ALGEBRA 1

Ron Larson   Laurie Boswell   Timothy D. Kanold   Lee Stiff

TEACHER'S EDITION

Contents

McDougal Littell
A DIVISION OF HOUGHTON MIFFLIN COMPANY
Evanston, Illinois • Boston • Dallas

About *Algebra 1*

The content of *Algebra 1* is organized around families of functions, with special emphasis on linear and quadratic functions. As students learn about each family of functions, they will learn to represent them in multiple ways—as verbal descriptions, equations, tables, and graphs. They will also learn to model real-world situations using functions in order to solve problems arising from those situations.

In addition to its algebra content, *Algebra 1* includes lessons on probability and data analysis as well as numerous examples and exercises involving geometry. These math topics often appear on standardized tests, so maintaining students' familiarity with them is important. To help students prepare for standardized tests, *Algebra 1* provides instruction and practice on standardized test questions in a variety of formats—multiple choice, short response, extended response, and so on. Technology support for both learning algebra and preparing for standardized tests is available at classzone.com.

Printed in Canada

ISBN-13: 978-0-6185-9556-3

ISBN-10: 0-618-59556-2   123456789—TBQ—09 08 07 06 05

Internet Web Site: http://www.mcdougallittell.com

About the Authors

Ron Larson is a professor of mathematics at Penn State University at Erie, where he has taught since receiving his Ph.D. in mathematics from the University of Colorado. Dr. Larson is well known as the author of a comprehensive program for mathematics that spans middle school, high school, and college courses. Dr. Larson's numerous professional activities keep him in constant touch with the needs of teachers and supervisors. He closely follows developments in mathematics standards and assessment.

Laurie Boswell is a mathematics teacher at The Riverside School in Lyndonville, Vermont, and has taught mathematics at all levels, elementary through college. A recipient of the Presidential Award for Excellence in Mathematics Teaching, she was also a Tandy Technology Scholar. She served on the NCTM Board of Directors (2002–2005), and she speaks frequently at regional and national conferences on topics related to instructional strategies and course content.

Timothy D. Kanold is the superintendent of Adlai E. Stevenson High School District 125 in Lincolnshire, Illinois. Dr. Kanold served as a teacher and director of mathematics for 17 years prior to becoming superintendent. He is the recipient of the Presidential Award for Excellence in Mathematics and Science Teaching, and a past president of the Council for Presidential Awardees in Mathematics. Dr. Kanold is a frequent speaker at national and international mathematics meetings.

Lee Stiff is a professor of mathematics education in the College of Education and Psychology of North Carolina State University at Raleigh and has taught mathematics at the high school and middle school levels. He served on the NCTM Board of Directors and was elected President of NCTM for the years 2000–2002. He is a recipient of the W. W. Rankin Award for Excellence in Mathematics Education presented by the North Carolina Council of Teachers of Mathematics.

Advisers and Reviewers

Curriculum Advisers and Reviewers

Cindy Branson
Mathematics Teacher
Creekview High School
Carrollton, TX

Ronald J. Labrocca
District Math Coordinator K–12
Manhasset Public Schools
Manhasset, NY

Richard Parr
Director of Educational
Technology, School
Mathematics Project
Rice University
Houston, TX

Rhonda Foote
Secondary Math Resource Specialist
North Kansas City School District
Kansas City, MO

John McHugh
Mathematics Department Chair
Holbrook Middle School
Lowell, NC

Rebecca S. Poe
Mathematics Teacher
Winnsboro High School
Winnsboro, TX

Ruth Hadnot
Mathematics Department Chair
Chicago Military Academy–Bronzeville
Chicago, IL

Fizza Munaim
Mathematics Teacher
Eastwood High School
El Paso, TX

Peggy S. Winfree White
Mathematics Teacher
Caprock High School
Amarillo, TX

Michael J. Klein
Educational Consultant
Macomb ISD
Clinton Township, MI

Anne Papakonstantinou
Director, School Mathematics Project
Rice University
Houston, TX

California Panel

Monette Bartel
Associate Adjunct Professor
College of the Canyons
Valencia, CA

Alberto Hernandez Galindo
Mathematics Department Chair
San Jose High Academy
San Jose, CA

Alvin E. Nash, Jr.
Mathematics Teacher
Pasadena High School
Pasadena, CA

Janice Beauchamp
Mathematics Teacher
Buchanan High School
Clovis, CA

Tom Griffith
Mathematics Department Chair
Scripps Ranch High School
San Diego, CA

Jon Simon
Mathematics Teacher
Casa Grande High School
Petaluma, CA

Pauline Embree
Mathematics Department Chair
Rancho San Joaquin Middle School
Irvine, CA

Debra Konvalin
Mathematics Teacher
Hiram W. Johnson High School
Sacramento, CA

Kansas and Missouri Panel

Arlene Banks
Mathematics Teacher
Westridge Middle School
Overland Park, KS

Phillip Gegen
Mathematics Teacher
Oak Park High School
Kansas City, MO

Steve Snider
Mathematics Teacher
Spring Garden Middle School
St. Joseph, MO

Jan Berghaus
Mathematics Teacher
Shawnee Mission West High School
Overland Park, KS

Jason Godfrey
Mathematics Teacher
Grandview High School
Grandview, MO

Karen Stohlmann
Mathematics Teacher
Blue Valley Northwest High School
Overland Park, KS

Dennis Dickson
Mathematics Teacher
Leavenworth High School
Leavenworth, KS

Deborah Reilly
Mathematics Teacher
West Middle School
Leavenworth, KS

Deborah Sylvester
Mathematics Teacher
Manhattan High School
Manhattan, KS

Coleen Floberg
Mathematics Teacher
Highland Park High School
Topeka, KS

Karen S. Skinner
Mathematics Teacher
New Mark Middle School
Kansas City, MO

Maureen Williams
Mathematics Department Chair
Southwest Junior High School
Lawrence, KS

Texas Panel

Leticia Alvarado
Mathematics Department Chair
Hornedo Middle School
El Paso, TX

William Lee Littles
Mathematics Teacher
Central High School
Beaumont, TX

Bertha Stimac
Instructional Specialist
Elsik 9th Grade Center
Houston, TX

Leticia Gonzales-Reynolds
Mathematics Teacher
Crockett High School
Austin, TX

Maria Magdalena Lucio
Mathematics Department Chair
Homer Hanna High School
Brownsville, TX

Tommie L. Walsh
Mathematics Teacher
Smylie Wilson Junior High School
Lubbock, TX

Maria Gossett
Mathematics Department Chair
E.M. Daggett Middle School
Fort Worth, TX

Lori Rapp
Secondary Mathematics Specialist
Lewisville School District
The Colony, TX

Mary Warner
Mathematics Teacher
Richard King High School
Corpus Christi, TX

Chapter 1 Summary

Chapter 1 focuses on the basics of algebra, showing how **variables** are used in forming **algebraic expressions** and how expressions are used in forming **equations and inequalities**. Along the way, students evaluate expressions using the **order of operations** and solve equations and inequalities using **mental math**. Students also use equations to solve real-world problems as part of the four-step **problem solving plan**. The chapter concludes by looking at the dependence of one variable on another in the form of **functional relationships**. Students see that functions have **multiple representations**: verbal descriptions, rules, tables, and graphs.

Problem Solving, p. 29
$0.1s + 0.6 = 2$

Expressions, Equations, and Functions

Animated Algebra
classzone.com
Activities **1, 7, 9, 14, 21, 29, 34, 37, 50**

Chapter 1 Highlights

PROBLEM SOLVING

- Mixed Review of Problem Solving, 27, 51
- Multiple Representations, 33, 39
- Multi-Step Problems, 6, 11, 19, 27, 40, 51
- Using Alternative Methods, 34
- Real-World Problem Solving Examples, 4, 10, 17, 23, 28, 30, 35, 37, 45

★ ASSESSMENT

- Standardized Test Practice Examples, 10, 30
- Multiple Choice, 5, 6, 11, 18, 24, 25, 31, 38, 46
- Short Response/Extended Response, 7, 12, 20, 26, 27, 32, 33, 40, 48, 51, 58
- Writing/Open-Ended, 5, 10, 12, 18, 19, 24, 25, 27, 31, 38, 39, 45, 46, 47, 51, 53

⊘ TECHNOLOGY

At classzone.com:

- Animated Algebra, 1, 7, 9, 14, 21, 29, 34, 37, 50
- @Home Tutor, xxii, 6, 11, 13, 19, 25, 32, 39, 41, 47, 53
- Online Quiz, 7, 12, 20, 26, 33, 40, 48
- Electronic Function Library, 52
- State Test Practice, 27, 51, 61

Multiplying Real Numbers, p. 90
Elevation $= 6416 + (-0.12)(50)$

Properties of Real Numbers

Chapter 2 Highlights

PROBLEM SOLVING
• Mixed Review of Problem Solving, 86, 119
• Multiple Representations, 83, 93, 116
• Multi-Step Problems, 69, 78, 86, 107, 115, 119
• Using Alternative Methods, 102
• Real-World Problem Solving Examples, 65, 76, 81, 90, 98, 104, 111

★ ASSESSMENT
• Standardized Test Practice Examples, 98
• Multiple Choice, 68, 69, 78, 82, 92, 99, 106, 107, 108, 114
• Short Response/Extended Response, 70, 79, 83, 86, 92, 93, 100, 101, 108, 115, 119, 126
• Writing/Open-Ended, 67, 77, 82, 83, 86, 91, 99, 106, 107, 113, 114, 119

⌖ TECHNOLOGY
At *classzone.com*:
• Animated Algebra, 63, 73, 80, 90, 93, 98
• @Home Tutor, 62, 69, 78, 83, 92, 100, 107, 115, 121
• Online Quiz, 70, 79, 84, 93, 101, 108, 116
• State Test Practice, 86, 119, 129

Contents   ix

Chapter 2 Summary

Chapter 2 focuses on the set of **real numbers** and its various subsets, including integers, rational numbers, and irrational numbers. Students become proficient at **comparing and ordering** real numbers and **performing operations** on them. Students also learn the **properties** of real-number addition and multiplication, including the **distributive property**, which students use to simplify expressions. The chapter emphasizes logical reasoning by asking students to write **conditional statements** and to determine whether those statements are true or false. Students learn to provide **justifications** for true statements and **counterexamples** for false statements.

Chapter 3 Summary

Chapter 3 focuses on **solving linear equations** in one variable. In the first half of the chapter, students learn the **properties of equality** in the course of solving simple one-step equations, and they employ those properties to solve increasingly complex multi-step equations. In the second half of the chapter, students solve **proportions** using the multiplication property of equality as well as the cross products property, and they solve **percent problems** by using proportions as well as the percent equation. The chapter concludes by asking students to **rewrite functions and formulas** by solving for one variable in terms of the other(s).

Solving Equations, p. 143
$$8517 = 2117 + 64d$$

Solving Linear Equations

Animated Algebra classzone.com **Activities** 131, 133, 139, 154, 176, 185, 187

Chapter 3 Highlights

PROBLEM SOLVING
• **Mixed Review of Problem Solving,** 161, 190
• **Multiple Representations,** 139, 146, 147, 153, 159, 166, 172, 188
• **Multi-Step Problems,** 140, 146, 161, 167, 190
• **Using Alternative Methods,** 147
• **Real-World Problem Solving Examples,** 137, 143, 150, 155, 164, 170, 178, 186

★ ASSESSMENT
• **Standardized Test Practice Examples,** 149, 169
• **Multiple Choice,** 138, 144, 145, 151, 157, 165, 171, 179, 187, 198
• **Short Response/Extended Response,** 139, 140, 145, 146, 151, 152, 159, 161, 166, 167, 172, 173, 180, 181, 189, 190
• **Writing/Open-Ended,** 137, 139, 144, 150, 151, 157, 161, 165, 171, 179, 180, 181, 187, 188, 190

⚡ TECHNOLOGY
At classzone.com:
• **Animated Algebra,** 131, 133, 139, 154, 176, 185, 187
• **@Home Tutor,** 130, 139, 145, 152, 158, 160, 166, 172, 180, 188, 192
• **Online Quiz,** 140, 146, 153, 159, 167, 173, 181, 189
• **State Test Practice,** 161, 190, 201

Graphing Linear Equations, p. 231
$2x + y = 128$

Graphing Linear Equations and Functions

Chapter 4 Highlights

PROBLEM SOLVING
- **Mixed Review of Problem Solving,** 233, 269
- **Multiple Representations,** 211, 221, 230, 259, 260
- **Multi-Step Problems,** 211, 220, 231, 233, 241, 269
- **Using Alternative Methods,** 260, 261
- **Real-World Problem Solving Examples,** 208, 218, 227, 228, 237, 238, 245, 246, 255, 256, 265

★ ASSESSMENT
- **Standardized Test Practice Examples,** 215, 262
- **Multiple Choice,** 209, 219, 220, 230, 239, 247, 257, 266, 276
- **Short Response/Extended Response,** 212, 221, 232, 233, 242, 249, 258, 259, 267, 268, 269
- **Writing/Open-Ended,** 209, 210, 214, 219, 229, 230, 233, 239, 241, 247, 248, 256, 257, 265, 266, 269, 271

🖉 TECHNOLOGY
At _classzone.com_:
- **Animated Algebra,** 205, 207, 216, 226, 238, 245, 254
- **@Home Tutor,** 204, 210, 211, 220, 222, 230, 241, 248, 249, 258, 267, 271
- **Online Quiz,** 212, 221, 232, 242, 250, 259, 268
- **Electronic Function Library,** 270
- **State Test Practice,** 233, 269, 279

Contents   **xi**

Chapter 4 Summary

Chapter 4 focuses on **graphing linear equations** in two variables. Students learn a variety of graphing techniques, including making a table of values and plotting points, identifying and using just the **x- and y-intercepts**, and identifying and using just the **slope** and y-intercept. Students recognize that the slope of a line is constant and that slope can be interpreted as a **rate of change** in real-world graphs. Students examine a special type of linear relationship known as **direct variation**, and they use direct variation models to solve real-world problems. The chapter concludes by introducing students to **function notation** while examining the effects of m and b on the graph of $f(x) = mx + b$.

Chapter 5 Summary

Chapter 5 focuses on **writing linear equations** in two variables. Students learn to write equations in a various forms: **slope-intercept form**, **point-slope form**, and **standard form**. Students then solve real-world problems using these forms. For instance, given a real-world situation involving a starting value and a constant rate of change, students model the situation using a linear equation in slope-intercept form. Students also examine the relationships among slopes of **parallel and perpendicular lines** and write equations based on those relationships. The chapter concludes by showing students how to **fit lines to data** and **make predictions** from the resulting linear models.

Slopes of Lines, p. 321
$12y = -7x + 42$

Writing Linear Equations

Chapter 5 Highlights

PROBLEM SOLVING	★ ASSESSMENT	🌐 TECHNOLOGY
• **Mixed Review of Problem Solving,** 317, 343 • **Multiple Representations,** 288, 299, 315, 340 • **Multi-Step Problems,** 317, 343 • **Using Alternative Methods,** 300 • **Real-World Problem Solving Examples,** 285, 294, 295, 304, 313, 321, 326, 327, 337	• **Standardized Test Practice Examples,** 293 • **Multiple Choice,** 286, 297, 305, 306, 314, 322, 323, 329, 339 • **Short Response/Extended Response,** 288, 289, 297, 298, 306, 307, 315, 317, 322, 323, 324, 329, 330, 340, 343, 350 • **Writing/Open-Ended,** 286, 287, 296, 297, 305, 314, 317, 322, 323, 328, 329, 338, 339, 343, 345	*At classzone.com:* • **Animated Algebra,** 281, 283, 303, 307, 311, 327, 335 • **@Home Tutor,** 280, 288, 291, 298, 307, 315, 323, 330, 333, 339, 340, 342, 345 • **Online Quiz,** 289, 299, 308, 316, 324, 331, 341 • **State Test Practice,** 317, 343, 353

Graphing Inequalities, p. 356
$T \leq 134$

Solving and Graphing Linear Inequalities

Animated Algebra
classzone.com Activities 355, 358, 364, 382, 387, 390, 391, 399, 407

Chapter 6 Highlights

PROBLEM SOLVING
- **Mixed Review of Problem Solving,** 389, 413
- **Multiple Representations,** 361, 367, 374, 386, 402, 411
- **Multi-Step Problems,** 360, 389, 403, 411, 413
- **Using Alternative Methods,** 375, 376
- **Real-World Problem Solving Examples,** 358, 365, 371, 383, 392, 400, 408

★ ASSESSMENT
- **Standardized Test Practice Examples,** 365, 405
- **Multiple Choice,** 360, 372, 373, 385, 386, 393, 394, 401, 409, 411
- **Short Response/Extended Response,** 361, 368, 373, 374, 387, 389, 395, 402, 403, 411, 412, 413, 420
- **Writing/Open-Ended,** 359, 360, 366, 372, 384, 389, 393, 401, 409, 410, 413

⊘ TECHNOLOGY
At classzone.com:
- **Animated Algebra,** 355, 358, 364, 382, 387, 390, 391, 399, 407
- **@Home Tutor,** 354, 360, 367, 373, 385, 388, 394, 402, 410, 415
- **Online Quiz,** 361, 368, 374, 387, 395, 403, 412
- **State Test Practice,** 389, 413, 423

Chapter 6 Summary

Chapter 6 focuses on **solving linear inequalities** in one variable and **graphing linear inequalities** in two variables. Paralleling the development of Chapter 3, students use the **properties of inequality** to solve inequalities, starting with simple one-step inequalities and progressing to more complicated multi-step inequalities. Students then solve **compound inequalities** involving *and* and *or*, and students extend this skill to solving **absolute value equations and inequalities**. The chapter concludes by showing students how to graph a linear inequality in two variables by graphing the related equation (using techniques from Chapter 4) and shading the appropriate half-plane.

Contents **xiii**

T11

Chapter 7 Summary

Chapter 7 focuses on **solving systems of linear equations** and inequalities in two variables. Students learn various methods for solving systems of equations: by graphing and finding the point where the lines intersect (**graphing method**), by solving one equation for one of the variables and substituting into the other equation (**substitution method**), and by combining the equations to eliminate one of the variables (**elimination method**). Students also examine **special cases** where a system has no solution or has infinitely many solutions. The chapter concludes by showing students how to graph a system of inequalities using the method for graphing single inequalities from Chapter 6.

Solving Linear Systems, p. 446
$x - y = 4, x + y = 6$

Systems of Equations and Inequalities

Animated Algebra classzone.com **Activities** 425, 428, 435, 441, 446, 452, 459, 466

Chapter 7 Highlights

PROBLEM SOLVING
• **Mixed Review of Problem Solving,** 458, 473
• **Multiple Representations,** 433, 442, 449, 456
• **Multi-Step Problems,** 440, 450, 458, 465, 473
• **Using Alternative Methods,** 442
• **Real-World Problem Solving Examples,** 430, 438, 446, 453, 461, 468

★ ASSESSMENT
• **Standardized Test Practice Examples,** 429, 453
• **Multiple Choice,** 431, 432, 439, 447, 455, 463, 469, 470, 480
• **Short Response/Extended Response,** 432, 440, 441, 448, 450, 456, 458, 465, 470, 471, 473
• **Writing/Open-Ended,** 430, 431, 439, 440, 447, 454, 455, 456, 458, 462, 464, 469, 473

⊘ TECHNOLOGY
At classzone.com:
• **Animated Algebra,** 425, 428, 435, 441, 446, 452, 459, 466
• **@Home Tutor,** 424, 432, 434, 440, 449, 456, 464, 471, 475
• **Online Quiz,** 433, 441, 450, 457, 465, 472
• **State Test Practice,** 458, 473, 483

Scientific Notation, p. 516
9.065×10^9 miles

Exponents and Exponential Functions

Chapter 8 Highlights

PROBLEM SOLVING

- **Mixed Review of Problem Solving,** 511, 541
- **Multiple Representations,** 493, 500, 507, 517, 525, 528, 537
- **Multi-Step Problems,** 493, 511, 517, 525, 538, 541
- **Using Alternative Methods,** 528, 529
- **Real-World Problem Solving Examples,** 491, 498, 505, 514, 522, 523, 534

★ ASSESSMENT

- **Standardized Test Practice Examples,** 505, 523
- **Multiple Choice,** 492, 499, 506, 507, 515, 516, 524, 526, 535, 536, 548
- **Short Response/Extended Response,** 494, 501, 507, 508, 511, 516, 517, 526, 537, 541
- **Writing/Open-Ended,** 492, 493, 498, 499, 506, 511, 515, 516, 523, 524, 535, 536, 541, 543

🖋 TECHNOLOGY

At _classzone.com_:
- **Animated Algebra,** 487, 505, 512, 522, 534, 536
- **@Home Tutor,** 486, 493, 500, 507, 516, 519, 525, 537, 543
- **Online Quiz,** 494, 501, 508, 518, 527, 538
- **State Test Practice,** 511, 541, 551

Contents   **XV**

Chapter 8 Summary

Chapter 8 focuses on **working with exponents** and **graphing exponential functions**. Students learn the **properties of exponents** while working with positive exponents, then they extend the properties to **zero and negative exponents**. Students also learn to write numbers in **scientific notation** using positive, negative, and zero exponents and to compare and perform operations with numbers written in scientific notation. With an understanding of exponents, students are prepared to examine exponential functions, their first encounter with **nonlinear functions**. Students write and graph exponential functions and then use **exponential growth and decay models** to solve real-world problems.

Chapter 9 Summary

Chapter 9 focuses on **working with polynomials** and **solving polynomial equations**. In the first half of the chapter, students learn to **classify polynomials** by degree and by the number of terms and to **add, subtract, and multiply polynomials**, including recognizing patterns for **special products**. In the second half of the chapter, students learn to **factor polynomials** using several techniques: factoring out a common monomial factor, factoring a trinomial into a product of binomials, and factoring special products. Students then use factoring and the **zero product property** to solve polynomial equations, with particular emphasis on solving quadratic equations.

Subtracting Polynomials, p. 558
$B = -0.0262t^3 + 0.376t^2 - 0.574t + 9.67$

Polynomials and Factoring

Chapter 9 Highlights

PROBLEM SOLVING	**★ ASSESSMENT**	**⚙ TECHNOLOGY**
• **Mixed Review of Problem Solving,** 581, 614 • **Multiple Representations,** 573, 580, 589, 598 • **Multi-Step Problems,** 581, 614 • **Using Alternative Methods,** 590 • **Real-World Problem Solving Examples,** 556, 564, 571, 577, 585, 595, 602, 609	• **Standardized Test Practice Examples,** 564, 596 • **Multiple Choice,** 557, 565, 566, 572, 578, 580, 586, 589, 596, 597, 603, 610 • **Short Response/Extended Response,** 558, 559, 567, 568, 573, 574, 579, 581, 587, 588, 597, 598, 604, 612, 614, 622 • **Writing/Open-Ended,** 557, 565, 572, 578, 581, 586, 596, 603, 610, 611, 614, 616	**At _classzone.com:_** • **Animated Algebra,** 553, 555, 582, 592, 598, 601 • **@Home Tutor,** 552, 558, 560, 567, 573, 579, 588, 598, 604, 612, 616 • **Online Quiz,** 559, 568, 574, 580, 589, 599, 605, 613 • **State Test Practice,** 581, 614, 625

Solving Quadratic Equations, p. 648
$$y = -0.04x^2 + 1.2x$$

Quadratic Equations and Functions

Chapter 10 Highlights

PROBLEM SOLVING	★ ASSESSMENT	⚙ TECHNOLOGY
• Mixed Review of Problem Solving, 661, 694	• Standardized Test Practice Examples, 631, 671	**At classzone.com:**
• Multiple Representations, 658, 659, 667, 676, 690	• Multiple Choice, 632, 633, 638, 647, 655, 657, 666, 674, 681, 688, 690	• Animated Algebra, 627, 634, 636, 642, 662, 668, 672, 684
• Multi-Step Problems, 658, 661, 668, 675, 683, 694	• Short Response/Extended Response, 634, 640, 648, 649, 656, 657, 661, 668, 676, 682, 690, 694	• @Home Tutor, 626, 633, 639, 648, 651, 657, 667, 675, 682, 689, 690, 692, 696
• Using Alternative Methods, 659		• Online Quiz, 634, 640, 649, 658, 668, 676, 683, 691
• Real-World Problem Solving Examples, 631, 637, 646, 654, 665, 672, 680, 687	• Writing/Open-Ended, 632, 638, 639, 647, 655, 656, 661, 666, 667, 674, 681, 682, 688, 694	• Electronic Function Library, 695
		• State Test Practice, 661, 694, 705

Contents   **xvii**

Chapter 10 Summary

Chapter 10 focuses on **graphing quadratic functions** and **solving quadratic equations**. Students learn the effects of a and c on the graph of $y = ax^2 + c$ and then extend their understanding of quadratic graphs to $y = ax^2 + bx + c$. Students are able to solve quadratic equations graphically by interpreting the solutions as the x-intercepts of related graphs. Students also solve quadratic equations by **completing the square**, and this method leads to the **quadratic formula** when applied to the general equation $ax^2 + bx + c = 0$. Students see that the **discriminant** in the quadratic formula determines the number of solutions that a quadratic equation has. The chapter concludes by comparing linear models (from Chapter 5), exponential models (from Chapter 8), and **quadratic models** and asking students to choose an appropriate model for a given set of data.

Chapter 11 Summary

Chapter 11 focuses on **working with radicals** and **connections to geometry**. In the first half of the chapter, students learn to **graph square root functions**. Students then **simplify square root expressions** using the properties of radicals and **solve square root equations** by squaring both sides. In the second half of the chapter, students look at geometric situations involving square roots. In particular, students solve right-triangle problems using the **Pythagorean theorem and its converse**, and they solve coordinate-plane problems using the **distance and midpoint formulas**.

Solving Radical Equations, p. 731
$$s = 1.34\sqrt{\ell}$$

Radicals and Geometry Connections

Animated Algebra classzone.com **Activities** 709, 711, 719, 722, 731, 737, 746

Chapter 11 Highlights

PROBLEM SOLVING	★ ASSESSMENT	⚙ TECHNOLOGY
• Mixed Review of Problem Solving, 735, 752 • Multiple Representations, 725 • Multi-Step Problems, 715, 725, 733, 735, 748, 752 • Using Alternative Methods, 751 • Real-World Problem Solving Examples, 713, 722, 731, 738, 739, 746	• Standardized Test Practice Examples, 738, 746 • Multiple Choice, 713, 714, 723, 732, 740, 741, 747, 748 • Short Response/Extended Response, 716, 726, 734, 735, 742, 749, 752 • Writing/Open-Ended, 713, 723, 724, 732, 733, 735, 740, 741, 747, 748, 752	*At classzone.com:* • Animated Algebra, 709, 711, 719, 722, 731, 737, 746 • @Home Tutor, 708, 715, 717, 725, 733, 741, 748, 749, 754, 755 • Online Quiz, 716, 726, 734, 742, 750 • State Test Practice, 735, 752, 761

Dividing Rational Expressions, p. 807
$$T = \frac{100 + 2.2x}{1 - 0.014x}$$

Rational Equations and Functions

Chapter 12 Highlights

Chapter 12 Summary

Chapter 12 focuses on **rational expressions and equations**. In the first half of the chapter, students learn to **graph rational functions** whose numerators and denominators have degree 0 or 1, including the special case of **inverse variation**. Students also extend their work with polynomials in Chapter 9 by using **polynomial division** to put rational functions in a form for graphing. In the second half of the chapter, students learn to **simplify and perform operations** on rational expressions, and they use graphs to check their work visually. Students then learn to **solve rational equations** and check for extraneous solutions.

Using Permutations, p. 855
$$\text{Probability} = \frac{_5P_5}{_7P_7}$$

Chapter 13 Summary

Chapter 13 focuses on **probability and combinatorics** as well as **data analysis**. In the first half of the chapter, students learn to find probabilities of **simple and compound events**. Students also learn to calculate **permutations and combinations**, which are in turn used to find probabilities. In the second half of the chapter, students learn to recognize potential bias in **sampling methods and survey questions**. Students also learn to find **measures of central tendency and dispersion** and to display data using **stem-and-leaf plots**, **histograms**, and **box-and-whisker plots**.

Probability and Data Analysis

Animated Algebra
classzone.com
Activities 841, 845, 848, 856, 875, 887

Chapter 13 Highlights

PROBLEM SOLVING	★ ASSESSMENT	🌐 TECHNOLOGY
• **Mixed Review of Problem Solving,** 870, 894 • **Multiple Representations,** 854, 866 • **Multi-Step Problems,** 870, 894 • **Using Alternative Methods,** 868 • **Real-World Problem Solving Examples,** 844, 852, 853, 857, 863, 871, 872, 876, 882, 888, 889	• **Standardized Test Practice Examples,** 845, 889 • **Multiple Choice,** 846, 847, 854, 858, 864, 865, 873, 877, 883, 890 • **Short Response/Extended Response,** 847, 848, 855, 858, 859, 866, 870, 874, 877, 878, 885, 891, 894 • **Writing/Open-Ended,** 846, 853, 858, 864, 865, 870, 873, 877, 883, 884, 889, 894, 896	**At *classzone.com*:** • **Animated Algebra,** 841, 845, 848, 856, 875, 887 • **@Home Tutor,** 840, 847, 854, 859, 860, 866, 874, 877, 878, 884, 886, 890, 891, 893, 896 • **Online Quiz,** 848, 855, 859, 867, 874, 878, 885, 892 • **State Test Practice,** 870, 894, 905

Contents
of Student Resources

McDougal Littell
ALGEBRA 1
Where great lessons begin

- Engages students in active learning
- Adaptable to different teaching styles and student abilities
- Ongoing assessment integrated with instruction

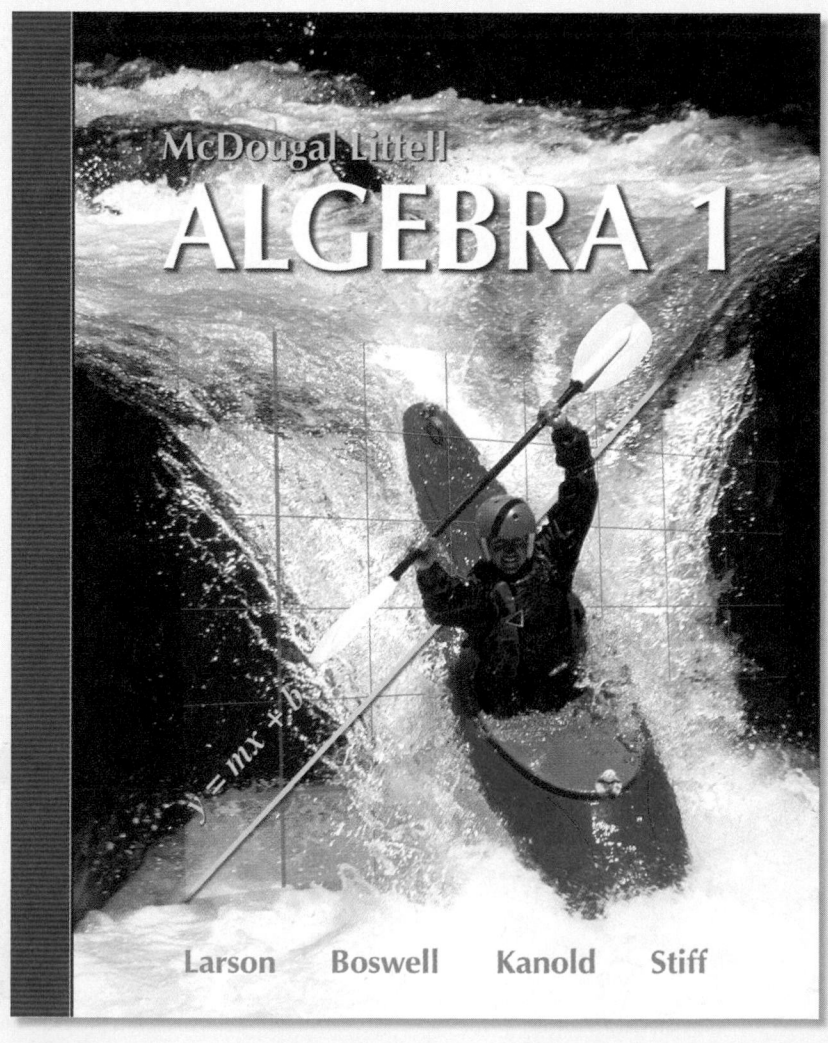

McDougal Littell

ALGEBRA 1

Larson   Boswell   Kanold   Stiff

1 Expressions, Equations, and Functions

1.1 Evaluate Expressions
1.2 Apply Order of Operations
1.3 Write Expressions
1.4 Write Equations and Inequalities
1.5 Use a Problem Solving Plan
1.6 Represent Functions as Rules and Tables
1.7 Represent Functions as Graphs

Now

In Chapter 1, you will apply the big ideas listed below and reviewed in the Chapter Summary on page 52. You will also use the key vocabulary listed below.

Big Ideas

1 Writing and evaluating algebraic expressions
2 Using expressions to write equations and inequalities
3 Representing functions as verbal rules, equations, tables, and graphs

KEY VOCABULARY

- variable, p. 2
- algebraic expression, p. 2
- power, exponent, base, p. 3
- order of operations, p. 8
- verbal model, p. 16

- rate, unit rate, p. 17
- open sentence, p. 21
- equation, inequality, p. 21
- solution of an equation or inequality, p. 22

- formula, p. 30
- function, p. 35
- domain, range, p. 35
- independent variable, p. 36
- dependent variable, p. 36

Before

In previous courses, you learned the following skills, which you'll use in Chapter 1: using fractions and percents, and finding perimeter and area.

Prerequisite Skills

VOCABULARY CHECK

Copy and complete the statement.

1. In the fraction $\frac{2}{3}$, $\underline{}$ is the numerator and $\underline{}$ is the denominator.

2. Two fractions that represent the same number are called $\underline{}$ fractions.

3. The word *percent* (%) means "divided by $\underline{}$."

SKILLS CHECK

Perform the indicated operation. *(Review pp. 914–915 for 1.1, 1.2.)*

4. $\frac{2}{3} + \frac{3}{5}$ 5. $\frac{5}{6} - \frac{3}{4}$ 6. $\frac{3}{5} \times \frac{2}{3}$ 7. $\frac{1}{2} \div \frac{5}{8}$

Write the percent as a decimal. *(Review p. 916 for 1.5.)*

8. 4%   9. 23%   10. 1.5%   11. 2.5%

12. Find the perimeter and area of the rectangle. *(Review p. 924 for 1.5.)*

$4\frac{1}{2}$ in.

11 in.

@**HomeTutor** Prerequisite skills practice at classzone.com

Why?

You can use multiple representations to describe a real-world situation. For example, you can solve an equation, make a table, or draw a diagram to determine a running route.

Animated Algebra

The animation illustrated below for Example 1 on page 28 helps you answer this question: How does the number of blocks you run affect the total distance?

Your goal is to find a 2 mile running path around the long and short city blocks.

Click on a point on the graph to move the runner and see the distance covered.

Animated Algebra at classzone.com

Other animations for Chapter 1: pages 7, 9, 14, 21, 37, 50, and 52

1

Animated Algebra

Animated Algebra includes interactive electronic activities that provide insights into both the how and the why of math.

- Each chapter opens with an animated activity related to a real-world problem in the chapter. Throughout the chapter, additional activities support and extend specific examples and exercises.

- The Electronic Function Library allows students to explore the properties of functions and their graphs.

Clear Instruction

New concepts and methods are presented using clear, student-friendly language and visuals, and examples are carefully stepped out for easier understanding. Vocabulary and key ideas are highlighted.

Connect

New topics are related to what students have already studied and are applied to real-world problems.

Guide

Students are made aware of common errors, other solution methods, vocabulary connections, and so on.

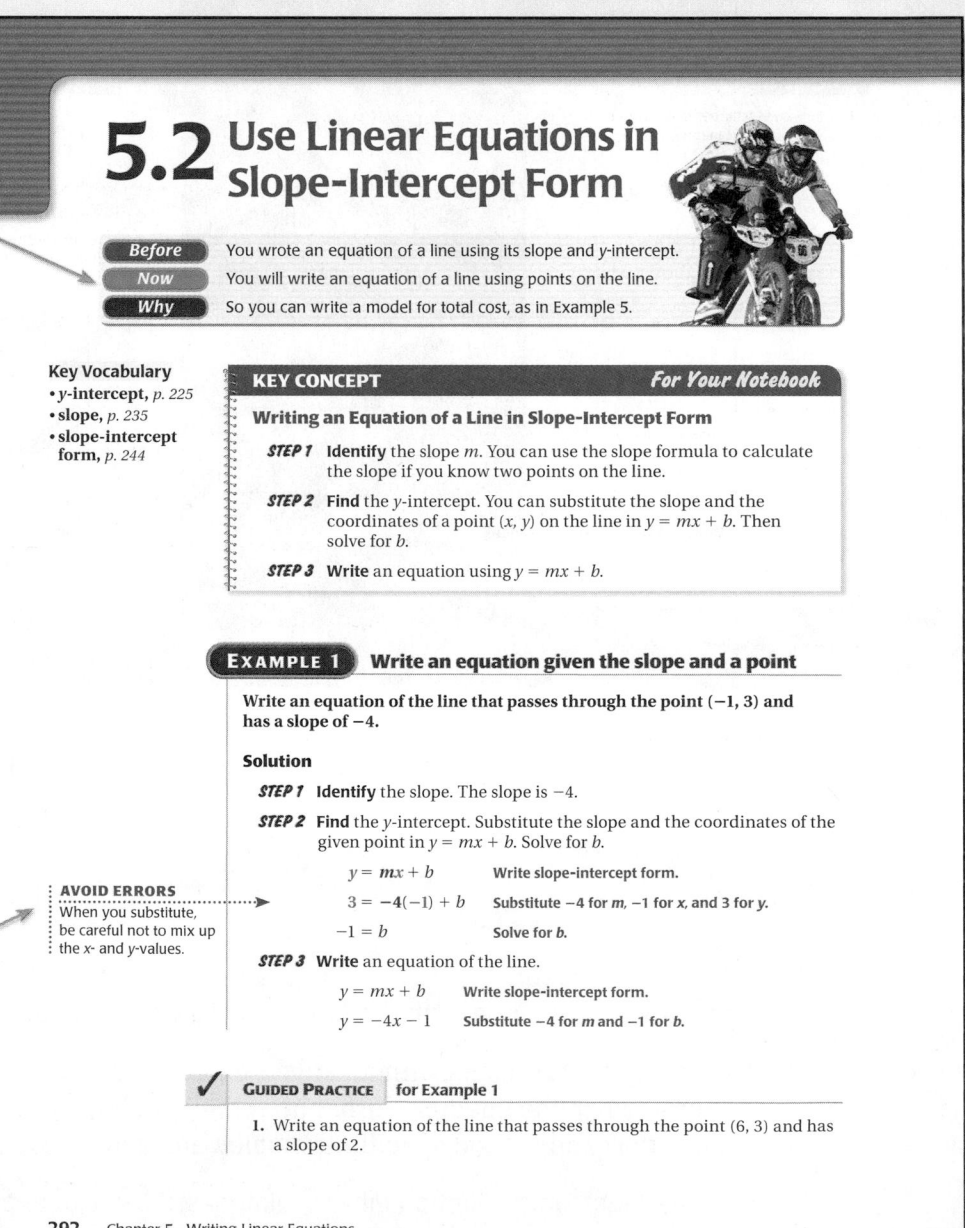

5.2 Use Linear Equations in Slope-Intercept Form

Before	You wrote an equation of a line using its slope and y-intercept.
Now	You will write an equation of a line using points on the line.
Why	So you can write a model for total cost, as in Example 5.

Key Vocabulary
• *y*-intercept, p. 225
• slope, p. 235
• slope-intercept form, p. 244

KEY CONCEPT — *For Your Notebook*

Writing an Equation of a Line in Slope-Intercept Form

STEP 1 Identify the slope m. You can use the slope formula to calculate the slope if you know two points on the line.

STEP 2 Find the y-intercept. You can substitute the slope and the coordinates of a point (x, y) on the line in $y = mx + b$. Then solve for b.

STEP 3 Write an equation using $y = mx + b$.

EXAMPLE 1 **Write an equation given the slope and a point**

Write an equation of the line that passes through the point $(-1, 3)$ and has a slope of -4.

Solution

STEP 1 Identify the slope. The slope is -4.

STEP 2 Find the y-intercept. Substitute the slope and the coordinates of the given point in $y = mx + b$. Solve for b.

$$y = mx + b \qquad \text{Write slope-intercept form.}$$
$$3 = -4(-1) + b \qquad \text{Substitute } -4 \text{ for } m, -1 \text{ for } x, \text{ and } 3 \text{ for } y.$$
$$-1 = b \qquad \text{Solve for } b.$$

STEP 3 Write an equation of the line.

$$y = mx + b \qquad \text{Write slope-intercept form.}$$
$$y = -4x - 1 \qquad \text{Substitute } -4 \text{ for } m \text{ and } -1 \text{ for } b.$$

AVOID ERRORS
When you substitute, be careful not to mix up the x- and y-values.

✓ **GUIDED PRACTICE** for Example 1

1. Write an equation of the line that passes through the point $(6, 3)$ and has a slope of 2.

292 Chapter 5 Writing Linear Equations

How to Write Equations in Slope-Intercept Form

For Your Notebook

Given slope *m* and *y*-intercept *b*

Substitute *m* and *b* in the equation *y = mx + b*.

Given slope *m* and one point

Substitute *m* and the coordinates of the point in *y = mx + b*. Solve for *b*. Write the equation.

Given two points

Use the points to find the slope *m*. Then follow the same steps described at the left.

MODELING REAL-WORLD SITUATIONS You can model a real-world situation that involves a constant rate of change with an equation in slope-intercept form.

EXAMPLE 4 Solve a multi-step problem

GYM MEMBERSHIP Your gym membership costs $33 per month after an initial membership fee. You paid a total of $228 after 6 months. Write an equation that gives the total cost as a function of the length of your gym membership (in months). Find the total cost after 9 months.

Solution

STEP 1 Identify the rate of change and sta

Rate of change, *m*: monthly co
Starting value, *b*: initial memb

STEP 2 Write a verbal model. Then write a

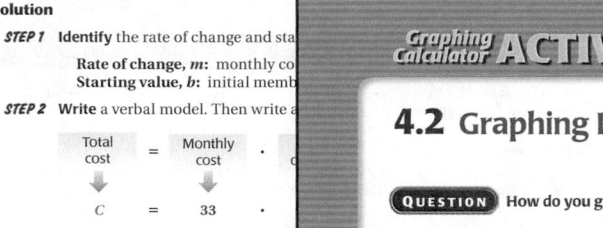

Total cost	=	Monthly cost	·	
C	=	33	·	

STEP 3 Find the starting value. Membersh
can substitute 6 for *t* and 228 for *C*

$228 = 33(6) + b$ Substitute 6 fo

$30 = b$ Solve for *b*.

STEP 4 Write an equation. Use the functio

$C = 33t + 30$ Substitute 30

STEP 5 Evaluate the function when *t* = 9.

$C = 33(9) + 30 = 327$ Substitut

▶ Your total cost after 9 months is $327.

294   Chapter 5   Writing Linear Equations

Visualize

Graphs and diagrams help students visualize problems so that they can work toward a solution.

Model

Stepped-out examples model how to think about problems. Students see how to move from words to an equation.

Graphing Calculator **ACTIVITY**   *Use after Lesson 4.2*

@HomeTutor
classzone.com
Keystrokes

4.2 Graphing Linear Equations

QUESTION How do you graph an equation on a graphing calculator?

EXAMPLE Use a graph to solve a problem

The formula to convert temperature from degrees Fahrenheit to degrees Celsius is $C = \frac{5}{9}(F - 32)$. Graph the equation. At what temperature are degrees Fahrenheit and degrees Celsius equal?

STEP 1 *Rewrite and enter equation*

Rewrite the equation using *x* for *F* and *y* for *C*. Enter the equation into the Y= screen. Put parentheses around the fraction $\frac{5}{9}$.

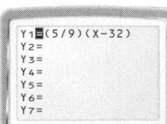

STEP 2 *Set window*

The screen is a "window" that lets you look at part of a coordinate plane. Press WINDOW to set the borders of the graph. A friendly window for this equation is $-94 \le x \le 94$ and $-100 \le y \le 100$.

STEP 3 *Graph and trace equation*

Press TRACE and use the left and right arrows to move the cursor along the graph until the *x*-coordinate and *y*-coordinate are equal. From the graph, you can see that degrees Fahrenheit and degrees Celsius are equal at −40.

PRACTICE

Graph the equation. Find the unknown value in the ordered pair.

1. $y = 8 - x$; (2.4, ?)   **2.** $y = 2x + 3$; (?, 0.8)   **3.** $y = -4.5x + 1$; (1.4, ?)

4. SPEED OF SOUND The speed *s* (in meters per second) of sound in air can be modeled by $s = 331.1 + 0.61T$ where *T* is the air temperature in degrees Celsius. Graph the equation. Estimate the speed of sound when the temperature is 20°C.

222   Chapter 4   Graphing Linear Equations and Functions

Varied, Leveled Practice

The wide variety of skill and problem solving exercises is carefully paced, ensuring that students build skills and feel confident about their work. The @Home Tutor and Animated Algebra features provide additional support.

Support

Exercises are correlated to examples, providing homework support and fostering independent student learning.

Analyze

Error analysis exercises give students the opportunity to analyze mathematical thinking.

6.1 EXERCISES

HOMEWORK KEY
○ = WORKED-OUT SOLUTIONS on p. WS1 for Exs. 7, 15, and 33
★ = STANDARDIZED TEST PRACTICE Exs. 2, 29, 34, 35, and 38
◆ = MULTIPLE REPRESENTATIONS Ex. 37

SKILL PRACTICE

1. **VOCABULARY** Copy and complete: To graph $x < -8$, you draw a(n) __?__ circle at -8, and you draw an arrow to the __?__ .

2. ★ **WRITING** Are $x + 7 \geq 18$ and $x \geq 25$ equivalent inequalities? *Explain.*

EXAMPLE 1
on p. 356
for Exs. 3–5

WRITING AND GRAPHING INEQUALITIES Write and graph an inequality that describes the situation.

3. The speed limit on a highway is 60 miles per hour.

4. You must be at least 16 years old to go on a field trip.

5. A child must be taller than 48 inches to get on an amusement park ride.

EXAMPLE 2
on p. 356
for Exs. 6–9

WRITING INEQUALITIES Write an inequality represented by the graph.

6.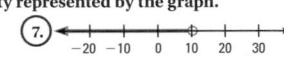

7.

8.

9.

EXAMPLES 3 and 4
on pp. 357–358
for Exs. 10–23

SOLVING INEQUALITIES Solve the inequality. Graph your solution.

10. $x + 4 < 5$

11. $-8 \leq 8 + y$

12. $-1\frac{1}{4} \leq m + 3$

13. $n + 17 \leq 16\frac{4}{5}$

14. $8.2 + v > -7.6$

15. $w + 14.9 > -2.7$

16. $r - 4 < -5$

17. $1 \leq s - 8$

18. $-1\frac{1}{3} \leq p - 8\frac{1}{3}$

19. $q - 1\frac{1}{3} > -2\frac{1}{2}$

20. $2.1 \geq c - 6.7$

21. $d - 1.92 > -8.76$

ERROR ANALYSIS *Describe* and correct the error in solving the inequality or in graphing the solution.

22.

23.

TRANSLATING SENTENCES Write the verbal sentence as an inequality. Then solve the inequality and graph your solution.

24. The sum of 11 and m is greater than -23.

25. The difference of n and 15 is less than or equal to 37.

26. The difference of c and 13 is less than -19.

6.1 Solve Inequalities Using Addition and Subtraction   **359**

EXAMPLE 4
on p. 595
for Exs. 58, 60

58. DIVING You dive from a platform when your center of gravity is 32 feet above the surface of a swimming pool. Your initial vertical velocity leaving the platform is 28 feet per second. After how many seconds does your center of gravity enter the water?

@HomeTutor for problem solving help at classzone.com

EXAMPLE 5
on p. 596
for Exs. 59, 61

59. SCRAPBOOK DESIGN You plan to make a scrapbook. On the cover, you want to show three pictures with space between them, as shown. Each of the pictures is twice as long as it is wide.

  a. Write a polynomial that represents the area of the scrapbook cover.

  b. The area of the cover will be 96 square centimeters. Find the length and width of the pictures you will use.

@HomeTutor for problem solving help at classzone.com

60. ★ SHORT RESPONSE You throw a ball into the air with an initial vertical velocity of 31 feet per second. The ball leaves your hand when it is 6 feet above the ground. You catch the ball when it reaches a height of 4 feet. After how many seconds do you catch the ball? *Explain* how you can use the solutions of an equation to find your answer.

61. PARTHENON The Parthenon in Athens, Greece, is an ancient structure that has a rectangular base. The length of the Parth... 8 meters more than twice its width. The area of the ... 2170 square meters. Find the length and width of th...

62. ◆ MULTIPLE REPRESENTATIONS An African cat called a serval leaps from the ground in an attempt to catch a bird. The serval's initial vertical velocity is 24 feet per second.

  a. Writing an Equation Write an equation that gives the serval's height (in feet) as a function of the time (in seconds) since it left the ground.

  b. Making a Table Use the equation from part (a) to make a table that shows the height of the serval for $t = 0, 0.3, 0.6, 0.9, 1.2,$ and 1.5 seconds.

  c. Drawing a Graph Plot the ordered pairs in the table as points in a coordinate plane. Connect the points with a smooth curve. After how many seconds does the serval reach a height of 9 feet? *Justify* your answer using the equation from part (a).

Animated Algebra at classzone.com

598

○ = WORKED-OUT SOLUTIONS
on p. WS1

★ = STANDARDIZ...
TEST PRACTIC...

Challenge

Students with strong abilities find challenging skill and problem solving exercises in every lesson.

CHALLENGE Use the given surface area S of the cylinder to find the radius r to the nearest tenth. (Use 3.14 for π.)

47. $S = 251 \text{ ft}^2$

6 ft

48. $S = 716 \text{ m}^2$

13 m

49. $S = 1074 \text{ cm}^2$

10 cm

GRAPHING CALCULATOR You may wish to use a graphing calculator to complete the following Problem Solving exercises.

EXAMPLE 6
on p. 646
for Exs. 50–52

50. SOCCER The height y (in feet) of a soccer ball after it is kicked can be modeled by the graph of the equation $y = -0.04x^2 + 1.2x$ where x is the horizontal distance (in feet) that the ball travels. The ball is not touched, and it lands on the ground. Find the distance that the ball was kicked.

@HomeTutor for problem solving help at classzone.com

51. SURVEYING To keep water off a road, the road's surface is shaped like a parabola as in the cross section below. The surface of the road can be modeled by the graph of $y = -0.0017x^2 + 0.041x$ where x and y are measured in feet. Find the width of the road to the nearest tenth of a foot.

@HomeTutor for problem solving help at classzone.com

52. DIVING During a cliff diving competition, a diver begins a dive with his center of gravity 70 feet above the water. The initial vertical velocity of his dive is 8 feet per second.

  a. Write an equation that models the height h (in feet) of the diver's center of gravity as a function of time t (in seconds).

  b. How long after the diver begins his dive does his center of gravity reach the water?

53. ★ SHORT RESPONSE An arc of water sprayed from the nozzle of a fountain can be modeled by the graph of $y = -0.75x^2 + 6x$ where x is the horizontal distance (in feet) from the nozzle and y is the vertical distance (in feet). The diameter of the circle formed by the arcs on the surface of the water is called the display diameter. Find the display diameter of the fountain. *Explain* your reasoning.

Display diameter

648

○ = WORKED-OUT SOLUTIONS
on p. WS1

★ = STANDARDIZED
TEST PRACTICE

● Represent

By representing problems in more than one way, students make important mathematical connections.

Explain ●

Concepts and writing skills are developed through exercises that ask students to explain their reasoning.

Focused Review

Throughout each chapter, carefully coordinated summaries and reviews focus on key concepts, vocabulary, and problem solving skills.

Synthesize

"Big ideas" introduced at the beginning of each chapter and reinforced in the chapter summary help students synthesize what they have learned.

Organize

Tables, charts, and visuals help students organize their thinking about mathematical concepts.

---

5 CHAPTER SUMMARY

BIG IDEAS
For Your Notebook

Big Idea 1

Writing Linear Equations in a Variety of Forms

Using given information about a line, you can write an equation of the line in three different forms.

Form	Equation	Important information
Slope-intercept form	$y = mx + b$	• The slope of the line is m. • The y-intercept of the line is b.
Point-slope form	$y - y_1 = m(x - x_1)$	• The slope of the line is m. • The line passes through (x_1, y_1).
Standard form	$Ax + By = C$	• A, B, and C are real numbers. • A and B are not both zero.

Big Idea 2

Using Linear Models to Solve Problems

You can write a linear equation that models a situation involving a constant rate of change. Analyzing given information helps you choose a linear model.

Choosing a Linear Model	
If this is what you know . . .	**. . . then use this equation form**
constant rate of change and initial value	slope-intercept form
constant rate of change and one data pair	slope-intercept form or point-slope form
two data pairs and the fact that the rate of change is constant	slope-intercept form or point-slope form
the sum of two variable quantities is constant	standard form

Big Idea 3

Modeling Data with a Line of Fit

You can use a line of fit to model data that have a positive or negative correlation. The line or an equation of the line can be used to make predictions.

Step 1 Make a scatter plot of the data.

Step 2 Decide whether the data can be modeled by a line.

Step 3 Draw a line that appears to follow the trend in data closely.

Step 4 Write an equation using two points on the line.

Step 5 Interpolate (between known values) or extrapolate (beyond known values) using the line or its equation.

344 Chapter 5 Writing Linear Equations

STATE TEST PRACTICE
classzone.com

Lessons 7.1–7.4

1. **MULTI-STEP PROBLEM** Flying into the wind, a helicopter takes 15 minutes to travel 15 kilometers. The return flight takes 12 minutes. The wind speed remains constant during the trip.

   a. Find the helicopter's average speed (in kilometers per hour) for each leg of the trip.

   b. Write a system of linear equations that represents the situation.

   c. What is the helicopter's average speed in still air? What is the speed of the wind?

2. **SHORT RESPONSE** At a grocery store, a customer pays a total of $9.70 for 1.8 pounds of potato salad and 1.4 pounds of coleslaw. Another customer pays a total of $6.55 for 1 pound of potato salad and 1.2 pounds of coleslaw. How much do 2 pounds of potato salad and 2 pounds of coleslaw cost? *Explain.*

3. **GRIDDED ANSWER** During one day, two computers are sold at a computer store. The two customers each arrange payment plans with the salesperson. The graph shows the amount *y* of money (in dollars) paid for the computers after *x* months. After how many months will each customer have paid the same amount?

4. **OPEN-ENDED** *Describe* a real-world problem that can be modeled by a linear system. Then solve the system and interpret the solution in the context of the problem.

5. **SHORT RESPONSE** A hot air balloon is launched at Kirby Park, and it ascends at a rate of 7200 feet per hour. At the same time, a second hot air balloon is launched at Newman Park, and it ascends at a rate of 4000 feet per hour. Both of the balloons stop ascending after 30 minutes. The diagram shows the altitude of each park. Are the hot air balloons ever at the same height at the same time? *Explain.*

Kirby Park | Newman Park

3960 ft

1705 ft

SEA LEVEL   *Not drawn to scale*

---

5 CHAPTER REVIEW

5.6 Fit a Line to Data
pp. 323–331

EXAMPLE

The table shows the time needed to roast turkeys of different weights. Make a scatter plot of the data. *Describe* **the correlation of the data.**

Weight (pounds)	6	8	12	14	18	20	24
Roast time (hours)	2.75	3.00	3.50	4.00	4.25	4.75	5.25

Treat the data as ordered pairs. Let *x* represent the turkey weight (in pounds), and let *y* represent the time (in hours) it takes to roast the turkey. Plot the ordered pairs as points in a coordinate plane.

The scatter plot shows a positive correlation, which means that heavier turkeys tend to require more time to roast.

EXERCISES

EXAMPLE 2
on p. 326
for Ex. 21

21. **AIRPORTS** The table shows the number of airports in the Unites States for several years during the period 1990–2001. Make a scatter plot of the data. *Describe* the correlation of the data.

Years	1990	1995	1998	1999	2000	2001
Airports (thousands)	17.5	18.2	18.8	19.1	19.3	19.3

5.7 Predict with Linear Models
pp. 335–341

EXAMPLE

Use the scatter plot from the example for Lesson 5.6 above to estimate the time (in hours) it takes to roast a 10 pound turkey.

Draw a line that appears to fit the points in the scatter plot closely. There should be approximately as many points above the line as below it.

Find the point on the line whose *x*-coordinate is 10. At that point, you can see that the *y*-coordinate is about 3.25.

▶ It takes about 3.25 hours to roast a 10 pound turkey.

EXERCISES

EXAMPLE 2
on p. 336
for Ex. 22

22. **COOKING TIMES** Use the graph in the Example above to estimate the time (in hours) it takes to roast a turkey that weighs 30 pounds. *Explain* how you found your answer.

Differentiating Instruction

Exercises are easily adapted to a range of abilities. For each lesson, both skill and problem solving exercises are labeled A-, B-, and C-level in the teacher's edition.

10.2 EXERCISES

● Differentiate

Leveled exercise sets move from basic skills and problem solving to more challenging exercises.

SKILL PRACTICE

1. **VOCABULARY** *Explain* how you can tell whether a quadratic function has a maximum value or minimum value without graphing the function.

2. ★ **WRITING** *Describe* the steps you would take to graph a quadratic function in standard form.

EXAMPLE 1
on p. 635
for Exs. 3–14

FINDING AXIS OF SYMMETRY AND VERTEX Find the axis of symmetry and the vertex of the graph of the function.

3. $y = 2x^2 - 8x + 6$

4. $y = x^2 - 6x + 11$

6. $y = -x^2 - 10x$

7. $y = 6x^2 + 6x$

9. $y = -\frac{2}{3}x^2 - 1$

10. $y = \frac{1}{2}x^2 + 8x - 9$

12. ★ **MULTIPLE CHOICE** What is the vertex of the graph of $y = -3x^2 + 18x - 13$?

(A) $(-3, -94)$ (B) $(-3, -14)$ (C) $(3,$

ERROR ANALYSIS *Describe* and correct the error in fi symmetry of the graph of the given function.

13. $y = 2x^2 + 16x - 1$

14. $y =$

$$x = \frac{b}{2a} = \frac{16}{2(2)} = 4$$
The axis of symmetry is $x = 4$.

EXAMPLE 2
on p. 636
for Exs. 15–27

GRAPHING QUADRATIC FUNCTIONS Graph the functi and axis of symmetry.

15. $y = x^2 + 6x + 2$

16. $y = x^2 + 4x + 8$

18. $y = 5x^2 + 10x - 3$

19. $y = 4x^2 + x - 32$

21. $y = -3x^2 - 2x - 5$

22. $y = -8x^2 - 12x + 1$

24. $y = \frac{1}{3}x^2 + 6x - 9$

25. $y = -\frac{1}{2}x^2 + 6x + 3$

27. ★ **MULTIPLE CHOICE** Which function has the graph shown?

(A) $y = -2x^2 + 8x + 3$

(B) $y = -\frac{1}{2}x^2 + 2x + 3$

(C) $y = \frac{1}{2}x^2 + 2x + 3$

(D) $y = 2x^2 + 8x + 3$

EXAMPLE 3
on p. 637
for Exs. 28–36

MAXIMUM AND MINIMUM VALUES Tell whether the function has a *minimum value* or a *maximum value*. Then find the minimum or maximum value.

28. $f(x) = x^2 - 6$

29. $f(x) = -5x^2 + 7$

30. $f(x) = 4x^2 + 32x$

31. $f(x) = -3x^2 + 12x - 20$

32. $f(x) = x^2 + 7x + 8$

33. $f(x) = -2x^2 - x + 10$

34. $f(x) = \frac{1}{2}x^2 - 2x + 5$

35. $f(x) = -\frac{3}{8}x^2 + 9x$

36. $f(x) = \frac{1}{4}x^2 + 7x + 11$

37. ★ **WRITING** Compare the graph of $y = x^2 + 4x + 1$ with the graph of $y = x^2 - 4x + 1$.

38. **REASONING** Follow the steps below to justify the equation for the axis of symmetry for the graph of $y = ax^2 + bx + c$. Because the graph of $y = ax^2 + bx + c$ is a vertical translation of the graph of $y = ax^2 + bx$, the two graphs have the same axis of symmetry. Use the function $y = ax^2 + bx$ in place of $y = ax^2 + bx + c$.

   a. Find the x-intercepts of the graph of $y = ax^2 + bx$. (You can do this by finding the zeros of the function $y = ax^2 + bx$ using factoring.)

   b. Because a parabola is symmetric about its axis of symmetry, the axis of symmetry passes through a point halfway between the x-intercepts of the parabola. Find the x-coordinate of this point. What is an equation of the vertical line through this point?

39. **CHALLENGE** Write a function of the form $y = ax^2 + bx$ whose graph contains the points $(1, 6)$ and $(3, 6)$.

PROBLEM SOLVING

GRAPHING CALCULATOR You may wish to use a graphing calculator to complete the following Problem Solving exercises.

EXAMPLE 4
on p. 637
for Exs. 40–42

40. **SPIDERS** Fishing spiders can propel themselves across water and leap vertically from the surface of the water. During a vertical jump, the height of the body of the spider can be modeled by the function $y = -4500x^2 + 820x + 43$ where x is the duration (in seconds) of the jump and y is the height (in millimeters) of the spider above the surface of the water. After how many seconds does the spider's body reach its maximum height? What is the maximum height?

@**HomeTutor** for problem solving help at classzone.com

41. **ARCHITECTURE** The parabolic arches that support the roof of the Dallas Convention Center can be modeled by the graph of the equation $y = -0.0019x^2 + 0.71x$ where x and y are measured in feet. What is the height h at the highest point of the arch as shown in the diagram?

@**HomeTutor** for problem solving help at classzone.com

Reason

In both skill and problem solving exercises, students are asked questions that promote conceptual thinking.

EXAMPLE 4 Solve a multi-step problem

SCUBA DIVING As a scuba diver descends into deeper water, the pressure of the water on the diver's body steadily increases.

The pressure at the surface of the water is 2117 pounds per square foot (lb/ft²). The pressure increases at a rate of 64 pounds per square foot for each foot the diver descends. Find the depth at which a diver experiences a pressure of 8517 pounds per square foot.

ANOTHER WAY
For an alternative method for solving Example 4, turn to page 147 for the **Problem Solving Workshop**.

Solution

STEP 1 Write a verbal model. Then write an equation.

| Pressure at given depth (lb/ft²) | = | Pressure at surface (lb/ft²) | + | Rate of change of pressure (lb/ft² per foot of depth) | · | Diver's depth (ft) |

$$P \quad = \quad$$

STEP 2 Find the depth at wh

$$P = 2117$$
$$8517 = 2117$$
$$8517 - 2117 = 2117$$
$$6400 = 64d$$
$$\frac{6400}{64} = \frac{64d}{64}$$
$$100 = d$$

▶ A diver experiences a pressu depth of 100 feet.

CHECK $P = 2117 + 64d$
$$8517 \overset{?}{=} 2117 + 64($$
$$8517 \overset{?}{=} 2117 + 640$$
$$8517 = 8517 ✓$$

✓ **GUIDED PRACTICE** for Exam

9. **WHAT IF?** In Example 4, 5317 pounds per square f

10. **JOBS** Kim has a job wher Kim made $53 dollars, $1 she work?

PROBLEM SOLVING WORKSHOP
LESSON 3.2

Using ALTERNATIVE METHODS

Another Way to Solve Example 4, page 143

MULTIPLE REPRESENTATIONS In Example 4 on page 143, you saw how to solve a problem about scuba diving by using an equation. You can also solve the problem using a table.

PROBLEM

SCUBA DIVING As a scuba diver descends into deeper water, the pressure of the water on the diver's body steadily increases. The pressure at the surface of the water is 2117 pounds per square foot (lb/ft²). The pressure increases at a rate of 64 pounds per square foot for each foot the diver descends. Find the depth at which a diver experiences a pressure of 8517 pounds per square foot.

METHOD

Making a Table An alternative approach is to make a table.

STEP 1 Make a table that shows the pressure as the depth increases. Because you are looking for a fairly high pressure, use larger increments in depth, such as 20 feet.

> Every 1 ft of depth increases the pressure by 64 lb/ft².

> Every 20 ft of depth increases the pressure by 64(20) = 1280 lb/ft².

Depth (ft)	Pressure (lb/ft²)
0	2117
1	2181
2	2245
20	3397
40	4677
60	5957
80	7237
100	8517

STEP 2 Look for the depth at which the pressure reaches 8517 pounds per square foot. This happens at a depth of 100 feet.

PRACTICE

1. **BASKETBALL** A sports club offers an organized basketball league. A team pays $600 to join the league. In addition to paying their share of the $600, team members who are not members of the sports club must pay a $25 fee to play. A team pays a total of $775. How many team members who are not club members are on the team? Solve this problem using two different methods.

2. **WHAT IF?** In Exercise 1, suppose you are on a team, but not a club member. The $600 cost is divided equally among the team members. How many players must there be on your team for you to pay $100 to play? Make a table to find the answer.

3. **FURNITURE** You have $370 to spend on a dining table and chairs. A table costs $220, and each chair costs $35. How many chairs can you buy in addition to the table? Solve this problem using two different methods.

Using Alternative Methods   **147**

Interpret

Seeing alternative worked-out solutions helps students interpret problem solving situations.

Varying Instruction

Algebra 1 supports teaching in a variety of ways, including direct instruction, hands-on activities, paper-and-pencil explorations, and calculator-assisted solutions.

◉ Model

Using algebra tiles helps students model algebraic concepts and skills, such as multiplying binomials.

Investigating Algebra **ACTIVITY** *Use before Lesson 9.2*

9.2 Multiplication with Algebra Tiles

MATERIALS · algebra tiles

QUESTION How can you multiply binomials using algebra tiles?

You can use the following algebra tiles to model polynomials. Notice that the value of each tile is the same as its area.

1-tile   x-tile   x²-tile

EXPLORE Multiply binomials

Find the product $(x + 3)(2x + 1)$.

STEP 1 *Model the rectangle's dimensions*
Model each binomial with algebra tiles. Arrange the first binomial vertically and the second horizontally, as shown. These polynomials model the length and width of a rectangle.

STEP 2
Fill in th algebra

STEP 3 *Find the product*
The rectangle you created represents the polynomial $2x^2 + 7x +$. So, $(x + 3)(2x + 1) = 2x^2 + 7x + 3$.

DRAW CONCLUSIONS Use your observations to complete

Use algebra tiles to find the product. Include a drawing of your

1. $(x + 1)(x + 3)$ 2. $(x + 5)(x + 4)$ 3. $(2x + 1)($
4. $(3x + 2)(x + 1)$ 5. $(3x + 2)(2x + 1)$ 6. $(4x + 1)($
7. **REASONING** Find the product $x(2x + 1)$ and the product $3(2$ sum of these two products? What do your answers suggest y the product $(x + 3)(2x + 1)$?

9.2 Multiply Polynomials

Before You added and subtracted polynomials.
Now You will multiply polynomials.
Why? So you can determine areas, as in Example 7.

Key Vocabulary
• polynomial, *p. 554*
• binomial, *p. 555*

The diagram shows that a rectangle with width x and length $2x + 3$ has an area of $2x^2 + 3x$. You can also find this product by using the distributive property.

$$x(2x + 3) = x(2x) + x(3) = 2x^2 + 3x$$

In this lesson, you will learn several methods for multiplying polynomials. Each method is based on the distributive property.

EXAMPLE 1 Multiply a monomial and a polynomial

Find the product $2x^3(x^3 + 3x^2 - 2x + 5)$.

$2x^3(x^3 + 3x^2 - 2x + 5)$ **Write product.**
$= 2x^3(x^3) + 2x^3(3x^2) - 2x^3(2x) + 2x^3(5)$ **Distributive property**
$= 2x^6 + 6x^5 - 4x^4 + 10x^3$ **Product of powers property**

REVIEW PROPERTIES OF EXPONENTS
For help with using the properties of exponents, see p. 489.

EXAMPLE 2 Multiply polynomials using a table

Find the product $(x - 4)(3x + 2)$.

Solution

STEP 1 Write subtraction as addition in each polynomial.
$$(x - 4)(3x + 2) = [x + (-4)](3x + 2)$$

STEP 2 Make a table of products.

	3x	2
x	3x²	
-4		

	3x	2
x	3x²	2x
-4	-12x	-8

▶ The product is $3x^2 + 2x - 12x - 8$, or $3x^2 - 10x - 8$.

✓ GUIDED PRACTICE for Examples 1 and 2

Find the product.

1. $x(7x^2 + 4)$ 2. $(a + 3)(2a + 1)$ 3. $(4n - 1)(n + 5)$

Reason

Stepped-out examples that apply algebraic properties help students learn to reason mathematically.

8.6 Exponential Models

MATERIALS · yarn · scissors

QUESTION How can you model a situation using an exponential function?

EXPLORE Collect data so that you can write exponential models

STEP 1 *Fold and cut* Take about 1 yard of yarn and consider it to be 1 unit long. Fold it in half and cut, as shown. You are left with two pieces of yarn, each half the length of the original piece of yarn.

STEP 2 *Copy and complete* Copy the table. Notice that the row for stage 1 has the data from Step 1. For each successive stage, fold *all* the pieces of yarn in half and cut. Then record the number of new pieces and the length of each new piece until the table is complete.

Stage	Number of pieces	Length of each new piece
1	2	$\frac{1}{2}$
2	?	?
3	?	?
4	?	?
5	?	?

DRAW CONCLUSIONS Use your observations to complete thes

1. Use the data in the first and second columns of the table.
   a. Do the data represent an exponential function? *Explain* how y
   b. Write a function that models the number of pieces of yarn at st
   c. Use the function to find the number of pieces of yarn at stage

2. Use the data in the first and third columns of the table.
   a. Do the data represent an exponential function? *Explain* how y
   b. Write a function that models the length of each new piece of y stage *x*.
   c. Use the function to find the length of each new piece of yarn at

530 Chapter 8 Exponents and Exponential Functions

EXAMPLE 5 Solve a multi-step problem

TRIP EXPENSES Your art club is planning a bus trip to an art museum. The cost for renting a bus is $495, and the cost will be divided equally among the people who are going on the trip. A museum ticket costs $12.50 per person.

- Write an equation that gives the cost *C* (in dollars per person) of the trip as a function of the number *p* of people going on the trip.

- Graph the equation. *Describe* the change in the cost as the number of people increases.

- Use the graph to approximate the number of people who need to go on the trip so that the cost is about $25 per person.

San Francisco Art Museum

Solution

STEP 1 Write a verbal model. Then write an equation.

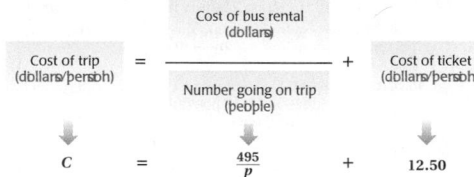

$$C = \frac{495}{p} + 12.50$$

STEP 2 Graph $C = \frac{495}{p} + 12.50$ on a graphing calculator. The vertical asymptote is $p = 0$. The horizontal asymptote is $C = 12.5$. As the number of people increases, the cost decreases.

STEP 3 Approximate the number of people needed in order for the cost to be about $25. When $C \approx 25$, the value of p is about 40. So, if about 40 people go on the trip, each person will pay about $25.

Trace
X=39.89   Y=24.90

✓ **GUIDED PRACTICE** for Example 5

7. **WHAT IF?** In Example 5, suppose the club rents a larger bus for $610. Write and graph an equation that gives the cost *C* (in dollars per person) of the trip as a function of the number *p* of people going on the trip. Then approximate the number of people who need to go on the trip so that the cost is about $25 per person.

778 Chapter 12 Rational Equations and Functions

● **Explore**

Hands-on explorations allow students to develop conceptual understanding of important ideas.

Graph ●

Using graphs to visualize real-world problems contributes to students' understanding.

Integrating Assessment

Ongoing assessment is embedded so that you can measure students' understanding and progress in each lesson and chapter.

Strategize

Standardized Test Practice examples develop math skills and suggest test-taking strategies.

COMPOUND INTEREST Compound interest is interest earned on both an initial investment and on previously earned interest. Compounding of interest can be modeled by exponential growth where a is the initial investment, r is the annual interest rate, and t is the number of years the money is invested.

★ **EXAMPLE 5** Standardized Test Practice

You put $250 in a savings account that earns 4% annual interest compounded yearly. You do not make any deposits or withdrawals. How much will your investment be worth in 5 years?

Ⓐ $300 Ⓑ $304.16 Ⓒ $1344.56 Ⓓ $781,250

ESTIMATE
You can use the simple interest formula, $I = prt$, to estimate the amount of interest earned: $(250)(0.04)(5) = 50$. Compounding interest will result in slightly more than $50.

Solution

$y = a(1 + r)^t$ Write exponential growth model.

$= 250(1 + 0.04)^5$ Substitute 250 for a, 0.04 for r, and 5 for t.

$= 250(1.04)^5$ Simplify.

≈ 304.16 Use a calculator.

You will have $304.16 in 5 years.

▶ The correct answer is B. Ⓐ Ⓑ Ⓒ Ⓓ

✓ **GUIDED PRACTICE** for Examples 4 and 5

5. **WHAT IF?** In Example 4, suppose the owner of the car sold it in 1994. Find the value of the car to the nearest dollar.

6. **WHAT IF?** In Example 5, suppose the annual interest rate is 3.5%. How much will your investment be worth in 5 years?

8.5 EXERCISES

HOMEWORK KEY
○ = **WORKED-OUT SOLUTIONS**
on p. WS1 for Exs. 13 and 41
★ = **STANDARDIZED TEST PRACTICE**
Exs. 3, 8, 34, 35, 42, 43, 46, and 50
◆ = **MULTIPLE REPRESENTATIONS**
Ex. 41

SKILL PRACTICE

1. **VOCABULARY** In the exponential growth model $y = a(1 + r)^t$, the quantity $1 + r$ is called the __?__.

2. **VOCABULARY** For what values of b does the exponential function $y = ab^x$ (where $a > 0$) represent exponential growth?

3. ★ **WRITING** How does the graph of $y = 2 \cdot 5^x$ compare with the graph of $y = 5^x$? Explain.

8.5 Write and Graph Exponential Growth Functions   **523**

---

42. ★ **SHORT RESPONSE** A company sells advertising blim[ps] shows the costs of advertising blimps of different leng[ths] represent an exponential function? Explain.

Length, ℓ (feet)	10	15	20
Cost, c (dollars)	400.00	700.00	1225.00

43. ★ **MULTIPLE CHOICE** A weblog, or blog, refers to a web[site or] personal journal. According to one analyst, over one [year the] number of blogs in existence doubled about every 6 m[onths. It is] estimated that there were about 600,000 blogs at the b[eginning of the] period. How many blogs were there at the end of the p[eriod?]

Ⓐ 660,000 Ⓑ 1,200,000 Ⓒ 4,800,00[0]

44. **TELECOMMUNICATIONS** For the period 1991–2001, the [number] y (in millions) of Internet users worldwide can be mod[eled by the] function $y = 4.67(1.65)^x$ where x is the number of years [since 1991.]

  a. Identify the initial amount, the growth factor, and t[he ...]

  b. Graph the function. Identify its domain and range.

  c. Use the graph to estimate the year in which the num[ber of Internet] users worldwide was about 21 million.

45. **GRAPHING CALCULATOR** The frequency (in hertz) of a [note on a] piano is a function of the position of the key that creat[es it. The] position of some piano keys and the frequencies of the [notes created by] the keys are shown below. Use the exponential regres[sion feature of a] graphing calculator to find an exponential model for t[he frequency of] piano notes. What is the frequency of the note created [by ...]

46. ★ **EXTENDED RESPONSE** In 1830, the population of th[e U.S.] was 12,866,020. By 1890, the population was 62,947,714.

  a. **Model** Assume the population growth from 1830 to 1890 was linear. Write a linear model for the U.S. population from 1830 to 1890. By about how much did the population grow per year from 1830 to 1890?

  b. **Model** Assume the population growth from 1830 to 1890 was exponential. Write an exponential model for the U.S. population from 1830 to 1890. By approximately what percent did the population grow per year from 1830 to 1890?

  c. **Explain** The U.S. population was 23,191,876 in 1850 and 38,558,371 in 1870. Which of the models in parts (a) and (b) is a better approximation of actual U.S. population for the time period 1850–1890? Explain.

★ = **STANDARDIZED TEST PRACTICE**

● Prepare

Solving a variety of test-format questions prepares students for high-stakes tests.

CONTEXT-BASED
MULTIPLE CHOICE QUESTIONS

Some of the information you need to solve a context-based multiple choice question may appear in a table, a diagram, or a graph.

PROBLEM 1

A recipe from a box of pancake mix is shown. The number p of pancakes you can make varies directly with the number m of cups of mix you use. A full box of pancake mix contains 9 cups of mix. How many pancakes can you make when you use the full box?

(A) 63   **(B)** 65

(C) 126   **(D)** 131

> 2 cups pancake mix
> 1 cup milk
> 2 eggs
> Combine ingredients. Pour batter on hot greased griddle. Flip when edges are dry. Makes 14 pancakes.

Interpret

Learning how to interpret information is a critical problem solving skill.

Plan

INTERPRET THE INFORMATION Use the number of pancakes and the number of cups of mix given in the recipe to write a direct variation equation. Then use the equation to find the number of pancakes that you can make when you use 9 cups of mix.

Solution

STEP 1
Use the values given in the recipe to find a direct variation equation.

Because the number p of pancakes you can make varies directly with the number m of cups of mix you use, you can write the equation $p = am$. From the recipe, you know that $p = 14$ when $m = 2$.

$p = am$	**Write direct variation equation.**
$14 = a(2)$	**Substitute.**
$7 = a$	**Solve for a.**

So, a direct variation equation that relates p and m is $p = 7m$.

STEP 2
Substitute 9 for m in the direct variation equation and solve for p.

Use the direct variation equation to find the number of pancakes you can make when you use a full box of mix.

$p = 7m$	**Write direct variation equation.**
$p = 7(9)$	**Substitute 9 for m.**
$p = 63$	**Simplify.**

You can make 63 pancakes when you use a full box of mix.

The correct answer is A. **(A) (B) (C) (D)**

276   Chapter 4   Graphing Linear Equations and Functions

TEST PRACTICE

...h below.

...on. Which ...e function?

...present a ...ncluded?

...2, 0)

...−1)

In Exercises 3 and 4, use the graph below, which shows a traveler's movements through an airport to a terminal. The traveler has to walk and take a shuttle bus to get to the terminal.

Distance (feet) vs Time (minutes)
Points: (4, 1000), (12, 1000), (13, 3000), (15, 3500)

Practice

Thorough practice builds students' confidence and skills.

3. For how many minutes does the traveler wait for the shuttle bus?

(A) 1 min   **(B)** 2 min

(C) 4 min   **(D)** 8 min

4. For about what distance does the traveler ride on the shuttle bus?

(A) 100 ft   **(B)** 100 ft

(C) 2000 ft   **(D)** 3000 ft

In Exercises 5–7, use the following information.
At a yoga studio, new members pay a sign-up fee of $50 plus a monthly fee of $25. The total cost C (in dollars) of a new membership is given by $C = 25m + 50$ where m is the number of months of membership. The owner of the studio is considering changing the cost of a new membership. A graph of four different options for changing the cost is shown.

Cost (dollars) vs Number of months — Option 1, Option 2, Option 3, Option 4

5. For which option are the sign-up fee and monthly fee kept the same?

(A) Option 1   **(B)** Option 2

(C) Option 3   **(D)** Option 4

6. For which option is the sign-up fee kept the same and the monthly fee raised?

(A) Option 1   **(B)** Option 2

(C) Option 3   **(D)** Option 4

7. For which option is the monthly fee kept the same and the sign-up fee raised?

(A) Option 1   **(B)** Option 2

(C) Option 3   **(D)** Option 4

8. The table shows the cost of a therapeutic massage for a given amount of time. What is the cost per minute?

Time (minutes)	30	45	60
Cost (dollars)	42.00	63.00	84.00

(A) $.71   **(B)** $1.40

(C) $2.80   **(D)** $14.00

278   Chapter 4   Graphing Linear Equations and Functions

PROGRAM OVERVIEW

Algebra 1 provides a complete set of resources organized for ease of use.

Pupil Edition

eEdition
CD-ROM and online

Teacher's Edition

Resource Manager

Activity Generator

**Power Presentations:
The Electronic Classroom**
with Animated Algebra

Best Practices Toolkit

Easy Planner
DVD-ROM
and
Easy Planner Plus
online

English Learners Package

Special Topics Library

Assessment and Intervention

**eWorkbook
ClassZone**

Test Generator
CD-ROM

@Home Tutor
CD-ROM and online

Workbooks

McDougal Littell Assessment System

ClassZone

RESOURCE MANAGER

The Resource Manager contains Chapter Resource Books and Transparency Books to help you adapt the program to your teaching style and to the needs of your students.

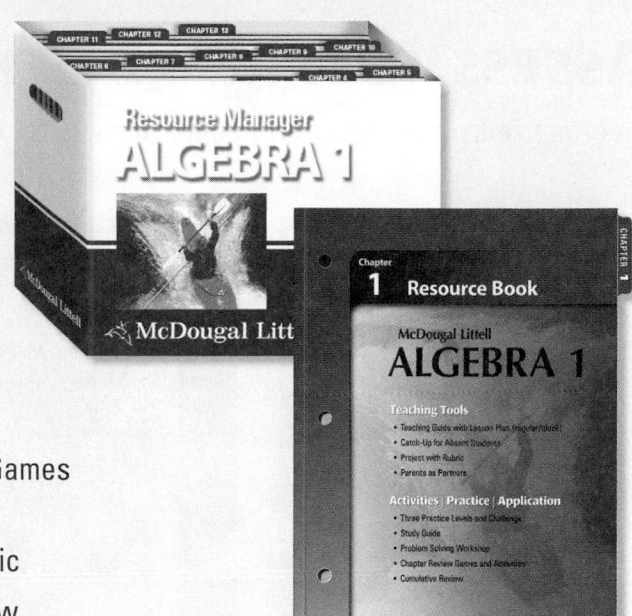

CHAPTER RESOURCE BOOKS

- Parents as Partners
- Teaching Guide with Lesson Plan (regular/block)
- Practice (Levels A, B, and C)
- Study Guide
- Problem Solving Workshop
- Challenge
- Catch-Up for Absent Students

- Activities
- Applications
- Chapter Review Games and Activities
- Project with Rubric
- Cumulative Review
- Answers

Note: There is one resource book for each chapter in the book.

CHAPTER TRANSPARENCY BOOKS

- Warm-Up and Daily Homework Quiz
- Notetaking Guide (transparencies)
- Answers (evens and odds)

Note: There is one transparency book for each chapter in the book.

WORKED-OUT SOLUTION KEY

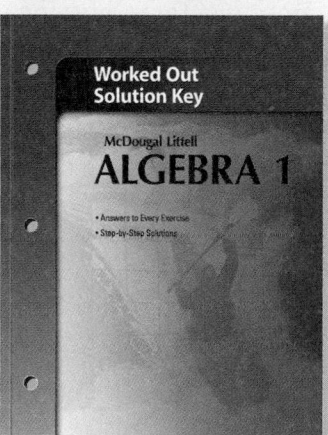

WORKBOOKS

- Practice Workbook
- Notetaking Guide (PE and TE)

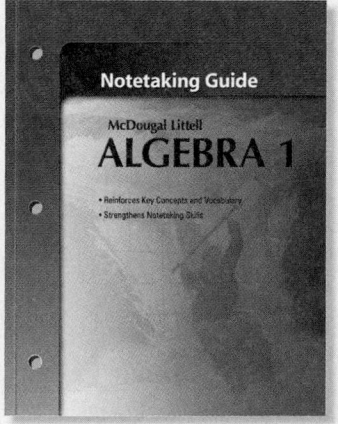

ASSESSMENT AND INTERVENTION SYSTEM

An organized set of resources helps you keep track of ongoing progress.

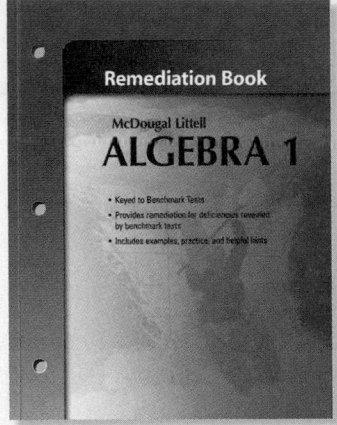

BEST PRACTICES TOOLKIT

The teaching resource contains professional materials such as suggestions for in-service workshops, professional articles on various aspects of teaching, and tips for new teachers.

Strategies For Effective Teaching

- The Bigger Picture of Mathematics
- Research-Based Solutions for Your Classroom
- Reading, Writing, Notetaking
- Differentiated Instruction
- English Learners
- Inclusion
- Strategies for Success with Sample Worksheets
- Using Technology in the Classroom
- Tips for New Teachers

- Math Background Notes
- Assessment Strategies and Rubrics with Samples

Pre-AP Resources

- Pre-AP* Overview
- Pre-AP Pacing and Assignment Guide
- Pre-AP Best Practices
- Pre-AP Copymasters

Teacher Survival Activities

- Start-of-School Activities
- Before-Vacation Activities
- Substitute Teachers' Activities
- Quick Change-of-Pace Activities
- Bulletin Board Ideas

Teacher Tool Transparencies

- Includes graphic organizers and tools such as overhead algebra tiles, protractor, and coordinate grids.

Answers

- Includes Answers to Activities and Worksheets

*Pre-AP is a registered trademark of the College Entrance Examination Board, which was not involved in the production of and does not endorse this product.

ENGLISH LEARNERS PACKAGE

A variety of resources are available to help you address the needs of English learners.

Student Resources in Spanish (PE)
Textbook exercises, chapter reviews, and chapter standardized test preparation and practice pages are translated into Spanish.

Spanish Study Guide
Provides examples and extra practice in Spanish.

Assessment Book
English Assessment Book in Spanish

Multi-Language Visual Glossary
A visual math glossary is translated into nine languages.

Quick Reference: English Learner Strategies for Math
This quick reference guide offers strategies for helping English learners in your math classroom.

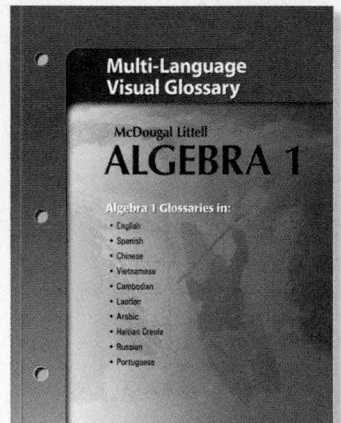

SPECIAL TOPICS LIBRARY

These student materials focus on topics of high interest. New materials are added to the library on an ongoing basis.

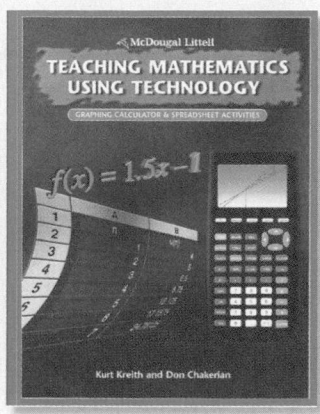

TECHNOLOGY RESOURCES

McDougal Littell offers flexible, easy-to-navigate resources online and on CD-ROM for planning, motivation, instruction, and assessment.

Power Presentations: The Electronic Classroom CD-ROM

- All the classroom resources you need to teach an interactive lesson

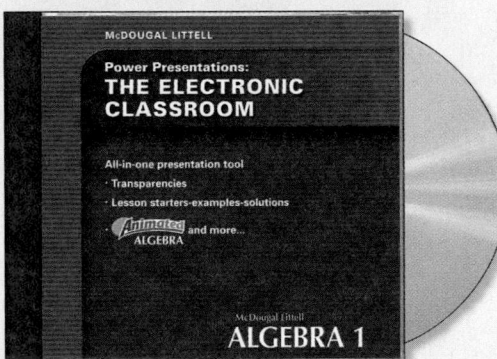

Activity Generator CD-ROM

- Leveled activities (A, B, C) for each lesson
- Teaching commentary to guide students from concrete to abstract

Easy Planner DVD

- Lesson plans you can customize
- All print teaching resources

 classzone.com

McDougal Littell's companion website provides full support for the student at home.

- Extra examples
- Vocabulary support
- Animations
- eWorkbook
- Quizzes

CD-Rom and Online Formats

@HomeTutor

- Animated examples and instruction
- Self-scoring exercises
- Customized student progress reports

ASSESSMENT

McDougal Littell Assessment System
- Innovative standards-based system
- Helps you test, score, report, reteach
- Tests and answer sheets can be printed on plain paper

Test Generator

Animated Algebra CD-ROM
- Engaging, interactive activities that support textbook lessons and exercises

Now available **Larson Learning courseware** provides multi-sensory learning to enhance core instruction in McDougal Littell textbooks. For more information about Larson Learning products, visit **mcdougallittell.com**

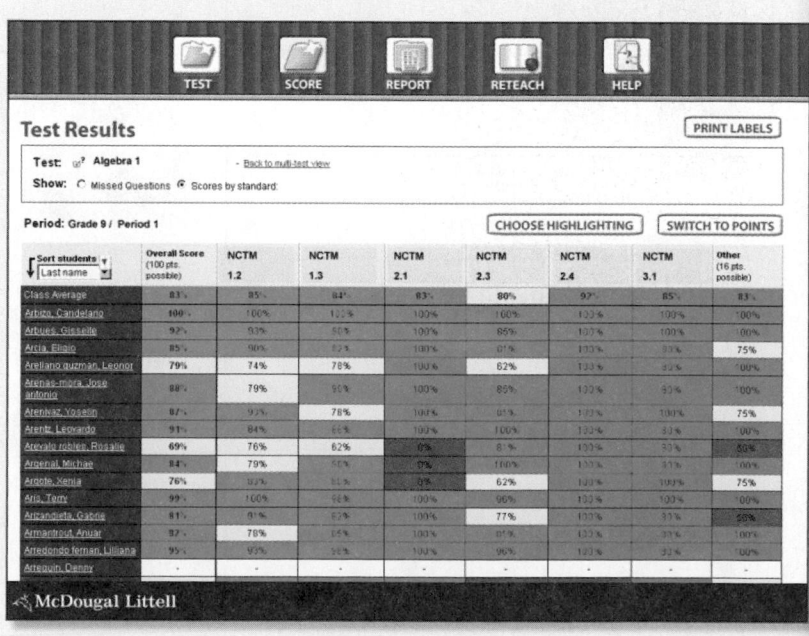

Planning the Chapter

4 Pacing and Assignment Guide

REGULAR SCHEDULE
Pre-AP For pacing and assignments for a Pre-AP course, see the *Algebra 1 Toolkit*.

Lesson	Les. Day	BASIC	AVERAGE	ADVANCED
4.1	Day 1	SRH p. 921 Exs. 7–21 odd; pp. 209–212 Exs. 1, 2, 3–11 odd, 13–17, 22–30, 36–39, 42–54 even	pp. 209–212 Exs. 1, 2, 7–13 odd, 16–22 even, 23, 24–32 even, 33–40, 43–53 odd	pp. 209–212 Exs. 1, 2, 10–13, 19–23, 26–28, 31–35*, 38–41*, 43–53 odd
4.2	Day 1	EP p. 938 Exs. 33–36; pp. 219–221 Exs. 1–10, 11–21 odd, 23–25, 42–47	pp. 219–221 Exs. 1–10, 16–25, 42–47	pp. 219–221 Exs. 1, 2, 5–10, 17–25, 34*, 42–47
	Day 2	pp. 219–221 Exs. 26–29, 35–39, 48–55	pp. 219–221 Exs. 26–32 even, 33, 35–40, 48–55	pp. 219–221 Exs. 29–33, 36–41*, 48–55
4.3	Day 1	EP p. 940 Exs. 1–7 odd; pp. 229–232 Exs. 1–10, 16–21, 28–33, 37, 44–47, 51–56	pp. 229–232 Exs. 1–3, 10–15, 22–27, 29, 30, 34–41, 44–49, 51–55 odd	pp. 229–232 Exs. 1, 2, 12–15, 24–27, 29, 30, 35–37, 39–43*, 46–50*, 52–56 even
4.4	Day 1	SRH p. 934 Exs. 6–14; pp. 239–242 Exs. 1–18, 42–56 even	pp. 239–242 Exs. 1–7, 11–18, 24–28, 43–55 odd	pp. 239–242 Exs. 1, 2, 12–18, 24–32, 43–55 odd
	Day 2	pp. 239–242 Exs. 19–27, 36–39, 57–62	pp. 239–242 Exs. 19–23, 31–33, 36–40, 57–62	pp. 239–242 Exs. 19–23, 35–41*, 57–62
4.5	Day 1	pp. 247–250 Exs. 1–13, 17–24, 30–33, 40–43, 46–56 even	pp. 247–250 Exs. 1–5, 9, 10, 13–20, 25–31, 32–38 even, 40–44, 46–56 even	pp. 247–250 Exs. 1, 2, 6–10, 14–19, 27–39*, 41–45*, 47–57 odd
4.6	Day 1	pp. 256–259 Exs. 1, 2, 3–9 odd, 10–22 even, 23–28, 40–45, 48–62 even	pp. 256–259 Exs. 1, 2, 6–10, 18–28, 29–35 odd, 40–46, 53–56, 60	pp. 256–259 Exs. 1, 2, 7–9, 19–22,
4.7	Day 1	pp. 265–268 Exs. 1, 3–11 odd, 12–18, 39–41, 46–54	pp. 265–268 Exs. 1, 7–13, 16–, 46–54	
	Day 2	pp. 265–268 Exs. 2, 19–29, 42, 55–60	pp. 265–268 Exs. 2, 27–37, 4, 55–60	
Review	Day 1	pp. 271–274 Exs. 1–34	pp. 271–274 Exs. 1–34	
Assess	Day 1	Chapter 4 Test	Chapter 4 Test	
Yearly Pacing		Chapter 4 Total – 12 days	Chapters 1–4 Total – 46 days	

*Challenge Exercises   EP

BLOCK SCHEDULE

DAY 1	DAY 2	DAY 3	DAY 4
4.1	**4.2 (CONT.)**	**4.4**	**4.5**
pp. 209–212 Exs. 1, 2, 7–13 odd, 16–22 even, 23, 24–32 even, 33–40, 43–53 odd	pp. 219–221 Exs. 26–32 even, 33, 35–40, 48–55	pp. 239–242 Exs. 1–7, 11–18, 31–33, 36–40, 43–55 odd, 57–62	pp. 247–250 Exs. 1–5, 9, 10, 13–2, 25–31, 32–38 even, 40–44, 46–56 even
4.2	**4.3**		**4.6**
pp. 219–221 Exs. 1–10, 16–25, 42–47	pp. 229–232 Exs. 1–3, 10–15, 22–27, 29, 30, 34–41, 44–49, 51–55 odd		pp. 256–259 Exs. 1, 2, 6–10, 18–2 29–35 odd, 40–46, 53–56, 60–62
Yearly Pacing	Chapter 4 Total – 6 days	Chapters 1–4 Total – 23 days	

204A

Chapter Resource Guide 4

RESOURCE MANAGER

Chapter Resource Book

CHAPTER SUPPORT

Parents as Partners (Chapter Overview with home involvement exercises and activity)						p. 1	

LESSON SUPPORT	**4.1**	**4.2**	**4.3**	**4.4**	**4.5**	**4.6**	**4.7**
Teaching Guide/Lesson Plan	p. 3	p. 16	p. 31	p. 45	p. 58	p. 75	p. 88
Activity Masters		p. 18					p. 90
Technology Activities & Keystrokes		p. 19			p. 60		
Activity Support Masters					p. 62		
Practice (3 levels)	p. 5	p. 20	p. 33	p. 47	p. 64	p. 77	p. 91
Study Guide	p. 11	p. 26	p. 39	p. 53	p. 70	p. 83	p. 97
Catch-Up for Absent Students	p. 13	p. 28	p. 41	p. 55	p. 72	p. 85	p. 99
Problem Solving/Application	p. 14	p. 29	p. 42	p. 56	p. 73	p. 86	p. 100
Challenge Practice	p. 15	p. 30	p. 44	p. 57	p. 74	p. 87	p. 101

REVIEW							
Chapter Review Games and Activities	p. 102			Cumulative Practice		p. 104	
Project with Rubric	p. 103			Resource Book Answers		A1	

Transparencies	**4.1**	**4.2**	**4.3**	**4.4**	**4.5**	**4.6**	**4.7**
Warm-Up/Daily Homework Quiz	✔	✔	✔	✔	✔	✔	✔
Notetaking Guide	✔	✔	✔	✔	✔	✔	✔
Teacher Support	✔	✔	✔	✔	✔	✔	✔
Answer Transparencies	✔	✔	✔	✔	✔	✔	✔

ASSESSMENT BOOK

Quizzes	p. 46	SAT/ACT Chapter Test	p. 57
Chapter Tests (3 levels)	p. 49	Alternative Assessment with Rubric	p. 59
Standardized Chapter Test	p. 55		

TECHNOLOGY

- Easy Planner
- Test and Practice Generator
- Power Presentations
- @HomeTutor
- Activity Generator
- Animated Algebra
- Classzone.com
- eEdition Plus Online
- eWorkbook Plus Online
- Easy Grader Online

ADDITIONAL RESOURCES

- Worked-Out Solution Key
- Notetaking Guide
- Practice Wookbook
- Algebra 1 Toolkit
- Benchmark Tests
- Reteaching and Remediation
- Spanish Study Guide
- Spanish Assessment Book
- Student Resources in Spanish
- Multi-Language Visual Glossary

204B

Regular and Block schedules for pacing the course

A handy guide for integrating resource materials into your lessons

Reduced facsimiles with annotations from the Teacher's Resource Package allow you to see and grade resources at a glance.

Planning the Lesson

Plan and Prepare
- Warm-Up Exercises
- Notetaking Guide
- Pacing summary

Focus and Motivate
- Essential Question
- Motivating the Lesson

4.3 Graph Using Intercepts

Before	You graphed a linear equation using a table of values.
Now	You will graph a linear equation using intercepts.
Why	So you can find a submersible's location, as in Example 5.

Key Vocabulary
- *x*-intercept
- *y*-intercept

You can use the fact that two points determine a line to graph a linear equation. Two convenient points are the points where the graph crosses the axes.

An **x-intercept** of a graph is the *x*-coordinate of a point where the graph crosses the *x*-axis. A **y-intercept** of a graph is the *y*-coordinate of a point where the graph crosses the *y*-axis.

To find the *x*-intercept of the graph of a linear equation, find the value of *x* when $y = 0$. To find the *y*-intercept of the graph, find the value of *y* when $x = 0$.

EXAMPLE 1 Find the intercepts of the graph of an equation

Find the *x*-intercept and the *y*-intercept of the graph of $2x + 7y = 28$.

Solution

To find the *x*-intercept, substitute 0 for *y* and solve for *x*.

$$2x + 7y = 28 \qquad \text{Write original equation.}$$
$$2x + 7(0) = 28 \qquad \text{Substitute 0 for } y.$$
(Solve for *x*.)

(substitute 0 for *x* and solve for *y*.)
(Write original equation.)
(Substitute 0 for *x*.)
(Solve for *y*.)
(*y*-intercept is 4.)

(Example 1)
(the *y*-intercept of the graph of the equation.)

2. $4x - 2y = 10$ **2.5, −5**   3. $-3x + 5y = -15$ **5, −3**

4.3 Graph Using Intercepts **225**

---

1 PLAN AND PREPARE

Warm-Up Exercises
Transparency Available
Evaluate the expression when $x = -3$.

1. $3x + 4$ **−5**
2. $-2x + 6$ **12**
3. $4x - 3$ **−15**
4. The amount *a* that a taxi service charges is given by $a = 1.5m$ where *m* is the number of miles. Find *a* when *m* is 7. **$10.50**

Notetaking Guide
Transparency Available
Promotes interactive learning and notetaking skills, pp. 80–82.

Pacing
Basic: 1 day
Average: 1 day
Advanced: 1 day
Block: 0.5 block with 4.2
- See *Teaching Guide/Lesson Plan.*

2 FOCUS AND MOTIVATE

Essential Question
Big Idea 1, p. 205
How do you use intercepts to graph equations? Tell students they will learn how to answer this question by finding and using the *x*- and *y*-intercepts of the graph of an equation.

NCTM STANDARDS
Standard 3: Specify locations using coordinate geometry
Standard 10: Use representations to communicate mathematical ideas

---

Interactive Technology
- Easy Planner
- Power Presentations CD-ROM
- Activity Generator CD-ROM
- Animated Algebra
- Test Generator CD-ROM
- Online Quiz
- eWorkbook
- eEdition
- @HomeTutor

Resources for English Learners
- Quick Reference for English Learners
- Spanish Study Guide
- Multi-Language Visual Glossary
- Student Resources in Spanish

See also the *Algebra 1 Toolkit* for more strategies for meeting individual needs.

225

Guide (pp. 80–82)
Workbook (pp. 52–54)
Options
Presentations CD-ROM
dynamic electronic teaching for the classroom.
Generator CD-ROM provides activities for all ability levels.

Motivating the Lesson
You know that your school sells T-shirts and sweatshirts with the school name on them. T-shirts cost $9 and sweatshirts cost $12. You have $144. By writing an equation and finding the intercepts of the graph of the equation, you can find the possible numbers of T-shirts and sweatshirts you can buy.

3 TEACH

Extra Example 1
Find the *x*-intercept and the *y*-intercept of the graph of $3x - 4y = 12$. **x-intercept: 4, y-intercept: −3**

Key Question to Ask for Example 1
- What coordinates are associated with the *x*-intercept and the *y*-intercept? **(14, 0), (0, 4)**

Extra Example 2
Graph the equation $4x + 8y = 24$.

Key Question to Ask for Example 2
- Why is using intercepts an efficient way to graph an equation? Since $x = 0$ and $y = 0$, it is easier to find the intercepts than other points on the line.

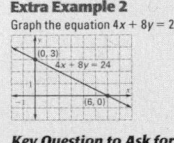
Animated Algebra classzone.com

An **Animated Algebra** activity is available on-line for **Example 2**. This activity is also available on the **Power Presentations CD-ROM**.

EXAMPLE 2 Use intercepts to graph an equation

Graph the equation $x + 2y = 4$.

Solution

STEP 1 Find the intercepts.

$$x + 2y = 4 \qquad\qquad x + 2y = 4$$
$$x + 2(0) = 4 \qquad\qquad 0 + 2y = 4$$
$$x = 4 \leftarrow \textit{x-intercept} \qquad y = 2 \leftarrow \textit{y-intercept}$$

CHECK A GRAPH
Be sure to check the graph by finding a third solution of the equation and checking to see that the corresponding point is on the graph.

STEP 2 Plot points. The *x*-intercept is 4, so plot the point (4, 0). The *y*-intercept is 2, so plot the point (0, 2). Draw a line through the points.

Animated Algebra at classzone.com

EXAMPLE 3 Use a graph to find intercepts

The graph crosses the *x*-axis at (2, 0). The *x*-intercept is 2. The graph crosses the *y*-axis at (0, −1). The *y*-intercept is −1.

✓ GUIDED PRACTICE for Examples 2 and 3

4. Graph $6x + 7y = 42$. Label the points where the line crosses the axes. **See margin.**

5. Identify the *x*-intercept and the *y*-intercept of the graph shown at the right. **−4, 2**

KEY CONCEPT *For Your Notebook*

Relating Intercepts, Points, and Graphs

Intercepts	Points
The *x*-intercept of a graph is *a*.	The graph crosses the *x*-axis at (*a*, 0).
The *y*-intercept of a graph is *b*.	The graph crosses the *y*-axis at (0, *b*).

226 Chapter 4 Graphing Linear Equations and Functions

Differentiated Instruction

Visual Learners To help students remember how to find the intercepts in problems similar to Example 2, have them make the following table.

x-intercept	*y* = 0
y-intercept	*x* = 0

Have them connect the entries in this table with an "X," pairing "*x*-intercept" with "*y* = 0" and pairing "*y*-intercept" with "*x* = 0." See also the *Algebra 1 Toolkit* for more strategies.

226

Teach
- Extra Example for each example in the book
- Key Questions to Ask for examples in the book
- Closing the Lesson summary and Essential Question at the end of each lesson
- Differentiated Instruction notes ... AND MORE

4.3 EXERCISES

HOMEWORK KEY
○ = WORKED-OUT SOLUTIONS
on p. WS1 for Exs. 21 and 47
★ = STANDARDIZED TEST PRACTICE
Exs. 2, 37, 41, 49, and 50
◆ = MULTIPLE REPRESENTATIONS
Ex. 44

SKILL PRACTICE

A 1. **VOCABULARY** Copy and complete: The __?__ of the graph of an equation is the value of x when y is zero. **x-intercept**

2. **★ WRITING** What are the x-intercept and the y-intercept of the line passing through the points $(0, 3)$ and $(-4, 0)$? *Explain.*

2. −4, 3; the x-intercept is when y is 0, so the point (−4, 0) gives the x-intercept. The y-intercept is when x is 0, so the point (0, 3) gives the y-intercept.

3. **ERROR ANALYSIS** *Describe* and correct the error in finding the intercepts of the line shown. **The intercepts are switched around; the x-intercept is −2, and the y-intercept is 1.**

> The x-intercept is 1, and the y-intercept is −2. ✗

EXAMPLE 1
on p. 225
for Exs. 4–15

FINDING INTERCEPTS Find the x-intercept and the y intercept of the graph of the equation.

4. $5x - y = 35$ **7, −35**
5. $3x - 3y = 9$ **3, −3**
6. $-3x + 9y = -18$ **6, −2**

7. $4x + y = 4$ **1, 4**
8. $2x + y = 10$ **5, 10**
9. $2x - 8y = 24$ **12, −3**

10. $3x + 0.5y = 6$ **2, 12**
11. $0.2x + 3.2y = 12.8$ **64, 4**
12. $2x + 24$ **−12, 24**

13. $y = -14x + 7$ **½, 7**
14. $y = -4.8x + 1.2$ **0.25, 1.2**
15. $y = \frac{3}{5}x - 12$ **20, −12**

EXAMPLE 2
on p. 226
for Exs. 16–27

GRAPHING LINES Graph the equation. Label the points where the line crosses the axes. **16–27. See margin.**

16. $y = x + 3$
17. $y = x - 2$
18. $y = 4x - 8$

19. $y = 5 + 10x$
20. $y = -2 + 8x$
㉑ $y = -4x + 3$

22. $3x + y = 15$
23. $x - 4y = 18$
24. $8x - 5y = 80$

25. $-2x + 5y = 15$
26. $0.5x + 3y = 9$
27. $y = \frac{1}{2}x + \frac{1}{4}$

...tify the x-intercept and the

29.

30.

$-4, 3$

4.3 Graph Using Intercepts **229**

C 50. **★ EXTENDED RESPONSE** You borrow $180 from a friend who doesn't charge you interest. You work out a payment schedule in which you will make weekly payments to your friend. The balance B (in dollars) of the loan is given by the function $B = 180 - pn$ where p is the weekly payment and n is the number of weeks you make payments.

a. **Interpret** Without finding the intercepts, state what they represent.

b. **Graph** Graph the function if you make weekly payments of $20. **See margin.**

c. **Identify** Find the domain and range of the function in part (b). How long will it take to pay back your friend? **domain: $0 \le n \le 9$, range: $0 \le B \le 180$; 9 wk**

d. **CHALLENGE** Suppose you make payments of $20 for three weeks. Then you make payments of $15 until you have paid your friend back. How does this affect the graph? How many payments do you make? **The graph is two line segments; 11 payments.**

50a. The B-intercept is the balance of the loan after 0 weeks, the n-intercept is the amount of time it takes to pay off the loan.

MIXED REVIEW

REVIEW GRAPHS
For help with line graphs, see p. 934.

In Exercises 51–53, use the line graph, which shows the number of points Alex scored in five basketball games. *(p. 934)*

51. How many points did Alex score in game 4? **16 points**

52. In which game did Alex score the most points? **game 2**

53. How many more points did Alex score in game 5 than in game 1? **12 more points**

PREVIEW
Prepare for Lesson 4.4 in Exs. 54–56.

Solve the proportion. *(p. 934)*

54. $\frac{3}{5} = \frac{x}{30}$ **18**
55. $\frac{x}{x+6} = \frac{7}{6}$ **−42**
56. $\frac{t-3}{12} = \frac{2t-2}{9}$ **−$\frac{1}{5}$**

QUIZ for Lessons 4.1–4.3

Plot the point in a coordinate plane. *Describe* the location of the point. *(p. 206)*
1–3. See margin for art.

1. $(-7, 2)$ **Quadrant II**
2. $(0, -5)$ **y-axis**
3. $(2, -6)$ **Quadrant IV**

Graph the equation. *(p. 215)* **4–6. See margin.**

4. $-4x - 2y = 12$
5. $y = -5$
6. $x = 6$

Find the x-intercept and the y-intercept of the graph of the equation. *(p. 225)*

7. $y = x + 7$ **−7, 7**
8. $y = x - 3$ **3, −3**
9. $y = -5x + 2$ **$\frac{2}{5}$, 2**
10. $x + 3y = 15$ **15, 5**
11. $3x - 6y = 36$ **12, −6**
12. $-2x - 5y = 22$ **−11, −$4\frac{2}{5}$**

13. **SWIMMING POOLS** A public swimming pool that holds 45,000 gallons of water is going to be drained for maintenance at a rate of 100 gallons per minute. The amount of water w (in gallons) in the pool after t minutes is given by the function $w = 45,000 - 100t$. Graph the function. Identify its domain and range. How much water is in the pool after 60 minutes? How many minutes will it take to empty the pool? *(p. 225)* **See margin for art; domain: $0 \le t \le 450$, range: $0 \le w \le 45,000$; 39,000 gal; 450 min.**

232

EXTRA PRACTICE for Lesson 4.3, p. 941 ⏺ **ONLINE QUIZ** at classzone.com

---

Pacing the Course

The Pacing Chart below shows the number of days allotted for each chapter. The Regular Schedule requires 160 days. The Block Schedule requires 80 days. These time frames include days for review and assessment: 2 days per chapter for the Regular Schedule and 1 day per chapter for the Block Schedule. Semester and trimester divisions are indicated by blue and green rules, respectively.

CHAPTER	SEMESTER 1							SEMESTER 2					
	1	2	3	4	5	6	7	8	9	10	12	12	13
Regular Schedule	10	12	12	12	12	12	10	12	14	16	10	14	14
Block Schedule	5	6	6	6	6	6	5	6	7	8	5	7	7
	Trimester 1					Trimester 2				Trimester 3			

Assignments are provided with each lesson for a basic course, an average course, an advanced course, and a block-schedule course. Each of the four courses covers all thirteen chapters.

Basic Course

The basic course is intended for students who enter with below-average mathematical and problem solving skills. Assignments include:
- spiral review of pre-course and on-level topics through Skills Review Handbook and Extra Practice references
- substantial work with the skills and concepts presented in the lesson
- straightforward applications of these skills and concepts
- test preparation and mixed review exercises

Average Course

The average course is intended for students who enter with typical mathematical and problem-solving skills. Assignments include:
- substantial work with the skills and concepts presented in the lesson
- applications of these skills and concepts
- test preparation and mixed review exercises

Advanced Course

The advanced course is intended for students who enter with above-average mathematical and problem-solving skills. Assignments include:
- substantial work with the skills and concepts presented in the lesson
- more complex applications and challenge exercises
- test preparation and mixed review exercises
- optional extra challenge exercises provided in the Chapter Resource Books

Block-Schedule Course

The block-schedule course is intended for schools that use a block schedule. It covers the same content as the regular-schedule course. The exercises assigned are comparable to the exercises for the average course.

The Pacing and Assignment Guide for each chapter is located on the interleaved pages preceding the chapter. Part of the Pacing Chart for Chapter 4 is shown here.

Regular-Schedule Chart
This chart provides pacing for the basic, average, and advanced courses.

REGULAR SCHEDULE

Lesson	Les. Day	BASIC	AVERAGE	ADVANCED
4.1	Day 1	SRH p. 921 Exs. 7–21 odd; pp. 209–212 Exs. 1, 2, 3–11 odd, 13–17, 22–30, 36–39, 42–54 even	pp. 209–212 Exs. 1, 2, 7–13 odd, 16–22 even, 23, 24–32 even, 33–40, 43–53 odd	pp. 209–212 Exs. 1, 2, 10–13, 19–23, 26–28, 31–35*, 38–41*, 43–53 odd
4.2	Day 1	EP p. 938 Exs. 33–36; pp. 219–221 Exs. 1–10, 11–21 odd, 23–25, 42–47	pp. 219–221 Exs. 1–10, 16–25, 42–47	pp. 219–221 Exs. 1, 2, 5–10, 17–25, 34*, 42–47
	Day 2	pp. 219–221 Exs. 26–29, 35–39, 48–55	pp. 219–221 Exs. 26–32 even, 33, 35–40, 48–55	pp. 219–221 Exs. 29–33, 36–41*, 48–55
4.3	Day 1	EP p. 940 Exs. 1–7 odd; pp. 229–232 Exs. 1–10, 16–21, 28–33, 37, 44–47, 51–56	pp. 229–232 Exs. 1–3, 10–15, 22–27, 29, 30, 34–41, 44–49, 51–55 odd	pp. 229–232 Exs. 1, 2, 12–15, 24–27, 29, 30, 35–37, 39–43*, 46–50*, 52–56 even

Block-Schedule Chart
This chart provides pacing for the block-schedule course.

BLOCK SCHEDULE

DAY 1	DAY 2	DAY 3	DAY 4	DAY 5	DAY 6
4.1	**4.2 (CONT.)**	**4.4**	**4.5**	**4.7**	**REVIEW**
pp. 209–212 Exs. 1, 2, 7–13 odd, 16–22 even, 23, 24–32 even, 33–40, 43–53 odd	pp. 219–221 Exs. 26–32 even, 33, 35–40, 48–55	pp. 239–242 Exs. 1–7, 11–28, 31–33, 36–40, 43–55 odd, 57–62	pp. 247–250 Exs. 1–5, 9, 10, 13–20, 25–31, 32–38 even, 40–44, 46–56 even	pp. 265–268 Exs. 1, 2, 7–13, 16–22, 27–37, 39–44, 46–60	pp. 271–274 Exs. 1–34
4.2	**4.3**		**4.6**		**ASSESS**
pp. 219–221 Exs. 1–10, 16–25, 42–47	pp. 229–232 Exs. 1–3, 10–15, 22–27, 29, 30, 34–41, 44–49, 51–55 odd		pp. 256–259 Exs. 1, 2, 6–10, 18–28, 29–35 odd, 40–46, 53–56, 60–62		Chapter 4 Test

Assignment Guide
An assignment guide for each lesson is provided at the beginning of the exercise set. Assignments are given for basic, average, advanced, and block-schedule courses.

Assignment Guide
Basic
Day 1: SRH p. 921 Exs. 7–21 odd; pp. 209–212 Exs. 1, 2, 3–11 odd, 13–17, 22–30, 42–54 even

Average
Day 1: pp. 209–212 Exs. 1, 2, 7–13 odd, 16–22 even, 23, 24–32 even, 33–40, 43–53 odd

Advanced
Day 1: pp. 209–212 Exs. 1, 2, 10–13, 19–23, 26–28, 31–35*, 38–41*, 43–53 odd

Block
pp. 209–212 Exs. 1, 2, 7–13 odd, 16–22 even, 23, 24–32 even, 33–40, 43–53 odd (with 4.2)

Meeting your planning and teaching needs

Contents

The following pages include information about the *Algebra 1* program and explain how it reflects current research in mathematics instruction.

A letter from the authors

Dear Colleagues,

We wanted to create a program that would help your students succeed in mathematics and make your teaching job easier. To achieve these objectives, we reviewed and addressed the curriculum and assessment guidelines of many states and of the National Council of Teachers of Mathematics. We also developed an extensive collection of teacher resources to assist you in the classroom. Our overall goal was to prepare your students both for important assessments and for future mathematics courses.

Our commitment has always been to writing books that contain accurate mathematics, sound pedagogy, and student-friendly presentations. We believe that a balance of teaching approaches is generally most effective. Therefore, we combine clear, straightforward instruction in concepts and skills with thought-provoking student activities, relevant real-life applications, and powerful strategies for problem solving and communication. We have also incorporated feedback from many teachers and students nationwide who have used earlier editions or pilot materials in the classroom.

During more than 16 years of working together as an author team, we have remained dedicated to helping students at all levels achieve high mathematics standards. Our textbooks provide differentiated instruction for struggling students, carefully constructed examples and practice for the majority of students, and demanding challenge exercises for more advanced students.

We wish you success as you strive to give every student in your classroom a quality mathematics education.

Ron Larson

Laurie Boswell

Tim Kanold

Lee Stiff

A Program You Can Trust

A program you can count on to help students gain understanding and achieve success

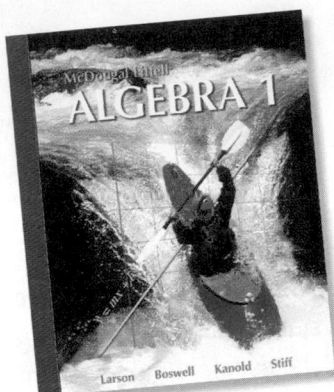

McDougal Littell Algebra 1 is a program you can count on to teach the mathematical concepts and methods your students need to know to meet high curriculum standards and succeed on high-stakes tests. Including the appropriate content, however, is not enough. The math must be presented in a way that students can understand and that will motivate them to learn. The distinguished author team of *McDougal Littell Algebra 1* and the thorough, research-based planning and development process ensure that students gain conceptual understanding and achieve success on important assessments.

Distinguished Author Team

The experienced, expert author team of Ron Larson, Laurie Boswell, Timothy Kanold, and Lee Stiff brings a wealth of mathematical expertise, writing talent, and classroom teaching and curriculum planning experience from middle school through college to the creation of this program. Lead author Ron Larson has been writing highly-respected and widely-used textbooks for more than 20 years, and each new book benefits from the comments of the many teachers and students who used earlier editions.

Standards-Based Instruction and Assessment

In planning the outline and writing the textbook, the authors paid careful attention to state curriculum standards and state assessment objectives from all states to make sure that the important mathematical concepts and skills were included and given appropriate emphasis. The authors also made sure that the outline and course content fully addressed the standards of national organizations such as the National Council of Teachers of Mathematics (see pages T57–T58) and the National Assessment of Educational Progress (see page T59).

... validated by research

Supporting Best Practices from Research

Recent research studies have confirmed strategies for increasing student achievement. These strategies, which reflect the best practices of successful teachers, can help all students learn more effectively. The authors kept this research in mind as they planned and wrote *Algebra 1*, so that the content, organization, and instructional strategies in the program would make it easy for you to implement best-practice instruction in your classroom.

Comprehensive Research and Review

Several years prior to publication, the authors and teams of editors, consultants, graphic designers, professional researchers, and experts in content, instruction, and technology began gathering and analyzing the extensive data on which this program is based. Data were gathered in the following ways:

- **Classroom Visits** Discussions and classroom observations took place in schools throughout the country to determine the key needs of teachers and students, the obstacles that they face in achieving their goals, and the types of materials that can help them achieve success.

- **Nationwide Research Surveys** Comprehensive mail surveys on Algebra 1 curriculum needs, instructional practices, student achievement levels, and teacher preferences regarding instructional materials were conducted early in the development process to guide the planning of the program.

- **Teacher Panels** Panels of expert teachers from different areas of the country participated in the development of the program by identifying instructional and curriculum needs, reviewing prototype outlines and sample materials for both print and electronic materials, and providing suggestions for teaching-support publications.

- **Student Discussion Groups** Discussion groups were held with Algebra 1 students to determine the textbook characteristics that make it easy or hard for them to learn and the extent to which they have access to and feel comfortable using electronic products.

- **Focus Tests** Focus tests in which teachers discussed their instructional goals and evaluated sample student and teacher materials were held in different areas of the country. The teachers were chosen to represent the wide range of types of schools, philosophies of instruction, and teacher characteristics (like number of years of teaching) in the teaching population. The feedback from these diverse groups was used to revise and refine the project plans.

- **Curriculum Advisers and Reviewers** The Curriculum Advisers and Reviewers listed on pages T4–T5 participated in planning the program and read all the proof for the student edition in detail with regard to clarity, accuracy, and appropriateness for classroom use. Other teacher reviewers read selected chapters for these characteristics.

- **Learner Verification** The *Algebra 1, Geometry, Algebra 2 Research-Based Framework and Learner Verification* book provides information about the instructional research on which the program was based as well as classroom research demonstrating the effectiveness of the program.

What is mathematics?

The Bigger Picture of Mathematics

by Dr. Ron Larson,
Lead Author of the
Larson Mathematics Series

What is Mathematics? You would think that this is an easy question to answer. But, it isn't.

Was mathematics discovered or was it invented? Is mathematics a logical system that exists devoid of applications or is mathematics a problem solving language whose very essence is solving real-life problems? Is correct calculation an important part of mathematics or is it only important to be able to "set the problem up" correctly? Is mathematics a system of rules or is mathematics a way of thinking?

As mathematics teachers, it is important for us to realize that mathematics is all of these things. We need to be careful to pass this understanding on to our students so that they will not have a narrow answer to the question "What is Mathematics?" We need to show them the bigger picture of mathematics.

Mathematics as Calculation

Most people equate mathematics with calculation. While this view of mathematics is too limited, it is still true that calculation plays a critical role in mathematics.

I worry when I hear educators dismissing calculation as "something best left to calculators" or even worse, as "drill and kill." I prefer to think about other phrases that describe the importance of calculation, such as "practice makes perfect."

... in our world

When I drive across a bridge, I am thankful that the teacher of the civil engineer who designed the bridge believed in the importance of correct calculation.

The point is that part of our job as mathematics teachers is to help prepare skilled professionals who can fly planes, prescribe medicines, and do any of thousands of other technically difficult jobs.

But, there may be a stronger reason for teaching students to calculate correctly. It is simply the way that students learn best. They learn specific examples first. Generalization comes later.

After a career in mathematics, it is clear to me that we derive important insights into a mathematical theory when we see how it relates to actual calculations.

Mathematics as a Field of Study

Mathematics, of course, is not simply a collection of techniques for calculating sums, products, slopes, and so on. Mathematics has content. It has a vocabulary of defined and undefined terms. It has a collection of axioms and theorems.

The vocabulary and rules of mathematics comprise much of the curriculum we teach from grade school through high school.

Like it or not, the vocabulary of mathematics is formal. It has to be in order to provide for clear communication. It is important that students know the difference between an expression and an equation. We *evaluate* an expression. We *solve* an equation.

The rules of mathematics are also formal—they are rigid and unforgiving. We don't do students favors when we allow them to approach mathematics in a sloppy manner. Mathematics

must be approached carefully, with the confidence that comes from knowing its rules.

Mathematics as a Modeling Language

It is difficult to know which of the many faces of mathematics was the first to show itself on our planet. Surely, one of the first was the use of symbols and calculations to model and solve real-life problems.

To me, the perennial debate about the virtues of applied versus pure mathematics isn't productive. From a historical point of view, it seems clear that both must be taught—hand-in-hand—from grade school through high school.

To be good at mathematics, students must understand the various types of models we use: linear, quadratic, cubic, radical, rational, exponential, logarithmic, and trigonometric. They must learn to translate real-life situations to mathematical models, obtain mathematical solutions, and then translate those solutions back into the context of the real-life application.

Mathematics as Logical Thought

Perhaps the most difficult task we face as mathematics teachers is to teach our students to think logically.

The real world is filled with logical fallacy—such as some advertisements and political slogans that contain illogical arguments. As mathematics teachers, we can improve our nation and our world by teaching careful logical thought to our students.

In light of all these things, I hope that this text helps your students get a view of the bigger picture of mathematics.

The Bigger Picture
in *Algebra 1*

The following chart shows how the various ways of looking at mathematics described in the article on pages T50–T51 are developed across the *Algebra 1* book.

Because these strands of thought are integrated throughout the book, the lesson references here are selected examples in each category, not a comprehensive listing.

Mathematics as Calculation

Performing calculations	Order of operations (1.2), operations with integers (2.2, 2.3, 2.4, 2.6), solving equations (3.1, 3.2, 3.3, 3.4), solving proportions (3.6), finding slope (4.4), solving systems (7.3, 7.4), using the Pythagorean theorem and distance formula (11.4, 11.5), permutations and combinations (13.2, 13.3)

Mathematics as a Field of Study

Using mathematical vocabulary	Functions (1.6), coordinate plane (4.1), slope (4.4), compound inequalities (6.4), exponents (8.3), probability and odds (13.1), measures of central tendency and dispersion (13.6)
Knowing mathematical principles	Properties of addition (2.2), properties of multiplication (2.4), distributive property (2.5), properties of equality (3.1), properties of inequality (6.1, 6.2), rules of exponents (8.1, 8.2, 8.3)

Mathematics as a Modeling Language

Using mathematical models	Direct variation (4.6), linear functions (4.7), lines of fit (5.6), predicting with linear models (5.7), exponential growth and decay (8.5, 8.6), quadratic functions (10.1, 10.2), comparing linear, exponential, and quadratic models (10.8), square root functions (11.1), inverse variation (12.1), rational functions (12.2)
Translating real-life situations to mathematical models, obtaining solutions, then translating solutions back into real-life contexts	Elections (1.7), speed of sound (2.7), batting average (3.1), membership fees (3.4), event planning (4.3), cooking (5.2), sales tax (6.3), job earnings (6.7), investments (7.4), nutrition (7.6), music frequency (8.5), depreciation (8.6), genetic traits (9.3), vertical motion (9.4), long jump (11.1), electric circuits (12.6)

Mathematics as Logical Thought

Thinking logically	Conditional statements and counterexamples (2.1), deductive and inductive reasoning (2.7 Ext.), proof (11.2 Ext.), Venn diagrams (6.4 Act., 13.4), error analysis and reasoning exercises (throughout)

Providing Universal Access

We want *all* students to develop computational, procedural, and problem solving skills to provide a solid foundation for further study in mathematics. In most classrooms, however, students present a variety of achievement levels, skills, and needs, and they do not arrive at competencies at the same time or in the same way.

Algebra 1 is organized so that much of the differentiation for special needs students is built into the program. Simpler concepts are introduced before more complex ones. Activities provide students with models for conceptual understanding of the mathematical reasoning behind each key concept. Ample practice is provided, and each lesson includes exercises that recall and use skills and understandings from previous chapters. Mathematical reasoning is emphasized and challenge exercises are included throughout each chapter.

You can use the table below to help plan your approach to students with various needs. See also the *Algebra 1 Best Practices Toolkit* for more suggestions.

FOUR BASIC STUDENT GROUPS

Advanced Group	Grade Level Group	Underachieving Group	Intensive Needs Group
Advanced students have already completed some of the grade-level material. They make rapid progress and become bored with repetition. They may have been formally identified as gifted or talented in the area of mathematics.	Students achieving at grade level may have minor, occasional difficulties but they can be assisted to maintain their progress with extra practice and individual or group assistance on an as-needed basis.	These learners are not achieving at expected grade level but can, with a program that provides targeted assistance. Systematic differentiation such as preteaching, reteaching, and additional instructional time should be planned.	Intensive needs students are those whose performance is two or more standard deviations below the mean on standardized measures. These students will probably already be eligible for special education services.
SUGGESTED PLAN	**SUGGESTED PLAN**	**SUGGESTED PLAN**	**SUGGESTED PLAN**
1. Assess what these students already know.	1. Assess what these students already know.	1. Assess what these students already know.	1. Assess what these students already know.
2. Allow these students to "test out" of chapters or assignments.	2. Progress through *Algebra 1* at the recommended pace and sequence.	2. Provide additional scaffolding and the instructional variations suggested in this book.	2. Determine if these students have an IEP.
3. Substitute challenging assignments for easier ones.	3. On an ad hoc basis, review or provide additional practice as needed.	3. Focus on the key concepts and present material systematically.	3. Refer students for special education testing or child study team discussion; enlist the help of specialists.
4. Modify instruction so that it is more complex or more in-depth.		4. Vary the kinds of instruction so that students have several opportunities to understand.	4. Carefully consider each student's most appropriate placement in mathematics.
		5. Provide additional practice homework.	5. Use the specific suggestions for underachieving learners.

Maximizing Success for English Learners

Accommodating various levels of reading and math achievement

English learners in your classroom may be at, behind, or ahead of grade expectations in mathematics. You can maximize success for English learners by assessing each student's competencies in mathematics and English to form a basis for program planning. The table below summarizes the attributes of various English learners and how you can help accommodate their needs.

Prior to each chapter in *Algebra 1*, you will find suggestions to help you modify curriculum and instruction so the content is accessible to English learners. The suggestions and activities are designed to teach mathematical vocabulary, explain mathematical concepts in a variety of ways, and dissect the structure of word problems. See also the *Algebra 1 Best Practices Toolkit* for more suggestions.

Low Mathematics Achievement

Low Reading Achievement

Who is the student?
- Student may be new to the class, school, or country.
- Student may have had inadequate schooling.
- Student may have moved a lot.
- Student may be unmotivated or have test anxiety.
- Low reading achievement may be depressing mathematics scores.
- Student may have gaps and holes in knowledge.
- Student may need special education assistance.

What to do?
- Examine cumulative folder for other testing, notes, etc.
- Ask questions about language use and prior schooling.
- Delay any testing for a week or two. Help student feel comfortable in the class during that period of time.
- Administer mathematics achievement test and reading test, in an individual setting.
- Assess this student at weekly intervals and monitor classroom work to determine if progress is being made.
- Look at the English Learners suggestions in each chapter.

High Reading Achievement

Who is the student?
- Student may have been designated as an English learner because oral skills lag behind reading skills.
- Student may not test well in mathematics.
- Most students can make rapid progress in mathematics; a few may have learning difficulties that require the help of a specialist.

What to do?
- Assess mathematics achievement in a variety of ways.
- Concentrate on developing oral fluency.
- Focus on vocabulary specific to mathematics.
- Use a student's reading ability to improve his or her math scores.

High Mathematics Achievement

Low Reading Achievement

Who is the student?
- Student has had good prior mathematics instruction.
- Mathematics is an area where this student can excel.
- Math achievement level may actually be higher than scores indicate. (Limited English reading skills affect math achievement as well.)
- Word problems will be especially difficult.

What to do?
- Mathematics instruction should proceed at normal or near normal pace.
- Student should be involved in a systematic English language development program and intensive reading program outside of mathematics class.
- Spend part of each class period on vocabulary study.
- Provide student with a bilingual dictionary or math glossary and a mathematics text in the home language.
- Look at the English Learners suggestions in each chapter for those that are most useful.

High Reading Achievement

Who is the student?
- Student may be ready for designation as a fluent English speaker.
- May need extra study in the specialized vocabulary of mathematics. Complex syntax may present obstacles to performance.
- Given systematic instruction, this student should be able to achieve at or above grade level.

What to do?
- Scan all of the suggestions for English learners in each chapter and progress through the ones the student needs as quickly as possible.
- Monitor carefully to make sure this student continues to progress at a reasonable pace.

Differentiating Instruction

All students, whether they are struggling, average, or advanced learners, must have opportunities to make continuing progress in developing the skills they need to become successful adults. To develop these skills, students need to participate in courses that are based on challenging curriculum standards and assessment objectives. *McDougal Littell Algebra 1* has been designed around sound, challenging curriculum standards. Through ongoing assessment and practice with test-taking skills and standardized test formats, this program prepares students for high-stakes tests.

The *McDougal Littell Algebra 1* program provides you with helpful materials for differentiating instruction to reach all students, for assessing student progress throughout the course, and for diagnosing student understanding in order to provide appropriate prescription and remediation. The charts below illustrate some of the ways in which this program helps you differentiate for the diverse classroom.

PLANNING AND MOTIVATING THE LESSON

Feature	Description
Student Edition: Chapter Prerequisite Skills	Exercises at the beginning of each chapter that review pre-chapter vocabulary and skills
Student Edition: Investigating Algebra Activities	Pre-lesson activities where students explore concepts and discover mathematical results
Teacher's Edition: Pacing and Assignment Guides	Schedules for teaching the lessons of each chapter, along with three levels of exercise assignments for every lesson (basic, average, and advanced)
Teacher's Edition: Warm-Up Exercises	Exercises that review skills needed for the upcoming lesson; also available on transparencies
Teaching Guides with Lesson Plans (in Chapter Resource Books)	Tips for getting students ready for each lesson, teaching the lesson, assigning homework, and assessing students' knowledge
Best-Practices Toolkit	A collection of effective teaching strategies, pre-AP resources, "teacher survival" activities (for use at the start of the school year, before vacation, etc.), and teacher tool transparencies
Easy Planner	Software that provides customizable lesson plans as well as all print teaching resources in an electronic format
Activity Generator	Software that offers leveled activities for each lesson and teaching commentary to guide students from the concrete to the abstract
Animated Algebra	Interactive electronic activities that support textbook lessons and exercises

... in the diverse classroom

TEACHING THE LESSON

Feature	Description
Student Edition: Guided Practice	Problems for each example that help you monitor how well students are grasping concepts and skills as you present the lesson
Student Edition: Leveled Exercise Sets	Exercise sets for each lesson that are divided into three difficulty levels (A, B, and C); levels are labeled in the Teacher's Edition
Student Edition: Problem Solving Workshops	Features that present alternative methods for solving an example from the preceding lesson
Teacher's Edition: Extra Examples	Additional examples modeled after each example in the textbook
Teacher's Edition: Differentiated Instruction Notes	Tips for tailoring instruction to students of different abilities and learning styles
Chapter Resource Books	Booklets for every chapter that include a chapter study guide, a project, catch-up for absent students, and additional activities, applications, cumulative review, and challenge exercises
Notetaking Guide	A workbook that gives students a framework for recording the key concepts of every lesson
@HomeTutor	Software that provides animated examples and instruction, self-scoring exercises, and customized student progress reports
Power Presentations: The Electronic Classroom	All the classroom resources needed to teach an interactive lesson using Microsoft PowerPoint

REVIEWING AND ASSESSING

Feature	Description
Student Edition: Skills Review Handbook	Examples and practice for reviewing essential prerequisite skills from earlier courses
Student Edition: Extra Practice	Exercises for each chapter that can be used by students who need more practice or who want to review for chapter tests
Benchmark Tests	Tests for measuring student progress, including a Pre-Course Test and End-of-Course Tests
Remediation Book	A guide containing examples, practice, and helpful hints for remediating deficiencies revealed by benchmark tests
Assessment Book (English and Spanish)	A resource that provides quizzes, three levels of chapter tests, SAT/ACT chapter tests, cumulative tests, and alternative assessment
Spanish Study Guide	Extra examples and practice in Spanish
Student Resources in Spanish	Chapter reviews, chapter tests, and standardized test preparation and practice in Spanish
Test Generator	Software that creates customized, editable tests and practice worksheets based on topics you select
McDougal Littell Assessment System	Innovative standards-based assessment software that helps you test, score, report, and reteach

National Council of Teachers of Mathematics

The chart below lists the lessons and other features in the textbook that address the NCTM Content Standards. These five standards cover the content areas of number and operations, algebra, geometry, measurement, and data analysis and probability.

CONTENT STANDARDS

1. NUMBER AND OPERATIONS

Understand numbers, ways of representing numbers, relationships among numbers, and number systems; understand meanings of operations and how they relate to one another; compute fluently and make reasonable estimates.

1.1 through 1.2 Tech. Act., 2.1, 2.2 Act. through 2.4, 2.5, 2.6, 2.7, 3.1 through 3.4 Tech. Act., 3.7, 3.7 Ext., 6.2 Act., 8.1 Act. through 8.4 Tech. Act., 8.6 Act., 11.2 Act., 11.2, 13.2 through 13.3 Tech. Act., 13.6, 13.6 Ext., Skills Review Handbook

2. ALGEBRA

Understand patterns, relations, and functions; represent and analyze mathematical situations and structures using algebraic symbols; use mathematical models to represent and understand quantitative relationships; analyze change in various contexts.

1.3 Act. through 1.6, 1.7, 1.7 Ext., 2.1 Ext., 2.4 through 2.5, 3.1 Act. through 3.3, 3.5 through 3.6 Ext., 3.8, 4.2, 4.2 Ext. through 4.7, 5.1, 5.3, 5.4, 5.5, 6.1 through 6.3 Ext., 6.4 through 6.6, 6.7, 7.1 Act., 7.1, 7.2 through 7.6, 8.1 Act. through 8.2, 8.3 Act., 8.3, 8.4, 8.5 through 8.6 Ext., 9.1 through 9.8, 10.1 through 10.6, 10.7 through 10.8 Tech. Act., 11.1 through 11.4 Act., 11.5, 12.1 Act. through 12.7

3. GEOMETRY

Analyze characteristics and properties of two- and three-dimensional geometric shapes and develop mathematical arguments about geometric relationships; specify locations and describe spatial relationships using coordinate geometry and other representational systems; apply transformations and use symmetry to analyze mathematical situations; use visualization, spatial reasoning, and geometric modeling to solve problems.

3.6 Ext., 4.1 through 4.2 Tech. Act., 4.3, 4.4, 4.6, 4.7, 5.1 through 5.3, 5.5, 6.3 Ext., 6.5 Ext., 6.7 Act., 6.7, 7.1, 7.1 Tech. Act., 7.5, 7.6, 8.5, 8.6, 9.1 Tech. Act., 10.1 through 10.3 Tech. Act., 10.5 Ext., 10.7 Act., 10.8 Tech. Act., 11.1, 11.1 Tech. Act., 11.4 Act. through 11.5, 12.1 Act. through 12.2, 12.3 Tech. Act., Skills Review Handbook

4. MEASUREMENT

Understand measurable attributes of objects and the units, systems, and processes of measurement; apply appropriate techniques, tools, and formulas to determine measurements.

1.5, 3.6, 3.6 Ext., 3.8, 4.4 Act., 4.4, 5.1 Act., 5.1, 6.5, Skills Review Handbook

5. DATA ANALYSIS AND PROBABILITY

Formulate questions that can be addressed with data and collect, organize, and display relevant data to answer them; select and use appropriate statistical methods to analyze data; develop and evaluate inferences and predictions that are based on data; understand and apply basic concepts of probability.

1.7 Act., 2.6, 5.6 through 5.7 Tech. Act., 6.6, 10.8, 10.8 Tech. Act., 13.1 Act. through 13.3, 13.4 through 13.8 Tech. Act., Skills Review Handbook

National Council of Teachers of Mathematics

The chart below lists the lessons and other features in the textbook that address the NCTM Process Standards. These five standards cover the processes of problem solving, reasoning and proof, communication, connections, and representation.

PROCESS STANDARDS

6. PROBLEM SOLVING

Build new mathematical knowledge through problem solving; solve problems that arise in mathematics and in other contexts; apply and adapt a variety of appropriate strategies to solve problems; monitor and reflect on the process of mathematical problem solving.

Occurs throughout. E.g.: 1.3 through 1.5, 2.4, 2.5, 2.5 PSW, 3.2, 3.5, 3.8, 4.2, 4.3, 4.6, 5.1, 5.2, 5.3, 5.4, 5.7, 6.3, 6.3 PSW, 6.4, 7.2, 7.3, 7.6, 8.2, 8.4, 9.2, 9.4, 9.5, 9.6 through 9.8, 10.3, 10.4, 10.5, 10.7, 10.8, 11.2, 11.3, 11.4, 11.5 PSW, 12.1, 12.3, 12.5, 12.7, 13.1, 13.2, 13.3, 13.4, 13.5, Skills Review Handbook

7. REASONING AND PROOF

Recognize reasoning and proof as fundamental aspects of mathematics; make and investigate mathematical conjectures; develop and evaluate mathematical arguments and proofs; select and use various types of reasoning and methods of proof.

Occurs throughout. E.g.: 2.1, 2.7 Act., 2.7 Ext., 4.7, 5.5 Act., 6.4 Act., 6.4, 7.3, 11.2 Ext., 13.1 Act.; Reasoning exs.: 2.4, 4.1, 5.2, 8.2, 10.2, 13.3; Error analysis exs.: 1.6, 3.3, 6.5, 7.2, 9.6, 11.1, 12.4

8. COMMUNICATION

Organize and consolidate their mathematical thinking through communication; communicate their mathematical thinking coherently and clearly to peers, teachers, and others; analyze and evaluate the mathematical thinking and strategies of others; use the language of mathematical ideas precisely.

Occurs throughout. E.g.: 1.5, 1.7 Act., 2.7 Act., 4.5, 4.6, 4.7, 5.1 Tech. Act., 5.2, 7.6, 8.3, 9.2, 9.3, 10.6, 12.3 Act., 13.1 Ext., 13.5, 13.7, 13.8; Explain exs.: 2.4, 3.6, 5.3, 6.1, 8.1, 10.1, 11.4, 12.7; Writing exs.: 1.7, 3.3, 4.1, 6.6, 7.4, 9.8, 11.2, 13.7

9. CONNECTIONS

Recognize and use connections among mathematical ideas; understand how mathematical ideas interconnect and build on one another to produce a coherent whole; recognize and apply mathematics in contexts outside of mathematics.

Occurs throughout. E.g.: 1.7 Act., 1.7, 2.3, 2.4 Ext., 3.3, 3.4, 3.5 through 3.6 Ext., 4.5, 4.6, 5.3 Ext., 5.5 through 5.7 Tech. Act., 6.7, 7.1, 7.1 Tech. Act., 7.5, 8.3 Ext., 8.5 through 8.6 Ext., 10.7 Act. through 10.8 Tech. Act., 11.4 Act., 11.4, 11.5, 12.2, 12.7

10. REPRESENTATION

Create and use representations to organize, record, and communicate mathematical ideas; select, apply, and translate among mathematical representations to solve problems; use representations to model and interpret physical, social, and mathematical phenomena.

Occurs throughout. E.g.: 1.3, 1.4, 1.6 through 1.7 Ext., 2.1 Ext., 2.3 Tech. Act., 3.1 Act., 3.4, 3.4 Tech. Act., 4.1 through 4.3, 4.4, 4.5 Ext. through 4.7, 5.1, 5.3 Ext., 5.6 through 5.7 Tech. Act., 6.1, 6.2, 6.3 Ext., 6.4 Act., 6.4 Tech. Act., 6.5 Ext., 6.7 Act., 6.7, 7.1 Act. through 7.1 Tech. Act., 7.4, 7.5, 8.5 through 8.6, 9.1, 9.2, 9.3, 9.5 Act., 9.6 Act. through 9.8, 10.1, 10.3, 10.5 Act., 10.8 Act. through 10.8 Tech. Act., 11.1, 12.2 Act., 12.2, 12.3 Tech. Act., 12.7, 13.4, 13.7 through 13.8 Tech. Act.; Multiple Representations examples and exercises: 3.4, 5.7, 8.5, 10.8, 11.1, 13.4

National Assessment of Educational Progress

The NAEP is used to assess student understanding of math across the nation. The chart below lists the topics assessed by the NAEP, and lessons and features from *McDougal Littell Algebra 1* that address them.

Number Properties and Operations

1. Number sense	2.1, 2.2 Act., 2.2, 2.7, 6.1, 6.2, 8.4, 11.5, 11.5 Act., 13.1–13.3, Skills Review Handbook
2. Estimation	1.4, 1.5, 2.7, 3.1, 3.2, 5.6, 5.7, 8.2, 10.7 Act., 10.7, Skills Review Handbook
3. Number operations	1.1–1.3, 1.5, 2.1–2.4, 2.6, 3.6 Ext., 3.7, 4.4, 7.3, 7.4, 8.1, 8.2, 9.1, 9.2, 11.4, 11.4 Act., 13.1–13.6
4. Ratios and proportional reasoning	3.5–3.7, 13.3–13.6, Skills Review Handbook
5. Properties of number and operations	1.1, 2.1–2.6, 9.5 Act.–9.8

Measurement

1. Measuring physical attributes	1.5, 3.3 (Exs. 33, 34), 3.4 (Exs. 44–46), 3.5, 3.8, 8.5, 8.6, 10.3 (Exs. 47–49), 10.4 (Exs. 47–49), 11.4 Act.
2. Systems of measurement	1.5, 3.1 (Ex. 60), 11.4, 11.5, Skills Review Handbook

Geometry

1. Dimension and shape	1.5, 11.5, 12.1 Act., Skills Review Handbook
2. Transformation of shapes and preservation of properties	3.6, 9.2 Act., 9.5 Act., 9.6 Act., 11.4 Act., 10.5 Ext., Skills Review Handbook
3. Relationships between geometric figures	5.5, 7.1 Act.–7.6, 11.4 Act., 11.4, Skills Review Handbook
4. Position and direction	5.5, 7.5, 10.1 (Ex. 40), 11.4, 11.5 Act., 11.5, Skills Review Handbook
5. Mathematical reasoning	11.4 Act., 11.4, 11.5 (Ex. 51), Skills Review Handbook

Data Analysis and Probability

1. Data representation	1.7 Act., 1.7, 4.1, 5.6 Act., 5.6, 5.7 Act., 5.7, 13.7 Act., 13.7, 13.8 Act., 13.8
2. Characteristics of data sets	6.6, 10.8 Act., 13.4–13.8
3. Experiments and samples	13.5, 13.6
4. Probability	13.1–13.6

Algebra

1. Patterns, relations, and functions	1.6, 1.7, 1.7 Ext., 4.1–4.7, 5.3, 5.3 Ext., 5.5–5.7, 10.8, 11.4 Act.
2. Algebraic representations	1.3, 1.5–1.7, 4.1, 4.3, 7.1–7.5, 8.5, 8.6, 10.8, 11.1, 12.2
3. Variables, expressions, and operations	1.1–1.6, 3.1–3.8, 5.1–5.3, 7.1–7.6, 8.1–8.6
4. Equations and inequalities	1.4, 3.1–3.4, 3.6–3.8, 4.3–4.5, 5.1–5.5, 6.1–6.6, 7.1–7.6

Pacing and Assignment Guide

1

Pre-AP For pacing and assignments for a Pre-AP course, see the *Algebra 1 Toolkit*.

Lesson	Les. Day	BASIC	AVERAGE	ADVANCED
1.1	Day 1	SRH p. 914 Exs. 11–15; pp. 5–7 Exs. 1, 2, 3–13 odd, 15–25, 27–41 odd, 48–52, 56–65	pp. 5–7 Exs. 1, 2, 4–14 even, 15, 16–22 even, 24, 25, 26–44 even, 45, 46, 49–54, 57–65	pp. 5–7 Exs. 1, 2, 10–14, 15–23 odd, 32–44 even*, 45–47, 50–63*
1.2	Day 1	SRH p. 915 Exs. 11–15; pp. 10–12 Exs. 1, 2, 3–17 odd, 19–26, 28–30, 34–38, 41–52	pp. 10–12 Exs. 1, 2, 8–18 even, 20–39, 41–52	pp. 10–12 Exs. 1, 2, 13–19, 25–33*, 36–40*, 43–52
1.3	Day 1	SRH p. 929 Exs. 1–6; pp. 18–20 Exs. 1, 2, 3–11 odd, 13, 14, 15–21 odd, 22–27, 31–35, 38–46 even	pp. 18–20 Exs. 1, 2, 4–12 even, 13–29, 32–37, 41–46	pp. 18–20 Exs. 1, 2, 9–14, 18–25, 28–30*, 33–37*, 44–46
1.4	Day 1	pp. 24–26 Exs. 1, 2, 3–13 odd, 14–16, 17–35 odd, 39–45, 49–57 odd	pp. 24–26 Exs. 1, 2, 7–11, 13–16, 21–28, 32–38, 41–46, 50–56 even	pp. 24–26 Exs. 1, 2, 9–13, 16, 22–28 even, 32–38*, 42–48*, 50, 51, 56, 57
1.5	Day 1	SRH p. 937 Exs. 1–4; pp. 31–33 Exs. 1–10, 14–20, 24–32	pp. 31–33 Exs. 1, 2, 4–13, 16–22, 24–32	pp. 31–33 Exs. 1, 2, 4, 5, 8–13*, 17–23*, 25–31 odd
1.6	Day 1	pp. 38–40 Exs. 1–15	pp. 38–40 Exs. 1, 2, 4, 5, 7–16	pp. 38–40 Exs. 1, 2, 5, 8, 11–13, 18, 19, 22*
	Day 2	pp. 38–40 Exs. 16–20, 23–27, 30–36	pp. 38–40 Exs. 17–28, 30–36	pp. 38–40 Exs. 23–36*
1.7	Day 1	pp. 46–48 Exs. 1–11, 15–19, 21–30	pp. 46–48 Exs. 1, 2, 4–13, 15–19, 21–30	pp. 46–48 Exs. 1, 2, 6–8, 11–20*, 23–30
Review	Day 1	pp. 53–56 Exs. 1–40	pp. 53–56 Exs. 1–40	pp. 53–56 Exs. 1–40
Assess	Day 1	Chapter 1 Test	Chapter 1 Test	Chapter 1 Test
Yearly Pacing		Chapter 1 Total – 10 days	Chapter 1 Total – 10 days	Remaining – 150 days

*Challenge Exercises   EP = Extra Practice   SRH = Skills Review Handbook

DAY 1	DAY 2	DAY 3	DAY 4	DAY 5
1.1	**1.3**	**1.5**	**1.6 (CONT.)**	**REVIEW**
pp. 5–7 Exs. 1, 2, 4–14 even, 15, 16–22 even, 24, 25, 26–44 even, 45, 46, 49–54, 57–65	pp. 18–20 Exs. 1, 2, 3–11 odd, 13–29, 32–37, 41–46	pp. 31–33 Exs. 1, 2, 4–13, 16–22, 24–32	pp. 38–40 Exs. 17–28, 30–36	pp. 53–56 Exs. 1–40
1.2	**1.4**	**1.6**	**1.7**	**ASSESS**
pp. 10–12 Exs. 1, 2, 8–18 even, 20–39, 41–52	pp. 24–26 Exs. 1, 2, 7–11, 13–16, 21–28, 32–38, 41–46, 50–56 even	pp. 38–40 Exs. 1, 2, 4, 5, 7–16	pp. 46–48 Exs. 1, 2, 4–13, 15–19, 21–30	Chapter 1 Test
Yearly Pacing	Chapter 1 Total – 5 days	Chapter 1 Total – 5 days	Remaining – 75 days	

RESOURCE MANAGER

Chapter Resource Book

CHAPTER SUPPORT

Parents as Partners (Chapter Overview with home involvement exercises and activity)						p. 1	

LESSON SUPPORT

	1.1	1.2	1.3	1.4	1.5	1.6	1.7
Teaching Guide/Lesson Plan	p. 3	p. 15	p. 27	p. 37	p. 49	p. 59	p. 70
Activity Masters		p. 17		p. 39			
Technology Activities & Keystrokes	p. 5	p. 18				p. 61	
Activity Support Masters							
Practice (3 levels)	p. 7	p. 19	p. 29	p. 40	p. 51	p. 62	p. 72
Study Guide	p. 10	p. 23	p. 32	p. 43	p. 54	p. 65	p. 78
Catch-Up for Absent Students	p. 12	p. 24	p. 34	p. 45	p. 56	p. 67	p. 80
Problem Solving/Application	p. 13	p. 25	p. 35	p. 46	p. 57	p. 68	p. 81
Challenge Practice	p. 14	p. 26	p. 36	p. 48	p. 58	p. 69	p. 82

REVIEW

Chapter Review Games and Activities	p. 83	Cumulative Practice	p. 85
Project with Rubric	p. 84	Resource Book Answers	A1

Transparencies

	1.1	1.2	1.3	1.4	1.5	1.6	1.7
Warm-Up/Daily Homework Quiz	✔	✔	✔	✔	✔	✔	✔
Notetaking Guide	✔	✔	✔	✔	✔	✔	✔
Teacher Support			✔			✔	✔
Answer Transparencies	✔	✔	✔	✔	✔	✔	✔

ASSESSMENT BOOK

Quizzes	p. 1	SAT/ACT Chapter Test	p. 12
Chapter Tests (3 levels)	p. 4	Alternative Assessment with Rubric	p. 14
Standardized Chapter Test	p. 10		

TECHNOLOGY

- Easy Planner
- Test and Practice Generator
- Power Presentations
- @HomeTutor
- Activity Generator
- Animated Algebra
- Classzone.com
- eEdition Plus Online
- eWorkbook Plus Online
- Easy Grader Online

ADDITIONAL RESOURCES

- Worked-Out Solution Key
- Notetaking Guide
- Practice Workbook
- Algebra 1 Toolkit
- Benchmark Tests
- Reteaching and Remediation
- Spanish Study Guide
- Spanish Assessment Book
- Student Resources in Spanish
- Multi-Language Visual Glossary

Lesson Practice Level B

LESSON 1.1 Practice B
For use with pages 2–7

Evaluate the expression.

1. $y + 12$ when $y = 29$ 41
2. $47 - x$ when $x = 38$ 9
3. $0.8a$ when $a = 7.5$ 6
4. $12.5 + m$ when $m = 7.6$ 20.1
5. $r(4.6)$ when $r = 8.1$ 37.26
6. $6.25 \div g$ when $g = 2.5$ 2.5
7. $\frac{x}{0.9}$ when $x = 54$ 60
8. $\frac{62}{d}$ when $d = 3.1$ 20
9. $\frac{4}{7} \cdot t$ when $t = \frac{7}{8}$ $\frac{1}{2}$
10. $r(8.3)$ when $r = 10.2$ 84.66
11. $w + \frac{2}{5}$ when $w = \frac{1}{2}$ $\frac{9}{10}$
12. $\frac{n}{2.4}$ when $n = 12$ 5

Write the power in words and as a product.

13. 8^7 eight to the seventh power; $8 \cdot 8 \cdot 8 \cdot 8 \cdot 8 \cdot 8 \cdot 8$
14. $(0.1)^4$ one tenth to the fourth power; $0.1 \cdot 0.1 \cdot 0.1 \cdot 0.1$
15. x^5 x to the fifth power; $x \cdot x \cdot x \cdot x \cdot x$

Evaluate the power.

16. 9^2 81
17. 2^6 64
18. $(0.4)^3$ 0.064

Evaluate the expression.

19. x^2 when $x = \frac{1}{5}$ $\frac{1}{25}$
20. m^4 when $m = 0.6$ 0.1296
21. $2y^3$ when $y = 4$ 128

22. **Side Table** A side table has interior storage space in the shape of a cube. What is the volume of the storage space if the interior length is 12 inches? 1728 in.³

12 in.
12 in.
12 in.

23. **Playing Cards** There are 52 cards in a standard deck of playing cards. You are combining decks of cards so that you can play a game with a large number of people. The expression $52d$ represents the number of cards in d decks. If you combine 4 decks of cards, how many cards will you have altogether? 208 cards

24. **Sales Tax** An item costs c dollars and 6% sales tax is charged. The total cost including sales tax is given by the expression $1.06c$. You are buying a skateboard that costs $75. What is the cost of the skateboard including sales tax? $74.50

25. **Flower Arranging** You are creating a flower arrangement for a friend. The total cost (in dollars) for one vase and f flowers is given by the expression $8 + 2.5f$. How much will it cost to make an arrangement with 8 flowers? $28

LESSON 1.2 Practice B
For use with pages 8–13

Evaluate the expression.

1. $16 \div 8 \cdot 5$ 10
2. $7^2 - 24 \div 3$ 41
3. $5 + 1.2 \div 0.3$ 9
4. $18 \div 6 + 4 \cdot 3$ 15
5. $13 - 15 \div 5 + 9$ 19
6. $\frac{2}{3} \cdot 3^2 - 5$ 1
7. $8(6 - 2) + 4$ 36
8. $28 - 3(4 + 5)$ 1
9. $1.2 \cdot 5 - 6 \div 3$ 4
10. $(11 + 15) \div 13$ 2
11. $35 - 3^2 \cdot 2$ 17
12. $\frac{4}{5}(3 \cdot 20) - 17$ 31

Evaluate the expression.

13. $3x^4 - 5$ when $x = 5$ 1870
14. $8m^3 \div 6$ when $m = 3$ 36
15. $200 - 3y^2$ when $y = 8$ 8
16. $5c^2 - 2c$ when $c = 9$ 387
17. $3 \cdot 18t^2$ when $t = \frac{1}{3}$ 6
18. $\frac{42}{n} + n$ when $n = 6$ 13
19. $7(x + 5)$ when $x = 10$ 105
20. $\frac{5a}{a - 6}$ when $a = 8$ 20
21. $\frac{4d^2}{d + 1}$ when $d = 3$ 9

22. Was the expression evaluated correctly using the order of operations? If not, find and correct the error.

$$80 - \frac{1}{3}(15)^2 = 80 - 5^2 = 80 - 25 = 55 \quad \text{no; } 80 - \frac{1}{3}(15)^2 = 80 - \frac{1}{3}(225) = 80 - 75 = 5$$

23. **Tournament** During a bowling tournament, you bowled three games with scores of 110, 130, and 129, respectively. Your average bowling score is given by $\frac{110 + 130 + 129}{3}$. What is your average score? 123

24. **Painting** Three weeks ago, an art supply store started selling a paint kit for 75% of the original price. Now the kit is 15% off of the sale price. The expression $0.75x - 0.15(0.75x)$ represents the current price of the paint kit where x is the kit's original price (in dollars). Find the current price of the kit if it originally cost $48. $30.60

25. **Crown Molding** You are decorating the perimeter of the ceiling of your living room with crown molding. The expression $2x + 2y$ represents the total amount of molding you need where x is the width of the room (in feet) and y is the length of the room (in feet). Find the total amount of wood you need if the room is 11 feet wide and 10.5 feet long. 43 ft

26. **Core Sample** Before a structure is built on a plot of land, it is sometimes necessary to test the surface beneath the plot of land to determine its integrity. So, it may be necessary to take a core sample which is cylindrical in shape. Find the volume of the core sample shown by using the expression $\pi r^2 h$ where r is the radius (in inches) and h is the height (in inches) of the cylinder. Use 3.14 for π. 1017.36 in.³

3 in.

36 in.

LESSON 1.3 Practice B
For use with pages 14–20

Translate the verbal phrase into an expression.

1. The difference of 9 and a number n $9 - n$
2. The quotient of a number y and 22 $\frac{y}{22}$
3. The sum of 57 and a number b $57 + b$
4. $\frac{2}{3}$ of a number x $\frac{2}{3}x$
5. 18 less than a number c $c - 18$
6. 25 more than twice a number m $25 + 2m$
7. The quotient of 8 and twice a number z $\frac{8}{2z}$
8. The sum of 2 and the square of a number r $2 + r^2$

Write an expression for the situation.

9. The amount of money you spent if you started with $40 and now have d dollars $40 - d$
10. The total height of a 1-foot tall birdbath if it is placed on a base that is b feet tall $b + 1$
11. Each person's share of baseball cards if 4 people share c cards equally $\frac{c}{4}$
12. Number of minutes in h hours $60h$

Find the unit rate.

13. $\frac{\$75}{5 \text{ video games}}$ $15/video game
14. $\frac{600 \text{ students}}{8 \text{ classes}}$ 75 students/class
15. $\frac{32 \text{ pencils}}{4 \text{ boxes}}$ 8 pencils/box

16. **Candle Making** You are making candles for your friends. A mold for the candles costs $22.50 and wax to make one candle costs $5. Write an algebraic expression for the total cost of making x candles. You make 8 candles. Find the total cost. $22.5 + 5x$; $62.50

17. **Baseball** Last season, a baseball player scored 14 runs in 18 games. This season, the baseball player scored 12 runs in 15 games. Find the number of runs scored per game in each season. Round your answers to the nearest hundredth. Then identify the season in which the player scored more runs per game. Last season: 0.78 runs/game; This season: 0.80 runs/game; This season

18. **Car Trip** You are getting ready to make a 640-mile car trip. In general, your car can drive 160 miles on 5 gallons of gasoline. How many gallons of gasoline will you use for the trip? You started out with 4 gallons of gasoline in your car and gasoline is $2.05 per gallon. How much money will you spend on gasoline on the trip? 20 gal; $32.80

19. **Plant Trellis** You are building the wood trellis shown in the figure so that you can grow a vine up the side of your home. Write an expression for the total number of feet of wood needed to build the trellis. *Hint:* Write separate expressions for the number of feet of vertical pieces needed and the number of feet of horizontal pieces needed. Then find the total number of feet of wood needed if the trellis is 8 feet tall and 2 feet wide.

$6x + 3y$; 36 ft

x ft
y ft

LESSON 1.4 Practice B
For use with pages 21–26

Write an equation or an inequality.

1. The difference of a number c and 17 is more than 33. $c - 17 > 33$
2. The product of 3 and a number x is at most 21. $3x \leq 21$
3. The sum of 14 and twice a number y is equal to 78. $14 + 2y = 78$
4. The difference of 22 and the quotient of a number m and 4 is 54. $22 - \frac{m}{4} = 54$
5. The sum of 7 and three times a number b is at least 12. $7 + 3b \geq 12$

Check whether the given number is a solution of the equation or inequality.

6. $6x + 7 = 25$; 3 yes
7. $22 - 5c = 8$; 3 no
8. $\frac{b}{4} - 7 = 1$; 36 no
9. $7a + 4 \geq 20$; 2.7 yes
10. $4y - 3 > 12$; 4 yes
11. $\frac{m}{3} + 14 < 33$; 9 yes

Solve the equation using mental math.

12. $x + 9 = 17$ 8
13. $y - 5 = 12$ 17
14. $8w = 48$ 6
15. $\frac{m}{4} = 16$ 64
16. $2x - 1 = 15$ 8
17. $3x + 2 = 20$ 6

18. **Computers** You are buying a new printer and a new scanner for your computer, and you cannot spend over $150. The printer you want costs $80. Write an inequality that describes the most that you can spend on the scanner and still stay within your budget. If you buy a scanner that costs $75, will you remain within your budget? $80 + x \leq 150$; no

19. **Go-Carts** You and three of your friends are going to race go-carts. The last time you went, you had a coupon for $3 off each admission and paid $48 for the 4 admissions. What was the total price without the coupon? You pay the regular price this time and share it equally. How much does each person pay? $60; $15

20. **Bracelets** You are making beaded bracelets for your friends. You want to use 30 beads for each bracelet and want to use no more than 145 beads. Write an inequality that models this situation. Can you make 4 bracelets? $30x \leq 145$; yes

21. **Staircase** When building a staircase, you need to be concerned with the height of the riser and the depth of the tread so that people can go up and down the stairs comfortably. One rule of thumb used to determine proper riser height and tread depth is that the sum of the tread depth (in inches) and twice the riser height (in inches) should equal 26 inches. Write an equation that models this situation. The riser height of a set of steps is 5 inches. What should the depth be? $t + 2r = 26$; 16 in.

tread
riser

In Exercises 1 and 2, identify what you know and what you need to find out. You do *not* need to solve the problem. See below.

1. You are making cookies for a bake sale and need to make enough cookies to fill 24 boxes containing 6 cookies each. How many dozen cookies do you need to make?

2. The cellular phone plan you signed up for gives you 400 minutes a month for $35 and charges $.15 for each additional minute over 400 minutes. How long can you talk on the phone each month and stay within a budget of $45?

In Exercises 3 and 4, state the formula that is needed to solve the problem. You do *not* need to solve the problem.

3. You invest $200 into a savings account that earns 2% simple interest. How long will it take to earn $50 in interest? $I = Prt$

4. It takes you half an hour to travel 26 miles to work. What is your average speed? $d = rt$

5. **Sticker Collection** Your sticker collection consists of 175 stickers. Each sticker is either an animated cartoon character or an animal. There are 42 less stickers that are animated characters than stickers that are animals. Let x be the number of stickers that are animals. Which equation correctly models this situation? c
   a. $x - 42 = 175$
   b. $x + (x + 47) = 175$
   c. $x + (x - 42) = 175$

6. **Bookshelf** You installed a bookshelf on the wall to organize some of your books. The books that you absolutely want on the shelf weigh a total of $6\frac{3}{4}$ pounds. The bookshelf can handle no more than 9 pounds. You plan on filling the rest of the shelf with your paperbacks that each weigh about $\frac{1}{8}$ pound. Assuming you won't run out of room, how many paperback books can you add to the shelf? 18

7. **Camping** You are responsible for buying supplies for an upcoming camping trip. You can buy packages of stew that just need water added and then are heated. Each package costs $4.95 and contains enough stew for 2 people. You need to buy enough packages so that you can have stew for 3 days of the trip. There will be 8 people on the trip. How many packages do you need? What is the total cost? 12; $59.40

8. **Banking** You are going to open a certificate of deposit (CD) that earns simple interest. One bank offers a CD in which you must deposit $500 for 3 years with 2% interest. Another bank offers a CD in which you must deposit $250 for 4 years with 3% interest. Which CD will earn more interest? Neither; they both earn the same amount.

1. Know: Number of boxes and number of cookies in one box; Need to find out: How many dozen cookies need made

2. Know: Charge for 400 minutes of service, charge per minute over 400 minutes, and amount you can spend; Need to find out: How many minutes over 400 you can talk

---

Complete the sentence.

1. The input variable is called the __?__ variable. independent

2. The output variable is called the __?__ variable. dependent

6.
Domain	1	2	3	4
Range	2	6	10	14

Tell whether the pairing is a function.

3.
Input	Output
1	15
3	20
5	15
7	20

function

4.
Input	Output
5	5
6	5
7	5
8	5

function

5.
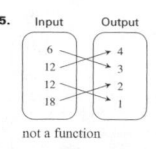

not a function

Make a table for the function. Identify the range of the function.

6. $y = 4x - 2$
   Domain: 1, 2, 3, 4
   See above.

7. $y = 0.1x + 3$
   Domain: 10, 20, 30, 40
   See below.

8. $y = \frac{1}{2}x + 2$
   Domain: 6, 7, 8, 9
   See below.

Write a rule for the function.

9.
Input, x	1	2	3	4
Output, y	5	10	15	20

$y = 5x$

10.
Input, x	10	11	12	13
Output, y	3	4	5	6

$y = x - 7$

11. **Shoe Sizes** The table shows men's shoe sizes in the United States and Australia. Write a rule for the Australian size as a function of the United States' size.

U.S. size	5	6	7	8	9	10
Australian size	3	4	5	6	7	8

$y = x - 2$

7.
Domain	10	20	30	40
Range	4	5	6	7

12. **Balloon Bunches** You are making balloon bunches to attach to tables for a charity event. You plan on using 8 balloons in each bunch. Write a rule for the total number of balloons used as a function of the number of bunches created. Identify the independent and dependent variables. How many balloons will you use if you make 10 bunches? $y = 8x$; independent: number of balloon bunches; dependent: number of balloons; 80 balloons

13. **Baking** A baker has baked 10 loaves of bread so far today and plans on baking 3 loaves more each hour for the rest of his shift. Write a rule for the total number of loaves baked as a function of the number of hours left in the baker's shift. Identify the independent and dependent variables. How many loaves will the baker make if he has 4 hours left in his shift?
   $y = 10 + 3x$; independent: number of hours left in shift; dependent: number of loaves baked; 22 loaves

8.
Domain	6	7	8	9
Range	5	5.5	6	6.5

Graph the ordered pairs.

1. (3, 4), (4, 7), (5, 10), (6, 13), (7, 16)

2. (2, 5), (6, 7), (4, 6), (12, 10), (10, 9)

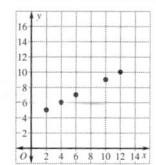

Complete the input-output table for the function.

3. $y = 3x + 2$

x	0	1	2	3
y	2	5	8	11

4. $y = 4x - 1$

x	1	2	3	4
y	3	7	11	15

Graph the function.

5. $y = 6 - x$
   Domain: 6, 5, 4, 3, 2

6. $y = \frac{1}{3}x$
   Domain: 6, 9, 12, 15, 18

7. $y = 4x - 3$
   Domain: 1, 2, 3, 4, 5

8. $y = 1.2x$
   Domain: 1, 2, 3, 4, 5

Write a rule for the function represented by the graph. Identify the domain and range of the function. 10. $y = 4x - 1$; Domain: 1, 2, 3, 4; Range: 3, 7, 11, 15

9.

10.

11.
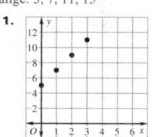

9. $y = x + 6$; Domain: 0, 1, 2, 3; Range: 6, 7, 8, 9 11. $y = 2x + 5$; Domain: 0, 1, 2, 3; Range: 5, 7, 9, 11

12.

13.

14.
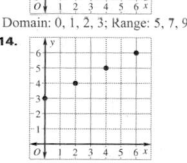

12. $y = \frac{1}{3}x$; Domain: 3, 6, 9, 12; Range: 1, 2, 3, 4 13. $y = 6x - 4$; Domain: 1, 2, 3, 4; Range: 2, 8, 14, 20

15. **High Temperatures** The table shows the high temperature H (in degrees Fahrenheit) in a city during the week as a function of the number of days d since Monday. Graph the function. Describe how the high temperatures change as the week progresses. 15. Answers will vary.

Number of days since Monday, d	0	1	2	3	4	5
High temperature (degrees Fahrenheit), H	24	34	41	39	37	39

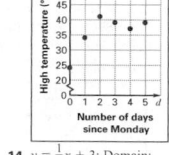

14. $y = \frac{1}{2}x + 3$; Domain: 0, 2, 4, 6; Range: 3, 4, 5, 6

16. **Metal Screws** The table shows the number of threads per inch on a screw as a function of screw size.

Screw size number, x	0	1	2	3	4	5	6
Number of threads per inch, y	80	72	64	56	48	44	40

a. Graph the function.
b. Describe how the number of threads per inch changes as the screw size increases.
c. Would it be reasonable to expect a #8 screw to have 32 threads per inch? *Explain*. 16. c. Yes. Answers will vary.

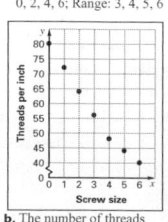

16. b. The number of threads decrease as the screw size increases.

1D

1 Assessment

CHAPTER 1 Quiz 1
For use after Lessons 1.1–1.3

Evaluate the expression.

1. $8 + a$ when $a = 5$
2. $27 - h$ when $h = 21$
3. $\frac{p}{4}$ when $p = 16$
4. $7 + y^2$ when $y = 3$
5. $\frac{2m + 9}{m}$ when $m = 2$
6. $\frac{3x}{x - 1}$ when $x = 3$

Translate the verbal phrase into an expression.

7. 10 more than $\frac{1}{2}$ of a number r
8. Twice a number d
9. The difference of 19 and t
10. The sum of a number n and the square of a number b

Answers

1. _____ 13 _____
2. _____ 6 _____
3. _____ 4 _____
4. _____ 16 _____
5. _____ $6\frac{1}{2}$ _____
6. _____ $4\frac{1}{2}$ _____
7. _____ $10 + \frac{1}{2}r$ _____
8. _____ $2d$ _____
9. _____ $19 - t$ _____
10. _____ $p + b^2$ _____

CHAPTER 1 Quiz 2
For use after Lessons 1.4–1.5

Write an equation or an inequality.

1. The sum of twice a number d and 3 is 12.
2. Six less than four times a number j is 18.
3. The product of 8 and a number q is at least 32.
4. The difference of 10 and a number w is no more than 8.

In Exercises 5–8, check whether the given number is a solution of the equation or inequality.

5. $z - 4 = 9;\ 12$
6. $2x - 9 \geq 11;\ 10$
7. $k - 8.2 < 10;\ 18$
8. $4d + 1 < 13;\ 3$
9. What is the interest on $950 invested for 4 years in an account that earns simple interest at a rate of 3% per year?
10. A car travels 210 miles in 3.5 hours. What is the average speed of the car?

Answers

1. _____ $2d + 3 = 12$ _____
2. _____ $4j - 6 = 18$ _____
3. _____ $8q \geq 32$ _____
4. _____ $10 - w \leq 8$ _____
5. _____ no _____
6. _____ yes _____
7. _____ yes _____
8. _____ no _____
9. _____ $114 _____
10. _____ 60 mi/h _____

CHAPTER 1 Quiz 3
For use after Lessons 1.6–1.7

Identify the domain and range of the function.

1.
Input	Output
0	1
2	5
4	9
6	13

2.
Input	Output
1	2
2	5
3	8
4	11

Tell whether the pairing is a function.

3.

4.
Input	Output
3	5
4	7
5	9
6	11

Graph the function.

5. $y = x - 2$; Domain: 2, 3, 4, 5, 6
6. $y = \frac{1}{2}x + 3$; Domain: 0, 2, 4, 6, 8

In Exercises 7–9, use the graph at the right.

7. Write a rule for the function represented by the graph.
8. Identify the domain of the function.
9. Identify the range of the function.

Answers

1. domain: 0, 2, 4, 6; range: 1, 5, 9, 13
2. domain: 1, 2, 3, 4; range: 2, 5, 8, 11
3. _____ no _____
4. _____ yes _____
5. _____ See left. _____
6. _____ See left. _____
7. _____ $y = x + 2$ _____
8. domain: 1, 2, 3, 4, 5
9. range: 3, 4, 5, 6, 7

CHAPTER 1 Chapter Test B
For use after Chapter 1

Evaluate the expression.

1. $34.5x$ when $x = 4$
2. $\frac{1}{3}y$ when $y = \frac{9}{10}$

Evaluate the power.

3. 5^4
4. 1^7
5. $\left(\frac{1}{2}\right)^5$

6. You can convert temperatures in degrees Fahrenheit to degrees Celsius by using the expression $\frac{9}{5}C + 32$, where C is the temperature (in degrees Celsius). Convert 35°C to degrees Fahrenheit.

Evaluate the expression.

7. $16 \div (4 - 2) - 3$
8. $3[15 - (2^3 - 6)^2]$

Evaluate the expression for the given values of the variables.

9. $3m - n$ when $m = 5$ and $n = 4$
10. $2u^2 + v$ when $u = 3$ and $v = 7$

11. A rectangular box is created by cutting out squares of equal sides of lengths x from a piece of cardboard 10 inches by 15 inches and folding up the sides as shown in the figure. The volume of the box is given by $V = x(10 - 2x)(15 - 2x)$. Find the volume of the box when the side length of the square is 3 inches.

Write an algebraic expression, an equation, or an inequality.

12. The quotient of the square of a number t and 14
13. Amount you earn if you make 6.5 dollars an hour for h hours
14. The product of 6 and the quantity 2 more than a number x is at least 45.
15. The sum of 4 and the quotient of a number k and 9 is 12.

Answers

1. _____ 138 _____
2. _____ $\frac{3}{10}$ _____
3. _____ 625 _____
4. _____ 1 _____
5. _____ $\frac{1}{32}$ _____
6. _____ 95°F _____
7. _____ 5 _____
8. _____ 33 _____
9. _____ 11 _____
10. _____ 25 _____
11. _____ 108 in.³ _____
12. _____ $\frac{t^2}{14}$ _____
13. _____ $6.5h$ _____
14. _____ $6(2 + x) \geq 45$ _____
15. _____ $4 + \frac{k}{9} = 12$ _____

Check whether the given number is a solution of the equation or the inequality.

16. $7z + 8 > 20; 2$

17. $\frac{r}{5} + 15 = 20; 25$

18. A carpet outlet advertises a price of $470.40 to carpet a 12-foot by 16-foot room. If a customer was given a price of $725.20 for carpeting a room that is 16 feet wide, what is the length of the room?

Write a rule for the function.

19.

Input, x	1	3	5	7
Output, y	2	6	10	14

20.

Input, x	12	15	18	21
Output, y	4	5	6	7

Find the range of the function. Then graph the function.

21. $y = \frac{1}{2}x + 3$

Domain: 0, 1, 2, 3, 4

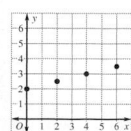

22. $y = x - 6$

Domain: 10, 12, 14, 16, 18

Answers

16.	yes
17.	yes
18.	$18\frac{1}{2}$ ft
19.	$y = 2x$
20.	$y = \frac{x}{3}$
21.	Range: 3, 3.5, 4, 4.5, 5
	See left.
22.	Range: 4, 6, 8, 10, 12
	See left.

Multiple Choice

1. What is the value of $3.2n$ when $n = 5$?   C

(A) 0.16   **(B)** 1.6   **(C)** 16   **(D)** 161

2. What is the value of 5^4?   C

(A) 20   **(B)** 54   **(C)** 625   **(D)** 1024

3. Let d be the number of dollars you spent on gas and let g be the number of gallons you purchased. Which expression represents the price you paid per gallon?   D

(A) $d + g$ **(B)** $\frac{g}{d}$

(C) dg **(D)** $\frac{d}{g}$

4. What is the value of $3[1^2(5 - 3 + 1)^3 \div 9]$?   B

(A) $\frac{1}{3}$ **(B)** 9   **(C)** 18   **(D)** 6

5. What is the value of $\frac{108}{x^2} + 4x$ when $x = 6$?   A

(A) 27   **(B)** 33   **(C)** 42   **(D)** 55

6. Which expression represents the phrase "twice the quotient of 5 less than a number m and 6"?   B

(A) $2\left(\frac{5 - m}{6}\right)$ **(B)** $2\left(\frac{m - 5}{6}\right)$

(C) $\frac{2m - 5}{6}$ **(D)** $\frac{2(5) - m}{6}$

7. Which inequality corresponds to the sentence "Five less than the product of a number n and -6 is at least 8."?   D

(A) $5 - (-6n) \geq 8$ **(B)** $-6n - 5 \leq 8$
(C) $-\frac{n}{6} - 5 \geq 8$ **(D)** $-6n - 5 \geq 8$

8. What is the solution of the equation $\frac{x}{4} - 12 = -4$?   C

(A) -64 **(B)** -32 **(C)** 32   **(D)** 64

9. A car travels an average speed of 45 miles per hour. How many hours would it take to travel 540 miles?   A

(A) 12 hours   **(B)** 12.5 hours
(C) 13 hours   **(D)** 14 hours

10. The temperature is 77°F. What is the temperature in degrees Celsius?   B

(A) 11°C   **(B)** 25°C
(C) 61°C   **(D)** 225°C

11. The range of the function $y = 3x - 2$ is 1, 7, 13, 16, and 19. Which number is in the domain of the function?   C

(A) 2   **(B)** 4   **(C)** 6   **(D)** 8

12. Each output of a function is 0.25 greater than the corresponding input. Which equation is a rule for the function?   A

(A) $y = x + 0.25$ **(B)** $y = x - 0.25$
(C) $y = 0.25x$ **(D)** $y = \frac{x}{0.25}$

13. Which set of numbers represents the domain of the function in the table?   D

Input	Output
-2	6
0	0
2	-6
4	-12

(A) $-12, -6, 0, 6$
(B) $-12, -6, -2, 0, 2, 4, 6$
(C) $-2, 2, 4$
(D) $-2, 0, 2, 4$

---

14. Which ordered pair is a solution of the function $y = 2x + 5$?   B

(A) $(7, 1)$ **(B)** $(0, 5)$
(C) $(-2, 9)$ **(D)** $(0, 0)$

15. The relation in the table is a function. Which ordered pair can be included with this relation to form a new relation that is also a function?   D

Input	-5	0	5	10
Output	12	15	18	21

(A) $(5, 7)$ **(B)** $(0, 2)$
(C) $(-5, 5)$ **(D)** $(2, 16)$

16. The graph of what function is shown?   A

(A) $y = \frac{1}{4}x + 2$ **(B)** $y = \frac{1}{4}x + 4$
(C) $y = 2x + \frac{1}{4}$ **(D)** $y = 4x + 2$

Gridded Answer

17. What is the value of the expression $\frac{1}{3}x^2 + 4$ when $x = 9$?

19. b.

Short Response

18. You need to buy school supplies. Notebooks are $1.95 each and folders are $1.25 each. You only have $7.35 to spend.

   a. Write an inequality for this situation. Let n represent the number of notebooks you can buy and let f represent the number of folders you can buy. $1.95n + 1.25f \leq 7.35$

   b. What is the maximum number of notebooks you can buy if you want to buy one folder?   3

   c. Would you have enough money left to buy a binder for $2.49 if you purchased two notebooks and one folder? *Explain.* See below.

Extended Response

19. Use the table to complete parts a–c.

Input	Output
0	2
1	4
2	6
3	8
4	10

   a. Write a rule for the function represented by the table. Identify the domain and range of the function.

   b. Graph the function.   See left.

   c. Write a problem that involves a real-world situation that can be solved using the rule for the function you wrote in part a. *Explain.*

19. a. $y = 2x + 2$; domain: 0, 1, 2, 3, 4; range: 2, 4, 6, 8, 10

Answers will vary.

18. c. No; If you buy 2 notebooks and 1 folder, you only have $2.20 left, which is not enough to buy a binder.

Journal

1. Explain the difference between an algebraic expression and an equation. Write an example of each, and explain what it means to evaluate an algebraic expression.

Multi-Step Problem

2. A local pizza shop offers the following special every Tuesday: buy one large pizza with one topping at regular price, and get as many medium one topping pizza as you would like for $6.25 each.

   a. If the cost of a large pizza with one topping is $13.50, how much would it cost to purchase one large and five medium pizzas?

   b. Complete the table by calculating the total cost of purchasing one large pizza and the indicated number of medium pizzas.

Number of medium pizzas	0	1	2	3	4
Total cost	?	?	?	?	?

   c. Graph the function for total cost using your work in the table above.

   d. Write a rule for the function representing the total cost of purchasing one large pizza with one topping and m medium pizzas.

   e. You and a group of friends decide to pool your money to have a pizza party. If you have a total of $100 and purchase one large pizza, how many medium pizzas can you buy?

   f. Your parents decide to purchase one large pizza and five medium pizzas. Determine the total area (in square inches) of pizza if a large pizza has a radius of 8 inches and a medium pizza has a radius of 5 inches. (*Hint:* $A = \pi r^2$. Use 3.14 for π. Round your answer to the nearest inch.)

   g. What is the cost per square inch of pizza if one large and five medium pizzas are purchased?

1. Complete answers should include: a clear distinction that an equation contains the equal sign and algebraic expressions do not; one example of an algebraic expression and one example of an equation; a written explanation describing how to replace the variable(s) in the expression with particular values to evaluate the expression.

2. a. $44.75   **b.** $13.50; $19.75; $26.00; $32.25; $38.50

c.

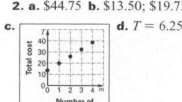

d. $T = 6.25m + 13.50$

e. 13 medium pizzas   **f.** about 594 in.^{2} **g.** about $.08 per square inch

1F

Main Ideas

In Chapter 1, students write and evaluate expressions, equations, and inequalities. They learn to apply the order of operations and to use a problem solving plan to solve real-world problems. Students represent functions as rules and as tables. They also graph functions given a rule or table of values.

Prerequisite Skills

• Using fractions and percents
• Finding perimeter and area

Additional resources for reviewing prerequisite skills are:

• Skills Review Handbook, pp. 909–937
• @HomeTutor

1 Expressions, Equations, and Functions

1.1 **Evaluate Expressions**

1.2 **Apply Order of Operations**

1.3 **Write Expressions**

1.4 **Write Equations and Inequalities**

1.5 **Use a Problem Solving Plan**

1.6 **Represent Functions as Rules and Tables**

1.7 **Represent Functions as Graphs**

Before

In previous courses, you learned the following skills, which you'll use in Chapter 1: using fractions and percents, and finding perimeter and area.

Prerequisite Skills

VOCABULARY CHECK

Copy and complete the statement.

1. In the fraction $\frac{2}{3}$, _?_ is the numerator and _?_ is the denominator. **2, 3**

2. Two fractions that represent the same number are called _?_ fractions. **equivalent**

3. The word *percent* (%) means "divided by _?_." **100**

SKILLS CHECK

Perform the indicated operation. *(Review pp. 914–915 for 1.1, 1.2.)*

4. $\frac{2}{3} + \frac{3}{5}$ **$1\frac{4}{15}$**

5. $\frac{5}{6} - \frac{3}{4}$ **$\frac{1}{12}$**

6. $\frac{3}{5} \times \frac{2}{3}$ **$\frac{2}{5}$**

7. $\frac{1}{2} \div \frac{5}{8}$ **$\frac{4}{5}$**

Write the percent as a decimal. *(Review p. 916 for 1.5.)*

8. 4% **0.04**

9. 23% **0.23**

10. 1.5% **0.015**

11. 2.5% **0.025**

12. Find the perimeter and area of the rectangle. *(Review p. 924 for 1.5.)* **31 in., $49\frac{1}{2}$ in.²**

$4\frac{1}{2}$ in.

11 in.

 @HomeTutor Prerequisite skills practice at classzone.com

xxii

Chapter Planning Guide

Chapter 1 Resource Book
• Teaching Guide/Lesson Plan (pp. 3, 15, 27, 37, 49, 59, 70)
• Project with Rubric (p. 84)

Assessment and Intervention
• Assessment Book (pp. 1–15)
• Benchmark Tests
• Reteaching and Remediation Book

Interactive Technology
• Easy Planner
• Power Presentations CD-ROM
• Activity Generator CD-ROM
• Animated Algebra
• Test Generator CD-ROM
• Online Quizzes
• eWorkbook
• eEdition
• @HomeTutor

Resources for English Learners
• Quick Reference for English Learners
• Spanish Study Guide
• Multi-Language Visual Glossary
• Student Resources in Spanish

In Chapter 1, you will apply the big ideas listed below and reviewed in the Chapter Summary on page 52. You will also use the key vocabulary listed below.

Big Ideas

① Writing and evaluating algebraic expressions

② Using expressions to write equations and inequalities

③ Representing functions as verbal rules, equations, tables, and graphs

KEY VOCABULARY

- variable, *p. 2*
- algebraic expression, *p. 2*
- power, exponent, base, *p. 3*
- order of operations, *p. 8*
- verbal model, *p. 16*

- rate, unit rate, *p. 17*
- open sentence, *p. 21*
- equation, inequality, *p. 21*
- solution of an equation or inequality, *p. 22*

- formula, *p. 30*
- function, *p. 35*
- domain, range, *p. 35*
- independent variable, *p. 36*
- dependent variable, *p. 36*

Why?

You can use multiple representations to describe a real-world situation. For example, you can solve an equation, make a table, or draw a diagram to determine a running route.

Animated Algebra

The animation illustrated below for Example 1 on page 28 helps you answer this question: How does the number of blocks you run affect the total distance?

Your goal is to find a 2 mile running path around the long and short city blocks.

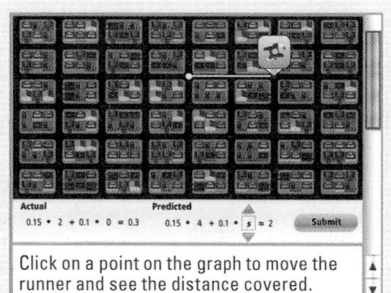

Click on a point on the graph to move the runner and see the distance covered.

Animated Algebra at classzone.com

Other animations for Chapter 1: pages 7, 9, 14, 21, 37, 50, and 52

Algebra 1 Toolkit

- Reading Strategies for Chapter 1, pp. 9–10
- Differentiated Instruction Notes, pp. 41–44
- English Learners Notes, pp. 97–98
- Inclusion Notes, pp. 129–130
- Teaching Strategies with Sample Worksheets, pp. 155–178
- Using Technology in the Classroom, pp. 179–184
- Tips for New Teachers, pp. 185–186
- Math Background Notes, pp. 211–212
- Pre-AP Strategies and Copymasters, pp. 279, 304–312
- Teacher Survival Activities, pp. 555–556, 581–582
- Bulletin Board Idea, p. 607
- Teacher Tool Transparencies, following p. 620

1.1 Evaluate Expressions

Before	You used whole numbers, fractions, and decimals.
Now	You will evaluate algebraic expressions and use exponents.
Why	So you can calculate sports statistics, as in Ex. 50.

Key Vocabulary
• variable
• algebraic expression
• power
• base
• exponent

A **variable** is a letter used to represent one or more numbers. The numbers are the values of the variable. An **algebraic expression**, or *variable expression*, consists of numbers, variables, and operations.

Algebraic expression			Meaning	Operation
$5(n)$	$5 \cdot n$	$5n$	5 times n	Multiplication
$\frac{14}{y}$	$14 \div y$		14 divided by y	Division
$6 + c$			6 plus c	Addition
$8 - x$			8 minus x	Subtraction

To **evaluate an algebraic expression**, substitute a number for the variable, perform the operation(s), and simplify the result, if necessary. The resulting number is the value of the expression.

EXAMPLE 1 Evaluate algebraic expressions

Evaluate the expression when $n = 3$.

AVOID ERRORS
Use the multiplication symbol $\cdot$ instead of $\times$ in algebraic expressions to avoid confusing $\times$ with the variable x.

a. $13 \cdot n = 13 \cdot 3$ Substitute 3 for n.
$= 39$ Multiply.

b. $\frac{9}{n} = \frac{9}{3}$ Substitute 3 for n.
$= 3$ Divide.

c. $n - 1 = 3 - 1$ Substitute 3 for n.
$= 2$ Subtract.

d. $n + 8 = 3 + 8$ Substitute 3 for n.
$= 11$ Add.

✓ **GUIDED PRACTICE** for Example 1

Evaluate the expression when $y = 2$.

1. $6y$ **12**
2. $\frac{8}{y}$ **4**
3. $y + 4$ **6**
4. $11 - y$ **9**

2   Chapter 1 Expressions, Equations, and Functions

EXAMPLE 2 Evaluate an expression

MOVIES The total cost of seeing a movie at a theater can be represented by the expression $a + r$ where a is the cost (in dollars) of admission and r is the cost (in dollars) of refreshments. Suppose you pay $7.50 for admission and $7.25 for refreshments. Find the total cost.

Solution

$$\text{Total cost} = a + r \qquad \text{Write expression.}$$
$$= 7.50 + 7.25 \qquad \text{Substitute 7.50 for } a \text{ and 7.25 for } r.$$
$$= 14.75 \qquad \text{Add.}$$

▶ The total cost is $14.75.

EXPRESSIONS USING EXPONENTS A **power** is an expression that represents repeated multiplication of the same factor. For example, 81 is a power of 3 because $81 = 3 \cdot 3 \cdot 3 \cdot 3$. A power can be written in a form using two numbers, a **base** and an **exponent**. The exponent represents the number of times the base is used as a factor, so 81 can be written as 3^4.

$$\underset{\text{power}}{3^4} = \underset{\text{4 factors of 3}}{3 \cdot 3 \cdot 3 \cdot 3}$$

base → ↗ exponent

EXAMPLE 3 Read and write powers

Write the power in words and as a product.

WRITE EXPONENTS
For a number raised to the first power, you usually do not write the exponent 1. For instance, you write 7^1 simply as 7.

Power	Words	Product
a. 7^1	seven to the first power	7
b. 5^2	five to the second power, or five *squared*	$5 \cdot 5$
c. $\left(\dfrac{1}{2}\right)^3$	one half to the third power, or one half *cubed*	$\dfrac{1}{2} \cdot \dfrac{1}{2} \cdot \dfrac{1}{2}$
d. z^5	z to the fifth power	$z \cdot z \cdot z \cdot z \cdot z$

✓ **GUIDED PRACTICE** for Examples 2 and 3

5. WHAT IF? In Example 2, suppose you go back to the theater with a friend to see an afternoon movie. You pay for both admissions. Your total cost (in dollars) can be represented by the expression $2a$. If each admission costs $4.75, what is your total cost? **$9.50**

Write the power in words and as a product.

6. 9^5 nine to the fifth power, $9 \cdot 9 \cdot 9 \cdot 9 \cdot 9$

7. 2^8 two to the eighth power, $2 \cdot 2 \cdot 2 \cdot 2 \cdot 2 \cdot 2 \cdot 2 \cdot 2$

8. n^4 n to the fourth power, $n \cdot n \cdot n \cdot n$

Differentiated Instruction

English Learners Some mathematical terms can be associated with more common English definitions. For example, the *base* is the lower part or bottom of something. Therefore, in any power expression, the base is the number at the bottom (and the exponent is the number at the top).

See also the *Algebra 1 Toolkit* for more strategies.

Motivating the Lesson
You want to save money to buy a digital music player. If you know how much it costs, you can determine how much you need to save each week depending on whether you want to purchase it in 2, 3, 4, or more weeks. You can do this by evaluating an expression that involves a variable.

❸ TEACH

Extra Example 1
Evaluate the expression when $c = 4$.
a. $4c$ **16**
b. $\dfrac{8}{c}$ **2**
c. $15 + c$ **19**

Extra Example 2
You are ordering a skateboard and a helmet from an on-line store. The total weight of the two items can be represented by $s + h$, where s is the weight of the skateboard and h is the weight of the helmet. Find the total weight if the helmet weighs 1.3 kilograms and the skateboard weighs 5.4 kilograms. **7.1 kg**

Key Question to Ask for Example 2
• How are the letters used as variables appropriate for this situation? **The first letter in the word *admission* is *a* and the first letter in the word *refreshments* is *r*.**

Extra Example 3
Write the power in words and as a product.
a. $\left(\dfrac{1}{5}\right)^1$ one fifth to the first power; $\dfrac{1}{5}$
b. 6^2 six squared; $6 \cdot 6$
c. 3^4 three to the fourth power; $3 \cdot 3 \cdot 3 \cdot 3$
d. p^3 p to the third power or p cubed; $p \cdot p \cdot p$

EXAMPLE 4 Evaluate powers

Evaluate the expression.

a. x^4 when $x = 2$

b. n^3 when $n = 1.5$

Solution

a. $x^4 = 2^4$

$\quad = 2 \cdot 2 \cdot 2 \cdot 2$

$\quad = 16$

b. $n^3 = 1.5^3$

$\quad = (1.5)(1.5)(1.5)$

$\quad = 3.375$

 GUIDED PRACTICE for Example 4

Evaluate the expression.

9. x^3 when $x = 8$ **512**

10. k^2 when $k = 2.5$ **6.25**

11. d^4 when $d = \dfrac{1}{3}$ $\dfrac{1}{81}$

REVIEW AREA AND VOLUME

For help with area and volume, see pp. 924 and 927.

AREA AND VOLUME Exponents are used in the formulas for the area of a square and the volume of a cube. In fact, the words *squared* and *cubed* come from the formula for the area of a square and the formula for the volume of a cube.

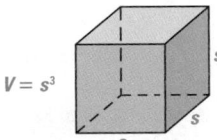

$A = s^2$ $\qquad$ $V = s^3$

EXAMPLE 5 Evaluate a power

STORAGE CUBES Each edge of the medium-sized pop-up storage cube shown is 14 inches long. The storage cube is made so that it can be folded flat when not in use. Find the volume of the storage cube.

Solution

$V = s^3$ $\qquad$ Write formula for volume.

$\quad = 14^3$ $\qquad$ Substitute 14 for *s*.

$\quad = 2744$ $\qquad$ Evaluate power.

▶ The volume of the storage cube is 2744 cubic inches.

 GUIDED PRACTICE for Example 5

12. **WHAT IF?** In Example 5, suppose the storage cube is folded flat to form a square. Find the area of the square. **196 in.²**

1.1 EXERCISES

SKILL PRACTICE

A 1. **VOCABULARY** Identify the exponent and the base in the expression 6^{12}.
exponent: 12, base: 6

2. ★ **WRITING** *Describe* the steps you would take to evaluate the expression n^5 when $n = 3$. Then evaluate the expression. **Substitute 3 for *n*. Then write 3^5 as the product $3 \cdot 3 \cdot 3 \cdot 3 \cdot 3$ and multiply; 243.**

EVALUATING EXPRESSIONS Evaluate the expression.

3. $15x$ when $x = 4$ **60**   4. $0.4r$ when $r = 6$ **2.4**   5. $w - 8$ when $w = 20$ **12**

6. $1.6 - g$ when $g = 1.2$ **0.4**   7. $5 + m$ when $m = 7$ **12**   8. $0.8 + h$ when $h = 3.7$ **4.5**

9. $\frac{24}{f}$ when $f = 8$ **3**   10. $\frac{t}{5}$ when $t = 4.5$ **0.9**   11. $2.5m$ when $m = 4$ **10**

12. $\frac{1}{2}k$ when $k = \frac{2}{3}$ **$\frac{1}{3}$**   13. $y - \frac{1}{2}$ when $y = \frac{5}{6}$ **$\frac{1}{3}$**   14. $h + \frac{1}{3}$ when $h = 1\frac{1}{3}$ **$1\frac{2}{3}$**

15. ★ **MULTIPLE CHOICE** What is the value of $2.5m$ when $m = 10$? **D**

    Ⓐ 0.25   Ⓑ 2.5   Ⓒ 12.5   Ⓓ 25

WRITING POWERS Write the power in words and as a product. **16, 18–20. See margin.**

16. 12^5 17. 7^3 **seven to the third power, $7 \cdot 7 \cdot 7$**   18. $(3.2)^2$ 19. $(0.3)^4$

20. $\left(\frac{1}{2}\right)^8$ 21. n^7 ***n* to the seventh power, $n \cdot n \cdot n \cdot n \cdot n \cdot n \cdot n$**   22. y^6 ***y* to the sixth power, $y \cdot y \cdot y \cdot y \cdot y \cdot y$**   23. t^4 ***t* to the fourth power, $t \cdot t \cdot t \cdot t$**

ERROR ANALYSIS *Describe* and correct the error in evaluating the power. **24, 25. See margin.**

24.

$(0.4)^2 = 2(0.4) = 0.8$ ✗

25.

$5^4 = 4 \cdot 4 \cdot 4 \cdot 4 \cdot 4 = 1024$ ✗

EVALUATING POWERS Evaluate the power.

26. 3^2 **9**   27. 10^2 **100**   28. 1^5 **1**   29. 11^3 **1331**

30. 5^3 **125**   31. 3^5 **243**   32. 2^6 **64**   33. 6^4 **1296**

34. $\left(\frac{1}{4}\right)^2$ **$\frac{1}{16}$**   ㉟ $\left(\frac{3}{5}\right)^3$ **$\frac{27}{125}$**   36. $\left(\frac{2}{3}\right)^4$ **$\frac{16}{81}$**   37. $\left(\frac{1}{6}\right)^3$ **$\frac{1}{216}$**

B **EVALUATING EXPRESSIONS** Evaluate the expression.

38. x^2 when $x = \frac{3}{4}$ **$\frac{9}{16}$**   39. p^2 when $p = 1.1$ **1.21**

40. $x + y$ when $x = 11$ and $y = 6.4$ **17.4**   41. kn when $k = 9$ and $n = 4.5$ **40.5**

42. $w - z$ when $w = 9.5$ and $z = 2.8$ **6.7**   43. $\frac{b}{c}$ when $b = 24$ and $c = 2.5$ **9.6**

44. ★ **MULTIPLE CHOICE** Which expression has the greatest value when $x = 10$ and $y = 0.5$? **C**

    Ⓐ xy Ⓑ $x - y$ Ⓒ $\frac{x}{y}$ Ⓓ $\frac{y}{x}$

Left margin notes:

16. twelve to the fifth power, $12 \cdot 12 \cdot 12 \cdot 12 \cdot 12$

EXAMPLE 1
on p. 2
for Exs. 3–15

18. three and two tenths squared, $3.2 \cdot 3.2$

19. three tenths to the fourth power, $0.3 \cdot 0.3 \cdot 0.3 \cdot 0.3$

EXAMPLE 3
on p. 3
for Exs. 16–25

20. one half to the eighth power, $\frac{1}{2} \cdot \frac{1}{2} \cdot \frac{1}{2} \cdot \frac{1}{2} \cdot \frac{1}{2} \cdot \frac{1}{2} \cdot \frac{1}{2} \cdot \frac{1}{2}$

EXAMPLE 4
on p. 4
for Exs. 26–37

24. 0.4 was multiplied by 2 instead of squared; $(0.4)^2 = (0.4)(0.4) = 0.16$.

25. The base was used as the exponent and the exponent was used as the base; $5^4 = 5 \cdot 5 \cdot 5 \cdot 5 = 625$.

Differentiated Instruction

Auditory Learners For students who begin learning algebra, the concept of a variable is a new idea. When saying the word *variable* out loud to students, stress the sounds "vary" and "able" as in "able to vary." Explain that letters such as *x* are called variables because they represent a number that varies, or changes. For example, in **Exercise 3**, $x = 4$; but in **Exercise 38**, $x = \frac{3}{4}$.

See also the *Algebra 1 Toolkit* for more strategies.

---

④ **PRACTICE AND APPLY**

Assignment Guide

📘 **Answer Transparencies** available for all exercises

Basic:
Day 1: SRH p. 914 Exs. 11–15
pp. 5–7
Exs. 1, 2, 3–13 odd, 15–25,
27–41 odd, 48–52, 56–65

Average:
Day 1: pp. 5–7
Exs. 1, 2, 4–14 even, 15, 16–22 even,
24, 25, 26–44 even, 45, 46, 49–54,
57–65

Advanced:
Day 1: pp. 5–7
Exs. 1, 2, 10–14, 15–23 odd,
32–44 even*, 45–47, 50–63*

Block:
pp. 5–7
Exs. 1, 2, 4–14 even, 15, 16–22 even,
24, 25, 26–44 even, 45, 46, 49–54,
57–65 (with 1.2)

Differentiated Instruction

See *Algebra 1 Best Practices Toolkit* for suggestions on addressing the needs of a diverse classroom.

Homework Check

For a quick check of student understanding of key concepts, go over the following exercises:
Basic: 5, 18, 30, 48, 51
Average: 10, 20, 32, 49, 51
Advanced: 12, 22, 34, 50, 52

Extra Practice

• Student Edition, p. 938
• Chapter 5 Resource Book:
  Practice levels A, B, C, pp. 7–9

Practice Worksheet

An easily-readable reduced practice page (with answers) for this lesson can be found on p. 1C.

5

45. ★ **MULTIPLE CHOICE** Let b be the number of tokens you bought at an arcade, and let u be the number you have used. Which expression represents the number of tokens remaining? **B**

(A) $b + u$ (B) $b - u$ (C) bu (D) $\dfrac{b}{u}$

46. **COMPARING POWERS** Let x and y be whole numbers greater than 0 with $y > x$. Which has the greater value, 3^x or 3^y? *Explain.* **3^y; if $y > x$, then 3^y is raised to a higher power than 3^x.**

47. **CHALLENGE** For which whole number value(s) of x greater than 0 is the value of x^2 greater than the value of 2^x? *Explain.* **3; $3^2 = 9$ and $2^3 = 8$. For values of x greater than 3, $2^x > x^2$.**

PROBLEM SOLVING

EXAMPLE 2 A
on p. 3
for Exs. 48–50

48. **GEOMETRY** The perimeter of a square with a side length of s is given by the expression $4s$. What is the perimeter of the square shown? **30 m**

7.5 m

@HomeTutor for problem solving help at classzone.com

49. **LEOPARD FROG** You can estimate the distance (in centimeters) that a leopard frog can jump using the expression 13ℓ where ℓ is the frog's length (in centimeters). What distance can a leopard frog that is 12.5 centimeters long jump? **162.5 cm**

@HomeTutor for problem solving help at classzone.com

50. **MULTI-STEP PROBLEM** Jen was the leading scorer on her soccer team. She scored 120 goals and had 20 assists in her high school career.

  a. The number n of points awarded for goals is given by $2g$ where g is the number of goals scored. How many points did Jen earn for goals? **240 points**

  b. The point total is given by $n + a$ where a is the number of assists. Use your answer from part (a) to find Jen's point total. **260 points**

EXAMPLE 5
on p. 4
for Exs. 51–52

51. **MULTI-STEP PROBLEM** You are buying a tank for three fish. You have a flame angel that is 3.5 inches long, a yellow sailfin tang that is 5.5 inches long, and a coral beauty that is 3 inches long. The area (in square inches) of water surface the fish need is given by the expression $12f$ where f is the sum of the lengths (in inches) of all the fish in the tank.

  a. What is the total length of the three fish? **12 in.**

  b. How many square inches of water surface do the fish need? **144 in.²**

B **52.** ★ **MULTIPLE CHOICE** For a snow sculpture contest, snow is packed into a cube-shaped box with an edge length of 8 feet. The box is frozen and removed, leaving a cube of snow. One cubic foot of the snow weighs about 30 pounds. You can estimate the weight (in pounds) of the cube using the expression $30V$ where V is the volume (in cubic feet) of the snow. About how much does the uncarved cube weigh? **C**

(A) 240 pounds   (B) 1920 pounds

(C) 15,360 pounds   (D) 216,000 pounds

○ = **WORKED-OUT SOLUTIONS**
   on p. WS1

★ = **STANDARDIZED TEST PRACTICE**

6

53. FOOTBALL A football team's net score for the regular season is given by the expression $a - b$ where a is the total number of points the team scored and b is the total number of points scored against the team. The table shows the point totals for the 2003 National Football League Conference Champions. Which team's net score was greater? **New England Patriots**

Team	Points scored, a	Points scored against, b
New England Patriots	336	238
Carolina Panthers	325	304

C 54. ★ **EXTENDED RESPONSE** A manufacturer produces three different sizes of cube-shaped stacking bins with edge lengths as shown.

Bin A 6 in.   Bin B 12 in.   Bin C 18 in.

54d. *Sample answer:* The volume of the cube is multiplied by n^3. The edge length of Bin B is 2 times the edge length of Bin A, so the volume of Bin B is 2^3 or 8 times the volume of Bin A. The edge length of Bin C is 3 times the edge length of Bin A, so the volume of Bin C is 3^3 or 27 times the volume of Bin A.

   a. **Evaluate** Find the volume of each bin. **216 in.³; 1728 in.³; 5832 in.³**

   b. **Compare** How many times greater is the edge length of bin B than the edge length of bin A? How many times greater is the volume of bin B than the volume of bin A? **2; 8**

   c. **Compare** Answer the questions in part (b) for bin A and bin C. **3; 27**

   d. **CHALLENGE** *Explain* how multiplying the edge length of a cube by a number n affects the volume of the cube. *Justify* your explanation.

   Animated Algebra at classzone.com

55. **CHALLENGE** You purchase a set of 100 cube-shaped miniature magnets, each with an edge length of $\frac{1}{8}$ inch. You arrange the cubes to form larger cubes, each one with a different edge length. How many cubes can you form? What is their total volume? **4 cubes; about 0.1953 in.³**

MIXED REVIEW

PREVIEW
Prepare for
Lesson 1.2 in
Exs. 56–59.

Perform the indicated operation.

56. $\frac{13}{16} - \frac{1}{8}$ *(p. 914)* $\frac{11}{16}$ **57.** $\frac{3}{4} + \frac{1}{3}$ *(p. 914)* $1\frac{1}{12}$ **58.** $\frac{4}{7} \times \frac{7}{9}$ *(p. 915)* $\frac{4}{9}$ **59.** $\frac{3}{20} \div \frac{5}{8}$ *(p. 915)* $\frac{6}{25}$

Write the percent as a decimal and as a fraction. *(p. 916)*

60. 37% $0.37, \frac{37}{100}$ **61.** 15% $0.15, \frac{3}{20}$ **62.** 125% $1.25, 1\frac{1}{4}$ **63.** 0.2% $0.002, \frac{1}{500}$

Find the perimeter of the rectangle or square. *(p. 924)*

64. 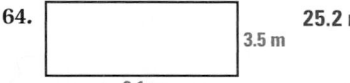 25.2 m   3.5 m   9.1 m

65. 56 in.   14 in.   14 in.

---

⑤ ASSESS AND RETEACH

Daily Homework Quiz

📄 **Transparency Available**

Evaluate the expression or power.

1. $13g$ when $g = 7$ **91**

2. $1.65 - a$ when $a = 0.75$ **0.9**

3. 5^4 **625**

4. $\left(\frac{1}{3}\right)^3$ $\frac{1}{27}$

5. Emily is saving for a $300 bicycle. She has saved $128.25. The amount she still needs to save is given by the expression $c - s$, where c is the cost of the bicycle and s is the amount she has saved. How much does she have left to save? **$171.75**

⟳ **Online Quiz**

Available at **classzone.com**

Diagnosis/Remediation

• Practice A, B, C in Chapter 1 Resource Book, pp. 7–9
• Study Guide in Chapter 1 Resource Book, pp. 10–11
• Practice Workbook, pp. 1–2
• @HomeTutor

Challenge

Additional challenge is available in the Chapter 1 Resource Book, p. 14.

❶ PLAN AND PREPARE

Warm-Up Exercises
📠 Transparency Available

Evaluate the expression.

1. $a + 5.7$ when $a = 1.3$ **7**

2. b^3 when $b = 4$ **64**

3. The number of weeks it takes you to read a novel is given by $\frac{n}{p}$, where n is total pages in the novel and p is pages read per week. How long will it take you to read a 340-page novel if you read 85 pages per week? **4 weeks**

Notetaking Guide
📠 Transparency Available

Promotes interactive learning and notetaking skills, pp. 4–6.

Pacing
Basic: 1 day
Average: 1 day
Advanced: 1 day
Block: 0.5 block with 1.1
• See *Teaching Guide/Lesson Plan.*

❷ FOCUS AND MOTIVATE

Essential Question
Big Idea 1, p. 1

How do you use the order of operations to evaluate an expression?
Tell students they will learn how to answer this question by using an algorithm (an ordered series of steps).

NCTM STANDARDS
Standard 1: Understand how operations are related; Compute fluently

Before You evaluated algebraic expressions and used exponents.

Now You will use the order of operations to evaluate expressions.

Why? So you can determine online music costs, as in Ex. 35.

Key Vocabulary
• order of operations

Mathematicians have established an **order of operations** to evaluate an expression involving more than one operation.

KEY CONCEPT *For Your Notebook*

Order of Operations

STEP 1 **Evaluate** expressions inside grouping symbols.

STEP 2 **Evaluate** powers.

STEP 3 **Multiply** and **divide** from left to right.

STEP 4 **Add** and **subtract** from left to right.

EXAMPLE 1 Evaluate expressions

Evaluate the expression $27 \div 3^2 \times 2 - 3$.

STEP 1 There are no grouping symbols, so go to Step 2.

STEP 2 **Evaluate** powers.

$$27 \div 3^2 \times 2 - 3 = 27 \div 9 \times 2 - 3 \qquad \text{Evaluate power.}$$

STEP 3 **Multiply** and **divide** from left to right.

$$27 \div 9 \times 2 - 3 = 3 \times 2 - 3 \qquad \text{Divide.}$$

$$3 \times 2 - 3 = 6 - 3 \qquad \text{Multiply.}$$

STEP 4 **Add** and **subtract** from left to right.

$$6 - 3 = 3 \qquad \text{Subtract.}$$

▶ The value of the expression $27 \div 3^2 \times 2 - 3$ is 3.

✓ **GUIDED PRACTICE** for Example 1

Evaluate the expression.

1. $20 - 4^2$ **4**

2. $2 \cdot 3^2 + 4$ **22**

3. $32 \div 2^3 + 6$ **10**

4. $15 + 6^2 - 4$ **47**

Resource Planning Guide

Chapter Resource Book
• Teaching Guide/Lesson Plan (pp. 15–16)
• Activity Master (p. 17)
• Practice levels A, B, C (pp. 19–21)
• Study Guide (pp. 22–23)
• Catch-up for Absent Students (p. 24)
• Application (p. 25)
• Challenge (p. 26)

Workbooks
• Notetaking Guide (pp. 4–6)
• Practice Workbook (pp. 3–4)

Teaching Options
• **Power Presentations CD-ROM** provides dynamic electronic teaching resources for the classroom.
• **Activity Generator CD-ROM** provides editable activities for all ability levels.

Interactive Technology
• Easy Planner
• Power Presentations CD-ROM
• Activity Generator CD-ROM
• Animated Algebra
• Test Generator CD-ROM
• Online Quiz
• eWorkbook
• eEdition
• @HomeTutor

Resources for English Learners
• Quick Reference for English Learners
• Spanish Study Guide
• Multi-Language Visual Glossary
• Student Resources in Spanish

See also the *Algebra 1 Toolkit* for more strategies for meeting individual needs.

GROUPING SYMBOLS Grouping symbols such as parentheses ( ) and brackets [ ] indicate that operations inside the grouping symbols should be performed first. For example, to evaluate $2 \cdot 4 + 6$, you multiply first, then add. To evaluate $2(4 + 6)$, you add first, then multiply.

EXAMPLE 2 Evaluate expressions with grouping symbols

Evaluate the expression.

a. $7(13 - 8) = 7(5)$ Subtract within parentheses.

     $= 35$ Multiply.

b. $24 - (3^2 + 1) = 24 - (9 + 1)$ Evaluate power.

     $= 24 - 10$ Add within parentheses.

     $= 14$ Subtract.

c. $2[30 - (8 + 13)] = 2[30 - 21]$ Add within parentheses.

     $= 2[9]$ Subtract within brackets.

     $= 18$ Multiply.

AVOID ERRORS
When grouping symbols appear inside other grouping symbols, work from the innermost grouping symbols outward.

FRACTION BARS A fraction bar can act as a grouping symbol. Evaluate the numerator and denominator before you divide:

$$\frac{8 + 4}{5 - 2} = (8 + 4) \div (5 - 2) = 12 \div 3 = 4$$

EXAMPLE 3 Evaluate an algebraic expression

Evaluate the expression when $x = 4$.

$\dfrac{9x}{3(x + 2)} = \dfrac{9 \cdot 4}{3(4 + 2)}$ Substitute 4 for x.

$= \dfrac{9 \cdot 4}{3 \cdot 6}$ Add within parentheses.

$= \dfrac{36}{18}$ Multiply.

$= 2$ Divide.

Animated Algebra at classzone.com

✓ **GUIDED PRACTICE**   for Examples 2 and 3

Evaluate the expression.

5. $4(3 + 9)$ **48**   **6.** $3(8 - 2^2)$ **12**   **7.** $2[(9 + 3) \div 4]$ **6**

Evaluate the expression when $y = 8$.

8. $y^2 - 3$ **61**   **9.** $12 - y - 1$ **3**   **10.** $\dfrac{10y + 1}{y + 1}$ **9**

1.2 Apply Order of Operations   **9**

Motivating the Lesson
On a 3-day trip, the Browns drove 186 miles the first day, 168 miles the second day, and 255 miles the third day. Ask students what series of calculations they would use to find the average number of miles driven each day. Then ask them how they would write a single numerical expression to calculate this average.

❸ TEACH

Extra Example 1
Evaluate the expression $6 + 12 \div 3 \times 4^2$. **70**

Extra Example 2
Evaluate the expression.
a. $24 \div (4 - 1)$ **8**
b. $48 - (6 + 5^2)$ **17**
c. $3[32 \div (2 + 6)]$ **12**

Key Questions to Ask for Example 2

• How are the expressions in Example 2 different from those in Example 1? **The expressions in Example 2 involve grouping symbols.**

• In part c, why is the addition done first? **You evaluate the expression in the innermost grouping symbols first.**

Extra Example 3
Evaluate the expression $\dfrac{10x}{2(x + 2)}$ when $x = 3$. **3**

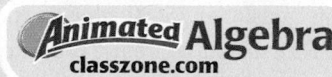
Animated Algebra
classzone.com

An **Animated Algebra** activity is available on-line for **Example 3**. This activity is also available on the **Power Presentations CD-ROM**.

Differentiated Instruction

Inclusion Students having difficulty using basic arithmetic operations may be allowed to rely on calculators. Have students work in groups with a variety of calculators. Include a calculator that does *not* follow the order of operations. Present each group with a simple expression to evaluate on the calculator, such as $2 + 3 \cdot 4$. For different calculators, the answer will be 14 or 20. Help students understand how to use their own calculator to evaluate numerical expressions.

See also the *Algebra 1 Toolkit* for more strategies.

EXAMPLE 2 **Standardized Test Practice**

A group of 12 students volunteers to collect litter for one day. A sponsor provides 3 juice drinks and 2 sandwiches for each student and pays \$30 for trash bags. The sponsor's cost (in dollars) is given by the expression $12(3j + 2s) + 30$ where j is the cost of a juice drink and s is the cost of a sandwich. A juice drink costs \$1.25. A sandwich costs \$2. What is the sponsor's cost?

(A) \$79 (B) \$123 (C) \$129 (D) \$210

ELIMINATE CHOICES
You can eliminate choices A and D by estimating. When j is about 1 and s is 2, the value of the expression is about $12(3 + 4) + 30$, or \$114.

Solution

$$12(3j + 2s) + 30 = 12(3 \cdot \mathbf{1.25} + 2 \cdot 2) + 30 \qquad \text{Substitute 1.25 for } j \text{ and 2 for } s.$$
$$= 12(3.75 + 4) + 30 \qquad \text{Multiply within parentheses.}$$
$$= 12(7.75) + 30 \qquad \text{Add within parentheses.}$$
$$= 93 + 30 \qquad \text{Multiply.}$$
$$= 123 \qquad \text{Add.}$$

▶ The sponsor's cost is \$123. The correct answer is B. (A) (B) (C) (D).

✓ **GUIDED PRACTICE** **for Example 4**

11. **WHAT IF?** In Example 4, suppose the number of volunteers doubles. Does the sponsor's cost double as well? *Explain.* **No; the total cost of the juice drinks and sandwiches will double, but the cost of the trash bags will not.**

1.2 EXERCISES

HOMEWORK KEY
○ = **WORKED-OUT SOLUTIONS** on p. WS1 for Exs. 16 and 35
★ = **STANDARDIZED TEST PRACTICE** Exs. 2, 19, 31, 37, 39, and 40

SKILL PRACTICE

A

1. **VOCABULARY** According to the order of operations, which operation would you perform first in simplifying $50 - 5 \times 4^2 \div 2$? **Square 4.**

2. ★ **WRITING** *Describe* the steps you would use to evaluate the expression $2(3x + 1)^2$ when $x = 3$. **Substitute 3 for x; multiply $3 \cdot 3$; add $9 + 1$; square 10; multiply $2 \cdot 100$. The result is 200.**

EXAMPLES 1 and 2 on pp. 8–9 for Exs. 3–21

EVALUATING EXPRESSIONS Evaluate the expression.

3. $13 - 8 + 3$ **8**
4. $8 - 2^2$ **4**
5. $3 \cdot 6 - 4$ **14**
6. $5 \cdot 2^3 + 7$ **47**

7. $48 \div 4^2 + \frac{3}{5}$ **$3\frac{3}{5}$**
8. $1 + 5^2 \div 50$ **82**
9. $2^4 \cdot 4 - 2 \div 8$ **$63\frac{3}{4}$**
10. $4^3 \div 8 + 8$ **16**

11. $(12 + 72) \div 4$ **21**
12. $24 + 4(3 + 1)$ **40**
13. $12(6 - 3.5)^2 - 1.5$ **73.5**
14. $24 \div (8 + 4^2)$ **1**

15. $\frac{1}{2}(21 + 2^2)$ **$12\frac{1}{2}$**
16. $\frac{1}{6}(6 + 18) - 2^2$ **0**
17. $\frac{3}{4}[13 - (2 + 3)]^2$ **48**
18. $8[20 - (9 - 5)^2]$ **32**

19. ★ **MULTIPLE CHOICE** What is the value of $3[20 - (7 - 5)^2]$? **A**

    (A) 48   (B) 56   (C) 192   (D) 972

20. 7 + 7 was added before dividing 14 by 7; $(1 + 13) \div 7 + 7$ $= 14 \div 7 + 7 = 2 + 7 = 9$

ERROR ANALYSIS *Describe* and correct the error in evaluating the expression. 20, 21. See margin.

20.
$$(1 + 13) \div 7 + 7 = 14 \div 7 + 7$$
$$= 14 \div 14$$
$$= 1$$
✗

21.
$$20 - \frac{1}{2} \cdot 6^2 = 20 - 3^2$$
$$= 20 - 9$$
$$= 11$$
✗

EXAMPLE 3 B
on p. 9
for Exs. 22–31

21. $\frac{1}{2}$ was multiplied by 6 before squaring 6; $20 - \frac{1}{2} \cdot 6^2 =$ $20 - \frac{1}{2} \cdot 36 =$ $20 - 18 = 2.$

EVALUATING EXPRESSIONS Evaluate the expression.

22. $4n - 12$ when $n = 7$ **16**   **23.** $2 + 3x^2$ when $x = 3$ **29**   **24.** $6t^2 - 13$ when $t = 2$ **11**

25. $11 + r^3 - 2r$ when $r = 5$ **126**   **26.** $5(w - 4)$ when $w = 7$ **15**   **27.** $3(m^2 - 2)$ when $m = 1.5$ **0.75**

28. $\frac{9x + 4}{3x + 1}$ when $x = 7$ **$3\frac{1}{22}$**   **29.** $\frac{k^2 - 1}{k + 3}$ when $k = 5$ **3**   **30.** $\frac{b^3 - 21}{5b + 9}$ when $b = 3$ **$\frac{1}{4}$**

31. ★ **MULTIPLE CHOICE** What is the value of $\frac{x^2}{25} + 3x$ when $x = 10$? **B**

    (A) 26   (B) 34   (C) 43   (D) 105

C **CHALLENGE** Insert grouping symbols in the expression so that the value of the expression is 14.

32. $9 + 39 + 22 \div 11 - 9 + 3$
    $(9 + 39 + 22) \div (11 - 9 + 3)$

33. $2 \times 2 + 3^2 - 4 + 3 \times 5$
    $(2 \times 2 + 3)^2 - (4 + 3) \times 5$

PROBLEM SOLVING

EXAMPLE 4 A
on p. 10
for Exs. 34–37

34. SALES Your school's booster club sells school T-shirts. Half the T-shirts come from one supplier at a cost of $5.95 each, and half from another supplier at a cost of $6.15 each. The average cost (in dollars) of a T-shirt is given by the expression $\frac{5.95 + 6.15}{2}$. Find the average cost. **$6.05**

@HomeTutor for problem solving help at classzone.com

35. MULTI-STEP PROBLEM You join an online music service. The total cost (in dollars) of downloading 3 singles at $.99 each and 2 albums at $9.95 each is given by the expression $3 \cdot 0.99 + 2 \cdot 9.95$.

    a. Find the total cost. **$22.87**

    b. You have $25 to spend. How much will you have left? **$2.13**

@HomeTutor for problem solving help at classzone.com

36. PHYSIOLOGY If you know how tall you were at the age of 2, you can estimate your adult height (in inches). Girls can use the expression $25 + 1.17h$ where h is the height (in inches) at the age of 2. Boys can use the expression $22.7 + 1.37h$. Estimate the adult height of each person to the nearest inch.

    a. A girl who was 34 inches tall at age 2 **65 in.**

    b. A boy who was 33 inches tall at age 2 **68 in.**

1.2 Apply Order of Operations   **11**

PRACTICE
AND APPLY

Assignment Guide

📖 Answer Transparencies available for all exercises

Basic:
Day 1: SRH p. 915 Exs. 11–15
pp. 10–12
Exs. 1, 2, 3–17 odd, 19–26, 28–30, 34–38, 41–52

Average:
Day 1: pp. 10–12
Exs. 1, 2, 8–18 even, 20–39, 41–52

Advanced:
Day 1: pp. 10–12
Exs. 1, 2, 13–19, 25–33*, 36–40*, 43–52

Block:
pp. 10–12
Exs. 1, 2, 8–18 even, 20–39, 41–52 (with 1.1)

Differentiated Instruction

See *Algebra 1 Best Practices Toolkit* for suggestions on addressing the needs of a diverse classroom.

Homework Check

For a quick check of student understanding of key concepts, go over the following exercises:
Basic: 8, 14, 22, 34, 35
Average: 10, 16, 24, 35, 36
Advanced: 13, 18, 28, 36, 37

Extra Practice
• Student Edition, p. 938
• Chapter 5 Resource Book: Practice levels A, B, C, pp. 19–21

Practice Worksheet

An easily-readable reduced practice page (with answers) for this lesson can be found on p. 1C.

Differentiated Instruction

Below Level Point out that the fraction bars appearing in **Exercises 28–30** are grouping symbols. To help students evaluate the expressions in these exercises, suggest that they use this algorithm: *evaluate the numerator, then evaluate the denominator, and divide the value of the numerator by the value of the denominator.* You might suggest that they remember *numerator/denominator/divide* as a shortened version of the algorithm.

See also the *Algebra 1 Toolkit* for more strategies.

11

Evaluate the expression.

1. $3^3 \div 9 + 4 \cdot 3$ **15**

2. $12 + (5 - 3)^2$ **16**

3. $2(c^2 + 4)$ when $c = 4$ **40**

4. $\dfrac{g^2 - 8}{2g - 5}$ when $g = 6$ **4**

5. The cost (in dollars) to buy p posters at the Posters Plus online store is given by the expression $3.5p + 6.75$. At the More Posters online store, the cost is given by $4.25p + 2.55$. Which store has the lower cost for 5 posters? **More Posters**

Online Quiz

Available at **classzone.com**

Diagnosis/Remediation

• Practice A, B, C in Chapter 1 Resource Book, pp. 19–21
• Study Guide in Chapter 1 Resource Book, pp. 22–23
• Practice Workbook, pp. 3–4
• @HomeTutor

Challenge

Additional challenge is available in the Chapter 1 Resource Book, p. 26.

40a. *Sample answer:* First place votes are worth 3 points which is $3f$, second place votes are worth 2 points which is $2s$, third place votes are worth 1 point which is $1t$. A player's point total is $3f + 2s + t$.

40c. Yes. *Sample answer:* Change each of the first place votes to third place votes, change each of the second place votes to first place votes, and change each of the third place votes to second place votes.

---

37. ★ **OPEN-ENDED**   Write a numerical expression including parentheses that has the same value when you remove the parentheses. *Sample answer:* $(3 \times 4) + 5$

B **38.** **ONLINE SHOPPING** The regular shipping fee (in dollars) for an online computer store is given by the expression $0.5w + 4.49$ where w is the weight (in pounds) of the item. The fee (in dollars) for rush delivery is given by $0.99w + 6.49$. You purchase a 26.5 pound computer. How much do you save using regular shipping instead of rush delivery? **$14.99**

39. ★ **SHORT RESPONSE** You make and sell flags for $10 each. Each flag requires $4.50 worth of fabric. You pay $12.99 for a kit to punch holes to hang the flags. Your expenses (in dollars) are given by the expression $4.50m + 12.99$ where m is the number of flags you make. Your income is given by the expression $10s$ where s is the number of flags you sell. Your profit is equal to the difference of your income and your expenses.

   a. You make 50 flags and sell 38 of them. Find your income and your expenses. Then find your profit. **$380, $237.99; $142.01**

   b. *Explain* how you could use a single expression to determine your profit *Sample answer:* **You could write an expression showing the difference of your income and expenses as $P = 10s - (4.50m + 12.99)$.**

C **40.** ★ **EXTENDED RESPONSE** Each year Heisman Trophy voters select the outstanding college football player. Each voter selects three players ranked first to third. A first place vote is worth 3 points, a second place vote is worth 2 points, and a third place vote is worth 1 point. Let f, s, and t be, respectively, the number of first place, second place, and third place votes a player gets. The table shows the votes for the winner and the runner-up in 2003.

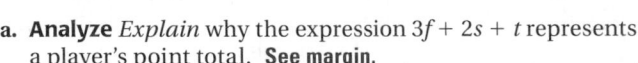

Player	First place	Second place	Third place
Jason White	319	204	116
Larry Fitzgerald	253	233	128

   a. **Analyze** *Explain* why the expression $3f + 2s + t$ represents a player's point total. **See margin.**

   b. **Calculate** Use the expression in part (a) to determine how many more points Jason White got than Larry Fitzgerald got. **128 points**

   c. **CHALLENGE** Can you rearrange the order of the votes for each player in such a way that Larry Fitzgerald would have won? *Explain*.

MIXED REVIEW

PREVIEW
Prepare for Lesson 1.3 in Exs. 41–48.

Copy and complete. *(p. 929)*

41. $360 \text{ in.} = \underline{\ ?\ } \text{ ft}$ **30**

42. $250 \text{ g} = \underline{\ ?\ } \text{ kg}$ **0.25**

43. $8 \text{ ft}^2 = \underline{\ ?\ } \text{ in.}^2$ **1152**

44. $80 \text{ L} = \underline{\ ?\ } \text{ mL}$ **80,000**

Find the value of the expression when $x = 5$. *(p. 2)*

45. $x + 4.7$ **9.7**

46. $19.3 - x$ **14.3**

47. $\frac{1}{2}x$ **$2\frac{1}{2}$**

48. $x - \frac{3}{4}$ **$4\frac{1}{4}$**

Evaluate the power. *(p. 2)*

49. 6^2 **36**

50. 10^4 **10,000**

51. $(0.2)^2$ **0.04**

52. $\left(\frac{2}{3}\right)^3$ **$\frac{8}{27}$**

1.2 Use Order of Operations

QUESTION How can you use a graphing calculator to evaluate an expression?

You can use a graphing calculator to evaluate an expression. When you enter the expression, it is important to use grouping symbols so that the calculator performs operations in the correct order.

EXAMPLE Evaluate an expression

Use a graphing calculator to evaluate an expression.

Lean body mass is the mass of the skeleton, muscles, and organs. Physicians use lean body mass to determine dosages of medicine.

Scientists have developed separate formulas for the lean body masses of men and women based on their mass m (in kilograms) and height h (in meters). Lean body mass in measured in units called BMI (Body Mass Index) units.

Men: $1.10m - \dfrac{128m^2}{10{,}000h^2}$ **Women:** $1.07m - \dfrac{148m^2}{10{,}000h^2}$

Find the lean body mass (in BMI units) of a man who is 1.8 meters tall and has a mass of 80 kilograms.

Solution

Enter the expression for men in the calculator. Substitute 80 for m and 1.8 for h. Because the fraction bar is a grouping symbol, enter the denominator using parentheses.

Use the following keystrokes.

1.10 [X] 80 [−] 128 [X] 80 [x²] [÷] [(] 10000 [X] 1.8 [x²] [)]

```
1.10*80-128*80²/
(10000*1.8²)
        62.71604938
```

▸ The lean body mass of a man who is 1.8 meters tall and has a mass of 80 kilograms is about 62.7 BMI units.

PRACTICE

Use a calculator to evaluate the expression for $n = 4$. Round to the nearest thousandth.

1. $3 + 5 \cdot n \div 10$ **5**

2. $2 + \dfrac{3n^2}{4}$ **14**

3. $\dfrac{83}{3n^2} - 1.3$ **0.429**

4. $\dfrac{14.2n}{8 + n^3}$ **0.789**

5. $\dfrac{7 - n}{n^2}$ **0.188**

6. $5n^2 + \dfrac{4n^3 + 1}{3}$ **165.667**

7. Find the lean body mass (to the nearest tenth of a BMI unit) of a woman who is 1.6 meters tall and has a mass of 54 kilograms. **40.9 BMI units**

---

① PLAN AND PREPARE

Learn the Method

- Students will learn how to use a graphing calculator to evaluate an algebraic expression.
- After completing the activity, students can use their graphing calculators to check their answers for Exercises 3–19 and 22–31 in Lesson 1.2. They can also use their calculators to test various placements of grouping symbols in the expressions given in Exercises 32 and 33.

Keystroke Help

Keystrokes for several models of calculators are available in black-line format in the *Chapter 1 Resource Book*.

② TEACH

Tips for Success

In the keystroking shown, point out the use of parentheses around the denominator since the expression involves a fraction bar. Stress that the right parenthesis comes after the second x^2 key.

Extra Example

A person's body mass index (BMI) indicates if they are overweight and at risk for health problems. BMI is calculated using the formula $\dfrac{w}{h^2} \cdot 703$, where w is the person's weight in pounds and h is their height in inches. Calculate the BMI for a person who weighs 120 pounds and is 64.5 inches tall. **about 20.3**

③ ASSESS AND RETEACH

Use a calculator to evaluate the expression for $b = 2$. Round to the nearest thousandth.

1. $7 + \dfrac{9b^2}{3}$ **19**

2. $\dfrac{83}{4b^3 - 7.4}$ **3.374**

13

1 PLAN AND PREPARE

Explore the Concept
- Students will describe a pattern.
- This activity leads into the study of writing an algebraic expression in Example 2 in Lesson 1.3.

Materials
Each student or pair of students will need graph paper.

Recommended Time
Work activity: 10 min
Discuss results: 5 min

Grouping
Students can work individually or in pairs. If students work in pairs, one student can draw and label the figures and the other can write the numerical expression.

2 TEACH

Tips for Success
To visually reinforce the pattern, in Figures 2 and 3 have students shade those squares that appeared in the previous figure. Students should readily see that four new squares at added at each stage.

classzone.com

An **Animated Algebra** activity is available on-line. This activity is also available on the **Power Presentations CD-ROM**.

Key Discovery
Algebraic expressions can be used to determine the *n*th number in a pattern.

3 ASSESS AND RETEACH

Without drawing it, how can you find the number of squares in the 15th figure of the pattern?
Multiply 4 × 15 and add 1.

1.3 Patterns and Expressions

MATERIALS · graph paper

QUESTION How can you use an algebraic expression to describe a pattern?

EXPLORE Create and describe a pattern

STEP 1

STEP 2

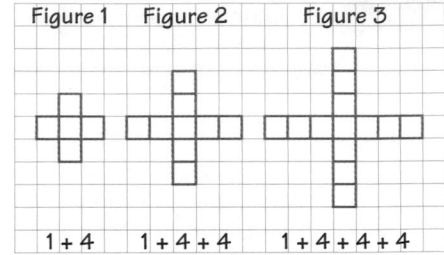

1 + 4	1 + 4 + 4	1 + 4 + 4 + 4

Draw a figure Draw a unit square on graph paper. Then draw a unit square against each side of the first square to form figure 1.

Copy figure 1 and draw a square on each "arm" to form figure 2. Use the same method to form figure 3.

Write expressions For each figure, write a numerical expression that describes the number of squares in the figure.

DRAW CONCLUSIONS Use your observations to complete these exercises

In Exercises 1–3, use the pattern in Steps 1 and 2 above.

1. How is the figure number related to the number of times 4 is added in the numerical expression? Predict the number of squares in the fourth figure. Create figure 4 and check your prediction. **The figure number is equal to the number of times 4 is added in the numerical expression; 17 squares; see margin.**

2. *Describe* how to calculate the number of squares in the *n*th figure. **Find the sum of 1 and the quantity 4 times *n*.**

3. Write an algebraic expression for the number of squares in the *n*th figure. (*Hint:* Remember that repeated addition can be written as multiplication.) **1 + 4*n***

4. Write an algebraic expression for the number of squares in the *n*th figure of the pattern shown. **2*n***

Figure 1   **Figure 2**   **Figure 3**   **Figure 4**

1.

1.3 Write Expressions

Before	You evaluated expressions.
Now	You will translate verbal phrases into expressions.
Why?	So you can find the time needed to do a job, as in Ex. 36.

Key Vocabulary
• verbal model
• rate
• unit rate

To translate verbal phrases into expressions, look for words that indicate mathematical operations.

KEY CONCEPT   *For Your Notebook*

Translating Verbal Phrases

Operation	Verbal Phrase	Expression
Addition: sum, plus, total, more than, increased by	The sum of 2 and a number x	$2 + x$
	A number n plus 7	$n + 7$
Subtraction: difference, less than, minus, decreased by	The difference of a number n and 6	$n - 6$
	A number y minus 5	$y - 5$
Multiplication: times, product, multiplied by, of	12 times a number y	$12y$
	$\frac{1}{3}$ of a number x	$\frac{1}{3}x$
Division: quotient, divided by, divided into	The quotient of a number k and 2	$\frac{k}{2}$

Order is important when writing subtraction and division expressions. For instance, "the difference of a number n and 6" is written $n - 6$, *not* $6 - n$, and "the quotient of a number k and 2" is written $\frac{k}{2}$, *not* $\frac{2}{k}$.

EXAMPLE 1 **Translate verbal phrases into expressions**

AVOID ERRORS

When you translate verbal phrases, the words "the quantity" tell you what to group. In part (a), you write $6n - 4$, *not* $(6 - 4)n$.

Verbal Phrase	Expression
a. 4 less than the quantity 6 times a number n	$6n - 4$
b. 3 times the sum of 7 and a number y	$3(7 + y)$
c. The difference of 22 and the square of a number m	$22 - m^2$

 GUIDED PRACTICE for Example 1

1. Translate the phrase "the quotient when the quantity 10 plus a number x is divided by 2" into an expression. $\dfrac{10 + x}{2}$

---

❶ PLAN AND PREPARE

Warm-Up Exercises
📑 Transparency Available
1. Evaluate $2[54 \div (4^2 + 2)]$. **6**
2. Evaluate $\dfrac{5x}{x + 2}$ when $x = 3$. **3**
3. Eight students each ordered 2 drawing kits and 4 drawing pencils. The expression $8(2k + 4p)$ gives the total cost, where k is the cost of a kit and p is the cost of a pencil. Find the total cost if a kit costs \$25 and a pencil costs \$1.25. **\$440**

Notetaking Guide
📑 Transparency Available
Promotes interactive learning and notetaking skills, pp. 7–9.

Pacing
Basic: 1 day
Average: 1 day
Advanced: 1 day
Block: 0.5 block with 1.4
• See *Teaching Guide/Lesson Plan.*

❷ FOCUS AND MOTIVATE

Essential Question
Big Idea 1, p. 1
How do you write an expression to represent a real-world situation? **Tell students they will learn how to answer this question by using variables, symbols, and a verbal model to describe the situation.**

NCTM STANDARDS
Standard 2: Represent situations using algebraic symbols
Standard 10: Use representations to solve problems

Resource Planning Guide

Chapter Resource Book
• Teaching Guide/Lesson Plan (pp. 27–28)
• Practice levels A, B, C (pp. 29–31)
• Study Guide (pp. 32–33)
• Catch-up for Absent Students (p. 34)
• Problem Solving Workshop (p. 35)
• Challenge (p. 36)

Workbooks
• Notetaking Guide (pp. 7–9)
• Practice Workbook (pp. 5–6)

Teaching Options
• **Power Presentations CD-ROM** provides dynamic electronic teaching resources for the classroom.
• **Activity Generator CD-ROM** provides editable activities for all ability levels.

Interactive Technology
• Easy Planner
• Power Presentations CD-ROM
• Activity Generator CD-ROM
• Animated Algebra
• Test Generator CD-ROM
• Online Quiz
• eWorkbook
• eEdition
• @HomeTutor

Resources for English Learners
• Quick Reference for English Learners
• Spanish Study Guide
• Multi-Language Visual Glossary
• Student Resources in Spanish

See also the *Algebra 1 Toolkit* for more strategies for meeting individual needs.

15

EXAMPLE 2   Write an expression

❸ TEACH

Extra Example 1

Translate the verbal phrase into an expression.

a. 8 times the quantity 4 plus a number n **$8(4 + n)$**

b. 12 decreased by a number x **$12 - x$**

c. The quotient of the square of a number w and 5 **$\dfrac{w^2}{5}$**

Extra Example 2

The length of a building is 20 feet more than its width w. Write an expression for the length of the building. **$w + 20$**

Extra Example 3

You and 4 friends meet to have dinner at a restaurant. Everyone decides to order the nightly special. Write an expression for the total cost of the meals. **$5s$, where s is the cost of the nightly special**

Key Questions to Ask for Example 3

• Why is the amount of money in the jar represented by a variable? **The amount changes each day.**

• What phrase in the problem indicates division? **"share the amount in the jar equally"**

• Why is the number of people given as 6 and not 5? **You need to include yourself in the total.**

CHOOSE A VARIABLE
To write an expression for a real-world problem, choose a letter that reminds you of the quantity represented, such as ℓ for length.

EXAMPLE 2   **Write an expression**

CUTTING A RIBBON A piece of ribbon ℓ feet long is cut from a ribbon 8 feet long. Write an expression for the length (in feet) of the remaining piece.

Solution

Draw a diagram and use a specific case to help you write the expression.

Suppose the piece cut is 2 feet long.

Suppose the piece cut is ℓ feet long.

The remaining piece is $(8 - 2)$ feet long.

The remaining piece is $(8 - \ell)$ feet long.

▶ The expression $8 - \ell$ represents the length (in feet) of the remaining piece.

VERBAL MODEL A **verbal model** describes a real-world situation using words as labels and using math symbols to relate the words. You can replace the words with numbers and variables to create a *mathematical model*, such as an expression, for the real-world situation.

EXAMPLE 3   **Use a verbal model to write an expression**

TIPS You work with 5 other people at an ice cream stand. All the workers put their tips into a jar and share the amount in the jar equally at the end of the day. Write an expression for each person's share (in dollars) of the tips.

Solution

STEP 1 **Write** a verbal model.

STEP 2 **Translate** the verbal model into an algebraic expression. Let a represent the amount (in dollars) in the jar.

Amount in jar	÷	Number of people
↓		↓
a	÷	6

▶ An expression that represents each person's share (in dollars) is $\dfrac{a}{6}$.

AVOID ERRORS
Read the statement of the problem carefully. The number of people sharing tips is 6.

✓ **GUIDED PRACTICE**   for Examples 2 and 3

2. **WHAT IF?** In Example 2, suppose that you cut the original ribbon into p pieces of equal length. Write an expression that represents the length (in feet) of each piece. $\dfrac{\ell}{p}$

3. **WHAT IF?** In Example 3, suppose that each of the 6 workers contributes an equal amount for an after-work celebration. Write an expression that represents the total amount (in dollars) contributed. **$6d$, where d represents the amount contributed by each worker.**

Differentiated Instruction

Inclusion Students with conceptual processing difficulties may have a hard time with the many verbal descriptions and symbolic notations for expressing the same operation. For example, "k divided by 2" or "the quotient of k and 2" can be written as $\dfrac{k}{2}$, $k/2$, and $k \div 2$. Students with such difficulties should be provided with resource sheets listing as many possible descriptions and notations for each standard operation. See also the *Algebra 1 Toolkit* for more strategies.

RATES A **rate** is a fraction that compares two quantities measured in different units. If the denominator of the fraction is 1 unit, the rate is called a **unit rate**.

EXAMPLE 4 Find a unit rate

READING
Per means "for each" or "for every" and can also be represented using the symbol /, as in mi/h.

A car travels 110 miles in 2 hours. Find the unit rate.

$$\frac{110 \text{ miles}}{2 \text{ hours}} = \frac{110 \text{ miles} \div 2}{2 \text{ hours} \div 2} = \frac{55 \text{ miles}}{1 \text{ hour}}$$

▶ The unit rate is 55 miles per hour, or 55 mi/h.

EXAMPLE 5 Solve a multi-step problem

CELL PHONES Your basic monthly charge for cell phone service is $30, which includes 300 free minutes. You pay a fee for each extra minute you use. One month you paid $3.75 for 15 extra minutes. Find your total bill if you use 22 extra minutes.

Solution

STEP 1 **Calculate** the unit rate.

$$\frac{3.75}{15} = \frac{0.25}{1} = \$.25 \text{ per minute}$$

STEP 2 **Write** a verbal model and then an expression. Let m be the number of extra minutes.

Basic charge (dollars)	+	Rate for extra minutes (dollars/minute)	·	Number of extra minutes (minutes)
30	+	0.25	·	m

USE UNIT ANALYSIS
You expect the answer, which is a cost, to be in dollars. You can use unit analysis to check that the expression produces an answer in dollars.

Use *unit analysis* to check that the expression $30 + 0.25m$ is reasonable.

$$\text{dollars} + \frac{\text{dollars}}{\text{minute}} \cdot \text{minutes} = \text{dollars} + \text{dollars} = \text{dollars}$$

Because the units are dollars, the expression is reasonable.

STEP 3 **Evaluate** the expression when $m = 22$.

$$30 + 0.25(22) = 35.5$$

▶ The total bill is $35.50.

✓ **GUIDED PRACTICE** for Examples 4 and 5

4. Suppose your friends share cell phone service. They pay a basic charge of $35 and $8.80 for 40 extra minutes. Find their total bill if they use 35 extra minutes. **$42.70**

1.3 Write Expressions **17**

Extra Example 4
A 16-ounce box of cereal costs $2.99. Find the unit rate to the nearest cent. **19¢/oz**

Key Questions to Ask for Example 4
• Why do you divide by 2? **So the denominator of the fraction is 1 hour.**
• Why do you divide *both* the numerator and the denominator by 2? **So the resulting unit rate is equivalent to the original rate.**

Extra Example 5
You have a membership in a local ski club. The membership costs you $40 per month, which includes 10 lift passes. You must pay a fee for each lift pass after the tenth one. Two months ago you paid $13.50 for 3 extra lift passes. Find your total cost for last month if you bought 7 extra lift passes. **$71.50**

Key Question to Ask for Example 5
• Why do you need to know the unit rate? **So you can determine the cost to talk for 22 minutes.**

Closing the Lesson
Have students summarize the major points of the lesson and answer the Essential Question: How do you write an expression to represent a real-world situation?
• Certain words and phrases indicate the operation(s) to be used in a real-world situation.
• A verbal model can be used to write an expression that models a real-world situation.
• Use division to change a given rate to a unit rate.
Translate the verbal phrases in the problem into operations and variables, create a verbal model, and then translate the verbal model into an expression.

1.3 EXERCISES

HOMEWORK KEY
○ = WORKED-OUT SOLUTIONS
on p. WS1 for Exs. 11, 21, and 33

★ = STANDARDIZED TEST PRACTICE
Exs. 2, 13, 14, 34, and 37

SKILL PRACTICE

A 1. **VOCABULARY** Copy and complete: A(n) __?__ is a fraction that compares two quantities measured in different units. **rate**

2. ★ **WRITING** *Explain* how to write $\frac{20 \text{ miles}}{4 \text{ hours}}$ as a unit rate. **See margin.**

TRANSLATING PHRASES **Translate the verbal phrase into an expression.**

EXAMPLE 1
on p. 15
for Exs. 3–14

2. Divide the numerator and the denominator by 4; $\frac{20 \text{ miles} \div 4}{4 \text{ hours} \div 4}$
$= \frac{5 \text{ mi}}{1\text{h}}$ or 5 mi/h.

9. $\frac{2t}{12}$

3. 8 more than a number x **$x + 8$**

4. The product of 6 and a number y **$6y$**

5. $\frac{1}{2}$ of a number m **$\frac{1}{2}m$**

6. 50 divided by a number h **$\frac{50}{h}$**

7. The difference of 7 and a number n **$7 - n$**

8. The sum of 15 and a number x **$15 + x$**

9. The quotient of twice a number t and 12

10. 3 less than the square of a number p **$p^2 - 3$**

⑪. 7 less than twice a number k **$2k - 7$**

12. 5 more than 3 times a number w **$3w + 5$**

13. ★ **MULTIPLE CHOICE** Which expression represents the phrase "the product of 15 and the quantity 12 more than a number x"? **C**

Ⓐ $15 + 12 \times x$ Ⓑ $(15 + 12)x$ Ⓒ $15(x + 12)$ Ⓓ $15 \times 12 + x$

14. ★ **MULTIPLE CHOICE** Which expression represents the phrase "twice the quotient of 50 and the sum of a number y and 8"? **C**

Ⓐ $\frac{2 \cdot 50}{y} + 8$ Ⓑ $2\left(\frac{50 + y}{8}\right)$ Ⓒ $2\left(\frac{50}{y + 8}\right)$ Ⓓ $\frac{2}{50} + (y + 8)$

EXAMPLES 2 and 3
on p. 16
for Exs. 15–21

WRITING EXPRESSIONS **Write an expression for the situation.**

15. Number of tokens needed for v video games if each game takes 4 tokens **$4v$**

16. Number of pages of a 5 page article left to read if you've read p pages **$5 - p$**

17. Each person's share if p people share 16 slices of pizza equally **$\frac{16}{p}$**

18. Amount you spend if you buy a shirt for $20 and jeans for j dollars **$20 + j$**

19. Number of days left in the week if d days have passed so far **$7 - d$**

20. Number of hours in m minutes **$\frac{m}{60}$**

㉑. Number of months in y years **$12y$**

EXAMPLE 4
on p. 17
for Exs. 18–23

UNIT RATES **Find the unit rate.**

22. $\frac{32 \text{ students}}{4 \text{ groups}}$
8 students per group

23. $\frac{4.5 \text{ pints}}{3 \text{ servings}}$
1.5 pints per serving

24. $\frac{12 \text{ runs}}{5 \text{ innings}}$
2.4 runs per inning

25. $\frac{\$136}{20 \text{ shares}}$
$6.80 per share

B **ERROR ANALYSIS** *Describe* and correct the error in the units.

26. $\frac{\$2}{\text{foot}} \cdot 24 \text{ feet} = \frac{\$48}{\text{ft}^2}$

Feet should cancel out, not be squared; $48.

27. $9 \text{ yards} \cdot \frac{3 \text{ feet}}{1 \text{ yard}} \cdot \frac{\$2}{\text{foot}} = \frac{\$54}{\text{ft}}$ ✗

Feet should cancel out; $54.

COMPARING RATES In Exercises 28 and 29, tell which rate is greater.

28. $1\frac{1}{4}$ miles in 2 minutes and 4 seconds, or $1\frac{3}{16}$ miles in 1 minute and 55 seconds

$1\frac{3}{16}$ **mi in 1 min 55 sec**

29. $1.60 for 5 minutes, or $19.50 for 1 hour **$19.50 for 1 h**

C 30. **CHALLENGE** Look for a pattern in the expressions shown below. Use the pattern to write an expression for the sum of the whole numbers from 1 to n. Then find the sum of the whole numbers from 1 to 50.

$$1 + 2 = \frac{2 \cdot 3}{2} \qquad 1 + 2 + 3 = \frac{3 \cdot 4}{2} \qquad 1 + 2 + 3 + 4 = \frac{4 \cdot 5}{2} \qquad \frac{n \cdot (n + 1)}{2}; 1275$$

PROBLEM SOLVING

EXAMPLE 5 A
on p. 17
for Exs. 31–34

31. **TICKET PRICES** Tickets to a science museum cost $19.95 each. There is a $3 charge for each order no matter how many tickets are ordered. Write an expression for the cost (in dollars) of ordering tickets. Then find the total cost if you order 5 tickets. **19.95t + 3; $102.75**

 @HomeTutor for problem solving help at classzone.com

32. **FOSSIL FUELS** Fossil fuels are produced by the decay of organic material over millions of years. To make one gallon of gas, it takes about 98 tons of organic material, roughly the amount of wheat that could be harvested in a 40 acre field. Write an expression for the amount (in tons) of organic material it takes to make g gallons of gas. How many tons would it take to make enough gas to fill a car's 20 gallon gas tank? **98g; 1960 tons**

@HomeTutor for problem solving help at classzone.com

33. **MULTI-STEP PROBLEM** A 48 ounce container of juice costs $2.64. A 64 ounce container of the same juice costs $3.84.

a. Find the cost per ounce of each container. **$.055, $.06**

b. Which size container costs less per ounce? **48 oz container**

c. You want to buy 192 ounces of juice. How much do you save using the container size from your answer to part (b)? **$.96**

34. ★ **OPEN-ENDED** *Describe* a real-world situation that can be modeled by the rate $\frac{30}{x}$ where x is a period of time (in hours). Identify the units for 30. Choose a value for x and find the unit rate.

34. *Sample answer:* You earn 30 dollars for shoveling driveways in a certain amount of time. If $x = 4$ hours, the unit rate is $7.50 per hour.

35. **WILDLIFE EDUCATION** A wildlife center presents a program about birds of prey. The center charges a basic fee of $325 and an additional fee for each bird exhibited. If 5 birds are exhibited, the additional fee is $125. What is the total cost if 7 birds are exhibited? **$500**

B 36. **DIGITAL PHOTOS** Your printer takes 36 seconds to print a small photo and 60 seconds to print a large one. Write an expression for the time (in seconds) your printer would take to print a batch including both small and large photos. Then find the time your printer would take to print 12 small photos and 5 large photos.

36s + 60ℓ; 732 sec

1.3 Write Expressions **19**

Ⓒ **37.** ★ **EXTENDED RESPONSE** A national survey determines the champion tree in a species. The champion is the tree with the greatest score, based on the tree's girth, its height, and its crown spread as shown.

A tree's score is the sum of the girth in inches, the height in feet, and $\frac{1}{4}$ the crown spread in feet. The data for three champion trees are given. Note that the girth is given in feet.

Species	Girth (ft)	Height (ft)	Crown spread (ft)
Narrowleaf cottonwood	12	97	24
Green ash	21.5	95	95
Green buttonwood	14.5	51	68

a. Write Write an expression for a tree's score. $12g + h + \frac{1}{4}c$

b. Evaluate Find the score for each tree in the table. **247; 376.75; 242**

c. CHALLENGE Let *n* be any number greater than 0. Which change would have the greatest effect on a tree's score, an increase of *n* feet in the girth, in the height, or in the crown spread? *Explain* your reasoning. **Girth; because it is multiplied by 12.**

MIXED REVIEW

Find the area of the rectangle. *(p. 924)*

38.
12 in. 5 in. **60 in.²**

39.
3.5 cm 2 cm **7 cm²**

40.
2.1 m 1.5 m **3.15 m²**

PREVIEW
Prepare for Lesson 1.4 in Exs. 41–46.

Evaluate the expression.

41. $18x$ when $x = 5$ *(p. 2)* **90**   **42.** $y - 6$ when $y = 22$ *(p. 2)* **16**   **43.** $5 + z$ when $z = 11$ *(p. 2)* **16**

44. $\frac{g}{7} + 2$ when $g = 35$ *(p. 10)* **7**   **45.** $5 - 2y^2$ when $y = 1$ *(p. 10)* **3**   **46.** $\frac{a + 9}{2}$ when $a = 4$ *(p. 10)* **6.5**

QUIZ for Lessons 1.1–1.3

Evaluate the expression.

1. $y + 10$ when $y = 43$ *(p. 2)* **53**   **2.** $15 - b$ when $b = 9$ *(p. 2)* **6**   **3.** t^2 when $t = 20$ *(p. 2)* **400**

4. $3n - 5$ when $n = 8$ *(p. 8)* **19**   **5.** $2y^2 - 1$ when $y = 5$ *(p. 8)* **49**   **6.** $\frac{3x - 6}{8}$ when $x = 8$ *(p. 8)* $2\frac{1}{4}$

Translate the verbal phrase into an expression. *(p. 15)*

7. 7 less than a number *y* $y - 7$ **8.** 5 more than a number *t* $t + 5$ **9.** Twice a number *k* **2k**

10. **CAMPING** The rental cost for a campsite is $25 plus $2 per person. Write an expression for the total cost. Then find the total cost for 5 people. *(p. 15)* **25 + 2p; $35**

1.4 Write Equations and Inequalities

Before You translated verbal phrases into expressions.

Now You will translate verbal sentences into equations or inequalities.

Why So you can calculate team competition statistics, as in Ex. 41.

Key Vocabulary
• open sentence
• equation
• inequality
• solution of an equation
• solution of an inequality

An **open sentence** is a mathematical statement that contains two algebraic expressions and a symbol that compares them.

An **equation** is an open sentence that contains the symbol =. An **inequality** is an open sentence that contains one of the symbols <, ≤, >, or ≥.

KEY CONCEPT
For Your Notebook

Symbol	Meaning	Associated Words
=	is equal to	the same as
<	is less than	fewer than
≤	is less than or equal to	at most, no more than
>	is greater than	more than
≥	is greater than or equal to	at least, no less than

COMBINING INEQUALITIES Sometimes two inequalities are combined. For example, the inequalities $x > 4$ and $x < 9$ can be combined to form the inequality $4 < x < 9$, which is read "x is greater than 4 and less than 9."

EXAMPLE 1 Write equations and inequalities

Verbal Sentence	Equation or Inequality
a. The difference of twice a number k and 8 is 12.	$2k - 8 = 12$
b. The product of 6 and a number n is at least 24.	$6n \geq 24$
c. A number y is no less than 5 and no more than 13.	$5 \leq y \leq 13$

 Animated Algebra at classzone.com

✓ **GUIDED PRACTICE** for Example 1

1. Write an equation or an inequality: The quotient of a number p and 12 is at least 30. $\dfrac{p}{12} \geq 30$

---

① PLAN AND PREPARE

Warm-Up Exercises
📖 Transparency Available

1. Write an expression for the phrase: 4 times the difference of 6 and a number y. **$4(6 - y)$**

2. A museum charges $50 for an annual membership and then a reduced price of $2 per ticket. Write an expression to represent the situation. Then find the total cost to join the museum and buy 9 tickets. **$50 + 2t$, where t is the number of tickets; $68**

Notetaking Guide
📖 Transparency Available

Promotes interactive learning and notetaking skills, pp. 10–12.

Pacing
Basic: 1 day
Average: 1 day
Advanced: 1 day
Block: 0.5 block with 1.3
• See *Teaching Guide/Lesson Plan.*

② FOCUS AND MOTIVATE

Essential Question
Big Idea 2, p. 1

How do you write equations and inequalities? **Tell students they will learn how to answer this question by translating sentences into equations or inequalities.**

NCTM STANDARDS

Standard 2: Represent situations using algebraic symbols

Standard 6: Solve problems in math and other contexts

Resource Planning Guide

Chapter Resource Book
• Teaching Guide/Lesson Plan (pp. 37–38)
• Activity Master (p. 39)
• Practice levels A, B, C (pp. 40–42)
• Study Guide (pp. 43–44)
• Catch-up for Absent Students (p. 45)
• Problem Solving Workshop (p. 46)
• Challenge (p. 48)

Workbooks
• Notetaking Guide (pp. 10–12)
• Practice Workbook (pp. 7–8)

Teaching Options
• **Power Presentations CD-ROM** provides dynamic electronic teaching resources for the classroom.
• **Activity Generator CD-ROM** provides editable activities for all ability levels.

Interactive Technology
• Easy Planner
• Power Presentations CD-ROM
• Activity Generator CD-ROM
• Animated Algebra
• Test Generator CD-ROM
• Online Quiz
• eWorkbook
• eEdition
• @HomeTutor

Resources for English Learners
• Quick Reference for English Learners
• Spanish Study Guide
• Multi-Language Visual Glossary
• Student Resources in Spanish

See also the *Algebra 1 Toolkit* for more strategies for meeting individual needs.

SOLUTIONS When you substitute a number for the variable in an open sentence like $x + 2 = 5$ or $2y > 6$, the resulting statement is either true or false. If the statement is true, the number is a **solution of the equation** or a **solution of the inequality**.

EXAMPLE 2 Check possible solutions

Check whether 3 is a solution of the equation or inequality.

Equation/Inequality	Substitute	Conclusion
a. $8 - 2x = 2$	$8 - 2(3) \stackrel{?}{=} 2$	$2 = 2$ ✓ 3 is a solution.
b. $4x - 5 = 6$	$4(3) - 5 \stackrel{?}{=} 6$	$7 = 6$ ✗ 3 is *not* a solution.
c. $2z + 5 > 12$	$2(3) + 5 \stackrel{?}{>} 12$	$11 > 12$ ✗ 3 is *not* a solution.
d. $5 + 3n \leq 20$	$5 + 3(3) \stackrel{?}{\leq} 20$	$14 \leq 20$ ✓ 3 is a solution.

USING MENTAL MATH Some equations are simple enough to solve using mental math. Think of the equation as a question. Once you answer the question, check the solution.

EXAMPLE 3 Use mental math to solve an equation

Equation	Think	Solution	Check
a. $x + 4 = 10$	What number plus 4 equals 10?	6	$6 + 4 = 10$ ✓
b. $20 - y = 8$	20 minus what number equals 8?	12	$20 - 12 = 8$ ✓
c. $6n = 42$	6 times what number equals 42?	7	$6(7) = 42$ ✓
d. $\frac{a}{5} = 9$	What number divided by 5 equals 9?	45	$\frac{45}{5} = 9$ ✓

✓ **GUIDED PRACTICE** for Examples 2 and 3

Check whether the given number is a solution of the equation or inequality.

2. $9 - x = 4$; 5 **solution**   **3.** $b + 5 < 15$; 7 **solution**   **4.** $2n + 3 \geq 21$; 9 **solution**

Solve the equation using mental math.

5. $m + 6 = 11$ **5**   **6.** $5x = 40$ **8**   **7.** $\frac{r}{4} = 10$ **40**

EXAMPLE 4 Solve a multi-step problem

MOUNTAIN BIKING The last time you and 3 friends went to a mountain bike park, you had a coupon for $10 off and paid $17 for 4 tickets. What is the regular price of 4 tickets? If you pay the regular price this time and share it equally, how much does each person pay?

Solution

STEP 1 **Write** a verbal model. Let p be the regular price of 4 tickets. Write an equation.

Regular price	−	Amount of coupon	=	Amount paid
p	−	10	=	17

STEP 2 **Use** mental math to solve the equation $p - 10 = 17$. Think: 10 less than what number is 17? Because $27 - 10 = 17$, the solution is 27.

▸ The regular price for 4 tickets is $27.

STEP 3 **Find** the cost per person: $\dfrac{\$27}{4 \text{ people}} = \$6.75$ per person

▸ Each person pays $6.75.

EXAMPLE 5 Write and check a solution of an inequality

BASKETBALL A basketball player scored 351 points last year. If the player plays 18 games this year, will an average of 20 points per game be enough to beat last year's total?

Solution

STEP 1 **Write** a verbal model. Let p be the average number of points per game. Write an inequality.

Number of games	·	Points per game	>	Total points last year
18	·	p	>	351

USE UNIT ANALYSIS
Unit analysis shows that $\text{games} \cdot \dfrac{\text{points}}{\text{games}} = \text{points}$, so the inequality is reasonable.

STEP 2 **Check** that 20 is a solution of the inequality $18p > 351$. Because $18(20) = 360$ and $360 > 351$, 20 is a solution. ✓

▸ An average of 20 points per game will be enough.

✓ **GUIDED PRACTICE** for Examples 4 and 5

8. **WHAT IF?** In Example 4, suppose that the price of 4 tickets with a half-off coupon is $15. What is each person's share if you pay full price? **$7.50**

9. **WHAT IF?** In Example 5, suppose that the player plays 16 games. Would an average of 22 points per game be enough to beat last year's total? **yes**

1.4 Write Equations and Inequalities   **23**

1.4 EXERCISES

HOMEWORK KEY
○ = WORKED-OUT SOLUTIONS
on p. WS1 for Exs. 7 and 41

★ = STANDARDIZED TEST PRACTICE
Exs. 2, 16, 36, 44, 45, and 46

SKILL PRACTICE

A 1. **VOCABULARY** Give an example of an open sentence. *Sample answer:* $3x + 5 = 20$

2. ★ **WRITING** *Describe* the difference between an expression and an equation. **An expression does not contain an equal sign but an equation does.**

EXAMPLE 1
on p. 21
for Exs. 3–16

WRITING OPEN SENTENCES Write an equation or an inequality.

3. The sum of 42 and a number n is equal to 51. $42 + n = 51$

4. The difference of a number z and 11 is equal to 35. $z - 11 = 35$

5. The difference of 9 and the quotient of a number t and 6 is 5. $9 - \frac{t}{6} = 5$

6. The sum of 12 and the quantity 8 times a number k is equal to 48. $12 + 8k = 48$

⑦. The product of 9 and the quantity 5 more than a number t is less than 6. $9(t + 5) < 6$

8. The product of 4 and a number w is at most 51. $4w \le 51$

9. The sum of a number b and 3 is greater than 8 and less than 12. $8 < b + 3 < 12$

10. The product of 8 and a number k is greater than 4 and no more than 16. $4 < 8k \le 16$

11. The difference of a number t and 7 is greater than 10 and less than 20. $10 < t - 7 < 20$

STORE SALES Write an inequality for the price p (in dollars) described.

12.

$p \le \$10$

13.

Prices start at $\$12^{.99}$

$p \ge \$12.99$

ERROR ANALYSIS *Describe* and correct the error in writing the verbal sentence as an equation or an inequality.

14. The sum of a number n and 4 is no more than 13.

$n + 4 < 13$ ✗ The wrong inequality symbol is used; $n + 4 \le 13$.

15. The quotient of a number t and 4.2 is at most 15.

$\frac{t}{4.2} > 15$ ✗ The wrong inequality symbol is used; $\frac{t}{4.2} \le 15$.

16. ★ **MULTIPLE CHOICE** Which equation corresponds to the sentence "The product of a number b and 3 is no less than 12"? **D**

Ⓐ $3b < 12$ Ⓑ $3b \le 12$ Ⓒ $3b > 12$ Ⓓ $3b \ge 12$

EXAMPLE 2
on p. 22
for Exs. 17–28

CHECK POSSIBLE SOLUTIONS Check whether the given number is a solution of the equation or inequality.

17. $x + 9 = 17$; 8 **solution**

18. $9 + 4y = 17$; 1 **not a solution**

19. $6f - 7 = 29$; 5 **not a solution**

20. $\frac{k}{5} + 9 = 11$; 10 **solution**

21. $\frac{r}{3} - 4 = 4$; 12 **not a solution**

22. $\frac{x - 5}{3} \ge 2.8$; 11 **not a solution**

23. $15 - 4y > 6$; 2 **solution**

24. $y - 3.5 < 6$; 9 **solution**

25. $2 + 3x \le 8$; 2 **solution**

26. $2p - 1 \ge 7$; 3 **not a solution**

27. $4z - 5 < 3$; 2 **not a solution**

28. $3z + 7 > 20$; 4 **not a solution**

EXAMPLE 3
on p. 22
for Exs. 29–34

MENTAL MATH Solve the equation using mental math.

29. $x + 8 = 13$ **5**   30. $y + 16 = 25$ **9**   31. $z - 11 = 1$ **12**

32. $5w = 20$ **4**   33. $8b = 72$ **9**   34. $\frac{f}{6} = 4$ **24**

EQUATIONS AND INEQUALITIES In Exercises 35 and 36, write an open sentence. Then check whether $3\frac{1}{2}$ is a solution of the open sentence.

B 35. 2 less than the product of 3 and a number x is equal to the sum of x and 5.
$3x - 2 = x + 5$; solution

36. 4 more than twice a number k is no greater than the sum of k and 11.
$2k + 4 \leq k + 11$; solution

37. ★ **MULTIPLE CHOICE** Which equation has the same solution as $z - 9 = 3$? **C**

   Ⓐ $z - 4 = 16$ Ⓑ $\frac{1}{2}z = 7$ Ⓒ $z + 15 = 27$ Ⓓ $5z = 45$

C 38. **CHALLENGE** Use mental math to solve the equation $3x + 4 = 19$. *Explain* your thinking. **5; ask what number times 3 plus 4 equals 19.**

PROBLEM SOLVING

EXAMPLES A
4 and 5
on p. 23
for Exs. 39–43

39. **CHARITY WALK** You are taking part in a charity walk, and you have walked 12.5 miles so far. Your goal is to walk 20 miles. How many more miles do you need to walk to meet your goal? **7.5 mi**

   @HomeTutor for problem solving help at classzone.com

40. **COMPACT DISCS** You buy a storage rack that holds 40 CDs. You have 27 CDs. Write an inequality that describes how many more CDs you can buy and still have no more CDs than the rack can hold. You buy 15 CDs. Will they all still fit? **$27 + c \leq 40$; no**

   @HomeTutor for problem solving help at classzone.com

41. **ECO-CHALLENGE** Eco-Challenge Fiji was a competition that included jungle trekking, ocean swimming, mountain biking, and river kayaking. In 2002, the U.S. team finished second about 6 hours after the winning team from New Zealand. The U.S. team finished in about 173 hours. What was the winning team's time? **167 h**

42. **No.** *Sample answer:* Since each batch of cookies takes 2.5 cups of flour and you want to make 8 batches, you need to multiply 2.5 by 8, which gives you 20 cups. Since you only have 18 cups, you do not have enough.

42. **BAKING MEASUREMENTS** You are baking batches of cookies for a bake sale. Each batch takes 2.5 cups of flour. You have 18 cups of flour. Can you bake 8 batches? *Explain*.

43. **EMPLOYMENT** Your friend takes a job cleaning up a neighbor's yard and mowing the grass, and asks you and two other friends to help. Your friend divides the amount the neighbor pays equally among all the members of the group. Each of you got $25. How much did the neighbor pay? **$100**

44. ★ **OPEN-ENDED** Describe a real-world situation you could model using the equation $5x = 50$. Use mental math to solve the equation. *Explain* what the solution means in this situation. **See margin.**

Vocabulary

Exercise 38 Some students may be confused by the words "less" and "less than" since they both indicate subtraction. Point out that "less than" means "subtracted from" while "less" means "minus." So, "2 less than the product of 3 and a number x" means 2 subtracted from $3x$, or $3x - 2$.

Mathematical Reasoning

Exercise 41 Point out that $3x$ must have a value of 15 in order for x to be a solution of the equation. Students should then see that the solution of the equation $3x = 15$ is the solution of the given equation.

Reading Strategy

Exercise 43 Students may want to reword the third sentence of this exercise. The following sentence may be easier for students to decipher: *Write an inequality that describes the number of additional CDs you can buy without having too many to fit in the storage rack.*

Avoiding Common Errors

Exercise 46 Watch for students who use 3 as the number of workers in the group. Suggest they give names to each of the persons discussed in the problem as they read it. Then ask them to count the number of workers; they will discover that there are 4 workers.

44. *Sample answer:* You want to buy $5 gift certificates to a music store for your friends. If you have $50, how many certificates can you buy? 10 certificates; you can buy 10 $5 gift certificates for $50.

Write an equation or an inequality.

1. 3 less than twice a number n is 12. $2n - 3 = 12$

2. The product of 5 and a number k is no more than 30. $5k \leq 30$

3. Check whether 2 is a solution of the inequality $3p + 2 > 8$. $8 \not> 8$; 2 is *not* a solution.

4. You need to practice a gymnastic routine for at least 25 hours. You have already practiced 8.5 hours. If you practice for another 16.5 hours, will you reach your goal? Explain. **Yes; the inequality $h + 8.5 \geq 25$ represents the situation. If you substitute 16.5 for h, $16.5 + 8.5 = 25$ and $25 \geq 25$.**

Online Quiz

Available at **classzone.com**

Diagnosis/Remediation

- Practice A, B, C in Chapter 1 Resource Book, pp. 40–42
- Study Guide in Chapter 1 Resource Book, pp. 43–44
- Practice Workbook, pp. 7–8
- @HomeTutor

Challenge

Additional challenge is available in the Chapter 1 Resource Book, p. 48.

B **45.** ★ **SHORT RESPONSE** You have two part-time jobs. You earn $6 per hour running errands and $5 per hour walking dogs. You can work a total of 10 hours this weekend and hope to earn at least $55. Let r be the number of hours you spend running errands.

   a. Write an inequality that describes the situation. Your inequality should involve only one variable, r. $6r + 5(10 - r) \geq 55$

   b. If you spend the same amount of time at each job, will you meet your goal? *Explain.* **Yes; you will earn $30 running errands and $25 walking dogs; 30 + 25 = 55.**

   c. Can you meet your goal by working all 10 hours at only one job? *Explain.* **Yes; if you work 10 hours running errands, you will earn $60. You will not meet your goal if you work all 10 hours walking dogs.**

46. ★ **EXTENDED RESPONSE** Your school's service club is sponsoring a dance in the school gym to raise money for a local charity. The expenses will be $600. The club members will sell tickets for $10. They hope to raise enough money to cover the expenses and have enough left to donate $1000 to the charity.

   a. How many tickets must they sell to cover their expenses? **60 tickets**

   b. How many tickets must they sell to cover their expenses and meet their goal? **160 tickets**

   c. The school allows no more than 200 students in the gymnasium for a dance. Can the club members sell enough tickets to exceed their goal? What is the greatest possible amount by which they can exceed their goal? *Explain* your reasoning. **Yes; $400; if they sell 200 tickets they will bring in $2000, which is $400 over their goal.**

C **47.** **CHALLENGE** You and your friend are reading the same series of science fiction books. You tell your friend, "I've read 3 times as many books as you have." Your friend replies, "You've read only 4 more books than I have." How many books have each of you read? **friend: 2 books; you: 6 books**

48. **CHALLENGE** Each of the long sides of a rectangle has a length of x inches. Each of the other sides is 1 inch shorter than the long sides. The perimeter of the rectangle is 22 inches. Find the length and the width of the rectangle. *Justify* your answer. **6 in., 5 in.; $P = 2\ell + 2w$, $2(6) + 2(5) = 12 + 10 = 22$**

MIXED REVIEW

PREVIEW
Prepare for Lesson 1.5 in Exs. 49–54.

Write the percent as a decimal. *(p. 916)*

49. 3% **0.03** **50.** 3.5% **0.035** **51.** 5.25% **0.0525**

Find the perimeter of the triangle or rectangle. *(p. 924)*

52.
$1\frac{3}{4}$ in. $1\frac{3}{4}$ in.
$1\frac{3}{4}$ in. $5\frac{1}{4}$ in.

53.
0.9 m
1.6 m

54.
7 ft
$4\frac{1}{2}$ ft
5 m
23 ft

Evaluate the expression. *(p. 8)*

55. $9 \cdot 3^2 - 2$ **79** **56.** $4 \div 2^2 + \frac{1}{7}$ **$1\frac{1}{7}$** **57.** $5 \div 0.25 \cdot 3$ **60**

EXTRA PRACTICE for Lesson 1.4, p. 938   💿 **ONLINE QUIZ** at classzone.com

Lessons 1.1–1.4

1. MULTI-STEP PROBLEM You are making a photo quilt by transferring photos to squares of fabric. Each square should be big enough so that you can turn over an edge $\frac{5}{8}$ inch long on each side and have a finished square with a side length of $5\frac{3}{4}$ inches.

  a. What are the dimensions of each fabric square? **7 in. by 7 in.**

  b. How many square inches of fabric do you need if you want to include 48 squares? **2352 in.²**

  c. The fabric you buy is 36 inches wide. How long a piece of fabric do you need? **70 in.**

  d. You buy a piece of fabric that has the length you found in part (c). Once you've cut all the squares, how many square inches of fabric are left over? **168 in.²**

2. MULTI-STEP PROBLEM A rule of thumb states that the ideal weight (in ounces) of a baseball bat for a high school baseball player is 5 ounces more than one third of the player's height (in inches).

  a. Write an expression that describes the ideal weight (in ounces) of a bat for a high school baseball player who is h inches tall. $\frac{1}{3}h + 5$

  b. One player was 66 inches tall last year. This year the player is 69 inches tall. How much heavier should the player's new bat be than the bat used last year? **1 oz**

3. SHORT RESPONSE You collect miniature cars and display them on shelves that hold 20 cars each.

  a. Which expression would you evaluate to find the number of shelves you need for x cars: $20x$, $\frac{x}{20}$, or $\frac{20}{x}$? *Justify* your choice. **See margin.**

  b. Find the number of shelves you need to display 120 cars. **6 shelves**

4. OPEN-ENDED *Describe* a real-world situation that you could model with the inequality $3x < 15$. *Explain* what a solution of the inequality means in this situation. **See margin.**

5. SHORT RESPONSE You pay $7.50 for 3 quarts of strawberries. You realize that you need more strawberries for your recipe. You return to the store with $4.50. Will you have enough money to buy 2 more quarts of strawberries? *Explain* your reasoning. **No; each quart cost $2.50, so you will need $5 for 2 quarts.**

6. EXTENDED RESPONSE The number of calories in one serving of any food is the sum of the calories from fat, protein, and carbohydrate. The table shows the calories in 1 gram of each of the three food components.

Component	Calories in 1 gram
Fat	9
Protein	4
Carbohydrate	4

  a. Write an expression for the total number of calories in a serving of food that contains f grams of fat, p grams of protein, and c grams of carbohydrate. $9f + 4p + 4c$

  b. A serving of cheddar cheese contains 14 grams of fat, 11 grams of protein, and 1 gram of carbohydrate. How many calories are in a serving of cheddar cheese? **174 calories**

  c. A 100 pound teenager requires about 45 grams of protein per day. If the teenager tried to get all the required protein for one day from cheddar cheese, how many calories would the teenager consume? *Explain.* **See margin.**

7. GRIDDED ANSWER You are comparing two dorm-size refrigerators, both with cube-shaped interiors. One model has an interior edge length of 14 inches. Another model has an interior edge length of 16 inches. How many more cubic inches of storage space does the larger model have? **1352 in.³**

3a. $\frac{x}{20}$; if you divide the number of cars you have by 20 you will know how many shelves you need.

4. *Sample answer:* A basketball player scores less than 15 points in a game. What is the most 3-point field goals the player could have scored? The solution $x < 5$ means the player scored less than 5 3-point field goals.

6c. About 713 calories; the teenager would need about 4.1 servings of cheese to get 45 grams of protein. So, 4.1 times 174 calories per serving is about 713 calories.

① PLAN AND PREPARE

Warm-Up Exercises

📄 **Transparency Available**

1. Mr. Lu is planting trees around the perimeter of a rectangular park. The park measures 72 feet by 48 feet. The trees need to be spaced 12 feet apart. A tree is to be planted in each corner. How many trees are needed? **20 trees**

2. In an aviary, there are three times as many finches as mockingbirds. If there are 48 birds, how many mockingbirds are there? **12 mockingbirds**

Notetaking Guide

📄 **Transparency Available**

Promotes interactive learning and notetaking skills, pp. 13–15.

Pacing

Basic: 1 day
Average: 1 day
Advanced: 1 day
Block: 0.5 block with 1.6
• See *Teaching Guide/Lesson Plan*.

② FOCUS AND MOTIVATE

Essential Question

Big Idea 2, p. 1

How can you use a problem solving plan to solve a problem? **Tell students they will learn how to answer this question by working through the steps of a problem solving plan.**

NCTM STANDARDS

Standard 6: Solve problems in math and other contexts; Apply/adapt strategies to solve problems

1.5 Use a Problem Solving Plan

Before You used problem solving strategies.

Now You will use a problem solving plan to solve problems.

Why? So you can determine a route, as in Example 1.

Key Vocabulary
• formula

KEY CONCEPT *For Your Notebook*

A Problem Solving Plan

STEP 1 Read and Understand Read the problem carefully. Identify what you know and what you want to find out.

STEP 2 Make a Plan Decide on an approach to solving the problem.

STEP 3 Solve the Problem Carry out your plan. Try a new approach if the first one isn't successful.

STEP 4 Look Back Once you obtain an answer, check that it is reasonable.

EXAMPLE 1 Read a problem and make a plan

RUNNING You run in a city where the short blocks on north-south streets are 0.1 mile long. The long blocks on east-west streets are 0.15 mile long. You will run 2 long blocks east, a number of short blocks south, 2 long blocks west, then back to your starting point. You want to run 2 miles. How many short blocks should you run?

0.1 mi

0.15 mi

Solution

ANOTHER WAY
For an alternative method for solving the problem in Example 1, turn to page 34 for the **Problem Solving Workshop**.

STEP 1 Read and Understand

What do you know?

You know the length of each size block, the number of long blocks you will run, and the total distance you want to run.

You can conclude that you must run an even number of short blocks because you run the same number of short blocks in each direction.

What do you want to find out?

You want to find out the number of short blocks you should run so that, along with the 4 long blocks, you run 2 miles.

STEP 2 Make a Plan Use what you know to write a verbal model that represents what you want to find out. Then write an equation and solve it, as in Example 2.

28 Chapter 1 Expressions, Equations, and Functions

Resource Planning Guide

Chapter Resource Book
• Teaching Guide/Lesson Plan (pp. 49–50)
• Practice levels A, B, C (pp. 51–53)
• Study Guide (pp. 54–55)
• Catch-up for Absent Students (p. 56)
• Problem Solving Workshop (p. 57)
• Challenge (p. 58)

Workbooks
• Notetaking Guide (pp. 13–15)
• Practice Workbook (pp. 9–10)

Teaching Options
• **Power Presentations CD-ROM** provides dynamic electronic teaching resources for the classroom.
• **Activity Generator CD-ROM** provides editable activities for all ability levels.

Interactive Technology
• Easy Planner
• Power Presentations CD-ROM
• Activity Generator CD-ROM
• Animated Algebra
• Test Generator CD-ROM
• Online Quiz
• eWorkbook
• eEdition
• @HomeTutor

Resources for English Learners
• Quick Reference for English Learners
• Spanish Study Guide
• Multi-Language Visual Glossary
• Student Resources in Spanish

See also the *Algebra 1 Toolkit* for more strategies for meeting individual needs.

EXAMPLE 2 Solve a problem and look back

Solve the problem in Example 1 by carrying out the plan. Then check your answer.

Solution

STEP 3 **Solve the Problem** Write a verbal model. Then write an equation. Let *s* be the number of short blocks you run.

Length of short block (miles/block)	·	Number of short blocks (blocks)	+	Length of long block (miles/block)	·	Number of long blocks (blocks)	=	Total distance (miles)
0.1	·	s	+	0.15	·	4	=	2

REVIEW PROBLEM SOLVING
To review problem solving strategies, see p. 936.

The equation is $0.1s + 0.6 = 2$. One way to solve the equation is to use the strategy *guess, check, and revise*.

Guess an even number that is easily multiplied by 0.1. Try 20.

Check whether 20 is a solution.

$$0.1s + 0.6 = 2 \qquad \text{Write equation.}$$
$$0.1(20) + 0.6 \stackrel{?}{=} 2 \qquad \text{Substitute 20 for } s.$$
$$2.6 = 2 \; \text{✗} \qquad \text{Simplify; 20 does not check.}$$

Revise. Because $2.6 > 2$, try an even number less than 20. Try 14.

Check whether 14 is a solution.

$$0.1s + 0.6 = 2 \qquad \text{Write equation.}$$
$$0.1(14) + 0.6 \stackrel{?}{=} 2 \qquad \text{Substitute 14 for } s.$$
$$2 = 2 \; \text{✓} \qquad \text{Simplify.}$$

▶ To run 2 miles, you should run 14 short blocks along with the 4 long blocks you run.

STEP 4 **Look Back** Check your answer by making a table. You run 0.6 mile on long blocks. Each two short blocks add 0.2 mile.

Short blocks	0	2	4	6	8	10	12	14
Total distance	0.6	0.8	1.0	1.2	1.4	1.6	1.8	2.0

The total distance is 2 miles when you run 4 long blocks and 14 short blocks. The answer in Step 3 is correct.

Animated **Algebra** at classzone.com

 GUIDED PRACTICE for Examples 1 and 2

1. **WHAT IF?** In Example 1, suppose that you want to run a total distance of 3 miles. How many short blocks should you run? **24 short blocks**

Differentiated Instruction

Below Level In Step 1 of **Example 1**, some students may not be able to conclude that there must be an even number of short blocks. Have these students draw a diagram of the route and label it using the information in the problem. The diagram should enable them to see that the number of short blocks must be even. Suggest they use the diagram to create a verbal model for the problem.

See also the *Algebra 1 Toolkit* for more strategies.

Motivating the Lesson
Ask students to recount a complex situation they have had to resolve, such as allocating time for homework, activities, and chores after school each day. After they share some problems, tell them that this lesson offers a plan for solving complex math problems.

❸ TEACH

Extra Example 1
You are designing the layout for a newspaper about teen issues. The newspaper will be $22\frac{1}{2}$ inches wide. You plan to have 5 columns with $\frac{1}{8}$-inch gaps between them and $\frac{3}{8}$-inch margins on the left and right sides. How wide will each column be? **Step 1: I know the width of the newspaper, the number of columns, the size of the margins, and the size of the gaps between the columns. I want to find out how many gaps there are, so I can determine the width of each column. Step 2: I can use a diagram to find the number of gaps and then use what I know to make a verbal model. Next, I can write an equation and solve it.**

Extra Example 2
Solve the problem in Extra Example 1 by carrying out the plan. Then check your answer. **Step 3: Let *w* be the width of each column. There are two margins and four gaps. The problem is modeled by $5w + 2\left(\frac{3}{8}\right) + 4\left(\frac{1}{8}\right) = 22\frac{1}{2}$. Using the guess, check, and revise strategy, the width of each column should be $4\frac{1}{4}$ inches. Step 4: Substituting $4\frac{1}{4}$ into the equation for *w* results in a true statement.**

Extra Example 3

A builder lays sod on the lawns of new homes. The installed cost for sod is $.38 per square foot. What is the cost of installing sod on a rectangular lawn that is 32 feet long and 18 feet wide? **D**

- **(A)** $19.00
- **(B)** $38.00
- **(C)** $184.32
- **(D)** $218.88

Key Question to Ask for Example 3

- Why do you use the formula $A = \ell w$? **The piece of leather is described as being rectangular and the words *square inches* indicate area, so the formula $A = \ell w$ is needed to solve the problem.**

Closing the Lesson

Have students summarize the major points of the lesson and answer the Essential Question: How can you use a problem solving plan to solve a problem?

- **A problem solving plan is a guide that helps you organize the steps of the work necessary to solve a problem.**
- **Any problem solving strategy can be utilized within the problem solving plan.**

By following the steps in the plan, you can identify what you need to know, decide on a strategy to use, carry out the strategy, and then check that the answer you calculate is reasonable.

FORMULAS A **formula** is an equation that relates two or more quantities. You may find it helpful to use formulas in problem solving.

> **KEY CONCEPT** *For Your Notebook*
>
> **Formulas**
>
> **Temperature**
>
> $C = \frac{5}{9}(F - 32)$ where F = degrees Fahrenheit and C = degrees Celsius
>
> **Simple interest**
>
> $I = Prt$ where I = interest, P = principal, r = interest rate (as a decimal), and t = time
>
> **Distance traveled**
>
> $d = rt$ where d = distance traveled, r = rate (constant or average speed), and t = time
>
> **Profit**
>
> $P = I - E$ where P = profit, I = income, and E = expenses

REVIEW FORMULAS
For additional formulas, see pp. 924–928 and the Table of Formulas on pp. 952–953.

 EXAMPLE 3 **Standardized Test Practice**

You are making a leather book cover. You need a rectangular piece of leather as shown. Find the cost of the piece if leather costs $.25 per square inch.

Short Stories   11 in.

18 in.

- **(A)** $14.50
- **(B)** $49.50
- **(C)** $58.00
- **(D)** $198.00

ELIMINATE CHOICES
You can eliminate choices A and D by estimating. The area of the piece of leather is about 200 square inches, and $.25(200) is about $50.

Solution

Use the formula for the area of a rectangle, $A = \ell w$, with $\ell = 18$ inches and $w = 11$ inches.

$A = \ell w$ **Write area formula.**

$ = 18(11)$ **Substitute 18 for ℓ and 11 for *w*.**

$ = 198$ **Simplify.**

The area is 198 square inches, so the total cost is $.25(198) = $49.50.

▶ The correct answer is B. (A) (B) (C) (D)

✓ **GUIDED PRACTICE** for Example 3

2. **GARDENING** A gardener determines the cost of planting daffodil bulbs to be $2.40 per square foot. How much will it cost to plant daffodil bulbs in a rectangular garden that is 12 feet long and 5 feet wide? **D**

- **(A)** $40.80
- **(B)** $60
- **(C)** $81.60
- **(D)** $144

Differentiated Instruction

Visual Learners A diagram is often the most helpful way to solve a word problem. If a diagram such as the one in **Example 3** is given, that is a sign to use it. Encourage visual learners to construct diagrams whenever possible. Have them construct a similar diagram for **Guided Practice Exercise 2**.

See also the *Algebra 1 Toolkit* for more strategies.

1.5 EXERCISES

HOMEWORK KEY

○ = WORKED-OUT SOLUTIONS
on p. WS1 for Exs. 5 and 17

★ = STANDARDIZED TEST PRACTICE
Exs. 2, 11, 12, 20, and 22

◆ = MULTIPLE REPRESENTATIONS
Ex. 21

SKILL PRACTICE

A 1. **VOCABULARY** Give an example of a formula. *Sample answer:* $d = rt$

2. ★ **WRITING** *Describe* how you can use a formula to solve the following problem: The inner edges of a cube-shaped pot have a length of 1.5 feet. How much does it cost to fill the planter if soil costs $4 per cubic foot? **See margin.**

EXAMPLES 1 and 2
on pp. 28–29
for Exs. 3–5

READING AND UNDERSTANDING In Exercises 3–5, identify what you know and what you need to find out. You do *not* need to solve the problem.

3. **CRAFT SHOW** You make 35 dog collars and anticipate selling all of them at a craft show. You spent $85 for materials and hope to make a profit of $90. How much should you charge for each collar? **See margin.**

4. **DISTANCE RUNNING** A runner ran at a rate of 0.15 mile per minute for 40 minutes. The next day, the runner ran at a rate of 0.16 mile per minute for 50 minutes. How far did the runner run altogether? **14 mi**

5. **TEMPERATURE** One day, the temperature in Rome, Italy, was 30°C. The temperature in Dallas, Texas, was 83°F. Which temperature was higher? **See margin.**

ERROR ANALYSIS *Describe* and correct the error(s) in solving the problem. A town is fencing a rectangular field that is 200 feet long and 150 feet wide. At $10 per foot, how much will it cost to fence the field? **6, 7. See margin.**

6.

$$P = 200 + 150 = 350$$
$$\$10(350) = \$3500$$

7.

$$A = (200)(150) = 30,000$$
$$\$10(30,000) = \$300,000$$

EXAMPLE 3 **B**
on p. 30
for Exs. 8–12

CHOOSING A FORMULA In Exercises 8–10, state the formula that is needed to solve the problem. You do *not* need to solve the problem.

8. The temperature is 68°F. What is the temperature in degrees Celsius? $C = \frac{5}{9}(F - 32)$

9. A store buys a baseball cap for $5 and sells it for $20. What is the profit? $P = I - E$

10. Find the area of a triangle with a base of 25 feet and a height of 8 feet. $A = \frac{1}{2}bh$

11. ★ **MULTIPLE CHOICE** What is the interest on $1200 invested for 2 years in an account that earns simple interest at a rate of 5% per year? **C**

    (A) $12   **(B)** $60   **(C)** $120   **(D)** $240

12. ★ **MULTIPLE CHOICE** A car travels at an average speed of 55 miles per hour. How many miles does the car travel in 2.5 hours? **D**

    (A) 22 miles   **(B)** 57.5 miles   **(C)** 110 miles   **(D)** 137.5 miles

C 13. **CHALLENGE** Write a formula for the length ℓ of a rectangle given its perimeter P and its width w. *Justify* your thinking.
$\ell = \frac{P}{2} - w$. *Sample answer:* Dividing the perimeter by 2 will give the sum of the length and the width. Subtracting the width will give the length.

Differentiated Instruction

Advanced You may wish to pair advanced students with other students who are struggling with the word problems in the exercises of this lesson. Both students will benefit from this interaction—the advanced student must follow the steps of the problem solving plan for each problem when they often might not while working on their own, and the assisted student receives the guidance they need to succeed.

See also the *Algebra 1 Toolkit* for more strategies.

2. *Sample answer:* Since you are filling a cubic container, you need to use the volume formula $V = s^3$ where s is the length of an edge. Substituting 1.5 for s gives $V = 1.5^3 = 3.375$ cubic feet. If the soil costs $4 per cubic foot, $3.375 \cdot 4 = \$13.50$ to fill the planter.

3. You know how many collars you've made, how much you have spent to make them, and how much money you want to make. You need to find what to charge for each collar so you make $90.

5–7. See Additional Answers beginning on p. AA1.

Assignment Guide

📖 Answer Transparencies available for all exercises

Basic:
Day 1: SRH p. 937 Exs. 1–4
pp. 31–33
Exs. 1–10, 14–20, 24–32

Average:
Day 1: pp. 31–33
Exs. 1, 2, 4–13, 16–22, 24–32

Advanced:
Day 1: pp. 31–33
Exs. 1, 2, 4, 5, 8–13*, 17–23*, 25–31 odd

Block:
pp. 31–33
Exs. 1, 2, 4–13, 16–22, 24–32
(with 1.6)

Differentiated Instruction

See *Algebra 1 Best Practices Toolkit* for suggestions on addressing the needs of a diverse classroom.

Homework Check

For a quick check of student understanding of key concepts, go over the following exercises:

Basic: 3, 4, 8, 14, 16
Average: 4, 5, 9, 16, 17
Advanced: 4, 5, 10, 17, 18

Extra Practice

- Student Edition, p. 938
- Chapter 5 Resource Book: Practice levels A, B, C, pp. 51–53

Practice Worksheet

An easily-readable reduced practice page (with answers) for this lesson can be found on p. 1C.

EXAMPLES A
1, 2, and 3
on pp. 28–30
for Exs. 14–18

14. DVD STORAGE A stackable storage rack holds 22 DVDs and costs $21. How much would it cost to buy enough racks to hold 127 DVDs? **$126**

@HomeTutor for problem solving help at classzone.com

15. FRAMING For an art project, you make a square print with a side length of 8 inches. You make a frame using strips of wood $1\frac{1}{4}$ inches wide. What is the area of the frame? **110.25 in.²**

@HomeTutor for problem solving help at classzone.com

16. MOUNTAIN BOARDS You have saved $70 to buy a mountain board that costs $250. You plan to save $10 each week. How many weeks will it take to save for the mountain board? **18 wk**

17. HIKING You are hiking. The total weight of your backpack and its contents is $13\frac{3}{8}$ pounds. You want to carry no more than 15 pounds. How many extra water bottles can you add to your backpack if each bottle weighs $\frac{3}{4}$ pound? **2 water bottles**

18. PIZZA Thick crust pizza requires about 0.15 ounce of dough per square inch of surface area. You have two rectangular pans, one that is 16 inches long and 14 inches wide, and one that is 15.5 inches long and 10 inches wide. How much more dough do you need to make a thick crust pizza in the larger pan than in the smaller one? **10.35 oz**

19. SONAR A diver uses a sonar device to determine the distance to her diving partner. The device sends a sound wave and records the time it takes for the wave to reach the diving partner and return to the device. Suppose the wave travels at a rate of about 4800 feet per second.

a. The wave returns 0.2 second after it was sent. How far did the wave travel? **960 ft**

b. How far away is the diving partner? **480 ft**

B **20. ★ EXTENDED RESPONSE** A gardener is reseeding a city park that has the shape of a right triangle with a base of 150 feet and a height of 200 feet. The third side of the park is 250 feet long.

a. One bag of grass seed covers 3750 square feet and costs $27.50. How many bags are needed? What is the total cost? **4 bags; $110**

b. Wire fencing costs $23.19 for each 50 foot roll. How much does it cost to buy fencing to enclose the area? **$278.28**

c. Fence posts cost $3.19 each and should be placed every 5 feet. How many posts are needed, and how much will they cost altogether? *Explain.* **See margin.**

○ = WORKED-OUT SOLUTIONS
on p. WS1

★ = STANDARDIZED
TEST PRACTICE

◆ = MULTIPLE
REPRESENTATIONS

21a.

Room size (feet)	1 by 1	2 by 2	3 by 3	4 by 4	5 by 5
Remaining area (square feet)	431	428	423	416	407

21. ◆ **MULTIPLE REPRESENTATIONS** Homeowners are building a square closet in a rectangular room that is 24 feet long and 18 feet wide. They want the remaining floor area to be at least 400 square feet. Because they don't want to cut any of the 1 foot by 1 foot square floor tiles, the side length of the closet floor should be a whole number of feet.

   a. Making a Table Make a table showing possible side lengths of the closet floor and the remaining area for each side length. **See margin.**

   b. Writing an Inequality Write an inequality to describe the situation. Use your table to find the greatest possible side length of the closet floor.
   $1 \le s \le 5$; **5 ft**

22. ★ **SHORT RESPONSE** A farmer plans to build a fence around a rectangular pen that is 16 feet long. The area of the pen is 80 square feet. Is 40 feet of fencing enough to fence in the pen? *Explain.* **No.** *Sample answer:* **The width of the pen is 5 feet long. The farmer would need 2(5) + 2(16) = 42 feet of fencing.**

C **23. CHALLENGE** You and your friend live 12 miles apart. You leave home at the same time and travel toward each other. You walk at a rate of 4 miles per hour and your friend bicycles at a rate of 11 miles per hour.

   a. How long after you leave home will you meet? How far from home will each of you be? **48 min; you: 3.2 mi, your friend: 8.8 mi**

   b. Suppose your friend bicycles at a rate of 12 miles per hour. How much sooner will you meet? How far from home will each of you be?
   3 min; you: 3 mi, your friend: 9 mi

MIXED REVIEW

Write the decimal as a fraction and as a percent. *(p. 916)*

24. 0.85 $\frac{17}{20}$; **85%**   **25.** 1.25 $1\frac{1}{4}$; **125%**   **26.** 0.245 $\frac{49}{200}$; **24.5%**   **27.** 0.007 $\frac{7}{1000}$; **0.7%**

28. Find the surface area and volume of the rectangular prism. *(p. 927)*
52 ft², 24 ft³

PREVIEW
Prepare for Lesson 1.6 in Exs. 29–32.

Translate the verbal phrase into an expression. *(p. 15)*

29. $\frac{1}{3}$ multiplied by a number v $\frac{1}{3}v$ **30.** 22 divided by a number h $\frac{22}{h}$

31. 7 more than twice a number m
  2m + 7   **32.** Twice the sum of a number y and 3
  2(y + 3)

QUIZ *for Lessons 1.4–1.5*

Write an equation or an inequality. *(p. 21)*

1. 4 more than twice a number n is equal to 25. **2n + 4 = 25**

2. The quotient of a number x and 2 is no more than 9. $\frac{x}{2} \le 9$

Check whether the given number is a solution of the equation or inequality. *(p. 21)*

3. $13 - 2x = 5$; 4   **solution**   **4.** $5d - 4 \ge 16$; 4   **solution**   **5.** $4y + 3 \ge 15$; 3   **solution**

6. CAR TRAVEL One car travels about 28.5 miles on each gallon of gas. Suppose the average price of gas is $2 per gallon. About how much would the gas for a 978 mile trip cost? *(p. 28)* **about $68.63**

EXTRA PRACTICE for Lesson 1.5, p. 938   ◆ **ONLINE QUIZ** at classzone.com   33

⑤ **ASSESS AND RETEACH**

Daily Homework Quiz
📄 **Transparency Available**

1. Gerry is borrowing money from a friend at a simple interest rate of 4%. If she borrows $2000 and plans to pay it back in 2 years, how much interest will she owe? **$160**

2. A migrating whale is traveling at an average speed of 5.4 kilometers per hour. How far will the whale travel in 18 hours at this rate? **97.2 km**

3. Skye sells baskets that she weaves from sweet grass. She makes a profit of $68 per basket and her expenses are $2.50 per basket. How much does she charge a customer for 3 baskets? **$211.50**

🧭 **Online Quiz**

Available at **classzone.com**

Diagnosis/Remediation
- Practice A, B, C in Chapter 1 Resource Book, pp. 51–53
- Study Guide in Chapter 1 Resource Book, pp. 54–55
- Practice Workbook, pp. 9–10
- @HomeTutor

Challenge
Additional challenge is available in the Chapter 1 Resource Book, p. 58.

Quiz

An easily-readable reduced copy of the quiz (with answers) on Lessons 1.4–1.5 from the Assessment Book can be found on p. 1E.

Alternative Strategy

Example 1 on page 28 can be solved by drawing a diagram. This method allows students to visualize the solution and will help them to better understand the algebraic solution given in Example 2 on page 29.

Teaching Strategy

Stress that each pair of rectangles represents running 4 long blocks and 2 short blocks. Point out how each figure is labeled to indicate the total distance along its outer edges. Emphasize that carefully drawing an accurate diagram improves one's chances of avoiding errors and solving the problem correctly.

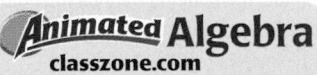
classzone.com

An **Animated Algebra** activity is available on-line for the **Problem**. This activity is also available on the **Power Presentations CD-ROM**.

1. 9 pieces of cake; Draw a diagram of a 9 inch by 11 inch pan and divide it into 3 inch by 3 inch pieces. From the diagram you see that the cake can be divided into 9 pieces of cake.

2. 2 ft. *Sample answer:* Method 1: Draw a diagram of the rope showing two of the floats 3 feet from each end. Divide the remaining rope so that the 4 floats are equally spaced. From the diagram you can see that there is 2 feet between consecutive floats.

3 ft | 2 ft | 2 ft | 2 ft | 3 ft

Method 2: Use the equation $3x + 6 = 12$ where 3 is the number of spaces between the floats, x is the length of space in between the floats, 6 is the total space at each end of the rope, and 12 is the total length of the rope. Solving the equation gives $x = 2$.

Another Way to Solve Example 1, page 28

MULTIPLE REPRESENTATIONS In Example 1 on page 28, you saw how to solve a problem about running using an equation. You can also solve the problem by using the strategy *draw a diagram*.

PROBLEM

RUNNING You run in a city where the short blocks on north-south streets are 0.1 mile long. The long blocks on east-west streets are 0.15 mile long. You will run 2 long blocks east, a number of short blocks south, 2 long blocks west, then back to your starting point. You want to run a total of 2 miles. How many short blocks should you run?

METHOD

Drawing a Diagram You can draw a diagram to solve the problem.

STEP 1 **Read** the problem carefully. It tells you the lengths of a short block and a long block. You plan to run 4 long blocks and a distance of 2 miles.

STEP 2 **Draw** a pair of rectangles to represent running 1 short block in each direction. The total distance is $4(0.15) + 2(0.1) = 0.8$ mile. Continue adding pairs of rectangles until the total distance run is 2 miles.

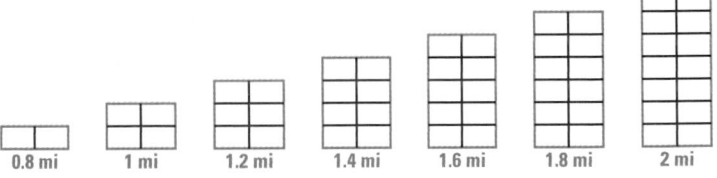

0.8 mi | 1 mi | 1.2 mi | 1.4 mi | 1.6 mi | 1.8 mi | 2 mi

▸ You should run 14 short blocks.

Animated Algebra at classzone.com

PRACTICE

1–4. See margin.

1. **BAKING** A cake pan is 9 inches wide and 11 inches long. How many 3 inch by 3 inch square pieces can you cut? Solve this problem using an equation. Then draw a diagram. *Explain* why a diagram is useful.

2. **SWIMMING** A 12 foot rope strung through 4 floats marks off the deep end of a pool. Each end of the rope is 3 feet from a float. The floats are equally spaced. How far apart are they? Solve this problem using two different methods.

3. **ERROR ANALYSIS** *Describe* and correct the error in solving Exercise 2.

$4x + 6 = 12$
$4(1.5) + 6 = 12$

The buoys are 1.5 feet apart.

4. **GEOMETRY** The length of a rectangle is twice its width. The perimeter is 72 inches. What is its length? Solve this problem using two different methods.

34   Chapter 1   Expressions, Equations, and Functions

---

3. The equation should be $3x + 6 = 12$ because there are only 3 spaces between the 4 floats; $3(2) + 6 = 12$.

4. 24 in. *Sample answer:* Method 1: Use the formula $P = 2\ell + 2w$ to find the length. Substitute 72 for P and $2w$ for ℓ to get the equation $72 = 2(2w) + 2w$. Solving the equation gives $w = 12$. If the length is $2w$, the length is 24 inches. Method 2: Draw a diagram of the rectangle. Label the width, w, and the length, $2w$. If you add up the sides to find the perimeter you will get the equation $6w = 72$. Solving the equation gives $w = 12$, so the length must be 24 inches.

1.6 Represent Functions as Rules and Tables

Before You wrote algebraic expressions and equations.

Now You will represent functions as rules and as tables.

Why? So you can describe consumer costs, as in Example 1.

Key Vocabulary
• function
• domain
• range
• independent variable
• dependent variable

When you pump gas, the total cost depends on the number of gallons pumped. The total cost is a *function* of the number of gallons pumped.

A **function** consists of:

• A set called the **domain** containing numbers called **inputs**, and a set called the **range** containing numbers called **outputs**.

• A pairing of inputs with outputs such that each input is paired with exactly one output.

EXAMPLE 1 Identify the domain and range of a function

The input-output table shows the cost of various amounts of regular unleaded gas from the same pump. Identify the domain and range of the function.

Input (gallons)	10	12	13	17
Output (dollars)	19.99	23.99	25.99	33.98

Solution

▸ The domain is the set of inputs: 10, 12, 13, and 17. The range is the set of outputs: 19.99, 23.99, 25.99, and 33.98.

✓ **GUIDED PRACTICE** for Example 1

1. Identify the domain and range of the function.
   domain: 0, 1, 2, and 4,
   range: 1, 2, and 5

Input	0	1	2	4
Output	5	2	2	1

MAPPING DIAGRAMS A function may be represented by a *mapping diagram*. Notice that an output may be paired with more than one input, but no input is paired with more than one output.

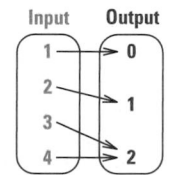

---

① PLAN AND PREPARE

Warm-Up Exercises

▢ **Transparency Available**

1. Write an expression: 7 more than a number *x*. **$x + 7$**

2. Determine if 3 is a solution of $2x - 4 = 2$. **2 = 2; 3 is a solution.**

3. Gae spent $4 more than twice as much as Casey at a store. If Casey spent $6, how much did Gae spend? **$16**

Notetaking Guide

▢ **Transparency Available**

Promotes interactive learning and notetaking skills, pp. 16–18.

Pacing

Basic: 2 days
Average: 2 days
Advanced: 2 days
Block: 0.5 block with 1.5
0.5 block with 1.7
• See *Teaching Guide/Lesson Plan.*

② FOCUS AND MOTIVATE

Essential Question

Big Idea 3, p. 1

How do you represent functions as tables and rules? **Tell students they will learn how to answer this question by describing the relationships between domain and range, between input and output, and between independent and dependent variables.**

NCTM STANDARDS

Standard 2: Understand functions; Use models to understand relationships

---

Resource Planning Guide

Chapter Resource Book
• Teaching Guide/Lesson Plan (pp. 59–60)
• Activity Master (p. 61)
• Practice levels A, B, C (pp. 62–64)
• Study Guide (pp. 65–66)
• Catch-up for Absent Students (p. 67)
• Application (p. 68)
• Challenge (p. 69)

Workbooks
• Notetaking Guide (pp. 16–18)
• Practice Workbook (pp. 11–12)

Teaching Options
• **Power Presentations CD-ROM** provides dynamic electronic teaching resources for the classroom.
• **Activity Generator CD-ROM** provides editable activities for all ability levels.

Interactive Technology
• Easy Planner
• Power Presentations CD-ROM
• Activity Generator CD-ROM
• Animated Algebra
• Test Generator CD-ROM
• Online Quiz
• eWorkbook
• eEdition
• @HomeTutor

Resources for English Learners
• Quick Reference for English Learners
• Spanish Study Guide
• Multi-Language Visual Glossary
• Student Resources in Spanish

See also the *Algebra 1 Toolkit* for more strategies for meeting individual needs.

EXAMPLE 2   Identify a function

Motivating the Lesson

Students have already encountered situations where numerical data is presented in a table, such as the shipping costs for various package weights when ordering from a catalog. Ask them about other real-world situations where they have encountered data given in a table.

❸ TEACH

Extra Example 1

The input-output table shows the amount of money Miguel earns at his job for several numbers of hours. Identify the domain and range of the function.

Input (hours)	2	5	7	8
Output (dollars)	14	35	49	56

domain: 2, 5, 7, 8
range: 14, 35, 49, 56

Extra Example 2

Tell whether the pairing is a function.

a. Input   Output

The pairing is a function, because each input is paired with exactly one output.

b.

Input	1	2	2	4
Output	2	3	4	6

The pairing is *not* a function, because the input 2 is paired with both 3 and 4.

Extra Example 3

The domain of the function $y = x + 4$ is 0, 2, 3, 6, and 7. Make a table for the function. Identify the range.   range: 4, 6, 7, 10, 11

x	0	2	3	6	7
$y = x + 4$	4	6	7	10	11

EXAMPLE 2   Identify a function

Tell whether the pairing is a function.

a.

b.

Input	Output
0	0
1	2
4	8
6	12

The pairing is *not* a function because the input 0 is paired with both 2 and 3.

The pairing is a function because each input is paired with exactly one output.

✓ GUIDED PRACTICE   for Example 2

Tell whether the pairing is a function.

2.

Input	3	6	9	12
Output	1	2	2	1

function

3.

Input	2	2	4	7
Output	0	1	2	3

not a function

FUNCTION RULES A function may be represented using a rule that relates one variable to another. The input variable is called the **independent variable.** The output variable is called the **dependent variable** because its value depends on the value of the input variable.

READING
....
Function rules typically give the dependent variable in terms of the independent variable. In an equation like $y = x + 3$, you know that y is the dependent variable.

KEY CONCEPT   *For Your Notebook*

Functions

Verbal Rule	Equation	Table				
The output is 3 more than the input.	$y = x + 3$					

Input, x	0	1	2	3	4
Output, y	3	4	5	6	7

EXAMPLE 3   Make a table for a function

The domain of the function $y = 2x$ is 0, 2, 5, 7, and 8. Make a table for the function, then identify the range of the function.

Solution

x	0	2	5	7	8
$y = 2x$	$2(0) = 0$	$2(2) = 4$	$2(5) = 10$	$2(7) = 14$	$2(8) = 16$

The range of the function is 0, 4, 10, 14, and 16.

Differentiated Instruction

Visual Learners To help students remember that the input is the domain and the output is the range, show that the word pairings (domain, range) and (input, output) are both in alphabetical order. Emphasize that the first words in each pairing are associated with each other, as are the second words. This type of association can also be shown later in Lesson 1.7 with ordered pairs (x, y).

See also the *Algebra 1 Toolkit* for more strategies.

EXAMPLE 4 Write a function rule

Write a rule for the function.

Input	0	1	4	6	10
Output	2	3	6	8	12

Solution

Let *x* be the input, or independent variable, and let *y* be the output, or dependent variable. Notice that each output is 2 more than the corresponding input. So, a rule for the function is $y = x + 2$.

EXAMPLE 5 Write a function rule for a real-world situation

CONCERT TICKETS You are buying concert tickets that cost $15 each. You can buy up to 6 tickets. Write the amount (in dollars) you spend as a function of the number of tickets you buy. Identify the independent and dependent variables. Then identify the domain and the range of the function.

Solution

> **CHOOSE A VARIABLE**
> To write a function rule for a real-world situation, choose letters for the variables that remind you of the quantities represented.

Write a verbal model. Then write a function rule. Let *n* represent the number of tickets purchased and *A* represent the amount spent (in dollars).

Amount spent (dollars)	=	Cost per ticket (dollars/ticket)	·	Tickets purchased (tickets)
A	=	15	·	*n*

So, the function rule is $A = 15n$. The amount spent depends on the number of tickets bought, so *n* is the independent variable and *A* is the dependent variable.

Because you can buy up to 6 tickets, the domain of the function is 0, 1, 2, 3, 4, 5, and 6. Make a table to identify the range.

Number of tickets, *n*	0	1	2	3	4	5	6
Amount (dollars), *A*	0	15	30	45	60	75	90

The range of the function is 0, 15, 30, 45, 60, 75, and 90.

Animated Algebra at classzone.com

✓ **GUIDED PRACTICE** for Examples 3, 4, and 5

4. Make a table for the function $y = x - 5$ with domain 10, 12, 15, 18, and 29. Then identify the range of the function. **range: 5, 7, 10, 13, and 24**

5. Write a rule for the function. Identify the domain and the range.
   $y = 8x$; domain: 1, 2, 3, and 4, range: 8, 16, 24, and 32

Time (hours)	1	2	3	4
Pay (dollars)	8	16	24	32

1.6 Represent Functions as Rules and Tables **37**

Extra Example 4

Write a rule for the function.

Input	1	2	4	7	9
Output	0	1	3	6	8

$y = x - 1$

Extra Example 5

At a community center, art lessons are offered at night. The fee is $12 per lesson. You plan to attend up to 5 lessons. Write the amount you will spend as a function of the number of lessons you attend. Identify the independent and dependent variables. Then identify the domain and the range of the function. **$A = 12n$; independent variable: *n*; dependent variable: *A*; domain: 0, 1, 2, 3, 4, 5; range: 0, 12, 24, 36, 48, 60**

Animated Algebra
classzone.com

An **Animated Algebra** activity is available on-line for **Example 5**. This activity is also available on the **Power Presentations CD-ROM**.

Closing the Lesson

Have students summarize the major points of the lesson and answer the Essential Question: How do you represent functions as tables and as rules?

- For a function, no input value is paired with more than one output value.
- A function rule describes what must be done to the input to obtain the output.

To create a table for a function, use the domain of the function as the input values and apply the function rule to each input to find its corresponding output. To write a rule for a function, determine the pattern that links each dependent variable (output *y*) to its corresponding independent variable (input *x*).

HOMEWORK KEY

○ = **WORKED-OUT SOLUTIONS**
on p. WS1 for Exs. 7 and 23

★ = **STANDARDIZED TEST PRACTICE**
Exs. 2, 11, 12, 13, 26, and 27

◆ = **MULTIPLE REPRESENTATIONS**
Exs. 23 and 24

SKILL PRACTICE

Ⓐ 1. **VOCABULARY** Copy and complete: A(n) ? is a number in the domain of a function. A(n) ? is a number in the range of a function. **input; output**

2. ★ **WRITING** In the equation $b = a - 2$, which variable is the independent variable and which is the dependent variable? *Explain.* **a, b; the value of b depends on a.**

DOMAIN AND RANGE Identify the domain and range of the function.

EXAMPLES 1 and 2
on pp. 35–36
for Exs. 3–11

3.

Input	Output
0	5
1	7
2	15
3	44

domain: 0, 1, 2, and 3, range: 5, 7, 15, and 44

4.
domain: 3, 5, 7, and 8, range: 2, 3, 5, and 7

5.

Input	Output
6	5
12	7
21	10
42	17

domain: 6, 12, 21, and 42, range: 5, 7, 10, and 17

IDENTIFYING FUNCTIONS Tell whether the pairing is a function.

6.

Input	Output
0	7.5
1	9.5
2	11.5
3	13.5

function

7.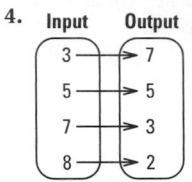
not a function

8.

Input	Output
7	13
11	8
21	13
35	20

function

ERROR ANALYSIS In Exercises 9 and 10, describe and correct the error(s) related to the function represented by the table.
9, 10. See margin.

Input, x	1	2	3	4	5
Output, y	6	7	8	6	9

9.
The pairing is not a function. One output is paired with two inputs.

10.
The pairing is a function. The range is 1, 2, 3, 4, and 5.

11. ★ **OPEN-ENDED** Draw a mapping diagram for a function with 6 inputs. Then make a table to represent the function. **See margin.**

EXAMPLES 3 and 4
on pp. 36–37
for Exs. 12–21

12. ★ **MULTIPLE CHOICE** The domain of the function $y = 5x - 1$ is 1, 3, 4, 5, and 6. Which number is in the range of the function? **B**

Ⓐ 0 Ⓑ 4 Ⓒ 9 Ⓓ 15

13. ★ **MULTIPLE CHOICE** Each output of a function is 0.5 less than the corresponding input. Which equation is a rule for the function? **A**

Ⓐ $y = x - 0.5$ Ⓑ $y = x + 0.5$ Ⓒ $y = 0.5 - x$ Ⓓ $y = 0.5x$

9. The pairing is a function. Each input is paired with only one output.

10. The numbers listed are the domain, not the range. The range of the function is 6, 7, 8, and 9.

11. *Sample:*

Input	Output
0	5
1	6
2	7
3	7
4	9
5	10

TABLES Make a table for the function. Identify the range of the function.
14–19. See margin.

14. $y = x - 3$
Domain: 12, 15, 22, 30

15. $y = x + 3.5$
Domain: 4, 5, 7, 8, 12

16. $y = 3x + 4$
Domain: 0, 5, 7, 10

17. $y = \frac{1}{2}x + 3$
Domain: 4, 6, 9, 11

18. $y = \frac{2}{3}x + \frac{1}{3}$
Domain: 4, 6, 8, 12

19. $y = \frac{0.5x + 1}{2}$
Domain: 0, 2, 4, 6

FUNCTION RULES Write a rule for the function.

20.

Input, x	0	1	2	3
Output, y	2.2	3.2	4.2	5.2

$y = x + 2.2$

21.

Input, x	15	20	21	30	42
Output, y	7	12	13	22	34

$y = x - 8$

22. CHALLENGE Fill in the table in such a way that when t is the independent variable, the pairing is a function, and when t is the dependent variable, the pairing is not a function.

Sample answer:

t	? 1	? 2	? 3	? 4
v	? 2	? 2	? 3	? 3

PROBLEM SOLVING

EXAMPLE 5 [A]
on p. 37
for Exs. 23–26

23a. the number of quarters left; the number of quarters used

23. ◆ **MULTIPLE REPRESENTATIONS** You have 10 quarters that you can use for a parking meter.

a. **Describing in Words** Copy and complete: Each time you put 1 quarter in the meter, you have 1 less quarter, so ? is a function of ? .

b. **Writing a Rule** Write a rule for the number y of quarters that you have left as a function of the number x of quarters you have used so far. Identify the domain of the function. $y = 10 - x$; domain: 0, 1, 2, 3, 4, 5, 6, 7, 8, 9, and 10

c. **Making a Table** Make a table and identify the range of the function.

@HomeTutor for problem solving help at classzone.com

Range: 0, 1, 2, 3, 4, 5, 6, 7, 8, 9, and 10; see margin.

24. ◆ **MULTIPLE REPRESENTATIONS** At a yard sale, you find 5 paperback books by your favorite author. Each book is priced at $.75.

a. **Describing in Words** Copy and complete: For each book you buy, you spend $.75, so ? is a function of ? . amount of money you spend; the number of books you buy

b. **Writing a Rule** Write a rule for the amount (in dollars) you spend as a function of the number of books you buy. Identify the domain of the function. $y = \$.75x$; domain: 0, 1, 2, 3, 4, and 5

c. **Making a Table** Make a table and identify the range of the function.

@HomeTutor for problem solving help at classzone.com

Range: 0, 0.75, 1.5, 2.25, 3, and 3.75; see margin.

25. SAVINGS You have $100 saved and plan to save $20 each month. Write a rule for the amount saved (in dollars) as a function of the number of months from now. Identify the independent and dependent variables, the domain, and the range. How much will you have saved altogether 12 months from now? $y = 100 + 20m$; independent variable: m, the number of months; dependent variable: y, the amount of money saved; domain: $m > 0$, range: $y \geq 100$; $340

26. ★ **OPEN-ENDED** Write a function rule that models a real-world situation. Identify the independent variable and the dependent variable. *Sample answer:* $W = 8h$, where W is wages and h is hours worked; the independent variable is h, the dependent variable is W.

Vocabulary

Exercises 3–8 For students who confuse the connection between the terms *input* and *domain* and between the terms *output* and *range*, suggest they use the memory clue "*i* comes before *o* like *d* comes before *r*, so *input* goes with *domain* and *output* goes with *range*."

Avoiding Common Errors

Exercises 20–21 Some students may write the input as a function of the output. Remind them that the output is always a result of having done something with the input. Stress that they need to look at what must be done with the input value in order to obtain the corresponding output value.

Study Strategy

Exercise 25 To help students solve this problem, suggest they use Example 5 as a model. Point out that the problem states $100 is already saved, so students will need to show the addition of this amount in their rule.

14.

Input	12	15	22	30
Output	9	12	19	27

range: 9, 12, 19, and 27

15. See below.

16.

Input	0	5	7	10
Output	4	19	25	34

range: 4, 19, 25, and 34

17.

Input	4	6	9	11
Output	5	6	7.5	8.5

range: 5, 6, 7.5, and 8.5

18.

Input	4	6	8	12
Output	3	$4\frac{1}{3}$	$5\frac{2}{3}$	$8\frac{1}{3}$

range: 3, $4\frac{1}{3}$, $5\frac{2}{3}$, and $8\frac{1}{3}$

19.

Input	0	2	4	6
Output	$\frac{1}{2}$	1	$1\frac{1}{2}$	2

range: $\frac{1}{2}$, 1, $1\frac{1}{2}$, and 2

15.

Input	4	5	7	8	12
Output	7.5	8.5	10.5	11.5	15.5

range: 7.5, 8.5, 10.5, 11.5, and 15.5

23c.

Input	0	1	2	3	4	5	6	7	8	9	10
Output	10	9	8	7	6	5	4	3	2	1	0

24c.

Input	0	1	2	3	4	5
Output	0	0.75	1.5	2.25	3	3.75

1. The domain of the function $y = \frac{2}{3}x + 1$ is 0, 3, 6, and 9. Make a table for the function. Identify the range of the function.

x	0	3	6	9
y	1	3	5	7

range: 1, 3, 5, 7

2. Write a rule for the function.

Input, x	2	3	4	5
Output, y	3	4.5	6	7.5

$y = 1.5x$

3. Jasmine sells bracelets. Her profit on each bracelet is $8. Write a rule that shows her total profit p as a function of the number of bracelets b she sells. Write the range of the function if the domain is 5, 10, 15, 20, and 25. $p = 8b$; range: 40, 80, 120, 160, 200

Online Quiz

Available at **classzone.com**

Diagnosis/Remediation

- Practice A, B, C in Chapter 1 Resource Book, pp. 62–64
- Study Guide in Chapter 1 Resource Book, pp. 65–66
- Practice Workbook, pp. 11–12
- @HomeTutor

Challenge

Additional challenge is available in the Chapter 1 Resource Book, p. 69.

27a–b. See Additional Answers beginning on p. AA1.
30–33.

27a, b.
See margin.

B **27.** ★ **SHORT RESPONSE** Consider a pairing of the digits 2 through 9 on a telephone keypad with the associated letters.

a. Make a table showing the pairing with the digits as inputs and the letters as outputs. Is the pairing a function? *Explain.*

b. Make a table showing the pairing with the letters as inputs and the digits as outputs. Is the pairing a function? *Explain.*

28. **MULTI-STEP PROBLEM** The table shows the fuel efficiency of four compact cars from one manufacturer for model year 2004.

City fuel efficiency (mi/gal), c	24	26	27	28
Highway fuel efficiency (mi/gal), h	32	34	35	36

a. **Write a Rule** Use the table to write a rule for the cars' highway fuel efficiency as a function of their city fuel efficiency. $h = c + 8$

b. **Predict** Another of the manufacturer's compact cars has a city fuel efficiency of 30 miles per gallon. Predict the highway fuel efficiency. **38 mi/gal**

c. **Calculate** A study found that if gas costs $2 per gallon, you can use the expression $\frac{11{,}550}{c} + \frac{9450}{h}$ to estimate a car's annual fuel cost (in dollars) for a typical driver. Evaluate the expression for the car in part (b). **about $634**

C **29.** **CHALLENGE** Each week you spend a total of 5 hours exercising. You swim part of the time and bike the rest.

300 calories per hour   440 calories per hour

a. Write a rule for the total number of calories you burn for the whole 5 hours as a function of the time you spend swimming. $c = 300s + 440(5 - s)$

b. One week you spend half the time swimming. How many calories do you burn during the whole 5 hours? **1850 cal**

MIXED REVIEW

PREVIEW
·············
Prepare for
Lesson 1.7 in
Exs. 30–33.

Plot the point in a coordinate plane. *(p. 921)* 30–33. See margin.

30. $A(1, 3)$ **31.** $B(3, 1)$ **32.** $C(2, 4)$ **33.** $D(6, 2)$

Write an equation or an inequality. *(p. 21)*

34. The difference of 13 and a number w is 5. $13 - w = 5$

35. The quotient of 21 and a number d is no less than 7. $\frac{21}{d} \geq 7$

36. **TRAVEL** On a 1375 mile flight, an airplane's average speed is 550 miles per hour. The flight is within a single time zone and leaves at 10 A.M. What time will the airplane arrive at its destination? *(p. 28)* **12:30 P.M.**

EXTRA PRACTICE for Lesson 1.6, p. 938   **ONLINE QUIZ** at classzone.com

@HomeTutor
classzone.com
Keystrokes

1.6 Make a Table

QUESTION How can you use a graphing calculator to create a table for a function?

You can use a graphing calculator to create a table for a function when you want to display many pairs of input values and output values or when you want to find the input value that corresponds to a given output value.

In the example below, you will make a table to compare temperatures in degrees Celsius and temperatures in degrees Fahrenheit for temperatures at or above the temperature at which water freezes, 32°F.

EXAMPLE Use a graphing calculator to make a table

The formula $C = \frac{5}{9}(F - 32)$ gives the temperature in degrees Celsius as a function of the temperature in degrees Fahrenheit. Make a table for the function.

STEP 1 *Enter equation*
Rewrite the function using x for F and y for C. Press **Y=** and enter $\frac{5}{9}(x - 32)$.

STEP 2 *Set up table*
Go to the TABLE SETUP screen. Use a starting value (TblStart) of 32 and an increment ($\triangle$Tbl) of 1.

STEP 3 *View table*
Display the table. Scroll down to see pairs of inputs and outputs.

```
Y1∎(5/9)(X-32)
Y2=
Y3=
Y4=
Y5=
Y6=
Y7=
```

```
TABLE SETUP
 TblStart=32
 △Tbl=1
 Indpnt:Auto Ask
 Depend:Auto Ask
```

```
X    │Y1     │Y2
32   │     0 │
33   │.55556 │
34   │1.1111 │
35   │1.6667 │
36   │2.2222 │
37   │2.7778 │
```

PRACTICE

1. You see a sign that indicates that the outdoor temperature is 10°C. Find the temperature in degrees Fahrenheit. *Explain* how you found your answer.
50°F; scroll down until you see the output 10, look to see that the input is 50.
2. Water boils at 100°C. What is the temperature in degrees Fahrenheit?
212°F

Make a table for the function. Use the given starting value and increment. **3–6. See margin.**

3. $y = \frac{3}{4}x + 5$
TblStart = 0, $\triangle$Tbl = 1

4. $y = 4x + 2$
TblStart = 0, $\triangle$Tbl = 0.5

5. $y = 7.5x - 0.5$
TblStart = 1, $\triangle$Tbl = 1

6. $y = 0.5x + 6$
TblStart = 3, $\triangle$Tbl = 3

1.6 Represent Functions as Rules and Tables **41**

3.
Input	0	1	2	3
Output	5	5.75	6.5	7.25

4.
Input	0	0.5	1	1.5
Output	2	4	6	8

5.
Input	1	2	3	4
Output	7	14.5	22	29.5

6.
Input	3	6	9	12
Output	7.5	9	10.5	12

---

1 PLAN AND PREPARE

Learn the Method
• Students will use a graphing calculator to make a table for a function.
• Students can use the skills learned in this activity to check their tables in Exercises 14–19 in Lesson 1.6.

Keystroke Help
Keystrokes for several models of calculators are available in blackline format in the *Chapter 1 Resource Book*.

2 TEACH

Tips for Success
When discussing Step 3, point out to students that the values for x and y are shown in the columns labeled X and Y_1, respectively. You may also wish to point out the unused column labeled Y_2. Remind students that the values in the X column are those for the variable F in the formula, and the values in the Y_1 column are those for the variable C.

Extra Example
Use your calculator to make a table for the function $y = 2x + 4$. Use a starting value of 4 and an increment of 0.25. Use your table to find the output when the input is 8.75. **21.5**

3 ASSESS AND RETEACH

1. What are the key items you need to enter into the calculator to have it set up a table? **the function, the starting value, and the increment**

2. Explain how you would use the table in Step 3 to find the Celsius temperature that is equivalent to 98°F. **Scroll down the table until you locate the value 98 in the X-column, and read the corresponding value in the Y_1-column.**

1.7 Scatter Plots and Functions

MATERIALS · tape measure · graph paper

QUESTION How can you tell whether a graph represents a function?

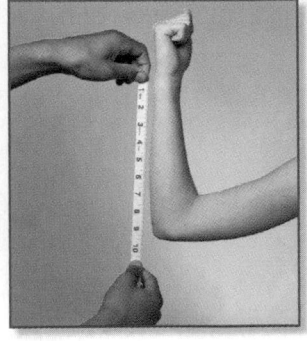

A *scatter plot* is a type of display for paired data. Each data pair is plotted as a point. In this activity, you will work in a group to make a scatter plot. You will measure the height of each student in your group and the length of his or her forearm. The length of the forearm is the distance from the elbow to the wrist.

EXPLORE Collect data and make a scatter plot

STEP 1 *Collect data* Measure the height of each student in your group and the length of his or her forearm. Record the results for each student in one row of a table like the one shown.

Height (inches)	Forearm length (inches)
63	10
?	?

STEP 2 *Make a scatter plot* Use graph paper to draw axes labeled as shown. Then plot the data pairs (*height, forearm length*). For example, plot the point (**63**, **10**) for a student with a height of 63 inches and a forearm length of 10 inches.

(63, 10)

The symbol ⌇ on an axis represents a break in the axis.

DRAW CONCLUSIONS Use your observations to complete these exercises

1. Examine your scatter plot. What does it suggest about the relationship between a person's height and the person's forearm length?
   Sample answer: **The greater the person's height, the greater the length of the forearm.**

2. Compare your table with those of the other groups in your class. Determine which of the tables represent functions and which do not.
   Answers will vary. Tables that are functions should have only one forearm length for each height.

3. Is it possible to determine whether a table represents a function by looking at the corresponding scatter plot? *Explain.*
   Yes; if there is more than one y for an x it is not a function.

1.7 Represent Functions as Graphs

Before	You represented functions as rules and tables.
Now	You will represent functions as graphs.
Why?	So you can describe sales trends, as in Example 4.

Key Vocabulary
• **function**, *p. 35*
• **domain**, *p. 35*
• **range**, *p. 35*

You can use a graph to represent a function. Given a table that represents a function, each corresponding pair of input and output values forms an ordered pair of numbers that can be plotted as a point. The *x*-coordinate is the input. The *y*-coordinate is the output.

REVIEW THE COORDINATE PLANE
For help with the coordinate plane, see p. 921.

Table

Input, x	Output, y
1	2
2	3
4	5

Ordered Pairs
(input, output)

(1, 2)

(2, 3)

(4, 5)

Graph

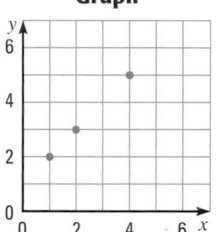

The horizontal axis of the graph is labeled with the input variable. The vertical axis is labeled with the output variable.

EXAMPLE 1 Graph a function

Graph the function $y = \frac{1}{2}x$ with domain 0, 2, 4, 6, and 8.

Solution

STEP 1 Make an input-output table.

x	0	2	4	6	8
y	0	1	2	3	4

STEP 2 Plot a point for each ordered pair (x, y).

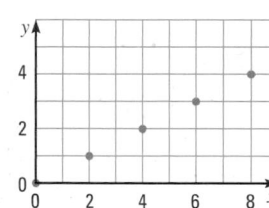

✓ **GUIDED PRACTICE** for Example 1

1. Graph the function $y = 2x - 1$ with domain 1, 2, 3, 4, and 5. **See margin on p. 45.**

Warm-Up Exercises
⬙ **Transparency Available**

1. Make a table for $y = 2x + 3$ with domain 0, 3, 6, and 9.

x	0	3	6	9
y	3	9	15	21

2. Write a rule for the function.

Input, x	0	2	4	9
Output, y	1	7	13	28

$y = 3x + 1$

Notetaking Guide
⬙ **Transparency Available**
Promotes interactive learning and notetaking skills, pp. 19–21.

Pacing
Basic: 1 day
Average: 1 day
Advanced: 1 day
Block: 0.5 block with 1.6
• See *Teaching Guide/Lesson Plan*.

② FOCUS AND MOTIVATE

Essential Question
Big Idea 3, p. 1

How do you represent functions as graphs? **Tell students they will learn how to answer this question by using the function's domain, range, and a table of values.**

NCTM STANDARDS
Standard 2: Understand functions; Use models to understand relationships

---

Resource Planning Guide

Chapter Resource Book
• Teaching Guide/Lesson Plan (pp. 70–71)
• Practice levels A, B, C (pp. 72–77)
• Study Guide (pp. 78–79)
• Catch-up for Absent Students (p. 80)
• Problem Solving Workshop (p. 81)
• Challenge (p. 82)

Workbooks
• Notetaking Guide (pp. 19–21)
• Practice Workbook (pp. 13–15)

Teaching Options
• **Power Presentations CD-ROM** provides dynamic electronic teaching resources for the classroom.
• **Activity Generator CD-ROM** provides editable activities for all ability levels.

Interactive Technology
• Easy Planner
• Power Presentations CD-ROM
• Activity Generator CD-ROM
• Animated Algebra
• Test Generator CD-ROM
• Online Quiz
• eWorkbook
• eEdition
• @HomeTutor

Resources for English Learners
• Quick Reference for English Learners
• Spanish Study Guide
• Multi-Language Visual Glossary
• Student Resources in Spanish

See also the *Algebra 1 Toolkit* for more strategies for meeting individual needs.

44

Motivating the Lesson

Tell students that graphs help to visualize the relationships between data values and that makes these relationships easier to recognize. Ask students to share instances where graphs have helped them to more easily visualize relationships.

❸ TEACH

Extra Example 1

Graph the function $y = 2x - 3$ with domain 2, 3, 4, and 5.

Extra Example 2

The table shows the profit p (in thousands of dollars) at a small toy store each year from 2000 to 2004 as a function of the time t in years since 2000. Graph the function.

t	0	1	2	3	4
p	19.5	20.3	22.7	21.1	21.8

Extra Example 3

Write a rule for the function represented by the graph. Identify the domain and the range of the function.

$y = x - 1$;
domain: 1, 3, 5, 7;
range: 0, 2, 4, 6

EXAMPLE 2 Graph a function

SAT SCORES The table shows the average score s on the mathematics section of the Scholastic Aptitude Test (SAT) in the United States from 1997 to 2003 as a function of the time t in years since 1997. In the table, 0 corresponds to the year 1997, 1 corresponds to 1998, and so on. Graph the function.

Years since 1997, t	0	1	2	3	4	5	6
Average score, s	511	512	511	514	514	516	519

Solution

> **READING**
> The symbol ↓ on the vertical number line represents a break in the axis.

STEP 1 **Choose** a scale. The scale should allow you to plot all the points on a graph that is a reasonable size.

- The t-values range from 0 to 6, so label the t-axis from 0 to 6 in increments of 1 unit.

- The s-values range from 511 to 519, so label the s-axis from 510 to 520 in increments of 2 units.

STEP 2 **Plot** the points.

✓ **GUIDED PRACTICE** for Example 2

2. **WHAT IF?** In Example 2, suppose that you use a scale on the s-axis from 0 to 520 in increments of 1 unit. *Describe* the appearance of the graph.
   Sample answer: **The graph would be very large with all the points near the top of the graph.**

EXAMPLE 3 Write a function rule for a graph

Write a rule for the function represented by the graph. Identify the domain and the range of the function.

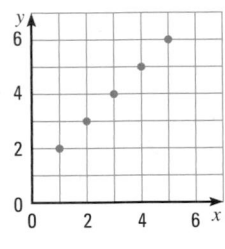

Solution

STEP 1 **Make** a table for the graph.

x	1	2	3	4	5
y	2	3	4	5	6

STEP 2 **Find** a relationship between the inputs and the outputs. Notice from the table that each output value is 1 more than the corresponding input value.

STEP 3 **Write** a function rule that describes the relationship: $y = x + 1$.

▶ A rule for the function is $y = x + 1$. The domain of the function is 1, 2, 3, 4, and 5. The range is 2, 3, 4, 5, and 6.

Differentiated Instruction

Inclusion Some students may find it counterintuitive to think of x-values increasing to the right and y-values increasing upward. Due to this, they may have difficulty constructing graphs on a coordinate plane. Have these students draw coordinate planes by first drawing the x- and y-axes with the arrows properly indicating the increasing direction of the x- and y-values.

See also the *Algebra 1 Toolkit* for more strategies.

Write a rule for the function represented by the graph. Identify the domain and the range of the function.

3.

$y = 5 - x$; domain: 0, 1, 2, 3, and 4, range: 1, 2, 3, 4, and 5

4.

$y = 5x + 5$; domain: 1, 2, 3, and 4, range: 10, 15, 20, and 25

EXAMPLE 4   Analyze a graph

GUITAR SALES The graph shows guitar sales (in millions of dollars) for a chain of music stores for the period 1999–2005. Identify the independent variable and the dependent variable. Describe how sales changed over the period and how you would expect sales in 2006 to compare to sales in 2005.

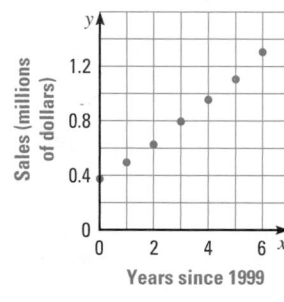

Solution

The independent variable is the number of years since 1999. The dependent variable is the sales (in millions of dollars). The graph shows that sales were increasing. If the trend continued, sales would be greater in 2006 than in 2005.

✓ **GUIDED PRACTICE** for Example 4

5. **REASONING** Based on the graph in Example 4, is $1.4 million a reasonable prediction of the chain's sales for 2006? *Explain.*
   Yes; the graph seems to increase about $0.2 million every two years.

CONCEPT SUMMARY   *For Your Notebook*

Ways to Represent a Function

You can use a verbal rule, an equation, a table, or a graph to represent a function.

Verbal Rule	Equation	Table	Graph
The output is 1 less than twice the input.	$y = 2x - 1$		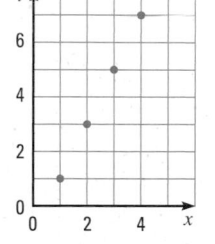

Table:

x	y
1	1
2	3
3	5
4	7

Extra Example 4

The graph shows the average number of video rentals per month at a video store for the years 2000–2006. Identify the independent variable and the dependent variable. Describe how the average number of rentals changed over the period and how you would expect the average number of rentals in 2006 to compare to the number in 2007.

independent variable: years since 2000; dependent variable: average number of video rentals per month; The graph shows that the average number of video rentals per month was decreasing. If the trend continued, the average number of rentals in 2007 would be less than in 2006.

Closing the Lesson

Have students summarize the major points of the lesson and answer the Essential Question: How do you represent functions as graphs?

• **You can use a graph to represent a function.**

• **An input-output table can be used to write a rule for a function whose graph is given.**

You can graph a function by using its domain and function rule to create an input-output table, and then by graphing points for each ordered pair in the table.

---

p. 43

1.

1.7 EXERCISES

HOMEWORK KEY
○ = **WORKED-OUT SOLUTIONS**
on p. WS1 for Exs. 3 and 17

★ = **STANDARDIZED TEST PRACTICE**
Exs. 2, 13, 18, 19, and 20

④ PRACTICE AND APPLY

Assignment Guide

📖 Answer Transparencies available for all exercises

Basic:
Day 1: pp. 46–48
Exs. 1–11, 15–19, 21–30

Average:
Day 1: pp. 46–48
Exs. 1, 2, 4–13, 15–19, 21–30

Advanced:
Day 1: pp. 46–48
Exs. 1, 2, 6–8, 11–20*, 23–30

Block:
pp. 46–48
Exs. 1, 2, 4–13, 15–19, 21–30
(with 1.6)

Differentiated Instruction

See *Algebra 1 Best Practices Toolkit* for suggestions on addressing the needs of a diverse classroom.

Homework Check

For a quick check of student understanding of key concepts, go over the following exercises:
Basic: 3, 6, 10, 15, 18
Average: 5, 11, 16, 18, 19
Advanced: 6, 12, 17, 18, 19

Extra Practice

• Student Edition, p. 938
• Chapter 5 Resource Book:
  Practice levels A, B, C, pp. 72–77

Practice Worksheet

An easily-readable reduced practice page (with answers) for this lesson can be found on p. 1C.

3–8. See Additional Answers beginning on p. AA1.

9.

SKILL PRACTICE

A 1. **VOCABULARY** Copy and complete: Each point on the graph of a function corresponds to an ordered pair (x, y) where x is in the __?__ of the function and y is in the __?__ of the function. **domain; range**

2. ★ **WRITING** Given the graph of a function, describe how to write a rule for the function. **Find a relationship between the input values and the output values.**

EXAMPLE 1
on p. 43
for Exs. 3–9

GRAPHING FUNCTIONS Graph the function. **3–8. See margin.**

③ $y = x + 3$; domain: 0, 1, 2, 3, 4, and 5

4. $y = \frac{1}{2}x + 1$; domain: 0, 1, 2, 3, 4, and 5

5. $y = 2x + 2$; domain: 0, 2, 5, 7, and 10

6. $y = 3x - 1$; domain: 1, 2, 3, 4, and 5

7. $y = x + 5$; domain: 0, 2, 4, 6, 8, and 10

8. $y = 2.5x$; domain: 0, 1, 2, 3, and 4

9. **ERROR ANALYSIS** *Describe* and correct the error in graphing the function $y = x - 1$ with domain 1, 2, 3, 4, and 5.
The domain and range are graphed backwards; see margin.

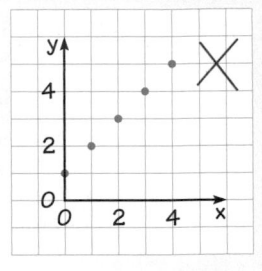

EXAMPLE 3 **B**
on p. 44
for Exs. 10–12

WRITING FUNCTION RULES Write a rule for the function represented by the graph. Identify the domain and the range of the function. **10–12. See margin.**

10.   11.   12.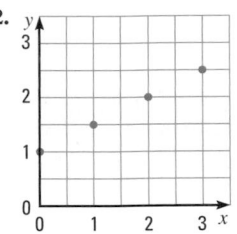

13. ★ **MULTIPLE CHOICE** The graph of which function is shown? **C**

Ⓐ $y = \frac{1}{2}x + \frac{1}{2}$ Ⓑ $y = x + \frac{1}{2}$

Ⓒ $y = \frac{3}{2}x + \frac{1}{2}$ Ⓓ $y = 2x + \frac{1}{2}$

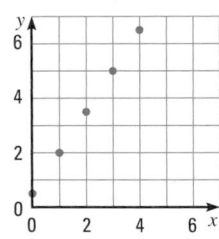

---

46 Chapter 1 Expressions, Equations, and Functions

---

10. $y = x$; domain: 0, 1, 2, 3, 4, 5, and 6, range: 0, 1, 2, 3, 4, 5, and 6

11. $y = 2x - 2$; domain: 1, 2, 3, and 4, range: 0, 2, 4, and 6

12. $y = \frac{1}{2}x + 1$; domain: 0, 1, 2, and 3, range: 1, $1\frac{1}{2}$, 2, $2\frac{1}{2}$

15.

14. CHALLENGE The graph represents a function.

    a. Write a rule for the function. $\frac{1}{2}x^2$

    b. Find the value of y so that $(1.5, y)$ is on the graph of the function. **1.125**

PROBLEM SOLVING

EXAMPLE 2 **A**
on p. 44
for Exs. 15–17

15. ADVERTISING The table shows the cost C (in millions of dollars) of a 30 second Super Bowl ad on TV as a function of the time t (in years) since 1997. Graph the function. **See margin.**

Years since 1997, t	0	1	2	3	4	5	6	7
Cost (millions of dollars), C	1.2	1.3	1.6	2.1	2.1	1.9	2.1	2.3

@HomeTutor for problem solving help at classzone.com

16. CONGRESS The table shows the number r of U.S. representatives for Texas as a function of the time t (in years) since 1930. Graph the function. **See margin.**

Years since 1930, t	0	10	20	30	40	50	60	70
Number of representatives, r	21	21	22	23	24	27	30	32

@HomeTutor for problem solving help at classzone.com

17. ELECTIONS The table shows the number v of voters in U.S. presidential elections as a function of the time t (in years) since 1984. First copy and complete the table. Round to the nearest million. Then graph the function represented by the first and third columns. **See margin for art.**

Years since 1984	Voters	Voters (millions)
0	92,652,680	? **93**
4	91,594,693	? **92**
8	104,405,155	? **104**
12	96,456,345	? **96**
16	105,586,274	? **106**

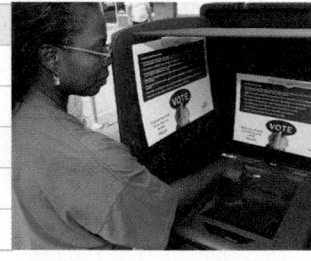

EXAMPLE 4
on p. 45
for Exs. 18–19

18. ★ WRITING The graph shows the number of hours of daylight in Houston, Texas, on the fifteenth day of the month, with 1 representing January, and so on. Identify the independent variable and the dependent variable. *Describe* how the number of hours of daylight changes over a year. **Independent variable: the month, dependent variable: the hours of daylight; the number of daylight hours increases from January to May and then decreases through December.**

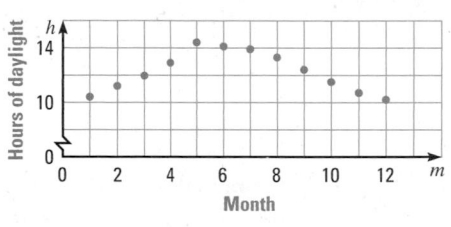

Month

1.7 Represent Functions as Graphs   **47**

Avoiding Common Errors

Exercises 3–8 Students sometimes mistakenly reverse the x- and y-coordinates of a point when they plot it. Remind them that the domain values of a function are the x-coordinates of the points. Point out that they can quickly compare the given domain values to the labels of the vertical grid lines that have plotted points located on them.

Study Strategy

Exercises 10–12 Instruct students to use the solution steps shown in Example 3. Emphasize that a table will help them identify the relationship between the corresponding values of x and y.

Exercises 15–17 Suggest that students review Step 1 in Example 2 before graphing the functions. This will remind them to choose an appropriate scale and uniform increments for their graphs.

Mathematical Reasoning

Exercise 13 Lead students to see that the points are rising by $1\frac{1}{2}\left(\text{or } \frac{3}{2}\right)$ units on the y-axis for each increase of 1 unit on the x-axis. This suggests that answer C may be correct and should be checked first.

Internet Reference

Exercise 15 Additional information about the Super Bowl, including a link to commercials, can be found at the official Super Bowl website www.superbowl.com.

Exercise 16 For information about the number of U.S. Representatives from other states, visit the official website for the U.S. House of Representatives at www.house.gov.

Differentiated Instruction

Advanced Ask students if it is possible to write a rule for the functions given in **Exercises 15 and 16.** Challenge them to explain why they can write rules for some functions and not for others. Suggest they graph a real-world situation in which they can write a rule for the function and then compare it to their graphs in Exercise 15 and 16. This will lead them into thinking about the differences between functions and prepare them for the concept of linear functions.

See also the *Algebra 1 Toolkit* for more strategies.

16.

Years since 1930

17.

Years since 1984

Daily Homework Quiz

📄 Transparency Available

1. Graph the function $y = \frac{1}{2}x + 2$ with domain 2, 4, 6, and 8.

2. Write a rule for the function represented by the graph. Identify the domain and the range of the function.

$y = -\frac{1}{2}x + 6$; domain: 0, 2, 4, 6, 8; range: 2, 3, 4, 5, 6

📡 Online Quiz

Available at **classzone.com**

Diagnosis/Remediation

- Practice A, B, C in Chapter 1 Resource Book, pp. 72–77
- Study Guide in Chapter 1 Resource Book, pp. 78–79
- Practice Workbook, pp. 13–15
- @HomeTutor

Challenge

Additional challenge is available in the Chapter 1 Resource Book, p. 82.

Quiz

An easily-readable reduced copy of the quiz (with answers) on Lessons 1.6–1.7 from the Assessment Book can be found on p. 1E.

20a, Quiz 1, 4, 5. See Additional Answers beginning on p. AA1.

48

---

19. ★ **SHORT RESPONSE** A field biologist collected and measured alligator snapping turtle eggs. The graph shows the mass m (in grams) of an egg as a function of its length ℓ (in millimeters).

a. Describe As the lengths of the eggs increase, what happens to the masses of the eggs? **increases**

b. Estimate Is 27.5 g a reasonable estimate for the mass of an egg that is 38 mm long? *Explain*.
Yes; 27.5 grams is between the mass of an egg that is just under 38 millimeters long and an egg that is just over 38 millimeters long.

20. ★ **SHORT RESPONSE** Women first officially ran in the Boston Marathon in 1972. The graph shows the winning time t (in minutes) for both men and women as a function of the number n of years since 1972 for that year and every five years thereafter.

a. CHALLENGE *Explain* how you can estimate the difference in the men's and women's winning time for any year shown. **See margin.**

b. CHALLENGE *Compare* any trends you see in the graphs.
Sample answer: **Between 1982 and 2002 the men's times are all within about 5 minutes of each other and the women's times are all within about 10 minutes of each other.**

MIXED REVIEW

PREVIEW
Prepare for Lesson 2.1 in Exs. 21–24.

Copy and complete the statement using <, >, or =. *(p. 909)*

21. 0.53 ? 0.5 **>** **22.** 3.9 ? 4.0 **<** **23.** 1.64 ? 1.66 **<** **24.** 0.80 ? 0.8 **=**

Solve the equation using mental math. *(p. 21)*

25. $x + 12 = 20$ **8** **26.** $12z = 480$ **40** **27.** $x - 8 = 5$ **13** **28.** $\frac{n}{2} = 32$ **64**

Write a rule for the function. *(p. 35)*

29.

Input, x	2	3	7	10
Ouput, y	8	7	3	0

$y = 10 - x$

30.

Input, x	0	4	8	12
Ouput, y	5	7	9	11

$y = \frac{1}{2}x + 5$

QUIZ for Lessons 1.6–1.7

1. The domain of the function $y = 12 - 2x$ is 0, 2, 3, 4, and 5. Make a table for the function, then identify the range of the function. *(p. 35)*
Range: 2, 4, 6, 8, and 12; see margin.

Tell whether the pairing is a function. *(p. 35)*

2.

x	5	6	7	11
y	1	2	3	7

function

3.

x	4	6	9	15
y	1	3	6	3

function

Graph the function. *(p. 43)* **4, 5. See margin.**

4. $y = 2x - 5$; domain: 5, 6, 7, 8, and 9 **5.** $y = 7 - x$; domain: 1, 2, 3, 4, and 5

Determine Whether a Relation Is a Function

GOAL Determine whether a relation is a function when the relation is represented by a table or a graph.

Key Vocabulary
• relation, *p. 49*

A **relation** is any pairing of a set of inputs with a set of outputs. Every function is a relation, but not every relation is a function. A relation is a function if for every input there is exactly one output.

EXAMPLE 1 Determine whether a relation is a function

Determine whether the relation is a function.

a.

Input	4	4	5	6	7
Output	0	1	2	3	4

b.

Input	3	5	7	9
Output	1	2	3	2

Solution

a. The input 4 has two different outputs, 0 and 1. So, the relation is *not* a function.

b. Every input has exactly one output, so the relation is a function.

USING THE GRAPH OF A RELATION You can use the *vertical line test* to determine whether a relation represented by a graph is a function. When a relation is *not* a function, its graph contains at least two points with the same *x*-coordinate and different *y*-coordinates. Those points lie on a vertical line.

KEY CONCEPT *For Your Notebook*

Vertical Line Test

Words

A relation represented by a graph is a function provided that no vertical line passes through more than one point on the graph.

Graphs

Function	Function	*Not* a function

EXAMPLE 2 Use the vertical line test

Determine whether the graph represents a function.

a.

b.

You can draw a vertical line through the points (1, 2) and (1, 4). The graph does *not* represent a function.

No vertical line can be drawn through more than one point. The graph represents a function.

 Animated Algebra at classzone.com

PRACTICE

EXAMPLE 1
on p. 49
for Exs. 1–3

IDENTIFYING FUNCTIONS Determine whether the relation is a function.

1.

Input	Output
0	1
2	6
5	12
7	5
8	4

function

2.

Input	Output
3	7
4	8
4	9
5	10
6	11

not a function

3.

Input	Output
0.7	1.9
1.2	2.4
3.5	4.7
7.5	8.7
7.5	9.7

not a function

EXAMPLE 2
on p. 50
for Exs. 4–6

IDENTIFYING FUNCTIONS Determine whether the graph represents a function.

4.

function

5.

function

6.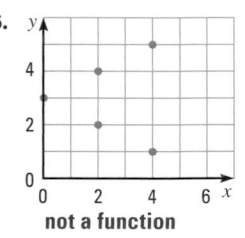

not a function

REASONING Tell whether the pairing of *x*-values and *y*-values is necessarily a function. *Explain* your reasoning. **7, 8. See margin.**

7. A teacher makes a table that lists the number *x* of letters in the first name and the number *y* of letters in the last name of each student in the class.

8. Your doctor records your height *x* (in inches) and your weight *y* (in pounds) each time you have a medical exam.

9. You have a record of your age *x* (in years) and your height *y* (in inches) on each of your birthdays since you were born.
Function; for each of your birthdays, you have only one height.

7. Not a function. *Sample answer:* There could be many students whose first names have 4 letters, for instance, but their last names could all have a different number of letters.

8. Not a function. *Sample answer:* If your height stays the same, you could lose or gain weight, giving more than one output for an input.

---

③ TEACH

Extra Example 1

Determine whether the relation is a function. **yes**

Input	2	3	4	5	6
Output	9	4	1	0	1

Extra Example 2

Determine whether the graph represents a function. **no**

classzone.com

An **Animated Algebra** activity is available on-line for **Example 2**. This activity is also available on the **Power Presentations CD-ROM**.

Closing the Lesson

Have students summarize the major points of the lesson and answer the Essential Question: How do you determine whether a relation shown in a table or a graph is a function?

- **A relation is a function if for every input there is exactly one output.**
- **A relation is a function if no vertical line passes through more than one point when the relation is graphed.**

In a table, check that each input has exactly one output; in a graph, check that no vertical line passes through more than one point.

④ PRACTICE AND APPLY

Teaching Strategy

Exercises 8–9 Have students work in groups to create tables of realistic values and then have them graph them. Working with actual values may help students see the relationships more readily.

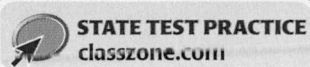

Lessons 1.5–1.7

1. **MULTI-STEP PROBLEM** A pizza shop charges $7 for a large cheese pizza plus $.95 for each topping.

   a. Use a verbal model to write an equation for the total cost C (in dollars) of a pizza with n toppings. **1a, b. See margin.**

   b. The pizza shop offers 10 toppings. Write an input-output table for the total cost (in dollars) of a pizza as a function of the number n of toppings. *Explain* why the table represents a function and describe the domain and range of the function.

   c. You have $15 to spend on a large pizza. What is the greatest number of toppings you can afford? **8 toppings**

2. **SHORT RESPONSE** Your class is planning a car wash. You need $75 worth of materials.

   a. Use a verbal model to write an equation that relates your profit to the number of cars you wash. Find your profit if you wash 120 cars. **2a, b. See margin.**

   b. Does doubling the number of cars you wash double your profit? *Explain.*

3. **MULTI-STEP PROBLEM** You are painting a room in a community center. The room has four walls that are each 9 feet high and 25 feet long. There are two rectangular windows and two rectangular doors that do not need to be painted. Each window is 3.5 feet wide and 4 feet high. Each door is 3.5 feet wide and 7 feet high.

   a. Find the combined area of the windows and doors. **77 ft²**

   b. Find the combined area of all four walls, excluding the windows and the doors. **823 ft²**

   c. A gallon of paint covers about 400 square feet. How many gallons of paint will you need in order to give the room one coat of paint? **3 gal**

   d. The paint costs $24.95 per gallon. How much will it cost for one coat of paint? **$74.85**

4. **GRIDDED ANSWER** You consider 68°F to be a comfortable room temperature. The temperature in a room is 18°C. How many degrees Celsius should you raise the temperature so that it will be 68°F? **2°C**

5. **SHORT RESPONSE** Your family is driving from Charleston, South Carolina, to Jacksonville, Florida, a total distance of about 250 miles. You leave Charleston at 1:00 P.M. You travel at an average speed of 55 miles per hour without stopping. Will you get to Jacksonville before the 5:00 P.M. rush hour? *Explain.* **See margin.**

6. **GRIDDED ANSWER** A person invests $1200 in an account earning 3% simple annual interest. How much will be in the account after 2 years? **$1272**

7. **OPEN-ENDED** Write a problem that involves a real-world situation and that can be solved using the formula for distance traveled. Solve the problem and explain what the solution means in the situation. **See margin.**

8. **EXTENDED RESPONSE** You pay $40 per hour for windsurfing lessons and rent equipment for $20 per hour. The cost (in dollars) of lessons and the cost (in dollars) of rentals are both functions of the time (in hours).

   a. Write a rule for each function. **$c = 40t$, $c = 20t$**

   b. Let the domains of the functions be the whole numbers from 0 to 6. Graph each function. **See margin.**

   c. You rent equipment for every lesson you take. What function gives your total cost? How would the graph of this function compare with the graphs in part (b)? **$c = 60t$; this graph would begin higher on the *y*-axis and it would be steeper.**

1a. total cost = cost of cheese + (number of toppings)(cost of each topping)

1b. See below.

2a. profit = (number of cars) · (price per car) − cost of materials; $525

2b. No; your materials cost is the same. Only the income doubled, not the profit.

5. No; it will take your family about $4\frac{1}{2}$ hours to get to Jacksonville, so it will be after 5:30 P.M.

7. *Sample answer:* You are riding your bike to your friend's house, 5 miles away. You need to be there in a half hour. What should your average speed be to get there in time? $r = 10$, you must ride your bike at 10 miles per hour to get to your friend's house in a half hour.

8b.

1b.

Toppings	0	1	2	3	4	5
Cost (dollars)	7	7.95	8.90	9.85	10.80	11.75

Toppings	6	7	8	9	10
Cost (dollars)	12.70	13.65	14.60	15.55	16.50

There is exactly one cost for each number of toppings, so the table represents a function. The domain is 0, 1, 2, 3, 4, 5, 6, 7, 8, 9, and 10. The range is 7, 7.95, 8.90, 9.85, 10.80, 11.75, 12.70, 13.65, 14.60, 15.55, and 16.50.

Additional Resources

The following resources are available to help review the materials in this chapter.

Chapter 1 Resource Book

- Chapter Review Games and Activities, p. 83
- Cumulative Practice, Ch. 1, pp. 85–86

Student Resources in Spanish

eWorkbook

@HomeTutor

Vocabulary Practice

Vocabulary practice is available at **classzone.com**

BIG IDEAS   *For Your Notebook*

Big Idea ❶

Writing and Evaluating Algebraic Expressions

The cost of admission for one student at a planetarium is $6. You can use a verbal model to write an expression for the total cost of admission for any number of students.

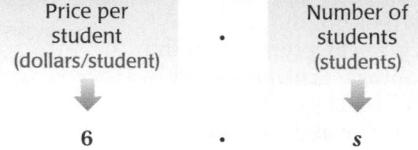

Price per student (dollars/student)	•	Number of students (students)
6	•	s

An expression is 6s. Because $\dfrac{dollars}{student} \cdot students = dollars$, the expression produces an answer in dollars. The expression is reasonable.

Big Idea ❷

Using Expressions to Write Equations and Inequalities

You can use symbols to write an equation or inequality that compares the expression 6s to another expression.

The total cost of admission to the planetarium for s students at a rate of $6 per student is $150.

$$6s = 150 \qquad \textbf{Equation}$$

The total cost of admission to the planetarium for s students at a rate of $6 per student is no more than $150.

$$6s \le 150 \qquad \textbf{Inequality}$$

Big Idea ❸

Representing Functions as Verbal Rules, Equations, Tables, and Graphs

You can use a verbal description, an equation, a table, or a graph to represent a function.

Words The total cost (in dollars) of admission to the planetarium is 6 times the number of students.

Equation

$C = 6s$

Table

Input, s	Input, C
0	0
1	6
2	12
3	18

Graph

Extra Example 1.1
Evaluate $\frac{36}{g}$ when $g = 4$. **9**

REVIEW KEY VOCABULARY

- variable, value of a variable, *p. 2*
- algebraic expression, *p. 2*
- evaluate an algebraic expression, *p. 2*
- power, exponent, base, *p. 3*
- order of operations, *p. 8*
- verbal model, *p. 16*
- rate, unit rate, *p. 17*
- open sentence, *p. 21*
- equation, inequality, *p. 21*
- solution of an equation or inequality, *p. 22*
- formula, *p. 30*
- function, *p. 35*
- input, output, *p. 35*
- domain, range, *p. 35*
- independent variable, *p. 36*
- dependent variable, *p. 36*

VOCABULARY EXERCISES

In Exercises 1–3, copy and complete the statement.

1. In the power 7^{12}, __?__ is the base and __?__ is the exponent. **7, 12**

2. A(n) __?__ is an open sentence that contains an equal sign. **equation**

3. A(n) __?__ consists of numbers, variables, and operations. **algebraic expression**

4. **WRITING** *Describe* how you can tell by looking at the graph of a function which variable is the input variable and which is the output variable.
   When looking at the graph of a function the variable along the *x*-axis is the input variable and the variable along the *y*-axis is the output variable.

REVIEW EXAMPLES AND EXERCISES

Use the review examples and exercises below to check your understanding of the concepts you have learned in each lesson of Chapter 1.

1.1 Evaluate Expressions
pp. 2–7

EXAMPLE

Evaluate $6 - n$ when $n = 4$.

$6 - n = 6 - 4$ **Substitute 4 for *n*.**

$\quad\quad = 2$ **Simplify.**

EXERCISES

EXAMPLES
1, 4, and 5
on pp. 2–4
for Exs. 5–12

Evaluate the expression.

5. $3 + x$ when $x = 13$ **16**

6. $y - 2$ when $y = 18$ **16**

7. $\frac{20}{k}$ when $k = 2$ **10**

8. $40w$ when $w = 0.5$ **20**

9. z^2 when $z = 20$ **400**

10. w^3 when $w = 0.1$ **0.001**

11. **DVD STORAGE** A plastic storage sleeve for a DVD has the shape of a square with an edge length of 5 inches. What is the area of the sleeve? **25 in.²**

12. **NOTEPAPER** You store square notepaper in a cube-shaped box with an inside edge length of 3 inches. What is the volume of the box? **27 in.³**

Extra Example 1.2

Evaluate $32 - (4^2 + 8) \div 4$. **26**

Extra Example 1.3

Write an expression for the height of a tree over time if the tree was 2.5 feet tall when planted and it grows at an average rate of 2 feet per year. **$2t + 2.5$, where t represents the time in years**

1.2 Apply Order of Operations
pp. 8–12

EXAMPLE

Evaluate $(5 + 3)^2 \div 2 \times 3$.

$(5 + 3)^2 \div 2 \times 3 = 8^2 \div 2 \times 3$ Add within parentheses.

$= 64 \div 2 \times 3$ Evaluate power.

$= 32 \cdot 3$ Divide.

$= 96$ Multiply.

EXERCISES

EXAMPLES 1, 2, and 3 on p. 8–9 for Exs. 13–21

Evaluate the expression.

13. $12 - 6 \div 2$ **9**
14. $1 + 2 \cdot 9^2$ **163**
15. $3 + 2^3 - 6 \div 2$ **8**

16. $15 - (4 + 3^2)$ **2**
17. $\frac{20 - 12}{5^2 - 1}$ **$\frac{1}{3}$**
18. $50 - [7 + (3^2 \div 2)]$ **$38\frac{1}{2}$**

Evaluate the expression when $x = 4$.

19. $15x - 8$ **52**
20. $3x^2 + 4$ **52**
21. $2(x - 1)^2$ **18**

1.3 Write Expressions
pp. 15–20

EXAMPLE

Write an expression for the entry fee in a jazz band competition if there is a base fee of $50 and a charge of $1 per member.

Write a verbal model. Then translate the verbal model into an algebraic expression. Let n represent the number of band members.

▸ An expression for the entry fee (in dollars) is $50 + n$.

EXERCISES

EXAMPLES 1, 2, and 3 on pp. 15–16 for Exs. 22–27

Translate the verbal phrase into an expression.

22. The sum of a number k and 7 **$k + 7$**
23. 5 less than a number z **$z - 5$**
24. The quotient of a number k and 12 **$\frac{k}{12}$**
25. 3 times the square of a number x **$3x^2$**

26. TOLL ROADS A toll road charges trucks a toll of $3 per axle. Write an expression for the total toll for a truck. **$3a$**

27. SCHOOL SUPPLIES You purchase some notebooks for $2.95 each and a package of pens for $2.19. Write an expression for the total amount (in dollars) that you spend. **$2.95n + 2.19$**

1.4 Write Equations and Inequalities
pp. 21–26

EXAMPLE

Write an inequality for the sentence "The sum of 3 and twice a number k is no more than 15". Then check whether 4 is a solution of the inequality.

An inequality is $3 + 2k \le 15$.

To check whether 4 is a solution of the inequality, substitute 4 for k.

$3 + 2(4) \overset{?}{\le} 15$ **Substitute 4 for k.**

$11 \le 15$ ✓ **The solution checks. So, 4 is a solution.**

EXERCISES

EXAMPLES 1 and 2
on pp. 21–22
for Fxs. 28–32

Write an equation or an inequality.

28. The product of a number z and 12 is 60. **$12z = 60$**

29. The sum of 13 and a number t is at least 24. **$13 + t \ge 24$**

Check whether the given number is a solution of the equation or inequality.

30. $3x - 4 = 10$; 5
not a solution

31. $4y - 2 \ge 2$; 3
solution

32. $2d + 4 < 9d - 7$; 3
solution

1.5 Use a Problem Solving Plan
pp. 28–33

EXAMPLE

A rectangular banner is 12 feet long and has an area of 60 square feet. What is the perimeter of the banner?

STEP 1 **Read and Understand** You know the length of the rectangular banner and its area. You want to find the perimeter.

STEP 2 **Make a Plan** Use the area formula for a rectangle to find the width. Then use the perimeter formula for a rectangle.

STEP 3 **Solve the Problem** Substituting 12 for ℓ in the formula $A = \ell w$, $60 = 12w$. Because $12 \cdot 5 = 60$, $w = 5$. Then substituting 12 for ℓ and 5 for w in the formula $P = 2\ell + 2w$, $P = 2(12) + 2(5) = 34$ feet.

STEP 4 **Look Back** Use estimation. Since $\ell \approx 10$ and $A = 60$, $w \approx 6$. Then $P \approx 2(10) + 2(6) = 32$ feet, so your answer is reasonable.

EXERCISES

EXAMPLES 1, 2, and 3
on p. 28–30
for Exs. 33–34

33. **U.S. HISTORY** The flag that inspired the national anthem was a rectangle 30 feet wide and 42 feet long. Pieces of the flag have been lost. It is now 30 feet wide and 34 feet long. How many square feet have been lost? **240 ft^2**

34. **PATTERNS** A grocery clerk stacks three rows of cans of fruit for a display. Each of the top two rows has 2 fewer cans than the row beneath it. There are 30 cans altogether. How many cans are there in each row? **8 cans, 10 cans, and 12 cans**

Chapter Review **55**

Extra Example 1.4
Write an equation for the sentence "Nine more than the quantity 6 less than a number n is 18." Then check whether 10 is a solution of the equation. $9 + (n - 6) = 18$; **10 is not a solution since $9 + (10 - 6) = 13$ and $13 \ne 18$.**

Extra Example 1.5
The floor of a rectangular building is 52 feet long and has a perimeter of 174 feet. What is the area of the floor? **1820 ft^2**

1.6 Represent Functions as Rules and Tables

pp. 35–40

EXAMPLE

The domain of the function $y = 3x - 5$ is 2, 3, 4, and 5. Make a table for the function, then identify the range of the function.

x	2	3	4	5
$y = 3x - 5$	$3(2) - 5 = 1$	$3(3) - 5 = 4$	$3(4) - 5 = 7$	$3(5) - 5 = 10$

The range of the function is 1, 4, 7, and 10.

EXERCISES

EXAMPLES 1, 3, and 4 on p. 35–37 for Exs. 35–38

Make a table for the function. Identify the range of the function.

35. $y = x - 5$
Domain: 10, 12, 15, 20, 21
Range: 5, 7, 10, 15, and 16; see margin.

36. $y = 3x + 1$
Domain: 0, 2, 3, 5, 10
Range: 1, 7, 10, 16, and 31; see margin.

Write a rule for the function.

37.
Input, x	0	2	4	5
Output, y	4	6	8	9

$y = x + 4$

38.
Input, x	0	3	4	6
Output, y	0	15	20	30

$y = 5x$

1.7 Represent Functions as Graphs

pp. 43–48

EXAMPLE

Write a rule for the function represented by the graph. Identify the domain and the range of the function.

Make a table for the graph.

x	2	3	4	5	6
y	0	1	2	3	4

Each y-value is 2 less than the corresponding x-value. A rule for the function is $y = x - 2$. The domain is 2, 3, 4, 5, and 6. The range is 0, 1, 2, 3, and 4.

EXERCISES

EXAMPLES 1, 3, and 4 on pp. 43–45 for Exs. 39–40

39. Graph the function $y = 4x - 3$ with domain 1, 2, 3, 4, and 5. **See margin.**

40. Write a rule for the function represented by the graph. Identify the domain and the range of the function.

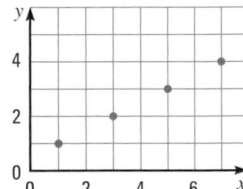

$\frac{1}{2}x + \frac{1}{2}$; domain: 1, 3, 5, and 7, range: 1, 2, 3, and 4

Evaluate the expression.

1. $7 + 3^2 \cdot 2$ **25**

2. $(5^2 + 17) \div 7$ **6**

3. $(24 - 11) - (3 + 2) \div 4$ **11.75**

4. $\frac{x}{5}$ when $x = 30$ **6**

5. n^3 when $n = 20$ **8000**

6. $15 - t$ when $t = 11$ **4**

7. $12 + 4x$ when $x = 1\frac{1}{2}$ **18**

8. $3z^2 - 7$ when $z = 6$ **101**

9. $2(4n + 5)$ when $n = 2$ **26**

Write an expression, an equation, or an inequality.

10. The sum of 19 and the cube of a number x **$19 + x^3$**

11. The product of 3 and a number y is no more than 21. **$3y \leq 21$**

12. Twice the difference of a number z and 12 is equal to 10. **$2(z - 12) = 10$**

Check whether the given number is a solution of the equation or inequality.

13. $2 + 3x = 10$; 2 **not a solution**
14. $8 + 3b > 15$; 2 **not a solution**
15. $11y - 5 \leq 30$; 3 **solution**

16. Refer to the graph.

    a. *Explain* why the graph represents a function.

    b. Identify the domain and the range.

    c. Write a rule for the function. **$y = x + 2$**

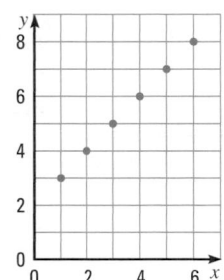

16a. There is exactly one output for each input.

16b. domain: 1, 2, 3, 4, 5, and 6, range: 3, 4, 5, 6, 7, and 8

17. **FOOD PREPARATION** You buy tomatoes at $1.29 per pound and peppers at $3.99 per pound to make salsa. Write an expression for the total cost of the ingredients. Then find the total cost of 5 pounds of tomatoes and 2 pounds of peppers. **$c = 1.29t + 3.99p$; $14.43**

18. **CAR EXPENSES** A family determined the average cost of maintaining and operating the family car to be about $.30 per mile. On one trip, the family drove at an average rate of 50 miles per hour for a total of 6.5 hours. On a second trip, they drove at an average rate of 55 miles per hour for a total of 6 hours. Which trip cost more? How much more? **the second trip; $1.50**

19. **SHOE SIZES** A man's size 6 shoe is the same size as a woman's size $7\frac{1}{2}$.

    The table shows other corresponding sizes of men's and women's shoes.

Men's size, x	6	$6\frac{1}{2}$	7	$7\frac{1}{2}$	8	$8\frac{1}{2}$	9
Women's size, y	$7\frac{1}{2}$	8	$8\frac{1}{2}$	9	$9\frac{1}{2}$	10	$10\frac{1}{2}$

19a. $y = x + 1\frac{1}{2}$; domain: 6, $6\frac{1}{2}$, 7, $7\frac{1}{2}$, 8, $8\frac{1}{2}$, and 9, range: $7\frac{1}{2}$, 8, $8\frac{1}{2}$, 9, $9\frac{1}{2}$, 10, and $10\frac{1}{2}$

    a. Using the data in the table, write a rule for women's shoe size as a function of men's shoe size. Identify the domain and the range.

    b. Graph the function. **See margin.**

Additional Resources

Assessment Book

- Chapter Test, Levels A, B, C, pp. 4–9
- Standardized Chapter Test, pp. 10–11
- SAT/ACT Chapter Test, pp. 12–13
- Alternative Assessment, pp. 14–15

Test Generator CD-ROM

Chapter Test

Easily-readable reduced copies (with answers) of Chapter Test B, the Standardized Chapter Test, and the Alternative Assessment from the Assessment Book can be found on pp. 1E–1F.

19b.

Using Rubrics

The rubric given on the pupil page is a sample of a three-level rubric. Other rubrics may contain four, five, or six levels. For more information on rubrics, see the *Algebra 1 Toolkit*.

Test-Taking Strategy

Encourage students to read short response questions carefully as they often contain more than one part, but the parts generally are not labeled. Suggest that they underline or circle each part of the question that must be answered. When they finish, they can refer back to the underlined or circled parts to verify that they have answered all parts of the question.

Mathematical Reasoning

Multiple Representations As shown here in the Problem, students may be able to use algebra, a graph, or a table to determine a solution to a question. Encourage students to use the method with which they are most proficient. If they should encounter difficulty using one method, suggest that they switch to another. Remind students that whatever method they use, they should be sure to include explanations of all the steps they followed in order to arrive at the solution.

Scoring Rubric

Full Credit
- solution is complete and correct

Partial Credit
- solution is complete but has errors,
  or
- solution is without error but incomplete

No Credit
- no solution is given,
  or
- solution makes no sense

SHORT RESPONSE QUESTIONS

PROBLEM

Mike and Aaron are inflating helium balloons for a graduation party. Mike can inflate 3 balloons per minute, and Aaron can inflate 2 balloons per minute. If Mike and Aaron start inflating balloons at the same time, how many minutes will it take them to inflate a total of 30 balloons? *Explain* your answer.

Below are sample solutions to the problem. Read each solution and the comments in blue to see why the sample represents full credit, partial credit, or no credit.

SAMPLE 1: Full credit solution

For each person, the number of balloons inflated is a function of the number of minutes. Let t be the time (in minutes) that Mike and Aaron have been inflating balloons, and let b be the number of balloons inflated.

The function rules are correct. The tables and explanation show how the problem was solved.

Mike: $b = 3t$

t	1	2	3	4	5	6
b	3	6	9	12	15	18

Aaron: $b = 2t$

t	1	2	3	4	5	6
b	2	4	6	8	10	12

The tables show that in 6 minutes Mike will have inflated 18 balloons, and Aaron will have inflated 12 balloons.

The solution is correct.

Since $18 + 12 = 30$, it will take Mike and Aaron 6 minutes to inflate a total of 30 balloons.

SAMPLE 2: Partial credit solution

The reasoning and the function rule are correct.

Since Mike can inflate 3 balloons per minute and Aaron can inflate 2 balloons per minute, together they can inflate 5 balloons per minute.

Use the function $b = 5t$ where t is the time (in minutes) and b is the number of balloons inflated.

The solution is incorrect. The student substituted 30 for x instead of for y.

$$b = 5t$$
$$= 5(30)$$
$$= 150$$

So, it will take 150 minutes, or 2.5 hours, to inflate 30 balloons.

SAMPLE 3: Partial credit solution

The solution is without error but incomplete. There is no explanation of how the graph was used to find the answer.

Mike can inflate 3 balloons per minute, and Aaron can inflate 2 balloons per minute. Let t represent the time in minutes and b represent the total number of balloons the friends inflate. Graph the function $b = 5t$.

It will take 6 minutes to inflate 30 balloons.

SAMPLE 4: No credit solution

The solution makes no sense. Each boy takes less time working alone.

Mike takes $30 \div 3 = 10$ minutes to inflate 30 balloons. Aaron takes $30 \div 2 = 15$ minutes to inflate 30 balloons. Because $10 + 15 = 25$, it will take Mike and Aaron 25 minutes to inflate 30 balloons.

PRACTICE Apply the Scoring Rubric

Score the solution to the problem below as *full credit, partial credit,* or *no credit. Explain* your reasoning.

> **PROBLEM** Jessica and Graciela start exercising at the same time. Jessica jogs at a rate of 600 feet per minute. Graciela walks in the same direction at a rate of 400 feet per minute. If the girls start at the same time, in how many minutes will they be 4000 feet apart? *Explain*.

1. Partial credit; the calculation $4000 \div 200$ is the correct one to use, and the answer is correct, but the solution does not explain why the calculation $4000 \div 200$ produces the correct answer.

2. No credit; the answer is incorrect and the student's reasoning is incorrect. The equation $d = 1000t$ is a valid equation but it cannot be used to answer the question.

3. Full credit; the function rules are correct, and the student has explained what the variables represent. The tables and explanation show how the problem was solved, and the question is answered correctly.

1. Because $4000 \div 200 = 20$, Jessica and Graciela will be 4000 feet apart after 20 minutes.

2. For every minute they exercise, the girls travel a total of 1000 feet. Let t be time (in minutes) and d be distance (in feet). Then $d = 1000t$, and when $t = 4$, $d = 4000$. The answer is 4 minutes.

3. Let t be the time (in minutes) and d be the distance (in feet). For Jessica, $d = 600t$. For Graciela, $d = 400t$.

t	5	10	15	20
d	3000	6000	9000	12,000

t	5	10	15	20
d	2000	4000	6000	8000

When $t = 20$, $600t = 12,000$ and $400t = 8000$, so the girls are 4000 feet apart. The answer is 20 minutes.

1. Between 120 and 140 calories; 128 calories. *Sample answer:* The punch is $\frac{2}{5}$ pineapple juice and $\frac{3}{5}$ apple juice, so the number of calories in 1 cup of punch is $\frac{2}{5}(140) + \frac{3}{5}(120) = 56 + 72 = 128$ calories.

2. A and B. *Sample answer:* **Ming will spend at least 100($.99) = $99 on songs, so she has $340 − $99 = $241 to spend on the MP3 player. Models C and D cost more than $241, so she should not consider purchasing those.**

3a. $12. *Sample answer:* **The price per calendar should be (cost per calendar) + (profit per calendar). For a profit of $1800, the profit per calendar must be $1800 ÷ 200 = $9, so the price should be $9 + $3 = $12.**

3b. $13. *Sample answer:* **For a profit of $2000, the profit per calendar must be $2000 ÷ 200 = $10, so the price should be $10 + $3 = $13.**

4. $408. *Sample answer:* **On a weekday Mark earns $8.50 per hour, or $8.50(8) = $68 per day. On a weekend day Mark earns 1.5($8.50) = $12.75 per hour, or $12.75(8) = $102 per day. The most weekend days he can work in a week is 2, so he will earn the maximum amount by working 2 weekend days and 3 weekdays. The maximum amount is 2($102) + 3($68) = $408.**

5. *Sample answer:* **Option 1 is preferable if the child's current allowance is more than $6 per week; Option 2 is preferable if the child's current allowance is not more than $6 per week. For Option 1 to be preferable one-half of the current allowance must be more than $3, so the current allowance must be more than 2($3) = $6.**

SHORT RESPONSE

1. A punch recipe uses 2 parts pineapple juice to 3 parts apple juice. The table shows the number of calories in each type of juice.

Juice	Calories in one cup
pineapple	140
apple	120

Would you expect there to be fewer than 120 calories, between 120 and 140 calories, or more than 140 calories in 1 cup of the punch? Exactly how many calories are there in 1 cup of the punch? *Explain.* **1–8 See margin.**

2. Ming has saved $340 to spend on an MP3 player and music. Music for the MP3 player costs $.99 per song, and Ming wants to buy at least 100 songs. Which models of MP3 player should she consider purchasing? *Explain* your reasoning.

Model	Price (dollars)
A	230
B	241
C	275
D	299

3. An animal shelter has 200 calendars to sell at a fair as a fundraiser. Each of the calendars costs $3 to make. The shelter hopes to sell all the calendars and make a total profit of $1800.

  a. What should the selling price of each calendar be?

  b. If the shelter hopes to make a profit of $2000, what should the selling price of each calendar be? *Explain* your reasoning.

4. Mark works at a grocery store where employees make one and a half times their regular hourly wage when they work on a Saturday or a Sunday. Mark works an 8 hour shift 5 days per week, sometimes including weekends. His regular hourly wage is $8.50. What is the maximum amount that he could earn in one week? *Explain* your reasoning.

5. The Ruizes offer each of their children two different options for increasing the child's weekly allowance.

  Option 1: Increase the allowance by one half of the current allowance.

  Option 2: Increase the allowance by $3 per week.

Describe under what conditions each option is preferable. *Justify* your answers.

6. A pizzeria charges $11 for a large cheese pizza. The pizzeria is offering a special deal. If you buy 3 large cheese pizzas, you can choose to get a fourth cheese pizza free.

  a. Make a table showing the cost (in dollars) of 1, 2, 3, or 4 pizzas.

  b. Is the cost of the pizzas a function of the number of pizzas purchased? *Explain.*

  c. Is the number of pizzas purchased a function of the cost (in dollars)? *Explain.*

7. You buy 5 feet of ribbon to decorate the edge of a rectangular placemat. You have 6 inches of ribbon left over after you decorate the placemat. What is the width of the placemat? *Explain* your method.

x in.
16 in.

8. Two buses leave the same stop at the same time and travel the same route. One is an express bus and doesn't make any stops along the way. The other is a local bus and makes stops along the way.

The express bus travels at an average speed of 40 miles per hour, and the local bus travels at an average speed of 30 miles per hour. The route is 10 miles long and the local bus makes 5 two-minute stops. How many minutes do you save by taking the express bus instead of the local bus? *Explain.*

60 Chapter 1 Expressions, Equations, and Functions

6a.

Number of pizzas	1	2	3	4
Cost (dollars)	11	22	33	33

6b. Yes. *Sample answer:* **When "number of pizzas" is the input, each input is paired with exactly one output.**

6c. No; when "cost" is the input, there is an input, $33, that is paired with two different outputs, 3 and 4.

MULTIPLE CHOICE

9. Which is a rule for the function given by the input-output table? **A**

Input, x	8	10	12	14
Output, y	5	7	9	11

ⓐ $y = x - 3$ ⓑ $y = x - 2$

ⓒ $y = x + 3$ ⓓ $y = x - 2$

10. The number of adult tickets sold at a school talent show is 5 less than 3 times the number c of children's tickets sold. Which expression represents the number of adult tickets sold? **D**

ⓐ $3c + 5$ ⓑ $5 - 3c$

ⓒ $5c + 3$ ⓓ $3c - 5$

11. The function $y = 2x + 4$ has a domain of 2, 3, 5, 7, and 8. Which number is *not* in the range of the function? **B**

ⓐ 8   ⓑ 12

ⓒ 18   ⓓ 20

GRIDDED ANSWER

12. What is the value of the expression $202 - 2(2 + 3)^2$? **152**

13. What is the value of $x^2 - 2x + 7$ when $x = 3$? **10**

14. What is the solution of the equation $54 = 9x$? **6**

15. What is the volume (in cubic inches) of the cube? **729 in.³**

9 in.
9 in.
9 in.

16. A rectangular field is twice as long as it is wide. A golf cart traveling at 12 miles per hour takes 7.5 minutes to travel the perimeter of the field. What is the length (in miles) of the field? **0.5 mi**

17. The table represents a function that can also be represented by a rule. What is the missing value in the table? **1**

Input, x	7	8	11	12
Output, y	0	?	4	5

EXTENDED RESPONSE

18. Mario deposits $140 in an account that earns simple interest at a rate of 5% per year. On the same day, Andy deposits $150 in an account that earns simple interest at a rate of 3% per year. Mario and Andy plan to keep the accounts for at least 5 years, but make no additional deposits. **18a–c. See margin.**

  a. For each account, write a rule for the the amount I (in dollars) of interest as a function of the time t (in years) that the account has been open.

  b. Let the domain of each function in part (a) be 1, 2, 3, 4, and 5. Make a table for each function.

  c. After how many years will the total amount in each account be the same? How much will be in each account? *Justify* your answer.

19. A dance floor is made from square wooden tiles with a side length of 1 foot. The floor can be laid out as a square or as a rectangle. The width of the rectangular floor is 10 feet less than the width of the square floor, and its length is 15 feet greater than the length of the square floor. **19a, b. See margin.**

  a. How much greater is the length of the rectangular dance floor than the width? *Justify* your answer.

  b. The perimeter of the rectangular dance floor is 130 feet. What are the length and width of the dance floor? *Explain* your reasoning.

  c. How many square tiles make up the dance floor? **900 tiles**

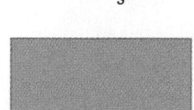

s

s

Standardized Test Practice   **61**

7. 11 in. *Sample answer:* The perimeter is 6 inches less than 5 feet, or $5(12) - 6 = 54$ inches. Length plus width equals one-half the perimeter, so $16 + x = 27$ inches. Using mental math to solve the equation, the value of x is $27 - 16 = 11$ inches.

8. 15 min. *Sample answer:* Since 10 miles $= \frac{1}{4}(40$ miles$)$, the express bus takes $\frac{1}{4}(60$ minutes$) = 15$ minutes to travel the route. Because 10 miles $= \frac{1}{3}(30$ miles$)$, the local bus takes $\frac{1}{3}(60$ minutes$) = 20$ minutes to travel the route. The local bus is stopped for $5(2) = 10$ minutes, so its total trip time is $20 + 10 = 30$ minutes; thus, taking the express bus saves $30 - 15 = 15$ minutes.

18a. Mario's account: $I = 7t$, Andy's account: $I = 4.5t$

18b–c. See below.

19a. 25 ft. *Sample answer:* If s feet is the length of the side of the square dance floor, then the length and the width of the rectangular dance floor are $(s + 15)$ feet and $(s - 10)$ feet. The difference is $(s + 15) - (s - 10) = s + 15 - s + 10 = 25$ feet.

19b. 45 ft, 20 ft. *Sample answer:* Length plus width equals one-half the perimeter, so $(s - 10) + (s + 15) = \frac{1}{2}(130)$, or $2s + 5 = 65$.

Using the guess, check, and revise strategy to solve the equation, the value of s is 30 feet, so the length is $30 + 15 = 45$ feet and the width is $30 - 10 = 20$ feet.

18b. Mario's account:

t (years)	1	2	3	4	5
I (dollars)	7	14	21	28	35

Andy's account:

t (years)	1	2	3	4	5
I (dollars)	4.5	9	13.5	18	22.5

18c. 4 yr. *Sample answer:* Mario's account begins with $10 less than Andy's account. The tables show that after the fourth year Mario's account has earned $10 more in interest than Andy's account has. After four years, Mario's account has $140 + $28 = $168, and Andy's account has $150 + $18 = $168.

2 Pacing and Assignment Guide

REGULAR SCHEDULE

Pre-AP For pacing and assignments for a Pre-AP course, see the *Algebra 1 Toolkit*.

Lesson	Les. Day	BASIC	AVERAGE	ADVANCED
2.1	Day 1	SRH p. 930 Exs. 1–4; pp. 67–70 Exs. 1, 3, 5–10, 14–19, 53, 54, 57, 67–75	pp. 67–70 Exs. 1, 3, 8–13, 17–22, 53, 54, 57–59, 67–75 odd	pp. 67–70 Exs. 1, 3, 10–13, 19–22, 53, 54, 57–60*, 68–74 even
	Day 2	pp. 67–70 Exs. 2, 4, 23–30, 35–44, 55, 56, 58, 61–66	pp. 67–70 Exs. 2, 4, 27–39 odd, 40–51, 55, 56, 61–66	pp. 67–70 Exs. 2, 4, 28–38 even, 39, 41–52*, 55, 56, 63, 65, 66
2.2	Day 1	SRH p. 914 Exs. 21–25; pp. 77–79 Exs. 1, 2, 3–23 odd, 24–31, 33–43 odd, 53–57, 60–66	pp. 77–79 Exs. 1, 2, 6–22 even, 24–31, 34–50 even, 53–59, 60–66 even	pp. 77–79 Exs. 1, 2, 8–22 even, 27–49 odd, 51–53*, 55–59*, 61–65 odd
2.3	Day 1	pp. 82–84 Exs. 1–16, 17–35 odd, 42–46, 49–55 odd	pp. 82–84 Exs. 1, 2, 6–14 even, 15, 16, 20–30 even, 32–46, 50–56 even	pp. 82–84 Exs. 1, 2, 10–14, 20–30 even, 32–41*, 43–48*, 52, 56
2.4	Day 1	pp. 91–93 Exs. 1–11, 19–41 odd, 43, 44, 50–54, 58–64 even	pp. 91–93 Exs. 1, 2, 10–42 even, 43–48, 50–55, 58–64 even	pp. 91–93 Exs. 1, 2, 12–42 even, 43–49*, 51–56*, 57–63 odd
2.5	Day 1	SRH p. 925 Exs. 1, 2, 4, 5, 12; pp. 99–101 Exs. 1–15, 21–24, 62–67	pp. 99–101 Exs. 1–4, 9–20, 23–27, 62–67	pp. 99–101 Exs. 1, 2, 11–20, 23–27, 65–67
	Day 2	pp. 99–101 Exs. 27–42, 50–53, 56–61	pp. 99–101 Exs. 32–48, 50–54, 56–61	pp. 99–101 Exs. 34–49*, 51–61*
2.6	Day 1	pp. 106–108 Exs. 1, 2, 3–23 odd, 24–28, 33–37, 42–45, 52–55, 59–63 odd	pp. 106–108 Exs. 1, 2, 7–10, 15–23 odd, 28–32, 37–49, 53, 60–64 even	pp. 106–108 Exs. 1, 2, 8–10, 19–23, 29–32, 38–41, 44–52*, 54–58*
2.7	Day 1	SRH p. 909 Exs. 11–17 odd; pp. 113–116 Exs. 1–10, 15–20, 23, 47–50, 56–63	pp. 113–116 Exs. 1, 2, 7–14, 17–23, 47–50, 56–63	pp. 113–116 Exs. 1, 2, 9–14, 19–23, 47–52, 56–62 even
	Day 2	pp. 113–116 Exs. 24–37, 51–53, 64–71	pp. 113–116 Exs. 24–32 even, 34–45, 51–54, 65–71 odd	pp. 113–116 Exs. 26–32 even, 36–46*, 53–55*, 64–70 even
Review	Day 1	pp. 121–124 Exs. 1–60	pp. 121–124 Exs. 1–60	pp. 121–124 Exs. 1–60
Assess	Day 1	Chapter 2 Test	Chapter 2 Test	Chapter 2 Test
Yearly Pacing		Chapter 2 Total – 12 days	Chapters 1–2 Total – 22 days	Remaining – 138 days

*Challenge Exercises   EP = Extra Practice   SRH = Skills Review Handbook

BLOCK SCHEDULE

DAY 1	DAY 2	DAY 3	DAY 4	DAY 5	DAY 6
2.1	2.2	2.4	2.5 (CONT.)	2.7	REVIEW
pp. 67–70 Exs. 1–4, 8–13, 17–22, 27–39 odd, 40–51, 53–59, 61–66, 67–75 odd	pp. 77–79 Exs. 2, 6–22 even, 24–31, 34–50 even, 53–59, 60–66 even	pp. 91–93 Exs. 1, 2, 10–42 even, 43–48, 50–55, 58–64 even	pp. 99–101 Exs. 32–48, 50–54, 56–61	pp. 113–116 Exs. 1, 2, 7–14, 17–23, 24–32 even, 34–45, 47–54, 56–63, 65–71 odd	pp. 121–124 Exs. 1–60
	2.3	2.5	2.6		ASSESS
	pp. 82–84 Exs. 1, 2, 6–14 even, 15, 16, 20–30 even, 32–46, 50–56 even	pp. 99–101 Exs. 1–4, 9–20, 23–27, 62–67	pp. 106–108 Exs. 1, 2, 7–10, 15–23 odd, 28–32, 37–49, 60–64 even		Chapter 2 Test
Yearly Pacing	Chapter 2 Total – 6 days	Chapters 1–2 Total – 11 days	Remaining – 69 days		

RESOURCE MANAGER

Chapter Resource Book

CHAPTER SUPPORT

Parents as Partners (Chapter Overview with home involvement exercises and activity)						p. 1	

LESSON SUPPORT

	2.1	2.2	2.3	2.4	2.5	2.6	2.7
Teaching Guide/Lesson Plan	p. 3	p. 13	p. 24	p. 37	p. 47	p. 58	p. 70
Activity Masters			p. 26				
Technology Activities & Keystrokes			p. 27			p. 60	
Activity Support Masters		p. 15			p. 49		
Practice (3 levels)	p. 5	p. 16	p. 28	p. 39	p. 50	p. 62	p. 72
Study Guide	p. 8	p. 19	p. 31	p. 42	p. 53	p. 65	p. 75
Catch-Up for Absent Students	p. 10	p. 21	p. 33	p. 44	p. 55	p. 67	p. 77
Problem Solving/Application	p. 11	p. 22	p. 34	p. 45	p. 56	p. 68	p. 78
Challenge Practice	p. 12	p. 23	p. 36	p. 46	p. 57	p. 69	p. 79

REVIEW

Chapter Review Games and Activities	p. 80	Cumulative Practice	p. 82
Project with Rubric	p. 81	Resource Book Answers	A1

Transparencies

	2.1	2.2	2.3	2.4	2.5	2.6	2.7
Warm-Up/Daily Homework Quiz	✔	✔	✔	✔	✔	✔	✔
Notetaking Guide	✔	✔	✔	✔	✔	✔	✔
Teacher Support	✔	✔					✔
Answer Transparencies	✔	✔	✔	✔	✔	✔	✔

ASSESSMENT BOOK

Quizzes	p. 16	SAT/ACT Chapter Test	p. 27
Chapter Tests (3 levels)	p. 19	Alternative Assessment with Rubric	p. 29
Standardized Chapter Test	p. 25		

TECHNOLOGY

- Easy Planner
- Test and Practice Generator
- Power Presentations
- @HomeTutor
- Activity Generator
- Animated Algebra
- Classzone.com
- eEdition Plus Online
- eWorkbook Plus Online
- Easy Grader Online

ADDITIONAL RESOURCES

- Worked-Out Solution Key
- Notetaking Guide
- Practice Wookbook
- Algebra 1 Toolkit
- Benchmark Tests
- Reteaching and Remediation
- Spanish Study Guide
- Spanish Assessment Book
- Student Resources in Spanish
- Multi-Language Visual Glossary

LESSON 2.1 Practice B
For use with pages 64–70

4. whole number: none; integer: -3; **5.** whole number: 0; integer: 0, -2;
rational number: $-1.9, \frac{3}{4}, 0.8, -3$; rational number: $1.3, -2, \frac{1}{2}, 0; -2,$
$-3, -1.9, \frac{3}{4}, 0.8$ $0, \frac{1}{2}, 1.3$

Graph the numbers on a number line. Then order the numbers from least to greatest.

1. 2, -3, and 0 $-3, 0, 2$ **2.** -5, 7, and -8 $-8, -5, 7$ **3.** -9, -12, and 6 $-12, -9, 6$

Tell whether each number in the list is a whole number, an integer, or a rational number. Then order the numbers from least to greatest.

4. $-1.9, \frac{3}{4}, 0.8, -3$ **5.** $1.3, -2, \frac{1}{2}, 0$ **6.** $2.5, -\frac{7}{8}, -0.5, \frac{1}{3}$

6. whole number: none; integer: none; rational number: $2.5, -\frac{7}{8}, -0.5, \frac{1}{3}; -\frac{7}{8}, -0.5, \frac{1}{3}, 2.5$

For the given value of a, find $-a$ and $|a|$.

7. $a = 10.2$ $-10.2; 10.2$ **8.** $a = -14$ $14; 14$ **9.** $a = \frac{1}{2}$ $-\frac{1}{2}; \frac{1}{2}$

Identify the hypothesis and conclusion of the conditional statement. Tell whether the statement is *true* or *false*. If it is false, give a counterexample.

10. If a number is negative, then its opposite is positive.   **10.** hypothesis: a number is negative; conclusion: its opposite is positive; true

11. If a number is even, then its opposite is a whole number.   **11.** hypothesis: a number is even; conclusion: its opposite is a whole number; false; 2

Evaluate the expression when $x = -2.5$.

12. $-x$ 2.5 **13.** $|x| + 3$ 5.5 **14.** $|x| - 4$ -1.5

15. Fairbanks, Alaska The table shows the monthly normal temperatures in Fairbanks, Alaska, during the winter months. Which monthly temperature is the lowest? Which months had temperatures below $-5°F$?   January; December and January

Month	December	January	February	March
Temperature (°F)	$-7°$	$-10°$	$-4°$	$11°$

16. Stock Market The gains and losses of a stock for a week are shown in the table. Which day showed the greatest gain? Which day showed the greatest loss?   Monday; Wednesday

Day	Monday	Tuesday	Wednesday	Thursday	Friday
Gain or loss	$+0.02$	-0.05	-0.12	-0.08	-0.01

17. Class Enrollment The table shows the growth in enrollment of the senior class at a high school between 1999 and 2004. Which year showed the greatest increase in class size? Which year showed the greatest decrease in class size?   2000; 2002

Year	1999	2000	2001	2002	2003	2004
Increase	15	22	-7	-12	10	18

Algebra 1
Chapter 2 Resource Book   **6**

LESSON 2.2 Practice B
For use with pages 71–77

Use a number line to find the sum.

1. $-8 + 9$ 1   **2.** $13 + (-4)$ 9   **3.** $-5 + (-11)$ -16

4. $-6 + (-7)$ -13 **5.** $-15 + 6$ -9 **6.** $-21 + 10$ -11

Find the sum.

7. $-4.2 + 6.5$ 2.3   **8.** $14.2 + (-9.1)$ 5.1   **9.** $7.8 + (-3.9)$ 3.9

10. $2\frac{2}{3} + \left(-1\frac{1}{3}\right)$ $1\frac{1}{3}$ **11.** $-7\frac{1}{2} + 10\frac{3}{4}$ $3\frac{1}{4}$ **12.** $8\frac{2}{3} + \left(-9\frac{1}{6}\right)$ $-\frac{1}{2}$

13. $-10 + (-23) + 18$ -15 **14.** $-1.25 + 2.5 + 3.5$ 4.75   **15.** $-2.6 + 7.5 + 5.6$ 10.5

Evaluate the expression for the given value of x.

16. $6 + x + (-11); x = 8$ 3   **17.** $-14 + x + 14; x = 9$ 9

18. $2.2 + x + (-3.4); x = -2.5$ -3.7 **19.** $-4.3 + (-x) + 1.5; x = 3.1$ -5.9

20. $-2.8 + (-x) + 8.1; x = -3.6$ 8.9   **21.** $-6.8 + |x| + 2.6; x = -3.2$ -1

Solve the equation.

22. $x + 15 + (-15) = 6$ $x = 6$ **23.** $6 + x + (-3) = 0$ $x = -3$ **24.** $x + (-2.5) + 6.8 = 0$ $x = -4.3$

25. Delivery Driver A furniture delivery driver is given three deliveries for the morning. The first delivery is 7 miles west of the furniture store. The second delivery is 14 miles east of the first house, and the last delivery before lunch is 3 miles west of the second house. How far is the delivery driver from the store after the last delivery?   4 miles

1st   Furniture   3rd   2nd
House   store   House   House

7 miles west
14 miles east
3 miles west
Not drawn to scale

26. Homework Your history teacher gives you an extra credit question on each homework assignment. You've been keeping track of how many points you are above or below the number of regular points you can earn on each assignment. How many total points do you have if there are 125 regular homework points for the five assignments?   128 points

Assignment	1	2	3	4	5
Number of points above and below	-2	4	-1	5	-3

27. Company Profits The table shows the profits earned by a small company during the first six months of the year. Did the company make a positive profit for the first six months? If so, how much?   yes; $500

Month	January	February	March	April	May	June
Profit	$1500	$-2000	$1000	$3000	$-2000	$-1000

Algebra 1
Chapter 2 Resource Book   **17**

LESSON 2.3 Practice B
For use with pages 78–83

Find the difference.

1. $12 - (-7)$ 19   **2.** $22 - (-28)$ 50   **3.** $-6 - (-13)$ 7

4. $-15 - (-9)$ -6 **5.** $5.8 - (-7.9)$ 13.7   **6.** $-4.1 - (-3.6)$ -0.5

7. $-6.2 - (-3.6)$ -2.6 **8.** $3.8 - (-5.9)$ 9.7   **9.** $-2.6 - (-10.2)$ 7.6

10. $\frac{1}{3} - \frac{4}{9}$ $-\frac{1}{9}$ **11.** $\frac{1}{2} - \left(-\frac{7}{8}\right)$ $1\frac{3}{8}$ **12.** $-\frac{2}{3} - \left(-\frac{3}{8}\right)$ $-\frac{7}{24}$

Evaluate the expression when $x = -6.4$ and $y = 10.8$.

13. $y - x$ 17.2   **14.** $x - (-y)$ 4.4   **15.** $x - y$ -17.2

16. $-y - x$ -4.4 **17.** $x - y - 2.6$ -19.8 **18.** $y - 5.4 - x$ 11.8

19. $-7.3 - x + y$ 9.9   **20.** $6.4 + y - x$ 23.6   **21.** $10.8 - x - y$ 6.4

22. $y - (-x) + 6.4$ 10.8   **23.** $7.2 + y - x$ 24.4   **24.** $4.25 - x - y$ -0.15

Find the change in temperature or elevation.

25. From $15°C$ to $-5°C$ $-20°C$ **26.** From -250 meters to 175 meters   425 m

27. Planet Temperatures The average temperature on the surface of Venus is $480°C$ and the average temperature on the surface of Mars is $-65°C$. How many degrees hotter is the temperature on Venus' surface than on Mars' surface? $545°C$

28. Manned Submersibles Alvin, a manned submersible used in deep-sea exploration, has a maximum depth of $-14,764$ feet. Its first untethered dive was -35 feet. How many feet deeper is Alvin's maximum depth than the depth of its first dive?   14,729 ft

29. Banana Prices The table shows the weekly prices (in dollars) of a pound of bananas during a month at a local supermarket. Determine the change in the price per pound each week. Find the total of these changes to determine the total change in the price per pound over the 4 weeks.

Week	1	2	3	4
Price per pound (dollars)	0.49	0.49	0.39	0.49

Week 1 to Week 2: $0;
Week 2 to Week 3: $-.10;
Week 3 to Week 4: $.10; $0

30. State Temperatures The table shows the record high and low temperatures for several states. Find the difference between the record high and low temperatures for each state. Which state has the greatest temperature difference?

State	Alaska	North Dakota	Wyoming	Virginia	Nevada
High temperature (°F)	$100°$	$121°$	$115°$	$110°$	$125°$
Low temperature (°F)	$-80°$	$-60°$	$-66°$	$-30°$	$-50°$

Alaska: 180°; North Dakota: 181°; Wyoming: 181°; Virginia: 140°;
Nevada: 175°; North Dakota and Wyoming

Algebra 1
Chapter 2 Resource Book   **29**

LESSON 2.4 Practice B
For use with pages 86–91

Find the product.

1. $10(-9)$ -90 **2.** $-12(-3)$ 36   **3.** $-11(7)$ -77

4. $2.6(-8)$ -20.8 **5.** $-3.2(15)$ -48 **6.** $-9.5(5)$ -47.5

7. $-\frac{1}{2}(28)$ -14 **8.** $-\frac{2}{3}(-21)$ 14   **9.** $\frac{4}{5}(-20)$ -16

10. $-6(4)(-3.5)$ 84   **11.** $-2.1(-10)(-5)$ -105 **12.** $-6.5(21)(-6)$ 819

Identify the property illustrated.

13. $5.6 \cdot (-3.2) = -3.2 \cdot 5.6$ **14.** $0 \cdot 2.1 = 0$ **15.** $-1 \cdot (-1.5) = 1.5$
Commutative prop. of mult.   Multiplicative property of 0   Multiplicative property of -1

Find the product. Justify your steps.   See below.

16. $-3(-5)(-4x)$ **17.** $-\frac{3}{4}(-20)(7y)$ **18.** $8x(4.2)(-5)$

Evaluate the expression when $x = -3$ and $y = 4.1$.

19. $x + 2y$ 5.2   **20.** $y - 4x$ 16.1   **21.** $5.2x - y$ -19.7

22. $xy - 10.1$ -22.4 **23.** $14.3 - xy$ 26.6   **24.** $3x - |y|$ -13.1

25. Death Valley The lowest point in North America is Death Valley, California. Its elevation is at -86 meters. What is this elevation in feet? *Hint:* Use the fact that 1 meter ≈ 3.281 feet. -282.166 m

26. Lava Flow A kind of lava, block lava, is moving away from the base of a volcano at a rate of 1.5 meters per day. If the lava continues to flow at this rate, how far away has the lava flowed from the base of the volcano in 30 days?   45 m

27. Snow Melt After a recent snowfall, the snow on the ground in a shaded area is melting at a rate of 0.01 inch per minute. Currently, there are 4 inches of snow on the ground. If the snow continues melting at this rate, how much snow will be on the ground in 6 hours? How much snow has melted?   0.4 in.; 3.6 in.

28. City Population In 1990, the population of Pittsburgh, Pennsylvania was 2468 thousand people. The table shows the average rate of change in the population for two periods of time. Find the total population in 2000 and 2002.

Time period	Rate of change (thousand people/yr)
1990–2000	-3.7
2000–2002	-6.5

1990 to 2000: 2431
2000: 2431 thousand people
2002: 2418 thousand people

16. $-3(-5)(-4x)$
$= 15(-4x)$ Product of -3 and -5 is 15.
$= [15(-4)]x$ Assoc. prop. of mult.
$= -60x$ Product of 15 and -4 is -60.

17. $-\frac{3}{4}(-20)(7y)$
$= 15(7y)$ Product of $-\frac{3}{4}$ and -20 is 15.
$= (15 \cdot 7)y$ Assoc. prop. of mult.
$= 105y$ Product of 15 and 7 is 105.

18. $8x(4.2)(-5)$
$= 8x(-21)$ Product of 4.2 and -5 is -21.
$= 8(-21)x$ Comm. prop. of mult.
$= -168x$ Product of 8 and -21 is -168.

Algebra 1
Chapter 2 Resource Book   **40**

Practice B

For use with pages 94–100

Use the distributive property to write an equivalent expression.

1. $5(x + 11)$ $5x + 55$ **2.** $3(x - 12)$ $3x - 36$ **3.** $-4(x + 8)$ $-4x - 32$

4. $9(2x + 1)$ $18x + 9$ **5.** $(x - 7)(-10)$ $-10x + 70$ **6.** $(4x + 3)5$ $20x + 15$

7. $x(4x - 1)$ $4x^2 - x$ **8.** $2x(x - 1)$ $2x^2 - 2x$ **9.** $-x(5x + 2)$ $-5x^2 - 2x$

Identify the terms, like terms, coefficients, and constant terms of the expression. **10.** Terms: $-8, 2x, 5, 11x$; Like terms: $2x$ and $11x$, -8 and 5; Coefficients: 2, 11; Constant terms: -8, 5

10. $-8 + 2x + 5 + 11x$ **11.** $4x^2 + 1 - 3x^2 + 5$

12. $7y^2 - 6 + 3y^2 - 15$ See below. **13.** $3xy + 5 - 2xy + 10$ See below.

11. Terms: $4x^2, 1, -3x^2, 5$; Like terms: $4x^2$ and $-3x^2$, 1 and 5; Coefficients: 4, -3; Constant terms: 1, 5

Simplify the expression.

14. $6 + 10x + 3$ $10x + 9$ **15.** $2(3x + 1) + 4x$ $10x + 2$ **16.** $6(5 - x) + 12x$ $6x + 30$

17. $7(x - 1) - 5$ $7x - 12$ **18.** $8x + 3(2x - 1)$ $14x - 3$ **19.** $-2(x + 4) - 3$ $-2x - 11$

20. $11x - (x + 7)$ $10x - 7$ **21.** $9 - 2(x - 4)$ $-2x + 17$ **22.** $7x - 3(4 - 2x)$ $13x - 12$

23. **Curtains** You are making curtains by alternating strips of solid colored fabric and patterned fabric. The solid colored fabric costs $.99 per strip and the patterned fabric costs $1.25 per strip. You need 7 strips for one curtain. Write an equation that gives the total cost c as a function of the number n of solid colored strips used. Then find the total cost if you use 3 solid colored strips. $c = 0.99n + 1.25(7 - n)$; $7.97

24. **Shoe Boxes** A department store is selling its plastic shoe boxes for $1.50 off the regular price of a shoe box. You buy 4 shoe boxes. Write an equation that gives the total cost t as a function of the regular cost r of a shoe box. Then find the total cost if the boxes regularly cost $3.59 each. $t = 4(r - 1.5)$; $8.36

25. **Delivering Papers** You and your friend share a paper route. You can deliver 4 papers in one minute and your friend can deliver 3 papers in one minute. Seventy-five papers have to be delivered each day on the route. Let n be the number of papers you deliver.

    a. Use the verbal model to write an equation that you can use to find out how long it will take the both of you together to deliver the papers. $t = \frac{1}{4}n + \frac{1}{3}(75 - n)$

Total amount of time (min)	=	Your rate (min/paper)	·	Number of papers you deliver (papers)	+	Friend's rate (min/papers)	·	Number of papers friend delivers (papers)

    b. How long will it take the both of you to deliver the papers if you deliver 38 papers? 50 papers? about 21.8 min; about 20.8 min

12. Terms: $7y^2, -6, 3y^2, -15$; Like terms: $7y^2$ and $3y^2$, -6 and -15; Coefficients: 7, 3; Constant terms: $-6, -15$

13. Terms: $3xy, 5, -2xy, 10$; Like terms: $3xy$ and $-2xy$, 5 and 10; Coefficients: 3, -2; Constant terms: 5, 10

Practice B

For use with pages 101–106

Find the multiplicative inverse of the number.

1. -7 $-\frac{1}{7}$ **2.** $-\frac{1}{5}$ -5 **3.** $-\frac{7}{8}$ $-\frac{8}{7}$

Find the quotient.

4. $-32 \div (-2)$ 16 **5.** $-1 \div \left(-\frac{6}{5}\right)$ $\frac{5}{6}$ **6.** $14 \div \left(-\frac{2}{7}\right)$ -49

7. $17 \div \left(-2\frac{1}{8}\right)$ -8 **8.** $-\frac{3}{4} \div 4$ $-\frac{3}{16}$ **9.** $-\frac{1}{3} \div \frac{1}{5}$ $-1\frac{2}{3}$

10. $-\frac{1}{9} \div (-8)$ $\frac{1}{72}$ **11.** $-\frac{6}{11} \div (-3)$ $\frac{2}{11}$ **12.** $\frac{5}{8} \div \left(-2\frac{1}{2}\right)$ $-\frac{1}{4}$

Find the mean of the numbers.

13. $1, -3, -10$ -4 **14.** $-15, 4, -22$ -11 **15.** $-7.5, 3, -6.5$ $-3\frac{2}{3}$

Simplify the expression.

16. $\frac{-8x + 27}{9}$ $-\frac{8}{9}x + 3$ **17.** $\frac{15x - 5}{-5}$ $1 - 3x$ **18.** $\frac{12x - 20}{-4}$ $5 - 3x$

19. **Melting Point** The melting point of the element fluorine is $-219.62°C$. The melting point of the element bromine is $-7.2°C$. How many times lower is the melting point of fluorine than the melting point of bromine? Round your answer to the nearest tenth. about 30.5

20. **Website Traffic** During a 3-month period, the traffic to a website dropped by 126,000 visitors. Find the average rate of change in the traffic to the website (in visitors per month) over the 3-month period. $-42,000$ visitors/month

21. **Average Velocity** The velocity of an object indicates the object's speed and the direction in which the object is traveling. A negative velocity indicates that the object is moving downward or backward. A hawk is diving downward at a rate of 50 feet in 28 seconds. Find the hawk's average velocity (in feet per second). Round your answer to the nearest tenth. -1.8 ft/sec

22. **Health Club** The table below shows change in the number of memberships at a health club. What is the average change in the number of memberships (in members per month)? 5.6 memberships/month

Month	Nov.	Dec.	Jan.	Feb.	Mar.
Change in number of memberships	18	10	40	-25	-15

23. **Bank Account Activity** During a 14-day period, there is the following activity on your bank account. You deposit $100, withdraw $75, deposit $85, and withdraw $150. What is the rate of change (in dollars per day) in your bank account? Round your answer to the nearest cent. about $-$2.86/day

---

Practice B

For use with pages 107–114

Evaluate the expression.

1. $\pm\sqrt{81}$ ± 9 **2.** $\pm\sqrt{25}$ ± 5 **3.** $-\sqrt{400}$ -20

4. $\sqrt{625}$ 25 **5.** $\sqrt{4900}$ 70 **6.** $\pm\sqrt{169}$ ± 13

Approximate the square root to the nearest integer.

7. $-\sqrt{29}$ -5 **8.** $\sqrt{108}$ 10 **9.** $-\sqrt{53}$ -7

10. $\sqrt{138}$ 12 **11.** $-\sqrt{55}$ -7 **12.** $\sqrt{640}$ 25

Tell whether each number in the list is a real number, a rational number, an irrational number, an integer, or a whole number. Then order the numbers from least to greatest. See below.

13. $-\sqrt{16}, 3.2, -\frac{3}{2}, \sqrt{9}$ **14.** $\sqrt{5}, -6, 2.5, -\frac{24}{5}$

Evaluate the expression for the given value of x.

15. $14 + \sqrt{x}$ when $x = 16$ 18 **16.** $\sqrt{x} - 5.5$ when $x = 4$ -3.5

17. $-9 \cdot \sqrt{x}$ when $x = 25$ -45 **18.** $2\sqrt{x} - 1$ when $x = 100$ 19

19. **Park** A local park is in the shape of a square and covers an area of 3600 square feet. Find the side length of the park. 60 ft

20. **Wall Poster** You are considering buying a square wall poster that has an area of 6.25 square feet. Find the side length of the wall poster. 2.5 ft

21. **Road Sign** The U.S. Department of Transportation determines the sizes of the traffic control signs that you see along the roadways. The square Pennsylvania state route sign at the right has an area of 1296 square inches. Find the side length of the sign. 36 in.

22. **Flower Bed** You are building the square flower bed shown using railroad ties. You want to place another railroad tie on the diagonal to form two triangular beds. Find the length of the diagonal by using the expression $\sqrt{2s^2}$ where s is the side length of the flower bed. Round your answer to the nearest tenth. about 7.1 ft

$\vdash$ 5 ft $\dashv$

13. real number: $-\sqrt{16}, 3.2, -\frac{3}{2}, \sqrt{9}$; rational number: $-\sqrt{16}, 3.2, -\frac{3}{2}, \sqrt{9}$; irrational number: none; integer: $-\sqrt{16}, \sqrt{9}$; whole number: $\sqrt{9}$; $-\sqrt{16}, -\frac{3}{2}, \sqrt{9}, 3.2$

14. real number: $-6, -\frac{24}{5}, \sqrt{5}, 2.5$; rational number: $-6, -\frac{24}{5}, 2.5$; irrational number: $\sqrt{5}$; integer: -6; whole number: none; $-6, -\frac{24}{5}, \sqrt{5}, 2.5$

2 Assessment

Identify the property illustrated.

1. $x + (-7) = -7 + x$

2. $5 + (-5) = 0$

3. $(3 + 2) + 9 = 3 + (2 + 9)$

4. $0 + 12 = 12$

Find the sum or difference.

5. $2.7 + (-5.2)$

6. $18 - (-4)$

7. $-3 - (-5)$

Evaluate the expression when $x = 10$ and $y = -3$.

8. $-x + y + 4$

9. $y + |y| - 7$

10. $6 - x - y$

Answers

1. Commutative property of addition
2. Inverse property of addition
3. Associative property of addition
4. Identity property of addition
5. -2.5
6. 22
7. 2
8. -9
9. -7
10. -1

Identify the property illustrated.

1. $(-8 \cdot 2) \cdot 3 = -8 \cdot (2 \cdot 3)$

2. $5 \cdot (-1) = -5$

3. $3 \cdot (-6) = -6 \cdot 3$

4. $14 \cdot 0 = 0$

Find the product.

5. $3(-8)$

6. $-4(-5)$

7. $2(3)(-1)$

8. $(-6x) \cdot (-5)$

9. $-\frac{3}{4}x \cdot 28$

10. $1.8 \cdot x \cdot (-4.6)$

Use the distributive property to write an equivalent expression.

11. $-(3x + 1)$

12. $-9(y - 7)$

13. $(4x + 3)3$

Answers

1. Associative property of multiplication
2. Property of -1
3. Commutative property of multiplication
4. Property of zero
5. -24
6. 20
7. -6
8. $30x$
9. $-21x$
10. $-8.28x$
11. $-3x - 1$
12. $-9y + 63$
13. $12x + 9$

Find the multiplicative inverse of the number.

1. $-\frac{1}{3}$

2. 8

Find the quotient.

3. $-30 \div 3$

4. $-24 \div (-4)$

5. $-\frac{3}{4} \div 2$

Simplify the expression.

6. $\frac{35 - 14x}{7}$

7. $\frac{-16x + 8}{-4}$

Evaluate the expression.

8. $\sqrt{49}$

9. $\pm\sqrt{4}$

10. $-\sqrt{16}$

Answers

1. -3
2. $\frac{1}{8}$
3. -10
4. 6
5. $-\frac{3}{8}$
6. $5 - 2x$
7. $4x - 2$
8. 7
9. 2 and -2
10. -4

Tell whether each number is a real number, a rational number, an irrational number, an integer, or a whole number.

1. -0.75 2. $\sqrt{12}$ 3. 10

Tell whether the statement is *true* or *false*. If it is false, give a counterexample.

4. If a number is positive, then its opposite is negative.

5. If a number is an integer, then the number is an irrational number.

Order the numbers in the list from least to greatest.

6. $-\frac{1}{5}, -0.25, \frac{1}{3}, 1$ 7. $-\frac{14}{3}, -4.6, -4.07, -4\frac{1}{3}$

Identify the property being illustrated.

8. $(x \cdot 0.5) \cdot 8 = x \cdot (0.5 \cdot 8)$

9. $x + (-y) = -y + x$

10. $2(5z - 9) = 10z - 18$

11. $3a + (-3a) = 0$

Find the sum or the difference.

12. $3 - (-12)$ 13. $-22 + 16$

14. $-0.8 + (-8.9)$ 15. $-16 - (-25.2)$

16. $\frac{1}{2} - \frac{7}{10}$ 17. $7\frac{4}{5} + -2\frac{1}{4}$

In Exercises 18 and 19, use the table below.

Name	Double eagle	Eagle	Birdie	Par	Bogey	Double bogey
Score	-3	-2	-1	0	1	2

18. In golf, the best total score is the lowest score. In 4 holes, you score a birdie, a par, a double eagle, and a double bogey. Your friend scores an eagle, a double eagle, a bogey, and a par. Who has the better total score?

19. What is the difference between your friend's total score and your total score?

Answers

1. real number, rational number
2. real number, irrational number
3. real number, rational number, integer, whole number
4. true
5. false; 5
6. $-0.25, -\frac{1}{5}, \frac{1}{3}, 1$
7. $-\frac{14}{3}, -4.6, -4\frac{1}{3}, -4.07$
8. Assoc. prop. of mult.
9. Commutative property of addition
10. Distributive prop.
11. Inverse prop. of add.
12. 15
13. -6
14. -9.7
15. 9.2
16. $-\frac{1}{5}$
17. $5\frac{11}{20}$
18. your friend
19. -2

Evaluate the expression when $x = -5.4$ and $y = 2.8$.

20. $y - x - 1.4$

21. $x + |y - 10|$

Find the product or the quotient.

22. $-6(-12)$

23. $45 \div (-3)$

24. $\frac{5}{9}\left(-\frac{3}{4}\right)$

25. $-7.2 \div 8$

26. $-4 \div \left(-\frac{2}{9}\right)$

27. $-\frac{2}{3}(18)\left(-\frac{1}{4}\right)$

28. A person buys items and sells them on a website. The table shows the profit earned for each item. Suppose that in one week the person sells 8 mantel clocks, 5 framed mirrors, and 3 candles. Find the average daily profit.

Item	Mantel clock	Framed mirror	Candle
Profit	$4.13	-$1.65	$2.36

Simplify the expression.

29. $10x - (x + 3)$

30. $-2x(x - 6)$

31. $\frac{-6x + 15}{-10}$

32. Use the distributive property and mental math to find the total cost of 6 notebooks at $3.95 each.

33. Find the perimeter and area of the rectangle with the given dimensions.

$4 + 2w$

Approximate the square root to the nearest integer.

34. $\sqrt{35}$

35. $-\sqrt{150}$

36. $\sqrt{18}$

37. The area of a town's square is 14,400 square feet. Find the side length of the square.

Evaluate the expression for the given value of x.

38. $2 - \sqrt{x}$ when $x = 25$

39. $4\sqrt{x} + 9$ when $x = 1$

Answers

20. ___6.8___
21. ___1.8___
22. ___72___
23. ___-15___
24. ___$-\frac{5}{12}$___
25. ___-0.9___
26. ___18___
27. ___3___
28. ___$4.55___
29. ___$9x - 3$___
30. ___$-2x^2 + 12x$___
31. ___$\frac{3}{5}x - \frac{3}{2}$___
32. ___$6(4 - 0.05)$ = $23.70___
33. ___$P = 20 + 4w$; $A = 24 + 12w$___
34. ___6___
35. ___-12___
36. ___4___
37. ___120 ft___
38. ___-3___
39. ___13___

Multiple Choice

1. Which list of numbers is ordered from least to greatest? C

Ⓐ $-\frac{1}{2}, -1, \frac{3}{8}, 5$ Ⓑ $\frac{1}{2}, \frac{1}{3}, \frac{1}{4}, \frac{1}{5}$

Ⓒ $-\frac{1}{2}, 0.66, \frac{2}{3}, \frac{7}{8}$ Ⓓ $-0.16, -\frac{1}{6}, 0, 3$

2. Which number is an integer? A

Ⓐ $-\frac{32}{8}$ Ⓑ $\frac{1}{5}$

Ⓒ $|-3.8|$ Ⓓ $\left|\frac{24}{5}\right|$

3. What is the value of $5(-x)$ when $x = -\frac{1}{10}$? C

Ⓐ $-2\frac{1}{2}$ Ⓑ $\frac{4}{5}$

Ⓒ $\frac{1}{2}$ Ⓓ $4\frac{9}{10}$

4. Which number is a solution of $5 + |m| = 7.3$? B

Ⓐ -12.3 Ⓑ -2.3

Ⓒ 7.3 Ⓓ 12.3

5. What is the value of $-5.06 + -2.3$? B

Ⓐ -7.9 Ⓑ -7.36

Ⓒ 3.3 Ⓓ 3.76

6. What property is being illustrated in the equation $-12 + 12 = 0$? D

Ⓐ Associative Property

Ⓑ Commutative Property

Ⓒ Identity Property

Ⓓ Inverse Property

7. What is the solution of the equation $-9.7 + x - 5.4 = 12.1$? D

Ⓐ -3 Ⓑ 3 Ⓒ 16.5 Ⓓ 27.2

8. What is the value of $-\frac{5}{6} - \left(-\frac{2}{3}\right)$? C

Ⓐ $-1\frac{1}{2}$ Ⓑ $-\frac{7}{9}$

Ⓒ $-\frac{1}{6}$ Ⓓ $1\frac{1}{2}$

9. What is the change in temperature from $-26°F$ to $78°F$? D

Ⓐ $-104°F$ Ⓑ $-52°F$

Ⓒ $52°F$ Ⓓ $104°F$

10. What is the value of $|z - y| - x$ where $x = 25.3, y = -7.2, z = 15.8$? B

Ⓐ -16.7 Ⓑ -2.3

Ⓒ 2.3 Ⓓ 16.7

11. What property is being illustrated in the equation $-2 \cdot (5 \cdot 2) = (-2 \cdot 5) \cdot 2$? A

Ⓐ Associative Property

Ⓑ Commutative Property

Ⓒ Identity Property

Ⓓ Inverse Property

12. What is the product of $-\frac{1}{5}(-a)(-a)\left(\frac{5}{9}\right)$? A

Ⓐ $-\frac{1}{9} \cdot a^2$ Ⓑ $\frac{1}{9} \cdot a^2$

Ⓒ $-\frac{2}{9} \cdot a$ Ⓓ $\frac{2}{9} \cdot a$

13. What is the value of $|n| + m^2$ where $m = -2.4$ and $n = -3.8$? C

Ⓐ -1 Ⓑ 1.96

Ⓒ 9.56 Ⓓ 16.84

14. Which pair of terms are like terms? D

Ⓐ $2x, 2y$ Ⓑ $3x, 2x^2$

Ⓒ $-4, -4y$ Ⓓ $x^3, 5x^3$

15. Simplify the expression $4(n - 3) - 2(-3 + n)$. A

Ⓐ $2n - 6$ Ⓑ $2n + 6$

Ⓒ $4n - 18$ Ⓓ $6n - 2$

16. What is the perimeter of the rectangle? D

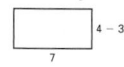

$4 - 3y$

7

Ⓐ $-3y + 11$ Ⓑ $-21y + 28$

Ⓒ $-3y + 28$ Ⓓ $-6y + 22$

17. If $-\frac{4}{5}x = 1$, what is the value of x? B

Ⓐ $-1\frac{2}{5}$ Ⓑ $-1\frac{1}{4}$

Ⓒ $\frac{4}{5}$ Ⓓ $-1\frac{1}{5}$

18. Simplify the expression $\frac{27 - 6y}{-3}$. C

Ⓐ $-6y - 9$ Ⓑ $2y + 27$

Ⓒ $2y - 9$ Ⓓ $-7y$

19. Which number is between -20 and -15? C

Ⓐ $-\sqrt{1089}$ Ⓑ $-\sqrt{441}$

Ⓒ $-\sqrt{289}$ Ⓓ $-\sqrt{196}$

20. Which expression is a perfect square if $x = 81$? A

Ⓐ $2 \cdot \sqrt{x} + 31$ Ⓑ $\sqrt{x} + 3 \cdot 3$

Ⓒ $9 - 5\sqrt{x}$ Ⓓ $2 + 6\sqrt{x}$

21. Which number is irrational? D

Ⓐ $-\frac{5}{3}$ Ⓑ -2.4

Ⓒ $\sqrt{16}$ Ⓓ $\sqrt{18}$

Gridded Answer

22. What is the value of $\frac{5(2x - 6)}{x}$ when $x = -2$?

```
          | 2 | 5
  Ⓞ Ⓞ Ⓞ Ⓞ
  ① ① ① ①
  ② ● ② ②
  ③ ③ ③ ③
  ④ ④ ④ ④
  ⑤ ⑤ ● ⑤
  ⑥ ⑥ ⑥ ⑥
  ⑦ ⑦ ⑦ ⑦
  ⑧ ⑧ ⑧ ⑧
  ⑨ ⑨ ⑨ ⑨
```

Short Response

23. a. $C = \$.15t + \$.10m$

23. Suppose you have a pre-paid cell phone where you pay a certain amount up front and the amount used is deducted. You pay $.15 per minute and $.10 per text message.

a. Write an equation for the total cost C where t represents each minute used and m represents each text message sent.

b. You have pre-paid $20 on your phone. If you have used 104 minutes and have sent 7 text messages, what is your remaining balance? *Explain.* $3.70

Extended Response

24. A gardener has a square garden with an area of 5476 square feet.

a. How many feet of fencing would the gardener need to fence around his garden?   296 ft

b. Fencing is sold in 50 feet rolls. Partial rolls cannot be purchased. How many rolls of fencing must the gardener purchase? *Explain.*   6 rolls

c. How many feet of fencing will the gardener have leftover? Explain.   4 ft

d. Each roll of fencing costs $45.65 plus 6% tax. How much will the gardener pay for the fencing? Round to the nearest cent. *Explain.* $290.33

Journal

1. Describe the relationship between integers and rational numbers. Explain the difference between rational numbers and irrational numbers, and provide an example of each type of number.

Multi-Step Problem

2. To discourage random guessing on a multiple-choice exam, a professor assigns 7 points for a correct answer, -3 points for an incorrect answer, and -1 point for leaving the question blank.

a. What is the score for a student who had 19 correct answers, 4 incorrect answers, and 2 questions left blank?

b. What is the maximum number of points available on the exam from part (a)?

c. The following calculation was used to compute Pete's score on the exam: $17(7) + 2(-1) + 6(-3)$. Determine the score for this student and describe Pete's performance on the exam.

d. Katie took the exam and had 19 correct answers, 3 incorrect answers, and left 3 questions blank. Katie calculated her score on the exam as shown.

$19(7) + 3(-3) + 3(-1) = 19(7) + 3(-3 - 1)$

Verify that both sides of this equation result in the same score and name the property that guarantees the equality.

e. Jason answered 20 questions correctly and 5 questions incorrectly. What fraction of the total points did Jason earn? Write your answer in simplest form.

f. Erin answered 18 questions correctly, 1 incorrectly, and left 6 blank. Stephen answered 19 questions correctly, 5 incorrectly, and left 1 blank. Who had the higher score on the exam?

g. If a student answers every question on the exam, the following expression can be used to calculate the number of points earned, where x represents the number of questions answered correctly.

$7x + (25 - x)(-3)$

Explain why this expression can be used to calculate the total number of points earned. Then simplify the expression.

h. Evaluate your expression from part (g) to determine the points earned by a student who answered all of the questions and had 16 correct answers.

1. Complete answers should include: an explanation that a rational number is a ratio of two integers; an explanation that irrational numbers cannot be expressed as a ratio of two integers, or a discussion of the differences between the decimal representations of rational numbers and irrational numbers; an example of a rational number and an example of an irrational number.

2. a. 199 points **b.** 175 points **c.** 99 points; 17 correct answers, 6 incorrect answers, 2 left blank **d.** 121 points; distributive property **e.** $\frac{5}{7}$ **f.** Neither; both scored 177 points. **g.** Explanations may vary; $10x - 75$ **h.** 85 points

Main Ideas

In Chapter 2, students will learn about the real number system. They will classify real numbers, compare and order integers and rational numbers, perform basic operations, find square roots, apply properties to evaluate and simplify expressions, and use the Distributive Property to write equivalent expressions. Students will use conditional statements and logical reasoning to reason with real numbers.

Prerequisite Skills

- Comparing and ordering numbers
- Evaluating expressions
- Applying order of operations

Additional resources for reviewing prerequisite skills are:

- Skills Review Handbook, pp. 909–937
- @HomeTutor

2 Properties of Real Numbers

2.1 Use Integers and Rational Numbers

2.2 Add Real Numbers

2.3 Subtract Real Numbers

2.4 Multiply Real Numbers

2.5 Apply the Distributive Property

2.6 Divide Real Numbers

2.7 Find Square Roots and Compare Real Numbers

Before

In previous courses and in Chapter 1, you learned the following skills, which you'll use in Chapter 2: comparing and ordering numbers, evaluating expressions, and applying the order of operations.

Prerequisite Skills

VOCABULARY CHECK

In Exercises 1 and 2, copy and complete the statement.

1. The **least common denominator** of the fractions $\frac{3}{8}$ and $\frac{5}{12}$ is _?_. **24**

2. The **variable** in the expression $5x - 3$ is _?_. **x**

3. According to the **order of operations**, what is the first step in simplifying the expression $(3 + 4)^2 - 8$? **Add 3 + 4.**

SKILLS CHECK

Copy and complete the statement using <, >, or =. *(Review p. 909 for 2.1, 2.7.)*

4. 26.70 _?_ 29.69   5. 15.09 _?_ 15.1   6. 0.333 _?_ 0.34   7. 2.5 _?_ 2.500
     <   **<**   **>**   **=**

Evaluate the expression when $x = 5$. *(Review p. 2 for 2.2–2.4, 2.6.)*

8. $52 - x$ **47**   9. $1.7x$ **8.5**   10. $x + 39$ **44**   11. $\frac{125}{x}$ **25**

Evaluate the expression. *(Review p. 8 for 2.5.)*

12. $5m - 9$ when $m = 6$ **21**   13. $16 - r - 3$ when $r = 10$ **3**

@HomeTutor Prerequisite skills practice at classzone.com

62

Chapter 2 Resource Book
- Teaching Guide/Lesson Plan (pp. 3, 13, 24, 37, 47, 58, 70)
- Project with Rubric (p. 81)

Assessment and Intervention
- Assessment Book (pp. 16–30)
- Benchmark Tests
- Reteaching and Remediation Book

Interactive Technology
- Easy Planner
- Power Presentations CD-ROM
- Activity Generator CD-ROM
- Animated Algebra
- Test Generator CD-ROM
- Online Quizzes
- eWorkbook
- eEdition
- @HomeTutor

Resources for English Learners
- Quick Reference for English Learners
- Spanish Study Guide
- Multi-Language Visual Glossary
- Student Resources in Spanish

In Chapter 2, you will apply the big ideas listed below and reviewed in the Chapter Summary on page 120. You will also use the key vocabulary listed below.

Big Ideas

1 Performing operations with real numbers
2 Applying properties of real numbers
3 Classifying and reasoning with real numbers

KEY VOCABULARY
- whole numbers, integers, *p. 64*
- rational number, *p. 64*
- opposites, absolute value, *p. 66*
- conditional statement, *p. 66*
- additive identity, *p. 76*
- additive inverse, *p. 76*

- multiplicative identity, *p. 89*
- equivalent expressions, *p. 96*
- distributive property, *p. 96*
- term, coefficient, constant term, like terms, *p. 97*
- multiplicative inverse, *p. 103*

- square root, radicand, *p. 110*
- perfect square, *p. 111*
- irrational number, *p. 111*
- real numbers, *p. 112*

Why?

You can use multiple representations to solve a problem about a real-world situation. For example, you can write an equation and make a table to find a skydiver's altitude over time.

Animated Algebra

The animation illustrated below for Exercise 54 on page 93 helps you answer this question: How does the time spent in free fall after a skydiver reaches terminal velocity affect the altitude of the skydiver?

A skydiver in freefall wants to open the parachute at an altitude of 2500 feet.

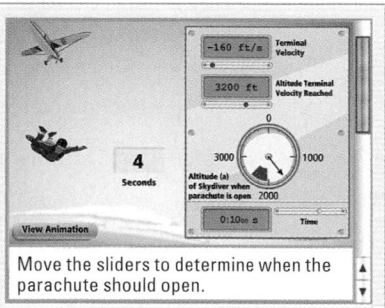

Move the sliders to determine when the parachute should open.

Animated Algebra at classzone.com

Other animations for Chapter 2: pages 73, 80, 90, and 98

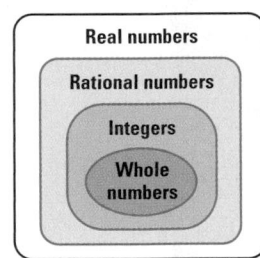

① PLAN AND PREPARE

Warm-Up Exercises

📄 **Transparency Available**

Complete the statement using <, >, or =.

1. 1.3 <u>?</u> 1.03 **>**   **2.** $\frac{5}{8}$ <u>?</u> $\frac{6}{9}$ **<**

3. Order from least to greatest:
$\frac{1}{2}$, 0.04, $\frac{3}{7}$, 0.45 **0.04, $\frac{3}{7}$, 0.45, $\frac{1}{2}$**

4. A hobby store has balsa wood strips in three thicknesses (in inches): $\frac{3}{16}$, $\frac{5}{32}$, and $\frac{1}{8}$. Which strip is the thickest? **$\frac{3}{16}$-inch strip**

Notetaking Guide

📄 **Transparency Available**

Promotes interactive learning and notetaking skills, pp. 23–26.

Pacing

Basic: 2 days
Average: 2 days
Advanced: 2 days
Block: 1 block
• See *Teaching Guide/Lesson Plan.*

② FOCUS AND MOTIVATE

Essential Question

Big Idea 3, p. 63

How do you compare positive and negative numbers? **Tell students they will learn how to answer this question by graphing integers.**

NCTM STANDARDS

Standard 1: Understand relationships among numbers; Understand number systems

Before You performed operations with whole numbers.

Now You will graph and compare positive and negative numbers.

Why? So you can compare temperatures, as in Ex. 58.

Key Vocabulary
• whole numbers
• integers
• rational number
• opposites
• absolute value
• conditional statement

Whole numbers are the numbers 0, 1, 2, 3, . . . and **integers** are the numbers . . . , −3, −2, −1, 0, 1, 2, 3, ... (The dots indicate that the numbers continue without end in both directions.) **Positive integers** are integers that are greater than 0. **Negative integers** are integers that are less than 0. The integer 0 is neither negative nor positive.

Zero is neither negative nor positive.

EXAMPLE 1   Graph and compare integers

Graph −3 and −4 on a number line. Then tell which number is greater.

▶ On the number line, −3 is to the right of −4. So, −3 > −4.

RATIONAL NUMBERS The integers belong to the set of *rational numbers*. A **rational number** is a number $\frac{a}{b}$ where a and b are integers and $b \neq 0$. For example, $-\frac{1}{2}$ is a rational number because it can be written as $\frac{-1}{2}$ or $\frac{1}{-2}$. The rational numbers belong to the set of numbers called the *real numbers*.

READING
Although you can write a negative fraction in different ways, you usually write it with the negative sign in front of the fraction.

Real numbers
Rational numbers
Integers
Whole numbers

✓ GUIDED PRACTICE   for Example 1

1–3. Check students' graphs.
Graph the numbers on a number line. Then tell which number is greater.

1. 4 and 0 **4**   **2.** 2 and −5 **2**   **3.** −1 and −6 **−1**

64   Chapter 2   Properties of Real Numbers

Resource Planning Guide

Chapter Resource Book
• Teaching Guide/Lesson Plan (pp. 3–4)
• Practice levels A, B, C (pp. 5–7)
• Study Guide (pp. 8–9)
• Catch-up for Absent Students (p. 10)
• Application (p. 11)
• Challenge (p. 12)

Workbooks
• Notetaking Guide (pp. 23–26)
• Practice Workbook (pp. 16–17)

Teaching Options
• **Power Presentations CD-ROM** provides dynamic electronic teaching resources for the classroom.
• **Activity Generator CD-ROM** provides editable activities for all ability levels.

Interactive Technology
• Easy Planner
• Power Presentations CD-ROM
• Activity Generator CD-ROM
• Animated Algebra
• Test Generator CD-ROM
• Online Quiz
• eWorkbook
• eEdition
• @HomeTutor

Resources for English Learners
• Quick Reference for English Learners
• Spanish Study Guide
• Multi-Language Visual Glossary
• Student Resources in Spanish

See also the *Algebra 1 Toolkit* for more strategies for meeting individual needs.

REVIEW FRACTIONS
For help with writing fractions as decimals, see p. 916.

DECIMALS In decimal form, a rational number either terminates or repeats. For example, $\frac{3}{4} = 0.75$ is a *terminating decimal*, and $\frac{1}{3} - 0.333\ldots$ is a *repeating decimal*.

EXAMPLE 2 Classify numbers

Tell whether each of the following numbers is a whole number, an integer, or a rational number: 5, 0.6, $-2\frac{2}{3}$, and -24.

Number	Whole number?	Integer?	Rational number?
5	Yes	Yes	Yes
0.6	No	No	Yes
$-2\frac{2}{3}$	No	No	Yes
-24	No	Yes	Yes

JUSTIFY AN ANSWER
The number 0.6 is a rational number because it can be written as a quotient of two integers: $\frac{3}{5}$.

EXAMPLE 3 Order rational numbers

ASTRONOMY A star's color index is a measure of the temperature of the star. The greater the color index, the cooler the star. Order the stars in the table from hottest to coolest.

Star	Rigel	Arneb	Denebola	Shaula
Color index	-0.03	0.21	0.09	-0.22

Solution

Begin by graphing the numbers on a number line.

Read the numbers from left to right: -0.22, -0.03, 0.09, 0.21.

▶ From hottest to coolest, the stars are Shaula, Rigel, Denebola, and Arneb.

---

4. 3: whole number, integer, rational number, -1.2: rational number, -2: integer, rational number, 0: whole number, integer, rational number; -2, -1.2, 0, 3

5. 4.5: rational number, $-\frac{3}{4}$: rational number, -2.1: rational number, 0.5: rational number; -2.1, $-\frac{3}{4}$, 0.5, 4.5

6. 3.6: rational number, -1.5: rational number, -0.31: rational number, -2.8: rational number; -2.8, -1.5, -0.31, 3.6

7. $\frac{1}{6}$: rational number, 1.75: rational number, $-\frac{2}{3}$: rational number, 0: whole number, integer, rational number; $-\frac{2}{3}$, 0, $\frac{1}{6}$, 1.75

✓ **GUIDED PRACTICE** for Examples 2 and 3

Tell whether each number in the list is a whole number, an integer, or a rational number. Then order the numbers from least to greatest.
4–7. See margin.

4. 3, -1.2, -2, 0
5. 4.5, $-\frac{3}{4}$, -2.1, 0.5
6. 3.6, -1.5, -0.31, -2.8
7. $\frac{1}{6}$, 1.75, $-\frac{2}{3}$, 0

Motivating the Lesson
Ask students to give examples of situations where they might use negative numbers. Tell them by learning to compare positive and negative numbers they can determine who has a lower golf score.

3 TEACH

Extra Example 1
Graph 0 and -2 on a number line. Then tell which number is greater. $0 > -2$

Extra Example 2
Tell whether each of the following numbers is a whole number, an integer, or a rational number: -19, 7, 0.3, and $-1\frac{1}{5}$. -19: integer, rational number; 7: whole number, integer, rational number; 0.3: rational number; $-1\frac{1}{5}$: rational number

Key Question to Ask for Example 2
• Why are all the numbers rational numbers? **They can all be written in the form** $\frac{a}{b}$. $5 = \frac{5}{1}$; $0.6 = \frac{3}{5}$; $-2\frac{2}{3} = \frac{-8}{3}$; $-24 = \frac{-24}{1}$

Extra Example 3
The apparent magnitude of a star is its brightness as observed from Earth. The greater the magnitude, the dimmer the star. Order the stars from brightest to dimmest.

Star	Magnitude
Arcturus	-0.06
Sirius	-1.47
Vega	0.03

Sirius, Arcturus, Vega

Differentiated Instruction

Below Level Students performing below level may not realize that all the numbers in **Guided Practice Exercises 4–7** are rational numbers. To help them see this fact, have these students write each of the numbers as a quotient of two integers. You may wish to do this as an activity in which below level students are paired with advanced students. If so, advanced students can give help where needed.

See also the *Algebra 1 Toolkit* for more strategies.

OPPOSITES Two numbers that are the same distance from 0 on a number line but are on opposite sides of 0 are called **opposites**. For example, 4 and −4 are opposites because they are both 4 units from 0 but are on opposite sides of 0. The opposite of 0 is 0. You read the expression $-a$ as "the opposite of a."

EXAMPLE 4 Find opposites of numbers

> **READING**
> Do not assume that $-a$ is a negative number. Notice that for $a = -2.5$, $-a = 2.5$.

a. If $a = -2.5$, then $-a = -(-2.5) = 2.5$.

b. If $a = \frac{3}{4}$, then $-a = -\frac{3}{4}$.

ABSOLUTE VALUE The **absolute value** of a number a is the distance between a and 0 on a number line. The symbol $|a|$ represents the absolute value of a.

KEY CONCEPT   *For Your Notebook*

Absolute Value of a Number

Words If a is positive, then $|a| = a$.   **Example** $|2| = 2$

Words If a is 0, then $|a| = 0$.   **Example** $|0| = 0$

Words If a is negative, then $|a| = -a$.   **Example** $|-2| = -(-2) = 2$

EXAMPLE 5 Find absolute values of numbers

> **AVOID ERRORS**
> The absolute value of a number is never negative. If a number a is negative, then its absolute value, $-a$, is positive.

a. If $a = -\frac{2}{3}$, then $|a| = \left|-\frac{2}{3}\right| = -\left(-\frac{2}{3}\right) = \frac{2}{3}$.

b. If $a = 3.2$, then $|a| = |3.2| = 3.2$.

CONDITIONAL STATEMENTS A **conditional statement** has a hypothesis and a conclusion. An **if-then statement** is a form of a conditional statement. The *if* part contains the hypothesis. The *then* part contains the conclusion.

conditional statement

If a is a positive number, then $|a| = a$.

hypothesis   conclusion

In mathematics, if-then statements are either true or false. An if-then statement is true if the conclusion is always true when the hypothesis is satisfied. An if-then statement is false if for just one example, called a **counterexample**, the conclusion is false when the hypothesis is satisfied.

Differentiated Instruction

Visual Learners Some students may not remember the distinction between whole numbers and integers. Whole numbers are integers greater than or equal to 0, and "$0 \geq$" looks like the letters "OL" in "WHOLE."

See also the *Algebra 1 Toolkit* for more strategies.

EXAMPLE 6 Analyze a conditional statement

Identify the hypothesis and the conclusion of the statement "If a number is a rational number, then the number is an integer." Tell whether the statement is *true* or *false*. If it is false, give a counterexample.

Solution

Hypothesis: a number is a rational number

Conclusion: the number is an integer

The statement is false. The number 0.5 is a counterexample, because 0.5 is a rational number but not an integer.

 GUIDED PRACTICE for Examples 4, 5, and 6

For the given value of *a*, find −*a* and |*a*|.

8. *a* = 5.3 **−5.3, 5.3**

9. *a* = −7 **7, 7**

10. *a* = $-\frac{4}{9}$ $\frac{4}{9}, \frac{4}{9}$

Identify the hypothesis and the conclusion of the statement. Tell whether the statement is *true* or *false*. If it is false, give a counterexample.

11. Hypothesis: a number is a rational number, conclusion: the number is positive; false. *Sample answer:* −1 is rational, but not positive.

11. If a number is a rational number, then the number is positive.

12. If the absolute value of a number is positive, then the number is positive.
Hypothesis: the absolute value of a number is positive, conclusion: the number is positive; false. *Sample answer:* The absolute value of −2 is 2, but −2 is negative.

2.1 EXERCISES

HOMEWORK KEY

○ = **WORKED-OUT SOLUTIONS**
on p. WS1 for Exs. 7, 29, and 53

★ = **STANDARDIZED TEST PRACTICE**
Exs. 3, 4, 39, 50, 56, and 59

SKILL PRACTICE

 A

1. VOCABULARY Copy and complete: A number is a(n) __?__ if it can be written in the form $\frac{a}{b}$ where *a* and *b* are integers and *b* ≠ 0. **rational number**

2. VOCABULARY What is the opposite of −2? **2**

3. ★ WRITING *Describe* the difference between whole numbers and positive integers. **Zero is in the set of whole numbers, but not in the set of positive integers.**

4. ★ WRITING For a negative number *x*, is the absolute value of *x* a *positive number* or a *negative number*? *Explain.* **Positive number; the absolute value of a negative number is always positive.**

EXAMPLE 1
on p. 64
for Exs. 5–13

GRAPHING AND COMPARING INTEGERS Graph the numbers on a number line. Then tell which number is greater. **5–13. Check students' graphs.**

5. 0 and 7 **7**

6. 0 and −4 **0**

7. −5 and −6 **−5**

8. −2 and −3 **−2**

9. 5 and −2 **5**

10. −12 and 8 **8**

11. −1 and −5 **−1**

12. 3 and −13 **3**

13. −20 and −2 **−2**

Extra Example 6
Identify the hypothesis and conclusion of the statement "If a number is an integer, then the number is either positive or negative." Then tell whether the statement is *true* or *false*. If it is false, give a counterexample. **Hypothesis: a number is an integer; Conclusion: the number is positive or negative; false: 0 is an integer and it is neither positive nor negative.**

Key Question to Ask for Example 6
• If you switch the hypothesis and conclusion so that the statement reads "If a number is an integer, then it is a rational number," is the statement true or false? Why? **True; an integer can be written as the quotient of two integers.**

Closing the Lesson
Have students summarize the major points of the lesson and answer the Essential Question: How do you compare positive and negative numbers?

• A rational number can be written as the quotient of two integers.
• The absolute value of a number is the distance between the number and 0 on a number line. Opposites are the same distance from 0, but on opposite sides.
• Conditional statements contain a hypothesis and a conclusion, and can be either true or false.

Graph numbers on a number line so you can compare them and order them from least to greatest.

4 PRACTICE AND APPLY

Assignment Guide

📄 Answer Transparencies available for all exercises

Basic:
Day 1: SRH p. 930 Exs. 1–4
pp. 67–70
Exs. 1, 3, 5–10, 14–19, 53, 54, 57, 67–75
Day 2: pp. 67–70
Exs. 2, 4, 23–30, 35–44, 55, 56, 58, 61–66

Average:
Day 1: pp. 67–70
Exs. 1, 3, 8–13, 17–22, 53, 54, 57–59, 67–75 odd
Day 2: pp. 67–70
Exs. 2, 4, 27–39 odd, 40–51, 55, 56, 61–66

Advanced:
Day 1: pp. 67–70
Exs. 1, 3, 10–13, 19–22, 53, 54, 57–60*, 68–74 even
Day 2: pp. 67–70
Exs. 2, 4, 28–38 even, 39, 41–52*, 55, 56, 63, 65, 66

Block:
pp. 67–70
Exs. 1–4, 8–13, 17–22, 27–39 odd, 40–51, 53–59, 61–66, 67–75 odd

Differentiated Instruction

See *Algebra 1 Best Practices Toolkit* for suggestions on addressing the needs of a diverse classroom.

Homework Check

For a quick check of student understanding of key concepts, go over the following exercises:

Basic: 16, 25, 35, 53, 55
Average: 18, 31, 37, 53, 56
Advanced: 20, 32, 38, 56, 57

Extra Practice

• Student Edition, p. 939
• Chapter 2 Resource Book: Practice levels A, B, C, pp. 5–7

Practice Worksheet

An easily-readable reduced practice page (with answers) for this lesson can be found on p. 62C.

EXAMPLES
2 and 3
on p. 65
for Exs. 14–22

CLASSIFYING AND ORDERING NUMBERS Tell whether each number in the list is a whole number, an integer, or a rational number. Then order the numbers from least to greatest. **14–22. See margin.**

14. $3, -5, -2.4, 1$ **15.** $1.6, 1, -4, 0$ **16.** $0.25, -0.5, 0.2, -2$

17. $-\frac{2}{3}, -0.6, -1, \frac{1}{3}$ **18.** $-0.01, 0.1, 0, -\frac{1}{10}$ **19.** $16, -1.66, \frac{5}{3}, -1.6$

20. $-2.7, \frac{1}{2}, 0.3, -7$ **21.** $-4.99, 5, \frac{16}{3}, -5.1$ **22.** $-\frac{3}{5}, -0.4, -1, -0.5$

EXAMPLES
4 and 5
on p. 66
for Exs. 23–34

FINDING OPPOSITES AND ABSOLUTE VALUES For the given value of a, find $-a$ and $|a|$.

23. $a = 6$ **−6, 6**   **24.** $a = -3$ **3, 3**   **25.** $a = -18$ **18, 18**   **26.** $a = 0$ **0, 0**

27. $a = 13.4$ **−13.4, 13.4**   **28.** $a = 2.7$ **−2.7, 2.7**   **㉙.** $a = -6.1$ **6.1, 6.1**   **30.** $a = -7.9$ **7.9, 7.9**

31. $a = -1\frac{1}{9}$ **$1\frac{1}{9}, 1\frac{1}{9}$**   **32.** $a = -\frac{5}{6}$ **$\frac{5}{6}, \frac{5}{6}$**   **33.** $a = \frac{3}{4}$ **$-\frac{3}{4}, \frac{3}{4}$**   **34.** $a = 1\frac{1}{3}$ **$-1\frac{1}{3}, 1\frac{1}{3}$**

EXAMPLE 6
on p. 67
for Exs. 35–38

ANALYZING CONDITIONAL STATEMENTS Identify the hypothesis and the conclusion of the conditional statement. Tell whether the statement is *true* or *false*. If it is false, give a counterexample.

35. If a number is a positive integer, then the number is a whole number.
Hypothesis: a number is a positive integer, conclusion: the number is a whole number; true.

36. If a number is negative, then its absolute value is negative.

37. If a number is positive, then its opposite is positive.

38. If a number is an integer, then the number is a rational number.
Hypothesis: a number is an integer, conclusion: the number is a rational number; true.

39. ★ **MULTIPLE CHOICE** Which number is a whole number? **A**

Ⓐ $\left|-\frac{18}{9}\right|$ Ⓑ $-\frac{4}{3}$ Ⓒ 1.6 Ⓓ $-(-7.963)$

36. Hypothesis: a number is negative, conclusion: its absolute value is negative; false. *Sample answer:* $|-3|$ is 3, a positive integer.

37. Hypothesis: a number is positive, conclusion: its opposite is positive; false. *Sample answer:* The opposite of 2 is −2, a negative number.

Ⓑ **ERROR ANALYSIS** *Describe* and correct the error in the statement. **40, 41. See margin.**

40.

The numbers $-(-2), -4,$ $-|8|,$ and -0.3 are negative numbers.

41.

The numbers $|-3.4|, -(-8),$ $-|-0.2|,$ and 0.87 are positive numbers.

40. $-(-2)$ is not negative. *Sample answer:* In the number $-(-2)$, replace the parentheses with absolute value bars.

41. $-|-0.2|$ is a negative number. *Sample answer:* In the number $-|-0.2|$, remove both negative signs.

Ⓒ **EVALUATING EXPRESSIONS** Evaluate the expression when $x = -0.75$.

42. $-x$ **0.75**   **43.** $|x| + 0.25$ **1**   **44.** $|x| - 0.75$ **0**   **45.** $1 + |-x|$ **1.75**

46. $2 \cdot (-x)$ **1.5**   **47.** $(-x) \cdot 3$ **2.25**   **48.** $|x| + |x|$ **1.5**   **49.** $-x + |x|$ **1.5**

50. ★ **MULTIPLE CHOICE** Which number is a solution of $|x| + 1 = 1.3$? **B**

Ⓐ -2.3 Ⓑ -0.3 Ⓒ 1.3 Ⓓ 2.3

51. **CHALLENGE** What can you conclude about the opposite of the opposite of a number? *Explain* your reasoning. **It is the original number.** *Sample answer:* The opposite of a is $-a$ and the opposite of $-a$ is a, which is the original number.

52. **CHALLENGE** For what values of a is the opposite of a greater than a? less than a? equal to a? **See margin.**

○ = **WORKED-OUT SOLUTIONS** on p. WS1   ★ = **STANDARDIZED TEST PRACTICE**

68

14. 3: whole number, integer, rational number, −5: integer, rational number, −2.4: rational number, 1: whole number, integer, rational number; −5, −2.4, 1, 3

15. 1.6: rational number, 1: whole number, integer, rational number, −4: integer, rational number, 0: whole number, integer, rational number; −4, 0, 1, 1.6

16. 0.25: rational number, −0.5: rational number, 0.2: rational number, −2: integer, rational number; −2, −0.5, 0.2, 0.25

PROBLEM SOLVING

EXAMPLE 3 [A]
on p. 65
for Exs. 53, 57

53. Fondo,
Frink, Alamorio,
Calexico,
Date City

53. **GEOGRAPHY** The map shows various locations in Imperial County, California, and their elevations above or below sea level. Order the locations from lowest elevation to highest elevation.

@HomeTutor for problem solving help at classzone.com

Imperial County, CA
• Frink: —170 ft
• Fondo: —206 ft
• Alamorio: —135 ft
• Date City: 5 ft
Calexico: 2 ft

54. **SPORTS** In golf, the goal is to have the least score among all the players. Which golf score, −8 or −12, is the better score? **−12**

@HomeTutor for problem solving help at classzone.com

EXAMPLE 5
on p. 66
for Exs. 55–56

55. **MUSIC** A guitar tuner is a device that tunes a guitar string to its exact pitch. Some tuners use the measure *cents* to indicate how far above or below the exact pitch, marked as 0 cents, the string tone is. Suppose that one string tone measures −3.4 cents, and a second string tone measures −3.8 cents. Which string tone is closer to the exact pitch? *Explain.* **−3.4; the absolute value of −3.4 is less than the absolute value of −3.8, so it is closer to 0, the exact pitch.**

56. ★ **MULTIPLE CHOICE** The change in value of a share of a stock was −$.45 on Monday, −$1.32 on Tuesday, $.27 on Wednesday, and $1.03 on Thursday. On which day was the absolute value of the change the greatest? **B**

(A) Monday   (B) Tuesday   (C) Wednesday   (D) Thursday

57. **MULTI-STEP PROBLEM** An equalizer on a stereo system is used to increase or decrease the intensity of sounds at different frequencies. The intensity is measured in decibels (dB), and the frequencies are measured in hertz (Hz). The table shows the intensity at different frequencies on a stereo system.

Frequency (Hz)	32	64	125	250	500	1000	2000	4000	8000
Intensity (dB)	8.8	7.1	5.8	1.5	−2.8	−1.5	2.7	2.8	2.9

a. Which frequency has the least sound intensity? **500 Hz**

b. *Describe* the change in sound intensity as the frequency increases from 32 hertz to 8000 hertz. **The intensity decreases until 1000 Hz and then increases.**

[B]

58. **WEATHER** A wind chill index describes how much colder it feels outside when wind speed is considered with air temperature. The table shows the wind chill temperatures for given pairs of air temperature and wind speed.

a. **Compare** Which feels colder, an air temperature of 0°F with a wind speed of 30 miles per hour, or an air temperature of −10°F with a wind speed of 10 miles per hour?

58a. −10°F with a wind speed of 10 miles per hour

Wind Chill Temperatures (°F)					
Wind speed (mi/h)	Air temperature (°F)				
	20	10	0	−10	−20
0	20	10	0	−10	−20
10	9	−4	−16	−28	−41
20	4	−9	−22	−35	−48
30	1	−12	−26	−39	−53

b. **Analyze** How does the wind chill temperature change under constant wind speed and decreasing air temperature? under constant air temperature and increasing wind speed? **decreases; decreases**

2.1   Use Integers and Rational Numbers   **69**

17. $-\frac{2}{3}$: rational number, −0.6: rational number, −1: integer, rational number, $\frac{1}{3}$: rational number; −1, $-\frac{2}{3}$, −0.6, $\frac{1}{3}$

18. −0.01: rational number, 0.1: rational number, 0: whole number, integer, rational number, $-\frac{1}{10}$: rational number; $-\frac{1}{10}$, −0.01, 0, 0.1

19. 16: whole number, integer, rational number, −1.66: rational number, $\frac{5}{3}$: rational number, −1.6: rational number; −1.66, −1.6, $\frac{5}{3}$, 16

Study Strategy

Exercises 23–34 Remind students that −a is read "the opposite of a." Give an example such as, "if a is −1, then the opposite of a is the opposite of −1."

Avoiding Common Errors

Exercises 42–49 Some students may read −x as −0.75 rather than −(−0.75). Suggest that students use parenthesis around x to avoid this error.

Exercises 53–55 You may want to mention that students can avoid errors by graphing the numbers in these problems on a number line.

Reading Strategy

Exercise 56 Tell students to look for key words when they are reading a problem. Point out that this exercise asks for the day on which the *absolute value* of the change was the greatest.

Vocabulary

Exercise 58b Some students may need help with the word "constant." Tell these students that constant means that something does not change. Direct their attention to the chart so they can see that constant wind speed and decreasing air temperature are read in rows across the chart and constant air temperature and increasing wind speed are read in columns down the chart.

20. −2.7: rational number, $\frac{1}{2}$: rational number, 0.3: rational number, −7: integer, rational number; −7, −2.7, 0.3, $\frac{1}{2}$

21. −4.99: rational number, 5: whole number, integer, rational number, $\frac{16}{3}$: rational number, −5.1: rational number; −5.1, −4.99, 5, $\frac{16}{3}$

22. $-\frac{3}{5}$: rational number, −0.4: rational number, −1: integer, rational number, −0.5: rational number; −1, $-\frac{3}{5}$, −0.5, −0.4

52. See Additional Answers beginning on p. AA1.

1. Graph −3 and −5 on a number line. Then tell which number is greater. **−3 > −5**

2. Tell whether each number is a whole number, an integer, or a rational number: $-2.24, 6, 3\frac{1}{4}$,

−16. **−2.24: rational number; 6: whole number, integer, rational number; $3\frac{1}{4}$: rational number; −16: integer, rational number**

3. The table shows the boiling-point temperatures of some elements. Order the elements from lowest boiling-point temperature to highest.

Element	Temperature
Hydrogen	−2593°C
Mercury	357°C
Nitrogen	−196°C
Oxygen	−183°C

Hydrogen, Nitrogen, Oxygen, Mercury

Online Quiz

Available at **classzone.com**

Diagnosis/Remediation

• Practice A, B, C in Chapter 2 Resource Book, pp. 5–7
• Study Guide in Chapter 2 Resource Book, pp. 8–9
• Practice Workbook, pp. 16–17
• @HomeTutor

Challenge

Additional challenge is available in the Chapter 2 Resource Book, p. 12.

59b. Rigel's apparent magnitude is greater than the Sun's apparent magnitude, so it is dimmer than the Sun; Rigel's absolute magnitude is less than the Sun's absolute magnitude, so it is brighter than the Sun.

59c. No. *Sample answer:* The apparent magnitude of Arcturus is less than the apparent magnitude of Achernar, but the absolute magnitude of Arcturus is greater than the absolute magnitude of Achernar.

---

59. ★ **EXTENDED RESPONSE** A star's apparent magnitude measures how bright the star appears to a person on Earth. A star's absolute magnitude measures its brightness if it were a distance of 33 light-years, or about 194 trillion miles, from Earth. The greater the magnitude, the dimmer the star.

Star	Arcturus	Achernar	Canopus	Capella	Sirius	Sun
Apparent magnitude	−0.04	0.46	−0.72	0.08	−1.46	−26.72
Absolute magnitude	0.2	−1.3	−2.5	0.4	1.4	4.8

Orion Constellation

a. Order Order the stars in the table from brightest to dimmest when viewed from Earth. Then order the stars from brightest to dimmest if they were 33 light-years from Earth.

b. Compare The star Rigel has an apparent magnitude of 0.12 and an absolute magnitude of −8.1. *Compare* its brightness with the Sun's brightness using both apparent magnitude and absolute magnitude.

c. Analyze Can you use the apparent magnitudes of two stars to predict which star is brighter in terms of absolute magnitude? *Explain* your answer using a comparison of the apparent and absolute magnitudes of two stars in the table.

59a. Sun, Sirius, Canopus, Arcturus, Capella, Achernar; Canopus, Achernar, Arcturus, Capella, Sirius, Sun

60. CHALLENGE In an academic contest, the point values of the questions are given by the expression $50x$ where $x = 1, 2, 3,$ and 4. You earn $50x$ points for a correct answer to a question and $-(50x)$ points for an incorrect answer. Order from least to greatest all the possible points you can earn when answering a question. **−200, −150, −100, −50, 50, 100, 150, 200**

MIXED REVIEW

PREVIEW
Prepare for Lesson 2.2 in Exs. 61–66.

Add. *(p. 914)*

61. $\frac{1}{2} + \frac{1}{3}$ **$\frac{5}{6}$**

62. $\frac{5}{6} + \frac{1}{6}$ **1**

63. $2\frac{1}{2} + 1\frac{3}{4}$ **$4\frac{1}{4}$**

Find the perimeter of the triangle or rectangle. *(p. 924)*

64.

5.8 cm, 4.2 cm, 6.3 cm **16.3 cm**

65.

$1\frac{1}{3}$ ft, $2\frac{1}{4}$ ft, 3 ft, $6\frac{7}{12}$ ft

66.

3.7 m, 5.1 m **17.6 m**

Check whether the given number is a solution of the inequality. *(p. 21)*

67. $x + 2 < 3; 2$ **not a solution**
68. $y − 8 < 6; 13$ **solution**
69. $9 − 2z \le 3; 3$ **solution**

70. $2y + 3 \ge 14; 5$ **not a solution**
71. $3 < 7x − 4; 1$ **not a solution**
72. $2a \ge 15; 7$ **not a solution**

Make a table for the function. Identify the range of the function. *(p. 43)* **73–75. See margin.**

73. $y = x − 3$
Domain: 5, 8, 14, 30

74. $y = 1.5x$
Domain: 0, 2, 6, 10

75. $y = 2x − 3$
Domain: 2, 4, 7, 11

---

73. range: 2, 5, 11, 27

x	y
5	2
8	5
14	11
30	27

74. range: 0, 3, 9, 15

x	y
0	0
2	3
6	9
10	15

75. range: 1, 5, 11, 19

x	y
2	1
4	5
7	11
11	19

Apply Sets to Numbers and Functions

GOAL Apply set theory to numbers and functions.

Key Vocabulary
• set
• element
• empty set
• universal set
• union
• intersection

A **set** is a collection of distinct objects. Each object in a set is called an **element** or *member* of the set. You can use *set notation* to write a set by enclosing the elements of the set in braces. For example, if A is the set of whole numbers less than 6, then $A = \{0, 1, 2, 3, 4, 5\}$.

Two special sets are the *empty set* and the *universal set*. The set with no elements is called the **empty set** and is written as $\emptyset$. The set of all elements under consideration is called the **universal set** and is written as U.

KEY CONCEPT   *For Your Notebook*

Union and Intersection of Two Sets

The **union** of two sets A and B is the set of all elements in *either* A or B and is written as $A \cup B$.

The **intersection** of two sets A and B is the set of all elements in *both* A and B and is written as $A \cap B$.

$A \cup B$

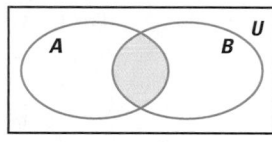

$A \cap B$

EXAMPLE 1   **Find the union and intersection of two sets**

Let U be the set of integers from 1 to 9. Let $A = \{2, 4, 6, 8\}$ and $B = \{2, 3, 5, 7\}$. Find (a) $A \cup B$ and (b) $A \cap B$.

Solution

a. The union of A and B consists of the elements that are in either set.

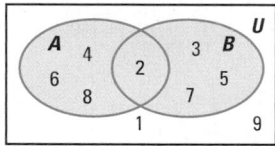

▶ $A \cup B = \{2, 3, 4, 5, 6, 7, 8\}$

b. The intersection of A and B consists of the elements that are in both sets.

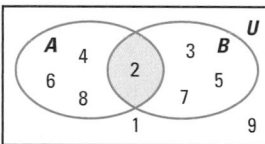

▶ $A \cap B = \{2\}$

---

① PLAN AND PREPARE

Warm-Up Exercises

Find the range of the given function with the given domain.
1. $y = 2x$; Domain: 3, 5, 7 **6, 10, 14**
2. $y = x + 5$; Domain: 2, 5, 8 **7, 10, 13**
3. $y = x - 2$; Domain: 2, 4, 6 **0, 2, 4**

② FOCUS AND MOTIVATE

Essential Question
Big Idea 3, p. 63

How do you apply sets to numbers and functions? **Tell students they will learn how to answer this question by finding the union and intersection of two sets of numbers and by using set notation to write a function and its range.**

③ TEACH

Extra Example 1
Let U be the set of rational numbers from -3 to 6.5. Let $A = \{-3, 1, 5\frac{1}{4}, 6.2\}$ and $B = \{-2, 1.5, 4, 6\}$. Find (a) $A \cup B$ and (b) $A \cap B$.
a. $A \cup B = \{-3, -2, 1, 1.5, 4, 5\frac{1}{4}, 6, 6.2\}$
b. $A \cap B = \emptyset$

NCTM STANDARDS

Standard 2: Understand functions; Use models to understand relationships

FUNCTIONS AND SETS You can write the domain and range of a function as sets of input values and output values and the function as a set of ordered pairs, as illustrated for the mapping diagram below.

$f = \{(1, 2), (2, 3), (3, 3), (5, 4)\}$

EXAMPLE 2 Write a function and its range as sets

Consider the function $y = x + 2$ with domain $D = \{0, 1, 2, 3\}$. Write the range and function using set notation.

Solution

x	0	1	2	3
y	$0 + 2 = 2$	$1 + 2 = 3$	$2 + 2 = 4$	$3 + 2 = 5$

▶ The range is $R = \{2, 3, 4, 5\}$.
The function is $f = \{(0, 2), (1, 3), (2, 4), (3, 5)\}$.

PRACTICE

EXAMPLE 1
on p. 71
for Exs. 1–4

Let U be the set of whole numbers from 0 to 10. Find $A \cup B$ and $A \cap B$ for the specified sets A and B.

1. $A = \{1, 3, 5, 7, 9\}$ and $B = \{3, 6, 9\}$ **{1, 3, 5, 6, 7, 9}, {3, 9}**

2. $A = \{1, 2, 3, 4, 5, 6\}$ and $B = \{4, 5, 6, 7, 8\}$ **{1, 2, 3, 4, 5, 6, 7, 8}, {4, 5, 6}**

3. $A = \{0, 2, 4, 6, 8, 10\}$ and $B = \{1, 3, 5, 7, 9\}$ **{0, 1, 2, 3, 4, 5, 6, 7, 8, 9, 10}, ∅**

4. $A = \{0, 5, 10\}$ and $B = \{1, 4, 7, 10\}$ **{0, 1, 4, 5, 7, 10}, {10}**

EXAMPLE 2
on p. 72
for Exs. 5–8

In Exercises 5–8, consider the specified function and domain. Write the range and function using set notation.

5. $y = 2x$ with domain $D = \{1, 2, 3, 4, 5\}$ **$R = \{2, 4, 6, 8, 10\}$, $f = \{(1, 2), (2, 4), (3, 6), (4, 8), (5, 10)\}$**

6. $y = x - 1$ with domain $D = \{2, 4, 6, 8, 10\}$ **$R = \{1, 3, 5, 7, 9\}$, $f = \{(2, 1), (4, 3), (6, 5), (8, 7), (10, 9)\}$**

7. $R = \{4, 8, 12, 16, 20\}$, $f = \{(1, 4), (5, 8), (9, 12), (13, 16), (17, 20)\}$

7. $y = x + 3$ with domain $D = \{1, 5, 9, 13, 17\}$

8. $y = 3x + 2$ with domain $D = \{1, 2, 3, 4, 5\}$ **$R = \{5, 8, 11, 14, 17\}$, $f = \{(1, 5), (2, 8), (3, 11), (4, 14), (5, 17)\}$**

9. Let A be the set of positive integers, and let B be the set of negative integers and 0. Find $A \cup B$ and $A \cap B$. **the set of integers, ∅**

10. Let A be the set of integers, and let B be the set of rational numbers. Find $A \cup B$ and $A \cap B$. **the set of rational numbers, the set of integers**

2.2 Addition of Integers

MATERIALS · algebra tiles

QUESTION   How can you use algebra tiles to find the sum of two integers?

You can use algebra tiles to model addition of integers. Each $+$ represents 1, and each $-$ represents -1. Pairing a $+$ with a $-$ results in a sum of 0.

EXPLORE   Find the sum of two integers

Find the sum $-7 + 4$.

STEP 1   Model -7 and 4 using algebra tiles.

-7 4

STEP 2   Group pairs of positive and negative tiles. Count the remaining tiles.

Each pair has a sum of 0.   ······▸

STEP 3   Copy and complete the statement: $-7 + 4 = \underline{\ ?\ }$.   **$-3$**

DRAW CONCLUSIONS   Use your observations to complete these exercises

Use algebra tiles to find the sum.

1. $3 + 8$ **11**
2. $5 + (-1)$ **4**
3. $-9 + 6$ **-3**
4. $-2 + (-3)$ **-5**
5. $-4 + 4$ **0**
6. $-7 + 5$ **-2**
7. $5 + (-7)$ **-2**
8. $-6 + 0$ **-6**

REASONING In Exercises 9–13, answer the question and give an example from Exercises 1–8 to support your answer.

9. Is the sum of two positive integers *positive* or *negative*?   **positive, Ex. 1**

10. Is the sum of two negative integers *positive* or *negative*?   **negative, Ex. 4**

11. Is the sum of a positive integer and a negative integer *always* positive?   **no, Ex. 6**

12. What is the sum of an integer and its opposite?   **0, Ex. 5**

13. What is the sum of an integer and 0?   **the integer, Ex. 8**

14. In Exercises 6 and 7, the two integers being added are the same, but the order is reversed. What does this suggest about the sums $a + b$ and $b + a$ where a and b are integers?   **It does not affect the answer.**

---

① PLAN AND PREPARE

Explore the Concept
- Students will model integer addition with algebra tiles.
- This activity leads into the study of adding integers in Example 1 in Lesson 2.2.

Materials
Each student will need:
- algebra tiles
- Activity Support Master (*Chapter 2 Resource Book*, p. 15)

Recommended Time
Work activity: 10 min
Discuss results: 5 min

Grouping
Students should work individually.

② TEACH

Tips for Success
Tell students that since the sum of a negative tile and a positive tile is zero, each such pair of tiles has no effect on the actual sum. Explain that this is why they need to pair one positive tile with one negative tile, and that they need to continue doing this until there are no pairs left.

Key Discovery
Students should see that the sum of an integer and its opposite is 0, the sum of two integers with the same sign has that same sign, and the sum of two integers with different signs has the sign of the integer modeled by the greater number of tiles.

③ ASSESS AND RETEACH

1. How many zero pairs can you make if you want to find the sum of $2 + (-5)$?   **2**

2. Can you make zero pairs if you want to find the sum of $-2 + (-3)$? Explain.   **No, only one negative and one positive tile form a zero pair.**

Before	You added positive numbers.
Now	You will add positive and negative numbers.
Why?	So you can calculate a sports score, as in Ex. 57.

Key Vocabulary
• additive identity
• additive inverse

One way to add two real numbers is to use a number line. Start at the first number. Use the sign of the second number to decide whether to move left or right. Then use the absolute value of the second number to decide how many units to move. The number where you stop is the sum of the two numbers.

To add a positive number, move to the right.

To add a negative number, move to the left.

EXAMPLE 1 Add two integers using a number line

Use a number line to find the sum.

a. $-3 + 6$

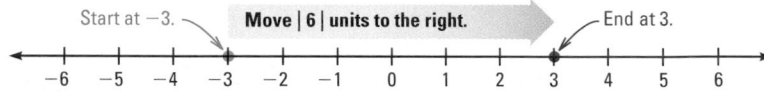

Start at −3. **Move |6| units to the right.** End at 3.

▶ The final position is 3. So, $-3 + 6 = 3$.

b. $-4 + (-5)$

End at −9. **Move |−5| units to the left.** Start at −4.

▶ The final position is −9. So, $-4 + (-5) = -9$.

✓ GUIDED PRACTICE for Example 1

Use a number line to find the sum.

1. $7 + (-2)$ **5**   **2.** $8 + (-11)$ **−3**   **3.** $-8 + 4$ **−4**   **4.** $-1 + (-4)$ **−5**

For Your Notebook

Rules of Addition

Words To add two numbers with the *same* sign, add their absolute values. The sum has the same sign as the numbers added.

Examples $8 + 7 = 15$ $-6 + (-10) = -16$

Words To add two numbers with *different* signs, subtract the lesser absolute value from the greater absolute value. The sum has the same sign as the number with the greater absolute value.

Examples $-12 + 7 = -5$ $18 + (-4) = 14$

EXAMPLE 2 **Add real numbers**

Find the sum.

a. $-5.3 + (-4.9) = -(|-5.3| + |-4.9|)$ Rule of same signs

$\qquad = -(5.3 + 4.9)$ Take absolute values.

$\qquad = -10.2$ Add.

b. $19.3 + (-12.2) = |19.3| - |-12.2|$ Rule of different signs

$\qquad = 19.3 - 12.2$ Take absolute values.

$\qquad = 7.1$ Subtract.

PROPERTIES OF ADDITION Notice that both $3 + (-2)$ and $-2 + 3$ have the same sum, 1. So, $3 + (-2) = -2 + 3$. This is an example of the *commutative property of addition*. The properties of addition are listed below.

For Your Notebook

Properties of Addition

COMMUTATIVE PROPERTY The order in which you add two numbers does not change the sum.

Algebra $a + b = b + a$ **Example** $3 + (-2) = -2 + 3$

ASSOCIATIVE PROPERTY The way you group three numbers in a sum does not change the sum.

Algebra $(a + b) + c = a + (b + c)$ **Example** $(-3 + 2) + 1 = -3 + (2 + 1)$

IDENTITY PROPERTY The sum of a number and 0 is the number.

Algebra $a + 0 = 0 + a = a$ **Example** $-5 + 0 = -5$

INVERSE PROPERTY The sum of a number and its opposite is 0.

Algebra $a + (-a) = -a + a = 0$ **Example** $-6 + 6 = 0$

Motivating the Lesson

Have students imagine that they need to balance a checkbook, track a club's finances, or monitor a fund-raiser. Explain that learning how to add positive and negative numbers in this lesson will help them oversee activities that have money coming in and money going out.

❸ TEACH

Extra Example 1

Use a number line to find the sum.

a. $-4 + 2$ **−2**

b. $3 + (-4)$ **−1**

Key Questions to Ask for Example 1

• In Example 1a, why do you start at −3? **−3 is the first number in the sum −3 + 6.**

• How do you know whether to move left or right? **Move right when the sign of the second number is positive and left when the sign is negative.**

Extra Example 2

Find the sum.

a. $-8.4 + (-0.7)$ **−9.1**

b. $-12.6 + 7.3$ **−5.3**

Key Question to Ask for Example 2

• In Example 2b, will −12.2 + 19.3 have the same answer as 19.3 + (−12.2)? Why? **Yes, to add two numbers with different signs, you subtract the lesser absolute value from the greater absolute value, so for both, you will subtract 12.2 from 19.3.**

Identify the property being illustrated.

a. $-11.9 + 11.9 = 0$ **Inverse property of addition**

b. $-8 + (-x) = -x + (-8)$ **Commutative property of addition**

c. $-2 + 0 = 2$ **Identity property of addition**

Extra Example 4

The table shows how much weight two dieters lost or gained per month. Which dieter had the greater weight loss at the end of three months? **dieter A**

Month	Dieter A	Dieter B
1	−3.3	−7.8
2	−5.1	+1.2
3	+0.5	−0.8

Closing the Lesson

Have students summarize the major points of the lesson and answer the Essential Question: How do you add positive and negative numbers?

• **Use the rules for like signs and different signs to add real numbers.**

• **Use the properties of addition to make adding easier, such as using the associative property to associate numbers that are easy to add.**

Using the rules of addition, add the absolute value of two numbers with the same sign and use the sign of the numbers for the sum. If two numbers have different signs, subtract the lesser absolute value from the greater absolute value and use the sign of the greater absolute value for the sum.

The identity property states that the sum of a number a and 0 is a. The number 0 is the **additive identity**. The inverse property states that the sum of a number a and its opposite is 0. The opposite of a is its **additive inverse**.

EXAMPLE 3   Identify properties of addition

Statement	Property illustrated
a. $(x + 9) + 2 = x + (9 + 2)$	Associative property of addition
b. $8.3 + (-8.3) = 0$	Inverse property of addition
c. $-y + 0.7 = 0.7 + (-y)$	Commutative property of addition

EXAMPLE 4   Solve a multi-step problem

BUSINESS The table shows the annual profits of two piano manufacturers. Which manufacturer had the greater total profit for the three years?

Year	Profit (millions) for manufacturer A	Profit (millions) for manufacturer B
1	−$5.8	−$6.5
2	$8.7	$7.9
3	$6.8	$8.2

Solution

STEP 1   **Calculate** the total profit for each manufacturer.

Manufacturer A:

$$\text{Total profit} = -5.8 + 8.7 + 6.8$$
$$= -5.8 + (8.7 + 6.8)$$
$$= -5.8 + 15.5$$
$$= 9.7$$

Manufacturer B:

$$\text{Total profit} = -6.5 + 7.9 + 8.2$$
$$= -6.5 + (7.9 + 8.2)$$
$$= -6.5 + 16.1$$
$$= 9.6$$

ANOTHER WAY
You can also find the sums by adding from left to right, as shown for manufacturer A:
$-5.8 + 8.7 + 6.8 =$
$2.9 + 6.8 = 9.7.$

STEP 2   **Compare** the total profits: $9.7 > 9.6$.

▶ Manufacturer A had the greater total profit.

✓ **GUIDED PRACTICE**   for Examples 2, 3, and 4

Find the sum.

5. $-0.6 + (-6.7)$ **−7.3**   **6.** $10.1 + (-16.2)$ **−6.1**   **7.** $-13.1 + 8.7$ **−4.4**

Identify the property being illustrated.

Commutative property of addition

8. $7 + (-7) = 0$ **9.** $-12 + 0 = -12$ **10.** $4 + 8 = 8 + 4$
Inverse property of addition   **Identity property of addition**

11. WHAT IF? In Example 4, suppose that the profits for year 4 are −$1.7 million for manufacturer A and −$2.1 million for manufacturer B. Which manufacturer has the greater total profit for the four years? **manufacturer A**

2.2 EXERCISES

HOMEWORK KEY

◯ = **WORKED-OUT SOLUTIONS**
on p. WS1 for Exs. 13, 35, and 55

★ = **STANDARDIZED TEST PRACTICE**
Exs. 2, 50, 56, 57, and 58

SKILL PRACTICE

[A] **1. VOCABULARY** What number is called the additive identity? **0**

2. ★ WRITING Without actually adding, how can you tell if the sum of two numbers will be zero? **If they are opposites, their sum will be zero.**

EXAMPLE 1
on p. 74
for Exs. 3–11

USING A NUMBER LINE Use a number line to find the sum.

3. $-11 + 3$ **−8**   **4.** $-1 + 6$ **5**   **5.** $13 + (-7)$ **6**

6. $5 + (-10)$ **−5**   **7.** $-9 + (-4)$ **−13**   **8.** $-8 + (-2)$ **−10**

9. $-14 + 8$ **−6**   **10.** $6 + (-12)$ **−6**   **11.** $-11 + (-9)$ **−20**

EXAMPLE 2
on p. 75
for Exs. 12–25

FINDING SUMS Find the sum.

12. $-2.4 + 3.9$ **1.5**   ◯**13.** $-8.7 + 4.2$ **−4.5**   **14.** $4.3 + (-10.2)$ **−5.9**

15. $9.1 + (-2.5)$ **6.6**   **16.** $-6.5 + (-7.1)$ **−13.6**   **17.** $-11.4 + (-3.8)$ **−15.2**

18. $4\frac{1}{5} + \left(-9\frac{1}{2}\right)$ **$-5\frac{3}{10}$**   **19.** $8\frac{2}{3} + \left(-1\frac{3}{5}\right)$ **$7\frac{1}{15}$**   **20.** $-12\frac{3}{4} + 6\frac{9}{10}$ **$-5\frac{17}{20}$**

21. $-\frac{4}{9} + 1\frac{4}{5}$ **$1\frac{16}{45}$**   **22.** $-3\frac{3}{7} + \left(-14\frac{3}{4}\right)$ **$-18\frac{5}{28}$**   **23.** $-7\frac{1}{12} + \left(-13\frac{7}{8}\right)$ **$-20\frac{23}{24}$**

ERROR ANALYSIS *Describe* and correct the error in finding the sum.

24.
$$-13 + (-15) = 28 \quad ✗$$
The answer should be negative,
$-13 + (-15) = -28.$

25.
$$17 + (-31) = -48 \quad ✗$$
The numbers have different signs, so their absolute values should have been subtracted,
$17 + (-31) = -14.$

EXAMPLE 3
on p. 76
for Exs. 26–31

IDENTIFYING PROPERTIES Identify the property being illustrated.

26. $-3 + 3 = 0$ **Inverse property of addition**

27. $(-6 + 1) + 7 = -6 + (1 + 7)$ **Associate property of addition**

28. $9 + (-1) = -1 + 9$ **Commutative property of addition**

29. $-8 + 0 = -8$ **Identity property of addition**

30. $(x + 2) + 3 = x + (2 + 3)$ **Associative property of addition**

31. $y + (-4) = -4 + y$ **Commutative property of addition**

EXAMPLE 4
on p. 76
for Exs. 32–37

FINDING SUMS Find the sum.

32. $-13 + 5 + (-7)$ **−15**   **33.** $-18 + (-12) + (-19)$ **−49**

34. $0.47 + (-1.8) + (-3.8)$ **−5.13**   ◯**35.** $-2.6 + (-3.4) + 7.6$ **1.6**

36. $-3\frac{1}{2} + \left(-7\frac{2}{5}\right) + \left(-9\frac{3}{10}\right)$ **$-20\frac{1}{5}$**   **37.** $8\frac{2}{3} + \left(-6\frac{3}{5}\right) + 3\frac{1}{4}$ **$5\frac{19}{60}$**

[B] **EVALUATING EXPRESSIONS** Evaluate the expression for the given value of x.

38. $3 + x + (-7); x = 6$ **2**   **39.** $x + (-5) + 5; x = -3$ **−3**

40. $9.6 + (-x) + 2.3; x = -8.5$ **20.4**   **41.** $-1.7 + (-5.4) + (-x); x = 2.4$ **−9.5**

42. $1\frac{1}{4} + |x| + \left(-3\frac{1}{2}\right); x = -8\frac{2}{5}$ **$6\frac{3}{20}$**   **43.** $|x| + \left(-3\frac{1}{4}\right) + \left(7\frac{3}{10}\right); x = -3\frac{1}{3}$ **$7\frac{23}{60}$**

2.2 Add Real Numbers   **77**

---

④ PRACTICE AND APPLY

Assignment Guide

🗐 Answer Transparencies available for all exercises

Basic:
Day 1: SRH p. 914 Exs. 21–25
pp. 77–79
Exs. 1, 2, 3–23 odd, 24–31,
33–43 odd, 53–57, 60–66

Average:
Day 1: pp. 77–79
Exs. 1, 2, 6–22 even, 24–31,
34–50 even, 53–59, 60–66 even

Advanced:
Day 1: pp. 77–79
Exs. 1, 2, 8–22 even, 27–49 odd,
51–53*, 55–59*, 61–65 odd

Block:
pp. 77–79
Exs. 2, 6–22 even, 24–31,
34–50 even, 53–59, 60–66 even
(with 2.3)

Differentiated Instruction

See *Algebra 1 Best Practices Toolkit* for suggestions on addressing the needs of a diverse classroom.

Homework Check

For a quick check of student understanding of key concepts, go over the following exercises:

Basic: 7, 15, 28, 34, 54
Average: 8, 18, 30, 36, 54
Advanced: 10, 31, 37, 55, 57

Extra Practice

• Student Edition, p. 939
• Chapter 2 Resource Book:
  Practice levels A, B, C, pp. 16–18

Practice Worksheet

An easily-readable reduced practice page (with answers) for this lesson can be found on p. 62C.

Differentiated Instruction

Kinesthetic Learners While working on **Exercises 3–11**, some students may need to trace their fingertip along a number line in order to complete the exercises. Have them begin at the starting number, and trace to the right to add a positive number or to the left to add a negative number.

See also the *Algebra 1 Toolkit* for more strategies.

Teaching Strategy

Exercises 3–11 Some students may prefer using algebra tiles or the rules of addition to find the sums. Have these students find the sums using a number line and then check their answers using algebra tiles or the rules of addition.

Exercise 50 Tell students it may be easier to determine the answer if they first substitute real numbers for *a* and *b*.

Avoiding Common Errors

Exercises 12–23 Watch for students who add the greater absolute value to the lesser absolute value when adding numbers of different signs. Remind them that when the numbers have different signs, they need to subtract the lesser absolute value from the greater absolute value. This means if the lesser absolute value is the first number, it will become the second number when they subtract, such that $2.5 + (-8.2)$ becomes $8.2 - 2.5$ when they take the absolute values and subtract.

Mathematical Reasoning

Exercise 56 Suggest that students first look for ways to eliminate answers before adding the numbers. Point out that the answers for A and B overlap for the years 2000 and 2001. To determine which three-year period had the greater profit, all they need to do is compare profits for 1999 and 2002. They can do the same for answers C and D. After they eliminate two of the answers, they can add and then compare the profits for the remaining three-year periods.

Internet Reference

Exercise 58 For more information about atoms, visit the Jefferson Lab website at http://education.jlab.org/atomtour/index.html

51. 0; $|2x|$. *Sample answer:* If $x = 2$, then $|2| + (-2) = 2 + (-2) = 0$. If $x = -2$, then $|-2| + (-(-2)) = |-2| + |-2| = 4$.

FINDING SOLUTIONS Solve the equation using mental math.

44. $x + (-9) + 9 = 8$ **8**

45. $(-8) + x + (-2) = -10$ **0**

46. $x + (-2.8) + 9.2 = 0$ **-6.4**

47. $-8.7 + x + 1.3 = 0$ **7.4**

TRANSLATING PHRASES In Exercises 48 and 49, translate the verbal phrase into an addition expression. Then find the sum.

48. The sum of the absolute value of -4 and the additive identity $|-4| + 0; 4$

49. The sum of the opposite of -18 and its additive inverse $-(-18) + (-18); 0$

50. ★ **MULTIPLE CHOICE** If $a + b$ is negative, which statement must be true?   **D**

   A $a < 0, b < 0$ **B** $a < 0$ **C** $a < 0, b > 0$ **D** $a < -b$

51. CHALLENGE Consider the expression $|x| + (-x)$. Write a simplified expression for the sum if x is positive. Then write a simplified expression for the sum if x is negative. Give examples to support your answers.   **See margin.**

51. 0; $|2x|$. *Sample answer:* If $x = 2$, then $|2| + (-2) = 2 + (-2) = 0$.   **C** If $x = -2$, then $|-2| + (-(-2)) = |-2| + |-2| = 4$.

52. CHALLENGE Evaluate $-50 + (-49) + (-48) + \cdots + 48 + 49 + 50$. *Explain* how you can use the properties of addition to obtain the sum.
0; use the commutative property of addition to add each negative number and its opposite. By the additive inverse property, it will equal 0.

PROBLEM SOLVING

EXAMPLE 1 **A**
on p. 74
for Ex. 53

53. WEATHER The temperature in your city at 6 A.M. was $-8°$F and increased by $15°$F by noon. What was the temperature at noon?
7°F

  @HomeTutor for problem solving help at classzone.com

EXAMPLE 2
on p. 75
for Exs. 54–55

54. PARKING GARAGES The bottom level of a parking garage has an elevation of -45 feet. The top level of the garage is 100 feet higher. What is the elevation of the top level?   **55 ft**

  @HomeTutor for problem solving help at classzone.com

55. **MULTI-STEP PROBLEM** In optometry, the strength of an eyeglass lens is measured in diopters. Two lenses can be combined to create a new lens, and the sum of their strengths is the strength of the new lens.

  a. A lens of -4.75 diopters is combined with a lens of 6.25 diopters to form a new lens. What is the strength of the new lens?   **1.5 diopters**

  b. A lens of -2.5 diopters is combined with a lens of -1.25 diopters to form a new lens. What is the strength of the new lens?   **-3.75 diopters**

  c. The greater the absolute value of the strength of a lens, the stronger the lens. Which new lens is stronger, the one in part (a) or in part (b)?   **part (b)**

EXAMPLE 4
on p. 76
for Exs. 56–57

56. ★ **MULTIPLE CHOICE** The table shows the profits for a company from 1999 to 2004. Which three-year period had the greatest total profit?   **C**

Year	1999	2000	2001	2002	2003	2004
Profit (millions of dollars)	-13.76	54.91	38.54	-21.33	123.90	-14.82

  A 1999–2001   **B** 2000–2002   **C** 2001–2003   **D** 2002–2004

  ○ = **WORKED-OUT SOLUTIONS**
    on p. WS1

  ★ = **STANDARDIZED TEST PRACTICE**

57. ★ **SHORT RESPONSE** In golf, your score on a hole is the number of strokes above or below an expected number of strokes needed to hit a ball into the hole. As shown in the table, each score has a name. When you compare two scores, the lesser score is the better score.

Name	Double eagle	Eagle	Birdie	Par	Bogey	Double bogey
Score	−3	−2	−1	0	1	2

  a. Compare For three holes, you score an eagle, a double bogey, and a birdie. Your friend scores a double eagle, a bogey, and a par. Who has the better total score? **your friend**

  b. Explain Your friend scores a double eagle and an eagle for the next two holes. Is it possible for you to have a better score on all five holes after your next two holes? *Explain* your reasoning.
No, if you score 2 double eagles, you will have the same score.

58. ★ **EXTENDED RESPONSE** Atoms consist of protons, electrons, and neutrons. A group of x protons has a charge of x. A group of x electrons has a charge of $-x$. Neutrons have a charge of 0.

  a. Calculate The total charge of an atom is the sum of the charges of its protons and electrons. Find the total charge of an atom that has 13 protons, 10 electrons, and 14 neutrons. **3**

  b. Interpret An atom is an ion only when it has a positive or a negative total charge. Is the atom in part (a) an ion? **yes**

  c. Explain In an atom, only the number of electrons can change. Suppose an atom has a total charge of 5. For the atom not to be an ion, how should the number of electrons change? Your answer should include an algebraic equation that models the situation and an explanation of how you solved the equation.

58c. **5 electrons should be added.** *Sample answer*: **5 + x = 0. For the expression to equal 0, add the additive inverse of 5, which is −5.**

59. **CHALLENGE** You sold three items in an Internet auction. The table shows the profit earned for each item. You now plan to sell a floor lamp. What is the least profit that you can earn on the lamp and have a positive total profit for the four items? *Explain* your answer. **$12.40; if you add each profit, the total is $12.39, to get a positive profit, you need to earn at least $12.40.**

Item	Profit (dollars)
Mantel clock	4.13
Framed mirror	−10.65
Metal lunch box	−5.87

MIXED REVIEW

PREVIEW Prepare for Lesson 2.3 in Exs. 60–63.

Evaluate the expression.

60. $t - 7$ when $t = 21$ *(p. 2)* **14**

61. $1.7 - y$ when $y = 0.8$ *(p. 2)* **0.9**

62. $-a$ when $a = -13.5$ *(p. 64)* **13.5**

63. $|c|$ when $c = -9.6$ *(p. 64)* **9.6**

State the formula that is needed to solve the problem. Then solve the problem. *(p. 28)*

64. What is the interest on $800 invested for 3 years in an account that earns simple interest at a rate of 1.5% per year? $I = prt$; **$36**

65. Find the perimeter of a rectangle that is 28 feet wide and 40 feet long. $P = 2\ell + 2w$; **136 ft**

66. The temperature is 50°F. What is the temperature in degrees Celsius? $C = \frac{5}{9}(F - 32)$; **10°C**

EXTRA PRACTICE for Lesson 2.2, p. 939   🖉 **ONLINE QUIZ** at classzone.com   **79**

5 ASSESS AND RETEACH

Daily Homework Quiz
📋 Transparency Available

Find the sum.

1. $7.6 + (-9)$ **−1.4**

2. $-23.7 + 28.2 + 8.3$ **12.8**

3. What property is illustrated by $(-y + 3) + 6 = -y + (3 + 6)$? **Associative property of addition**

4. The table shows the account ledgers for the Science Club and the Astronomy Club. Which club has the greater assets at the end of 3 weeks?

Week	Science Club	Astronomy Club
1	−$44.50	$106.00
2	$150.55	−$48.50
3	−$15.50	$35.00

The Astronomy Club has greater assets since $92.50 > $90.55.

 Online Quiz

Available at **classzone.com**

Diagnosis/Remediation

• Practice A, B, C in Chapter 2 Resource Book, pp. 16–18
• Study Guide in Chapter 2 Resource Book, pp. 19–20
• Practice Workbook, pp. 18–19
• @HomeTutor

Challenge

Additional challenge is available in the Chapter 2 Resource Book, p. 23.

Before	You added real numbers.
Now	You will subtract real numbers.
Why?	So you can find a change in temperature, as in Ex. 43.

Key Vocabulary
• opposites, p. 66

Because the expressions $12 - 3$ and $12 + (-3)$ have the same value, 9, you can conclude that $12 - 3 = 12 + (-3)$. Subtracting 3 from 12 is equivalent to adding the opposite of 3 to 12. This example illustrates the *subtraction rule.*

KEY CONCEPT   *For Your Notebook*

Subtraction Rule

Words To subtract b from a, add the opposite of b to a.

Algebra $a - b = a + (-b)$ **Example** $14 - 8 = 14 + (-8)$

EXAMPLE 1   Subtract real numbers

Find the difference.

a. $-12 - 19 = -12 + (-19)$ b. $18 - (-7) = 18 + 7$
    $\qquad\quad = -31$ $\qquad\qquad = 25$

 Animated Algebra at classzone.com

✓ **GUIDED PRACTICE**   for Example 1

Find the difference.

1. $-2 - 7$ **−9**   2. $11.7 - (-5)$ **16.7**   3. $\frac{1}{3} - \frac{1}{2}$ **$-\frac{1}{6}$**

EXAMPLE 2   Evaluate a variable expression

Evaluate the expression $y - x + 6.8$ when $x = -2$ and $y = 7.2$.

$y - x + 6.8 = 7.2 - (-2) + 6.8$ Substitute −2 for x and 7.2 for y.

$\qquad\qquad = 7.2 + 2 + 6.8$ Add the opposite of −2.

$\qquad\qquad = 16$ Add.

80   Chapter 2   Properties of Real Numbers

EVALUATING CHANGE You can use subtraction to find the change in a quantity, such as elevation or temperature. The change in a quantity is the difference of the new amount and the original amount. If the new amount is greater than the original amount, the change is positive. If the new amount is less than the original amount, the change is negative.

EXAMPLE 3   Evaluate change

TEMPERATURES One of the most extreme temperature changes in United States history occurred in Fairfield, Montana, on December 24, 1924. At noon, the temperature was 63°F. By midnight, the temperature fell to −21°F. What was the change in temperature?

Solution

The change C in temperature is the difference of the temperature m at midnight and the temperature n at noon.

STEP 1 **Write** a verbal model. Then write an equation.

| Change in temperature | = | Temperature at midnight | − | Temperature at noon |

$$C = m - n$$

STEP 2 **Find** the change in temperature.

$$C = m - n$$ Write equation.
$$= -21 - 63$$ Substitute values.
$$= -21 + (-63)$$ Add the opposite of 63.
$$= -84$$ Add −21 and −63.

▸ The change in temperature was −84°F.

> **AVOID ERRORS**
> When a quantity decreases, the change is negative. So, the change found in Example 3 should be a negative number.

USING A CALCULATOR To enter a negative number on a calculator, use the $\boxed{(-)}$ key. To enter a subtraction sign, use the $\boxed{-}$ key. You can use a calculator to check your answer in Example 3 using the following keystrokes.

$\boxed{(-)}$ 21 $\boxed{-}$ 63 $\boxed{\text{ENTER}}$

```
-21-63
              -84
```

✓ GUIDED PRACTICE   for Examples 2 and 3

Evaluate the expression when $x = -3$ and $y = 5.2$.

4. $x - y + 8$ **−0.2**   **5.** $y - (x - 2)$ **10.2**   **6.** $(y - 4) - x$ **4.2**

7. CAR VALUES A new car is valued at $15,000. One year later, the car is valued at $12,300. What is the change in the value of the car? **−$2700**

2.3   Subtract Real Numbers   **81**

Differentiated Instruction

Visual Learners On a calculator, some students may confuse the subtraction key with the negation key. Show them that the four operation keys $(+, -, \times, \div)$ are always together in a group. The negation key is not only set apart from the other keys, but it is often a different color.

See also the *Algebra 1 Toolkit* for more strategies.

Motivating the Lesson
Tell students that learning to subtract real numbers allows them to evaluate changes in quantities, such as the change in value of a $1500 computer that is valued at $975 after two years.

❸ TEACH

Extra Example 1
Find the difference.
a. −18 − 3 **−21**   **b.** −9 − (−12) **3**

Animated Algebra
classzone.com

An **Animated Algebra** activity is available on-line for **Example 1**. This activity is also available on the **Power Presentations CD-ROM**.

Extra Example 2
Evaluate the expression $x - y + 2.3$ when $x = 8.8$ and $y = -1.4$. **12.5**

Extra Example 3
The temperature one morning was 14°C. By midday, the temperature was −3°C. What was the change in temperature? **−17°C**

Closing the Lesson
Have students summarize the major points of the lesson and answer the Essential Question: How do you subtract real numbers?

- Subtracting b from a is the same as adding the opposite of b to a, so $a - b = a + (-b)$.
- The change in a quantity is the difference of the new amount and the original amount. If the quantity increases, the change is positive and if it decreases, the change is negative.

To subtract two numbers, add the opposite of the second number to the first number.

81

2.3 **EXERCISES**

HOMEWORK
KEY

○ = **WORKED-OUT SOLUTIONS**
on p. WS1 for Exs. 3, 21, and 43

★ = **STANDARDIZED TEST PRACTICE**
Exs. 2, 38, 39, 40, and 46

◆ = **MULTIPLE REPRESENTATIONS**
Ex. 45

4 **PRACTICE**
AND **APPLY**

Assignment Guide

📖 Answer Transparencies
available for all exercises

Basic:
Day 1: pp. 82–84
Exs. 1–16, 17–35 odd, 42–46,
49–55 odd

Average:
Day 1: pp. 82–84
Exs. 1, 2, 6–14 cvon, 15, 16,
20–30 even, 32–46, 50–56 even

Advanced:
Day 1: pp. 82–84
Exs. 1, 2, 10–14, 20–30 even,
32–41*, 43–48*, 52, 56

Block:
pp. 82–84
Exs. 1, 2, 6–14 even, 15, 16,
20–30 even, 32–46, 50–56 even
(with 2.2)

Differentiated Instruction

See *Algebra 1 Best Practices Toolkit*
for suggestions on addressing the
needs of a diverse classroom.

Homework Check

For a quick check of student understanding of key concepts, go over
the following exercises:

Basic: 7, 19, 23, 27, 42
Average: 10, 22, 28, 32, 42
Advanced: 13, 24, 30, 35, 43

Extra Practice

• Student Edition, p. 939
• Chapter 2 Resource Book:
  Practice levels A, B, C, pp. 28–30

Practice Worksheet

An easily-readable reduced
practice page (with answers)
for this lesson can be found
on p. 62C.

SKILL PRACTICE

A **1. VOCABULARY** Use the subtraction rule to rewrite the expression $-3 - 6$
as an addition expression. **$-3 + (-6)$**

2. ★ WRITING Without actually subtracting, how can you tell whether a
change in a quantity will be negative? **If the second number is larger than the first number.**

EXAMPLE 1
on p. 80
for Exs. 3–14

FINDING DIFFERENCES Find the difference.

3. $13 - (-5)$ **18**   4. $16 - 32$ **−16**   5. $-11 - (-3)$ **−8**   6. $-15 - 29$ **−44**

7. $-35.9 - (-50)$ **14.1**   8. $14.7 - (-2.3)$ **17**   9. $-3.6 - 22.2$ **−25.8**   10. $-18.2 - (-15.4)$ **−2.8**

11. $\frac{1}{2} - \frac{5}{6}$ **$-\frac{1}{3}$**   12. $-\frac{5}{3} - \frac{8}{3}$ **$-4\frac{1}{3}$**   13. $\frac{1}{2} - \left(-\frac{1}{4}\right)$ **$\frac{3}{4}$**   14. $-\frac{7}{10} - \left(-\frac{2}{5}\right)$ **$-\frac{3}{10}$**

EXAMPLE 2
on p. 80
for Exs. 15–25

15. 8 was
substituted for y
instead of -8;
$3 - (-8) + 2 =$
$3 + 8 + 2 = 13.$

16. The opposite
of -12 was not
added in step 3;
$3 - [-4 + (-8)]$
$= 3 - (-12) =$
$3 + 12 = 15.$

ERROR ANALYSIS *Describe* and correct the error in evaluating the
expression when $x = 3$ and $y = -8$.

15.
$$x - y + 2 = 3 - 8 + 2$$
$$= 3 + (-8) + 2$$
$$= -5 + 2$$
$$= -3$$ ✗

16.
$$x - (-4 + y) = 3 - [-4 + (-8)]$$
$$= 3 - (-12)$$
$$= 3 - 12$$
$$= -9$$ ✗

EVALUATING EXPRESSIONS Evaluate the expression when $x = 7.1$ and $y = -2.5$.

17. $x - (-y)$ **4.6**   18. $y - x - 12$ **−21.6**   19. $x - (-6) + y$ **10.6**

20. $x - (y - 13)$ **22.6**   21. $-y - (1.9 - x)$ **7.7**   22. $-y - x$ **−4.6**

23. $x - y - 2$ **7.6**   24. $5.3 - (y - x)$ **14.9**   25. $x + y - 2.8$ **1.8**

EXAMPLE 3
on p. 81
for Exs. 26–31

EVALUATING CHANGE Find the change in temperature or elevation.

26. From $-5°C$ to $-13°C$ **−8°C**   27. From $-45°F$ to $62°F$ **107°F**

28. From -300 feet to -100 feet **200 ft**   29. From 1200 meters to -80 meters **−1280 m**

30. From $4.8°F$ to $-12.6°F$ **−17.4°F**   31. From -90.7 miles to 36.4 miles **127.1 mi**

B **EVALUATING EXPRESSIONS** Evaluate the expression when $x = 3.6$, $y = 6.6$,
and $z = -11$.

32. $(x - y) - |z|$ **−14**   33. $(x - |-y|) - z$ **8**   34. $x - |y - z|$ **−14**

35. $(-x - y) - z - 5$ **−4.2**   36. $x + y - z + 12.9$ **34.1**   37. $-z + y - x - (-2.4)$ **16.4**

38. ★ MULTIPLE CHOICE If the value of the expression $a - b$ is negative,
which statement must be true? **C**

(A) $a > b$ (B) $a = 0$ (C) $a < b$ (D) $b = 0$

39. *Sample answer:* You are overdrawn on your ohooking account by $23. You write two more checks for $14 and $8. What is your balance?; −$45

39. ★ **OPEN-ENDED** Write a real-world problem that can be modeled by the expression −23 − 14 − 8. Then solve the problem.

40. ★ **WRITING** Tell whether the associative property and the commutative property hold for subtraction. Give examples to support your answers. **No.** *Sample answer:* (2 − 3) − 4 ≠ 2 − (3 − 4), 2 − 5 ≠ 5 − 2

41. **CHALLENGE** Let a and b be negative numbers. Tell whether the value of the expression is positive or negative. *Explain* your reasoning. **See margin.**

a. $|a + b|$ b. $-a - b$ c. $-|a| - |b|$ d. $a + b$

PROBLEM SOLVING

EXAMPLE 3 **A**
on p. 81
for Exs. 42–43

42. **VOLCANOES** Mahukona is a Hawaiian volcano whose summit has an elevation of −3600 feet. The summit once had an elevation of 800 feet. What was the change in elevation of the volcano's summit? **−4400 ft**

@**HomeTutor** for problem solving help at classzone.com

43. **CAVES** The temperature inside Mammoth Cave in Kentucky is about 12.2°C year round. If the temperature outside the cave is −2.4°C, what is the change in temperature from outside to inside the cave? **14.6°C**

@**HomeTutor** for problem solving help at classzone.com

44. **FOOTBALL** In four plays a football team gains 3 yards, loses 7 yards, loses 2 yards, and gains 15 yards. How many yards did the team gain after four plays? **9 yd**

45a. $d = t - 342$

45b.

t	d
341.7	20.3
343.8	1.8
340.9	21.1
342.7	0.7

341.7 and 340.9; you can tell if $t - 342$ is negative.

45. ◆ **MULTIPLE REPRESENTATIONS** In order to qualify for a girls' regional 1500 meter race, an athlete's personal best time for the season must be under the qualifying time of 5 minutes 42 seconds.

a. **Writing an Equation** Write an equation that expresses d as the difference of the athlete's personal best time t (in seconds) and the qualifying time (in seconds).

b. **Making a Table** Make a table that gives the values of d for $t = 341.7$, 343.8, 340.9, and 342.7. Which values of t in the table are under the qualifying time? How can you tell from the differences?

B

46. ★ **SHORT RESPONSE** A trade surplus or deficit is the difference of the value of all exports and the value of all imports. A positive difference is a surplus, and a negative difference is a deficit. The table shows the values of the United States' imports and exports for the period 2000–2003.

Year	2000	2001	2002	2003
Value of exports (trillions of dollars)	1.071	1.007	0.976	1.021
Value of imports (trillions of dollars)	1.449	1.369	1.398	1.517

a. **Calculate** Find the trade surplus or deficit for each year. **−$.378 trillion; −$.362 trillion; −$.422 trillion; −$.496 trillion**

b. **Describe** *Describe* any trends in the surplus or deficit over the years. *Sample answer:* There is a deficit each year and it has increased each year.

2.3 Subtract Real Numbers **83**

Avoiding Common Errors

Exercises 26–31 Remind students that a change is positive if the new amount is greater than the original and negative if the new amount is less than the original. Point out that the new amount could be greater than the original amount and still be a negative number.

📱 **Graphing Calculator**

Exercises 26–31, 46 Students can use their calculators to check their answers for exercises 26–31 and to calculate trade surpluses and deficits for exercise 46. Tell them to use the instructions for the calculator in Example 3. Note that they do not need to use negative numbers for exercise 46.

🔎 **Internet Reference**

Exercise 42 Additional information about volcanoes can be found at http://www.geology.sdsu.edu/how_volcanoes_work

Study Strategy

Exercises 42–43 Instruct students to write out detailed solutions for these exercises using Example 3 as a model. This will help them determine the original quantity and the new quantity and avoid confusing the two.

Reading Strategy

Exercise 45 Point out to students that part a on writing an equation states that the best time and the qualifying time are in seconds.

Exercise 47 Encourage students to read the introduction on snowboards and study the diagram before answering part a.

41a. Positive; the absolute value of a negative number is positive.

41b. Positive; if $-a - b$ is written as a sum, $-a + (-b)$, then the opposite of a negative number is positive. The sum of two positive numbers is positive.

41c. Negative; if $-|a| - |b|$ is written as a sum, $-|a| + (-|b|)$, the opposite of the absolute value of a number is negative. The sum of two negative numbers is negative.

41d. Negative; the sum of two negative numbers is negative.

47. SNOWBOARDS Snowboarders can rotate the shoe bindings on their snowboards. The binding setup shown below is written +24°/−18°. This means that the front angle is 24° counterclockwise from vertical, and the rear angle is 18° clockwise from vertical.

a. An instructor suggests a binding setup of +30°/+15° for beginners. Your setup is initially +24°/−4°. Find the changes in angle measures needed to match the instructor's suggestion. **6°; 19°**

b. A mirror setup is a setup of +n°/−n° where n is between 0 and 90. Your setup is initially +13°/−6°. You change the front angle measure by −3°. Find the change in the rear angle measure needed for a mirror setup. **−4°**

C **48. CHALLENGE** Greenwich Mean Time (GMT) is the time at the Royal Observatory in Greenwich, England. A location that is +n hours from GMT is n hours ahead of GMT, and a location that is −n hours from GMT is n hours behind GMT. Costa Rica is −6 hours from GMT, and India is +5.5 hours from GMT. If it is 7:45 A.M. in India, what time is it in Costa Rica? **8:15 P.M.**

MIXED REVIEW

Evaluate the expression.

49. $20x$ when $x = 15$ *(p. 2)* **300**

50. $3x + 8$ when $x = 12$ *(p. 8)* **44**

51. $15.5 + x$ when $x = -30.2$ *(p. 74)* **−14.7**

52. $-x + 19.4$ when $x = 8.2$ *(p. 74)* **11.2**

PREVIEW Prepare for Lesson 2.4 in Exs. 53–56.

Identify the property illustrated. *(p. 74)*

53. $1 + 7 = 7 + 1$ **Commutative property of addition**

54. $-4.8 + 4.8 = 0$ **Inverse property of addition**

55. $0 + (-9) = -9$ **Identity property of addition**

56. $(2 + 3) + 4 = 2 + (3 + 4)$ **Associative property of addition**

QUIZ *for Lessons 2.1–2.3*

1. Tell whether each of the following numbers is a whole number, an integer, or a rational number: $-\frac{5}{6}$, -8.2, 0, -9. Then order the numbers from least to greatest. *(p. 64)* $-\frac{5}{6}$**: rational number, −8.2: rational number, 0: whole number, integer, rational number, −9: integer, rational number;** $-9, -8.2, -\frac{5}{6}, 0$

Find the sum or difference.

2. $5 + (-36)$ *(p. 74)* **−31**

3. $-8.2 + (-2.3)$ *(p. 74)* **−10.5**

4. $3\frac{1}{2} + (-2)$ *(p. 74)* $1\frac{1}{2}$

5. $-18 - (-9)$ *(p. 80)* **−9**

6. $-11.2 - 21.7$ *(p. 80)* **−32.9**

7. $4\frac{1}{2} - \left(-\frac{1}{5}\right)$ *(p. 80)* $4\frac{7}{10}$

Evaluate the expression when $x = 2.5$ and $y = -3.4$. *(p. 80)*

8. $x + y - 9$ **−9.9**

9. $x - (y - 5.1)$ **11**

10. $12.1 - (y - x)$ **18**

@HomeTutor
classzone.com
Keystrokes

2.3 Subtract Real Numbers

QUESTION How can you use a spreadsheet to subtract the same number from various numbers?

In a spreadsheet, the columns are identified by letters, and the rows are identified by numbers. Each cell has a name that is made up of a letter and a number. For example, B2 is the cell in column B and row 2. A cell can contain a label, a number, or a formula.

	A	B
1		
2		

EXAMPLE Find the difference of two numbers

A manufacturing company is making foam hand grips for bicycles and jump ropes. The ideal length of a hand grip is 5 inches. In a batch of ten hand grips, the actual lengths (in inches) are 4.878, 4.902, 5.115, 5.13, 4.877, 4.874, 4.799, 4.819, 4.879, and 5.124. Create a spreadsheet to find the difference of the actual length and the ideal length for each hand grip.

Solution

STEP 1 *Enter data*

Enter the labels in the first row of the spreadsheet. Then enter the grip numbers and grip lengths in successive rows.

	A	B	C
1	Grip	Length (inches)	Difference
2	1	4.878	
3	2	4.902	

STEP 2 *Calculate differences*

For each hand grip, enter the formula for the difference of the actual and ideal lengths in the appropriate cell in column C. **See margin.**

	A	B	C
1	Grip	Length (inches)	Difference
2	1	4.878	=B2−5
3	2	4.902	=B3−5

After you enter a formula, the cell should display the difference of the length of the grip and the ideal length. For example, C2 should display −0.122, and C3 should display −0.098.

DRAW CONCLUSIONS

1. The manufacturer will consider a hand grip acceptable if the absolute value of the difference of the actual length and the ideal length is at most 0.125 inch. How many hand grips from the batch are acceptable? **6 hand grips**

2. What are the least and greatest possible lengths that a hand grip can have and still be acceptable? *Explain* your reasoning. **4.875 in., 5.125 in.; adding and subtracting 0.125 from 5 will give the greatest and least acceptable lengths of a hand grip.**

3. For which of the ten hand grips is the length closest to the ideal length? How can you tell from the differences in column C? **4.902; the difference in the lengths has the smallest absolute value.**

4. In another batch of ten hand grips, the actual lengths (in inches) are 4.871, 5.019, 5.112, 4.987, 5.067, 4.899, 4.859, 5.132, 5.126, and 5.093. Create a spreadsheet to find the difference of the actual length and the ideal length for each hand grip. **See margin.**

2.3 Subtract Real Numbers **85**

@HomeTutor
classzone.com
Keystrokes

❶ PLAN AND PREPARE

Learn the Method

• Students will use a spreadsheet to subtract real numbers.

• After the activity, students can use a spreadsheet to check their table calculations in Exercise 46, Lesson 2.3.

❷ TEACH

Alternative Strategy

Show students that they do not need to enter the formula in each cell in Step 2. Demonstrate that they can enter the formula for cell C2, click on the cell, move the cursor to the bottom right corner of the cell until the plus icon appears, click on the icon, and then move the cursor to the bottom of row 11. Students can check that the correct formula is entered by clicking on a cell. The formula will appear in the *fx* box at the top of the page. Warn that this works only if they have already entered all of the grip lengths in column B.

Extra Example

A manufacturing plant fills boxes with dog biscuits. The ideal weight per box is 12 ounces. In a batch of ten boxes, the actual weights (in ounces) are 11.025, 11.280, 11.275, 12.024, 11.685, 12.3, 11.45, 12.54, 11.955, and 12.2. Create a spreadsheet to find the difference of the actual weight and the ideal weight for each box of dog biscuits. **Enter box numbers in column A, actual weights in column B, and the formulas =B2−12, =B3−12, and so on in column C.**

❸ ASSESS AND RETEACH

Suppose you made a spreadsheet to find the differences of the ideal and actual lengths of the grips. What would be the formula? Would the results be the same? **=5−B2, =5−B3, =5−B4, . . . ; yes**

Step 2, 4. See Additional Answers beginning on p. AA1.

Lessons 2.1–2.3

4. *Sample answer:* You start a babysitting service. It costs you $35.50 for a training course and then you spend $12.43 on games to bring with you. After your first week, you've earned $50.43. The expression −35.50 + (−12.43) + 50.43 represents the profit or loss from the first week of business; $2.50.

5. −14; −444; −579; −515; −222. *Sample answer:* Each year more people migrate out of the city than migrate into it.

1. MULTI-STEP PROBLEM The table shows the record low temperatures for several states in the United States.

State	Temperature (°F)
Alaska	−80
Arkansas	−29
California	−45
Hawaii	12
Kentucky	−37

a. Order the temperatures from least to greatest. **−80°F, −45°F, −37°F, −29°F, 12°F**

b. The record low temperature in Arizona is −40°F. Which states in the table have record low temperatures less than −40°F? **Alaska and California**

2. MULTI-STEP PROBLEM Your bank charges a $35 fee when the balance in your checking account is negative. You have a balance of $150 in your account. You withdraw $165 using your debit card.

a. What will the balance in your account be after the fee is charged? **−$50**

b. How much money do you need to deposit into the account so that the balance is $0? **$50**

3. GRIDDED ANSWER At the close of trading on the New York Stock Exchange on Monday, the value of a share of a certain stock was $10.65. Over the next three days, the change in value of a share was −$.56, then −$1.09, and then $.89. What was the value of a share of the stock at the end of the three days? **$9.89**

4. OPEN-ENDED *Describe* a real-world situation that can be modeled by the expression −35.50 + (−12.43) + 50.43. Then find the value of the expression. **See margin.**

5. SHORT RESPONSE Net migration flow is the difference of the number of people migrating into a place and the number of people migrating out of a place. The table shows the number of people who migrated into and out of a certain city during the period 2001–2005.

Year	Number migrating into city	Number migrating out of city
2001	3302	3316
2002	3179	3623
2003	3053	3632
2004	3180	3695
2005	3174	3396

Find the net migration flow for each year. Then describe any trends in the city's net migration flow during this period. **See margin.**

6. EXTENDED RESPONSE In meteorology, the lifted index measures the likelihood of a thunderstorm. The greater the lifted index, the less likely a storm will occur. The table shows the lifted index for two cities at various times during a day.

Time	Lifted index for city A	Lifted index for city B
12 A.M.	−5.6	−0.8
4 A.M.	−4.3	−1.8
8 A.M.	−3.8	−2.3
12 P.M.	−2.5	−2.6
4 P.M.	−3.0	−1.4
8 P.M.	−4.5	0.8

a. At what time during that day is a storm least likely to occur in city A? **12 P.M.**

b. Compare the likelihood of a storm between 12 A.M. and 8 P.M. for the two cities on that day. *Sample answer:* **A storm is less likely in city B except at 12 P.M.**

c. Would you expect a storm in city B but not in city A at 8 P.M. that day? *Explain.* **No, because the lifted index is greater in city B.**

2.4 Multiplication by −1

MATERIALS · paper and pencil

QUESTION   What is the product of any integer *a* and −1?

You can rewrite a multiplication expression as repeated addition. For example, 3 · 8 can be rewritten as 8 + 8 + 8. Because the sum is 24, you can conclude that 3 · 8 = 24.

EXPLORE   Find the product of an integer and −1

STEP 1   Copy and complete the table.

Multiplication Expression	Addition Expression	Sum
5 · (−1)	−1 + (−1) + (−1) + (−1) + (−1)	−5
4 · (−1)	?	?
3 · (−1)	?	?
2 · (−1)	?	?

−1 + (−1) + (−1) + (−1); −4

−1 + (−1) + (−1); −3

−1 + (−1); −2

STEP 2   Copy and complete the multiplication equations below.

$5 \cdot (-1) = \underline{?} \ \mathbf{-5}$
$4 \cdot (-1) = \underline{?} \ \mathbf{-4}$ Complete using the table from Step 1.
$3 \cdot (-1) = \underline{?} \ \mathbf{-3}$
$2 \cdot (-1) = \underline{?} \ \mathbf{-2}$

$1 \cdot (-1) = \underline{?} \ \mathbf{-1}$
$0 \cdot (-1) = \underline{?} \ \mathbf{0}$
$-1 \cdot (-1) = \underline{?} \ \mathbf{1}$ Complete by extending the pattern in the first four products.
$-2 \cdot (-1) = \underline{?} \ \mathbf{2}$
$-3 \cdot (-1) = \underline{?} \ \mathbf{3}$

DRAW CONCLUSIONS   Use your observations to complete these exercises

1. Copy and complete: For any integer *a*, *a* · (−1) = $\underline{?}$.   **−a**

Find the product.

2. 12 · (−1) **−12**
3. 10 · (−1) **−10**
4. −23 · (−1) **23**
5. −47 · (−1) **47**
6. −18 · (−1) **18**
7. 15 · (−1) **−15**

2.4   Multiply Real Numbers   **87**

---

① PLAN AND PREPARE

Explore the Concept

- Students will multiply an integer by −1.
- This activity leads into the study of properties of multiplication in Example 2 in Lesson 2.4.

Recommended Time

Work activity: 10 min
Discuss results: 5 min

Grouping

Students can work individually or in pairs. If students work in pairs, one student can copy and complete the table in Step 1 and the other student can copy and complete the multiplication equations in Step 2. Each student can check the work of the other.

② TEACH

Key Questions

- What can you conclude from the table in Step 1? **The product of a positive integer and −1 is the opposite of the integer.**
- What is the pattern in Step 2? **At each step, add 1 to the product from the step before.**

Key Discovery

The product of an integer and −1 is the opposite of the integer.

③ ASSESS AND RETEACH

1. What is the sign of *a* · (−1) if *a* is a negative integer? **positive**
2. What is the sign of *a* · (−1) if *a* is a positive integer? **negative**

Before You added and subtracted real numbers.

Now You will multiply real numbers.

Why So you can calculate an elevation, as in Example 4.

Key Vocabulary
• multiplicative identity

In the activity on page 87, you saw that $a \cdot (-1) = -a$ for any integer a. This rule not only lets you write the product of a and -1 as $-a$, but it also lets you write $-a$ as $(-1)a$ and $a(-1)$. Using this rule, you can multiply any two real numbers. Here are two examples:

$$-2(3) = -1(2)(3) \qquad (-2)(-3) = -2(3)(-1)$$
$$= -1(6) \qquad\qquad\quad = -6(-1)$$
$$= -6 \qquad\qquad\qquad\quad = 6$$

KEY CONCEPT *For Your Notebook*

The Sign of a Product

Words The product of two real numbers with the *same* sign is positive.

Examples $3(4) = 12$ $\qquad\qquad -6(-3) = 18$

Words The product of two real numbers with *different* signs is negative.

Examples $2(-5) = -10$ $\qquad\qquad -7(2) = -14$

EXAMPLE 1 **Multiply real numbers**

Find the product.

MULTIPLY NEGATIVES
....
• A product is negative if it has an *odd* number of negative numbers.
• A product is positive if it has an *even* number of negative numbers.

a. $-3(6) = -18$ $\qquad$ Different signs; product is negative.

b. $2(-5)(-4) = (-10)(-4)$ $\qquad$ Multiply 2 and -5.
$\qquad\qquad\qquad = 40$ $\qquad$ Same signs; product is positive.

c. $-\frac{1}{2}(-4)(-3) = 2(-3)$ $\qquad$ Multiply $-\frac{1}{2}$ and -4.
$\qquad\qquad\qquad = -6$ $\qquad$ Different signs; product is negative.

 GUIDED PRACTICE for Example 1

Find the product.

1. $-2(-7)$ **14** $\qquad$ 2. $-0.5(-4)(-9)$ **−18** $\qquad$ 3. $\frac{4}{3}(-3)(7)$ **−28**

PROPERTIES OF MULTIPLICATION Notice that both $4(-5)$ and $-5(4)$ have a product of -20, so $4(-5) = -5(4)$. This equation is an example of the *commutative property of multiplication*. Properties of multiplication are listed below.

KEY CONCEPT *For Your Notebook*

Properties of Multiplication

COMMUTATIVE PROPERTY The order in which you multiply two numbers does not change the product.

Algebra $a \cdot b = b \cdot a$ **Example** $4 \cdot (-5) = -5 \cdot 4$

ASSOCIATIVE PROPERTY The way you group three numbers in a product does not change the product.

Algebra $(a \cdot b) \cdot c = a \cdot (b \cdot c)$ **Example** $(-2 \cdot 7) \cdot 4 = -2 \cdot (7 \cdot 4)$

IDENTITY PROPERTY The product of a number and 1 is that number.

Algebra $a \cdot 1 = 1 \cdot a = a$ **Example** $(-5) \cdot 1 = -5$

PROPERTY OF ZERO The product of a number and 0 is 0.

Algebra $a \cdot 0 = 0 \cdot a = 0$ **Example** $-3 \cdot 0 = 0$

PROPERTY OF −1 The product of a number and −1 is the opposite of the number.

Algebra $a \cdot (-1) = -1 \cdot a = -a$ **Example** $-2 \cdot (-1) = 2$

The identity property states that the product of a number a and 1 is a. The number 1 is called the **multiplicative identity**.

EXAMPLE 2 **Identify properties of multiplication**

Statement	Property illustrated
a. $(x \cdot 7) \cdot 0.5 = x \cdot (7 \cdot 0.5)$	Associative property of multiplication
b. $8 \cdot 0 = 0$	Multiplicative property of zero
c. $-6 \cdot y = y \cdot (-6)$	Commutative property of multiplication
d. $9 \cdot (-1) = -9$	Multiplicative property of −1
e. $1 \cdot v = v$	Identity property of multiplication

 GUIDED PRACTICE for Example 2

Identify the property illustrated.

4. $-1 \cdot 8 = -8$
Multiplicative property of −1
6. $(y \cdot 4) \cdot 9 = y \cdot (4 \cdot 9)$
Associative property of multiplication
8. $-5 \cdot (-6) = -6 \cdot (-5)$
Commutative property of multiplication

5. $12 \cdot x = x \cdot 12$
Commutative property of multiplication
7. $0 \cdot (-41) = 0$
Multiplicative property of zero
9. $-13 \cdot (-1) = 13$
Multiplicative property of −1

2.4 Multiply Real Numbers   **89**

EXAMPLE 3 Use properties of multiplication

Find the product $(-4x) \cdot 0.25$. Justify your steps.

$(-4x) \cdot 0.25 = 0.25 \cdot (-4x)$		Commutative property of multiplication
$= [0.25 \cdot (-4)]x$		Associative property of multiplication
$= -1 \cdot x$		Product of 0.25 and -4 is -1.
$= -x$		Multiplicative property of -1

Animated Algebra   at classzone.com

EXAMPLE 4 Solve a multi-step problem

LAKES In 1900 the elevation of Mono Lake in California was about 6416 feet. From 1900 to 1950, the average rate of change in elevation was about -0.12 foot per year. From 1950 to 2000, the average rate of change was about -0.526 foot per year. Approximate the elevation in 2000.

Solution

STEP 1 **Write** a verbal model.

New elevation (feet)	=	Original elevation (feet)	+	Average rate of change (feet/year)	·	Time passed (years)

STEP 2 **Calculate** the elevation in 1950. Use the elevation in 1900 as the original elevation. The time span is $1950 - 1900 = 50$ years.

New elevation $= 6416 + (-0.12)(50)$	**Substitute values.**
$= 6416 + (-6)$	**Multiply -0.12 and 50.**
$= 6410$	**Add 6416 and -6.**

STEP 3 **Calculate** the elevation in 2000. Use the elevation in 1950 as the original elevation. The time span is $2000 - 1950 = 50$ years.

New elevation $= 6410 + (-0.526)(50)$	**Substitute values.**
$= 6410 + (-26.3)$	**Multiply -0.526 and 50.**
$= 6383.7$	**Add 6410 and -26.3.**

▸ The elevation in 2000 was about 6383.7 feet above sea level.

  GUIDED PRACTICE for Examples 3 and 4

Find the product. *Justify* your steps. 10–12. See margin.

10. $\frac{3}{10}(5y)$ 11. $0.8(-x)(-1)$ 12. $(-y)(-0.5)(-6)$

13. Using the data in Example 4, approximate the elevation of Mono Lake in 1925 and in 1965. **about 6413 ft; about 6402.11 ft**

2.4 EXERCISES

HOMEWORK
KEY
○ = WORKED-OUT SOLUTIONS
on p. WS1 for Exs. 11, 31, and 51

★ = STANDARDIZED TEST PRACTICE
Exs. 2, 48, 52, 53, and 55

◆ = MULTIPLE REPRESENTATIONS
Ex. 54

SKILL PRACTICE

Ⓐ 1. **VOCABULARY** What number is called the multiplicative identity? **1**

2. ★ **WRITING** *Describe* the difference between the identity property of multiplication and the multiplicative property of −1. **See margin.**

EXAMPLE 1
on p. 88
for Exs. 3–18

FINDING PRODUCTS Find the product.

3. −4(7) **−28**   4. 11(−2) **−22**   5. −9(−10) **90**   6. −8(−11) **88**

7. 5(−7.2) **−36**   8. (−2.5)(−1.3) **3.25**   9. $-42\left(-\frac{1}{6}\right)$ **7**   10. $-\frac{1}{2}(-32)$ **16**

11. −1.9(3.3)(7)
    −43.89
12. 0.5(−20)(−3) **30**   13. $-\frac{5}{6}(-12)(-4)$ **−40**   14. $-\frac{3}{4}(2)(-6)$ **9**

15. −8(−4)(−2.5) **−80**   16. −1.6(−2)(−10)
    −32
17. $18\left(-\frac{2}{3}\right)\left(-\frac{1}{5}\right)$ $2\frac{2}{5}$ 18. $-\frac{3}{4}\left(-\frac{1}{3}\right)\left(-\frac{8}{9}\right)$ $-\frac{2}{9}$

EXAMPLE 2
on p. 89
for Exs. 19–27

IDENTIFYING PROPERTIES Identify the property illustrated. **19–27. See margin.**

19. $-\frac{2}{5} \cdot 0 = 0$ 20. $0.3 \cdot (-3) = -3 \cdot 0.3$ 21. $-143 \cdot 1 = -143$

22. $-1 \cdot (-6) = 6$ 23. $(-2 \cdot 5) \cdot 4 = -2 \cdot (5 \cdot 4)$ 24. $0 \cdot (-76.3) = 0$

25. $1 \cdot (ab) = ab$ 26. $(3x)y = 3(xy)$ 27. $s \cdot (-1) = -s$

EXAMPLE 3
on p. 90
for Exs. 28–36

USING PROPERTIES Find the product. *Justify* your steps. **28–36. See margin.**

28. $y(-2)(-8)$ 29. $-18(-x)$ 30. $\frac{3}{5}(-5q)$

31. −2(−6)(−7z)   32. $-5(-4)(-2.1)(-z)$ 33. $-\frac{1}{5}(-10)(4)(-5c)$

34. $-5t(-t)$ 35. $-6r(-2.8r)$ 36. $\frac{1}{3}\left(-\frac{9}{10}\right)(-m)(-m)$

Ⓑ **EVALUATING EXPRESSIONS** Evaluate the expression when $x = -2$ and $y = 3.6$.

37. $2x + y$ **−0.4**   38. $-x - 3y$ **−8.8**   39. $xy - 5.4$ **−12.6**

40. $|y| - 4x$ **11.6**   41. $1.5x - |-y|$ **−6.6**   42. $x^2 - y^2$ **−8.96**

43. −1(7) = −7,
not 7;
−1(7)(−3)(−2x)
= −7(−3)(−2x)
= 21(−2x) =
[21 · (−2)]x =
−42x

44. (−8)(−5) =
40, not −40;
(−8)(−5)(z)(z) =
40(z · z) = 40z²

ERROR ANALYSIS *Describe* and correct the error in finding the product.

43.
$$-1(7)(-3)(-2x) = 7(-3)(-2x)$$
$$= -21(-2x)$$
$$= [-21 \cdot (-2)]x$$
$$= 42x$$

44.
$$(-5z)(-8)(z) = (-8)(-5z)(z)$$
$$= (-8)(-5)(z)(z)$$
$$= -40(z \cdot z)$$
$$= -40z^2$$

○
4 **PRACTICE**
AND **APPLY**

Assignment Guide
🖳 **Answer Transparencies available for all exercises**

Basic:
Day 1: pp. 91–93
Exs. 1–11, 19–41 odd, 43, 44, 50–54, 58–64 even

Average:
Day 1: pp. 91–93
Exs. 1, 2, 10–42 even, 43–48, 50–55, 58–64 even

Advanced:
Day 1: pp. 91–93
Exs. 1, 2, 12–42 even, 43–49*, 51–56*, 57–63 odd

Block:
pp. 91–93
Exs. 1, 2, 10–42 even, 43–48, 50–55, 58–64 even (with 2.5)

Differentiated Instruction
See *Algebra 1 Best Practices Toolkit* for suggestions on addressing the needs of a diverse classroom.

Homework Check
For a quick check of student understanding of key concepts, go over the following exercises:
Basic: 7, 21, 29, 37, 50
Average: 12, 22, 32, 38, 51
Advanced: 16, 26, 34, 40, 52

Extra Practice
• Student Edition, p. 939
• Chapter 2 Resource Book:
  Practice levels A, B, C, pp. 39–41

Practice Worksheet

An easily-readable reduced practice page (with answers) for this lesson can be found on p. 62C.

2. *Sample answer:* The identity property of multiplication states that the product of a number and 1 is the number. The multiplicative property of −1 states that the product of a number and −1 is the *opposite* of the number.
19. Multiplicative property of zero
20. Commutative property of multiplication
21. Identity property of multiplication
22. Multiplicative property of −1
23. Associative property of multiplication

24. Multiplicative property of zero
25. Identity property of multiplication
26. Associative property of multiplication
27. Multiplicative property of −1
28–36. See Additional Answers beginning on p. AA1.

REASONING In Exercises 45–47, tell whether the statement is *true* or *false*. If it is false, give a counterexample.

45. If x is negative, then x^2 is positive. **true**

46. If the product of three numbers is positive, then all three numbers are positive. **False. Sample answer:** $(-1)(-2)(3) = 6$

47. If the product of four numbers is 0, then at least one of the numbers is 0. **true**

48. ★ **MULTIPLE CHOICE** Let a be a negative number. If the product abc is positive, which statement must be true? **B**

    (A) $bc > 0$ **(B)** $bc < 0$ **(C)** $ac > 0$ **(D)** $ab < 0$

49. **CHALLENGE** The product of n factors is negative. What is the greatest possible number of negative factors if n is even? if n is odd? Give several examples to support your answers. **$n - 1$; n. Sample answer: If you have 4 factors, $(-1)(-2)(-3)(4)$, the most that can be negative is 3, or $4 - 1$, for the product to be negative. If you have 5 factors, $(-1)(-2)(-3)(-4)(-5)$, all of them can be negative for the product to be negative.**

PROBLEM SOLVING

EXAMPLE 4 A
on p. 90
for Exs. 50–53

50. **DEAD SEA** In 1940 the surface area of the Dead Sea was about 980 square kilometers. From 1940 to 2001, the average rate of change in surface area was about –5.7 square kilometers per year. Find the surface area of the Dead Sea in 2001. **about 632.3 km²**

@HomeTutor for problem solving help at classzone.com

51. **STOCKS** An investor purchases 50 shares of a stock at $3.50 per share. The next day, the change in value of a share of the stock is –$.25. What is the total value of the shares the next day? **$162.50**

@HomeTutor for problem solving help at classzone.com

52b. about 0.47658 km³; find the total change in the volume of the glaciers between 1913 and 1994, then multiply the change by $\frac{1}{3}$.

52. ★ **SHORT RESPONSE** In 1913 the total volume of the glaciers on Mount Rainier was 5.62 cubic kilometers. The table shows the average rate of change in the volume for two periods of time.

Time period	Rate of change (km³/yr)
1913–1971	–0.02241
1971–1994	–0.00565

   a. Find the total volume of the glaciers in 1971 and in 1994. **4.32022 km³; 4.19027 km³**

   b. About one third of the change in volume during the period 1913–1994 took place in the northeastern glaciers. Find the change in the volume of the northeastern glaciers. *Explain* your steps.

53. ★ **MULTIPLE CHOICE** The Rialto Bridge in Venice, Italy, is a footbridge built in the late 16th century. The maximum clearance between the water and the bridge is about 7.32 meters. Because of a rising sea level and a gradual sinking of the city, the clearance changes at an average rate of about –2 millimeters per year. Approximate the clearance after 15 years. **C**

   (A) 5.32 meters   **(B)** 7.02 meters

   (C) 7.29 meters   **(D)** 7.318 meters

○ = **WORKED-OUT SOLUTIONS** on p. WS1   ★ = **STANDARDIZED TEST PRACTICE**   ◆ = **MULTIPLE REPRESENTATIONS**

B 54. ◆ **MULTIPLE REPRESENTATIONS** A skydiver in free fall will eventually reach a constant velocity, called terminal velocity. A skydiver reaches a terminal velocity of −160 feet per second at an altitude of 3200 feet.

4400 feet: Plane flies at this altitude.

3200 feet: Skydiver reaches terminal velocity.

2500 feet: Parachute opens.

   a. **Writing an Equation** Write an equation for the altitude a (in feet) of the skydiver as a function of the time t (in seconds) after reaching terminal velocity. $a = 3200 + (−160t)$

   b. **Making a Table** Make a table of values for $t = 1, 2, 3, 4$, and 5 seconds. The skydiver wants to open the parachute after reaching an altitude of about 2500 feet. After how many seconds should the skydiver open the parachute? **See margin.**

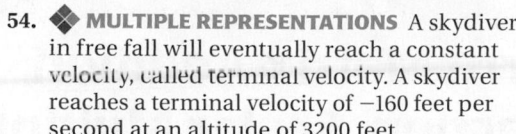 at classzone.com

55. ★ **EXTENDED RESPONSE** The table shows the fuel capacities of two ferries in Puget Sound, Washington, and the average rates of change in tank fuel when the ferries are burning fuel.

Ferry	Fuel capacity (gal)	Rate of change (gal/h)
Rhododendron	11,250	−30
Spokane	135,000	−240

   a. **Model** For each ferry, write an equation that gives the amount of tank fuel f (in gallons) as a function of the time t (in hours) that fuel is burned. $f = 11,250 + (−30t), f = 135,000 + (−240t)$

   b. **Calculate** Both ferries start with a full tank. How many gallons of fuel will each ferry have left after 3 hours? **11,160 gal, 134,280 gal**

   c. **Explain** If both ferries continue to burn fuel without refueling, which ferry will run out of fuel first? How many gallons will the other ferry have at that time? Your answer should include the following: **See margin.**

     • the number of hours that each ferry will take to burn all of its fuel

     • an explanation of how you used the equations in part (a)

C 56. **CHALLENGE** Due to soil erosion, the surface area of Dongting Lake in China is decreasing. Its surface area was about 2626.5 square kilometers in 1995. From 1950 to 1995, the average rate of change in surface area was about −38.3 square kilometers per year. From 1825 to 1950, the average rate of change was about −13.2 square kilometers per year. Approximate the surface area in 1825. **6000 km²**

MIXED REVIEW

PREVIEW
Prepare for
Lesson 2.5
in Exs. 57–60.

Evaluate the expression for the given value of the variable. *(p. 8)*

57. $1 + 9y^2$ when $y = 3$ **82**

58. $z^2 \cdot 2$ when $z = 6$ **72**

59. $2(x − 19)$ when $x = 24$ **10**

60. $9(17 + w)$ when $w = 8$ **225**

Find the sum or difference.

61. $−3 + (−6)$ *(p. 74)* **−9**

62. $7.8 + (−6.4) + (−9.4)$ *(p. 74)* **−8**

63. $−19.4 − (−6.4)$ *(p. 80)* **−13**

64. $−\frac{4}{7} − \frac{3}{14}$ *(p. 80)* $−\frac{11}{14}$

EXTRA PRACTICE for Lesson 2.4, p. 939   ⟳ **ONLINE QUIZ** at classzone.com   **93**

54b.

t	$3200 + (−160t)$
1	3040
2	2880
3	2720
4	2560
5	2400

4 sec

---

⑤**ASSESS** AND **RETEACH**

Daily Homework Quiz

📄 **Transparency Available**

Find the product.

1. $−6.5(4)(−2)$ **52**

2. $7.4(−1.2)(3)$ **−26.64**

Identify the property illustrated.

3. $r \cdot 0 = 0$ **Multiplicative property of zero**

4. $−y \cdot (−1) = y$ **Multiplicative property of −1**

5. Since Javier began setting his thermostat lower, his energy bills have been declining at a rate of −0.88 dollar per year. If his average bill was $130 in 1990, estimate his average bill in 2005. **$116.80**

⟳ **Online Quiz**

Available at **classzone.com**

Diagnosis/Remediation

• Practice A, B, C in Chapter 2 Resource Book, pp. 39–41

• Study Guide in Chapter 2 Resource Book, pp. 42–43

• Practice Workbook, pp. 22–23

• @HomeTutor

Challenge

Additional challenge is available in the Chapter 2 Resource Book, p. 46.

55c. Rhododendron; 45,000 gal; the Rhododendron takes 375 hours to burn all of its fuel; the Spokane takes 562.5 hours to burn all of its fuel; to find the number of hours the Rhododendron will take to burn all its fuel, use the equations in part (a) and find the additive inverse of 11,250, then divide it by −30; to find the number of hours the Spokane will take to burn all its fuel, use the equations in part (a) and find the additive inverse of 135,000, then divide it by −240.

Perform Matrix Addition, Subtraction, Scalar Multiplication

GOAL Perform operations on matrices.

1 PLAN AND PREPARE

Warm-Up Exercises

Perform the indicated operation.

1. $12.1 + (-15.2)$ **−3.1**

2. $-6 - (-9.8)$ **3.8**

3. $-15(-2.4)$ **36**

4. $4.8 \cdot (-5.5)(3)$ **−79.2**

2 FOCUS AND MOTIVATE

Essential Question

Big Idea 1, p. 63

How do you perform operations on matrices? **Tell students they will learn how to answer this question by adding and subtracting two matrices and by performing scalar multiplication.**

3 TEACH

Extra Example 1

Perform the indicated operation, if possible.

a. $\begin{bmatrix} 10 & -4 & -2 \\ 4 & -6 & 5 \end{bmatrix} - \begin{bmatrix} 11 & -1 & 3 \\ -4 & 0 & -8 \end{bmatrix}$

$\begin{bmatrix} -1 & -3 & -5 \\ 8 & -6 & 13 \end{bmatrix}$

b. $\begin{bmatrix} -5 & 14 & 0 \\ 6 & -7 & -4 \end{bmatrix} + \begin{bmatrix} -5 & -11 & -3 \\ -3 & -1 & 4 \end{bmatrix}$

$\begin{bmatrix} -10 & 3 & -3 \\ 3 & -8 & 0 \end{bmatrix}$

NCTM STANDARDS

Standard 2: Understand patterns

Standard 9: Use connections among mathematical ideas

Key Vocabulary
• matrix
• dimensions of a matrix
• element
• scalar multiplication
• scalar

A **matrix** is a rectangular arrangement of numbers in rows and columns. If a matrix has m rows and n columns, the **dimensions of the matrix** are written as $m \times n$. For example, matrix A below has two rows and three columns. The dimensions of matrix A are 2×3 (read "2 by 3"). Each number in a matrix is called an **element**, or *entry*. In matrix A, the element in the first row and second column is 4.

$$A = \begin{bmatrix} 0 & 4 & -1 \\ -3 & 2 & 5 \end{bmatrix} \text{2 rows}$$
$$\text{3 columns}$$

MATRIX ADDITION AND SUBTRACTION To add or subtract matrices (the plural of *matrix*), you add or subtract corresponding elements. You can add or subtract matrices only if they have the same dimensions.

EXAMPLE 1 Add or subtract two matrices

Perform the indicated operation, if possible.

a. $\begin{bmatrix} 0 & 4 & -1 \\ -3 & 2 & 5 \end{bmatrix} + \begin{bmatrix} 2 & 1 & 3 \\ -2 & -6 & 4 \end{bmatrix} = \begin{bmatrix} 0+2 & 4+1 & -1+3 \\ -3+(-2) & 2+(-6) & 5+4 \end{bmatrix}$

$= \begin{bmatrix} 2 & 5 & 2 \\ -5 & -4 & 9 \end{bmatrix}$

b. $\begin{bmatrix} -10 & 2 \\ -4 & 7 \\ 7 & -13 \end{bmatrix} - \begin{bmatrix} 9 & -2 \\ 4 & 8 \\ -5 & -11 \end{bmatrix} = \begin{bmatrix} -10-9 & 2-(-2) \\ -4-4 & 7-8 \\ 7-(-5) & -13-(-11) \end{bmatrix}$

$= \begin{bmatrix} -10+(-9) & 2+2 \\ -4+(-4) & 7+(-8) \\ 7+5 & -13+11 \end{bmatrix}$

$= \begin{bmatrix} -19 & 4 \\ -8 & -1 \\ 12 & -2 \end{bmatrix}$

c. You can't perform the subtraction $\begin{bmatrix} 6 & -4 & -8 \end{bmatrix} - \begin{bmatrix} 1 \\ 12 \\ -6 \end{bmatrix}$ because the first matrix is a 1×3 matrix and the second matrix is a 3×1 matrix.

94 Chapter 2 Properties of Real Numbers

SCALAR MULTIPLICATION In **scalar multiplication**, every element in a matrix is multiplied by a real number called a **scalar**.

EXAMPLE 2 Perform scalar multiplication

Perform the indicated operation.

a. $6\begin{bmatrix} -7 & -\frac{1}{3} \\ \frac{1}{2} & 11 \end{bmatrix} = \begin{bmatrix} 6(-7) & 6\left(-\frac{1}{3}\right) \\ 6\left(\frac{1}{2}\right) & 6(11) \end{bmatrix}$

$= \begin{bmatrix} -42 & -2 \\ 3 & 66 \end{bmatrix}$

b. $-2\begin{bmatrix} 0.5 \\ -3.2 \\ 8.1 \end{bmatrix} = \begin{bmatrix} -2(0.5) \\ -2(-3.2) \\ -2(8.1) \end{bmatrix}$

$= \begin{bmatrix} -1 \\ 6.4 \\ -16.2 \end{bmatrix}$

PRACTICE

**EXAMPLES
1 and 2**
on pp. 94–95
for Exs. 1–10

Perform the indicated operation, if possible.

1. $\begin{bmatrix} 7 & 6 \\ 3 & 2 \end{bmatrix} + \begin{bmatrix} 9 & -2 \\ 5 & 10 \end{bmatrix}$ $\begin{bmatrix} \mathbf{16} & \mathbf{4} \\ \mathbf{8} & \mathbf{12} \end{bmatrix}$

2. $\begin{bmatrix} -8 \\ -4 \\ 1 \end{bmatrix} + \begin{bmatrix} 11 \\ -9 \\ -6 \end{bmatrix}$ $\begin{bmatrix} \mathbf{3} \\ \mathbf{-13} \\ \mathbf{-5} \end{bmatrix}$

3. $\begin{bmatrix} -8 & -1 & -9 \\ -4 & -3 & 2 \end{bmatrix} - \begin{bmatrix} 7 & 3 & 0 \\ -2 & -5 & 7 \end{bmatrix}$
   See margin.

4. $\begin{bmatrix} 11 & -12 \\ 15 & -22 \end{bmatrix} - \begin{bmatrix} 7 \\ 8 \end{bmatrix}$
   Cannot be performed.

5. $\begin{bmatrix} -9.1 & 5.4 & 3.7 \end{bmatrix} + \begin{bmatrix} 1.3 & -6.7 \end{bmatrix}$
   Cannot be performed.

6. $\begin{bmatrix} \frac{3}{4} & -2 \\ 6 & -3 \end{bmatrix} - \begin{bmatrix} 8 & -2 \\ 6 & -\frac{5}{6} \end{bmatrix}$ $\begin{bmatrix} \mathbf{-7\frac{1}{4}} & \mathbf{0} \\ \mathbf{0} & \mathbf{-2\frac{1}{6}} \end{bmatrix}$

7. $7\begin{bmatrix} -4 & -7 \\ \frac{1}{2} & \frac{4}{9} \end{bmatrix}$ $\begin{bmatrix} \mathbf{-28} & \mathbf{-49} \\ \mathbf{3\frac{1}{2}} & \mathbf{3\frac{1}{9}} \end{bmatrix}$

8. $2\begin{bmatrix} 1.5 & -6 \\ -4.5 & 0 \end{bmatrix}$ $\begin{bmatrix} \mathbf{3} & \mathbf{-12} \\ \mathbf{-9} & \mathbf{0} \end{bmatrix}$

9. $-6\begin{bmatrix} 12 \\ -3.4 \\ -0.7 \end{bmatrix}$ $\begin{bmatrix} \mathbf{-72} \\ \mathbf{20.4} \\ \mathbf{4.2} \end{bmatrix}$

10. $-\frac{1}{2}\begin{bmatrix} 18 & -26 & \frac{7}{4} \\ -\frac{2}{3} & 20 & -2 \end{bmatrix}$ $\begin{bmatrix} \mathbf{-9} & \mathbf{13} & \mathbf{-\frac{7}{8}} \\ \mathbf{\frac{1}{3}} & \mathbf{-10} & \mathbf{1} \end{bmatrix}$

11. **NUTRITION** The matrix shows the amounts (in milligrams) of calcium and potassium in one ounce of different types of milk. Write a matrix for the amounts of calcium and potassium in 8 ounces of each type of milk.

	Calcium (mg)	Potassium (mg)	Calcium (mg)	Potassium (mg)
Lowfat milk	32.940	36.295	**263.52**	**290.36**
Reduced fat milk	33.855	42.700	**270.84**	**341.6**
Whole milk	30.805	40.565	**246.44**	**324.52**

CHALLENGE Perform the indicated operations.

12. $9\left(\begin{bmatrix} 1 & -12 & 8 \\ -7 & 10 & -4 \end{bmatrix} + \begin{bmatrix} 3 & -3 & -7 \\ -5 & -21 & -12 \end{bmatrix}\right)$
    See margin.

13. $\begin{bmatrix} -6 & -8 \\ 8 & 14 \end{bmatrix} - 7\begin{bmatrix} 5 & 13 \\ -10 & -11 \end{bmatrix}$ $\begin{bmatrix} \mathbf{-41} & \mathbf{-99} \\ \mathbf{78} & \mathbf{91} \end{bmatrix}$

Extra Example 2
Perform the indicated operation.

a. $4\begin{bmatrix} -8 & 0.5 \\ \frac{1}{4} & -\frac{1}{2} \end{bmatrix}$ $\begin{bmatrix} \mathbf{-32} & \mathbf{2} \\ \mathbf{1} & \mathbf{-2} \end{bmatrix}$

b. $-2\begin{bmatrix} -1.6 \\ 2.4 \\ -5.5 \end{bmatrix}$ $\begin{bmatrix} \mathbf{3.2} \\ \mathbf{-4.8} \\ \mathbf{11} \end{bmatrix}$

Closing the Lesson

Have students summarize the major points of the lesson and answer the Essential Question: How do you perform operations on matrices?

• Matrices must have the same dimensions to add or subtract.

• To perform scalar multiplication, multiply each element in the matrix by the scalar.

To add or subtract matrices with the same dimensions, add or subtract corresponding elements. For scalar multiplication, multiply all elements in the matrix by the scalar.

④ PRACTICE AND APPLY

Avoiding Common Errors

Exercises 1–10 Instruct students to write out the solutions, using Examples 1 and 2 as models. This will help them avoid adding, subtracting, or multiplying the wrong elements. It will also help them tell when two matrices do not have the same dimensions.

Reading Strategy

Exercise 11 For students who are having trouble solving this problem, ask whether it would make sense to add 8 ounces to find the number of milligrams of calcium and potassium, to subtract 8 ounces, or to multiply by 8 ounces.

3. $\begin{bmatrix} -15 & -4 & -9 \\ -2 & 2 & -5 \end{bmatrix}$

12. $\begin{bmatrix} 36 & -135 & 9 \\ -108 & -99 & -144 \end{bmatrix}$

95

Before You used properties to add and multiply real numbers.

Now You will apply the distributive property.

Why? So you can find calories burned, as in Example 5.

Key Vocabulary
• **equivalent expressions**
• **distributive property**
• **term**
• **coefficient**
• **constant term**
• **like terms**

The models below show two methods for finding the area of a rectangle that has a length of $(x + 2)$ units and a width of 3 units.

Area = 3(x + 2)

Area = 3(x) + 3(2)

The expressions $3(x + 2)$ and $3(x) + 3(2)$ are equivalent because they represent the same area. Two expressions that have the same value for all values of the variable are called **equivalent expressions**. The equation $3(x + 2) = 3(x) + 3(2)$ illustrates the **distributive property**, which can be used to find the product of a number and a sum or difference.

KEY CONCEPT *For Your Notebook*

The Distributive Property

Let a, b, and c be real numbers.

Words	Algebra	Examples
The product of a and $(b + c)$:	$a(b + c) = ab + ac$	$3(4 + 2) = 3(4) + 3(2)$
	$(b + c)a = ba + ca$	$(3 + 5)2 = 3(2) + 5(2)$
The product of a and $(b - c)$:	$a(b - c) = ab - ac$	$5(6 - 4) = 5(6) - 5(4)$
	$(b - c)a = ba - ca$	$(8 - 6)4 = 8(4) - 6(4)$

EXAMPLE 1 **Apply the distributive property**

AVOID ERRORS
Be sure to distribute the factor outside of the parentheses to *all* of the numbers inside the parentheses, not just to the first number.

Use the distributive property to write an equivalent expression.

a. $4(y + 3) = 4y + 12$

b. $(y + 7)y = y^2 + 7y$

c. $n(n - 9) = n^2 - 9n$

d. $(2 - n)8 = 16 - 8n$

EXAMPLE 2 **Distribute a negative number**

Use the distributive property to write an equivalent expression.

$$
\begin{aligned}
\textbf{a.} \quad -2(x + 7) &= -2(x) + (-2)(7) &&\text{Distribute } -2.\\
&= -2x - 14 &&\text{Simplify.}\\
\textbf{b.} \quad (5 - y)(-3y) &= 5(-3y) - y(-3y) &&\text{Distribute } -3y.\\
&= -15y + 3y^2 &&\text{Simplify.}\\
\textbf{c.} \quad -(2x - 11) &= (-1)(2x - 11) &&\text{Multiplicative property of } -1\\
&= (-1)(2x) - (-1)(11) &&\text{Distribute } -1.\\
&= -2x + 11 &&\text{Simplify.}
\end{aligned}
$$

TERMS AND COEFFICIENTS The parts of an expression that are added together are called **terms**. The number part of a term with a variable part is called the **coefficient** of the term.

READING
Note that $-x$ has a coefficient of -1 even though the 1 isn't written. Similarly, x has a coefficient of 1.

Terms

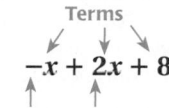

$$-x + 2x + 8$$

Coefficients are -1 and 2.

A **constant term** has a number part but no variable part, such as 8 in the expression above. **Like terms** are terms that have the same variable parts, such as $-x$ and $2x$ in the expression above. Constant terms are also like terms.

EXAMPLE 3 **Identify parts of an expression**

Identify the terms, like terms, coefficients, and constant terms of the expression $3x - 4 - 6x + 2$.

Solution

Write the expression as a sum: $3x + (-4) + (-6x) + 2$

Terms: $3x, -4, -6x, 2$ **Like terms:** $3x$ and $-6x$; -4 and 2

Coefficients: $3, -6$ **Constant terms:** $-4, 2$

✓ **GUIDED PRACTICE** for Examples 1, 2, and 3

Use the distributive property to write an equivalent expression.

1. $2(x + 3)$ **2.** $-(4 - y)$ **3.** $(m - 5)(-3m)$ **4.** $(2n + 6)\left(\dfrac{1}{2}\right)$
$2x + 6$ $-4 + y$ $-3m^2 + 15m$ $n + 3$

5. Identify the terms, like terms, coefficients, and constant terms of the expression $-7y + 8 - 6y - 13$.
terms: $-7y, 8, -6y, -13$; like terms: $-7y$ and $-6y$, 8 and -13;
coefficients: $-7, -6$; constant terms: 8, -13

COMBINING LIKE TERMS The distributive property allows you to combine like terms that have variable parts. For example, $5x + 6x = (5 + 6)x = 11x$. A quick way to combine like terms with variable parts is to mentally add the coefficients and use the common variable part. An expression is *simplified* if it has no grouping symbols and if all of the like terms have been combined.

2.5 Apply the Distributive Property   **97**

EXAMPLE 4   Standardized Test Practice

ANOTHER WAY
In Example 4, you can
rewrite the expression
$4(n + 9) - 3(2 + n)$ as
$4(n + 9) + (-3)(2 + n)$
and then distribute -3
to the terms in $2 + n$.

Simplify the expression $4(n + 9) - 3(2 + n)$.

(A) $5n + 30$ (B) $n + 30$ (C) $5n + 3$ (D) $n + 3$

$$4(n + 9) - 3(2 + n) = 4n + 36 - 6 - 3n \qquad \text{Distributive property}$$
$$= n + 30 \qquad \text{Combine like terms.}$$

▶ The correct answer is B. (A) (B) (C) (D)

EXAMPLE 5   Solve a multi-step problem

EXERCISING Your daily workout plan involves a total of
50 minutes of running and swimming. You burn 15 calories
per minute when running and 9 calories per minute when
swimming. Let r be the number of minutes that you run. Find
the number of calories you burn if you run for 20 minutes.

ANOTHER WAY
For an alternative
method for solving the
problem in Example 5,
turn to page 102 for
the **Problem Solving
Workshop**.

Solution
The workout lasts 50 minutes, and your running time is
r minutes. So, your swimming time is $(50 - r)$ minutes.

STEP 1 Write a verbal model. Then write an equation.

Amount burned (calories)	=	Burning rate when running (calories/minute)	·	Running time (minutes)	+	Burning rate when swimming (calories/minute)	·	Swimming time (minutes)
C	=	15	·	r	+	9	·	$(50 - r)$

$$C = 15r + 9(50 - r) \qquad \text{Write equation.}$$
$$= 15r + 450 - 9r \qquad \text{Distributive property}$$
$$= 6r + 450 \qquad \text{Combine like terms.}$$

STEP 2 Find the value of C when $r = 20$.

$$C = 6r + 450 \qquad \text{Write equation.}$$
$$= 6(20) + 450 = 570 \qquad \text{Substitute 20 for } r. \text{ Then simplify.}$$

▶ You burn 570 calories if you run for 20 minutes and swim for 30 minutes.

Animated Algebra at classzone.com

✓ **GUIDED PRACTICE**   for Examples 4 and 5

6. Simplify the expression $5(6 + n) - 2(n - 2)$. **$34 + 3n$**

7. **WHAT IF?** In Example 5, suppose your workout lasts 45 minutes. How many
calories do you burn if you run for 20 minutes? 30 minutes? **525 calories;
585 calories**

21. terms: $-7, 13x, 2x, 8$; like terms:
-7 and 8, $13x$ and $2x$; coefficients:
13, 2; constant terms: -7, 8

22. terms: $9, 7y, -2, -5y$; like terms:
9 and -2, $7y$ and $-5y$; coefficients:
7, -5; constant terms: 9, -2

2.5 EXERCISES

HOMEWORK KEY
○ = **WORKED-OUT SOLUTIONS**
on p. WS1 for Exs. 9, 23, and 51
★ = **STANDARDIZED TEST PRACTICE**
Exs. 2, 27, 52, and 54

SKILL PRACTICE

A
1. **VOCABULARY** What are the coefficients of the expression $4x + 8 - 9x + 2$? **4, −9**

2. ★ **WRITING** Are the expressions $2(x + 1)$ and $2x + 1$ equivalent? *Explain.*
No; the 2 was not distributed to the 1, $2(x + 1) = 2x + 2$.

ERROR ANALYSIS *Describe* and correct the error in simplifying the expression.
3. **The negative was not distributed to the −8; $5y − (2y − 8) = 5y − 2y + 8 = 3y + 8$.**

3.
$$5y - (2y - 8) = 5y - 2y - 8$$
$$= 3y - 8 \quad \times$$

4.
$$8 + 2(4 + 3x) = 8 + 8 + 6x$$
$$= 22x \quad \times$$

4. **Unlike terms cannot be combined; $8 + 2(4 + 3x) = 8 + 8 + 6x = 16 + 6x$.**

EXAMPLES 1 and 2
on pp. 96–97
for Exs. 5–20

USING THE DISTRIBUTIVE PROPERTY Use the distributive property to write an equivalent expression.

5. $4(x + 3)$ **$4x + 12$**
6. $8(y + 2)$ **$8y + 16$**
7. $(m + 5)5$ **$5m + 25$**
8. $(n + 6)3$ **$3n + 18$**

○ 9. $(p − 3)(−8)$ **$−8p + 24$**
10. $−4(q − 4)$ **$−4q + 16$**
11. $2(2r − 3)$ **$4r − 6$**
12. $(s − 9)9$ **$9s − 81$**

13. $6v(v + 1)$ **$6v^2 + 6v$**
14. $−w(2w + 7)$ **$−2w^2 − 7w$**
15. $−2x(3 − x)$ **$2x^2 − 6x$**
16. $3y(y − 6)$ **$3y^2 − 18y$**

17. $\frac{1}{2}\left(\frac{1}{2}m − 4\right)$ **$\frac{1}{4}m − 2$**
18. $−\frac{3}{4}(p − 1)$ **$−\frac{3}{4}p + \frac{3}{4}$**
19. $\frac{2}{3}(6n − 9)$ **$4n − 6$**
20. $\frac{5}{6}r(r − 1)$ **$\frac{5}{6}r^2 − \frac{5}{6}r$**

EXAMPLE 3
on p. 97
for Exs. 21–26

IDENTIFYING PARTS OF AN EXPRESSION Identify the terms, like terms, coefficients, and constant terms of the expression. **21–26. See margin.**

21. $−7 + 13x + 2x + 8$
22. $9 + 7y − 2 − 5y$

○ 23. $7x^2 − 10 − 2x^2 + 5$
24. $−3y^2 + 3y^2 − 7 + 9$

25. $2 + 3xy − 4xy + 6$
26. $6xy − 11xy + 2xy − 4xy + 7xy$

27. ★ **MULTIPLE CHOICE** Which two terms are like terms? **B**

   (A) $−2, −5x$ **(B)** $4x, −x$ **(C)** $−2, −2y$ **(D)** $5x, −3y$

EXAMPLE 4
on p. 98
for Exs. 28–39

SIMPLIFYING EXPRESSIONS Simplify the expression.

28. $7x + (−11x)$ **$−4x$**
29. $6y − y$ **$5y$**
30. $5 + 2n + 2$ **$2n + 7$**

31. $(4a − 1)2 + a$ **$9a − 2$**
32. $3(2 − c) − c$ **$6 − 4c$**
33. $6r + 2(r + 4)$ **$8r + 8$**

34. $15t − (t − 4)$ **$14t + 4$**
35. $3(m + 5) − 10$ **$3m + 5$**
36. $−6(v + 1) + v$ **$−5v − 6$**

37. $7(w − 5) + 3w$ **$10w − 35$**
38. $6(5 − z) + 2z$ **$30 − 4z$**
39. $(s − 3)(−2) + 17s$ **$15s + 6$**

B ⬡ **GEOMETRY** Find the perimeter and area of the rectangle.

40.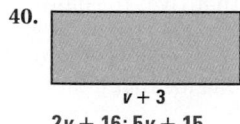
5
$v + 3$
$2v + 16$; $5v + 15$

41.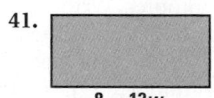
9
$8 − 12w$
$34 − 24w$; $72 − 108w$

42.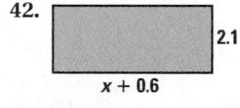
2.1
$x + 0.6$
$2x + 5.4$; $2.1x + 1.26$

---

23. terms: $7x^2$, −10, $−2x^2$, 5; like terms: $7x^2$ and $−2x^2$, −10 and 5; coefficients: 7, −2; constant terms: −10, 5
24. terms: $−3y^2$, $3y^2$, −7, 9; like terms: $−3y^2$ and $3y^2$, −7 and 9; coefficients: −3, 3; constant terms: −7, 9
25. terms: 2, $3xy$, $−4xy$, 6; like terms: 2 and 6, $3xy$ and $−4xy$; coefficients: 3, −4; constant terms: 2, 6
26. terms: $6xy$, $−11xy$, $2xy$, $−4xy$, $7xy$; like terms: $6xy$, $−11xy$, $2xy$, $−4xy$, and $7xy$; coefficients: 6, −11, 2, −4, 7; constant terms: none

---

④ PRACTICE AND APPLY

Assignment Guide

🖥 Answer Transparencies available for all exercises

Basic:
Day 1: SRH p. 925 Exs. 1, 2, 4, 5, 12
pp. 99–101
Exs. 1–15, 21–24, 62–67
Day 2: pp. 99–101
Exs. 27–42, 50–53, 56–61

Average:
Day 1: pp. 99–101
Exs. 1–4, 9–20, 23–27, 62–67
Day 2: pp. 99–101
Exs. 32–48, 50–54, 56–61

Advanced:
Day 1: pp. 99–101
Exs. 1, 2, 11–20, 23–27, 65–67
Day 2: pp. 99–101
Exs. 34–49*, 51–61*

Block:
pp. 99–101
Exs. 1–4, 9–20, 23–27, 62–67
(with 2.4)
pp. 99–101
Exs. 32–48, 50–54, 56–61 (with 2.6)

Differentiated Instruction

See *Algebra 1 Best Practices Toolkit* for suggestions on addressing the needs of a diverse classroom.

Homework Check

For a quick check of student understanding of key concepts, go over the following exercises:
Basic: 6, 10, 22, 31, 50
Average: 11, 15, 24, 35, 51
Advanced: 16, 18, 25, 37, 52

Extra Practice

• Student Edition, p. 939
• Chapter 2 Resource Book: Practice levels A, B, C, pp. 50–52

Practice Worksheet

An easily-readable reduced practice page (with answers) for this lesson can be found on p. 62C.

USING MENTAL MATH In Exercises 43–46, use the example below to find the total cost.

> **EXAMPLE** Use the distributive property and mental math
>
> Use the distributive property and mental math to find the total cost of 5 picture frames at $1.99 each.
>
> | | |
> |---|---|
> | Total cost $= 5(1.99)$ | Write expression for total cost. |
> | $= 5(2 - 0.01)$ | Rewrite 1.99 as $2 - 0.01$. |
> | $= 5(2) - 5(0.01)$ | Distributive property |
> | $= 10 - 0.05$ | Multiply using mental math. |
> | $= 9.95$ | Subtract. The total cost is $9.95. |

43. 3 CDs at $12.99 each **$38.97**   **44.** 5 magazines at $3.99 each **$19.95**

45. 6 pairs of socks at $1.98 per pair **$11.88**   **46.** 25 baseballs at $2.98 each **$74.50**

TRANSLATING PHRASES In Exercises 47 and 48, translate the verbal phrase into an expression. Then simplify the expression.

47. Twice the sum of 6 and x, increased by 5 less than x
$2(6 + x) + (x - 5); 3x + 7$

48. Three times the difference of x and 2, decreased by the sum of x and 10
$3(x - 2) - (x + 10); 2x - 16$

C **49.** **CHALLENGE** How can you use $a(b + c) = ab + ac$ to show that $(b + c)a = ba + ca$ is also true? *Justify* your steps.
$(b + c)a = a(b + c)$, Commutative property of multiplication; $= ab + ac$, Given statement; $= ba + ca$, Commutative property of multiplication

PROBLEM SOLVING

EXAMPLE 5 A
on p. 98
for Exs. 50–52

50. **SPORTS** An archer shoots 6 arrows at a target. Some arrows hit the 9 point ring, and the rest hit the 10 point bull's-eye. Write an equation that gives the score s as a function of the number a of arrows that hit the 9 point ring. Then find the score if 2 arrows hit the 9 point ring. $s = -a + 60; 58$

@HomeTutor for problem solving help at classzone.com

9 points   10 points

52. $C = 2.5 + 0.1(m - 10);$ 10 minutes today and 15 minutes tomorrow; the cost of using the phone 10 minutes today and 15 minutes tomorrow is $2.5 + 2.5 + 0.1(5) = 5.50; the cost of using the phone for 25 minutes today is $2.5 + 0.1(15) = $4.

51. **MOVIES** You have a coupon for $2 off the regular cost per movie rental. You rent 3 movies, and the regular cost of each rental is the same. Write an equation that gives the total cost C (in dollars) as a function of the regular cost r (in dollars) of a rental. Then find the total cost if a rental regularly costs $3.99. $C = 3r - 6; 5.97

@HomeTutor for problem solving help at classzone.com

52. ★ **SHORT RESPONSE** Each day you use your pay-as-you-go cell phone you pay $.25 per minute for the first 10 minutes and $.10 per minute for any time over 10 minutes. Write an equation that gives the daily cost C (in dollars) as a function of the time t (in minutes) when usage exceeds 10 minutes. Which costs more, using the phone for 10 minutes today and 15 minutes tomorrow, or using the phone for 25 minutes today? *Explain.*

100

◯ = **WORKED-OUT SOLUTIONS** on p. WS1

★ = **STANDARDIZED TEST PRACTICE**

B **53. DIVING** In a diving competition, a diver's score is the product of the difficulty level d of a dive and the sum of the scores x, y, and z of 3 judges. Write a simplified expression that represents the diver's score.
$s = d(x + y + z)$

54. ★ **EXTENDED RESPONSE** During the summer you give one hour saxophone lessons to 20 students each week. Use the information in the advertisement.

   a. Model Write an equation that gives your weekly earnings y (in dollars) as a function of the number x of beginning students that you teach. $y = -15x + 700$

   b. Calculate Find your weekly earnings if 15 of your 20 students are beginners. **$475**

   c. Explain Suppose that you plan to teach for 10 weeks and want to earn $4000 for the summer. How many advanced students should you teach? Your answer should include the following:

     • a table of values generated by the equation in part (a)

     • an explanation of your method for answering the question **See margin.**

SAXOPHONE LESSONS
$20 per hour beginner
$35 per hour advanced
Learn from the best!

C **55. CHALLENGE** A drama club plans to sell 100 tickets to a school musical. An adult ticket costs $6, and a student ticket costs $4. Students who attend the school get a $1 discount. The club expects two thirds of the student tickets to be discounted. Write an equation that gives the total revenue r (in dollars) as a function of the number a of adult tickets sold. $r = \frac{8}{3}a + \frac{1000}{3}$

MIXED REVIEW

PREVIEW
Prepare for Lesson 2.6 in Exs. 56–61.

Multiply or divide. *(p. 915)*

56. $\frac{1}{2} \cdot \frac{2}{5}$ $\frac{1}{5}$ **57.** $\frac{4}{7} \cdot \frac{1}{8}$ $\frac{1}{14}$ **58.** $1\frac{2}{3} \cdot 2\frac{3}{10}$ $3\frac{5}{6}$

59. $\frac{1}{5} \div \frac{3}{10}$ $\frac{2}{3}$ **60.** $\frac{2}{3} \div \frac{4}{9}$ $1\frac{1}{2}$ **61.** $2\frac{3}{4} \div 1\frac{5}{8}$ $1\frac{9}{13}$

Find the sum, difference, or product.

62. $-7 + (-4)$ *(p. 74)* **−11**   **63.** $8 + (-11)$ *(p. 74)* **−3**   **64.** $12 - 23$ *(p. 80)* **−11**

65. $-9 - 6$ *(p. 80)* **−15**   **66.** $(-11)(-2.1)$ *(p. 88)* **23.1**   **67.** $15(3.5)$ *(p. 88)* **52.5**

QUIZ *for Lessons 2.4–2.5*

Find the product. *(p. 88)*

1. $-5 \cdot (-5)$ **25**   **2.** $18 \cdot \left(-\frac{7}{6}\right)$ **−21**   **3.** $8 \cdot \frac{4}{5} \cdot (-10)$ **−64**   **4.** $9 \cdot (-7) \cdot (-1.2)$ **75.6**

5. $(-3x) \cdot (-4)$ **12x**   **6.** $-\frac{2}{3}x \cdot 15$ **−10x**   **7.** $x \cdot 1.5 \cdot (-6.4)$ **−9.6x**   **8.** $(-2)(13x)$ **−26x**

Use the distributive property to write an equivalent expression. *(p. 96)*

9. $7(x + 14)$ **7x + 98**   **10.** $-4(5x + 9)$ **−20x −36**   **11.** $-5(2x - 6)$ **−10x +30**   **12.** $(3 - x)6$ **18 − 6x**

EXTRA PRACTICE for Lesson 2.5, p. 939   **ONLINE QUIZ** at classzone.com   **101**

54c. You do not need to teach any advanced students.

Number of beginner students	Weekly pay (dollars)
15	475
16	460
17	445
18	430
19	415
20	400

You need to earn $4000 ÷ 10 = $400 a week. A table of values shows how much you can earn based on the number of beginner students you teach.

Using ALTERNATIVE METHODS

Alternative Strategy

Example 5 on page 98 can be solved by breaking the problem into parts. This method allows students to see the components of the problem and will help them better understand the algebraic solution given in Lesson 2.5.

Avoiding Common Errors

Students may confuse the time spent running with the time swimming or the number of calories burned per minute running with the number of calories burned per minute swimming. Have them check that their calculations match the numbers in the problem.

Teaching Strategy

Students may want to use this strategy for Exercises 50–55 in Lesson 2.5.

1. $330; method 1: write an equation for *c*, the total cost as a function of *n*, the number of nights you spend at a campground; $c = 15n + 60(10 − n)$ or $c = −45n + 600$. Substitute 6 for *n*, giving you $c = \$330$; method 2: break the problem into parts. Find the cost of staying at the campground for 6 nights: $15 per night · 6 nights = $90. Find the number of nights spent at the motel: $10 − 6 = 4$ nights. Find the cost of staying at the motel for 4 nights: $60 per night · 4 nights = $240. Add the cost of the campground to the cost of the motel: $90 + $240 = $330.

2. $450; method 1: write an equation for *c*, the total cost, as a function of *n*, the number of nights you spend at a campground; $c = 15n + 60(12 − n)$ or $c = −45n + 720$. Substitute 6 for *n*, giving you $c = \$450$; method 2: break the problem into parts. Find the cost of staying at the campground for 6 nights: $15 per night · 6 nights = $90. Find the number of nights spent at the motel: $12 − 6 = 6$ nights. Find the cost of staying at the motel for 6 nights: $60 per night · 6 nights = $360. Add the cost of the campground to the cost of the motel: $90 + $360 = $450.

Another Way to Solve Example 5, page 98

MULTIPLE REPRESENTATIONS In Example 5 on page 98, you saw how to solve a problem about exercising using a verbal model and an equation. You can also solve the problem by breaking it into parts.

PROBLEM

> **EXERCISING** Your daily workout plan involves a total of 50 minutes of running and swimming. You burn 15 calories per minute when running and 9 calories per minute when swimming. Find the number of calories you burn if you run for 20 minutes.

METHOD **Breaking into Parts** You can solve the problem by breaking it into parts.

STEP 1 Find the number of calories you burn when running.

$$\frac{15 \text{ calories}}{\text{per minute}} \cdot 20 \text{ minutes} = 300 \text{ calories}$$

Your running time is 20 minutes, so your swimming time is $50 − 20 = 30$ minutes.

STEP 2 Find the calories you burn when swimming.

$$\frac{9 \text{ calories}}{\text{per minute}} \cdot 30 \text{ minutes} = 270 \text{ calories}$$

STEP 3 Add the calories you burn when doing each activity. You burn a total of 570 calories.

$$300 \text{ calories} + 270 \text{ calories} = 570 \text{ calories}$$

PRACTICE

1–4. See margin.

1. **VACATIONING** Your family is taking a vacation for 10 nights. You will spend some nights at a campground and the rest of the nights at a motel. A campground stay costs $15 per night, and a motel stay costs $60 per night. Find the total cost of lodging if you stay at a campground for 6 nights. Solve this problem using two different methods.

2. **WHAT IF?** In Exercise 1, suppose the vacation lasts 12 days. Find the total cost of lodging if you stay at the campground for 6 nights. Solve this problem using two different methods.

3. **FLORIST** During the summer, you work 35 hours per week at a florist shop. You get paid $8 per hour for working at the register and $9.50 per hour for making deliveries. Find the total amount you earn this week if you spend 5 hours making deliveries. Solve this problem using two different methods.

4. **ERROR ANALYSIS** *Describe* and correct the error in solving Exercise 3.

$8 per hour · 5 hours = $40
$9.50 per hour · 30 hours = $285
$40 + $285 = $325

3. See Additional Answers beginning on p. AA1.

4. You earn $9.50 per hour making deliveries, not working at the register; $9.50 per hour · 5 hours = $47.50; $8 per hour · 30 hours = $240; $47.50 + $240 = $287.50.

2.6 Divide Real Numbers

Before You multiplied real numbers.

Now You will divide real numbers.

Why? So you can calculate volleyball statistics, as in Ex. 57.

Key Vocabulary
- multiplicative inverse
- reciprocal, *p. 915*
- mean, *p. 918*

Reciprocals like $\frac{2}{3}$ and $\frac{3}{2}$ have the property that their product is 1:

$$\frac{2}{3} \cdot \frac{3}{2} = 1$$

The reciprocal of a nonzero number a, written $\frac{1}{a}$, is called the **multiplicative inverse** of a. Zero does not have a multiplicative inverse because there is no number a such that $0 \cdot a = 1$.

> ### KEY CONCEPT
> *For Your Notebook*
>
> **Inverse Property of Multiplication**
>
> **Words** The product of a nonzero number and its multiplicative inverse is 1.
>
> **Algebra** $a \cdot \frac{1}{a} = \frac{1}{a} \cdot a = 1, a \neq 0$ **Example** $8 \cdot \frac{1}{8} = 1$

EXAMPLE 1 **Find multiplicative inverses of numbers**

WRITE INVERSES
You can find the inverse of $-\frac{6}{7}$ as follows:

$$\frac{1}{-\frac{6}{7}} \cdot 1 = \frac{1}{-\frac{6}{7}} \cdot \frac{7}{7}$$

$$= -\frac{7}{6}$$

a. The multiplicative inverse of $-\frac{1}{5}$ is -5 because $-\frac{1}{5} \cdot (-5) = 1$.

b. The multiplicative inverse of $-\frac{6}{7}$ is $-\frac{7}{6}$ because $-\frac{6}{7} \cdot \left(-\frac{7}{6}\right) = 1$.

DIVISION Because the expressions $4 \div \frac{2}{3}$ and $4 \cdot \frac{3}{2}$ have the same value, 6, you can conclude that $4 \div \frac{2}{3} = 4 \cdot \frac{3}{2}$. This example illustrates the *division rule*.

> ### KEY CONCEPT
> *For Your Notebook*
>
> **Division Rule**
>
> **Words** To divide a number a by a nonzero number b, multiply a by the multiplicative inverse of b.
>
> **Algebra** $a \div b = a \cdot \frac{1}{b}, b \neq 0$ **Example** $5 \div 2 = 5 \cdot \frac{1}{2}$

① PLAN AND PREPARE

Warm-Up Exercises
📄 Transparency Available

Find the quotient.

1. $84 \div 14$ **6**

2. $1.2 \div 5$ **0.24**

3. $\frac{2}{3} \div 3$ **$\frac{2}{9}$**

4. $\frac{5}{8} \div \frac{1}{5}$ **$3\frac{1}{8}$**

5. The points Jeri scored in her last five basketball games were 28, 34, 19, 26, and 38. How many points did she average per game? **29 points**

Notetaking Guide
📄 Transparency Available

Promotes interactive learning and notetaking skills, pp. 39–41.

Pacing
Basic: 1 day
Average: 1 day
Advanced: 1 day
Block: 0.5 block with 2.5
- See *Teaching Guide/Lesson Plan.*

② FOCUS AND MOTIVATE

Essential Question
Big Idea 1, p. 63

How do you divide real numbers? **Tell students they will learn how to answer this question by using the division rule and sign rules for products and quotients.**

NCTM STANDARDS
Standard 1: Understand meanings of operations; Understand how operations are related

Resource Planning Guide

Chapter Resource Book
- Teaching Guide/Lesson Plan (pp. 58–59)
- Activity Master (p. 60)
- Practice levels A, B, C (pp. 62–64)
- Study Guide (pp. 65–66)
- Catch-up for Absent Students (p. 67)
- Application (p. 68)
- Challenge (p. 69)

Workbooks
- Notetaking Guide (pp. 39–41)
- Practice Workbook (pp. 26–27)

Teaching Options
- **Power Presentations CD-ROM** provides dynamic electronic teaching resources for the classroom.
- **Activity Generator CD-ROM** provides editable activities for all ability levels.

Interactive Technology
- Easy Planner
- Power Presentations CD-ROM
- Activity Generator CD-ROM
- Animated Algebra
- Test Generator CD-ROM
- Online Quiz
- eWorkbook
- eEdition
- @HomeTutor

Resources for English Learners
- Quick Reference for English Learners
- Spanish Study Guide
- Multi-Language Visual Glossary
- Student Resources in Spanish

See also the *Algebra 1 Toolkit* for more strategies for meeting individual needs.

103

104

Motivating the Lesson

A top golfer has scores of -4, -3, -6 and -3 in four rounds of golf on a new course. In this lesson, you will learn how to find the average score on this course.

③ TEACH

Extra Example 1

Find the multiplicative inverse of the number.

a. $-\dfrac{1}{7}$ **-7**   b. $-\dfrac{5}{3}$ **$-\dfrac{3}{5}$**

Key Question to Ask for Example 1

• What is the multiplicative inverse of $\dfrac{a}{b}$, where $a \neq 0$ and $b \neq 0$? $\dfrac{b}{a}$

Extra Example 2

Find the quotient

a. $18 \div (-3)$ **-6**   b. $-16 \div \left(-\dfrac{8}{3}\right)$ **6**

Extra Example 3

Andy recorded the low temperature each night at his home during January. Over five consecutive nights, he recorded the temperatures $-2°C$, $-10°C$, $6°C$, $-1°C$, and $2°C$. What was the mean low temperature at his home for these nights? **$-1°C$**

Key Question to Ask for Example 3

• Why do you divide by 5 in Example 3? **because there are 5 values in the data set, one for each day**

Vocabulary

In Example 3, remind students that the mean is sometimes referred to as the "average" of a set of data.

SIGN OF A QUOTIENT Because division can be expressed as multiplication, the sign rules for division are the same as the sign rules for multiplication.

> **AVOID ERRORS**
> You cannot divide a real number by 0, because 0 does not have a multiplicative inverse.

KEY CONCEPT
For Your Notebook

The Sign of a Quotient

• The quotient of two real numbers with the *same* sign is positive.
• The quotient of two real numbers with *different* signs is negative.
• The quotient of 0 and any nonzero real number is 0.

EXAMPLE 2   Divide real numbers

Find the quotient.

a. $-16 \div 4 = -16 \cdot \dfrac{1}{4}$

$\qquad\qquad\quad = -4$

b. $-20 \div \left(-\dfrac{5}{3}\right) = -20 \cdot \left(-\dfrac{3}{5}\right)$

$\qquad\qquad\qquad\quad = 12$

✓ **GUIDED PRACTICE**   for Examples 1 and 2

Find the multiplicative inverse of the number.

1. -27 $-\dfrac{1}{27}$ 2. -8 $-\dfrac{1}{8}$ 3. $-\dfrac{4}{7}$ $-\dfrac{7}{4}$ 4. $-\dfrac{1}{3}$ -3

Find the quotient.

5. $-64 \div (-4)$ **16**   6. $-\dfrac{3}{8} \div \left(\dfrac{3}{10}\right)$ **$-1\dfrac{1}{4}$**   7. $18 \div \left(-\dfrac{2}{9}\right)$ **-81**   8. $-\dfrac{2}{5} \div 18$ **$-\dfrac{1}{45}$**

EXAMPLE 3   Find the mean

TEMPERATURES The table gives the daily minimum temperatures (in degrees Fahrenheit) in Barrow, Alaska, for the first 5 days of February 2004. Find the mean daily minimum temperature.

Day in February	1	2	3	4	5
Minimum temperature (°F)	-21	-29	-39	-39	-22

Point Barrow Observatory

Solution

To find the mean daily minimum temperature, find the sum of the minimum temperatures for the 5 days and then divide the sum by 5.

> **REVIEW MEAN**
> For help with finding a mean, see p. 918.

$\text{Mean} = \dfrac{-21 + (-29) + (-39) + (-39) + (-22)}{5}$

$\qquad\quad = -\dfrac{150}{5} = -30$

▸ The mean daily minimum temperature was $-30°F$.

Differentiated Instruction

Inclusion Some students may find it easier to divide real numbers by first determining the sign of the final answer and then proceeding with the division of the numbers without regard to the sign. Give grouped examples like the following: $-4 \div 2 = -(4 \div 2) = -2$, $4 \div (-2) = -(4 \div 2) = -2$, $-4 \div (-2) = +(4 \div 2) = 2$. In these examples, once the sign was determined, the problem was reduced to dividing 4 by 2.

See also the *Algebra 1 Toolkit* for more strategies.

EXAMPLE 4 **Simplify an expression**

Simplify the expression $\dfrac{36x - 24}{6}$.

ANOTHER WAY

You can simplify the expression by first rewriting it as a difference of two fractions: $\dfrac{36x - 24}{6} = \dfrac{36x}{6} - \dfrac{24}{6} = 6x - 4$.

$\dfrac{36x - 24}{6} = (36x - 24) \div 6$ **Rewrite fraction as division.**

$= (36x - 24) \cdot \dfrac{1}{6}$ **Division rule**

$= 36x \cdot \dfrac{1}{6} - 24 \cdot \dfrac{1}{6}$ **Distributive property**

$= 6x - 4$ **Simplify.**

✔ **GUIDED PRACTICE**   for Examples 3 and 4

9. Find the mean of the numbers -3, 4, 2.8, and -1.5.   **0.575**

10. **TEMPERATURES** Find the mean daily maximum temperature (in degrees Fahrenheit) in Barrow, Alaska, for the first 5 days of February 2004.   **$-16.8°$F**

Day in February	1	2	3	4	5
Maximum temperature (°F)	-3	-20	-21	-22	-18

Simplify the expression.

11. $\dfrac{2x - 8}{-4}$ $-\dfrac{1}{2}x + 2$ 12. $\dfrac{-6y + 18}{3}$ $-2y + 6$ 13. $\dfrac{-10z - 20}{-5}$ $2z + 4$

OPERATIONS ON REAL NUMBERS In this chapter, you saw how to find the sum, difference, product, and quotient of two real numbers a and b. You can use the values of a and b to determine whether the result is positive, negative, or 0.

CONCEPT SUMMARY   *For Your Notebook*

Rules for Addition, Subtraction, Multiplication, and Division

Let a and b be real numbers.

Expression	$a + b$	$a - b$	$a \cdot b$	$a \div b$
Positive if...	the number with the greater absolute value is positive.	$a > b$.	a and b have the same sign ($a \neq 0, b \neq 0$).	a and b have the same sign ($a \neq 0, b \neq 0$).
Negative if...	the number with the greater absolute value is negative.	$a < b$.	a and b have different signs ($a \neq 0, b \neq 0$).	a and b have different signs ($a \neq 0, b \neq 0$).
Zero if...	a and b are additive inverses.	$a = b$.	$a = 0$ or $b = 0$.	$a = 0$ and $b \neq 0$.

2.6   Divide Real Numbers   **105**

Extra Example 4

Simplify the expression $\dfrac{40x + 32}{8}$.
$5x + 4$

Reading Strategy

Be certain that students read and understand the Another Way note next to Example 4. This note presents another approach to simplifying expressions that some students may find preferable to use.

Closing the Lesson

Have students summarize the major points of the lesson and answer the Essential Question: How do you divide real numbers?

- To divide a number a by a nonzero number b, find the product $a \cdot \dfrac{1}{b}$.
- The sign rules for division are the same as for multiplication.
- The product of a nonzero number and its multiplicative inverse is 1.

To divide two real numbers, multiply the first number by the multiplicative inverse of the second number.

2.6 EXERCISES

HOMEWORK
KEY

○ = WORKED-OUT SOLUTIONS
on p. WS1 for Exs. 13, 35, and 53

★ = STANDARDIZED TEST PRACTICE
Exs. 2, 23, 48, 49, 55, 56, and 57

SKILL PRACTICE

A
1. **VOCABULARY** Copy and complete: The product of a nonzero number and
   its __?__ is 1. **multiplicative inverse**

2. ★ **WRITING** How can you tell whether the mean of n numbers is negative
   without actually dividing the sum of the numbers by n? *Explain.*
   If their sum is negative, the mean will be negative.

EXAMPLE 1
on p. 103
for Exs. 3–10, 23

FINDING INVERSES Find the multiplicative inverse of the number.

3. -18 $-\dfrac{1}{18}$

4. -9 $-\dfrac{1}{9}$

5. -1 -1

6. $-\dfrac{1}{2}$ -2

7. $-\dfrac{3}{4}$ $-1\dfrac{1}{3}$

8. $-\dfrac{5}{9}$ $-1\dfrac{4}{5}$

9. $-4\dfrac{1}{3}$ $-\dfrac{3}{13}$

10. $-2\dfrac{2}{5}$ $-\dfrac{5}{12}$

EXAMPLE 2
on p. 104
for Exs. 11–22

FINDING QUOTIENTS Find the quotient.

11. $-21 \div 3$ -7

12. $-18 \div (-6)$ 3

13. $-1 \div \left(-\dfrac{7}{2}\right)$ $\dfrac{2}{7}$

14. $15 \div \left(-\dfrac{3}{4}\right)$ -20

15. $13 \div \left(-4\dfrac{1}{3}\right)$ -3

16. $-\dfrac{2}{3} \div 2$ $-\dfrac{1}{3}$

17. $-\dfrac{1}{2} \div \dfrac{1}{5}$ $-2\dfrac{1}{2}$

18. $-\dfrac{1}{5} \div (-6)$ $\dfrac{1}{30}$

19. $-\dfrac{4}{7} \div (-2)$ $\dfrac{2}{7}$

20. $-1 \div \left(-\dfrac{6}{5}\right)$ $\dfrac{5}{6}$

21. $8 \div \left(-\dfrac{4}{11}\right)$ -22

22. $-\dfrac{1}{3} \div \dfrac{5}{3}$ $-\dfrac{1}{5}$

23. ★ **MULTIPLE CHOICE** If $-\dfrac{5}{7}x = 1$, what is the value of x? **A**

   Ⓐ $-1\dfrac{2}{5}$
   Ⓑ $\dfrac{5}{7}$
   Ⓒ 1
   Ⓓ $\dfrac{12}{5}$

EXAMPLE 3
on p. 104
for Exs. 24–32

FINDING MEANS Find the mean of the numbers.

24. $-10, -8, 3$ -5

25. $12, -8, -9$ $-1\dfrac{2}{3}$

26. $18, -9, 0, -5$ 1

27. $-2, 9, -3, 5$ $2\dfrac{1}{4}$

28. $-1, -4, -5, 10$ 0

29. $7, -4, 1, -9, -6$ $-2\dfrac{1}{5}$

30. $-5.3, -2, 1.3$ -2

31. $0.25, -4, -0.75, -1, 6$ 0.1

32. $-0.6, 0.18, -2, 5, -0.5$ 0.416

EXAMPLE 4
on p. 105
for Exs. 33–43

SIMPLIFYING EXPRESSIONS Simplify the expression.

33. $\dfrac{6x - 14}{2}$ $3x - 7$

34. $\dfrac{12y - 8}{-4}$ $-3y + 2$

35. $\dfrac{9z - 6}{-3}$ $-3z + 2$

36. $\dfrac{-6p + 15}{6}$ $-p + 2\dfrac{1}{2}$

37. $\dfrac{5 - 25q}{10}$ $\dfrac{1}{2} - 2\dfrac{1}{2}q$

38. $\dfrac{-18 - 21r}{-12}$ $3\dfrac{1}{4}r$

39. $\dfrac{-24a - 10}{-8}$ $3a + 1\dfrac{1}{4}$

40. $\dfrac{-20b + 12}{-5}$ $4b - 2\dfrac{2}{5}$

41. $\dfrac{36 - 27c}{9}$ $4 - 3c$

ERROR ANALYSIS *Describe* and correct the error in simplifying the
expression. **42, 43. See margin.**

42.
$$\dfrac{12 - 18x}{6} = (12 - 18x) \cdot \left(-\dfrac{1}{6}\right)$$
$$= 12\left(-\dfrac{1}{6}\right) - 18x\left(-\dfrac{1}{6}\right)$$
$$= -2 + 3x$$

43.
$$\dfrac{-15x - 10}{-5} = (-15x - 10) \cdot \left(-\dfrac{1}{5}\right)$$
$$= -15x\left(-\dfrac{1}{5}\right) - 10\left(-\dfrac{1}{5}\right)$$
$$= 3x - 2$$

42. The multiplicative inverse of 6 is $\dfrac{1}{6}$, not $-\dfrac{1}{6}$. $\dfrac{12 - 18x}{6} =$

$(12 - 18x) \cdot \left(\dfrac{1}{6}\right) = 12\left(\dfrac{1}{6}\right) - 18x\left(\dfrac{1}{6}\right) = 2 - 3x.$

43. -2 was added instead of subtracted; $\dfrac{-15x - 10}{-5} =$

$(-15x - 10) \cdot \left(-\dfrac{1}{5}\right) = -15x\left(-\dfrac{1}{5}\right) - 10\left(-\dfrac{1}{5}\right) = 3x + 2.$

EVALUATING EXPRESSIONS Evaluate the expression.

44. $\dfrac{2y - x}{x}$ when $x = 1$ and $y = -4$ **9**

45. $\dfrac{4r}{3y + x}$ when $x = 6$ and $y = -8$ **$-1\frac{1}{3}$**

46. $\dfrac{-9x}{y^2 - 1}$ when $x = -3$ and $y = -2$ **9**

47. $\dfrac{y - x}{xy}$ when $x = -6$ and $y = -2$ **$\frac{1}{3}$**

48. No; no.
Sample answer:
$4 \div 2 = 2$ but
$2 \div 4 = \frac{1}{2}$,
$(20 \div 4) \div 2 =$
$2\frac{1}{2}$ but $20 \div$
$(4 \div 2) = 10$.

48. ★ **WRITING** Tell whether division is commutative and associative. Give examples to support your answer.

49. ★ **MULTIPLE CHOICE** Let a and b be positive numbers, and let c and d be negative numbers. Which quotient has a value that is always negative?   **C**

Ⓐ $\dfrac{a}{b} \div \dfrac{c}{d}$ Ⓑ $\dfrac{a}{c} \div \dfrac{b}{d}$ Ⓒ $\dfrac{c^2}{a} \div \dfrac{b}{d}$ Ⓓ $\dfrac{a}{cd} \div b$

C

50. CHALLENGE Find the mean of the integers from -410 to 400. *Explain* how you got your answer.   **See margin.**

51. CHALLENGE What is the mean of a number and three times its opposite? *Explain* your reasoning.   **The opposite of the number; if you add x and 3 times $-x$, you get $-2x$; $-2x \div 2 = -x$.**

PROBLEM SOLVING

EXAMPLE 2 Ⓐ
on p. 104
for Ex. 52

52. SPORTS Free diving means diving without the aid of breathing equipment. Suppose that an athlete free dives to an elevation of -42 meters in 60 seconds. Find the average rate of change in the diver's elevation.   **$-\dfrac{7}{10}$ m/sec**

@HomeTutor for problem solving help at classzone.com

EXAMPLE 3
on p. 104
for Exs. 53–54

53. WEATHER The daily mean temperature is the mean of the high and low temperatures for a given day. The high temperature for Boston, Massachusetts, on January 10, 2004, was $-10.6°C$. The low temperature was $-18.9°C$. Find the daily mean temperature for that day.   **$-14.75°C$**

@HomeTutor for problem solving help at classzone.com

54. MULTI-STEP PROBLEM The table shows the changes in the values of one share of stock A and one share of stock B over 5 days.

Day of week	Monday	Tuesday	Wednesday	Thursday	Friday
Change in share value for stock A (dollars)	-0.45	-0.32	0.66	-1.12	1.53
Change in share value for stock B (dollars)	-0.37	0.14	0.59	-0.53	1.02

54c. Yes. *Sample answer:* Over the first four days, stock A's average change in value was -0.3075 whereas stock B's was -0.0425.

a. Find the average daily change in share value for each stock.   **$.06; $.17**

b. Which stock performed better over the 5 days? How much more money did the better performing stock earn, on average, per day?   **stock B; $.11**

c. Can you conclude that the stock that performed better over all 5 days also performed better over the first 4 days of the week? *Explain* your reasoning.

Study Strategy

Exercises 33–41 In preparation for these exercises, students may want to review Example 4. Note that some students may find it easier to use the alternative method for simplifying expressions that is mentioned in "Another Way."

Avoiding Common Errors

Exercises 44–47 Students often substitute incorrectly when replacement values involve a negative sign. Encourage them to use parentheses to insert the values. This will help them avoid computational errors.

Reading Strategy

Exercise 56 Urge students to read all parts of the question carefully before completing part b. Note that the original prediction was off by 3.5 meters, which changes the rate of change for the whole period.

50. -5. *Sample answer:* Using additive inverses you can determine that the sum of the integers -400 to 400 is 0. The sum of the integers from -410 to -401 is -4055. Divide this sum by the number of integers from -410 to 400, which is 811; $-4055 \div 811 = -5$.

⑤ ASSESS AND RETEACH

Daily Homework Quiz

🔲 **Transparency Available**

Find the quotient.

1. $-14 \div 2\frac{1}{2}$ $-5\frac{3}{5}$

2. $-\frac{3}{4} \div (-4)$ $\frac{3}{16}$

Simplify the expression.

3. $\frac{9x - 15}{-3}$ $-3x + 5$

4. $\frac{-8x + 12}{5}$ $-1.6x + 2.4$

5. Ethan's team scored the following numbers of points in six rounds of a statewide History Quiz Contest: 86, −14, 58, −26, 74, and 20. What was the team's mean score? **33**

🔵 **Online Quiz**

Available at **classzone.com**

Diagnosis/Remediation

• Practice A, B, C in Chapter 2 Resource Book, pp. 62–64
• Study Guide in Chapter 2 Resource Book, pp. 65–66
• Practice Workbook, pp. 26–27
• @HomeTutor

Challenge

Additional challenge is available in the Chapter 2 Resource Book, p. 69.

57c. If the player had the same number of aces as service errors, then $a = e$, so $f = \frac{a - a}{s} = 0$; if all the serves were aces, a would be equal to s and e would be 0, so $f = \frac{s - 0}{s} = \frac{s}{s} = 1$; if all the serves were errors, then $e = s$ and $a = 0$, so $f = \frac{0 - s}{s} = \frac{-s}{s} = -1$.

Ⓑ **55.** ★ **MULTIPLE CHOICE** In a trivia competition, your team earned 60, −100, 300, 120, and −80 points on 5 questions. The sixth question has a value of 300 points. By how many points will your team's mean score per question change if you answer the sixth question correctly? **A**

Ⓐ 40 points   Ⓑ 50 points   Ⓒ 60 points   Ⓓ 100 points

56. ★ **SHORT RESPONSE** The South Aral Sea in Russia was about 57 meters above sea level in 1965. Scientists once predicted that the elevation would be about 34 meters above sea level in 2002.

  a. Estimate the average rate of change in elevation for the period 1965–2002 using the scientists' prediction. Round to the nearest hundredth of a meter per year. **−0.62 meter per year**

  b. More recent research suggests that the elevation decreased to about 30.5 meters above sea level in 2002. Use this information to predict the elevation in 2010. *Explain* the steps of your solution. **About 24.74 m.** *Sample answer:* Find the average rate of change based on the actual elevation in 2002, −0.72; use the equation 30.5 + (−0.72)(8) to predict the elevation on 2010.

South Aral Sea, 1973   South Aral Sea, 2000

57. ★ **EXTENDED RESPONSE** In volleyball, an ace is a serve that the opponent doesn't hit. Ace efficiency is a measure of a player's ability to hit aces while minimizing service errors. The ace efficiency f is given by the formula $f = \frac{a - e}{s}$ where a is the number of aces, e is the number of service errors, and s is the total number of serves.

  a. **Calculate** Find the ace efficiency for a player who has 108 aces and 125 service errors in 500 serves. **−0.034**

  b. **Compare** If the player makes 30 more aces and 20 more service errors in the next 100 serves, will the ace efficiency improve? *Explain.* **Yes; it will improve to −0.012.**

  c. **Justify** Under what conditions would a player's ace efficiency be 0? 1? −1? *Justify* your answers algebraically. **See margin.**

Ⓒ **58.** **CHALLENGE** The average daily balance of a checking account is the sum of the daily balances in a given period divided by the number of days in the period. Suppose that a period has 30 days. Find the average daily balance of an account that has a balance of $110 for 18 days, −$300 for 10 days, and $100 for the rest of the period. **−$27.33**

MIXED REVIEW

Evaluate the expression.

59. $6x$ when $x = 15$ *(p. 2)* **90**   **60.** $4x + 2y$ when $x = 3$ and $y = 7$ *(p. 8)* **26**

61. $x - y - 2$ when $x = 3$ and $y = -4$ *(p. 80)* **5**   **62.** $-4xy$ when $x = -2$ and $y = -1.4$ *(p. 88)* **−11.2**

PREVIEW

Prepare for Lesson 2.7 in Exs. 63–64.

Identify the hypothesis and the conclusion of the statement. Tell whether the statement is *true* or *false*. If it is false, give a counterexample. *(p. 64)* **63, 64. See margin.**

63. If a number is a whole number, then the number is a rational number.

64. If a number is a rational number, then the number is an integer.

63. Hypothesis: a number is a whole number, conclusion: the number is a rational number; true.

64. Hypothesis: a number is a rational number, conclusion: the number is an integer; false. *Sample answer:* $\frac{2}{3}$ is a rational number, but not an integer.

2.7 Writing Statements in If-Then Form

MATERIALS • paper and pencil

QUESTION   How can you write an *all* or *none* statement in if-then form?

EXPLORE   Tell whether certain statements are true about a group

STEP 1 *Answer questions*   Copy the questions below and write your answers beside them.

1. Do you play an instrument?
2. Do you participate in a school sport?
3. Are you taking an art class?
4. Do you walk to school?

STEP 2 *Write if-then statements*   Each of the *all* or *none* statements below can be written in if-then form. Copy each statement and complete its equivalent if-then form. The first one is done for you as an example.

1. All of the students in our group play an instrument.
   If a student is in our group, then the student plays an instrument.

2. None of the students in our group participates in a school sport.
   If _?_ , then _?_ . **a student is in our group; the student doesn't participate in a school sport**

3. None of the students in our group is taking an art class.
   If _?_ , then _?_ . **a student is in our group; the student is not taking an art class**

4. All of the students in our group walk to school.
   If _?_ , then _?_ . **if a student is in our group; the student walks to school**

STEP 3 *Analyze statements*   Form a group with 2 or 3 classmates. Tell whether each if-then statement in Step 2 is *true* or *false* for your group. If the statement is false, give a counterexample.

DRAW CONCLUSIONS   Use your observations to complete these exercises

1. *Describe* the similarity and difference in the if-then forms of the **Both statements begin with "If a** following statements: **student is in our group" but the conclusion of the statement containing the word** "all" **is positive and the conclusion of the statement containing the word "none" is negative.**

   All of the students in our group listen to rock music.

   None of the students in our group listens to rock music.

Rewrite the given conditional statement in if-then form. Then tell whether the statement is *true* or *false*. If it is false, give a counterexample.

2. All of the positive numbers are integers.   **If a number is positive, then it is an integer; false.**
   Sample answer: $\frac{2}{3}$ **is a positive number, but it is not an integer.**

3. All of the rational numbers can be written as fractions.
   If a number is rational, then it can be written as a fraction; true.

4. None of the negative numbers is a whole number.
   If a number is negative, then it is not a whole number; true.

5. None of the rational numbers has an opposite equal to itself.
   If a number is rational, then it does not have an opposite equal to itself; false;
   0 is a rational number and its opposite is 0.

2.7   Find Square Roots and Compare Real Numbers   **109**

---

❶ PLAN AND PREPARE

Explore the Concept

- Students will write statements in if-then form.
- This activity leads into the study of rewriting conditional statements in Example 5 in Lesson 2.7.

Recommended Time

Work activity: 10 min
Discuss results: 5 min

Grouping

Students should work in groups of 3–4. All students should answer the questions in Step 1. In Step 2, all students should write the if-then statements and then check that all the statements are written correctly. Students should complete Step 3 as a group.

❷ TEACH

Tips for Success

In Step 2, point out that the "if" part of the if-then statement is the same for all of the statements and the "then" part of the if-then statement begins with "then the student."

Key Discovery

Generalizations that are true for all members of a set or for no members of a set can be written in if-then form.

❸ ASSESS AND RETEACH

How many counterexamples does it take to prove that an if-then statement is false? **one**

2.7 Find Square Roots and Compare Real Numbers

Before You found squares of numbers and compared rational numbers.

Now You will find square roots and compare real numbers.

Why? So you can find side lengths of geometric shapes, as in Ex. 54.

① PLAN AND PREPARE

Warm-Up Exercises

🗂 Transparency Available

Find the square of the number.

1. 14 **196**   **2.** 16 **256**

Complete the statements using <, >, or =.

3. $-2.5 \underline{\ ?\ } -\frac{19}{8}$ <   **4.** $\frac{5}{6} \underline{\ ?\ } \frac{21}{25}$ <

5. A square room has a side length of 25 feet. What is its area? **625 ft²**

Notetaking Guide

🗂 Transparency Available

Promotes interactive learning and notetaking skills, pp. 42–44.

Pacing

Basic: 2 days

Average: 2 days

Advanced: 2 days

Block: 1 block

• See *Teaching Guide/Lesson Plan*.

② FOCUS AND MOTIVATE

Essential Question

Big Idea 3, p. 63

How do you evaluate a square root and compare real numbers? **Tell students they will learn how to answer this question by finding and approximating square roots and graphing numbers on a number line.**

NCTM STANDARDS

Standard 1: Understand relationships among numbers; Understand number systems

Key Vocabulary
• square root
• radicand
• perfect square
• irrational number
• real numbers

Recall that the square of 4 is $4^2 = 16$ and the square of -4 is $(-4)^2 = 16$. The numbers 4 and -4 are called the *square roots* of 16. In this lesson, you will find the square roots of nonnegative numbers.

KEY CONCEPT   *For Your Notebook*

Square Root of a Number

Words If $b^2 = a$, then b is a **square root** of a.

Example $3^2 = 9$ and $(-3)^2 = 9$, so 3 and -3 are square roots of 9.

All positive real numbers have two square roots, a positive square root (or *principal* square root) and a negative square root. A square root is written with the radical symbol $\sqrt{\ }$. The number or expression inside a radical symbol is the **radicand**.

$$\text{radical symbol} \longrightarrow \sqrt{a} \longleftarrow \text{radicand}$$

Zero has only one square root, 0. Negative real numbers do not have real square roots because the square of every real number is either positive or 0.

EXAMPLE 1   Find square roots

Evaluate the expression.

READING

The symbol $\pm$ is read as "plus or minus" and refers to both the positive square root and the negative square root.

a. $\pm\sqrt{36} = \pm 6$ **The positive and negative square roots of 36 are 6 and -6.**

b. $\sqrt{49} = 7$ **The positive square root of 49 is 7.**

c. $-\sqrt{4} = -2$ **The negative square root of 4 is -2.**

✓ GUIDED PRACTICE   for Example 1

Evaluate the expression.

1. $-\sqrt{9}$ **-3**   **2.** $\sqrt{25}$ **5**   **3.** $\pm\sqrt{64}$ **± 8**   **4.** $-\sqrt{81}$ **-9**

Resource Planning Guide

Chapter Resource Book
• Teaching Guide/Lesson Plan (pp. 70–71)
• Practice levels A, B, C (pp. 72–74)
• Study Guide (pp. 75–76)
• Catch-up for Absent Students (p. 77)
• Problem Solving Workshop (p. 78)
• Challenge (p. 79)

Workbooks
• Notetaking Guide (pp. 42–44)
• Practice Workbook (pp. 28–29)

Teaching Options
• **Power Presentations CD-ROM** provides dynamic electronic teaching resources for the classroom.
• **Activity Generator CD-ROM** provides editable activities for all ability levels.

Interactive Technology
• Easy Planner
• Power Presentations CD-ROM
• Activity Generator CD-ROM
• Animated Algebra
• Test Generator CD-ROM
• Online Quiz
• eWorkbook
• eEdition
• @HomeTutor

Resources for English Learners
• Quick Reference for English Learners
• Spanish Study Guide
• Multi-Language Visual Glossary
• Student Resources in Spanish

See also the *Algebra 1 Toolkit* for more strategies for meeting individual needs.

PERFECT SQUARES The square of an integer is called a **perfect square**. As shown in Example 1, the square root of a perfect square is an integer. As you will see in Example 2, you need to approximate a square root if the radicand is a whole number that is *not* a perfect square.

 EXAMPLE 2 **Approximate a square root**

FURNITURE The top of a folding table is a square whose area is 945 square inches. Approximate the side length of the tabletop to the nearest inch.

Solution

You need to find the side length s of the tabletop such that $s^2 = 945$. This means that s is the positive square root of 945. You can use a table to determine whether 945 is a perfect square.

Number	28	29	30	31	32
Square of number	784	841	900	961	1024

As shown in the table, 945 is *not* a perfect square. The greatest perfect square less than 945 is 900. The least perfect square greater than 945 is 961.

$900 < 945 < 961$ **Write a compound inequality that compares 945 with both 900 and 961.**

$\sqrt{900} < \sqrt{945} < \sqrt{961}$ **Take positive square root of each number.**

$30 < \sqrt{945} < 31$ **Find square root of each perfect square.**

Because 945 is closer to 961 than to 900, $\sqrt{945}$ is closer to 31 than to 30.

▶ The side length of the tabletop is about 31 inches.

USING A CALCULATOR In Example 2, you can use a calculator to obtain a better approximation of the side length of the tabletop.

[2nd] [√] 945 [)] [ENTER]

√(945)
              30.74085

The side length is about 30.74 inches, which is closer to 31 than to 30.

 GUIDED PRACTICE   **for Example 2**

Approximate the square root to the nearest integer.

5. $\sqrt{32}$ **6**   6. $\sqrt{103}$ **10**   7. $-\sqrt{48}$ **−7**   8. $-\sqrt{350}$ **−19**

IRRATIONAL NUMBERS The square root of a whole number that is not a perfect square is an example of an *irrational number*. An **irrational number**, such as $\sqrt{945} = 30.74085\ldots$, is a number that cannot be written as a quotient of two integers. The decimal form of an irrational number neither terminates nor repeats.

Differentiated Instruction

Visual Learners Mathematicians chose the symbol √ for a square root because it is a distorted letter *r*, which is the first letter of the word "root." Be sure that students do not confuse it with the symbol ⌐ used in long division.
See also the *Algebra 1 Toolkit* for more strategies.

Motivating the Lesson
A square garden has an area of 225 square feet. You want to know how much fencing you should buy to go around the garden without measuring. By knowing how to find square roots, you can find the side length and then determine how much fencing you should buy.

3 TEACH

Extra Example 1
Evaluate the expression.
a. $\pm\sqrt{100}$ **±10**
b. $\sqrt{121}$ **11**
c. $-\sqrt{400}$ **−20**

Key Questions to Ask for Example 1
• How is Example 1a different from Examples 1b and 1c? **The symbol ± in Example 1a means that the expression represents *both* the positive and negative square roots. In Examples 1b and 1c, only a *single* square root is indicated.**
• In Example 1c, how is $-\sqrt{4}$ different from $\sqrt{-4}$? **$-\sqrt{4}$ means the negative square root of 4; $\sqrt{-4}$ means the square root of −4, which is not a real number.**

Extra Example 2
The top of a square box has an area of 320 square inches. Approximate the side length of the box top to the nearest inch. **18 in.**

Teaching Strategy
When discussing Example 2, suggest that students make a list of the squares of numbers to 50 to use as a reference in approximating square roots.

REAL NUMBERS The set of **real numbers** is the set of all rational and irrational numbers, as illustrated in the Venn diagram below. Every point on the real number line represents a real number.

REAL NUMBERS

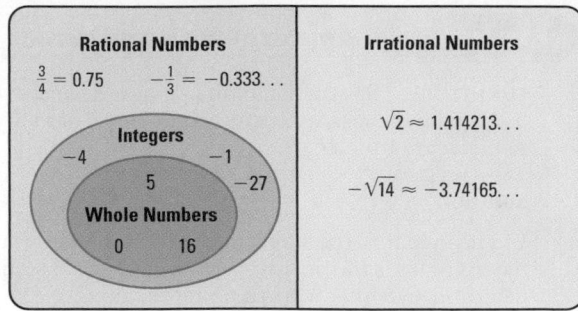

EXAMPLE 3 Classify numbers

Tell whether each of the following numbers is a real number, a rational number, an irrational number, an integer, or a whole number: $\sqrt{24}$, $\sqrt{100}$, $-\sqrt{81}$.

Number	Real number?	Rational number?	Irrational number?	Integer?	Whole number?
$\sqrt{24}$	Yes	No	Yes	No	No
$\sqrt{100}$	Yes	Yes	No	Yes	Yes
$-\sqrt{81}$	Yes	Yes	No	Yes	No

EXAMPLE 4 Graph and order real numbers

Order the numbers from least to greatest: $\frac{4}{3}$, $-\sqrt{5}$, $\sqrt{13}$, -2.5, $\sqrt{9}$.

Solution

Begin by graphing the numbers on a number line.

▸ Read the numbers from left to right: -2.5, $-\sqrt{5}$, $\frac{4}{3}$, $\sqrt{9}$, $\sqrt{13}$.

✓ **GUIDED PRACTICE** for Examples 3 and 4

9. Tell whether each of the following numbers is a real number, a rational number, an irrational number, an integer, or a whole number: $-\frac{9}{2}$, 5.2, 0, $\sqrt{7}$, 4.1, $-\sqrt{20}$. Then order the numbers from least to greatest. **See margin.**

CONDITIONAL STATEMENTS In the activity on page 109, you saw that a conditional statement not in if-then form can be written in that form.

EXAMPLE 5 Rewrite a conditional statement in if-then form

Rewrite the given conditional statement in if-then form. Then tell whether the statement is *true* or *false*. If it is false, give a counterexample.

Solution

a. **Given:** No integers are irrational numbers.

   If-then form: If a number is an integer, then it is not an irrational number.

   The statement is true.

b. **Given:** All real numbers are rational numbers.

   If-then form: If a number is a real number, then it is a rational number.

   The statement is false. For example, $\sqrt{2}$ is a real number but *not* a rational number.

✓ **GUIDED PRACTICE** for Example 5

11. If a number is a repeating decimal, then it is an irrational number; false. *Sample answer:* 0.333… is a repeating decimal and can be written as $\frac{1}{3}$, so it is a rational number.

Rewrite the conditional statement in if-then form. Then tell whether the statement is *true* or *false*. If it is false, give a counterexample.

10. All square roots of perfect squares are rational numbers.
    If a number is the square root of a perfect square, then it is a rational number; true.
11. All repeating decimals are irrational numbers.

12. No integers are irrational numbers.
    If a number is an integer, then it is not an irrational number; true.

2.7 EXERCISES

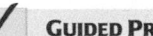

HOMEWORK KEY
○ = **WORKED-OUT SOLUTIONS** on p. WS1 for Exs. 9, 19, and 49
★ = **STANDARDIZED TEST PRACTICE** Exs. 2, 23, 42, 43, 44, 50, and 53
◆ = **MULTIPLE REPRESENTATIONS** Ex. 54

SKILL PRACTICE

A 1. **VOCABULARY** Copy and complete: The set of all rational and irrational numbers is called the set of __?__. **real numbers**

2. ★ **WRITING** Without calculating, how can you tell whether the square root of a whole number is rational or irrational?
   If it is not a perfect square, the square root is irrational.

EXAMPLE 1
on p. 110
for Exs. 3–14

EVALUATING SQUARE ROOTS Evaluate the expression.

3. $\sqrt{4}$ **2**   4. $-\sqrt{49}$ **−7**   5. $-\sqrt{9}$ **−3**   6. $\pm\sqrt{1}$ **±1**

7. $\sqrt{196}$ **14**   8. $\pm\sqrt{121}$ **±11**   9. $\pm\sqrt{2500}$ **±50**   10. $-\sqrt{256}$ **−16**

11. $-\sqrt{225}$ **−15**   12. $\sqrt{361}$ **19**   13. $\pm\sqrt{169}$ **±13**   14. $-\sqrt{1600}$ **−40**

113

EXAMPLE 2
on p. 111
for Exs. 15–22

APPROXIMATING SQUARE ROOTS Approximate the square root to the nearest integer.

15. $\sqrt{10}$ **3**
16. $-\sqrt{18}$ **−4**
17. $-\sqrt{3}$ **−2**
18. $\sqrt{150}$ **12**
19. $-\sqrt{86}$ **−9**
20. $\sqrt{40}$ **6**
21. $\sqrt{200}$ **14**
22. $-\sqrt{65}$ **−8**

23. ★ **MULTIPLE CHOICE** Which number is between −30 and −25? **B**

(A) $-\sqrt{1610}$ (B) $-\sqrt{680}$ (C) $-\sqrt{410}$ (D) $-\sqrt{27}$

EXAMPLES 3 and 4
on p. 112
for Exs. 24–29

CLASSIFYING AND ORDERING REAL NUMBERS Tell whether each number in the list is a real number, a rational number, an irrational number, an integer, or a whole number. Then order the numbers from least to greatest.

24. $\sqrt{49}$, 8, $-\sqrt{4}$, −3 **24–29. See margin.**

25. $-\sqrt{12}$, −3.7, $\sqrt{9}$, 2.9

26. −11.5, $-\sqrt{121}$, −10, $\frac{25}{2}$, $\sqrt{144}$

27. $\sqrt{8}$, $-\frac{2}{5}$, −1, 0.6, $\sqrt{6}$

28. $-\frac{8}{3}$, $-\sqrt{5}$, 2.6, −1.5, $\sqrt{5}$

29. −8.3, $-\sqrt{80}$, $-\frac{17}{2}$, −8.25, $-\sqrt{100}$

EXAMPLE 5
on p. 113
for Exs. 30–33

ANALYZING CONDITIONAL STATEMENTS Rewrite the conditional statement in if-then form. Then tell whether the statement is *true* or *false*. If it is false, give a counterexample. **30–33. See margin.**

30. All whole numbers are real numbers.

31. All real numbers are irrational numbers.

32. No perfect squares are whole numbers.

33. No irrational numbers are whole numbers.

B   **EVALUATING EXPRESSIONS** Evaluate the expression for the given value of x.

34. $3 + \sqrt{x}$ when $x = 9$ **6**
35. $11 - \sqrt{x}$ when $x = 81$ **2**

36. $4 \cdot \sqrt{x}$ when $x = 49$ **28**
37. $-7 \cdot \sqrt{x}$ when $x = 36$ **−42**

38. $-3 \cdot \sqrt{x} - 7$ when $x = 121$ **−40**
39. $6 \cdot \sqrt{x} + 3$ when $x = 100$ **63**

40. $\frac{\sqrt{x}}{x}$ when $x = 4$ **$\frac{1}{2}$**
41. $\frac{\sqrt{x}}{5} - 17$ when $x = 25$ **−16**

42. *Sample answer:* −5, −4.5, −4; $-\sqrt{26}$ is a little less than −5 and $-\sqrt{15}$ is a little more than −4, therefore −4, −4.5, and −5 are between $-\sqrt{26}$ and $-\sqrt{15}$.

42. ★ **OPEN-ENDED** Without using a calculator, find three rational numbers between $-\sqrt{26}$ and $-\sqrt{15}$. *Explain* how you found the numbers.

43. ★ **MULTIPLE CHOICE** If $x = 36$, the value of which expression is a perfect square? **B**

(A) $\sqrt{x} + 17$ (B) $87 - \sqrt{x}$ (C) $5 \cdot \sqrt{x}$ (D) $8 \cdot \sqrt{x} + 2$

44. ★ **WRITING** Simplify $\sqrt{x^2}$ using the definition of square root. Then verify your answer using several values of x that are perfect squares. *Sample answer:* If $x^2 = a$, then x is the square root of a, therefore $\sqrt{x^2}$ is x; $\sqrt{4^2} = \sqrt{16} = 4$; $\sqrt{3^2} = \sqrt{9} = 3$; $\sqrt{2^2} = \sqrt{4} = 2$.

C 45. **CHALLENGE** Find the first five perfect squares x such that $2 \cdot \sqrt{x}$ is also a perfect square. *Describe* your method. **4, 64, 324, 1024, 2500; take $\frac{1}{2}$ of an even perfect square, and then square it.**

46. **CHALLENGE** Let n be any whole number from 1 to 1000. For how many values of n is $\sqrt{n}$ a rational number? *Explain* your reasoning. **31; the square root of 1000 is between 31 and 32, so there are 31 perfect squares less than 1000.**

○ = **WORKED-OUT SOLUTIONS** on p. WS1   ★ = **STANDARDIZED TEST PRACTICE**

114

24–29. See Additional Answers beginning on p. AA1.

30. If a number is a whole number, then it is a real number; true.

31. If a number is a real number, then it is an irrational number; false. *Sample answer:* 3 is a real number and a rational number.

32. If a number is a perfect square, then it is not a whole number; false. *Sample answer:* 9 is a perfect square and a whole number.

33. If a number is an irrational number, then it is not a whole number; true.

PROBLEM SOLVING

EXAMPLE 1 **A**
on p. 110
for Exs. 47, 49

47. ART The area of a square painting is 3600 square inches. Find the side length of the painting. **60 in.**

@HomeTutor for problem solving help at classzone.com

EXAMPLE 2
on p. 111
for Exs. 48, 50

48. SOCCER Some soccer drills are practiced in a square section of a field. If the section of a field for a soccer drill is 1620 square yards, find the side length of the section. Round your answer to the nearest yard. **40 yd**

@HomeTutor for problem solving help at classzone.com

49. MAZES The table shows the locations and areas of various life-size square mazes. Find the side lengths of the mazes. Then tell whether the side lengths are *rational* or *irrational* numbers.
35 ft; 24 ft; 48 ft; 30 ft; they are all rational numbers.

Maze at Corona, New York

Location of maze	Area (ft²)
Dallas, Texas	1225
San Francisco, California	576
Corona, New York	2304
Waterville, Maine	900

50. ★ SHORT RESPONSE You plan to use a square section of a park for a small outdoor concert. The section should have an area of 1450 square feet. You have 150 feet of rope to use to surround the section. Do you have enough rope? *Explain* your reasoning. **No; each side is a little more than 38 feet. 38 feet times 4 is 152 feet, which is more than 150 feet.**

51. 3; square each fraction, $\left(\frac{265}{153}\right)^2 < 3,$ $\left(\frac{1351}{780}\right)^2 > 3$ **so the value of x is 3.**

51. MATH HISTORY To calculate the value of the irrational number π, the Greek mathematician Archimedes first estimated the square root of a certain integer x. He found that $\sqrt{x}$ was between $\frac{265}{153}$ and $\frac{1351}{780}$. Find the value of x. *Explain* how you got your answer.

B

52. MULTI-STEP PROBLEM The Kelvin temperature scale was invented by Lord Kelvin in the 19th century and is often used for scientific measurements. To convert a temperature from degrees Celsius (°C) to kelvin (K), you add 273 to the temperature in degrees Celsius.

a. Convert 17°C to kelvin. **290 K**

b. The speed s (in meters per second) of sound in air is given by the formula $s = 20.1 \cdot \sqrt{K}$ where K is the temperature in kelvin. Find the speed of sound in air at 17°C. Round your answer to the nearest meter per second. **342 m/sec**

53. ★ SHORT RESPONSE A homeowner is building a square patio and will cover the patio with square tiles. Each tile has an area of 256 square inches and costs $3.45. The homeowner has $500 to spend on tiles.

a. Calculate How many tiles can the homeowner buy? **144 tiles**

b. Explain Find the side length (in feet) of the largest patio that the homeowner can build. *Explain* how you got your answer. **See margin.**

Graphing Calculator

Exercises 15–23 It may be helpful for students to use calculators to approximate the square roots. Tell them to use the instructions on how to approximate square roots on page 111.

Teaching Strategy

Exercise 42 For students who have difficulty with this exercise, suggest they first identify the opposites of the perfect squares closest to 26 and 15.

Study Strategy

Exercise 48 Students may be tempted to use their calculators to solve this problem. Encourage them to use their calculators to check their answers, but use the solution model for Example 2 to solve the problem. Explain that by using the model, they will develop a better understanding of square roots. By learning to approximate the square root of a number, they will develop estimation skills that can help them judge whether they entered numbers in their calculators incorrectly.

Avoiding Common Errors

Exercise 52 Some students overlook the different parts of a problem and then make errors because they lack information necessary to solve the problem. Some students may use 27°C for K in part b of this exercise. Remind students to read all parts of a problem before proceeding.

53b. 16 ft. *Sample answer:* If the homeowner can buy 144 tiles that are each 256 square inches, then the total area is (144 tiles) • (256 square inches per tile) = 36,864 square inches. Divide 36,864 square inches by 144 square inches to find the number of square feet, 256 square feet. If the area of the square is 256 square feet, take the square root of 256 to find the side length, 16 feet.

⑤ ASSESS AND RETEACH

Daily Homework Quiz
📄 **Transparency Available**

Evaluate the expression.

1. $\pm\sqrt{289}$ **±17**

2. $-\sqrt{36}$ **−6**

Approximate the square root to the nearest integer.

3. $-\sqrt{21}$ **−5**

4. $\sqrt{620}$ **25**

5. A square courtyard has an area of 272 square feet. What is the side length of the courtyard to the nearest foot? **16 ft**

🌐 Online Quiz
Available at **classzone.com**

Diagnosis/Remediation
• Practice A, B, C in Chapter 2 Resource Book, pp. 72–74
• Study Guide in Chapter 2 Resource Book, pp. 75–76
• Practice Workbook, pp. 28–29
• @HomeTutor

Challenge
Additional challenge is available in the Chapter 2 Resource Book, p. 79.

Quiz

An easily-readable reduced copy of the quiz (with answers) on Lessons 2.6–2.7 from the Assessment Book can be found on p. 62E.

54a. See Additional Answers beginning on p. AA1.
Quiz
6. −3: real number, rational number, integer, −√5: real number, irrational number, −3.7: real number, rational number, √3: real number, rational number; −3.7, −3, −√5, √3

---

54. ◆ **MULTIPLE REPRESENTATIONS** The diagram shows the approximate areas (in square meters) of the square bases for the pyramids of Giza. **See margin.**

Menkaure 11,772 m²   Khafre 46,440 m²   Khufu 54,056 m²

    a. Making a Table Make a table that gives the following quotients (rounded to the nearest tenth) for each of the 3 pairs of pyramids:

       • (area of larger base) ÷ (area of smaller base)

       • (side length of larger base) ÷ (side length of smaller base)

    For each pair of pyramids, how are the two quotients related?

    b. Writing an Equation Write an equation that gives the quotient q of the side lengths as a function of the quotient r of the areas. $q = \sqrt{r}$

$\boxed{C}$ **55. CHALLENGE** Write an equation that gives the edge length ℓ of a cube as a function of the surface area A of the cube. $\ell = \sqrt{\dfrac{A}{6}}$

MIXED REVIEW

Evaluate the expression. *(p. 8)*

56. $11 + 6 - 3$ **14**   **57.** $18 - 3^2$ **9**   **58.** $9 \cdot 2^2 - 1$ **35**   **59.** $6(4^2 + 4)$ **120**

60. $12 \cdot 3 + 15$ **51**   **61.** $6 \cdot 4 + 7 \cdot 5$ **59**   **62.** $9(15 - 2 \cdot 4)$ **63**   **63.** $5^2 - 2^3$ **17**

PREVIEW
Prepare for Lesson 3.1 in Exs. 64–71.

Solve the equation using mental math. *(p. 21)*

64. $8 + x = 13$ **5**   **65.** $x - 20 = 15$ **35**   **66.** $4x = 32$ **8**   **67.** $\dfrac{x}{7} = 5$ **35**

68. $x - 14 = 30$ **44**   **69.** $x + 11 = 27$ **16**   **70.** $\dfrac{x}{9} = 10$ **90**   **71.** $6x = 48$ **8**

QUIZ *for Lessons 2.6–2.7*

Find the quotient. *(p. 103)*

1. $-20 \div (-5)$ **4**   **2.** $-12 \div \dfrac{2}{3}$ **−18**   **3.** $\dfrac{4}{5} \div \left(-\dfrac{3}{10}\right)$ **$-2\dfrac{2}{3}$**   **4.** $-18.2 \div (-3)$ **$6\dfrac{1}{15}$**

5. Simplify the expression $\dfrac{15x - 6}{3}$. *(p. 103)* **$5x - 2$**

6. Tell whether each of the following numbers is a real number, a rational number, an irrational number, an integer, or a whole number: -3, $-\sqrt{5}$, -3.7, $\sqrt{3}$. Then order the numbers from least to greatest. *(p. 110)* **See margin.**

7. If a number is irrational, then it is not a negative number; false. *Sample answer:* $-\sqrt{5}$ is an irrational number and it is negative.

7. Rewrite the following conditional statement in if-then form: "No irrational numbers are negative numbers." Tell whether the statement is *true* or *false*. If it is false, give a counterexample. *(p. 110)*

Use Logical Reasoning

GOAL Use inductive and deductive reasoning.

When you make a conclusion based on several examples, you are using **inductive reasoning**. A conclusion reached using inductive reasoning is an example of a *conjecture*. A **conjecture** is a statement that is believed to be true but not yet shown to be true.

EXAMPLE 1 Use inductive reasoning

Your friend asks you to perform the following number trick: *Choose any number. Then double the number. Then add 8. Then multiply by 3. Then divide by 6. Then subtract 4.* Perform the number trick for three different numbers. Then make a conjecture based on the results.

Solution

	Step		
Step 1: Choose any number.	Choose 5.	Choose 14.	Choose −6.
Step 2: Double the number.	10	28	−12
Step 3: Add 8.	18	36	−4
Step 4: Multiply by 3.	54	108	−12
Step 5: Divide by 6.	9	18	−2
Step 6: Subtract 4.	5	14	−6

Conjecture: The result in Step 6 is the same as the number in Step 1.

EXAMPLE 2 Show that a conjecture is true

Show that the conjecture made in Example 1 is true for all numbers x.

Solution

Step 1: Choose any number.	Choose x.
Step 2: Double the number.	$2x$
Step 3: Add 8.	$2x + 8$
Step 4: Multiply by 3.	$3(2x + 8) = 6x + 24$
Step 5: Divide by 6.	$\frac{6x + 24}{6} = x + 4$
Step 6: Subtract 4.	$(x + 4) - 4 = x$

The result in Step 6 is the same as the number chosen in Step 1. So, the conjecture made in Example 1 is true for all numbers x.

① PLAN AND PREPARE

Warm-Up Exercises

Tell whether each statement is *true* or *false*. If it is false, give a counterexample.

1. If a number is negative, then it is a rational number. **False;** $-\sqrt{20}$ **is a negative number and it is not rational.**

2. If a number is an integer, then it is not a whole number. **False; 7 is an integer and also a whole number.**

② FOCUS AND MOTIVATE

Essential Question

Big Idea 3, p. 63

How do you use reasoning with real numbers? **Tell students they will learn how to answer this question by analyzing and proving conjectures.**

③ TEACH

Extra Example 1

Choose any number. Then double it. Then subtract 4. Then multiply by 5. Then divide by 10. Then add 2. Perform the number trick for three different numbers. Then make a conjecture based on the results. **Conjecture: The result in Step 6 is the same as the number in Step 1.**

NCTM STANDARDS

Standard 7: Make mathematical conjectures; Investigate mathematical conjectures

Extra Example 2

Show that the conjecture in Example 1 is true for all numbers x.
Step 1: Choose x.
Step 2: $2x$
Step 3: $2x - 4$
Step 4: $5(2x - 4) = 10x - 20$
Step 5: $\dfrac{10x - 20}{10} = x - 2$
Step 6: $(x - 2) + 2 = x$

Extra Example 3

Show that $\dfrac{5(2x - 4)}{10} + 2 = x$. Justify each step.

$\dfrac{5(2x - 4)}{10} + 2 = \dfrac{10x - 20}{10} + 2$
$= (x - 2) + 2$
$= (x + (-2)) + 2$
$= x + (-2 + 2)$
$= x + 0$
$= x$

Justifications:
Step 1: Distributive property
Step 2: Divide $10x - 20$ by 10.
Step 3: Subtraction rule
Step 4: Associative property of addition
Step 5: Inverse property of addition
Step 6: Identity property of addition

Closing the Lesson

Have students summarize the major points of the lesson and answer the Essential Question: How do you use reasoning with real numbers?

- Inductive reasoning uses examples to draw conclusions.
- Deductive reasoning uses true statements, whether assumed true or shown to be true, to draw conclusions.
- A conjecture is a conclusion based on inductive reasoning.

You can use inductive and deductive methods to analyze statements about real numbers and determine if they are true or false.

DEDUCTIVE REASONING In Example 2, you simplified the expression at each step. Had you not done this, you would have obtained the expression $\dfrac{3(2x + 8)}{6} - 4$. You can still show that $\dfrac{3(2x + 8)}{6} - 4 = x$ by applying *deductive reasoning*. When you make a conclusion based on statements that are assumed or shown to be true, you are using **deductive reasoning**.

EXAMPLE 3 Use deductive reasoning

Show that $\dfrac{3(2x + 8)}{6} - 4 = x$. Justify each step.

Solution

Step	Justification
$\dfrac{3(2x + 8)}{6} - 4 = \dfrac{6x + 24}{6} - 4$	Distributive property
$= (x + 4) - 4$	Divide $(6x + 24)$ by 6.
$- (x + 4) + (-4)$	Subtraction rule
$= x + [4 + (-4)]$	Associative property of addition
$= x + 0$	Inverse property of addition
$= x$	Identity property of addition

PRACTICE

EXAMPLES
1, 2, and 3
on pp. 117–118
for Exs. 1–3

In Exercises 1 and 2, perform the given number trick for three numbers. Make a conjecture based on the results. Then show that your conjecture is true for all numbers. 1, 2. See margin.

1. Choose any number. Then subtract 5. Then multiply by 6. Then divide by 3. Then add 10.

2. Choose any number. Then double it. Then add 12. Then multiply by 4. Then divide by 8. Then subtract the number you chose.

3. The steps below show that $\dfrac{4(3x + 5) - 20}{12} = x$. *Justify* each step.

$\dfrac{4(3x + 5) - 20}{12} = \dfrac{(12x + 20) - 20}{12}$	__?__ **Distributive property**
$= \dfrac{(12x + 20) + (-20)}{12}$	__?__ **Subtraction rule**
$= \dfrac{12x + [20 + (-20)]}{12}$	__?__ **Associative property of addition**
$= \dfrac{12x + 0}{12}$	__?__ **Inverse property of addition**
$= \dfrac{12x}{12}$	__?__ **Identity property of addition**
$= x$	__?__ **Divide**

118   Chapter 2   Properties of Real Numbers

PRACTICE
4 **AND APPLY**

Avoiding Common Errors

Exercises 1–2 Students sometimes skip steps and then cannot prove their conclusions. Tell students to follow the step-by-step solutions offered in the three examples.

1. *Sample answer:* $3 - 5 = -2$, $-2(6) = -12$, $-12 \div 3 = -4$, $-4 + 10 = 6$; $-2 - 5 = -7$, $-7(6) = -42$, $-42 \div 3 = -14$, $-14 + 10 = -4$; $10 - 5 = 5$, $5(6) = 30$, $30 \div 3 = 10$, $10 + 10 = 20$; double the number; $\dfrac{(x - 5)6}{3} + 10 = (x - 5)2 + 10 = 2x - 10 + 10 = 2x$

2. *Sample answer:* $4(2) = 8$, $8 + 12 = 20$, $20(4) = 80$, $80 \div 8 = 10$, $10 - 4 = 6$; $(-5)(2) = 10$, $-10 + 12 = 2$, $2(4) = 8$, $8 \div 8 = 1$, $1 - (-5) = 6$; $10(2) = 20$, $20 + 12 = 32$, $32(4) = 128$, $128 \div 8 = 16$, $16 - 10 = 6$; the answer will be 6; $\dfrac{(2x + 12)4}{8} - x = \dfrac{8x + 48}{8} - x = x + 6 - x = 6$.

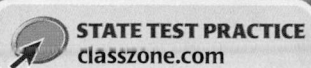
Lessons 2.4–2.7

1. **MULTI-STEP PROBLEM** The modern pentathlon consists of 5 events, including a distance run. For the men's run, every athlete starts with 1000 points. The athlete earns 2 points for every 0.5 second under a finishing time of 10 minutes and −2 points for every 0.5 second over 10 minutes.

   a. An athlete finishes the race in 9 minutes 34 seconds. How many points does he have now? **1104 points**

   b. His competitor finishes in 11 minutes 2.5 seconds. How many more points than his competitor does he have?
   354 points

2. **MULTI-STEP PROBLEM** The troposphere is the lowest layer of the atmosphere. It extends to a height of 11,000 meters. On average, the temperature is 15°C at the bottom of the troposphere and changes by about −0.0065°C for every meter of increase in elevation.

   a. Write an equation that gives the temperature T (in degrees Celsius) as a function of the elevation e (in meters) within the troposphere. $T = 15 + (-0.0065)e$

   b. Find the temperature at the top of the troposphere. **−56.5°C**

3. **GRIDDED ANSWER** The table shows the areas of two square rugs that a store sells. How many inches longer is the sorrel rug than the shaw rug? **3 in.**

Type of rug	Area (in.²)
Sorrel rug	8281
Shaw rug	7744

4. **SHORT RESPONSE** Your friend is comparing two 6-sided cubic storage bins. The yellow bin has a surface area of 9600 square centimeters and costs $25. The blue bin has a surface area of 7350 square centimeters and costs $20.

   a. Find the edge length of each bin. **40 cm; 35 cm**

   b. Which bin costs less per cubic centimeter? *Explain* your reasoning. **See margin.**

5. **SHORT RESPONSE** The table shows the costs of three items at a baseball stadium in 2002 and 2004.

Item	Cost in 2002	Cost in 2004
Ticket	$20.44	$17.90
Soda	$2.75	$2.00
Hot dog	$2.75	$2.75

   a. Write an equation that gives the change c in the total amount spent from 2002 to 2004 when buying x of each item. Then find the value of c when $x = 4$. $c = -3.29x$; **−$13.16**

   b. Suppose that from 2004 to 2006 the cost of a ticket decreases, and the costs of the other two items increase. Can you conclude that the change in the total amount spent from 2004 to 2006 is positive? *Explain*. **No; it depends on the amount of change for each item.**

6. **EXTENDED RESPONSE** A farmer is planting corn and soybeans in the rectangular field shown. The farmer spends $.09 per square yard to plant corn and $.07 per square yard to plant soybeans.

   a. Write an equation that gives the cost C of planting the field as a function of the length x (in yards) of the corn section. $C = 4x + 5600$

   b. How much money will the farmer spend on planting the field if the corn section has a length of 100 yards? **$6000**

   c. Suppose that the farmer has $6500 to plant the entire field. Will the farmer have enough money if the soybean section has a length of 250 yards? *Explain*. **Yes; the cost will be $6200.**

7. **OPEN-ENDED** *Describe* a real-world situation that can be modeled by the expression $\dfrac{8.90 + (-2.34) + (-1.15)}{3}$. Then find the value of the expression. **See margin.**

4b. The yellow bin. *Sample answer:* For each bin, divide the cost by the surface area; the yellow bin costs less per cubic centimeter.

7. *Sample answer:* A stock increases in value by $8.90 one week, decreases by $2.34 the next week and decreases $1.15 the following week. The expression $\dfrac{8.90 + (-2.34) + (-1.15)}{3}$ represents the stock's average change over 3 weeks; $1.80.

Additional Resources

The following resources are available to help review the materials in this chapter.

Chapter 2 Resource Book

- Chapter Review Games and Activities, p. 80
- Cumulative Practice, Chs. 1–2, pp. 82–83

Student Resources in Spanish

eWorkbook

@HomeTutor

Vocabulary Practice

Vocabulary practice is available at **classzone.com**

Big Idea 1

Performing Operations with Real Numbers

To add or multiply two real numbers a and b, you can use the following rules:

Expression	Rule when a and b have the same sign	Rule when a and b have different signs
$a + b$	Add $\lvert a \rvert$ and $\lvert b \rvert$. The sum has the same sign as a and b.	Subtract the lesser absolute value from the greater absolute value. The sum has the same sign as the number with the greater absolute value.
ab	The product is positive.	The product is negative.

You can use these rules to subtract or divide numbers, but first you rewrite the difference or quotient using the subtraction rule or the division rule.

Big Idea 2

Applying Properties of Real Numbers

You can apply the properties of real numbers to evaluate and simplify expressions. Many of the properties of addition and multiplication are similar.

Property	Addition	Multiplication
Commutative property	$a + b = b + a$	$ab = ba$
Associative property	$(a + b) + c = a + (b + c)$	$(ab)c = a(bc)$
Identity property	$a + 0 = 0 + a = a$	$a \cdot 1 = 1 \cdot a = a$
Inverse property	$a + (-a) = -a + a = 0$	$a \cdot \frac{1}{a} = \frac{1}{a} \cdot a = 1, a \neq 0$
Distributive property	$a(b + c) = ab + ac$ (and three variations)	

Big Idea 3

Classifying and Reasoning with Real Numbers

Being able to classify numbers can help you tell whether a conditional statement about real numbers is true or false. For example, the following statement is false: "All real numbers are integers." A counterexample is 3.5.

Numbers	Description
Whole numbers	The numbers 0, 1, 2, 3, 4, . . .
Integers	The numbers . . . , $-3, -2, -1, 0, 1, 2, 3, . . .$
Rational numbers	Numbers of the form $\frac{a}{b}$ where a and b are integers and $b \neq 0$
Irrational numbers	Numbers that cannot be written as a quotient of two integers
Real numbers	All rational and irrational numbers

@HomeTutor

classzone.com
• Multi-Language Glossary
• Vocabulary practice

REVIEW KEY VOCABULARY

- whole numbers, integers, positive integer, negative integer, *p. 64*
- rational number, *p. 64*
- opposites, absolute value, *p. 66*
- conditional statement, *p. 66*
- if-then statement, *p. 66*

- counterexample, *p. 66*
- additive identity, *p. 76*
- additive inverse, *p. 76*
- multiplicative identity, *p. 89*
- equivalent expressions, *p. 96*
- distributive property, *p. 96*

- term, coefficient, constant term, like terms, *p. 97*
- multiplicative inverse, *p. 103*
- square root, radicand, *p. 110*
- perfect square, *p. 111*
- irrational number, *p. 111*
- real numbers, *p. 112*

VOCABULARY EXERCISES

Identify the terms, coefficients, constant terms, and like terms of the expression. **1, 2. See margin.**

1. $-3x - 5 - 7x - 9$

2. $-10c - 6 + c$

Tell whether the number is a real number, a rational number, an irrational number, an integer, or a whole number.

3. 0.3
real number,
rational number

4. $-\sqrt{8}$
real number,
irrational number

5. -15
real number,
rational number,
integer

6. $\sqrt{49}$
real number,
rational number,
integer, whole number

REVIEW EXAMPLES AND EXERCISES

Use the review examples and exercises below to check your understanding of the concepts you have learned in each lesson of Chapter 2.

2.1 Use Integers and Rational Numbers   *pp. 64–67*

EXAMPLE

Order the following numbers from least to greatest: $\frac{1}{5}, -0.10, 0.25, -\frac{1}{6}$.

From least to greatest, the numbers are $-\frac{1}{6}, -0.10, \frac{1}{5}$, and 0.25.

EXERCISES

EXAMPLES
3, 4, and 5
on pp. 65–66
for Exs. 7–12

Order the numbers in the list from least to greatest.

7. $-5.2, -\frac{3}{8}, -6, 0.3, -\frac{1}{4}$ $-6, -5.2, -\frac{3}{8}, -\frac{1}{4}, 0.3$ **8.** $2.1, 0, -\frac{13}{10}, -1.38, \frac{3}{5}$ $-1.38, -\frac{13}{10}, 0, \frac{3}{5}, 2.1$

For the given value of a, find $-a$ and $|a|$.

9. $a = -0.2$ **0.2, 0.2**   **10.** $a = 3$ **$-3, 3$**   **11.** $a = \frac{7}{8}$ $-\frac{7}{8}, \frac{7}{8}$ **12.** $a = -\frac{6}{11}$ $\frac{6}{11}, \frac{6}{11}$

Extra Example 2.2

Find the sum.

a. $-12.8 + 6$ **−6.8**

b. $\dfrac{5}{8} + \left(-\dfrac{3}{4}\right)$ **−$\dfrac{1}{8}$**

Extra Example 2.3

Find the difference.

a. $-14 - 8$ **−22**

b. $6.3 - (-2.9)$ **9.2**

2.2 Add Real Numbers

pp. 74–76

EXAMPLE

Find the sum.

a.
$$-3.6 + (-5.5) = -(|-3.6| + |-5.5|)$$ Rule of same signs

$$= -(3.6 + 5.5)$$ Take absolute values.

$$= -9.1$$ Add.

b.
$$16.1 + (-9.3) = |16.1| - |-9.3|$$ Rule of different signs

$$= 16.1 - 9.3$$ Take absolute values.

$$= 6.8$$ Subtract.

EXERCISES

EXAMPLES
1, 2, and 4
on pp. 74–76
for Exs. 13–19

Find the sum.

13. $-2 + 5$ **3**

14. $-6 + (-4)$ **−10**

15. $6.2 + (-9.7)$ **−3.5**

16. $-4.61 + (-0.79)$ **−5.4**

17. $-\dfrac{4}{7} + \left(-\dfrac{9}{14}\right)$ **−1$\dfrac{3}{14}$**

18. $-\dfrac{4}{5} + \dfrac{11}{12}$ **$\dfrac{7}{60}$**

19. **BUSINESS** A company has a profit of $2.07 million in its first year, −$1.54 million in its second year, and −$.76 million in its third year. Find the company's total profit for the three years. **−$.23 million**

2.3 Subtract Real Numbers

pp. 80–81

EXAMPLE

Find the difference.

a.
$$12 - 19 = 12 + (-19)$$ Add the opposite of 19.

$$= -7$$ Simplify.

b.
$$8.2 - (-1.6) = 8.2 + 1.6$$ Add the opposite of −1.6.

$$= 9.8$$ Simplify.

EXERCISES

EXAMPLES
1 and 2
on p. 80
for Exs. 20–28

Find the difference.

20. $-8 - 3$ **−11**

21. $1 - 11$ **−10**

22. $7.7 - 16.3$ **−8.6**

23. $-20.3 - (-14.2)$ **−6.1**

24. $\dfrac{7}{3} - \dfrac{11}{3}$ **−1$\dfrac{1}{3}$**

25. $-\dfrac{4}{9} - \dfrac{5}{12}$ **−$\dfrac{31}{36}$**

Evaluate the expression when $x = 2$ and $y = -3$.

26. $(x - 7) + y$ **−8**

27. $\dfrac{3}{2} - x - y$ **2$\dfrac{1}{2}$**

28. $y - (2.4 - x)$ **−3.4**

2.4 Multiply Real Numbers
pp. 88–90

EXAMPLE

Find the product.

a. $-4(12) = -48$ Different signs; product is negative.

b. $\frac{1}{2}(-6)(-3) = -3(-3)$ Multiply $\frac{1}{2}$ and -6.

        $= 9$ Same signs; product is positive.

EXERCISES

EXAMPLES
1, 3, and 4
on pp. 88–90
for Exs. 29–35

Find the product.

29. $15(-4)$ **−60**   **30.** $-7.5(-8)$ **60**   **31.** $-\frac{2}{5}(-5)(-9)$ **−18**

Find the product. *Justify* your steps. **32–34. See margin.**

32. $-4(-y)(-7)$ **33.** $-\frac{1}{3}x \cdot (-18)$ **34.** $2.5(-4z)(-2)$

35. SWIMMING POOLS The water level of a swimming pool is 3.3 feet and changes at an average rate of -0.14 feet per day due to water evaporation. What will the water level of the pool be after 4 days? **2.74 ft**

2.5 Apply the Distributive Property
pp. 96–98

EXAMPLE

Use the distributive property to write an equivalent expression.

a. $5(x + 3) = 5(x) + 5(3)$ Distribute 5.

       $= 5x + 15$ Simplify.

b. $(7 - y)(-2y) = 7(-2y) - y(-2y)$ Distribute $-2y$.

       $= -14y + 2y^2$ Simplify.

EXERCISES

EXAMPLES
1, 2, 4, and 5
on pp. 96–98
for Exs. 36–42

Use the distributive property to write an equivalent expression.

36. $8(5 - x)$ **40 − 8x**   **37.** $-3(y + 9)$ **−3y − 27**   **38.** $(z - 4)(-z)$ **−z² + 4z**

Simplify the expression.

39. $3(x - 2) + 14$ **3x + 8**   **40.** $9.1 - 4(m + 3.2)$ **−3.7 − 4m**   **41.** $5n + \frac{1}{2}(8n - 7)$ **9n − 3½**

42. PARTY COSTS You are buying 10 pizzas for a party. Cheese pizzas cost $11 each, and single topping pizzas cost $13 each. Write an equation that gives the total cost C (in dollars) as a function of the number p of cheese pizzas that you buy. Then find the total cost if you buy 4 cheese pizzas. **$C = -2p + 130$; $122**

Chapter Review   **123**

Extra Example 2.4
Find the product.

a. $-8(-2.5)$ **20**

b. $-\frac{1}{3}(9)(2)$ **−6**

Extra Example 2.5
Use the distributive property to write an equivalent expression.

a. $-6(y - 2)$ **−6y + 12**

b. $(5 - x)(-x)$ **−5x + x²**

32. $-28y$; $-4(-y)(-7) = -4(-7)(-y)$, commutative property of multiplication; $28(-y)$, product of -4 and -7; $-28y$, multiply

33. $6x$; $-\frac{1}{3}x \cdot (-18) = -\frac{1}{3}(-18)(x)$, commutative property of multiplication; $6(x)$, product of $-\frac{1}{3}$ and -18; $6x$, multiply

34. $20z$; $2.5(-4z)(-2) = 2.5(-2)(-4z)$, commutative property of multiplication, $-5(-4z)$, product of 2.5 and -2; $[(-5)(-4)]z$, associative property of multiplication, $20z$, multiply

Extra Example 2.6
Find the quotient.
a. $-112 \div (-8)$ **14**

b. $\frac{12}{21} \div \left(-\frac{6}{7}\right)$ **$-\frac{2}{3}$**

Extra Example 2.7
Order the following numbers from least to greatest: $\sqrt{12}, 3.8, -\sqrt{64}, -8.2, 3.$ **$-8.2, -\sqrt{64}, 3, \sqrt{12}, 3.8$**

2.6 | Divide Real Numbers
pp. 103–105

EXAMPLE
Find the quotient.

a. $196 \div (-7) = 196 \cdot \left(-\frac{1}{7}\right)$
$= -28$

b. $-\frac{14}{15} \div \left(-\frac{7}{3}\right) = -\frac{14}{15} \cdot \left(-\frac{3}{7}\right)$
$= \frac{2}{5}$

EXERCISES

EXAMPLES 2, 3, and 4 on pp. 104–105 for Exs. 43–49

Find the quotient.

43. $56 \div (-4)$ **−14**

44. $-6 \div \frac{3}{13}$ **−26**

45. $-\frac{4}{9} \div \left(-\frac{2}{3}\right)$ **$\frac{2}{3}$**

46. **SCIENCE** A scientist studies the diving abilities of three seals and records the elevations they reach before swimming back up to the surface. Find the mean of the following elevations (in meters) recorded: $-380, -307, -354.$ **−347 m**

Simplify the expression.

47. $\frac{24x - 40}{8}$ **$3x - 5$**

48. $\frac{-36m + 18}{6}$ **$-6m + 3$**

49. $\frac{-18n - 9}{-9}$ **$2n + 1$**

2.7 | Find Square Roots and Compare Real Numbers
pp. 110–113

EXAMPLE
Order the following numbers from least to greatest: $\sqrt{25}, -\sqrt{18}, -4, 3.2.$

From least to greatest, the numbers are $-\sqrt{18}, -4, 3.2,$ and $\sqrt{25}.$

EXERCISES

EXAMPLES 1, 2, 4, and 5 on pp. 110–113 for Exs. 50–60

Evaluate the expression.

50. $\sqrt{121}$ **11**

51. $-\sqrt{36}$ **−6**

52. $\pm\sqrt{81}$ **±9**

53. $\pm\sqrt{225}$ **±15**

Approximate the square root to the nearest integer.

54. $\sqrt{97}$ **10**

55. $-\sqrt{48}$ **−7**

56. $-\sqrt{142}$ **−12**

57. $\sqrt{300}$ **17**

Order the numbers in the list from least to greatest.

58. $-\sqrt{49}, -6.8, 2, \sqrt{3}, 1.58$
    $-\sqrt{49}, -6.8, 1.58, \sqrt{3}, 2$

59. $1.25, \sqrt{11}, -0.3, 0, -\sqrt{4}$
    $-\sqrt{4}, -0.3, 0, 1.25, \sqrt{11}$

60. Rewrite the following conditional statement in if-then form: "All real numbers are irrational numbers." Tell whether the statement is *true* or *false*. If it is false, give a counterexample. **If a number is a real number, then it is irrational; false.** *Sample answer:* **5 is a real number and it is rational.**

Tell whether the number is a real number, a rational number, an irrational number, an integer, or a whole number.

1. $-\dfrac{1}{4}$
real number, rational number

2. $\sqrt{90}$
real number, irrational number

3. $-\sqrt{144}$
real number, rational number, integer

4. 8.95
real number, rational number

Order the numbers in the list from least to greatest.

5. $-\dfrac{5}{3}, -2, 3, \dfrac{1}{2}, -1.07$ $-2, -\dfrac{5}{3}, -1.07, \dfrac{1}{2}, 3$

6. $\sqrt{15}, -4.3, 4.2, 0, -\sqrt{25}$
$-\sqrt{25}, -4.3, 0, \sqrt{15}, 4.2$

Find the sum, difference, product, or quotient.

7. $-5 + 2$ -3

8. $1.3 + (-10.4)$ -9.1

9. $-\dfrac{1}{3} + \dfrac{1}{6}$ $-\dfrac{1}{6}$

10. $-\dfrac{2}{7} - \dfrac{5}{14}$ $-\dfrac{9}{14}$

11. $-41 - 32$ -73

12. $7.2 - (-11.6)$ 18.8

13. $-11(-7)$ 77

14. $-4.5(20)(2)$ -180

15. $-\dfrac{1}{5}(-20)(-5)$ -20

16. $-36 \div (-6)$ 6

17. $-\dfrac{3}{5} \div 12$ $-\dfrac{1}{20}$

18. $5 \div \left(-\dfrac{10}{11}\right)$ $-5\dfrac{1}{2}$

Evaluate the expression when $x = -6$ and $y = -10$.

19. $-x$ 6

20. $|y|$ 10

21. $8 - (x - y)$ 4

22. $-4x + y$ 14

Simplify the expression.

23. $-9(y - 7)$
$-9y + 63$

24. $8(x - 4) - 10x$
$-2x - 32$

25. $\dfrac{-7w - 21}{7}$
$-w - 3$

26. $\dfrac{-16v + 8}{-4}$
$4v - 2$

In Exercises 27 and 28, rewrite the conditional statement in if-then form. Then tell whether the statement is *true* or *false*. If it is false, give a counterexample.

27. No rational numbers are integers.   **If a number is rational, then it is not an integer; false.**
Sample answer: -2 is a rational number and an integer.

28. All irrational numbers are real numbers.
If a number is irrational, then it is a real number; true.

29. **MUSIC** The revenue from sales of digital pianos in the United States was $152.4 million in 2001 and $149.0 million in 2002. Find the change in revenue from 2001 to 2002.   **$-\$3.4$ million**

30. **ELEVATORS** An elevator moves at a rate of -5.8 feet per second from a height of 300 feet above the ground. It takes 3 seconds for the elevator to make its first stop. How many feet above the ground is the elevator now?   **282.6 ft**

31. **SUMMER JOBS** You plan to work a total of 25 hours per week at two summer jobs. You will earn $8.75 per hour working at a cafe and $10.50 per hour working at an auto shop. Write an equation that gives your weekly pay p (in dollars) as a function of the time t (in hours) spent working at the cafe. Then find your weekly pay if you work 10 hours at the cafe.   **$p = -1.75t + 262.5$; $245**

32. **TEMPERATURES** The low temperatures for Montreal, Quebec, in Canada on February 12 for each year during the period 2000–2004 are $-6.7°F$, $-4.2°F$, $4.1°F$, $-3.6°F$, and $0.3°F$. Find the mean of the temperatures.   **$-2.02°F$**

Additional Resources

Assessment Book
- Chapter Test, Levels A, B, C, pp. 19–24
- Standardized Chapter Test, pp. 25–26
- SAT/ACT Chapter Test, pp. 27–28
- Alternative Assessment, pp. 29–30

Test Generator CD-ROM

Chapter Test

Easily-readable reduced copies (with answers) of Chapter Test B, the Standardized Chapter Test, and the Alternative Assessment from the Assessment Book can be found on pp. 62E–62F.

Using Rubrics

The rubric given on the pupil pages is a sample of a three-level rubric. Other rubrics may contain four, five, or six levels. For more information on rubrics, see the *Algebra 1 Toolkit*.

Test-Taking Strategy

Encourage students to read the question fully before beginning their work on a solution. Suggest that they take a few moments to organize the steps in their mind before starting to write down their work. This approach will help organize their solution into a logical sequence of steps leading to their answer.

Avoiding Common Errors

When using more than one equation, students often transpose numbers in the equations. Caution students to check their equations for the correct numbers before they begin their calculations.

Scoring Rubric

Full Credit
- solution is complete and correct

Partial Credit
- solution is complete but errors are made, *or*
- solution is without error but incomplete

No Credit
- no solution is given, *or*
- solution makes no sense

EXTENDED RESPONSE QUESTIONS

PROBLEM

The *Alvin* is an HOV (human-operated vehicle) used to explore the ocean. A new HOV is being built that will carry explorers deeper and faster. The table shows the capabilities of the two vehicles.

Vehicle	Lowest elevation (m)	Velocity (m/sec)
Alvin	−4500	−30
New HOV	−6500	−44

a. For each vehicle, write an equation that gives the elevation e (in meters) to which the vehicle dives as a function of the elapsed time t (in seconds) of the dive.

b. If both vehicles begin diving from the surface of the ocean at the same time, what will their elevations be after 90 seconds?

c. If both vehicles continue diving, which vehicle will reach its lowest elevation first? *Explain* how you can use the equations you wrote in part (a) to find the answer.

Below are sample solutions to the problem. Read each solution and the comments in blue to see why the sample represents full credit, partial credit, or no credit.

Full credit solution

The correct equations are given. →

a. Alvin: $e = -30t$ **New HOV:** $e = -44t$

b. Alvin: $e = -30t$ **New HOV:** $e = -44t$

$\qquad = -30(90) \qquad\qquad\qquad = -44(90)$

$\qquad = -2700 \qquad\qquad\qquad\quad = -3960$

The correct calculations are performed, and the correct elevations are given. →

Alvin will be at an elevation of −2700 meters, and the new HOV will be at an elevation of −3960 meters.

c.

t (sec)	Elevation of Alvin (m)	Elevation of new HOV (m)
100	$e = -30(100) = -3000$	$e = -44(100) = -4400$
125	$e = -30(125) = -3750$	$e = -44(125) = -5500$
150	$e = -30(150) = -4500$	$e = -44(150) = -6600$

The reasoning is correct, and it includes use of the equations. The answer is correct. →

After 150 seconds, Alvin reaches its lowest elevation, −4500 feet. Because −6600 < −6500, the new HOV has reached its lowest elevation in less than 150 seconds. So, the new HOV reaches its lowest elevation first.

126   Chapter 2   Properties of Real Numbers

Partial credit solution

The correct equations and elevations are given.

a. **Alvin:** $e = -30t$ **New HOV:** $e = -44t$

b. **Alvin:** $e = -30(90)$ **New HOV:** $e = -44(90)$

$= -2700$ $= -3960$

Alvin will be at an elevation of -2700 meters, and the new HOV will be at an elevation of -3960 meters.

The answer is correct, but the reasoning is incorrect. The lowest elevations were not considered.

c. The velocity of Alvin is -30 meters per second, and the velocity of the new HOV is -44 meters per second. So, each second the new HOV descends 14 meters more than Alvin. This means that the new HOV will reach its lowest elevation first.

No credit solution

The equations are incorrect and the elevations are incorrect.

a. **Alvin:** $e = \dfrac{-4500}{t}$ **New HOV:** $e = \dfrac{-6500}{t}$

b. **Alvin:** $e = \dfrac{-4500}{90} = -50$ **New HOV:** $e = \dfrac{-6500}{90} \approx -72$

Alvin will be at an elevation of -50 meters, and the new HOV will be at an elevation of about -72 meters.

The student's reasoning is incorrect and does not use the equations. The answer is incorrect.

c. Alvin has to travel only to -4500 meters, while the new HOV has to travel to -6500 meters. So, Alvin will reach its lowest elevation first.

PRACTICE Apply the Scoring Rubric

1. Full credit; for part (a), the correct equations are given. For part (b), the correct calculations are performed, and the correct elevations are given. For part (c), the reasoning is correct and includes use of the equations from part (b). The solution is correct.

1. A student's solution to the problem on the previous page is given below. Score the solution as *full credit*, *partial credit*, or *no credit*. *Explain* your reasoning. If you choose *partial credit* or *no credit*, explain how you would change the solution so that it earns a score of full credit.

a. Alvin: $e = -30t$ New HOV: $e = -44t$

b. Alvin: $e = -30(90)$ New HOV: $e = -44(90)$

$= -2700$ meters $= -3960$ meters

c. The time it takes Alvin to reach its lowest elevation can be found by solving $-4500 = -30t$. Using mental math, I found that $t = 150$ seconds.

The time it takes the new HOV to reach its lowest elevation can be found by solving $-6500 = -44t$.

Try $t = 145$: $-44(145) = -6380$

Try $t = 150$: $-44(150) = -6600$

The new HOV reaches its lowest elevation, -6500 feet, after more than 145 seconds but less than 150 seconds. So, the new HOV will reach its lowest elevation first.

Study Strategy

Remind students to label their answers according to the labels given in the extended response question. Tell them that reviewers expect the same organization in the answers as in the questions. Similarly, tell students to organize each part of the answer so that the answer is clear and the reviewer does not have to look in several places to put the answer together. If one part of an answer has multiple steps, such as part (c) in the Practice, suggest that students write a summary statement at the end that ties the steps together and shows the relationship between the steps.

2c. No;

$\vdash$10 × 2.5 in. = 25 in.$\dashv$

6 × 2.5 in. = 15 in.

$\leftarrow$ 1 in.

Sample answer: **From the diagram, you can see that sixty 2.5-inch squares can be cut from the 16 inch by 25 inch piece of wood. The leftover 1 inch by 25 inch piece contains enough area to cover the remaining four 2.5 inch squares that are needed, but no square 2.5 inches on a side can be cut from this piece.**

EXTENDED RESPONSE

1. Your friend owns a business designing and selling personalized greeting cards. The table shows the profits for the first five years of the business.

Year	1	2	3	4	5
Profit (dollars)	−680	−1259	−963	2795	1507

a. Find the total profit for the five years. Then tell whether the profit was a *gain* or a *loss*. **$1400; gain**

b. In which year did the business have the least profit? the greatest profit? **year 2; year 4**

c. Can you use the table to determine the year with the greatest expenses and the year with the greatest income? *Justify* your answer. **No.** *Sample answer:* **Since profit = income − expenses, many different incomes and expenses can produce the same profit.**

2. The area of the playing region of a checkerboard has 64 small squares of equal size arranged as shown.

a. Write an equation that gives the side length *s* of the playing region as a function of the area *A* of the playing region. $s = \sqrt{A}$

b. The area of the playing region of a certain checkerboard is 256 square inches. What is the side length of a small square on the checkerboard? *Explain* your answer.

c. You want to make a checkerboard out of a rectangular piece of wood that measures 16 inches by 25 inches. Each small square will have a side length of 2.5 inches. Can you cut 64 whole small squares from the piece of wood? *Justify* your answer using a diagram. **See margin.**

2b. 2 in. *Sample answer:* **The side length *s* of the playing region is $\sqrt{256} = 16$ inches. Eight small squares fit along each side, so the side length of each small square is 16 ÷ 8 = 2 inches.**

3. The table shows the changes in elevation from one mile marker to the next mile marker on each of two trails. Trail A is 6 miles long, and trail B is 8 miles long.

Mile markers	0 to 1	1 to 2	2 to 3	3 to 4	4 to 5	5 to 6	6 to 7	7 to 8
Elevation change on trail A (ft)	420	−60	−16	425	470	345	—	—
Elevation change on trail B (ft)	−135	430	465	410	390	−40	−60	405

a. Find the total change in elevation for each trail. Which trail has the greater total change in elevation? **trail A: 1584 ft, trail B: 1865 ft; trail B**

b. The average trail grade is the total elevation change (in feet) divided by the trail length (in feet). The lesser the average trail grade is, the easier it is to hike the trail. Which is easier to hike, *trail A* or *trail B*? *Explain.*

c. If trail B is extended by 1 mile, is it possible for trail B to have the same average trail grade as trail A? Your answer should include the following:

- a table of values that gives the average trail grade of trail B for various elevation changes from mile 8 to mile 9

- an explanation of how you used the table to answer the question **See margin.**

3b. Trail B. *Sample answer:* **The average trail grade for trail A is $\frac{1584}{6} = 264$ feet per mile, and the average trail grade for trail B is $\frac{1865}{8} \approx 233$ feet per mile. Since trail B has a lesser average trail grade, it is the easier trail to hike.**

3c. Yes; for elevation change *x* from mile 8 to 9, the average trail grade will be $\frac{1865 + x}{9}$ feet per mile. Make a table of values showing the average trail grades for values of *x*, and look for an average trail grade value of 264 feet per mile, the average trail grade of trail A.

Elevation change (ft)	450	475	500	525
Average trail grade (ft/mi)	about 257	about 260	about 263	about 266

Since 264 is between 263 and 266, there is an elevation change between 500 and 525 feet that will give an average trail grade of 264 feet per mile.

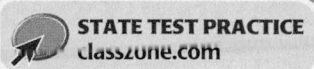

MULTIPLE CHOICE

4. Which description does not apply to $-\sqrt{9}$? **B**

- **(A)** Real number
- **(B)** Whole number
- **(C)** Integer
- **(D)** Rational number

5. Which list of numbers is in order from least to greatest? **C**

- **(A)** $-\dfrac{10}{3}, -\sqrt{16}, -\sqrt{20}, -4.5$
- **(B)** $-4.5, -\dfrac{10}{3}, -\sqrt{16}, -\sqrt{20}$
- **(C)** $-4.5, -\sqrt{20}, -\sqrt{16}, -\dfrac{10}{3}$
- **(D)** $-\sqrt{20}, -4.5, -\sqrt{16}, -\dfrac{10}{3}$

6. Which statement illustrates the associative property of multiplication? **D**

- **(A)** $(-5 \cdot 3) + 7 = 7 + (-5 \cdot 3)$
- **(B)** $8 + (9 + 10) = (8 + 9) + 10$
- **(C)** $4 \cdot (2 \cdot 12) = (2 \cdot 12) \cdot 4$
- **(D)** $11 \cdot (4 \cdot 7) = (11 \cdot 4) \cdot 7$

GRIDDED ANSWER

7. The table shows the change in the balance of your bank account when you withdraw money from an automated teller machine (ATM).

Change in Balance after Withdrawal of $x	
Your bank's ATM	**Another bank's ATM**
$-x$	$-x - 1.50$

You have $230 in your bank account. You make 8 withdrawals of $20 each, and 3 of the withdrawals are made from your bank's ATM. How much money is in your account now? **$62.50**

8. The table shows the scores earned by two teams in each of three rounds of an academic contest. What is the difference of the greater total score and the lesser total score? **350**

Round	Team A's score	Team B's score
1	−125	100
2	300	−75
3	150	−50

SHORT RESPONSE

9. A homeowner is dividing a rectangular room into two rooms as shown. The homeowner plans to install carpet in the living room and wood flooring in the dining room. Carpet costs $2.50 per square foot, and wood flooring costs $4.25 per square foot.

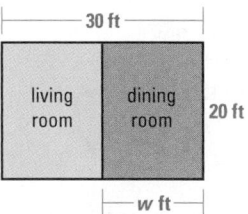

a. Write an equation that gives the total cost C (in dollars) of the project as a function of the width w (in feet) of the dining room. $C = 35w + 1500$

b. How much money will the homeowner save by making the width of the dining room 12 feet instead of making the rooms the same size? *Explain* your answer.

10. A certain swimming pool contains 22,900 gallons of water when full. Due to evaporation, the amount of water in the pool changes at a rate of about −160 gallons per week.

a. If water is not added to the pool, find the approximate amount of water that will be left in the pool after 12 weeks. **about 20,980 gal**

b. A garden hose adds 2 gallons of water to the pool per minute. Estimate the time (in minutes) each day that the hose would need to add water in order to make up for the daily loss of water. *Explain* how you estimated the time. **See margin.**

10b. About 11.5 min. *Sample answer:* Divide the loss per week by 7 to get the daily loss: $\dfrac{-160}{7} \approx$ −23 gallons per day. The garden hose adds 2 gallons per minute, so to add 23 gallons, the hose will need to add water for $\dfrac{23 \text{ gal}}{2 \text{ gal/min}} =$ 11.5 minutes.

9b. $105. *Sample answer:* If the rooms are the same size, they both have a width of 30 ÷ 2 = 15 feet. For $w = 15$, $C = 35(15) + 1500 = 2025. For $w = 12$, $C = 35(12) + 1500 = 1920. The difference in cost is $2025 − $1920 = $105.

REGULAR SCHEDULE

Pre-AP For pacing and assignments for a Pre-AP course, see the *Algebra 1 Toolkit*.

Lesson	Les. Day	BASIC	AVERAGE	ADVANCED
3.1	Day 1	SRH p. 915 Exs. 16–20; pp. 137–140 Exs. 1, 2, 3–13 odd, 15, 16, 17–27 odd, 29–42, 53–59, 64–75	pp. 137–140 Exs. 1, 2, 8–14 even, 15, 16, 20–28 even, 29, 30, 32–50 even, 54–61, 64–75 even	pp. 137–140 Exs. 1, 2, 11–16, 20–26 even, 34–48 even, 49–52*, 56–63*, 69–75 odd
3.2	Day 1	SRH p. 938 Exs. 21–24; pp. 144–146 Exs. 1, 2, 3–21 odd, 22–29, 37–41, 46–60	pp. 144–146 Exs. 1, 2, 6–20 even, 21–26, 30–36, 38–44, 46–60	pp. 144–146 Exs. 1, 2, 8–14 even, 19–21, 24–26, 32–36*, 39–45*, 49–51, 54–60 even
3.3	Day 1	pp. 150–153 Exs. 1–18, 27, 28, 44–47	pp. 150–153 Exs. 1, 2, 4–10 even, 12–18, 27–32, 35, 45, 46	pp. 150–153 Exs. 1, 9–11, 15–18, 29–32, 35, 37*, 45, 46
	Day 2	pp. 150–153 Exs. 19–26, 29, 30, 38–41, 48–56	pp. 150–153 Exs. 19–26, 33, 34, 36, 38–42, 49–55 odd	pp. 150–153 Exs. 22–24, 33, 34, 36, 38–43*, 54–56
3.4	Day 1	EP p. 939 Exs. 38–41; pp. 157–159 Exs. 1, 2, 3–13 odd, 15–37, 49–52, 56–64 even	pp. 157–159 Exs. 1, 2, 7–13 odd, 15–29, 31–43 odd, 44–47, 49–53, 56–64 odd	pp. 157–159 Exs. 1, 7, 8, 12–26, 29, 38–48*, 50–55*, 58–64 even
3.5	Day 1	SRH p. 912 Exs. 6–10; pp. 165–167 Exs. 1–6, 7–17 odd, 19–26, 45–52, 56–66	pp. 165–167 Exs. 1, 2, 5, 6, 10–18 even, 19–22, 23–43 odd, 47–54, 56–66 even	pp. 165–167 Exs. 1, 2, 15–20, 27–30, 32–42 even, 43–55*, 57–65 odd
3.6	Day 1	pp. 171–173 Exs. 1–18, 19–25 odd, 33–39 odd, 40, 44–54 even	pp. 171–173 Exs. 1, 2, 4–14 even, 15–18, 19–29 odd, 31–42, 44–54 even	pp. 171–173 Exs. 1, 2, 11–16, 24–30 even, 31–34*, 37–43*, 46, 47, 53–55
3.7	Day 1	SRH p. 917 Exs. 11–17 odd; pp. 179–181 Exs. 1–14, 22, 23, 47–52	pp. 179–181 Exs. 1, 2, 3–13 odd, 22, 23, 26–29, 47–52	pp. 179–181 Exs. 1, 6–8, 12–14, 22, 23, 26–29
	Day 2	pp. 179–181 Exs. 15–21, 24, 25, 33–37, 41–46	pp. 179–181 Exs. 16, 19–21, 24, 25, 30, 31, 35–39, 41–46	pp. 179–181 Exs. 17–19, 24, 25, 30–32*, 35–40*, 42, 46
3.8	Day 1	pp. 187–189 Exs. 1–10, 11–19 odd, 20–25, 32–35, 38–45	pp. 187–189 Exs. 1, 2, 4, 6, 8–10, 12–18 even, 20–30, 32–36, 38–45	pp. 187–189 Exs. 1, 7, 8, 16–31*, 34–37*, 38–44 even
Review	Day 1	pp. 192–196 Exs. 1–61	pp. 192–196 Exs. 1–61	pp. 192–196 Exs. 1–61
Assess	Day 1	Chapter 3 Test	Chapter 3 Test	Chapter 3 Test
Yearly Pacing		Chapter 3 Total – 12 days	Chapters 1–3 Total – 34 days	Remaining – 126 days

*Challenge Exercises   EP = Extra Practice   SRH = Skills Review Handbook

BLOCK SCHEDULE

DAY 1	DAY 2	DAY 3	DAY 4	DAY 5	DAY 6
3.1	**3.3**	**3.4**	**3.6**	**3.7 (CONT.)**	**REVIEW**
pp. 137–140 Exs. 1, 2, 8–14 even, 15, 16, 20–28 even, 29, 30, 32–50 even, 54–61, 64–75 even	pp. 150–153 Exs. 1, 2, 4–10 even, 12–36, 38–42, 45, 46, 49–55 odd	pp. 157–159 Exs. 1, 2, 7–13 odd, 15–29, 31–43 odd, 44–47, 49–53, 56–64 odd	pp. 171–173 Exs. 1, 2, 4–14 even, 15–18, 19–29 odd, 31–42, 44–54 even	pp. 179–181 Exs. 16, 19–21, 24, 25, 30, 31, 35–39, 41–46	pp. 192–196 Exs. 1–61
3.2		**3.5**	**3.7**	**3.8**	**ASSESS**
pp. 144–146 Exs. 1, 2, 6–20 even, 21–26, 30–36, 38–44, 46–60		pp. 165–167 Exs. 1, 2, 5, 6, 10–18 even, 19–22, 23–43 odd, 47–54, 56–66 even	pp. 179–181 Exs. 1, 2, 3–13 odd, 22, 23, 26–29, 47–52	pp. 187–189 Exs. 1, 2, 4, 6, 8–10, 12–18 even, 20–30, 32–36, 38–45	Chapter 3 Test
Yearly Pacing		Chapter 3 Total – 6 days	Chapters 1–3 Total – 17 days	Remaining – 63 days	

RESOURCE MANAGER

Chapter Resource Book

CHAPTER SUPPORT

| Parents as Partners (Chapter Overview with home involvement exercises and activity) | | | | | | | p. 1 | |

LESSON SUPPORT	3.1	3.2	3.3	3.4	3.5	3.6	3.7	3.8
Teaching Guide/Lesson Plan	p. 3	p. 14	p. 25	p. 37	p. 50	p. 60	p. 70	p. 80
Activity Masters		p. 16		p. 39				
Technology Activities & Keystrokes			p. 27	p. 40				
Activity Support Masters	p. 5							
Practice (3 levels)	p. 6	p. 17	p. 29	p. 41	p. 52	p. 62	p. 72	p. 82
Study Guide	p. 9	p. 20	p. 32	p. 44	p. 55	p. 65	p. 75	p. 85
Catch-Up for Absent Students	p. 11	p. 22	p. 34	p. 46	p. 57	p. 67	p. 77	p. 87
Problem Solving/Application	p. 12	p. 23	p. 35	p. 47	p. 58	p. 68	p. 78	p. 88
Challenge Practice	p. 13	p. 24	p. 36	p. 49	p. 59	p. 69	p. 79	p. 89

REVIEW

Chapter Review Games and Activities	p. 90	Cumulative Practice	p. 92
Project with Rubric	p. 91	Resource Book Answers	A1

Transparencies

Transparencies	3.1	3.2	3.3	3.4	3.5	3.6	3.7	3.8
Warm-Up/Daily Homework Quiz	✔	✔	✔	✔	✔	✔	✔	✔
Notetaking Guide	✔	✔	✔	✔	✔	✔	✔	✔
Teacher Support	✔							
Answer Transparencies	✔	✔	✔	✔	✔	✔	✔	✔

ASSESSMENT BOOK

Quizzes	p. 31	SAT/ACT Chapter Test	p. 42
Chapter Tests (3 levels)	p. 34	Alternative Assessment with Rubric	p. 44
Standardized Chapter Test	p. 40		

TECHNOLOGY

- Easy Planner
- Test and Practice Generator
- Power Presentations
- @HomeTutor
- Activity Generator
- Animated Algebra
- Classzone.com
- eEdition Plus Online
- eWorkbook Plus Online
- Easy Grader Online

ADDITIONAL RESOURCES

- Worked-Out Solution Key
- Notetaking Guide
- Practice Wookbook
- Algebra 1 Toolkit
- Benchmark Tests
- Reteaching and Remediation
- Spanish Study Guide
- Spanish Assessment Book
- Student Resources in Spanish
- Multi-Language Visual Glossary

3 Lesson Practice Level B

LESSON 3.1 Practice B
For use with pages 134–140

Solve the equation.

1. $x + 16 = 25$ $x = 9$
2. $n - 9 = 17$ $n = 26$
3. $-30 = w + 8$ $w = -38$
4. $y + 5 = -13$ $y = -18$
5. $a - 17 = -10$ $a = 7$
6. $41 = 52 + m$ $m = -11$
7. $c - 2.4 = 1.8$ $c = 4.2$
8. $z + 4.1 = 9.6$ $z = 5.5$
9. $-3.2 = 4.5 + p$ $p = -7.7$
10. $9x = 54$ $x = 6$
11. $-5b = 55$ $b = -11$
12. $-42 = 3m$ $m = -14$
13. $-52 = -4y$ $y = 13$
14. $\frac{1}{3}n = 36$ $n = 108$
15. $-\frac{3}{4}a = 12$ $a = -16$
16. $0.5y = 17$ $y = 34$
17. $-1.4a = 2.8$ $a = -2$
18. $-6.5 = -1.3m$ $m = 5$

The rectangle or triangle has area A. Write and solve an equation to find the value of x.

19. $A = 70$ in.^{2} $10x = 70; x = 7$ in.
20. $A = 30$ in.^{2} $\frac{1}{2}(12x) = 30; x = 5$ in.

x
10 in.

x
12 in.

21. **Caves** Cumberland Caverns in Tennessee is 44.4 kilometers long. This cave is 10.9 kilometers longer than Carlsbad Caverns in New Mexico. How long is Carlsbad Caverns?   33.5 km

22. **Bocce** Bocce is a lawn bowling game that originated in Italy. The bocce court below has an area of 1032 square feet. The width of the court is 12 feet. What is the length of the court?   86 ft

12 ft

23. **Olympics** In the 2002 Winter Olympics, Cartriona LeMay Doan won the 500-meter race. Her winning time was 74.75 seconds. Find her average speed to the nearest tenth of a meter per second.   6.7 m/sec

24. **Part-Time Job** You work at a grocery store part-time. You estimate that you spend $\frac{3}{5}$ of your time stocking shelves. You work 20 hours each week. How many hours of your work week do you spend stocking shelves?   12 h

LESSON 3.1

LESSON 3.2 Practice B
For use with pages 141–146

Solve the equation.

1. $3n + 14 = 35$ $n = 7$
2. $7y - 10 = 11$ $y = 3$
3. $14 = 9 - x$ $x = -5$
4. $9c - 5 = 13$ $c = 2$
5. $4.6 = 4m - 3.4$ $m = 2$
6. $1.2 = 2.4 - 3b$ $b = 0.4$
7. $\frac{p}{6} + 9 = 14$ $p = 30$
8. $\frac{w}{7} - 2 = 9$ $w = 77$
9. $\frac{z}{3} - 8 = -4$ $z = 12$

Write an equation for the function described. Then find the input.

10. The output of a function is 5 more than 2 times the input. Find the input when the output is 17. $y = 2x + 5$; 6

11. The output of a function is 10 more than 4 times the input. Find the input when the output is -26. $y = 4x + 10$; -9

12. The output of a function is 14 less than 6 times the input. Find the input when the output is 22. $y = 6x - 14$; 6

Solve the equation.

13. $9a + 4a = 26$ $a = 2$
14. $14y - 6y = 48$ $y = 6$
15. $38 = 26x - 7x$ $x = 2$
16. $16x - 3x = -52$ $x = -4$
17. $-9 = 11m - 8m$ $m = -3$
18. $4.5z - 2.5z = 24$ $z = 12$

19. **Yoga Class** A fitness center offers yoga classes for $10 per class and sells yoga mats for $19.95. A person paid a total of $139.95 to the fitness center for yoga classes and a mat. Find the number of yoga classes the person took.   12 classes

20. **Library Books** Your school has a $1200 grant to buy books and magazine subscriptions for the school library. The average cost of a magazine subscription is $30. Your school decides to spend $870 on books and the remaining amount on magazine subscriptions. How many magazine subscriptions can the school buy?   11 subscriptions

21. **Walking** You have already walked 5 miles of an 18-mile trail. If you walk the rest of the trail at a pace of 1 mile in 17 minutes, how many hours will it take you to finish the trail? Use the following verbal model to answer the question. Round your answer to the nearest tenth.   about 3.7 h

Walking rate (mi/min)	·	Number of minutes (min)	+	Number of miles already walked (mi)	=	Total number of miles walked (mi)

22. **Swimming Pool** The capacity of a small children's swimming pool is 106 gallons of water. There are currently 15 gallons of water in the pool. You are filling the pool with water at a rate of 2 gallons per minute.

  a. Write an equation that gives the amount y (in gallons) of water in the pool as a function of the number x of minutes from now. $y = 15 + 2x$

  b. After how many minutes will the pool be full?   45.5 min

LESSON 3.2

LESSON 3.3 Practice B
For use with pages 148–153

Solve the equation.

1. $16x - 15 - 9x = 13$ $x = 4$
2. $15m + 4 - 9m = -32$ $m = -6$
3. $3b - 9 - 8b = 11$ $b = -4$
4. $-31 = 8 - 6p - 7p$ $p = 3$
5. $9 + 4(x + 1) = 25$ $x = 3$
6. $7(d - 5) + 12 = 5$ $d = 4$
7. $10a + 5(a - 3) = 15$ $a = 2$
8. $19a - 3(a - 6) = 66$ $a = 3$
9. $\frac{1}{4}(x - 8) = 7$ $x = 36$
10. $\frac{1}{3}(d + 9) = -12$ $d = -45$
11. $\frac{3}{4}(n + 3) = 9$ $n = 9$
12. $-\frac{5}{2}(w - 1) = 15$ $w = -5$
13. $6.4 + 2.1(z - 2) = 8.5$ $z = 3$
14. $4.5 - 1.5(6m + 2) = 6$ $m = -0.5$
15. $15 = 4.3n - 2.1(n - 4)$ $n = 3$

Find the value of x for the triangle or rectangle.

16. Perimeter = 23 feet $x = 5$
17. Perimeter = 24 meters $x = 3$

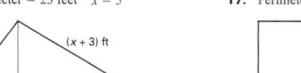
x ft   (x + 3) ft
2x ft

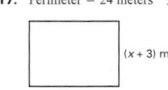
(x + 3) m
2x m

18. **Wrapping a Package** It takes 70 inches of ribbon to make a bow and wrap the ribbon around a box. The bow takes 32 inches of ribbon. The width of the box is 14 inches. What is the height of the box?   5 in.

14 in.

19. **Vacation** You are driving to a vacation spot that is 1500 miles away. Including rest stops, it takes you 42 hours to get to the vacation spot. You estimate that you drove at an average speed of 50 miles per hour. How many hours were you *not* driving?   12 h

20. **Moving** You helped a friend move a short distance recently. The friend rented a truck for $15 an hour and rented a dolly for $5. Your friend paid a total of $80 for the rental. How long did your friend rent the truck for?   5 h

21. **Painting** You and your friend are painting the walls in your apartment. You estimate that there is 1000 square feet of space to be painted. You paint at a rate of 4 square feet per minute and your friend paints at a rate of 3 square feet per minute. Your friend shows up to help you paint 45 minutes after you have already started painting.

  a. Write an equation that gives the total number of square feet y as a function of the number of minutes x it takes to paint all of the walls. $y = 4(x + 45) + 3x$

  b. How long will it take you and your friend to finish painting? Round your answer to the nearest minute.   about 117 min

LESSON 3.3

LESSON 3.4 Practice B
For use with pages 154–159

1. $5x + 11 = 4x + 18$
   $x + 11 = 18$ Subtract 4x from each side.
   $x = 7$ Subtract 11 from each side.

Solve the equation and describe each step you use.

1. $5x + 11 = 4x + 18$
2. $11p - 4 = 6p + 1$ See below.
3. $-6 = 2(w + 5)$ See below.

Solve the equation, if possible.

4. $15x - 8 = 14x + 13$ $x = 21$
5. $9n - 7 = 5n + 5$ $n = 3$
6. $4z - 15 = 4z + 11$ no solution
7. $-7a + 9 = 3a + 49$ $a = -4$
8. $4(w + 3) = w - 15$ $w = -9$
9. $8(y - 5) = 6y - 18$ $y = 11$
10. $14m - 10 = 3(4 + m)$ $m = 2$
11. $7 + x = \frac{1}{2}(4x - 2)$ $x = 8$
12. $8b + 11 - 3b = 2b + 2$ $b = -3$
13. $10d - 6 = 4d - 15 - 3d$ $d = -1$
14. $16p - 4 = 4(2p - 3)$ $p = -1$
15. $0.25(8z - 4) = z + 8 - 2z$ $z = 3$

Write an expression for the perimeter of the square.

16. $16x - 16$ 5x − 8 ; 3x
17. $32x + 16$ 10x ; 6x + 8
18. $18x - 30$ 7x − 15 ; 2x

19. **Saving and Spending** Currently, you have $80 and your sister has $145. You decide to save $6 of your allowance each week, while your sister decides to spend her whole allowance plus $7 each week. How long will it be before you have as much money as your sister?   5 weeks

20. **Botanical Gardens** The membership fee for joining a gardening association is $24 per year. A local botanical garden charges members of the gardening association $3 for admission to the garden. Nonmembers of the association are charged $6. After how many visits to the garden is the total cost for members, including the membership fee, the same as the total cost for nonmembers?   8 visits

21. **College Enrollment** Information about students' choices of majors at a small college is shown in the table. In how many years will there be 2 times as many students majoring in engineering than in business? In how many years will there be 2 times as many students majoring in engineering than in biology?   3 years; 7.6 years

Major	Number of students enrolled in major	Average rate of change
Engineering	120	22 more students each year
Business	105	4 fewer students each year
Biology	98	6 more students each year

2. $11p - 4 = 6p + 1$
   $5p - 4 = 1$ Subtract 6p from each side.
   $5p = 5$ Add 4 to each side.
   $p = 1$ Divide each side by 5.

3. $-6 = 2(w + 5)$
   $-6 = 2w + 10$ Distribute 2 to $(w + 5)$.
   $-16 = 2w$ Subtract 10 from each side.
   $-8 = w$ Divide each side by 2.

LESSON 3.4

130C

Tell whether the ratio is in simplest form. If not, write it in simplest form.

1. 16 to 34   no; 8 to 17

2. 17 : 65   yes

3. $\frac{33}{108}$ no; $\frac{11}{36}$

Solve the proportion.

4. $\frac{1}{2} = \frac{p}{14}$ $p = 7$

5. $\frac{2}{3} = \frac{x}{21}$ $x = 14$

6. $\frac{14}{8} = \frac{y}{20}$ $y = 35$

7. $\frac{y}{6} = \frac{15}{9}$ $y = 10$

8. $\frac{10}{15} = \frac{m}{39}$ $m = 26$

9. $\frac{b}{8} = \frac{50}{20}$ $b = 20$

10. $\frac{8}{2.5} = \frac{d}{0.5}$ $d = 1.6$

11. $\frac{1.4}{1.6} = \frac{z}{10}$ $z = 8.75$

12. $\frac{n}{4} = \frac{0.3}{1.5}$ $n = 0.8$

Write the sentence as a proportion. Then solve the proportion.

13. 5 is to 12 as x is to 48. $\frac{5}{12} = \frac{x}{48}$; $x = 20$

14. w is to 9 as 7 is to 36. $\frac{w}{9} = \frac{7}{36}$; $w = \frac{7}{4}$

15. d is to 4 as 32 is to 56. $\frac{d}{4} = \frac{32}{56}$; $d = \frac{16}{7}$

16. 22 is to 50 as x is to 500. $\frac{22}{50} = \frac{x}{500}$; $x = 220$

17. 10 is to 45 as b is to 225. $\frac{10}{45} = \frac{b}{225}$; $b = 50$

18. n is to 18 as 64 is to 72. $\frac{n}{18} = \frac{64}{72}$; $n = 16$

19. **Books** Over the summer, you read 20 books. Eight of these books were biographies.

   a. Find the ratio of biographies to the total number of books. $\frac{2}{5}$

   b. Find the ratio of non-biographies to biographies. $\frac{3}{2}$

   c. Find the ratio of non-biographies to the total number of books. $\frac{3}{5}$

20. **Fitness Center** The table shows the number of people attending classes at a fitness center during a recent evening.

Class	Aerobics	Spinning	Yoga
Number of people	32	28	16

   a. Find the ratio of the number of people taking yoga to the number of people taking spinning class. $\frac{4}{7}$

   b. Find the ratio of the number of people taking aerobics to the total number of people taking classes. $\frac{8}{19}$

21. **Mailroom** You work in the local mailroom at a college. One of your duties is to sort local mail from all of the other mail. You can sort 8 pieces of mail in 10 seconds. How many pieces of mail should you be able to sort in 45 minutes?   2160 pieces of mail

22. **Music** A music downloading website reports that nearly 5 out of every 7 songs downloaded are classified as pop music. According to this information, predict how many of the next 500 songs downloaded will be pop songs. Round your answer to the nearest whole number.   about 357 songs

Name the cross products of the proportion.

1. $\frac{n}{11} = \frac{40}{55}$ $55n$ and $11(40)$

2. $\frac{4}{9} = \frac{1}{x}$ $4x$ and $9(1)$

3. $\frac{1.8}{1.9} = \frac{b}{3.8}$ $1.8(3.8)$ and $1.9b$

4. $\frac{a+6}{21} = \frac{4}{7}$ $7(a+6)$ and $21(4)$

5. $\frac{5x}{x+1} = \frac{30}{9}$ $9(5x)$ and $30(x+1)$

6. $\frac{2.2}{3.3} = \frac{a-2}{a-1}$ $2.2(a-1)$ and $3.3(a-2)$

Solve the proportion.

7. $\frac{3}{5} = \frac{21}{m}$ $m = 35$

8. $\frac{12}{7} = \frac{60}{d}$ $d = 35$

9. $\frac{24}{x} = \frac{48}{60}$ $x = 30$

10. $\frac{5}{7} = \frac{3w}{21}$ $w = 5$

11. $\frac{2w}{10} = \frac{30}{80}$ $w = 3$

12. $\frac{2z}{24} = \frac{6}{24}$ $z = 9$

13. $\frac{8}{9} = \frac{30+a}{45}$ $a = 10$

14. $\frac{9-y}{44} = \frac{5}{22}$ $y = -1$

15. $\frac{26}{15} = \frac{104}{70-w}$ $w = 10$

16. $\frac{35}{16} = \frac{c-8}{2}$ $c = 12.375$

17. $\frac{1}{9} = \frac{a}{a+24}$ $a = 3$

18. $\frac{2}{n} = \frac{14}{n+30}$ $n = 5$

A map has a scale of 1 in. : 38 ft. Use the given map distance to find the actual distance.

19. 5.5 in.   209 ft

20. 2.25 in.   85.5 ft

21. 1.75 in.   66.5 ft

22. **Concrete** You are making up your own mix of concrete to patch a set of stairs. In order to have the proper mix, you need to mix 1 part of Portland cement with 2 parts of sand and 3 parts of gravel.

   a. How many total parts are in one batch of concrete?   6

   b. You make a mix with 4 parts of sand. How many total parts of cement, sand, and gravel are in your mix?   12 parts

23. **Architectural Firm** An architectural firm makes a model of a science center they are building. The ratio of the model to the actual size is 1 in. : 85 ft. Estimate the height of the building if the model is 1.5 inches tall.   127.5 ft

1.5 in.

24. **Tall Buildings** You made a model of the Space Needle in Seattle, Washington, for a report on architecture in the United States. You used a scale of 1 in. : 50 ft. Your model is 12.1 inches tall. Estimate the actual height of the Space Needle.   605 ft

Use a proportion to answer the question.

1. What percent of 125 is 25?   20%

2. What percent of 70 is 14?   20%

3. What number is 15% of 80?   12

4. What number is 65% of 180?   117

5. 3 is 2% of what number?   150

6. 384 is 64% of what number?   600

Use the percent equation to answer the question.

7. What percent of 64 is 16?   25%

8. What percent of 160 is 128?   80%

9. What number is 12% of 225?   27

10. What number is 85% of 360?   306

11. 4.8 is 8% of what number?   60

12. 25.8 is 86% of what number?   30

Find the percent. Round your answer to the nearest whole percent when necessary.

13. $6 tip for a $40 dinner   15%

14. $8.10 tax on an item priced at $135   6%

15. 46 musicians out of 230 people   20%

16. 18 action movies out of 45 movies   40%

17. **Antarctica** Antarctica comprises about 10.5% of the total land area on Earth. Antarctica has a surface area of about 5,400,000 square miles. What is the total land area on Earth?   51,428,571.43 mi^2

18. **Part-Time Job** So far this week, you have worked 10 hours at your part-time job. This is 80% of the number of hours you work each week. How many hours do you work each week?   12.5 h

19. **Class Times** The circle graph shows the results of a survey in which 500 college students were asked which time they preferred to start classes for the day.

Class Starting Time Survey
9 A.M. 25%
8 A.M. 2%
11 A.M. 38%
10 A.M. 35%

   a. How many students who participated in the survey want to start classes at 8 A.M.?   10 students

   b. How many students who participated in the survey want to start classes at 9 A.M.?   125 students

   c. How many students who participated in the survey want to start classes at either 10 or 11 A.M.?   365 students

20. **Boots** Last year you bought a pair of designer boots on sale for $84. Your friend bought the same boots this year for $120. Which statements are correct?   a and c

   a. You paid 30% less than your friend paid.

   b. Your friend paid 50% more than you did.

   c. You paid 70% of what your friend paid.

Write the equation in function form.

1. $4x + y = -10$ $y = -4x - 10$

2. $6 - y = 17x$ $y = 6 - 17x$

3. $y - 3x - 11 = 0$ $y = 3x + 11$

4. $2x + 2y = 8$ $y = 4 - x$

5. $6x - 3y = 12$ $y = 2x - 4$

6. $16 - 8y = 4x$ $y = 2 - \frac{1}{2}x$

7. $5x - 7y = 14$ $y = \frac{5}{7}x - 2$

8. $9y - 4x - 9 = 0$ $y = \frac{4}{9}x + 1$

9. $15 + 3y = -24x$ $y = -8x - 5$

10. $4 + 6y = 12x - 2$ $y = 2x - 1$

11. $4 - 10y = 22 - 6x$ $y = \frac{3}{5}x - \frac{9}{5}$

12. $8x - 2y - 5 = 11$ $y = 4x - 8$

Solve the literal equation.

13. Solve $R = R_1 + R_2$ for R_2. $R_2 = R - R_1$

14. Solve $I - Prt$ for r. $r = \frac{I}{Pt}$

15. Solve $C = \frac{Q}{V}$ for V. $V = \frac{Q}{C}$

16. Solve $y = mx + b$ for m. $m = \frac{y - b}{x}$

Solve the formula for the indicated variable.

17. Area of a trapezoid: $A = \frac{h}{2}(a + b)$. Solve for h. $h = \frac{2A}{a + b}$

18. Area of a rhombus: $A = \frac{1}{2}d_1 d_2$. Solve for d_1. $d_1 = \frac{2A}{d_2}$

19. **Guitar Practice** You practice playing your guitar every day. You spend 15 minutes practicing chords and the rest of the time practicing a new song. So the total number of minutes y you practice for the week is given by $y = 7(15 + x)$, where x is the number of minutes you spend on practicing a new song.

   a. Solve the equation for x. $x = \frac{y}{7} - 15$

   b. How many minutes did you spend on a new song if you practiced 210 minutes last week? 245 minutes? 315 minutes?   15 min; 20 min; 30 min

20. **Discounts** Solve for r in the formula $S = L - rL$ where S is the sale price, L is the list price, and r is the discount rate. $r = \frac{L - S}{L}$

   a. An item with a list price of $128 goes on sale for $51.20. Find the discount rate.   60%

   b. An item with a list price of $56.80 goes on sale for $36.92. Find the discount rate.   35%

21. **Cookbook** You bought a cookbook while on a recent trip overseas. All of the oven temperatures are in degrees Celsius and the only formula you can remember for temperature is how to convert Fahrenheit to Celsius: $C = \frac{5}{9}(F - 32)$.

   a. Solve the equation for F. $F = \frac{9}{5}C + 32$

   b. A recipe tells you to bake a pie in the oven at 149°C. What is this temperature in degrees Fahrenheit? Round your answer to the nearest whole degree.   about 300°F

CHAPTER 3 Quiz 1
For use after Lessons 3.1–3.3

Solve the equation. Check your solution.

1. $-112 = 7n$

2. $\frac{2}{3}t = 18$

3. $\frac{f}{-3} = -30$

4. $-28 = 10w - 3w$

5. $\frac{d}{5} + 1 = 7$

6. $\frac{9}{4}y - 2 = 25$

7. $24 = 13z - 4z + 6$

8. $7(h + 3) + 4 = -3$

9. $\frac{2}{3}(4x - 7) = -2$

10. A contractor purchases ceramic tile to remodel a kitchen floor. Each tile costs \$4, and the adhesive and grouting material costs \$17.82. If the contractor is charged a total of \$545.82, how many ceramic tiles did the contractor purchase?

Answers

1. $n = -16$
2. $t = 27$
3. $f = 90$
4. $w = -4$
5. $d = 30$
6. $y = 12$
7. $z = 2$
8. $h = -4$
9. $x = 1$
10. 132 tiles

CHAPTER 3 Quiz 2
For use after Lessons 3.4–3.6

Solve the equation, if possible.

1. $6 - 11x = 7x - 12$

2. $2y + 5 = 3(4y - 5)$

3. $12(x + 3) = 24 + 12x$

Solve the proportion. Check your solution.

4. $\frac{t}{65} = \frac{5}{13}$

5. $\frac{1.9}{2.1} = \frac{b}{8.4}$

6. $\frac{j + 4}{6} = \frac{18}{12}$

7. $\frac{m + 18}{m} = \frac{5}{2}$

8. $\frac{d + 4}{2d + 2} = \frac{3}{4}$

9. $\frac{f - 9}{-3} = \frac{11 - f}{5}$

10. At a pet show, the ratio of dogs to cats is $4 : 3$. If the number of cats is 45, find the number of dogs at the show.

Answers

1. $x = 1$
2. $y = 2$
3. no solution
4. $t = 25$
5. $b = 7.6$
6. $j = 5$
7. $m = 12$
8. $d = 5$
9. $f = 6$
10. 60 dogs

CHAPTER 3 Quiz 3
For use after Lessons 3.7–3.8

Use the percent equation to answer the question.

1. 9 is 36 percent of what number?

2. What percent of 125 is 65?

3. What number is 15% of 120?

4. What percent of 110 is 8.8?

5. 62.4 is 48% of what number?

6. What number is 118% of 80?

Write the equation in function form.

7. $4 = 8x + 5y$

8. $2y - 10x = 16$

9. $10 + 7x = 19 - 3y$

10. The formula for simple interest is $I = Prt$ where P is the principal, r is the interest rate, and t is time. Solve the formula for r.

Answers

1. 25
2. 52%
3. 18
4. 8%
5. 130
6. 94.4
7. $y = -\frac{8}{5}x + \frac{4}{5}$
8. $y = 5x + 8$
9. $y = -\frac{7}{3}x + 3$
10. $r = \frac{I}{Pt}$

CHAPTER 3 Chapter Test B
For use after Chapter 3

Solve the equation, if posssible.

1. $-7 = -2 + x$

2. $b - \frac{2}{5} = \frac{3}{5}$

3. $-\frac{2}{3}d = 8$

4. $17 = 14 + 6y$

5. $2t - 5t = 9$

6. $13 - 9w = -14$

7. $7m - 4 - 2m = 6$

8. $\frac{3}{4}(c + 4) = 3$

9. $5(3 - 2y) + 4y = 3$

10. $4x - 1 = 2(2x + 3)$

11. $7a - 3.9a = 6.2$

12. $9 - 5z = 12 - (6z + 7)$

13. A new plasma-screen television costs \$5250. A family makes a down payment of \$552 and pays off the balance in 24 equal monthly payments. Write and solve an equation to find the monthly payment.

14. On a class trip, there were 45 more girls than boys. The total number of students on the trip was 211. Write and solve an equation to find the number of girls and the number of boys on the class trip.

Solve the proportion.

15. $\frac{4}{5} = \frac{12}{y}$

16. $\frac{1.1}{1.2} = \frac{w}{3.6}$

17. $\frac{16}{9} = \frac{-4t}{27}$

18. $\frac{8}{m + 3} = \frac{4}{m}$

19. $\frac{6}{x + 4} = \frac{12}{5x - 13}$

20. $\frac{5}{3z - 4} = \frac{-3}{1 - 2z}$

21. On Monday, biologists tagged 150 sunfish from a lake. On Friday, the biologists counted 12 tagged fish out of a sample of 400 sunfish from the same lake. Estimate the total number of sunfish in the lake.

Answers

1. $x = -5$
2. $b = 1$
3. $d = -12$
4. $y = \frac{1}{2}$
5. $t = -3$
6. $w = 3$
7. $m = 2$
8. $c = 0$
9. $y = 2$
10. no solution
11. $a = 2$
12. $z = -4$
13. $24x + 552 = 5250;$ \$195.75
14. $x + x + 45 = 211;$ 128 girls; 83 boys
15. $y = 15$
16. $w = 3.3$
17. $t = -12$
18. $m = 3$
19. $x = 7$
20. $z = -7$
21. 5000 sunfish

22. A recipe for oatmeal raisin cookies calls for $1\frac{2}{3}$ cups of flour to make 4 dozen cookies. How many cups of flour are needed to make 6 dozen cookies?

Solve the percent problem.

23. 3 is 1.5% of what number?　　**24.** 9 is what percent of 6?

25. What is 26.5% of 46?　　**26.** 70 is 200% of what number?

27. In a renovation project, a football stadium increased its 60,000-seat capacity by 15%. How many seats will be available when the project is completed?

Write the equation in function form.

28. $5x - y = 7$　　**29.** $10x + 3y + 2 = 9x + 8$

In Exercises 30–32, use the following information.
Anthropologists can estimate the height of a woman by measuring the length of her radius bone (from the wrist to the elbow). The length of the radius bone b is given by $b = 0.26h - 18.85$ where h is the height (in centimeters) of the woman.

30. Solve the equation for h.

31. If the length of a woman's radius bone is 25 centimeters, estimate the height of the woman. Round your answer to the nearest centimeter.

32. If 1 in. = 2.54 cm, convert the woman's height to inches. Round your answer to the nearest inch.

Answers

22. $2\frac{1}{2}$ cups of flour

23. 200

24. 150%

25. 12.19

26. 35

27. 69,000 seats

28. $y = 5x - 7$

29. $y = -\frac{1}{3}x + 2$

30. $h = \frac{b + 18.85}{0.26}$

31. about 169 cm

32. about 67 in.

Multiple Choice

1. What is the solution of the equation $-25 = x - 12$?　B

　Ⓐ -37　Ⓑ -13　Ⓒ 13　Ⓓ 37

2. What is the solution of the equation $\frac{m}{3.6} = -1.2$?　A

　Ⓐ -4.32　　Ⓑ -3

　Ⓒ 2.4　　Ⓓ 4.8

3. What is the solution of the equation $15 = \frac{3}{5}n$?　D

　Ⓐ 5　Ⓑ 9　Ⓒ $15\frac{3}{5}$　Ⓓ 25

4. What is the solution of the equation $\frac{2}{3}c + 6 = -12$?　A

　Ⓐ -27　　Ⓑ -18

　Ⓒ -9　　Ⓓ 3

5. What is the first step in solving the equation $5 + \frac{12}{x} = -1$?　C

　Ⓐ Add 1 to each side.

　Ⓑ Divide each side by 12.

　Ⓒ Subtract 5 from each side.

　Ⓓ Add 5 to each side.

6. Examine the problem below. Which line contains an error?　A

$$6x - 2(x - 5) = 22 \qquad \text{Line 1}$$
$$6x - 2x - 10 = 22 \qquad \text{Line 2}$$
$$4x - 10 = 22 \qquad \text{Line 3}$$
$$4x = 32 \qquad \text{Line 4}$$
$$x = 8 \qquad \text{Line 5}$$

　Ⓐ Line 2　　Ⓑ Line 3

　Ⓒ Line 4　　Ⓓ Line 5

7. What is the solution of the equation $8x - 4(5 - x) = -44$?　B

　Ⓐ -6　Ⓑ -2　Ⓒ 5　Ⓓ 8

8. The perimeter of the triangle is 37 centimeters. What is the value of x?　B

　Ⓐ $2\frac{1}{4}$　　Ⓑ 4

　Ⓒ $4\frac{3}{7}$　　Ⓓ 25

9. What is the solution of the equation $4t - 3(t - 2) = t + 6$?　D

　Ⓐ -16　　Ⓑ -9

　Ⓒ -7　　Ⓓ 0

10. What equation does *not* have a solution?　D

　Ⓐ $3y - 2 = \frac{y}{2}$

　Ⓑ $5(x - 3) = 2x + 7$

　Ⓒ $4m - 15 = m - 15$

　Ⓓ $3(6 - n) = -3(n - 8)$

11. What is the value of r in the proportion $\frac{2}{5} = \frac{18}{r}$?　C

　Ⓐ 10　　Ⓑ 40

　Ⓒ 45　　Ⓓ 90

12. What is the value of p in the proportion $\frac{2}{3} = \frac{p}{35}$?　A

　Ⓐ $23\frac{1}{3}$　　Ⓑ $52\frac{1}{2}$

　Ⓒ 70　　Ⓓ 105

---

13. Which proportion represents the statement 5 is to 4 as x is to 24?　B

　Ⓐ $\frac{5}{x} = \frac{24}{4}$　　Ⓑ $\frac{5}{4} = \frac{x}{24}$

　Ⓒ $\frac{5}{24} = \frac{4}{x}$　　Ⓓ $\frac{4}{5} = \frac{x}{24}$

14. Which ratio represents the number of dogs to birds?　C

Dogs	Cats	Birds
243	372	195

　Ⓐ $\frac{81}{124}$　　Ⓑ $\frac{65}{81}$

　Ⓒ $\frac{81}{65}$　　Ⓓ $\frac{124}{65}$

15. What is the value of y in the proportion $\frac{6}{y - 5} = \frac{18}{y + 1}$?　C

　Ⓐ $\frac{1}{2}$　　Ⓑ 5

　Ⓒ 8　　Ⓓ 23

16. What number is 65% of 92?　B

　Ⓐ 5.98　　Ⓑ 59.8

　Ⓒ 598　　Ⓓ 5980

17. What percent of 150 is 30?　C

　Ⓐ 2%　　Ⓑ 5%

　Ⓒ 20%　　Ⓓ 500%

18. Which equation is *not* equivalent to the formula $C = \frac{5}{9}(F - 32)$?　A

　Ⓐ $C - \frac{5}{9}F = -32$　Ⓑ $C = \frac{5}{9}F - \frac{160}{9}$

　Ⓒ $\frac{9}{5}C = F - 32$　Ⓓ $C + 17\frac{7}{9} = \frac{5}{9}F$

Gridded Answer

19. What is the solution of the equation $15t - 3(t - 7) = 57$?

```
              3
     ⊘ ⊘
   ⊙ ⊙ ⊙ ⊙
   ⓪ ⓪ ⓪ ⓪
   ① ① ① ①
   ② ② ② ②
   ③ ③ ● ③
   ④ ④ ④ ④
   ⑤ ⑤ ⑤ ⑤
   ⑥ ⑥ ⑥ ⑥
   ⑦ ⑦ ⑦ ⑦
   ⑧ ⑧ ⑧ ⑧
   ⑨ ⑨ ⑨ ⑨
```

Short Response

20. You are shopping for a new jacket and find that your favorite store has jackets 35% off.

　a. Write an equation representing the cost C before taxes where P represents the original price.

　b. If the sale price of the jacket you want is $55.25, what was the original price? *Explain.*　$85　**20. a.** $C = 0.75P$ or $C = P - 0.35P$

Extended Response

21. The formula for simple interest is $I = Prt$ where I is the interest, P is the principal, r is the interest rate, and t is time in years.

　a. Calculate the amount of interest you would pay if you borrowed $15,000 at a rate of 7.25% for 5 years.　$5437.50

　b. Calculate the *total* amount of interest you would pay on a $25,000 loan at a rate of 5.25% for 5 years. *Explain.*

　c. Rewrite the formula for simple interest so that you can easily calculate the principal given the interest, rate, and time.　$P = \frac{I}{rt}$

　d. If the simple interest on a loan at a rate of 6.5% for 4 years is $3250, what was the principal?　$12,500

21. b. $31,562.50; The simple interest calculates to be $6562.50. This amount must be added to the original $25,000 borrowed for a total of $31,562.50.

Journal　**1.** Explain the difference between a ratio and a proportion. Write an example of each, and explain how to solve a proportion.

Multi-Step Problem　**2.** A car rental agency charges $25 per day to rent an economy class car, and also charges $.08 per mile for each mile that the car is driven.

　a. Write an equation that gives the cost C of a 3 day car rental as a function of the number of miles m that the car is driven.

　b. Juanita needs to rent a car for a 3 day period. If she has $150 budgeted to pay for the rental car, how many miles can she drive the car and not go over her budget? Write your answer in whole numbers of miles.

　c. If Juanita changes her plans so that her rental is for 2 days, how many more miles can she drive the rental car and still stay within her $150 budget? Write your answer in whole numbers of miles.

　d. Write an equation that gives the cost C of a car rental for which 1000 miles were driven as a function of the number of days d that the car is rented.

　e. Stephen needs to rent a car and knows that he will need to drive a total of 1000 miles. If Stephen has $250 to spend on the rental car, how many days is he able to rent the car? Write your answer in whole numbers of days.

　f. If Stephen decides to reduce the number of miles he drives to 800, how many more days is he able to rent the car? Write your answer in whole numbers of days.

1. Complete answers should include: an explanation that a ratio is a relationship between two quantities; an explanation that a proportion is created by equating two ratios; one example of a ratio and one example of a proportion; a written explanation describing how to solve a proportion.

2. a. $C = 75 + 0.08m$　**b.** 937 miles　**c.** 313 more miles　**d.** $C = 25d + 80$　**e.** 6 days　**f.** 1 more day

130F

Main Ideas

In Chapter 3, students use properties of equality to solve one-step, two-step, and multi-step equations in one variable. They also use properties of equality and the distributive property to solve equations with variables on both sides. Students write ratios and proportions, solve proportions using cross products, and solve percent problems, such as finding the percent of a number, a base, and part of a base. Finally, students rewrite equations in function form and solve formulas and literal equations for a given variable.

Prerequisite Skills

• Simplifying expressions

• Writing percents as decimals

• Using formulas

Additional resources for reviewing prerequisite skills are:

• Skills Review Handbook, pp. 909–937

• @HomeTutor

3 Solving Linear Equations

3.1 **Solve One-Step Equations**

3.2 **Solve Two-Step Equations**

3.3 **Solve Multi-Step Equations**

3.4 **Solve Equations with Variables on Both Sides**

3.5 **Write Ratios and Proportions**

3.6 **Solve Proportions Using Cross Products**

3.7 **Solve Percent Problems**

3.8 **Rewrite Equations and Formulas**

Before

In previous courses and chapters, you learned the following skills, which you'll use in Chapter 3: simplifying expressions, writing percents as decimals, and using formulas.

Prerequisite Skills

VOCABULARY CHECK

Copy and complete the statement.

1. In the expression $3x + 7 + 7x$, __?__ and __?__ are like terms. **3x, 7x**

2. The reciprocal of $\frac{5}{8}$ is __?__. $\frac{8}{5}$

SKILLS CHECK

Simplify the expression. *(Review p. 96 for 3.2–3.6.)*

3. $5x - (6 - x)$ **6x − 6**

4. $3(x - 9) - 16$ **3x − 43**

5. $23 + 4(x + 2)$ **4x + 31**

6. $x(7 + x) + 9x^2$ **10x² + 7x**

Write the percent as a decimal. *(Review p. 916 for 3.7.)*

7. 54% **0.54**

8. 99% **0.99**

9. 12.5% **0.125**

10. 150% **1.5**

Find the perimeter of the rectangle. *(Review p. 924 for 3.8.)*

11. 7 ft / 16 ft **46 ft**

12. 14 cm / 20 cm **68 cm**

13. 4 in. / 11 in. **30 in.**

@HomeTutor Prerequisite skills practice at classzone.com

Chapter Planning Guide

Chapter 3 Resource Book

• Teaching Guide/Lesson Plan (pp. 3, 14, 25, 37, 50, 60, 70, 80)

• Project with Rubric (p. 91)

Assessment and Intervention

• Assessment Book (pp. 31–45)

• Benchmark Tests

• Reteaching and Remediation Book

Interactive Technology

• Easy Planner

• Power Presentations CD-ROM

• Activity Generator CD-ROM

• Animated Algebra

• Test Generator CD-ROM

• Online Quizzes

• eWorkbook

• eEdition

• @HomeTutor

Resources for English Learners

• Quick Reference for English Learners

• Spanish Study Guide

• Multi-Language Visual Glossary

• Student Resources in Spanish

In Chapter 3, you will apply the big ideas listed below and reviewed in the Chapter Summary on page 191. You will also use the key vocabulary listed below.

Big Ideas

1. **Solving equations in one variable**
2. **Solving proportion and percent problems**
3. **Rewriting equations in two or more variables**

KEY VOCABULARY
- inverse operations, *p. 134*
- equivalent equations, *p. 134*
- identity, *p. 156*
- ratio, *p. 162*
- proportion, *p. 163*
- cross product, *p. 168*
- scale drawing, *p. 170*
- scale model, *p. 170*
- scale, *p. 170*
- literal equation, *p. 184*

Why?

Knowing how to solve a linear equation can help you solve problems involving distance, rate, and time. For example, you can solve an equation to find the time it takes a jellyfish to travel a given distance at a given rate.

Animated Algebra

The animation illustrated below for Exercise 59 on page 139 helps you answer this question: How long does it take the jellyfish to travel 26 feet?

You have to find the time it takes for the jellyfish to travel 26 feet.

Click the up or down arrows until you reach the desired distance.

Animated Algebra at classzone.com

Other animations for Chapter 3: pages 133, 154, 176, 185, and 187

Algebra 1 Toolkit
- Reading Strategies for Chapter 3, pp. 13–14
- Differentiated Instruction Notes, pp. 49–52
- English Learners Notes, pp. 101–102
- Inclusion Notes, pp. 133–134
- Teaching Strategies with Sample Worksheets, pp. 155–178
- Using Technology in the Classroom, pp. 179–184
- Tips for New Teachers, pp. 189–190
- Math Background Notes, pp. 215–216
- Pre-AP Strategies and Copymasters, pp. 282–283, 329–344
- Teacher Survival Activities, pp. 559–560, 585–586
- Bulletin Board Idea, p. 609
- Teacher Tool Transparencies, following p. 620

1 PLAN AND PREPARE

Explore the Concept

- Students will use algebra tiles to model and solve one-step equations.
- This activity leads into the study of solving equations in Example 1 in Lesson 3.1.

Materials

Each student will need:
- algebra tiles
- Activity Support Master (*Chapter 3 Resource Book*, p. 5)

Recommended Time

Work activity: 10 min
Discuss results: 5 min

Grouping

Students should work individually.

2 TEACH

Tips for Success

In Explore 1, some students may think they should remove one 1-tile from each side of the equation since $1 + 1 = 2$. Point out that since there are two 1-tiles on the left side of the equation, they need to remove two 1-tiles to isolate the x-tile.

Key Questions

- In Explore 1, why do you remove the same number of 1-tiles from each side of the equation? **to keep the equation balanced**
- In Explore 2, why do you divide the 1-tiles into equal groups according to the number of x-tiles? **Since you want to isolate the x-tile, you need to find how many 1-tiles correspond to each x-tile.**

3.1 Modeling One-Step Equations

MATERIALS · algebra tiles

QUESTION How can you use algebra tiles to solve one-step equations?

You can model one-step equations using algebra tiles.

1-tile

x-tile

A 1-tile represents the number 1.   An x-tile represents the variable x.

EXPLORE 1 Solve an equation using subtraction

Solve $x + 2 = 5$.

STEP 1 Model $x + 2 = 5$ using algebra tiles.

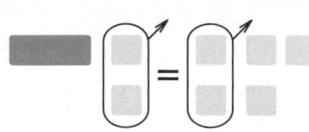

STEP 2 To find the value of x, isolate the x-tile on one side of the equation. You can do this by removing two 1-tiles from each side.

STEP 3 The x-tile is equal to three 1-tiles. So, the solution of $x + 2 = 5$ is 3.

PRACTICE

Write the equation modeled by the algebra tiles.

1.

$x + 2 = 6$

2.

$7 = x + 6$

Use algebra tiles to model and solve the equation.

3. $x + 3 = 9$ **6**   4. $x + 2 = 7$ **5**   5. $x + 8 = 8$ **0**   6. $x + 3 = 7$ **4**

7. $x + 2 = 12$ **10**   8. $x + 7 = 12$ **5**   9. $15 = x + 5$ **10** 10. $13 = x + 10$ **3**

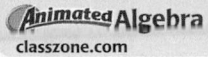

EXPLORE 2 Solve an equation using division

Solve $2x = 12$.

STEP 1 Model $2x = 12$ using algebra tiles.

STEP 2 There are two x-tiles, so divide the x-tiles and 1-tiles into two equal groups.

STEP 3 An x-tile is equal to six 1-tiles. So, the solution of $2x = 12$ is 6.

PRACTICE

Write the equation modeled by the algebra tiles.

11.

$4x = 4$

12.

$7 = 3x$

Use algebra tiles to model and solve the equation.

13. $2x = 10$ **5**   14. $3x = 12$ **4**   15. $3x = 18$ **6**   16. $4x = 16$ **4**

17. $6 = 2x$ **3**   18. $12 = 4x$ **3**   19. $20 = 5x$ **4**   20. $21 = 7x$ **3**

DRAW CONCLUSIONS Use your observations to complete these exercises

21. An equation and explanation that correspond to each step in Explore 1 are shown below. Copy and complete the equations and explanations.

$$x + 2 = 5 \qquad \text{Original equation}$$
$$x + 2 - \underline{?}^{\,2} = 5 - \underline{?}^{\,2} \qquad \text{Subtract } \underline{?}^{\,2} \text{ from each side.}$$
$$x = \underline{?}^{\,3} \qquad \text{Simplify. Solution is } \underline{?}^{\,3}.$$

22. Write an equation that corresponds to the algebra tile equation in each step of Explore 2. Based on your results, describe an algebraic method that you can use to solve $12x = 180$. Then use your method to find the solution. $2x = 12, \frac{2x}{2} = \frac{12}{2}, x = 6$; divide each side by 12; 15.

An **Animated Algebra** activity is available on-line. This activity is also available on the **Power Presentations CD-ROM**.

Key Discovery

Subtract to isolate the variable in a one-step addition equation and divide to isolate the variable in a one-step multiplication equation.

❸ ASSESS AND RETEACH

1. If you were modeling the solution of $x + 7 = 12$, how many 1-tiles would you remove from each side of the equation? **7**

2. How many equal groups do you form when using algebra tiles to model and solve the equation $4x = 12$? Explain. **Form 4 equal groups since there are 4 x-tiles.**

Warm-Up Exercises

▣ **Transparency Available**

Solve using mental math.

1. $x + 2 = 17$ **15** **2.** $\frac{x}{6} = 4$ **24**

3. $x - 7 = 3$ **10** **4.** $9x = 54$ **6**

5. Katrina divided her photos into three albums. Each album contains 26 photos. How many photos did Katrina have to begin with? **78 photos**

Notetaking Guide

▣ **Transparency Available**

Promotes interactive learning and notetaking skills, pp. 47–51.

Pacing

Basic: 1 day
Average: 1 day
Advanced: 1 day
Block: 0.5 block with 3.2
• See *Teaching Guide/Lesson Plan.*

❷ FOCUS AND MOTIVATE

Essential Question

Big Idea 1, p. 131

How do you solve one-step equations using subtraction, addition, division, and multiplication? **Tell students they will learn how to answer this question by using properties of equality and reciprocals to solve equations.**

NCTM STANDARDS

Standard 1: Understand meanings of operations; Understand how operations are related

3.1 Solve One-Step Equations

Before	You solved equations using mental math.
Now	You will solve one-step equations using algebra.
Why?	So you can determine a weight limit, as in Ex. 56.

Key Vocabulary
• inverse operations
• equivalent equations
• reciprocal, *p. 915*

Inverse operations are two operations that undo each other, such as addition and subtraction. When you perform the same inverse operation on each side of an equation, you produce an *equivalent equation*. **Equivalent equations** are equations that have the same solution(s).

KEY CONCEPT   *For Your Notebook*

Addition Property of Equality

Words Adding the same number to each side of an equation produces an equivalent equation.

Algebra If $x - a = b$, then $x - a + a = b + a$, or $x = b + a$.

Subtraction Property of Equality

Words Subtracting the same number from each side of an equation produces an equivalent equation.

Algebra If $x + a = b$, then $x + a - a = b - a$, or $x = b - a$.

EXAMPLE 1 Solve an equation using subtraction

Solve $x + 7 = 4$.

AVOID ERRORS
To obtain an equivalent equation, be sure to subtract the same number from each side.

$$x + 7 = 4 \qquad \text{Write original equation.}$$
$$x + 7 - 7 = 4 - 7 \qquad \text{Use subtraction property of equality: Subtract 7 from each side.}$$
$$x = -3 \qquad \text{Simplify.}$$

▸ The solution is -3.

CHECK Substitute -3 for x in the original equation.

$$x + 7 = 4 \qquad \text{Write original equation.}$$
$$-3 + 7 \stackrel{?}{=} 4 \qquad \text{Substitute } -3 \text{ for } x.$$
$$4 = 4 \checkmark \qquad \text{Simplify. Solution checks.}$$

Resource Planning Guide

Chapter Resource Book
• Teaching Guide/Lesson Plan (pp. 3–4)
• Practice levels A, B, C (pp. 6–8)
• Study Guide (pp. 9–10)
• Catch-up for Absent Students (p. 11)
• Application (p. 12)
• Challenge (p. 13)

Workbooks
• Notetaking Guide (pp. 47–51)
• Practice Workbook (pp. 30–31)

Teaching Options
• **Power Presentations CD-ROM** provides dynamic electronic teaching resources for the classroom.
• **Activity Generator CD-ROM** provides editable activities for all ability levels.

Interactive Technology
• Easy Planner
• Power Presentations CD-ROM
• Activity Generator CD-ROM
• Animated Algebra
• Test Generator CD-ROM
• Online Quiz
• eWorkbook
• eEdition
• @HomeTutor

Resources for English Learners
• Quick Reference for English Learners
• Spanish Study Guide
• Multi-Language Visual Glossary
• Student Resources in Spanish

See also the *Algebra 1 Toolkit* for more strategies for meeting individual needs.

EXAMPLE 2   Solve an equation using addition

USE HORIZONTAL FORMAT
In Example 2, both horizontal and vertical formats are used. In the rest of the book, equations will be solved using the horizontal format.

Solve $x - 12 = 3$.

Horizontal format		Vertical format
$x - 12 = 3$	Write original equation.	$x - 12 = 3$
$x - 12 + 12 = 3 + 12$	Add 12 to each side.	$\underline{+\ 12 \quad +\ 12}$
$x = 15$	Simplify.	$x = 15$

MULTIPLICATION AND DIVISION EQUATIONS Multiplication and division are inverse operations. So, the multiplication property of equality can be used to solve equations involving division, and the division property of equality can be used to solve equations involving multiplication.

KEY CONCEPT   *For Your Notebook*

Multiplication Property of Equality

Words Multiplying each side of an equation by the same nonzero number produces an equivalent equation.

Algebra If $\frac{x}{a} = b$ and $a \neq 0$, then $a \cdot \frac{x}{a} = a \cdot b$, or $x = ab$.

Division Property of Equality

Words Dividing each side of an equation by the same nonzero number produces an equivalent equation.

Algebra If $ax = b$ and $a \neq 0$, then $\frac{ax}{a} = \frac{b}{a}$, or $x = \frac{b}{a}$.

EXAMPLE 3   Solve an equation using division

Solve $-6x = 48$.

$-6x = 48$	Write original equation.
$\dfrac{-6x}{-6} = \dfrac{48}{-6}$	Divide each side by -6.
$x = -8$	Simplify.

 GUIDED PRACTICE   for Examples 1, 2, and 3

Solve the equation. Check your solution.

1. $y + 7 = 10$ **3**   2. $x - 5 = 3$ **8**   3. $q - 11 = -5$ **6**   4. $6 = t - 2$ **8**

5. $4x = 48$ **12**   6. $-65 = -5y$ **13**   7. $6w = -54$ **−9**   8. $24 = -8n$ **−3**

3.1 Solve One-Step Equations   **135**

Motivating the Lesson

In 1979, Susan Montgomery set a world's record for blowing the biggest gum bubble—48.2 centimeters in diameter. She broke that record in 1994 by blowing a bubble with a 58.4-centimeter diameter. By knowing how to solve equations, you can compare and determine world records in feats such as Susan's or in sports and other activities.

③ TEACH

Extra Example 1
Solve $x + 9 = 3$. **−6**

Extra Example 2
Solve $x - 2 = 11$. **13**

Key Questions to Ask for Example 2

- How are Examples 1 and 2 alike and how are they different? **Both use inverse operations of addition and subtraction. In Example 1 you subtract to obtain an equivalent equation, while in Example 2 you add.**

- Why do you perform the same operation on both sides of the equation? Explain. **You need to produce an equation equivalent to the original equation so they have the same solution.**

Extra Example 3
Solve $-4x = -28$. **7**

Key Questions to Ask for Example 3

- Which property of equality do you use to solve the equation? Why? **You use the division property of equality to undo multiplication of −6 times *m*.**

- Why do you divide by −6? **You want *x* to have a coefficient of 1.**

136

EXAMPLE 4   Solve an equation using multiplication

Solve $\frac{x}{4} = 5$.

Solution

$\frac{x}{4} = 5$	Write original equation.
$4 \cdot \frac{x}{4} = 4 \cdot 5$	Multiply each side by 4.
$x = 20$	Simplify.

✓ **GUIDED PRACTICE**   for Example 4

Solve the equation. Check your solution.

9. $\frac{t}{-3} = 9$ **−27**   10. $6 = \frac{c}{7}$ **42**   11. $13 = \frac{z}{-2}$ **−26**   12. $\frac{a}{5} = -11$ **−55**

USING RECIPROCALS Recall that the product of a number and its reciprocal is 1. You can isolate a variable with a fractional coefficient by multiplying each side of the equation by the reciprocal of the fraction.

EXAMPLE 5   Solve an equation by multiplying by a reciprocal

Solve $-\frac{2}{7}x = 4$.

REVIEW RECIPROCALS
For help with finding reciprocals, see p. 915.

Solution

The coefficient of x is $-\frac{2}{7}$. The reciprocal of $-\frac{2}{7}$ is $-\frac{7}{2}$.

$-\frac{2}{7}x = 4$	Write original equation.
$-\frac{7}{2}\left(-\frac{2}{7}x\right) = -\frac{7}{2}(4)$	Multiply each side by the reciprocal, $-\frac{7}{2}$.
$x = -14$	Simplify.

▶ The solution is −14. Check by substituting −14 for x in the original equation.

CHECK

$-\frac{2}{7}x = 4$	Write original equation.
$-\frac{2}{7}(-14) \overset{?}{=} 4$	Substitute −14 for x.
$4 = 4$ ✓	Simplify. Solution checks.

✓ **GUIDED PRACTICE**   for Example 5

Solve the equation. Check your solution.

13. $\frac{5}{6}w = 10$ **12**   14. $\frac{2}{3}p = 14$ **21**   15. $9 = -\frac{3}{4}m$ **−12**   16. $-8 = -\frac{4}{5}v$ **10**

Differentiated Instruction

EXAMPLE 6 **Write and solve an equation**

OLYMPICS In the 2004 Olympics, Shawn Crawford won the 200 meter dash. His winning time was 19.79 seconds. Find his average speed to the nearest tenth of a meter per second.

Solution

Let r represent Crawford's speed in meters per second. Write a verbal model. Then write and solve an equation.

Distance (meters)	=	Rate (meters/second)	·	Time (seconds)
200	=	r	·	19.79

$$\frac{200}{19.79} = \frac{19.79r}{19.79}$$

$$10.1 \approx r$$

▶ Crawford's average speed was about 10.1 meters per second.

✓ **GUIDED PRACTICE** for Example 6

17. WHAT IF? In Example 6, suppose Shawn Crawford ran 100 meters at the same average speed he ran the 200 meters. How long would it take him to run 100 meters? Round your answer to the nearest tenth of a second. **9.9 sec**

3.1 EXERCISES

HOMEWORK KEY
- ○ = **WORKED-OUT SOLUTIONS** on p. WS1 for Exs. 13 and 55
- ★ = **STANDARDIZED TEST PRACTICE** Exs. 2, 15, 16, 57, 58, and 61
- ◆ = **MULTIPLE REPRESENTATIONS** Ex. 59

SKILL PRACTICE

A

1. **VOCABULARY** Copy and complete: Two operations that undo each other are called __?__. **inverse operations**

2. ★ **WRITING** Which property of equality would you use to solve the equation $14x = 35$? *Explain.* **Division property of equality; to solve 14x = 35, you need to divide each side by 14.**

SOLVING ADDITION AND SUBTRACTION EQUATIONS Solve the equation. Check your solution.

EXAMPLES 1 and 2 on pp. 134–135 for Exs. 3–14

3. $x + 5 = 8$ **3**
4. $m + 9 = 2$ **−7**
5. $11 = f + 6$ **5**
6. $13 = 7 + z$ **6**
7. $6 = 9 + h$ **−3**
8. $-3 = 5 + a$ **−8**
9. $y - 4 = 3$ **7**
10. $t - 5 = 7$ **12**
11. $14 = k - 3$ **17**
12. $6 = w - 7$ **13**
13. $-2 = n - 6$ **4**
14. $-11 = b - 9$ **−2**

EXAMPLES 1 and 2
on pp. 134–135
for Exs. 15, 16

15. ★ **MULTIPLE CHOICE** What is the solution of $-8 = d - 13$? **C**

   (A) -21 (B) -5 (C) 5 (D) 21

16. ★ **MULTIPLE CHOICE** What is the solution of $22 + v = -65$? **A**

   (A) -87 (B) -43 (C) 43 (D) 87

EXAMPLES 3 and 4
on pp. 135–136
for Exs. 17–30

SOLVING MULTIPLICATION AND DIVISION EQUATIONS Solve the equation. Check your solution.

17. $5g = 20$ **4**   18. $-4q = 52$ **−13**   19. $48 = 8c$ **6**

20. $-108 = 9j$ **−12**   21. $15 = -h$ **−15**   22. $187 = -17r$ **−11**

23. $\frac{y}{3} = 5$ **15**   24. $\frac{m}{2} = 14$ **28**   25. $8 = \frac{x}{6}$ **48**

26. $7 = \frac{t}{-7}$ **−49**   27. $-11 = \frac{z}{-2}$ **22**   28. $-3 = \frac{d}{14}$ **−42**

29. 3.8 should
have been
subtracted from
both sides; $x + 3.8 - 3.8 = 2.3 - 3.8$, $x = -1.5$.

30. Both sides
should have been
multiplied
by 3; $3 \cdot \frac{x}{3} = 27 \cdot 3$, $x = 81$.

ERROR ANALYSIS *Describe* and correct the error in solving the equation.

29.
$$x + 3.8 = 2.3$$
$$x + 3.8 - 3.8 = 2.3 + 3.8$$
$$x = 6.1$$ ✗

30.
$$\frac{x}{3} = 27$$
$$3 \cdot \frac{x}{3} = \frac{27}{3}$$
$$x = 9$$ ✗

B   **SOLVING EQUATIONS** Solve the equation. Check your solution.

31. $b - 0.4 = 3.1$ **3.5**   32. $-3.2 + z = -7.4$ **−4.2**   33. $-5.7 = w - 4.6$ **−1.1**

34. $-6.1 = p + 2.2$ **−8.3**   35. $8.2 = -4g$ **−2.05**   36. $-3.3a = 19.8$ **−6**

37. $\frac{3}{4} = \frac{1}{8} + v$ $\frac{5}{8}$ 38. $\frac{n}{4.6} = -2.5$ **−11.5**   39. $-0.12 = \frac{y}{-0.5}$ **0.06**

EXAMPLE 5
on p. 136
for Exs. 40–48

40. $\frac{1}{2}m = 21$ **42**   41. $\frac{1}{3}c = 32$ **96**   42. $-7 = \frac{1}{5}x$ **−35**

43. $\frac{3}{2}k = 18$ **12**   44. $-21 = -\frac{3}{5}t$ **35**   45. $-\frac{2}{7}v = 16$ **−56**

46. $\frac{8}{5}x = \frac{4}{15}$ $\frac{1}{6}$ 47. $\frac{1}{3}y = \frac{1}{5}$ $\frac{3}{5}$ 48. $-\frac{4}{3} = \frac{2}{3}z$ **−2**

C   ⬥ **GEOMETRY** The rectangle or triangle has area A. Write and solve an equation to find the value of x.

49. $A = 54$ in.²   **$54 = 12x$; 4.5 in.**

12 in.

50. $A = 72$ cm²   **$72 = \frac{1}{2}(16)x$; 9 cm**

16 cm

CHALLENGE Find the value of b using the given information.

51. $4a = 6$ and $b = a - 2$ **−0.5**   52. $a - 6.7 = 3.1$ and $b = 5a$ **49**

○ = **WORKED-OUT SOLUTIONS** on p. WS1   ★ = **STANDARDIZED TEST PRACTICE**   ◆ = **MULTIPLE REPRESENTATIONS**

EXAMPLE 6 [A]
on p. 137
for Exs. 53–57

53. THE DEAD SEA For the period 1999–2004, the maximum depth of the Dead Sea decreased by 9.9 feet. The maximum depth in 2004 was 1036.7 feet. What was the maximum depth in 1999? **1046.6 ft**

@HomeTutor for problem solving help at classzone.com

54. CRAFTS You purchase a cane of polymer clay to make pendants for necklaces. The cane is 50 millimeters long. How thick should you make each pendant so that you will have 20 pendants of uniform thickness? **2.5 mm**

50 mm

@HomeTutor for problem solving help at classzone.com

55. TRAMPOLINES A rectangular trampoline has an area of 187 square feet. The length of the trampoline is 17 feet. What is its width? **11 ft**

56. WHEELCHAIRS The van used to transport patients to and from a rehabilitation facility is equipped with a wheelchair lift. The maximum lifting capacity for the lift is 300 pounds. The wheelchairs used by the facility weigh 55 pounds each. What is the maximum weight of a wheelchair occupant who can use the lift? **245 lb**

57. ★ SHORT RESPONSE In Everglades National Park in Florida, there are 200 species of birds that migrate. This accounts for $\frac{4}{7}$ of all the species of birds sighted in the park.

   a. Write an equation to find the number of species of birds that have been sighted in Everglades National Park. $\frac{4}{7}x = 200$

   b. There are 600 species of plants in Everglades National Park. Are there more species of birds or of plants in the park? *Explain.*
   Plants; if you solve the equation in part (a) you find that there are 350 species of birds.

[B] **58. ★ OPEN-ENDED** *Describe* a real-world situation that can be modeled by the equation $15x = 135$. Solve the equation and explain what the solution means in this situation.

59. ◆ MULTIPLE REPRESENTATIONS A box jellyfish can travel at a rate of 6.5 feet per second.

   a. **Making a Table** Make a table that shows the distance d the jellyfish can travel after 1, 2, 3, 4, and 5 seconds. **See margin.**

   b. **Drawing a Graph** Graph the ordered pairs from the table in a coordinate plane. How long does it take the jellyfish to travel 26 feet? **See margin for art.;4 sec.**

   c. **Writing an Equation** Write and solve an equation to find the time it takes the jellyfish to travel 26 feet. **26 = 6.5t; 4 sec**

   Animated Algebra at classzone.com

58. Sample answer: Each member of the drama club needs to sell tickets to the upcoming play. If there are 15 members and you want to sell 135 tickets, how many tickets should each member sell? $x = 9$; each member should sell 9 tickets.

3.1 Solve One-Step Equations **139**

Reading Strategy

Exercises 3–48 Some students may be confused when the variable is on the right side of the equation. Explain that the solution is the same whether the variable is on the right or the left side. If students find it distracting, they can rewrite the equation so that the variable is on the left side.

Exercises 47–48 Tell students to make sure they multiply by the reciprocal of the coefficient.

Avoiding Common Errors

Exercises 31–34 Remind students to align decimals when they add or subtract. They may want to use a vertical model for these exercises.

Study Strategy

Exercises 53–57 Encourage students to write a verbal model for each of these exercises using the model in Example 6 as a guide. This will help them organize all of the information in the problems so they write appropriate equations to solve the problems.

 Internet Reference

Exercise 53 To learn more about the Dead Sea, visit i-cias.com/e.o/dead_sea.htm.

Exercise 57 More information about Everglades National Park can be found on the National Park Service's website www.nps.gov/ever.

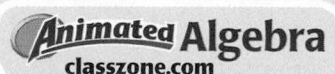 *Animated* Algebra
classzone.com

An **Animated Algebra** activity is available on-line for **Exercise 59**. This activity is also available on the **Power Presentations CD-ROM**.

59a.

t	D
1	6.5
2	13
3	19.5
4	26
5	32.5

59b.

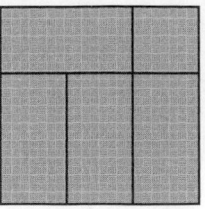

60. MULTI-STEP PROBLEM Tatami mats are a floor covering used in Japan. Tatami mats are equal in size, unless they are cut in half. The floor shown has an area of 81 square feet and is covered with 4.5 tatami mats.

a. What is the area of one tatami mat? **18 ft²**

b. What is the length of one tatami mat if it has a width of 3 feet? **6 ft**

61. ★ EXTENDED RESPONSE In baseball, a player's batting average is calculated by dividing the number of hits by the number of at bats.

a. **Calculate** Use the information in the table to find the number of hits Bill Mueller had in the 2003 Major League Baseball regular season. Round your answer to the nearest whole number. **171 hits**

Player	Team	Batting average	At bats
Bill Mueller	Boston Red Sox	0.326	524

b. **Calculate** The number of hits Bill Mueller had was 44 less than the number of hits Vernon Wells of the Toronto Blue Jays had in the 2003 regular season. How many hits did Vernon Wells have? **215 hits**

c. **Compare** In the 2003 regular season, Mueller had a higher batting average than Wells. Did Wells have fewer at bats than Mueller? *Explain* your reasoning. **No; if Mueller had less hits than Wells but had a higher batting average, he must have had less at bats than Wells.**

C **62. AMERICAN FLAGS** An American flag has a length that is 1.9 times its width. What is the area of a flag that has a length of 9.5 feet? **47.5 ft²**

63. CHALLENGE At a farm where you can pick your own strawberries, the cost of picked strawberries is calculated using only the weight of the strawberries. The total weight of a container full of strawberries is 2.1 pounds. The cost of the strawberries is $4.68. The weight of the container is 0.3 pound. What is the cost per pound for strawberries? **$2.60**

MIXED REVIEW

Translate the verbal phrase into an expression. *(p. 15)*

64. 4 more than a number k **$k + 4$**

65. The product of 8 and a number x **$8x$**

66. 40 divided by a number y **$\frac{40}{y}$**

67. 10 less than twice a number w **$2w - 10$**

PREVIEW
Prepare for
Lesson 3.2 in
Exs. 68–75.

A verbal description for a function and its domain are given. Write an equation for the function. Then describe the range. *(p. 35)*

68. The output is 9 more than the input. Domain: $-1, 0, 1, 2$
$y = x + 9$; range: 8, 9, 10, 11

69. The output is 3 times the input. Domain: $-4, -2, 0, 2$
$y = 3x$; range: $-12, -6, 0, 6$

Simplify the expression. *(p. 103)*

70. $-9x + 15x$ **$6x$**

71. $5x - 4x$ **x**

72. $12 + 3x - 3x$ **12**

73. $5x + 8 - x - 2$ **$4x + 6$**

74. $7.1x - 2.6x$ **$4.5x$**

75. $-0.7x + 11.3x$ **$10.6x$**

Solve the equation. Check your solution.

1. $-6 + a = -2$ **4**

2. $8 = m - 7$ **15**

3. $9k = -72$ **-8**

4. $12 = \dfrac{x}{-5}$ **-60**

5. Earth orbits the Sun at an average speed of 29.79 kilometers per second. Find how long it takes, to the nearest hundredth of a second, for Earth to travel 500 kilometers.   **16.78 sec**

 Online Quiz

Available at **classzone.com**

Diagnosis/Remediation
- Practice A, B, C in Chapter 3 Resource Book, pp. 6–8
- Study Guide in Chapter 3 Resource Book, pp. 9–10
- Practice Workbook, pp. 30–31
- @HomeTutor

Challenge
Additional challenge is available in the Chapter 3 Resource Book, p. 13.

3.2 Solve Two-Step Equations

Before	You solved one-step equations.
Now	You will solve two-step equations.
Why?	So you can find a scuba diver's depth, as in Example 4.

Key Vocabulary
- **like terms**, *p. 97*
- **input**, *p. 35*
- **output**, *p. 35*

The equation $\frac{x}{2} + 5 = 11$ involves two operations performed on x: division by 2 and addition by 5. You typically solve such an equation by applying the inverse operations in the reverse order of the order of operations. This is shown in the table below.

Operations performed on x	Operations to isolate x
1. Divide by 2.	1. Subtract 5.
2. Add 5.	2. Multiply by 2.

EXAMPLE 1 Solve a two-step equation

Solve $\frac{x}{2} + 5 = 11$.

$\frac{x}{2} + 5 = 11$	Write original equation.
$\frac{x}{2} + 5 - 5 = 11 - 5$	Subtract 5 from each side.
$\frac{x}{2} = 6$	Simplify.
$2 \cdot \frac{x}{2} = 2 \cdot 6$	Multiply each side by 2.
$x = 12$	Simplify.

▶ The solution is 12. Check by substituting 12 for x in the original equation.

CHECK	$\frac{x}{2} + 5 = 11$	Write original equation.
	$\frac{12}{2} + 5 \stackrel{?}{=} 11$	Substitute 12 for x.
	$11 = 11$ ✓	Simplify. Solution checks.

GUIDED PRACTICE for Example 1

Solve the equation. Check your solution.

1. $5x + 9 = 24$ **3**   2. $4y - 4 = 16$ **5**   3. $-1 = \frac{z}{3} - 7$ **18**

Resource Planning Guide

Chapter Resource Book
- Teaching Guide/Lesson Plan (pp. 14–15)
- Activity Master (p. 16)
- Practice levels A, B, C (pp. 17–19)
- Study Guide (pp. 20–21)
- Catch-up for Absent Students (p. 22)
- Application (p. 23)
- Challenge (p. 24)

Workbooks
- Notetaking Guide (pp. 52–54)
- Practice Workbook (pp. 32–33)

Teaching Options
- **Power Presentations CD-ROM** provides dynamic electronic teaching resources for the classroom.
- **Activity Generator CD-ROM** provides editable activities for all ability levels.

Interactive Technology
- Easy Planner
- Power Presentations CD-ROM
- Activity Generator CD-ROM
- Animated Algebra
- Test Generator CD-ROM
- Online Quiz
- eWorkbook
- eEdition
- @HomeTutor

Resources for English Learners
- Quick Reference for English Learners
- Spanish Study Guide
- Multi-Language Visual Glossary
- Student Resources in Spanish

See also the *Algebra 1 Toolkit* for more strategies for meeting individual needs.

---

① PLAN AND PREPARE

Warm-Up Exercises
◢ **Transparency Available**
Solve the equation.
1. $3x = -18$ **−6**
2. $b + 21 = 11$ **−10**
3. Simplify the expression $3(x + 2) - 4x + 1$. **−x + 7**
4. There are three times as many goats as sheep in a petting zoo. Find the number of sheep if the total number of goats and sheep is 28. **7 sheep**

Notetaking Guide
◢ **Transparency Available**
Promotes interactive learning and notetaking skills, pp. 52–54.

Pacing
Basic: 1 day
Average: 1 day
Advanced: 1 day
Block: 0.5 block with 3.1
- See *Teaching Guide/Lesson Plan*.

② FOCUS AND MOTIVATE

Essential Question
Big Idea 1, p. 131
How do you solve two-step equations? **Tell students they will learn how to answer this question by solving equations with more than one operation or with like terms.**

NCTM STANDARDS
Standard 1: Understand meanings of operations; Understand how operations are related

REVIEW LIKE TERMS
For help with combining like terms, see p. 97.

Motivating the Lesson

Ask students if they have shipped a package at a shipping outlet or bought items online. Tell them that outlets or online stores often charge handling fees, such as $.37 per ounce, on top of the cost of the items or the cost of shipping the package. Invite students to share some of their experiences. Tell them that these are examples of two-step equations that they will be solving in Lesson 3.2.

❸ TEACH

Extra Example 1

Solve $\frac{x}{4} - 3 = 2$. **20**

Key Questions to Ask for Example 1

- Could you multiply 2 by first? If so, what else would change? **Yes, you could multiply by 2 first to get $x + 10 = 22$. Then you would subtract 10 from each side.**

- Why is it simpler to subtract and then multiply? **There are fewer steps. If you multiply first, you have to multiply all of the terms of the equation by 2, which adds a step.**

Extra Example 2

Solve $5b - 7b = 4$. **−2**

Key Question to Ask for Example 2

- How do you use the distributive property to combine like terms? **Add the coefficients mentally, and then write the common variable.**

Extra Example 3

The output of a function is 7 more than 2 times the input. Write an equation for the function and then find the input when the output is 15. **$y = 2x + 7$; 4**

EXAMPLE 2 Solve a two-step equation by combining like terms

Solve $7x - 4x = 21$.

$7x - 4x = 21$	Write original equation.
$3x = 21$	Combine like terms.
$\dfrac{3x}{3} = \dfrac{21}{3}$	Divide each side by 3.
$x = 7$	Simplify.

EXAMPLE 3 Find an input of a function

The output of a function is 3 less than 5 times the input. Find the input when the output is 17.

Solution

STEP 1 Write an equation for the function. Let x be the input and y be the output.

$y = 5x - 3$ y is 3 less than 5 times x.

STEP 2 Solve the equation for x when $y = 17$.

$y = 5x - 3$	Write original function.
$17 = 5x - 3$	Substitute 17 for y.
$17 + 3 = 5x - 3 + 3$	Add 3 to each side.
$20 = 5x$	Simplify.
$\dfrac{20}{5} = \dfrac{5x}{5}$	Divide each side by 5.
$4 = x$	Simplify.

▶ An input of 4 produces an output of 17.

CHECK	$y = 5x - 3$	Write original function.
	$17 \stackrel{?}{=} 5(4) - 3$	Substitute 17 for y and 4 for x.
	$17 \stackrel{?}{=} 20 - 3$	Multiply 5 and 4.
	$17 = 17$ ✓	Simplify. Solution checks.

✓ **GUIDED PRACTICE**   for Examples 2 and 3

Solve the equation. Check your solution.

4. $4w + 2w = 24$ **4**   5. $8t - 3t = 35$ **7**   6. $-16 = 5d - 9d$ **4**

7. The output of a function is 5 more than -2 times the input. Find the input when the output is 11. **−3**

8. The output of a function is 4 less than 4 times the input. Find the input when the output is 3. **$1\frac{3}{4}$**

EXAMPLE 4 Solve a multi-step problem

SCUBA DIVING As a scuba diver descends into deeper water, the pressure of the water on the diver's body steadily increases.

The pressure at the surface of the water is 2117 pounds per square foot (lb/ft²). The pressure increases at a rate of 64 pounds per square foot for each foot the diver descends. Find the depth at which a diver experiences a pressure of 8517 pounds per square foot.

ANOTHER WAY

For an alternative method for solving Example 4, turn to page 147 for the **Problem Solving Workshop**.

Solution

STEP 1 Write a verbal model. Then write an equation.

Pressure at given depth (lb/ft²)	=	Pressure at surface (lb/ft²)	+	Rate of change of pressure (lb/ft² per foot of depth)	·	Diver's depth (ft)
P	=	2117	+	64	·	d

STEP 2 Find the depth at which the pressure is 8517 pounds per square foot.

$P = 2117 + 64d$	**Write equation.**
$8517 = 2117 + 64d$	**Substitute 8517 for P.**
$8517 - \mathbf{2117} = 2117 - \mathbf{2117} + 64d$	**Subtract 2117 from each side.**
$6400 = 64d$	**Simplify.**
$\dfrac{6400}{64} = \dfrac{64d}{64}$	**Divide each side by 64.**
$100 = d$	**Simplify.**

▸ A diver experiences a pressure of 8517 pounds per square foot at a depth of 100 feet.

CHECK		
	$P = 2117 + 64d$	**Write original equation.**
	$8517 \stackrel{?}{=} 2117 + 64(100)$	**Substitute 8517 for P and 100 for d.**
	$8517 \stackrel{?}{=} 2117 + 6400$	**Multiply 64 and 100.**
	$8517 = 8517 ✓$	**Simplify. Solution checks.**

✓ GUIDED PRACTICE for Example 4

9. **WHAT IF?** In Example 4, suppose the diver experiences a pressure of 5317 pounds per square foot. Find the diver's depth. **50 ft**

10. **JOBS** Kim has a job where she makes $8 per hour plus tips. Yesterday, Kim made $53 dollars, $13 of which was from tips. How many hours did she work? **5 h**

Differentiated Instruction

Inclusion Students need to organize their solution steps. It may be helpful to refer to a mnemonic device such as "My Dear Aunt Sally" to remember the order of operations Multiplication, Division, Addition, and Subtraction. For the method of solving linear equations, the mnemonic is reversed; to isolate the variable, first do Subtraction or Addition, then do Division or Multiplication.

See also the *Algebra 1 Toolkit* for more strategies.

Extra Example 4

To rent a booth at the county fairgrounds costs $42 per day plus a one-time equipment fee of $85. Find the number of days Mr. Batzle rented a booth if he paid a total of $337. **6 days**

Key Questions to Ask for Example 4

- How is Example 4 like the output and input of the function in Example 3? **The output is P, the pressure at a given depth, and the input is d, the diver's depth.**

- Which are the dependent and independent variables? **P is the dependent variable and d is the independent variable.**

- Why do you subtract and then divide to solve the equation? **This is using inverse operations in the reverse order of the operations performed on d. Since you multiplied d by 64 and then added 2117, you subtract 2117 and then divide by 64 to apply inverse operations in the reverse order.**

Closing the Lesson

Have students summarize the major points of the lesson and answer the Essential Question: How do you solve two-step equations?

- **To solve equations efficiently, apply inverse operations in the reverse order of the operations performed on the variable.**

- **Combine like terms before solving equations.**

First look for like terms and combine them when solving two-step equations. For equations with two operations, look at the original equation and apply the inverse operations in the reverse order.

143

HOMEWORK
KEY

○ = **WORKED-OUT SOLUTIONS**
on p. WS1 for Exs. 13, 19, and 39

★ = **STANDARDIZED TEST PRACTICE**
Exs. 2, 21, 40, 41, and 44

◆ = **MULTIPLE REPRESENTATIONS**
Ex. 43

④ PRACTICE AND APPLY

Assignment Guide

📖 Answer Transparencies
available for all exercises

Basic:
Day 1: SRH p. 938 Exs. 21–24
pp. 144–146
Exs. 1, 2, 3–21 odd, 22–29, 37–41,
46–60

Average:
Day 1: pp. 144–146
Exs. 1, 2, 6–20 even, 21–26, 30–36,
38–44, 46–60

Advanced:
Day 1: pp. 144–146
Exs. 1, 2, 8–14 even, 19–21, 24–26,
32–36*, 39–45*, 49–51, 54–60 even

Block:
pp. 144–146
Exs. 1, 2, 6–20 even, 21–26, 30–36,
38–44, 46–60 (with 3.1)

Differentiated Instruction

See *Algebra 1 Best Practices Toolkit*
for suggestions on addressing the
needs of a diverse classroom.

Homework Check

For a quick check of student understanding of key concepts, go over
the following exercises:

Basic: 7, 13, 17, 24, 37
Average: 8, 14, 18, 25, 38
Advanced: 10, 14, 20, 26, 39

Extra Practice

• Student Edition, p. 940
• Chapter 3 Resource Book:
Practice levels A, B, C, pp. 17–19

Practice Worksheet

An easily-readable reduced
practice page (with answers)
for this lesson can be found
on p. 130C.

SKILL PRACTICE

A 1. **VOCABULARY** Copy and complete: To solve the equation $2x + 3x = 20$, you would begin by combining $2x$ and $3x$ because they are __?__ . **like terms**

2. ★ **WRITING** *Describe* the steps you would use to solve the equation $4x + 7 = 15$. **First, subtract 7 from each side to get $4x = 8$, then divide each side by 4 to get $x = 2$.**

EXAMPLE 1
on p. 141
for Exs. 3–14

SOLVING TWO-STEP EQUATIONS Solve the equation. Check your solution.

3. $3x + 7 = 19$ **4**   4. $5h + 4 = 19$ **3**   5. $7d - 1 = 13$ **2**

6. $2g - 13 = 3$ **8**   7. $10 = 7 - m$ **−3**   8. $11 = 12 - q$ **1**

9. $\frac{a}{3} + 4 = 6$ **6**   10. $17 = \frac{w}{5} + 13$ **20**   11. $\frac{b}{2} - 9 = 11$ **40**

12. $-6 = \frac{z}{4} - 3$ **−12**   ⑬ $7 = \frac{5}{6}c - 8$ **18**   14. $10 = \frac{2}{7}n + 4$ **21**

EXAMPLE 2
on p. 142
for Exs. 15–23

COMBINING LIKE TERMS Solve the equation. Check your solution.

15. $8y + 3y = 44$ **4**   16. $2p + 7p = 54$ **6**   17. $11x - 9x = 18$ **9**

18. $36 = 9x - 3x$ **6**   ⑲ $-32 = -5k + 13k$ **−4**   20. $6 = -7f + 4f$ **−2**

21. ★ **MULTIPLE CHOICE** What is the first step you can take to solve the equation $6 + \frac{x}{3} = -2$? **D**

Ⓐ Subtract 2 from each side.   Ⓑ Add 6 to each side.

Ⓒ Divide each side by 3.   Ⓓ Subtract 6 from each side.

ERROR ANALYSIS *Describe* and correct the error in solving the equation.

22.
$$7 - 3x = 12$$
$$4x = 12$$
$$x = 3$$
| Unlike terms were combined; $-3x = 5$, $x = -\frac{5}{3}$.

23. **See margin.**
$$-2x + x = 10$$
$$\frac{-2x + x}{-2} = \frac{10}{-2}$$
$$x = -5$$

EXAMPLE 3
on p. 142
for Exs. 24–26

FINDING AN INPUT OF A FUNCTION Write an equation for the function described. Then find the input.

24. The output of a function is 7 more than 3 times the input. Find the input when the output is -8. $y = 3x + 7$; **−5**

25. The output of a function is 4 more than 2 times the input. Find the input when the output is -10. $y = 2x + 4$; **−7**

26. The output of a function is 9 less than 10 times the input. Find the input when the output is 11. $y = 10x - 9$; **2**

23. The division of $-2x + x$ by -2 is done incorrectly. *Sample answer:* If like terms are combined as the first step, the second line would be $-x = 10$ and the final result would be $x = -10$.

SOLVING EQUATIONS Solve the equation. Check your solution.

27. $5.6 = 1.1p + 1.2$ **4**   **28.** $7.2y + 4.7 = 62.3$ **8**   **29.** $1.2j - 4.3 = 1.7$ **5**

30. $16 - 2.4d = -8$ **10**   **31.** $14.4m - 5.1 = 2.1$ **0.5**   **32.** $-5.3 = 2.2v - 8.6$ **1.5**

33. $\frac{c}{5.3} + 8.3 = 11.3$ **15.9**   **34.** $3.2 + \frac{x}{2.5} = 4.6$ **3.5**   **35.** $-1.2 = \frac{z}{4.6} - 2.7$ **6.9**

C **36.** **CHALLENGE** Solve the equations $3x + 2 = 5$, $3x + 2 = 8$, and $3x + 2 = 11$.
Predict the solution of the equation $3x + 2 = 14$. *Explain.* **1, 2, 3; 4; the output of each equation is increased by 3 because x is multiplied by 3, each solution increases by 1.**

PROBLEM SOLVING

EXAMPLE 4 **A**
on p. 143
for Exs. 37–40

37. **DANCE CLASSES** A dance academy charges $24 per class and a one-time registration fee of $15. A student paid a total of $687 to the academy. Find the number of classes the student took. **28 classes**

@*HomeTutor* for problem solving help at classzone.com

38. **CAR REPAIR** Tyler paid $124 to get his car repaired. The total cost for the repairs was the sum of the amount paid for parts and the amount paid for labor. Tyler was charged $76 for parts and $32 per hour for labor. Find the amount of time it took to repair his car. **1.5 h**

@*HomeTutor* for problem solving help at classzone.com

39. **ADVERTISING** A science museum wants to promote an upcoming exhibit by advertising on city buses for one month. The costs of the two types of advertisements being considered are shown. The museum has budgeted $6000 for the advertisements. The museum decides to have 1 full bus wrap advertisement. How many half-side advertisements can the museum have?

5 half-side advertisements

Full bus wrap advertisement
$2000 for one month

Half-side advertisement
$800 for one month

41. Yes; the equation $542 = $50 + 6x gives the monthly cost of a guitar that costs $542. Solving the equation gives x = $82 per month, so you can afford the guitar.

40. ★ **MULTIPLE CHOICE** A skateboarding park charges $7 per session to skate and $4 per session to rent safety equipment. Jared rents safety equipment every time he skates. During one year, he spends $99 for skating charges and equipment rentals. Which equation can be used to find x, the number of sessions Jared attended? **B**

  Ⓐ $99 = 7x$ Ⓑ $99 = 7x + 4x$ Ⓒ $99 = 7x + 4$ Ⓓ $99 = 4x + 7$

B **41.** ★ **SHORT RESPONSE** A guitar store offers a finance plan where you give a $50 down payment on a guitar and pay the remaining balance in 6 equal monthly payments. You have $50 and you can afford to pay up to $90 per month for a guitar. Can you afford a guitar that costs $542? *Explain.*

3.2 Solve Two-Step Equations   **145**

Avoiding Common Errors

Exercises 3–14 Students often use the wrong operation when solving an equation. Suggest they work with a partner prior to solving the equations to go over the operations they should use in each of the exercises. Refer them to the box in the explanation before Example 1. Have them go through each of the exercises using the box as a model to determine which operations they should use and in which order.

Reading Strategy

Exercises 13–14 Caution students to read these exercises carefully. Note that the coefficients are slightly different than those in Exercises 9–12.

Teaching Strategy

Exercises 24–26 It may be useful to review Example 3 and functions in general before students work on these exercises. Remind students that functions typically give the output y in terms of the input x.

Exercise 36 For students who request help on this exercise, tell them to look for a pattern in the equations and for a pattern in the value of x. They may want to line up the equations, one underneath the other, to visualize the pattern. Tell them to use the patterns to explain their prediction.

Exercises 37–40 Suggest that students first determine the variable in the problem. This will help them determine the coefficient of the variable and the constant.

Solve the equation.

1. $\frac{a}{4} + 6 = -14$ **−80**

2. $6r - 12 = 6$ **3**

3. $-36 = 7y + 2y$ **−4**

4. The output of a function is 9 less than 3 times the input. Write an equation for the function and then find the input when the output is −6. $y = 3x - 9$; **1**

5. A bank charges $5.00 per month plus $.30 per check for a standard checking account. Find the number of checks Justine wrote if she paid $8.30 in fees last month. **11 checks**

Online Quiz

Available at **classzone.com**

Diagnosis/Remediation
- Practice A, B, C in Chapter 3 Resource Book, pp. 17–19
- Study Guide in Chapter 3 Resource Book, pp. 20–21
- Practice Workbook, pp. 32–33
- @HomeTutor

Challenge
Additional challenge is available in the Chapter 3 Resource Book, p. 24.

43b. See Additional Answers beginning on p. AA1.

43c.

(graph with points plotted, y-axis marked 0, 12, 24, 36, 48, 60; x-axis marked 0, 1, 2, 3, 4, 5)

---

42. Sample answer: Estimate the number of days to be about 1200; 3,000,000 + 1600(1200) = 3,000,000 + 1,920,000 = 4,920,000 so the solution makes sense.

42. MULTI-STEP PROBLEM The capacity of a landfill is 4,756,505 tons. The landfill currently holds 2,896,112 tons. A cell is added to the landfill every day, and each cell averages 1600 tons.

a. Write an equation that gives the amount y (in tons) in the landfill as a function of the number x of days from now. $y = 2{,}896{,}112 + 1600x$

b. After how many days will the landfill reach capacity? Round your answer to the nearest day. **1163 days**

c. Use estimation to check your answer to part (b).

Trash is compacted into a pocket called a cell.

Cells are separated by layers of soil.

43. ◆ **MULTIPLE REPRESENTATIONS** Two computer technicians are upgrading the software on the 54 computers in a school. On average, Marissa upgrades 5 computers in 1 hour and Ryan upgrades 7 computers in 1 hour.

a. **Writing an Equation** Write an equation that gives the number y of computers upgraded as a function of the number x of hours worked. $y = 12x$

b. **Making a Table** Make a table that shows the number of computers upgraded by each technician and the total number of computers upgraded after 1, 2, 3, 4, and 5 hours. **See margin.**

c. **Drawing a Graph** Graph the ordered pairs that represent the total number y of computers upgraded after x hours. Use the graph to estimate the number of hours it took to upgrade all of the computers. **See margin for art; about 4.5 h.**

44. ★ **SHORT RESPONSE** At a restaurant, customers can dine inside the restaurant or pick up food at the take-out window. On an average day, 400 customers are served inside the restaurant, and 120 customers pick up food at the take-out window. After how many days will the restaurant have served 2600 customers? *Explain.* **5 days; the restaurant serves 400 + 120 = 520 customers each day, use the equation 2600 = 520x to find x = 5.**

C **45. CHALLENGE** During a 1 mile race, one runner is running at a rate of 14.6 feet per second, and another runner is running at a rate of 11.3 feet per second. One lap around the track is 660 feet. After how many seconds will the faster runner be exactly one lap ahead of the other runner? **200 sec**

MIXED REVIEW

Find the sum, difference, or product.

46. $14 + (-6)$ *(p. 74)* **8**

47. $-7 + (-13)$ *(p. 74)* **−20**

48. $16 - 21$ *(p. 80)* **−5**

49. $-9 - (-10)$ *(p. 80)* **1**

50. $(3a)(-3a)(a)$ *(p. 88)* **−9a³**

51. $-2(-12)(2t)$ *(p. 88)* **48t**

Use the distributive property to write an equivalent expression. *(p. 96)*

52. $2(9z + 4)$ **18z + 8**

53. $-3(5b - 8)$ **−15b + 24**

54. $(2k - 7)(-5)$ **−10k + 35**

PREVIEW
Prepare for Lesson 3.3 in Exs. 55–60.

Solve the equation. Check your solution. *(p. 134)*

55. $x + 9 = 2$ **−7**

56. $m + 2 = 5$ **3**

57. $y - 18 = 12$ **30**

58. $-7r = 56$ **−8**

59. $30s = 1200$ **40**

60. $-\frac{1}{9}c = -8$ **72**

EXTRA PRACTICE for Lesson 3.2, p. 940   🧭 **ONLINE QUIZ** at classzone.com

Using ALTERNATIVE METHODS

Another Way to Solve Example 4, page 143

MULTIPLE REPRESENTATIONS In Example 4 on page 143, you saw how to solve a problem about scuba diving by using an equation. You can also solve the problem using a table.

PROBLEM

SCUBA DIVING As a scuba diver descends into deeper water, the pressure of the water on the diver's body steadily increases. The pressure at the surface of the water is 2117 pounds per square foot (lb/ft^2). The pressure increases at a rate of 64 pounds per square foot for each foot the diver descends. Find the depth at which a diver experiences a pressure of 8517 pounds per square foot.

METHOD

Making a Table An alternative approach is to make a table.

STEP 1 **Make** a table that shows the pressure as the depth increases. Because you are looking for a fairly high pressure, use larger increments in depth, such as 20 feet.

> Every 1 ft of depth increases the pressure by 64 lb/ft^2.

> Every 20 ft of depth increases the pressure by 64(20) = 1280 lb/ft^2.

Depth (ft)	Pressure (lb/ft²)
0	2117
1	2181
2	2245
20	3397
40	4677
60	5957
80	7237
100	8517

STEP 2 **Look** for the depth at which the pressure reaches 8517 pounds per square foot. This happens at a depth of 100 feet.

PRACTICE

1. **BASKETBALL** A sports club offers an organized basketball league. A team pays $600 to join the league. In addition to paying their share of the $600, team members who are not members of the sports club must pay a $25 fee to play. A team pays a total of $775. How many team members who are not club members are on the team? Solve this problem using two different methods. **See margin.**

2. **WHAT IF?** In Exercise 1, suppose you are on a team, but not a club member. The $600 cost is divided equally among the team members. How many players must there be on your team for you to pay $100 to play? Make a table to find the answer.
8 players; see margin for table.

3. **FURNITURE** You have $370 to spend on a dining table and chairs. A table costs $220, and each chair costs $35. How many chairs can you buy in addition to the table? Solve this problem using two different methods.
See margin.

Alternative Strategy

Example 4 on page 143 can be solved using a table. This method allows the student to grasp and solve a complex problem in which the numbers are large and the measurements are most likely unfamiliar. The table can also be used to help the student understand the algebraic solution given in Lesson 3.2.

Mathematical Reasoning

Multiple Representations Using a table to solve a problem is a useful strategy when students have a difficult time writing an equation. It is particularly helpful in Example 4 because students may feel overwhelmed by the numbers or the concepts and may be discouraged in finding a solution. By using the table alongside the algebraic solution, students are more likely to see the relationships in the equation between pressure at the surface, the rate of change, and the diver's depth. Once they see these interconnections, it could help them write an equation to model the problem. Have students discuss advantages and disadvantages of using tables to solve problems. One advantage is they can see how the pressure changes at different depths and thereby get a sense for a reasonable solution to the problem. Some disadvantages include more possibilities for making errors in calculations and missing the actual depth because they are using an increment that misses the target pressure.

1. See Additional Answers beginning on p. AA1.

2.

Team members	Your cost (dollars)
1	625
2	325
3	225
4	175
5	145
6	125
7	110.71
8	100

3. See Additional Answers beginning on p. AA1.

1 PLAN AND PREPARE

Warm-Up Exercises
Transparency Available

1. Simplify the expression $9x + 2(x - 1) + 7$. **$11x + 5$**

Solve the equation.

2. $5g - 7 = 58$ **13**

3. $\frac{2}{3}x = 18$ **27**

4. A surf shop charges $85 for surfing lessons and $35 per hour to rent a surfboard. Anna paid $225. Find the number of hours she spent surfing. **4 h**

Notetaking Guide
Transparency Available

Promotes interactive learning and notetaking skills, pp. 55–56.

Pacing

Basic: 2 days
Average: 2 days
Advanced: 2 days
Block: 1 block
• See *Teaching Guide/Lesson Plan.*

2 FOCUS AND MOTIVATE

Essential Question

Big Idea 1, p. 131

How do you solve multi-step equations? **Tell students they will learn how to answer this question by combining like terms, using the distributive property, and multiplying by a reciprocal.**

NCTM STANDARDS

Standard 1: Understand how operations are related

Standard 9: Understand how mathematical ideas build on one another

Before You solved one-step and two-step equations.
Now You will solve multi-step equations.
Why? So you can solve a problem about lifeguarding, as in Ex. 40.

Key Vocabulary
• **like terms,** *p. 97*
• **distributive property,** *p. 96*
• **reciprocal,** *p. 915*

Solving a linear equation may take more than two steps. Start by simplifying one or both sides of the equation, if possible. Then use inverse operations to isolate the variable.

EXAMPLE 1 Solve an equation by combining like terms

Solve $8x - 3x - 10 = 20$.

$8x - 3x - 10 = 20$	Write original equation.
$5x - 10 = 20$	Combine like terms.
$5x - 10 + 10 = 20 + 10$	Add 10 to each side.
$5x = 30$	Simplify.
$\dfrac{5x}{5} = \dfrac{30}{5}$	Divide each side by 5.
$x = 6$	Simplify.

EXAMPLE 2 Solve an equation using the distributive property

Solve $7x + 2(x + 6) = 39$.

Solution

When solving an equation, you may feel comfortable doing some steps mentally. Method 2 shows a solution where some steps are done mentally.

REVIEW PROPERTIES
For help with using the distributive property, see p. 96.

METHOD 1 Show All Steps	**METHOD 2** Do Some Steps Mentally
$7x + 2(x + 6) = 39$	$7x + 2(x + 6) = 39$
$7x + 2x + 12 = 39$	$7x + 2x + 12 = 39$
$9x + 12 = 39$	$9x + 12 = 39$
$9x + 12 - 12 = 39 - 12$	$9x = 27$
$9x = 27$	$x = 3$
$\dfrac{9x}{9} = \dfrac{27}{9}$	
$x = 3$	

Resource Planning Guide

Chapter Resource Book
• Teaching Guide/Lesson Plan (pp. 25–26)
• Activity Master (p. 27)
• Practice levels A, B, C (pp. 29–31)
• Study Guide (pp. 32–33)
• Catch-up for Absent Students (p. 34)
• Problem Solving Workshop (p. 35)
• Challenge (p. 36)

148

Workbooks
• Notetaking Guide (pp. 55–56)
• Practice Workbook (pp. 34–35)

Teaching Options
• **Power Presentations CD-ROM** provides dynamic electronic teaching resources for the classroom.
• **Activity Generator CD-ROM** provides editable activities for all ability levels.

Interactive Technology
• Easy Planner
• Power Presentations CD-ROM
• Activity Generator CD-ROM
• Animated Algebra
• Test Generator CD-ROM
• Online Quiz
• eWorkbook
• eEdition
• @HomeTutor

Resources for English Learners
• Quick Reference for English Learners
• Spanish Study Guide
• Multi-Language Visual Glossary
• Student Resources in Spanish

See also the *Algebra 1 Toolkit* for more strategies for meeting individual needs.

EXAMPLE 3 **Standardized Test Practice**

Which equation represents Step 2 in the solution process?

Step 1 $5x - 4(x - 3) = 17$

Step 2   [＿＿＿＿＿＿]

Step 3 $x + 12 = 17$

Step 4 $x = 5$

(A) $5x - 4x - 12 = 17$ (B) $5x - 4x - 3 = 17$

(C) $5x - 4x + 3 = 17$ (D) $5x - 4x + 12 = 17$

ELIMINATE CHOICES
You can eliminate choices B and C because -4 has not been distributed to *both* terms in the parentheses.

Solution

In Step 2, the distributive property is used to simplify the left side of the equation. Because $-4(x - 3) = -4x + 12$, Step 2 should be $5x - 4x + 12 = 17$.

▶ The correct answer is D. (A) (B) (C) (D)

✓ **GUIDED PRACTICE**   **for Examples 1, 2, and 3**

Solve the equation. Check your solution.

1. $9d - 2d + 4 = 32$ **4**   **2.** $2w + 3(w + 4) = 27$ **3**   **3.** $6x - 2(x - 5) = 46$ **9**

USING RECIPROCALS Although you can use the distributive property to solve an equation such as $\frac{3}{2}(3x + 5) = -24$, it is easier to multiply each side of the equation by the reciprocal of the fraction.

EXAMPLE 4 **Multiply by a reciprocal to solve an equation**

Solve $\frac{3}{2}(3x + 5) = -24$.

$\frac{3}{2}(3x + 5) = -24$	**Write original equation.**
$\frac{2}{3} \cdot \frac{3}{2}(3x + 5) = \frac{2}{3}(-24)$	**Multiply each side by $\frac{2}{3}$, the reciprocal of $\frac{3}{2}$.**
$3x + 5 = -16$	**Simplify.**
$3x = -21$	**Subtract 5 from each side.**
$x = -7$	**Divide each side by 3.**

✓ **GUIDED PRACTICE**   **for Example 4**

Solve the equation. Check your solution.

4. $\frac{3}{4}(z - 6) = 12$ **22**   **5.** $\frac{2}{5}(3r + 4) = 10$ **7**   **6.** $-\frac{4}{5}(4a - 1) = 28$ **−8.5**

            3.3   Solve Multi-Step Equations   **149**

Motivating the Lesson

Inform students that real-world problems often involve many parts. For example, you might want to know how long it takes to ride one section of a bike trail if you ride the whole trail in 55 minutes, pedaling at 14 miles per hour for part of the trail and 8 miles per hour for the rest. Tell students that this lesson offers several methods to solve problems such as this and others with many steps.

 TEACH

Extra Example 1
Solve $9x + x - 7 = 13$. **2**

Extra Example 2
Solve $4x - 7(x - 2) = 26$. **−4**

Key Question to Ask for Example 2

• Suppose you use Method 2 to solve Example 1. Which steps might you do mentally? **Add 10 to each side; divide each side by 5.**

Extra Example 3
Which equation represents Step 2 in the solution process? **C**
Step 1 $-3x + 4(x - 2) = 15$
Step 2   [＿＿＿＿＿]
Step 3 $x - 8 = 15$
Step 4 $x = 23$
(A) $-3x + 4x - 2 = 15$
(B) $-3x + 4x + 2 = 15$
(C) $-3x + 4x - 8 = 15$
(D) $-3x + 4x + 8 = 15$

Extra Example 4
Solve $\frac{3}{5}(2x - 4) = 18$. **17**

EXAMPLE 5 Write and solve an equation

BIRD MIGRATION A flock of cranes migrates from Canada to Texas. The cranes take 14 days (336 hours) to travel 2500 miles. The cranes fly at an average speed of 25 miles per hour. How many hours of the migration are the cranes *not* flying?

Solution

Let x be the amount of time the cranes are not flying. Then $336 - x$ is the amount of time the cranes are flying.

Distance (miles)	=	Rate (miles/hour)	·	Time spent flying (hours)
2500	=	25	·	$(336 - x)$

ANOTHER WAY
You can also begin solving the equation by dividing each side of the equation by 25.

$2500 = 25(336 - x)$ Write equation.

$2500 = 8400 - 25x$ Distributive property

$-5900 = -25x$ Subtract 8400 from each side.

$236 = x$ Divide each side by −25.

▶ The cranes were not flying for 236 hours of the migration.

✓ **GUIDED PRACTICE** for Example 5

7. WHAT IF? Suppose the cranes take 12 days (288 hours) to travel the 2500 miles. How many hours of this migration are the cranes *not* flying? **188 h**

3.3 EXERCISES

HOMEWORK KEY

○ = WORKED-OUT SOLUTIONS on p. WS1 for Exs. 17 and 39

★ = STANDARDIZED TEST PRACTICE Exs. 2, 18, 35, 36, and 41

◆ = MULTIPLE REPRESENTATIONS Ex. 42

SKILL PRACTICE

A   **1. VOCABULARY** What is the reciprocal of the fraction in the equation $\frac{3}{5}(2x + 8) = 18$? $\frac{5}{3}$

2. ★ WRITING *Describe* the steps you would use to solve the equation $3(4y - 7) = 6$. **Use the distributive property to get $12y - 21 = 6$, then add 21 to each side to get $12y = 27$, divide each side by 12 to get $y = 2.25$.**

EXAMPLE 1 on p. 148 for Exs. 3–11

COMBINING LIKE TERMS Solve the equation. Check your solution.

3. $p + 2p - 3 = 6$ **3**   **4.** $12v + 14 + 10v = 80$ **3**   **5.** $11w - 9 - 7w = 15$ **6**

6. $5a + 3 - 3a = -7$ **−5**   **7.** $6c - 8 - 2c = -16$ **−2**   **8.** $9 = 7z - 13z - 21$ **−5**

9. $-2 = 3y - 18 - 5y$ **−8**   **10.** $23 = -4m + 2 + m$ **−7**   **11.** $35 = -5 + 2x - 7x$ **−8**

150   Chapter 3 Solving Linear Equations

Extra Example 5

Edmund and Roberto took a 7-day (168 hours), 90-mile canoe trip down the Allagash River. If they paddled at an average rate of 2.5 miles per hour, how many hours did they spend *not* paddling? Write and solve an equation to find the answer. **$90 = 2.5(168 - x)$; 132 h**

Key Question to Ask for Example 5

• The Another Way sentence beside Example 5 suggests dividing by 25 as an alternative first step when solving the equation. When would it *not* be advantageous to divide by 25 as the first step? **if the distance traveled was not a multiple of 25**

Teaching Strategy

Ask a student to write the steps to solve Example 5 using the method presented on p. 147. Then have students discuss which method they prefer and why.

Closing the Lesson

Have students summarize the major points of the lesson and answer the Essential Question: How do you solve multi-step equations?

• To solve multi-step equations, first simplify one or both sides and then use inverse operations.

• If a fraction is being multiplied by a quantity, use reciprocals to simplify instead of the distributive property.

To solve a multi-step equation, first simplify and combine like terms. After simplifying, use inverse operations to isolate the variable.

EXAMPLES
2 and 3
on pp. 148–149
for Exs. 12–18, 25

USING THE DISTRIBUTIVE PROPERTY Solve the equation. Check your solution.

12. $3 + 4(z + 5) = 31$ **2**   **13.** $14 + 2(4g - 3) = 40$ **4**   **14.** $5m + 2(m + 1) = 23$ **3**

15. $5h + 2(11 - h) = -5$ **–9**   **16.** $27 = 3c - 3(6 - 2c)$ **5**   **⑰** $-3 = 12y - 5(2y - 7)$ **–19**

18. ★ **MULTIPLE CHOICE** What is the solution of $7v - (6 - 2v) = 12$? **C**

     Ⓐ -3.6 Ⓑ -2 Ⓒ 2 Ⓓ 3.6

EXAMPLE 4
on p. 149 for
Exs. 19–24, 26

MULTIPLYING BY A RECIPROCAL Solve the equation. Check your solution.

19. $\frac{1}{3}(d + 3) = 5$ **12**   **20.** $\frac{3}{2}(x - 5) = -6$ **1**   **21.** $\frac{4}{3}(7 - n) = 12$ **–2**

22. $4 = \frac{2}{9}(4y - 2)$ **5**   **23.** $-32 = \frac{8}{7}(3w - 1)$ **–9**   **24.** $-14 = \frac{2}{5}(9 - 2b)$ **22**

ERROR ANALYSIS *Describe* and correct the error in solving the equation.

25. -3 times -6
is 18, not -18;
$5x - 3x + 18 = 2,$
$2x + 18 = 2,$
$2x = -16,$
$x = -8.$

25.

26.

Multiply each
side by 2, not $\frac{1}{2}$;
$2x - 10 = 8,$
$2x = 18, x = 9.$

Ⓑ SOLVING EQUATIONS Solve the equation. Check your solution.

27. $8.9 + 1.2(3a - 1) = 14.9$ **2**   **28.** $-11.2 + 4(2.1 + q) = -0.8$ **0.5**

29. $1.3t + 3(t + 8.2) = 37.5$ **3**   **30.** $1.6 = 7.6 - 5(k + 1.1)$ **0.1**

31. $0.5 = 4.1x - 2(1.3x - 4)$ **–5**   **32.** $8.7 = 3.5m - 2.5(5.4 - 6m)$ **1.2**

GEOMETRY Find the value of *x* for the triangle or rectangle.

33. Perimeter = 24 feet **2**   **34.** Perimeter = 26 meters $5\frac{1}{3}$

$(x + 4)$ ft $4x$ ft

$10(x - 1)$ ft

$(2x - 6)$ m

$(x + 3)$ m

36. You should
divide each side
of the equation
by the number
outside the
parentheses
when the number
is a factor of the
number on the
other side of the
equals sign or it
is a fraction.

35. ★ **WRITING** The length of a rectangle is 3.5 inches more than its width.
The perimeter of the rectangle is 31 inches. Find the length and the width
of the rectangle. *Explain* your reasoning. **9.5 in., 6 in.; if you use the perimeter formula**
$P = 2\ell + 2w$ **and substitute** $3.5 + w$ **for** ℓ**, the solution is** $w = 6.$

36. ★ **SHORT RESPONSE** Solve each equation by first dividing each side of
the equation by the number outside the parentheses. When would you
recommend using this method to solve an equation? *Explain.*

     a. $9(x - 4) = 72$ **12**   **b.** $8(x + 5) = 60$ **2.5**

Ⓒ 37. CHALLENGE An even integer can be represented by the expression $2n$.
Find three consecutive even integers that have a sum of 54. **16, 18, 20**

3.3   Solve Multi-Step Equations   **151**

Differentiated Instruction

English Learners While discussing **Exercise 37**, point out
that the word "consecutive" comes from a Latin word meaning
"to follow." Students may be more familiar with the related word
"sequence," which is an ordered list. Show them examples of a
list of consecutive integers, a list of consecutive even integers,
and a list of consecutive odd integers.

See also the *Algebra 1 Toolkit* for more strategies.

---

④ PRACTICE AND **APPLY**

Assignment Guide

🗇 **Answer Transparencies**
available for all exercises

Basic:
Day 1: pp. 150–153
Exs. 1–18, 27, 28, 44–47
Day 2: pp. 150–153
Exs. 19–26, 29, 30, 38–41, 48–56

Average:
Day 1: pp. 150–153
Exs. 1, 2, 4–10 even, 12–18, 27–32,
35, 45, 46
Day 2: pp. 150–153
Exs. 19–26, 33, 34, 36, 38–42,
49–55 odd

Advanced:
Day 1: pp. 150–153
Exs. 1, 9–11, 15–18, 29–32, 35, 37*,
45, 46
Day 2: pp. 150–153
Exs. 22–24, 33, 34, 36, 38–43*,
54–56

Block:
pp. 150–153
Exs. 1, 2, 4–10 even, 12–36, 38–42,
45, 46, 49–55 odd

Differentiated Instruction

See *Algebra 1 Best Practices Toolkit*
for suggestions on addressing the
needs of a diverse classroom.

Homework Check

For a quick check of student understanding of key concepts, go over
the following exercises:

Basic: 4, 13, 18, 20, 38

Average: 8, 14, 18, 22, 39

Advanced: 11, 16, 18, 23, 40

Extra Practice

• Student Edition, p. 940
• Chapter 3 Resource Book:
Practice levels A, B, C, pp. 29–31

Practice Worksheet

An easily-readable reduced
practice page (with answers)
for this lesson can be found
on p. 130C.

151

41c. After the work crews merged; before the work crews merged they were working at a rate of 117 + 137 = 254 feet per month, and after merging at a rate of 307 feet per month.

EXAMPLE 5 Ⓐ
on p. 150
for Exs. 38–40

38. BASKETBALL A ticket agency sells tickets to a professional basketball game. The agency charges $32.50 for each ticket, a convenience charge of $3.30 for each ticket, and a processing fee of $5.90 for the entire order. The total charge for an order is $220.70. How many tickets were purchased? **6 tickets**

@HomeTutor for problem solving help at classzone.com

39. HANGING POSTERS You want to hang 3 equally-sized travel posters on the wall in your room so that the posters on the ends are each 3 feet from the end of the wall. You want the spacing between posters to be equal. How much space should you leave between the posters? **0.75 ft**

@HomeTutor for problem solving help at classzone.com

13.5 ft

40. LIFEGUARD TRAINING To qualify for a lifeguard training course, you have to swim continuously for 500 yards using either the front crawl or the breaststroke. You swim the front crawl at a rate of 45 yards per minute and the breaststroke at a rate of 35 yards per minute. You take 12 minutes to swim 500 yards. How much time did you spend swimming the front crawl? Use the verbal model below. **8 min**

$$\text{Distance} = \begin{pmatrix}\text{Rate for}\\\text{front}\\\text{crawl}\end{pmatrix} \cdot \begin{pmatrix}\text{Time}\\\text{for front}\\\text{crawl}\end{pmatrix} + \begin{pmatrix}\text{Rate for}\\\text{breaststroke}\end{pmatrix}\begin{pmatrix}\text{Total}\\\text{time}\end{pmatrix} - \begin{pmatrix}\text{Time}\\\text{for front}\\\text{crawl}\end{pmatrix}$$

Ⓑ **41. ★ EXTENDED RESPONSE** The Busk-Ivanhoe Tunnel on the Colorado Midland Railway was built in the 1890s with separate work crews starting on opposite ends at different times. The crew working from Ivanhoe started 0.75 month later than the crew working from Busk.

Ivanhoe crews completed 115 feet per month.
Busk crews completed 137 feet per month.

Cutaway of Busk-Ivanhoe Tunnel

a. Starting at the time construction began on the Busk end, find the time it took to complete a total of 8473 feet of the tunnel. Round your answer to the nearest month. **34 mo**

b. After 8473 feet were completed, the work crews merged under the same supervision. The combined crew took 3 months to complete the remaining 921 feet of the tunnel. Find the rate at which the remainder of the tunnel was completed. **307 ft per mo**

c. Was the tunnel being completed more rapidly before or after the work crews merged? *Explain* your reasoning.

○ = WORKED-OUT SOLUTIONS on p. WS1   ★ = STANDARDIZED TEST PRACTICE   ◆ = MULTIPLE REPRESENTATIONS

152

42. **MULTIPLE REPRESENTATIONS** A roofing contractor gives estimates for shingling a roof in cost per square, where a square is a 10 foot by 10 foot section of roof. The contractor estimates $27.50 per square for materials, $17 per square for labor, $30 per square for overhead and profit, and a total of $750 for miscellaneous expenses.

    a. Writing an Equation Write an equation that gives the estimate y (in dollars) as a function of the number x of squares of a roof. The contractor gives an estimate of $2314.50. About how many squares does the roof have? **$y = 74.5x + 750$; 21 squares**

    b. Making a Table Make a table that shows the estimates for shingling a roof that has 5, 10, 15, 20, or 25 squares. Use your table to check your answer to part (a). **See margin.**

C **43. CHALLENGE** A person has quarters and dimes that total $2.80. The number of dimes is 7 more than the number of quarters. How many of each coin does the person have? **6 quarters and 13 dimes**

MIXED REVIEW

Evaluate the expression for the given value(s) of the variable(s).

44. $x - y$ when $x = -7$ and $y = 2$ *(p. 80)* **−9**   **45.** $x - (-y)$ when $x = -4$ and $y = 5$ *(p. 80)* **1**

46. $\dfrac{x - 9}{4}$ when $x = 9$ *(p. 103)* **0**   **47.** $\dfrac{4y + 7}{3}$ when $y = 5$ *(p. 103)* **9**

PREVIEW
Prepare for Lesson 3.4 in Exs. 48–56.

Solve the equation. Check your solution. *(p. 141)*

48. $5x + 1 = 26$ **5**   **49.** $-x + 4 = 13$ **−9**   **50.** $3x - 5 = -14$ **−3**

51. $3 - 2x = 19$ **−8**   **52.** $\dfrac{x}{3} - 4 = 1$ **15**   **53.** $8 + \dfrac{x}{4} = -\dfrac{3}{4}$ **−35**

54. $11x + 5x = 48$ **3**   **55.** $-4x + 11x = -28$ **−4**   **56.** $\dfrac{2}{5}x - \dfrac{3}{5}x = -7$ **35**

QUIZ for Lessons 3.1–3.3

Solve the equation. Check your solution.

1. $x + 9 = 7$ *(p. 134)* **−2**   **2.** $y - 5 = -11$ *(p. 134)* **−6**

3. $-7b = -56$ *(p. 134)* **8**   **4.** $\dfrac{z}{4} = 6$ *(p. 134)* **24**

5. $-\dfrac{4}{3}t = -12$ *(p. 134)* **9**   **6.** $9w - 4 = 14$ *(p. 141)* **2**

7. $23 = 1 - d$ *(p. 141)* **−22**   **8.** $66 = 4m + 7m$ *(p. 141)* **6**

9. $-104 = -5p - 3p$ *(p. 141)* **13**   **10.** $2v + 5v - 8 = 13$ *(p. 148)* **3**

11. $2a - 6(a - 4) = -4$ *(p. 148)* **7**   **12.** $\dfrac{6}{5}(5 - 4g) = -18$ *(p. 148)* **5**

13. INTERNET SHOPPING Dan purchases DVDs from a website. Each DVD costs $11, and the shipping and handling fees are $6.95. Dan is charged a total of $50.95. How many DVDs did he purchase? *(p. 141)* **4 DVDs**

EXTRA PRACTICE for Lesson 3.3, p. 940   **ONLINE QUIZ** at classzone.com   153

42b.

Squares	Cost (dollars)
5	1122.50
10	1495
15	1867.50
20	2240
25	2612.50

3.4 Solve Equations with Variables on Both Sides

Before You solved equations with variables on one side.

Now You will solve equations with variables on both sides.

Why? So you can find the cost of a gym membership, as in Ex. 52.

❶ PLAN AND PREPARE

Warm-Up Exercises

🗎 **Transparency Available**

Solve the equation.

1. $2m - 6 + 4m = 12$ **3**

2. $6a - 5(a - 1) = 11$ **6**

3. A charter bus company charges $11.25 per ticket plus a handling charge of $.50 per ticket, and a $15 fee for booking the bus. If a group pays $297 to charter a bus, how many tickets did they buy? **24 tickets**

Notetaking Guide

🗎 **Transparency Available**

Promotes interactive learning and notetaking skills, pp. 57–59.

Pacing

Basic: 1 day

Average: 1 day

Advanced: 1 day

Block: 0.5 block with 3.5

• See *Teaching Guide/Lesson Plan.*

❷ FOCUS AND MOTIVATE

Essential Question

Big Idea 1, p. 131

How do you solve equations with variables on both sides? **Tell students they will learn how to answer this question by collecting variable terms on one side and constants on the other.**

NCTM STANDARDS

Standard 1: Understand how operations are related

Standard 9: Recognize math in contexts outside of mathematics

Key Vocabulary
• **identity**

Some equations have variables on both sides. To solve such equations, you can collect the variable terms on one side of the equation and the constant terms on the other side of the equation.

EXAMPLE 1 **Solve an equation with variables on both sides**

Solve $7 - 8x = 4x - 17$.

ANOTHER WAY

You could also begin solving the equation by subtracting $4x$ from each side to obtain $7 - 12x = -17$. When you solve this equation for x, you get the same solution, 2.

$7 - 8x = 4x - 17$	Write original equation.
$7 - 8x + 8x = 4x - 17 + 8x$	Add $8x$ to each side.
$7 = 12x - 17$	Simplify each side.
$24 = 12x$	Add 17 to each side.
$2 = x$	Divide each side by 12.

▸ The solution is 2. Check by substituting 2 for x in the original equation.

CHECK		
	$7 - 8x = 4x - 17$	Write original equation.
	$7 - 8(2) \stackrel{?}{=} 4(2) - 17$	Substitute 2 for x.
	$-9 \stackrel{?}{=} 4(2) - 17$	Simplify left side.
	$-9 = -9$ ✓	Simplify right side. Solution checks.

Animated Algebra at classzone.com

EXAMPLE 2 **Solve an equation with grouping symbols**

Solve $9x - 5 = \frac{1}{4}(16x + 60)$.

$9x - 5 = \frac{1}{4}(16x + 60)$	Write original equation.
$9x - 5 = 4x + 15$	Distributive property
$5x - 5 = 15$	Subtract $4x$ from each side.
$5x = 20$	Add 5 to each side.
$x = 4$	Divide each side by 5.

Resource Planning Guide

Chapter Resource Book
• Teaching Guide/Lesson Plan (pp. 37–38)
• Activity Master (p. 39)
• Practice levels A, B, C (pp. 41–43)
• Study Guide (pp. 44–45)
• Catch-up for Absent Students (p. 46)
• Problem Solving Workshop (p. 47)
• Challenge (p. 48)

Workbooks
• Notetaking Guide (pp. 57–59)
• Practice Workbook (pp. 36–37)

Teaching Options
• **Power Presentations CD-ROM** provides dynamic electronic teaching resources for the classroom.
• **Activity Generator CD-ROM** provides editable activities for all ability levels.

Interactive Technology
• Easy Planner
• Power Presentations CD-ROM
• Activity Generator CD-ROM
• Animated Algebra
• Test Generator CD-ROM
• Online Quiz
• eWorkbook
• eEdition
• @HomeTutor

Resources for English Learners
• Quick Reference for English Learners
• Spanish Study Guide
• Multi-Language Visual Glossary
• Student Resources in Spanish

See also the *Algebra 1 Toolkit* for more strategies for meeting individual needs.

Solve the equation. Check your solution.

1. $24 - 3m = 5m$ **3**
2. $20 + c = 4c - 7$ **9**
3. $9 - 3k = 17 - 2k$ **−8**

4. $5z - 2 = 2(3z - 4)$ **6**
5. $3 - 4a = 5(a - 3)$ **2**
6. $8y - 6 = \frac{2}{3}(6y + 15)$ **4**

❖ **EXAMPLE 3**   Solve a real-world problem

CAR SALES A car dealership sold 78 new cars and 67 used cars this year. The number of new cars sold by the dealership has been increasing by 6 cars each year. The number of used cars sold by the dealership has been decreasing by 4 cars each year. If these trends continue, in how many years will the number of new cars sold be twice the number of used cars sold?

Solution

Let x represent the number of years from now. So, $6x$ represents the increase in the number of new cars sold over x years and $-4x$ represents the decrease in the number of used cars sold over x years. Write a verbal model.

New cars sold this year	+	Increase in new cars sold over x years	= 2 (	Used cars sold this year	+	Decrease in used cars sold over x years	)
78	+	6x	= 2 (	67	+	(−4x)	)

$$78 + 6x = 2(67 - 4x) \qquad \text{Write equation.}$$
$$78 + 6x = 134 - 8x \qquad \text{Distributive property}$$
$$78 + 14x = 134 \qquad \text{Add 8x to each side.}$$
$$14x = 56 \qquad \text{Subtract 78 from each side.}$$
$$x = 4 \qquad \text{Divide each side by 14.}$$

▶ The number of new cars sold will be twice the number of used cars sold in 4 years.

CHECK   You can use a table to check your answer.

Year	0	1	2	3	4
Used cars sold	67	63	59	55	51
New cars sold	78	84	90	96	102

The number of new cars sold is twice the number of used cars sold in 4 years.

7. WHAT IF? In Example 3, suppose the car dealership sold 50 new cars this year instead of 78. In how many years will the number of new cars sold be twice the number of used cars sold?   **6 yr**

Motivating the Lesson

Learning how to write and solve equations with variables on both sides allows you to determine when two quantities equal each other. Suppose you offer a dog grooming service to earn money during the summer. One plan could be to charge customers a flat fee of $150 for two months of service, plus $5 per comb out and shampoo. Another plan could be to charge $10 per comb out and $5 per shampoo. By setting these options equal to each other, you can find when the earnings from the two plans would be the same. This can help you decide which plan to use.

③ TEACH

Extra Example 1
Solve $13 + 5x = 2x - 8$.   **−7**

An **Animated Algebra** activity is available on-line for **Example 1**. This activity is also available on the **Power Presentations CD-ROM**.

Extra Example 2
Solve $4x - 5 = \frac{1}{5}(5x + 20)$.   **3**

Key Question to Ask for Example 2
• Another way is suggested for solving the equation in Example 1. What is another way to solve the equation in Example 2? **You could start by mutiplying each side by 4 to get $36x - 20 = 16x + 60$. Then $20x = 80$ and $x = 4$.**

NUMBER OF SOLUTIONS Equations do not always have one solution. An equation that is true for all values of the variable is an **identity**. So, the solution of an identity is all real numbers. Some equations have no solution.

EXAMPLE 4 **Identify the number of solutions of an equation**

Solve the equation, if possible.

a. $3x = 3(x + 4)$

b. $2x + 10 = 2(x + 5)$

Solution

a. $3x = 3(x + 4)$ **Original equation**

$3x = 3x + 12$ **Distributive property**

The equation $3x = 3x + 12$ is not true because the number $3x$ cannot be equal to 12 more than itself. So, the equation has no solution. This can be demonstrated by continuing to solve the equation.

$3x - 3x = 3x + 12 - 3x$ **Subtract $3x$ from each side.**

$0 = 12$ ✗   **Simplify.**

▶ The statement $0 = 12$ is not true, so the equation has no solution.

b. $2x + 10 = 2(x + 5)$ **Original equation**

$2x + 10 = 2x + 10$ **Distributive property**

▶ Notice that the statement $2x + 10 = 2x + 10$ is true for all values of x. So, the equation is an identity, and the solution is all real numbers.

✓ **GUIDED PRACTICE**   for Example 4

Solve the equation, if possible.

8. $9z + 12 = 9(z + 3)$ **9.** $7w + 1 = 8w + 1$ **10.** $3(2a + 2) = 2(3a + 3)$

        no solution   0   identity

SOLVING LINEAR EQUATIONS You have learned several ways to transform an equation to an equivalent equation. These methods are combined in the steps listed below.

CONCEPT SUMMARY   *For Your Notebook*

Steps for Solving Linear Equations

STEP 1 **Use** the distributive property to remove any grouping symbols.

STEP 2 **Simplify** the expression on each side of the equation.

STEP 3 **Use** properties of equality to collect the variable terms on one side of the equation and the constant terms on the other side of the equation.

STEP 4 **Use** properties of equality to solve for the variable.

STEP 5 **Check** your solution in the original equation.

Differentiated Instruction

Below Level As you discuss **Example 4**, it may be difficult for students to understand the concept of no solution or a solution that is true for all values of the variable. Have these students substitute 5 to 10 different values for x in the equations in parts a and b. After they have done this, ask them to describe why the equation in part a has no solution and why any value satisfies the equation in part b. Check their understanding by asking them to explain the solutions to **Guided Practice Exercises 8 and 10**.

Advanced For some students, the equations in **Example 4** and the **Guided Practice** may seem obvious. Challenge these students to create complicated equations with no solution, one solution, or infinitely many solutions. Ask them to create five of each and then exchange them with other students to solve. Remind them to mix the equations.

See also the *Algebra 1 Toolkit* for more strategies.

3.4 EXERCISES

HOMEWORK KEY
○ = **WORKED-OUT SOLUTIONS**
on p. WS1 for Exs. 13 and 51
★ = **STANDARDIZED TEST PRACTICE**
Exs. 2, 15, 16, 17, 29, and 53
◆ = **MULTIPLE REPRESENTATIONS**
Ex. 52

SKILL PRACTICE

[A] 1. **VOCABULARY** Copy and complete: An equation that is true for all values of the variable is called a(n) __?__ . **identity**

2. ★ **WRITING** *Explain* why the equation $4x + 3 = 4x + 1$ has no solution.
A number plus 3 can't be equal to itself plus 1. If you solve the equation, you get $0 = 2$.

SOLVING EQUATIONS Solve the equation. Check your solution.

EXAMPLES 1 and 2
on p. 154
for Exs. 3–17

3. $8t + 5 = 6t + 1$ **−2**   4. $k + 1 = 3k - 1$ **1**   5. $8c + 5 = 4c - 11$ **−4**

6. $8 + 4m = 9m - 7$ **3**   7. $10b + 18 = 8b + 4$ **−7**   8. $19 - 13p = -17p - 5$ **−6**

9. $9a = 6(a + 4)$ **8**   10. $5h - 7 = 2(h + 1)$ **3**   11. $3(d + 12) = 8 - 4d$ **−4**

12. $7(r + 7) = 5r + 59$ **5**   (13.) $40 + 14j = 2(-4j - 13)$ **−3**   14. $5(n + 2) = \frac{3}{5}(5 + 10n)$ **7**

17. Sample answer:
Distribute the 3 to get $6z - 15 = 2z + 13$, then subtract $2z$ from each side to get $4z - 15 = 13$, next add 15 to each side to get $4z = 28$, finally divide each side by 4 to get $z = 7$.

15. ★ **MULTIPLE CHOICE** What is the solution of the equation $8x + 2x = 15x - 10$? **C**

(A) −2   (B) 0.4   (C) 2   (D) 5

16. ★ **MULTIPLE CHOICE** What is the solution of the equation $4y + y + 1 = 7(y - 1)$? **D**

(A) −4   (B) −3   (C) 3   (D) 4

17. ★ **WRITING** *Describe* the steps you would use to solve the equation $3(2z - 5) = 2z + 13$.

EXAMPLE 4
on p. 156
for Exs. 18–28

SOLVING EQUATIONS Solve the equation, if possible.

18. $w + 3 = w + 6$ **no solution**   19. $16d = 22 + 5d$ **2**   20. $8z = 4(2z + 1)$ **no solution**

27. The 3 was not distributed to both terms; $3x + 15 = 3x + 15$, $15 = 15$, so the equation is an identity.

21. $12 + 5v = 2v - 9$ **−7**   22. $22x + 70 = 17x - 95$ **−33**   23. $2 - 15n = 5(-3n + 2)$ **no solution**

24. $12y + 6 = 6(2y + 1)$ **identity**   25. $5(1 + 4m) = 2(3 + 10m)$ **no solution**   26. $2(3g + 2) = \frac{1}{2}(12g + 8)$ **identity**

28. When the equation is $0 = 0$, it means that it is true for all values of y, not just 0; the solution is an identity.

ERROR ANALYSIS *Describe* and correct the error in solving the equation.

27.
$$3(x + 5) = 3x + 15$$
$$3x + 5 = 3x + 15$$
$$5 = 15$$
The equation has no solution. ✗

28.
$$6(2y + 6) = 4(9 + 3y)$$
$$12y + 36 = 36 + 12y$$
$$12y = 12y$$
$$0 = 0$$
The solution is $y = 0$. ✗

[B] 29. ★ **OPEN-ENDED** Give an example of an equation that has no solution. *Explain* why your equation does not have a solution.
Sample answer: $5x + 4 = 5x$; the number $5x$ cannot be equal to 4 more than itself.

3.4 Solve Equations with Variables on Both Sides   **157**

④ **PRACTICE AND APPLY**

Assignment Guide
📖 Answer Transparencies available for all exercises

Basic:
Day 1: EP p. 939 Exs. 38–41
pp. 157–159
Exs. 1, 2, 3–13 odd, 15–37, 49–52, 56–64 even

Average:
Day 1: pp. 157–159
Exs. 1, 2, 7–13 odd, 15–29, 31–43 odd, 44–47, 49–53, 56–64 odd

Advanced:
Day 1: pp. 157–159
Exs. 1, 7, 8, 12–17, 18–26, 29, 38–48*, 50–55*, 58–64 even

Block:
pp. 157–159
Exs. 1, 2, 7–13 odd, 15–29, 31–43 odd, 44–47, 49–53, 56–64 odd (with 3.5)

Differentiated Instruction
See *Algebra 1 Best Practices Toolkit* for suggestions on addressing the needs of a diverse classroom.

Homework Check
For a quick check of student understanding of key concepts, go over the following exercises:
Basic: 5, 11, 19, 31, 49
Average: 7, 13, 22, 37, 50
Advanced: 8, 14, 24, 39, 51

Extra Practice
• Student Edition, p. 940
• Chapter 3 Resource Book:
Practice levels A, B, C, pp. 41–43

Practice Worksheet
An easily-readable reduced practice page (with answers) for this lesson can be found on p. 130C.

30. $8w - 8 - 6w = 4w - 7$ $-\frac{1}{2}$ **31.** $3x - 4 = 2x + 8 - 5x$ **2**

32. $-15c + 7c + 1 = 3 - 8c$ **no solution** **33.** $\frac{3}{2} + \frac{3}{4}a = \frac{1}{4}a - \frac{1}{2}$ **−4**

34. $\frac{5}{8}m - \frac{3}{8} = \frac{1}{2}m + \frac{7}{8}$ **10** **35.** $n - 10 = \frac{5}{6}n - 7 - \frac{1}{3}n$ **6**

36. $3.7b + 7 = 8.1b - 19.4$ **6** **37.** $6.2h + 5 - 1.4h = 4.8h + 5$ **identity**

38. $0.7z + 1.9 + 0.1z = 5.5 - 0.4z$ **3** **39.** $5.4t + 14.6 - 10.1t = 12.8 - 3.5t - 0.6$ **2**

40. $\frac{1}{8}(5y + 64) = \frac{1}{4}(20 + 2y)$ **−24** **41.** $14 - \frac{1}{5}(j - 10) = \frac{2}{5}(25 + j)$ **10**

42. $5(1.2k + 6) = 7.1k + 34.4$ **−4** **43.** $-0.25(4v - 8) = 0.5(4 - 2v)$ **identity**

GEOMETRY Find the perimeter of the square.

44.

$8x - 10$ **28x − 20**
$6x$

45.

$5x$ **16x + 12**
$3x + 6$

46.

$3x + 7$ **14x + 10**
$4x - 2$

C | **CHALLENGE** Find the value(s) of a for which the equation is an identity.

47. $a(2x + 3) = 9x + 12 - x$ **4** **48.** $10x - 35 + 3ax = 5ax - 7a$ **5**

PROBLEM SOLVING

EXAMPLE 3 **A**
on p. 155
for Exs. 49–51

49. CAMPING The membership fee for joining a camping association is $45. A local campground charges members of the camping association $35 per night for a campsite and nonmembers $40 per night for a campsite. After how many nights of camping is the total cost for members, including the membership fee, the same as the total cost for nonmembers? **9 nights**

@HomeTutor for problem solving help at classzone.com

50. HIGH-SPEED INTERNET Dan and Sydney are getting high-speed Internet access at the same time. Dan's provider charges $60 for installation and $42.95 per month. Sydney's provider has free installation and charges $57.95 per month. After how many months will Dan and Sydney have paid the same amount for high-speed Internet service? **4 mo**

@HomeTutor for problem solving help at classzone.com

51. **LANGUAGES** Information about students who take Spanish and students who take French at a high school is shown in the table. If the trends continue, in how many years will there be 3 times as many students taking Spanish as French? **about 4 yr**

Language	Students enrolled this year	Average rate of change
Spanish	555	33 more students each year
French	230	2 fewer students each year

◯ = WORKED-OUT SOLUTIONS on p. WS1 ★ = STANDARDIZED TEST PRACTICE ◆ = MULTIPLE REPRESENTATIONS

[B] **52.** ◆ **MULTIPLE REPRESENTATIONS** For $360, a rock-climbing gym offers a yearly membership where members can climb as many days as they want and pay $4 per day for equipment rental. Nonmembers pay $10 per day to use the gym and $6 per day for equipment rental.

a. **Writing an Equation** Write an equation to find the number of visits after which the total cost for a member and the total cost for a nonmember are the same. Then solve the equation. **$360 + 4x = 16x$; 30 visits**

b. **Making a Table** Make a table for the costs of members and nonmembers after 5, 10, 15, 20, 25, 30, and 35 visits. Use the table to check your answer to part (a). **See margin.**

53. ★ **EXTENDED RESPONSE** Flyball is a relay race for dogs. In each of the four legs of the relay, a dog jumps over hurdles, retrieves a ball from a flybox, and runs back over the hurdles. The last leg of a relay is shown below. The collie starts the course 0.3 second before the sheepdog.

flybox

The collie is running 23.4 feet per second.

The sheepdog is running 24 feet per second.

51 ft

53c. No; it would take 12 seconds for the sheepdog to catch up to the collie and it only takes 4.4 seconds for the collie to complete the last leg.

a. Let t represent the time (in seconds) it takes the collie to run the last leg. Write and solve an equation to find the number of seconds after which the sheepdog would catch up with the collie. **$23.4t = 24(t − 0.3)$; 12 sec**

b. How long does it take the collie to run the last leg? **about 4.4 sec**

c. Use your answers from parts (a) and (b) to determine whether the sheepdog catches up and passes the collie during the last leg of the relay. *Explain* your reasoning.

[C] **CHALLENGE** Find the length and the width of the rectangle described.

54. The length is 12 units more than the width. The perimeter is 7 times the width. **20, 8**

55. The length is 4 units less than 3 times the width. The perimeter is 22 units more than twice the width. **11, 5**

MIXED REVIEW

PREVIEW
Prepare for Lesson 3.5 in Exs. 56–64.

Write the fraction in simplest form. *(p. 912)*

56. $\frac{5}{15}$ **$\frac{1}{3}$**   **57.** $\frac{10}{12}$ **$\frac{5}{6}$**   **58.** $\frac{4}{14}$ **$\frac{2}{7}$**   **59.** $\frac{18}{48}$ **$\frac{3}{8}$**

Solve the equation. *(p. 134)*

60. $\frac{w}{3} = 6$ **18**   **61.** $\frac{x}{18} = 2$ **36**   **62.** $-11 = \frac{m}{4}$ **−44**   **63.** $12 = \frac{z}{-9}$ **−108**

64. **FOOTBALL** The average rushing yards per game for a football player is found by dividing the total rushing yards for the season by the number of games played. How many total rushing yards did a player have if he played in 12 games and averaged 22 yards per game? *(p. 134)* **264 rushing yards**

EXTRA PRACTICE for Lesson 3.4, p. 940   ⬥ **ONLINE QUIZ** at classzone.com   **159**

---

⑤**ASSESS** AND **RETEACH**

Daily Homework Quiz

🗐 **Transparency Available**

Solve the equation, if possible.

1. $3(3x + 6) = 9(x + 2)$ **The equation is an identity.**

2. $7(h − 4) = 2h + 17$ **9**

3. $8 − 2w = 6w − 8$ **2**

4. $4g + 3 = 2(2g + 3)$ **The equation has no solution.**

5. Bryson is looking for a repair service for general household maintenance. One service charges $75 to join the service and $30 per hour. Another service charges $45 per hour. After how many hours of service is the total cost for the two services the same? **5 h**

 Online Quiz

Available at **classzone.com**

Diagnosis/Remediation

• Practice A, B, C in Chapter 3 Resource Book, pp. 41–43
• Study Guide in Chapter 3 Resource Book, pp. 44–45
• Practice Workbook, pp. 36–37
• @HomeTutor

Challenge

Additional challenge is available in the Chapter 3 Resource Book, p. 48.

52b. See Additional Answers beginning on p. AA1.

3.4 Solve Equations Using Tables

QUESTION   How can you use a spreadsheet to solve an equation with variables on both sides?

You can use a spreadsheet to solve an equation with variables on both sides by evaluating the left side of the equation and the right side of the equation using the same value of the variable. If the left side and right side are equal, then the value of the variable is a solution.

EXAMPLE   Solve an equation using a spreadsheet

Solve $19(x - 1) - 72 = 6x$.

STEP 1 *Enter data and formulas*

Label columns for possible solutions, left side, and right side in row 1. Enter the integers from 0 through 10 as possible solutions in column A. Then enter the formulas for the left side and the right side of the equation in columns B and C.

	A	B	C
	Possible solutions	Left side	Right side
1			
2	0	=19*(A2−1)−72	=6*A2
3	1	=19*(A3−1)−72	=6*A3
...	...	...	...
12	10	=19*(A12−1)−72	=6*A12

STEP 2 *Compare columns*

Compare the values of the left side and the values of the right side. The left side and right side values are equal when $x = 7$. So, the solution is 7.

	A	B	C
	Possible solutions	Left side	Right side
1			
...	...	...	...
8	6	23	36
9	7	42	42
10	8	61	48

DRAW CONCLUSIONS   Use your observations to complete these exercises

In Exercises 1–3, use a spreadsheet to solve the equation.

1. $15x + 6 = 6x + 24$ **2**   **2.** $8x - 17 = 5x + 70$ **29**   **3.** $18 - 2(x + 3) = x$ **4**

4. Not all equations have integer solutions. Consider the equation $4.9 + 4.8(7 - x) = 6.2x$.

   a. Follow Step 1 above using $4.9 + 4.8(7 - x) = 6.2x$. **See answer to part (b).**

   b. Add a fourth column that shows the difference of the value of the left side and the value of the right side. Find consecutive possible solutions between which the differences of the values of the left side and right side change sign. **See margin for spreadsheet; 3 and 4.**

   c. Repeat Step 1. This time use the lesser of the two possible solutions from part (b) as the first possible solution, and increase each possible solution by 0.1. Can you identify a solution now? If so, what is it? **yes; 3.5**

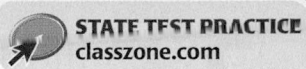
Lessons 3.1–3.4

1. MULTI-STEP PROBLEM A phone company charges $.25 for the first minute of a long-distance call and $.07 for each additional minute.

   a. Write an equation that gives the cost *C* of a long-distance call as a function of the length *t* (in minutes) of the call. **$C = 0.25 + 0.07(t − 1)$**

   b. Find the duration of a long-distance call that costs $2. **26 min**

2. GRIDDED ANSWER A veterinary assistant steps on a scale while holding a cat. The weight of the cat and assistant is 175 pounds. The assistant weighs 162 pounds. Find the weight (in pounds) of the cat. **13 lb**

3. EXTENDED RESPONSE A bowling alley charges $1.50 for bowling shoes and $3.75 for each game. Paul and Brandon each have $15 to spend at the bowling alley.

   a. Paul brings his own bowling shoes. How many games can he bowl? **4 games**

   b. Brandon needs to pay for bowling shoes. How many games can he bowl? Round your answer down to the nearest whole number. **3 games**

   c. Both Paul and Brandon decide to bowl the number of games that Brandon can afford to bowl. Does Paul have enough money to buy a slice of pizza and a soda that cost a total of $3.25? *Explain* your reasoning. **See margin.**

4. GRIDDED ANSWER The triangle has a perimeter of 82 inches. What is *x*? **4**

10(x − 1) in.   (4x + 14) in.

22 in.

5. SHORT RESPONSE You are folding origami cranes that will be used as decorations at a wedding. If you make cranes for 1 hour without a break, you can make 40 cranes. During a 3 hour period, you make 100 cranes. How much time did you spend *not* making cranes? *Explain* your reasoning. **See margin.**

6. SHORT RESPONSE A ski resort offers a super-saver pass for $90. The lift ticket rates with and without the super-saver pass are listed below.

Pass	Weekday lift ticket	Weekend/holiday lift ticket
With	$22.50	$36.00
Without	$45.00	$48.00

Suppose a skier skis only on weekdays. After how many visits to the ski resort will the cost for the super-saver pass and the lift tickets be equal to the cost of the lift tickets without the pass? *Explain* your reasoning. **See margin.**

7. SHORT RESPONSE The eruption of Mount St. Helens in 1980 decreased its elevation by 1313 feet. The current elevation is 8364 feet. What was the elevation of the volcano before the eruption? *Explain* your reasoning. **See margin.**

8. EXTENDED RESPONSE A garden supply store sells daffodil bulbs for $.60 per bulb.

   a. Jen spends $24 on daffodil bulbs. How many daffodil bulbs did she purchase? **40 daffodil bulbs**

   b. Jen decides to plant the daffodil bulbs along one side of her house that is 30 feet long. How many inches apart should she plant the bulbs so that they are equally spaced? **9 in.**

   c. Jen thinks that the daffodils will look better if the bulbs are planted 6 inches apart. How many more bulbs does she need? *Explain* your reasoning. **See margin.**

9. OPEN-ENDED *Describe* a real-world situation that can be modeled by the equation $4x + 15 = 47$. Then solve the equation and explain what your solution means in this situation. **See margin.**

3c. Yes; if Paul bowls only 3 games, he will have $3.75 left over.

5. 30 min; if you make 40 cranes in an hour, it will take 2.5 hours to make 100 cranes, so you spent 30 minutes not making cranes.

6. 4 visits; use an equation to find when the cost of skiing with a pass is the same as skiing without a pass. Solve $90 + 22.50x = 45x$ to find that $x = 4$.

7. 9677 ft; if you add 1313 feet to the current elevation, you will get the elevation before the eruption.

8c. 20 daffodil bulbs. *Sample answer:* If she plants bulbs 6 inches apart she will need 360 inches ÷ 6 inches = 60, so she needs 60 − 40 = 20 more bulbs.

9. *Sample answer:* You want to buy a video game for $47, if you have $15 and plan on saving money from a paper route each week for 4 weeks, how much money should you save each week? $x = 8$; you need to save $8 each week for 4 weeks to have enough money to buy the video game.

3.5 Write Ratios and Proportions

Before You solved equations involving division.

Now You will find ratios and write and solve proportions.

Why? So you can find a ratio involving a contest, as in Ex. 46.

Key Vocabulary
• ratio
• proportion
• simplest form, p. 912

Throughout this book you have been using rates, such as 50 miles per hour. A rate is a special type of *ratio*.

KEY CONCEPT   *For Your Notebook*

Ratios

A **ratio** uses division to compare two quantities. You can write the ratio of two quantities a and b, where b is not equal to 0, in three ways.

$$a \text{ to } b \qquad a:b \qquad \frac{a}{b}$$

Each ratio is read "the ratio of a to b." Ratios should be written in simplest form.

EXAMPLE 1 Write a ratio

VOLLEYBALL A volleyball team plays 14 home matches and 10 away matches.

  a. Find the ratio of home matches to away matches.

  b. Find the ratio of home matches to all matches.

Solution

  a. $\dfrac{\text{home matches}}{\text{away matches}} = \dfrac{14}{10} = \dfrac{7}{5}$

  b. $\dfrac{\text{home matches}}{\text{all matches}} = \dfrac{14}{14 + 10} = \dfrac{14}{24} = \dfrac{7}{12}$

 GUIDED PRACTICE for Example 1

Derek and his brother decide to combine their CD collections. Derek has 44 CDs, and his brother has 52 CDs. Find the specified ratio.

  1. The number of Derek's CDs to the number of his brother's CDs $\frac{11}{13}$

  2. The number of Derek's CDs to the number of CDs in the entire collection $\frac{11}{24}$

PROPORTIONS A **proportion** is an equation that states that two ratios are equivalent. The general form of a proportion is given below.

READING
This proportion is read
"*a* is to *b* as *c* is to *d*."

$$\frac{a}{b} = \frac{c}{d} \text{ where } b \neq 0, d \neq 0$$

If one of the numbers in a proportion is unknown, you can solve the proportion to find the unknown number. To solve a proportion with a variable in the numerator, you can use the same methods you used to solve equations.

EXAMPLE 2 Solve a proportion

Solve the proportion $\frac{11}{6} = \frac{x}{30}$.

$\frac{11}{6} = \frac{x}{30}$	Write original proportion.
$30 \cdot \frac{11}{6} = 30 \cdot \frac{x}{30}$	Multiply each side by 30.
$\frac{330}{6} = x$	Simplify.
$55 = x$	Divide.

✔ **GUIDED PRACTICE** for Example 2

Solve the proportion. Check your solution.

3. $\frac{w}{35} = \frac{4}{7}$ **20**
4. $\frac{9}{2} = \frac{m}{12}$ **54**
5. $\frac{z}{54} = \frac{5}{9}$ **30**

SETTING UP A PROPORTION There are different ways to set up a proportion. Consider the following problem.

A recipe for tomato salsa calls for 30 tomatoes to make 12 pints of salsa. How many tomatoes are needed to make 4 pints of salsa?

The tables below show two ways of arranging the information from the problem. In each table, *x* represents the number of tomatoes needed to make 4 pints of salsa. The proportions follow from the tables.

AVOID ERRORS
You cannot write a proportion that compares pints to tomatoes and tomatoes to pints.

$\frac{\text{pints}}{\text{tomatoes}} \neq \frac{\text{tomatoes}}{\text{pints}}$

	Tomatoes	Pints
Smaller recipe	*x*	4
Normal recipe	30	12

Proportion: $\frac{x}{30} = \frac{4}{12}$

	Smaller recipe	Normal recipe
Tomatoes	*x*	30
Pints	4	12

Proportion: $\frac{x}{4} = \frac{30}{12}$

3.5 Write Ratios and Proportions **163**

Motivating the Lesson
Tell students that ratios and proportions are used to solve a wide range of problems in which the relationship between quantities is important. For example, you can use ratios to compare the number of math books to English books in the library, the number of boys to girls in drama classes, and the number of airplanes to cars at an airfield. Proportions can be used to find distance, time, speed, and cost, among other things.

❸ TEACH

Extra Example 1
At a carwash fund raiser, 18 ninth grade students and 14 tenth grade students worked the first shift.
a. Find the ratio of ninth grade students to tenth grade students. $\frac{9}{7}$
b. Find the ratio of ninth grade students to all students. $\frac{9}{16}$

Key Question to Ask for Example 1
- Is the ratio of away matches to home matches the same as the ratio of home matches to away matches? Explain. **No, the ratio of away matches to home matches is 10 to 14 or 5 to 7, while the ratio of home matches to away matches is 7 to 5.**

Extra Example 2
Solve the proportion $\frac{12}{h} = \frac{3}{17}$. **68**

Key Question to Ask for Example 2
- Why do you multiply by 30 and not by the reciprocal of $\frac{11}{6}$? **Multiplying by 30 isolates the variable.**

EXAMPLE 3 Solve a multi-step problem

ELEVATORS The elevator that takes passengers from the lobby of the John Hancock Center in Chicago to the observation level travels 150 feet in 5 seconds. The observation level is located on the 94th floor, at 1029 feet above the ground. Find the time it takes the elevator to travel from the lobby to the observation level.

Solution

STEP 1 **Write** a proportion involving two ratios that compare the amount of time the elevator has ascended with the distance traveled.

$$\frac{5}{150} = \frac{x}{1029} \quad \longleftarrow \text{ seconds} \\ \longleftarrow \text{ feet}$$

STEP 2 **Solve** the proportion.

$\frac{5}{150} = \frac{x}{1029}$	Write proportion.
$1029 \cdot \frac{5}{150} = 1029 \cdot \frac{x}{1029}$	Multiply each side by 1029.
$\frac{5145}{150} = x$	Simplify.
$34.3 = x$	Use a calculator.

▸ The elevator travels from the lobby to the observation level in 34.3 seconds.

CHECK You can use a table to check the reasonableness of your answer.

Time (sec)	5	10	15	20	25	30	35
Distance traveled (ft)	150	300	450	600	750	900	1050

The solution, 34.3 seconds, is slightly less than 35 seconds, and 1029 feet is slightly less than 1050 feet. So, the solution is reasonable.

 GUIDED PRACTICE for Example 3

6. **WHAT IF?** In Example 3, suppose the elevator travels 125 feet in 5 seconds. Find the time it will take for the elevator to travel from the lobby to the observation level. **41.16 sec**

7. **ASTRONOMY** When two full moons appear in the same month, the second full moon is called a blue moon. On average, 2 blue moons occur every 5 years. Find the number of blue moons that are likely to occur in the next 25 years. **10 blue moons**

3.5 EXERCISES

HOMEWORK KEY

○ = **WORKED-OUT SOLUTIONS**
on p. WS1 for Exs. 17 and 49

★ = **STANDARDIZED TEST PRACTICE**
Exs. 2, 19, 20, 43, and 54

◆ = **MULTIPLE REPRESENTATIONS**
Ex. 52

SKILL PRACTICE

A 1. **VOCABULARY** Copy and complete: A proportion is an equation that states that two __?__ are equal. **ratios**

2. ★ **WRITING** Write a ratio of two quantities in three different ways. **Sample answer:** $\frac{2}{5}$, 2:5, 2 to 5

SIMPLIFYING RATIOS Tell whether the ratio is in simplest form. If not, write it in simplest form.

3. 14 to 18 **no; 7 to 9**   4. 5 : 13 **yes**   5. $\frac{24}{25}$ **yes**   6. 28 to 32 **no; 7 to 8**

EXAMPLE 2
on p. 163
for Exs. 7–22

SOLVING PROPORTIONS Solve the proportion. Check your solution.

7. $\frac{2}{5} = \frac{x}{3}$ **6** $\frac{6}{5}$ 8. $\frac{4}{1} = \frac{z}{16}$ **64**   9. $\frac{c}{8} = \frac{11}{4}$ **22**   10. $\frac{36}{12} = \frac{x}{2}$ **6**

11. $\frac{16}{7} = \frac{m}{21}$ **48**   12. $\frac{k}{9} = \frac{10}{18}$ **5**   13. $\frac{5}{8} = \frac{t}{24}$ **15**   14. $\frac{d}{5} = \frac{80}{100}$ **4**

15. $\frac{v}{20} = \frac{8}{4}$ **40**   16. $\frac{r}{60} = \frac{40}{50}$ **48**   (17.) $\frac{16}{48} = \frac{n}{36}$ **12**   18. $\frac{49}{98} = \frac{s}{112}$ **56**

19. ★ **MULTIPLE CHOICE** What is the value of x in the proportion $\frac{8}{5} = \frac{x}{20}$? **C**

  (A) 2   (B) 23   (C) 32   (D) 40

20. ★ **MULTIPLE CHOICE** What is the value of z in the proportion $\frac{z}{15} = \frac{28}{35}$? **B**

  (A) 8   (B) 12   (C) 18.75   (D) 425

ERROR ANALYSIS *Describe* and correct the error in solving the proportion.
21, 22. See margin.

21.
$$\frac{3}{4} = \frac{x}{6}$$
$$\frac{1}{6} \cdot \frac{3}{4} = \frac{1}{6} \cdot \frac{x}{6}$$
$$\frac{1}{8} = x$$ ✗

22.
$$\frac{m}{10} = \frac{50}{20}$$
$$10 \cdot \frac{m}{10} = 20 \cdot \frac{50}{20}$$
$$m = 50$$ ✗

B **WRITING AND SOLVING PROPORTIONS** Write the sentence as a proportion. Then solve the proportion.

25. $\frac{x}{4} = \frac{8}{16}$; 2

26. $\frac{y}{20} = \frac{9}{5}$; 36

29. $\frac{12}{18} = \frac{d}{27}$; 18

30. $\frac{t}{21} = \frac{40}{28}$; 30

23. 3 is to 8 as x is to 32. $\frac{3}{8} = \frac{x}{32}$; 12

24. 5 is to 7 as a is to 49. $\frac{5}{7} = \frac{a}{49}$; 35

25. x is to 4 as 8 is to 16.

26. y is to 20 as 9 is to 5.

27. b is to 10 as 7 is to 2. $\frac{b}{10} = \frac{7}{2}$; 35

28. 4 is to 12 as n is to 3. $\frac{4}{12} = \frac{n}{3}$; 1

29. 12 is to 18 as d is to 27.

30. t is to 21 as 40 is to 28.

3.5 Write Ratios and Proportions **165**

21. Multiply each side by 6, not $\frac{1}{6}$; $6 \cdot \frac{3}{4} = 6 \cdot \frac{x}{6}$, $4\frac{1}{2} = x$.

22. Multiply each side by 10, not one side by 10 and the other side by 20; $10 \cdot \frac{m}{10} = 10 \cdot \frac{50}{20}$, $m = 25$.

---

④ PRACTICE AND APPLY

Assignment Guide

▱ Answer Transparencies available for all exercises

Basic:
Day 1: SRH p. 912 Exs. 6–10
pp. 165–167
Exs. 1–6, 7–17 odd, 19–26, 45–52, 56–66

Average:
Day 1: pp. 165–167
Exs. 1, 2, 5, 6, 10–18 even, 19–22, 23–43 odd, 47–54, 56–66 even

Advanced:
Day 1: pp. 165–167
Exs. 1, 2, 15–20, 27–30, 32–42 even, 43–55*, 57–65 odd

Block:
pp. 165–167
Exs. 1, 2, 5, 6, 10–18 even, 19–22, 23–43 odd, 47–54, 56–66 even (with 3.4)

Differentiated Instruction

See *Algebra 1 Best Practices Toolkit* for suggestions on addressing the needs of a diverse classroom.

Homework Check

For a quick check of student understanding of key concepts, go over the following exercises:
Basic: 11, 14, 45, 47, 50
Average: 12, 16, 46, 48, 51
Advanced: 15, 20, 47, 48, 52

Extra Practice

- Student Edition, p. 940
- Chapter 3 Resource Book: Practice levels A, B, C, pp. 52–54

Practice Worksheet

An easily-readable reduced practice page (with answers) for this lesson can be found on p. 130C.

SOLVING PROPORTIONS Solve the proportion. Check your solution.

31. $\frac{b}{0.5} = \frac{9}{2.5}$ **1.8**   **32.** $\frac{1.1}{1.2} = \frac{n}{3.6}$ **3.3**   **33.** $\frac{2.1}{7.7} = \frac{v}{8.8}$ **2.4**   **34.** $\frac{36}{54} = \frac{2x}{6}$ **2**

35. $\frac{3a}{4} = \frac{36}{12}$ **4**   **36.** $\frac{10h}{108} = \frac{5}{9}$ **6**   **37.** $\frac{6r}{10} = \frac{36}{15}$ **4**   **38.** $\frac{12}{42} = \frac{4w}{56}$ **4**

39. $\frac{m+3}{8} = \frac{40}{64}$ **2**   **40.** $\frac{5}{13} = \frac{k-4}{39}$ **19**   **41.** $\frac{7}{112} = \frac{c-3}{8}$ **3.5**   **42.** $\frac{6+n}{60} = \frac{15}{90}$ **4**

43. ★ **SHORT RESPONSE** Is it possible to write a proportion using the numbers 3, 4, 6, and 8? *Explain* your reasoning. **Yes.** *Sample answer:* $\frac{3}{6} = \frac{4}{8}$

C **44.** **CHALLENGE** If $\frac{a}{b} = \frac{c}{d}$ for nonzero numbers a, b, c, and d, is it also true

that $\frac{a}{c} = \frac{b}{d}$? *Explain.* **Yes; multiply each side by b to get the equation $a = \frac{cb}{d}$, then divide each side by c to get $\frac{a}{c} = \frac{b}{d}$.**

PROBLEM SOLVING

EXAMPLE 1 A
on p. 162
for Exs. 45–49

45. **GOVERNMENT** There are 435 representatives in the U.S. House of Representatives. Of the 435 representatives, 6 are from Kentucky. Find the ratio of the number of representatives from Kentucky to the total number of representatives. $\frac{2}{145}$

@HomeTutor for problem solving help at classzone.com

46. **CONTEST** Of the 30 champions of the National Spelling Bee from 1974 to 2003, 16 are boys. Find the ratio of the number of champions who are girls to the number who are boys. $\frac{7}{8}$

@HomeTutor for problem solving help at classzone.com

PIZZA SALES The table shows the number of pizzas sold at a pizzeria during a week. Use the information to find the specified ratio.

47. Small pizzas to large pizzas $\frac{2}{5}$

48. Medium pizzas to large pizzas $\frac{3}{5}$

49. Large pizzas to all pizzas $\frac{1}{2}$

Size	Small	Medium	Large
Pizzas	96	144	240

EXAMPLE 3
on p. 164
for Exs. 50–52

50. **READING** A student can read 7 pages of a book in 10 minutes. How many pages of the book can the student read in 30 minutes? **21 pages**

51. **SOCCER** In the first 4 games of the season, a soccer team scored a total of 10 goals. If this trend continues, how many goals will the team score in the 18 remaining games of the season? **45 goals**

B **52.** ◆ **MULTIPLE REPRESENTATIONS** A movie is filmed so that the ratio of the length to the width of the image on the screen is 1.85 : 1.

a. **Writing a Proportion** Write and solve a proportion to find the length of the image on the screen when the width of the image is 38 feet. *Sample answer:* $\frac{1.85}{1} = \frac{x}{38}$, **70.3 ft**

b. **Making a Table** Make a table that shows the length of an image when the width of the image is 20, 25, 30, 35, and 40 feet. Use your table to check the reasonableness of your answer to part (a). **See margin.**

166

○ = **WORKED-OUT SOLUTIONS**
on p. WS1

★ = **STANDARDIZED**
TEST PRACTICE

◆ = **MULTIPLE**
REPRESENTATIONS

Study Strategy

Exercises 7–18 Remind students that they solve proportions in the same way they solve equations, by isolating the variable. Also note that the variable can be on either side of the equation.

Exercises 34–42 Even though these proportions are more complex than those in the previous exercises, students should stay focused on isolating the variable.

Reading Strategy

Exercises 23–30 Before beginning these exercises, you may want to refer students to the reading note on page 163. Students can use this model to help them write the sentences as proportions.

Avoiding Common Errors

Exercises 45–49 Students often compare the wrong quantities when they write ratios. Point out that they should compare quantities in the same order as the words. For example, if they want to find the ratio between medium pizzas and small pizzas, the number for medium pizzas is first in the ratio and the number for small pizzas is second.

Exercises 50–52 Caution students to be sure to set up each proportion correctly. Suggest they reread the section on setting up proportions on page 163. They can then look over their proportions to make sure they are writing like quantities in the same location in each ratio.

52b.

Width (ft)	Length (ft)
20	37
25	46.25
30	55.5
35	64.75
40	74

53. MULTI-STEP PROBLEM One day, the ratio of skiers to snowboarders on the mountain at a ski resort was 13 : 10. The resort sold a total of 253 lift tickets during the day.

    a. Find the ratio of snowboarders on the mountain to all of the skiers and snowboarders on the mountain. $\frac{10}{23}$

    b. Use the ratio from part (a) to find the number of lift tickets sold to snowboarders during the day. **110 lift tickets**

    c. During the same day, the ratio of snowboarders who rented snowboards to snowboarders that have their own snowboards is 4 : 7. Find the number of snowboarders who rented a snowboard. **40 snowboarders**

54. ★ **EXTENDED RESPONSE** You and a friend are waiting in separate lines to purchase concert tickets.

    a. Interpret Every 10 minutes, the cashier at the head of your line helps 3 people. There are 11 people in line in front of you. Write a proportion that can be used to determine how long you will have to wait to purchase tickets. *Sample answer:* $\frac{10}{3} = \frac{x}{11}$

    b. Interpret Every 5 minutes, the cashier at the head of your friend's line helps 2 people. There are 14 people in line in front of your friend. Write a proportion that can be used to determine how long your friend will have to wait to purchase tickets. *Sample answer:* $\frac{5}{2} = \frac{x}{14}$

    c. Compare Will you or your friend be able to purchase concert tickets first? *Explain.* **Your friend; you will wait in line for $36\frac{2}{3}$ minutes and your friend will wait only 35 minutes.**

C **55. CHALLENGE** A car traveling 50 miles per hour goes 15 miles farther in the same amount of time as a car traveling 30 miles per hour. Find the distance that each car travels. **37.5 mi, 22.5 mi**

MIXED REVIEW

Tell whether the pairing is a function. *(p. 35)*

56.

Input	−4	−2	0	2	2
Output	2	2	0	−1	−2

not a function

57.

Input	−1	0	1	2	3
Output	5	5	5	5	5

function

Write a rule for the function represented by the graph. Identify the domain and range of the function. *(p. 43)* **58–60. See margin.**

58.

59.

60.

Solve the equation. Check your solution.

61. $-2y = 18$ *(p. 134)* **−9**

62. $20x = 40$ *(p. 134)* **2**

63. $56 = 7(z + 5)$ *(p. 148)* **3**

64. $16(r + 3) = -48$ *(p. 148)* **−6**

65. $5(c - 12) = 2c$ *(p. 154)* **20**

66. $b + 11 = 3(b - 1)$ *(p. 154)* **7**

EXTRA PRACTICE for Lesson 3.5, p. 940   ⊘ **ONLINE QUIZ** at classzone.com   **167**

58. $y = \frac{1}{2}x + 1$; domain: 0, 2, 4, and 6, range: 1, 2, 3, and 4

59. $y = x - 1$; domain: 2, 3, 4, 5, and 6, range: 1, 2, 3, 4, and 5

60. $y = x + 2$; domain: 0, 1, 2, and 3, range: 2, 3, 4, and 5

PREVIEW
Prepare for
Lesson 3.6
in Exs. 61–66.

---

5 ASSESS AND RETEACH

Daily Homework Quiz

⊟ **Transparency Available**

1. A chocolate chip cookie recipe calls for $2\frac{1}{4}$ cups of flour and $\frac{3}{4}$ cup of brown sugar. Find the ratio of brown sugar to flour. $\frac{1}{3}$

Solve the proportion.

2. $\frac{a}{7} = \frac{9}{21}$ **3**

3. $\frac{32}{28} = \frac{m}{14}$ **16**

4. A printer can print 12 color pages in 3 minutes. How many color pages can the printer print in 9 minutes? Write and solve a proportion to find the answer. $\frac{12}{3} = \frac{x}{9}$; **36 color pages**

🖱 **Online Quiz**

Available at **classzone.com**

Diagnosis/Remediation

- Practice A, B, C in Chapter 3 Resource Book, pp. 52–54
- Study Guide in Chapter 3 Resource Book, pp. 55–56
- Practice Workbook, pp. 38–39
- @HomeTutor

Challenge

Additional challenge is available in the Chapter 3 Resource Book, p. 59.

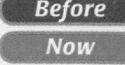

3.6 Solve Proportions Using Cross Products

Before You solved proportions using the multiplication property of equality.

Now You will solve proportions using cross products.

Why? So you can find the height of a scale model, as in Ex. 39.

Key Vocabulary
• cross product
• scale drawing
• scale model
• scale

In a proportion, a **cross product** is the product of the numerator of one ratio and the denominator of the other ratio. The following property involving cross products can be used to solve proportions.

KEY CONCEPT   *For Your Notebook*

Cross Products Property

Words The cross products of a proportion are equal.

Example $\frac{3}{4} = \frac{6}{8}$ $4 \cdot 6 = 24$
$3 \cdot 8 = 24$

Algebra If $\frac{a}{b} = \frac{c}{d}$ where $b \neq 0$ and $d \neq 0$, then $ad = bc$.

The proportion $\frac{3}{4} = \frac{6}{8}$ can be written as $3:4 = 6:8$. In this form, 4 and 6 are called the *means* of the proportion, and 3 and 8 are called the *extremes* of the proportion. This is why the cross products property is also called the *means-extremes property*.

EXAMPLE 1 **Use the cross products property**

Solve the proportion $\frac{8}{x} = \frac{6}{15}$.

$\frac{8}{x} = \frac{6}{15}$ Write original proportion.

$8 \cdot 15 = x \cdot 6$ Cross products property

$120 = 6x$ Simplify.

$20 = x$ Divide each side by 6.

▶ The solution is 20. Check by substituting 20 for x in the original proportion.

CHECK $\frac{8}{20} \overset{?}{=} \frac{6}{15}$ Substitute 20 for x.

$8 \cdot 15 \overset{?}{=} 20 \cdot 6$ Cross products property

$120 = 120 \checkmark$ Simplify. Solution checks.

EXAMPLE 2 **Standardized Test Practice**

What is the value of x in the proportion $\frac{4}{x} = \frac{8}{x-3}$?

(A) -6 (B) -3 (C) 3 (D) 6

Solution

ANOTHER WAY
Because 8 is twice 4, you can reason that $x - 3$ must be twice x:
$$x - 3 = 2x$$
$$-3 = x$$

$\frac{4}{x} = \frac{8}{x-3}$	Write original proportion.
$4(x - 3) = x \cdot 8$	Cross products property
$4x - 12 = 8x$	Simplify.
$-12 = 4x$	Subtract $4x$ from each side.
$-3 = x$	Divide each side by 4.

▶ The value of x is -3. The correct answer is B. (A) (B) (C) (D)

EXAMPLE 3 **Write and solve a proportion**

SEALS Each day, the seals at an aquarium are each fed 8 pounds of food for every 100 pounds of their body weight. A seal at the aquarium weighs 280 pounds. How much food should the seal be fed per day?

Solution

STEP 1 **Write** a proportion involving two ratios that compare the amount of food with the weight of the seal.

$$\frac{8}{100} = \frac{x}{280} \xleftarrow{\text{amount of food}}_{\text{weight of seal}}$$

STEP 2 **Solve** the proportion.

ANOTHER WAY
You can also solve the proportion by multiplying each side of the equation by 280.

$\frac{8}{100} = \frac{x}{280}$	Write proportion.
$8 \cdot 280 = 100 \cdot x$	Cross products property
$2240 = 100x$	Simplify.
$22.4 = x$	Divide each side by 100.

▶ A 280 pound seal should be fed 22.4 pounds of food per day.

 GUIDED PRACTICE for Examples 1, 2, and 3

Solve the proportion. Check your solution.

1. $\frac{4}{a} = \frac{24}{30}$ **5**   2. $\frac{3}{x} = \frac{2}{x-6}$ **18**   3. $\frac{m}{5} = \frac{m-6}{4}$ **30**

4. **WHAT IF?** In Example 3, suppose the seal weighs 260 pounds. How much food should the seal be fed per day? **20.8 lb**

Differentiated Instruction

Visual Learners To solve problems like the one in **Example 3**, students may want to organize the information in a table first.

	100-lb seal	280-lb seal
Amount of food (lb)	8	?
Weight of seal (lb)	100	280

Then the students can set up ratios vertically, $\frac{8}{100}$ and $\frac{x}{280}$, or horizontally, $\frac{8}{?}$ and $\frac{100}{280}$, to write a proportion.

See also the *Algebra 1 Toolkit* for more strategies.

Motivating the Lesson

Tell students that using cross products to solve proportions is useful in estimating actual distances on maps. Ask students to recount various times they have used the scale on a map to find the distance between two points. After a brief discussion, tell them they will learn how to use cross products to find map distances.

3 TEACH

Extra Example 1

Solve the proportion $\frac{4}{x} = \frac{12}{24}$. **8**

Key Questions to Ask for Example 1

- What are the means of the proportion? x **and 6**
- What are the extremes of the proportion? **8 and 15**

Extra Example 2

What is the value of x in the proportion $\frac{3}{x} = \frac{9}{x-4}$? **C**

(A) 4 (B) 2

(C) -2 (D) -4

Extra Example 3

Georgia is making her own potting soil. For every 4 buckets of peat moss, she mixes in 3 buckets of perlite. Suppose she uses 10 buckets of peat moss. How many buckets of perlite should she use? Write and solve a proportion to find the answer. $\frac{4}{3} = \frac{10}{x}$; **she should use 7.5 buckets of perlite.**

SCALE DRAWINGS AND SCALE MODELS The floor plan below is an example of a *scale drawing*. A **scale drawing** is a two-dimensional drawing of an object in which the dimensions of the drawing are in proportion to the dimensions of the object. A **scale model** is a three-dimensional model of an object in which the dimensions of the model are in proportion to the dimensions of the object.

A scale should be written as scale measure : actual measure.

The **scale** of a scale drawing or scale model relates the drawing's or model's dimensions and the actual dimensions. For example, the scale 1 in. : 12 ft on the floor plan means that 1 inch in the floor plan represents an actual distance of 12 feet.

EXAMPLE 4 Use the scale on a map

MAPS Use a metric ruler and the map of Ohio to estimate the distance between Cleveland and Cincinnati.

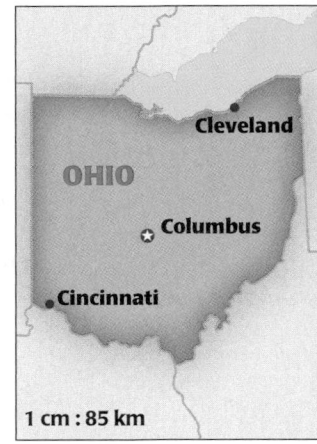

1 cm : 85 km

Solution

From the map's scale, 1 centimeter represents 85 kilometers. On the map, the distance between Cleveland and Cincinnati is about 4.2 centimeters.

Write and solve a proportion to find the distance d between the cities.

$$\frac{1}{85} = \frac{4.2}{d} \quad \begin{array}{l} \longleftarrow \textbf{centimeters} \\ \longleftarrow \textbf{kilometers} \end{array}$$

$$1 \cdot d = 85 \cdot 4.2 \quad \textbf{Cross products property}$$

$$d = 357 \quad \textbf{Simplify.}$$

▶ The actual distance between Cleveland and Cincinnati is about 357 kilometers.

✓ **GUIDED PRACTICE** for Example 4

5. Use a metric ruler and the map in Example 4 to estimate the distance (in kilometers) between Columbus and Cleveland. **about 212.5 km**

6. **MODEL SHIPS** The ship model kits sold at a hobby store have a scale of 1 ft : 600 ft. A completed model of the *Queen Elizabeth II* is 1.6 feet long. Estimate the actual length of the *Queen Elizabeth II*. **about 960 ft**

3.6 EXERCISES

HOMEWORK KEY

○ = WORKED-OUT SOLUTIONS
on p. WS1 for Exs. 13 and 39

★ = STANDARDIZED TEST PRACTICE
Exs. 2, 15, 16, 41, and 42

◆ = MULTIPLE REPRESENTATIONS
Ex. 40

SKILL PRACTICE

A 1. **VOCABULARY** Copy and complete: In a proportion, a(n) __?__ is the product of the numerator of one ratio and the denominator of the other ratio. **cross product**

2. ★ **WRITING** A scale drawing has a scale of 1 cm : 3 m. *Explain* how the scale can be used to find the actual distance between objects in the drawing. **Measure the distance in centimeters, in the drawing and then substitute the value in the proportion, $\frac{1}{3} = \frac{\text{distance in drawing}}{\text{actual distance}}$.**

EXAMPLES 1 and 2
on pp. 168–169
for Exs. 3–18

SOLVING PROPORTIONS Solve the proportion. Check your solution.

3. $\frac{2}{3} = \frac{4}{x}$ **6**

4. $\frac{3}{y} = \frac{15}{35}$ **7**

5. $\frac{13}{6} = \frac{52}{z}$ **24**

6. $\frac{10}{45} = \frac{v}{27}$ **6**

7. $\frac{5m}{6} = \frac{10}{12}$ **1**

8. $\frac{3k}{27} = \frac{2}{3}$ **6**

9. $\frac{-49}{7} = \frac{a+7}{6}$ **−49**

10. $\frac{6}{t+4} = \frac{42}{77}$ **7**

11. $\frac{8}{12} = \frac{r}{r+1}$ **2**

12. $\frac{n}{n-12} = \frac{9}{5}$ **27**

(13.) $\frac{11}{w} = \frac{33}{w+24}$ **12**

14. $\frac{18}{d+13} = \frac{6}{d-13}$ **26**

15. ★ **MULTIPLE CHOICE** What is the value of h in the proportion $\frac{15}{-2h} = \frac{5}{12}$? **B**

(A) −36   (B) −18   (C) 18   (D) 36

16. ★ **MULTIPLE CHOICE** What is the value of s in the proportion $\frac{7}{s-14} = \frac{21}{s+18}$? **D**

(A) −48   (B) −16   (C) 3   (D) 30

ERROR ANALYSIS *Describe* and correct the error in solving the proportion.

17.

$$\frac{4}{3} = \frac{16}{x}$$

$$4 \cdot 16 = 4 \cdot x$$

$$64 = 4x$$

$$16 = x$$

Use the cross products property to multiply 4 by x and 16 by 3; $4 \cdot x = 3 \cdot 16$, $4x = 48$, $x = 12$.

18.

$$\frac{18}{14} = \frac{b+2}{b}$$

$$18b = 14b + 2$$

$$4b = 2$$

$$b = 0.5$$

Distribute the 14 to both b and 2; $18b = 14b + 28$, $4b = 28$, $b = 7$.

B **SOLVING PROPORTIONS** Solve the proportion. Check your solution.

19. $\frac{7}{3} = \frac{2x+5}{x}$ **15**

20. $\frac{a}{9a-2} = \frac{1}{8}$ **2**

21. $\frac{24}{5z+4} = \frac{4}{z-1}$ **10**

22. $\frac{c-8}{-2} = \frac{11-4c}{11}$ **22**

23. $\frac{k-8}{7+k} = \frac{-1}{5}$ **5.5**

24. $\frac{2}{-3} = \frac{4v+4}{2v+14}$ **−2.5**

25. $\frac{m+1}{4} = \frac{3m+6}{7}$ **−3.4**

26. $\frac{6}{4+2w} = \frac{-2}{w-10}$ **5.2**

27. $\frac{n+0.3}{n-3.2} = \frac{9}{2}$ **4.2**

28. $\frac{-3}{11} = \frac{5-h}{h+1.4}$ **7.4**

29. $\frac{4}{b-3.9} = \frac{2}{b+1}$ **−5.9**

30. $\frac{16.5+3t}{3} = \frac{0.9-t}{-5}$ **−7.1**

3.6 Solve Proportions Using Cross Products **171**

---

④ PRACTICE AND APPLY

Assignment Guide

📖 Answer Transparencies available for all exercises

Basic:
Day 1: pp. 171–173
Exs. 1–18, 19–25 odd, 33–39 odd, 40, 44–54 even

Average:
Day 1: pp. 171–173
Exs. 1, 2, 4–14 even, 15–18, 19–29 odd, 31–42, 44–54 even

Advanced:
Day 1: pp. 171–173
Exs. 1, 2, 11–16, 24–30 even, 31–34*, 37–43*, 46, 47, 53–55

Block:
pp. 171–173
Exs. 1, 2, 4–14 even, 15–18, 19–29 odd, 31–42, 44–54 even (with 3.7)

Differentiated Instruction

See *Algebra 1 Best Practices Toolkit* for suggestions on addressing the needs of a diverse classroom.

Homework Check

For a quick check of student understanding of key concepts, go over the following exercises:

Basic: 7, 13, 15, 33, 35
Average: 10, 15, 23, 34, 37
Advanced: 12, 16, 29, 34, 39

Extra Practice

- Student Edition, p. 940
- Chapter 3 Resource Book: Practice levels A, B, C, pp. 62–64

Practice Worksheet

An easily-readable reduced practice page (with answers) for this lesson can be found on p. 130C.

31. REASONING The statements below justify the cross products property. Copy and complete the justification.

$$\frac{a}{b} = \frac{c}{d} \qquad \text{Given}$$

$$bd \cdot \frac{a}{b} = bd \cdot \frac{c}{d} \qquad \text{a. } \underline{\ ?\ } \quad \text{Multiplication property of equality}$$

$$\frac{bd \cdot a}{b} = \frac{bd \cdot c}{d} \qquad \text{b. } \underline{\ ?\ } \quad \text{Multiply}$$

$$ad = cb \qquad \text{c. } \underline{\ ?\ } \quad \text{Simplify}$$

C **32. CHALLENGE** In the proportion $\frac{5}{h} = \frac{k}{14}$, what happens to the value of h as the value of k increases? *Explain.* **Decreases; as k gets larger, the value of $\frac{k}{14}$ increases, so for the value of $\frac{5}{h}$ to increase, h must decrease.**

PROBLEM SOLVING

EXAMPLE 3
on p. 169
for Exs. 33–34

33. RECIPES A recipe that yields 12 buttermilk biscuits calls for 2 cups of flour. How much flour is needed to make 30 biscuits? **5 c**

@HomeTutor for problem solving help at classzone.com

34. DIGITAL PHOTOGRAPHS It took 7.2 minutes to upload 8 digital photographs from your computer to a website. At this rate, how long will it take to upload 20 photographs? **18 min**

@HomeTutor for problem solving help at classzone.com

EXAMPLE 4
on p. 170
for Exs. 35–39

MAPS A map has a scale of 1 cm : 15 km. Use the given map distance to find the actual distance.

35. 6 cm **90 km**   **36.** 3.2 cm **48 km**   **37.** 0.5 cm **7.5 km**   **38.** 4.7 cm **70.5 km**

39. SCALE MODEL An exhibit at Tobu World Square in Japan includes a scale model of the Empire State Building. The model was built using a scale of 1 m : 25 m. The height of the actual Empire State Building is 443.2 meters. What is the height of the model? **17.728 m**

B **40. ◆ MULTIPLE REPRESENTATIONS** The diameter of the burst of a firework is proportional to the diameter of the shell of the firework.

 a. **Writing a Proportion** Use the information in the diagram to find the burst diameter for a 4.75 inch shell. **213.75 ft**

 b. **Making a Table** Make a table of burst diameters for 2, 3, 4, 5, and 6 inch shells. Use the table to check your answer to part (a). **See margin.**

41. ★ SHORT RESPONSE The ratio of the length of a soccer field to the width of the field is 3 : 2. A scale drawing of a soccer field has a scale of 1 in. : 20 yd. The length of the field in the drawing is 6 inches. What is the actual width of the field? *Explain* your reasoning. **80 yd; find the actual length of the field by using the ratio 1 in. : 20 yd, then use that number to find the width of the soccer field by using the ratio 3 : 2.**

Burst

90 ft

Shell

2 in.

Not drawn to scale

○ = **WORKED-OUT SOLUTIONS**
on p. WS1

★ = **STANDARDIZED TEST PRACTICE**

◆ = **MULTIPLE REPRESENTATIONS**

172

40b.

Shell diameter (ft)	Burst diameter (ft)
2	90
3	135
4	180
5	225
6	270

42c. Nearly equal. *Sample answer:* The ratio of moles of hydrogen to moles of carbon is about 1.33 to 1, the ratio of moles of hydrogen to moles of oxygen is about 1.32 to 1. The two ratios are nearly the same.

42. ★ **EXTENDED RESPONSE** A mole is a unit of measurement used in chemistry. The masses of one mole of three elements are in the table.

Element	Mass of 1 mole
Hydrogen	1.008 grams
Carbon	12.011 grams
Oxygen	15.999 grams

a. A 100 gram sample of ascorbic acid contains 4.58 grams of hydrogen. To the nearest tenth, find the number of moles of hydrogen. **4.5 moles**

b. A 100 gram sample of ascorbic acid contains 54.5 grams of oxygen. To the nearest tenth, find the number of moles of oxygen in the sample. **3.4 moles**

c. The ratio of moles of hydrogen to moles of carbon in ascorbic acid is 4:3. How does this ratio compare with the ratio of moles of hydrogen to moles of oxygen in ascorbic acid? *Explain.*

[C] **43. CHALLENGE** At a typical National Football League game, the ratio of females to males in attendance is 2:3. Estimate the number of male and female spectators at a game that has 75,000 spectators. **45,000 males, 30,000 females**

MIXED REVIEW

Evaluate the expression for the given value of x. *(p. 110)*

44. $16 + \sqrt{x}$ when $x = 16$ **20**

45. $27 - \sqrt{x}$ when $x = 81$ **18**

46. $-3 \cdot \sqrt{x}$ when $x = 25$ **−15**

47. $2 \cdot \sqrt{x} + 11$ when $x = 144$ **35**

PREVIEW
Prepare for Lesson 3.7 in Exs. 48–55.

Solve the proportion. Check your solution. *(p. 162)*

48. $\frac{2}{3} = \frac{x}{21}$ **14**

49. $\frac{m}{6} = \frac{9}{2}$ **27**

50. $\frac{z}{11} = \frac{-10}{22}$ **−5**

51. $\frac{12}{5} = \frac{b}{25}$ **60**

52. $\frac{12}{36} = \frac{2c}{6}$ **1**

53. $\frac{9}{-8} = \frac{3w}{24}$ **−9**

54. $\frac{n-2}{50} = \frac{6}{30}$ **12**

55. $\frac{4}{13} = \frac{a+4}{39}$ **8**

QUIZ *for Lessons 3.4–3.6*

Solve the equation, if possible. *(p. 154)*

1. $y - 2 = y + 2$ **no solution**

2. $2x - 14 = -3x + 6$ **4**

3. $10z - 4 = 2(5z - 2)$ **identity**

4. $6m + 5 - 3m = 7(m - 1)$ **3**

5. $2(7 - g) = 9g + 14 - 11g$ **identity**

6. $13k + 3(k + 11) = 8k - 7$ **−5**

7. $\frac{1}{4}(8j - 3) = 2j - 3$ **no solution**

8. $8 - 4w = \frac{1}{3}(6w - 12)$ **2**

9. $\frac{2}{5}(10t - 50) = 4(9 - 6t)$ **2**

Solve the proportion. Check your solution. *(pp. 162, 168)*

10. $\frac{24}{20} = \frac{x}{5}$ **6**

11. $\frac{6}{-7} = \frac{3z}{42}$ **−12**

12. $\frac{14}{12} = \frac{w+11}{18}$ **10**

13. $\frac{18}{5a} = \frac{3}{-5}$ **−6**

14. $\frac{10}{17} = \frac{k}{2k-3}$ **10**

15. $\frac{h-1}{3} = \frac{2h+1}{9}$ **4**

16. **GEOMETRY** The ratio of the length to the width of a rectangle is 5:4. The length of the rectangle is 60 inches. What is the width? *(p. 168)* **48 in.**

Warm-Up Exercises

Solve the proportions.

1. $\frac{8}{k} = \frac{15}{6}$ **3.2**   2. $\frac{46}{25} = \frac{h}{35}$ **64.4**

3. $\frac{m}{2.5} = \frac{12}{6}$ **5**   4. $\frac{0.5}{13} = \frac{6.5}{x}$ **169**

5. The scale on a map is given as 1.5 cm : 8 km. The distance on the map between two cities is 2.25 centimeters. What is the actual distance between the cities? **12 km**

2 **FOCUS** AND **MOTIVATE**

Essential Question

Big Idea 2, p. 131

How do you use similar figures to solve problems? **Tell students they will learn how to answer this question by using similar figures to find unknown lengths of geometric figures and other objects that are difficult to measure.**

Extension   *Use after Lesson 3.6*

Apply Proportions to Similar Figures

GOAL Use similar figures to solve problems.

Key Vocabulary
- congruent figures
- similar figures
- corresponding parts

NAME SIMILAR FIGURES
When naming similar figures, list the letters of the corresponding vertices (corner points) in the same order.

Two figures are **congruent figures** if they have the same shape and size. The symbol $\cong$ indicates congruence. Of the triangles shown, $\triangle ABC \cong \triangle DEF$.

Two figures are **similar figures** if they have the same shape but not necessarily the same size. The symbol $\sim$ indicates that two figures are similar. All the triangles shown are similar; in particular, $\triangle ABC \sim \triangle JKL$.

The sides or angles that have the same relative position within two figures are called **corresponding parts**.

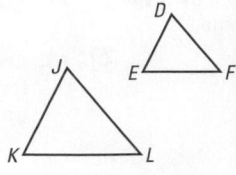

KEY CONCEPT   *For Your Notebook*

Properties of Similar Figures

In the diagram, $\triangle ABC \sim \triangle DEF$.

1. Corresponding angles of similar figures are congruent.

   $\angle A \cong \angle D$, $\angle B \cong \angle E$, $\angle C \cong \angle F$

NAME LENGTHS OF SIDES
AB represents the length of the side whose endpoints are A and B.

2. The ratios of the lengths of corresponding sides of similar figures are equal.

   $\frac{AB}{DE} = \frac{BC}{EF} = \frac{AC}{DF} = \frac{1}{2}$

EXAMPLE 1   **Find an unknown side length**

Given $\triangle JKL \sim \triangle QRS$, find QR.

Solution

Use the ratios of the lengths of corresponding sides to write a proportion.

$\frac{JK}{QR} = \frac{KL}{RS}$ **Write proportion involving QR.**

$\frac{18}{x} = \frac{8}{12}$ **Substitute.**

$216 = 8x$ **Cross products property**

$27 = x$ **Divide each side by 8.**

▶ QR is 27 centimeters.

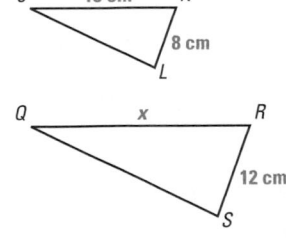

INDIRECT MEASUREMENT You can use similar figures to find lengths that are difficult to measure directly.

EXAMPLE 2 Use similar figures to measure indirectly

CAPE HATTERAS LIGHTHOUSE A man stands next to the Cape Hatteras Lighthouse in North Carolina. The lighthouse and the man are perpendicular to the ground. The sun's rays strike the lighthouse and the man at the same angle, forming two similar triangles. Use indirect measurement to approximate the height of the lighthouse.

83.2 ft

5.8 ft

Not drawn to scale   2.5 ft

Solution

Write and solve a proportion to find the height h (in feet) of the lighthouse.

ANOTHER WAY

You can also use the proportion below to find the height of the lighthouse.

$\dfrac{5.8}{2.5} = \dfrac{h}{83.2}$

$\begin{array}{l}\text{height} \longrightarrow \\ \text{height} \longrightarrow\end{array} \quad \dfrac{5.8}{h} = \dfrac{2.5}{83.2} \quad \begin{array}{l}\longleftarrow \text{ length of shadow} \\ \longleftarrow \text{ length of shadow}\end{array}$

$2.5h = 5.8 \cdot 83.2$ **Cross products property**

$2.5h = 482.56$ **Multiply.**

$h = 193.024$ **Divide each side by 2.5.**

▶ The height of the lighthouse is about 193 feet.

PRACTICE

EXAMPLE 1
on p. 174
for Exs. 1–4

1. Given $\triangle JKL \sim \triangle MNP$, find JL.   **24 in.**

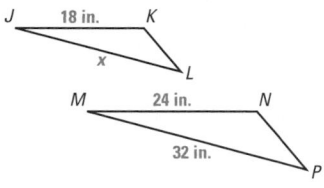

2. Given $\triangle EFG \sim \triangle UVW$, find UV.   **10 cm**

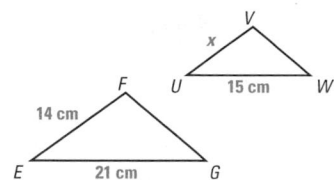

3. Given $ABCD \sim FGHJ$, find AD.   **16 m**

4. Given $JKLM \sim QRST$, find QT.   **40 ft**

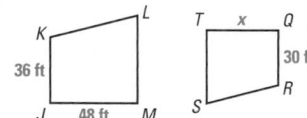

EXAMPLE 2
on p. 175
for Ex. 5

5. FLAGPOLES A 5 foot tall student stands near a flagpole. The flagpole and the student are perpendicular to the ground. The sun's rays strike the flagpole and the student at the same angle, forming two similar triangles. The flagpole casts a 15 foot shadow, and the student casts a 2 foot shadow. Use indirect measurement to find the height of the flagpole.   **37.5 ft**

Extension: Apply Proportions to Similar Figures   **175**

Key Questions to Ask for Example 1

- How do you know that $\overline{JK}$ corresponds to $\overline{QR}$? **The vertices appear in corresponding locations in the statement $\triangle JKL \sim \triangle QRS$.**
- Can you find JL? Explain. **No, you do not know the corresponding length QS in $\triangle QRS$.**

Extra Example 2

A woman 5.5 feet tall stands next to a lamp post. The woman and the lamp post are perpendicular to the ground. The Sun's rays strike the lamp post and the woman at the same angle, forming two similar triangles. The woman casts a 2.2-foot shadow, and the lamppost casts a 6.4-foot shadow. Use indirect measurement to find the height of the lamp post **16 ft**

Closing the Lesson

Have students summarize the major points of the lesson and answer the Essential Question: How do you use similar figures to solve problems?

- **In similar triangles, the ratios of the lengths of corresponding sides are equal.**
- **You can use similar figures to find unknown lengths.**

If two figures are similar, you can use the ratios of corresponding side lengths to determine missing side lengths or to measure objects that are difficult to measure.

④ PRACTICE AND APPLY

Avoiding Common Errors

Exercises 1–4 Some students may try to determine corresponding sides in similar figures visually. Explain that this is difficult to do and often leads to inaccurate results. Remind them that the statement of similarity indicates how the vertices correspond. When they are setting up proportions, they should use the similarity statement to determine the corresponding sides.

Before	You solved proportions.
Now	You will solve percent problems.
Why?	So you can solve a problem about racing, as in Ex. 34.

Key Vocabulary
• **percent,** *p. 916*
• **proportion,** *p. 163*

Recall that *percent* means "divided by 100." For example $27\% = \frac{27}{100}$.

By writing a percent as a fraction, you can use a proportion to solve a percent problem.

KEY CONCEPT *For Your Notebook*

Solving Percent Problems Using Proportions

You can represent "*a* is *p* percent of *b*" using the proportion

$$\frac{a}{b} = \frac{p}{100}$$

where *a* is a part of the base *b* and $\frac{p}{100}$, or *p*%, is the percent.

EXAMPLE 1 **Find a percent using a proportion**

What percent of 25 is 17?

Solution

Write a proportion where 25 is the base and 17 is a part of the base.

$\frac{a}{b} = \frac{p}{100}$	**Write proportion.**
$\frac{17}{25} = \frac{p}{100}$	**Substitute 17 for *a* and 25 for *b*.**
$1700 = 25p$	**Cross products property**
$68 = p$	**Divide each side by 25.**

▶ 17 is 68% of 25.

AVOID ERRORS
You can also solve for *p* by multiplying each side of the equation by 100.

 Animated **Algebra** at classzone.com

✓ **GUIDED PRACTICE** for Example 1

Use a proportion to answer the question.

1. What percent of 20 is 15? **75%**

2. What number is 30% of 90? **27**

---

1 PLAN AND PREPARE

Warm-Up Exercises
📄 **Transparency Available**

Write the percent as a decimal.
1. 27% **0.27**   **2.** 54.5% **0.545**

Solve the proportion.
3. $\frac{6}{25} = \frac{12}{n}$ **50**   **4.** $\frac{y}{18} = \frac{5}{8}$ **11.25**

5. A tennis ball machine throws 2 balls every 3 seconds. How many balls will the machine throw in 18 seconds? **12 balls**

Notetaking Guide
📄 **Transparency Available**

Promotes interactive learning and notetaking skills, pp. 66–69.

Pacing
Basic: 2 days
Average: 2 days
Advanced: 2 days
Block: 0.5 block with 3.6
0.5 block with 3.8
• See *Teaching Guide/Lesson Plan.*

2 FOCUS AND MOTIVATE

Essential Question
Big Idea 2, p. 131

How do you solve percent problems? Tell students they will learn how to answer this question by using proportions and the percent equation to find a percent or a part of a base.

NCTM STANDARDS
Standard 1: Understand numbers; Compute fluently

Resource Planning Guide

Chapter Resource Book
• Teaching Guide/Lesson Plan (pp. 70–71)
• Practice levels A, B, C (pp. 72–74)
• Study Guide (pp. 75–76)
• Catch-up for Absent Students (p. 77)
• Application (p. 78)
• Challenge (p. 79)

Workbooks
• Notetaking Guide (pp. 66–69)
• Practice Workbook (pp. 42–43)

Teaching Options
• **Power Presentations CD-ROM** provides dynamic electronic teaching resources for the classroom.
• **Activity Generator CD-ROM** provides editable activities for all ability levels.

Interactive Technology
• Easy Planner
• Power Presentations CD-ROM
• Activity Generator CD-ROM
• Animated Algebra
• Test Generator CD-ROM
• Online Quiz
• eWorkbook
• eEdition
• @HomeTutor

Resources for English Learners
• Quick Reference for English Learners
• Spanish Study Guide
• Multi-Language Visual Glossary
• Student Resources in Spanish

See also the *Algebra 1 Toolkit* for more strategies for meeting individual needs.

THE PERCENT EQUATION In Example 1, the proportion $\frac{a}{b} = \frac{p}{100}$ is used to find a percent. When you write $\frac{p}{100}$ as $p\%$ and solve for a, you get the equation $a = p\% \cdot b$.

KEY CONCEPT *For Your Notebook*

The Percent Equation

You can represent "a is p percent of b" using the equation

$$a = p\% \cdot b$$

where a is a part of the base b and $p\%$ is the percent.

EXAMPLE 2 Find a percent using the percent equation

What percent of 136 is 51?

DETERMINE THE BASE
When a problem talks about the percent *of* a number, the number is the base b, which is multiplied by the percent.

$a = p\% \cdot b$	Write percent equation.
$51 = p\% \cdot 136$	Substitute 51 for a and 136 for b.
$0.375 = p\%$	Divide each side by 136.
$37.5\% = p\%$	Write decimal as percent.

▶ 51 is 37.5% of 136.

CHECK Substitute 0.375 for $p\%$ in the original equation.

$51 = p\% \cdot 136$	Write original equation.
$51 \stackrel{?}{=} 0.375 \cdot 136$	Substitute 0.375 for $p\%$.
$51 = 51 \checkmark$	Multiply. Solution checks.

EXAMPLE 3 Find a part of a base using the percent equation

What number is 15% of 88?

$a = p\% \cdot b$	Write percent equation.
$= 15\% \cdot 88$	Substitute 15 for p and 88 for b.
$= 0.15 \cdot 88$	Write percent as decimal.
$= 13.2$	Multiply.

▶ 13.2 is 15% of 88.

 GUIDED PRACTICE for Examples 2 and 3

Use the percent equation to answer the question.

3. What percent of 56 is 49? **87.5%**
4. What percent of 55 is 11? **20%**
5. What number is 45% of 92? **41.4**
6. What number is 140% of 50? **70**

3.7 Solve Percent Problems **177**

Motivating the Lesson

Ask students to give examples of surveys they have participated in or surveys they have taken. After discussing real-world surveys, point out that a common theme of all of these surveys is determining some kind of percent. For example, what percent of respondents prefer to travel by bicycle? Ask students to give other examples of survey percents. Close the discussion by telling students that this lesson will prepare them for solving problems that involve percents.

❸ TEACH

Extra Example 1
What percent of 60 is 9? **15%**

An **Animated Algebra** activity is available on-line for **Example 1**. This activity is also available on the **Power Presentations CD-ROM**.

Extra Example 2
What percent of 20 is 13? **65%**

Key Questions to Ask for Example 2

- What is another way to write $p\%$? $\frac{p}{100}$, as in Example 1

- How would you write Example 2 as a proportion? $\frac{51}{136} = \frac{p}{100}$

- How do you know that 136 is the base, rather than 51? **136 follows the words "percent of".**

Extra Example 3
What number is 12% of 85? **10.2**

Extra Example 4
75 is 62.5% of what number? **120**

Differentiated Instruction

Visual Learners Remind students that "percent" means hundredths by writing familiar words like "centimeter" $\left(\frac{1}{100} \text{ of a meter}\right)$ and "centipede" (hundred legs). Circle the word stem "centi-" to emphasize hundred (the "cent" in percent). Also note the resemblance of the percent sign (%) to one of the symbols for division ($\div$) to remind students that percent means to divide, not multiply, by 100.

See also the *Algebra 1 Toolkit* for more strategies.

EXAMPLE 4 Find a base using the percent equation

20 is 12.5% of what number?

$a = p\% \cdot b$	Write percent equation.
$20 = 12.5\% \cdot b$	Substitute 20 for a and 12.5 for p.
$20 = 0.125 \cdot b$	Write percent as decimal.
$160 = b$	Divide each side by 0.125.

▶ 20 is 12.5% of 160.

EXAMPLE 5 Solve a real-world percent problem

SURVEY A survey asked 220 students to name their favorite pasta dish. Find the percent of students who chose the given pasta dish.

a. macaroni and cheese

b. lasagna

Type of Pasta	Students
Spaghetti	83
Lasagna	40
Macaroni and cheese	33
Fettucine alfredo	22
Baked ziti	16
Pasta primavera	15
Other	11

Solution

a. The survey results show that 33 of the 220 students chose macaroni and cheese.

$a = p\% \cdot b$	Write percent equation.
$33 = p\% \cdot 220$	Substitute 33 for a and 220 for b.
$0.15 = p\%$	Divide each side by 220.
$15\% = p\%$	Write decimal as percent.

▶ 15% of the students chose macaroni and cheese as their favorite dish.

b. The survey results show that 40 of the 220 students chose lasagna.

$a = p\% \cdot b$	Write percent equation.
$40 = p\% \cdot 220$	Substitute 40 for a and 220 for b.
$0.18 \approx p\%$	Divide each side by 220.
$18\% \approx p\%$	Write decimal as percent.

▶ About 18% of the students chose lasagna as their favorite dish.

✓ **GUIDED PRACTICE**   for Examples 4 and 5

In Exercises 7 and 8, use the percent equation to answer the question.

7. 65 is 62.5% of what number? **104**   8. 50 is 125% of what number? **40**

9. In Example 5, what percent of students chose fettucine alfredo? **10%**

CONCEPT SUMMARY
For Your Notebook

Types of Percent Problems

Percent problem	Example	Equation
Find a percent.	What percent of 136 is 51?	$51 = p\% \cdot 136$
Find part of a base.	What number is 15% of 88?	$a = 15\% \cdot 88$
Find a base.	20 is 12.5% of what number?	$20 = 12.5\% \cdot b$

3.7 EXERCISES

HOMEWORK KEY
○ = **WORKED-OUT SOLUTIONS**
on p. WS1 for Exs. 13 and 35

★ = **STANDARDIZED TEST PRACTICE**
Exs. 2, 19, 30, 31, 38, and 39

SKILL PRACTICE

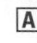 **A**

1. **VOCABULARY** Identify the percent, the base, and the part of the base in the following statement: 54 is 15% of 360. **percent: 15, base: 360, part: 54**

2. ★ **WRITING** Rewrite the statement "28 is 35% of 80" in the form $\frac{a}{b} = \frac{p}{100}$. *Explain* how you identified the values of *a*, *b*, and *p*. $\frac{28}{80} = \frac{35}{100}$; **the statement identifies 28 as part of 80 so 28 is the part, *a*, and 80 is the base, *b*; 35 is *p* because it is a percent.**

USING PROPORTIONS Use a proportion to answer the question.

EXAMPLE 1
on p. 176
for Exs. 3–8

3. What percent of 75 is 27? **36%**
4. What percent of 120 is 66? **55%**
5. What number is 35% of 80? **28**
6. What number is 60% of 85? **51**
7. 81 is 54% of what number? **150**
8. 42 is 200% of what number? **21**

USING THE PERCENT EQUATION Use the percent equation to answer the question.

EXAMPLES 2, 3, and 4
on pp. 177–178
for Exs. 9–21

9. What percent of 80 is 56? **70%**
10. What percent of 225 is 99? **44%**
11. What percent of 153 is 9.18? **6%**
12. What number is 18% of 150? **27**
13. What number is 115% of 60? **69**
14. What number is 82% of 215? **176.3**
15. 7 is 28% of what number? **25**
16. 189 is 90% of what number? **210**
17. 41.8 is 44% of what number? **95**
18. 71.5 is 52% of what number? **137.5**

19. ★ **MULTIPLE CHOICE** What number is 87.5% of 512? **B**

   (A) 5.85   (B) 448   (C) 585   (D) 4480

ERROR ANALYSIS *Describe* and correct the error in answering the question.

20. What percent of 95 is 19? **$p\%$ should be multiplied by 95; $19 = p\% \cdot 95$, $p\% = 20\%$.**

$$95 = p\% \cdot 19$$
$$5 = p\%$$
$$500\% = p\%$$

21. 153 is 76.5% of what number? **76.5% needs to be changed to 0.765; $153 = 0.765 \cdot b$, $b = 200$.**

$$153 = 76.5\% \cdot b$$
$$153 = 76.5 \cdot b$$
$$2 = b$$

3.7 Solve Percent Problems   **179**

④ **PRACTICE AND APPLY**

Assignment Guide
📖 **Answer Transparencies** available for all exercises

Basic:
Day 1: SRH p. 917 Exs. 11–17 odd
pp. 179–181
Exs. 1–14, 22, 23, 47–52
Day 2: pp. 179–181
Exs. 15–21, 24, 25, 33–37, 41–46

Average:
Day 1: pp. 179–181
Exs. 1, 2, 3–13 odd, 22, 23, 26–29, 47–52
Day 2: pp. 179–181
Exs. 16, 19–21, 24, 25, 30, 31, 35–39, 41–46

Advanced:
Day 1: pp. 179–181
Exs. 1, 6–8, 12–14, 22, 23, 26–29
Day 2: pp. 179–181
Exs. 17–19, 24, 25, 30–32*, 35–40*, 42, 46

Block:
pp. 179–181
Exs. 1, 2, 3–13 odd, 22, 23, 26–29, 47–52 (with 3.6)
pp. 179–181
Exs. 16, 19–21, 24, 25, 30, 31, 35–39, 41–46 (with 3.8)

Differentiated Instruction
See *Algebra 1 Best Practices Toolkit* for suggestions on addressing the needs of a diverse classroom.

Homework Check
For a quick check of student understanding of key concepts, go over the following exercises:
Basic: 5, 10, 13, 16, 33
Average: 7, 11, 13, 17, 34
Advanced: 8, 11, 14, 18, 35

Extra Practice
• Student Edition, p. 940
• Chapter 3 Resource Book:
  Practice levels A, B, C, pp. 72–74

Practice Worksheet

An easily-readable reduced practice page (with answers) for this lesson can be found on p. 130C.

Avoiding Common Errors

Exercises 3–18 To avoid confusing the base and part of a base, suggest that students reread the note "determine the base" for Example 2 on page 177 on how to determine a base. Students can write this information on a 3 × 5 card to use until they become proficient in distinguishing between a base and a part of a base.

Exercise 35 Caution students that errors can occur when many categories and percents are used in a problem. Urge them to double check that they used the correct category and the correct percent when solving parts (a) and (b).

Exercise 36 You may want to suggest that students identify the base and the part of a base for years 2001 and 2002.

Teaching Strategy

Exercises 8, 13 Both of these exercises require using percents greater than 1. You may want to review how to write such percents before students begin these exercises. Point out that in Exercise 8, the base will be less than 42 since 42 is 200% of a number, and that in Exercise 13, a part of the base will be greater than 60 since it is 115% of 60. In Exercise 8, some students may recognize that 200% of a number is twice the number, and use the fact that 42 is twice 21.

Study Strategy

Exercise 19 Point out that students can eliminate two choices because the exercise asks for a part of the base, which in this exercise must be less than the base 512.

Reading Strategy

Exercises 22–25 For students who ask for help on these problems, point out that the direction line gives them the value for *n*, and they need to solve for *n* before solving the percent problem.

B **SOLVING PERCENT PROBLEMS** Answer the question when $n = 25$.

22. What percent of 140 is $(n + 94)$? **85%** 23. What percent of $(4n)$ is 96? **96%**

24. What number is 52% of $(2n + 15)$? **33.8** 25. 25.5 is $(n - 8)$% of what number? **150**

SOLVING PERCENT PROBLEMS Find the percent. Round your answer to the nearest whole percent, if necessary.

26. $3.00 tip for a $18.70 taxi fare **16%** 27. $1.44 tax on an item priced at $24.00 **6%**

28. 90 rock CDs out of 125 CDs **72%** 29. 241 freshmen out of 804 students **30%**

30. ★ **WRITING** Would you use a proportion or the percent equation to solve the following problem: What number is 25% of 600? *Explain.* *Sample answer:* **Percent equation; you just need to multiply the percent by the base to find the part.**

31. ★ **SHORT RESPONSE** The side length of a square is 40% of the side length of another square. Is the area of the smaller square 40% of the area of the larger square? *Explain.* **No.** *Sample answer:* **The area of the smaller square would be 16% of the area of the larger square because the percent needs to be squared.**

C 32. **CHALLENGE** Let *y* be 10% of a number. What is 50% of the number? Write your answer in terms of *y*. **5y**

PROBLEM SOLVING

EXAMPLE 5 A
on p. 178
for Exs. 33–36

33. **SCHOOL TRANSPORTATION** In a school transportation survey of 225 students, 18 of the students surveyed said that they walk to school. What percent of the students surveyed walk to school? **8%**

@HomeTutor for problem solving help at classzone.com

34. **DAYTONA 500** After completing 10 laps in the Daytona 500, a driver has completed 5% of the race. How many laps does the race have? **200 laps**

@HomeTutor for problem solving help at classzone.com

REVIEW CIRCLE GRAPHS
For help with using a circle graph, see p. 935.

35. **MUSIC** The circle graph shows the results of a radio survey in which 250 listeners were asked to rate a song.

a. How many of the listeners who participated in the survey are "tired of" the song? **90 listeners**

b. How many of the listeners who participated in the survey "love" the song? **35 listeners**

Radio Survey

Tired of 36%
Like 26%
Love 14%
Dislike 13%
Not familiar with 11%

36. **HIKING** The table gives data about the number of people who started hiking the Appalachian Trail in Georgia and the number of those people who completed the trail in Maine. Copy and complete the table.

Year	Hikers who started	Hikers who completed	Percent completion
2001	2380	**? 395**	16.6%
2002	**? 1880**	376	20%
2003	1750	352	**? 20%**

○ = **WORKED-OUT SOLUTIONS** on p. WS1

★ = **STANDARDIZED TEST PRACTICE**

B **37. ART** The Louvre Museum, which is an art museum in France, has virtual tours of its exhibits on its website. The website can be viewed in four different languages. The table shows the number of hits received by each version of the website during one day. Find the percent of hits for each version of the website. **59.3%; 16.5%; 13.2%; 11%**

Version	English	French	Spanish	Japanese
Number of hits	4860	1350	1080	900

38. ★ OPEN-ENDED Write a real-world percent problem that can be solved using the proportion $\frac{x}{75} = \frac{15}{100}$. Then find the value of x and explain what the solution means in this situation. *Sample answer:* **You want to leave a 15% tip at a restaurant. If the bill came to $75, what tip should you leave? $x = 11.25$; you should leave $11.25 for a tip.**

39. ★ EXTENDED RESPONSE Two different stores are selling a bicycle that you want to buy.

   a. Solve At one store, the bicycle is on sale for 20% off the original price of $240. How much money will you save by purchasing the bicycle on sale at this store? **$48**

   b. Solve At the other store, the bicycle is on sale for 25% off the original price of $265. How much money will you save by purchasing the bicycle on sale at this store? **$66.25**

   c. Compare Which bicycle should you buy? *Explain.* **The bicycle in part (a); it will cost $192, the bicycle in part (b) will cost $198.75.**

C **40. CHALLENGE** Julia deposits 20% of her paycheck in her savings account. Then she deposits 60% of the remaining money in her checking account. She deposits $108.24 in her checking account. How much money did she deposit in her savings account? **$45.10**

MIXED REVIEW

PREVIEW
Prepare for Lesson 3.8 in Exs. 41–46.

Find the area of the triangle or rectangle. *(p. 924)*

41. 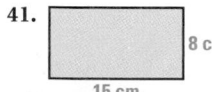 **120 cm²**

8 cm
15 cm

42. **143 in.²**

13 in.
22 in.

Make a table for the function. Identify the range of the function. *(p. 35)*
43–46. See margin for tables.

43. $y = x - 7$
Domain: −5, −2, 1, 4 **−12, −9, −6, −3**

44. $y = x + 4$
Domain: −6, −4, −2, 0 **−2, 0, 2, 4**

45. $y = 6x + 3$
Domain: −1, 1, 3, 5 **−3, 9, 21, 33**

46. $y = 5x - 5$
Domain: −2, −1, 0, 1 **−15, −10, −5, 0**

Find the sum or difference.

47. $-65 + (-27)$ *(p. 74)* **−92**

48. $33 + (-58)$ *(p. 74)* **−25**

49. $-43.9 + 89.4$ *(p. 74)* **45.5**

50. $91.2 - (-20.3)$ *(p. 80)* **111.5**

51. $-13 - 78$ *(p. 80)* **−91**

52. $28 - (-35)$ *(p. 80)* **63**

EXTRA PRACTICE for Lesson 3.7, p. 940   **ONLINE QUIZ** at classzone.com   181

Daily Homework Quiz

 Transparency Available

Solve the percent problem.

1. What percent of 50 is 1? **2%**

2. What percent of 128 is 48? **37.5%**

3. What number is 16% of 45? **7.2**

4. 12 is 12.5% of what number? **96**

5. Leonard has read 1001 pages out of 1456 of Tolstoy's *War and Peace*. What percent of the novel has he read? **68.75%**

⊘ Online Quiz

Available at **classzone.com**

Diagnosis/Remediation

- Practice A, B, C in Chapter 3 Resource Book, pp. 72–74
- Study Guide in Chapter 3 Resource Book, pp. 75–76
- Practice Workbook, pp. 42–43
- @HomeTutor

Challenge

Additional challenge is available in the Chapter 3 Resource Book, p. 79.

43.

x	y
−5	−12
−2	−9
1	−6
4	−3

44.

x	y
−6	−2
−4	0
−2	2
0	4

45.

x	y
−1	−3
1	9
3	21
5	33

46.

x	y
−2	−15
−1	10
0	−5
1	0

Find Percent of Change

Key Vocabulary
• percent of change
• percent of increase
• percent of decrease

GOAL Solve percent of change problems.

A **percent of change** indicates how much a quantity increases or decreases with respect to the original amount. If the new amount is greater than the original amount, the percent of change is called a **percent of increase**. If the new amount is less than the original amount, the percent of change is called a **percent of decrease**.

KEY CONCEPT   *For Your Notebook*

Percent of Change

The percent of change is the ratio of the amount of increase or decrease to the original amount.

$$\text{Percent of change, } p\% = \frac{\text{Amount of increase or decrease}}{\text{Original amount}}$$

The amount of increase is the new amount minus the original amount. The amount of decrease is the original amount minus the new amount.

EXAMPLE 1 **Find a percent of change**

Identify the percent of change as an *increase* or *decrease*. Then find the percent of change.

a. Original: 140
   New: 189

b. Original: 70
   New: 59.5

Solution

a. Because the new amount is greater than the original amount, the percent of change is an increase.

$$p\% = \frac{\text{Amount of increase}}{\text{Original amount}}$$

$$= \frac{189 - 140}{140}$$

$$= \frac{49}{140}$$

$$= 0.35$$

$$= 35\%$$

▸ The percent of increase is 35%.

b. Because the new amount is less than the original amount, the percent of change is a decrease.

$$p\% = \frac{\text{Amount of decrease}}{\text{Original amount}}$$

$$= \frac{70 - 59.5}{70}$$

$$= \frac{10.5}{70}$$

$$= 0.15$$

$$= 15\%$$

▸ The percent of decrease is 15%.

CHECK REASONABLENESS
Because 50 is one third (about 33%) of 150, it is reasonable that 49 is 35% of 140.

FINDING A NEW AMOUNT If you know the original amount and the percent of change, you can find the new amount.

- For a $p\%$ increase, multiply the original amount by $(100\% + p\%)$.
- For a $p\%$ decrease, multiply the original amount by $(100\% - p\%)$.

EXAMPLE 2 Find a new amount

SHOPPING Find the sale price of the pair of jeans described in the table.

Original price	$48.00
Discount	40%
Sale price	?

Solution

The sale price is a decrease from the original price, so multiply the original price by $(100\% - p\%)$.

$$\text{Sale price} = \textbf{Original price} \cdot (100\% - p\%)$$
$$= \textbf{48} \cdot (100\% - \textbf{40}\%) \quad \text{Substitute.}$$
$$= 48 \cdot 0.6 \quad\quad\quad \text{Subtract percents. Then write as a decimal.}$$
$$= 28.8 \quad\quad\quad\quad \text{Multiply.}$$

▶ The sale price of the pair of jeans is $28.80.

ANOTHER WAY
You can also find the sale price by first finding the change in price:
$$0.4 \cdot 48 = 19.2.$$
Then subtract the change in price from the original price:
$$\$48.00 - \$19.20 = \$28.80.$$

PRACTICE

EXAMPLE 1
on p. 182
for Exs. 1–6

Identify the percent of change as an *increase* or *decrease*. Then find the percent of change.

1. Original: 16 **increase; 25%**
   New: 20

2. Original: 35 **increase; 40%**
   New: 49

3. Original: 80 **decrease; 45%**
   New: 44

4. Original: 120 **decrease; 35%**
   New: 78

5. Original: 360 **decrease; 33%**
   New: 241.2

6. Original: 170 **increase; 67%**
   New: 283.9

EXAMPLE 2
on p. 183
for Exs. 7–14

Find the new amount.

7. Increase 14 by 45%. **20.3**

8. Increase 78 by 80%. **140.4**

9. Decrease 44 by 20%. **35.2**

10. Decrease 108 by 90%. **10.8**

11. **SUBWAY** The price for a token to ride a city's subway system is changing from $1.25 to $1.50. Find the percent of change. **20% increase**

12. **DVDS** The average price of a new DVD in 1998 was $24. In 2003, the average price was $21.12. Find the percent of change. **12% decrease**

13. **POPULATION** In Arizona, the population increased by 48.6% from 1990 to 2002. Use the information in the table to find the population density in Arizona in 2002. **48.0 people per square mile**

14. **DEPRECIATION** A new car is valued at $14,500. In one year, the car's value will depreciate, or decrease, by 15%. Find the value of the car after one year. **$12,325**

Year	Population density
1990	32.3 people per square mile
2002	?

Extension: Find Percent of Change **183**

Before You wrote functions and used formulas.

Now You will rewrite equations and formulas.

Why? So you can solve a problem about bowling, as in Ex. 33.

1 PLAN AND PREPARE

Warm-Up Exercises

📄 Transparency Available

1. Write an equation for "3 more than twice *a* is 24." $2a + 3 = 24$

2. A square has a side length of 8 feet. Find the area of the square using the formula $A = s^2$. **64 ft²**

3. A rectangular serving tray is 26 inches long and 18 inches wide. What is the tray's serving area? **468 in.²**

Notetaking Guide

📄 Transparency Available

Promotes interactive learning and notetaking skills, pp. 70–71.

Pacing

Basic: 1 day
Average: 1 day
Advanced: 1 day
Block: 0.5 block with 3.7
• See *Teaching Guide/Lesson Plan.*

2 FOCUS AND MOTIVATE

Essential Question

Big Idea 3, p. 131

How do you rewrite equations? Tell students they will learn how to answer this question by rewriting equations and formulas with two or more variables so that any given variable is a function of the other variables.

NCTM STANDARDS

Standard 2: Represent situations using algebraic symbols; Analyze situations using algebraic symbols

Key Vocabulary
• literal equation
• formula, *p. 30*

The equations $2x + 5 = 11$ and $6x + 3 = 15$ have the general form $ax + b = c$. The equation $ax + b = c$ is called a **literal equation** because the coefficients and constants have been replaced by letters. When you solve a literal equation, you can use the result to solve any equation that has the same form as the literal equation.

EXAMPLE 1 Solve a literal equation

Solve $ax + b = c$ for x. Then use the solution to solve $2x + 5 = 11$.

Solution

STEP 1 Solve $ax + b = c$ for x.

$$ax + b = c \qquad \text{Write original equation.}$$

$$ax = c - b \qquad \text{Subtract } b \text{ from each side.}$$

$$x = \frac{c - b}{a} \qquad \text{Assume } a \neq 0. \text{ Divide each side by } a.$$

STEP 2 Use the solution to solve $2x + 5 = 11$.

$$x = \frac{c - b}{a} \qquad \text{Solution of literal equation}$$

$$= \frac{11 - 5}{2} \qquad \text{Substitute 2 for } a, 5 \text{ for } b, \text{ and 11 for } c.$$

$$= 3 \qquad \text{Simplify.}$$

▶ The solution of $2x + 5 = 11$ is 3.

VARIABLES IN DENOMINATORS In Example 1, you must assume that $a \neq 0$ in order to divide by a. In general, if you have to divide by a variable when solving a literal equation, you should assume that the variable does not equal 0.

 GUIDED PRACTICE for Example 1

Solve the literal equation for x. Then use the solution to solve the specific equation.

1. $a - bx = c$; $12 - 5x = -3$ $\quad x = \frac{a - c}{b}$; **3**

2. $ax = bx + c$; $11x = 6x + 20$ $\quad x = \frac{c}{a - b}$; **4**

Resource Planning Guide

Chapter Resource Book
• Teaching Guide/Lesson Plan (pp. 80–81)
• Practice levels A, B, C (pp. 82–84)
• Study Guide (pp. 85–86)
• Catch-up for Absent Students (p. 87)
• Problem Solving Workshop (p. 88)
• Challenge (p. 89)

Workbooks
• Notetaking Guide (pp. 70–71)
• Practice Workbook (pp. 44–45)

Teaching Options
• **Power Presentations CD-ROM** provides dynamic electronic teaching resources for the classroom.
• **Activity Generator CD-ROM** provides editable activities for all ability levels.

Interactive Technology
• Easy Planner
• Power Presentations CD-ROM
• Activity Generator CD-ROM
• Animated Algebra
• Test Generator CD-ROM
• Online Quiz
• eWorkbook
• eEdition
• @HomeTutor

Resources for English Learners
• Quick Reference for English Learners
• Spanish Study Guide
• Multi-Language Visual Glossary
• Student Resources in Spanish

See also the *Algebra 1 Toolkit* for more strategies for meeting individual needs.

TWO OR MORE VARIABLES An equation in two variables, such as $3x + 2y = 8$, or a formula in two or more variables, such as $A = \frac{1}{2}bh$, can be rewritten so that one variable is a function of the other variable(s).

EXAMPLE 2 Rewrite an equation

Write $3x + 2y = 8$ so that y is a function of x.

$3x + 2y = 8$	Write original equation.
$2y = 8 - 3x$	Subtract $3x$ from each side.
$y = 4 - \frac{3}{2}x$	Divide each side by 2.

EXAMPLE 3 Solve and use a geometric formula

The area A of a triangle is given by the formula $A = \frac{1}{2}bh$ where b is the base and h is the height.

a. Solve the formula for the height h.

b. Use the rewritten formula to find the height of the triangle shown, which has an area of 64.4 square meters.

14 m

Solution

a.

$A = \frac{1}{2}bh$	Write original formula.
$2A = bh$	Multiply each side by 2.
$\frac{2A}{b} = h$	Divide each side by b.

b. Substitute 64.4 for A and 14 for b in the rewritten formula.

USE UNIT ANALYSIS
When area is measured in square meters and the base is measured in meters, dividing twice the area by the base gives a result measured in meters.

$h = \frac{2A}{b}$	Write rewritten formula.
$ = \frac{2(64.4)}{14}$	Substitute 64.4 for A and 14 for b.
$ = 9.2$	Simplify.

▶ The height of the triangle is 9.2 meters.

*Animated*Algebra at classzone.com

✓ **GUIDED PRACTICE** for Examples 2 and 3

3. Write $5x + 4y = 20$ so that y is a function of x. $y = 5 - \frac{5}{4}x$

4a. $w = \dfrac{P - 2\ell}{2}$ or $w = \dfrac{P}{2} - \ell$

4. The perimeter P of a rectangle is given by the formula $P = 2\ell + 2w$ where ℓ is the length and w is the width.

a. Solve the formula for the width w.

b. Use the rewritten formula to find the width of the rectangle shown. **2.4 ft**

$P = 19.2$ ft w

7.2 ft

3.8 Rewrite Equations and Formulas   **185**

Motivating the Lesson
Tell students that in this lesson they will learn how to rewrite formulas to isolate different variables. Explain that often it is easier to solve a problem if they isolate a variable before they substitute numbers for the other variables. As an example, suppose they want to find how long it will take to drive to the beach. Instead of substituting values for the formula $d = rt$ and then isolating the variable t, they can isolate t as $t = \frac{d}{r}$ and then substitute values for d and r.

❸ TEACH

Extra Example 1
Solve $p + qx = r$ for x. Then use the solution to solve $3 + 5x = -7$.
$x = \frac{r - p}{q}; -2$

Key Question to Ask for Example 1
• How would you solve $2x + 5 = 11$ directly? **Subtract 5 from both sides and then divide by 2.**

Extra Example 2
Write $-2x + 3y = 6$ so that y is a function of x. $y = \frac{2}{3}x + 2$

Extra Example 3
The area for a rectangle is given by the formula $A = \ell w$, where ℓ is the length and w is the width.
a. Solve the formula for the length ℓ.
$\ell = \frac{A}{w}$
b. Use the rewritten formula to find the length of this rectangle.

$A = 351$ cm^2 13 cm

27 cm

Extra Example 4

Irina deposited $650 in a savings account. After two years her account balance was $682.50. Find the rate of interest for the two years. Use the formula $A = P(1 + rt)$, where A is the account balance, P is principal, r is rate, and t is time. Rewrite the formula to isolate r and then solve.

$r = \dfrac{A - P}{Pt}$; $r = 0.025$ or 2.5%

Key Question to Ask for Example 4

• Do you have to rewrite the formula to find the low temperatures in degrees Fahrenheit? Explain. **No, you can use the given formula but the calculations are easier if you solve the given formula for F before you substitute 14°C or 10°C.**

Closing the Lesson

Have students summarize the major points of the lesson and answer the Essential Question: How do you rewrite equations?

• **In a literal equation, coefficients and constants have been replaced by letters. You can solve a literal equation for any variable.**

• **Use inverse operations when solving a formula or equation for a given variable.**

To rewrite an equation so that y is a function of x, rewrite the equation so that y is isolated on one side of the equation. For all literal equations, solve for the given variable by using properties of equality and inverse operations.

EXAMPLE 4 Solve a multi-step problem

TEMPERATURE You are visiting Toronto, Canada, over the weekend. A website gives the forecast shown. Find the low temperatures for Saturday and Sunday in degrees Fahrenheit. Use the formula $C = \frac{5}{9}(F - 32)$ where C is the temperature in degrees Celsius and F is the temperature in degrees Fahrenheit.

3 Day Forecast for Toronto		
Friday	**Saturday**	**Sunday**
Sunny High 21°C Low 13°C	Sunny High 22°C Low 14°C	Partly Cloudy High 16°C Low 10°C

REWRITE FORMULAS
When using a formula for multiple calculations, you may find it easier to rewrite the formula first.

Solution

 STEP 1 **Rewrite** the formula. In the problem, degrees Celsius are given and degrees Fahrenheit need to be calculated. The calculations will be easier if the formula is written so that F is a function of C.

$$C = \frac{5}{9}(F - 32) \qquad \text{Write original formula.}$$

$$\frac{9}{5} \cdot C = \frac{9}{5} \cdot \frac{5}{9}(F - 32) \qquad \text{Multiply each side by } \frac{9}{5}, \text{ the reciprocal of } \frac{5}{9}.$$

$$\frac{9}{5}C = F - 32 \qquad \text{Simplify.}$$

$$\frac{9}{5}C + 32 = F \qquad \text{Add 32 to each side.}$$

▶ The rewritten formula is $F = \frac{9}{5}C + 32$.

STEP 2 **Find** the low temperatures for Saturday and Sunday in degrees Fahrenheit.

Saturday (low of 14°C)

$$F = \frac{9}{5}C + 32$$

$$= \frac{9}{5}(14) + 32$$

$$= 25.2 + 32$$

$$= 57.2$$

▶ The low for Saturday is 57.2°F.

Sunday (low of 10°C)

$$F = \frac{9}{5}C + 32$$

$$= \frac{9}{5}(10) + 32$$

$$= 18 + 32$$

$$= 50$$

▶ The low for Sunday is 50°F.

✓ **GUIDED PRACTICE** for Example 4

5. Use the information in Example 4 to find the high temperatures for Saturday and Sunday in degrees Fahrenheit. **71.6°F, 60.8°F**

3.8 EXERCISES

SKILL PRACTICE

A 1. **VOCABULARY** Copy and complete: When you write the equation
$3x + 2 = 8$ as $ax + b = c$, the equation $ax + b = c$ is called a(n) __?__
because the coefficients and constants have been replaced by letters. **literal equation**

2. ★ **WRITING** Describe the steps you would take to solve $I = prt$ for t.
Divide each side by pr to get $\frac{I}{pr} = t$.

LITERAL EQUATIONS Solve the literal equation for x. Then use the solution
to solve the specific equation.

3. $ax = bx - c$; $8x = 3x - 10$ $x = \frac{c}{b-a}$; -2 4. $a(x + b) = c$; $2(x + 1) = 9$ $x = \frac{c}{a} - b$; 3.5

5. $c = \frac{x+a}{b}$; $2 = \frac{x+5}{7}$ $x = bc - a$; 9 6. $\frac{x}{a} = \frac{b}{c}$; $\frac{x}{8} = \frac{4.5}{12}$ $x = \frac{ab}{c}$; 3

7. $\frac{x}{a} + b = c$; $\frac{x}{4} + 6 = 13$ $x = a(c - b)$; 28 8. $ax + b = cx - d$; $2x + 9 = 7x - 1$
$x = \frac{b+d}{c-a}$; 2

9. *b* should have been subtracted from both sides, not added; $ax = -b$, $x = \frac{-b}{a}$.

ERROR ANALYSIS Describe and correct the error in solving the equation for x.

9.
$$ax + b = 0$$
$$ax = b$$
$$x = \frac{b}{a}$$ ✗

10. Both sides should have been divided by $(a - b)$, not multiplied; $x = \frac{c}{a-b}$.

10.
$$c = ax - bx$$
$$c = (a - b)x$$
$$c(a - b) = x$$ ✗

REWRITING EQUATIONS Write the equation so that y is a function of x.

11. $2x + y = 7$ $y = 7 - 2x$ 12. $5x + 4y = 10$ $y = \frac{5}{2} - \frac{5}{4}x$ 13. $12 = 9x + 3y$ $4 - 3x = y$

14. $18x - 2y = 26$ $y = -13 + 9x$ 15. $14 = 7y - 6x$ $2 + \frac{6}{7}x = y$ 16. $8x - 8y = 5$ $y = x - \frac{5}{8}$

17. $30 = 9x - 5y$ $\frac{9}{5}x - 6 = y$ 18. $3 + 6x = 11 - 4y$ $2 - \frac{3}{2}x = y$ 19. $2 + 6y = 3x + 4$ $y = \frac{1}{2}x + \frac{1}{3}$

REWRITING FORMULAS Solve the formula for the indicated variable.

20. Volume of a rectangular prism: $V = \ell wh$. Solve for w. $w = \frac{V}{\ell h}$

21. Surface area of a prism: $S = 2B + Ph$. Solve for h. $h = \frac{S - 2B}{P}$

22. Length of movie projected at 24 frames per second: $\ell = 24f$. Solve for f. $f = \frac{\ell}{24}$

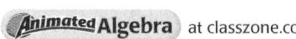 **Animated Algebra** at classzone.com

23. ★ **MULTIPLE CHOICE** The formula for the area of a trapezoid is
$A = \frac{1}{2}(b_1 + b_2)h$. Which equation is *not* equivalent to the formula? **C**

Ⓐ $h = \frac{2A}{b_1 + b_2}$ Ⓑ $b_1 = \frac{2A}{h} - b_2$ Ⓒ $b_2 = \frac{2A}{b_1} - h$ Ⓓ $b_2 = \frac{2A}{h} - b_1$

B **REWRITING EQUATIONS** Write the equation so that y is a function of x.
$y = 2.1x - 8.4$ $y = 18 - 5x$ $y = -\frac{1}{2}x + \frac{5}{2}$
24. $4.2x - 2y = 16.8$ 25. $9 - 0.5y = 2.5x$ 26. $8x - 5x + 21 = 36 - 6y$

Differentiated Instruction

Auditory Learners While working on **Exercises 20–23**, students may benefit from reading the formulas aloud, including their meaning, in order to solve for a given variable. For example, in **Exercise 21**, students could read "Surface area is equal to twice the base area plus the product of the perimeter and the height" instead of just reading the formula as "S equals $2B$ plus Ph."

See also the *Algebra 1 Toolkit* for more strategies.

---

④ PRACTICE AND APPLY

Assignment Guide

📑 Answer Transparencies available for all exercises

Basic:
Day 1: pp. 187–189
Exs. 1–10, 11–19 odd, 20–25, 32–35, 38–45

Average:
Day 1: pp. 187–189
Exs. 1, 2, 4, 6, 8–10, 12–18 even, 20–30, 32–36, 38–45

Advanced:
Day 1: pp. 187–189
Exs. 1, 7, 8, 16–31*, 34–37*, 38–44 even

Block:
pp. 187–189
Exs. 1, 2, 4, 6, 8–10, 12–18 even, 20–30, 32–36, 38–45 (with 3.7)

Differentiated Instruction

See *Algebra 1 Best Practices Toolkit* for suggestions on addressing the needs of a diverse classroom.

Homework Check

For a quick check of student understanding of key concepts, go over the following exercises:

Basic: 3, 6, 13, 20, 32
Average: 6, 16, 21, 24, 33
Advanced: 8, 18, 22, 26, 34

Extra Practice

• Student Edition, p. 940
• Chapter 3 Resource Book:
Practice levels A, B, C, pp. 82–84

Practice Worksheet

An easily-readable reduced practice page (with answers) for this lesson can be found on p. 130C.

27. Surface area of a cone:
$S = \pi r l + \pi r^2$.
Solve for l. Find l when
$S = 283$ cm^2 and $r = 5$ cm.
$l = \dfrac{S}{\pi r} - r$; **13.03 cm**

28. Area of a circular ring:
$A = 4\pi p w$.
Solve for p. Find p when
$A = 905$ ft^2 and $w = 9$ ft.
$p = \dfrac{A}{4\pi w}$; **8.01 ft**

29. ★ **OPEN-ENDED** *Describe* a real-world situation where you would want to solve the distance traveled formula $d = rt$ for t. *Sample answer:* **You want to find how long it will take to drive 150 miles if you drive at an average rate of 55 miles per hour.**

C **CHALLENGE** Solve the literal equation for a.

30. $x = \dfrac{a + b + c}{ab}$ $a = \dfrac{b + c}{bx - 1}$

31. $y = x\left(\dfrac{ab}{a - b}\right)$ $a = \dfrac{by}{y - bx}$

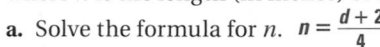
PROBLEM SOLVING

EXAMPLE 4 A
on p. 186
for Exs. 32–34

32. CARPENTRY The penny size d of a nail is given by $d = 4n - 2$ where n is the length (in inches) of the nail.

a. Solve the formula for n. $n = \dfrac{d + 2}{4}$

b. Use the new formula to find the lengths of nails with the following penny sizes: 5, 12, 16, and 20. **1.75 in., 3.5 in., 4.5 in., 5.5 in.**

@HomeTutor for problem solving help at classzone.com

33. BOWLING To participate in a bowling league, you pay a $25 sign-up fee and $12 for each league night that you bowl. So, the total cost C (in dollars) is given by the equation $C = 12x + 25$ where x is the number of league nights you bowled.

a. Solve the equation for x. $x = \dfrac{C - 25}{12}$

b. How many league nights have you bowled if you spent a total of $145? $181? $205? **10 league nights; 13 league nights; 15 league nights**

@HomeTutor for problem solving help at classzone.com

34. ◆ **MULTIPLE REPRESENTATIONS** An athletic facility is building an indoor track like the one shown. The perimeter P (in feet) of the track is given by $P = 2\pi r + 2x$.

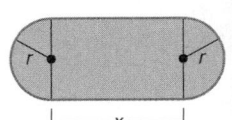

a. Writing an Equation Solve the formula for x. $x = \dfrac{P - 2\pi r}{2}$

b. Making a Table The perimeter of the track will be 660 feet. Use the rewritten formula to make a table that shows values of x to the nearest foot when r is 50 feet, 51 feet, 52 feet, and 53 feet. (Use 3.14 for π.) **See margin.**

c. Drawing a Graph Plot the ordered pairs from your table. Look for a pattern in the points. Use the pattern to find x when r is 54 feet.
See margin for art; 160.44 ft.

B **35.** ★ **WRITING** You work as a server at a restaurant. During your shift, you keep track of the bills that you give the tables you serve and the tips you receive from the tables. You want to calculate the tip received from each table as a percent of the bill. *Explain* how to rewrite the percent equation to make it easier to calculate the percent tip from each table.

Divide each side by the total bill, b, to get $\dfrac{a}{b} = p\%$.

36. ★ **EXTENDED RESPONSE** One type of stone formation found in Carlsbad Caverns in New Mexico is called a column. This cylindrical stone formation is connected to the ceiling and the floor of a cave.

  a. Rewrite the formula for the circumference of a circle, $C = 2\pi r$, so that you can easily calculate the radius of a column given its circumference. $r = \dfrac{C}{2\pi}$

36b. 1.1 ft; 1.3 ft; 1.4 ft

  b. What is the radius, to the nearest tenth of a foot, of a column that has a circumference of 7 feet? 8 feet? 9 feet? (Use 3.14 for π.)

  c. *Explain* how you can find the *area* of a cross section of a column if you know its circumference. **Solve for r using $\dfrac{C}{2\pi} = r$, then substitute r into the equation $A = \pi r^2$.**

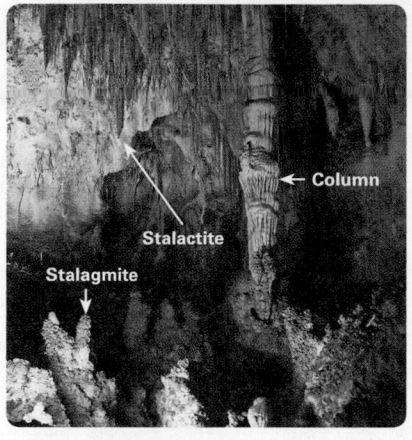
← Column

Stalactite

Stalagmite

C **37. CHALLENGE** The distance d (in miles) traveled by a car is given by $d = 55t$ where t is the time (in hours) the car has traveled. The distance d (in miles) traveled is also given by $d = 20g$ where g is the number of gallons of gasoline used by the car. Write an equation that expresses g as a function of t. $g = \dfrac{11t}{4}$

MIXED REVIEW

PREVIEW
Prepare for
Lesson 4.1 in
Exs. 38–39.

Graph the function. *(p. 43)* **38, 39. See margin.**

38. $y = x + 4$; domain: 0, 2, 4, 6, and 8   **39.** $y = 2x - 1$; domain: 1, 2, 3, 4, and 5

Use the distributive property to write an equivalent expression. *(p. 96)*

40. $3(2x + 3)$ **$6x + 9$**   **41.** $-2(x + 5)$ **$-2x - 10$**   **42.** $(3x - 5)(-5)$ **$-15x + 25$**   **43.** $(7x + 6)2$ **$14x + 12$**

Use the percent equation to answer the question. *(p. 176)*

44. What percent of 80 is 64? **80%**   **45.** What number is 95% of 120? **114**

QUIZ *for Lessons 3.7–3.8*

Use the percent equation to answer the question. *(p. 176)*

  1. What percent of 150 is 72? **48%**   **2.** What percent of 310 is 93? **30%**

  3. 31 is 5% of what number? **620**   **4.** What number is 46% of 55? **25.3**

Write the equation so that y is a function of x. *(p. 184)*

  5. $5x - 3y = 9$ $y = \dfrac{5}{3}x - 3$ **6.** $3x + 2y + 5x = 12$ $y = 6 - 4x$ **7.** $4(2x - y) = 6$ $y = 2x - \dfrac{3}{2}$

  8. ✏ **GEOMETRY** The volume V of a cylinder is given by the formula $V = \pi r^2 h$ where r is the radius of the cylinder and h is the height of the cylinder. Solve the formula for h. *(p. 184)* $h = \dfrac{V}{\pi r^2}$

EXTRA PRACTICE for Lesson 3.8, p. 940   ✐ **ONLINE QUIZ** at classzone.com   **189**

38.

39.

Daily Homework Quiz

📄 **Transparency Available**

1. Write the equation $15 = 5y - 4x$ so that y is a function of x.
$y = \dfrac{4}{5}x + 3$

2. Solve $C = 2\pi r$ for r. $r = \dfrac{C}{2}\pi$

3. Solve $V = \dfrac{1}{3}Bh$ for B. $B = \dfrac{3V}{h}$

4. On a round-trip bicycle trip from Santa Barbara to Canada, Phil rode 2850 miles in 63 days. Find his average miles per day for the trip. Use the formula $d = rt$ where d is distance, r is rate, and t is time. Solve for r to find the rate in miles per day to the nearest mile. **about 45 miles per day**

 Online Quiz

Available at **classzone.com**

Diagnosis/Remediation

• Practice A, B, C in Chapter 3 Resource Book, pp. 82–84
• Study Guide in Chapter 3 Resource Book, pp. 85–86
• Practice Workbook, pp. 44–45
• @HomeTutor

Challenge

Additional challenge is available in the Chapter 3 Resource Book, p. 89.

> **Quiz**
>
> **An easily-readable reduced copy of the quiz (with answers) on Lessons 3.7–3.8 from the Assessment Book can be found on p. 130E.**

3. $70. *Sample answer:* Use the proportion $\frac{7}{154} = \frac{x}{700}$ to find that you will need about 35 gallons of gas. Multiply 35 by $2 per gallon.

4. Solve $Q = \frac{3}{r}$ for r to get $r = \frac{3}{Q}$; substitute $\frac{3}{Q}$ for r in the formula $d = 2r$ to get $d = \frac{6}{Q}$.

7. Multiply each side by 2 and divide each side by d_2 to get $d_1 = \frac{2A}{d_2}$.

Lessons 3.5–3.8

1. MULTI-STEP PROBLEM The table below shows the results of a survey in which students at a school were asked to name their favorite sport to watch on TV.

Sport	Students
Baseball	7
Basketball	6
Football	10
Other	8

a. There are 1209 students at the school. Write a proportion that you can use to predict the number of students at the school who would name baseball as their favorite sport to watch on TV. *Sample answer:* $\frac{7}{31} = \frac{x}{1209}$

b. Solve the proportion. **273 students**

2. MULTI-STEP PROBLEM The ratio of male students to female students in the freshman class at a high school is $4:5$. There are 216 students in the freshman class.

a. Find the ratio of female students to all students. $\frac{5}{9}$

b. Use the ratio to find the number of female students in the freshman class. **120 females**

3. SHORT RESPONSE During a vacation, your family's car used 7 gallons of gasoline to travel 154 miles. Your family is planning another vacation in which you will travel 770 miles by car. If gasoline costs about $2 per gallon, how much money should your family budget for gasoline for this vacation? *Explain* your reasoning. **See margin.**

4. SHORT RESPONSE In biology, the surface-area-to-volume quotient Q of a single spherical cell is given by the formula $Q = \frac{3}{r}$ where r is the radius of the cell. Suppose you need to calculate the diameters of cells given the surface-area-to-volume quotients of the cells. Given that $d = 2r$, explain how to write a formula for the diameter d of a cell given its surface-area-to-volume quotient. **See margin.**

5. GRIDDED ANSWER A basketball player made 60% of his free-throws during a season. The player made 84 free-throws. How many free-throw attempts did he have? **140 attempts**

6. EXTENDED RESPONSE When a real estate agent sells a house, the agent receives 6% of the sale price as a commission. The agent lists the sale price for a house as $208,000.

a. How much of a commission should the agent expect to receive for selling this house at full price? **$12,480**

b. The house actually sells for $205,000. How much of a commission does the agent receive? **$12,300**

c. The real estate agent gives 10% of her commission to her assistant. What percent of the selling price does the agent's assistant receive? *Explain* your reasoning. **0.6%; find that $1230 is 10% of $12,300, then find $1230 is what percent of $205,000.**

7. SHORT RESPONSE The area A of a rhombus is given by the formula $A = \frac{1}{2}d_1 d_2$ where d_1 and d_2 are the lengths of the diagonals.

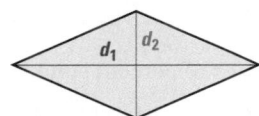

Suppose you need to find d_1 for different values of A and d_2. *Explain* how to rewrite the area formula to make it easier to find values for d_1. **See margin.**

8. OPEN-ENDED *Describe* how the dimensions of the rectangular garden below can be altered to increase the area of the garden by 25%. *Sample answer:* **Increase the length, 16 feet, by 4 feet.**

10 ft

16 ft

BIG IDEAS
For Your Notebook

Big Idea 1

Solving Equations in One Variable

You can solve equations in one variable by adding, subtracting, multiplying by, or dividing by the same number on each side.

Property	Words	Algebra
Addition Property of Equality	Add the same number to each side.	If $x - a = b$, then $x - a + a = b + a$, or $x = b + a$.
Subtraction Property of Equality	Subtract the same number from each side.	If $x + a = b$, then $x + a - a = b - a$, or $x = b - a$.
Multiplication Property of Equality	Multiply each side by the same nonzero number.	If $\frac{x}{a} = b$ and $a \neq 0$, then $a \cdot \frac{x}{a} = a \cdot b$, or $x = ab$.
Division Property of Equality	Divide each side by the same nonzero number.	If $ax = b$ and $a \neq 0$, then $\frac{ax}{a} = \frac{b}{a}$, or $x = \frac{b}{a}$.

Big Idea 2

Solving Proportion and Percent Problems

When solving a proportion, you can take the cross products, then use properties of equality.

$\dfrac{x - 3}{40} = \dfrac{4}{5}$ **Original proportion**

$5(x - 3) = 40 \cdot 4$ **Cross products property**

$5x - 15 = 160$ **Simplify.**

$5x = 175$ **Addition property of equality: Add 15 to each side.**

$x = 35$ **Division property of equality: Divide each side by 5.**

Big Idea 3

Rewriting Equations in Two or More Variables

If you have an equation in two or more variables, you can solve for one variable in terms of the others using properties of equality. For example, the formula for the perimeter P of a rectangle can be solved for the length ℓ.

$P = 2\ell + 2w$ w

ℓ

$P = 2\ell + 2w$ **Original formula**

$P - 2w = 2\ell$ **Subtraction property of equality: Subtract 2w from each side.**

$\dfrac{P - 2w}{2} = \ell$ **Division property of equality: Divide each side by 2.**

3 CHAPTER REVIEW

@*HomeTutor*
classzone.com
• Multi-Language Glossary
• Vocabulary practice

Extra Example 3.1
Solve $6x = -96$. **-16**

REVIEW KEY VOCABULARY

• inverse operations, *p. 134*	• proportion, *p. 163*	• scale model, *p. 170*
• equivalent equations, *p. 134*	• cross product, *p. 168*	• scale, *p. 170*
• identity, *p. 156*	• scale drawing, *p. 170*	• literal equation, *p. 184*
• ratio, *p. 162*		

VOCABULARY EXERCISES

1. Copy and complete: A(n) __?__ is a two-dimensional drawing of an object in which the dimensions of the drawing are in proportion to the dimensions of the object. **scale drawing**

2. Copy and complete: When you perform the same inverse operation on each side of an equation, you produce a(n) __?__ equation. **equivalent**

3. *Explain* why the equation $2x + 8x = 3x + 7x$ is an identity.
   If you collect like terms you get $10x = 10x$, so any value of x will make it true.

4. Copy and complete: In the proportion $\frac{7}{8} = \frac{28}{32}$, $7 \cdot 32$ and $8 \cdot 28$ are __?__. **cross products**

5. *Describe* the steps you would take to write the equation $6x - 2y = 16$ in function form. **Subtract $6x$ from each side, then divide each side by -2.**

REVIEW EXAMPLES AND EXERCISES

Use the review examples and exercises below to check your understanding of the concepts you have learned in each lesson of Chapter 3.

3.1 Solve One-Step Equations
pp. 134–140

EXAMPLE

Solve $\frac{x}{5} = 14$.

$\frac{x}{5} = 14$	**Write original equation.**
$5 \cdot \frac{x}{5} = 5 \cdot 14$	**Multiply each side by 5.**
$x = 70$	**Simplify.**

EXERCISES

**EXAMPLES
1, 2, 3, 4 and 5**
on pp. 134–136
for Exs. 6–12

Solve the equation. Check your solution.

6. $x - 4 = 3$ **7**
7. $-8 + a = 5$ **13**
8. $4m = -84$ **-21**
9. $-5z = 75$ **-15**
10. $11 = \frac{r}{6}$ **66**
11. $-27 = \frac{3}{4}w$ **-36**

12. **PARKS** A rectangular city park has an area of 211,200 square feet. If the length of the park is 660 feet, what is the width of the park? **320 ft**

3.2 Solve Two-Step Equations

pp. 141–146

EXAMPLE

Solve $4x - 9 = 3$.

$$4x - 9 = 3 \qquad \text{Write original equation.}$$
$$4x - 9 + 9 = 3 + 9 \qquad \text{Add 9 to each side.}$$
$$4x = 12 \qquad \text{Simplify.}$$
$$\frac{4x}{4} = \frac{12}{4} \qquad \text{Divide each side by 4.}$$
$$x = 3 \qquad \text{Simplify.}$$

EXERCISES

Solve the equation. Check your solution.

EXAMPLES
1 and 2
on pp. 141–142
for Exs. 13–18

13. $9b + 5 = 23$ **2**   **14.** $11 = 5y - 4$ **3**   **15.** $\frac{n}{3} - 4 = 2$ **18**

16. $\frac{3}{2}v + 2 = 20$ **12**   **17.** $3t + 9t = 60$ **5**   **18.** $-110 = -4c - 6c$ **11**

3.3 Solve Multi-Step Equations

pp. 148–153

EXAMPLE

Solve $5x - 2(4x + 3) = 9$.

$$5x - 2(4x + 3) = 9 \qquad \text{Write original equation.}$$
$$5x - 8x - 6 = 9 \qquad \text{Distributive property}$$
$$-3x - 6 = 9 \qquad \text{Combine like terms.}$$
$$-3x = 15 \qquad \text{Add 6 to each side.}$$
$$x = -5 \qquad \text{Divide each side by } -3.$$

EXERCISES

Solve the equation. Check your solution.

EXAMPLES
1, 2, 3 and 4
on pp. 148–149
for Exs. 19–28

19. $3w + 4w - 2 = 12$ **2**   **20.** $z + 5 - 4z = 8$ **−1**   **21.** $c + 2c - 5 - 5c = 7$ **−6**

22. $4y - (y - 4) = -20$ **−8**   **23.** $8a - 3(2a + 5) = 13$ **14**   **24.** $16h - 4(5h - 7) = 4$ **6**

25. $\frac{3}{2}(b + 1) = 3$ **1**   **26.** $\frac{4}{3}(2x - 1) = -12$ **−4**   **27.** $\frac{6}{5}(8k + 2) = -36$ **−4**

28. FOOTBALL You purchase 5 tickets to a football game from an Internet ticket agency. In addition to the cost per ticket, the agency charges a convenience charge of $2.50 per ticket. You choose to pay for rush delivery, which costs $15. The total cost of your order is $352.50. What is the price per ticket not including the convenience charge? **$65**

Extra Example 3.4

Solve the equation, if possible.

a. $6(w - 4) = -2(12 - 3w)$ **The equation is an identity.**

b. $4a + 3 = 4(a + 3)$ **The equation has no solution.**

Extra Example 3.5

You know you can buy 6 tickets to the county fair for $18. How many tickets can you buy for $51?

17 tickets

3.4 **Solve Equations with Variables on Both Sides** *pp. 154–159*

EXAMPLE

Solve the equation, if possible.

a.

$-2(x - 5) = 7 - 2x$	Original equation
$-2x + 10 = 7 - 2x$	Distributive property
$-2x + 3 = -2x$	Subtract 7 from each side.

▸ The equation $-2x + 3 = -2x$ is not true because the number $-2x$ cannot be equal to 3 more than itself. So, the equation has no solution.

b.

$5(3 - 2x) = -(10x - 15)$	Original equation
$15 - 10x = -10x + 15$	Distributive property
$15 - 10x = 15 - 10x$	Rearrange terms.

▸ The statement $15 - 10x = 15 - 10x$ is true for all values of x. So, the equation is an identity.

EXERCISES

Solve the equation, if possible.

EXAMPLES 1, 2, and 4 on pp. 154–156 for Exs. 29–37

29. $-3z - 1 = 8 - 3z$ **no solution**

30. $16 - 2m = 5m + 9$ **1**

31 $2.9w + 5 = 4.7w - 7.6$ **7**

32. $2y + 11.4 = 2.6 - 0.2y$ **−4**

33. $4(x - 3) = -2(6 - 2x)$ **identity**

34. $6(2a + 10) = 5(a + 5)$ **−5**

35. $\frac{1}{12}(48 + 24b) = 2(17 - 4b)$ **3**

36. $1.5(n + 20) = 0.5(3n + 60)$ **identity**

37. ⊘ **GEOMETRY** Refer to the square shown.

a. Find the value of x. **4**

b. Find the perimeter of the square. **116**

$6x + 5$

$8x - 3$

3.5 **Write Ratios and Proportions** *pp. 162–167*

EXAMPLE

You know that 5 pizzas will feed 20 people. How many pizzas do you need to order to feed 88 people?

$\dfrac{5}{20} = \dfrac{x}{88}$ ◀— number of pizzas
◀— number of people

$88 \cdot \dfrac{5}{20} = 88 \cdot \dfrac{x}{88}$ Multiply each side by 88.

$22 = x$ Simplify.

▸ You need to order 22 pizzas.

EXAMPLES
2 and 3
on pp. 163–164
for Exs. 38–44

EXERCISES

Solve the proportion. Check your solution.

38. $\frac{56}{16} = \frac{x}{2}$ **7**

39. $\frac{y}{9} = \frac{25}{15}$ **15**

40. $\frac{2}{7} = \frac{m}{91}$ **26**

41. $\frac{5z}{3} = \frac{105}{6}$ **10.5**

42. $\frac{9}{4} = \frac{3a}{20}$ **15**

43. $\frac{c+2}{45} = \frac{8}{5}$ **70**

44. **PAINTING** The label on a can of paint states that one gallon of the paint will cover 560 square feet. How many gallons of that paint are needed to cover 1400 square feet? **2.5 gal**

3.6 Solve Proportions Using Cross Products *pp. 168–173*

EXAMPLE

Solve the proportion $\frac{3}{10} = \frac{12}{x}$.

$\frac{3}{10} = \frac{12}{x}$ **Write original proportion.**

$3 \cdot x = 10 \cdot 12$ **Cross products property**

$3x = 120$ **Simplify.**

$x = 40$ **Divide each side by 3.**

EXAMPLE

A map has a scale of 1 cm : 15 km. The distance between two cities on the map is 7.2 centimeters. Estimate the actual distance between the cites.

$\frac{1}{15} = \frac{7.2}{d}$ ⟵ **centimeters** ⟵ **kilometers**

$1 \cdot d = 15 \cdot 7.2$ **Cross products property**

$d = 108$ **Simplify.**

▶ The distance between the two cities is about 108 kilometers.

EXERCISES

EXAMPLES
1, 3, and 4
on pp. 168–170
for Exs. 45–52

Solve the proportion. Check your solution.

45. $\frac{5}{7} = \frac{20}{r}$ **28**

46. $\frac{6}{z} = \frac{12}{5}$ **2.5**

47. $\frac{126}{56} = \frac{9}{4b}$ **1**

48. $\frac{10}{3m} = \frac{-5}{6}$ **−4**

49. $\frac{n+8}{5n-2} = \frac{3}{8}$ **10**

50. $\frac{5-c}{3} = \frac{2c+2}{-4}$ **−13**

51. **TYPING RATES** A student can type 65 words in 2 minutes. How many words can the student type in 20 minutes? **650 words**

52. **MAPS** A map has a scale of 1 cm : 12 km. The distance between two cities on the map is 6.8 centimeters. Estimate the actual distance between the cities.

about 81.6 km

Chapter Review **195**

Extra Examples 3.6

1. Solve the proportion $\frac{3}{5} = \frac{s}{4}$. **2.4**

2. A map has a scale of 1 cm : 8 km. The distance between 2 cities on the map is 6.5 centimeters. Estimate the actual distance between the cities. **The distance between the two cities is about 52 kilometers.**

Extra Example 3.7

What percent of 45 is 18? **40%**

Extra Example 3.8

Write $ax + by = c$ so that y is a function of x. $y = \dfrac{c - ax}{b}$ or $y = -\dfrac{a}{b}x + \dfrac{c}{b}$

3.7 Solve Percent Problems

pp. 176–181

EXAMPLE

42 is 40% of what number?

$a = p\% \cdot b$	Write percent equation.
$42 = 40\% \cdot b$	Substitute 42 for a and 40 for p.
$42 = 0.4 \cdot b$	Write percent as decimal.
$105 = b$	Divide each side by 0.4.

▶ 42 is 40% of 105.

EXERCISES

Use the percent equation to answer the question.

EXAMPLES
2, 3, 4, and 5
on pp. 177–179
for Exs. 53–57

53. What number is 30% of 55? **16.5**

54. 117 is 78% of what number? **150**

55. What percent of 56 is 21? **37.5%**

56. What percent of 60 is 18? **30%**

57. CONCERTS There were 7500 tickets sold for a concert, 20% of which were general admission tickets. How many general admission tickets were sold?

1500 general admission tickets

3.8 Rewrite Equations and Formulas

pp. 184–189

EXAMPLE

Write $5x + 4y - 7 = 5$ so that y is a function of x.

$5x + 4y - 7 = 5$	Write original equation.
$5x + 4y = 12$	Add 7 to each side.
$4y = 12 - 5x$	Subtract $5x$ from each side.
$y = 3 - \dfrac{5}{4}x$	Divide each side by 4.

EXERCISES

Write the equation so that y is a function of x.

EXAMPLES
2 and 3
on p. 185
for Exs. 58–61

58. $x + 7y = 0$ $y = \dfrac{-x}{7}$

59. $3x = 2y - 18$ $y = \dfrac{3}{2}x + 9$

60. $4y - x = 20 - y$ $y = \dfrac{1}{5}x + 4$

61. AQUARIUMS A pet store sells aquariums that are rectangular prisms. The volume V of an aquarium is given by the formula $V = \ell wh$ where ℓ is the length, w is the width, and h is the height.

a. Solve the formula for h. $h = \dfrac{V}{\ell w}$

b. Use the rewritten formula to find the height of the aquarium shown, which has a volume of 5850 cubic inches. **15 in.**

h in.

30 in.   13 in.

CHAPTER TEST

Solve the equation. Check your solution.

1. $5 + r = -19$ **−24**

2. $z - 8 = -12$ **−4**

3. $-11x = -77$ **7**

4. $\frac{a}{9} = 6$ **54**

5. $15q - 17 = 13$ **2**

6. $3y + 2 = 26$ **8**

7. $\frac{b}{4} + 5 = 14$ **36**

8. $\frac{m}{10} - 6 = 20$ **260**

9. $6j + 5j = 33$ **3**

10. $4k - 9k = 10$ **−2**

11. $14c - 8c + 7 = 37$ **5**

12. $4w - 21 + 5w = 51$ **8**

13. $-19.4 - 15d + 22d = 4.4$ **3.4**

14. $-12h + 39 = -4h - 17$ **7**

15. $-5.7v - 44.2 = -8.3v$ **17**

16. $-6.5t + 15 = -9.7t + 43.8$ **9**

17. $3(3n + 4) = 54 + 6n$ **14**

18. $\frac{1}{3}(24p - 66) = 3p + 43$ **13**

Solve the proportion. Check your solution.

19. $\frac{3}{4} = \frac{z}{16}$ **12**

20. $\frac{72}{45} = \frac{8}{w}$ **5**

21. $\frac{k}{9} = \frac{63}{81}$ **7**

22. $\frac{-5n}{4} = \frac{15}{2}$ **−6**

23. $\frac{34}{6} = \frac{2x + 1}{3}$ **8**

24. $\frac{-4a - 1}{-10a} = \frac{3}{8}$ **−4**

Use the percent equation to answer the question.

25. What percent of 84 is 21? **25%**

26. What percent of 124 is 93? **75%**

27. What number is 15% of 64? **9.6**

28. What number is 44% of 24.5? **10.78**

29. 90 is what percent of 250? **36%**

30. 79.8 is what percent of 95? **84%**

Write the equation so that y is a function of x.

31. $8x + y = 14$ **$y = 14 - 8x$**

32. $-9x + 3y = 18$ **$y = 3x + 6$**

33. $4x = -2y + 26$ **$13 - 2x = y$**

34. **MOVIES** The ticket prices at a movie theater are shown in the table. A family purchases tickets for 2 adults and 3 children, and the family purchases 3 boxes of popcorn of the same size. The family spent a total of $40.25. How much did each box of popcorn cost? **$2.25**

Ticket	Price
Adults	$8.50
Children	$5.50

35. **ICE SKATING** To become a member of an ice skating rink, you have to pay a $30 membership fee. The cost of admission to the rink is $5 for members and $7 for nonmembers. After how many visits to the rink is the total cost for members, including the membership fee, the same as the total cost for nonmembers? **15 visits**

36. **SCALE DRAWING** You are making a scale drawing of your classroom using the scale 1 inch : 3 feet. The floor of your classroom is a rectangle with a length of 21 feet and a width of 18 feet. What should the length and width of the floor in your drawing be? **7 in., 6 in.**

37. **SURVEYS** A survey asks high school seniors whether they would be willing to pay $5 for their yearbook. Out of the 225 seniors surveyed, 198 said "yes." What percent of the seniors said "yes"? **88%**

Additional Resources

Assessment Book
- Chapter Test, Levels A, B, C, pp. 34–39
- Standardized Chapter Test, pp. 40–41
- SAT/ACT Chapter Test, pp. 42–43
- Alternative Assessment, pp. 44–45

Test Generator CD-ROM

Chapter Test

Easily-readable reduced copies (with answers) of Chapter Test B, the Standardized Chapter Test, and the Alternative Assessment from the Assessment Book can be found on pp. 130E–130F.

MULTIPLE CHOICE QUESTIONS

If you have difficulty solving a multiple choice problem directly, you may be able to use another approach to eliminate incorrect answer choices and obtain the correct answer.

PROBLEM 1

Sid's car gets 34 miles per gallon when driven on the highway and 26 miles per gallon when driven in the city. If Sid drove 414 miles on 13 gallons of gas, how many highway miles and how many city miles did Sid drive?

(A) 91 highway miles, 323 city miles

(B) 182 highway miles, 232 city miles

(C) 232 highway miles, 182 city miles

(D) 323 highway miles, 91 city miles

METHOD 1

SOLVE DIRECTLY Write and solve an equation for the situation.

STEP 1 Write an equation. Let x represent the amount of gas (in gallons) used for highway driving. Then $13 - x$ represents the amount of gas used for city driving

$$414 = 34x + 26(13 - x)$$

STEP 2 Solve the equation.

$$414 = 34x + 338 - 26x$$

$$414 = 8x + 338$$

$$76 = 8x$$

$$9.5 = x$$

STEP 3 Calculate the number of highway miles driven.

$$34(9.5) = 323$$

STEP 4 Calculate the number of city miles driven.

$$26(13 - 9.5) = 91$$

Sid drove 323 highway miles and 91 city miles.

The correct answer is D. (A) (B) (C) (**D**)

METHOD 2

ELIMINATE CHOICES Another method is to consider the extremes to eliminate incorrect answer choices.

STEP 1 Consider driving all highway miles and all city miles.

All highway: $13 \text{ gal} \cdot \frac{34 \text{ mi}}{1 \text{ gal}} = 442 \text{ mi}$

All city: $13 \text{ gal} \cdot \frac{26 \text{ mi}}{1 \text{ gal}} = 338 \text{ mi}$

Because 414 is closer to 442 than to 338, you know that more highway miles were driven than city miles. So, you can eliminate choices A and B.

STEP 2 Calculate the gallons of gas that would be used for the remaining choices.

Choice C: $232 \text{ mi} \cdot \frac{1 \text{ gal}}{34 \text{ mi}} \approx 6.8 \text{ gal}$

$182 \text{ mi} \cdot \frac{1 \text{ gal}}{26 \text{ mi}} = 7 \text{ gal}$

Choice D: $323 \text{ mi} \cdot \frac{1 \text{ gal}}{34 \text{ mi}} = 9.5 \text{ gal}$

$91 \text{ mi} \cdot \frac{1 \text{ gal}}{26 \text{ mi}} = 3.5 \text{ gal}$

In choice D, the total number of gallons of gas is 13.

The correct answer is D. (A) (B) (C) (**D**)

PROBLEM 2

What is the value of x in the proportion $\dfrac{3}{2x-10} = \dfrac{12}{x+9}$?

Ⓐ 4   Ⓑ 6   Ⓒ 7   Ⓓ 8

METHOD 1

SOLVE DIRECTLY Find the value of x by using the cross products property to solve the proportion.

$$\dfrac{3}{2x-10} = \dfrac{12}{x+9}$$

$$3(x+9) = (2x-10)\cdot 12$$

$$3x + 27 = 24x - 120$$

$$147 = 21x$$

$$7 = x$$

The correct answer is C. Ⓐ Ⓑ Ⓒ Ⓓ

METHOD 2

ELIMINATE CHOICES Substitute each answer choice for x in the proportion and simplify.

Choice A: $\dfrac{3}{2(4)-10} \overset{?}{=} \dfrac{12}{5+9}$

$$\dfrac{3}{-2} = \dfrac{12}{14} \ \text{✗}$$

Choice B: $\dfrac{3}{2(6)-10} \overset{?}{=} \dfrac{12}{6+9}$

$$\dfrac{3}{2} = \dfrac{4}{5} \ \text{✗}$$

Choice C: $\dfrac{3}{2(7)-10} \overset{?}{=} \dfrac{12}{7+9}$

$$\dfrac{3}{4} = \dfrac{3}{4} \ \text{✓}$$

The correct answer is C. Ⓐ Ⓑ Ⓒ Ⓓ

EXERCISES

Explain why you can eliminate the highlighted answer choice. 1–4. See margin.

1. What is the solution of the equation $5(x+13) = 8(4+x)$?

   Ⓐ −11   Ⓑ −4   Ⓒ✗ 0   Ⓓ 11

2. 45 is 80% of what number?

   Ⓐ✗ 36   Ⓑ 56.25   Ⓒ 60   Ⓓ 64.5

3. A grocery store sells apples by the pound. A 3 pound bag of apples costs $2.99. About how much does a 5 pound bag of apples cost?

   Ⓐ $3.24   Ⓑ $3.45   Ⓒ $4.98   Ⓓ✗ $5.98

4. The surface area S of a cylinder is given by the formula $S = 2\pi rh + 2\pi r^2$ where r is the radius and h is the height of the cylinder. Which of the given formulas is *not* equivalent to the original formula?

   Ⓐ $S = 2\pi rh(h+r)$ Ⓑ $S = 2\pi rS + 2\pi r^2$

   Ⓒ✗ $h = \dfrac{S - 2\pi r^2}{2\pi r}$ Ⓓ $h = \dfrac{S}{2\pi r} - r$

Avoiding Common Errors

When students solve equations, recommend that they check their solutions using substitution in the original equation. This will help them avoid choosing answers that result from calculation errors.

Teaching Strategy

After students complete Exercises 2 and 3, you may want to use these exercises to demonstrate the advantages of using estimation and number sense to eliminate choices.

1. Substituting 0 for x into the equation gives $65 = 32$, which is not true.

2. 36 is less than 45, because 45 is only 80% of the number, the number must be greater than 45.

3. $5.98 is two times $2.99. Because 5 pounds is less than two times 3 pounds, the cost of the 5 pound bag should be less than two times the cost of the 3 pound bag.

4. Subtract $2\pi r^2$ from both sides of $S = 2\pi rh + 2\pi r^2$, and then divide both sides by $2\pi r$. The result is the formula given in answer C.

15a. $24w + 28(5 - w) = 132$, $w = 2$, 2 cans of white paint and 3 cans of blue paint

15b. $4; Kendra would have bought 2 cans of blue paint and 3 cans of white paint for a total of $2(\$28) + 3(\$24) = \$128$. The difference in cost is $\$132 - \$128 = \$4$.

16. Sandy; Sandy knits 40 rows per hour, or $\frac{2}{3}$ row per minute. It takes her $88 \div \frac{2}{3} = 132$ minutes to knit 88 rows. Kim knits 36 rows per hour, or $\frac{3}{5}$ row per minute. It takes her $84 \div \frac{3}{5} = 140$ minutes to knit 84 rows. Sandy finishes $140 - 132 = 8$ minutes ahead of Kim.

17a. The cost of buying from the website, $109.99, is about $4 more than the cost of buying from the store, $106.

17b. The cost of buying from the website, $209.99, is about $2 less than the cost of buying from the store, $212.

17c. $x + 9.99 = x + 0.06x$; write an expression in terms of x for each cost and then set the two cost expressions equal to each other.

MULTIPLE CHOICE

1. How many solutions does the equation $3(x - 3) = 3x - 6$ have? **A**

ⓐ None ⓑ 1

ⓒ 2 ⓓ Infinitely many

2. A karate studio offers a 6 week session for $175. How much would you expect to pay for a 9 week session? **D**

ⓐ $117 ⓑ $200

ⓒ $229 ⓓ $262.50

3. Andrew decides to get cable TV for $43 per month. Doug buys a satellite dish for $104 and pays $30 per month for satellite TV. After how many months will Andrew and Doug have paid the same amount for their TV services? **B**

ⓐ 7 ⓑ 8

ⓒ 9 ⓓ 10

4. The rates for using a swimming facility are given below. After how many visits will a family of 4 save money by having a membership rather than paying for all 4 family members for each visit? **B**

Admission Prices	
One-day visit	$3 per person
Family membership (unlimited visits)	$150

ⓐ 12 ⓑ 13

ⓒ 38 ⓓ 50

5. The record for the longest distance and longest time ever flown by a model airplane was set in 2003 by Maynard Hill. The airplane flew 1888 miles from Canada to Ireland in 38 hours and 53 minutes. What was the plane's average speed? **C**

ⓐ About 36 mi/h ⓑ About 45 mi/h

ⓒ About 49 mi/h ⓓ About 71,744 mi/h

6. The perimeter of the triangle shown is 16.5 inches. What is the length of the shortest side? **B**

ⓐ 3.5 in. ⓑ 4 in.

ⓒ 4.5 in. ⓓ 9 in.

7. Jeanie completed a 27 mile duathlon (a race that is a combination of running and biking) in exactly 2 hours. She ran an average speed of 8.5 miles per hour and biked an average speed of 16 miles per hour. For how long did Jeanie bike during the race? **A**

ⓐ 1 hour 20 minutes

ⓑ 1 hour 15 minutes

ⓒ 45 minutes

ⓓ 40 minutes

8. A model of the Gateway Arch in St. Louis, Missouri, was built using a scale of 1 ft : 500 ft. The model is 1.26 feet tall. What is the actual height of the Gateway Arch? **C**

ⓐ 75.6 ft ⓑ 396.8 ft

ⓒ 630 ft ⓓ 7560 ft

9. A mountain biking park has a total of 48 trails, 37.5% of which are beginner trails. The rest are divided evenly between intermediate and expert trails. How many of each kind of trail is there? **B**

ⓐ 12 beginner, 18 intermediate, 18 expert

ⓑ 18 beginner, 15 intermediate, 15 expert

ⓒ 18 beginner, 12 intermediate, 18 expert

ⓓ 30 beginner, 9 intermediate, 9 expert

10. What percent of 256 is 140.8? **D**

ⓐ 45% ⓑ 50%

ⓒ 52.5% ⓓ 55%

GRIDDED ANSWER

11. The circumference of a circle is 12 feet. What is the radius (in feet) of the circle? Round your answer to the nearest tenth. **1.9 ft**

12. What is the value of x in the equation $75 = 15x - 6(x + 7)$? **13**

13. The perimeter of the rectangle shown is 41 centimeters. What is the value of x? **2.5**

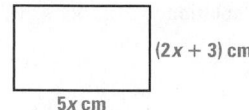
$(2x + 3)$ cm
$5x$ cm

14. Chris pays \$.29 for each digital photo he has printed. Debbie buys a photo printer for \$180. It costs \$.14 per photo for ink and paper to print a photo using the printer. After how many prints will Chris and Debbie have paid the same amount? **1200 prints**

EXTENDED RESPONSE

17. You are deciding whether to order some tools from a company's website and pay \$9.99 in shipping charges, or to go to one of the company's stores and pay 6% sales tax on your purchase. The marked prices of the tools are the same at both places. **a–d. See margin.**

   a. Compare the costs of buying \$100 worth of tools from each place.

   b. Compare the costs of buying \$200 worth of tools from each place.

   c. Write an equation you could use to find for what dollar amount x of tools the costs of buying the tools are the same. *Explain* how you wrote the equation.

   d. Solve the equation from part (c). How can the solution help you to decide from which place you should buy the tools? *Explain*.

18. The circle graph shows the results of a survey that asked 225 randomly selected people how they get driving directions.

   a. How many people said that they get directions from the Internet? **135 people**

   b. Suppose 15 more people were surveyed, and all 15 said that they get directions from the Internet. Calculate the new percent for the "From the Internet" category. *Explain* how you found your answer. **b–c. See margin.**

   c. Instead of 15 more people, suppose x more people are surveyed and they all said that they get directions from the Internet. What value of x would make the percent for the "From the Internet" category be 70%? Your response should include a proportion and an explanation of how you used the proportion to find your answer.

SHORT RESPONSE

15. Kendra is painting her dining room white and her living room blue. She spends a total of \$132 on 5 cans of paint. The white paint costs \$24 per can, and the blue paint costs \$28 per can.

   a. Write and solve an equation to find the number of cans of each color paint that Kendra bought. **a–b. See margin.**

   b. How much would Kendra have saved by switching the colors of the dining room and living room? *Explain*.

16. Kim and Sandy are each knitting a scarf. Kim can knit 3 rows in 5 minutes. Sandy can knit 4 rows in 6 minutes. They start knitting at the same time and do not take any breaks. Kim wants her scarf to be 84 rows long. Sandy wants her scarf to be 88 rows long. Who will finish her scarf first? *Explain*.
   See margin.

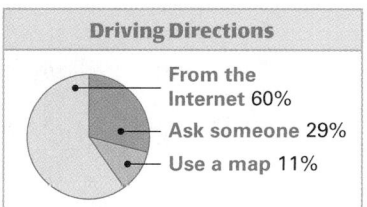

Driving Directions

From the Internet 60%
Ask someone 29%
Use a map 11%

17d. 166.5; the solution $x = 166.5$ means that if you want to buy \$166.50 worth of tools, the cost will be the same whether you buy them from the website or from the store. Combining this information with the results of parts (a) and (b), we know that if you are buying less than \$166.50 worth of tools it is better to buy them from the store, and if you are buying more than \$166.50 worth of tools it is better to buy them from the website.

18b. 62.5%; from part (a), 135 out of 225 people get directions from the Internet. The new number of people who get directions from the Internet is $135 + 15 = 150$ people, and the new total number of people surveyed is $225 + 15 = 240$ people. The new percent of people who get directions from the Internet is $\frac{150}{240} = 0.625$, or 62.5%.

18c. 75 people; following the method described in part (b), write the proportion $\frac{135 + x}{225 + x} = \frac{70}{100}$. Solve the proportion for x, the number of additional people surveyed.

Evaluate the expression. *(p. 8)*

1. $3 \cdot 4^2 - 21$ **27**

2. $4 + 4^2 \div 8$ **6**

3. $77 \div (11 - 4)$ **11**

4. $\frac{1}{2}(8 \cdot 6) - 4^2$ **8**

5. $3[50 - (13 - 7)^2]$ **42**

6. $\frac{3}{4}[(6 + 4)^2 - 40]$ **45**

Check whether the given number is a solution of the equation or inequality. *(p. 21)*

7. $7t - 11 = 52; 9$ **solution**

8. $3b - 2 = 2b + 3; 4$ **not a solution**

9. $8z - 11 > 21; 4$ **not a solution**

10. $5a + 3 \le 13; 2$ **solution**

11. $5 - y \ge 5; 3$ **not a solution**

12. $8x - 15 < 8; 7$ **not a solution**

Find the sum or difference.

13. $-2\frac{1}{6} + \left(-4\frac{2}{3}\right)$ *(p. 74)* $-6\frac{5}{6}$

14. $2.5 - (-2.05)$ *(p. 80)* **4.55**

15. $-24.6 - (-5.5)$ *(p. 80)* -19.1

Find the product or quotient.

16. $\frac{5}{2}(-8)(-5)$ *(p. 88)* **100**

17. $9 \div \left(-\frac{3}{7}\right)$ *(p. 103)* -21

18. $-\frac{7}{8} \div \frac{1}{2}$ *(p. 103)* $-1\frac{3}{4}$

Evaluate the expression for the given value of the variable(s).

19. $\frac{32}{w} - 2$ when $w = 4$ *(p. 8)* **6**

20. $7 + 3m^2 - 8m$ when $m = 5$ *(p. 8)* **42**

21. $\frac{5y}{32 - y^3}$ when $y = 3$ *(p. 8)* **3**

22. $5.15 + (-h) + 6.6$ when $h = 4.3$ *(p. 74)* **7.45**

23. $17.4 - |-p|$ when $p = 3.5$ *(p. 80)* **13.9**

24. $k^2 - 12.2k$ when $k = -1.6$ *(p. 88)* **22.08**

25. $8.3x - (-y)$ when $x = 6$ and $y = 9$ *(p. 88)* **58.8**

26. $\frac{y}{5x - y}$ when $x = 2$ and $y = 4$ *(p. 103)* $\frac{2}{3}$

Solve the equation. Check your solution.

27. $m + 16 = 5$ *(p. 134)* -11

28. $-4 = \frac{w}{7}$ *(p. 134)* -28

29. $5 + 3x = 23$ *(p. 141)* **6**

30. $\frac{a}{3} - 4 = 29$ *(p. 141)* **99**

31. $-4 = -2b - 18 + 5b$ *(p. 148)* $4\frac{2}{3}$

32. $\frac{3}{8}(16n + 48) = 72$ *(p. 148)* **9**

33. $-8z + 18 = 2(2z - 9)$ *(p. 154)* **3**

34. $(15c + 30) = \frac{1}{3}(102 - 12c)$ *(p. 154)* $\frac{4}{19}$

Solve the proportion. *(p. 168)*

35. $\frac{6}{d} = \frac{12}{17}$ **8.5**

36. $\frac{4}{7} = \frac{20}{m}$ **35**

37. $\frac{1}{9} = \frac{5}{3x}$ **15**

38. $\frac{3}{6h} = \frac{12}{72}$ **3**

39. $\frac{2}{11} = \frac{4}{t - 1}$ **23**

40. $\frac{12}{a + 1} = \frac{132}{35}$ $2\frac{2}{11}$

41. $\frac{w + 2}{8} = \frac{w}{3}$ **1.2**

42. $\frac{4}{9} = \frac{z}{z + 10}$ **8**

43. GARDENS You want to put edging around a rectangular flower garden that is 15 feet long and 12 feet wide. The edging comes in 3 foot pieces, as shown. How many pieces of edging do you need to buy? *(p. 28)* **18 pieces**

|—— 3 ft ——|

44. MUSIC The table shows the amount of time m (in hours per person per year) that adults listened to recorded music as a function of the time t (in years) since 1996. Graph the function. *(p. 43)* **See margin.**

Years since 1996, t	0	1	2	3	4	5
Hours listening to music, m	292	270	283	289	263	250

45. STOCKS The daily change in the price of a share of stock is the difference of the price of a share when trading closes and the price of a share when trading opened earlier that day. The table shows the prices of a share of stock during a 5 day period. Find the change in price for each day. *(p. 80)* **−$.34; −$.45; −$.25; $1.02; $.08**

Day	1	2	3	4	5
Opening price (dollars)	39.16	38.82	38.37	38.12	39.14
Closing price (dollars)	38.82	38.37	38.12	39.14	39.22

46. CRAFTS You want to make a square mirror by applying silver leaf to a piece of glass. You have enough silver leaf to cover 854 square inches. Determine the side length of the square piece of glass you need to have cut for this project. Round your answer to the nearest inch. *(p. 110)* **29 in.**

47. BANQUETS The senior class at your high school has its prom at a banquet facility. The banquet facility charges $15.95 per person for a dinner buffet and $400 to rent the banquet hall for an evening. The class paid the banquet facility a total of $2633 for the dinner buffet and use of the banquet hall. How many people attended the prom? *(p. 141)* **140 people**

48. TELEVISIONS The ratio of the length to the width of two different television screens is shown. The width of each screen is 16.2 inches. Find the length of each screen. *(p. 162)* **21.6 in., 28.8 in.**

Standard

Wide screen

49. BASKETBALL The circle graph shows the positions of the 20 players on a basketball team. *(p. 176)*

a. How many players on the team play center? **2 players**

b. How many players on the team play guard? **7 players**

c. How many players on the team play forward? **11 players**

Team Positions
Center 10%
Guard 35%
Forward 55%

44.

(graph showing points plotted with m-axis from 250 to 300 and x-axis from 0 to 5)

REGULAR SCHEDULE

Pre-AP For pacing and assignments for a Pre-AP course, see the *Algebra 1 Toolkit*.

Lesson	Les. Day	BASIC	AVERAGE	ADVANCED
4.1	Day 1	SRH p. 921 Exs. 7–21 odd; pp. 209–212 Exs. 1, 2, 3–11 odd, 13–17, 22–30, 36–39, 42–54 even	pp. 209–212 Exs. 1, 2, 7–13 odd, 16–22 even, 23, 24–32 even, 33–40, 43–53 odd	pp. 209–212 Exs. 1, 2, 10–13, 19–23, 26–28, 31–35*, 38–41*, 43–53 odd
4.2	Day 1	EP p. 938 Exs. 33–36; pp. 219–221 Exs. 1–10, 11–21 odd, 23–25, 42–47	pp. 219–221 Exs. 1–10, 16–25, 42–47	pp. 219–221 Exs. 1, 2, 5–10, 17–25, 34*, 42–47
	Day 2	pp. 219–221 Exs. 26–29, 35–39, 48–55	pp. 219–221 Exs. 26–32 even, 33, 35–40, 48–55	pp. 219–221 Exs. 29–33, 36–41*, 48–55
4.3	Day 1	EP p. 940 Exs. 1–7 odd; pp. 229–232 Exs. 1–10, 16–21, 28–33, 37, 44–47, 51–56	pp. 229–232 Exs. 1–3, 10–15, 22–27, 29, 30, 34–41, 44–49, 51–55 odd	pp. 229–232 Exs. 1, 2, 12–15, 24–27, 29, 30, 35–37, 39–43*, 46–50*, 52–56 even
4.4	Day 1	SRH p. 934 Exs. 6–14; pp. 239–242 Exs. 1–18, 42–56 even	pp. 239–242 Exs. 1–7, 11–18, 24–28, 43–55 odd	pp. 239–242 Exs. 1, 2, 12–18, 24–32, 43–55 odd
	Day 2	pp. 239–242 Exs. 19–27, 36–39, 57–62	pp. 239–242 Exs. 19–23, 31–33, 36–40, 57–62	pp. 239–242 Exs. 19–23, 35–41*, 57–62
4.5	Day 1	pp. 247–250 Exs. 1–13, 17–24, 30–33, 40–43, 46–56 even	pp. 247–250 Exs. 1–5, 9, 10, 13–20, 25–31, 32–38 even, 40–44, 46–56 even	pp. 247–250 Exs. 1, 2, 6–10, 14–19, 27–39*, 41–45*, 47–57 odd
4.6	Day 1	pp. 256–259 Exs. 1, 2, 3–9 odd, 10–22 even, 23–28, 40–45, 48–62 even	pp. 256–259 Exs. 1, 2, 6–10, 18–28, 29–35 odd, 40–46, 53–56, 60–62	pp. 256–259 Exs. 1, 2, 7–9, 19–22, 24–28, 33–39*, 41–47*, 54–56, 60–62
4.7	Day 1	pp. 265–268 Exs. 1, 3–11 odd, 12–18, 39–41, 46–54	pp. 265–268 Exs. 1, 7–13, 16–22, 39–41, 46–54	pp. 265–268 Exs. 1, 7–11, 13, 17–22, 37–41*, 46–54 even
	Day 2	pp. 265–268 Exs. 2, 19–29, 42, 55–60	pp. 265–268 Exs. 2, 27–37, 42–44, 55–60	pp. 265–268 Exs. 2, 28–36, 42–45*, 55–60
Review	Day 1	pp. 271–274 Exs. 1–34	pp. 271–274 Exs. 1–34	pp. 271–274 Exs. 1–34
Assess	Day 1	Chapter 4 Test	Chapter 4 Test	Chapter 4 Test
Yearly Pacing		Chapter 4 Total – 12 days	Chapters 1–4 Total – 46 days	Remaining – 114 days

*Challenge Exercises   EP = Extra Practice   SRH = Skills Review Handbook

BLOCK SCHEDULE

DAY 1	DAY 2	DAY 3	DAY 4	DAY 5	DAY 6
4.1	**4.2 (CONT.)**	**4.4**	**4.5**	**4.7**	**REVIEW**
pp. 209–212 Exs. 1, 2, 7–13 odd, 16–22 even, 23, 24–32 even, 33–40, 43–53 odd	pp. 219–221 Exs. 26–32 even, 33, 35–40, 48–55	pp. 239–242 Exs. 1–7, 11–28, 31–33, 36–40, 43–55 odd, 57–62	pp. 247–250 Exs. 1–5, 9, 10, 13–20, 25–31, 32–38 even, 40–44, 46–56 even	pp. 265–268 Exs. 1, 2, 7–13, 16–22, 27–37, 39–44, 46–60	pp. 271–274 Exs. 1–34
4.2	**4.3**		**4.6**		**ASSESS**
pp. 219–221 Exs. 1–10, 16–25, 42–47	pp. 229–232 Exs. 1–3, 10–15, 22–27, 29, 30, 34–41, 44–49, 51–55 odd		pp. 256–259 Exs. 1, 2, 6–10, 18–28, 29–35 odd, 40–46, 53–56, 60–62		Chapter 4 Test
Yearly Pacing	Chapter 4 Total – 6 days	Chapters 1–4 Total – 23 days	Remaining – 57 days		

RESOURCE MANAGER

Chapter Resource Book

CHAPTER SUPPORT

| Parents as Partners (Chapter Overview with home involvement exercises and activity) | | | | | | p. 1 | |

LESSON SUPPORT	4.1	4.2	4.3	4.4	4.5	4.6	4.7
Teaching Guide/Lesson Plan	p. 3	p. 16	p. 31	p. 45	p. 58	p. 75	p. 88
Activity Masters		p. 18					p. 90
Technology Activities & Keystrokes		p. 19			p. 60		
Activity Support Masters					p. 62		
Practice (3 levels)	p. 5	p. 20	p. 33	p. 47	p. 64	p. 77	p. 91
Study Guide	p. 11	p. 26	p. 39	p. 53	p. 70	p. 83	p. 97
Catch-Up for Absent Students	p. 13	p. 28	p. 41	p. 55	p. 72	p. 85	p. 99
Problem Solving/Application	p. 14	p. 29	p. 42	p. 56	p. 73	p. 86	p. 100
Challenge Practice	p. 15	p. 30	p. 44	p. 57	p. 74	p. 87	p. 101

REVIEW

Chapter Review Games and Activities	p. 102	Cumulative Practice	p. 104
Project with Rubric	p. 103	Resource Book Answers	A1

Transparencies

Transparencies	4.1	4.2	4.3	4.4	4.5	4.6	4.7
Warm-Up/Daily Homework Quiz	✔	✔	✔	✔	✔	✔	✔
Notetaking Guide	✔	✔	✔	✔	✔	✔	✔
Teacher Support	✔	✔	✔	✔	✔	✔	✔
Answer Transparencies	✔	✔	✔	✔	✔	✔	✔

ASSESSMENT BOOK

Quizzes	p. 46	SAT/ACT Chapter Test	p. 57
Chapter Tests (3 levels)	p. 49	Alternative Assessment with Rubric	p. 59
Standardized Chapter Test	p. 55		

TECHNOLOGY

- Easy Planner
- Test and Practice Generator
- Power Presentations
- @HomeTutor
- Activity Generator
- Animated Algebra
- Classzone.com
- eEdition Plus Online
- eWorkbook Plus Online
- Easy Grader Online

ADDITIONAL RESOURCES

- Worked-Out Solution Key
- Notetaking Guide
- Practice Wookbook
- Algebra 1 Toolkit
- Benchmark Tests
- Reteaching and Remediation
- Spanish Study Guide
- Spanish Assessment Book
- Student Resources in Spanish
- Multi-Language Visual Glossary

4 Lesson Practice Level B

Give the coordinates of the points labeled A, B, C, and D.

1.

2.

$A(-4, 1), B(1, -2), C(3, 2), D(0, 3)$

3.

$A(-3, 0), B(-2, 4), C(3, 2), D(1, -3)$

$A(2, 0), B(-1, -4), C(-2, 2), D(1, 3)$

Plot the point in a coordinate plane. *Describe* the location of the point.

4. $A(-4, 3)$ Point A is located 4 units to the left of the origin and 3 units above the x-axis.

5. $P(5, -6)$ Point P is located 5 units to the right of the origin and 6 units below the x-axis.

6. $Q(0, 7)$ Point Q is located 7 units above the origin on the y-axis.

7. $B(-7, -5)$ Point B is located 7 units to the left of the origin and 5 units below the x-axis.

8. $W(-5, 0)$ Point W is located 5 units to the left of the origin on the x-axis.

9. $V(-3, -3)$ Point V is located 3 units to the left of the origin and 3 units below the x-axis.

Graph the function with the given domain. Then identify the range of the function.

10. $y = x + 4$; domain: $-2, -1, 0, 1, 2$ Range: 2, 3, 4, 5, 6

11. $y = 2x - 5$; domain: $-2, -1, 0, 1, 2$ Range: $-9, -7, -5, -3, -1$

---

12. $y = 3x - 1$; domain: $-2, -1, 0, 1, 2$ Range: $-7, -4, -1, 2, 5$

13. $y = 6x - 2$; domain: $-2, -1, 0, 1, 2$ Range: $-14, -8, -2, 4, 10$

16. Because both coordinates are negative, $(-4, -2)$ lies in Quadrant III.

14. $y = 4x + 3$; domain: $-2, -1, 0, 1, 2$ Range: $-5, -1, 3, 7, 11$

15. $y = \frac{1}{2}x + 1$; domain: $-4, -2, 0, 2, 4$ Range: $-1, 0, 1, 2, 3$

17. Because the first coordinate is positive and the second coordinate is negative, $(9, -2)$ lies in Quadrant IV.

18. Because the first coordinate is negative and the second coordinate is positive, $(-1, 8)$ lies in Quadrant II.

Without plotting the point, tell whether it is in Quadrant I, Quadrant II, Quadrant III, or Quadrant IV. *Explain* your reasoning. See above.

16. $(-4, -2)$ **17.** $(9, -2)$ **18.** $(-1, 8)$

19. Jupiter's Moons The table shows some of the moons of Jupiter, their mean distances from Jupiter (in thousand kilometers), and their orbital periods (in Earth days). Graph the data from the table. Does the graph represent a function? Why or why not?

Mean distance (thousands of kilometers)

Moon	Io	Thebe	Ganymede	Callisto	Europa
Mean distance (thousand kilometers)	422	222	1070	1883	671
Orbital period (Earth days)	1.8	0.7	7.2	16.7	3.6

The graph represents a function because each input has exactly one output.

20. Cell Phone Use The table shows the number of cellular telephone subscribers in the United States since 1998.

Years since 1998	0	1	2	3	4
Subscribers (millions)	69	86	109	128	141

a. Graph the data from the table. Does the graph represent a function? Why or why not?

The graph represents a function because each input has exactly one output.

b. *Describe* any trend in the change in the number of subscribers.
The number of subscribers keeps increasing as time goes on.

Decide which of the two points lies on the graph of the line.

1. $2x + y = 10$ b
  a. $(4, 3)$ **b.** $(-4, 18)$

2. $x - 3y = 12$ b
  a. $(9, 1)$ **b.** $(6, -2)$

3. $2y - x = 9$ b
  a. $(5, 1)$ **b.** $(1, 5)$

Solve the equation for y.

4. $-6x + y = 11$ $y = 6x + 11$
5. $8x + 2y = 10$ $y = -4x + 5$
6. $6x - 3y = -9$ $y = 2x + 3$

7. $-4x + 2y = 16$ $y = 2x + 8$
8. $10x - 5y = 25$ $y = 2x - 5$
9. $3x + 2y = -8$ $y = -\frac{3}{2}x - 4$

Graph the equation.

10. $y + x = 14$

11. $y - 5x = 2$

12. $2y - 4x = 10$

13. $x = -6$

14. $y = 4$

15. $3x - 2y = 0$

Graph the function with the given domain. Then identify the range of the function.

16. $y = 2x - 2$; domain: $x \geq 0$ Range: $y \geq -2$

17. $y = -3x + 1$; domain: $x \leq 0$ Range: $y \geq 1$

---

18. $y = 3$; domain: $x \leq 2$ Range: $y = 3$

19. $y = -1$; domain: $x \geq -1$ Range: $y = -1$

23. a. Domain: $0 \leq p \leq 128$; Range: $0 \leq s \leq 3456$; 128 pots
b. Domain: $0 \leq p \leq 100$; Range: $0 \leq s \leq 2700$; 2700 in.^{3}

Identify the range of the function with the given domain.

20. $x + 3y = -8$; domain $x > 0$ $y < -\frac{8}{3}$

21. $6x - 3y = 9$; domain: $x < 1$ $y < -1$

22. Bicycle Rental A bicycle rental shop rents bicycles for $8 per hour. The total cost c (in dollars) for renting a bicycle h hours is given by the function $c = 8h$. Once you get to the rental shop, you figure you can rent a bicycle for at most 5 hours. Graph the function and identify its domain and range. What is the most that you will pay for renting the bicycle?   Domain: $0 \leq h \leq 5$; Range: $0 \leq c \leq 40$; $40

Bicycle Rental

24. Domain: $m \geq 0$; Range: $C \geq 700$; Rent for one year: Domain: $0 \leq m \leq 12$; Range: $0 \leq C \leq 6700$; The original graph was a ray. By restricting the domain, the graph becomes a line segment.

23. Plant Nursery A gardener at a nursery is filling pots with soil to prepare to transplant seedlings into these larger pots. Each new pot needs about 27 cubic inches of soil. The amount of soil s (in cubic inches) it takes to fill p pots is given by the function $s = 27p$. See above.

Plant Nursery

a. The gardener is filling the pots from a bag of soil that contains 3456 cubic inches of soil. Graph the function and identify its domain and range. How many pots can be filled from the bag?

b. Suppose the gardener needs to fill 100 pots. Graph the function on the same coordinate plane in part (a) and identify its domain and range. How much soil (in cubic inches) will the gardener need?

24. Apartment Lease Whenever you sign a lease for an apartment, you typically have to pay a security deposit in case you have caused any wear or tear on the apartment that has to be repaired before it can be re-leased. If no repairs need to be made, you get your entire deposit back. One apartment building has apartments that rent for $500 a month and a security deposit of $700. The total cost C (in dollars it costs to rent the apartment for m months is given by the function $C = 500m + 700$. Graph the function and identify its domain and range. Identify the domain and range if a renter only leases an apartment for one year and then moves out and doesn't get the security deposit back. How does this change the appearance of the graph? *Explain*.   See above.

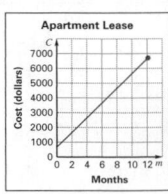

Apartment Lease

Practice B
For use with pages 225–232

Find the x-intercept and the y-intercept of the graph of the equation.

1. $x + y = 1$ $x = 1; y = 1$
2. $x - y = -5$ $x = -5; y = 5$
3. $6x - 3y = -3$ $x = -\frac{1}{2}; y = 1$
4. $5x + 10y = 30$ $x = 6; y = 3$
5. $9y - 5x = 20$ $x = -4; y = \frac{20}{9}$
6. $8x - 2y = 16$ $x = 2; y = -8$
7. $7x + 8y = 18$ $x = \frac{18}{7}; y = \frac{9}{4}$
8. $2y - 12x = -6$ $x = \frac{1}{2}; y = -3$
9. $2x - 0.5y = 8$ $x = 4; y = -16$

Draw the line that has the given intercepts.

10. x-intercept: 5
    y-intercept: 4
11. x-intercept: −1
    y-intercept: 6
12. x-intercept: 2
    y-intercept: −3

Graph the equation. Label the points where the line crosses the axes.

13. $y = -x - 4$
14. $y = 6 + 3x$
15. $y = 8x - 7$

16. $y = 1 - 3x$
17. $7x - 7y = 42$
18. $3y + 2x = -5$

Practice B continued
For use with pages 225–232

19. $4x - 9y = 16$
20. $y = 0.5x - 2$
21. $y = 3x + 0.2$

Match the equation with its intercepts.

22. $7y = 28 - 4x$ C
23. $7x = 4y + 28$ A
24. $4y = 7x + 28$ B

A. x-intercept: 4
   y-intercept: −7
B. x-intercept: −4
   y-intercept: 7
C. x-intercept: 7
   y-intercept: 4

25. **Rabbit Hutch** The cage that you keep your rabbit in has a perimeter of 118 inches. Let x be the cage's width (in inches) and let y be its length (in inches).
   a. Write an equation for the perimeter. $2x + 2y = 118$
   b. Find the intercepts of the graph of the equation you wrote. Then graph the equation. $x = 59; y = 59$

27. b. x-intercept: number of calories burnt when the man only bikes; y-intercept: number of calories burnt when the man only skates.

26. **Home and Garden Show** Admission to a home and garden show costs $7 per person during the week and $9 per person on the weekend. During one week of the show, a total of $142,506 was paid in admissions. This situation can be represented by the equation $7x + 9y = 142,506$ where x is the number of tickets sold during the week and y is the number of tickets sold on the weekend.
   a. Find the intercepts of the graph of the equation. Graph the equation. $x = 20,358; y = 15,834$
   b. Give three possibilities for the number of each kind of ticket that could have been sold for the week.   Answers will vary.

27. **Burning Calories** A man burns 10 calories per minute mountain biking and 7.5 calories per minute in-line skating. His goal is to burn approximately 420 calories daily. This situation can be represented by the equation $10x + 7.5y = 420$ where x is the number of minutes spent mountain biking and y is the number of minutes spent in-line skating.
   a. Find the intercepts of the graph of the equation. Graph the equation. $x = 42; y = 56$
   b. What do the intercepts mean in this situation?   See above.
   c. What are three possible numbers of minutes of biking and skating the man could do to reach his goal? Answers will vary.

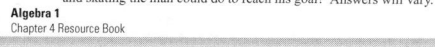

Practice B
For use with pages 235–242

Plot the points and draw a line through them. Without calculating, tell whether the slope of the line is positive, negative, zero, or undefined.

1. $(1, -4)$ and $(5, -8)$ negative
2. $(-3, 6)$ and $(-3, 0)$ undefined
3. $(-3, 3)$ and $(7, -1)$ negative

4. $(0, 2)$ and $(9, -5)$ negative
5. $(7, 1)$ and $(-2, 1)$ zero
6. $(-3, -1)$ and $(6, -2)$ negative

7. $(-4, -5)$ and $(-3, -2)$ positive
8. $(-7, 1)$ and $(-7, -8)$ undefined
9. $(2, -10)$ and $(12, 10)$ positive

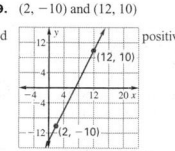

Find the slope of the line that passes through the points.

10. $\frac{2}{3}$
11. $-\frac{4}{5}$
12. 0

Practice B continued
For use with pages 235–242

13. $-\frac{3}{5}$
14. $\frac{3}{5}$
15. undefined

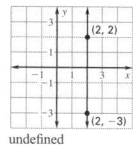

Find the slope of the line that passes through the points.

16. $(1, 2)$ and $(7, 7)$ $\frac{5}{6}$
17. $(3, 4)$ and $(-5, 0)$ $\frac{1}{2}$
18. $(5, -2)$ and $(5, 8)$ undefined
19. $(3, 1)$ and $(-5, 3)$ $-\frac{1}{4}$
20. $(-7, 1)$ and $(1, 5)$ $\frac{1}{2}$
21. $(2, -5)$ and $(5, -2)$ 1
22. $(3, 0)$ and $(8, 0)$ 0
23. $(-6, -6)$ and $(-2, -2)$ 1
24. $(-5, -4)$ and $(1, -2)$ $\frac{1}{3}$

Find the value of x or y so that the line passing through the two points has the given slope.

25. $(-3, y), (-9, -2); m = 1$ 4
26. $(-1, 4), (x, 3); m = \frac{1}{5}$ −6
27. $(8, 1), (1, y); m = -1$ 8
28. $(x, -7), (1, 2); m = 3$ −2
29. $(9, y), (3, 2); m = \frac{2}{3}$ 6
30. $(7, 5), (x, 2); m = \frac{3}{4}$ 3

31. **Trolley Bus** The table shows the number of trolley buses in operation in the United States during certain years.

Year	1980	1985	1990	1995	2000
Number of buses	823	676	832	885	951

   a. *Describe* the rates of change in the number of buses during the time period.   See below.
   b. Determine the time intervals during which the number of trolley buses showed the greatest and least rates of change.   Greatest: From 1985 to 1990; Least: From 1990 to 1995

32. **Postage Rate** The graph shows the cost (in dollars) (in dollars) to mail a letter that weighs one ounce during certain years.
   a. Determine the time interval during which the cost to mail a one-ounce letter showed the greatest rate of change.   From 2001 to 2002
   b. Determine the time interval during which the cost to mail a one-ounce letter showed the least rate of change.   From 1995 to 1999

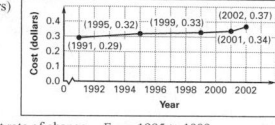

33. **Heart Rate** The graph shows the heart rate of a person during 30 minutes of exercise. Give a verbal description of the workout.   The person's heartrate increased for 0 to 12 minutes, then it slowly decreased until the end of the workout.

31. a. From 1980 to 1985: −29.4 buses per year; From 1985 to 1990: 31.2 buses per year; From 1990 to 1995: 10.6 buses per year; From 1995 to 2000: 13.2 buses per year; From 1980 to 1985, the number of buses decreased, but then the number of buses increased after that.

LESSON 4.5 Practice B
For use with pages 244–250

Identify the slope and y-intercept of the line with the given equation. See below.

1. $y = 5x - 4$
2. $y = 10 - 4x$
3. $9x + y = 8$
4. $12x + 3y = 9$
5. $6x - 2y = 2$
6. $2x + 5y = 10$
7. $9x - 3y = -1$
8. $4y + 6x = 2$
9. $8y - 2x = 5$
10. $5x + 5y = 3$
11. $-4y = 16$
12. $6x = 12$

Match the equation with its graph.

13. $3x + 4y = 12$ C
14. $3x + 4y = -12$ B
15. $3x - 4y = 12$ A

A.
B.
C.

Graph the equation.

16. $y = -7x + 2$
17. $y = 5x + 4$
18. $y = -x + 9$

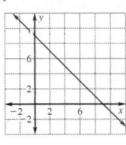

19. $y = \frac{1}{5}x$
20. $y = -\frac{2}{3}x + 1$
21. $y = \frac{4}{3}x - 5$

1. Slope: 5; y-intercept: -4
2. Slope: -4; y-intercept: 10
3. Slope: -9; y-intercept: 8
4. Slope: -4; y-intercept: 3
5. Slope: 3; y-intercept: -1
6. Slope: $-\frac{2}{5}$; y-intercept: 2
7. Slope: 3, y-intercept: $\frac{1}{3}$
8. Slope: $-\frac{3}{2}$; y-intercept: $\frac{1}{2}$
9. Slope: $\frac{1}{4}$; y-intercept: $\frac{5}{8}$
10. Slope: -1; y-intercept: $\frac{3}{5}$
11. Slope: 0; y-intercept: -4
12. Slope: undefined; y-intercept: none

LESSON 4.5 Practice B continued
For use with pages 244–250

Determine which lines are parallel.

22.

23.
line through $(-3, 9)$ and $(-1, 1)$ and line through $(-2, 10)$ and $(1, -2)$

line through $(-1, -4)$ and $(0, 2)$ and line through $(1, 3)$ and $(2, 9)$

Tell whether the graphs of the two equations are parallel lines.

24. $y = 8x - 3$, $8x + y = 3$ no
25. $2x + y = 5$, $-6 + 2x = y$ no
26. $2x + y = 5$, $y = 0.5x - 3$ no
27. $y = -0.6x + 2$, $5y + 3x = 8$ yes
28. $8x + 3y = 9$, $3y - 4 = 8x$ yes
29. $10x + 2y = 7$, $5x - y = 6$ no

30. **Squirrels** A family of squirrels takes up residence in the roof of your house. You call a company to get rid of the squirrels. The company traps the squirrels and then releases them in a wooded area. The company charges \$30 to drop off the traps and then charges \$15 for each squirrel it traps. The total cost C (in dollars) is given by the equation $C = 30 + 15s$ where s is the number of squirrels that are taken away.

  a. Graph the equation.

  b. Suppose the company raises its fee to \$18 to take away each squirrel so that the total cost for s squirrels is given by the equation $C = 30 + 18s$. Graph the equation in the same coordinate plane as the equation in part (a).

  c. How much more does it cost for the company to trap 4 squirrels after the fee is raised?   \$12

31. **Water Usage** A new toilet model has two different flush settings in order to conserve water. One setting uses 1.6 gallons of water per flush and the other setting uses 0.8 gallon of water per flush. The total amount w (in gallons) of water used in the first setting is given by the equation $w = 1.6f$ where f is the number of times the toilet is flushed. The total amount of water used in the second setting is given by the equation $w = 0.8f$.

  a. Graph both equations in the same coordinate plane. What do the slopes and the w-intercepts mean in this situation?

  b. How much more water is used by the first setting if the toilet is flushed 10 times?   8 gal

31. a. The slopes indicate the number of gallons of water used per flush. The w-intercepts show how much water is used when the toilet is not flushed at all.

LESSON 4.6 Practice B
For use with pages 253–259

Tell whether the equation represents direct variation. If so, identify the constant of variation.

1. $y = 8x$ yes; 8
2. $y = 2x + 1$ no
3. $3x + y = 6$ no

Graph the direct variation equation.

4. $y = 9x$
5. $y = -7x$
6. $3y = 4x$

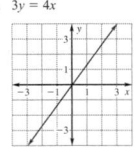

7. $4y = -12x$
8. $8y = x$
9. $8y = 6x$

The graph of a direct variation equation is shown. Write the direct variation equation. Then find the value of y when $x = 10$.

10.

(1, 6)

$y = 6x$; 60

11.

$(-2, 5)$

$y = -\frac{5}{2}x$; -25

12.

(2, 3)

$y = \frac{3}{2}x$; 15

13.

$(-4, -2)$

$y = \frac{1}{2}x$; 5

14.

(3, 2)

$y = \frac{2}{3}x$; $\frac{20}{3}$

15.

$(-1, 5)$

$y = -5x$; -50

LESSON 4.6 Practice B continued
For use with pages 253–259

16.

$(-3, 1)$

$y = -\frac{1}{3}x$; $-\frac{10}{3}$

17.

$(-2, -2)$

$y = x$; 10

18.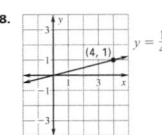

(4, 1)

$y = \frac{1}{4}x$; $\frac{5}{2}$

Tell whether the table represents direct variation. If so, write the direct variation equation.

19.

x	0.5	3	-2	1	-8
y	9	54	-36	18	-144

yes; $y = 18x$

20.

x	-5	3	-2	10	20
y	-2	1.2	-0.8	4	8

yes; $y = 0.4x$

21.

x	8	2	-4	-0.5	14
y	7	28	7	-112	4

no

22.

x	-0.2	-2	1	12	18
y	30	3	-6	-0.5	3

no

Given that y varies directly with x, use the specified values to write a direct variation equation that relates x and y.

23. $x = 24, y = 3$ $y = \frac{1}{8}x$
24. $x = -16, y = -4$ $y = \frac{1}{4}x$
25. $x = 28, y = -4$ $y = -\frac{1}{7}x$
26. $x = 5, y = -30$ $y = -6x$
27. $x = \frac{1}{6}, y = 1$ $y = 6x$
28. $x = 8, y = -3$ $y = -\frac{3}{8}x$
29. $x = 6, y = 102$ $y = 17x$
30. $x = -8, y = 64$ $y = -8x$
31. $x = 15, y = 9$ $y = \frac{3}{5}x$

32. **Hooke's Law** The force F required to stretch a spring varies directly with the amount the spring is stretched s. Eight pounds is needed to stretch a spring 8 inches.

  a. Write a direct variation equation that relates F and s. $F = s$

  b. How much force is required to stretch a spring 25 inches?   25 lb

33. **Basement Waterproofing** One way to keep moisture out of your basement is to paint the walls with a waterproof paint. The number g (of gallons) of paint you need varies directly with the area A of the basement. One gallon of paint covers 100 square feet.

  a. Write a direct variation equation that relates g and A. $g = 0.01A$

  b. How many gallons do you need to cover 530 square feet?   5.3 gal

  c. How many square feet does 8.5 gallons of paint cover?   850 ft^2

34. **Downloading Files** The table shows the amount of time t (in seconds) it takes to download a file of size s (in kilobytes).

Time, t (sec)	File size, s (kb)
15	420
30	840
45	1260

  a. *Explain* why s varies directly with t.

  b. Write a direct variation equation that relates s and t. $s = 28t$

  c. How long will it take to download an 800-kilobyte file? Round your answer to the nearest second.   about 29 sec

34. a. Because the ratios for each data pair is 28, s varies directly with t.

Evaluate the function when $x = -3$, 0, and 2.

1. $f(x) = 15x + 4$ $-41; 4; 34$
2. $g(x) = -9x + 1$ $28; 1; -17$
3. $p(x) = -7x - 5$ $16; -5; -19$
4. $h(x) = 3.25x$ $-9.75; 0; 6.5$
5. $m(x) = -4.4x$ $13.2; 0; -8.8$
6. $f(x) = 6.1x - 3.3$ $-21.6; -3.3; 8.9$
7. $s(x) = \frac{4}{5}x - 2$ $-\frac{22}{5}; -2; -\frac{2}{5}$
8. $d(x) = -\frac{5}{3}x + 4$ $9; 4; \frac{2}{3}$
9. $h(x) = \frac{3}{8}x - 6$ $-\frac{57}{8}; -6; -\frac{21}{4}$
10. $f(x) = -2.5x + 7$ $14.5; 7; 2$
11. $h(x) = 4.2x - 3$ $-15.6; -3; 5.4$
12. $g(x) = 6.1x - 2.2$ $-20.5; -2.2; 10$

Find the value of x so that the function has the given value.

13. $f(x) = 4x - 2; 18$ 5
14. $n(x) = 7x + 4; 39$ 5
15. $q(x) = 6 - 5x; 21$ -3
16. $g(x) = -3x + 8; 14$ -2
17. $h(x) = 9x - 13; 23$ 4
18. $m(x) = 12x - 30; 30$ 5
19. $s(x) = -4x - 9; 3$ -3
20. $m(x) = 8.5x - 3; 82$ 10
21. $p(x) = -2.4x + 6; 18$ -5
21. $d(x) = 3.3x - 1.1; 31.9$ 10

Graph the function. *Compare* your graph to the graph of $f(x) = x$.

23. $h(x) = x - 4$

The graph of h is the graph of f shifted down 4 units.

24. $g(x) = x + 7$

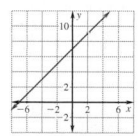

The graph of g is the graph of f shifted up 7 units.

25. $m(x) = 5x$

The graph of m is a dilation of the graph of f using a scale factor of 5.

26. $m(x) = 8x$

The graph of m is a dilation of the graph of f using a scale factor of 8.

27. $p(x) = \frac{1}{3}x$

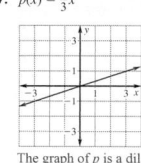

The graph of p is a dilation of the graph of f using a scale factor of $\frac{1}{3}$.

28. $n(x) = -2x$

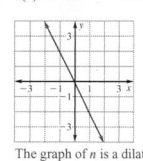

The graph of n is a dilation of the graph of f using a scale factor of 2 and a reflection in the x-axis.

---

29. $p(x) = -\frac{1}{4}x$ See below.
30. $d(x) = x - 1.5$ See below.
31. $g(x) = x + 4.5$ See below.

Match the function with the description of its graph in relation to the graph of $f(x) = x$.

32. $g(x) = 4x$ **C**
33. $g(x) = x + 4$ **A**
34. $g(x) = x - 4$ **B**

A. graph of f shifted up 4 units
B. graph of f shifted down 4 units
C. graph of f dilated by factor of 4

35. **Video Games** The number of hours people in the United States spend playing video games each year from 1998 to 2001 can be modeled by the function $f(x) = 11.9x + 46.4$ where x is the number of years since 1998. **a.** Domain: $0 \le x \le 3$ Range: $46.4 \le f(x) \le 82.1$

   a. Graph the function and identify its domain and range.

   b. Find the value of $f(x)$ when $x = 2$. *Explain* what the solution means in this situation.

   b. $f(2) = 70.2$; In 2000, people spent 70.2 hours each year playing video games.

   c. Find the value of x so that $f(x) = 60$. *Explain* what the solution means in this situation.   See below.

36. **Pool Membership** A pool membership during the summer costs $7 per week. The total cost of a membership is given by $f(x) = 7x$. The pool also rents out lockers for $2 per week. The total cost of a membership and a rental is given by $g(x) = 9x$.

   a. Graph both functions. How is the graph of f related to the graph of g?   See below.

   b. What is the difference between a 12-week membership if you get a locker and if you don't? *Explain* how you got your answer. $24; Because the difference is $2 per week, multiply 2 by 12.

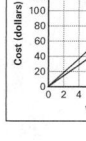

29. The graph of p is a dilation of the graph of f using a scale factor of $\frac{1}{4}$ and the reflection of f in the x-axis.

30. The graph of d is the graph of f shifted down 1.5 units.

31. The graph of s is the graph of f shifted up 4.5 units.

35. **c.** $f(1.1) \approx 60$; Near the beginning of 1999, people spent 60 hours each year playing video games.

36. **a.** The graphs have the same y-intercept but the slope of g is steeper than the slope of f.

204F

4 Assessment

Quiz 1

Plot the point in a coordinate plane. Describe the location of the point.

1. $(1, -4)$

2. $(-3, -2)$

Graph the equation.

3. $x = 3$

4. $y = -3$

5. $y - 3x = 1$

Find the x-intercept and the y-intercept of the graph of the equation.

6. $y = 7x - 3$

7. $-4y + x = 8$

8. $2x - 5y = 20$

9. Your school is selling tickets for a student concert. The total ticket sales can be modeled by the equation $90 = 6a + 3s$ where a is the number of adult tickets sold and s is the number of student tickets sold. Find the intercepts of the graph of the equation.

Answers

1. _____ See left.

    Quadrant IV

2. _____ See left.

    Quadrant III

3. _____ See left.

4. _____ See left.

5. _____ See left.

6. _____ x-intercept: $\left(\frac{3}{7}, 0\right)$;

    y-intercept: $(0, -3)$

7. _____ x-intercept: $(8, 0)$;

    y-intercept: $(0, -2)$

8. _____ x-intercept: $(10, 0)$;

    y-intercept: $(0, \quad 4)$

9. _____ a-intercept: $(15, 0)$;

    s-intercept: $(0, 30)$

Quiz 2

Find the slope of the line that passes through the points.

1. $(-4, 3)$ and $(7, 5)$

2. $(1, 2)$ and $(-2, 2)$

3. $(4, -1)$ and $(4, 3)$

Identify the slope and the y-intercept of the line with the given equation.

4. $y = 7x + 2$

5. $10x - 5y = 30$

6. $3x - 8y = -24$

Graph the equation.

7. $y = -\frac{7}{2}x - 1$

8. $-4x + 6y = 12$

9. $9x + 2y = -7$

10. A campsite charges $12 per day for the site rental and $8 for parking. The total campsite charge C (in dollars) is given by $C = 12d + 8$ where d is the number of days that the site is rented. Graph the equation.

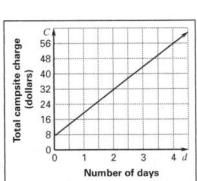

Answers

1. _____ $\frac{2}{11}$

2. _____ 0

3. _____ undefined

4. _____ 7; $(0, 2)$

5. _____ 2; $(0, -6)$

6. _____ $\frac{3}{8}$; $(0, 3)$

7. _____ See left.

8. _____ See left.

9. _____ See left.

10. _____ See left.

Quiz 3

Given that y varies directly with x, use the specified values to write a direct variation equation that relates x and y.

1. $x = 4, y = 12$

2. $x = 6, y = 8$

3. $x = 3, y = -6$

Evaluate the function.

4. $f(x) = 7x + 2$ when $x = 5$

5. $h(x) = 0.3x + 9.7$ when $x = 15$

6. $p(x) = \frac{2}{5}x + \frac{1}{2}$ when $x = 3$

Graph the function. Compare the graph to the graph of $f(x) = x$.

7. $p(x) = x + 4$

8. $g(x) = 3x$

9. $h(x) = \frac{1}{2}x$

10. The area A of a square varies directly as the square of the side s. Write a direct variation equation that relates s and A.

Answers

1. _____ $y = 3x$

2. _____ $y = \frac{4}{3}x$

3. _____ $y = -2x$

4. _____ 37

5. _____ 14.2

6. _____ $\frac{17}{10}$

7. _____ See left.
    Have the same slope; lines are parallel; the y-intercept of the graph of p is 4 more than the y-intercept of the graph of f.

8. _____ See left.
    Slope of the graph of $g >$ the slope of the graph of f; graph of g rises faster from left to right; the y-intercept for both graphs is 0; both lines pass through the origin

9. _____ See left.
    Slope of the graph of $h <$ the slope of the graph of f; graph of h rises more slowly from left to right; the y-intercept for both graphs is 0; both lines pass through the origin

10. _____ $A = ks^2$

Chapter Test

Plot the point in the coordinate plane. Describe the location of the point.

1. $A(-1, 3)$

2. $B(4, 0)$

3. $C(2, -2)$

4. $D(-1, -1)$

Graph the equation.

5. $3x - y = 5$

6. $3y - 2x = -3$

7. $y = -3$

Find the x-intercept and the y-intercept of the graph of the equation.

8. $6x - 4y = 12$

9. $-2x + 5y = -10$

10. $y = \frac{1}{2}x - 2$

In Exercises 11–16, use the following information.

The graph shows the distance of a car traveling along a straight road for 8 hours. A positive velocity is motion to the right, and a negative velocity is motion to the left.

11. Determine the rates of change in distance with respect to time.

12. Between what two times is the car not moving?

13. Between what two times is the car traveling to the right?

14. Between what two times is the car traveling to the left?

15. Between what two times is the car traveling the fastest?

16. What does the x-intercept represent in this situation?

Answers

1. _____ See left.

    Quadrant II

2. _____ See left.

    x-axis

3. _____ See left.

    Quadrant IV

4. _____ See left.

    Quadrant III

5. _____ See left.

6. _____ See left.

7. _____ See left.

8. _____ x-intercept $= 2$,

    y-intercept $= -3$

9. _____ x-intercept $= 5$,

    y-intercept $= -2$

10. _____ x-intercept $= 4$,

    y-intercept $= -2$

11. _____ 30 mi/h, 60 mi/h,

    0 mi/h, -30 mi/h

12. _____ hours 3 and 4

13. _____ first 3 hours

14. _____ hours 4 and 8

15. _____ hours 2 and 3

16. _____ After 8 hours, the car returns to its starting position.

Identify the slope and *y*-intercept of the line with the given equation.

17. $y = 8x - 3$ **18.** $2x + 9y = 9$ **19.** $-3x - 4y = -16$

Determine whether the equation represents direct variation. If so, identify the constant of variation.

20. $y = -x$ **21.** $4x - 3y = 0$ **22.** $2x + y = 4$

Complete the table for the function.

23. $f(x) = 6 + x$

x	−1	−4	0
f(x)	5	2	6

24. $f(x) = -\frac{7}{2}x$

x	0	2	−4
f(x)	0	−7	14

In Exercises 25–27, use the following information.

An advertising company charges $150,000 each time a 30-second commercial is aired. The cost (in thousands of dollars) to produce the commercial and air it *x* times is given by the function $C(x) = 150x + 300$.

25. Graph the function.

26. Identify the domain and the range of the function.

27. How many times could the station air the commercial if it wants to spend $900,000?

Answers

17. $m = 8, b = -3$

18. $m = -\frac{2}{9}, b = 1$

19. $m = -\frac{3}{4}, b = 4$

20. yes; $a = -1$

21. yes; $a = \frac{4}{3}$

22. no

23. See left.

24. See left.

25. See left.

26. domain: $x \geq 0$;

    range: $C \geq 300$

27. 4 times

Multiple Choice

1. A point is located 5 units to the right of the origin and 4 units down. What are the coordinates of the point?   **D**

Ⓐ (5, 4)   Ⓑ (−4, 5)

Ⓒ (4, 5)   Ⓓ (5, −4)

2. In which quadrant is the point $(-2, 3)$ located?   **B**

Ⓐ Quadrant I   Ⓑ Quadrant II

Ⓒ Quadrant III   Ⓓ Quadrant IV

3. Which ordered pair is a solution of $5x + 4y = 18$?   **A**

Ⓐ (−2, 7)   Ⓑ (8, 2)

Ⓒ (−3, 6)   Ⓓ (2, 4)

4. Which statement is true for the function whose graph is shown?   **B**

Ⓐ The domain is unrestricted.

Ⓑ The domain is $x \leq 0$.

Ⓒ The range is unrestricted.

Ⓓ The range is $y \leq 0$.

5. What is the *x*-intercept of the equation $3x - 2y = -12$?   **C**

Ⓐ (0, 6)   Ⓑ (0, −4)

Ⓒ (−4, 0)   Ⓓ (6, 0)

6. The slope of the line that passes through the points $(-2, 4)$ and $(-3, 7)$ is __?__.   **A**

Ⓐ negative   Ⓑ positive

Ⓒ undefined   Ⓓ zero

7. What is the slope of the line that passes through the points $(5, -3)$ and $(-7, 5)$?   **B**

Ⓐ $-\frac{1}{6}$ Ⓑ $-\frac{2}{3}$ Ⓒ −1   Ⓓ $-\frac{3}{2}$

8. What is the value of *y* for the line that has a slope of $-\frac{3}{2}$ and passes through the points $(3, 5)$ and $(7, y)$?   **C**

Ⓐ −11   Ⓑ −10

Ⓒ −1   Ⓓ 20

9. What is the slope of the line $y = \frac{1}{2}x + 2$?   **C**

Ⓐ −2   Ⓑ $-\frac{1}{2}$ Ⓒ $\frac{1}{2}$ Ⓓ 2

10. What is the *y*-intercept of the line $5x - 4y = -12$?   **D**

Ⓐ −3   Ⓑ $-\frac{5}{4}$ Ⓒ $\frac{5}{4}$ Ⓓ 3

11. Which line is parallel to the line $y = 4x - 2$?   **B**

Ⓐ $12x - 4y = 8$ Ⓑ $4y - 16x = 10$

Ⓒ $5y - 25x = -10$ Ⓓ $-x + 4y = -8$

12. What is the value of *m* if Lines 1 and 2 are parallel?   **A**

Line 1: $(-2, -5)$ and $(0, 0)$

Line 2: $(m, 12)$ and $(-3, 2)$

Ⓐ 1   Ⓑ 5   Ⓒ 7   Ⓓ 22

13. Which equation represents direct variation?   **A**

Ⓐ $-2x = 3y$ Ⓑ $5y - x = 4$

Ⓒ $12x - 3 = 4y$ Ⓓ $5x - 2y + 3 = 0$

14. What is the constant of variation in the equation $5x - 3y = 0$?   **B**

Ⓐ −3   Ⓑ $-\frac{5}{3}$ Ⓒ $-\frac{3}{5}$ Ⓓ 5

---

15. The graph of which function is shown?   **A**

Ⓐ $f(x) = -2x + 2$ Ⓑ $f(x) = 2x + 2$

Ⓒ $f(x) = -2x - 2$ Ⓓ $f(x) = 2x - 2$

16. Examine the problem below. Which line contains an error?   **B**

$g(x) = -\frac{2}{3}x - \frac{5}{6}$

$g(36) = -\frac{2}{3}(36) - \frac{5}{6}$ Line 1

$g(36) = -24 - \frac{5}{6}$ Line 2

$g(36) = -\frac{152}{6} - \frac{5}{6}$ Line 3

$g(36) = \frac{157}{6}$ Line 4

$g(36) = 26\frac{1}{6}$ Line 5

Ⓐ Line 2   Ⓑ Line 3

Ⓒ Line 4   Ⓓ Line 5

Gridded Answer

17. What is the value of $f(-3)$ if $f(x) = -4.2x + 6$?

18. a.

Short Response

18. You and a classmate are reading a short story that is 15 pages long. You read at a rate of 1 page per minute. Your classmate reads at a rate of 0.75 page per minute. The models below give the number of *p* pages you and your classmate have left to read after reading for *m* minutes.

You: $p = -m + 15$

Classmate: $p = -0.75m + 15$

a. Graph both equations on the same coordinate plane.   See below.

b. How many more minutes would it take your classmate to read the short story than you? *Explain* how you used the graph to determine this information.
    5 min

Extended Response

19. The table shows the difference *d* (in cents) of this year's average monthly gas price and the previous year's average monthly gas price. For example, in month 1, $d = -2$. So, the average gas price was 2 cents below the previous year's gas price.

Month M	1	2	3	4	5	6
Difference d (in cents)	−2	5	10	5	0	9

a. *Explain* how you know the table represents a function.

b. Graph the function and identify its domain and range.

c. What does a point in Quadrant IV mean in terms of this situation?

19. a. This table represents a function because for every month *M* there is exactly one difference *d*.

b. Domain = 1, 2, 3, 4, 5, and 6; Range = −2, 0, 5, 9, and 10   **c.** A point in Quadrant IV represents a decrease in the price of gas as compared to the average price that same month in the previous year.

Journal

1. List the three different methods that can be used to graph a linear equation. Then briefly describe how to graph $2x + y = 3$ using each method.

Multi-Step Problem

2. You are planning an ornamental garden that has a total area of 200 square feet. There are two sizes of ornamental plants you have chosen for your garden. Each small plant requires 2.5 square feet of space and each large plant requires 8 square feet of space. This situation can be modeled by the equation $2.5x + 8y = 200$ where *x* is the number of small plants and *y* is the number of large plants to be placed in the garden.

a. Find the intercepts of the graph of the equation.

b. Graph the equation.

c. What do the intercepts mean in this situation?

d. What are three possible numbers of small plants and large plants that you can plant in the garden?

e. What is the slope of this line?

f. Write the equation in slope-intercept form.

g. You decide to enlarge the space for the garden to a total of 240 square feet which means the new model will be $2.5x + 8y = 240$. Graph this equation on the same coordinate plane you used in part (b).

h. As you compare the two graphs, did increasing the size of the garden change the slope or *y*-intercept? Describe any changes that occurred.

1. Complete answers should include: a list of the three methods that can be used to graph a linear equation: make a table, use intercepts, and use the slope and *y*-intercept; an explanation of how to graph $2x + y = 3$ using each method.   **2. a.** *x*-intercept: 80; *y*-intercept: 25   **b.**

c. The *x*-intercept represents the number of small plants that can be placed in the garden if no large plants are used. The *y*-intercept represents the number of large plants that can be placed in the garden if no small plants are used.   **d.** *Sample answer:* 16 small and 20 large; 32 small and 15 large; 48 small and 10 large   **e.** $-\frac{5}{16}$ **f.** $y = -\frac{5}{16}x + 25$

g.

h. The slope remained the same, but the *y*-intercept increased by 5 units.

Main Ideas

In Chapter 4, students learn how to plot points in a coordinate plane and use tables, *x*- and *y*-intercepts, and the slope and *y*-intercept to graph linear equations and functions. They interpret slope as a rate of change in real-world situations and explore how changing the slope and *y*-intercept changes the graph. They use slope to identify parallel lines. They write and graph direct variation equations and use them to solve real-world problems. They learn how to use function notation and they compare families of graphs.

Prerequisite Skills

- Plotting ordered pairs
- Making a table of values for a function
- Graphing functions
- Writing equations in function form

Additional resources for reviewing prerequisite skills are:

- Skills Review Handbook, pp. 909–937
- @HomeTutor

4 Graphing Linear Equations and Functions

4.1 Plot Points in a Coordinate Plane

4.2 Graph Linear Equations

4.3 Graph Using Intercepts

4.4 Find Slope and Rate of Change

4.5 Graph Using Slope-Intercept Form

4.6 Model Direct Variation

4.7 Graph Linear Functions

Before

In previous chapters, you learned the following skills, which you'll use in Chapter 4: graphing functions and writing equations and functions.

Prerequisite Skills

VOCABULARY CHECK

Copy and complete the statement.

1. The set of inputs of a function is called the ___?___ of the function. The set of outputs of a function is called the ___?___ of the function. **domain; range**

2. A(n) ___?___ uses division to compare two quantities. **ratio**

SKILLS CHECK

Graph the function. *(Review p. 43 for 4.1–4.7.)* **3–8. See margin.**

3. $y = x + 6$; domain: 0, 2, 4, 6, and 8
4. $y = 2x + 1$; domain: 0, 1, 2, 3, and 4

5. $y = \frac{2}{3}x$; domain: 0, 3, 6, 9, and 12
6. $y = x - \frac{1}{2}$; domain: 1, 2, 3, 4, and 5

7. $y = x - 4$; 5, 6, 7, and 9
8. $y = \frac{1}{2}x + 1$; 2, 4, 6, and 8

Write the equation so that *y* is a function of *x*. *(Review p. 184 for 4.5.)*

9. $6x + 4y = 16$
$y = -\frac{3}{2}x + 4$

10. $x + 2y = 5$
$y = -\frac{1}{2}x + \frac{5}{2}$

11. $-12x + 6y = -12$
$y = 2x - 2$

 @HomeTutor Prerequisite skills practice at classzone.com

Chapter Planning Guide

Chapter 4 Resource Book
- Teaching Guide/Lesson Plan (pp. 3, 16, 31, 45, 58, 75, 88)
- Project with Rubric (p. 103)

Assessment and Intervention
- Assessment Book (pp. 46–60)
- Benchmark Tests
- Reteaching and Remediation Book

Interactive Technology
- Easy Planner
- Power Presentations CD-ROM
- Activity Generator CD-ROM
- Animated Algebra
- Test Generator CD-ROM
- Online Quizzes
- eWorkbook
- eEdition
- @HomeTutor

Resources for English Learners
- Quick Reference for English Learners
- Spanish Study Guide
- Multi-Language Visual Glossary
- Student Resources in Spanish

In Chapter 4, you will apply the big ideas listed below and reviewed in the Chapter Summary on page 270. You will also use the key vocabulary listed below.

Big Ideas

1 Graphing linear equations and functions using a variety of methods

2 Recognizing how changes in linear equations and functions affect their graphs

3 Using graphs of linear equations and functions to solve real-world problems

KEY VOCABULARY

- quadrant, *p. 206*
- standard form of a linear equation, *p. 216*
- linear function, *p. 217*
- *x*-intercept, *p. 225*
- *y*-intercept, *p. 225*

- slope, *p. 235*
- rate of change, *p. 237*
- slope-intercept form, *p. 244*
- parallel, *p. 246*
- direct variation, *p. 253*

- constant of variation, *p. 253*
- function notation, *p. 262*
- family of functions, *p. 263*
- parent linear function, *p. 263*

Why?

You can graph linear functions to solve problems involving distance. For example, you can graph a linear function to find the time it takes and in-line skater to travel a particular distance at a particular speed.

Animated Algebra

The animation illustrated below for Exercise 41 on page 267 helps you answer this question: How can you graph a function that models the distance an in-line skater travels over time?

You want to graph a function that gives the distance traveled by an in-line skater.

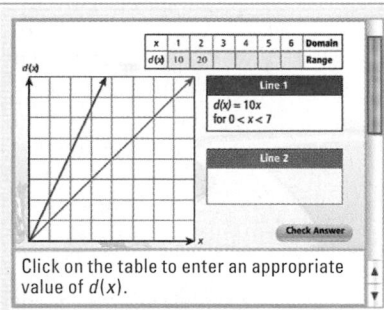

Click on the table to enter an appropriate value of $d(x)$.

Animated Algebra at classzone.com

Other animations for Chapter 4: pages 207, 216, 226, 238, 245, and 254

205

Algebra 1 Toolkit

- Reading Strategies for Chapter 4, pp. 15–16
- Differentiated Instruction Notes, pp. 53–56
- English Learners Notes, pp. 103–104
- Inclusion Notes, pp. 135–136
- Teaching Strategies with Sample Worksheets, pp. 155–178
- Using Technology in the Classroom, pp. 179–184
- Tips for New Teachers, pp. 191–192
- Math Background Notes, pp. 217–218
- Pre-AP Strategies and Copymasters, pp. 284–285, 345–359
- Teacher Survival Activities, pp. 561–562, 587–588
- Bulletin Board Idea, p. 610
- Teacher Tool Transparencies, following p. 620

5.

6.

7.

8.

3.

4.

4.1 Plot Points in a Coordinate Plane

Before	You graphed numbers on a number line.
Now	You will identify and plot points in a coordinate plane.
Why?	So you can interpret photos of Earth taken from space, as in Ex. 36.

Key Vocabulary
• quadrants
• coordinate plane, *p. 921*
• ordered pair, *p. 921*

In Chapter 1, you used a coordinate plane to graph ordered pairs whose coordinates were nonnegative. If you extend the *x*-axis and *y*-axis to include negative values, you divide the coordinate plane into four regions called **quadrants**, labeled I, II, III, and IV as shown.

Points in Quadrant I have two positive coordinates. Points in the other three quadrants have at least one negative coordinate.

READING

The *x*-coordinate of a point is sometimes called the *abscissa*. The *y*-coordinate of a point is sometimes called the *ordinate*.

For example, point *P* is in Quadrant IV and has an *x*-coordinate of 3 and a *y*-coordinate of −2. A point on an axis, such as point *Q*, is not considered to be in any of the four quadrants.

EXAMPLE 1 Name points in a coordinate plane

Give the coordinates of the point.

a. *A*   **b.** *B*

Solution

a. Point *A* is 3 units to the left of the origin and 4 units up. So, the *x*-coordinate is −3, and the *y*-coordinate is 4. The coordinates are (−3, 4).

b. Point *B* is 2 units to the right of the origin and 3 units down. So, the *x*-coordinate is 2, and the *y*-coordinate is −3. The coordinates are (2, −3).

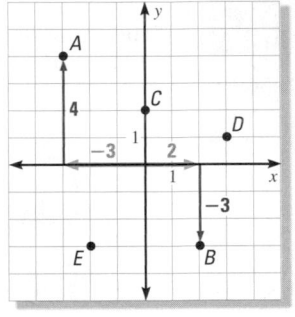

✓ **GUIDED PRACTICE** for Example 1

1. Use the coordinate plane in Example 1 to give the coordinates of points *C*, *D*, and *E*. *C* (0,2), *D* (3, 1), *E* (−2, −3)

2. What is the *y*-coordinate of any point on the *x*-axis? **0**

206   Chapter 4   Graphing Linear Equations and Functions

EXAMPLE 2 Plot points in a coordinate plane

Plot the point in a coordinate plane. Describe the location of the point.

a. $A(-4, 4)$ **b.** $B(3, -2)$ **c.** $C(0, -4)$

Solution

a. Begin at the origin. First move 4 units to the left, then 4 units up. Point A is in Quadrant II.

b. Begin at the origin. First move 3 units to the right, then 2 units down. Point B is in Quadrant IV.

c. Begin at the origin and move 4 units down. Point C is on the y-axis.

Animated Algebra at classzone.com

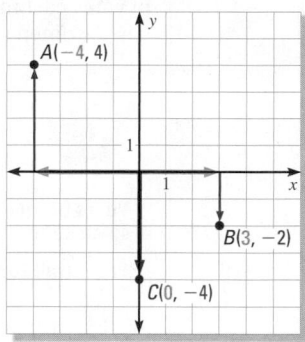

EXAMPLE 3 Graph a function

Graph the function $y = 2x - 1$ with domain $-2, -1, 0, 1,$ and 2. Then identify the range of the function.

Solution

STEP 1 Make a table by substituting the domain values into the function.

STEP 2 List the ordered pairs: $(-2, -5)$, $(-1, -3)$, $(0, -1)$, $(1, 1)$, $(2, 3)$. Then graph the function.

x	$y = 2x - 1$
-2	$y = 2(-2) - 1 = -5$
-1	$y = 2(-1) - 1 = -3$
0	$y = 2(0) - 1 = -1$
1	$y = 2(1) - 1 = 1$
2	$y = 2(2) - 1 = 3$

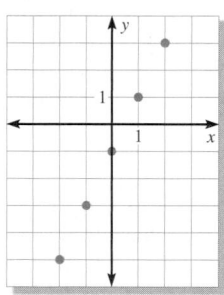

> **ANALYZE A FUNCTION**
> The function in Example 3 is called a *discrete* function. To learn about discrete functions, see p. 223.

STEP 3 Identify the range. The range consists of the y-values from the table: $-5, -3, -1, 1,$ and 3.

✓ **GUIDED PRACTICE** for Examples 2 and 3

Plot the point in a coordinate plane. *Describe* the location of the point.
3–6. See margin for art.

3. $A(2, 5)$ **Quadrant I** **4.** $B(-1, 0)$ **x-axis** **5.** $C(-2, -1)$ **Quadrant III** **6.** $D(-5, 3)$ **Quadrant II**

7. Graph the function $y = -\frac{1}{3}x + 2$ with domain $-6, -3, 0, 3,$ and 6.

Then identify the range of the function. **See margin for art; range: 0, 1, 2, 3, and 4.**

4.1 Plot Points in a Coordinate Plane **207**

Differentiated Instruction

Below Level Students who confuse x- and y-coordinates and quadrants may want to create a note card with a model of a coordinate plane and instructions on how to plot points. Suggest they show the four quadrants, the origin, and the signs of the x- and y-coordinates in each quadrant. Instructions should indicate that they start at the origin, move right for positive x-coordinates and left for negative, and then up for positive y-coordinates and down for negative.

See also the *Algebra 1 Toolkit* for more strategies.

Motivating the Lesson

You can use graphs in a coordinate plane to analyze trends that include negative quantities. For example, a member of the school golf team could plot her score above or below par for each round she plays, with round 0 being the first day of competition and rounds $-1, -2, -3, \ldots$ being earlier practice rounds

③ TEACH

Extra Example 1
Give the coordinates of the point.
a. A $(-2, 1)$ **b.** B $(4, -2)$

Extra Example 2
Plot the point in a coordinate plane. Describe the location of the point.
a. $A(-3, 0)$ **b.** $B(1, -4)$ **c.** $C(-4, -3)$

a. Point A is on the x-axis.
b. Point B is in Quadrant IV.
c. Point C is in Quadrant III.

Animated Algebra
classzone.com

An **Animated Algebra** activity is available on-line for **Example 2**. This activity is also available on the **Power Presentations CD-ROM**.

3–7. See Additional Answers beginning on p. AA1.

208

Extra Example 3

Graph the function $y = -\frac{1}{2}x + 1$
with domain $-4, -2, 0, 2,$ and $4.$
Then identify the range.

range: 3, 2, 1, 0, −1

Extra Example 4

The table shows attendance at a school carnival before and after the school added game booths in 2002.

Years, x, before or since 2002	−2	−1	0	1
Attendance, y (hundreds)	2.6	2.2	3.1	3.5

a. Explain how you know the table represents a function. **Each input has only one output.**

b. Graph the function.

c. Describe any trends. **Before 2002, attendance was below 300 and decreasing. After 2002, it increased to over 300 and it continued to climb in 2003.**

Closing the Lesson

Have students summarize the major points of the lesson and answer the Essential Question: How do you plot points in a coordinate plane?

• A coordinate plane consists of four regions called quadrants.

• You plot points in a coordinate plane by moving left or right from the origin and then up or down from the x-axis.

Begin at the origin and move to the right if the x-coordinate is positive and left if negative. Then move up if the y-coordinate is positive and down if negative.

 EXAMPLE 4 **Graph a function represented by a table**

VOTING In 1920 the ratification of the 19th amendment to the United States Constitution gave women the right to vote. The table shows the number (to the nearest million) of votes cast in presidential elections both before and since women were able to vote.

| −4 means 4 years before 1920, or 1916. | | 0 represents the year 1920. |

Presidential campaign button

Years before or since 1920	−12	−8	−4	0	4	8	12
Votes (millions)	15	15	19	27	29	37	40

a. Explain how you know that the table represents a function.

b. Graph the function represented by the table.

c. Describe any trend in the number of votes cast.

Solution

a. The table represents a function because each input has exactly one output.

b. To graph the function, let x be the number of years before or since 1920. Let y be the number of votes cast (in millions).

The graph of the function is shown.

c. In the three election years before 1920, the number of votes cast was less than 20 million. In 1920, the number of votes cast was greater than 20 million. The number of votes cast continued to increase in the three election years since 1920.

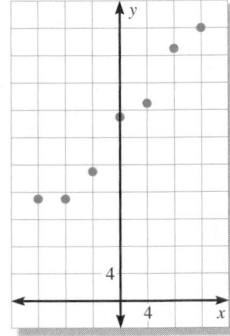

✓ **GUIDED PRACTICE** **for Example 4**

8. VOTING The presidential election in 1972 was the first election in which 18-year-olds were allowed to vote. The table shows the number (to the nearest million) of votes cast in presidential elections both before and since 1972.

Years before or since 1972	−12	−8	−4	0	4	8	12
Votes (millions)	69	71	73	78	82	87	93

8a. The table represents a function because each input has exactly one output.

a. *Explain* how you know the graph represents a function.

b. Graph the function represented by the table. **See margin.**

c. *Describe* any trend in the number of votes cast. **Sample answer: Before 1972 the number of voters increased by 2 million every 4 years. In 1972 the number increased by 5 million and continued to increase by more than 2 million every 4 years since 1972.**

8b.

Differentiated Instruction

Inclusion If you use the words *abscissa* and *ordinate*, students sometimes cannot remember which coordinate is the ordinate and which is the abscissa. One way to avoid confusion is to point out that the words in the ordered pair (abscissa, ordinate) and the letters in the ordered pair (x, y) are both in alphabetical order.

See also the *Algebra 1 Toolkit* for more strategies.

4.1 EXERCISES

HOMEWORK KEY:
○ = WORKED-OUT SOLUTIONS
on p. WS1 for Exs. 15, 25, and 37

★ = STANDARDIZED TEST PRACTICE
Exs. 2, 13, 23, 33, and 41

◆ = MULTIPLE REPRESENTATIONS
Ex. 40

SKILL PRACTICE

A 1. **VOCABULARY** What is the *x*-coordinate of the point (5, −3)? What is the *y*-coordinate? **5; −3**

2. ★ **WRITING** One of the coordinates of a point is negative while the other is positive. Can you determine the quadrant in which the point lies? *Explain.* **No; the point could lie in either Quadrant II or Quadrant IV.**

EXAMPLE 1
on p. 206
for Exs. 3–13

NAMING POINTS Give the coordinates of the point.

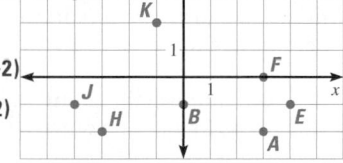

3. *A* **(3, −2)**   4. *B* **(0, −1)**

5. *C* **(4, 4)**   6. *D* **(−4, 3)**

7. *E* **(4, −1)**   8. *F* **(3, 0)**

9. *G* **(−5, 4)**   10. *H* **(−3, −2)**

11. *J* **(−4, −1)**   12. *K* **(−1, 2)**

13. ★ **MULTIPLE CHOICE** A point is located 3 units to the left of the origin and 6 units up. What are the coordinates of the point? **B**

    (A) (3, 6)   **(B)** (−3, 6)   **(C)** (6, 3)   **(D)** (6, −3)

EXAMPLE 2
on p. 207
for Exs. 14–22

PLOTTING POINTS Plot the point in a coordinate plane. *Describe* the location of the point. **14–21. See margin for art.**

14. *P*(5, 5) **Quadrant I**   **15.** *Q*(−1, 5) **Quadrant II** 16. *R*(−3, 0) **x-axis**   17. *S*(0, 0) **origin**

18. *T*(−3, −4) **Quadrant III**   19. *U*(0, 6) **y-axis**   20. *V*(1.5, 4) **Quadrant I** 21. *W*(3, −2.5) **Quadrant IV**

22. **ERROR ANALYSIS** *Describe* and correct the error in describing the location of the point *W*(6, −6). **The description of the location is backwards, the point is 6 units to the right of the origin and 6 units down.**

> Point *W*(6, −6) is 6 units to the left of the origin and 6 units up.

EXAMPLE 3
on p. 207
for Exs. 23–27

23. ★ **MULTIPLE CHOICE** Which number is in the range of the function whose graph is shown? **B**

    (A) −2   **(B)** −1

    (C) 0   **(D)** 2

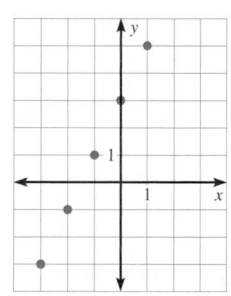

4.1   Plot Points in a Coordinate Plane   **209**

---

④ PRACTICE AND APPLY

Assignment Guide
📖 Answer Transparencies available for all exercises

Basic:
Day 1: SRH p. 921 Exs. 7–21 odd
pp. 209–212
Exs. 1, 2, 3–11 odd, 13–17, 22–30, 36–39, 42–54 even

Average:
Day 1: pp. 209–212
Exs. 1, 2, 7–13 odd, 16–22 even, 23, 24–32 even, 33–40, 43–53 odd

Advanced:
Day 1: pp. 209–212
Exs. 1, 2, 10–13, 19–23, 26–28, 31–35*, 38–41*, 43–53 odd

Block:
pp. 209–212
Exs. 1, 2, 7–13 odd, 16–22 even, 23, 24–32 even, 33–40, 43–53 odd (with 4.2)

Differentiated Instruction
See *Algebra 1 Best Practices Toolkit* for suggestions on addressing the needs of a diverse classroom.

Homework Check
For a quick check of student understanding of key concepts, go over the following exercises:
Basic: 7, 16, 24, 36, 37
Average: 9, 18, 26, 36, 38
Advanced: 12, 20, 27, 38, 39

Extra Practice
• Student Edition, p. 941
• Chapter 4 Resource Book:
Practice levels A, B, C, pp. 5–10

Practice Worksheet
An easily-readable reduced practice page (with answers) for this lesson can be found on p. 204C.

14–21.

Avoiding Common Errors

Exercises 3–21 Since students may switch *x*- and *y*-coordinates, you may want to remind them that the *x*-coordinate is the first number in an ordered pair and the *y*-coordinate the second.

Study Strategy

Exercise 23 Remind students that the range represents the *y*-values of the function. Have them rephrase the question as "Which *y*-value below is shown on the graph?"

Teaching Strategy

Exercise 35 Encourage students to create and use a visual model, such as the model of the coordinate plane shown in the introduction on page 206, to help determine the quadrant of each of the points.

24.

25.

26.

27.

28.

GRAPHING FUNCTIONS Graph the function with the given domain. Then identify the range of the function. **24–27. See margin for art.**

24. $y = -x + 1$; domain: $-2, -1, 0, 1, 2$
$-1, 0, 1, 2, 3$

25. $y = 2x - 5$; domain: $-2, -1, 0, 1, 2$
$-9, -7, -5, -3, -1$

26. $y = -\frac{2}{3}x - 1$; domain: $-6, -3, 0, 3, 6$
$-5, -3, -1, 1, 3$

27. $y = \frac{1}{2}x + 1$; domain: $-6, -4, -2, 0, 2$
$-2, -1, 0, 1, 2$

B **28.** ⊘ **GEOMETRY** Plot the points $W(-4, -2)$, $X(-4, 4)$, $Y(4, 4)$, and $Z(4, -2)$ in a coordinate plane. Connect the points in order. Connect point Z to point W. Identify the resulting figure. Find its perimeter and area.
See margin for art; rectangle; perimeter: 28 units; area: 48 square units.

REASONING Without plotting the point, tell whether it is in Quadrant I, II, III, or IV. *Explain* your reasoning. **29–32. See margin.**

29. $(4, -11)$ **30.** $(40, -40)$ **31.** $(-18, 15)$ **32.** $(-32, -22)$

33. ★ WRITING *Explain* how can you tell by looking at the coordinates of a point whether the point is on the *x*-axis or on the *y*-axis.

> **33.** If the *x*-coordinate is 0, then the point is on the *y*-axis. If the *y*-coordinate is 0, then the point is on the *x*-axis.

C **34. REASONING** Plot the point $J(-4, 3)$ in a coordinate plane. Plot three additional points in the same coordinate plane so that each of the four points lies in a different quadrant and the figure formed by connecting the points is a square. *Explain* how you located the points. **See margin.**

35. CHALLENGE Suppose the point (a, b) lies in Quadrant IV. *Describe* the location of the following points: (b, a), $(2a, -2b)$, and $(-b, -a)$. *Explain* your reasoning. **See margin.**

PROBLEM SOLVING

A **36. ASTRONAUT PHOTOGRAPHY** Astronauts use a coordinate system to describe the locations of objects they photograph from space. The *x*-axis is the equator, 0° latitude. The *y*-axis is the prime meridian, 0° longitude. The names and coordinates of some lakes photographed from space are given. Use the map to determine on which continent each lake is located.

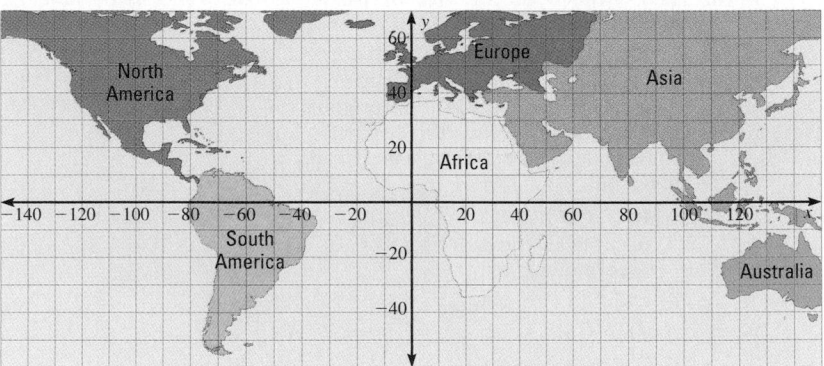

a. Lake Kulundinskoye: $(80, 53)$ **Asia**   **b.** Lake Champlain: $(-73, 45)$ **North America**

c. Lake Van: $(43, 39)$ **Asia**   **d.** Lake Viedma: $(-73, -50)$ **South America**

e. Lake Saint Clair: $(-83, 43)$ **North America**   **f.** Starnberger Lake: $(12, 48)$ **Europe**

@HomeTutor for problem solving help at classzone.com

○ = **WORKED-OUT SOLUTIONS** on p. WS1   ★ = **STANDARDIZED TEST PRACTICE**   ◆ = **MULTIPLE REPRESENTATIONS**

210

29–32. See Additional Answers beginning on p. AA1.

34. *Sample answer:*

Decide on a side length of a square that is greater than 4, like 5, so the other points will be in different quadrants. Add 5 to the *x*-coordinate of *J*, -4, to find the point $(1, 3)$ in Quadrant I. Then subtract 5 from the *y*-coordinate of *J* to find the point $(-4, -2)$ in Quadrant 3. Then add 5 to the *x*-coordinate of $(-4, -2)$ and add 5 to the *y*-coordinate of $(1, 3)$ to find the point $(1, -2)$ in Quadrant IV.

EXAMPLE 4
on p. 208
for Exs. 37–39

37. There is exactly one low temperature for each day in February; see margin for art.

(37.) RECORD TEMPERATURES The table shows the record low temperatures (in degrees Fahrenheit) for Odessa, Texas, for each day in the first week of February. *Explain* how you know the table represents a function. Graph the data from the table.

Day in February	1	2	3	4	5	6	7
Record low (degrees Fahrenheit)	−8	−11	10	8	10	9	11

@HomeTutor for problem solving help at classzone.com

38. STOCK VALUE The table shows the change in value (in dollars) of a stock over five days.

Day	1	2	3	4	5
Change in value (dollars)	−0.30	0.10	0.15	0.35	0.11

  a. *Explain* how you know the table represents a function. Graph the data from the table. **There is exactly one change in value for each day; see margin for art.**

  b. *Describe* any trend in the change in value of the stock.
    Sample answer: **The change in value increases until day 4, and then decreases.**

[B] 39. MULTI-STEP PROBLEM The difference between what the federal government collects and what it spends during a fiscal year is called the federal surplus or deficit. The table shows the federal surplus or deficit (in billions of dollars) in the 1990s. (A negative number represents a deficit.)

Years since 1990	0	1	2	3	4	5	6	7	8	9
Surplus or deficit (billions)	−221	−269	−290	−255	−203	−164	−108	−22	69	126

  a. Graph the function represented by the table. **See margin.**

  b. What conclusions can you make from the graph?
    Sample answer: **From 1992 to 1999 the federal deficit was decreasing.**

40. ◆ MULTIPLE REPRESENTATIONS Low-density lipoproteins (LDL) transport cholesterol in the bloodstream throughout the body. A high LDL number is associated with an increased risk of cardiovascular disease. A patient's LDL number in 1999 was 189 milligrams per deciliter (mg/dL). To lower that number, the patient went on a diet. The annual LDL numbers for the patient in years after 1999 are 169, 154, 145, 139, and 136.

Years since 1999	1	2	? 3	? 4	? 5
Changes in LDL (mg/dL)	−20	−15	?−9	?−6	?−3

  a. Making a Table Use the given information to copy and complete the table that shows the change in the patient's LDL number since 1999.

  b. Drawing a Graph Graph the ordered pairs from the table. **See margin.**

  c. Describing in Words Based on the graph, what can you conclude about the diet's effectiveness in lowering the patient's LDL number?
    Sample answer: **The diet is lowering the patient's LDL number.**

4.1 Plot Points in a Coordinate Plane **211**

35. For (*b*, *a*): Quadrant II; since (*a*, *b*) is in Quadrant IV, *a* must be positive and *b* must be negative, so the coordinates of (*b*, *a*) must be negative and positive. For (2*a*, −2*b*): Quadrant I; since (*a*, *b*) is in Quadrant IV, *a* must be positive and *b* must be negative, so the coordinates of (2*a*, −2*b*) must both be positive. For (−*b*, −*a*): Quadrant IV; since (*a*, *b*) is in Quadrant IV, *a* must be positive and *b* must be negative, so the coordinates of (−*b*, −*a*) must be positive and negative.

Vocabulary

Exercise 39 Students may be confused by the term "fiscal year." Tell them that a fiscal year refers to an accounting period of 12 months or 365 days, but the period may or may not correspond to the calendar year. The federal fiscal year runs from October through September.

Mathematical Reasoning

Exercises 39, 40 You may want to point out that both tables show years since a certain date, but the table in Exercise 39 begins with year 0, whereas the table in Exercise 40 begins with year 1. Lead students to see why the table in Exercise 40 must begin with year 1 and not year 0.

🌐 Internet Reference

Exercise 40 For more information about low-density lipoproteins, visit my.webmd.com/hw/cholesterol_management/hw207814.asp

37.

38a.

39a.

40b.

C **41.** ★ **EXTENDED RESPONSE** In a scientific study, researchers asked men to report their heights and weights. Then the researchers measured the actual heights and weights of the men. The data for six men are shown in the table. One row of the table represents the data for one man.

	Height (inches)			Weight (pounds)		
	Reported	Measured	Difference	Reported	Measured	Difference
	70	68	70 − 68 = 2	154	146	154 − 146 = 8
	70	67.5	? **2.5**	141	143	? **−2**
	78.5	77.5	? **1**	165	168	? **−3**
	68	69	? **−1**	146	143	? **3**
	71	72	? **−1**	220	223	? **−3**
	70	70	? **0**	176	176	? **0**

a. Calculate Copy and complete the table.

b. Graph For each participant, write an ordered pair (x, y) where x is the difference of the reported and measured heights and y is the difference of the reported and measured weights. Then plot the ordered pairs in a coordinate plane. **(2, 8), (2.5, −2), (1, −3), (−1, 3), (−1, −3), (0, 0); see margin for art.**

40c. Sample answer: A person who reported the same information that was measured.

c. CHALLENGE What does the origin represent in this situation?

d. CHALLENGE Which quadrant has the greatest number of points? *Explain* what it means for a point to be in that quadrant. **Quadrant IV; the person reported a greater height than was measured and a lesser weight than was measured.**

MIXED REVIEW

Evaluate the expression.

42. $4 + 2x^2$ when $x = 6$ *(p. 2)* **76**

43. $6 \cdot 2a^2$ when $a = 3$ *(p. 2)* **108**

44. $4 + 2(−7) + 3$ *(p. 8)* **−7**

45. $3(35 − 18)$ *(p. 8)* **51**

Use the distributive property to write an equivalent expression. *(p. 96)*

46. $6(x + 20)$ **$6x + 120$**

47. $3x(x + 9)$ **$3x^2 + 27x$**

48. $−(4 − 5y)$ **$−4 + 5y$**

49. TRAVEL You are traveling on the highway at an average speed of 55 miles per hour. How long will it take you to drive 66 miles? *(p. 168)* **1.2 h or 1 h 12 min**

PREVIEW

Prepare for Lesson 4.2 in Exs. 50–54.

Write the equation so that y is a function of x. *(p. 184)*

50. $4x + y = 6$ **$y = −4x + 6$**

51. $x + 7y = 14$ **$y = −\frac{1}{7}x + 2$**

52. $4(y − 6x) = 12$ **$y = 6x + 3$**

Tell whether the pairing is a function. *(p. 35)*

53.

Input	−5	−4	−3	−2
Output	−2	0	2	4

function

54.

Input	−1	0	1	2
Output	10	10	4	1

function

Perform Transformations

GOAL Perform and describe transformations in a coordinate plane.

Key Vocabulary
• transformation
• translation
• vertical stretch or shrink
• reflection

For a given set of points, a **transformation** produces an image by applying a rule to the coordinates of the points. Some types of transformations are *translations*, *vertical stretches*, *vertical shrinks*, and *reflections*.

A **translation** moves every point in a figure the same distance in the same direction either horizontally, vertically, or both. You can describe translations algebraically.

Horizontal translation: $(x, y) \rightarrow (x + h, y)$ **Vertical translation:** $(x, y) \rightarrow (x, y + k)$

EXAMPLE 1 Perform a translation

READ TRANSFORMATIONS
If a transformation is performed on a point *A*, the new location of point *A* is indicated by *A'* (read "*A* prime").

The transformation $(x, y) \rightarrow (x, y + 3)$ moves $\triangle ABC$ up 3 units.

Original		Image
$A(3, 0)$	$\rightarrow$	$A'(3, 3)$
$B(4, 2)$	$\rightarrow$	$B'(4, 5)$
$C(5, 0)$	$\rightarrow$	$C'(5, 3)$

The result of the transformation is $\triangle A'B'C'$.

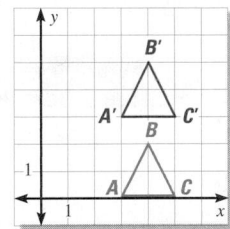

A **vertical stretch or shrink** moves every point in a figure away from the *x*-axis (a vertical stretch) or toward the *x*-axis (a vertical shrink), while points on the *x*-axis remain fixed. A **reflection** flips a figure in a line. You can describe vertical stretches and shrinks with or without reflection in the *x*-axis algebraically.

Vertical stretch:
$(x, y) \rightarrow (x, ay)$ where $a > 1$

Vertical shrink:
$(x, y) \rightarrow (x, ay)$ where $0 < a < 1$

Vertical stretch with reflection in the *x*-axis:
$(x, y) \rightarrow (x, ay)$ where $a < -1$

Vertical shrink with reflection in the *x*-axis:
$(x, y) \rightarrow (x, ay)$ where $-1 < a < 0$

EXAMPLE 2 Perform a vertical stretch with reflection

The transformation $(x, y) \rightarrow (x, -2y)$ vertically stretches $\triangle ABC$ and reflects it in the *x*-axis.

Original		Image
$A(3, 0)$	$\rightarrow$	$A'(3, 0)$
$B(4, 2)$	$\rightarrow$	$B'(4, -4)$
$C(5, 0)$	$\rightarrow$	$C'(5, 0)$

The result of the transformation is $\triangle A'B'C'$.

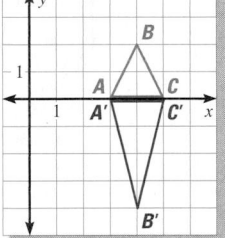

Extension: Perform Transformations **213**

① **PLAN AND PREPARE**

Warm-Up Exercises
Plot the points in a coordinate plane.
1. $A(-2, 1)$ **2.** $B(-1, -3)$
3. $C(4, -2)$ **4.** $D(1, 0)$

② **FOCUS AND MOTIVATE**

Essential Question
Big Idea 2, p. 205
How do you transform figures in the coordinate plane? Tell students they will learn how to answer this question by describing and performing translations, dilations, and reflections on figures in the coordinate plane.

③ **TEACH**

Extra Example 1
Describe the transformation of $\triangle ABC$ to $\triangle A'B'C'$. The transformation is $(x, y) \rightarrow (x - 4, y)$. $\triangle ABC$ is moved left 4 units.

NCTM STANDARDS

Standard 3: Apply transformations to math situations

Standard 10: Use representations to communicate mathematical ideas

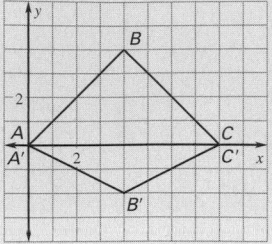
CONCEPT SUMMARY   *For Your Notebook*

Identifying Transformations

Translation		Vertical stretch or shrink	
Horizontal	**Vertical**	**Without reflection**	**With reflection**
$(x, y) \rightarrow (x + h, y)$	$(x, y) \rightarrow (x, y + k)$	$(x, y) \rightarrow (x, ay)$ where $a > 0$	$(x, y) \rightarrow (x, ay)$ where $a < 0$

PRACTICE

1. **VOCABULARY** Does a translation or a vertical stretch always produce a figure that is
   the same size and shape as the original figure? *Explain.* **See margin.**

2. ★ **WRITING** *Describe* the vertical shrink $(x, y) \rightarrow (x, \frac{1}{2}y)$ in words.
   Multiply each y-coordinate by $\frac{1}{2}$.

DESCRIBING TRANSFORMATIONS Use words to describe the transformation
of the blue figure to the red figure.

Subtract 4 from each y-coordinate.   Add 2 to each y-coordinate.

3.   4.   5.

  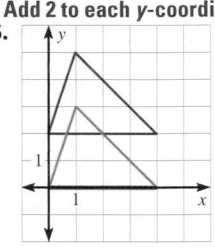

Multiply each y-coordinate by $-\frac{1}{2}$.

PERFORMING TRANSFORMATIONS Square *ABCD* has vertices at (0, 0),
(0, 2), (2, 2), and (2, 0). Perform the indicated transformation. Then give the
coordinates of figure A'B'C'D'.

6. $(x, y) \rightarrow (x, y - 5)$
   (0, −5), (0, −3), (2, −3), (2, −5)

7. $(x, y) \rightarrow (x, y + 1)$
   (0, 1), (0, 3), (2, 3), (2, 1)

8. $(x, y) \rightarrow (x, y - 7)$
   (0, −7), (0, −5), (2, −5), (2, −7)

9. $(x, y) \rightarrow (x, -y)$
   (0, 0), (0, −2), (2, −2), (2, 0)

10. $(x, y) \rightarrow (x, 4y)$
    (0, 0), (0, 8), (2, 8), (2, 0)

11. $(x, y) \rightarrow (x, -\frac{1}{2}y)$
    (0, 0), (0, −1), (2, −1), (2, 0)

12. $(x, y) \rightarrow (x + 2, y + 3)$
    (2, 3), (2, 5), (4, 5), (4, 3)

13. $(x, y) \rightarrow (x - 1, y + 4)$
    (−1, 4), (−1, 6), (1, 6), (1, 4)

14. $(x, y) \rightarrow (x + 3, y)$
    (3, 0), (3, 2), (5, 2), (5, 0)

15. ★ **WRITING** A square has vertices at (0, 0), (0, 3), (3, 3), and (3, 0).
    Tell how you could use a transformation to move the square so
    that it has new vertices at (0, 0), (0, −3), (3, −3), and (3, 0).
    Use the transformation $(x, y) \rightarrow (x, -y)$.

4.2 Graph Linear Equations

Before	You plotted points in a coordinate plane.
Now	You will graph linear equations in a coordinate plane.
Why?	So you can find how meteorologists collect data, as in Ex. 40.

Key Vocabulary
- standard form of a linear equation
- linear function

An example of an equation in two variables is $2x + 5y = 8$. A **solution of an equation in two variables**, x and y, is an ordered pair (x, y) that produces a true statement when the values of x and y are substituted into the equation.

★ EXAMPLE 1 Standardized Test Practice

> Which ordered pair is a solution of $3x - y = 7$?
>
> Ⓐ $(3, 4)$ Ⓑ $(1, -4)$ Ⓒ $(5, -3)$ Ⓓ $(-1, -2)$

Solution

Check whether each ordered pair is a solution of the equation.

Test $(3, 4)$:	$3x - y = 7$	**Write original equation.**
	$3(3) - 4 \stackrel{?}{=} 7$	**Substitute 3 for x and 4 for y.**
	$5 = 7$ ✗	**Simplify.**
Test $(1, -4)$:	$3x - y = 7$	**Write original equation.**
	$3(1) - (-4) \stackrel{?}{=} 7$	**Substitute 1 for x and -4 for y.**
	$7 = 7$ ✓	**Simplify.**

So, $(3, 4)$ is *not* a solution, but $(1, -4)$ is a solution of $3x - y = 7$.

▸ The correct answer is B. Ⓐ Ⓑ Ⓒ Ⓓ

✓ **GUIDED PRACTICE** for Example 1

1. Tell whether $\left(4, -\frac{1}{2}\right)$ is a solution of $x + 2y = 5$. **not a solution**

GRAPHS The **graph of an equation in two variables** is the set of points in a coordinate plane that represent all solutions of the equation. If the variables in an equation represent real numbers, one way to graph the equation is to make a table of values, plot enough points to recognize a pattern, and then connect the points. When making a table of values, choose convenient values of x that include negative values, zero, and positive values.

---

① PLAN AND PREPARE

Warm-Up Exercises
📠 **Transparency Available**

1. Graph $y = -x - 2$ with domain $-2, -1, 0, 1,$ and 2.

Rewrite the equation so y is a function of x.

2. $3x + 4y = 16$ $y = -\frac{3}{4}x + 4$

3. $-6x - 2y = -12$ $y = -3x + 6$

Notetaking Guide
📠 **Transparency Available**
Promotes interactive learning and notetaking skills, pp. 76–79.

Pacing
Basic: 2 days
Average: 2 days
Advanced: 2 days
Block: 0.5 block with 4.1
      0.5 block with 4.3
- See *Teaching Guide/Lesson Plan.*

② FOCUS AND MOTIVATE

Essential Question
Big Idea 1, p. 205
How do you graph linear equations? **Tell students they will learn how to answer this question by using tables to graph linear equations.**

NCTM STANDARDS
Standard 2: Use models to understand relationships

Standard 10: Use representations to communicate mathematical ideas

---

Resource Planning Guide

Chapter Resource Book
- Teaching Guide/Lesson Plan (pp. 16–17)
- Activity Master (p. 18)
- Practice levels A, B, C (pp. 20–25)
- Study Guide (pp. 26–27)
- Catch-up for Absent Students (p. 28)
- Problem Solving Workshop (p. 29)
- Challenge (p. 30)

Workbooks
- Notetaking Guide (pp. 76–79)
- Practice Workbook (pp. 49–51)

Teaching Options
- **Power Presentations CD-ROM** provides dynamic electronic teaching resources for the classroom.
- **Activity Generator CD-ROM** provides editable activities for all ability levels.

Interactive Technology
- Easy Planner
- Power Presentations CD-ROM
- Activity Generator CD-ROM
- Animated Algebra
- Test Generator CD-ROM
- Online Quiz
- eWorkbook
- eEdition
- @HomeTutor

Resources for English Learners
- Quick Reference for English Learners
- Spanish Study Guide
- Multi-Language Visual Glossary
- Student Resources in Spanish

See also the *Algebra 1 Toolkit* for more strategies for meeting individual needs.

215

❸ TEACH

Extra Example 1
Which ordered pair is a solution of $-x + 2y = 8$? **D**

Ⓐ $(2, 3)$ Ⓑ $(-2, 5)$
Ⓒ $(-1, 4)$ Ⓓ $(-2, 3)$

Key Questions to Ask for Example 1
• Are there other solutions of the equation? Explain. **Yes. Any ordered pair that produces a true statement is a solution.**
• What are some other solutions? **(3, 2), (2, −1), (0, −7)**

Extra Example 2
Graph the equation $2x + y = 2$.

Key Question to Ask for Example 2
• How many points on the line represent solutions of the equation? Explain. **Every point on the line is a solution of the equation, so there are an infinite number of solutions.**

❖ EXAMPLE 2 Graph an equation

Graph the equation $-2x + y = -3$.

Solution

> **DRAW A GRAPH**
> If you continued to find solutions of the equation and plotted them, the line would fill in.

STEP 1 **Solve** the equation for y.
$$-2x + y = -3$$
$$y = 2x - 3$$

STEP 2 **Make** a table by choosing a few values for x and finding the values of y.

x	−2	−1	0	1	2
y	−7	−5	−3	−1	1

STEP 3 **Plot** the points. Notice that the points appear to lie on a line.

STEP 4 **Connect** the points by drawing a line through them. Use arrows to indicate that the graph goes on without end.

LINEAR EQUATIONS A **linear equation** is an equation whose graph is a line, such as the equation in Example 2. The **standard form** of a linear equation is
$$Ax + By = C$$
where A, B, and C are real numbers and A and B are not both zero.

Consider what happens when $A = 0$ or when $B = 0$. When $A = 0$, the equation becomes $By = C$, or $y = \frac{C}{B}$. Because $\frac{C}{B}$ is a constant, you can write $y = b$. Similarly, when $B = 0$, the equation becomes $Ax = C$, or $x = \frac{C}{A}$, and you can write $x = a$.

EXAMPLE 3 Graph $y = b$ and $x = a$

Graph (a) $y = 2$ and (b) $x = -1$.

Solution

> **FIND A SOLUTION**
> The equations $y = 2$ and $0x + 1y = 2$ are equivalent. For any value of x, the ordered pair $(x, 2)$ is a solution of $y = 2$.

a. For every value of x, the value of y is 2. The graph of the equation $y = 2$ is a horizontal line 2 units above the x-axis.

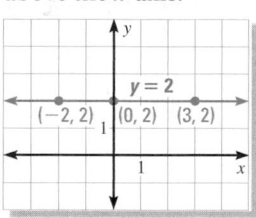

b. For every value of y, the value of x is −1. The graph of the equation $x = -1$ is a vertical line 1 unit to the left of the y-axis.

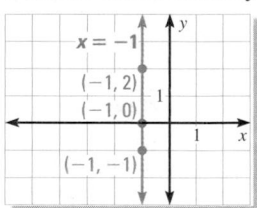

Animated Algebra at classzone.com

Differentiated Instruction

English Learners In Example 2, caution students that the figure is called a "graph of a line," and should not be confused with a *line graph* (p. 934). A line graph is a graph that uses line segments to connect data points. A graph of a line is a graph of a linear equation.

See also the *Algebra 1 Toolkit* for more strategies.

                            For Your Notebook

Equations of Horizontal and Vertical Lines

The graph of $y = b$ is a horizontal line. The line passes through the point $(0, b)$.

The graph of $x = a$ is a vertical line. The line passes through the point $(a, 0)$.

✓ **GUIDED PRACTICE**   for Examples 2 and 3

Graph the equation.   **2–4. See margin.**

2. $y + 3x = -2$ **3.** $y = 2.5$ **4.** $x = -4$

LINEAR FUNCTIONS In Example 3, $y = 2$ is a function, while $x = -1$ is not a function. The equation $Ax + By = C$ represents a **linear function** provided $B \neq 0$ (that is, provided the graph of the equation is not a vertical line). If the domain of a linear function is not specified, it is understood to be all real numbers. The domain can be restricted, as shown in Example 4.

EXAMPLE 4   **Graph a linear function**

Graph the function $y = -\frac{1}{2}x + 4$ with domain $x \geq 0$. Then identify the range of the function.

Solution

ANALYZE A FUNCTION
The function in Example 4 is called a *continuous* function. To learn about continuous functions, see p. 223.

STEP 1   **Make** a table.

x	0	2	4	6	8
y	4	3	2	1	0

STEP 2   **Plot** the points.

STEP 3   **Connect** the points with a ray because the domain is restricted.

STEP 4   **Identify** the range. From the graph, you can see that all points have a y-coordinate of 4 or less, so the range of the function is $y \leq 4$.

✓ **GUIDED PRACTICE**   for Example 4

5. Graph the function $y = -3x + 1$ with domain $x \leq 0$. Then identify the range of the function.   **See margin for art; $y \geq 1$.**

4.2   Graph Linear Equations   **217**

2–4. See Additional Answers beginning on p. AA1.

5.

$y = -3x + 1$

Extra Example 3

Graph (a) $y = -3$ and (b) $x = 2$.

a.

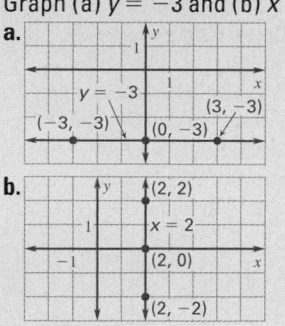

$y = -3$ $(-3, -3)$ $(3, -3)$ $(0, -3)$

b.

$(2, 2)$ $x = 2$ $(2, 0)$ $(2, -2)$

Key Question to Ask for Example 3

• Why is the graph of $y = b$ a horizontal line for any value of b? **All the y-coordinates are the same, so a line connecting points on the graph is horizontal.**

Animated Algebra
classzone.com

An **Animated Algebra** activity is available on-line for **Example 3**. This activity is also available on the **Power Presentations CD-ROM**.

Extra Example 4

Graph the function $y = \frac{1}{2}x - 1$ with domain $x \leq 0$. Then identify the range of the function.   **range: $y \leq -1$**

$y = \frac{1}{2}x - 1$

Key Questions to Ask for Example 4

• Why do the x-values in the table begin with 0? **It is the least value in the domain $x \geq 0$.**

• Does the range include negative numbers? Explain. **Yes; when $x > 8$, the values of y are negative.**

Extra Example 5

The number of pages a student types is given by $p = 4t$ where t is the time (in hours) spent typing. The student plans to type for at most 2.5 hours. Graph the function and identify its domain and range. **domain: $0 \le t \le 2.5$; range: $0 \le p \le 10$**

Extra Example 6

Suppose the student in Extra Example 5 plans to type at most 14 pages. Graph the function and identify its domain and range. **domain: $0 \le t \le 3.5$; range: $0 \le p \le 14$**

Closing the Lesson

Have students summarize the major points of the lesson and answer the Essential Question: How do you graph linear equations?

- **All points on the graph of a linear equation are solutions of the equation.**

- **Use a line to connect points when the domain is unrestricted, a ray when it is restricted, and a segment when both domain and range are restricted.**

Make a table of appropriate *x*-values, determine corresponding *y*-values, plot the points from the table, and connect the points with a line.

EXAMPLE 5   Solve a multi-step problem

RUNNING The distance d (in miles) that a runner travels is given by the function $d = 6t$ where t is the time (in hours) spent running. The runner plans to go for a 1.5 hour run. Graph the function and identify its domain and range.

Solution

STEP 1 **Identify** whether the problem specifies the domain or the range. You know the amount of time the runner plans to spend running. Because time is the independent variable, the domain is specified in this problem. The domain of the function is $0 \le t \le 1.5$.

> **ANALYZE GRAPHS**
> In Example 2, the domain is unrestricted, and the graph is a *line*. In Example 4, the domain is restricted to $x \ge 0$, and the graph is a *ray*. Here, the domain is restricted to $0 \le t \le 1.5$, and the graph is a *line segment*.

STEP 2 **Graph** the function. Make a table of values. Then plot and connect the points.

t (hours)	0	0.5	1	1.5
d (miles)	0	3	6	9

STEP 3 **Identify** the unspecified domain or range. From the table or graph, you can see that the range of the function is $0 \le d \le 9$.

EXAMPLE 6   Solve a related problem

WHAT IF? Suppose the runner in Example 5 instead plans to run 12 miles. Graph the function and identify its domain and range.

Solution

STEP 1 **Identify** whether the problem specifies the domain or the range. You are given the distance that the runner plans to travel. Because distance is the dependent variable, the range is specified in this problem. The range of the function is $0 \le d \le 12$.

STEP 2 **Graph** the function. To make a table, you can substitute d-values (be sure to include 0 and 12) into the function $d = 6t$ and solve for t.

> **SOLVE FOR t**
> To find the time it takes the runner to run 12 miles, solve the equation $6t = 12$ to get $t = 2$.

t (hours)	0	1	2
d (miles)	0	6	12

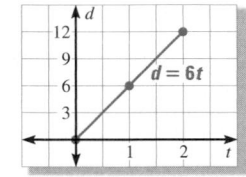

STEP 3 **Identify** the unspecified domain or range. From the table or graph, you can see that the domain of the function is $0 \le t \le 2$.

✓ **GUIDED PRACTICE**   for Examples 5 and 6

6. **GAS COSTS** For gas that costs $2 per gallon, the equation $C = 2g$ gives the cost C (in dollars) of pumping g gallons of gas. You plan to pump $10 worth of gas. Graph the function and identify its domain and range.
   See margin for art; domain: $0 \le g \le 5$, range: $0 \le C \le 10$.

6.

4.2 EXERCISES

HOMEWORK
KEY

○ = WORKED-OUT SOLUTIONS
on p. WS1 or Exs. 3, 11, and 37

★ = STANDARDIZED TEST PRACTICE
Exs. 2, 10, 32, 33, 39, and 41

◆ = MULTIPLE REPRESENTATIONS
Ex. 40

PRACTICE
AND APPLY

SKILL PRACTICE

[A] 1. **VOCABULARY** The equation $Ax + By = C$ represents a(n) _?_ provided $B \neq 0$. **linear function**

2. ★ **WRITING** Is the equation $y = 6x + 4$ in standard form? *Explain.*
No, to be in standard form it should be in the form $Ax + By = C$, so it should be $-6x + y = 4$.

CHECKING SOLUTIONS Tell whether the ordered pair is a solution of the equation.

EXAMPLE 1
on p. 215
for Exs. 3–10

3. $2y + x = 4$; $(-2, 3)$ **solution**   4. $3x - 2y = -5$; $(-1, 1)$ **solution**   5. $x = 9$; $(9, 6)$ **solution**

6. $y = -7$; $(-7, 0)$ **not a solution**   7. $-7x - 4y = 1$; $(-3, -5)$ **not a solution**   8. $-5y - 6x = 0$; $(-6, 5)$ **not a solution**

9. **ERROR ANALYSIS** *Describe* and correct the error in determining whether $(8, 11)$ is a solution of $y - x = -3$. **The 8 should be substituted for *x* and 11 for *y*, $11 - 8 \neq -3$, so (8, 11) is not a solution.**

$y - x = -3$
$8 - 11 = -3$
$-3 = -3$ (8, 11) is a solution.

10. ★ **MULTIPLE CHOICE** Which ordered pair is a solution of $6x + 3y = 18$? **B**

(A) $(-2, -10)$ (B) $(-2, 10)$ (C) $(2, 10)$ (D) $(10, -2)$

EXAMPLES 2 and 3
on p. 216
for Exs. 11–25

GRAPHING EQUATIONS Graph the equation. **11–22. See margin.**

11. $y + x = 2$ 12. $y - 2x = 5$ 13. $y - 3x = 0$ 14. $y + 4x = 1$

15. $2y - 6x = 10$ 16. $3y + 4x = 12$ 17. $x - 2y = 3$ 18. $3x + 2y = 8$

19. $x = 0$ 20. $y = 0$ 21. $y = -4$ 22. $x = 2$

MATCHING EQUATIONS WITH GRAPHS Match the equation with its graph.

23. $y - x = 0$ **C**   24. $x = -2$ **A**   25. $y = -1$ **B**

A.   B.   C.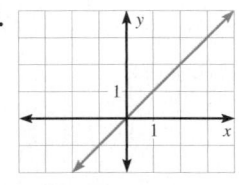

EXAMPLE 4 [B]
on p. 217
for Exs. 26–31

GRAPHING FUNCTIONS Graph the function with the given domain. Then identify the range of the function. **26–31. See margin for art.**

26. $y = 3x - 2$; domain: $x \geq 0$ $y \geq -2$ 27. $y = -5x + 3$; domain: $x \leq 0$ $y \geq 3$

28. $y = 4$; domain: $x \leq 5$ $y = 4$ 29. $y = -6$; domain: $x \geq 5$ $y = -6$

30. $y = 2x + 3$; domain: $-4 \leq x \leq 0$ $-5 \leq y \leq 3$ 31. $y = -x - 1$; domain: $-1 \leq x \leq 3$ $-4 \leq y \leq 0$

32. ★ **OPEN-ENDED** Graph $x - y = 3$ and $2x - 2y = 6$. *Explain* why the equations look different but have the same graph. Find another equation that looks different from the two given equations but has the same graph. **See margin for art; the equations are the same, each term in the first equation was multiplied by 2 to get the second equation. *Sample answer:* $3x - 3y = 9$**

4.2 Graph Linear Equations   **219**

Assignment Guide

Answer Transparencies available for all exercises

Basic:
Day 1: EP p. 938 Exs. 33–36
pp. 219–221
Exs. 1–10, 11–21 odd, 23–25, 42–47
Day 2: pp. 219–221
Exs. 26–29, 35–39, 48–55

Average:
Day 1: pp. 219–221
Exs. 1–10, 16–25, 42–47
Day 2: pp. 219–221
Exs. 26–32 even, 33, 35–40, 48–55

Advanced:
Day 1: pp. 219–221
Exs. 1, 2, 5–10, 17–25, 34, 42–47
Day 2: pp. 219–221
Exs. 29–33, 36–41*, 48–55

Block:
pp. 219–221
Exs. 1–10, 16–25, 42–47 (with 4.1)
pp. 219–221
Exs. 26–32 even, 33, 35–40, 48–55 (with 4.3)

Differentiated Instruction

See *Algebra 1 Best Practices Toolkit* for suggestions on addressing the needs of a diverse classroom.

Homework Check

For a quick check of student understanding of key concepts, go over the following exercises:
Basic: 4, 14, 21, 26, 35
Average: 6, 17, 22, 28, 36
Advanced: 7, 18, 30, 37, 38

Extra Practice

• Student Edition, p. 941
• Chapter 4 Resource Book:
Practice levels A, B, C, pp. 20–25

Practice Worksheet

An easily-readable reduced practice page (with answers) for this lesson can be found on p. 204C.

11–22, 26–31. See Additional Answers beginning on p. AA1.

32.

$x - y = 3$
$2x - 2y = 6$

219

35.

36.

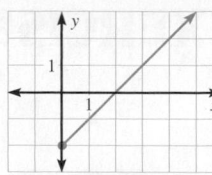

33. ★ **MULTIPLE CHOICE** Which statement is true for the function whose graph is shown? **D**

   Ⓐ The domain is unrestricted.

   Ⓑ The domain is $x \le -2$.

   Ⓒ The range is $y \le -2$.

   Ⓓ The range is $y \ge -2$.

34. **CHALLENGE** If $(3, n)$ is a solution of $Ax + 3y = 6$ and $(n, 5)$ is a solution of $5x + y = 20$, what is the value of A? **−1**

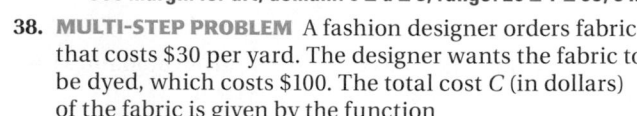

PROBLEM SOLVING

35. **BAKING** The weight w (in pounds) of a loaf of bread that a recipe yields is given by the function $w = \frac{1}{2}f$ where f is the number of cups of flour used. You have 4 cups of flour. Graph the function and identify its domain and range. What is the weight of the largest loaf of bread you can make?

@HomeTutor for problem solving help at classzone.com

   See margin for art; domain: $0 \le f \le 4$, range: $0 \le w \le 2$; 2 lb.

36. **TRAVEL** After visiting relatives who live 200 miles away, your family drives home at an average speed of 50 miles per hour. Your distance d (in miles) from home is given by $d = 200 - 50t$ where t is the time (in hours) spent driving. Graph the function and identify its domain and range. What is your distance from home after driving for 1.5 hours?

@HomeTutor for problem solving help at classzone.com

   See margin for art; domain: $0 \le t \le 4$, range: $0 \le d \le 200$; 125 mi.

37. **EARTH SCIENCE** The temperature T (in degrees Celsius) of Earth's crust can be modeled by the function $T = 20 + 25d$ where d is the distance (in kilometers) from the surface.

   a. A scientist studies organisms in the first 4 kilometers of Earth's crust. Graph the function and identify its domain and range. What is the temperature at the deepest part of the section of crust?
   See margin for art; domain: $0 \le d \le 4$, range: $20 \le T \le 120$; 120°C.

   b. Suppose the scientist studies organisms in a section of the crust where the temperature is between 20°C and 95°C. Graph the function and identify its domain and range. How many kilometers deep is the section of crust?
   See margin for art; domain: $0 \le d \le 3$, range: $20 \le T \le 95$; 3 km.

Ⓑ **38.** **MULTI-STEP PROBLEM** A fashion designer orders fabric that costs $30 per yard. The designer wants the fabric to be dyed, which costs $100. The total cost C (in dollars) of the fabric is given by the function

$$C = 30f + 100$$

where f is the number of yards of fabric.

38b. $13\frac{1}{3}$ yd; substitute 500 in for C and solve for f.

   a. The designer orders 3 yards of fabric. How much does the fabric cost? *Explain.* **$190; substitute 3 in for f and solve.**

   b. Suppose the designer can spend $500 on fabric. How many yards of fabric can the designer buy? *Explain.*

220

○ = **WORKED-OUT SOLUTIONS** on p. WS1

★ = **STANDARDIZED TEST PRACTICE**

◆ = **MULTIPLE REPRESENTATIONS**

37a.

37b.

39. ★ **SHORT RESPONSE** An emergency cell phone charger requires you to turn a small crank in order to create the energy needed to recharge the phone's battery. If you turn the crank 120 times per minute, the total number r of revolutions that you turn the crank is given by

$$r = 120t$$

where t is the time (in minutes) spent turning the crank.

  a. Graph the function and identify its domain and range.

  b. Identify the domain and range if you stop turning the crank after 4 minutes. *Explain* how this affects the appearance of the graph.

40. ◆ **MULTIPLE REPRESENTATIONS** The National Weather Service releases weather balloons twice daily at over 90 locations in the United States in order to collect data for meteorologists. The height h (in feet) of a balloon is a function of the time t (in seconds) after the balloon is released, as shown.

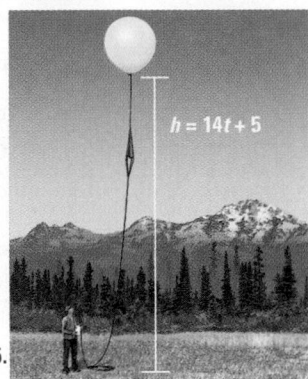

$h = 14t + 5$

  a. **Making a Table** Make a table showing the height of a balloon after t seconds for $t = 0$ through $t = 10$. **See margin.**

  b. **Drawing a Graph** A balloon bursts after a flight of about 7200 seconds. Graph the function and identify the domain and range.
  See margin for art; domain: $0 \leq t \leq 7200$, range: $5 \leq h \leq 100,805$.

Ⓒ **41.** ★ **EXTENDED RESPONSE** Students can pay for lunch at a school in one of two ways. Students can either make a payment of $30 per month or they can buy lunch daily for $2.50 per lunch.

  a. **Graph** Graph the function $y = 30$ to represent the monthly payment plan. Using the same coordinate plane, graph the function $y = 2.5x$ to represent the daily payment plan. **See margin.**

  b. **CHALLENGE** What are the coordinates of the point that is a solution of both functions? What does that point mean in this situation?

  c. **CHALLENGE** A student eats an average of 15 school lunches per month. How should the student pay, daily or monthly? *Explain.*
  Monthly; if he pays daily it will cost $37.50, if he pays monthly it will cost only $30.

MIXED REVIEW

Solve the equation.

42. $12x = 144$ *(p. 134)* **12**

43. $-4x = 30$ *(p. 134)* **−7.5**

44. $5.7x - 2x = 14.8$ *(p. 141)* **4**

45. $x - 4(x + 13) = 26$ *(p. 148)* **−26**

46. $6x - 4x + 13 = 27 - 2x$ *(p. 154)* **3.5**

47. $5x - \frac{1}{4}(24 + 8x) = 2x - 5$ *(p. 154)* **1**

Plot the point in a coordinate plane. *Describe* the location of the point. *(p. 206)*
48–55. See margin for art.

48. (3, 5) **Quadrant I**   **49.** (−3, 2) **Quadrant II** **50.** (0, −2) **y-axis**   **51.** (−5, 0) **x-axis**

52. (−2, −2)   **53.** $\left(\frac{1}{3}, 0\right)$ **x-axis**   **54.** $\left(-\frac{1}{2}, \frac{3}{4}\right)$ **Quadrant II** **55.** (0, 6.2) **y-axis**
Quadrant III

48–55.

1 PLAN AND PREPARE

Learn the Method
- Students will graph an equation on a graphing calculator and use the equation to solve a problem.
- After the activity, students can use a graphing calculator to check their solutions in Exercises 35–40 in Lesson 4.2.

Keystroke Help
Keystrokes for several models of calculators are available in black line format in the *Chapter 4 Resource Book*.

2 TEACH

Tips for Success
As students are working on Step 2, mention that they can change existing minimums and maximums of a window by entering new data or by using the zoom feature on their calculators.

Extra Example
The total cost *C* to buy a water cooler and bottles of water can be modeled by $C = 115 + 5.65b$ where *b* is the number of bottles. Graph the equation. Estimate the total cost when the number of bottles is 18.
about $217

3 ASSESS AND RETEACH

The fee *f* to use a photo lab can be modeled by $f = 12 + 4.25v$ where *v* is the number of visits.
1. Find the fee after 15 visits.
   $75.75
2. Find the number of visits if the fee is $63. **12 visits**

4.2 Graphing Linear Equations

QUESTION How do you graph an equation on a graphing calculator?

EXAMPLE Use a graph to solve a problem

The formula to convert temperature from degrees Fahrenheit to degrees Celsius is $C = \frac{5}{9}(F - 32)$. Graph the equation. At what temperature are degrees Fahrenheit and degrees Celsius equal?

STEP 1 *Rewrite and enter equation*

Rewrite the equation using *x* for *F* and *y* for *C*. Enter the equation into the ▢Y= screen. Put parentheses around the fraction $\frac{5}{9}$.

STEP 2 *Set window*

The screen is a "window" that lets you look at part of a coordinate plane. Press ▢WINDOW to set the borders of the graph. A friendly window for this equation is $-94 \le x \le 94$ and $-100 \le y \le 100$.

STEP 3 *Graph and trace equation*

Press ▢TRACE and use the left and right arrows to move the cursor along the graph until the *x*-coordinate and *y*-coordinate are equal. From the graph, you can see that degrees Fahrenheit and degrees Celsius are equal at −40.

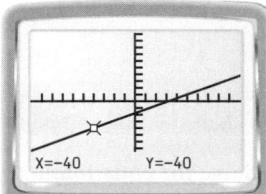

PRACTICE

Graph the equation. Find the unknown value in the ordered pair.

1. $y = 8 - x$; (2.4, _?_) **5.6**
2. $y = 2x + 3$; (_?_, 0.8) **−1.1**
3. $y = -4.5x + 1$; (1.4, _?_) **−5.3**

4. **SPEED OF SOUND** The speed *s* (in meters per second) of sound in air can be modeled by $s = 331.1 + 0.61T$ where *T* is the air temperature in degrees Celsius. Graph the equation. Estimate the speed of sound when the temperature is 20°C. **343.3 m/sec**

Identify Discrete and Continuous Functions

GOAL Graph and classify discrete and continuous functions.

Key Vocabulary
• discrete function
• continuous function

The graph of a function can consist of individual points, as in the graph in Example 3 on page 207. The graph of a function can also be a line or a part of a line with no breaks, as in the graph in Example 4 on page 217.

> ### KEY CONCEPT *For Your Notebook*
>
> **Identifying Discrete and Continuous Functions**
>
> A **discrete function** has a graph that consists of isolated points.
>
> A **continuous function** has a graph that is unbroken.
>
>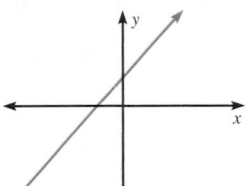

EXAMPLE 1 **Graph and classify a function**

Graph the function $y = 2x - 1$ with the given domain. Classify the function as discrete or continuous.

a. Domain: $x = 0, 1, 2, 3$

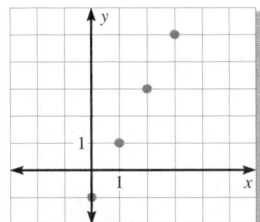

The graph consists of individual points, so the function is discrete.

b. Domain: $x \geq 0$

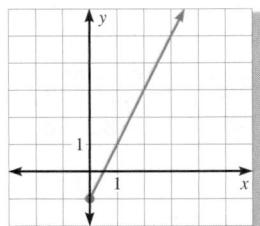

The graph is unbroken, so the function is continuous.

GRAPHS As a general rule, you can tell that a function is continuous if you do not have to lift your pencil from the paper to draw its graph, as in part (b) of Example 1.

---

① PLAN AND PREPARE

Warm-Up Exercises

1. What is the range of $y = -x + 3$ with domain 0, 1, 2, and 4.
   3, 2, 1, −1

2. Graph $y = \frac{1}{3}x + 1$.

② FOCUS AND MOTIVATE

Essential Question
Big Idea 1, p. 205

How do you tell if a function is discrete or continuous? **Tell students they will learn how to answer this question by graphing functions with individual points and lines or parts of lines.**

③ TEACH

Extra Example 1

Graph the function $y = \frac{1}{2}x + 1$ with the domain $x \geq 0$. Classify the function as discrete or continuous.

continuous

NCTM STANDARDS

Standard 2: Understand functions

Standard 10: Use representations to communicate mathematical ideas

EXAMPLE 2   Classify and graph a real-world function

Extra Example 2

Tell whether the function represented by the table is discrete or continuous. Explain. If continuous, graph the function and find the value of y when $x = 2.5$.

Hours hiked, x	1	2	3
Distance (mi), y	2.5	5	7.5

Since it makes sense to talk about the number of miles hiked after any amount of time, the table represents a continuous function. The distance hiked after 2.5 hours is about 6.25 miles.

Closing the Lesson

Have students summarize the major points of the lesson and answer the Essential Question: How do you identify discrete and continuous functions?

- **A discrete function has a graph consisting of isolated points.**
- **A continuous function has a graph with no breaks in it.**

Given a situation or domain, determine whether you should represent the function with individual points or an unbroken line or part of a line.

④ PRACTICE AND APPLY

Study Strategy

Exercises 7–9 Instruct students to think in terms of what makes sense, as in Example 2, when considering whether the functions are discrete or continuous.

1–6. See Additional Answers beginning on p. AA1.

Tell whether the function represented by the table is discrete or continuous. Explain. If continuous, graph the function and find the value of y when $x = 1.5$.

Duration of storm (hours), x	1	2	3
Amount of rain (inches), y	0.5	1	1.5

Solution

Although the table shows the amount of rain that has fallen after whole numbers of hours only, it makes sense to talk about the amount of rain after any amount of time during the storm. So, the table represents a continuous function.

The graph of the function is shown. To find the value of y when $x = 1.5$, start at 1.5 on the x-axis, move up to the graph, and move over to the y-axis. The y-value is about 0.75. So, about 0.75 inch of rain has fallen after 1.5 hours.

Storm Precipitation

PRACTICE

EXAMPLE 1
on p. 223
for Exs. 1–6

Graph the function with the given domain. Classify the function as discrete or continuous. 1–6. See margin for art.

1. $y = -2x + 3$; domain: $-2, -1, 0, 1, 2$
   discrete
2. $y = x$; domain: all real numbers
   continuous
3. $y = -\frac{1}{3}x + 1$; domain: $-12, -6, 0, 6, 12$
   discrete
4. $y = 0.5x$; domain: $-2, -1, 0, 1, 2$
   discrete
5. $y = 3x - 4$; domain: $x \leq 0$
   continuous
6. $y = \frac{2}{3}x + \frac{1}{3}$; domain: $x \geq -2$
   continuous

EXAMPLE 2
on p. 224
for Exs. 7–9

Tell whether the function represented by the table is discrete or continuous. *Explain*. If continuous, graph the function and find the value of y when $x = 3.5$. Round your answer to the nearest hundredth.

7.

Number of DVD rentals, x	1	2	3	4
Cost of rentals (dollars), y	4.50	9.00	13.50	18.00

Discrete; you can only rent a whole number of DVDs.

8. Continuous; it makes sense to talk about the distance driven for any amount of time during the drive; 175.

8.

Hours since 12 P.M., x	2	4	6	8
Distance driven (miles), y	100	200	300	400

9.

Volume of water (cubic inches), x	3	6	9	12
Approximate weight of water (pounds), y	0.1	0.2	0.3	0.4

Continuous; it makes sense to talk about the weight of water for any volume of water; about 0.12.

8.

9.

4.3 Graph Using Intercepts

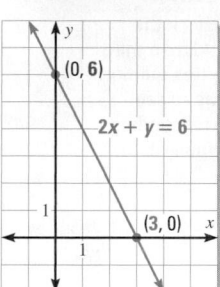

Before You graphed a linear equation using a table of values.

Now You will graph a linear equation using intercepts.

Why So you can find a submersible's location, as in Example 5.

Key Vocabulary
• *x*-intercept
• *y*-intercept

You can use the fact that two points determine a line to graph a linear equation. Two convenient points are the points where the graph crosses the axes.

An *x*-intercept of a graph is the *x*-coordinate of a point where the graph crosses the *x*-axis. A *y*-intercept of a graph is the *y*-coordinate of a point where the graph crosses the *y*-axis.

To find the *x*-intercept of the graph of a linear equation, find the value of *x* when $y = 0$. To find the *y*-intercept of the graph, find the value of *y* when $x = 0$.

[Graph showing line $2x + y = 6$ passing through (0, 6) and (3, 0)]

EXAMPLE 1 Find the intercepts of the graph of an equation

Find the *x*-intercept and the *y*-intercept of the graph of $2x + 7y = 28$.

Solution

To find the *x*-intercept, substitute 0 for *y* and solve for *x*.

$2x + 7y = 28$	**Write original equation.**
$2x + 7(0) = 28$	**Substitute 0 for y.**
$x = \dfrac{28}{2} = 14$	**Solve for x.**

To find the *y*-intercept, substitute 0 for *x* and solve for *y*.

$2x + 7y = 28$	**Write original equation.**
$2(0) + 7y = 28$	**Substitute 0 for x.**
$y = \dfrac{28}{7} = 4$	**Solve for y.**

▶ The *x*-intercept is 14. The *y*-intercept is 4.

 GUIDED PRACTICE for Example 1

Find the *x*-intercept and the *y*-intercept of the graph of the equation.

1. $3x + 2y = 6$ **2, 3**   **2.** $4x - 2y = 10$ **2.5, −5**   **3.** $-3x + 5y = -15$ **5, −3**

4.3 Graph Using Intercepts **225**

① PLAN AND PREPARE

Warm-Up Exercises
📄 **Transparency Available**

Evaluate the expression when $x = -3$.

1. $3x + 4$ **−5**

2. $-2x + 6$ **12**

3. $4x - 3$ **−15**

4. The amount *a* that a taxi service charges is given by $a = 1.5m$ where *m* is the number of miles. Find *a* when *m* is 7. **$10.50**

Notetaking Guide
📄 **Transparency Available**

Promotes interactive learning and notetaking skills, pp. 80–82.

Pacing

Basic: 1 day
Average: 1 day
Advanced: 1 day
Block: 0.5 block with 4.2
• See *Teaching Guide/Lesson Plan.*

② FOCUS AND MOTIVATE

Essential Question
Big Idea 1, p. 205

How do you use intercepts to graph equations? **Tell students they will learn how to answer this question by finding and using the *x*- and *y*-intercepts of the graph of an equation.**

NCTM STANDARDS

Standard 3: Specify locations using coordinate geometry

Standard 10: Use representations to communicate mathematical ideas

Resource Planning Guide

Chapter Resource Book
• Teaching Guide/Lesson Plan (pp. 31–32)
• Practice levels A, B, C (pp. 33–38)
• Study Guide (pp. 39–40)
• Catch-up for Absent Students (p. 41)
• Problem Solving Workshop (p. 42)
• Challenge (p. 44)

Workbooks
• Notetaking Guide (pp. 80–82)
• Practice Workbook (pp. 52–54)

Teaching Options
• **Power Presentations CD-ROM** provides dynamic electronic teaching resources for the classroom.
• **Activity Generator CD-ROM** provides editable activities for all ability levels.

Interactive Technology
• Easy Planner
• Power Presentations CD-ROM
• Activity Generator CD-ROM
• Animated Algebra
• Test Generator CD-ROM
• Online Quiz
• eWorkbook
• eEdition
• @HomeTutor

Resources for English Learners
• Quick Reference for English Learners
• Spanish Study Guide
• Multi-Language Visual Glossary
• Student Resources in Spanish

See also the *Algebra 1 Toolkit* for more strategies for meeting individual needs.

225

Motivating the Lesson

You know that your school sells T-shirts and sweatshirts with the school name on them. T-shirts cost $9 and sweatshirts cost $12. You have $144. By writing an equation and finding the intercepts of the graph of the equation, you can find the possible numbers of T-shirts and sweatshirts you can buy.

❸ TEACH

Extra Example 1

Find the x-intercept and the y-intercept of the graph of $3x - 4y = 12$. **x-intercept: 4, y-intercept: −3**

Key Question to Ask for Example 1

- What coordinates are associated with the x-intercept and the y-intercept? **(14, 0), (0, 4)**

Extra Example 2

Graph the equation $4x + 8y = 24$.

Key Question to Ask for Example 2

- Why is using intercepts an efficient way to graph an equation? **Since $x = 0$ and $y = 0$, it is easier to find the intercepts than other points on the line.**

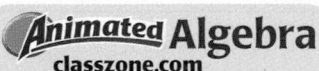
Animated Algebra
classzone.com

An **Animated Algebra** activity is available on-line for **Example 2**. This activity is also available on the **Power Presentations CD-ROM**.

EXAMPLE 2 Use intercepts to graph an equation

Graph the equation $x + 2y = 4$.

Solution

STEP 1 Find the intercepts.

$$x + 2y = 4 \qquad\qquad x + 2y = 4$$
$$x + 2(0) = 4 \qquad\qquad 0 + 2y = 4$$
$$x = 4 \leftarrow \textbf{\textit{x-intercept}} \qquad\qquad y = 2 \leftarrow \textbf{\textit{y-intercept}}$$

CHECK A GRAPH
Be sure to check the graph by finding a third solution of the equation and checking to see that the corresponding point is on the graph.

STEP 2 Plot points. The x-intercept is 4, so plot the point (4, 0). The y-intercept is 2, so plot the point (0, 2). Draw a line through the points.

Animated Algebra at classzone.com

EXAMPLE 3 Use a graph to find intercepts

The graph crosses the x-axis at (2, 0). The x-intercept is 2. The graph crosses the y-axis at (0, −1). The y-intercept is −1.

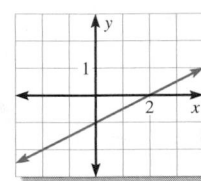

✓ **GUIDED PRACTICE** for Examples 2 and 3

4. Graph $6x + 7y = 42$. Label the points where the line crosses the axes. **See margin.**

5. Identify the x-intercept and the y-intercept of the graph shown at the right. **−4, 2**

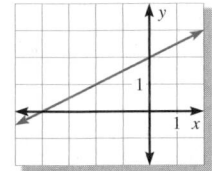

KEY CONCEPT *For Your Notebook*

Relating Intercepts, Points, and Graphs

Intercepts	Points
The x-intercept of a graph is a.	The graph crosses the x-axis at $(a, 0)$.
The y-intercept of a graph is b.	The graph crosses the y-axis at $(0, b)$.

Differentiated Instruction

Visual Learners To help students remember how to find the intercepts in problems similar to Example 2, have them make the following table.

x-intercept	$x = 0$
y-intercept	$y = 0$

Have them connect the entries in this table with an "X," pairing "x-intercept" with "$y = 0$" and pairing "y-intercept" with "$x = 0$."

See also the *Algebra 1 Toolkit* for more strategies.

EXAMPLE 4 **Solve a multi-step problem**

EVENT PLANNING You are helping to plan an awards banquet for your school, and you need to rent tables to seat 180 people. Tables come in two sizes. Small tables seat 4 people, and large tables seat 6 people. This situation can be modeled by the equation

$$4x + 6y = 180$$

where x is the number of small tables and y is the number of large tables.

- Find the intercepts of the graph of the equation.
- Graph the equation.
- Give four possibilities for the number of each size table you could rent.

Solution

STEP 1 **Find** the intercepts.

$4x + 6y = 180$	$4x + 6y = 180$
$4x + 6(0) = 180$	$4(0) + 6y = 180$
$x = 45 \leftarrow$ **x-intercept**	$y = 30 \leftarrow$ **y-intercept**

DRAW A GRAPH
Although x and y represent whole numbers, it is convenient to draw an unbroken line segment that includes points whose coordinates are not whole numbers.

STEP 2 **Graph** the equation.

The x-intercept is 45, so plot the point (45, 0). The y-intercept is 30, so plot the point (0, 30).

Since x and y both represent numbers of tables, neither x nor y can be negative. So, instead of drawing a line, draw the part of the line that is in Quadrant I.

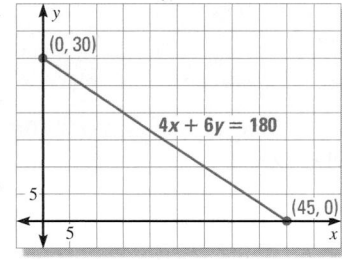

FIND SOLUTIONS
Other points, such as (12, 22), are also on the graph but are not as obvious as the points shown here because their coordinates are not multiples of 5.

STEP 3 **Find** the number of tables. For this problem, only whole-number values of x and y make sense. You can see that the line passes through the points **(0, 30), (15, 20), (30, 10),** and **(45, 0).**

So, four possible combinations of tables that will seat 180 people are: 0 small and 30 large, 15 small and 20 large, 30 small and 10 large, and 45 small and 0 large.

✓ **GUIDED PRACTICE** for Example 4

6. **WHAT IF?** In Example 4, suppose the small tables cost $9 to rent and the large tables cost $14. Of the four possible combinations of tables given in the example, which rental is the least expensive? *Explain.* **45 small tables and no large tables; if you rent 45 small tables it costs $405, all other combinations are more expensive.**

4.3 Graph Using Intercepts **227**

4.

Extra Example 3
Identify the x-intercept and y-intercept of the graph.

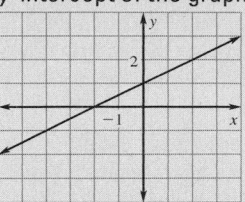

x-intercept: -2, y-intercept: 1

Extra Example 4
You make and sell decorative bows. You sell small bows for $3 and large bows for $5. You want to earn $60 per week. This situation can be modeled by $3x + 5y = 60$ where x is the number of small bows and y is the number of large bows.
- Find the intercepts of the graph.
- Graph the equation.
- Give three possibilities for the number of each type of bow you can sell to earn $60.

x-intercept: 20, y-intercept: 12

Possible combinations: 0 small and 12 large, 10 small and 6 large, 20 small and 0 large

Key Questions to Ask for Example 4

- How can you check the graph of the equation? Explain. **Test another point on the graph, such as (9, 24). If you substitute the values in the equation and they check, the graph is correct.**
- The point (10.5, 23) is a solution of the equation. Is it a solution of the problem? Explain. **No; you cannot rent 10.5 small tables.**

Teaching Strategy
In Step 2 of Example 5 on page 228, remind students that the scales on the x- and y-axes do not have to be the same and that it would be better in some situations to have two different scales.

227

EXAMPLE 5 Use a linear model

SUBMERSIBLES A submersible designed to explore the ocean floor is at an elevation of −13,000 feet (13,000 feet below sea level). The submersible ascends to the surface at an average rate of 650 feet per minute. The elevation e (in feet) of the submersible is given by the function

$$e = 650t - 13,000$$

where t is the time (in minutes) since the submersible began to ascend.

- Find the intercepts of the graph of the function and state what the intercepts represent.
- Graph the function and identify its domain and range.

Solution

STEP 1 Find the intercepts.

$$0 = 650t - 13,000 \qquad \qquad e = 650(0) - 13,000$$
$$13,000 = 650t \qquad \qquad e = -13,000 \leftarrow \textbf{\textit{e}-intercept}$$
$$20 = t \leftarrow \textbf{\textit{t}-intercept}$$

The t-intercept represents the number of minutes the submersible takes to reach an elevation of 0 feet (sea level). The e-intercept represents the elevation of the submersible after 0 minutes (the time the ascent begins).

STEP 2 Graph the function using the intercepts.

Elevation of a Submersible

The submersible starts at an elevation of −13,000 feet and ascends to an elevation of 0 feet. So, the range of the function is $-13,000 \le e \le 0$. From the graph, you can see that the domain of the function is $0 \le t \le 20$.

> **NAME INTERCEPTS**
> Because t is the independent variable, the horizontal axis is the t-axis, and you refer to the "t-intercept" of the graph of the function. Similarly, the vertical axis is the e-axis, and you refer to the "e-intercept."

✓ **GUIDED PRACTICE** for Example 5

7. **WHAT IF?** In Example 5, suppose the elevation of a second submersible is given by $e = 500t - 10,000$. Graph the function and identify its domain and range. **See margin for art; domain: $0 \le t \le 20$, range: $-10,000 \le e \le 0$.**

228   Chapter 4   Graphing Linear Equations and Functions

7.

4.3 EXERCISES

○ = **WORKED-OUT SOLUTIONS**
on p. WS1 for Exs. 21 and 47

★ = **STANDARDIZED TEST PRACTICE**
Exs. 2, 37, 41, 49, and 50

◆ = **MULTIPLE REPRESENTATIONS**
Ex. 44

④ PRACTICE AND APPLY

Assignment Guide

📄 **Answer Transparencies**
available for all exercises

Basic:
Day 1: EP p. 940 Exs. 1–7 odd
pp. 229–232
Exs. 1–10, 16–21, 28–33, 37, 44–47,
51–56

Average:
Day 1: pp. 229–232
Exs. 1–3, 10–15, 22–27, 29, 30,
34–41, 44–49, 51–55 odd

Advanced:
Day 1: pp. 229–232
Exs. 1, 2, 12–15, 24–27, 29, 30, 35–37,
39–43*, 46–50*, 52–56 even

Block:
pp. 229–232
Exs. 1–3, 10–15, 22–27, 29, 30, 34–41,
44–49, 51–55 odd (with 4.2)

Differentiated Instruction

See *Algebra 1 Best Practices Toolkit*
for suggestions on addressing the
needs of a diverse classroom.

Homework Check

For a quick check of student under-
standing of key concepts, go over
the following exercises:
Basic: 6, 17, 28, 44, 45
Average: 11, 24, 29, 46, 48
Advanced: 13, 26, 30, 48, 49

Extra Practice

• Student Edition, p. 941
• Chapter 4 Resource Book:
  Practice levels A, B, C, pp. 33–38

Practice Worksheet

An easily-readable reduced
practice page (with answers)
for this lesson can be found
on p. 204C.

SKILL PRACTICE

[A]

1. **VOCABULARY** Copy and complete: The __?__ of the graph of an equation is the value of *x* when *y* is zero. **x-intercept**

2. ★ **WRITING** What are the *x*-intercept and the *y*-intercept of the line passing through the points (0, 3) and (−4, 0)? *Explain.*

2. −4, 3; the *x*-intercept is when *y* is 0, so the point (−4, 0) gives the *x*-intercept. The *y*-intercept is when *x* is 0, so the point (0, 3) gives the *y*-intercept.

3. **ERROR ANALYSIS** *Describe* and correct the error in finding the intercepts of the line shown. **The intercepts are switched around; the x-intercept is −2, and the y-intercept is 1.**

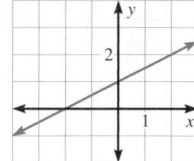

The x-intercept is 1, and the y-intercept is −2.

EXAMPLE 1
on p. 225
for Exs. 4–15

FINDING INTERCEPTS Find the *x*-intercept and the *y*-intercept of the graph of the equation.

4. $5x - y = 35$ **7, −35**
5. $3x - 3y = 9$ **3, −3**
6. $-3x + 9y = -18$ **6, −2**

7. $4x + y = 4$ **1, 4**
8. $2x + y = 10$ **5, 10**
9. $2x - 8y = 24$ **12, −3**

10. $3x + 0.5y = 6$ **2, 12**
11. $0.2x + 3.2y = 12.8$ **64, 4**
12. $y = 2x + 24$ **−12, 24**

13. $y = -14x + 7$ **$\frac{1}{2}$, 7**
14. $y = -4.8x + 1.2$ **0.25, 1.2**
15. $y = \frac{3}{5}x - 12$ **20, −12**

EXAMPLE 2
on p. 226
for Exs. 16–27

GRAPHING LINES Graph the equation. Label the points where the line crosses the axes. **16–27. See margin.**

16. $y = x + 3$
17. $y = x - 2$
18. $y = 4x - 8$

19. $y = 5 + 10x$
20. $y = -2 + 8x$
㉑ $y = -4x + 3$

22. $3x + y = 15$
23. $x - 4y = 18$
24. $8x - 5y = 80$

25. $-2x + 5y = 15$
26. $0.5x + 3y = 9$
27. $y = \frac{1}{2}x + \frac{1}{4}$

EXAMPLE 3
on p. 226
for Exs. 28–30

USING GRAPHS TO FIND INTERCEPTS Identify the *x*-intercept and the *y*-intercept of the graph.

28.
2, 1

29.
3, −2

30.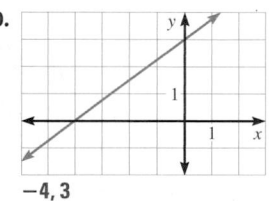
−4, 3

4.3 Graph Using Intercepts **229**

16–27. See Additional Answers beginning on p. AA1.

Avoiding Common Errors

Exercises 4–15 You may want to remind students before they begin these exercises that an intercept is either the *x*-coordinate or the *y*-coordinate of an ordered pair and therefore written as a number, not as an ordered pair.

Teaching Strategy

Exercises 31–36 Before students begin these exercises, suggest they write the ordered pairs that correspond to the intercepts.

31.

32.

33.

34.

35.

B **USING INTERCEPTS** Draw the line that has the given intercepts. **31–36. See margin.**

31. *x*-intercept: 3
y-intercept: 5

32. *x*-intercept: −2
y-intercept: 4

33. *x*-intercept: −5
y-intercept: 6

34. *x*-intercept: 9
y-intercept: −1

35. *x*-intercept: −8
y-intercept: −11

36. *x*-intercept: −2
y-intercept: −6

37. ★ **MULTIPLE CHOICE** The *x*-intercept of the graph of $Ax + 5y = 20$ is 2. What is the value of *A*? **D**

(A) 2   (B) 5   (C) 7.5   (D) 10

MATCHING EQUATIONS WITH GRAPHS Match the equation with its graph.

38. $2x - 6y = 6$ **C**

39. $2x - 6y = -6$ **B**

40. $2x - 6y = 12$ **A**

A.   **B.**   **C.**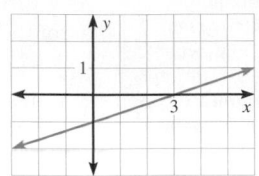

C **41.** ★ **WRITING** Is it possible for a line *not* to have an *x*-intercept? Is it possible for a line *not* to have a *y*-intercept? *Explain.* **Yes; yes; a horizontal line does not have an *x*-intercept if *y* ≠ 0, a vertical line does not have a *y*-intercept if *x* ≠ 0.**

42. **REASONING** Consider the equation $3x + 5y = k$. What values could *k* have so that the *x*-intercept and the *y*-intercept of the equation's graph would both be integers? *Explain.* **Sample answer: 15 and 30; *k* can be any multiple of both 3 and 5.**

43. **CHALLENGE** If $a \neq 0$, find the intercepts of the graph of $y = ax + b$ in terms of *a* and *b*. **$x = -\frac{b}{a}, y = b$**

PROBLEM SOLVING

EXAMPLES A
4 and 5
on pp. 227–228
for Exs. 44–47

44. ◆ **MULTIPLE REPRESENTATIONS** The perimeter of a rectangular park is 72 feet. Let *x* be the park's width (in feet) and let *y* be its length (in feet).

   a. Writing an Equation Write an equation for the perimeter. **$2x + 2y = 72$**

   b. Drawing a Graph Find the intercepts of the graph of the equation you wrote. Then graph the equation. **36, 36; see margin for art.**

   @HomeTutor for problem solving help at classzone.com

45. **RECYCLING** In one state, small bottles have a refund value of $.04 each, and large bottles have a refund value of $.08 each. Your friend returns both small and large bottles and receives $.56. This situation is given by $4x + 8y = 56$ where *x* is the number of small bottles and *y* is the number of large bottles. **$x = 14, y = 7$; see margin for art.**

   a. Find the intercepts of the graph of the equation. Graph the equation.

   b. Give three possibilities for the number of each size bottle your friend could have returned. *Sample answer:* **2 and 6, 4 and 5, 6 and 4**

   @HomeTutor for problem solving help at classzone.com

○ = **WORKED-OUT SOLUTIONS**
on p. WS1

★ = **STANDARDIZED TEST PRACTICE**

◆ = **MULTIPLE REPRESENTATIONS**

36.

44b.

Width (feet)

45a.

Small bottles

46. MULTI-STEP PROBLEM Before 1979, there was no 3-point shot in professional basketball; players could score only 2-point field goals and 1-point free throws. In a game before 1979, a team scored a total of 128 points. This situation is given by the equation $2x + y = 128$ where x is the possible number of field goals and y is the possible number of free throws.

  a. Find the intercepts of the graph of the equation. Graph the equation. **$x = 64$, $y = 128$; see margin for art.**

  b. What do the intercepts mean in this situation?

  c. What are three possible numbers of field goals and free throws the team could have scored?

  d. If the team made 24 free throws, how many field goals were made? **52 field goals**

1979–present   3 point line

Before 1979

47. COMMUNITY GARDENS A family has a plot in a community garden. The family is going to plant vegetables, flowers, or both. The diagram shows the area used by one vegetable plant and the area of the entire plot. The area f (in square feet) of the plot left for flowers is given by $f = 180 - 1.5v$ where v is the number of vegetable plants the family plants.

Area = 1.5 ft²

Area = 180 ft²

  a. Find the intercepts of the graph of the function and state what the intercepts represent.

  b. Graph the function and identify its domain and range.

  c. The family decides to plant 80 vegetable plants. How many square feet are left to plant flowers? **60 ft²**

48. CAR SHARING A member of a car-sharing program can use a car for $6 per hour and $.50 per mile. The member uses the car for one day and is charged $44. This situation is given by

$$6t + 0.5d = 44$$

where t is the time (in hours) the car is used and d is the distance (in miles) the car is driven. Give three examples of the number of hours the member could have used the car and the number of miles the member could have driven the car. *Sample answer:* **1 h and 76 mi, 2 h and 64 mi, 3 h and 52 mi**

49. ★ SHORT RESPONSE A humidifier is a device used to put moisture into the air by turning water to vapor. A humidifier has a tank that can hold 1.5 gallons of water. The humidifier can disperse the water at a rate of 0.12 gallon per hour. The amount of water w (in gallons) left in the humidifier after t hours of use is given by the function

$$w = 1.5 - 0.12t.$$

After how many hours of use will you have to refill the humidifier? *Explain* how you found your answer. **12.5 h.** *Sample answer:* **Since the tank will be empty when it needs to be refilled, replace *w* in the function with 0 and then solve the resulting equation for *t*.**

Graphing Calculator

Exercises 44–49 Students can use their graphing calculators to check their graphs. They can enter the equation using the $y=$ key, set parameters for the window using the Window key, and then graph using the Graph key. They can use the Table key to check *x*-intercepts, *y*-intercepts, and possible solutions for each of the exercises.

46a.

47b.

Daily Homework Quiz

📄 **Transparency Available**

1. Find the *x*-intercept and the *y*-intercept of the graph of $3x - y = 3$. **x-int: 1, y-int: −3**

2. A recycling company pays $1 per used ink jet cartridge and $2 per used laser cartridge. The company paid a customer $14. This situation is given by $x + 2y = 14$ where *x* is the number of ink jet cartridges and *y* the number of laser cartridges. Use intercepts to graph the equation. Give four possibilities for the number of each type of cartridge that could have been recycled. **(0, 7), (6, 4), (10, 2), (14, 0)**

🔄 **Online Quiz**

Available at **classzone.com**

Diagnosis/Remediation

• Practice A, B, C in Chapter 4 Resource Book, pp. 33–38
• Study Guide in Chapter 4 Resource Book, pp. 39–40
• Practice Workbook, pp. 52–54
• @HomeTutor

Challenge

Additional challenge is available in the Chapter 4 Resource Book, p. 44.

Quiz

An easily-readable reduced copy of the quiz (with answers) on Lessons 4.1–4.3 from the Assessment Book can be found on p. 204G.

50b, Quiz 1–6, 13. See Additional Answers beginning on p. AA1.

C **50.** ★ **EXTENDED RESPONSE** You borrow $180 from a friend who doesn't charge you interest. You work out a payment schedule in which you will make weekly payments to your friend. The balance *B* (in dollars) of the loan is given by the function $B = 180 - pn$ where *p* is the weekly payment and *n* is the number of weeks you make payments.

a. Interpret Without finding the intercepts, state what they represent.

b. Graph Graph the function if you make weekly payments of $20. **See margin.**

c. Identify Find the domain and range of the function in part (b). How long will it take to pay back your friend? **domain: $0 \le n \le 9$, range: $0 \le B \le 180$; 9 wk**

d. CHALLENGE Suppose you make payments of $20 for three weeks. Then you make payments of $15 until you have paid your friend back. How does this affect the graph? How many payments do you make?
The graph is two line segments; 11 payments.

50a. The *B*-intercept is the balance of the loan after 0 weeks, the *n*-intercept is the amount of time it takes to pay off the loan.

MIXED REVIEW

REVIEW GRAPHS
For help with line graphs, see p. 934.

In Exercises 51–53, use the line graph, which shows the number of points Alex scored in five basketball games. *(p. 934)*

51. How many points did Alex score in game 4? **16 points**

52. In which game did Alex score the most points? **game 2**

53. How many more points did Alex score in game 5 than in game 1? **12 more points**

PREVIEW
Prepare for Lesson 4.4 in Exs. 54–56.

Solve the proportion. *(p. 934)*

54. $\frac{3}{5} = \frac{x}{30}$ **18**

55. $\frac{x}{x + 6} = \frac{7}{6}$ **−42**

56. $\frac{t - 3}{12} = \frac{2t - 2}{9}$ **$-\frac{1}{5}$**

QUIZ *for Lessons 4.1–4.3*

Plot the point in a coordinate plane. *Describe* the location of the point. *(p. 206)*
1–3. See margin for art.

1. $(-7, 2)$ **Quadrant II**
2. $(0, -5)$ **y-axis**
3. $(2, -6)$ **Quadrant IV**

Graph the equation. *(p. 215)* **4–6. See margin.**

4. $-4x - 2y = 12$
5. $y = -5$
6. $x = 6$
$-11, -4\frac{2}{5}$

Find the x-intercept and the y-intercept of the graph of the equation. *(p. 225)*

7. $y = x + 7$ **−7, 7**
8. $y = x - 3$ **3, −3**
9. $y = -5x + 2$ **$\frac{2}{5}$, 2**
10. $x + 3y = 15$ **15, 5**
11. $3x - 6y = 36$ **12, −6**
12. $-2x - 5y = 22$ **$-11, -4\frac{2}{5}$**

13. SWIMMING POOLS A public swimming pool that holds 45,000 gallons of water is going to be drained for maintenance at a rate of 100 gallons per minute. The amount of water *w* (in gallons) in the pool after *t* minutes is given by the function $w = 45,000 - 100t$. Graph the function. Identify its domain and range. How much water is in the pool after 60 minutes? How many minutes will it take to empty the pool? *(p. 225)* **See margin for art; domain: $0 \le t \le 450$; range: $0 \le w \le 45,000$; 39,000 gal; 450 min.**

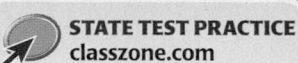
Lessons 4.1–4.3

1. MULTI-STEP PROBLEM An amusement park charges $20 for an all-day pass and $10 for a pass after 5 P.M. On Wednesday the amusement park collected $1000 in pass sales. This situation can be modeled by the equation $1000 = 20x + 10y$ where x is the number of all-day passes sold and y is the number of passes sold after 5 P.M.
a–c. See margin.
   a. Find the x-intercept of the graph of the equation. What does it represent?
   b. Find the y-intercept of the graph of the equation. What does it represent?
   c. Graph the equation using a scale of 10 on the x- and y-axes.

2. MULTI-STEP PROBLEM A violin player who plays every day received a violin with new strings. Players who play every day should replace the strings on their violins every 6 months. A particular brand of strings costs $24 per pack. The table shows the total spent a (in dollars) on replacement strings with respect to time t (in months).

t (months)	a (dollars)
6	24
12	48
18	72
24	96
30	120

   a. *Explain* how you know the table represents a function. **There is exactly one cost for each time.**
   b. Graph the function. **See margin.**

3. OPEN-ENDED Create a table that shows the number of minutes you think you will spend watching TV next week. Let Monday be day 1, Tuesday be day 2, and so on. Graph the data. Does the graph represent a function? *Explain.*
See margin for art; yes; there is exactly one number of minutes for each day.

4. SHORT RESPONSE You can hike at an average rate of 3 miles per hour. Your total hiking distance d (in miles) can be modeled by the function $d = 3t$ where t is the time (in hours) you hike. You plan on hiking for 10 hours this weekend.
   a. Is the domain or range specified in the problem? *Explain.* **Yes; the domain is specified because you plan on hiking for 10 hours.**
   b. Graph the function and identify its domain and range. Use the graph to find how long it takes to hike 6 miles. **See margin for art; domain: $0 \le t \le 10$, range: $0 \le d \le 30$; 2 h.**

5. EXTENDED RESPONSE The table shows the departure d (in degrees Fahrenheit) from the normal monthly temperature in New England for the first six months of 2004. For example, in month 1, $d = -3$. So, the average temperature was 3 degrees below the normal temperature for January.

M (month)	1	2	3	4	5	6
d (°F)	−3	−1	2	2	4	−1

   a. *Explain* how you know the table represents a function. **There is exactly one temperature departure for each month.**
   b. Graph the function and identify its domain and range. **See margin for art; domain: 1, 2, 3, 4, 5, and 6, range: −3, −1, 2, and 4.**
   c. What does a point in Quadrant IV mean in terms of this situation? **The temperature is below normal.**

6. GRIDDED ANSWER The graph shows the possible combinations of T-shirts and tank tops that you can buy with the amount of money you have. If you buy only T-shirts, how many can you buy? **6 T-shirts**

1a. 50; the number of all-day passes sold when no passes after 5 P.M. were sold

1b. 100; the number of passes sold after 5 P.M. when no all-day passes were sold

1c.

2b.

3.

4b.

5b.

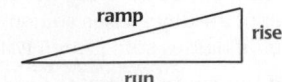

1 PLAN AND PREPARE

Explore the Concept
- Students will measure the slope of a ramp.
- This activity leads into the study of finding slope in Example 1 in Lesson 4.4.

Materials
Each student or group of students will need:
- several books
- two rulers

Recommended Time
Work activity: 10 min
Discuss results: 5 min

Grouping
Students can work individually or in groups of three. If students work in groups, one student can make a ramp with books and ruler, one can measure the rise and run of the ramp, and the other can record measurements and calculate and record the slope.

2 TEACH

Tips for Success
Use whole numbers for the run to make calculations easier. Do not let the ruler slip when measuring the rise and run.

Key Discovery
Slope is dependent on the ratio of rise to run.

3 ASSESS AND RETEACH

How does the slope of a ramp change if the rise of the ramp decreases and the run increases? **The slope decreases.**

4.4 Slopes of Lines

MATERIALS • several books • two rulers

QUESTION How can you use algebra to describe the slope of a ramp?

You can use the ratio of the vertical rise to the horizontal run to describe the *slope* of a ramp.

$$\text{slope} = \frac{\text{rise}}{\text{run}}$$

EXPLORE Calculate the slopes of ramps

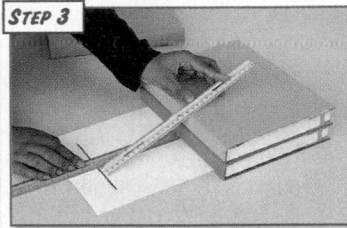

Make a ramp Make a stack of three books. Use a ruler as a ramp. Measure the rise and run of the ramp, and record them in a table. Calculate and record the slope of the ramp in your table.

Change the run Without changing the rise, make three ramps with different runs by moving the lower end of the ruler. Measure and record the rise and run of each ramp. Calculate and record each slope.

Change the rise Without changing the run, make three ramps with different rises by adding or removing books. Measure and record the rise and run of each ramp. Calculate and record each slope.

DRAW CONCLUSIONS Use your observations to complete these exercises

Describe how the slope of the ramp changes given the following conditions. Give three examples that support your answer.

1. The run of the ramp increases, and the rise stays the same. **The slope gets smaller.** *Sample answer:* $\frac{1}{4}, \frac{1}{5}, \frac{1}{6}$

2. The rise of the ramp increases, and the run stays the same. **The slope gets larger.** *Sample answer:* $\frac{1}{5}, \frac{2}{5}, \frac{3}{5}$

In Exercises 3–5, describe the relationship between the rise and the run of the ramp.

3. A ramp with a slope of 1 **The rise and the run are the same.**

4. A ramp with a slope greater than 1 **The rise is greater than the run.**

5. A ramp with a slope less than 1 **The rise is less than the run.**

6. Ramp A has a rise of 6 feet and a run of 2 feet. Ramp B has a rise of 10 feet and a run of 4 feet. Which ramp is steeper? How do you know? **Ramp A; the slope of ramp A is 3 while the slope of ramp B is $\frac{5}{2}$ or 2.5, and 3 > 2.5.**

234 Chapter 4 Graphing Linear Equations and Functions

4.4 Find Slope and Rate of Change

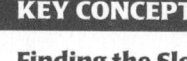

Before	You graphed linear equations.
Now	You will find the slope of a line and interpret slope as a rate of change.
Why?	So you can find the slope of a boat ramp, as in Ex. 23.

Key Vocabulary
• slope
• rate of change

The **slope** of a nonvertical line is the ratio of the vertical change (the *rise*) to the horizontal change (the *run*) between any two points on the line. The slope of a line is represented by the letter m.

> **KEY CONCEPT** *For Your Notebook*
>
> **Finding the Slope of a Line**
>
> **Words**
>
> The slope m of the nonvertical line passing through the two points (x_1, y_1) and (x_2, y_2) is the ratio of the rise (change in y) to the run (change in x).
>
> $$\text{slope} = \frac{\text{rise}}{\text{run}} = \frac{\text{change in } y}{\text{change in } x}$$
>
> **Symbols**
>
> $$m = \frac{y_2 - y_1}{x_2 - x_1}$$
>
> **Graph**
>
>

READING
Read x_1 as "x sub one." Think "x-coordinate of the first point."
Read y_1 as "y sub one." Think "y-coordinate of the first point."

EXAMPLE 1 Find a positive slope

Find the slope of the line shown.

Let $(x_1, y_1) = (-4, 2)$ and $(x_2, y_2) = (2, 6)$.

$$m = \frac{y_2 - y_1}{x_2 - x_1} \qquad \text{Write formula for slope.}$$

$$= \frac{6 - 2}{2 - (-4)} \qquad \text{Substitute.}$$

$$= \frac{4}{6} = \frac{2}{3} \qquad \text{Simplify.}$$

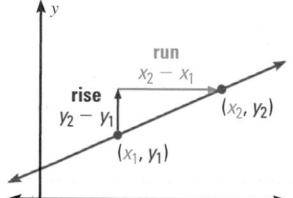

The line rises from left to right. The slope is positive.

AVOID ERRORS
Be sure to keep the x- and y-coordinates in the same order in both the numerator and denominator when calculating slope.

 GUIDED PRACTICE for Example 1

Find the slope of the line that passes through the points.

1. $(5, 2)$ and $(4, -1)$ **3**

2. $(-2, 3)$ and $(4, 6)$ **$\frac{1}{2}$**

3. $\left(\frac{9}{2}, 5\right)$ and $\left(\frac{1}{2}, -3\right)$ **2**

---

① PLAN AND PREPARE

Warm-Up Exercises
⬛ Transparency Available

Evaluate and simplify the ratios when $x = 2$ and $y = -2$.

1. $\frac{y + 3}{x - 5}$ $-\frac{1}{3}$ 2. $\frac{1 - y}{x - 6}$ $-\frac{3}{4}$

3. A cross-country skier traveled 14 miles in 3.5 hours. Use the formula $d = rt$ where d is distance, r is rate, and t is time, to find the average rate of speed. **4 mi/h**

Notetaking Guide
⬛ Transparency Available
Promotes interactive learning and notetaking skills, pp. 83–86.

Pacing
Basic: 2 days
Average: 2 days
Advanced: 2 days
Block: 1 block
• See *Teaching Guide/Lesson Plan.*

② FOCUS AND MOTIVATE

Essential Question
Big Idea 3, p. 205
How do you find the slope of a line and interpret slope as a rate of change? **Tell students they will learn how to answer this question by using the slope formula to find slope and to describe changes in a real-world situation.**

NCTM STANDARDS
Standard 2: Use models to understand relationships

Standard 4: Understand the units of measurement

Resource Planning Guide

Chapter Resource Book
• Teaching Guide/Lesson Plan (pp. 45–46)
• Practice levels A, B, C (pp. 47–52)
• Study Guide (pp. 53–54)
• Catch-up for Absent Students (p. 55)
• Application (p. 56)
• Challenge (p. 57)

Workbooks
• Notetaking Guide (pp. 83–86)
• Practice Workbook (pp. 55–57)

Teaching Options
• **Power Presentations CD-ROM** provides dynamic electronic teaching resources for the classroom.
• **Activity Generator CD-ROM** provides editable activities for all ability levels.

Interactive Technology
• Easy Planner
• Power Presentations CD-ROM
• Activity Generator CD-ROM
• Animated Algebra
• Test Generator CD-ROM
• Online Quiz
• eWorkbook
• eEdition
• @HomeTutor

Resources for English Learners
• Quick Reference for English Learners
• Spanish Study Guide
• Multi-Language Visual Glossary
• Student Resources in Spanish

See also the *Algebra 1 Toolkit* for more strategies for meeting individual needs.

235

EXAMPLE 2   Find a negative slope

Find the slope of the line shown.

Let $(x_1, y_1) = (3, 5)$ and $(x_2, y_2) = (6, -1)$.

$m = \dfrac{y_2 - y_1}{x_2 - x_1}$ Write formula for slope.

$= \dfrac{-1 - 5}{6 - 3}$ Substitute.

$= \dfrac{-6}{3} = -2$ Simplify.

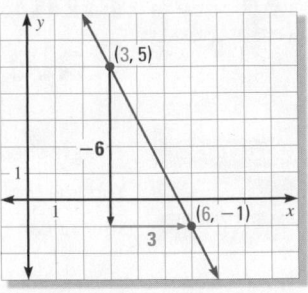

The line falls from left to right. The slope is negative.

EXAMPLE 3   Find the slope of a horizontal line

Find the slope of the line shown.

Let $(x_1, y_1) = (-2, 4)$ and $(x_2, y_2) = (4, 4)$.

$m = \dfrac{y_2 - y_1}{x_2 - x_1}$ Write formula for slope.

$= \dfrac{4 - 4}{4 - (-2)}$ Substitute.

$= \dfrac{0}{6} = 0$ Simplify.

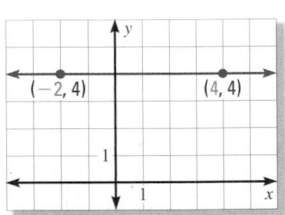

The line is horizontal. The slope is zero.

EXAMPLE 4   Find the slope of a vertical line

Find the slope of the line shown.

Let $(x_1, y_1) = (3, 5)$ and $(x_2, y_2) = (3, 1)$.

$m = \dfrac{y_2 - y_1}{x_2 - x_1}$ Write formula for slope.

$= \dfrac{1 - 5}{3 - 3}$ Substitute.

$= \dfrac{-4}{\cancel{0}}$ Division by zero is undefined.

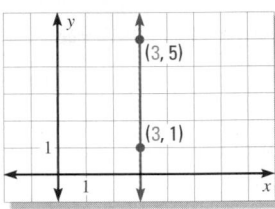

The line is vertical. The slope is undefined.

▶ Because division by zero is undefined, the slope of a vertical line is undefined.

✓ **GUIDED PRACTICE**   for Examples 2, 3, and 4

Find the slope of the line that passes through the points.

4. $(5, 2)$ and $(5, -2)$ **undefined**

5. $(0, 4)$ and $(-3, 4)$ **0**

6. $(0, 6)$ and $(5, -4)$ **−2**

For Your Notebook

Classification of Lines by Slope

A line with positive slope ($m > 0$) *rises* from left to right.	A line with negative slope ($m < 0$) *falls* from left to right.	A line with zero slope ($m = 0$) is *horizontal*.	A line with undefined slope is *vertical*.
			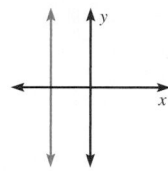

RATE OF CHANGE A **rate of change** compares a change in one quantity to a change in another quantity. For example, if you are paid $60 for working 5 hours, then your hourly wage is $12 per hour, a rate of change that describes how your pay increases with respect to time spent working.

EXAMPLE 5 Find a rate of change

INTERNET CAFE The table shows the cost of using a computer at an Internet cafe for a given amount of time. Find the rate of change in cost with respect to time.

Time (hours)	2	4	6
Cost (dollars)	7	14	21

Solution

ANALYZE UNITS
Because the cost is in dollars and time is in hours, the rate of change in cost with respect to time is expressed in dollars per hour.

$$\text{Rate of change} = \frac{\text{change in cost}}{\text{change in time}}$$

$$= \frac{14 - 7}{4 - 2} = \frac{7}{2} = 3.5$$

▸ The rate of change in cost is $3.50 per hour.

✓ **GUIDED PRACTICE** for Example 5

7. **EXERCISE** The table shows the distance a person walks for exercise. Find the rate of change in distance with respect to time. **0.05 mi/min**

Time (minutes)	Distance (miles)
30	1.5
60	3
90	4.5

Differentiated Instruction

Below Level After discussing **Example 5**, have students determine the rate of change using two sets of quantities different from the set used in the example. Ask what would be the rise and run if they graphed the data. Then ask them to describe the slope of the line in terms of the rise and run.

Advanced Have students explore rates of change that are averages as well as constants. In **Example 5**, ask students to consider that the cost for 6 hours at the café is $18 rather than $21. Have them describe how this affects the rate of change by comparing rates at 2 hours and 4 hours, 2 hours and 6 hours, and 4 hours and 6 hours.

See also the *Algebra 1 Toolkit* for more strategies.

238

SLOPE AND RATE OF CHANGE You can interpret the slope of a line as a rate of change. When given graphs of real-world data, you can compare rates of change by comparing slopes of lines.

EXAMPLE 6 **Use a graph to find and compare rates of change**

COMMUNITY THEATER A community theater performed a play each Saturday evening for 10 consecutive weeks. The graph shows the attendance for the performances in weeks 1, 4, 6, and 10. Describe the rates of change in attendance with respect to time.

Play Attendance

Solution

Find the rates of change using the slope formula.

INTERPRET RATE OF CHANGE
A negative rate of change indicates a decrease.

Weeks 1–4: $\dfrac{232 - 124}{4 - 1} = \dfrac{108}{3} = 36$ people per week

Weeks 4–6: $\dfrac{204 - 232}{6 - 4} = \dfrac{-28}{2} = -14$ people per week

Weeks 6–10: $\dfrac{72 - 204}{10 - 6} = \dfrac{-132}{4} = -33$ people per week

▶ Attendance increased during the early weeks of performing the play. Then attendance decreased, slowly at first, then more rapidly.

EXAMPLE 7 **Interpret a graph**

COMMUTING TO SCHOOL A student commutes from home to school by walking and by riding a bus. Describe the student's commute in words.

Solution

The first segment of the graph is not very steep, so the student is not traveling very far with respect to time. The student must be walking. The second segment has a zero slope, so the student must not be moving. He or she is waiting for the bus. The last segment is steep, so the student is traveling far with respect to time. The student must be riding the bus.

Animated Algebra at classzone.com

✓ **GUIDED PRACTICE** **for Examples 6 and 7**

8. **WHAT IF?** How would the answer to Example 6 change if you knew that attendance was 70 people in week 12? *Sample answer:* **The attendance did not decrease as rapidly between weeks 10 and 12.**

9. **WHAT IF?** Using the graph in Example 7, draw a graph that represents the student's commute from school to home. **See margin.**

4.4 EXERCISES

SKILL PRACTICE

A **1. VOCABULARY** Copy and complete: The __?__ of a nonvertical line is the ratio of the vertical change to the horizontal change between any two points on the line. **slope**

2. ★ WRITING Without calculating the slope, how can you tell that the slope of the line that passes through the points $(-5, -3)$ and $(2, 4)$ is positive?
The line between the two points rises from left to right.

3. ERROR ANALYSIS *Describe* and correct the error in calculating the slope of the line passing through the points $(5, 3)$ and $(2, 6)$. **The denominator should be** $2 - 5$, **not** $5 - 2$; $m = \dfrac{6-3}{2-5} = \dfrac{3}{-3} = -1$.

$$m = \frac{6-3}{5-2} = \frac{3}{3} = 1 \quad \diagup\!\!\!\!\!\diagdown$$

EXAMPLES
1, 2, 3, and 4
on pp. 235–236
for Exs. 4–18

FINDING SLOPE Tell whether the slope of the line is *positive*, *negative*, *zero*, or *undefined*. Then find the slope if it exists.

4.

positive; $\dfrac{2}{3}$

5.

undefined

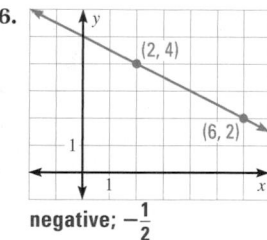

6.

negative; $-\dfrac{1}{2}$

7. ERROR ANALYSIS *Describe* and correct the error in calculating the slope of the line shown.

$$m = \frac{12-6}{0-3} = \frac{6}{-3} = -2 \quad \diagup\!\!\!\!\!\diagdown$$

The slope was calculated using $\dfrac{\text{run}}{\text{rise}}$, not $\dfrac{\text{rise}}{\text{run}}$; $m = \dfrac{0-3}{12-6} = \dfrac{-3}{6} = -\dfrac{1}{2}$.

FINDING SLOPE Find the slope of the line that passes through the points.

8. $(-2, -1)$ and $(4, 5)$ **1**

9. $(-3, -2)$ and $(-3, 6)$ **undefined**

10. $(5, -3)$ and $(-5, -3)$ **0**

⑪ $(1, 3)$ and $(3, -2)$ $-\dfrac{5}{2}$

12. $(-3, 4)$ and $(4, 1)$ $-\dfrac{3}{7}$

13. $(1, -3)$ and $(7, 3)$ **1**

14. $(0, 0)$ and $(0, -6)$ **undefined**

15. $(-9, 1)$ and $(1, 1)$ **0**

16. $(-10, -2)$ and $(-8, 8)$ **5**

17. ★ MULTIPLE CHOICE The slope of the line that passes through the points $(-2, -3)$ and $(8, -3)$ is __?__. **C**

Ⓐ positive   Ⓑ negative   Ⓒ zero   Ⓓ undefined

18. ★ MULTIPLE CHOICE What is the slope of the line that passes through the points $(7, -9)$ and $(-13, -6)$? **A**

Ⓐ $-\dfrac{3}{20}$ Ⓑ $\dfrac{3}{20}$ Ⓒ $\dfrac{3}{4}$ Ⓓ $\dfrac{5}{2}$

---

④ PRACTICE AND APPLY

Assignment Guide

📑 **Answer Transparencies**
available for all exercises

Basic:
Day 1: SRH p. 934 Exs. 6–14
pp. 239–242
Exs. 1–18, 42–56 even
Day 2: pp. 239–242
Exs. 19–27, 36–39, 57–62

Average:
Day 1: pp. 239–242
Exs. 1–7, 11–18, 24–28, 43–55 odd
Day 2: pp. 239–242
Exs. 19–23, 31–33, 36–40, 57–62

Advanced:
Day 1: pp. 239–242
Exs. 1, 2, 12–18, 24–32, 43–55 odd
Day 2: pp. 239–242
Exs. 19–23, 35–41*, 57–62

Block:
pp. 239–242
Exs. 1–7, 11–28, 31–33, 36–40,
43–55 odd, 57–62

Differentiated Instruction

See *Algebra 1 Best Practices Toolkit* for suggestions on addressing the needs of a diverse classroom.

Homework Check

For a quick check of student understanding of key concepts, go over the following exercises:

Basic: 4, 9, 19, 36, 38
Average: 11, 14, 20, 36, 39
Advanced: 12, 15, 20, 37, 39

Extra Practice

• Student Edition, p. 941
• Chapter 4 Resource Book:
  Practice levels A, B, C, pp. 47–52

Practice Worksheet

An easily-readable reduced practice page (with answers) for this lesson can be found on p. 204C.

EXAMPLE 5
on p. 237
for Exs. 19–20

19. MOVIE RENTALS The table shows the number of days you keep a rented movie before returning it and the total cost of renting the movie. Find the rate of change in cost with respect to time and interpret its meaning.

Time (days)	4	5	6	7
Total cost (dollars)	6.00	8.25	10.50	12.75

$2.25 per day, it costs $2.25 per day to rent a movie.

20. AMUSEMENT PARK The table shows the amount of time spent at an amusement park and the admission fee the park charges. Find the rate of change in the fee with respect to time spent at the park and interpret its meaning.

Time (hours)	4	5	6
Admission fee (dollars)	34.99	34.99	34.99

0, it does not matter how long a person stays at the park, the admission is the same.

FINDING SLOPE Find the slope of the object. Round to the nearest tenth.

21. Skateboard ramp **0.3**   **22.** Pet ramp **0.4**   **23.** Boat ramp **0.1**

15 in.
54 in.

24 in.
60 in.

4 ft
28 ft

B In Exercises 24–32, use the example below to find the value of *x* or *y* so that the line passing through the given points has the given slope.

EXAMPLE **Find a coordinate given the slope of a line**

Find the value of *x* so that the line that passes through the points (2, 3) and (*x*, 9) has a slope of $\frac{3}{2}$.

Solution

Let $(x_1, y_1) = (2, 3)$ and $(x_2, y_2) = (x, 9)$.

$$m = \frac{y_2 - y_1}{x_2 - x_1} \qquad \text{Write formula for slope.}$$

$$\frac{3}{2} = \frac{9 - 3}{x - 2} \qquad \text{Substitute values.}$$

$$3(x - 2) = 2(9 - 3) \qquad \text{Cross products property}$$

$$3x - 6 = 12 \qquad \text{Simplify.}$$

$$x = 6 \qquad \text{Solve for } x.$$

24. $(x, 4), (6, -1); m = \frac{5}{6}$ **12**   **25.** $(0, y), (-2, 1); m = -8$ **−15**   **26.** $(8, 1), (x, 7); m = -\frac{1}{2}$ **−4**

27. $(5, 4), (-5, y); m = \frac{3}{5}$ **−2**   **28.** $(-9, y), (0, -3); m = -\frac{7}{9}$ **4**   **29.** $(x, 9), (-1, 19); m = 5$ **−3**

30. $(9, 3), (-6, 7y); m = 3$ **−6**   **31.** $(-3, y + 1), (0, 4); m = 6$ **−15**   **32.** $\left(\frac{x}{2}, 7\right), (-10, 15); m = 4$ **−24**

○ = **WORKED-OUT SOLUTIONS**
on p. WS1

★ = **STANDARDIZED**
TEST PRACTICE

C

33. REASONING The point $(-1, 8)$ is on a line that has a slope of -3. Is the point $(4, -7)$ on the same line? *Explain* your reasoning.
Yes; the slope of the line containing both points is −3.

34. ★ WRITING Is a line with undefined slope the graph of a function? *Explain*.
No; a line with an undefined slope is a vertical line, which is not the graph of a function.

35. CHALLENGE Given two points (x_1, y_1) and (x_2, y_2) such that $x_1 \neq x_2$,

show that $\dfrac{y_2 - y_1}{x_2 - x_1} = \dfrac{y_1 - y_2}{x_1 - x_2}$. What does this result tell you about

calculating the slope of a line? **See margin.**

PROBLEM SOLVING

EXAMPLE 6 A
on p. 238
for Exs. 36–37

36. OCEANOGRAPHY Ocean water levels are measured hourly at a monitoring station. The table shows the water level (in meters) on one particular morning. *Describe* the rates of change in water levels throughout the morning. *Sample answer:* **The water level decreases until 8 A.M. and then it increases until 12 P.M.**

Hours since 12:00 A.M.	1	3	8	10	12
Water level (meters)	2	1.4	0.5	1	1.8

@HomeTutor for problem solving help at classzone.com

37. MULTI-STEP PROBLEM Firing a piece of pottery in a kiln takes place at different temperatures for different amounts of time. The graph shows the temperatures in a kiln while firing a piece of pottery (after the kiln is preheated to 250°F).

a. Determine the time interval during which the temperature in the kiln showed the greatest rate of change. **0 h to 1.5 h**

b. Determine the time interval during which the temperature in the kiln showed the least rate of change. **4.65 h to 8.95 h**

@HomeTutor for problem solving help at classzone.com

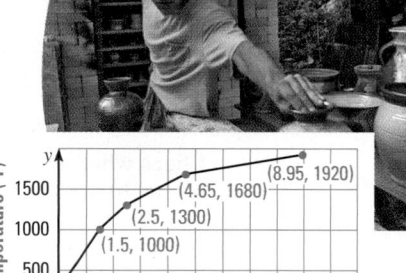

EXAMPLE 7
on p. 238
for Exs. 38–39

38. FLYING The graph shows the altitude of a plane during 4 hours of a flight. Give a verbal description of the flight. **See margin.**

39. HIKING The graph shows the elevation of a hiker walking on a mountain trail. Give a verbal description of the hike. **See margin.**

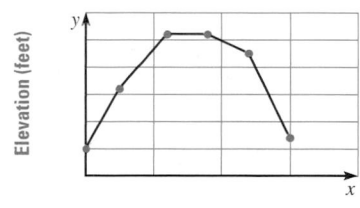

Study Strategy

Exercise 36 Tell students they can set up this problem using the solution in Example 6 as a model. Point out that instead of 3 intervals of time over weeks, there will be 4 intervals of time over hours for Exercise 36. Note that the independent variable is time and the dependent variable is water level. Ask students how this affects the use of the slope formula.

Exercises 38, 39 Suggest that students use Example 7 as a model for their descriptions. Note that the example describes the slope in each segment of the graph independently.

Internet Reference

Exercise 36 Additional information about oceanography can be found at the Office of Naval Research website at www.onr.navy.mil/focus/ocean

35. Multiply $\dfrac{y_2 - y_1}{x_2 - x_1}$ by $\dfrac{-1}{-1}$ to get

$\dfrac{-y_2 + y_1}{-x_2 + x_1}$, which, by the commutative property of addition, is equal

to $\dfrac{y_1 - y_2}{x_1 - x_2}$; it does not matter which point you choose to be (x_2, y_2) and which point is (x_1, y_1).

38. *Sample answer:* The altitude of the plane increases during the first 2 hours of the flight, then stays the same for about 45 minutes, and then decreases during the last hour and 45 minutes.

39. *Sample answer:* The elevation of the hiker increases for about 60 minutes, then stays the same for about 30 minutes, then decreases for the last 60 minutes.

📄 **Transparency Available**

Find the slope of the line that passes through the points.

1. $(12, -1)$ and $(-3, -1)$ **0**

2. $(-2, 6)$ and $(4, -3)$ $-\dfrac{3}{2}$

3. The graph shows the ticket sales for a school dance on day 1, day 3, day 6, and day 9 of ticket sales. Describe the rates of change in ticket sales with respect to time.

Ticket sales grew moderately, declined slightly, and then had another moderate rate of increase.

 Online Quiz

Available at **classzone.com**

Diagnosis/Remediation

- Practice A, B, C in Chapter 4 Resource Book, pp. 47–52
- Study Guide in Chapter 4 Resource Book, pp. 53–54
- Practice Workbook, pp. 55–57
- @HomeTutor

Challenge

Additional challenge is available in the Chapter 4 Resource Book, p. 57.

41a–c. See Additional Answers beginning on p. AA1.

40a. 1996 to 1998; about −1500 students per year

40b. 1998 to 2000; about 1500 students per year

40c. It increased. *Sample answer:* Although the number of engineering majors went down, it was not by as much as the number of biological science majors and liberal arts majors decreased.

40. ★ **EXTENDED RESPONSE** The graph shows the number (in thousands) of undergraduate students who majored in biological science, engineering, or liberal arts in the United States from 1990 to 2000.

a. During which two-year period did the number of engineering students decrease the most? Estimate the rate of change for this time period.

b. During which two-year period did the number of liberal arts students increase the most? Estimate the rate of change for this time period.

c. How did the total number of students majoring in biological science, engineering, and liberal arts change in the 10 year period? *Explain* your thinking.

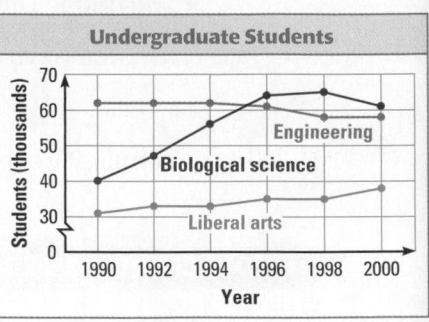

41. CHALLENGE Imagine the containers below being filled with water at a constant rate. Sketch a graph that shows the water level for each container during the time it takes to fill the container with water. **See margin.**

a.

b.

c.

MIXED REVIEW

Check whether the given number is a solution of the equation or inequality. *(p. 21)*

42. $4b - 7 = b + 11$; 6
solution

43. $x - 8 = -2x - 14$; -1
not a solution

44. $\dfrac{t}{4} + 9 = 13$; 16
solution

45. $a + 9 > 20$; 3
not a solution

46. $\dfrac{y + 3}{2} < 13$; 23
not a solution

47. $2(p + 5) \le 75$; 4
solution

Evaluate the expression. Approximate the square root to the nearest integer, if necessary. *(p. 110)*

48. $\sqrt{16}$ **4**

49. $-\sqrt{9}$ **−3**

50. $\pm\sqrt{45}$ **±7**

51. $\sqrt{136}$ **12**

52. $\pm\sqrt{64}$ **±8**

53. $-\sqrt{33}$ **−6**

54. $\pm\sqrt{154}$ **±12**

55. $\pm\sqrt{256}$ **±16**

56. $\sqrt{4761}$ **69**

PREVIEW
Prepare for Lesson 4.5 in Exs. 57–62.

Find the x-intercept and the y-intercept of the graph of the equation. *(p. 225)*

57. $y = x + 7$ **−7, 7**

58. $y = -x - 1$ **−1, −1**

59. $y = 8 - 2x$ **4, 8**

60. $y = 3x + 5$ **−1$\frac{2}{3}$, 5**

61. $y = 4x - 10$ **2$\frac{1}{2}$, −10**

62. $y = -9 + 6x$ **1$\frac{1}{2}$, −9**

EXTRA PRACTICE for Lesson 4.4, p. 941   **ONLINE QUIZ** at classzone.com

4.5 Slope and y-Intercept

QUESTION How can you use the equation of a line to find its slope and y-intercept?

EXPLORE Find the slopes and the y-intercepts of lines

STEP 1 *Find y when x = 0*
Copy the table below. Let $x_1 = 0$ and find y_1 for each equation. Use your answers to complete the second and fifth columns in the table.

STEP 2 *Find y when x = 2*
Let $x_2 = 2$ and find y_2 for each equation. Use your answers to complete the third column in the table.

STEP 3 *Compute the slope*
Use the slope formula and the ordered pairs you found in the second and third columns to complete the fourth column.

Line	$(0, y_1)$	$(2, y_2)$	Slope	y-intercept
$y = 4x + 3$	$(0, 3)$	$(2, 11)$	$\frac{11 - 3}{2 - 0} = 4$	3
$y = -2x + 3$	$(0, ?)$ **3**	$(2, ?)$ **−1**	? **−2**	? **3**
$y = \frac{1}{2}x + 4$	$(0, ?)$ **4**	$(2, ?)$ **5**	? $\frac{1}{2}$	? **4**
$y = -4x - 3$	$(0, ?)$ **−3**	$(2, ?)$ **−11**	? **−4**	? **−3**
$y = -\frac{1}{4}x - 3$	$(0, ?)$ **−3**	$(2, ?)$ **$-3\frac{1}{2}$**	? $-\frac{1}{4}$	? **−3**

DRAW CONCLUSIONS Use your observations to complete these exercises

1. *Compare* the slope of each line with the equation of the line. What do you notice? **It is the same as the coefficient of x in each equation.**

2. *Compare* the y-intercept of each line with the equation of the line. What do you notice? **It is the same as the constant in each equation.**

Predict the slope and the y-intercept of the line with the given equation. Then check your predictions by finding the slope and y-intercept as you did in the table above.

3. $y = -5x + 1$ **−5, 1**   4. $y = \frac{3}{4}x + 2$ **$\frac{3}{4}$, 2**   5. $y = -\frac{3}{2}x - 1$ **$-\frac{3}{2}$, −1**

6. **REASONING** Use the procedure you followed to complete the table above to show that the y-intercept of the graph of $y = mx + b$ is b and the slope of the graph is m. **If you substitute 0 for x you get y = b, giving the point (0, b). This shows the y-intercept is b. Substitute 2 in for x giving the point (2, 2m + b). Use the points (0, b) and (2, 2m + b) to find the slope. $\frac{(2m + b) - b}{2 - 0} = m$.**

4.5 Graph Using Slope-Intercept Form **243**

① PLAN AND PREPARE

Explore the Concept
- Students will use the equation of a line to find the slope and y-intercept of the line.
- This activity leads into the study of finding the slope and y-intercept of a line in Example 1 in Lesson 4.5.

Materials
Each student will need:
- Activity Support Master (*Chapter 4 Resource Book*, p. 62)

Recommended Time
Work activity: 10 min
Discuss results: 5 min

Grouping
Students should work individually.

② TEACH

Key Question
- What is the relationship between columns 2 and 5? **Column 2 gives the coordinates of the y-intercept in column 5.**

Key Discovery
The slope of a line written in the form $y = mx + b$ is m, the coefficient of x, and the y-intercept is the constant b.

③ ASSESS AND RETEACH

Predict the slope and y-intercept of the graph of $y = x$. Explain. **Since the coefficient of x is 1, the slope is 1. Since the equation is equivalent to y = x + 0, the constant is 0, and the y-intercept is 0.**

1. Rewrite $5x + y = 8$ so y is a function of x. $y = -5x + 8$

2. Find the slope of the line that passes through $(-5, 6)$ and $(0, 8)$. $\frac{2}{5}$

3. Find the intercepts of the graph of the function $a = 20t - 600$. a-intercept: -600, t-intercept: 30

Notetaking Guide

📄 **Transparency Available**

Promotes interactive learning and notetaking skills, pp. 87–90.

Pacing

Basic: 1 day

Average: 1 day

Advanced: 1 day

Block: 0.5 block with 4.6

• See *Teaching Guide/Lesson Plan*.

2 FOCUS AND MOTIVATE

Essential Question

Big Idea 1, p. 205

How do you graph linear equations given in slope-intercept form? **Tell students they will learn how to answer this question by using the *y*-intercept and the slope to determine two points on the graph.**

NCTM STANDARDS

Standard 2: Use models to understand relationships

Standard 8: Use the language of math to express ideas

4.5 Graph Using Slope-Intercept Form

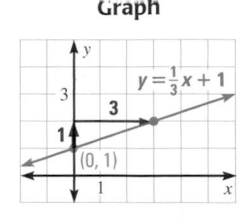

Before You found slopes and graphed equations using intercepts.

Now You will graph linear equations using slope-intercept form.

Why? So you can model a worker's earnings, as in Ex. 43.

Key Vocabulary
• slope-intercept form
• parallel

In the activity on page 243, you saw how the slope and y-intercept of the graph of a linear equation in the form $y = mx + b$ are related to the equation.

KEY CONCEPT *For Your Notebook*

Finding the Slope and *y*-Intercept of a Line

Words	Symbols	Graph
A linear equation of the form $y = mx + b$ is written in **slope-intercept form** where m is the slope and b is the y-intercept of the equation's graph.	$y = mx + b$ ↑ slope ↑ y-intercept ↓ ↓ $y = \frac{1}{3}x + 1$	$y = \frac{1}{3}x + 1$, passing through $(0, 1)$

EXAMPLE 1 Identify slope and *y*-intercept

Identify the slope and y-intercept of the line with the given equation.

a. $y = 3x + 4$

b. $3x + y = 2$

Solution

a. The equation is in the form $y = mx + b$. So, the slope of the line is 3, and the y-intercept is 4.

b. Rewrite the equation in slope-intercept form by solving for y.

$3x + y = 2$ **Write original equation.**

$y = -3x + 2$ **Subtract 3x from each side.**

▸ The line has a slope of -3 and a y-intercept of 2.

REWRITE EQUATIONS

When you rewrite a linear equation in slope-intercept form, you are expressing y as a function of x.

 GUIDED PRACTICE for Example 1

Identify the slope and y-intercept of the line with the given equation.

1. $y = 5x - 3$ **5, −3**

2. $3x - 3y = 12$ **1, −4**

3. $x + 4y = 6$ $-\frac{1}{4}, 1\frac{1}{2}$

Resource Planning Guide

Chapter Resource Book
• Teaching Guide/Lesson Plan (pp. 58–59)
• Activity Master (p. 60)
• Practice levels A, B, C (pp. 64–69)
• Study Guide (pp. 70–71)
• Catch-up for Absent Students (p. 72)
• Problem Solving Workshop (p. 73)
• Challenge (p. 74)

Workbooks
• Notetaking Guide (pp. 87–90)
• Practice Workbook (pp. 58–60)

Teaching Options
• **Power Presentations CD-ROM** provides dynamic electronic teaching resources for the classroom.
• **Activity Generator CD-ROM** provides editable activities for all ability levels.

Interactive Technology
• Easy Planner
• Power Presentations CD-ROM
• Activity Generator CD-ROM
• Animated Algebra
• Test Generator CD-ROM
• Online Quiz
• eWorkbook
• eEdition
• @HomeTutor

Resources for English Learners
• Quick Reference for English Learners
• Spanish Study Guide
• Multi-Language Visual Glossary
• Student Resources in Spanish

See also the *Algebra 1 Toolkit* for more strategies for meeting individual needs.

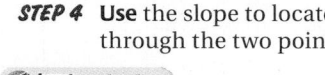

EXAMPLE 2 Graph an equation using slope-intercept form

Graph the equation $2x + y = 3$.

Solution

STEP 1 **Rewrite** the equation in slope-intercept form.

$$y = -2x + 3$$

STEP 2 **Identify** the slope and the y-intercept.

$$m = -2 \text{ and } b = 3$$

STEP 3 **Plot** the point that corresponds to the y-intercept, $(0, 3)$.

STEP 4 **Use** the slope to locate a second point on the line. Draw a line through the two points.

Animated **Algebra** at classzone.com

MODELING In real-world problems that can be modeled by linear equations, the y-intercept is often an initial value, and the slope is a rate of change.

EXAMPLE 3 Change slopes of lines

ESCALATORS To get from one floor to another at a library, you can take either the stairs or the escalator. You can climb stairs at a rate of 1.75 feet per second, and the escalator rises at a rate of 2 feet per second. You have to travel a vertical distance of 28 feet. The equations model the vertical distance d (in feet) you have left to travel after t seconds.

Stairs: $d = -1.75t + 28$ **Escalator:** $d = -2t + 28$

a. Graph the equations in the same coordinate plane.

b. How much time do you save by taking the escalator?

Solution

a. Draw the graph of $d = -1.75t + 28$ using the fact that the d-intercept is 28 and the slope is -1.75. Similarly, draw the graph of $d = -2t + 28$. The graphs make sense only in the first quadrant.

b. The equation $d = -1.75t + 28$ has a t-intercept of **16**. The equation $d = -2t + 28$ has a t-intercept of **14**. So, you save $16 - 14 = 2$ seconds by taking the escalator.

✓ **GUIDED PRACTICE**   for Examples 2 and 3

4. Graph the equation $y = -2x + 5$. **See margin.**

5. **WHAT IF?** In Example 3, suppose a person can climb stairs at a rate of 1.4 feet per second. How much time does taking the escalator save? **6 sec**

4.5   Graph Using Slope-Intercept Form   **245**

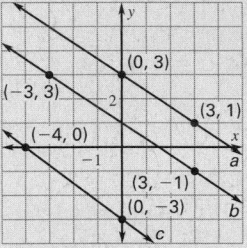
EXAMPLE 4 Change intercepts of lines

TELEVISION A company produced two 30 second commercials, one for $300,000 and the second for $400,000. Each airing of either commercial on a particular station costs $150,000. The cost C (in thousands of dollars) to produce the first commercial and air it n times is given by $C = 150n + 300$. The cost to produce the second and air it n times is given by $C = 150n + 400$.

a. Graph both equations in the same coordinate plane.

b. Based on the graphs, what is the difference of the costs to produce each commercial and air it 2 times? 4 times? What do you notice about the differences of the costs?

Solution

a. The graphs of the equations are shown.

b. You can see that the vertical distance between the lines is $100,000 when $n = 2$ and $n = 4$.

The difference of the costs is $100,000 no matter how many times the commercials are aired.

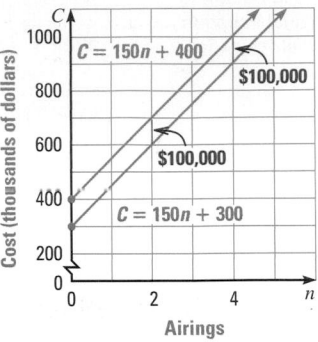

PARALLEL LINES Two lines in the same plane are **parallel** if they do not intersect. Because slope gives the rate at which a line rises or falls, two nonvertical lines with the same slope are parallel.

EXAMPLE 5 Identify parallel lines

Determine which of the lines are parallel.

Find the slope of each line.

Line a: $m = \dfrac{-1 - 0}{-1 - 2} = \dfrac{-1}{-3} = \dfrac{1}{3}$

Line b: $m = \dfrac{-3 - (-1)}{0 - 5} = \dfrac{-2}{-5} = \dfrac{2}{5}$

Line c: $m = \dfrac{-5 - (-3)}{-2 - 4} = \dfrac{-2}{-6} = \dfrac{1}{3}$

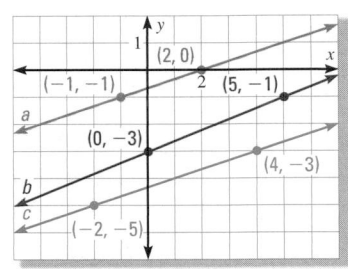

▶ Line a and line c have the same slope, so they are parallel.

✓ **GUIDED PRACTICE** for Examples 4 and 5

6. **WHAT IF?** In Example 4, suppose that the cost of producing and airing a third commercial is given by $C = 150n + 200$. Graph the equation. Find the difference of the costs of the second commercial and the third. **See margin for art; $200,000.**

7. Determine which lines are parallel: line a through $(-1, 2)$ and $(3, 4)$; line b through $(3, 4)$ and $(5, 8)$; line c through $(-9, -2)$ and $(-1, 2)$. **a and c**

6.

4.5 EXERCISES

HOMEWORK KEY
○ = WORKED-OUT SOLUTIONS
on p. WS1 for Exs. 11, 21, and 41
★ = STANDARDIZED TEST PRACTICE
Exs. 2, 9, 10, 36, 42, and 44

SKILL PRACTICE

A

1. **VOCABULARY** Copy and complete: Two lines in the same plane are __?__ if they do not intersect. **parallel**

2. ★ **WRITING** What is the slope-intercept form of a linear equation? *Explain* why this form is called slope-intercept form. **$y = mx + b$; because m is the slope and b is the y-intercept.**

EXAMPLE 1
on p. 244
for Exs. 3–16

SLOPE AND y-INTERCEPT Identify the slope and y-intercept of the line with the given equation.

3. $y = 2x + 1$ **2, 1**

4. $y = -x$ **-1, 0**

5. $y = 6 - 3x$ **-3, 6**

6. $y = -7 + 5x$ **5, -7**

7. $y = \frac{2}{3}x - 1$ **$\frac{2}{3}$, -1**

8. $y = -\frac{1}{4}x + 8$ **$-\frac{1}{4}$, 8**

9. ★ **MULTIPLE CHOICE** What is the slope of the line with the equation $y = -18x - 9$? **A**

(A) -18   (B) -9   (C) 9   (D) 18

10. ★ **MULTIPLE CHOICE** What is the y-intercept of the line with the equation $x - 3y = -12$? **C**

(A) -12   (B) -4   (C) 4   (D) 12

REWRITING EQUATIONS Rewrite the equation in slope-intercept form. Then identify the slope and the y-intercept of the line.

11. $4x + y = 1$
$y = -4x + 1; -4, 1$

12. $x - y = 6$ $y = x - 6; 1, -6$

13. $6x - 3y = -9$
$y = 2x + 3; 2, 3$

14. $-12x - 4y = 2$
$y = -3x - \frac{1}{2}; -3, -\frac{1}{2}$

15. $2x + 5y = -10$
$y = -\frac{2}{5}x - 2; -\frac{2}{5}, -2$

16. $-x - 10y = 20$
$y = -\frac{1}{10}x - 2; -\frac{1}{10}, -2$

EXAMPLE 2
on p. 245
for Exs. 17–29

MATCHING EQUATIONS WITH GRAPHS Match the equation with its graph.

17. $2x + 3y = 6$ **B**

18. $2x + 3y = -6$ **A**

19. $2x - 3y = 6$ **C**

A.   B.   C.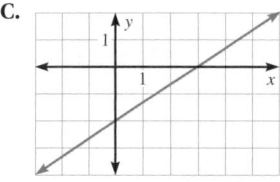

20. **ERROR ANALYSIS** *Describe* and correct the error in graphing the equation $y = 4x - 1$.
The y-intercept is -1, not 1; see margin for art.

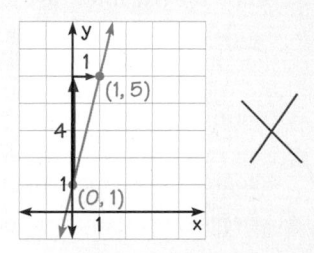

---

4 PRACTICE AND APPLY

Assignment Guide

📄 Answer Transparencies available for all exercises

Basic:
Day 1: pp. 247–250
Exs. 1–13, 17–24, 30–33, 40–43, 46–56 even

Average:
Day 1: pp. 247–250
Exs. 1–5, 9, 10, 13–20, 25–31, 32–38 even, 40–44, 46–56 even

Advanced:
Day 1: pp. 247–250
Exs. 1, 2, 6–10, 14–19, 27–39*, 41–45*, 47–57 odd

Block:
pp. 247–250
Exs. 1–5, 9, 10, 13–20, 25–31, 32–38 even, 40–44, 46–56 even (with 4.6)

Differentiated Instruction

See *Algebra 1 Best Practices Toolkit* for suggestions on addressing the needs of a diverse classroom.

Homework Check

For a quick check of student understanding of key concepts, go over the following exercises:

Basic: 12, 22, 30, 40, 42
Average: 15, 26, 32, 41, 43
Advanced: 16, 29, 34, 41, 44

Extra Practice

• Student Edition, p. 941
• Chapter 4 Resource Book:
Practice levels A, B, C, pp. 64–69

Practice Worksheet

An easily-readable reduced practice page (with answers) for this lesson can be found on p. 204C.

20.

21.

22.

23.

24.

GRAPHING EQUATIONS Graph the equation. 21–29. See margin.

21. $y = -6x + 1$ **22.** $y = 3x + 2$ **23.** $y = -x + 7$

24. $y = \frac{2}{3}x$ **25.** $y = \frac{1}{4}x - 5$ **26.** $y = -\frac{5}{2}x + 2$

27. $7x - 2y = -11$ **28.** $-8x - 2y = 32$ **29.** $-x - 0.5y = 2.5$

EXAMPLE 5
on p. 246
for Exs. 30–35

PARALLEL LINES Determine which lines are parallel.

30.

blue and green

31.

red, blue, and green

B **PARALLEL LINES Tell whether the graphs of the two equations are parallel lines. *Explain* your reasoning.**

32. $y = 5x - 7, 5x + y = 7$
Not parallel; the slopes are 5 and −5.
33. $y = 3x + 2, -7 + 3x = y$
Parallel; the slopes are both 3.
34. $y = -0.5x, x + 2y = 18$
Parallel; the slopes are both −0.5.
35. $4x + y = 3, x + 4y = 3$
Not parallel; the slopes are −4 and −$\frac{1}{4}$.

36. ★ OPEN-ENDED Write the equation of a line that is parallel to $6x + y = 24$. *Explain* your reasoning. **Sample answer: $y = -6x + 5$; the equation has the same slope as $6x + y = 24$, but a different y-intercept.**

REASONING Find the value of k so that the lines through the given points are parallel.

37. Line 1: $(-4, -2)$ and $(0, 0)$
Line 2: $(2, 7)$ and $(k, 5)$ **−2**
38. Line 1: $(-1, 9)$ and $(-6, -6)$
Line 2: $(-7, k)$ and $(0, -2)$ **−23**

C **39. CHALLENGE** Find the slope and y-intercept of the graph of the equation $Ax + By = C$ where $B \neq 0$. Use your results to find the slope and y-intercept of the graph of $3x + 2y = 18$. $m = -\frac{A}{B}$, y-intercept $= \frac{C}{B}$; $-\frac{3}{2}$, 9

PROBLEM SOLVING

EXAMPLES A
3 and 4
on pp. 245–246
for Exs. 40–44

40. HOCKEY Your family spends $60 on tickets to a hockey game and $4 per hour for parking. The total cost C (in dollars) is given by $C = 60 + 4t$ where t is the time (in hours) your family's car is parked.

  a. Graph the equation. **a–b. See margin.**

  b. Suppose the parking fee is raised to $5.50 per hour so that the total cost of tickets and parking for t hours is $C = 60 + 5.5t$. Graph the equation in the same coordinate plane as the equation in part (a).

  c. How much more does it cost to go to a game for 4 hours after the parking fee is raised? **$6**

@HomeTutor for problem solving help at classzone.com

25.

26.

27.

○ = **WORKED-OUT SOLUTIONS**
on p. WS1

★ = **STANDARDIZED TEST PRACTICE**

41. SPEED LIMITS In 1995 Pennsylvania changed its maximum speed limit on rural interstate highways, as shown below. The diagram also shows the distance d (in miles) a person could travel driving at the maximum speed limit for t hours both before and after 1995.

Before 1995 SPEED LIMIT 55 $d = 55t$

After 1995 SPEED LIMIT 65 $d = 65t$

a. Graph both equations in the same coordinate plane. **See margin.**

b. Use the graphs to find the difference of the distances a person could drive in 3 hours before and after the speed limit was changed. **30 mi**

@HomeTutor for problem solving help at classzone.com

42. ★ **SHORT RESPONSE** A service station charges $40 per hour for labor plus the cost of parts to repair a car. Parts can either be ordered from the car dealership for $250 or from a warehouse for $200. The equations below give the total repair cost C (in dollars) for a repair that takes t hours using parts from the dealership or from the warehouse.

Dealership: $C = 40t + 250$ **Warehouse:** $C = 40t + 200$

a. Graph both equations in the same coordinate plane. **See margin.**

b. Use the graphs to find the difference of the costs if the repair takes 3 hours. What if the repair takes 4 hours? What do you notice about the differences of the costs? *Explain.* **$50; $50; the difference is $50 no matter how many hours it takes to repair a car because the slopes are the same.**

B 43. **FACTORY SHIFTS** Welders at a factory can work one of two shifts. Welders on the first shift earn $12 per hour while workers on the second shift earn $14 per hour. The total amount a (in dollars) a first-shift worker earns is given by $a = 12t$ where t is the time (in hours) worked. The total amount a second-shift worker earns is given by $a = 14t$.

a. Graph both equations in the same coordinate plane. What do the slopes and the a-intercepts of the graphs mean in this situation?

b. How much more money does a welder earn for a 40 hour week if he or she works the second shift rather than the first shift? **$80**

44. ★ **EXTENDED RESPONSE** An artist is renting a booth at an art show. A small booth costs $350 to rent. The artist plans to sell framed pictures for $50 each. The profit P (in dollars) the artist makes after selling p pictures is given by $P = 50p - 350$.

a. Graph the equation. **a–b. See margin for art.**

b. If the artist decides to rent a larger booth for $500, the profit is given by $P = 50p - 500$. Graph this equation on the same coordinate plane you used in part (a).

c. The artist can display 80 pictures in the small booth and 120 in the larger booth. If the artist is able to sell all of the pictures, which booth should the artist rent? *Explain.* **Larger booth; if the artist rents the larger booth and sells all the paintings, the artist will make $5500, if the artist rents the smaller booth and sells all the paintings, the artist will make only $3650.**

Margin notes:

43a. See margin for art; the slopes are the amount of money earned per hour, the a-intercepts show the amount of money made at 0 hours.

Internet Reference

Exercise 41 To find a map showing the maximum speed limit on interstate highways for the entire United States, visit www.fhwa.dot.gov/policy/ohpi/speeds.htm

41a.

42a.

43a.

44a–b.

28.

29.

40a–b.

C **45. CHALLENGE** To use a rock climbing wall at a college, a person who does not attend the college has to pay a $5 certification fee plus $3 per visit. The total cost C (in dollars) for a person who does not attend the college is given by $C = 3v + 5$ where v is the number of visits to the rock climbing wall. A student at the college pays only an $8 certification fee, so the total cost for a student is given by $C = 8$.

  a. Graph both equations in the same coordinate plane. At what point do the lines intersect? What does the point of intersection represent?
  See margin for art; (1, 8); the point represents when the costs are equal.

  b. When will a nonstudent pay more than a student? When will a student pay more than a nonstudent? *Explain.* **A nonstudent pays more than a student after the first visit; a student pays more than a nonstudent when getting certified.**

MIXED REVIEW

Simplify the expression. *(p. 96)*

46. $3(x + 24)$ **$3x + 72$**   **47.** $5(x - 5)$ **$5x - 25$**   **48.** $8(x - 6)$ **$8x - 48$**

Solve the equation.

49. $3x + x = 8$ *(p. 141)* **2**   **50.** $5(x - 3x) = 15$ *(p. 148)* **−1.5**   **51.** $\frac{4}{3}(8x - 3) = 16$ *(p. 148)*
                                                                                                                    1.875

PREVIEW
Prepare for
Lesson 4.6
in Exs. 52–57.

Find the slope of the line that passes through the points. *(p. 235)*

52. $(3, 4)$ and $(9, 5)$ $\frac{1}{6}$ **53.** $(4, -4)$ and $(-2, 2)$ **−1**   **54.** $(-3, -7)$ and $(0, -7)$ **0**

Solve the proportion. Check your solution. *(p. 168)*

55. $\frac{4}{5} = \frac{x}{50}$ **40**   **56.** $\frac{2x}{x + 4} = \frac{8}{9}$ **3.2**   **57.** $\frac{7t - 2}{8} = \frac{3t - 4}{5}$ **−2**

QUIZ *for Lessons 4.4–4.5*

Find the slope of the line that passes through the points. *(p. 235)*

  1. $(3, -11)$ and $(0, 4)$ **−5**   **2.** $(2, 1)$ and $(8, 4)$ $\frac{1}{2}$ **3.** $(-4, -1)$ and $(-1, -1)$ **0**

Identify the slope and y-intercept of the line with the given equation. *(p. 244)*

  4. $y = -x + 9$ **−1, 9**   **5.** $2x + 9y = -18$ $-\frac{2}{9}, -2$ **6.** $-x + 6y = 21$ $\frac{1}{6}, 3\frac{1}{2}$

Graph the equation. *(p. 244)* **7–9. See margin.**

  7. $y = -2x + 11$ **8.** $y = \frac{5}{3}x - 8$ **9.** $-3x - 4y = -12$

10. RED OAKS Red oak trees grow at a rate of about 2 feet per year. You buy and plant two red oak trees, one that is 6 feet tall and one that is 8 feet tall. The height h (in feet) of the shorter tree can be modeled by $h = 2t + 6$ where t is the time (in years) since you planted the tree. The height of the taller tree can be modeled by $h = 2t + 8$. *(p. 244)*

  a. Graph both equations in the same coordinate plane. **See margin.**

  b. Use the graphs to find the difference of the heights of the trees 5 years after you plant them. What is the difference after 10 years? What do you notice about the difference of the heights of the two trees?
  2 ft; 2 ft; it is always 2 feet.

250   **EXTRA PRACTICE** for Lesson 4.5, p. 941   **ONLINE QUIZ** at classzone.com

Solve Linear Equations by Graphing

GOAL Use graphs to solve linear equations.

In Chapter 3, you learned how to solve linear equations in one variable algebraically. You can also solve linear equations graphically.

KEY CONCEPT *For Your Notebook*

Steps for Solving Linear Equations Graphically

Use the following steps to solve a linear equation in one variable graphically.

STEP 1 Write the equation in the form $ax + b = 0$.

STEP 2 Write the related function $y = ax + b$.

STEP 3 Graph the equation $y = ax + b$.

The solution of $ax + b = 0$ is the x-intercept of the graph of $y = ax + b$.

EXAMPLE 1 Solve an equation graphically

Solve $\frac{5}{2}x + 2 = 3x$ graphically. Check your solution algebraically.

Solution

STEP 1 Write the equation in the form $ax + b = 0$.

$$\frac{5}{2}x + 2 = 3x \qquad \text{Write original equation.}$$

$$-\frac{1}{2}x + 2 = 0 \qquad \text{Subtract 3x from each side.}$$

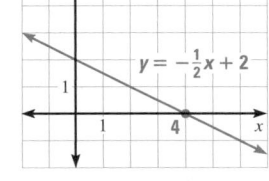
$y = -\frac{1}{2}x + 2$

STEP 2 Write the related function $y = -\frac{1}{2}x + 2$.

STEP 3 Graph the equation $y = -\frac{1}{2}x + 2$. The x-intercept is 4.

▶ The solution of $\frac{5}{2}x + 2 = 3x$ is 4.

CHECK Use substitution.

$$\frac{5}{2}x + 2 = 3x \qquad \text{Write original equation.}$$

$$\frac{5}{2}(4) + 2 \overset{?}{=} 3(4) \qquad \text{Substitute 4 for x.}$$

$$10 + 2 = 12 \qquad \text{Simplify.}$$

$$12 = 12 \checkmark \qquad \text{Solution checks.}$$

Extension: Solve Linear Equations by Graphing **251**

---

❶ PLAN AND PREPARE

Warm-Up Exercises
Solve the equation.
1. $-3n + 13 = 7$ **2**
2. $\frac{3}{4}x + 2 = -10$ **−16**
3. $-6 + 4d = 2d + 2$ **4**
4. You buy a petrified rock and 6 postcards on a trip to the Petrified Forest. The petrified rock costs $6.75. Find the cost of each postcard if your total cost is $14.25 before tax and all the postcards cost the same. **$1.25**

❷ FOCUS AND MOTIVATE

Essential Question
Big Idea 1, p. 205
How do you use graphs to solve linear equations in one variable? Tell students they will learn how to answer this question by writing equations and their related functions to find the *x*-intercept of a graph.

❸ TEACH

Extra Example 1
Solve $\frac{4}{3}x + 5 = 1$ graphically. **−3**

$y = \frac{4}{3}x + 4$

NCTM STANDARDS
Standard 2: Use models to understand relationships
Standard 10: Use representations to communicate mathematical ideas

Extra Example 2

The number s (in thousands) of subscribers to a local magazine can be modeled by the function $s = 3.128t + 12.58$ where t is the number of years since 1990. Use a graphing calculator to approximate the year when the number of subscribers will be 80 thousand.

X=21.263158 Y=−.9088421

about 21 years after 1990, or 2011

Closing the Lesson

Have students summarize the major points of the lesson and answer the Essential Question: How do you use graphs to solve linear equations in one variable?

• **To solve a linear equation in one variable by graphing, first find a related function.**

• **The x-intercept of the graph of the related function is the solution of the original equation.**

Rewrite the given equation so it is equal to zero. Then write and graph the related function. The x-intercept of the graph is the solution of the equation.

④ PRACTICE AND APPLY

Avoiding Common Errors

Exercises 7–9 Remind students to substitute the appropriate numbers for s, b, and m in the equations and then write each equation in $ax + b = 0$ form.

EXAMPLE 2 Approximate a real-world solution

POPULATION The United States population P (in millions) can be modeled by the function $P = 2.683t + 213.1$ where t is the number of years since 1975. In approximately what year will the population be 350 million?

Solution

Substitute 350 for P in the linear model. You can answer the question by solving the resulting linear equation $350 = 2.683t + 213.1$.

STEP 1 **Write** the equation in the form $ax + b = 0$.

$350 = 2.683t + 213.1$ **Write equation.**

$0 = 2.683t − 136.9$ **Subtract 350 from each side.**

$0 = 2.683x − 136.9$ **Substitute x for t.**

STEP 2 **Write** the related function: $y = 2.683x − 136.9$.

STEP 3 **Graph** the related function on a graphing calculator. Use the *trace* feature to approximate the x-intercept. You will know that you've crossed the x-axis when the y-values change from negative to positive. The x-intercept is about 51.

X=51.010638 Y=−.038457

▶ Because x is the number of years since 1975, you can estimate that the population will be 350 million about 51 years after 1975, or in 2026.

SET THE WINDOW

Use the following viewing window for Example 2.
Xmin=−5
Xmax=60
Xscl=5
Ymin=−150
Ymax=10
Yscl=10

PRACTICE

EXAMPLE 1
on p. 251
for Exs. 1–6

Solve the equation graphically. Then check your solution algebraically.

1. $6x + 5 = −7$ **−2**

2. $−7x + 18 = −3$ **3**

3. $2x − 4 = 3x$ **−4**

4. $\frac{1}{2}x − 3 = 2x$ **−2**

5. $−4 + 9x = −3x + 2$ $\frac{1}{2}$

6. $10x − 18x = 4x − 6$ $\frac{1}{2}$

EXAMPLE 2
on p. 252
for Exs. 7–9

7. CABLE TELEVISION The number s (in millions) of cable television subscribers can be modeled by the function $s = 1.79t + 51.1$ where t is the number of years since 1990. Use a graphing calculator to approximate the year when the number of subscribers was 70 million. **2000**

8. EDUCATION The number b (in thousands) of bachelor's degrees in Spanish earned in the U.S. can be modeled by the function $b = 0.281t + 4.26$ where t is the number of years since 1990. Use a graphing calculator to approximate the year when the number of degrees will be 9000. **2006**

9. TRAVEL The number of miles m (in billions) traveled by vehicles in New York can be modeled by $m = 2.56t + 113$ where t is the number of years since 1994. Use a graphing calculator to approximate the year in which the number of vehicle miles of travel in New York was 130 billion. **2000**

4.6 Model Direct Variation

Before You wrote and graphed linear equations.

Now You will write and graph direct variation equations.

Why? So you can model distance traveled, as in Ex. 40.

Key Vocabulary
• direct variation
• constant of variation

Two variables x and y show **direct variation** provided $y = ax$ and $a \neq 0$. The nonzero number a is called the **constant of variation**, and y is said to *vary directly* with x.

The equation $y = 5x$ is an example of direct variation, and the constant of variation is 5. The equation $y = x + 5$ is *not* an example of direct variation.

EXAMPLE 1 Identify direct variation equations

Tell whether the equation represents direct variation. If so, identify the constant of variation.

a. $2x - 3y = 0$ **b.** $-x + y = 4$

Solution

To tell whether an equation represents direct variation, try to rewrite the equation in the form $y = ax$.

a. $2x - 3y = 0$ Write original equation.

$-3y = -2x$ Subtract 2x from each side.

$y = \frac{2}{3}x$ Simplify.

▶ Because the equation $2x - 3y = 0$ can be rewritten in the form $y = ax$, it represents direct variation. The constant of variation is $\frac{2}{3}$.

b. $-x + y = 4$ Write original equation.

$y = x + 4$ Add x to each side.

▶ Because the equation $-x + y = 4$ cannot be rewritten in the form $y = ax$, it does not represent direct variation.

✓ **GUIDED PRACTICE** for Example 1

Tell whether the equation represents direct variation. If so, identify the constant of variation.

1. $-x + y = 1$
not direct variation

2. $2x + y = 0$
direct variation; -2

3. $4x - 5y = 0$
direct variation; $\frac{4}{5}$

① PLAN AND PREPARE

Warm-Up Exercises
🖴 Transparency Available
Rewrite the equation so y is a function of x.

1. $4x - 2y = -8$ $y = 2x + 4$
2. $-9x + 3y = 21$ $y = 3x + 7$

3. You are traveling by bus. After 4.5 hours, the bus has traveled 234 miles. Use the formula $d = rt$ where d is distance, r is rate, and t is time to find the average rate of speed of the bus. **52 mi/h**

Notetaking Guide
🖴 Transparency Available
Promotes interactive learning and notetaking skills, pp. 91–93.

Pacing
Basic: 1 day
Average: 1 day
Advanced: 1 day
Block: 0.5 block with 4.5
• See *Teaching Guide/Lesson Plan.*

② FOCUS AND MOTIVATE

Essential Question
Big Idea 3, p. 205

How do you write and graph direct variation equations? **Tell students they will learn how to answer this question by recognizing situations that represent direct variation and identifying the constant of variation.**

NCTM STANDARDS
Standard 2: Use models to understand relationships

Standard 8: Communicate thinking clearly to others

Resource Planning Guide

Chapter Resource Book
• Teaching Guide/Lesson Plan (pp. 75–76)
• Practice levels A, B, C (pp. 77–82)
• Study Guide (pp. 83–84)
• Catch-up for Absent Students (p. 85)
• Application (p. 86)
• Challenge (p. 87)

Workbooks
• Notetaking Guide (pp. 91–93)
• Practice Workbook (pp. 61–63)

Teaching Options
• **Power Presentations CD-ROM** provides dynamic electronic teaching resources for the classroom.
• **Activity Generator CD-ROM** provides editable activities for all ability levels.

Interactive Technology
• Easy Planner
• Power Presentations CD-ROM
• Activity Generator CD-ROM
• Animated Algebra
• Test Generator CD-ROM
• Online Quiz
• eWorkbook
• eEdition
• @HomeTutor

Resources for English Learners
• Quick Reference for English Learners
• Spanish Study Guide
• Multi-Language Visual Glossary
• Student Resources in Spanish

See also the *Algebra 1 Toolkit* for more strategies for meeting individual needs.

253

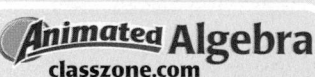
DIRECT VARIATION GRAPHS Notice that a direct variation equation, $y = ax$, is a linear equation in slope-intercept form, $y = mx + b$, with $m = a$ and $b = 0$. The graph of a direct variation equation is a line with a slope of a and a y-intercept of 0. So, the line passes through the origin.

EXAMPLE 2 Graph direct variation equations

Graph the direct variation equation.

a. $y = \dfrac{2}{3}x$

b. $y = -3x$

Solution

a. Plot a point at the origin. The slope is equal to the constant of variation, or $\dfrac{2}{3}$. Find and plot a second point, then draw a line through the points.

b. Plot a point at the origin. The slope is equal to the constant of variation, or -3. Find and plot a second point, then draw a line through the points.

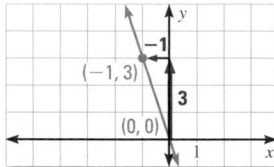

Animated Algebra at classzone.com

EXAMPLE 3 Write and use a direct variation equation

The graph of a direct variation equation is shown.

a. Write the direct variation equation.

b. Find the value of y when $x = 30$.

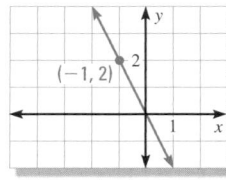

Solution

a. Because y varies directly with x, the equation has the form $y = ax$. Use the fact that $y = 2$ when $x = -1$ to find a.

$y = ax$ **Write direct variation equation.**

$2 = a(-1)$ **Substitute.**

$-2 = a$ **Solve for a.**

▶ A direct variation equation that relates x and y is $y = -2x$.

b. When $x = 30$, $y = -2(30) = -60$.

✓ GUIDED PRACTICE for Examples 2 and 3

4. Graph the direct variation equation $y = 2x$. **See margin.**

5. The graph of a direct variation equation passes through the point $(4, 6)$. Write the direct variation equation and find the value of y when $x = 24$.

$y = \dfrac{3}{2}x$, **36**

KEY CONCEPT   *For Your Notebook*

Properties of Graphs of Direct Variation Equations

- The graph of a direct variation equation is a line through the origin.
- The slope of the graph of $y = ax$ is a.

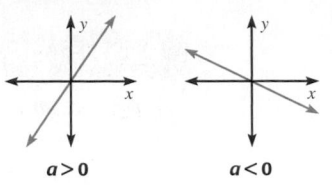

$a > 0$ $a < 0$

EXAMPLE 4   Solve a multi-step problem

ANOTHER WAY
For alternative methods for solving Example 4, turn to page 260 for the **Problem Solving Workshop**.

SALTWATER AQUARIUM The number s of tablespoons of sea salt needed in a saltwater fish tank varies directly with the number w of gallons of water in the tank. A pet shop owner recommends adding 100 tablespoons of sea salt to a 20 gallon tank.

- Write a direct variation equation that relates w and s.
- How many tablespoons of salt should be added to a 30 gallon saltwater fish tank?

Solution

STEP 1 **Write** a direct variation equation. Because s varies directly with w, you can use the equation $s = aw$. Also use the fact that $s = 100$ when $w = 20$.

RECOGNIZE RATE OF CHANGE
The value of a in Example 4 is a rate of change: 5 tablespoons of sea salt per gallon of water.

$s = aw$ **Write direct variation equation.**

$100 = a(20)$ **Substitute.**

$5 = a$ **Solve for a.**

▸ A direct variation equation that relates w and s is $s = 5w$.

STEP 2 **Find** the number of tablespoons of salt that should be added to a 30 gallon saltwater fish tank. Use your direct variation equation from Step 1.

$s = 5w$ **Write direct variation equation.**

$s = 5(30)$ **Substitute 30 for w.**

$s = 150$ **Simplify.**

▸ You should add 150 tablespoons of salt to a 30 gallon fish tank.

✓ **GUIDED PRACTICE**   for Example 4

6. **WHAT IF?** In Example 4, suppose the fish tank is a 25 gallon tank. How many tablespoons of salt should be added to the tank? **125 tbsp**

4.6 Model Direct Variation   **255**

4.

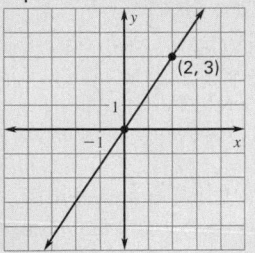

Extra Example 5
The table shows the cost of buying used DVDs at a music store.

Number of DVDs, d	Cost, c
3	$25.77
6	$51.54
9	$77.31

a. CHECK why C varies directly with d. **All of the data pairs have the same ratio, 8.59.**

b. Write a direct variation equation that relates d and C. **$C = 8.59d$**

Closing the Lesson

Have students summarize the major points of the lesson and answer the Essential Question: How do you write and graph direct variation equations?

• **A direct variation equation is of the form $y = ax$, with a not equal to 0.**

• **The graph of a direct variation equation is a line through the origin with slope a.**

Use facts in a real-world situation or the coordinates of a point for the values of x and y in the direct variation equation $y = ax$. Then solve for the constant of variation. To graph a direct variation equation, plot a point at the origin and then use the constant of variation, which is the slope, to plot a second point.

RATIOS The direct variation equation $y = ax$ can be rewritten as $\frac{y}{x} = a$ for $x \neq 0$. So, in a direct variation, the ratio of y to x is constant for all nonzero data pairs (x, y).

EXAMPLE 5 Use a direct variation model

ONLINE MUSIC The table shows the cost C of downloading s songs at an Internet music site.

Number of songs, s	Cost, C (dollars)
3	2.97
5	4.95
7	6.93

a. Explain why C varies directly with s.

b. Write a direct variation equation that relates s and C.

Solution

a. To explain why C varies directly with s, compare the ratios $\frac{C}{s}$ for all data pairs (s, C): $\frac{2.97}{3} = \frac{4.95}{5} = \frac{6.93}{7} = 0.99$.

Because the ratios all equal 0.99, C varies directly with s.

b. A direct variation equation is $C = 0.99s$.

 GUIDED PRACTICE for Example 5

7. WHAT IF? In Example 5, suppose the website charges a total of $1.99 for the first 5 songs you download and $.99 for each song after the first 5. Is it reasonable to use a direct variation model for this situation? *Explain.* **No; the equation that models this situation does not have the form $y = ax$.**

4.6 EXERCISES

HOMEWORK KEY

○ = **WORKED-OUT SOLUTIONS**
on p. WS1 for Exs. 7, 21, and 43

★ = **STANDARDIZED TEST PRACTICE**
Exs. 2, 9, 28, 38, 43, 44, and 46

◆ = **MULTIPLE REPRESENTATIONS**
Ex. 45

SKILL PRACTICE

[A] **1. VOCABULARY** Copy and complete: Two variables x and y show __?__ provided $y = ax$ and $a \neq 0$. **direct variation**

2. ★ WRITING A line has a slope of -3 and a y-intercept of 4. Is the equation of the line a direct variation equation? *Explain.* **No; a direct variation equation has a y-intercept of 0.**

EXAMPLE 1
on p. 253
for Exs. 3–10

IDENTIFYING DIRECT VARIATION EQUATIONS Tell whether the equation represents direct variation. If so, identify the constant of variation.

3. $y = x$ **direct variation; 1**

4. $y = 5x - 1$ **not direct variation**

5. $2x + y = 3$ **not direct variation**

6. $x - 3y = 0$ **direct variation; $\frac{1}{3}$**

 7. $8x + 2y = 0$ **direct variation; -4**

8. $2.4x + 6 = 1.2y$ **not direct variation**

Differentiated Instruction

English Learners The word *variation* means "a change," so students may be confused by the term *constant of variation* for a in the direct variation equation $y = ax$. Stress that a does not vary, but rather stays constant, in a given direct variation equation.

See also the *Algebra 1 Toolkit* for more strategies.

9. **★ MULTIPLE CHOICE** Which equation is a direct variation equation? **C**

    (A) $y = 7 - 3x$ **(B)** $3x - 7y = 1$ **(C)** $3x - 7y = 0$ **(D)** $3y = 7x - 1$

10. **ERROR ANALYSIS** *Describe* and correct the error in identifying the constant of variation for the direct variation equation $-5x + 3y = 0$. The coefficient of y should be 1, not 3; $y = \frac{5}{3}x$, the constant of variation is $\frac{5}{3}$.

> $-5x + 3y = 0$
> $3y = 5x$
> The constant of variation is 5. ✗

EXAMPLE 2
on p. 254
for Exs. 11–22

GRAPHING EQUATIONS Graph the direct variation equation. **11–22. See margin.**

11. $y = x$ 12. $y = 3x$ 13. $y = -4x$ 14. $y = 5x$

15. $y = \frac{4}{3}x$ 16. $y = \frac{1}{2}x$ 17. $y = -\frac{1}{3}x$ 18. $y = -\frac{3}{2}x$

19. $12y = -24x$ 20. $10y = 25x$ **21.** $4x + y = 0$ 22. $y - 1.25x = 0$

EXAMPLE 3
on p. 254
for Exs. 23–25

WRITING EQUATIONS The graph of a direct variation equation is shown. Write the direct variation equation. Then find the value of y when $x = 8$.

23.
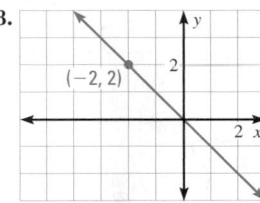
$(-2, 2)$

$y = -x;\ -8$

24.
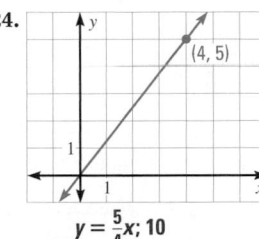
$(4, 5)$

$y = \frac{5}{4}x;\ 10$

25.
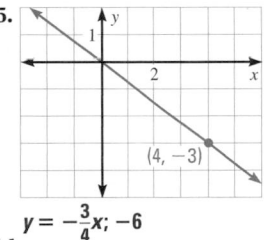
$(4, -3)$

$y = -\frac{3}{4}x;\ -6$

[B] **IDENTIFYING DIRECT VARIATION EQUATIONS** Tell whether the table represents direct variation. If so, write the direct variation equation.

26.

x	1	2	3	4	6
y	5	10	15	20	30

direct variation; $y = 5x$

27.

x	-3	-1	1	3	5
y	-2	0	2	4	6

not a direct variation

28. **★ WRITING** A student says that a direct variation equation can be used to model the data in the table. *Explain* why the student is mistaken.

x	2	4	8	16
y	1	2	4	6

Sample answer: Each of the ratios $\frac{y}{x}$ should be equal, $\frac{4}{8} \neq \frac{6}{16}$, so y does not vary directly with x.

WRITING EQUATIONS Given that y varies directly with x, use the specified values to write a direct variation equation that relates x and y.

29. $x = 3, y = 9$ $y = 3x$ 30. $x = 2, y = 26$ $y = 13x$ 31. $x = 14, y = 7$ $y = \frac{1}{2}x$

32. $x = 15, y = -5$ $y = -\frac{1}{3}x$ 33. $x = -2, y = -2$ $y = x$ 34. $x = -18, y = -4$ $y = \frac{2}{9}x$

35. $x = \frac{1}{4}, y = 1$ $y = 4x$ 36. $x = -6, y = 15$ $y = -\frac{5}{2}x$ 37. $x = -5.2, y = 1.4$ $y = -\frac{7}{26}x$

[C] 38. **★ WRITING** If y varies directly with x, does x vary directly with y? If so, what is the relationship between the constants of variation? *Explain.*

39. **CHALLENGE** The slope of a line is $-\frac{1}{3}$, and the point $(-6, 2)$ lies on the line. Use the formula for the slope of a line to determine if the equation of the line is a direct variation equation. **direct variation**

38. Yes; the constants of variation are reciprocals of each other; if $y = a_1x$, then $a_1 = \frac{y}{x}$ and if $x = a_2y$, then $a_2 = \frac{x}{y}$, which shows the constants of variation, a_1 and a_2 are reciprocals of each other.

4.6 Model Direct Variation   **257**

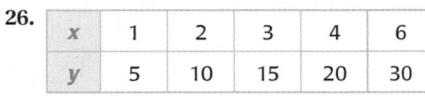

4 PRACTICE AND APPLY

Assignment Guide

📖 **Answer Transparencies** available for all exercises

Basic:
Day 1: pp. 256–259
Exs. 1, 2, 3–9 odd, 10–22 even, 23–28, 40–45, 48–62 even

Average:
Day 1: pp. 256–259
Exs. 1, 2, 6–10, 18–28, 29–35 odd, 40–46, 53–56, 60–62

Advanced:
Day 1: pp. 256–259
Exs. 1, 2, 7–9, 19–22, 24–28, 33–39*, 41–47*, 54–56, 60–62

Block:
pp. 256–259
Exs. 1, 2, 6–10, 18–28, 29–35 odd, 40–46, 53–56, 60–62 (with 4.5)

Differentiated Instruction
See *Algebra 1 Best Practices Toolkit* for suggestions on addressing the needs of a diverse classroom.

Homework Check
For a quick check of student understanding of key concepts, go over the following exercises:
Basic: 5, 14, 23, 40, 43
Average: 7, 19, 24, 41, 43
Advanced: 8, 20, 25, 42, 44

Extra Practice
• Student Edition, p. 941
• Chapter 4 Resource Book: Practice levels A, B, C, pp. 77–82

Practice Worksheet
An easily-readable reduced practice page (with answers) for this lesson can be found on p. 204C.

11–22. See Additional Answers beginning on p. AA1.

Avoiding Common Errors

Exercises 19–22 Some students may forget to rewrite the equations in the form $y = ax$. Remind them to do this before graphing.

Exercises 23–25 Caution students to substitute the coordinates correctly in the direct variation equation.

Exercises 26–28 Some students may notice that the increments in the table are not equal and assume that the ratios are not the same for all the data pairs. Tell students they need to test all the data pairs to see if the ratios are equal.

Internet Reference

Exercise 46 More statistical information for NCAA women's basketball can be found at www.ncaasports.com/basketball/womens/stats

EXAMPLE 4 A
on p. 255
for Exs. 40–42

40. BICYCLES The distance d (in meters) you travel on a bicycle varies directly with the number r of revolutions that the rear tire completes. You travel about 2 meters on a mountain bike for every revolution of the tire.

1 revolution   2 meters

a. Write a direct variation equation that relates r and d. **$d = 200r$**

b. How many meters do you travel in 1500 tire revolutions? **3000 m**

@HomeTutor for problem solving help at classzone.com

41. VACATION TIME At one company, the amount of vacation v (in hours) an employee earns varies directly with the amount of time t (in weeks) he or she works. An employee who works 2 weeks earns 3 hours of vacation.

a. Write a direct variation equation that relates t and v. **$v = \frac{3}{2}t$**

b. How many hours of vacation time does an employee earn in 8 weeks? **12 h**

@HomeTutor for problem solving help at classzone.com

42. LANDSCAPING Landscapers plan to spread a layer of stone on a path. The number s of bags of stone needed depends on the depth d (in inches) of the layer. They need 10 bags to spread a layer of stone that is 2 inches deep. Write a direct variation equation that relates d and s. Then find the number of bags needed to spread a layer that is 3 inches deep. **$s = 5d$; 15 bags**

EXAMPLE 5
on p. 256
for Exs. 43–44

43a. Compare the ratios, $\frac{f}{w}$, for all data pairs (w, f). Since the ratios all equal 0.25, f varies directly with w.

44a. Compare the ratios, $\frac{p}{\ell}$, for all data pairs (ℓ, p). Since the ratios all equal 1.25, p varies directly with ℓ.

43. ★ **SHORT RESPONSE** At a recycling center, computers and computer accessories can be recycled for a fee f based on weight w, as shown in the table.

a. *Explain* why f varies directly with w.

b. Write a direct variation equation that relates w and f. Find the total recycling fee for a computer that weighs 18 pounds and a printer that weighs 10 pounds. **$f = 0.25w$; $7**

Weight, w (pounds)	Fee, f (dollars)
10	2.50
15	3.75
30	7.50

44. ★ **SHORT RESPONSE** You can buy gold chain by the inch. The table shows the price of gold chain for various lengths.

Length, ℓ (inches)	7	9	16	18
Price, p (dollars)	8.75	11.25	20.00	22.50

a. *Explain* why p varies directly with ℓ.

b. Write a direct variation equation that relates ℓ and p. If you have $30, what is the longest chain that you can buy? **$p = 1.25\ell$; 24 in.**

○ = **WORKED-OUT SOLUTIONS** on p. WS1   ★ = **STANDARDIZED TEST PRACTICE**   ◆ = **MULTIPLE REPRESENTATIONS**

45. ◆ **MULTIPLE REPRESENTATIONS** The total cost of riding the subway to and from school every day is $1.50.

a. Making a Table Make a table that shows the number d of school days and the total cost C (in dollars) for trips to and from school for some values of d. Assume you travel to school once each school day and home from school once each school day. **See margin.**

b. Drawing a Graph Graph the ordered pairs from the table and draw a ray through them. **See margin.**

c. Writing an Equation Write an equation of the graph from part (b). Is it a direct variation equation? *Explain.* If there are 22 school days in one month, what will it cost to ride the subway to and from school for that month?
$C = 1.5d$; yes; it's in the form $y = ax$; $33.

46. ★ **EXTENDED RESPONSE** The table shows the average number of field goals attempted t and the average number of field goals made m per game for all NCAA Division I women's basketball teams for 9 consecutive seasons.

Attempted field goals, t	61.8	61.9	61.8	60.8	59.5	59.0	58.9	59.2	58.4
Field goals made, m	25.7	25.6	25.6	25.2	24.5	24.6	24.5	24.3	24.0

a. Write Why is it reasonable to use a direct variation model for this situation? Write a direct variation equation that relates t and m. Find the constant of variation to the nearest tenth. All of the ratios, $\frac{m}{t}$, are approximately equal to 0.4; $m = 0.4t$; 0.4.

b. Estimate The highest average number of attempted field goals in one season was 66.2. Estimate the number of field goals made that season. about 26 field goals

c. Explain If the average number of field goals made was increasing rather than decreasing and the number of attempted field goals continued to decrease, would the data show direct variation? *Explain.* No; the ratios, $\frac{m}{t}$, for each season would not be equal to each other.

47. CHALLENGE In Exercise 40, you found an equation showing that the distance traveled on a bike varies directly with the number of revolutions that the rear tire completes. The number r of tire revolutions varies directly with the number p of pedal revolutions. In a particular gear, you travel about 1.3 meters for every 5 revolutions of the pedals. Show that distance traveled varies directly with pedal revolutions.

47. Because $d = 200r$ and r varies directly with p, you can write the equation $r = ap$. When $d = 130$ centimeters, $r = 0.65$. Substitute 0.65 for r when $p = 5$, to get $0.65 = 5a$. Solve to find $a = 0.13$. If you substitute ap for r into the equation $d = 200r$, you get $d = 200(0.13)p$, giving the direct variation equation $d = 26p$.

MIXED REVIEW

Graph the equation. 48–56. See margin.

48. $y = -8$ *(p. 215)*   **49.** $x = 6$ *(p. 215)*   **50.** $2x + y = 4$ *(p. 225)*

51. $-2x + 5y = -30$ *(p. 225)*   **52.** $0.4x + 2y = 6$ *(p. 225)*   **53.** $y = 2x - 5$ *(p. 244)*

54. $y = \frac{1}{3}x$ *(p. 244)*   **55.** $y = -x + 3$ *(p. 244)*   **56.** $y = -\frac{3}{2}x + 2$ *(p. 244)*

Identify the slope and y-intercept of the line with the given equation. *(p. 244)*

57. $y = 3x + 5$ 3, 5   **58.** $y = -3x$ −3, 0   **59.** $y = 2x - 5$ 2, −5

60. $y = 4x - 11$ 4, −11   **61.** $y = \frac{4}{5}x - 3$ $\frac{4}{5}$, −3   **62.** $y = \frac{5}{4}x + 3.1$ $\frac{5}{4}$, 3.1

PREVIEW
Prepare for Lesson 4.7 in Exs. 57–62.

48–56. See Additional Answers beginning on p. AA1.

---

⑤ ASSESS AND RETEACH

Daily Homework Quiz

📄 **Transparency Available**

Tell whether the equation represents direct variation. If so, identify the constant of variation.

1. $5x - 6y = 2$ **no**

2. $x + y = 0$ **yes, −1**

3. The number p of parts a machine produces varies directly with the time t (in minutes) the machine is in operation. The machine produces 84 parts in 14 minutes. Write a direct variation equation that relates t and p. How many parts does the machine produce in 25 minutes? $p = 6t$; 150 parts

🧭 **Online Quiz**

Available at **classzone.com**

Diagnosis/Remediation
• Practice A, B, C in Chapter 4 Resource Book, pp. 77–82
• Study Guide in Chapter 4 Resource Book, pp. 83–84
• Practice Workbook, pp. 61–63
• @HomeTutor

Challenge
Additional challenge is available in the Chapter 4 Resource Book, p. 87.

45a. *Sample answer:*

d	C (dollars)
1	1.5
2	3
3	4.5

45b.

Alternative Strategy

Example 4 on page 255 can be solved by using a graph or by writing and solving a proportion. The method of using a graph allows students to visualize the solution. The method of using a proportion is useful when students cannot remember the direct variation equation. Both methods can help students understand the algebraic solution given in Lesson 4.6.

Reading Strategy

In Method 1, point out to students that the *x*-coordinates and *x*-values are color-coded blue and the *y*-coordinates and *y*-values are color-coded red for all three steps.

Another Way to Solve Example 4, page 255

MULTIPLE REPRESENTATIONS In Example 4 on page 255, you saw how to solve the problem about how much salt to add to a saltwater fish tank by writing and using a direct variation equation. You can also solve the problem using a graph or a proportion.

PROBLEM

SALTWATER AQUARIUM The number *s* of tablespoons of sea salt needed in a saltwater fish tank varies directly with the number *w* of gallons of water in the tank. A pet shop owner recommends adding 100 tablespoons of sea salt to a 20 gallon tank. How many tablespoons of salt should be added to a 30 gallon saltwater fish tank?

METHOD 1

Using a Graph An alternative approach is to use a graph.

STEP 1 **Read** the problem. It tells you an amount of salt for a certain size fish tank. You can also assume that if a fishtank has no water, then no salt needs to be added. Write ordered pairs for this information.

STEP 2 **Graph** the ordered pairs. Draw a line through the points.

The coordinates of points on the line give the amounts of salt that should be added to fish tanks of various sizes. ········▶

STEP 3 **Find** the point on the graph that has an *x*-coordinate of 30. The *y*-coordinate of this point is 150, so 150 tablespoons of salt should be added to a 30 gallon tank.

METHOD 2

Writing a Proportion Another alternative approach is to write and solve a proportion.

STEP 1 **Write** a proportion involving two ratios that each compare the amount of water (in gallons) to the amount of salt (in tablespoons).

$$\frac{20}{100} = \frac{30}{s} \longleftarrow \text{amount of water (gallons)}$$
$$\longleftarrow \text{amount of salt (tablespoons)}$$

STEP 2 **Solve** the proportion.

$\frac{20}{100} = \frac{30}{s}$	Write proportion.
$20s = 100 \cdot 30$	Cross products property
$20s = 3000$	Simplify.
$s = 150$	Divide each side by 20.

▶ You should add 150 tablespoons of salt to a 30 gallon tank.

CHECK Check your answer by writing each ratio in simplest form.

$$\frac{20}{100} = \frac{1}{5} \text{ and } \frac{30}{150} = \frac{1}{5}$$

Because each ratio simplifies to $\frac{1}{5}$, the answer is correct.

PRACTICE

1. **WHAT IF?** Suppose the fish tank in the problem above is a 22 gallon tank. How many tablespoons of salt should be added to the tank? *Describe* which method you used to solve this problem. **See margin.**

2. **ADVERTISING** A local newspaper charges by the word for printing classified ads. A 14 word ad costs $5.88. How much would a 21 word ad cost? Solve this problem using two different methods. **See margin.**

3. **REASONING** In Exercise 2, how can you quickly determine the cost of a 7 word ad? *Explain* how you could use the cost of a 7 word ad to solve the problem. **See margin.**

4. **NUTRITION** A company sells fruit smoothies in two sizes of bottles: 6 fluid ounces and 10 fluid ounces. You know that a 6 ounce bottle contains 96 milligrams of sodium. How many milligrams of sodium does a 10 ounce bottle contain? **160 mg**

5. **ERROR ANALYSIS** A student solved the problem in Exercise 4 as shown. *Describe* and correct the error made.

> Let x = the number of milligrams of sodium in a 10 ounce bottle.
> $$\frac{6}{x} = \frac{10}{96}$$
> $$576 = 10x$$
> $$57.6 = x$$

The proportion should be
$$\frac{6}{96} = \frac{10}{x},$$
$$\frac{6}{96} = \frac{10}{x},$$
$$960 = 6x,$$
$$x = 160.$$

6. **SLEEPING** You find an online calculator that calculates the number of calories you burn while sleeping. The results for various sleeping times are shown. About how many more calories would you burn by sleeping for 9.5 hours than for 8 hours? Choose any method for solving the problem. **90 calories**

Hours of sleep	6.5	7	8.5	9
Calories burned	390	420	510	540

Using Alternative Methods **261**

Warm-Up Exercises

📃 **Transparency Available**

Tell whether the ordered pair is a solution of the equation.

1. $2x + 3y = 2$; $(3, -2)$ **no**

2. $-x - 4y = -3$; $(-5, 2)$ **yes**

3. The weight of a person on Mars is given by the function $y = 0.371x$ where x is the weight of a person on Earth. A person weighs 130 pounds on Earth. Find the weight of the person on Mars. **48.23 lb**

Notetaking Guide

📃 **Transparency Available**

Promotes interactive learning and notetaking skills, pp. 94–97.

Pacing

Basic: 2 days

Average: 2 days

Advanced: 2 days

Block: 1 block

• See *Teaching Guide/Lesson Plan.*

2 FOCUS AND MOTIVATE

Essential Question

Big Idea 3, p. 205

What is function notation? **Tell** students they will learn how to answer this question by finding values of a function for given x-values, by finding x-values for given function values, and by graphing.

4.7 Graph Linear Functions

Before	You graphed linear equations and functions.
Now	You will use function notation.
Why?	So you can model an animal population, as in Example 3.

Key Vocabulary
• function notation
• family of functions
• parent linear function

You have seen linear functions written in the form $y = mx + b$. By naming a function f, you can write it using **function notation**.

$$f(x) = mx + b \qquad \text{Function notation}$$

The symbol $f(x)$ is another name for y and is read as "the value of f at x," or simply as "f of x." It does *not* mean f times x. You can use letters other than f, such as g or h, to name functions.

⭐ **EXAMPLE 1** **Standardized Test Practice**

> What is the value of the function $f(x) = 3x - 15$ when $x = -3$?
>
> (A) -24 (B) -6 (C) -2 (D) 8

Solution

$$f(x) = 3x - 15 \qquad \text{Write original function.}$$
$$f(-3) = 3(-3) - 15 \qquad \text{Substitute } -3 \text{ for } x.$$
$$= -24 \qquad \text{Simplify.}$$

▶ The correct answer is A. (A) (B) (C) (D)

✓ **GUIDED PRACTICE** for Example 1

1. Evaluate the function $h(x) = -7x$ when $x = 7$. **−49**

EXAMPLE 2 **Find an *x*-value**

For the function $f(x) = 2x - 10$, find the value of x so that $f(x) = 6$.

$$f(x) = 2x - 10 \qquad \text{Write original function.}$$
$$6 = 2x - 10 \qquad \text{Substitute 6 for } f(x).$$
$$8 = x \qquad \text{Solve for } x.$$

▶ When $x = 8$, $f(x) = 6$.

Resource Planning Guide

Chapter Resource Book
• Teaching Guide/Lesson Plan (pp. 88–89)
• Activity Master (p. 90)
• Practice levels A, B, C (pp. 91–96)
• Study Guide (pp. 97–98)
• Catch-up for Absent Students (p. 99)
• Problem Solving Workshop (p. 100)
• Challenge (p. 101)

Workbooks
• Notetaking Guide (pp. 94–97)
• Practice Workbook (pp. 64–66)

Teaching Options
• **Power Presentations CD-ROM** provides dynamic electronic teaching resources for the classroom.
• **Activity Generator CD-ROM** provides editable activities for all ability levels.

Interactive Technology
• Easy Planner
• Power Presentations CD-ROM
• Activity Generator CD-ROM
• Animated Algebra
• Test Generator CD-ROM
• Online Quiz
• eWorkbook
• eEdition
• @HomeTutor

Resources for English Learners
• Quick Reference for English Learners
• Spanish Study Guide
• Multi-Language Visual Glossary
• Student Resources in Spanish

See also the *Algebra 1 Toolkit* for more strategies for meeting individual needs.

DOMAIN AND RANGE The domain of a function consists of the values of x for which the function is defined. The range consists of the values of $f(x)$ where x is in the domain of f. The graph of a function f is the set of all points $(x, f(x))$.

EXAMPLE 3 Graph a function

GRAY WOLF The gray wolf population in central Idaho was monitored over several years for a project aimed at boosting the number of wolves. The number of wolves can be modeled by the function $f(x) = 37x + 7$ where x is the number of years since 1995. Graph the function and identify its domain and range.

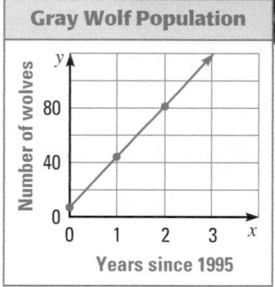

INTERPRET MODELS
The rate of change in the wolf population actually varied over time. The model simplifies the situation by assuming a steady rate of change.

Solution

To graph the function, make a table.

x	f(x)
0	$37(0) + 7 = 7$
1	$37(1) + 7 = 44$
2	$37(2) + 7 = 81$

Gray Wolf Population

The domain of the function is $x \geq 0$. From the graph or table, you can see that the range of the function is $f(x) \geq 7$.

✔ **GUIDED PRACTICE** for Examples 2 and 3

2. **WOLF POPULATION** Use the model from Example 3 to find the value of x so that $f(x) = 155$. *Explain* what the solution means in this situation.
   4; in 1999, 4 years after 1995, the wolf population will be 155.

FAMILIES OF FUNCTIONS A **family of functions** is a group of functions with similar characteristics. For example, functions that have the form $f(x) = mx + b$ constitute the family of *linear* functions.

KEY CONCEPT   *For Your Notebook*

Parent Function for Linear Functions

The most basic linear function in the family of all linear functions, called the **parent linear function**, is:

$$f(x) = x$$

The graph of the parent linear function is shown.

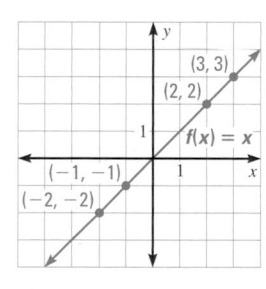

4.7 Graph Linear Functions **263**

Motivating the Lesson
You are comparing the costs of two veterinarians for the care of your horses. One veterinarian charges $50 per house call plus $25 per hour. Another charges $25 per house call plus $45 per hour. By learning how to use function notation, you can compare the two rates by graphing both functions on the same coordinate plane.

❸ TEACH

Extra Example 1
What is the value of the function $f(x) = 2x + 12$ when $x = -8$? **B**
Ⓐ −12   Ⓑ −4
Ⓒ 4   Ⓓ 28

Extra Example 2
For the function $f(x) = -2x + 4$, find the value of x so that $f(x) = 16$.
−6

Key Question to Ask for Example 2
• How is Example 2 different from Example 1? **In Example 1, x is replaced with a number to find $f(x)$; and in Example 2, $f(x)$ is replaced with a number to find x.**

Extra Example 3
A bowling alley charges $5 to rent shoes and $4 per game. The cost after playing x games is given by $f(x) = 4x + 5$. Graph the function and identify its domain and range.

domain: $x \geq 0$; range: $f(x) \geq 5$

Differentiated Instruction

Kinesthetic Learners Explain that $y = x$ is called the *parent function* because any linear function can be obtained by changing the slope from 1 and moving the y-intercept from 0. Changing m and b in the linear function $f(x) = mx + b$ generates the family of linear functions. Draw a line on a transparency and place it on a grid to show the graph of $y = x$. Then show how this can be used to create any line on the coordinate plane by moving the transparency.

See also the *Algebra 1 Toolkit* for more strategies.

EXAMPLE 4 Compare graphs with the graph $f(x) = x$

Graph the function. Compare the graph with the graph of $f(x) = x$.

a. $g(x) = x + 3$ **b.** $h(x) = 2x$

Solution

a.

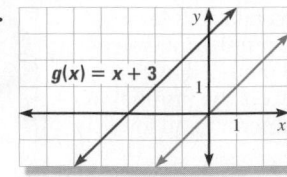

Because the graphs of g and f have the same slope, $m = 1$, the lines are parallel. Also, the y-intercept of the graph of g is 3 more than the y-intercept of the graph of f.

b.

Because the slope of the graph of h is greater than the slope of the graph of f, the graph of h rises faster from left to right. The y-intercept for both graphs is 0, so both lines pass through the origin.

 GUIDED PRACTICE for Example 4

3. Graph $h(x) = -3x$. Compare the graph with the graph of $f(x) = x$.
See margin for art; since the slope of the graph of h is negative the graph of h falls from left to right. The y-intercept for both graphs is 0, so both lines pass through the origin.

CONCEPT SUMMARY *For Your Notebook*

Comparing Graphs of Linear Functions with the Graph of $f(x) = x$

Changing m or b in the general linear function $g(x) = mx + b$ creates families of linear functions whose graphs are related to the graph of $f(x) = x$.

$g(x) = x + b$

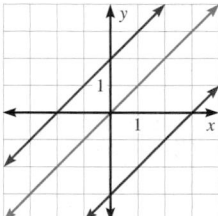

• The graphs have the same slope, but different y-intercepts.

• Graphs of this family are vertical translations of the graph of $f(x) = x$.

$g(x) = mx$ where $m > 0$

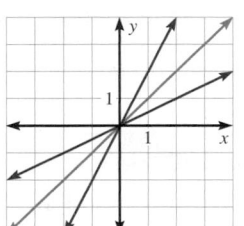

• The graphs have different (positive) slopes, but the same y-intercept.

• Graphs of this family are vertical stretches or shrinks of the graph of $f(x) = x$.

$g(x) = mx$ where $m < 0$

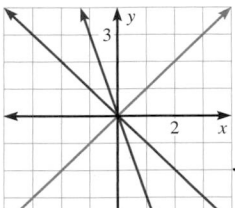

• The graphs have different (negative) slopes, but the same y-intercept.

• Graphs of this family are vertical stretches or shrinks with reflections in the x-axis of the graph of $f(x) = x$.

3.

EXAMPLE 5 Graph real-world functions

CABLE A cable company charges new customers $40 for installation and $60 per month for its service. The cost to the customer is given by the function $f(x) = 60x + 40$ where x is the number of months of service. To attract new customers, the cable company reduces the installation fee to $5. A function for the cost with the reduced installation fee is $g(x) = 60x + 5$. Graph both functions. How is the graph of g related to the graph of f?

Solution

The graphs of both functions are shown. Both functions have a slope of 60, so they are parallel. The y-intercept of the graph of g is 35 less than the graph of f. So, the graph of g is a vertical translation of the graph of f.

REVIEW TRANSFORMATIONS
For help with transformations, see pp. 922–923.

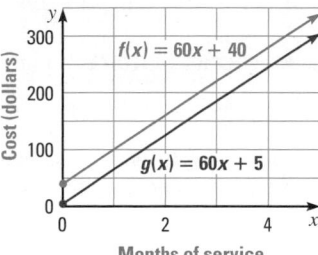

✓ **GUIDED PRACTICE** for Example 5

4. **WHAT IF?** In Example 5, suppose the monthly fee is $70 so that the cost to the customer is given by $h(x) = 70x + 40$. Graph f and h in the same coordinate plane. How is the graph of h related to the graph of f?
   See margin for art; since the slope of the graph of h is greater than the slope of the graph of f, the graph of h rises faster from left to right. The y-intercept for both graphs is 40, so both lines pass through (0, 40).

4.7 EXERCISES

HOMEWORK KEY
○ = **WORKED-OUT SOLUTIONS**
on p. WS1 for Exs. 3, 17, and 39

★ = **STANDARDIZED TEST PRACTICE**
Exs. 2, 13, 22, 35, 36, 44, and 45

SKILL PRACTICE

A

1. **VOCABULARY** When you write the function $y = 3x + 12$ as $f(x) = 3x + 12$, you are using __?__ . **function notation**

2. ★ **WRITING** Would the functions $f(x) = -9x + 12$, $g(x) = -9x - 2$, and $h(x) = -9x$ be considered a family of functions? *Explain.* **Yes; they are all linear functions.**

EXAMPLE 1
on p. 262
for Exs. 3–13

EVALUATING FUNCTIONS Evaluate the function when $x = -2$, 0, and 3.

3. $f(x) = 12x + 1$ **−23, 1, 37**
4. $g(x) = -3x + 5$ **11, 5, −4**
5. $p(x) = -8x - 2$ **14, −2, −26**
6. $h(x) = 2.25x$ **−4.5, 0, 6.75**
7. $m(x) = -6.5x$ **13, 0, −19.5**
8. $f(x) = -0.75x - 1$ **0.5, −1, −3.25**
9. $s(x) = \frac{2}{5}x + 3$ **$2\frac{1}{5}, 3, 4\frac{1}{5}$**
10. $d(x) = -\frac{3}{2}x + 5$ **8, 5, $\frac{1}{2}$**
11. $h(x) = \frac{3}{4}x - 6$ **$-7\frac{1}{2}, -6, -3\frac{3}{4}$**

12. **ERROR ANALYSIS** *Describe* and correct the error in evaluating the function $g(x) = -5x + 3$ when $x = -3$. **$g(-3)$ does not mean multiply −3 and g, it means to find the value of the function when $g = -3$, $g(-3) = 18$.**

$$g(-3) = -5(-3) + 3$$
$$-3g = 18$$
$$g = -6$$

4.7 Graph Linear Functions **265**

EXAMPLE 2
on p. 262
for Exs. 14–22

13. ★ **MULTIPLE CHOICE** Given $f(x) = -6.8x + 5$, what is the value of $f(-2)$? **D**

    (A) −18.6   (B) −8.6   (C) 8.6   (D) 18.6

FINDING X-VALUES Find the value of x so that the function has the given value.

14. $f(x) = 6x + 9$; 3   **−1**   15. $g(x) = -x + 5$; 2   **3**

16. $h(x) = -7x + 12$; −9   **3**   (17.) $j(x) = 4x + 11$; −13   **−6**

18. $m(x) = 9x - 5$; −2 $\frac{1}{3}$ 19. $n(x) = -2x - 21$; −6   **−7.5**

20. $p(x) = -12x - 36$; −3   **−2.75**   21. $q(x) = 8x - 32$; −4   **3.5**

22. ★ **MULTIPLE CHOICE** What value of x makes $f(x) = 5$ if $f(x) = -2x + 25$? **C**

    (A) −15   (B) −10   (C) 10   (D) 15

EXAMPLE 4 [B]
on p. 264
for Exs. 23–34

TRANSFORMATIONS OF LINEAR FUNCTIONS Graph the function. Compare the graph with the graph of $f(x) = x$. **23–34. See margin.**

23. $g(x) = x + 5$ 24. $h(x) = 6 + x$ 25. $q(x) = x - 1$

26. $m(x) = x - 6$ 27. $d(x) = x + 7$ 28. $t(x) = x - 3$

29. $r(x) = 4x$ 30. $w(x) = 5x$ 31. $h(x) = -3x$

32. $k(x) = -6x$ 33. $g(x) = \frac{1}{3}x$ 34. $m(x) = -\frac{7}{2}x$

35. ★ **MULTIPLE CHOICE** The graph of which function is shown? **B**

    (A) $f(x) = 3x + 8$

    (B) $f(x) = 3x - 8$

    (C) $f(x) = 8x + 3$

    (D) $f(x) = 8x - 3$

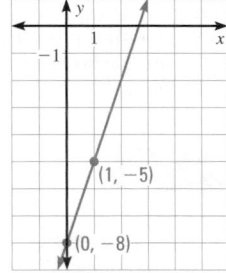

(1, −5)

(0, −8)

36. ★ **OPEN-ENDED** In this exercise you will compare the graphs of linear functions when their slopes and y-intercepts are changed.

    a. Choose a linear function of the form $f(x) = mx + b$ where $m \neq 0$. Then graph the function. **Sample answer: f(x) = 2x + 3; see margin for art.**

    b. Using the same m and b values as in part (a), graph the function $g(x) = 2mx + b$. How are the slope and y-intercept of the graph of g related to the slope and y-intercept of the graph of f? **See margin.**

    c. Using the same m and b values as in part (a), graph the function $h(x) = mx + (b - 3)$. How are the slope and y-intercept of the graph of h related to the slope and y-intercept of the graph of f? **See margin.**

[C] 37. **REASONING** How is the graph of $g(x) = 1$ related to the graph of $h(x) = -1$? **Since the graphs of g and h have the same slope, m = 0, the lines are parallel. The y-intercept of the graph of h is 2 less than the y-intercept of the graph of g.**

38. **CHALLENGE** Suppose that $f(x) = 4x + 7$ and $g(x) = 2x$. What is a rule for $g(f(x))$? What is a rule for $f(g(x))$? **8x + 14; 8x + 7**

○ = **WORKED-OUT SOLUTIONS**
on p. WS1

★ = **STANDARDIZED**
TEST PRACTICE

PRACTICE AND APPLY

4

Assignment Guide

📖 Answer Transparencies available for all exercises

Basic:
Day 1: pp. 265–268
Exs. 1, 3–11 odd, 12–18, 39–41, 46–54
Day 2: pp. 265–268
Exs. 2, 19–29, 42, 55–60

Average:
Day 1: pp. 265–268
Exs. 1, 7–13, 16–22, 39–41, 46–54
Day 2: pp. 265–268
Exs. 2, 27–37, 42–44, 55–60

Advanced:
Day 1: pp. 265–268
Exs. 1, 7–11, 13, 17–22, 37–41*, 46–54 even
Day 2: pp. 265–268
Exs. 2, 28–36, 42–45*, 55–60

Block:
pp. 265–268
Exs. 1, 2, 7–13, 16–22, 27–37, 39–44, 46–60

Differentiated Instruction

See *Algebra 1 Best Practices Toolkit* for suggestions on addressing the needs of a diverse classroom.

Homework Check

For a quick check of student understanding of key concepts, go over the following exercises:

Basic: 5, 16, 24, 39, 42
Average: 8, 18, 28, 40, 42
Advanced: 9, 20, 31, 41, 43

Extra Practice

• Student Edition, p. 941
• Chapter 4 Resource Book: Practice levels A, B, C, pp. 91–96

Practice Worksheet

An easily-readable reduced practice page (with answers) for this lesson can be found on p. 204C.

23–34, 36a–c. See Additional Answers beginning on p. AA1.

EXAMPLE 3 [A]
on p. 263
for Exs. 39–41

39a. See margin for art; domain: $0 \le x \le 20$, range: $2.75 \le f(x) \le 4.75$.

39b. 18; in 1998, 18 years after 1980, the price of a movie ticket was $4.55.

40a. See margin for art; domain: $0 \le x \le 5$, range: $330 \le f(x) \le 21,580$

41. See margin for art; domain: $x \ge 0$, range: $d(x) \ge 0$; 1.5 h; substitute 15 for $d(x)$ to get the equation $15 = 10x$, solve for x.

EXAMPLE 5 [B]
on p. 265
for Exs. 42–43

(39.) **MOVIE TICKETS** The average price of a movie ticket in the United States from 1980 to 2000 can be modeled by the function $f(x) = 0.10x + 2.75$ where x is the number of years since 1980.

  a. Graph the function and identify its domain and range.

  b. Find the value of x so that $f(x) = 4.55$. *Explain* what the solution means in this situation.

   @HomeTutor for problem solving help at classzone.com

40. **DVD PLAYERS** The number (in thousands) of DVD players sold in the United States from 1998 to 2003 can be modeled by $f(x) = 4250x + 330$ where x is the number of years since 1998.

  a. Graph the function and identify its domain and range.

  b. Find the value of x so that $f(x) = 13,080$. *Explain* what the solution means in this situation.

  @HomeTutor for problem solving help at classzone.com

  3; in 2001, 3 years after 1998, the number of DVD players sold was 13,080.

41. **IN-LINE SKATING** An in-line skater's average speed is 10 miles per hour. The distance traveled after skating for x hours is given by the function $d(x) = 10x$. Graph the function and identify its domain and range. How long did it take the skater to travel 15 miles? *Explain*.

  Animated Algebra at classzone.com

42. **HOME SECURITY** A home security company charges new customers $155 for the installation of security equipment and a monthly fee of $40. To attract more customers, the company reduces its installation fee to $75. The functions below give the total cost for x months of service:

  Regular fee: $f(x) = 40x + 155$ **Reduced fee:** $g(x) = 40x + 75$

  Graph both functions. How is the graph of g related to the graph of f? **See margin.**

43. **THEATERS** A ticket for a play at a theater costs $16. The revenue (in dollars) generated from the sale of x tickets is given by $s(x) = 16x$. The theater managers raise the cost of tickets to $20. The revenue generated from the sale of x tickets at that price is given by $r(x) = 20x$. Graph both functions. How is the graph of r related to the graph of s? **See margin.**

[C] **44.** ★ **EXTENDED RESPONSE** The cost of supplies, such as mustard and napkins, a pretzel vendor needs for one day is $75. Each pretzel costs the vendor $.50 to make. The total daily cost to the vendor is given by $C(x) = 0.5x + 75$ where x is the number of pretzels the vendor makes.

  a. **Graph** Graph the cost function. **See margin.**

  b. **Graph** The vendor sells each pretzel for $3. The revenue is given by $R(x) = 3x$ where x is the number of pretzels sold. Graph the function. **See margin.**

  c. **Explain** The vendor's profit is the difference of the revenue and the cost. *Explain* how you could use the graphs to find the vendor's profit for any given number of pretzels made and sold.
  Sample answer: Find the values of y on each graph for any value of x. Subtract $C(x)$ from $R(x)$ to find the vendor's profit.

Teaching Strategy

Exercises 3–11 To remind students that $f(x)$ does not mean f times x, you may wish to have them write the function name with x replaced by -2, 0, and 3. For example, students would write $f(-2) = -23$, $f(0) = 1$, and $f(3) = 37$ when answering Exercise 3.

Exercises 23–34 You may want to review the concept box on page 264 before the students begin these exercises. Ask students to give examples of vertical stretches and shrinks with and without reflections.

Reading Strategy

Exercises 14–21 Tell students to read the instruction line for the exercises carefully. They may want to review Examples 1 and 2 so they are clear on the difference between finding an x-value and finding the value of a function for a given x-value.

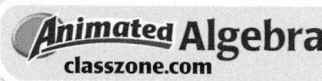
Animated Algebra
classzone.com

An **Animated Algebra** activity is available on-line for **Exercise 41**. This activity is also available on the **Power Presentations CD-ROM**.

42, 43. See Additional Answers beginning on p. AA1.

44a.

44b.

39a.

40a.

41.

5 ASSESS AND RETEACH

Daily Homework Quiz

📄 Transparency Available

1. Evaluate $f(x) = 8x - 4$ when $x = -3, 0$, and 2. **−28, −4, 12**

2. Find the value of x so $g(x) = -2x + 1$ has the value -3. **2**

3. A stable charges $25 for feed and $50 per day to stable horses. The cost is given by $f(x) = 50x + 25$. Recently, the stable raised its fee for food to $50. The new fee is given by $g(x) = 50x + 50$. Graph the functions and then compare the two graphs.

The graphs have the same slope. The y-intercept of g is 25 units greater than that of f, so g is a vertical translation.

🖱 Online Quiz

Available at **classzone.com**

Diagnosis/Remediation

- Practice A, B, C in Chapter 4 Resource Book, pp. 91–96
- Study Guide in Chapter 4 Resource Book, pp. 97–98
- Practice Workbook, pp. 64–66
- @HomeTutor

Challenge

Additional challenge is available in the Chapter 4 Resource Book, p. 101.

Quiz

An easily-readable reduced copy of the quiz (with answers) on Lessons 4.6–4.7 from the Assessment Book can be found on p. 204G.

45b, Quiz 8, 9. See Additional Answers beginning on p. AA1.

---

45. ★ **EXTENDED RESPONSE** The number of hours of daylight in Austin, Texas, during the month of March can be modeled by the function $\ell(x) = 0.03x + 11.5$ where x is the day of the month.

a. Graph Graph the function and identify its domain and range. **See graph in part (b); domain: $1 \le x \le 31$; range: $11.53 \le \ell(x) \le 12.43$**

b. Graph The number of hours of darkness can be modeled by the function $d(x) = 24 - \ell(x)$. Graph the function on the same coordinate plane as you used in part (a). Identify its domain and range. **See margin for art; domain: $11.53 \le \ell(x) \le 12.43$; range: $11.57 \le d(x) \le 12.47$**

c. CHALLENGE *Explain* how you could have obtained the graph of d from the graph of ℓ using translations and reflections. **The graph of d is a reflection of the line ℓ.**

d. CHALLENGE What does the point where the graphs intersect mean in terms of the number of hours of daylight and darkness?
The number of hours of daylight equals the number of hours of darkness.

MIXED REVIEW

Solve the equation or proportion.

46. $y - 7 = -3$ *(p. 134)* **4**
47. $4.5m = 49.5$ *(p. 134)* **11**
48. $4z + 5z = -36$ *(p. 141)* **−4**

49. $5(x - 4) = 20$ *(p. 148)* **8**
50. $3t + 4 + 5t = -4$ *(p. 148)* **−1**
51. $-5g = 3(g - 8)$ *(p. 154)* **3**

52. $9n = 4(2n + 1)$ *(p. 154)* **4**
53. $\frac{7}{6} = \frac{t}{42}$ *(p. 168)* **49**
54. $\frac{5}{6} = \frac{p}{15}$ *(p. 168)* **12.5**

PREVIEW
Prepare for Lesson 5.1 in Exs. 55–60.

Write the equation in slope-intercept form. Then graph the equation. *(p. 244)*
55–60. See margin for art.

55. $x + 6y = 12$ $\;y = -\frac{1}{6}x + 2$
56. $5x + y = -10$ $\;y = -5x - 10$
57. $2x - 2y = 3$ $\;y = x - \frac{3}{2}$

58. $-2x - 3y = 21$ $\;y = -\frac{2}{3}x - 7$
59. $-4x - 3y = -18$ $\;y = -\frac{4}{3}x + 6$
60. $2x - y = 10$ $\;y = 2x - 10$

QUIZ for Lessons 4.6–4.7

Given that y varies directly with x, use the specified values to write a direct variation equation that relates x and y. *(p. 253)*

1. $x = 5, y = 10$ $\;y = 2x$
2. $x = 4, y = 6$ $\;y = \frac{3}{2}x$
3. $x = 2, y = -16$ $\;y = -8x$

Evaluate the function. *(p. 262)*

4. $g(x) = 6x - 5$ when $x = 4$ **19**
5. $h(x) = 14x + 7$ when $x = 2$ **35**

6. $j(x) = 0.2x + 12.2$ when $x = 244$ **61**
7. $k(x) = \frac{5}{6}x + \frac{1}{3}$ when $x = 4$ **$3\frac{2}{3}$**

Graph the function. Compare the graph to the graph of $f(x) = x$. *(p. 262)* **8–9. See margin.**

8. $g(x) = -4x$
9. $h(x) = x - 2$

10. HOURLY WAGE The table shows the number of hours that you worked for each of three weeks and the amount that you were paid. What is your hourly wage? *(p. 253)* **$7/h**

Hours	12	16	14
Pay (dollars)	84	112	98

EXTRA PRACTICE for Lesson 4.7, p. 941   🖱 **ONLINE QUIZ** at classzone.com

55–60. See Additional Answers beginning on p. AA1.

Lessons 4.4–4.7

1. **MULTI-STEP PROBLEM** The amount of drink mix d (in tablespoons) that you need to add to w fluid ounces of water is given by $d = \frac{1}{4}w$.

   a. Graph the equation. **See margin.**

   b. Use the graph to find the amount of drink mix you need if you want to make enough drinks to serve 4 people. Assume 1 serving is 8 fluid ounces. **8 tbsp**

2. **MULTI-STEP PROBLEM** A water park charges $25 per ticket for adults. Let s be the amount of money the park receives from adult ticket sales, and let t be the number of adult tickets sold.

   a. Write a direct variation equation that relates t and s. **$s = 25t$**

   b. How much money does the park earn when 90 adult tickets are sold? **$2250**

   c. The park collected $3325 in adult ticket sales in one day. How many tickets did the park sell? **133 adult tickets**

3. **SHORT RESPONSE** You and your friend are each reading an essay that is 10 pages long. You read at a rate of 1 page per minute. Your friend reads at a rate of $\frac{2}{3}$ page per minute.

   The models below give the number p of pages you and your friend have left to read after reading for m minutes.

   You: $p = -m + 10$

   Your friend: $p = -\frac{2}{3}m + 10$

   Graph both equations in the same coordinate plane. *Explain* how you can use the graphs to find how many more minutes it took your friend to read the essay than it took you to read the essay. **See margin.**

4. **OPEN-ENDED** Draw a graph that represents going to a movie theater, watching a movie, and returning home from the theater. Let the x-axis represent time and the y-axis represent your distance from home. **See margin.**

5. **EXTENDED RESPONSE** A central observatory averages and then reports the number of sunspots recorded by various observatories. The table shows the average number of sunspots reported by the central observatory in years since 1995.

Years since 1995	Average number of sunspots
0	17.5
2	21.0
4	93.2
6	110.9

   a. Draw a line graph of the data. **See margin.**

   b. During which two-year period was the increase in sunspots the greatest? Find the rate of change for this time period. **1997 to 1999; 36.1 sunspots per year**

   c. During which two-year period was the increase in sunspots the least? Find the rate of change for this time period. **1995 to 1997; 1.75 sunspots per year**

   d. *Explain* how you could find the overall rate of change for the time period shown. **See margin.**

6. **GRIDDED ANSWER** To become a member at a gym, you have to pay a sign-up fee of $125 and a monthly fee of $40. To attract new customers, the gym lowers the sign-up fee to $75. The function f gives the total cost with the regular sign-up fee. The function g gives the total cost with the reduced sign-up fee. The graphs of f and g are shown. The graph of g is a vertical translation of the graph of f by how many units? **50 units down**

1a.

3. See below.

4. Sample:

5a.

5d. Subtract 17.5 from 110.9 and divide by 6 to find 15.6 sunspots per year.

3.

Find the m-intercepts of each line and subtract the m-intercept of your friend's line from the m-intercept of your line to find your friend takes 5 more minutes to read the essay.

BIG IDEAS   *For Your Notebook*

Big Idea ①

Graphing Linear Equations and Functions Using a Variety of Methods

You can graph a linear equation or function by making a table, using intercepts, or using the slope and y-intercept.

A taxi company charges a $2 fee to pick up a customer plus $1 per mile to drive to the customer's destination. The total cost C (in dollars) that a customer pays to travel d miles is given by $C = d + 2$. Graph this function.

Method: Make a table.

d	C
0	2
1	3
2	4
3	5

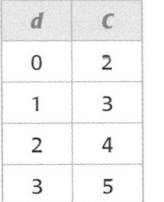

Method: Use slope and C-intercept.

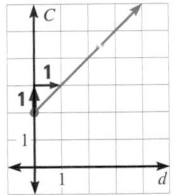

Big Idea ②

Recognizing How Changes in Linear Equations and Functions Affect Their Graphs

When you change the value of m or b in the equation $y = mx + b$, you produce an equation whose graph is related to the graph of the original equation.

Suppose the taxi company raises its rate to $1.50 per mile. The total amount that a customer pays is given by $C = 1.5d + 2$. Graph the function.

> You can see that the graphs have the same C-intercept, but different slopes. ......▶

Big Idea ③

Using Graphs of Linear Equations and Functions to Solve Real-world Problems

You can use the graphs of $C = d + 2$ and $C = 1.5d + 2$ to find out how much more a customer pays to travel 4 miles at the new rate than at the old rate.

> A customer pays $2 more to travel 4 miles at the new rate. ......▶

CHAPTER REVIEW

@HomeTutor
classzone.com
• Multi-Language Glossary
• Vocabulary practice

REVIEW KEY VOCABULARY

- quadrant, *p. 206*
- solution of an equation in two variables, *p. 215*
- graph of an equation in two variables, *p. 215*
- linear equation, *p. 216*

- standard form of a linear equation, *p. 216*
- linear function, *p. 217*
- *x*-intercept, *p. 225*
- *y*-intercept, *p. 225*
- slope, *p. 235*
- rate of change, *p. 237*

- slope-intercept form, *p. 244*
- parallel, *p. 246*
- direct variation, *p. 253*
- constant of variation, *p. 253*
- function notation, *p. 262*
- family of functions, *p. 263*
- parent linear function, *p. 263*

VOCABULARY EXERCISES

1. Copy and complete: The __?__ of a nonvertical line is the ratio of vertical change to horizontal change. **slope**

2. Copy and complete: When you write $y = 2x + 3$ as $f(x) = 2x + 3$, you use __?__. **function notation**

3. **WRITING** *Describe* three different methods you could use to graph the equation $5x + 3y = 12$. *Sample answer:* **Make a table, use intercepts, and use the slope and *y*-intercept.**

4. Tell whether the equation is written in slope-intercept form. If the equation is not in slope-intercept form, write it in slope-intercept form.

   a. $3x + y = 6$ **b.** $y = 5x + 2$ **c.** $x = 4y - 1$ **d.** $y = -x + 6$
   not slope-intercept   **slope-intercept**   **not slope-**   **slope-intercept form**
   form; $y = -3x + 6$ **form**   **intercept form;**

REVIEW EXAMPLES AND EXERCISES $y = \frac{1}{4}x + \frac{1}{4}$

Use the review examples and exercises below to check your understanding of the concepts you have learned in each lesson of Chapter 4.

4.1   Plot Points in a Coordinate Plane   *pp. 206–212*

EXAMPLE

Plot the points $A(-2, 3)$ and $B(0, -2)$ in a coordinate plane. Describe the location of the points.

Point $A(-2, 3)$: Begin at the origin and move 2 units to the left, then 3 units up. Point A is in Quadrant II.

Point $B(0, -2)$: Begin at the origin and move 2 units down. Point B is on the *y*-axis.

EXERCISES

EXAMPLE 2
on p. 207
for Exs. 5–7

Plot the point in a coordinate plane. *Describe* the location of the point.
5–7. See margin for art.

5. $A(3, 4)$ **6.** $B(-5, 0)$ **7.** $C(-7, -2)$
    Quadrant I   ***x*-axis**   **Quadrant III**

Chapter Review   **271**

Extra Example 4.1

Plot the points $A(0, 3)$ and $B(-2, -1)$ in a coordinate plane. Describe the location of the points.
Point $A(0, 3)$: Begin at the origin and move 3 units up. Point A is on the *y*-axis.
Point B: Begin at the origin and move to the left 2 points, then 1 unit down. Point B is in Quadrant III.

5–7.

Extra Example 4.2

Graph the equation $y + 2x = -3$.

Extra Example 4.3

Graph the equation $-2x + 4y = 12$ using intercepts.

8.

9.

10. (0, 9) (4, 9)

11. (0, 3) (-15, 0)

4.2 Graph Linear Equations
pp. 215–221

EXAMPLE

Graph the equation $y + 3x = 1$.

STEP 1 **Solve** the equation for y.

$y + 3x = 1$

$y = -3x + 1$

STEP 2 **Make** a table by choosing a few values for x and finding the values for y.

x	-1	0	1
y	4	1	-2

STEP 3 **Plot** the points.

STEP 4 **Connect** the points by drawing a line through them.

EXERCISES

EXAMPLE 2
on p. 216
for Exs. 8–10

Graph the equation. 8–10. See margin.

8. $y + 5x = -5$ **9.** $2x + 3y = 9$ **10.** $2y - 14 = 4$

4.3 Graph Using Intercepts
pp. 225–232

EXAMPLE

Graph the equation $-0.5x + 2y = 4$.

STEP 1 **Find** the intercepts.

$-0.5x + 2y = 4$ $-0.5x + 2y = 4$

$-0.5x + 2(0) = 4$ $-0.5(0) + 2y = 4$

$x = -8 \leftarrow$ **x-intercept** $y = 2 \leftarrow$ **y-intercept**

STEP 2 **Plot** the points that correspond to the intercepts: $(-8, 0)$ and $(0, 2)$.

STEP 3 **Connect** the points by drawing a line through them.

EXERCISES

EXAMPLES 2 and 4
on pp. 226–227
for Exs. 11–14

Graph the equation. 11–13. See margin.

11. $-x + 5y = 15$ **12.** $4x + 4y = -16$ **13.** $2x - 6y = 18$

14. CRAFT FAIR You sell necklaces for $10 and bracelets for $5 at a craft fair. You want to earn $50. This situation is modeled by the equation $10n + 5b = 50$ where n is the number of necklaces you sell and b is the number of bracelets you sell. Find the intercepts of the graph of the equation. Then graph the equation. Give three possibilities for the number of bracelets and necklaces that you could sell. *n-intercept: 5, b-intercept: 10; see margin for art. Sample answer:* 1 necklace and 8 bracelets, 2 necklaces and 6 bracelets, 3 necklaces and 4 bracelets

272   Chapter 4   Graphing Linear Equations and Functions

12.

(-4, 0) (0, -4)

13.

(9, 0) (0, -3)

14.

Number of bracelets

Number of necklaces

4.4 Find Slope and Rate of Change
pp. 235–242

EXAMPLE

Find the slope of the line shown.

Let $(x_1, y_1) = (2, -3)$ and $(x_2, y_2) = (4, -4)$.

$m = \dfrac{y_2 - y_1}{x_2 - x_1}$　Write formula for slope.

$= \dfrac{-4 - (-3)}{4 - 2}$　Substitute values.

$= -\dfrac{1}{2}$　Simplify.

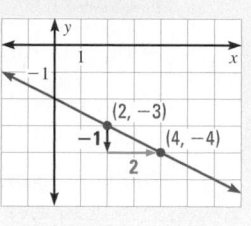

EXERCISES

EXAMPLES 1,2,3, and 4 on pp. 235–236 for Exs. 15–17

Find the slope of the line that passes through the points.

15. $(-1, 11)$ and $(2, 10)$　$-\dfrac{1}{3}$　**16.** $(-2, 0)$ and $(4, 9)$　$\dfrac{3}{2}$　**17.** $(-5, 4)$ and $(1, -8)$　-2

4.5 Graph Using Slope-Intercept Form
pp. 244–250

EXAMPLE

Graph the equation $2x + y = -1$.

STEP 1 Rewrite the equation in slope-intercept form.

$2x + y = -1 \rightarrow y = -2x - 1$

STEP 2 Identify the slope and the y-intercept.

$m = -2$ and $b = -1$

STEP 3 Plot the point that corresponds to the y-intercept, $(0, -1)$.

STEP 4 Use the slope to locate a second point on the line. Draw a line through the two points.

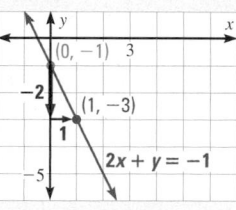

EXERCISES

EXAMPLES 2 and 3 on p. 245 for Exs. 18–21

Graph the equation. **18–20. See margin.**

18. $4x - y = 3$　　**19.** $3x - 6y = 9$　　**20.** $-3x + 4y - 12 = 0$

21. RUNNING One athlete can run a 60 meter race at an average rate of 7 meters per second. A second athlete can run the race at an average rate of 6 meters per second. The distance d (in meters) the athletes have left to run after t seconds is given by the following equations:

Athlete 1: $d = -7t + 60$　　**Athlete 2:** $d = -6t + 60$

Graph both models in the same coordinate plane. About how many seconds faster does the first athlete finish the race than the second athlete?

See margin for art; about 1.4 sec.

Chapter Review **273**

Extra Example 4.4
Find the slope of the line shown.

Extra Example 4.5
Graph the equation $3x + y = 2$ using slope-intercept form.

18.

19.

20.

21.

Extra Example 4.6
Graph the direct variation equation $y = \frac{1}{4}x$.

Extra Example 4.7
Evaluate the function $f(x) = 3x + 5$ when $x = -2$. **−1**

25.

26.

27.

31–33. See Additional Answers beginning on p. AA1.

34.

Number of years

4.6 Model Direct Variation
pp. 253–259

EXAMPLE

Graph the direct variation equation $y = -\frac{2}{3}x$.

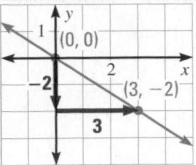

Plot a point at the origin. The slope is equal to the constant of variation, $-\frac{2}{3}$. Find and plot a second point, then draw a line through the points.

EXERCISES

EXAMPLES
1, 2, and 4
on pp. 253–255
for Exs. 22–28

Tell whether the equation represents direct variation. If so, identify the constant of variation.

22. $x - y = 3$
not direct variation

23. $x + 2y = 0$
direct variation; $-\frac{1}{2}$

24. $8x - 2y = 0$
direct variation; 4

Graph the direct variation equation. **25–27. See margin.**

25. $y = 4x$

26. $-5y = 3x$

27. $4x + 3y = 0$

28. SNOWSTORMS The amount s (in inches) of snow that fell during a snowstorm varied directly with the duration d (in hours) of the storm. In the first 2 hours of the storm 5 inches of snow fell. Write a direct variation equation that relates d and s. How many inches of snow fell in 6 hours? $s = \frac{5}{2}d$; 15 in.

4.7 Graph Linear Functions
pp. 262–268

EXAMPLE

Evaluate the function $f(x) = -6x + 5$ when $x = 3$.

$f(x) = -6x + 5$ Write function.

$f(3) = -6(3) + 5$ Substitute 3 for x.

$= -13$ Simplify.

EXERCISES

EXAMPLES
1 and 3
on pp. 262–263
for Exs. 29–34

Evaluate the function.

29. $g(x) = 2x - 3$ when $x = 7$ **11**

30. $h(x) = -\frac{1}{2}x - 7$ when $x = -6$ **−4**

Graph the function. Compare the graph with the graph of $f(x) = x$. **31–33. See margin.**

31. $j(x) = x - 6$

32. $k(x) = -2.5x$

33. $t(x) = 2x + 1$

34. MOUNT EVEREST Mount Everest is rising at a rate of 2.4 inches per year. The number of inches that Mount Everest rises in x years is given by the function $f(x) = 2.4x$. Graph the function and identify its domain and range. Find the value of x so that $f(x) = 250$. *Explain* what the solution means in this situation. **See margin for art; domain: $x \geq 0$, range: $f(x) \geq 0$; about 104; Mount Everest will have grown 250 inches in 104 years.**

Plot the point in a coordinate plane. *Describe* **the location of the point.**
1–3. See margin for art.

1. $A(7, 1)$ **Quadrant I**

2. $B(-4, 0)$ **x-axis**

3. $C(3, -9)$ **Quadrant IV**

Draw the line that has the given intercepts. **4–6. See margin.**

4. x-intercept: 2
y-intercept: −6

5. x-intercept: −1
y-intercept: 8

6. x-intercept: −3
y-intercept: −5

Find the slope of the line that passes through the points.

7. (2, 1) and (8, 4) $\frac{1}{2}$

8. (−2, 7) and (0, −1) **−4**

9. (3, 5) and (3, 14)
undefined

Identify the slope and y-intercept of the line with the given equation.

10. $y = -\frac{3}{2}x - 10$ $-\frac{3}{2}, -10$

11. $7x + 2y = -28$ $-\frac{7}{2}, -14$

12. $3x - 8y = 48$ $\frac{3}{8}, -6$

Tell whether the equation represents direct variation. If so, identify the constant of variation.

13. $x + 4y = 4$
not direct variation

14. $-\frac{1}{3}x - y = 0$
direct variation; $-\frac{1}{3}$

15. $3x - 3y = 0$
direct variation; 1

Graph the equation. **16–18. See margin.**

16. $x = 3$

17. $y + x = 6$

18. $2x + 8y = -32$

Evaluate the function for the given value.

19. $f(x) = -4x$ when $x = 2.5$ **−10**

20. $g(x) = \frac{5}{2}x - 6$ when $x = -2$ **−11**

21. BUSINESS To start a dog washing business, you invest $300 in supplies. You charge $10 per hour for your services. Your profit P (in dollars) for working t hours is given by $P = 10t - 300$. Graph the equation. You will break even when your profit is $0. Use the graph to find the number of hours you must work in order to break even. **See margin for art; 30 h.**

22. PEDIATRICS The dose d (in milligrams) of a particular medicine that a pediatrician prescribes for a patient varies directly with the patient's mass m (in kilograms). The pediatrician recommends a dose of 150 mg of medicine for a patient whose mass is 30 kg.

   a. Write a direct variation equation that relates m and d. **d = 5m**

   b. What would the dose of medicine be for a patient whose mass is 50 kg? **250 mg**

23. SCISSOR LIFT The scissor lift is a device that can lower and raise a platform. The maximum and minimum heights of the platform of a particular scissor lift are shown. The scissor lift can raise the platform at a rate of 3.5 inches per second. The height of the platform after t seconds is given by $h(t) = 3.5t + 48$. Graph the function and identify its domain and range. **See margin for art; domain: $0 \le t \le 58.3$, range: $48 \le h(t) \le 252$.**

252 in.

48 in.

Raised   Lowered

Additional Resources

Assessment Book
• Chapter Test, Levels A, B, C, pp. 49–54
• Standardized Chapter Test, pp. 55–56
• SAT/ACT Chapter Test, pp. 57–58
• Alternative Assessment, pp. 59–60

Test Generator CD-ROM

Chapter Test

Easily-readable reduced copies (with answers) of Chapter Test B, the Standardized Chapter Test, and the Alternative Assessment from the Assessment Book can be found on pp. 204G–204H.

5.

6.

16–18. See Additional Answers beginning on p. AA1.

21.

23.

1–3.

4.

Test-Taking Strategy

Point out to students that graphs, tables, and diagrams may contain all of the information they need to solve a problem or they may contain only some of the information. Encourage students to examine the graphic in a question to determine how the given information will help them solve the problem.

Teaching Strategy

You may want to stress that students can solve problems in more than one way, and they should choose the strategy with which they are most comfortable. In Problem 1, for example, they could solve the problem using a proportion.

CONTEXT-BASED MULTIPLE CHOICE QUESTIONS

Some of the information you need to solve a context-based multiple choice question may appear in a table, a diagram, or a graph.

PROBLEM 1

A recipe from a box of pancake mix is shown. The number p of pancakes you can make varies directly with the number m of cups of mix you use. A full box of pancake mix contains 9 cups of mix. How many pancakes can you make when you use the full box?

(A) 63   (B) 65

(C) 126   (D) 131

> 2 cups pancake mix
> 1 cup milk
> 2 eggs
> Combine ingredients. Pour batter on hot greased griddle. Flip when edges are dry. Makes 14 pancakes.

Plan

INTERPRET THE INFORMATION Use the number of pancakes and the number of cups of mix given in the recipe to write a direct variation equation. Then use the equation to find the number of pancakes that you can make when you use 9 cups of mix.

Solution

STEP 1
Use the values given in the recipe to find a direct variation equation.

➤ Because the number p of pancakes you can make varies directly with the number m of cups of mix you use, you can write the equation $p = am$. From the recipe, you know that $p = 14$ when $m = 2$.

$p = am$ **Write direct variation equation.**

$14 = a(2)$ **Substitute.**

$7 = a$ **Solve for a.**

So, a direct variation equation that relates p and m is $p = 7m$.

STEP 2
Substitute 9 for m in the direct variation equation and solve for p.

➤ Use the direct variation equation to find the number of pancakes you can make when you use a full box of mix.

$p = 7m$ **Write direct variation equation.**

$p = 7(9)$ **Substitute 9 for m.**

$p = 63$ **Simplify.**

You can make 63 pancakes when you use a full box of mix.

The correct answer is A. (A) (B) (C) (D)

PROBLEM 2

At a yard sale, Jack made $54 selling cassettes for $1 each and CDs for $3 each. This situation is modeled by the equation $x + 3y = 54$ where x is the number of cassettes and y is the number of CDs that Jack sold. The graph of the equation is shown. Which is a possible combination of cassettes and CDs that Jack sold?

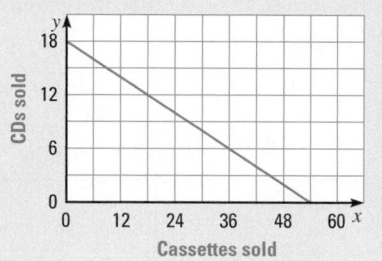

Ⓐ 12 cassettes, 4 CDs   Ⓑ 4 cassettes, 12 CDs

Ⓒ 18 cassettes, 12 CDs   Ⓓ 28.5 cassettes, 8.5 CDs

Avoiding Common Errors

Exercise 1 Caution students to read the labels on the axes of a graph carefully as the answers to a multiple-choice question often include values that appear on both axes.

Plan

INTERPRET THE INFORMATION Each point on the line represents a solution of the equation. Identify the answer choice that describes a point on the graph shown and that makes sense in the context of the problem.

Solution

STEP 1
Write an ordered pair for each answer choice.

The answer choices correspond to the following ordered pairs.

Ⓐ (12, 4)   Ⓑ (4, 12)   Ⓒ (18, 12)   Ⓓ (28.5, 8.5)

STEP 2
Eliminate points not on the line and points that don't make sense. Check ordered pairs not eliminated to find the solution.

You can eliminate answer choices A and B because the points do not lie on the graph shown. You can also eliminate answer choice D because only whole number solutions make sense in this situation. Check that (18, 12) is a solution of the equation.

$x + 3y = 54$ **Write original equation.**

$18 + 3(12) = 54$ **Substitute.**

$54 = 54$ ✓   **Solution checks.**

The correct answer is C. Ⓐ Ⓑ ⓒ Ⓓ

PRACTICE

1. In Problem 2, what is the greatest number of CDs Jack could have sold? **B**

   Ⓐ 3   Ⓑ 18   Ⓒ 36   Ⓓ 54

2. The table shows the total cost for a certain number of people to ice skate at a particular rink. What is the cost per person? **C**

   Ⓐ $.20   Ⓑ $1

   Ⓒ $5   Ⓓ $10

Number of people	Cost (dollars)
2	10
4	20
6	30

Standardized Test Preparation   **277**

MULTIPLE CHOICE

In Exercises 1 and 2, use the graph below.

1. The graph represents a function. Which number is in the domain of the function? **B**

   Ⓐ 22 Ⓑ −1

   Ⓒ 1 Ⓓ 4

2. The graph would no longer represent a function if which point were included? **D**

   Ⓐ (−4, −2) Ⓑ (−2, 0)

   Ⓒ (1, 3) Ⓓ (3, −1)

In Exercises 3 and 4, use the graph below, which shows a traveler's movements through an airport to a terminal. The traveler has to walk and take a shuttle bus to get to the terminal.

3. For how many minutes does the traveler wait for the shuttle bus? **D**

   Ⓐ 1 min Ⓑ 2 min

   Ⓒ 4 min Ⓓ 8 min

4. For about what distance does the traveler ride on the shuttle bus? **C**

   Ⓐ 100 ft Ⓑ 100 ft

   Ⓒ 2000 ft Ⓓ 3000 ft

In Exercises 5–7, use the following information.

At a yoga studio, new members pay a sign-up fee of $50 plus a monthly fee of $25. The total cost C (in dollars) of a new membership is given by $C = 25m + 50$ where m is the number of months of membership. The owner of the studio is considering changing the cost of a new membership. A graph of four different options for changing the cost is shown.

5. For which option are the sign-up fee and monthly fee kept the same? **D**

   Ⓐ Option 1 Ⓑ Option 2

   Ⓒ Option 3 Ⓓ Option 4

6. For which option is the sign-up fee kept the same and the monthly fee raised? **A**

   Ⓐ Option 1 Ⓑ Option 2

   Ⓒ Option 3 Ⓓ Option 4

7. For which option is the monthly fee kept the same and the sign-up fee raised? **C**

   Ⓐ Option 1 Ⓑ Option 2

   Ⓒ Option 3 Ⓓ Option 4

8. The table shows the cost of a therapeutic massage for a given amount of time. What is the cost per minute? **B**

Time (minutes)	30	45	60
Cost (dollars)	42.00	63.00	84.00

   Ⓐ $.71 Ⓑ $1.40

   Ⓒ $2.80 Ⓓ $14.00

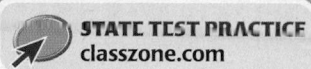

GRIDDED ANSWER

9. What is the slope of the line shown? **1**

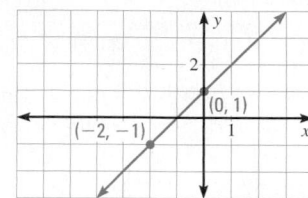

10. What is the y-intercept of the graph of the equation $4x + 8y = 16$? **2**

11. What is the value of $f(x) = -1.8x - 9$ when $x = -5$? **0**

12. The number w of cups of water varies directly with the number u of cups of uncooked rice. Use the table to find the value of the constant of variation a in the direct variation equation $w = au$. $\frac{3}{2}$

Uncooked rice, u (cups)	$\frac{1}{2}$	1	$1\frac{1}{2}$
Water, w (cups)	$\frac{3}{4}$	$1\frac{1}{2}$	$2\frac{1}{4}$

EXTENDED RESPONSE

14. A fog machine has a tank that holds 32 fluid ounces of fog fluid and has two settings: low and high. The low setting uses 0.2 fluid ounce of fluid per minute, and the high setting uses 0.25 fluid ounce per minute. The functions below give the amount f (in fluid ounces) of fluid left in the tank after t minutes when the machine starts with a full tank of fluid.

Low setting: $f = -0.2t + 32$ **High setting:** $f = -0.25t + 32$

a. Identify the slope and y-intercept of each function. **low: -0.2, 32; high: -0.25, 32**

b. Graph each function in the same coordinate plane. **See margin.**

c. How much longer can the machine be run on the low setting than on the high setting? *Explain* how you found your answer. **See margin.**

15. At a pizzeria, a cheese pizza costs $9. Toppings cost $1.50 each.

a. The cost of a pizza is given by the function $f(x) = 1.5x + 9$ where x is the number of toppings. Graph the function. **See margin.**

b. You have $14 and buy only a pizza. How many toppings can you get? **3 toppings**

c. The pizzeria's owner decides to change the price of toppings to $2 each. The new cost of a pizza is given by the function $g(x) = 2x + 9$. Graph the function in the same coordinate plane you used in part (a). **See margin.**

d. Can you get the same number of toppings at the new price as you did in part (b)? *Explain*. **See margin.**

SHORT RESPONSE

13. Patricia takes a bus to and from her job. She can either pay $1.75 each way or get a monthly bus pass for $58 and ride the bus an unlimited number of times. The functions below give the costs C (in dollars) of riding the bus n times in one month. The graphs of the functions are shown.

Monthly pass: $C = 58$
Pay per ride: $C = 1.75n$

How many days in a month would Patricia need to take the bus to and from work to make buying a monthly pass worth the cost? *Explain*. **See margin.**

13. 17 days. *Sample answer:* The two costs are equal when $58 = 1.75n$, or $n = 58 \div 1.75 \approx 33.14$. In this problem situation only whole-number values of n make sense. The graph shows that when $n < 34$, the pay-per-ride cost is lower; when $n \geq 34$, the monthly pass cost is lower. If Patricia rides the bus at least 34 times a month, it will be worth buying the monthly pass. Because she rides the bus to and from work, she rides twice a day, so the number of days is $34 \div 2 = 17$ days.

14b.

14c. 32 min; the machine can run until the amount of fog fluid is 0, so to find how many minutes the machine can run on each setting, set $f = 0$ in each equation and solve for t. For the low setting, solve $0 = -0.2t + 32$ to get $t = 160$ minutes, and for the high setting solve $0 = -0.25t + 32$ to get $t = 128$ minutes. The difference in time is $160 - 128 = 32$ minutes.

15a, c.

15d. No; at the new price, a pizza with 3 toppings would cost $g(3) = 2(3) + 9 = \$15$, which is more money than you have.

Pacing and Assignment Guide

REGULAR SCHEDULE **Pre-AP** For pacing and assignments for a Pre-AP course, see the *Algebra 1 Toolkit*.

Lesson	Les. Day	BASIC	AVERAGE	ADVANCED
5.1	Day 1	EP p. 941 Exs. 33–36; pp. 286–289 Exs. 1–5, 9–12, 16–20, 24–26, 30–32, 39, 40, 45–49, 53–63 odd	pp. 286–289 Exs. 1, 2, 6–9, 13–17, 21–24, 26, 28, 33–35, 39–43, 46–51, 56, 57, 62, 63	pp. 286–289 Exs. 1, 7–9, 13–15, 21–23, 27–29, 36–44*, 47–52*, 58, 64
5.2	Day 1	EP p. 941 Exs. 27–32; pp. 296–299 Exs. 1–5, 11–13, 17–19, 23–26, 55–58	pp. 296–299 Exs. 1, 2, 6–8, 14–16, 20–22, 25–29, 55–58	pp. 296–299 Exs. 1, 7, 8, 15, 16, 21, 22, 27–37, 57, 58
	Day 2	pp. 296–299 Exs. 9, 10, 29–35, 47–52, 59–64	pp. 296–299 Exs. 9, 10, 31–43 odd, 48–53, 59–64	pp. 296–299 Exs. 10, 38–46*, 49–54*, 63, 64
5.3	Day 1	EP p. 939 Exs. 42–45; pp. 305–308 Exs. 1–8, 12–17, 45–53	pp. 305–308 Exs. 1, 2, 6–13, 17–19, 45–53	pp. 305–308 Exs. 1, 2, 7–12, 17–19, 35*, 36*, 45–53 odd
	Day 2	pp. 305–308 Exs. 20–32, 37–42, 54–57	pp. 305–308 Exs. 20–28 even, 29–34, 37–43, 54–57	pp. 305–308 Exs. 24–28, 30–34, 37–44*, 55, 57
5.4	Day 1	EP p. 941 Exs. 37–40; pp. 314–316 Exs. 1–8, 11–19, 47–49	pp. 314–316 Exs. 1–4, 8–10, 14–22, 47–49	pp. 314–316 Exs. 1–4, 8–10, 16–22, 37*, 47–49
	Day 2	pp. 314–316 Exs. 23–32, 38–41, 45, 46	pp. 314–316 Exs. 23–29 odd, 30–36, 38–43, 45, 46	pp. 314–316 Exs. 26–28, 30–36, 41–46*
5.5	Day 1	pp. 322–324 Exs. 1–8, 12–22, 27, 28, 32–35, 38–42	pp. 322–324 Exs. 1, 2, 7–17, 23–30, 32–37, 39, 41, 42	pp. 322–324 Exs. 1, 2, 8–11, 13–17, 24–37*, 40–42
5.6	Day 1	EP p. 941 Exs. 1–7 odd; pp. 328–331 Exs. 1–12, 16–18, 22–28	pp. 328–331 Exs. 1, 2, 4–14, 16–20, 22–28	pp. 328–331 Exs. 1, 2, 4–8, 11–28*
5.7	Day 1	pp. 338–341 Exs. 1–15, 18–21, 24–32	pp. 338–341 Exs. 1–6, 9–16, 18–22, 24–32	pp. 338–341 Exs. 1–6, 10–14, 16–32*
Review	Day 1	pp. 345–348 Exs. 1–22	pp. 345–348 Exs. 1–22	pp. 345–348 Exs. 1–22
Assess	Day 1	Chapter 5 Test	Chapter 5 Test	Chapter 5 Test
Yearly Pacing		Chapter 5 Total – 12 days	Chapters 1–5 Total – 58 days	Remaining – 102 days

*Challenge Exercises   EP = Extra Practice   SRH = Skills Review Handbook

BLOCK SCHEDULE

DAY 1	DAY 2	DAY 3	DAY 4	DAY 5	DAY 6
5.1	**5.2 (CONT.)**	**5.3 (CONT.)**	**5.4 (CONT.)**	**5.6**	**REVIEW**
pp. 286–289 Exs. 1, 2, 6–9, 13–17, 21–24, 26, 28, 33–35, 39–43, 46–51, 56, 57, 62, 63	pp. 296–299 Exs. 9, 10, 31–43 odd, 48–53, 59–64	pp. 305–308 Exs. 20–28 even, 29–34, 37–43, 54–57	pp. 314–316 Exs. 23–29 odd, 30–36, 38–43, 45, 46	pp. 328–331 Exs. 1, 2, 4–14, 16–20, 22–28	pp. 345–348 Exs. 1–22
5.2	**5.3**	**5.4**	**5.5**	**5.7**	**ASSESS**
pp. 296–299 Exs. 1, 2, 6–8, 14–16, 20–22, 25–29, 55–58	pp. 305–308 Exs. 1, 2, 6–13, 17–19, 45–53	pp. 314–316 Exs. 1–4, 8–10, 14–22, 47–49	pp. 322–324 Exs. 1, 2, 7–17, 23–30, 32–37, 39, 41, 42	pp. 338–341 Exs. 1–6, 9–16, 18–22, 24–32	Chapter 5 Test
Yearly Pacing	Chapter 5 Total – 6 days	Chapters 1–5 Total – 29 days	Remaining – 51 days		

RESOURCE MANAGER

Chapter Resource Book

CHAPTER SUPPORT

Parents as Partners (Chapter Overview with home involvement exercises and activity)		p. 1

LESSON SUPPORT	5.1	5.2	5.3	5.4	5.5	5.6	5.7
Teaching Guide/Lesson Plan	p. 3	p. 14	p. 24	p. 38	p. 50	p. 60	p. 74
Activity Masters			p. 26	p. 40			
Technology Activities & Keystrokes	p. 5					p. 62	p. 76
Activity Support Masters							
Practice (3 levels)	p. 6	p. 16	p. 27	p. 41	p. 52	p. 63	p. 78
Study Guide	p. 9	p. 19	p. 33	p. 44	p. 55	p. 69	p. 84
Catch-Up for Absent Students	p. 11	p. 21	p. 35	p. 46	p. 57	p. 71	p. 86
Problem Solving/Application	p. 12	p. 22	p. 36	p. 47	p. 58	p. 72	p. 87
Challenge Practice	p. 13	p. 23	p. 37	p. 49	p. 59	p. 73	p. 88

REVIEW

Chapter Review Games and Activities	p. 89		Cumulative Practice	p. 91
Project with Rubric	p. 90		Resource Book Answers	A1

Transparencies	5.1	5.2	5.3	5.4	5.5	5.6	5.7
Warm-Up/Daily Homework Quiz	✔	✔	✔	✔	✔	✔	✔
Notetaking Guide	✔	✔	✔	✔	✔	✔	✔
Teacher Support	✔		✔	✔		✔	
Answer Transparencies	✔	✔	✔	✔	✔	✔	✔

ASSESSMENT BOOK

Quizzes	p. 61	SAT/ACT Chapter Test	p. 71
Chapter Tests (3 levels)	p. 63	Alternative Assessment with Rubric	p. 73
Standardized Chapter Test	p. 69		

TECHNOLOGY

- Easy Planner
- Test and Practice Generator
- Power Presentations
- @HomeTutor
- Activity Generator
- Animated Algebra
- Classzone.com
- eEdition Plus Online
- eWorkbook Plus Online
- Easy Grader Online

ADDITIONAL RESOURCES

- Worked-Out Solution Key
- Notetaking Guide
- Practice Wookbook
- Algebra 1 Toolkit
- Benchmark Tests
- Reteaching and Remediation
- Spanish Study Guide
- Spanish Assessment Book
- Student Resources in Spanish
- Multi-Language Visual Glossary

LESSON 5.1 Practice B
For use with pages 283–289

Write an equation of the line with the given slope and y-intercept.

1. slope: 7; y-intercept: 4
$y = 7x + 4$

2. slope: −3; y-intercept: 5
$y = -3x + 5$

3. slope: 1; y-intercept: −6
$y = x - 6$

Write an equation of the line shown.

4.
$y = -5x + 5$

5.
$y = 2x - 5$

6.
$y = \frac{3}{4}x + 3$

Write an equation of the line that passes through the given points.

7. (−1, 0), (0, −2) $y = -2x - 2$

8. (0, 4), (6, 13) $y = \frac{3}{2}x + 4$

9. (4, 5), (8, 2) $y = -\frac{3}{4}x + 8$

10. (−1, −9), (6, 5) $y = 2x - 7$

11. (2, −13), (−3, 12)
$y = -5x - 3$

12. (−4, −21), (1, −1)
$y = 4x - 5$

Write an equation for the linear function f with the given values.

13. $f(0) = -1, f(3) = -10$
$f(x) = -3x - 1$

14. $f(-4) = 5, f(2) = 2$
$f(x) = -\frac{1}{2}x + 3$

15. $f(-4) = -2, f(2) = 7$
$f(x) = \frac{3}{2}x + 4$

16. **Landscape Supply** A landscape supply business charges $30 to deliver mulch. The mulch costs $23 per cubic yard.

a. Write an equation that gives the total cost (in dollars) of having mulch delivered to a site as a function of the number of cubic yards ordered. $y = 23x + 30$

b. *Identify* the dependent and independent variables in this situation. **b.** independent: x, number of cubic yards ordered; dependent: y, total cost

c. Find the cost of having 8 cubic yards of mulch delivered to a site. $214

17. **Cable Television** A cable company charges $44 per month for basic service. Each premium channel costs an additional $16 per month.

a. Write an equation that gives the total cost (in dollars) of cable each month as a function of the number of premium channels. $y = 16x + 44$ **b.** independent: x, number of premium channels; dependent: y, total cost

b. *Identify* the dependent and independent variables in this situation.

c. *Explain* how you can use the equation from part (a) to approximate how many premium channels you can have for $80 a month. Substitute 80 for y in the equation and solve for x.

18. **Laser Printer** A laser printer has a "sleep" mode that is an energy-saving feature. When a job is sent to the printer, it takes 45 seconds for the printer to warm up and then the printer prints pages at a rate of 6 pages per minute.

a. Write the time it takes the printer to warm up in minutes. 0.75 min

b. Write an equation that gives the total amount of time (in minutes) it takes the printer to warm up and print a job as a function of the number of pages in the job. $y = \frac{1}{6}x + 0.75$

c. Find out how long it takes the printer to print a 50-page job if it must first warm up. about 9 min

LESSON 5.2 Practice B
For use with pages 292–299

Write an equation of the line that passes through the given point and has slope m.
$y = -2x + 23$

1. (−1, 6); m = 5 $y = 5x + 11$

2. (10, 3); m = −2

3. (2, −3); m = 7 $y = 7x - 17$

4. (−4, −9); m = 2 $y = 2x - 1$

5. (5, −4); m = $\frac{1}{3}$ $y = \frac{1}{3}x - \frac{17}{3}$

6. (−8, 1); m = $-\frac{3}{4}$
$y = -\frac{3}{4}x - 5$

Write an equation of the line shown.

7.

8.

9.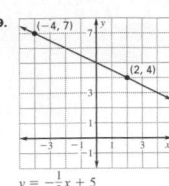

$y = -4x + 5$

$y = 3x + 8$

$y = -\frac{1}{2}x + 5$

Write an equation of the line that passes through the given points.

10. (−10, 7), (5, −3)
$y = -\frac{2}{3}x + \frac{1}{3}$

11. (−5, −2), (12, 17.4)
$y = 1.2x + 3$

12. (−8, 84), (5, −46)
$y = -10x + 4$

Write an equation for the linear function f with the given values.

13. $f(4) = -8, f(-3) = 1$
$f(x) = \frac{9}{7}x - \frac{20}{7}$

14. $f(6) = -4, f(9) = -9$
$f(x) = -\frac{5}{3}x + 6$

15. $f(-1) = -6, f(4) = -14$
$f(x) = -\frac{8}{5}x - \frac{38}{5}$

16. **Oil Changes** You are scheduled to start your job at an oil change shop 2 hours after the shop opens. Two hours after you start, a total of 11 cars have had their oil changed since the shop opened. Three hours later, a total of 14 cars have had their oil changed. At what rate are cars getting their oil changed since you started working? How many cars had their oil changed before you started work? 1 car per hour; 9 cars

17. **Motor Vehicle Licenses** The amount of revenue brought in by states from motor vehicle licenses increased at a relatively constant rate of 499.79 million dollars per year from 1990 to 2000. In 2000, the states brought in 15,099 million dollars in revenue from motor vehicle licenses.

a. What was the approximate revenue (in million dollars) from licenses in 1990? 10,101.1 million dollars

b. Write an equation that gives the revenue (in million dollars) as a function of the number of years since 1990. $y = 499.79x + 10,101.1$

c. Find the revenue from licenses in 1999. 14,599.21 million dollars

18. **Imports** The number of metric tons of fruits, nuts, and vegetables imported into the United States increased at a relatively constant rate of 437.5 thousand metric tons per year from 1990 to 2002. In 2002, about 9900.5 thousand metric tons of fruits, nuts, and vegetables were imported. Write an equation that gives the number of thousand metric tons imported as a function of the number of years since 1990. Find the year in which the number of metric tons reached 8000 thousand metric tons.
$y = 437.5x + 4650.5$; between 1997 and 1998

LESSON 5.3 Practice B
For use with pages 302–308

Write an equation in point-slope form of the line that passes through the given point and has the given slope m.

1. (1, 9); m = −3
$y - 9 = -3(x - 1)$

2. (4, −10); m = 2
$y + 10 = 2(x - 4)$

3. (−5, 6); m = 4
$y - 6 = 4(x + 5)$

4. (−2, −8); m = 3
$y + 8 = 3(x + 2)$

5. (−4, −7); m = $-\frac{1}{2}$
$y + 7 = -\frac{1}{2}(x + 4)$

6. (−9, 2); m = −5
$y - 2 = -5(x + 9)$

7. (6, −4); m = $\frac{2}{3}$
$y + 4 = \frac{2}{3}(x - 6)$

8. (0, 15); m = $\frac{4}{5}$
$y - 15 = \frac{4}{5}x$

9. (−8, 0); m = 2 $y = 2(x + 8)$

Graph the equation.

10. $y - 6 = 3(x - 4)$

11. $y + 1 = 2(x - 5)$

12. $y - 2 = -4(x + 3)$

13. $y + 2 = -(x - 1)$

14. $y = \frac{1}{2}(x - 5)$

15. $y + 3 = 5x$

16. $y + 1 = \frac{2}{3}(x + 1)$
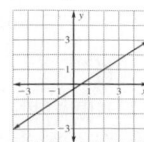

17. $y - 2 = -\frac{1}{2}(x - 3)$

18. $y + \frac{1}{2} = 2(x - 1)$

LESSON 5.3 Practice B *continued*
For use with pages 302–308

19. $y - 3 = 2(x + 2)$

20. $y - 6 = \frac{3}{4}(x - 4)$

21. $y + 8 = -3(x - 1)$

22. $y - 3 = \frac{5}{3}(x - 1)$

23. $y = -1(x - 3)$

24. $y - 2 = -x$

Write an equation of the line shown.

19.

20.

21.

22.

23.

24.

Write an equation of the line that passes through the given points.

25. (9, 4), (17, 6) $y - 4 = \frac{1}{4}(x - 9)$

26. (−3, 10), (4, 2) $y - 2 = -\frac{8}{7}(x - 4)$

27. (3, −8), (7, −2) $y + 8 = \frac{3}{2}(x - 3)$

28. (−4, −4), (2, 5) $y + 4 = \frac{3}{2}(x + 4)$

29. **Bryce Canyon National Park** From 1990 to 2000, the number of thousand visits by people to Bryce Canyon National Park increased by about 23.9 thousand visits per year. In 2000, there were about 1102.4 thousand visits to the park.

a. Write an equation that gives the number of thousand visits as a function of the number of years since 1990. $y - 1102.4 = 23.9(x - 10)$

b. How many visits were made to the park in 1995? 982.9 thousand visits

30. **Airmail Letter Rates** The table shows the cost of mailing different weights of airmail letters to Canada.

Weight (oz)	2	3	4	8
Cost (dollars)	0.85	1.10	1.35	2.35

a. *Explain* why the situation can be modeled using a linear equation. The slope between each pair of points is the same.

b. Write an equation that gives the cost (in dollars) as a function of the weight of an airmail letter (in ounces). $y - 0.85 = 0.25(x - 2)$

c. How much does it cost to mail a 5-ounce airmail letter to Canada? $1.60

31. **New Mexico** The population density of New Mexico increased at a relatively constant rate from 1980 to 1999. In 1985, the population density was about 11.62 people per square mile. In 1999, the population density was about 14.28 people per square mile. Write an equation that gives the population density (in people per square mile) as a function of the number of years since 1980. What was the population density in 1990?
$y - 11.62 = 0.19(x - 5)$; 12.57 people per square mile

LESSON 5.4 — Practice B
For use with pages 311–316

Write two equations in standard form that are equivalent to the given equation. 1–6. Answers will vary.

1. $6x + 24y = 18$
2. $8x - 14y = 2$
3. $6x + y = 1$

4. $-4x - 2y = 16$
5. $2x + 3y = 11$
6. $-9x + 4y = 5$

Write an equation in standard form of the line that passes through the given point and has the given slope m.

7. $(4, 3), m = 7$ $7x - y = 25$
8. $(5, -1), m = 2$ $2x - y = 11$
9. $(-2, 6), m = 1$ $x - y = -8$

10. $(-7, 8), m = -3$ $3x + y = -13$
11. $(9, -10), m = -4$ $4x + y = 26$
12. $(-15, -4), m = \frac{1}{2}$ $x - 2y = -7$

Write an equation in standard form of the line that passes through the given points.

13. $(2, 6), (3, 8)$ $2x - y = -2$
14. $(-1, 2), (5, 4)$ $x - 3y = -7$
15. $(7, -3), (4, 1)$ $4x + 3y = 19$

16. $(3, -8), (5, -9)$ $x + 2y = -13$
17. $(-5, 6), (2, -3)$ $9x + 7y = -3$
18. $(-3, -1), (6, -8)$ $7x + 9y = -30$

Write equations of the horizontal and the vertical lines that pass through the given point.

19. $(8, 3)$ $x = 8, y = 3$
20. $(-2, 6)$ $x = -2, y = 6$
21. $(5, -5)$ $x = 5, y = -5$

22. **Text Messaging** Your cell phone plan charges you $.02 to send a text message and $.07 to receive a text message. You plan to spend no more than $5 a month on text messaging.

a. Write an equation in standard form that models the possible combinations of sent text messages and received text messages. $0.02x + 0.07y = 5$

b. Graph the equation from part (a). *Explain* what the intercepts of the graph mean in this situation.

c. List three other possible combinations of the number of messages you can send and receive.   Answers will vary.

b. *x*-intercept: the number of messages you can send when no messages are received; *y*-intercept: the number of messages you can receive when no messages are sent

23. **Potting Soil Mix** You are making 24 pounds of your own potting soil mix of sphagnum peat moss and coarse sand. You buy the peat moss in bags that weigh approximately 2 pounds.

a. Last time you made potting soil, you used 9 bags of sphagnum peat moss and 4 bags of coarse sand. Use this information to find the number of pounds in a bag of coarse sand.   1.5 lb

b. Write an equation in standard form that models the possible combinations of bags of sphagnum peat moss and coarse sand you can use. $2x + 1.5y = 24$

c. List three possible combinations of whole bags of sphagnum peat moss and coarse sand you can use to make the potting soil.   Answers will vary.

LESSON 5.5 — Practice B
For use with pages 319–324

Write an equation of the line that passes through the given point and is parallel to the given line. See below.

1. $(4, 7), y = 5x - 3$
2. $(3, -2), y = \frac{2}{3}x + 1$
3. $(-6, 1), 4x + y = 7$

4. $(-5, -5), 6x - y = 1$
5. $(0, -8), 8x + 4y = 5$
6. $(-9, 11), 5x - 10y = 3$

Write an equation of the line that passes through the given point and is perpendicular to the given line. See below.

7. $(1, -1), y = 3x + 2$
8. $(5, 0), y = \frac{2}{3}x - 4$
9. $(3, -7), y = -\frac{1}{5}x + 1$

10. $(-9, 2), 10x - 5y = 6$
11. $(10, -11), -2x + 5y = 1$
12. $(-4, -8), 8x + 3y = 7$

Determine which of the following lines, if any, are parallel or perpendicular.

13. Line a: $y = 8x - 5$, Line b: $y = \frac{1}{8}x + 1$, Line c: $8x + y = 2$

14. Line a: $y = -2x + 5$, Line b: $2y - x = 3$, Line c: $2x + y = 1$

15. Line a: $6x + 2y = 5$, Line b: $y = \frac{1}{3}x - 4$, Line c: $y = -3x + 5$

13. Lines b and c are perpendicular.
14. Lines a and lines b and c are perpendicular. Lines a and c are parallel. 15. Lines a and b and lines b and c are perpendicular. Lines b and c are parallel.

16. **Kite Design** You are beginning to model a kite design on the coordinate plane, as shown.

1. $y - 7 = 5(x - 4)$
2. $y + 2 = \frac{2}{3}(x - 3)$
3. $y = -4(x + 6)$
4. $y + 5 = 6(x + 5)$
5. $y + 8 = -2x$
6. $y - 11 = \frac{1}{2}(x + 9)$
7. $y + 1 = -\frac{1}{3}(x - 1)$
8. $y = -\frac{3}{2}(x - 5)$
9. $y + 7 = 5(x - 3)$
10. $y - 2 = -\frac{1}{2}(x + 9)$
11. $y + 11 = -\frac{5}{2}(x - 10)$
12. $y + 8 = \frac{3}{8}(x + 4)$

17. a. you: $y = \frac{1}{2}x$; your friend: $y = \frac{1}{2}x + 5$

a. Write an equation that models part A of the kite. $y = \frac{2}{3}x + 4$

b. Write an equation that models part B of the kite. $y = -\frac{4}{3}x + 4$

c. Do the kite parts form a right angle? *Justify* your answer.   No. The lines for part A and part B are not perpendicular.

17. **Lunch Duty** Everyone at summer camp takes turns being on lunch duty. You and your friend are in charge of making turkey sandwiches. You both can make 1 sandwich in 2 minutes. Your friend arrives 10 minutes earlier and starts making sandwiches.

a. Write equations that model the number of sandwiches made as a function of the number of minutes it takes you and your friend to each make sandwiches.

b. How many sandwiches will each of you make in 20 minutes?   you: 10 sandwiches; your friend: 15 sandwiches

c. How are the graphs of the equations from part (a) related? *Justify* your answer.   The graphs are parallel; they have the same slope but different *y*-intercepts.

LESSON 5.6 — Practice B
For use with pages 325–331

Tell whether x and y show a *positive correlation*, a *negative correlation*, or relatively no correlation.

1.

2.

3.
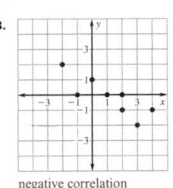

relatively no correlation   positive correlation   negative correlation

Make a scatter plot of the data. Draw a line of fit. Write an equation for the line.

4.
x	-2	-1	0	1	2	3
y	4	2	1	-2	-1	-2

Answers will vary.

5.
x	0	0	0.5	1.5	2	2.5
y	-4	-3	-1.5	1	3	4

Answers will vary.

6.
x	-3	-2	-1	0	1	2
y	1	-1	0	-2	-4	-5

Answers will vary.

7.
x	0	4	3	2	1	0
y	-3	-2	0	-1	1	1

Answers will vary.

LESSON 5.6 — Practice B *continued*
For use with pages 325–331

Make a scatter plot of the data. *Describe* the correlation of the data. If possible, fit a line to the data and write an equation of the line.

8.
x	-2	-2	-1	0	1	1	2
y	-4	-3	-2	-1	0	2	1

positive correlation
Answers will vary.

9.
x	-4	-3	-2	-2	-1	0	1
y	7	5	6	3	4	2	1

negative correlation
Answers will vary.

10. **Thermostat** The table shows the thermostat setting (in units called gas marks) on a British gas oven and the corresponding temperature in degrees Celsius.

Setting (gas mark)	2	3	4	5	6	7	8
Temperature (°C)	150	160	180	190	200	220	230

a. Make a scatter plot of the data where *x* represents the thermostat setting (in gas marks) and *y* represents the temperature (in degrees Celsius).

b. *Describe* the correlation of the data.   positive correlation

c. An oven set to gas mark 10 heats to a temperature of 260°C. Does this fit the trend shown by your scatter plot? *Explain* your reasoning.   Yes; tshe temperature increases as the setting increases.

11. **Fruits** The table shows the amount of energy (in kilocalories) and amount of carbohydrates (in grams) in a 100-gram serving of different fruits.

Fruit	Apple	Banana	Blueberries	Kiwi	Pear	Strawberries	Mango
Energy (kcal)	59	92	56	61	59	30	65
Carbohydrates (g)	15.25	23.43	14.13	14.88	15.11	7.02	17

a. Make a scatter plot of the data where *x* represents the energy (in kilocalories) and *y* represents the carbohydrates (in grams).

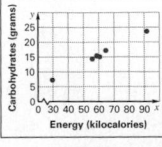

b. *Describe* the correlation of the data.   positive correlation

c. A 100-gram serving of an avocado contains 161 kilocalories of energy and 7.39 grams of carbohydrates. Does an avocado fit the trend shown by your scatter plot? *Explain* your reasoning.   No; the number of carbohydrates appears to increase as the number of kilocalories increases.

5 Lesson Practice Level B

Make a scatter plot of the data. Find the equation of the best-fitting line. Approximate the value of *y* for *x* = 3.

1.

x	−1	0	1	2	4
y	3	3	1	0	−3

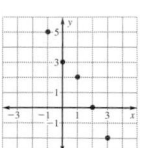
Answers will vary.

2.

x	−1	0	1	2	4
y	−1	1	2	1	5

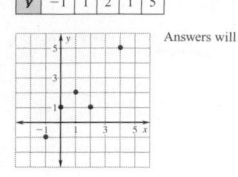
Answers will vary.

Make a scatter plot of the data. Find the equation of the best-fitting line. Approximate the value of *y* for *x* = 5.

3.

x	−1	0	1	2	3
y	5	3	2	0	−2

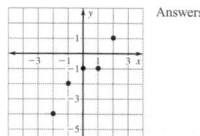
Answers will vary.

4.

x	−5	−3	−1	1	2
y	−4	−2	−1	1	0

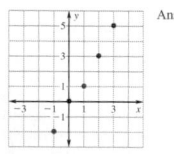
Answers will vary.

5.

x	−2	−1	0	1	2
y	−4	−2	−1	−1	1

Answers will vary.

6.

x	−1	0	1	2	3
y	−2	0	1	3	5

Answers will vary.

Find the zero of the function.

7. $f(x) = 16x − 4$ 0.25

8. $f(x) = 2 − 4x$ 0.5

9. $f(x) = 0.5x + 5$ −10

10. $f(x) = −0.1x − 3$ −30

11. $f(x) = \frac{3}{4}x − 3$ 4

12. $f(x) = −\frac{2}{5}x + 4$ 10

13. $f(x) = 0.25x + 0.5$ −2

14. $f(x) = 9 − 0.7x$ $\frac{90}{7}$

15. $f(x) = 1.2x + 10$ $−\frac{25}{3}$

16. $f(x) = \frac{1}{2}x − 6$ 12

17. $f(x) = −\frac{2}{5}x − 4$ −10

18. $f(x) = −0.8x + 15$ 18.75

19. $f(x) = 1.25x − 5$ 4

20. $f(x) = 6 − 0.2x$ 30

21. $f(x) = 2.5x − 3$ 1.2

22. Profit The table shows the monthly profit of a small company.

Month	January	February	March	April	May
Profit (dollars)	1200	1250	1400	1380	1450

a. Make a scatter plot of the data. Let *x* represent the number of months since January and let *y* represent the profit.

b. Find an equation that models the profit (in dollars) as a function of the number of months since January.   Answers will vary.

c. Approximate the profit in August.   Answers will vary.

23. Escape Velocity The table shows several planet diameters and escape velocities. The escape velocity is the velocity at which an object has to travel in order to escape the effect of a planet's gravity.

Planet	Mercury	Uranus	Earth	Mars	Venus
Diameter (km)	4879	51,118	12,756	6794	12,104
Escape velocity (km/sec)	4.3	21.3	11.186	5.03	10.36

a. Make a scatter plot of the data. Let *x* represent the diameter of the planet and let *y* represent the escape velocity.

b. Find an equation that models the escape velocity (in kilometers per second) as a function of the diameter (in kilometers).   Answers will vary.

c. Approximate the escape velocity of Neptune, which has a diameter of 49,528 kilometers.
Answers will vary.

CHAPTER 5 — Quiz 1
For use after Lessons 5.1–5.4

Write an equation in slope-intercept form of the line that passes through the given point and has the given slope m.

1. $(2, 3)$; $m = 2$

2. $(5, -4)$; $m = -1$

3. $(6, 2)$; $m = -\frac{1}{2}$

4. $(-3, -1)$; $m = \frac{4}{5}$

Write an equation in point-slope form of the line that passes through the given points.

5. $(2, -2)$, $(5, 7)$

6. $(6, 4)$, $(2, 1)$

Write an equation in standard form of the line that passes through the given points.

7. $(0, 3)$, $(2, -3)$

8. $(1, -1)$, $(4, 2)$

9. A racquetball club charges $10 for a one-month trial membership. After the trial month, the regular membership fee is $12 per month. Write an equation that gives the total cost of a membership C as a function of the length of membership m (in months).

10. Use your equation from Exercise 9 to find the total cost of membership after 8 months.

Answers

1. $y = 2x - 1$

2. $y = -x + 1$

3. $y = -\frac{1}{2}x + 5$

4. $y = \frac{4}{5}x + \frac{7}{5}$

5. $y + 2 = 3(x - 2)$ or $y - 7 = 3(x - 5)$

6. $y - 4 = \frac{3}{4}(x - 6)$ or $y - 1 = \frac{3}{4}(x - 2)$

7. $3x + y = 3$

8. $x - y = 2$

9. $C = 12(m - 1) + 10$

10. $94

CHAPTER 5 — Quiz 2
For use after Lessons 5.5–5.7

Write an equation of the line that passes through the given point and is parallel to the given line.

1. $(1, -2)$, $-5x + y = 9$

2. $(-3, -4)$, $2y = 4 + 3x$

Write an equation of the line that passes through the given point and is perpendicular to the given line.

3. $(5, -8)$, $y = \frac{5}{2}x + 4$

4. $(2, -3)$, $6y = -2x + 1$

Determine which of the following lines, if any, are parallel or perpendicular.

5. Line a: $3y + x = 6$, Line b: $y = 3x + 2$, Line c: $3x + y = 0$

6. Line a: $y = -\frac{4}{5}x - 2$, Line b: $y = -\frac{5}{4}x + 7$, Line c: $5y = -4x + 5$

Tell whether x and y show a *positive correlation*, a *negative correlation*, or *relatively no correlation*.

7.

8.

Find the zero of the function.

9. $f(x) = -13x + 52$

10. $f(x) = \frac{1}{6}x - 3$

Answers

1. $y = 5x - 7$

2. $y = \frac{3}{2}x + \frac{1}{2}$

3. $y = -\frac{2}{5}x - 6$

4. $y = 3x - 9$

5. Lines a and b are perpendicular.

6. Lines a and c are parallel.

7. relatively no correlation

8. negative correlation

9. 4

10. 18

CHAPTER 5 — Chapter Test B
For use after Chapter 5

Write an equation in slope-intercept form of the line shown.

1.

2.

In Exercises 3 and 4, use the following information.

A delivery service charges a base price for an overnight delivery of a package plus an extra charge for each pound the package weighs. A customer is billed $22.85 for shipping a 3-pound package and $40 for shipping a 10-pound package.

3. Write an equation that gives the total cost of shipping a package as a function of the weight of the package.

4. Find the cost of shipping a 15-pound package.

Find the missing coefficient in the equation of the line that passes through the given point.

5. $Ax + y = 3$; $(2, -5)$

6. $3x + By = -1$; $(2, 7)$

Graph the equation.

7. $y - 2 = \frac{2}{3}(x - 4)$

8. $y + 4 = -3(x + 2)$

In Exercises 9 and 10, use the table.

x	2	4	6	9	11
y	-3	5	13	25	33

9. Explain why the data can be modeled by a linear equation.

10. Write an equation in point-slope form that relates y to x.

Answers

1. $y = \frac{4}{3}x - 5$

2. $y = -x - 1$

3. $y = 2.45x + 15.50$

4. $52.25

5. $A = 4$

6. $B = -1$

7. See left.

8. See left.

9. The y-values increase at a constant rate of 4 for each x-value.

10. *Sample answer:* $y + 3 = 4(x - 2)$

CHAPTER 5 — Chapter Test B *continued*
For use after Chapter 5

Write an equation in standard form of the line that passes through the given point and has the given slope m or that passes through the given points.

11. $(-4, 3)$, $m = \frac{1}{2}$

12. $(2, -3)$, $m = -4$

13. $(-2, -1)$, $(2, -6)$

14. $(-2, 5)$, $(3, 5)$

In Exercises 15 and 16, use the following information.

A piggy bank contains only nickels and quarters. The total value in the bank is $3.80.

15. Write an equation in standard form that models the possible combinations of nickels and quarters in the piggy bank.

16. List two of these possible combinations.

17. Write an equation of the line that passes through the point $(-4, -1)$ and is (a) parallel to and (b) perpendicular to the line $2x + 7y = 14$.

In Exercises 18–22, use the table.

Fat (g)	31	39	19	34	43	39	35
Calories	580	680	410	590	660	640	570

18. Make a scatter plot of the data.

19. Describe the correlation.

20. Use technology to find the equation of the best-fitting line for the data.

21. Graph the best-fitting line for the data on the scatter plot.

22. Predict the number of calories in a hamburger that contains 34 grams of fat.

Answers

11. $y = \frac{1}{2}x + 5$

12. $4x + y = 5$

13. $5x + 4y = -14$

14. $y = 5$

15. $0.05n + 0.25q = 3.80$

16. *Sample answers:* 26 nickels and 10 quarters; 1 nickel and 15 quarters

17. Parallel: $y = -\frac{2}{7}x - \frac{15}{7}$; Perpendicular: $y = \frac{7}{2}x + 13$

18. See left.

19. The scatter plot shows a positive correlation. As the grams of fat increase, the number of calories tends to increase.

20. $y = 11x + 211$

21. See left.

22. 585 calories

Assessment

Multiple Choice

1. Which equation is an equation of the line with a slope of -2 and a y-intercept of 4? **D**
   - **A** $y = 4x - 2$
   - **B** $y = -2x - 4$
   - **C** $y = 2x - 4$
   - **D** $y = -2x + 4$

2. Which equation represents the line shown? **A**

   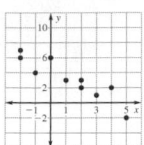

   - **A** $y = -\frac{1}{2}x - 2$
   - **B** $y = -2x - 2$
   - **C** $y = \frac{1}{2}x - 2$
   - **D** $y = -\frac{1}{2}x + 4$

3. Which function has the values $f(-3) = -11$ and $f(2) = -1$? **D**
   - **A** $f(x) = x - 8$
   - **B** $f(x) = -2x + 3$
   - **C** $f(x) = \frac{1}{3}x - 10$
   - **D** $f(x) = 2x - 5$

4. What is the equation of the line that passes through the points $(1, 8)$ and $(-2, -7)$? **B**
   - **A** $y = -x + 9$
   - **B** $y = 5x + 3$
   - **C** $y = 2x - 3$
   - **D** $y = \frac{1}{5}x - 5$

5. Which equation is an equation of the line that passes through the point $(2, -1)$ and has a slope of -1? **A**
   - **A** $y + 1 = -(x - 2)$
   - **B** $y - 1 = -(x - 2)$
   - **C** $y - 1 = -(x + 2)$
   - **D** $y + 1 = -(x + 2)$

6. Which equation is the point-slope equation of the line that passes through the points $(-2, -1)$ and $(7, -4)$? **C**
   - **A** $y + 1 = -3(x + 2)$
   - **B** $y - 1 = -\frac{1}{3}(x - 2)$
   - **C** $y + 4 = -\frac{1}{3}(x - 7)$
   - **D** $y + 4 = \frac{1}{3}(x - 7)$

7. What is the equation of the vertical line that passes through the point $(6, -2)$? **C**
   - **A** $y = -2$
   - **B** $y = 6$
   - **C** $x = 6$
   - **D** $x = -2$

8. Which equation is the standard form equation of the line that passes through the point $(-2, 0)$ and has a slope of 4? **D**
   - **A** $4x + y = 2$
   - **B** $4x - y = 8$
   - **C** $4x + y = -8$
   - **D** $-4x + y = 8$

9. The graph of the equation $Ax + 3y = -3$ is a line that passes through $(2, -5)$. What is the value of A? **B**
   - **A** 5
   - **B** 6
   - **C** 7
   - **D** 8

10. Which of the following statements is true of the given lines? **C**

    Line a: $2x + y = -4$
    Line b: $x + 2y = -10$
    Line c: $-2x + 4y = -12$
    - **A** Lines a and b are parallel.
    - **B** Lines b and c are parallel.
    - **C** Lines a and c are perpendicular.
    - **D** Lines b and c are perpendicular.

11. Which equation represents the line that passes through $(1, 1)$ and is parallel to the line passing through $(2, 3)$ and $(1, 5)$? **D**
    - **A** $y = \frac{1}{2}x + 1$
    - **B** $y = \frac{1}{2}x + 3$
    - **C** $y = -2x + 1$
    - **D** $y = -2x + 3$

12. Which equation best models the data in the scatter plot? **A**

    - **A** $y = -x + 4$
    - **B** $y = x + 5$
    - **C** $y = -5x + 2$
    - **D** $y = 3x - 2$

13. Given the function $y = -5.2x + 28$, for what value of x does $y = -206$? **C**
    - **A** -45
    - **B** 0
    - **C** 45
    - **D** 54

Gridded Answer

14. What is the zero of the function $f(x) = 4x - 5$?

    ```
    5 / 4
    ```

Short Response

15. You pay an activation fee and a monthly fee for cellular phone service. The table shows the total cost of cellular service over different numbers of months.

Months of Service	2	4	6	8	10
Total Cost (dollars)	137	209	281	353	425

   a. *Explain* why the situation can be modeled by a linear equation. See below.
   b. What is the activation fee? $65
   c. What is the monthly service fee? $36

Extended Response

16. If you sign up for a gym membership during the month of May, you are charged a joining fee of $78. Otherwise, you are charged a joining fee of $155. The monthly membership cost is $33.32.

   a. Write an equation that gives the total cost (in dollars) of membership as a function of the number of months of membership if you join in May.
   b. Write an equation that gives the total cost (in dollars) of membership as a function of the number of months of membership if you join in a month other than May. $C = 155 + 33.32m$
   c. How are the graphs of these functions related? *Explain*.
   d. After 6 months, what is the difference in total cost for a person who paid $78 to join and a person who paid $155 to join? After 12 months? *Explain*.

15. a. The situation can be modeled by a linear equation because the monthly fee is constant.
16. a. $C = 78 + 33.32m$ **c.** The graphs are parallel. The slopes of both lines are equal.
d. Regardless of the number of months, the difference will always be $77. They both pay the same amount each month. The only difference was in their joining fee.

Alternative Assessment and Math Journal

For use after Chapter 5

Journal

1. Explain the process that is used to fit a line to data.

Multi-Step Problem

2. A car wash charges a flat rate for the first 8 minutes of washing time and also charges a certain amount for each additional minute of washing time. Gina took 12 minutes to wash her car and it cost her a total of $5.00. Kris took 17 minutes to wash his truck at a total cost of $6.25.

   a. Write an equation that models the total cost of a car wash as a function of the number of minutes spent washing a vehicle.

   b. How much is the flat rate for the first 8 minutes?

   c. How much is charged for each additional minute of washing time?

   d. It took Jermaine 15 minutes to wash his car. How much did he spend?

   e. Darci has $10 to spend at the car wash. What is the maximum number of minutes she can take to wash her vehicle?

   f. What is the slope of a line parallel to the line in part (a)?

   g. What is the slope of a line perpendicular to the line in part (a)?

1. Complete answers should include mention of: making a scatter plot of the data; deciding if the data can be modeled by a line; sketching a line that follows the trend in the data; determining two points on the line drawn in order to determine the equation of the line.

2. a. $C = 0.25x + 2$ b. $4.00 c. $.25 d. $5.75 e. 32 minutes f. 0.25 g. -4

Alternative Assessment Rubric *continued*

For use after Chapter 5

Journal Solution

1. Complete answers should include mention of:
   - making a scatter plot of the data.
   - deciding if the data can be modeled by a line.
   - sketching a line that follows the trend in the data.
   - determining two points on the line drawn in order to determine the equation of the line.

Multi-Step Problem Solution

2. a. $C = 0.25x + 2$
   b. $4.00
   c. $.25
   d. $5.75
   e. 32 minutes
   f. 0.25
   g. -4

Multi-Step Problem Rubric

4 The student answers all parts of the problem correctly and completely. The student shows all work. The student's work is neat.

3 The student answers all parts of the problem. The student's work may contain one or two errors in the calculations or equation. The student shows most work. The student's work is neat.

2 The student answers all parts of the problem, but there are more than two errors in the calculations or equation. The student shows some work. The student's work is sloppy.

1 The student does not complete all parts of the problem. The student's work has several errors in the calculations and equation. The student's work is sloppy, or no work is shown.

Main Ideas

In Chapter 5, students write equations of lines in slope-intercept form given three situations: the slope and y-intercept; the slope and a point; or two points. Also, they write and graph equations using the slope and a point, using a graph of the line, or using real-world data. They write equations of lines in standard form, and use their equations to solve real-world problems. They write and find equations of lines parallel or perpendicular to a given line. They make scatter plots of data and use a line of fit to model and interpret the data. They perform linear regression to find the best-fitting line for data, and make predictions using the graph and the equation.

Prerequisite Skills

- Evaluating functions
- Finding the slope of lines
- Finding the y-intercept of lines

Additional resources for reviewing prerequisite skills are:

- Skills Review Handbook, pp. 909–937
- @HomeTutor

5 Writing Linear Equations

5.1 Write Linear Equations in Slope-Intercept Form

5.2 Use Linear Equations in Slope-Intercept Form

5.3 Write Linear Equations in Point-Slope Form

5.4 Write Linear Equations in Standard Form

5.5 Write Equations of Parallel and Perpendicular Lines

5.6 Fit a Line to Data

5.7 Predict with Linear Models

Before

In previous chapters, you learned the following skills, which you'll use in Chapter 5: evaluating functions and finding the slopes and y-intercepts of lines.

Prerequisite Skills

VOCABULARY CHECK

Copy and complete the statement.

1. In the equation $y = mx + b$, the value of m is the $\underline{\ ?\ }$ of the graph of the equation. **slope**

2. In the equation $y = mx + b$, the value of b is the $\underline{\ ?\ }$ of the graph of the equation. **y-intercept**

3. Two lines are $\underline{\ ?\ }$ if their slopes are equal. **parallel**

SKILLS CHECK

Find the slope of the line that passes through the points.
(Review p. 235 for 5.1–5.6.)

4. $(4, 5), (2, 3)$ **1**

5. $(0, -6), (8, 0)$ $\frac{3}{4}$

6. $(0, 0), (-1, 2)$ **−2**

Identify the slope and the y-intercept of the line with the equation.
(Review p. 244 for 5.1–5.6.)

7. $y = x + 1$ **1, 1**

8. $y = \frac{3}{4}x - 6$ $\frac{3}{4}, -6$

9. $y = -\frac{2}{5}x - 2$ $-\frac{2}{5}, -2$

Evaluate the function when $x = -2, 0,$ and 4. *(Review p. 262 for 5.7.)*

10. $f(x) = x - 10$
    −12, −10, −6

11. $f(x) = 2x + 4$
    0, 4, 12

12. $f(x) = -5x - 7$
    3, −7, −27

@HomeTutor Prerequisite skills practice at classzone.com

Chapter Planning Guide

Chapter 5 Resource Book
- Teaching Guide/Lesson Plan (pp. 3, 14, 24, 38, 50, 60, 74)
- Project with Rubric (p. 90)

Assessment and Intervention
- Assessment Book (pp. 61–74)
- Benchmark Tests
- Reteaching and Remediation Book

Interactive Technology
- Easy Planner
- Power Presentations CD-ROM
- Activity Generator CD-ROM
- Animated Algebra
- Test Generator CD-ROM
- Online Quizzes
- eWorkbook
- eEdition
- @HomeTutor

Resources for English Learners
- Quick Reference for English Learners
- Spanish Study Guide
- Multi-Language Visual Glossary
- Student Resources in Spanish

In Chapter 5, you will apply the big ideas listed below and reviewed in the Chapter Summary on page 344. You will also use the key vocabulary listed below.

Big Ideas

① Writing linear equations in a variety of forms
② Using linear models to solve problems
③ Modeling data with a line of fit

KEY VOCABULARY
- point-slope form, *p. 302*
- converse, *p. 319*
- perpendicular, *p. 320*
- scatter plot, *p. 325*

- correlation, *p. 325*
- line of fit, *p. 326*
- best-fitting line, *p. 335*
- linear regression, *p. 335*

- interpolation, *p. 335*
- extrapolation, *p. 336*
- zero of a function, *p. 337*

Why?

You can use linear equations to solve problems involving a constant rate of change. For example, you can write an equation that models how traffic delays affected excess fuel consumption over time.

Animated Algebra

The animation illustrated below for Exercise 40 on p. 307 helps you to answer the question: In what year was a certain amount of excess fuel consumed?

Find the year in which the given amount of excess fuel was consumed.

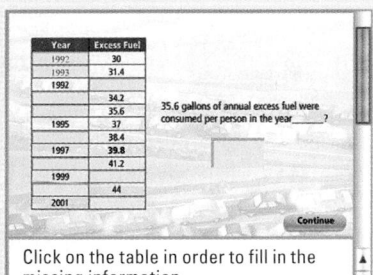

Click on the table in order to fill in the missing information.

Animated Algebra at classzone.com

Other animations for Chapter 5: pages 283, 303, 307, 311, 322, 327, and 335

1 PLAN AND PREPARE

Explore the Concept
- Students model a linear relationship using the perimeter formula.
- This activity leads into the study of writing linear equations in slope-intercept form in Example 5 in Lesson 5.1.

Materials
Each student or pair of students will need:
- 8.5 by 11-inch sheet of paper
- inch ruler

Recommended Time
Work activity: 10 min
Discuss results: 5 min

Grouping
Students can work individually or in pairs. If students work in pairs, one can measure and fold the paper and the other can find the paper's perimeter and record the data.

2 TEACH

Key Questions
- What are the independent and dependent variables? **Width of fold; perimeter**
- What is the starting value of the perimeter? **39 in.**
- What happens to the perimeter as the width of the fold increases by one inch? **It decreases by 2 inches.**

Key Discovery
Use a constant rate of change and a starting value to describe a linear relationship.

3 ASSESS AND RETEACH

How do you find the perimeter if the fold is 8 inches? **Multiply 8 by −2 and add 39 to get 23 inches.**

5.1 Modeling Linear Relationships

MATERIALS · 8.5 inch by 11 inch piece of paper · inch ruler

QUESTION How can you model a linear relationship?

You know that the perimeter of a rectangle is given by the formula $P = 2\ell + 2w$. In this activity, you will find a linear relationship using that formula.

EXPLORE Find perimeters of rectangles

STEP 1 *Find perimeter*
Find the perimeter of a piece of paper that is 8.5 inches wide and 11 inches long. Record the result in a table like the one shown.

STEP 2 *Change paper size*
Measure 1 inch from a short edge of the paper. Fold over 1 inch of the paper. You now have a rectangle with the same width and a different length than the original piece of paper. Find the perimeter of this new rectangle and record it in your table.

STEP 3 *Find additional perimeters*
Unfold the paper and repeat Step 2, this time folding the paper 2 inches from a short edge. Find the perimeter of this rectangle and record the result in your table. Repeat with a fold of 3 inches and a fold of 4 inches.

Width of fold (inches)	Perimeter of rectangle (inches)
0	39
1	?
2	?
3	?
4	?

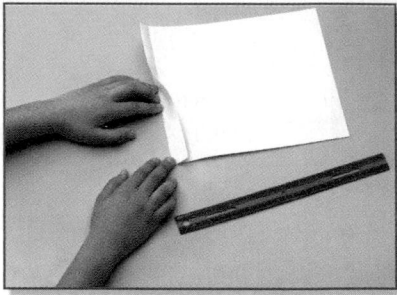

DRAW CONCLUSIONS Use your observations to complete these exercises

1. What were the length and the width of the piece of paper before it was folded? By how much did these dimensions change with each fold? **11 in., 8.5 in.; length: reduced by 1 in., width: did not change**

2. What was the perimeter of the piece of paper before it was folded? By how much did the perimeter change with each fold? **39 in.; reduced by 2 in.**

3. Use the values from your table to predict the perimeter of the piece of paper after a fold of 5 inches. *Explain* your reasoning.
29 in.; with each 1 inch fold, the perimeter is reduced by 2 inches.

4. Write a rule you could use to find the perimeter of the piece of paper after a fold of n inches. Use the data in the table to show that this rule gives accurate results. **39 − 2n; 39 − (2)(1) = 37; 39 − (2)(2) = 35; 39 − (2)(3) = 33; 39 − (2)(4) = 31**

282 Chapter 5 Writing Linear Equations

5.1 Write Linear Equations in Slope-Intercept Form

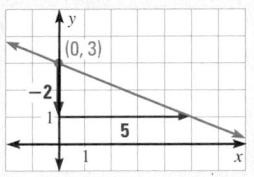

Before   You graphed equations of lines.

Now   You will write equations of lines.

Why?   So you can model distances in sports, as in Ex. 52.

Key Vocabulary
• y-intercept, *p. 225*
• slope, *p. 235*
• slope-intercept form, *p. 244*

Recall that the graph of an equation in slope-intercept form, $y = mx + b$, is a line with a slope of m and a y-intercept of b. You can use this form to write an equation of a line if you know its slope and y-intercept.

EXAMPLE 1   Use slope and y-intercept to write an equation

Write an equation of the line with a slope of −2 and a y-intercept of 5.

$y = mx + b$ Write slope-intercept form.

$y = -x + 5$ Substitute −2 for *m* and 5 for *b*.

EXAMPLE 2   Standardized Test Practice

Which equation represents the line shown?

(A) $y = -\frac{2}{5}x + 3$ **(B)** $y = -\frac{5}{2}x + 3$

(C) $y = -\frac{2}{5}x + 1$ **(D)** $y = 3x + \frac{2}{5}$

ELIMINATE CHOICES
In Example 2, you can eliminate choices C and D because the y-intercepts of the graphs of these equations are not 3.

The slope of the line is $\dfrac{\text{rise}}{\text{run}} = \dfrac{-2}{5} = -\dfrac{2}{5}$.

The line crosses the y-axis at (0, 3). So, the y-intercept is 3.

$y = mx + b$ Write slope-intercept form.

$y = -\frac{2}{5}x + 3$ Substitute $-\frac{2}{5}$ for *m* and 3 for *b*.

▸ The correct answer is A.   (A) (B) (C) (D)

Animated Algebra at classzone.com

GUIDED PRACTICE   for Examples 1 and 2

Write an equation of the line with the given slope and y-intercept.

1. Slope is 8; y-intercept is −7.
   $y = 8x - 7$

2. Slope is $\frac{3}{4}$; y-intercept is −3.
   $y = \frac{3}{4}x - 3$

① PLAN AND PREPARE

Warm-Up Exercises
🗐 Transparency Available
Find the slope of the line that passes through the points.

1. (2, −1), (4, 0) $\frac{1}{2}$

2. (−1, −3), (1, 5) **4**

3. A landscape architect charges $75 for a consulting fee and $30 per hour. Write an equation that shows the cost *C* as a function of time *t* (in hours). $C = 30t + 75$

Notetaking Guide
🗐 Transparency Available
Promotes interactive learning and notetaking skills, pp. 100–102.

Pacing
Basic: 1 day
Average: 1 day
Advanced: 1 day
Block: 0.5 block with 5.2
• See *Teaching Guide/Lesson Plan*.

② FOCUS AND MOTIVATE

Essential Question
Big Idea 1, p. 281
How do you write an equation of a line in slope-intercept form? **Tell** students they will learn how to answer this question by using the slope and y-intercept or two points to write an equation of the line.

NCTM STANDARDS
Standard 2: Use models to represent relationships

Standard 4: Understand the units of measurement

Resource Planning Guide

Chapter Resource Book
• Teaching Guide/Lesson Plan (pp. 3–4)
• Activity Master (p. 5)
• Practice levels A, B, C (pp. 6–8)
• Study Guide (pp. 9–10)
• Catch-up for Absent Students (p. 11)
• Application (p. 12)
• Challenge (p. 13)

Workbooks
• Notetaking Guide (pp. 100–102)
• Practice Workbook (pp. 67–68)

Teaching Options
• **Power Presentations CD-ROM** provides dynamic electronic teaching resources for the classroom.
• **Activity Generator CD-ROM** provides editable activities for all ability levels.

Interactive Technology
• Easy Planner
• Power Presentations CD-ROM
• Activity Generator CD-ROM
• Animated Algebra
• Test Generator CD-ROM
• Online Quiz
• eWorkbook
• eEdition
• @HomeTutor

Resources for English Learners
• Quick Reference for English Learners
• Spanish Study Guide
• Multi-Language Visual Glossary
• Student Resources in Spanish

See also the *Algebra 1 Toolkit* for more strategies for meeting individual needs.

❸ TEACH

Extra Example 1

Write an equation of the line with a slope of 4 and a y-intercept of -3.
$y = 4x - 3$

Extra Example 2

Which equation represents the line shown? **B**

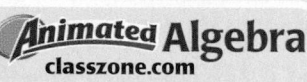

Ⓐ $y = \dfrac{3}{5}x - 2$

Ⓑ $y = \dfrac{5}{3}x - 2$

Ⓒ $y = -2x + \dfrac{3}{5}$

Ⓓ $-2x + \dfrac{5}{3}$

An **Animated Algebra** activity is available on-line for **Example 2**. This activity is also available on the **Power Presentations CD-ROM**.

Extra Example 3

Write an equation of the line shown.

$y = -\dfrac{3}{4}x + 2$

USING TWO POINTS If you know the point where a line crosses the y-axis and any other point on the line, you can write an equation of the line.

EXAMPLE 3 Write an equation of a line given two points

Write an equation of the line shown.

Solution

STEP 1 Calculate the slope.

$$m = \frac{y_2 - y_1}{x_2 - x_1} = \frac{-1 - (-5)}{3 - 0} = \frac{4}{3}$$

STEP 2 Write an equation of the line. The line crosses the y-axis at $(0, -5)$. So, the y-intercept is -5.

$y = mx + b$ Write slope-intercept form.

$y = \dfrac{4}{3}x \ \ 5$ Substitute $\dfrac{4}{3}$ for m and -5 for b.

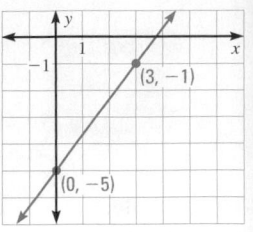

WRITING FUNCTIONS Recall that the graphs of linear functions are lines. You can use slope-intercept form to write a linear function.

REVIEW FUNCTIONS
For help with using function notation, see p. 262.

EXAMPLE 4 Write a linear function

Write an equation for the linear function f with the values $f(0) = 5$ and $f(4) = 17$.

Solution

STEP 1 Write $f(0) = 5$ as $(0, 5)$ and $f(4) = 17$ as $(4, 17)$.

STEP 2 Calculate the slope of the line that passes through $(0, 5)$ and $(4, 17)$.

$$m = \frac{y_2 - y_1}{x_2 - x_1} = \frac{17 - 5}{4 - 0} = \frac{12}{4} = 3$$

STEP 3 Write an equation of the line. The line crosses the y-axis at $(0, 5)$. So, the y-intercept is 5.

$y = mx + b$ Write slope-intercept form.

$y = 3x + 5$ Substitute 3 for m and 5 for b.

▶ The function is $f(x) = 3x + 5$.

✓ **GUIDED PRACTICE** for Examples 3 and 4

3. Write an equation of the line shown. $y = -\dfrac{1}{2}x + 1$

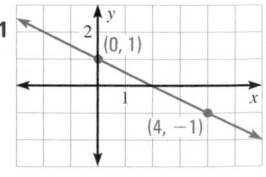

Write an equation for the linear function f with the given values.

4. $f(0) = -2, f(8) = 4$ $y = \dfrac{3}{4}x - 2$

5. $f(-3) = 6, f(0) = 5$ $y = -\dfrac{1}{3}x + 5$

READING

The value b is a starting value in a real-world situation modeled by $y = mx + b$, because when $x = 0$, the value of y is b.

MODELING REAL-WORLD SITUATIONS When a quantity y changes at a constant rate with respect to a quantity x, you can use the equation $y = mx + b$ to model the relationship. The value of m is the constant rate of change, and the value of b is an initial, or starting, value for y.

EXAMPLE 5 Solve a multi-step problem

RECORDING STUDIO A recording studio charges musicians an initial fee of $50 to record an album. Studio time costs an additional $35 per hour.

a. Write an equation that gives the total cost of an album as a function of studio time (in hours).

b. Find the total cost of recording an album that takes 10 hours of studio time.

Solution

a. The cost changes at a constant rate, so you can write an equation in slope-intercept form to model the total cost.

STEP 1 **Identify** the rate of change and the starting value.

Rate of change, m: cost per hour
Starting value, b: initial fee

STEP 2 **Write** a verbal model. Then write the equation.

Total cost (dollars)	=	Cost per hour (dollars per hour)	·	Studio time (hours)	+	Initial fee (dollars)
C	=	35	·	t	+	50

CHECK Use unit analysis to check the equation.

$$\text{dollars} = \frac{\text{dollars}}{\cancel{\text{hour}}} \cdot \cancel{\text{hours}} + \text{dollars} \checkmark$$

▸ The total cost C is given by the function $C = 35t + 50$ where t is the studio time (in hours).

b. Evaluate the function for $t = 10$.

$C = 35(10) + 50 = 400$ **Substitute 10 for t and simplify.**

▸ The total cost for 10 hours of studio time is $400.

✓ **GUIDED PRACTICE** for Example 5

6. **WHAT IF?** In Example 5, suppose the recording studio raises its initial fee to $75 and charges $40 per hour for studio time.

   a. Write an equation that gives the total cost of an album as a function of studio time (in hours). $C = 40t + 75$

   b. Find the total cost of recording an album that takes 10 hours of studio time. $475

Differentiated Instruction

Inclusion Students may have difficulty working with equations when the variables are not x and y. To graph the equation in **Example 5**, have students write the following two equations.

$C = 35t + 50$

$y = 35x + 50$

Because t matches up with x and C matches up with y, it is easy to explain why t is plotted on the x-axis and C is plotted on the y-axis.
See also the *Algebra 1 Toolkit* for more strategies.

5.1 EXERCISES

HOMEWORK KEY

○ = **WORKED-OUT SOLUTIONS**
on p. WS1 for Exs. 11, 19, and 47

★ = **STANDARDIZED TEST PRACTICE**
Exs. 2, 9, 40, 43, 48, and 50

◆ = **MULTIPLE REPRESENTATIONS**
Ex. 49

④ PRACTICE AND APPLY

Assignment Guide

📑 Answer Transparencies
available for all exercises

Basic:
Day 1: EP p. 941 Exs. 33–36
pp. 286–289
Exs. 1–5, 9–12, 16–20, 24–26, 30–32,
39, 40, 45–49, 53–63 odd

Average:
Day 1: pp. 286–289
Exs. 1, 2, 6–9, 13–17, 21–24, 26, 28,
33–35, 39–43, 46–51, 56, 57, 62, 63

Advanced:
Day 1: pp. 286–289
Exs. 1, 7–9, 13–15, 21–23, 27–29,
36–44*, 47–52*, 58, 64

Block:
pp. 286–289
Exs. 1, 2, 6–9, 13–17, 21–24, 26, 28,
33–35, 39–43, 46–51, 56, 57, 62,
63 (with 5.2)

Differentiated Instruction

See *Algebra 1 Best Practices Toolkit*
for suggestions on addressing the
needs of a diverse classroom.

Homework Check

For a quick check of student understanding of key concepts, go over
the following exercises:

Basic: 4, 10, 20, 32, 45
Average: 6, 13, 26, 34, 46
Advanced: 8, 14, 28, 38, 48

Extra Practice

- Student Edition, p. 942
- Chapter 5 Resource Book:
  Practice levels A, B, C, pp. 6–8

Practice Worksheet

An easily-readable reduced
practice page (with answers)
for this lesson can be found
on p. 280C.

SKILL PRACTICE

A 1. **VOCABULARY** Copy and complete: The ratio of the rise to the run
between any two points on a nonvertical line is called the __?__. **slope**

2. ★ **WRITING** *Explain* how you can use slope-intercept form to write an
equation of a line given its slope and *y*-intercept. **You can substitute the slope for *m* and
the *y*-intercept for *b* to get the equation of the line.**

EXAMPLE 1
on p. 283
for Exs. 3–9, 16

WRITING EQUATIONS Write an equation of the line with the given slope and
y-intercept.

3. slope: 2 $y = 2x + 9$
   y-intercept: 9

4. slope: 1 $y = x + 5$
   y-intercept: 5

5. slope: −3 $y = -3x$
   y-intercept: 0

6. slope: −7 $y = -7x + 1$
   y-intercept: 1

7. slope: $\frac{2}{3}$ $y = \frac{2}{3}x - 9$
   y-intercept: −9

8. slope: $\frac{3}{4}$ $y = \frac{3}{4}x - 6$
   y-intercept: −6

9. ★ **MULTIPLE CHOICE** Which equation represents the line with a slope
of −1 and a *y*-intercept of 2? **A**

   A $y = -x + 2$ **B** $y = 2x - 1$ **C** $y = x - 2$ **D** $y = 2x + 1$

EXAMPLE 2
on p. 283
for Exs. 10–15,
17

WRITING EQUATIONS Write an equation of the line shown.

10.
    $y = x - 4$

11.
    $y = -\frac{1}{2}x$

12.
    $y = -3x + 4$

13.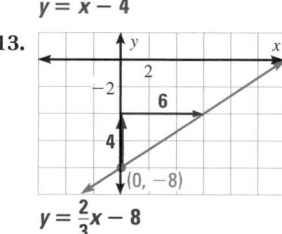
    $y = \frac{2}{3}x - 8$

14.
    $y = -x - 3$

15.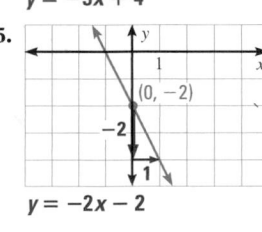
    $y = -2x - 2$

16. The given
slope and
y-intercept were
interchanged
in the slope-
intercept form of
the equation;
$y = 2x + 7$.

16. **ERROR ANALYSIS** *Describe* and correct the error in writing an
equation of the line with a slope of 2 and a *y*-intercept of 7.

$y = 7x + 2$ ✗

17. **ERROR ANALYSIS** *Describe* and
correct the error in writing an
equation of the line shown.

$slope = \frac{0 - 4}{0 - 5} = \frac{-4}{-5} = \frac{4}{5}$

✗ $y = \frac{4}{5}x + 4$

The slope should be $\frac{0 - 4}{5 - 0}$,

$y = -\frac{4}{5}x + 4$.

EXAMPLE 3
on p. 284
for Exs. 18–29

USING A GRAPH Write an equation of the line shown.

18.

$y = \frac{1}{3}x + 2$

19.

$y = 4x + 4$

20.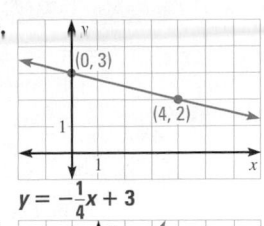

$y = -\frac{1}{4}x + 3$

21.

$y = -\frac{4}{3}x$

22.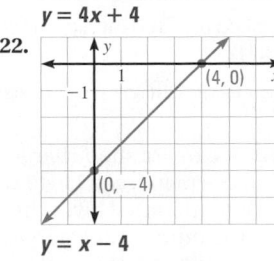

$y = x - 4$

23.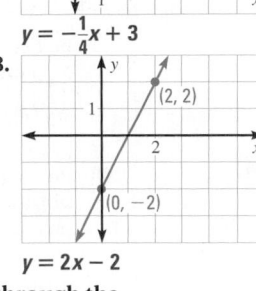

$y = 2x - 2$

USING TWO POINTS Write an equation of the line that passes through the given points.

24. $(-3, 1)$, $(0, -8)$
$y = -3x - 8$

25. $(2, -7)$, $(0, -5)$
$y = -x - 5$

26. $(2, -4)$, $(0, -4)$
$y = -4$

27. $(0, 4)$, $(8, 3.5)$
$y = -0.0625x + 4$

28. $(0, 5)$, $(1.5, 1)$
$y = -\frac{8}{3}x + 5$

29. $(-6, 0)$, $(0, -24)$
$y = -4x - 24$

EXAMPLE 4
on p. 284
for Exs. 30–38

WRITING FUNCTIONS Write an equation for the linear function f with the given values.

30. $f(0) = 2$, $f(2) = 4$
$y = x + 2$

31. $f(0) = 7$, $f(3) = 1$
$y = -2x + 7$

32. $f(0) = -2$, $f(4) = -3$
$y = -\frac{1}{4}x - 2$

33. $f(0) = -1$, $f(5) = -5$
$y = -\frac{4}{5}x - 1$

34. $f(-2) = 6$, $f(0) = -4$
$y = -5x - 4$

35. $f(-6) = -1$, $f(0) = 3$
$y = \frac{2}{3}x + 3$

36. $f(4) = 13$, $f(0) = 21$
$y = -2x + 21$

37. $f(0) = 9$, $f(3) = 0$
$y = -3x + 9$

38. $f(0.2) = 1$, $f(0) = 0.6$
$y = 2x + 0.6$

B **39. VISUAL THINKING** Write an equation of the line with a slope that is half the slope of the line shown and a y-intercept that is 2 less than the y-intercept of the line shown. $y = x - 3$

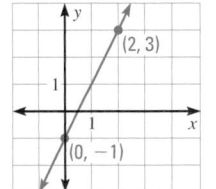

40. Sample answer: A health club offers an aerobics membership that charges $9 plus $4 per class.

40. ★ OPEN-ENDED *Describe* a real-world situation that can be modeled by the function $y = 4x + 9$.

USING A DIAGRAM OR TABLE Write an equation that represents the linear function shown in the mapping diagram or table.

41. 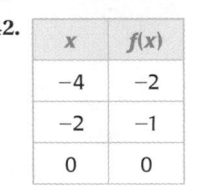 $y = -2x + 1$

42.

x	$f(x)$
-4	-2
-2	-1
0	0

$y = \frac{1}{2}x$

43. ★ WRITING A line passes through the points $(3, 5)$ and $(3, -7)$. Is it possible to write an equation of the line in slope-intercept form? *Justify* your answer. **No; the slope of the line is undefined, the equation is $x = 3$, which is not in slope-intercept form.**

C **44. CHALLENGE** Show that the equation of the line that passes through the points $(0, b)$ and $(1, b + m)$ is $y = mx + b$. *Explain* how you can be sure that the point $(-1, b - m)$ also lies on the line. **See margin.**

Avoiding Common Errors

Exercises 3–9 Students sometimes interchange the slope and the y-intercept when replacing m and b in the slope-intercept form of an equation of the line. Suggest that students double-check that m is the slope and b is the y-intercept in their equations.

Teaching Strategy

Exercises 10–15 Prior to these exercises, you may want to review how to use the ratio of rise to run to determine slope. In discussing the ratio, you might want to point out that a ratio of 4 to 4, for example, is 1, whereas a ratio of 4 to 1 is 4.

Study Strategy

Exercises 18–23 Tell students they can use the ratio of rise to run to check their slope calculations.

Reading Strategy

Exercises 30–38 Remind students that $f(x)$ is read "the value of f at x." When x in the parentheses is replaced by a number such as 3, it can be read "the value of f when x is 3."

44. Find the slope by substituting the values: $\frac{b + m - b}{1 - 0} = m$. The y-intercept is when $x = 0$, so the y-intercept is b. If you substitute $(-1, b - m)$ into the equation $y = mx + b$, you get $b - m = -m + b$ which is a true statement.

EXAMPLE 5 [A]
on p. 285
for Exs. 45–49

45. WEB SERVER The initial fee to have a website set up using a server is $48. It costs $44 per month to maintain the website.

 a. Write an equation that gives the total cost of setting up and maintaining a website as a function of the number of months it is maintained. **$C = 44m + 48$**

 b. Find the total cost of setting up and maintaining the website for 6 months. **$312**

 @HomeTutor for problem solving help at classzone.com

46. PHOTOGRAPHS A camera shop charges $3.99 for an enlargement of a photograph. Enlargements can be delivered for a charge of $1.49 per order. Write an equation that gives the total cost of an order with delivery as a function of the number of enlargements. Find the total cost of ordering 8 photograph enlargements with delivery. **$C = 3.99e + 1.49; 33.41**

 @HomeTutor for problem solving help at classzone.com

(47.) AQUARIUM Your family spends $30 for tickets to an aquarium and $3 per hour for parking. Write an equation that gives the total cost of your family's visit to the aquarium as a function of the number of hours that you are there. Find the total cost of 4 hours at the aquarium. **$C = 3h + 30; $42**

48. ★ **SHORT RESPONSE** Scientists found that the number of ant species in Clark Canyon, Nevada, increases at a rate of 0.0037 species per meter of elevation. There are approximately 3 ant species at sea level.

 a. Write an equation that gives the number of ant species as a function of the elevation (in meters). **$a = 0.0037e + 3$**

 b. Identify the dependent and independent variables in this situation.
 dependent variable: a, independent variable: e

 c. *Explain* how you can use the equation from part (a) to approximate the number of ant species at an elevation of 2 meters.
 Substitute 2 for e to get approximately 3.

[B] **49.** ◆ **MULTIPLE REPRESENTATIONS** The timeline shows the approximate total area of glaciers on Mount Kilimanjaro from 1970 to 2000.

Year	1970	1980	1990	2000
Area	5.2 km^2	4.1 km^2	3.0 km^2	1.9 km^2

 a. **Making a Table** Make a table that shows the number of years x since 1970 and the area of the glaciers y (in square kilometers). **See margin.**

 b. **Drawing a Graph** Graph the data in the table. *Explain* how you know the area of glaciers changed at a constant rate. **See margin for art; the area of the glaciers changed −1.1 square kilometers between every 10 year interval.**

 c. **Writing an Equation** Write an equation that models the area of glaciers as a function of the number of years since 1970. By how much did the area of the glaciers decrease each year from 1970 to 2000?
 $y = -0.11x + 5.2; -0.11$ km^2

◯ = **WORKED-OUT SOLUTIONS**
on p. WS1

★ = **STANDARDIZED TEST PRACTICE**

◆ = **MULTIPLE REPRESENTATIONS**

Reading Strategy

Exercise 49 Remind students to read instructions carefully. Point out in part a that x is the number of years since 1970. Tell them that this affects whether they use 0 or 1 to designate 1970 and, in turn, affects the numbers they use to designate subsequent years.

Internet Reference

Exercise 49 For more information about Mt. Kilimanjaro and its glaciers, visit nationalgeographic.com and do a search for "Mt. Kilimanjaro AND glaciers."

Mathematical Reasoning

Exercises 50–51 You may want to discuss with students how an equation of the form $y = mx + b$ can model these situations. Ask them to identify the independent and dependent variables, the values for m, and the values for b. The starting values of b may give students problems in both of these exercises. Point out that, depending on the context, a starting value may require calculation.

49a.

x (years since 1970)	y (km^2)
0	5.2
10	4.1
20	3.0
30	1.9

49b.

288

50. ★ EXTENDED RESPONSE The Harris Dam in Maine releases water into the Kennebec River. From 10:00 A.M. to 1:00 P.M. during each day of whitewater rafting season, water is released at a greater rate than usual.

Time interval	Release rate (gallons per hour)
12:00 A.M. to 10:00 A.M.	8.1 million
10:00 A.M. to 1:00 P.M.	130 million

   a. On a day during rafting season, how much water is released by 10:00 A.M.? **81 million gal**

   b. Write an equation that gives, for a day during rafting season, the total amount of water (in gallons) released as a function of the number of hours since 10:00 A.M. $y = 130{,}000{,}000h$

   c. What is the domain of the function from part (b)? *Explain.* $0 \le h \le 3$; water is only released for 3 hours after 10:00 A.M.

51. FIREFIGHTING The diagram shows the time a firefighting aircraft takes to scoop water from a lake, fly to a fire, and drop the water on the fire.

0.7 min per mile of distance to fly to fire

0.2 min to scoop water

1.8 min to drop water

   a. Model Write an equation that gives the total time (in minutes) that the aircraft takes to scoop, fly, and drop as a function of the distance (in miles) flown from the lake to the fire. $t = 0.7d + 2$

   b. Predict Find the time the aircraft takes to scoop, fly, and drop if it travels 20 miles from the lake to the fire. **16 min**

[C] **52. CHALLENGE** The elevation at which a baseball game is played affects the distance a ball travels when hit. For every increase of 1000 feet in elevation, the ball travels about 7 feet farther. Suppose a baseball travels 400 feet when hit in a ball park at sea level.

   a. Model Write an equation that gives the distance (in feet) the baseball travels as a function of the elevation of the ball park in which it is hit. $d = \frac{7}{1000}e + 400$

   b. Justify *Justify* the equation from part (a) using unit analysis. $d \text{ ft} = \frac{7}{1000} \cdot e \text{ ft} + 400 \text{ ft}$

   c. Predict If the ball were hit in exactly the same way at a park with an elevation of 3500 feet, how far would it travel? **424.5 ft**

MIXED REVIEW

Solve the equation. Check your solution.

53. $x + 11 = 6$ *(p. 134)* **−5**   **54.** $x - 7 = 13$ *(p. 134)* **20**   **55.** $0.2x = -1$ *(p. 134)* **−5**

56. $3x + 9 = 21$ *(p. 141)* **4**   **57.** $2x - 3 = 25$ *(p. 141)* **14**   **58.** $4x - 8 = -10$ *(p. 141)* **−0.5**

PREVIEW
Prepare for Lesson 5.2 in Exs. 59–64.

Find the slope of the line that passes through the points. *(p. 235)*

59. $(-4, 6), (0, -2)$ **−2**   **60.** $(-3, -2), (0, 1)$ **1**   **61.** $(5, 6), (-1, 3)$ $\frac{1}{2}$

62. $(-9, 3), (7, -1)$ $-\frac{1}{4}$ **63.** $(3, -12), (5, -7)$ $\frac{5}{2}$ **64.** $(10, 4), (-8, 2)$ $\frac{1}{9}$

EXTRA PRACTICE for Lesson 5.1, p. 942   **ONLINE QUIZ** at classzone.com   **289**

---

① PLAN AND PREPARE

Learn the Method

- Students will find the slope and the *y*-intercept of a line using a graphing calculator and then write an equation of the line.
- After the activity, students can use a graphing calculator to check their solutions in Exercises 24–38 in Lesson 5.1.

Keystroke Help

Keystrokes for several models of calculators are available in blackline format in the *Chapter 5 Resource Book*.

② TEACH

Tips for Success

In Example 1, remind students that a line with a positive slope rises from left to right and a line with a negative slope falls from left to right.

Extra Example 1

In the same viewing window, display the four lines that have slopes of −2, −1, 1, and 2 and a *y*-intercept of −3. Then use the graphs to determine which line passes through the point (1, −4). Write an equation of the line.

The line that passes through the point (1, −4) is the line with a slope of −1. An equation of the line is $y = -x - 3$.

5.1 Investigate Families of Lines

QUESTION How can you use a graphing calculator to find equations of lines using slopes and *y*-intercepts?

Recall from Chapter 4 that you can create families of lines by varying the value of either *m* or *b* in $y = mx + b$. The constants *m* and *b* are called *parameters*. Given the value of one parameter, you can determine the value of the other parameter if you also have information that uniquely identifies one member of the family of lines.

EXAMPLE 1 Find the slope of a line and write an equation

In the same viewing window, display the four lines that have slopes of −1, −0.5, 0.5, and 1 and a *y*-intercept of 2. Then use the graphs to determine which line passes through the point (12, 8). Write an equation of the line.

STEP 1 *Enter equations*

Press Y= and enter the four equations. Because the lines all have the same *y*-intercept, they constitute a family of lines and can be entered as shown.

STEP 2 *Display graphs*

Graph the equations in an appropriate viewing window. Press TRACE and use the left and right arrow keys to move along one of the lines until *x* = 12. Use the up and down arrow keys to see which line passes through (12, 8).

STEP 3 *Find the line*

The line that passes through (12, 8) is the line with a slope of 0.5. So, an equation of the line is $y = 0.5x + 2$.

PRACTICE

Display the lines that have the same *y*-intercept but different slopes, as given, in the same viewing window. Determine which line passes through the given point. Write an equation of the line.

1. Slopes: −3, −2, 2, 3; *y*-intercept: 5; point: (−3, 11) $y = -2x + 5$

2. Slopes: 4, −2.5, 2.5, 4; *y*-intercept: −1; point: (4, −11) $y = -2.5x - 1$

3. Slopes: −2, −1, 1, 2; *y*-intercept: 1.5; point: (1, 3.5) $y = 2x + 1.5$

290 Chapter 5 Writing Linear Equations

@HomeTutor
@HomeTutor
classzone.com
Keystrokes

EXAMPLE 2 Find the *y*-intercept of a line and write an equation

In the same viewing window, display the five lines that have a slope of 0.5 and *y*-intercepts of −2, −1, 0, 1, and 2. Then use the graphs to determine which line passes through the point (−2, −2). Write an equation of the line.

STEP 1 *Enter equations*	STEP 2 *Display graphs*	STEP 3 *Find the line*
Press Y= and enter the five equations. Because the lines all have the same slope, they constitute a family of lines and can be entered as shown below.	Graph the equations in an appropriate viewing window. Press TRACE and use the left and right arrow keys to move along one of the lines until *x* = −2. Use the up and down arrow keys to see which line passes through (−2, −2).	The line that passes through (−2, −2) is the line with a *y*-intercept of −1. So, an equation of the line is $y = 0.5x - 1$.

PRACTICE

Display the lines that have the same slope but different *y*-intercepts, as given, in the same viewing window. Determine which line passes through the given point. Write an equation of the line.

4. Slope: −3; *y*-intercepts: −2, −1, 0, 1, 2; point: (4, −13) $y = -3x - 1$

5. Slope: 1.5; *y*-intercepts: −2, −1, 0, 1, 2; point: (−2, −1) $y = 1.5x + 2$

6. Slope: −0.5; *y*-intercepts: −3, −1.5, 0, 1.5, 3; point: (−4, 3.5) $y = -0.5x + 1.5$

7. Slope: 4; *y*-intercepts: −3, −1, 0, 1, 3; point: (2, 5) $y = 4x - 3$

8. Slope: 2; *y*-intercepts: −6, −3, 0, 3, 6; point: (−2, −7) $y = 2x - 3$

DRAW CONCLUSIONS

9. Of all the lines having equations of the form $y = 0.5x + b$, which one passes through the point (2, 2)? *Explain* how you found your answer. $y = 0.5x + 1$; substitute 2 for *x*, 2 for *y*, and solve for *b*.

10. *Describe* a process you could use to find an equation of a line that has a slope of −0.25 and passes through the point (8, −2).
Sample answer: Substitute −0.25 for *m*, 8 for *x*, and −2 for *y* and solve for *b*.

Extra Example 2
In the same viewing window, display the five lines that have a slope of −2 and *y*-intercepts of −4, −2, 0, 2, and 4. Then use the graphs to determine which line passes through the point (−1, 2). Write an equation of the line.

The line that passes through the point (−1, 2) is the line with a *y*-intercept of 0. An equation of the line is $y = -2x$.

③ ASSESS AND RETEACH

1. Describe a process you could use to find an equation of a line that has a *y*-intercept of 1 and passes through the point (2, 4). **In the same viewing window, display graphs through (0, 1) with several slopes, such as 0.5, 1, 1.5, and 2. Then use trace to find the line that passes through (2, 4).**

2. Of all the lines having equations of the form $y = mx - 2$, which one passes through the point (3, 4)? Explain how you found your answer. **An equation of the line is $y = 2x - 2$. I first tried $y = x - 2$. That line passes through (3, 1), so in order to pass through (3, 4) I needed a greater slope. I graphed equations of lines through (0, −2) with slopes of 1.5, 2, and 2.5. I used trace to find that a line with a slope of 2 passes through (3, 4).**

1 PLAN AND PREPARE

Warm-Up Exercises
📄 Transparency Available
Find the slope of the line that passes through the points.

1. (0, −2), (1, 3) **5**

2. (3, 2), (5, −2) **−2**

3. Bill borrowed $75 from his parents. He is paying back $5 per week. Write an equation that models this situation.
$y = -5x + 75$

Notetaking Guide
📄 Transparency Available
Promotes interactive learning and notetaking skills, pp. 103–105.

Pacing
Basic: 2 days
Average: 2 days
Advanced: 2 days
Block: 0.5 block with 5.1
  0.5 block with 5.3
• See *Teaching Guide/Lesson Plan.*

2 FOCUS AND MOTIVATE

Essential Question
Big Idea 2, p. 281
How do you find the equation of a line given two points? **Tell students they will learn how to answer this question by using the slope formula and finding the y-intercept.**

NCTM STANDARDS
Standard 3: Describe spatial relationships using coordinate geometry

Standard 8: Use the language of math to express ideas

Before	You wrote an equation of a line using its slope and y-intercept.
Now	You will write an equation of a line using points on the line.
Why	So you can write a model for total cost, as in Example 5.

Key Vocabulary
• **y-intercept,** *p. 225*
• **slope,** *p. 235*
• **slope-intercept form,** *p. 244*

KEY CONCEPT   *For Your Notebook*

Writing an Equation of a Line in Slope-Intercept Form

STEP 1 Identify the slope m. You can use the slope formula to calculate the slope if you know two points on the line.

STEP 2 Find the y-intercept. You can substitute the slope and the coordinates of a point (x, y) on the line in $y = mx + b$. Then solve for b.

STEP 3 Write an equation using $y = mx + b$.

EXAMPLE 1 Write an equation given the slope and a point

Write an equation of the line that passes through the point $(-1, 3)$ and has a slope of -4.

Solution

STEP 1 Identify the slope. The slope is -4.

STEP 2 Find the y-intercept. Substitute the slope and the coordinates of the given point in $y = mx + b$. Solve for b.

$$y = mx + b \qquad \text{Write slope-intercept form.}$$
$$3 = -4(-1) + b \qquad \text{Substitute } -4 \text{ for } m, -1 \text{ for } x, \text{ and } 3 \text{ for } y.$$
$$-1 = b \qquad \text{Solve for } b.$$

STEP 3 Write an equation of the line.

$$y = mx + b \qquad \text{Write slope-intercept form.}$$
$$y = -4x - 1 \qquad \text{Substitute } -4 \text{ for } m \text{ and } -1 \text{ for } b.$$

AVOID ERRORS
When you substitute, be careful not to mix up the x- and y-values.

 GUIDED PRACTICE for Example 1

1. Write an equation of the line that passes through the point (6, 3) and has a slope of 2. $y = 2x - 9$

Resource Planning Guide

Chapter Resource Book
• Teaching Guide/Lesson Plan (pp. 14–15)
• Practice levels A, B, C (pp. 16–18)
• Study Guide (pp. 19–20)
• Catch-up for Absent Students (p. 21)
• Application (p. 22)
• Challenge (p. 23)

Workbooks
• Notetaking Guide (pp. 103–105)
• Practice Workbook (pp. 69–70)

Teaching Options
• **Power Presentations CD-ROM** provides dynamic electronic teaching resources for the classroom.
• **Activity Generator CD-ROM** provides editable activities for all ability levels.

Interactive Technology
• Easy Planner
• Power Presentations CD-ROM
• Activity Generator CD-ROM
• Animated Algebra
• Test Generator CD-ROM
• Online Quiz
• eWorkbook
• eEdition
• @HomeTutor

Resources for English Learners
• Quick Reference for English Learners
• Spanish Study Guide
• Multi-Language Visual Glossary
• Student Resources in Spanish

See also the *Algebra 1 Toolkit* for more strategies for meeting individual needs.

EXAMPLE 2 **Write an equation given two points**

EXAMPLE 2 Write an equation given two points

Write an equation of the line that passes through $(-2, 5)$ and $(2, -1)$.

Solution

STEP 1 **Calculate** the slope.

$$m = \frac{y_2 - y_1}{x_2 - x_1} = \frac{-1 - 5}{2 - (-2)} = \frac{-6}{4} = -\frac{3}{2}$$

ANOTHER WAY
You can also find the *y*-intercept using the coordinates of the other given point, $(2, -1)$:
$y = mx + b$
$-1 = -\frac{3}{2}(2) + b$
$2 = b$

STEP 2 **Find** the *y*-intercept. Use the slope and the point $(-2, 5)$.

$y = mx + b$ Write slope-intercept form.

$5 = -\frac{3}{2}(-2) + b$ Substitute $-\frac{3}{2}$ for *m*, -2 for *x*, and 5 for *y*.

$2 = b$ Solve for *b*.

STEP 3 **Write** an equation of the line.

$y = mx + b$ Write slope-intercept form.

$y = -\frac{3}{2}x + 2$ Substitute $-\frac{3}{2}$ for *m* and 2 for *b*.

★ ## EXAMPLE 3 Standardized Test Practice

Which function has the values $f(4) = 9$ and $f(-4) = -7$?

(A) $f(x) = 2x + 10$ (B) $f(x) = 2x + 1$

(C) $f(x) = 2x - 13$ (D) $f(x) = 2x - 14$

ELIMINATE CHOICES
You can also evaluate each function when $x = 4$ and $x = -4$. Eliminate any choices for which $f(4) \neq 9$ or $f(-4) \neq -7$.

STEP 1 **Calculate** the slope. Write $f(4) = 9$ as $(4, 9)$ and $f(-4) = -7$ as $(-4, -7)$.

$$m = \frac{y_2 - y_1}{x_2 - x_1} = \frac{-7 - 9}{-4 - 4} = \frac{-16}{-8} = 2$$

STEP 2 **Find** the *y*-intercept. Use the slope and the point $(4, 9)$.

$y = mx + b$ Write slope-intercept form.

$9 = 2(4) + b$ Substitute 2 for *m*, 4 for *x*, and 9 for *y*.

$1 = b$ Solve for *b*.

STEP 3 **Write** an equation for the function. Use function notation.

$f(x) = 2x + 1$ Substitute 2 for *m* and 1 for *b*.

▶ The answer is B. (A) (B) (C) (D)

✓ **GUIDED PRACTICE** for Examples 2 and 3

2. Write an equation of the line that passes through $(1, -2)$ and $(-5, 4)$. **$y = -x - 1$**

3. Write an equation for the linear function with the values $f(-2) = 10$ and $f(4) = -2$. **$y = -2x + 6$**

Motivating the Lesson

Knowing how to write a linear equation that represents a real-world situation will help you determine information about the situation. For example, if you know that one person paid $135 for a ski club membership and 5 ski lessons and another person paid $183 for membership and 9 lessons, you could determine the membership fee and the cost per ski lesson.

❸ TEACH

Extra Example 1
Write an equation of the line that passes through the point $(6, 3)$ and has a slope of -2.   **$y = -2x + 15$**

Extra Example 2
Write an equation of the line that passes through $(3, 0)$ and $(2, -4)$. **$y = 4x - 12$**

Key Questions to Ask for Example 2

• How is Example 2 different from Example 1? **In Example 1 you are given the slope and in Example 2 you have to use the two points to calculate the slope.**

• What values do you need from the graph of a line to write an equation of the line in slope-intercept form? **You need the coordinates of two points to calculate the slope and to determine the *y*-intercept.**

Extra Example 3
Which function has the values $f(2) = 8$ and $f(-2) = -4$? **A**
(A) $f(x) = 3x + 2$
(B) $f(x) = 3x + 14$
(C) $f(x) = 3x - 10$
(D) $f(x) = 3x - 12$

Extra Example 4

A carnival charges $2.50 per ride after an entrance fee. You paid a total of $22.50 after 6 rides. Write an equation that gives the total cost as a function of the number of rides. Find the total cost for 15 rides. $C = 2.5n + 7.5$, where C is the total cost and n is the number of rides. The total cost for 15 rides is $45.

Key Questions to Ask for Example 4

- In a graph of the situation, which values would you graph on the x-and y-axes? **Graph the independent variable, t, time in months, on the x-axis, and the dependent variable, C, total cost, on the y-axis.**

- What would be the coordinates of the y-intercept in a graph of the equation? **(0, 30)**

- Which are two other points that the graph of the equation would pass through? **(1, 63), (9, 327)**

- What do the points (x, y) on the graph represent? **The points represent the total cost y after x months.**

How to Write Equations in Slope-Intercept Form

Given slope m and y-intercept b

Substitute m and b in the equation $y = mx + b$.

Given slope m and one point

Substitute m and the coordinates of the point in $y = mx + b$. Solve for b. Write the equation.

Given two points

Use the points to find the slope m. Then follow the same steps described at the left.

MODELING REAL-WORLD SITUATIONS You can model a real-world situation that involves a constant rate of change with an equation in slope-intercept form.

EXAMPLE 4 Solve a multi-step problem

GYM MEMBERSHIP Your gym membership costs $33 per month after an initial membership fee. You paid a total of $228 after 6 months. Write an equation that gives the total cost as a function of the length of your gym membership (in months). Find the total cost after 9 months.

Solution

STEP 1 **Identify** the rate of change and starting value.

> **Rate of change, m:** monthly cost, $33 per month
> **Starting value, b:** initial membership fee

STEP 2 **Write** a verbal model. Then write an equation.

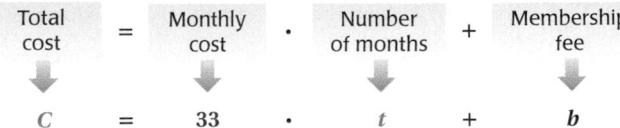

| Total cost | = | Monthly cost | · | Number of months | + | Membership fee |

$$C = 33 \cdot t + b$$

STEP 3 **Find** the starting value. Membership for 6 months costs $228, so you can substitute 6 for t and 228 for C in the equation $C = 33t + b$.

$228 = 33(6) + b$ **Substitute 6 for t and 228 for C.**

$30 = b$ **Solve for b.**

STEP 4 **Write** an equation. Use the function from Step 2.

$C = 33t + 30$ **Substitute 30 for b.**

STEP 5 **Evaluate** the function when $t = 9$.

$C = 33(9) + 30 = 327$ **Substitute 9 for t. Simplify.**

▶ Your total cost after 9 months is $327.

Differentiated Instruction

English Learners The letter t is used for the number of months in **Example 4** because it is a time (and this word begins with the letter t). Tell students that t is commonly used as a variable for most measures of time (seconds, minutes, hours, days, and so on) in algebraic expressions and equations.

See also the *Algebra 1 Toolkit* for more strategies.

EXAMPLE 5 Solve a multi-step problem

BMX RACING In Bicycle Moto Cross (BMX) racing, racers purchase a one year membership to a track. They also pay an entry fee for each race at that track. One racer paid a total of $125 after 5 races. A second racer paid a total of $170 after 8 races. How much does the track membership cost? What is the entry fee per race?

ANOTHER WAY
For alternative methods for solving the problem in Example 5, turn to page 300 for the **Problem Solving Workshop**.

Solution

STEP 1 **Identify** the rate of change and starting value.

> Rate of change, *m*: entry fee per race
> Starting value, *b*: track membership cost

STEP 2 **Write** a verbal model. Then write an equation.

| Total cost | = | Entry fee per race | · | Races entered | + | Membership cost |

$$C = m \cdot r + b$$

STEP 3 **Calculate** the rate of change. This is the entry fee per race. Use the slope formula. Racer 1 is represented by (5, 125). Racer 2 is represented by (8, 170).

$$m = \frac{y_2 - y_1}{x_2 - x_1} = \frac{170 - 125}{8 - 5} = \frac{45}{3} = 15$$

STEP 4 **Find** the track membership cost *b*. Use the data pair (5, 125) for racer 1 and the entry fee per race from Step 3.

$C = mr + b$	Write the equation from Step 2.
$125 = 15(5) + b$	Substitute 15 for *m*, 5 for *r*, and 125 for *C*.
$50 = b$	Solve for *b*.

▸ The track membership cost is $50. The entry fee per race is $15.

✓ **GUIDED PRACTICE**   for Examples 4 and 5

4. **GYM MEMBERSHIP** A gym charges $35 per month after an initial membership fee. A member has paid a total of $250 after 6 months. Write an equation that gives the total cost of a gym membership as a function of the length of membership (in months). Find the total cost of membership after 10 months. $C = 35m + 40$; $390

5. **BMX RACING** A BMX race track charges a membership fee and an entry fee per race. One racer paid a total of $76 after 3 races. Another racer paid a total of $124 after 7 races.

   a. How much does the track membership cost? **$40**

   b. What is the entry fee per race? **$12**

   c. Write an equation that gives the total cost as a function of the number of races entered. $C = 12r + 40$

5.2   Use Linear Equations in Slope-Intercept Form   **295**

HOMEWORK
KEY

○ = **WORKED-OUT SOLUTIONS**
on p. WS1 for Exs. 5, 11, and 49

★ = **STANDARDIZED TEST PRACTICE**
Exs. 2, 29, 34–37, 41, and 49

◆ = **MULTIPLE REPRESENTATIONS**
Ex. 53

5.2 EXERCISES

④ PRACTICE AND APPLY

Assignment Guide

📖 **Answer Transparencies available for all exercises**

Basic:
Day 1: EP p. 941 Exs. 27–32
pp. 296–299
Exs. 1–5, 11–13, 17–19, 23–26, 55–58
Day 2: pp. 296–299
Exs. 9, 10, 29–35, 47–52, 59–64

Average:
Day 1: pp. 296–299
Exs. 1, 2, 6–8, 14–16, 20–22, 25–29,
55–58
Day 2: pp. 296–299
Exs. 9, 10, 31–43 odd, 48–53, 59–64

Advanced:
Day 1: pp. 296–299
Exs. 1, 7, 8, 15, 16, 21, 22, 27–37,
57, 58
Day 2: pp. 296–299
Exs. 10, 38–46*, 49–54*, 63, 64

Block:
pp. 296–299
Exs. 1, 2, 6–8, 14–16, 20–22, 25–29,
55–58 (with 5.1)
pp. 296–299
Exs. 9, 10, 31–43 odd, 48–53, 59–64
(with 5.3)

Differentiated Instruction

See *Algebra 1 Best Practices Toolkit* for suggestions on addressing the needs of a diverse classroom.

Homework Check

For a quick check of student understanding of key concepts, go over the following exercises:

Basic: 4, 12, 25, 47, 48
Average: 7, 20, 31, 48, 49
Advanced: 8, 22, 32, 49, 50

Extra Practice

• Student Edition, p. 942
• Chapter 5 Resource Book:
Practice levels A, B, C, pp. 16–18

Practice Worksheet

An easily-readable reduced practice page (with answers) for this lesson can be found on p. 280C.

SKILL PRACTICE

[A] 1. **VOCABULARY** What is the y-coordinate of a point where a graph crosses the y-axis called? **y-intercept**

2. ★ **WRITING** If the equation $y = mx + b$ is used to model a quantity y as a function of the quantity x, why is b considered to be the starting value?
   It is the point where x is 0.

EXAMPLE 1
on p. 292
for Exs. 3–9

WRITING EQUATIONS Write an equation of the line that passes through the given point and has the given slope m.

3. $(1, 1)$; $m = 3$ **$y = 3x - 2$**

4. $(5, 1)$; $m = 2$ **$y = 2x - 9$**

5. $(-4, 7)$; $m = -5$
   $y = -5x - 13$

6. $(5, -5)$; $m = -2$
   $y = -2x + 5$

7. $(8, -4)$; $m = -\frac{3}{4}$
   $y = -\frac{3}{4}x + 2$

8. $(-3, -11)$; $m = \frac{1}{2}$
   $y = \frac{1}{2}x - \frac{19}{2}$

9. **ERROR ANALYSIS** *Describe* and correct the error in finding the y-intercept of the line that passes through the point $(6, -3)$ and has a slope of -2.
   −3 was substituted for x instead of y and 6 was substituted for y instead of x, $-3 = -2(6) + b$, $-3 = -12 + b$, $9 = b$.

$y = mx + b$
$6 = -2(-3) + b$
$6 = 6 + b$
$0 = b$ ✗

EXAMPLE 4
on p. 294
for Ex. 10

10. **ERROR ANALYSIS** An Internet service provider charges $18 per month plus an initial set-up fee. One customer paid a total of $81 after 2 months of service. *Describe* and correct the error in finding the set-up fee.
   18 should have been substituted for m, not b, $81 = (18)2 + b$, $81 = 36 + b$, $b = \$45$.

$C = mt + b$
$81 = m(2) + 18$
$63 = m(2)$ ✗
$31.50 = m$

EXAMPLE 2
on p. 293
for Exs. 11–22

USING TWO POINTS Write an equation of the line that passes through the given points.

11. $(1, 4)$, $(2, 7)$ **$y = 3x + 1$**

12. $(3, 2)$, $(4, 9)$ **$y = 7x - 19$**

13. $(10, -5)$, $(-5, 1)$
    $y = -\frac{2}{5}x - 1$

14. $(-2, 8)$, $(-6, 0)$ **$y = 2x + 12$**

15. $\left(\frac{9}{2}, 1\right)$, $\left(-\frac{7}{2}, 7\right)$ **$y = -\frac{3}{4}x + \frac{35}{8}$**

16. $\left(-5, \frac{3}{4}\right)$, $\left(-2, -\frac{3}{4}\right)$
    $y = -\frac{1}{2}x - \frac{7}{4}$

USING A GRAPH Write an equation of the line shown.

17. $y = 4x - 15$

18. $y = \frac{2}{5}x + \frac{4}{5}$

19. $y = -\frac{1}{2}x + \frac{1}{2}$

20. $y = -\frac{7}{6}x + \frac{11}{6}$

21. $y = \frac{1}{3}x - \frac{4}{3}$

22. $y = -3x - 7$

17.

(4, 1)
(3, −3)

18.

(3, 2)
(−2, 0)

19.
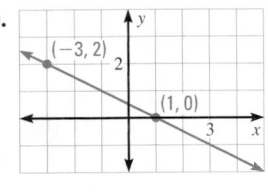
(−3, 2)
(1, 0)

20.
(−1, 3)
(2, −0.5)

21.
(−2, −2)
(1, −1)

22.
(−3, 2)
(−2, −1)

EXAMPLE 3
on p. 293
for Fxs. 23–33

WRITING LINEAR FUNCTIONS Write an equation for a linear function f that has the given values.

23. $f(-2) = 15, f(1) = 9$ $y = -2x + 11$

24. $f(-2) = -2, f(4) = -8$ $y = -x - 4$

25. $f(2) = 7, f(4) = 6$ $y = -\frac{1}{2}x + 8$

26. $f(-4) = -8, f(-8) = -11$ $y = \frac{3}{4}x - 5$

27. $f(3) = 1, f(6) = 4$ $y = x - 2$

28. $f(-5) = 9, f(11) = -39$ $y = -3x - 6$

29. ★ MULTIPLE CHOICE Which function has the values $f(4) = -15$ and $f(7) = 57$? **D**

(A) $f(x) = 14x - 71$

(B) $f(x) = 24x - 1361$

(C) $f(x) = 24x + 360$

(D) $f(x) = 24x - 111$

B **USING A TABLE OR DIAGRAM** Write an equation that represents the linear function shown in the table or mapping diagram.

30.

x	$f(x)$
-4	6
4	4
8	3
12	2

$y = -\frac{1}{4}x + 5$

31.

x	$f(x)$
-3	8
3	4
6	2
9	0

$y = -\frac{2}{3}x + 6$

32.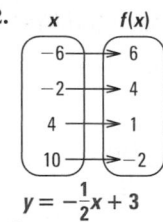

$y = -\frac{1}{2}x + 3$

33.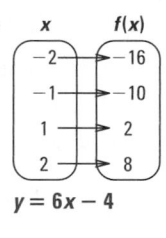

$y = 6x - 4$

★ SHORT RESPONSE Tell whether the given information is enough to write an equation of a line. *Justify* your answer. **34–37. See margin.**

34. Two points on the line

35. The slope and a point on the line

36. The slope of the line

37. Both intercepts of the line

USING A GRAPH In Exercises 38–41, use the graph at the right.

38. Write an equation of the line shown. $y = \frac{3}{2}x - \frac{1}{2}$

39. Write an equation of a line that has the same y-intercept as the line shown but has a slope that is 3 times the slope of the line shown. $y = \frac{9}{2}x - \frac{1}{2}$

40. Write an equation of a line that has the same slope as the line shown but has a y-intercept that is 6 more than the y-intercept of the line shown. $y = \frac{3}{2}x + \frac{11}{2}$

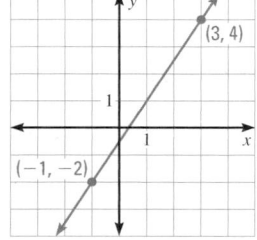

41. ★ WRITING Which of the lines from Exercises 38–40 intersect? Which of the lines never intersect? *Justify* your answers.

C **REASONING** Decide whether the three points lie on the same line. *Explain* how you know. If the points do lie on the same line, write an equation of the line that passes through all three points. **42–45. See margin.**

42. $(-4, -2), (2, 2.5), (8, 7)$

43. $(2, 2), (-4, 5), (6, 1)$

44. $(-10, 4), (-3, 2.8), (-17, 6.8)$

45. $(-5.5, 3), (-7.5, 4), (-4, 5)$

46. CHALLENGE A line passes through the points $(-2, 3), (2, 5)$, and $(6, k)$. Find the value of k. *Explain* your steps.
7; find the equation of the line through $(-2, 3)$ and $(2, 5)$ to be $y = \frac{1}{2}x + 4$, then substitute 6 for x to find k.

5.2 Use Linear Equations in Slope-Intercept Form **297**

---

*Left margin:*

41. The lines $y = \frac{3}{2}x - \frac{1}{2}$ and $y = \frac{9}{2}x - \frac{1}{2}$ and the lines $y = \frac{9}{2}x - \frac{1}{2}$ and $y = \frac{3}{2}x + \frac{11}{2}$ intersect because they have different slopes; the lines $y = \frac{3}{2}x - \frac{1}{2}$ and $y = \frac{3}{2}x + \frac{11}{2}$ will not intersect, they have the same slope, so they are parallel.

*Right margin:*

Avoiding Common Errors

Exercises 11–22 Students often make errors in computing slope. Remind them that it is helpful to write out the slope formula and then substitute the numbers before simplifying.

Exercises 18, 19 In these exercises, some students may use the x-intercept as the y-intercept. Remind those students that they are being given $(a, 0)$, not $(0, b)$.

Graphing Calculator

Exercises 11–22 Students can check their answers to these exercises by using the *calculate* feature. Students should enter their equation into the calculator, select *value* from the calculate menu, enter the x-values from the exercise, and use the calculator's y-values to check their answers.

42. The three points lie on the same line. If you find the equation of the line between two of the points and then check to see that the third point is a solution, you can see that all three points are on the line $y = \frac{3}{4}x + 1$.

43. The three points do not lie on the same line. If you find the equation of the line between two of the points and then check to see that the third point is a solution, you can see they do not lie on the same line.

44. The three points do not lie on the same line. If you find the equation of the line between two of the points and then check to see that the third point is a solution, you can see they do not lie on the same line.

45. The three points do not lie on the same line. If you find the equation of the line between two of the points and then check to see that the third point is a solution, you can see they do not lie on the same line.

---

*Bottom margin:*

34. Yes; you can find the slope and then substitute m and the coordinates of the point in $y = mx + b$, solve for b, and write the equation.

35. Yes; you can substitute m and the coordinates of the point in $y = mx + b$, solve for b, and write the equation.

36. No; many lines have the same slope but different y-intercepts.

37. Yes; you can find the slope of the line, then substitute the y-intercept for b, and write the equation.

EXAMPLES A
4 and 5
on pp. 294–295
for Exs. 47–50

47. BIOLOGY Four years after a hedge maple tree was planted, its height was 9 feet. Eight years after it was planted, the hedge maple tree's height was 12 feet. What is the growth rate of the hedge maple? What was its height when it was planted? $\frac{3}{4}$ ft/yr; 6 ft

@HomeTutor for problem solving help at classzone.com

48. TECHNOLOGY You have a subscription to an online magazine that allows you to view 25 articles from the magazine's archives. You are charged an additional fee for each article after the first 25 articles viewed. After viewing 28 archived articles, you paid a total of $34.80. After viewing 30 archived articles, you paid a total of $40.70.

   a. What is the cost per archived article after the first 25 articles viewed? **$2.95**

   b. What is cost of the magazine subscription? **$25.95**

@HomeTutor for problem solving help at classzone.com

49. 115 min or 1 h 55 min; substitute 30 for *m*, 2 for *x* and 85 for *y* into the equation *y* = *mx* + *b* to find *b* = 25. Then substitute 3 for *x* into the equation *y* = 30*x* + 25 to solve for *y*.

HINT
In part (b), let *t* represent the number of years since 1981.

(49.) ★ **SHORT RESPONSE** You are cooking a roast beef until it is well-done. You must allow 30 minutes of cooking time for every pound of beef, plus some extra time. The last time you cooked a 2 pound roast, it was well-done after 1 hour and 25 minutes. How much time will it take to cook a 3 pound roast? *Explain* how you found your answer. **See margin.**

50. TELEPHONE SERVICE The annual household cost of telephone service in the United States increased at a relatively constant rate of $27.80 per year from 1981 to 2001. In 2001 the annual household cost of telephone service was $914.

   a. What was the annual household cost of telephone service in 1981? **$358**

   b. Write an equation that gives the annual household cost of telephone service as a function of the number of years since 1981. ***y* = 27.8*x* + 358**

   c. Find the household cost of telephone service in 2000. **$886.20**

51. NEWSPAPERS Use the information in the article about the circulation of Sunday newspapers.

   a. About how many Sunday newspapers were in circulation in 1970? **about 584 newspapers**

   b. Write an equation that gives the number of Sunday newspapers in circulation as a function of the number of years since 1970. ***y* = 11.8*x* + 584**

   c. About how many Sunday newspapers were in circulation in 2000? **about 938 newspapers**

> **Sunday Edition C9**
>
> **SUNDAY PAPERS INCREASE**
> **From 1970 to 2000,** the number of Sunday newspapers in circulation increased at a relatively constant rate of 11.8 newspapers per year. In 1997 there were 903 Sunday newspapers in circulation.

B **52. AIRPORTS** From 1990 to 2001, the number of airports in the United States increased at a relatively constant rate of 175 airports per year. There were 19,306 airports in the United States in 2001.

   a. How many U.S. airports were there in 1990? **17,381 airports**

   b. Write an equation that gives the number of U.S. airports as a function of the number of years since 1990. ***y* = 175*x* + 17,381**

   c. Find the year in which the number of U.S. airports reached 19,500. **2002**

○ = WORKED-OUT SOLUTIONS on p. WS1   ★ = STANDARDIZED TEST PRACTICE   ◆ = MULTIPLE REPRESENTATIONS

53. ◆ **MULTIPLE REPRESENTATIONS** A hurricane is traveling at a constant speed on a straight path toward a coastal town, as shown below.

Hurricane position at 1:00 P.M.
216 mi town

Hurricane position at 5:00 P.M.
144 mi town

   a. Writing an Equation Write an equation that gives the distance (in miles) of the hurricane from the town as a function of the number of hours since 12:00 P.M. $d = -18t + 234$

   b. Drawing a Graph Graph the equation from part (a). *Explain* what the slope and the y-intercept of the graph mean in this situation. **b–c. See margin.**

   c. Describing in Words Predict the time at which the hurricane will reach the town. Your answer should include the following information:
   • an explanation of how you used your equation
   • a description of the steps you followed to obtain your prediction

C **54. CHALLENGE** An in-line skater practices at a race track. In two trials, the skater travels the same distance going from a standstill to his top racing speed. He then travels at his top racing speed for different distances.

Trial number	Time at top racing speed (seconds)	Total distance traveled (meters)
1	24	300
2	29	350

   a. Model Write an equation that gives the total distance traveled (in meters) as a function of the time (in seconds) at top racing speed. $d = 10t + 60$

   b. Justify What do the rate of change and initial value in your equation represent? *Explain* your answer using unit analysis. **See margin.**

   c. Predict One lap around the race track is 200 meters. The skater starts at a standstill and completes 3 laps. Predict the number of seconds the skater travels at his top racing speed. *Explain* your method.
   54 sec; the total distance is the length of the race track times 3 laps, 600 meters. If you substitute 600 for d, $t = 54$.

MIXED REVIEW

Solve the equation. Check your solution.

55. $3x + 2x - 3 = 12$ *(p. 148)* **3**   **56.** $-2(q + 13) - 8 = 2$ *(p. 148)* **−18**

57. $-3a + 15 = 45 + 7a$ *(p. 154)* **−3**   **58.** $7c + 25 = -19 + 2c$ *(p. 154)* **−8.8**

PREVIEW
Prepare for
Lesson 5.3
in Exs. 59–64.

Write an equation of the line that has the given characteristics. *(p. 283)*

59. Slope: -5; y-intercept: -2 $y = -5x - 2$ **60.** Slope: $\frac{2}{7}$; y-intercept: -3 $y = \frac{2}{7}x - 3$

61. Slope: 1; passes through $(0, -4)$ $y = x - 4$ **62.** Slope: 9; passes through $(0, 14)$ $y = 9x + 14$

63. Passes through $(0, 6)$, $(5, 2)$ $y = -\frac{4}{5}x + 6$ **64.** Passes through $(-12, 3)$, $(0, 2)$ $y = -\frac{1}{12}x + 2$

EXTRA PRACTICE for Lesson 5.2, p. 942   ⟳ **ONLINE QUIZ** at classzone.com   **299**

⑤ ASSESS AND RETEACH

Daily Homework Quiz
📄 **Transparency Available**

Write an equation of the line that passes through the given point with the given slope.

1. $(4, -1)$, $m = -1$ $y = -x + 3$
2. $(2, 0)$, $m = 4$ $y = 4x - 8$

Write an equation of the line that passes through the given points.

3. $(2, 3)$, $(4, 7)$ $y = 2x - 1$
4. $(-5, 7)$, $(2, \ \ 7)$ $y = -2x - 3$

5. A camp charges a registration fee and a daily amount. If the total bill for one camper was $338 for 12 days and the total bill for another camper was $506 for 19 days, how much will the bill be for a camper who enrolls for 30 days? **$770**

 Online Quiz

Available at **classzone.com**

Diagnosis/Remediation
• Practice A, B, C in Chapter 5 Resource Book, pp. 16–18
• Study Guide in Chapter 5 Resource Book, pp. 19–20
• Practice Workbook, pp. 69–70
• @HomeTutor

Challenge
Additional challenge is available in the Chapter 5 Resource Book, p. 23.

Alternative Strategy

Students can solve Example 5 on page 295 by using a graph or a table. A graph can help students visualize the racing problem, while a table can help students see the linear pattern. Both methods help students to understand the algebraic solution to the problem.

Mathematical Reasoning

Multiple Representations You may want to discuss the advantages of finding an algebraic solution of the racing problem, and using a graph or table to check the reasonableness of the solution. For example, an algebraic solution allows the student to calculate the total cost for any input value, whereas the graph and the table are limited by scale and by size. The graph readily shows the slope of the line and the table lends itself to calculating the y-intercept, both of which confirm the algebraic solution of the problem.

1. $5; $19; Method 1: Use a graph.

Graph the ordered pairs, (2, 43) and (4, 81), draw a line through the points and find the y-intercept, or the delivery fee, to be $5. Then find the slope of the line, or the cost per calendar, to be $\frac{38}{2} = 19;

Method 2: Use a table to calculate the cost of the calendars.

Number of calendars	Cost (dollars)
2	43
3	?
4	81

The number of calendars increased by 2 and the cost increased by $38, so the cost per calendar is $38 ÷ 2 = $19. The delivery fee is the cost when the number of calendars is 0. Use the cost per calendar and work backwards to fill in the table.
$43 − $19 = $24; $24 − $19 = $5.

Number of calendars	Cost (dollars)
0	5
1	24
2	43

The delivery fee is $5.
2. $119.18; Method 1: Use a graph.

Another Way to Solve Example 5, page 295

MULTIPLE REPRESENTATIONS In Example 5 on page 295, you saw how to solve a problem about BMX racing using an equation. You can also solve this problem using a graph or a table.

PROBLEM

BMX RACING In Bicycle Moto Cross (BMX) racing, racers purchase a one year membership to a track. They also pay an entry fee for each race at that track. One racer paid a total of $125 after 5 races. A second racer paid a total of $170 after 8 races. How much does the track membership cost? What is the entry fee per race?

METHOD 1   **Using a Graph** One alternative approach is to use a graph.

STEP 1 **Read** the problem. It tells you the number of races and amount paid for each racer. Write this information as ordered pairs.

Racer 1: (5, 125)
Racer 2: (8, 170)

STEP 2 **Graph** the ordered pairs. Draw a line through the points.

The y-intercept is 50.
So, the track membership is $50.

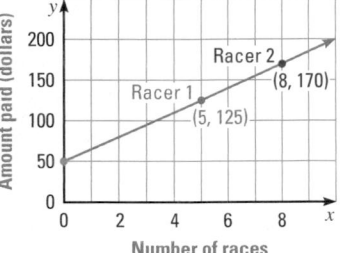

STEP 3 **Find** the slope of the line. This is the entry fee per race.

$$\text{Fee} = \frac{45 \text{ dollars}}{3 \text{ races}} = \$15 \text{ per race}$$

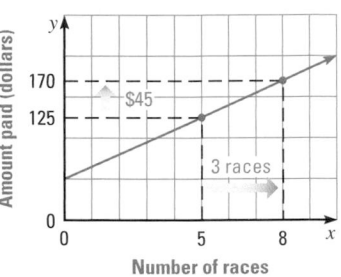

METHOD 2 **Using a Table** Another approach is to use a table showing the amount paid for various numbers of races.

STEP 1 Calculate the race entry fee.

Number of races	Amount paid
5	$125
6	?
7	?
8	$170

+3 ⟨ ⟩ +$45

The number of races increased by 3, and the amount paid increased by $45, so the race entry fee is $45 ÷ 3 = $15.

STEP 2 Find the membership cost.

Number of races	Amount paid	
0	$50	− $15
1	$65	− $15
2	$80	− $15
3	$95	− $15
4	$110	− $15
5	$125	

The membership cost is the cost with no races. Use the race entry fee and work backwards to fill in the table. The membership cost is $50.

PRACTICE

1. **CALENDARS** A company makes calendars from personal photos. You pay a delivery fee for each order plus a cost per calendar. The cost of 2 calendars plus delivery is $43. The cost of 4 calendars plus delivery is $81. What is the delivery fee? What is the cost per calendar? Solve this problem using two different methods. **See margin.**

2. **BOOKSHELVES** A furniture maker offers bookshelves that have the same width and depth but that differ in height and price, as shown in the table. Find the cost of a bookshelf that is 72 inches high. Solve this problem using two different methods. **See margin.**

Height (inches)	Price (dollars)
36	56.54
48	77.42
60	98.30

3. **WHAT IF?** In Exercise 2, suppose the price of the 60 inch bookshelf was $99.30. Can you still solve the problem? *Explain.* **See margin.**

4. **CONCERT TICKETS** All tickets for a concert are the same price. The ticket agency adds a fixed fee to every order. A person who orders 5 tickets pays $93. A person who orders 3 tickets pays $57. How much will 4 tickets cost? Solve this problem using two different methods. **See margin.**

5. **ERROR ANALYSIS** A student solved the problem in Exercise 4 as shown below. *Describe* and correct the error.

Let p = price paid for 4 tickets
$$\frac{57}{3} = \frac{p}{4}$$
$$228 = 3p$$
$$76 = p$$

The student assumes that there is no fixed fee by using a proportion; 93 − 57 = 36, 36 ÷ 2 = 18, 57 + 18 = 75.

Using Alternative Methods **301**

(Exercise 2 continued)

Graph the ordered pairs, (36, 56.54) and (48, 77.42), draw a line through the points and find the y-intercept to be −6.1. Then find the slope of the line to be $\frac{20.88}{12}$ = $1.74. Write the equation y = 1.74x − 6.1 and substitute 72 for x to find the cost to be $119.18; Method 2: Use a table to calculate the cost of the bookshelf.

Height (inches)	Cost (dollars)
36	56.54
48	77.42
60	98.30

The height increased by 12 and the cost increased by $20.88, so the cost per inch is $20.88 ÷ 12 = $1.74; 98.30 + 20.88 = 119.18.

The cost of a bookshelf that is 72 inches is $119.18.

---

① PLAN AND PREPARE

Warm-Up Exercises
📋 Transparency Available

Write an equation of the line.

1. passes through (3, 4), $m = 3$
$y = 3x - 5$

2. passes through $(-2, 2)$ and
(1, 8) $y = 2x + 6$

3. A carnival charges an entrance
fee and a ticket fee. One person
paid $27.50 and bought 5 tickets.
Another paid $45.00 and bought
12 tickets. How much will
22 tickets cost? **$70**

Notetaking Guide
📋 Transparency Available

Promotes interactive learning and
notetaking skills, pp. 106–108.

Pacing

Basic: 2 days

Average: 2 days

Advanced: 2 days

Block: 0.5 block with 5.2
0.5 block with 5.4

• See *Teaching Guide/Lesson Plan.*

② FOCUS AND MOTIVATE

Essential Question

Big Idea 1, p. 281

How do you write linear equations
in point-slope form? **Tell students
they will learn how to answer this
question by using two points, or the
slope and one point.**

NCTM STANDARDS

Standard 3: Describe spatial relationships using coordinate geometry

Standard 6: Solve problems in
math and other contexts

5.3 Write Linear Equations in Point-Slope Form

Before	You wrote linear equations in slope-intercept form.
Now	You will write linear equations in point-slope form.
Why?	So you can model sports statistics, as in Ex. 43.

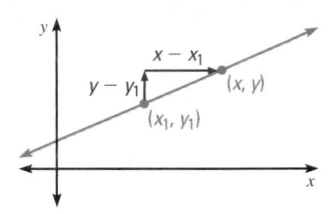

Key Vocabulary
• point-slope form

Consider the line that passes through the point (2, 3) with a slope of $\frac{1}{2}$.

Let (x, y) where $x \neq 2$ be another point on the line. You can write an equation relating x and y using the slope formula, with $(x_1, y_1) = (2, 3)$ and $(x_2, y_2) = (x, y)$.

$$m = \frac{y_2 - y_1}{x_2 - x_1} \qquad \text{Write slope formula.}$$

$$\frac{1}{2} = \frac{y - 3}{x - 2} \qquad \text{Substitute } \frac{1}{2} \text{ for } m, 3 \text{ for } y_1, \text{ and } 2 \text{ for } x_1.$$

$$\frac{1}{2}(x - 2) = y - 3 \qquad \text{Multiply each side by } (x - 2).$$

USE POINT-SLOPE FORM
When an equation is in point-slope form, you can read the x- and y-coordinates of a point on the line and the slope of the line.

➤ The equation in *point-slope form* is $y - 3 = \frac{1}{2}(x - 2)$.

KEY CONCEPT *For Your Notebook*

Point-Slope Form

The **point-slope form** of the equation of the nonvertical line through a given point (x_1, y_1) with a slope of m is $y - y_1 = m(x - x_1)$.

EXAMPLE 1 **Write an equation in point-slope form**

Write an equation in point-slope form of the line that passes through the point (4, −3) and has a slope of 2.

$$y - y_1 = m(x - x_1) \qquad \text{Write point-slope form.}$$

$$y + 3 = 2(x - 4) \qquad \text{Substitute 2 for } m, 4 \text{ for } x_1, \text{ and } -3 \text{ for } y_1.$$

✓ **GUIDED PRACTICE** for Example 1

1. Write an equation in point-slope form of the line that passes through the point (−1, 4) and has a slope of −2. $y - 4 = -2(x + 1)$

302 Chapter 5 Writing Linear Equations

Resource Planning Guide

Chapter Resource Book
• Teaching Guide/Lesson Plan (pp. 24–25)
• Activity Master (p. 26)
• Practice levels A, B, C (pp. 27–32)
• Study Guide (pp. 33–34)
• Catch-up for Absent Students (p. 35)
• Problem Solving Workshop (p. 36)
• Challenge (p. 38)

Workbooks
• Notetaking Guide (pp. 106–108)
• Practice Workbook (pp. 71–73)

Teaching Options
• **Power Presentations CD-ROM**
provides dynamic electronic teaching
resources for the classroom.
• **Activity Generator CD-ROM** provides
editable activities for all ability levels.

Interactive Technology
• Easy Planner
• Power Presentations CD-ROM
• Activity Generator CD-ROM
• Animated Algebra
• Test Generator CD-ROM
• Online Quiz
• eWorkbook
• eEdition
• @HomeTutor

Resources for English Learners
• Quick Reference for English Learners
• Spanish Study Guide
• Multi-Language Visual Glossary
• Student Resources in Spanish

See also the *Algebra 1 Toolkit* for more
strategies for meeting individual needs.

EXAMPLE 2 **Graph an equation in point-slope form**

Graph the equation $y + 2 = \frac{2}{3}(x - 3)$.

Solution

Because the equation is in point-slope form, you know that the line has a slope of $\frac{2}{3}$ and passes through the point $(3, -2)$.

Plot the point $(3, -2)$. Find a second point on the line using the slope. Draw a line through both points.

 GUIDED PRACTICE   for Example 2

2. Graph the equation $y - 1 = -(x - 2)$. **See margin.**

EXAMPLE 3   **Use point-slope form to write an equation**

Write an equation in point-slope form of the line shown.

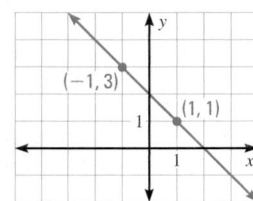

Solution

STEP 1   **Find** the slope of the line.

$$m = \frac{y_2 - y_1}{x_2 - x_1} = \frac{3 - 1}{-1 - 1} = \frac{2}{-2} = -1$$

STEP 2   **Write** the equation in point-slope form. You can use either given point.

Method 1 Use $(-1, 3)$.

$y - y_1 = m(x - x_1)$

$y - 3 = -(x + 1)$

Method 2 Use $(1, 1)$.

$y - y_1 = m(x - x_1)$

$y - 1 = -(x - 1)$

CHECK   Check that the equations are equivalent by writing them in slope-intercept form.

$y - 3 = -x - 1$

$y = -x + 2$

$y - 1 = -x + 1$

$y = -x + 2$

Animated Algebra   activity at classzone.com

 GUIDED PRACTICE   for Example 3

3. Write an equation in point-slope form of the line that passes through the points $(2, 3)$ and $(4, 4)$. $y - 3 = \frac{1}{2}(x - 2)$ or $y - 4 = \frac{1}{2}(x - 4)$

Differentiated Instruction

Auditory Learners To write the equation of a line in point-slope form, students need to know the slope and a point on the line. Students can state the point-slope form as follows. "For a given *point*, *y* minus the *y*-coordinate equals the *slope* times the quantity *x* minus the *x*-coordinate."

See also the *Algebra 1 Toolkit* for more strategies.

Motivating the Lesson

You need to print and bind a report for a project. You have a price list showing a printing company charges $10.50 for 10 pages, $11.75 for 15 pages, $14.25 for 25 pages, and $18 for 40 pages. You can use this list to determine if the company charges a constant rate to print each page. If so, you can determine the cost to print and bind your report.

③ TEACH

Extra Example 1

Write an equation in point-slope form of the line that passes through the point $(-3, 1)$ and has a slope of 3. $y - 1 = 3(x + 3)$

Extra Example 2

Graph $y - 2 = \frac{1}{2}(x + 2)$.

Extra Example 3

Write an equation in point-slope form of the line shown.

$y - 3 = -2(x + 2)$ or $y + 3 = -2(x - 1)$

2. See Additional Answers beginning on p. AA1.

Extra Example 4

A radio station charges $650 for the first minute of ad time and then $340 for each additional minute. Write an equation that gives the total cost (in dollars) to run an ad as a function of the number of minutes the ad runs. Find the cost of 7 minutes of ad time. $C = 340t + 310$, where C is total cost (in dollars) and t is time (in minutes). The cost to run the ad for 7 minutes is $2690.

Extra Example 5

The table shows the cost of renting a canoe for different times (in hours). Can the situation be modeled by a linear equation? *Explain.* If possible, write an equation that gives the cost as a function of time (in hours).

Time (hours)	Cost (dollars)
2	22
4	32
6	42
8	52
10	62

Because the cost increases at a constant rate of $5 per hour, the situation can be modeled by a linear equation. An equation that models the situation is $C = 5t + 12$, where C is the total cost (in dollars) and t is time (in hours).

Key Questions to Ask for Example 5

• When the equation is written in slope-intercept form, what does the y-intercept represent? **a one-time cost of $50**

• If you use the data pair $(12, 650)$, how does it affect the point-slope form and slope-intercept form of the equation? **The point-slope form changes to $C - 650 = 50(p - 12)$, but the slope-intercept form remains the same.**

EXAMPLE 4 **Solve a multi-step problem**

STICKERS You are designing a sticker to advertise your band. A company charges $225 for the first 1000 stickers and $80 for each additional 1000 stickers. Write an equation that gives the total cost (in dollars) of stickers as a function of the number (in thousands) of stickers ordered. Find the cost of 9000 stickers.

Solution

STEP 1 **Identify** the rate of change and a data pair. Let C be the cost (in dollars) and s be the number of stickers (in thousands).

> **Rate of change, m:** $80 per 1 thousand stickers
> **Data pair (s_1, C_1):** (1 thousand stickers, $225)

STEP 2 **Write** an equation using point-slope form. Rewrite the equation in slope-intercept form so that cost is a function of the number of stickers.

$$C - C_1 = m(s - s_1) \qquad \text{Write point-slope form.}$$
$$C - 225 = 80(s - 1) \qquad \text{Substitute 80 for } m, \text{ 1 for } s_1, \text{ and 225 for } C_1.$$
$$C = 80s + 145 \qquad \text{Solve for } C.$$

STEP 3 **Find** the cost of 9000 stickers.

$$C = 80(9) + 145 = 865 \qquad \text{Substitute 9 for } s. \text{ Simplify.}$$

▶ The cost of 9000 stickers is $865.

AVOID ERRORS
Remember that s is given in thousands. To find the cost of 9000 stickers, substitute 9 for s.

EXAMPLE 5 **Write a real-world linear model from a table**

WORKING RANCH The table shows the cost of visiting a working ranch for one day and night for different numbers of people. Can the situation be modeled by a linear equation? *Explain.* If possible, write an equation that gives the cost as a function of the number of people in the group.

Number of people	4	6	8	10	12
Cost (dollars)	250	350	450	550	650

Solution

STEP 1 **Find** the rate of change for consecutive data pairs in the table.

$$\frac{350 - 250}{6 - 4} = 50, \quad \frac{450 - 350}{8 - 6} = 50, \quad \frac{550 - 450}{10 - 8} = 50, \quad \frac{650 - 550}{12 - 10} = 50$$

Because the cost increases at a constant rate of $50 per person, the situation can be modeled by a linear equation.

STEP 2 **Use** point-slope form to write the equation. Let C be the cost (in dollars) and p be the number of people. Use the data pair $(4, 250)$.

$$C - C_1 = m(p - p_1) \qquad \text{Write point-slope form.}$$
$$C - 250 = 50(p - 4) \qquad \text{Substitute 50 for } m, \text{ 4 for } p_1, \text{ and 250 for } C_1.$$
$$C = 50p + 50 \qquad \text{Solve for } C.$$

4. **WHAT IF?** In Example 4, suppose a second company charges $250 for the first 1000 stickers. The cost of each additional 1000 stickers is $60.

    a. Write an equation that gives the total cost (in dollars) of the stickers as a function of the number (in thousands) of stickers ordered. $C = 60s + 190$

    b. Which company would charge you less for 9000 stickers? **second company**

5. **MAILING COSTS** The table shows the cost (in dollars) of sending a single piece of first class mail for different weights. Can the situation be modeled by a linear equation? *Explain*. If possible, write an equation that gives the cost of sending a piece of mail as a function of its weight (in ounces).

Weight (ounces)	1	4	5	10	12
Cost (dollars)	0.37	1.06	1.29	2.44	2.90

Yes; because the cost increases at a constant rate of $.23 per ounce, the situation can be modeled by a linear equation; $C = 0.23w + 0.14$.

5.3 EXERCISES

HOMEWORK KEY
○ = **WORKED-OUT SOLUTIONS**
   on p. WS1 for Exs. 3 and 39

★ = **STANDARDIZED TEST PRACTICE**
   Exs. 2, 12, 30–34, 38, and 41

SKILL PRACTICE

Ⓐ

1. **VOCABULARY** Identify the slope of the line given by the equation $y - 5 = -2(x + 5)$. Then identify one point on the line. $-2; (-5, 5)$

2. ★ **WRITING** *Describe* the steps you would take to write an equation in point-slope form of the line that passes through the points $(3, -2)$ and $(4, 5)$. **Find the slope and substitute it for m in the equation $y - y_1 = m(x - x_1)$. Then pick one of the points and substitute the coordinates in for y_1 and x_1.**

EXAMPLE 1
on p. 302
for Exs. 3–13

WRITING EQUATIONS Write an equation in point-slope form of the line that passes through the given point and has the given slope m.

3. $(2, 1)$, $m = 2$
  $y - 1 = 2(x - 2)$

4. $(3, 5)$, $m = -1$
  $y - 5 = -(x - 3)$

5. $(7, -1)$, $m = -6$
  $y + 1 = -6(x - 7)$

6. $(5, -1)$, $m = -2$
  $y + 1 = -2(x - 5)$

7. $(-8, 2)$, $m = 5$
  $y - 2 = 5(x + 8)$

8. $(-6, 6)$, $m = \frac{3}{2}$
  $y - 6 = \frac{3}{2}(x + 6)$

9. $(-11, -3)$, $m = -9$
  $y + 3 = -9(x + 11)$

10. $(-3, -9)$, $m = \frac{7}{3}$
  $y + 9 = \frac{7}{3}(x + 3)$

11. $(5, -12)$, $m = -\frac{2}{5}$
  $y + 12 = -\frac{2}{5}(x - 5)$

12. ★ **MULTIPLE CHOICE** Which equation represents the line that passes through the point $(-6, 2)$ and has a slope of -1? **C**

  Ⓐ $y + 2 = -(x + 6)$ Ⓑ $y + 2 = -(x - 6)$

  Ⓒ $y - 2 = -(x + 6)$ Ⓓ $y + 1 = -2(x + 6)$

13. **ERROR ANALYSIS** *Describe* and correct the error in writing an equation of the line that passes through the point $(1, -5)$ and has a slope of -2.
The form is $y - y_1$, so the left side should be $y - (-5)$ or $y + 5$; $y + 5 = -2(x - 1)$.

$y - 5 = -2(x - 1)$ ✗

Mathematical Reasoning

You may want to discuss the relationship between the point-slope form and the slope-intercept form of an equation. Tell students that data as ordered pairs fit well with the point-slope form. The ordered pairs allow them to determine quickly whether there is a constant rate of change, and the pairing allows them to plug the data directly into the point-slope form. Point out that to make calculations and graphing easier, they can rewrite the equation in slope-intercept form. Stress that they can use the form that works best in a situation, and then move from one form to the other as needed to help solve the problem.

Closing the Lesson

Have students summarize the major points of the lesson and answer the Essential Question: How do you write linear equations in point-slope form?

- **The point-slope form of an equation is $y - y_1 = m(x - x_1)$.**
- **The point-slope form uses the x-and y-coordinates of a point and the slope.**

If you are given two points, use the slope formula to find the slope. Substitute the slope and the coordinates of a given point into the point-slope form.

EXAMPLE 2
on p. 303
for Exs. 14–19

GRAPHING EQUATIONS Graph the equation. 14–19. See margin.

14. $y - 5 = 3(x - 1)$ **15.** $y + 3 = -2(x - 2)$ **16.** $y - 1 = 3(x + 6)$

17. $y + 8 = -(x + 4)$ **18.** $y - 1 = \frac{3}{4}(x + 1)$ **19.** $y + 4 = -\frac{5}{2}(x - 3)$

EXAMPLE 3
on p. 303
for Exs. 20–30

USING A GRAPH Write an equation in point-slope form of the line shown.

20.   **21.**   **22.**

$y - 1 = 2(x - 3)$ or $y + 3 = 2(x - 1)$ $y - 4 = (x - 1)$ or $y - 1 = (x + 2)$ $y - 4 = -\frac{1}{2}(x + 5)$

WRITING EQUATIONS Write an equation in point-slope form of the line $\quad$ or $y - 2 = -\frac{1}{2}(x + 1)$
that passes through the given points. 23–28. See margin.

23. $(7, 2), (2, 12)$ **24.** $(6, -2), (12, 1)$ **25.** $(-4, -1), (6, -7)$

26. $(4, 5), (-4, -5)$ **27.** $(3, -20), (4, 36)$ **28.** $(-5, -19), (5, 13)$

29. A point was
not substituted
into the
equation, the
y-coordinates
of the two
points were
substituted;
$y - 2 = \frac{2}{3}(x - 1)$.

29. ERROR ANALYSIS *Describe* and correct the error
in writing an equation of the line shown.

$$m = \frac{4 - 2}{4 - 1} = \frac{2}{3} \qquad y - 2 = \frac{2}{3}(x - 4)$$

30. ★ **MULTIPLE CHOICE** The graph of which equation is
shown? **B**

(A) $y + 4 = -3(x + 2)$ **(B)** $y - 4 = -3(x - 2)$

(C) $y - 4 = -3(x + 2)$ **(D)** $y + 4 = -3(x + 2)$

B ★ **SHORT RESPONSE** Tell whether the data in the table can be modeled by
a linear equation. *Explain*. If possible, write an equation in point-slope
form that relates y and x. 31–34. See margin.

31.

x	2	4	6	8	10
y	−1	5	15	29	47

32.

x	1	2	3	5	7
y	1.2	1.4	1.6	2	2.4

33.

x	1	2	3	4	5
y	2	−3	4	−5	6

34.

x	−3	−1	1	3	5
y	16	10	4	−2	−8

C **CHALLENGE** Find the value of k so that the line passing through the given
points has slope m. Write an equation of the line in point-slope form.

35. $(k, 4k), (k + 2, 3k), m = -1$
$2; y - 8 = -(x - 2)$ or $y - 6 = -(x - 4)$

36. $(-k + 1, 3), (3, k + 3), m = 3$
$-3; y - 3 = 3(x - 4)$ or $y = 3(x - 3)$

○ = **WORKED-OUT SOLUTIONS**
on p. WS1

★ = **STANDARDIZED**
TEST PRACTICE

14.

$y - 5 = 3(x - 1)$

15.

$y + 3 = -2(x - 2)$

16.

$y - 1 = 3(x + 6)$

Assignment Guide

📄 **Answer Transparencies**
available for all exercises

Basic:
Day 1: EP p. 939 Exs. 42–45
pp. 305–308
Exs. 1–8, 12–17, 45–53
Day 2: pp. 305–308
Exs. 20–32, 37–42, 54–57

Average:
Day 1: pp. 305–308
Exs. 1, 2, 6–13, 17–19, 45–53
Day 2: pp. 305–308
Exs. 20–28 even, 29–34, 37–43,
54–57

Advanced:
Day 1: pp. 305–308
Exs. 1, 2, 7–12, 17–19, 35*, 36*,
45–53 odd
Day 2: pp. 305–308
Exs. 24–28, 30–34, 37–44*, 55, 57

Block:
pp. 305–308
Exs. 1, 2, 6–13, 17–19, 45–53 (with 5.2)
pp. 305–308
Exs. 20–28 even, 29–34, 37–43,
54–57 (with 5.4)

Differentiated Instruction

See *Algebra 1 Best Practices Toolkit*
for suggestions on addressing the
needs of a diverse classroom.

Homework Check

For a quick check of student understanding of key concepts, go over
the following exercises:

Basic: 4, 16, 22, 37, 38
Average: 8, 17, 24, 38, 39
Advanced: 10, 18, 27, 38, 40

Extra Practice

• Student Edition, p. 942
• Chapter 5 Resource Book:
  Practice levels A, B, C, pp. 27–32

Practice Worksheet

**An easily-readable reduced
practice page (with answers)
for this lesson can be found
on p. 280C.**

EXAMPLE 4 [A]
on p. 304
for Exs. 37, 39, 40

37. TELEVISION In order to use an excerpt from a movie in a new television show, the television producer must pay the director of the movie $790 for the first 2 minutes of the excerpt and $130 per minute after that.

a. Write an equation that gives the total cost (in dollars) of using the excerpt as a function of the length (in minutes) of the excerpt. **$y = 130x + 530$**

b. Find the total cost of using an excerpt that is 8 minutes long. **$1570**

@HomeTutor for problem solving help at classzone.com

EXAMPLE 5
on p. 304
for Exs. 38, 40

38. Since the cost increases at a constant rate of $1714 per month, the situation can be modeled by a linear equation; $5950; $1714.

38. ★ SHORT RESPONSE A school district pays an installation fee and a monthly fee for Internet service. The table shows the total cost of Internet service for the school district over different numbers of months. *Explain* why the situation can be modeled by a linear equation. What is the installation fee? What is the monthly service fee?

Months of service	2	4	6	8	10	12
Total cost (dollars)	9,378	12,806	16,234	19,662	23,090	26,518

@HomeTutor for problem solving help at classzone.com

39. COMPANY SALES During the period 1994–2004, the annual sales of a small company increased by $10,000 per year. In 1997 the annual sales were $97,000. Write an equation that gives the annual sales as a function of the number of years since 1994. Find the sales in 2000.
$y = 10000x + 67000$; $127,000

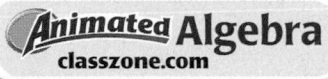
Animated Algebra at classzone.com

40. TRAFFIC DELAYS From 1990 to 2001 in Boston, Massachusetts, the annual excess fuel (in gallons per person) consumed due to traffic delays increased by about 1.4 gallons per person each year. In 1995 each person consumed about 37 gallons of excess fuel.

a. Write an equation that gives the annual excess fuel (in gallons per person) as a function of the number of years since 1990. **$y = 1.4x + 30$**

b. How much excess fuel was consumed per person in 2001? **45.4 gal**

Animated Algebra at classzone.com

41a. Since the cost increases at a constant rate of $.49 per print, the situation can be modeled by a linear equation.

41. ★ EXTENDED RESPONSE The table shows the cost of ordering sets of prints of digital photos from an online service. The cost per print is the same for the first 30 prints. There is also a shipping charge.

Number of prints	1	2	5	8
Total cost (dollars)	1.98	2.47	3.94	5.41

a. *Explain* why the situation can be modeled by a linear equation.

b. Write an equation in point-slope form that relates the total cost (in dollars) of a set of prints to the number of prints ordered. *Sample answer:* $y - 1.98 = 0.49(x - 1)$

c. Find the shipping charge for up to 10 prints. **$1.49**

d. The cost of 15 prints is $9.14. The shipping charge increases after the first 10 prints. Find the shipping charge for 15 prints. **$1.79**

Avoiding Common Errors

Exercises 3–11, 23–28 Watch for students who fail to write both the subtraction symbol and negative symbol when they substitute negative values in the point-slope form.

Exercises 31, 32, 38, 41 Caution students that intervals for the data pairs are not always equal. To avoid errors, suggest they model Step 1 in Example 5 on page 304.

Study Strategy

Exercises 23–28 Suggest that students follow Example 3 on page 303 and use both points to write equations in point-slope form. They can then check that the equations are equivalent by writing them in slope-intercept form.

Animated Algebra
classzone.com

An **Animated Algebra** activity is available on-line for **Exercise 40**. This activity is also available on the **Power Presentations CD-ROM**.

23. $y - 2 = -2(x - 7)$ or
$y - 12 = -2(x - 2)$

24. $y + 2 = \frac{1}{2}(x - 6)$ or
$y - 1 = \frac{1}{2}(x - 12)$

25. $y + 1 = -\frac{3}{5}(x + 4)$ or
$y + 7 = -\frac{3}{5}(x - 6)$

26. $y - 5 = \frac{5}{4}(x - 4)$ or
$y + 5 = \frac{5}{4}(x + 4)$

27. $y + 20 = 8(x + 3)$ or
$y - 36 = 8(x - 4)$

28. $y + 19 = \frac{16}{5}(x + 5)$ or
$y - 13 = \frac{16}{5}(x - 5)$

31–34. See Additional Answers beginning on p. AA1.

17.

$y + 8 = -(x + 4)$

18.

$y - 1 = \frac{3}{4}(x + 1)$

19.

$y + 4 = -\frac{5}{2}(x - 3)$

1. Write an equation in point-slope form of the line that passes through $(6, -4)$ and has slope 2. $y + 4 = -2(x - 6)$

2. Write an equation in point-slope form of the line that passes through $(-1, -6)$ and $(3, 10)$. $y + 6 = 4(x + 1)$ or $y - 10 = 4(x - 3)$

3. A travel company offers guided rafting trips for $875 for the first three days and $235 for each additional day. Write an equation that gives the total cost (in dollars) of a rafting trip as a function of the length of the trip. Find the cost for a 7-day trip. $C = 235t + 170$, where C is total cost and t is time (in days); $1815

Online Quiz

Available at **classzone.com**

Diagnosis/Remediation

- Practice A, B, C in Chapter 5 Resource Book, pp. 27–32
- Study Guide in Chapter 5 Resource Book, pp. 33–34
- Practice Workbook, pp. 71–73
- @HomeTutor

Challenge

Additional challenge is available in the Chapter 5 Resource Book, p. 37.

B 42. **AQUACULTURE** Aquaculture is the farming of fish and other aquatic animals. World aquaculture increased at a relatively constant rate from 1991 to 2002. In 1994 world aquaculture was about 20.8 million metric tons. In 2000 world aquaculture was about 35.5 million metric tons.

   a. Write an equation that gives world aquaculture (in millions of metric tons) as a function of the number of years since 1991. $y = 2.45x + 13.45$

   b. In 2001 China was responsible for 70.2% of world aquaculture. Approximate China's aquaculture in 2001. **about 26.64 million metric tons**

43. **MARATHON** The diagram shows a marathon runner's speed at several outdoor temperatures.

Temperature	Running Speed
75°F	16.7 ft/sec
70°F	17.0 ft/sec
65°F	17.3 ft/sec
60°F	17.6 ft/sec

Not drawn to scale

   a. Write an equation in point-slope form that relates running speed (in feet per second) to temperature (in degrees Fahrenheit). $y - 17.6 = -0.06(x - 60)$

   b. Estimate the runner's speed when the temperature is 80°F. **16.4 ft/sec**

C 44. **CHALLENGE** The number of cans recycled per pound of aluminum recycled in the U.S. increased at a relatively constant rate from 1972 to 2002. In 1977 about 23.5 cans per pound of aluminum were recycled. In 2000, about 33.1 cans per pound of aluminum were recycled.

   a. Write an equation that gives the number of cans recycled per pound of aluminum recycled as a function of the number of years since 1972. $y = 0.417391x + 21.413$

   b. In 2002, there were 53.8 billion aluminum cans collected for recycling. Approximately how many pounds of aluminum were collected? *Explain* how you found your answer.

44b. 1.59 billion lb; find the number of cans recycled per pound of aluminum in 2002 by substituting 30 for x to get about 33.9 cans per pound. Divide 53.8 million aluminum cans by 33.9 cans per pound to find the number of pounds of aluminum.

MIXED REVIEW

Evaluate the expression.

45. $|-3.2| - 2.8$ *(p. 80)* **0.4**   46. $-6.1 - (-8.4)$ *(p. 80)* **2.3**   47. $\sqrt{196}$ *(p. 110)* **14**

Graph the equation. 48–53. See margin.

48. $x = 0$ *(p. 215)*   49. $y = 8$ *(p. 215)*   50. $4x - 2y = 7$ *(p. 225)*

51. $-x + 5y = 1$ *(p. 225)*   52. $y = 2x - 7$ *(p. 244)*   53. $y = -\frac{3}{4}x + 2$ *(p. 244)*

PREVIEW
Prepare for Lesson 5.4 in Exs. 54–57.

Write an equation of the line that has the given characteristics.

54. Slope: -3; y-intercept: 5 *(p. 283)* $y = -3x + 5$

55. Slope: 8; passes through $(2, 15)$ *(p. 292)* $y = 8x - 1$

56. Passes through $(0, -3)$, $(6, 1)$ *(p. 283)* $y = \frac{2}{3}x - 3$

57. Passes through $(3, 3)$, $(6, -1)$ *(p. 292)* $y = -\frac{4}{3}x + 7$

48–53. See Additional Answers beginning on p. AA1.

Relate Arithmetic Sequences to Linear Functions

GOAL Identify, graph, and write the general form of arithmetic sequences.

Key Vocabulary
• sequence
• arithmetic sequence
• common difference

A **sequence** is an ordered list of numbers. The numbers in a sequence are called *terms*. In an **arithmetic sequence**, the difference between consecutive terms is constant. The constant difference is called the **common difference**.

An arithmetic sequence has the form $a_1, a_1 + d, a_1 + 2d, \ldots$ where a_1 is the first term and d is the common difference. For instance, if $a_1 = 2$ and $d = 6$, then the sequence $2, 2 + 6, 2 + 2(6), \ldots$ or $2, 8, 14, \ldots$ is arithmetic.

EXAMPLE 1 **Identify an arithmetic sequence**

Tell whether the sequence is arithmetic. If it is, find the next two terms.

   a. $-4, 1, 6, 11, 16, \ldots$ **b.** $3, 5, 9, 15, 23, \ldots$

Solution

  a. The first term is $a_1 = -4$. Find the differences of consecutive terms.

$$a_2 - a_1 = 1 - (-4) = 5 \qquad\qquad a_3 - a_2 = 6 - 1 = 5$$
$$a_4 - a_3 = 11 - 6 = 5 \qquad\qquad a_5 - a_4 = 16 - 11 = 5$$

   ▶ Because the terms have a common difference ($d = 5$), the sequence is arithmetic. The next two terms are $a_6 = 21$ and $a_7 = 26$.

  b. The first term is $a_1 = 3$. Find the differences of consecutive terms.

$$a_2 - a_1 = 5 - 3 = 2 \qquad\qquad a_3 - a_2 = 9 - 5 = 4$$
$$a_4 - a_3 = 15 - 9 = 6 \qquad\qquad a_5 - a_4 = 23 - 15 = 8$$

   ▶ There is no common difference, so the sequence is not arithmetic.

GRAPHING A SEQUENCE To graph a sequence, let a term's position number in the sequence be the *x*-value. The term is the corresponding *y*-value.

EXAMPLE 2 **Graph a sequence**

Graph the sequence $-4, 1, 6, 11, 16, \ldots$.
Make a table pairing each term with its position number.

Position, *x*	1	2	3	4	5
Term, *y*	−4	1	6	11	16

Plot the pairs in the table as points in a coordinate plane.

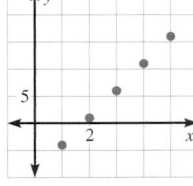

5.3 Extension: Relate Arithmetic Sequences to Linear Functions   **309**

Extra Example 2

Graph the sequence 13, 9, 5, 1, −3, ...

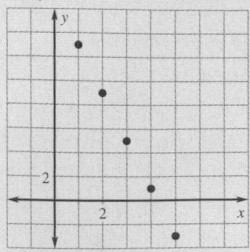

Extra Example 3

Write a rule for the nth term of the sequence 13, 9, 5, 1, −3, ... Find a_{100}. $a_n = 13 + (n - 1)-4$; −383

Closing the Lesson

Have students summarize the major points of the lesson and answer the Essential Question: How do you use a linear model to identify, graph, and write the general form of arithmetic sequences?

• A sequence is arithmetic if consecutive terms have a common difference.

• The rule for an arithmetic sequence is $a_n = a_1 + (n - 1)d$ where a_n is the nth term, a_1 is the first term, and d is the common difference.

Use the common difference between consecutive terms to find the next term. Pair a term with its position in the sequence to graph the sequence. Substitute the first term, the value of n, and the common difference into the arithmetic sequence rule to find the nth term.

4 PRACTICE AND APPLY

Avoiding Common Errors

Exercises 1–3 Some students may use a positive number as a common difference when it should be a negative number. Tell students that the common difference between consecutive terms can be a positive or a negative number. Remind them to subtract each term from the one right after it to find the common difference.

KEY CONCEPT   *For Your Notebook*

Rule for an Arithmetic Sequence

The nth term of an arithmetic sequence with first term a_1 and common difference d is given by $a_n = a_1 + (n - 1)d$.

EXAMPLE 3   **Write a rule for the nth term of a sequence**

Write a rule for the nth term of the sequence −4, 1, 6, 11, 16, ... Find a_{100}.

Solution

The first term of the sequence is $a_1 = -4$, and the common difference is $d = 5$.

$a_n = a_1 + (n - 1)d$ **Write general rule for an arithmetic sequence.**

$a_n = -4 + (n - 1)5$ **Substitute −4 for a_1 and 5 for d.**

Find a_{100} by substituting 100 for n.

$a_n = -4 + (n - 1)5$ **Write the rule for the sequence.**

$a_{100} = -4 + (100 - 1)5$ **Substitute 100 for n.**

$a_{100} = 491$ **Evaluate.**

PRACTICE

EXAMPLE 1
on p. 309
for Exs. 1–3

Tell whether the sequence is arithmetic. If it is, find the next two terms. If it is not, explain why not.   No; there is no common difference

1. 17, 14, 11, 8, 5, . . .   yes; 2, −1
2. 1, 4, 16, 64, 256, . . .
3. −8, −15, −22, −29, −36, . . .   yes; −43, −50

EXAMPLE 2
on p. 309
for Exs. 4–9

Graph the sequence. 4–9. See margin.

4. 1, 4, 7, 11, 14, . . .
5. 4, −3, −10, −17, −24, . . .
6. 5, −1, −7, −13, −19, . . .
7. 2, $3\frac{1}{2}$, 5, $6\frac{1}{2}$, 8, . . .
8. 0, 2, 4, 6, 8, . . .
9. −3, −4, −5, −6, −7, . . .

EXAMPLE 3
on p. 310
for Exs. 10–15

Write a rule for the nth term of the sequence. Find a_{100}. 10–15. See margin.

10. −12, −5, 2, 9, 16, . . .
11. 51, 72, 93, 114, 135, . . .
12. 0.25, −0.75, −1.75, −2.75, . . .
13. $\frac{1}{4}$, $\frac{3}{8}$, $\frac{1}{2}$, $\frac{5}{8}$, $\frac{3}{4}$, . . .
14. 0, −5, −10, −15, −20, . . .
15. 1, $1\frac{1}{3}$, $1\frac{2}{3}$, 2, $2\frac{1}{3}$, . . .

16. **REASONING** For an arithmetic sequence with a first term of a_1 and a common difference of d, show that $a_{n+1} - a_n = d$.
A term after the first term is the sum of the previous term and the common difference, so $a_{n+1} = a_n + d$, subtract a_n from both sides, $a_{n+1} - a_n = d$.

4–9. See Additional Answers beginning on p. AA1.

10. $a_n = -12 + (n - 1)7$; 681
11. $a_n = 51 + (n - 1)21$; 2130
12. $a_n = 0.25 + (n - 1)(-1)$; −98.75

13. $a_n = \frac{1}{4} + (n - 1)\frac{1}{8}$; $12\frac{5}{8}$
14. $a_n = (n - 1)(-5)$; −495
15. $a_n = 1 + (n - 1)\frac{1}{3}$; 34

5.4 Write Linear Equations in Standard Form

Before	You wrote equations in point-slope form.
Now	You will write equations in standard form.
Why?	So you can find possible combinations of objects, as in Ex. 41.

Key Vocabulary
• standard form, p. 215

Recall that the linear equation $Ax + By = C$ is in standard form, where A, B, and C are real numbers and A and B are not both zero. All linear equations can be written in standard form.

EXAMPLE 1 Write equivalent equations in standard form

Write two equations in standard form that are equivalent to $2x - 6y = 4$.

Solution

To write one equivalent equation, multiply each side by 2.	To write another equivalent equation, multiply each side by 0.5.
$4x - 12y = 8$	$x - 3y = 2$

EXAMPLE 2 Write an equation from a graph

Write an equation in standard form of the line shown.

Solution

STEP 1 Calculate the slope.

$$m = \frac{1 - (-2)}{1 - 2} = \frac{3}{-1} = -3$$

STEP 2 Write an equation in point-slope form. Use $(1, 1)$.

$y - y_1 = m(x - x_1)$ **Write point-slope form.**

$y - 1 = -3(x - 1)$ **Substitute 1 for y_1, −3 for m, and 1 for x_1.**

STEP 3 Rewrite the equation in standard form.

$3x + y = 4$ **Simplify. Collect variable terms on one side, constants on the other.**

Animated Algebra at classzone.com

✓ **GUIDED PRACTICE** for Examples 1 and 2

1. Write two equations in standard form that are equivalent to $x - y = 3$.
   Sample answer: $2x - 2y = 6$, $3x - 3y = 9$
2. Write an equation in standard form of the line through $(3, -1)$ and $(2, -3)$.
   $-2x + y = -7$

---

❶ PLAN AND PREPARE

Warm-Up Exercises
📄 **Transparency Available**

Write an equation in point-slope form of the line that passes through the given points.
1. $(1, 4)$, $(6, -1)$ $y - 4 = -(x - 1)$ or $y + 1 = -(x - 6)$
2. $(-1, -2)$, $(2, 7)$ $y + 2 = 3(x + 1)$ or $y - 7 = 3(x - 2)$
3. A store rents 3 DVDs for \$5, plus \$3 for each additional DVD. Find the cost of renting 20 DVDs. **\$56**

Notetaking Guide
📄 **Transparency Available**
Promotes interactive learning and notetaking skills, pp. 109–112.

Pacing
Basic: 2 days
Average: 2 days
Advanced: 2 days
Block: 0.5 block with 5.3
       0.5 block with 5.5
• See *Teaching Guide/Lesson Plan*.

❷ FOCUS AND MOTIVATE

Essential Question
Big Idea 1, p. 281

How do you write an equation in standard form? **Tell students they will learn how to answer this question by rewriting equations.**

NCTM STANDARDS
Standard 2: Use models to understand relationships

Standard 6: Apply/adapt strategies to solve problems

Resource Planning Guide

Chapter Resource Book
• Teaching Guide/Lesson Plan (pp. 38–39)
• Activity Master (p. 40)
• Practice levels A, B, C (pp. 41–43)
• Study Guide (pp. 44–45)
• Catch-up for Absent Students (p. 46)
• Problem Solving Workshop (p. 47)
• Challenge (p. 49)

Workbooks
• Notetaking Guide (pp. 109–112)
• Practice Workbook (pp. 74–75)

Teaching Options
• **Power Presentations CD-ROM** provides dynamic electronic teaching resources for the classroom.
• **Activity Generator CD-ROM** provides editable activities for all ability levels.

Interactive Technology
• Easy Planner
• Power Presentations CD-ROM
• Activity Generator CD-ROM
• Animated Algebra
• Test Generator CD-ROM
• Online Quiz
• eWorkbook
• eEdition
• @HomeTutor

Resources for English Learners
• Quick Reference for English Learners
• Spanish Study Guide
• Multi-Language Visual Glossary
• Student Resources in Spanish

See also the *Algebra 1 Toolkit* for more strategies for meeting individual needs.

HORIZONTAL AND VERTICAL LINES Recall that equations of horizontal lines have the form $y = a$. Equations of vertical lines have the form $x = b$. You cannot write an equation for a vertical line in slope-intercept form or point-slope form, because a vertical line has no slope. However, you can write an equation for a vertical line in standard form.

EXAMPLE 3 Write an equation of a line

Write an equation of the specified line.

a. Blue line   **b.** Red line

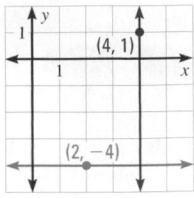

Solution

a. The y-coordinate of the given point on the blue line is -4. This means that all points on the line have a y-coordinate of -4. An equation of the line is $y = -4$.

b. The x-coordinate of the given point on the red line is 4. This means that all points on the line have an x-coordinate of 4. An equation of the line is $x = 4$.

EXAMPLE 4 Complete an equation in standard form

Find the missing coefficient in the equation of the line shown. Write the completed equation.

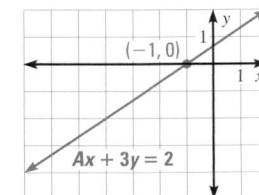

Solution

STEP 1 **Find** the value of A. Substitute the coordinates of the given point for x and y in the equation. Solve for A.

$$Ax + 3y = 2 \qquad \text{Write equation.}$$

$$A(-1) + 3(0) = 2 \qquad \text{Substitute } -1 \text{ for } x \text{ and } 0 \text{ for } y.$$

$$-A = 2 \qquad \text{Simplify.}$$

$$A = -2 \qquad \text{Divide by } -1.$$

STEP 2 **Complete** the equation.

$$-2x + 3y = 2 \qquad \text{Substitute } -2 \text{ for } A.$$

✓ **GUIDED PRACTICE**   for Examples 3 and 4

Write equations of the horizontal and vertical lines that pass through the given point.

3. $(-8, -9)$ $y = -9, x = -8$ **4.** $(13, -5)$ $y = -5, x = 13$

Find the missing coefficient in the equation of the line that passes through the given point. Write the completed equation.

5. $-4x + By = 7, (-1, 1)$ $3; -4x + 3y = 7$ **6.** $Ax + y = -3, (2, 11)$
$-7; -7x + y = -3$

❖ EXAMPLE 5 Solve a multi-step problem

LIBRARY Your class is taking a trip to the public library. You can travel in small and large vans. A small van holds 8 people and a large van holds 12 people. Your class could fill 15 small vans and 2 large vans.

a. Write an equation in standard form that models the possible combinations of small vans and large vans that your class could fill.

b. Graph the equation from part (a).

c. List several possible combinations.

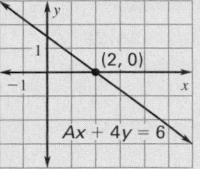

Solution

a. Write a verbal model. Then write an equation.

Capacity of small van	·	Number of small vans	+	Capacity of large van	·	Number of large vans	=	People on trip
8	·	s	+	12	·	ℓ	=	p

Because your class could fill 15 small vans and 2 large vans, use (15, 2) as the s- and ℓ-values to substitute in the equation $8s + 12\ell = p$ to find the value of p.

$$8(15) + 12(2) = p \qquad \text{Substitute 15 for } s \text{ and 2 for } \ell.$$

$$144 = p \qquad \text{Simplify.}$$

Substitute 144 for p in the equation $8s + 12\ell = p$.

▶ The equation $8s + 12\ell = 144$ models the possible combinations.

b. Find the intercepts of the graph.

Substitute 0 for s.   Substitute 0 for ℓ.

$$8(0) + 12\ell = 144 \qquad 8s + 12(0) = 144$$

$$\ell = 12 \qquad\qquad s = 18$$

LISTING COMBINATIONS
Other combinations of small and large vans are possible. Another way to find possible combinations is by substituting values for s or ℓ in the equation.

Plot the points (0, 12) and (18, 0). Connect them with a line segment. For this problem only nonnegative whole-number values of s and ℓ make sense.

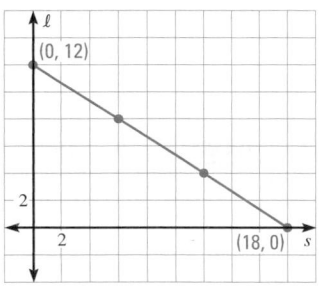

c. The graph passes through (0, 12), (6, 8), (12, 4), and (18, 0). So, four possible combinations are 0 small and 12 large, 6 small and 8 large, 12 small and 4 large, 8 small and 0 large.

✓ **GUIDED PRACTICE** for Example 5

7. WHAT IF? In Example 5, suppose that 8 students decide not to go on the class trip. Write an equation that models the possible combinations of small and large vans that your class could fill. List several possible combinations. **$8s + 12\ell = 136$. *Sample answer:* 17 small, 0 large; 14 small, 2 large; 11 small, 4 large; 8 small, 6 large; 5 small, 8 large; 2 small, 10 large**

5.4 Write Linear Equations in Standard Form   **313**

Extra Example 4

Find the missing coefficient in the equation of the line shown. Write the completed equation.

$$3x + 4y = 6$$

Extra Example 5

T-shirts at a flea market cost $4.50 each and shorts cost $6 each. You have enough money to buy exactly 12 T-shirts and 9 pairs of shorts.

a. Write an equation in standard form that models the possible combinations of T-shirts and shorts you can buy.
$$4.5t + 6s = 108$$

b. Graph the equation.

c. List several possible combinations. **0 T-shirts and 18 shorts; 8 T-shirts and 12 shorts; 24 T-shirts and 0 shorts**

Closing the Lesson

Have students summarize the major points of the lesson and answer the Essential Question: How do you write an equation in standard form?

• $Ax + By = C$ is the standard form of an equation where A, B, and C are real numbers, and A and B are not both 0.

Use the slope formula to find the slope. Write the equation in point-slope form. Collect variable terms on one side of the equation and constants on the other to rewrite the equation in standard form.

313

5.4 EXERCISES

HOMEWORK KEY
○ = WORKED-OUT SOLUTIONS
on p. WS1 for Exs. 17 and 39
★ = STANDARDIZED TEST PRACTICE
Exs. 4, 30, 40, and 42
◆ = MULTIPLE REPRESENTATIONS
Ex. 41

④ PRACTICE AND APPLY

Assignment Guide

📑 Answer Transparencies available for all exercises

Basic:
Day 1: EP p. 941 Exs. 37–40
pp. 314–316
Exs. 1–8, 11–19, 47–49
Day 2: pp. 314–316
Exs. 23–32, 38–41, 45, 46

Average:
Day 1: pp. 314–316
Exs. 1–4, 8–10, 14–22, 47–49
Day 2: pp. 314–316
Exs. 23–29 odd, 30–36, 38–43, 45, 46

Advanced:
Day 1: pp. 314–316
Exs. 1–4, 8–10, 16–22, 37*, 47–49
Day 2: pp. 314–316
Exs. 26–28, 30–36, 41–46*

Block:
pp. 314–316
Exs. 1–4, 8–10, 14–22, 47–49
(with 5.3)
pp. 314–316
Exs. 23–29 odd, 30–36, 38–43, 45, 46 (with 5.5)

Differentiated Instruction

See *Algebra 1 Best Practices Toolkit* for suggestions on addressing the needs of a diverse classroom.

Homework Check

For a quick check of student understanding of key concepts, go over the following exercises:
Basic: 6, 12, 24, 29, 38
Average: 9, 16, 27, 32, 39
Advanced: 10, 20, 27, 34, 40

Extra Practice

• Student Edition, p. 942
• Chapter 5 Resource Book: Practice levels A, B, C, pp. 41–43

Practice Worksheet

An easily-readable reduced practice page (with answers) for this lesson can be found on p. 280C.

SKILL PRACTICE

A **VOCABULARY** Identify the form of the equation.

1. $2x + 8y = -3$
   standard form

2. $y = -5x + 8$
   slope-intercept form

3. $y + 4 = 2(x - 6)$
   point-slope form

4. ★ **WRITING** *Explain* how to write an equation of a line in standard form when two points on the line are given. **Find the slope of the line then substitute the slope and one of the points into the point-slope form. Collect variables on one side and constants on the other side.**

EXAMPLE 1
on p. 311
for Exs. 5–10

EQUIVALENT EQUATIONS Write two equations in standard form that are equivalent to the given equation. **5–10. See margin.**

5. $x + y = -10$
6. $5x + 10y = 15$
7. $-x + 2y = 9$
8. $-9x - 12y = 6$
9. $9x - 3y = -12$
10. $-2x + 4y = -5$

EXAMPLE 2
on p. 311
for Exs. 11–22

17. $\frac{2}{3}x + y = -\frac{4}{3}$

19. $-\frac{4}{3}x + y = -1$

21. $-\frac{1}{2}x + y = 1$

WRITING EQUATIONS Write an equation in standard form of the line that passes through the given point and has the given slope m or that passes through the two given points.

11. $(-3, 2)$, $m = 1$
    $-x + y = 5$
12. $(4, -1)$, $m = 3$
    $-3x + y = -13$
13. $(0, 5)$, $m = -2$
    $2x + y = 5$
14. $(-8, 0)$, $m = -4$
    $4x + y = -32$
15. $(-4, -4)$, $m = -\frac{3}{2}$
    $\frac{3}{2}x + y = -10$
16. $(-6, -10)$, $m = \frac{1}{6}$
    $-\frac{1}{6}x + y = -9$
⑰ $(-8, 4)$, $(4, -4)$
18. $(-5, 2)$, $(-4, 3)$ $-x + y = 7$
19. $(0, -1)$, $(-6, -9)$
20. $(3, 9)$, $(1, 1)$
    $-4x + y = -3$
21. $(10, 6)$, $(-12, -5)$
22. $(-6, -2)$, $(-1, -2)$
    $y = -2$

EXAMPLE 3
on p. 312
for Exs. 23–28

HORIZONTAL AND VERTICAL LINES Write equations of the horizontal and vertical lines that pass through the given point.

23. $(3, 2)$ $y = 2$, $x = 3$
24. $(-5, -3)$ $y = -3$, $x = -5$
25. $(-1, 3)$ $y = 3$, $x = -1$
26. $(5, 3)$ $y = 3$, $x = 5$
27. $(-1, 4)$ $y = 4$, $x = -1$
28. $(-6, -2)$ $y = -2$, $x = -6$

EXAMPLE 4 **B**
on p. 312
for Exs. 29–36
29. $(1, -4)$ was substituted incorrectly, 1 should be substituted for x and -4 substituted for y, $A(1) - 3(-4) = 5$, $A + 12 = 5$, $A = -7$.

32. $\frac{1}{2}; \frac{1}{2}x - 4y = -1$

29. **ERROR ANALYSIS** *Describe* and correct the error in finding the value of A for the equation $Ax - 3y = 5$, if the graph of the equation passes through the point $(1, -4)$.

$$A(-4) - 3(1) = 5$$
$$A = -2$$ ✗

30. ★ **MULTIPLE CHOICE** The graph of the equation $Ax + 2y = -2$ is a line that passes through $(2, -2)$. What is the value of A? **B**

   (A) -1 **(B)** 1 **(C)** 2 **(D)** 3

COMPLETING EQUATIONS Find the missing coefficient in the equation of the line that passes through the given point. Write the completed equation.

31. $Ax + 3y = 5$, $(2, -1)$
    $4; 4x + 3y = 5$
32. $Ax - 4y = -1$, $(6, 1)$
33. $-x + By = 10$, $(-2, -2)$
    $-4; -x - 4y = 10$
34. $8x + By = 4$, $(-5, 4)$
    $11; 8x + 11y = 4$
35. $Ax - 3y = -5$, $(1, 0)$
    $-5; -5x - 3y = -5$
36. $2x + By = -4$, $(-3, 7)$
    $\frac{2}{7}; 2x + \frac{2}{7}y = -4$

C 37. **CHALLENGE** Write an equation in standard form of the line that passes through $(0, a)$ and $(b, 0)$ where $a \neq 0$ and $b \neq 0$. $\frac{a}{b}x + y = a$

5–10. Sample answers are given.

5. $2x + 2y = -20$, $3x + 3y = -30$

6. $x + 2y = 3$, $10x + 20y = 30$

7. $x - 2y = -9$, $-2x + 4y = 18$

8. $-3x - 4y = 2$, $-6x - 8y = 4$

9. $3x - y = -4$, $6x - 2y = -8$

10. $2x - 4y = 5$, $-4x + 8y = -10$

EXAMPLE 5 [A]
on p. 313
for Exs. 38–41

38. GARDENING The diagram shows the prices of two types of ground cover plants. Write an equation in standard form that models the possible combinations of vinca and phlox plants a gardener can buy for $300. List three of these possible combinations. **$2.5p + 1.2v = 300$; *Sample answer:* 120 phlox plants and 0 vinca plants, 0 phlox plants and 250 vinca plants, 60 phlox plants and 125 vinca plants**

Vinca
$1.20 per plant

Phlox
$2.50 per plant

@HomeTutor for problem solving help at classzone.com

39. NUTRITION A snack mix requires a total of 120 ounces of some corn cereal and some wheat cereal. Corn cereal comes in 12 ounce boxes.

   a. The last time you made this mix, you used 5 boxes of corn cereal and 4 boxes of wheat cereal. How many ounces are in a box of wheat cereal? **15 oz**

   b. Write an equation in standard form that models the possible combinations of boxes of wheat and corn cereal you can use. **$12c + 15w = 120$**

   c. List all possible combinations of whole boxes of wheat and corn cereal you can use to make the snack mix. **10 corn, 0 wheat; 5 corn, 4 wheat; 0 corn, 8 wheat**

@HomeTutor for problem solving help at classzone.com

40. $20n + 5t = 100$; see margin for art. The *n*-intercept, 5, is the number of nights of boarding the dog at the kennel without any treats. The *t*-intercept, 20, is the number of treats that can be bought without boarding the dog for any nights.

40. ★ SHORT RESPONSE A dog kennel charges $20 per night to board your dog. You can also have a doggie treat delivered to your dog for $5. Write an equation that models the possible combinations of nights at the kennel and doggie treats that you can buy for $100. Graph the equation. *Explain* what the intercepts of the graph mean in this situation.

[B] **41. ◆ MULTIPLE REPRESENTATIONS** As the student council treasurer, you prepare the budget for your class rafting trip. Each large raft costs $100 to rent, and each small raft costs $40 to rent. You have $1600 to spend.

   a. Writing an Equation Write an equation in standard form that models the possible combinations of small rafts and large rafts that you can rent. **$100\ell + 40s = 1600$**

   b. Drawing a Graph Graph the equation from part (a). **See margin.**

   c. Making a Table Make a table that shows several combinations of small and large rafts that you can rent. **See margin.**

42. ★ SHORT RESPONSE One bus ride costs $.75. One subway ride costs $1.00. A monthly pass can be used for unlimited subway and bus rides and costs the same as 36 subway rides plus 36 bus rides.

   a. Write an equation in standard form that models the possible combinations of bus and subway rides with the same value as the pass. **$0.75b + s = 63$**

   b. You ride the bus 60 times in one month. How many times must you ride the subway in order for the cost of the rides to equal the value of the pass? *Explain* your answer. **18 subway rides; if you ride the bus 60 times, it costs (0.75)$60 = $45 without the pass. The pass costs $63, you need to spend $18 on subway rides, $18 ÷ 1 = $18.**

5.4 Write Linear Equations in Standard Form **315**

Avoiding Common Errors

Exercises 5–10 Watch for students who overlook one of the terms of the equation or one of the sides of the equation when multiplying to write an equivalent equation. Remind these students that they must use every term of the equation as a factor to obtain an equivalent equation.

Teaching Strategy

Exercise 42 You may want to use this exercise to illustrate why it makes sense in some problems to substitute values in an equation to find possible combinations. Point out the side note to Example 5 which mentions the method of substitution as another way to find possible combinations. Point out that either method works well for Example 5. Then draw students' attention to Exercise 42. After they write the equation in part (a), ask them to find the intercepts of the equation. Discuss how the points (0, 63) and (84, 0) would make this a difficult problem to graph. Suggest that students pay attention to practical matters such as very large numbers when solving problems of this type.

41c.

Large rafts	Small rafts
16	0
14	5
12	10
10	15
8	20
6	25
4	30
2	35
0	40

40.

41b.

43. ⊕ **GEOMETRY** Write an equation in standard form that models the possible lengths and widths (in feet) of a rectangle having the same perimeter as a rectangle that is 10 feet wide and 20 feet long. Make a table that shows five possible lengths and widths of the rectangle.

$2\ell + 2w = 60$; see margin for table.

C **44.** **CHALLENGE** You are working in a chemistry lab. You have 1000 milliliters of pure acid. A dilution of acid is created by adding pure acid to water. A 40% dilution contains 40% acid and 60% water. You have been asked to make a 40% dilution and a 60% dilution of pure acid.

a. Write an equation in standard form that models the possible quantities of each dilution you can prepare using all 1000 milliliters of pure acid. **$0.4x + 0.6y = 1000$**

b. You prepare 700 milliliters of the 40% dilution. How much of the 60% dilution can you prepare? **1200 mL**

c. How much water do you need to prepare 700 milliliters of the 40% dilution? **420 mL**

MIXED REVIEW

PREVIEW
Prepare for Lesson 5.5 in Exs. 45–46.

Tell whether the graphs of the two equations are parallel lines. *Explain* your reasoning. *(p. 244)* **45–46. See margin.**

45. $1 - y = 4x$, $-6 = -4x - y$

46. $4x = 2y - 6$, $4 + y = -2x$

Write an equation in point-slope form of the line that passes through the given point and has the given slope m. *(p. 302)*

47. $(3, -4)$, $m = 1$
$y + 4 = x - 3$

48. $(-6, 6)$, $m = -2$
$y - 6 = -2(x + 6)$

49. $(-8, -1)$, $m = 5$
$y + 1 = 5(x + 8)$

QUIZ for Lessons 5.1–5.4

Write an equation in slope-intercept form of the line that passes through the given point and has the given slope m.

1. $(2, 5)$, $m = 3$ *(p. 292)*
$y = 3x - 1$

2. $(-1, 4)$, $m = -2$ *(p. 292)*
$y = -2x + 2$

3. $(0, -7)$, $m = 5$ *(p. 283)*
$y = 5x - 7$

Write an equation in slope-intercept form of the line that passes through the given points.

4. $(0, 2)$, $(9, 5)$ *(p. 283)*
$y = \frac{1}{3}x + 2$

5. $(5, 7)$, $(19, 14)$ *(p. 292)*
$y = \frac{1}{2}x + \frac{9}{2}$

6. $(4, 24)$, $(-11, 19)$ *(p. 292)*
$y = \frac{1}{3}x + \frac{68}{3}$

Write an equation in (a) point-slope form and (b) standard form of the line that passes through the given points. *(pp. 302, 311)* **7–9. See margin.**

7. $(-5, 2)$, $(-4, 3)$

8. $(0, -1)$, $(-6, -9)$

9. $(3, 9)$, $(1, 1)$

10. **DVDS** The table shows the price per DVD for different quantities of DVDs. Write an equation that models the price per DVD as a function of the number of DVDs purchased. *(p. 302)* **$y = -2x + 22$**

Number of DVDs purchased	1	2	3	4	5	6
Price per DVD (dollars)	20	18	16	14	12	10

45. Parallel; if you write each equation in slope-intercept form, you can see that the slopes are equal.

46. Not parallel; if you write each equation in slope-intercept form, you can see that the slopes are not equal.

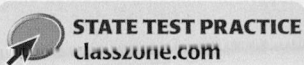

Lessons 5.1–5.4

1. **MULTI-STEP PROBLEM** A satellite radio company charges a monthly fee of $13 for service. To use the service, you must first buy equipment that costs $100.

   a. Identify the rate of change and starting value in this situation. **$13 per month; $100**

   b. Write an equation that gives the total cost of satellite radio as a function of the number of months of service. **$C = 13m + 100$**

   c. Find the total cost after 1 year of satellite radio service. **$256**

2. **MULTI-STEP PROBLEM** You hike 5 miles before taking a break. After your break, you continue to hike at an average speed of 3.5 miles per hour.

   a. Write an equation that gives the distance (in miles) that you hike as a function of the time (in hours) since your break. **$d = 3.5t + 5$**

   b. You hike for 4 hours after your break. Find the total distance you hike for the day. **19 mi**

3. **EXTENDED RESPONSE** The table shows the cost of a catered lunch buffet for different numbers of people.

Number of people	Cost (dollars)
12	192
18	288
24	384
30	480
36	576
42	672

   a. *Explain* why the situation can be modeled by a linear equation. **See margin.**

   b. Write an equation that gives the cost of the lunch buffet as a function of the number of people attending. **$C = 16p$**

   c. What is the cost of a lunch buffet for 120 people? **$1920**

4. **SHORT RESPONSE** You use a garden hose to fill a swimming pool at a constant rate. The pool is empty when you begin to fill it. The pool contains 15 gallons of water after 5 minutes. After 30 minutes, the pool contains 90 gallons of water. Write an equation that gives the volume (in gallons) of water in the pool as a function of the number of minutes since you began filling it. *Explain* how you can find the time it takes to put 150 gallons of water in the pool. **$V = 3t$; substitute 150 for V and solve for t; $t = 50$ minutes.**

5. **EXTENDED RESPONSE** A city is paving a bike path. The same length of path is paved each day. After 4 days, there are 8 miles of path remaining to be paved. After 6 more days, there are 5 miles of path remaining to be paved.

   a. *Explain* how you know the situation can be modeled by a linear equation. **See margin.**

   b. Write an equation that gives the distance (in miles) remaining to be paved as a function of the number of days since the project began. **$d = -\frac{1}{2}d + 10$**

   c. In how many more days will the entire path be paved? **20 days**

6. **OPEN-ENDED** Write an equation in standard form that models the possible combinations of nickels and dimes worth a certain amount of money (in dollars). List several of these possible combinations. **See margin.**

7. **GRIDDED ANSWER** You are saving money to buy a stereo system. You have saved $50 so far. You plan to save $20 each week for the next few months. How much money do you expect to have saved in 7 weeks? **$190**

8. **GRIDDED ANSWER** The cost of renting a moving van for a 26 mile trip is $62.50. The cost of renting the same van for a 38 mile trip is $65.50. The cost changes at a constant rate with respect to the length (in miles) of the trip. Find the total cost of renting the van for a 54 mile trip. **$69.50**

3a. Because the cost increases at a constant rate of $16 per person, the situation can be modeled by a linear equation.

5a. Because the same length of path is paved each day, the situation can be modeled by a linear equation.

6. *Sample answer:* $0.05n + 0.1d = 3$;

Nickels	Dimes
60	0
50	5
40	10
30	15
20	20
10	25
0	30

1 PLAN AND PREPARE

Explore the Concept

- Students will explore whether converses of conditional statements are true.

- This activity leads into the study of parallel lines and perpendicular lines in Lesson 5.5.

Materials

Each student will need 10 index cards.

Recommended Time

Work activity: 10 min
Discuss results: 5 min

Grouping

Students should work individually.

2 TEACH

Alternative Strategy

When you begin this activity, have one student select two cards, and then write the conditional statement on the board. If the statement is false, have the student write a counterexample. Ask a second student to write the converse of the conditional statement on the board. Ask the class whether the converse is true or false.

Key Discovery

The converse of a conditional statement may be true or false.

3 ASSESS AND RETEACH

If a conditional statement is false, is the converse always false? Always true? Justify your answer. **The converse of a false statement may be true or false. Examples: The statement "if it swims, it is a duck" is false, while its converse "if it is a duck, it swims" is true. The statement "If it is a tree, it has wings" is false, and its converse "if it has wings, it is a tree" also is false.**

5.5 If–Then Statements and Their Converses

MATERIALS • index cards

QUESTION Is the converse of a conditional statement true?

In Lesson 2.1, you learned that an if-then statement is a form of a conditional statement where the *if* part contains the hypothesis and the *then* part contains the conclusion. The *converse* of an if-then statement interchanges the hypothesis and conclusion of the original statement.

EXPLORE Write the converse

STEP 1 *Make cards*

Write each phrase below on a separate index card.

it swims	it is a tree	it flies	it needs water	it has wings
it is a duck	it grows	it is a bird	it is an airplane	it is a frog

STEP 2 *Write the conditional statement*

Place the cards face down. Select a card at random to be the hypothesis. Select another card at random to be the conclusion. Write the statement and determine whether it is true or false. If it is false, give a counterexample.

Hypothesis: it is a duck   Conclusion: it has wings

Statement: If it is a duck, then it has wings.
The statement is true. All ducks have wings.

STEP 3 *Write the converse*

Switch the order of the cards to create the converse statement. Determine whether the converse is true or false. If it is false, give a counterexample.

Hypothesis: it has wings   Conclusion: it is a duck

Statement: If it has wings, then it is a duck.
The statement is false. Airplanes have wings, but they are not ducks.

STEP 4 *Repeat*

Repeat Steps 2 and 3 ten times. Keep a record of your conditional statements and their converses.

DRAW CONCLUSIONS Use your observations to complete these exercises

1. **REASONING** If a conditional statement is true, can you be sure that its converse is true? *Justify* your answer. **See margin.**

2. **REASONING** If the converse of a statement is true, can you be sure that the original statement is true? *Justify* your answer. **No. *Sample answer:* If you picked *it needs water* and *it is a tree*, the converse would be *If it is a tree, then it needs water*, which is true. The original statement is *If it needs water, then it is a tree*, which is not true, a duck needs water, but it is not a tree.**

318 Chapter 5 Writing Linear Equations

1. No. *Sample answer:* If you picked *it is a bird* and *it flies*, the statement would be *If it is a bird, then it flies*, which is true. The converse statement is *If it flies, then it is a bird*, which is not true; an airplane flies, but it is not a bird.

5.5 Write Equations of Parallel and Perpendicular Lines

Before You used slope to determine whether lines are parallel.

Now You will write equations of parallel and perpendicular lines.

Why? So you can analyze growth rates, as in Ex. 33.

Key Vocabulary
• converse
• perpendicular lines
• conditional statement, *p. 66*

The **converse** of a conditional statement interchanges the hypothesis and conclusion. The converse of a true statement is not necessarily true.

In Chapter 4, you learned that the statement "If two nonvertical lines have the same slope, then they are parallel" is true. Its converse is also true.

KEY CONCEPT   *For Your Notebook*

Parallel Lines

• If two nonvertical lines in the same plane have the same slope, then they are parallel.

• If two nonvertical lines in the same plane are parallel, then they have the same slope.

EXAMPLE 1   Write an equation of a parallel line

Write an equation of the line that passes through $(-3, -5)$ and is parallel to the line $y = 3x - 1$.

Solution

STEP 1 **Identify** the slope. The graph of the given equation has a slope of 3. So, the parallel line through $(-3, -5)$ has a slope of 3.

STEP 2 **Find** the y-intercept. Use the slope and the given point.

$$y = mx + b \qquad \text{Write slope-intercept form.}$$
$$-5 = 3(-3) + b \qquad \text{Substitute 3 for } m, -3 \text{ for } x, \text{ and } -5 \text{ for } y.$$
$$4 = b \qquad \text{Solve for } b.$$

STEP 3 **Write** an equation. Use $y = mx + b$.

$$y = 3x + 4 \qquad \text{Substitute 3 for } m \text{ and 4 for } b.$$

CHECK REASONABLENESS
You can check that your answer is reasonable by graphing both lines.

✓ **GUIDED PRACTICE** for Example 1

1. Write an equation of the line that passes through $(-2, 11)$ and is parallel to the line $y = -x + 5$. $y = -x + 9$

Motivating the Lesson

Your dad is planning to plant two red oak trees in your backyard. He wants to know how tall they will be in six years. One tree is 56 inches high and the other is 63 inches high. Red oaks grow at an average rate of 24 inches per year. By writing two equations that model the growth of the trees, you can predict the height of each tree in six years.

③ TEACH

Extra Example 1

Write an equation of the line that passes through $(-3, 3)$ and is parallel to the line $y = -2x + 1$.
$y = -2x - 3$

Key Questions to Ask for Example 1

- How are the parallel lines different? **They have different y-intercepts.**
- If two lines have different y-intercepts, are they parallel? Explain. **No. The line $y = x + 3$ and the line $y = 2x + 1$ have different y-intercepts, but they are not parallel since they have different slopes.**

Extra Example 2

Determine which lines, if any, are parallel or perpendicular.
Line a: $-x + 3y = 1$
Line b: $y = -3x + 1$
Line c: $2x - 6y = 4$

Lines a and c have slopes of $\frac{1}{3}$, so they are parallel. Line b has a slope of -3, the negative reciprocal of $\frac{1}{3}$, so it is perpendicular to lines a and c.

PERPENDICULAR LINES Two lines in the same plane are **perpendicular** if they intersect to form a right angle. Horizontal and vertical lines are perpendicular to each other.

Compare the slopes of the perpendicular lines shown below.

Rotate the line 90° in a clockwise direction about the origin to find a perpendicular line.

USE FRACTIONS
The product of a nonzero number m and its negative reciprocal is -1:
$$m\left(-\frac{1}{m}\right) = -1.$$

KEY CONCEPT
For Your Notebook

Perpendicular Lines

- If two nonvertical lines in the same plane have slopes that are negative reciprocals, then the lines are perpendicular.

- If two nonvertical lines in the same plane are perpendicular, then their slopes are negative reciprocals.

EXAMPLE 2 Determine whether lines are parallel or perpendicular

Determine which lines, if any, are parallel or perpendicular.

Line a: $y = 5x - 3$ **Line b:** $x + 5y = 2$ **Line c:** $-10y - 2x = 0$

Solution

Find the slopes of the lines.

Line a: The equation is in slope-intercept form. The slope is 5.

Write the equations for lines b and c in slope-intercept form.

Line b: $x + 5y = 2$ **Line c:** $-10y - 2x = 0$

$$5y = -x + 2 \qquad\qquad -10y = 2x$$

$$y = -\frac{1}{5}x + \frac{2}{5} \qquad\qquad y = -\frac{1}{5}x$$

▶ Lines b and c have slopes of $-\frac{1}{5}$, so they are parallel. Line a has a slope of 5, the negative reciprocal of $-\frac{1}{5}$, so it is perpendicular to lines b and c.

✓ **GUIDED PRACTICE**   for Example 2

2. Determine which lines, if any, are parallel or perpendicular.

Line a: $2x + 6y = -3$ Line b: $y = 3x - 8$ Line c: $-1.5y + 4.5x = 6$

parallel: b and c; perpendicular: a and b, a and c

Differentiated Instruction

English Learners Some students may have trouble with the converse. The statements about parallel and perpendicular lines give examples with converses that are true. Give examples to illustrate that the converse of a logical statement is not always true. For example, "If a figure is a square, then it has four sides" is a true statement. The converse, "If a figure has four sides, then it is a square" is false (for example, the figure could be a rectangle).

See also the *Algebra 1 Toolkit* for more strategies.

EXAMPLE 3 Determine whether lines are perpendicular

STATE FLAG The Arizona state flag is shown in a coordinate plane. Lines *a* and *b* appear to be perpendicular. Are they?

Line *a*: $12y = -7x + 42$

Line *b*: $11y = 16x - 52$

Solution

Find the slopes of the lines. Write the equations in slope-intercept form.

Line *a*: $12y = -7x + 42$ Line *b*: $11y = 16x - 52$

$$y = -\frac{7}{12}x + \frac{42}{12}$$ $$y = \frac{16}{11}x - \frac{52}{11}$$

▶ The slope of line *a* is $-\frac{7}{12}$. The slope of line *b* is $\frac{16}{11}$. The two slopes are not

negative reciprocals, so lines *a* and *b* are not perpendicular.

EXAMPLE 4 Write an equation of a perpendicular line

Write an equation of the line that passes through $(4, -5)$ and is perpendicular to the line $y = 2x + 3$.

Solution

STEP 1 **Identify** the slope. The graph of the given equation has a slope of 2. Because the slopes of perpendicular lines are negative reciprocals, the slope of the perpendicular line through $(4, -5)$ is $-\frac{1}{2}$.

STEP 2 **Find** the *y*-intercept. Use the slope and the given point.

$y = mx + b$ Write slope-intercept form.

$-5 = -\frac{1}{2}(4) + b$ Substitute $-\frac{1}{2}$ for *m*, 4 for *x*, and -5 for *y*.

$-3 = b$ Solve for *b*.

STEP 3 **Write** an equation.

$y = mx + b$ Write slope-intercept form.

$y = -\frac{1}{2}x - 3$ Substitute $-\frac{1}{2}$ for *m* and -3 for *b*.

✓ **GUIDED PRACTICE** for Examples 3 and 4

3. Is line *a* perpendicular to line *b*? *Justify* your answer using slopes.

   Line *a*: $2y + x = -12$ Line *b*: $2y = 3x - 8$

4. Write an equation of the line that passes through $(4, 3)$ and is perpendicular to the line $y = 4x - 7$. $y = -\frac{1}{4}x + 4$

3. No; the slope of line *a* is $-\frac{1}{2}$, the slope of line *b* is $\frac{3}{2}$. The slopes are not negative reciprocals so the lines are not perpendicular.

Extra Example 3

The path of a golf ball bouncing off a curved wall on a miniature golf course is shown in a coordinate plane. Lines *a* and *b* of the path appear to be perpendicular. Are they?

Line *a*: $3y = 2x - 1$

Line *b*: $2y = -3x + 21$

The slope of line *a* is $\frac{2}{3}$. The slope of line *b* is $-\frac{3}{2}$. The two slopes are negative reciprocals, so the lines are perpendicular.

Extra Example 4

Write an equation of the line that passes through $(4, -2)$ and is perpendicular to the line $y = 4x + 2$.

$y = -\frac{1}{4}x - 1$

Closing the Lesson

Have students summarize the major points of the lesson and answer the Essential Question: How do you write equations of parallel and perpendicular lines?

• Two nonvertical lines have the same slope if and only if they are parallel.

• The slopes of two nonvertical lines are negative reciprocals if and only if the lines are perpendicular.

Identify the slope of the line. Use the same slope and a different *y*-intercept to write an equation of a parallel line. Use the negative reciprocal of the slope to write an equation of a perpendicular line.

5.5 **EXERCISES**

HOMEWORK
KEY
○ = **WORKED-OUT SOLUTIONS**
on p. WS1 for Exs. 19 and 33

★ = **STANDARDIZED TEST PRACTICE**
Exs. 2, 16, 17, 28, 30, 34, and 36

4 PRACTICE AND APPLY

Assignment Guide

📓 **Answer Transparencies**
available for all exercises

Basic:
Day 1: pp. 322–324
Exs. 1–8, 12–22, 27, 28, 32–35, 38–42

Average:
Day 1: pp. 322–324
Exs. 1, 2, 7–17, 23–30, 32–37, 39, 41, 42

Advanced:
Day 1: pp. 322–324
Exs. 1, 2, 8–11, 13–17, 24–37*, 40–42

Block:
pp. 322–324
Exs. 1, 2, 7–17, 23–30, 32–37, 39, 41, 42 (with 5.4)

Differentiated Instruction

See *Algebra 1 Best Practices Toolkit* for suggestions on addressing the needs of a diverse classroom.

Homework Check

For a quick check of student understanding of key concepts, go over the following exercises:
Basic: 6, 12, 16, 20, 32
Average: 8, 14, 24, 32, 34
Advanced: 10, 15, 26, 32, 34

Extra Practice

• Student Edition, p. 942
• Chapter 5 Resource Book:
  Practice levels A, B, C, pp. 52–54

Practice Worksheet

An easily-readable reduced practice page (with answers) for this lesson can be found on p. 280C.

SKILL PRACTICE

A

1. **VOCABULARY** Copy and complete: Two lines in a plane are _?_ if they intersect to form a right angle. **perpendicular**

2. ★ **WRITING** *Explain* how you can tell whether two lines are perpendicular, given the equations of the lines. **Identify the slopes of the lines. If the slopes are negative reciprocals, then the lines are perpendicular.**

EXAMPLE 1
on p. 319
for Exs. 3–11

PARALLEL LINES Write an equation of the line that passes through the given point and is parallel to the given line.

3. $(-1, 3)$, $y = 2x + 2$
$y = 2x + 5$

4. $(6, 8)$, $y = -\frac{5}{2}x + 10$
$y = -\frac{5}{2}x + 23$

5. $(5, -1)$, $y = -\frac{3}{5}x - 3$
$y = -\frac{3}{5}x + 2$

6. $(-1, 2)$, $y = 5x + 4$
$y = 5x + 7$

7. $(1, 7)$, $-6x + y = -1$
$y = 6x + 1$

8. $(18, 2)$, $3y = x - 12$
$y = \frac{1}{3}x - 4$

9. $(-2, 5)$, $2y = 4x - 6$
$y = 2x + 9$

10. $(9, 4)$, $y = x - 3$
$y = x - 5$

11. $(-10, 0)$, $-y + 3x = 16$
$y = 3x + 30$

EXAMPLE 2
on p. 320
for Exs. 12–16

PARALLEL OR PERPENDICULAR Determine which lines, if any, are parallel or perpendicular.

12. Line a: $y = 4x - 2$, Line b: $y = -\frac{1}{4}x$, Line c: $y = -4x + 1$
parallel: none; perpendicular: a and b

13. Line a: $y = \frac{3}{5}x + 1$, Line b: $5y = 3x - 2$, Line c: $10x - 6y = -4$
parallel: a and b; perpendicular: none

14. Line a: $y = 3x + 6$, Line b: $3x + y = 6$, Line c: $3y = 2x + 18$
parallel: none; perpendicular: none

15. Line a: $4x - 3y = 2$, Line b: $3x + 4y = -1$, Line c: $4y - 3x = 20$
parallel: none; perpendicular: a and b

17. The line through points (6, 4) and (4, 1) is perpendicular to the line through points (1, 3) and (4, 1); the slope of the line through the points (6, 4) and (4, 1) is $\frac{3}{2}$, the slope of the line through the points (1, 3) and (4, 1) is $-\frac{2}{3}$. The slopes are negative reciprocals, so the lines are perpendicular.

16. ★ **MULTIPLE CHOICE** Which statement is true of the given lines? **D**

Line a: $-2x + y = 4$ Line b: $2x + 5y = 2$ Line c: $x + 2y = 4$

(A) Lines a and b are parallel.
(B) Lines a and c are parallel.
(C) Lines a and b are perpendicular.
(D) Lines a and c are perpendicular.

17. ★ **SHORT RESPONSE** Determine which of the lines shown, if any, are parallel or perpendicular. *Justify* your answer using slopes.

Animated Algebra at classzone.com

EXAMPLE 4
on p. 321
for Exs. 18–27

PERPENDICULAR LINES Write an equation of the line that passes through the given point and is perpendicular to the given line.

18. $(3, -3)$, $y = x + 5$
$y = -x$

19. $(-9, 2)$, $y = 3x - 12$
$y = -\frac{1}{3}x - 1$

20. $(5, 1)$, $y = 5x - 2$
$y = -\frac{1}{5}x + 2$

21. $(7, 10)$, $y = 0.5x - 9$
$y = -2x + 24$

22. $(-2, -4)$, $y = -\frac{2}{7}x + 1$
$y = \frac{7}{2}x + 3$

23. $(-4, -1)$, $y = \frac{4}{3}x + 6$
$y = -\frac{3}{4}x - 4$

24. $(3, 3)$, $2y = 3x - 6$
$y = -\frac{2}{3}x + 5$

25. $(-5, 2)$, $y + 3 = 2x$
$y = -\frac{1}{2}x - \frac{1}{2}$

26. $(8, -1)$, $4y + 2x = 12$
$y = 2x - 17$

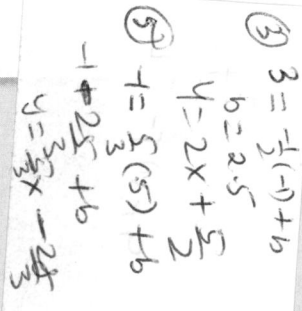

27. ERROR ANALYSIS *Describe* and correct the error in finding the *y*-intercept of the line that passes through (2, 1) and is perpendicular to the line $y = -\frac{1}{2}x + 3$.
(2, 1) was substituted incorrectly, 2 should be substituted for *x*, and 1 should be substituted for *y*; 1 = 2(2) + *b*, 1 = 4 + *b*, −3 = *b*.

$$y = mx + b$$
$$2 = 2(1) + b$$
$$0 = b$$

B **28. ★ MULTIPLE CHOICE** Which equation represents the line that passes through (0, 0) and is parallel to the line passing through (2, 3) and (6, 1)? **B**

(A) $y = \frac{1}{2}x$ (B) $y = -\frac{1}{2}x$ (C) $y = -2x$ (D) $y = 2x$

29. REASONING Is the line through (4, 3) and (3, −1) perpendicular to the line through (−3, 3) and (1, 2)? *Justify* your answer using slopes. **See margin.**

C **30. ★ OPEN-ENDED** Write equations of two lines that are parallel. Then write an equation of a line that is perpendicular to those lines.

30. *Sample answer:* $y = 2x + 1$ and $y = 2x + 3$; $y = -\frac{1}{2}x + 2$

31. CHALLENGE Write a formula for the slope of a line that is perpendicular to the line through the points (x_1, y_1) and

---

PROBLEM SOLVING

EXAMPLES A
3 and 4
on p. 321
for Exs. 32, 34

32. HOCKEY A hockey puck leaves the blad bounces off a wall, and travels in a new

a. Write an equation that models the p the blade of the hockey stick to the

b. Write an equation that models the path of the puck after it bounces off the wall. $y = -2x + 8$

c. Does the path of the puck form a right angle? *Justify* your answer.

32c. No; the slopes −2 and 2 are not negative reciprocals.

@HomeTutor for problem solving help at classzone.com

(33.) **BIOLOGY** While nursing, blue whale calves can gain weight at a rate of 200 pounds per day. Two particular calves weigh 6000 pounds and 6250 pounds at birth.

a. Write equations that model the weight of each calf as a function of the number of days since birth. $w_1 = 200d + 6000$; $w_2 = 200d + 6250$

b. How much is each calf expected to weigh 30 days after birth? **12,000 lb; 12,250 lb**

c. How are the graphs of the equations from part (a) related? *Justify* your answer.

33c. The graphs of the lines are parallel because they have the same slope, 200. The *w*-intercept of the second line is 250 more than the *w*-intercept of the first line.

@HomeTutor for problem solving help at classzone.com

34. ★ SHORT RESPONSE The map shows several streets in a city. Determine which of the streets, if any, are parallel or perpendicular. *Justify* your answer using slopes. **See margin.**

Park: $3y - 2x = 12$ Main: $y = -6x + 44$

2nd St.: $3y = 2x - 13$ Sea: $2y = -3x + 37$

5.5 Write Equations of Parallel and Perpendicular Lines   **323**

---

29. Yes; the slope of the line through (4, 3) and (3, −1) is 4 and the slope of the line through (−3, 3) and (1, 2) is $-\frac{1}{4}$. The slopes are negative reciprocals, so the lines are perpendicular.

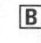
34. Parallel: 2nd Street and Park Street; the slope of both streets is $\frac{2}{3}$. Since they have the same slope, the streets are parallel. Perpendicular: 2nd Street and Sea Street, Park Street and Sea Street; the slope of Sea Street is $-\frac{3}{2}$, which is the negative reciprocal of $\frac{2}{3}$, the slope of 2nd Street and Park Street. Since the slopes are negative reciprocals, the streets are perpendicular.

Daily Homework Quiz

📑 **Transparency Available**

1. Write an equation of the line that passes through the point $(-1, 4)$ and is parallel to the line $y = 5x - 2$. **$y = 5x + 9$**

2. Write an equation of the line that passes through the point $(-1, -1)$ and is perpendicular to the line $y = -\frac{1}{4}x + 2$.

   $y = 4x + 3$

3. Paths a, b, and c are shown in the coordinate grid. Determine which paths, if any, are parallel or perpendicular. Justify your answer using slopes.

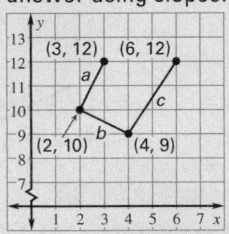

Paths a and b are perpendicular because their slopes, 2 and $-\frac{1}{2}$, are negative reciprocals. No paths are parallel.

Online Quiz

Available at **classzone.com**

Diagnosis/Remediation

- Practice A, B, C in Chapter 5 Resource Book, pp. 52–54
- Study Guide in Chapter 5 Resource Book, pp. 55–56
- Practice Workbook, pp. 76–77
- @HomeTutor

Challenge

Additional challenge is available in the Chapter 5 Resource Book, p. 59.

---

35. Different registration fees; because the lines are parallel, the rate of change, the monthly fee, for each must be equal. Therefore, the students paid different registration fees.

36c. The graphs of the lines are parallel; they have the same slope, 38.75. The C-intercept of the second graph is 100 more than the C-intercept of the first graph.

37b. The graphs of the lines are parallel; they have the same slope, -2.5. The y-intercept of the second line is 20 less than the y-intercept of the first line.

B 35. **SOFTBALL** A softball training academy charges students a monthly fee plus an initial registration fee. The total amounts paid by two students are given by the functions $f(x)$ and $g(x)$ where x is the numbers of months the students have been members of the academy. The graphs of f and g are parallel lines. Did the students pay different monthly fees or different registration fees? How do you know?

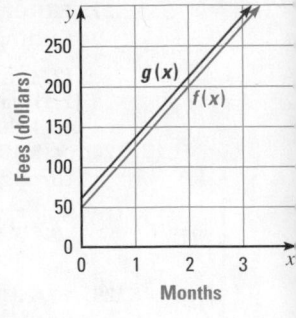

36. ★ **EXTENDED RESPONSE** If you are one of the first 100 people to join a new health club, you are charged a joining fee of $49. Otherwise, you are charged a joining fee of $149. The monthly membership cost is $38.75.

   a. Write an equation that gives the total cost (in dollars) of membership as a function of the number of months of membership if you are one of the first 100 members to join. **$C = 38.75m + 49$**

   b. Write an equation that gives the total cost (in dollars) of membership as a function of the number of months of membership if you are *not* one of the first 100 members to join. **$C = 38.75m + 149$**

   c. How are the graphs of these functions related? How do you know?

   d. After 6 months, what is the difference in total cost for a person who paid $149 to join and a person who paid $49 to join? after 12 months? **$100; $100**

C 37. **CHALLENGE** You and your friend have gift cards to a shopping mall. Your card has a value of $50, and your friend's card has a value of $30. If neither of you uses the cards, the value begins to decrease at a rate of $2.50 per month after 6 months.

   a. Write two equations, one that gives the value of your card and another that gives the value of your friend's card as functions of the number of months after 6 months of nonuse. **$y = -2.5x + 50; y = -2.5x + 30$**

   b. How are the graphs of these functions related? How do you know?

   c. What are the x-intercepts of the graphs of the functions, and what do they mean in this situation? **20; 12; the x-intercepts show the number of months of nonuse it would take for the value of the gift card to be $0.**

MIXED REVIEW

Solve the equation or proportion.

38. $5z + 6z = 77$ *(p. 141)* **7**   39. $-8n = 4(3n + 5)$ *(p. 148)* **−1**   40. $\frac{3}{5} = \frac{t}{7}$ *(p. 162)* **4.2**

PREVIEW
Prepare for Lesson 5.6 in Ex. 41.

41. **CAMPING** The table shows the cost C (in dollars) for one person to stay at a campground for n nights. *(p. 253)*

   a. *Explain* why C varies directly with n. **See margin.**

   b. Write a direct variation equation that relates C and n. **$c = 15n$**

Number of nights, n	1	3	5	9
Cost, C (in dollars)	15	45	75	135

42. Write an equation in standard form of the line that passes through the points $(3, -9)$ and $(12, 9)$. *(p. 311)* **$-2x + y = -15$**

41a. Compare the ratios, $\frac{c}{n}$, for all data pairs (n, c): $\frac{15}{1} = \frac{45}{3} = \frac{75}{5} = \frac{135}{9} = 15.$
Because the ratios all equal 15, c varies directly with n.

5.6 Fit a Line to Data

Before You modeled situations involving a constant rate of change.

Now You will make scatter plots and write equations to model data.

Why? So you can model scientific data, as in Ex. 19.

Key Vocabulary
• scatter plot
• correlation
• line of fit

A **scatter plot** is a graph used to determine whether there is a relationship between paired data. Scatter plots can show trends in the data.

  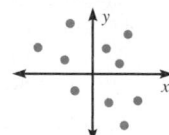

If *y* tends to increase as *x* increases, the paired data are said to have a **positive correlation**.

If *y* tends to decrease as *x* increases, the paired data are said to have a **negative correlation**.

If *x* and *y* have no apparent relationship, the paired data are said to have **relatively no correlation**.

EXAMPLE 1 Describe the correlation of data

Describe the correlation of the data graphed in the scatter plot.

a.

Hours of studying

b.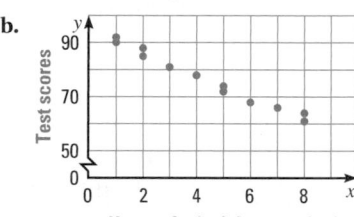

Hours of television watched

a. The scatter plot shows a positive correlation between hours of studying and test scores. This means that as the hours of studying increased, the test scores tended to increase.

b. The scatter plot shows a negative correlation between hours of television watched and test scores. This means that as the hours of television watched increased, the test scores tended to decrease.

✓ **GUIDED PRACTICE** for Example 1

1. Using the scatter plots in Example 1, predict a reasonable test score for 4.5 hours of studying and 4.5 hours of television watched.
   Sample answer: 72, 77

5.6 Fit a Line to Data **325**

Resource Planning Guide

Chapter Resource Book
• Teaching Guide/Lesson Plan (pp. 60–61)
• Activity Master (p. 62)
• Practice levels A, B, C (pp. 63–68)
• Study Guide (pp. 69–70)
• Catch-up for Absent Students (p. 71)
• Application (p. 72)
• Challenge (p. 73)

Workbooks
• Notetaking Guide (pp. 117–120)
• Practice Workbook (pp. 78–80)

Teaching Options
• **Power Presentations CD-ROM** provides dynamic electronic teaching resources for the classroom.
• **Activity Generator CD-ROM** provides editable activities for all ability levels.

Interactive Technology
• Easy Planner
• Power Presentations CD-ROM
• Activity Generator CD-ROM
• Animated Algebra
• Test Generator CD-ROM
• Online Quiz
• eWorkbook
• eEdition
• @HomeTutor

Resources for English Learners
• Quick Reference for English Learners
• Spanish Study Guide
• Multi-Language Visual Glossary
• Student Resources in Spanish

See also the *Algebra 1 Toolkit* for more strategies for meeting individual needs.

325

---

① PLAN AND PREPARE

Warm-Up Exercises
▭ Transparency Available

Find the slope of the line that passes through the point.

1. $(-4, 1)$ and $(6, -4)$ $-\frac{1}{2}$

2. $(2, -3)$ and $(-1, 6)$ -3

3. Your commission *c* varies directly with the number *s* of pairs you sell. You made $180 when you sold 15 pairs of shoes. Write a direct variation equation that relates *c* to *s*. $c = 12s$

Notetaking Guide
▭ Transparency Available

Promotes interactive learning and notetaking skills, pp. 117–120.

Pacing
Basic: 1 day
Average: 1 day
Advanced: 1 day
Block: 0.5 block with 5.7
• See *Teaching Guide/Lesson Plan*.

② FOCUS AND MOTIVATE

Essential Question
Big Idea 3, p. 281

How do you make scatter plots and write equations to model data?
Tell students they will learn how to answer this question by graphing data pairs and by finding a line of fit for the data pairs.

NCTM STANDARDS
Standard 5: Collect, organize, and display data; Select proper statistical methods to analyze data

EXAMPLE 2   Make a scatter plot

SWIMMING SPEEDS The table shows the lengths (in centimeters) and swimming speeds (in centimeters per second) of six fish.

Fish	Pike	Red gurnard	Black bass	Gurnard	Norway haddock
Length (cm)	37.8	19.2	21.3	26.2	26.8
Speed (cm/sec)	148	47	88	131	98

a. Make a scatter plot of the data.

b. *Describe* the correlation of the data.

Solution

a. Treat the data as ordered pairs. Let *x* represent the fish length (in centimeters), and let *y* represent the speed (in centimeters per second). Plot the ordered pairs as points in a coordinate plane.

b. The scatter plot shows a positive correlation, which means that longer fish tend to swim faster.

Fish Swimming Speeds

✓ **GUIDED PRACTICE**   for Example 2

2. Make a scatter plot of the data in the table. *Describe* the correlation of the data.

x	1	1	2	3	3	4	5	5	6
y	2	3	4	4	5	5	5	7	8

See margin for art; the scatter plot shows a positive correlation.

MODELING DATA When data show a positive or negative correlation, you can model the trend in the data using a **line of fit**.

KEY CONCEPT   *For Your Notebook*

Using a Line of Fit to Model Data

STEP 1 **Make** a scatter plot of the data.

STEP 2 **Decide** whether the data can be modeled by a line.

STEP 3 **Draw** a line that appears to fit the data closely. There should be approximately as many points above the line as below it.

STEP 4 **Write** an equation using two points on the line. The points do not have to represent actual data pairs, but they must lie on the line of fit.

326

EXAMPLE 3 **Write an equation to model data**

BIRD POPULATIONS The table shows the number of active red-cockaded woodpecker clusters in a part of the De Soto National Forest in Mississippi. Write an equation that models the number of active clusters as a function of the number of years since 1990.

Year	1992	1993	1994	1995	1996	1997	1998	1999	2000
Active clusters	22	24	27	27	34	40	42	45	51

Solution

STEP 1 **Make** a scatter plot of the data. Let x represent the number of years since 1990. Let y represent the number of active clusters.

STEP 2 **Decide** whether the data can be modeled by a line. Because the scatter plot shows a positive correlation, you can fit a line to the data.

Years since 1990

STEP 3 **Draw** a line that appears to fit the points in the scatter plot closely.

STEP 4 **Write** an equation using two points on the line. Use (2, 20) and (8, 42).

Find the slope of the line.

$$m = \frac{y_2 - y_1}{x_2 - x_1} = \frac{42 - 20}{8 - 2} = \frac{22}{6} = \frac{11}{3}$$

Find the y-intercept of the line. Use the point (2, 20).

$y = mx + b$	**Write slope-intercept form.**
$20 = \frac{11}{3}(2) + b$	**Substitute $\frac{11}{3}$ for m, 2 for x, and 20 for y.**
$\frac{38}{3} = b$	**Solve for b.**

An equation of the line of fit is $y = \frac{11}{3}x + \frac{38}{3}$.

▶ The number y of active woodpecker clusters can be modeled by the function $y = \frac{11}{3}x + \frac{38}{3}$ where x is the number of years since 1990.

Animated Algebra at classzone.com

✓ **GUIDED PRACTICE** **for Example 3**

3. Use the data in the table to write an equation that models y as a function of x.

x	1	2	3	4	5	6	8
y	3	5	8	9	11	12	14

Sample answer: $y = 1.6x + 2.3$

5.6 Fit a Line to Data **327**

2.

Extra Example 2

The table shows the carbohydrates (in grams) and the fiber (in grams) in six types of fruit.

Fruit	Fiber	Carb.
Apple	5	22
Banana	4	29
Blackberries	8	18
Figs	2	12
Guava	5	11
Peach	2	11

a. Make a scatter plot of the data.

Fruit Nutrition

Carbohydrates (grams) / Fiber (grams)

b. Describe the correlation of the data. **The scatter plot shows relatively no correlation, which means there is no general relationship between fiber and carbohydrates in fruit.**

Extra Example 3

The table shows the number of injured birds a person rehabilitated at a veterinary service. Write an equation that models the number of rehabilitated birds as a function of the number of years years since 1995.

Year	Birds
1997	8
1998	11
1999	12
2000	12
2001	15
2002	19
2003	21

The number of rehabilitated birds can be modeled by the function $y = 2.07x + 3.64$ where x is the number of years since 1995.

Extra Example 4

Refer to the model on the number of birds in Extra Example 3.

a. Describe the domain and range of the function. **The domain is the period 1997 to 2003. Since x is the number of years after 1995, the domain is $2 \leq x \leq 8$. The range is the number of birds given by the model, so the range is about $8 \leq y \leq 20$.**

b. At what rate did the number of rehabilitated birds change from 1997 to 2003? **The number of rehabilitated birds increased at a rate of 2 birds per year.**

Closing the Lesson

Have students summarize the major points of the lesson and answer the Essential Question: How do you make scatter plots and write equations to model data?

• A scatter plot shows whether there is a positive, negative, or no correlation in the data.

• A line of fit can model data. The points you use to find the equation must be on the line, but they do not have to be actual data values.

Plot paired data in a coordinate plane. For a positive or negative correlation, draw a line of fit, with about the same number of points above and below the line. Use two points on the line to find the slope and then use the slope and a point to find the y-intercept. Write an equation of the line.

2. When data has a positive correlation, the dependent variable tends to increase as the independent variable increases. When data has a negative correlation, the dependent variable tends to decrease as the independent variable increases. When data has relatively no correlation there is no apparent relationship between the independent variable and the dependent variable.

328

EXAMPLE 4 **Interpret a model**

Refer to the model for the number of woodpecker clusters in Example 3.

   a. *Describe* the domain and range of the function.

   b. At about what rate did the number of active woodpecker clusters change during the period 1992–2000?

Solution

   a. The domain of the function is the the period from 1992 to 2000, or $2 \leq x \leq 10$. The range is the the number of active clusters given by the function for $2 \leq x \leq 10$, or $20 \leq y \leq 49.3$.

   b. The number of active woodpecker clusters increased at a rate of $\frac{11}{3}$ or about 3.7 woodpecker clusters per year.

✓ **GUIDED PRACTICE**   **for Example 4**

   4. In Guided Practice Exercise 2, at about what rate does y change with respect to x? **about 1.6**

5.6 EXERCISES

SKILL PRACTICE

A **1. VOCABULARY** Copy and complete: When data have a positive correlation, the dependent variable tends to __?__ as the independent variable increases. **increase**

   2. ★ WRITING *Describe* how paired data with a positive correlation, a negative correlation, and relatively no correlation differ. **See margin.**

DESCRIBING CORRELATIONS Tell whether x and y show a *positive correlation*, a *negative correlation*, or *relatively no correlation*.

EXAMPLE 1
on p. 325
for Exs. 3–5, 10, 11

3.
positive correlation

4.
relatively no correlation

5.
negative correlation

EXAMPLES 2 and 3
on pp. 326–327
for Exs. 6–9

FITTING LINES TO DATA Make a scatter plot of the data in the table. Draw a line of fit. Write an equation of the line. 6–7. See margin for art.

6.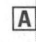

x	1	1	3	4	5	6	9
y	10	12	33	46	59	70	102

Sample answer: $y = 11.5x - 0.28$

7.

x	1.2	1.8	2.3	3.0	4.4	5.2
y	10	7	5	−1	−4	−8

Sample answer: $y = -4.4x + 14.88$

6.

7.

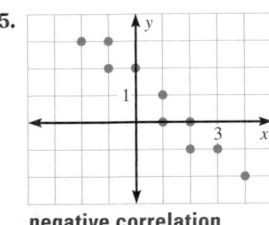

8. ★ **MULTIPLE CHOICE** Which equation best models the data in the scatter plot? **C**

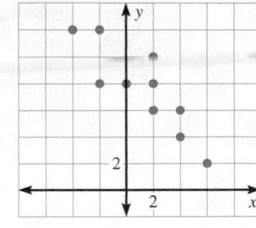

  A $y = -x - 6$ **B** $y = x - 6$

  C $y = -x + 8$ **D** $y = x + 8$

9. The line does not have approximately half the data above it and half below it; see margin for art.

10. The independent variable is *x*, not *y*; the dependent variable decreases as *x* increases.

9. ERROR ANALYSIS *Describe* and correct the error in fitting the line to the data in the scatter plot.

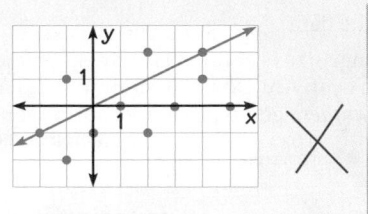

10. ERROR ANALYSIS *Describe* and correct the error in describing the correlation of the data in the scatter plot.

The data have a negative correlation. The independent variable decreases as x increases.

11. ★ **OPEN-ENDED** Give an example of a data set that shows a negative correlation. *Sample answer:* The amount of time driving a car and the amount of gas left in the gas tank.

B **12.** ★ **SHORT RESPONSE** Make a scatter plot of the data. *Describe* the correlation of the data. Is it possible to fit a line to the data? If so, write an equation of the line. If not, explain why.

12. See margin for art; relatively no correlation; no; because there is relatively no correlation in the data you cannot write an equation.

x	−12	−7	−4	−3	−1	2	5	6	7	9	15
y	150	50	15	10	1	5	22	37	52	90	226

MODELING DATA Make a scatter plot of the data. *Describe* the correlation of the data. If possible, fit a line to the data and write an equation of the line.

13–14. See margin for art.

13.

x	10	12	15	20	30	45	60	99
y	−2	4	9	16	32	55	87	128

positive correlation; *Sample answer:* $y = 1.49x - 13$

14.

x	−5	−3	−3	0	1	2	5	6
y	−4	12	10	−6	8	0	3	−9

relatively no correlation

C **15. CHALLENGE** Which line shown is a better line of fit for the scatter plot? *Explain* your reasoning.
Line *b*; line *a* has too many points below the line, but line *b* has about half the points above the line and about half the points below the line.

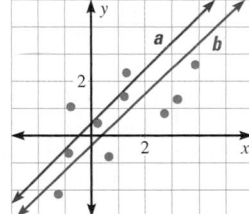

4 PRACTICE AND APPLY

Assignment Guide

📑 **Answer Transparencies available for all exercises**

Basic:
Day 1: EP p. 941 Exs. 1–7 odd
pp. 328–331
Exs. 1–12, 16–18, 22–28

Average:
Day 1: pp. 328–331
Exs. 1, 2, 4–14, 16–20, 22–28

Advanced:
Day 1: pp. 328–331
Exs. 1, 2, 4–8, 11–28*

Block:
pp. 328–331
Exs. 1, 2, 4–14, 16–20, 22–28
(with 5.7)

Differentiated Instruction

See *Algebra 1 Best Practices Toolkit* for suggestions on addressing the needs of a diverse classroom.

Homework Check

For a quick check of student understanding of key concepts, go over the following exercises:
Basic: 3, 6, 16, 17, 18
Average: 4, 7, 16, 17, 18
Advanced: 5, 7, 16, 17, 18

Extra Practice

• Student Edition, p. 942
• Chapter 5 Resource Book:
Practice levels A, B, C, pp. 63–68

Practice Worksheet

An easily-readable reduced practice page (with answers) for this lesson can be found on p. 280C.

9.

12.

13.

14.

Teaching Strategy

Exercise 8 You may want to point out to students that they can immediately eliminate the two choices with positive slope based on the correlation shown on the scatter plot.

 Internet Reference

Exercise 17 Additional information about the layers of Earth's atmosphere can be found at liftoff. msfc.nasa.gov/academy/space/atmosphere.html

Avoiding Common Errors

Exercises 17–21 Some students may draw a line through two of the points rather than a line of fit that models the data. Remind them that approximately the same number of points should lie above the line as below it, but that none of the points in the data set actually have to lie on the line.

Exercises 19–21 Some students may attempt to write an equation that models the data without making a scatter plot first. Remind these students that there is not a constant rate of change in the data, and that because of this, they need to plot the data so they can draw a line of fit.

16a.

17a.

EXAMPLE 2 A
on p. 326
for Exs. 16

16b. Positive correlation; the larger the home range size the larger the percent of pacing time.

EXAMPLES 3 and 4
on pp. 327–328
for Exs. 17–18

17b. *Sample answer:* $y = -2.2x + 111$

18. See margin for art; the growth rate of alligator 2 is slightly greater than the growth rate of alligator 1.

19. *Sample answer:*
$y = 12.6x + 32$

---

16. ★ **SHORT RESPONSE** The table shows the approximate home range size of big cats (members of the *Panthera* genus) in their natural habitat and the percent of time that the cats spend pacing in captivity.

Big cat (*Panthera* genus)	Lion	Jaguar	Leopard	Tiger
Home range size (km²)	148	90	34	48
Pacing (percent of time)	48	21	11	16

a. Make a scatter plot of the data. **See margin.**

b. *Describe* the correlation of the data.

c. The snow leopard's home range size is about 39 square kilometers. It paces about 7% of its time in captivity. Does the snow leopard fit the pacing trend of cats in the *Panthera* genus? *Explain* your reasoning. **No; it is below the expected percent of time spent pacing.**

@HomeTutor for problem solving help at classzone.com

17. **EARTH SCIENCE** The mesosphere is a layer of atmosphere that lies from about 50 kilometers above Earth's surface to about 90 kilometers above Earth's surface. The diagram shows the temperature at certain altitudes in the mesosphere.

a. Make a scatter plot of the data. **See margin.**

b. Write an equation that models the temperature (in degrees Celsius) as a function of the altitude (in kilometers) above 50 kilometers.

c. At about what rate does the temperature change with increasing altitude in the mesosphere? *Sample answer:* **−2.2 degrees per kilometers**

100 km	**Mesosphere**	
86 km	Altitude (km)	Temperature (°C)
	86	−86
	80	−65
52 km	75	−54
	70	−40
	65	−26
	60	−21
	52	−4
0 km		

@HomeTutor for problem solving help at classzone.com

18. B **ALLIGATORS** The table shows the weights of two alligators at various times during a feeding trial. Make two scatter plots, one for each alligator, where *x* is the number of weeks and *y* is the weight of the alligator. Draw lines of fit for both scatter plots. *Compare* the approximate growth rates.

Weeks	0	9	18	27	34	43	49
Alligator 1 weight (pounds)	6	8.6	10	13.6	15	17.2	19.8
Alligator 2 weight (pounds)	6	9.2	12.8	13.6	20.2	21.4	24.3

19. **GEOLOGY** The table shows the duration of several eruptions of the geyser Old Faithful and the interval between eruptions. Write an equation that models the interval as a function of an eruption's duration.

Duration (minutes)	1.5	2.0	2.5	3.0	3.5	4.0	4.5	5.0
Interval (minutes)	50	57	65	71	76	82	89	95

○ = **WORKED-OUT SOLUTIONS** on p. WS1   ★ = **STANDARDIZED TEST PRACTICE**

330

18.

20. DAYLIGHT The table shows the number of hours and minutes of daylight in Baltimore, Maryland, for ten days in January.

Day in January	5	6	7	8	9	10	11	12	13	14
Daylight (hours and minutes)	9:30	9:31	9:32	9:34	9:35	9:36	9:37	9:38	9:40	9:41

a. Write an equation that models the hours of daylight (in minutes in excess of 9 hours) as a function of the number of days since January 5.
Sample answer: $y = 1.2x + 30$

b. At what rate do the hours of daylight change over time in early January?
Sample answer: 1.2 min per day

c. Do you expect the trend described by the equation to continue indefinitely? *Explain.* **No; it will continue through June and then start decreasing.**

21c. Sample answer: $m = 13.884y + 39.808$; the function models the amount of money, *m*, spent on the Internet as a function of the number of years, *y*, since 1999.

21d. Yes, if you substitute the number of years since 1999 for *y*, you get about the amount of money, *m*, given in the data.

21. CHALLENGE The table shows the estimated amount of time and the estimated amount of money the average person in the U.S. spent on the Internet each year from 1999 to 2005.

Year	1999	2000	2001	2002	2003	2004	2005
Internet time (hours)	88	107	136	154	169	182	193
Internet spending (dollars)	40.55	49.64	68.70	84.73	97.76	110.46	122.67

a. Write an equation that models the amount of time *h* (in hours) spent on the Internet as a function of the number of years *y* since 1999.
Sample answer: $h = 17.8y + 93.6$

b. Write an equation that models the amount of money *m* spent on the Internet as a function of the time *h* (in hours) spent on the Internet.
Sample answer: $m = 0.78h - 33.2$

c. Substitute the expression that is equal to *h* from part (a) in the function from part (b). What does the new function tell you? **See margin.**

d. Does the function from part (c) agree with the data given? *Explain.*

MIXED REVIEW

PREVIEW
Prepare for Lesson 5.7 in Exs. 22–24.

Evaluate the function when $x = -2, 5,$ and 0. *(p. 262)*

22. $f(x) = 5x - 8$ **−18, 17, −8**   **23.** $g(x) = -10x$ **20, −50, 0**   **24.** $v(x) = 14 - 5x$ **24, −11, 14**

Write an equation of the line shown. *(p. 283)*

25.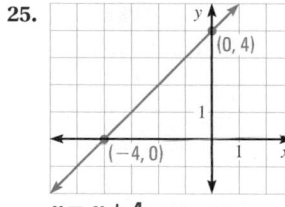

$y = x + 4$

26.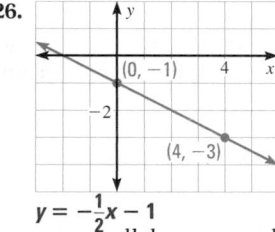

$y = -\frac{1}{2}x - 1$

27.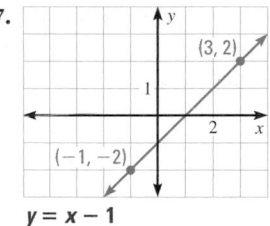

$y = x - 1$

28. Determine which lines, if any, are parallel or perpendicular. *(p. 319)*

Line *a*: $y = 2x - 5$ Line *b*: $2x + y = -5$ Line *c*: $4x - 2y = 3$
parallel: *a* and *c*

EXTRA PRACTICE for Lesson 5.6, p. 942   **ONLINE QUIZ** at classzone.com   **331**

⑤ ASSESS AND RETEACH

Daily Homework Quiz
Transparency Available

Tell whether *x* and *y* show a *positive correlation*, a *negative correlation*, or *relatively no correlation*.

1.
negative correlation

2. The table shows the body length and wingspan (both in inches) of seven birds. Write an equation that models the wingspan as a function of body length.

Bird	Body Length	Wing-span
Cuckoo	12	18
Falcon	16	41
Harrier	18	43
Hawk	19	51
Osprey	23	63
Sandpiper	9	22
Warbler	5	7

$y = 3.1x - 10.3$, where *x* is body length and *y* is wingspan

 Online Quiz

Available at **classzone.com**

Diagnosis/Remediation
• Practice A, B, C in Chapter 5 Resource Book, pp. 63–68
• Study Guide in Chapter 5 Resource Book, pp. 69–70
• Practice Workbook, pp. 78–80
• @HomeTutor

Challenge
Additional challenge is available in the Chapter 5 Resource Book, p. 73.

Use after Lesson 5.6

5.6 Perform Linear Regression

QUESTION How can you model data with the best-fitting line?

The line that most closely follows a trend in data is the *best-fitting line*. The process of finding the best-fitting line to model a set of data is called *linear regression*. This process can be tedious to perform by hand, but you can use a graphing calculator to make a scatter plot and perform linear regression on a data set.

EXAMPLE 1 Create a scatter plot

The table shows the total sales from women's clothing stores in the United States from 1997 to 2002. Make a scatter plot of the data. *Describe* the correlation of the data.

Year	1997	1998	1999	2000	2001	2002
Sales (billions of dollars)	27.9	28.7	30.2	32.5	33.1	34.3

STEP 1 **Enter data**

Press **STAT** and select Edit. Enter years since 1997 (0, 1, 2, 3, 4, 5) into List 1 (L_1). These will be the *x*-values. Enter sales (in billions of dollars) into List 2 (L_2). These will be the *y*-values.

STEP 2 **Choose plot settings**

Press **2nd** **Y=** and select Plot1. Turn Plot1 On. Select scatter plot as the type of display. Enter L_1 for the Xlist and L_2 for the Ylist.

STEP 3 **Make a scatter plot**

Press **ZOOM** 9 to display the scatter plot so that the points for all data pairs are visible.

STEP 4 **Describe the correlation**

Describe the correlation of the data in the scatter plot.

The data have a positive correlation. This means that with each passing year, the sales of women's clothing tended to increase.

---

① PLAN AND PREPARE

Learn the Method

- Students will use a graphing calculator to create a scatter plot and perform linear regression on a data set.
- After the activity, students can use a graphing calculator to check their solutions in Exercises 17–21 in Lesson 5.6.

Keystroke Help

Keystrokes for several models of calculators are available in blackline format in the *Chapter 5 Resource Book*.

② TEACH

Extra Example 1

The table shows the number of endangered plants in the U.S. from 1997 to 2002. Make a scatter plot of the data. *Describe* the correlation of the data.

Year	Endangered Plants
1997	553
1998	567
1999	581
2000	592
2001	595
2002	599

The data have a positive correlation. This means that with each passing year, the number of endangered plants tended to increase.

MODELING DATA The *correlation coefficient r* for a set of paired data measures how well the best-fitting line fits the data. You can use a graphing calculator to find a value for *r*.

For *r* close to 1, the data have a strong positive correlation. For *r* close to −1, the data have a strong negative correlation. For *r* close to 0, the data have relatively no correlation.

EXAMPLE 2 Find the best-fitting line

Find an equation of the best-fitting line for the scatter plot from Example 1. Determine the correlation coefficient of the data. Graph the best-fitting line.

STEP 1 *Perform regression*

Press **STAT**. From the CALC menu, choose LinReg(ax+b). The *a*- and *b*-values given are for an equation of the form $y = ax + b$. Rounding these values gives the equation $y = 1.36x + 27.7$. Because *r* is close to 1, the data have a strong positive correlation.

STEP 2 *Draw the best-fitting line*

Press **Y=** and enter $1.36x + 27.7$ for y_1. Press **GRAPH**.

PRACTICE

In Exercises 1–5, refer to the table, which shows the total sales from men's clothing stores in the United States from 1997 to 2002.

Year	1997	1998	1999	2000	2001	2002
Sales (billions of dollars)	10.1	10.6	10.5	10.8	10.3	9.9

1. Make a scatter plot of the data. *Describe* the correlation. **See art in Exercise 3; negative correlation.**

2. Find the equation of the best-fitting line for the data. **$S = -0.046y + 10.5$**

3. Draw the best-fitting line for the data. **See margin.**

DRAW CONCLUSIONS

4. What does the value of *r* for the equation in Exercise 2 tell you about the correlation of the data? **The data have relatively no correlation.**

5. **PREDICT** How could you use the best-fitting line to predict future sales of men's clothing? *Explain* your answer. **Sample answer: You cannot use the best-fitting line to predict future sales because the data do not show a strong correlation.**

Extra Example 2
Find an equation of the best-fitting line for the scatter plot from Extra Example 1. Determine the correlation coefficient of the data. Graph the best-fitting line. **Rounding the values from the graphing calculator, the equation of the best-fitting line is $y = 9.29x + 558$. The correlation coefficient is 0.965. Since *r* is close to 1, the data have a strong positive correlation.**

3 ASSESS AND RETEACH

A friend performs linear regression on a data set and tells you that the correlation coefficient is 0.213.

1. What does the value of *r* tell you about the data set? **Since the value of *r* is positive but close to zero, there is almost no correlation in the data even though the *y* values tend to increase as the *x* values increase.**

2. How reliable is the best-fitting line for predicting future trends in the data? **Since the correlation is low, the best-fitting line would not be accurate in predicting future trends.**

3.

333

5.7 Collecting and Organizing Data

MATERIALS • metric ruler

QUESTION How can you make a prediction using a line of fit?

EXPLORE Make a prediction using a line of fit

A student in your class draws a rectangle with a short side that is 4 centimeters in length. Predict the length of the long side of the rectangle.

STEP 1 *Collect data*

Ask each of 10 people to draw a rectangle. Do not let anyone drawing a rectangle see a rectangle drawn by someone else.

STEP 2 *Organize data*

Measure the lengths (in centimeters) of the short and long sides of the rectangles you collected. Create a table like the one shown.

Short side (cm)	2.7	2.7	1.8	2.6	1.4	1.5	1.2	0.8	3.8
Long side (cm)	4.4	6.5	3.4	6	3.4	3	2.8	1.6	6.5

STEP 3 *Graph data*

Make a scatter plot of the data where each point represents a rectangle that you collected. Let x represent the length of the short side of the rectangle, and let y represent the length of the long side.

STEP 4 *Model data*

Draw a line of fit.

STEP 5 *Predict*

Use the line of fit to find the length of the long side that corresponds to a short side with a length of 4 centimeters. In this case, the long side length predicted by the line of fit has a length of about 7 centimeters.

DRAW CONCLUSIONS Use your observations to complete these exercises
1–3. Answers may vary.

1. **COMPARE** What is the slope of your line of fit? How does this slope compare with the slope of the line shown above?

2. **PREDICT** Suppose a student in your class draws a rectangle that has a long side with a length of 5 centimeters. Predict the length of the shorter side. *Explain* how you made your prediction.

3. **EXTEND** The *golden ratio* appears frequently in architectural structures, paintings, sculptures, and even in nature. This ratio of the long side of a rectangle to its short side is approximately 1.618. How does this ratio compare with the slopes of the lines you compared in Exercise 1?

5.7 Predict with Linear Models

Before	You made scatter plots and wrote equations of lines of fit.
Now	You will make predictions using best-fitting lines.
Why?	So you can model trends, as in Ex. 21.

Key Vocabulary
- best-fitting line
- linear regression
- interpolation
- extrapolation
- zero of a function

The line that most closely follows a trend in data is called the **best-fitting line**. The process of finding the best-fitting line to model a set of data is called **linear regression**. You can perform linear regression using technology. Using a line or its equation to approximate a value between two known values is called **linear interpolation**.

EXAMPLE 1 Interpolate using an equation

CD SINGLES The table shows the total number of CD singles shipped (in millions) by manufacturers for several years during the period 1993–1997.

Year	1993	1995	1996	1997
CD singles shipped (millions)	7.8	22	43	67

a. Make a scatter plot of the data.

REVIEW REGRESSION
For help with performing a linear regression to find the best-fitting line, see p. 332.

b. Find an equation that models the number of CD singles shipped (in millions) as a function of the number of years since 1993.

c. Approximate the number of CD singles shipped in 1994.

Solution

a. Enter the data into lists on a graphing calculator. Make a scatter plot, letting the number of years since 1993 be the x-values (0, 2, 3, 4) and the number of CD singles shipped be the y-values.

b. Perform linear regression using the paired data. The equation of the best-fitting line is approximately $y = 14x + 2.4$.

ANOTHER WAY
You can also estimate the number of CDs shipped in 1994 by evaluating $y = 14x + 2.4$ when $x = 1$.

c. Graph the best-fitting line. Use the *trace* feature and the arrow keys to find the value of the equation when $x = 1$.

▶ About 16 million CD singles were shipped in 1994.

X=1   Y=16.4

Animated **Algebra** at classzone.com

Resource Planning Guide

Chapter Resource Book
- Teaching Guide/Lesson Plan (pp. 74–75)
- Activity Master (p. 76)
- Practice levels A, B, C (pp. 78–83)
- Study Guide (pp. 84–85)
- Catch-up for Absent Students (p. 86)
- Problem Solving Workshop (p. 87)
- Challenge (p. 88)

Workbooks
- Notetaking Guide (pp. 121–124)
- Practice Workbook (pp. 81–83)

Teaching Options
- **Power Presentations CD-ROM** provides dynamic electronic teaching resources for the classroom.
- **Activity Generator CD-ROM** provides editable activities for all ability levels.

Interactive Technology
- Easy Planner
- Power Presentations CD-ROM
- Activity Generator CD-ROM
- Animated Algebra
- Test Generator CD-ROM
- Online Quiz
- eWorkbook
- eEdition
- @HomeTutor

Resources for English Learners
- Quick Reference for English Learners
- Spanish Study Guide
- Multi-Language Visual Glossary
- Student Resources in Spanish

See also the *Algebra 1 Toolkit* for more strategies for meeting individual needs.

335

Motivating the Lesson
You have data that gives the yearly sea turtle strandings off North Carolina from 1993 to 2004, with the exception of 1995 and 1998. By using a best-fitting line, you can predict the number of strandings that occurred in 1995 and 1998. You can also predict the number of strandings that are likely in future years.

Motivating the Lesson
You have data that gives the yearly sea turtle strandings off North Carolina from 1993 to 2004, with the exception of 1995 and 1998. By using a best-fitting line, you can predict the number of strandings that occurred in 1995 and 1998. You can also predict the number of strandings that are likely in future years.

❸ TEACH

Extra Example 1
The table shows the number of hikers who have completed the Appalachian Trail from 1996 to 2000.

Year	Hikers completing trail
1996	405
1998	403
1999	552
2000	623

a. Make a scatter plot of the data.

b. Find an equation that models the number of hikers completing the trail as a function of the number of years since 1996. *Sample answer:* $y = 56x + 369$

c. Approximate the number of hikers who completed the entire trail in 1997. **about 425 hikers**

Animated Algebra
classzone.com

An **Animated Algebra** activity is available on-line for **Example 1**. This activity is also available on the **Power Presentations CD-ROM**.

EXAMPLE 2 Extrapolate using an equation

CD SINGLES Look back at Example 1.

a. Use the equation from Example 1 to approximate the number of CD singles shipped in 1998 and in 2000.

b. In 1998 there were actually 56 million CD singles shipped. In 2000 there were actually 34 million CD singles shipped. *Describe* the accuracy of the extrapolations made in part (a).

Solution

a. Evaluate the equation of the best-fitting line from Example 1 for $x = 5$ and $x = 7$.

The model predicts about 72 million CD singles shipped in 1998 and about 100 million CD singles shipped in 2000.

```
Y₁(5)
              72.4
Y₁(7)
             100.4
```

b. The differences between the predicted number of CD singles shipped and the actual number of CD singles shipped in 1998 and 2000 are 16 million CDs and 66 million CDs, respectively. The difference in the actual and predicted numbers increased from 1998 to 2000. So, the equation of the best-fitting line gives a less accurate prediction for the year that is farther from the given years.

ACCURACY As Example 2 illustrates, the farther removed an x-value is from the known x-values, the less confidence you can have in the accuracy of the predicted y-value. This is true in general but not in every case.

✔ **GUIDED PRACTICE** for Examples 1 and 2

1. **HOUSE SIZE** The table shows the median floor area of new single-family houses in the United States during the period 1995–1999.

Year	1995	1996	1997	1998	1999
Median floor area (square feet)	1920	1950	1975	2000	2028

a. Find an equation that models the floor area (in square feet) of a new single-family house as a function of the number of years since 1995. $y = 26.6x + 1921.4$

b. Predict the median floor area of a new single-family house in 2000 and in 2001. **about 2054.4 ft², about 2081 ft²**

c. Which of the predictions from part (b) would you expect to be more accurate? *Explain* your reasoning. **The prediction for 2000 because the farther removed an x-value is from the known x-values, the less confidence you can have in the accuracy of the predicted y-value.**

Differentiated Instruction

Auditory Learners Point out that linear *in*terpolation predicts a point *in*side the range of the data points. Linear *ex*trapolation predicts a point *ex*terior to, or outside of, the range of the data points.

See also the *Algebra 1 Toolkit* for more strategies.

EXAMPLE 3 **Predict using an equation**

SOFTBALL The table shows the number of participants in U.S. youth softball during the period 1997–2001. Predict the year in which the number of youth softball participants reaches 1.2 million.

Year	1997	1998	1999	2000	2001
Participants (millions)	1.44	1.4	1.411	1.37	1.355

Solution

STEP 1 Perform linear regression. Let x represent the number of years since 1997, and let y represent the number of youth softball participants (in millions). The equation for the best-fitting line is approximately $y = -0.02x + 1.435$.

ANOTHER WAY
You can also predict the year by substituting 1.2 for y in the equation and solving for x:
$y = 0.02x + 1.435$
$1.2 = -0.02x + 1.435$
$x = 11.75$

STEP 2 Graph the equation of the best-fitting line. Trace the line until the cursor reaches $y = 1.2$. The corresponding x-value is shown at the bottom of the calculator screen.

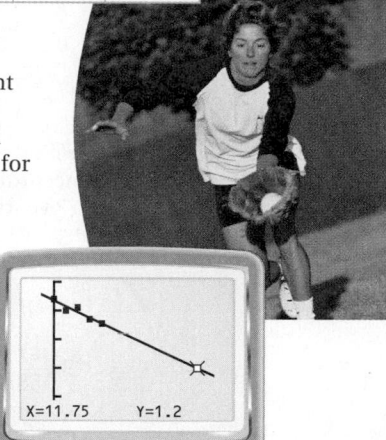

X=11.75   Y=1.2

▶ There will be 1.2 million participants about 12 years after 1997, or in 2009.

✓ **GUIDED PRACTICE** **for Example 3**

2. **SOFTBALL** In Example 3, in what year will there be 1.25 million youth softball participants in the U.S? **2006**

ZERO OF A FUNCTION A **zero of a function** $y = f(x)$ is an x-value for which $f(x) = 0$ (or $y = 0$). Because $y = 0$ along the x-axis of the coordinate plane, a zero of a function is an x-intercept of the function's graph.

KEY CONCEPT *For Your Notebook*

Relating Solutions of Equations, x-Intercepts of Graphs, and Zeros of Functions

In Chapter 3 you learned to solve an equation like $2x - 4 = 0$:

$2x - 4 = 0$

$2x = 4$

$x = 2$

The solution of $2x - 4 = 0$ is 2.

In Chapter 4 you found the x-intercept of the graph of a function like $y = 2x - 4$:

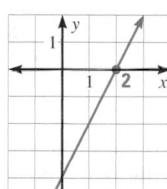

Now you are finding the zero of a function like $f(x) = 2x - 4$:

$f(x) = 0$

$2x - 4 = 0$

$x = 2$

The zero of $f(x) = 2x - 4$ is 2.

338

EXAMPLE 4 Find the zero of a function

SOFTBALL Look back at Example 3. Find the zero of the function. *Explain* what the zero means in this situation.

Solution

Substitute 0 for y in the equation of the best-fitting line and solve for x.

$y = -0.02x + 1.435$ **Write the equation.**

$0 = -0.02x + 1.435$ **Substitute 0 for y.**

$x \approx 72$ **Solve for x.**

▸ The zero of the function is about 72. The function has a negative slope, which means that the number of youth softball participants is decreasing. According to the model, there will be no youth softball participants 72 years after 1997, or in 2069.

 GUIDED PRACTICE for Example 4

3. **JET BOATS** The number y (in thousands) of jet boats purchased in the U.S. can be modeled by the function $y = -1.23x + 14$ where x is the number of years since 1995. Find the zero of the function. *Explain* what the zero means in this situation. **11.4; the function has a negative slope, which means that the number of jet boats purchased in the U.S. is decreasing. According to the model, there will be no jet boats purchased 11.4 years after 1995, or in 2006.**

5.7 **EXERCISES**

HOMEWORK KEY:
○ = **WORKED-OUT SOLUTIONS**
on p. WS1 for Exs. 3 and 19

★ = **STANDARDIZED TEST PRACTICE**
Exs. 2, 14, 16, and 21

◆ = **MULTIPLE REPRESENTATIONS**
Exs. 22

SKILL PRACTICE

A 1. **VOCABULARY** Copy and complete: Using a linear function to approximate a value within a range of known data values is called ? . **linear interpolation**

2. ★ **WRITING** *Explain* how extrapolation differs from interpolation. **See margin.**

EXAMPLE 1
on p. 335
for Exs. 3–4

LINEAR INTERPOLATION Make a scatter plot of the data. Find the equation of the best-fitting line. Approximate the value of y for $x = 5$. **3–4. See margin for art.**

3.

x	0	2	4	6	7
y	2	7	14	17	20

$y = 2.5x + 2$; 14.5

4.

x	2	4	6	8	10
y	6.2	22.5	40.2	55.4	72.1

$y = 8.2x - 10.1$; 30.9

EXAMPLE 2
on p. 336
for Exs. 5–6

LINEAR EXTRAPOLATION Make a scatter plot of the data. Find the equation of the best-fitting line. Approximate the value of y for $x = 10$. **5–6. See margin for art.**

5.

x	0	1	2	3	4
y	20	32	39	53	63

$y = 10.7x + 20$; 127

6.

x	1	3	5	7	9
y	0.4	1.4	1.9	2.3	3.2

Sample answer: $y = 0.33x + 0.22$; 3.52

Extra Example 4

Look back at Extra Example 3. Find the zero of the function. *Explain* what the zero means in this situation. **The zero of the function is about 11. The function has a negative slope, which means that the number of new issues of amateur radio licenses in the general class is decreasing. According to the model, there will be no new general licenses issued about 11 months after September, 2004, which will be August, 2005.**

Closing the Lesson

Have students summarize the major points of the lesson and answer the Essential Question: How can you use a best-fitting line to make predictions about data?

• You can approximate an unknown data value by using the equation of the best-fitting line found by linear regression.

• The zero of a function is the x value of the point where the line crosses the x-axis.

Make a scatter plot of the data and then perform a linear regression to find the equation of the best-fitting line. Use the trace feature of the graphing calculator to trace the line of the equation or evaluate the equation of the best-fitting line to find the predicted values. Substitute 0 for y in the equation to find the zero of the function.

2. Extrapolation is finding an approximate value outside the range of known values. Interpolation is finding an approximate value within the range of known values.

3.

4.

5.

6.

EXAMPLE 4
on p. 338
for Exs. 7–13

ZERO OF A FUNCTION Find the zero of the function.

7. $f(x) = 7.5x - 20$ $2\frac{2}{3}$

8. $f(x) = -x + 7$ **7**

9. $f(x) = \frac{1}{8}x + 2$ **−16**

10. $f(x) = 17x - 68$ **4**

11. $f(x) = -0.5x + 0.75$ **1.5**

12. $f(x) = 5x - 7$ **1.4**

13. **ERROR ANALYSIS** *Describe* and correct the error made in finding the zero of the function $y = 2.3x - 2$.
To find the zero of a function, substitute 0 for *y*, not *x*; $0 = 2.3x - 2$, $2 = 2.3x$, $x = \frac{20}{23}$.

$$y = 2.3(0) - 2$$
$$y = -2$$

14. ★ **MULTIPLE CHOICE** Given the function $y = 12.6x + 3$, for what *x*-value does $y = 66$? **B**

(A) 0.2 (B) 5 (C) 5.5 (D) 78.6

[B] 15. **ERROR ANALYSIS** *Describe* and correct the error in finding an equation of the best-fitting line using a graphing calculator.

Equation of the best-fitting line is
$y = 23.1x + 4.47$.

```
LinReg
 y=ax+b
 a=4.47
 b=23.1
 r²=.9989451055
 r=.9994724136
```

a and *b* were not substituted correctly; $y = 4.47x + 23.1$.

16. ★ **OPEN-ENDED** Give an example of a real-life situation in which you can use linear interpolation to find the zero of a function. *Explain* what the zero means in this situation. **Sample answer: Temperature on a mountain depends on the elevation. The zero indicates the elevation at which the temperature is 0°F.**

[C] 17. **CHALLENGE** A quantity increases rapidly for 10 years. During the next 10 years, the quantity decreases rapidly.

a. Can you fit a line to the data? *Explain.*
No; the data would first have a positive slope and then a negative slope.

b. How could you model the data using more than one line? *Explain* the steps you could take. **You could fit a line to the data for the first 10 years and then fit another line to the data for the following 10 years.**

PROBLEM SOLVING

EXAMPLE 1 [A]
on p. 335
for Ex. 18

18. **SAILBOATS** Your school's sailing club wants to buy a sailboat. The table shows the lengths and costs of sailboats.

Length (feet)	11	12	14	14	16	22	23
Cost (dollars)	600	500	1900	1700	3500	6500	6000

a. Make a scatter plot of the data. Let *x* represent the length of the sailboat. Let *y* represent the cost of the sailboat. **See margin.**

b. Find an equation that models the cost (in dollars) of a sailboat as a function of its length (in feet). $y = 513x - 5258$

c. Approximate the cost of a sailboat that is 20 feet long. **$5002**

@HomeTutor for problem solving help at classzone.com

5.7 Predict with Linear Models **339**

4 PRACTICE AND APPLY

Assignment Guide

📖 Answer Transparencies available for all exercises

Basic:
Day 1: pp. 338–341
Exs. 1–15, 18–21, 24–32

Average:
Day 1: pp. 338–341
Exs. 1–6, 9–16, 18–22, 24–32

Advanced:
Day 1: pp. 338–341
Exs. 1–6, 10–14, 16–32*

Block:
pp. 338–341
Exs. 1–6, 9–16, 18–22, 24–32
(with 5.6)

Differentiated Instruction

See *Algebra 1 Best Practices Toolkit* for suggestions on addressing the needs of a diverse classroom.

Homework Check

For a quick check of student understanding of key concepts, go over the following exercises:
Basic: 3, 5, 8, 20, 21
Average: 4, 5, 10, 20, 21
Advanced: 6, 12, 18, 20, 22

Extra Practice

• Student Edition, p. 942
• Chapter 5 Resource Book: Practice levels A, B, C, pp. 78–83

Practice Worksheet

An easily-readable reduced practice page (with answers) for this lesson can be found on p. 280C.

18a.

(19.) **FARMING** The table shows the living space recommended for pigs of certain weights.

Weight (pounds)	40	60	80	100	120	150	230
Area (square feet)	2.5	3	3.5	4	5	6	8

a. Make a scatter plot of the data. **See margin.**

b. Write an equation that models the recommended living space (in square feet) as a function of a pig's weight (in pounds). $y = 0.03x + 1.23$

c. About how much living space is recommended for a pig weighing 250 pounds? **about 8.73 ft²**

@HomeTutor for problem solving help at classzone.com

20. **TELEVISION STATIONS** The table shows the number of UHF and VHF broadcast television stations each year from 1996 to 2002.

Year	1996	1997	1998	1999	2000	2001	2002
Television stations	1551	1563	1583	1616	1730	1686	1714

a. Find an equation that models the number of broadcast television stations as a function of the number of years since 1996. $y = 31.5x + 1540$

b. At approximately what rate did the number of television stations change from 1996 to 2002? **31.5 stations per year**

c. Approximate the year in which there were 1750 television stations. **2002**

21. ★ **SHORT RESPONSE** The table shows the number of people who lived in high noise areas near U.S. airports for several years during the period 1985–2000.

a. Find an equation that models the number of people (in thousands) living in high noise areas as a function of the number of years since 1985. $y = -197.6x + 3542$

b. Find the zero of the function from part (a). *Explain* what the zero means in this situation. Is this reasonable?

People in High Noise Areas

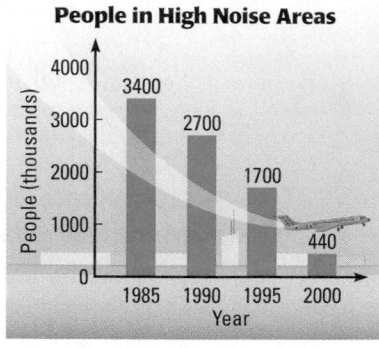

22. ◆ **MULTIPLE REPRESENTATIONS** The table shows the number of U.S. households with personal computers (PCs) from 1994 to 2002.

Year	1994	1995	1996	1997	1998	1999	2000	2001	2002
Households with PCs (millions)	32.0	33.6	38.8	44.0	51.2	61.1	66.0	69.1	72.7

a. **Drawing a Graph** Make a scatter plot of the data in the table. **See margin.**

b. **Writing an Equation** Find an equation that models the number of households with personal computers (in millions) as a function of the number of years since 1994. $y = 5.7x + 29.3$

c. **Describing in Words** Find the zero of the function from part (b). *Explain* what the zero means in this situation. **About −5.14; about 5.14 years before 1994, or 1988, the number of households with PCs was 0.**

22a.

○ = **WORKED-OUT SOLUTIONS** on p. WS1   ★ = **STANDARDIZED TEST PRACTICE**   ◆ = **MULTIPLE REPRESENTATIONS**

23a.

There is relatively no correlation in either scatter plot.

C **23. CHALLENGE** The table shows the estimated populations of mallard ducks and all ducks in North America for several years during the period 1975–2000.

Year	1975	1980	1985	1990	1995	2000
Mallards (thousands)	7727	7707	4961	5452	8269	9470
All ducks (thousands)	37,790	36,220	25,640	25,080	35,870	41,840

a. Make two scatter plots where x is the number of years since 1975 and y is the number of mallards (in thousands) for one scatter plot, while y is the number of ducks (in thousands) for the other scatter plot. *Describe* the correlation of the data in each scatter plot. **See margin.**

b. Can you use the mallard duck population to predict the total duck population? *Explain.* **No; because you cannot find a line of best fit for either correlation, you cannot use the mallard duck population to predict the total duck population.**

MIXED REVIEW

Find the sum, difference, product, or quotient.

24. $-19 + (-8)$ *(p. 74)* **−27**   **25.** $-7.3 + 5$ *(p. 74)* **−2.3**   **26.** $-4.03 + (-3.57)$ *(p. 74)* **−7.6**

27. $-2.8 - (-2.3)$ *(p. 80)* **−0.5**   **28.** $-4(5)(-5.5)$ *(p. 88)* **110**   **29.** $-25 \div (-5)$ *(p. 103)* **5**

PREVIEW

Prepare for
Lesson 6.1
in Exs. 30–32.

Solve the equation. Check your solution.

30. $x - (-9) = 8$ *(p. 134)* **−1**   **31.** $3x - 4 = -4$ *(p. 141)* **0**   **32.** $4x + 10x = 98$ *(p. 148)* **7**

QUIZ for Lessons 5.5–5.7

1. PARALLEL LINES Write an equation of the line that passes through $(-6, 8)$ and is parallel to the line $y = 3x - 15$. *(p. 319)* **$y = 3x + 26$**

PERPENDICULAR LINES Write an equation of the line that passes through the given point and is perpendicular to the given line. *(p. 319)*

2. $(5, 5), y = -x + 2$ **$y = x$**   **3.** $(10, -3), y = 2x + 24$ **$y = -\frac{1}{2}x + 2$**   **4.** $(2, 3), x + 2y = -7$ **$y = 2x - 1$**

5. CASSETTE TAPES The table shows the number of audio cassette tapes shipped for several years during the period 1994–2002. *(pp. 325, 335)*

Year	1994	1996	1998	2000	2002
Tapes shipped (millions)	345	225	159	76	31

5b. about −38.85 tapes per year

a. Write an equation that models the number of tapes shipped (in millions) as a function of the number of years since 1994. **$y = -38.85x + 322.6$**

b. At about what rate did the number of tapes shipped change over time?

c. Approximate the year in which 125 million tapes were shipped. **1999**

d. Find the zero of the function from part (a). *Explain* what the zero means in this situation.
About 8.3; 8.3 years after 1994, or 2002, there will be no tapes shipped.

EXTRA PRACTICE for Lesson 5.7, p. 942   **ONLINE QUIZ** at classzone.com   **341**

⑤ ASSESS AND RETEACH

Daily Homework Quiz

📋 **Transparency Available**

1. Find the zero of the function $f(x) = 2.5x - 6$. **2.4**

2. The table shows the number of video rentals at a store from 1998 to 2002. Find an equation that models the number of video rentals as a function of the number of years since 1998. Predict the number of rentals in 1999 and 2003.

Year	Video Rentals (thousands)
1998	2.3
2000	2.0
2001	1.85
2002	1.45

$y = -0.2x + 2.35$, where x is the number of years after 1998. The model predicts about 2150 video rentals in 1999 and 1350 video rentals in 2003.

 Online Quiz

Available at **classzone.com**

Diagnosis/Remediation

• Practice A, B, C in Chapter 5 Resource Book, pp. 78–83
• Study Guide in Chapter 5 Resource Book, pp. 84–85
• Practice Workbook, pp. 81–83
• @HomeTutor

Challenge

Additional challenge is available in the Chapter 5 Resource Book, p. 88.

Quiz

An easily-readable reduced copy of the quiz (with answers) on Lessons 5.5–5.7 from the Assessment Book can be found on p. 280F.

1 PLAN AND PREPARE

Learn the Method

- Students will find data on the Internet and use the data to make a prediction about the total U.S. voting-age population in 2010.
- After the activity, students can use the techniques they learned to find data for a real-life situation in Exercise 16 in Lesson 5.7, and then find the zero of the function.

2 TEACH

Tips for Success

Urge students to pay attention to the year of the data as there may be gaps in the years. Remind them that they need to enter the correct year to plot accurate data for the scatter plots.

Extra Example 1

Find data on U.S. postal rates for the first ounce of a letter since 1995. Use an equation that models the data to predict the cost of postage for the first ounce of a letter in 2010. You can find postal rates in the most recent "Transportation" document. **Using the data (1995, 32), (1999, 33), (2001, 34), (2002, 37), an equation is $y = 0.591x + 28.5$, where x is the number of years after 1990. The model predicts that in 2010 the first ounce of postage on a letter will be about 40 cents.**

3 ASSESS AND RETEACH

Looking at the online *Statistical Abstract*, name three different types of data that you can use to explore real-life situations.
Sample answer: Total energy consumption from 1996 to 2002; the number of oil spills from 1–100 gallons from 1998 to 2001; attendance at major league baseball games from 1985 to 2003.

5.7 Model Data from the Internet

QUESTION How can you find reliable data on the Internet and use it to predict the total U.S voting-age population in 2010?

EXAMPLE 1 Collect and analyze data

Find data for the total U.S. voting-age population over several years. Use an equation that models the data to predict the total U.S. voting-age population in 2010.

STEP 1 *Find a data source*

Reliable data about the U.S. population can be found in the online *Statistical Abstract*. Go to the address shown below. Click on a link to the most recent version of the *Statistical Abstract*.

> Address http://www.census.gov

Voting-Age Population	
Year	**Total (mil.)**
1980	157.1
1988	178.1
1990	182.1
1994	190.3
1996	193.7
1998	198.2

STEP 2 *Find an appropriate data set*

Choose the most recent "Elections" document. In this document, find the table of data entitled "Voting-Age Population."

STEP 3 *Find a model*

Use a graphing calculator to make a scatter plot. Let x represent the number of years since 1980. Let y represent the total U.S. voting-age population (in millions). Find an equation that models the total U.S. voting-age population (in millions) as a function of the number of years since 1980.

▶ $y = 2.23x + 159$

STEP 4 *Predict*

Use the model to predict the total voting-age population in 2010. You can either evaluate the equation for $x = 30$ or trace the graph of the equation, as shown.

▶ The total U.S. voting-age population will be about 225.9 million in 2010.

DRAW CONCLUSIONS 1–3. Answers may vary.

1. In the online *Statistical Abstract*, find data for the total value of agricultural imports over several years beginning with 1990.

2. Make a scatter plot of the data you found in Exercise 1. Find an equation that models the total value of agricultural imports (in millions of dollars) as a function of the number of years since 1990.

3. Predict the year in which the total value of agricultural imports will be $45,000 million. *Describe* the method you used.

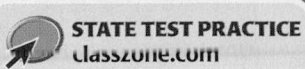
Lessons 5.5–5.7

1. MULTI-STEP PROBLEM The table shows the value of primary and secondary schools built in the U.S. each year from 1995 to 2000.

Year	Value (millions of dollars)
1995	1245
1996	1560
1997	2032
1998	2174
1999	2420
2000	2948

a. Make a scatter plot of the data. **See margin.**

b. Write an equation that models the value (in millions of dollars) of the schools built as a function of the number of years since 1995. $y = 321x + 1260$

c. At approximately what rate did the value change from 1995 to 2000? **about $321 million per year**

d. In what year would you predict the value of the schools built in the U.S. to be $3,600,000,000? **2002**

2. GRIDDED ANSWER A map of a city shows streets as lines on a coordinate grid. State Street has a slope of $-\frac{1}{2}$. Park Street runs perpendicular to State Street. What is the slope of Park Street on the map? **2**

3. OPEN-ENDED The graph represents the cost for one kayak owner for storing a kayak at a marina over time. The total cost includes a standard initial fee and a monthly storage fee. Suppose a different kayak owner pays a lower initial fee during a special promotion. Write an equation that could give the total cost as a function of the number of months of storage for this kayak owner. *Sample answer: y = 8x + 5*

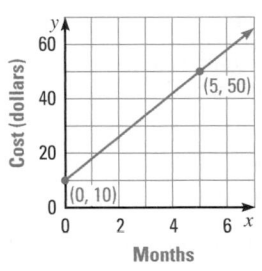

4. SHORT RESPONSE The table shows the heights and corresponding lengths of horses in a stable. Make a scatter plot of the data. *Describe* the correlation of the data. **See margin.**

Height (hands)	Length (inches)
17.0	76
16.0	72
16.2	74
15.3	71
15.1	69
16.3	75

5. EXTENDED RESPONSE The table shows the percent of revenue from U.S. music sales made through music clubs from 1998 through 2003.

Year	Percent of revenue
1998	9
1999	7.9
2000	7.6
2001	6.1
2002	4
2003	4.1

a. Find an equation that models the percent of revenue from music clubs as a function of the number of years since 1998. $y = -1.1x + 9.1$

b. At approximately what rate did the percent of revenue from music clubs change from 1998 to 2003? **about −1.1 percent per year**

c. Find the zero of the function. *Explain* what the zero means in this situation. **See margin.**

6. SHORT RESPONSE The cost of bowling includes a $4.00 fee per game and a shoe rental fee. Shoes for adults cost $2.25. Shoes for children cost $1.75. Write equations that give the total cost of bowling for an adult and for a child as functions of the number of games bowled. How are the graphs of the equations related? *Explain.* **See margin.**

1a.

[graph: Value (millions of dollars) vs. Years since 1995]

4.

[graph]

positive correlation

5c. 8.3; 8.3 years after 1998, or 2006 the percent of revenue from U.S. music sales made through music clubs will be 0.

6. $C = 4g + 2.25$, $C = 4g + 1.75$; the graphs have the same slopes, but different C-intercepts.

Additional Resources

The following resources are available to help review the materials in this chapter.

Chapter 5 Resource Book
- Chapter Review Games and Activities, p. 89
- Cumulative Practice, Chs. 1–5, pp. 91–92

Student Resources in Spanish

eWorkbook

@HomcTutor

Vocabulary Practice

Vocabulary practice is available at **classzone.com**

BIG IDEAS
For Your Notebook

Big Idea 1

Writing Linear Equations in a Variety of Forms

Using given information about a line, you can write an equation of the line in three different forms.

Form	Equation	Important information
Slope-intercept form	$y = mx + b$	• The slope of the line is m. • The y-intercept of the line is b.
Point-slope form	$y - y_1 = m(x - x_1)$	• The slope of the line is m. • The line passes through (x_1, y_1).
Standard form	$Ax + By = C$	• A, B, and C are real numbers. • A and B are not both zero.

Big Idea 2

Using Linear Models to Solve Problems

You can write a linear equation that models a situation involving a constant rate of change. Analyzing given information helps you choose a linear model.

Choosing a Linear Model	
If this is what you know . . .	**. . . then use this equation form**
constant rate of change and initial value	slope-intercept form
constant rate of change and one data pair	slope-intercept form or point-slope form
two data pairs and the fact that the rate of change is constant	slope-intercept form or point-slope form
the sum of two variable quantities is constant	standard form

Big Idea 3

Modeling Data with a Line of Fit

You can use a line of fit to model data that have a positive or negative correlation. The line or an equation of the line can be used to make predictions.

Step 1 Make a scatter plot of the data.

Step 2 Decide whether the data can be modeled by a line.

Step 3 Draw a line that appears to follow the trend in data closely.

Step 4 Write an equation using two points on the line.

Step 5 Interpolate (between known values) or extrapolate (beyond known values) using the line or its equation.

@HomeTutor
classzone.com
• Multi-Language Glossary
• Vocabulary practice

REVIEW KEY VOCABULARY

- point-slope form, *p. 302*
- converse, *p. 319*
- perpendicular, *p. 320*
- scatter plot, *p. 325*

- positive correlation, negative correlation, relatively no correlation, *p. 325*
- line of fit, *p. 326*
- best-fitting line, *p. 335*

- linear regression, *p. 335*
- interpolation, *p. 335*
- extrapolation, *p. 336*
- zero of a function, *p. 337*

VOCABULARY EXERCISES

1. Copy and complete: If a best-fitting line falls from left to right, then the data have a(n) __?__ correlation. **negative**

2. Copy and complete: Using a linear function to approximate a value beyond a range of known values is called __?__. **extrapolation**

3. **WRITING** What is the zero of a function, and how does it relate to the function's graph? *Explain.* **The zero of a function is the *x*-value of the function when *y* = 0; it is the *x*-intercept of the graph.**

REVIEW EXAMPLES AND EXERCISES

Use the review examples and exercises below to check your understanding of the concepts you have learned in each lesson of Chapter 5.

5.1 Write Linear Equations in Slope-Intercept Form
pp. 283–289

EXAMPLE

Write an equation of the line shown.

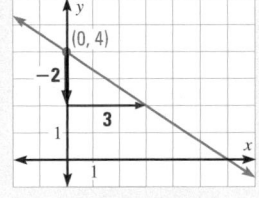

$y = mx + b$ — Write slope-intercept form.

$y = -\frac{2}{3}x + 4$ — Substitute $-\frac{2}{3}$ for *m* and 4 for *b*.

EXERCISES

EXAMPLES 1 and 5
on pp. 283, 285
for Exs. 4–7

Write an equation in slope-intercept form of the line with the given slope and *y*-intercept.

4. slope: 3
   y-intercept: −10
   $y = 3x - 10$

5. slope: $\frac{4}{9}$
   y-intercept: 5 $y = \frac{4}{9}x + 5$

6. slope: $-\frac{2}{11}$
   y-intercept: 7
   $y = -\frac{2}{11}x + 7$

7. **GIFT CARD** You have a $25 gift card for a bagel shop. A bagel costs $1.25. Write an equation that gives the amount (in dollars) that remains on the card as a function of the total number of bagels you have purchased so far. How much money is on the card after you buy 2 bagels? $y = -1.25x + 25; \$22.50$

Chapter Review **345**

Extra Example 5.1
Write an equation of the line shown.

$y = \frac{3}{4}x - 4$

Extra Example 5.2

Write an equation of the line that passes through the point (6, 4) and has a slope of 3. $y = 3x - 14$

Extra Example 5.3

Write an equation in point-slope form of the line shown.

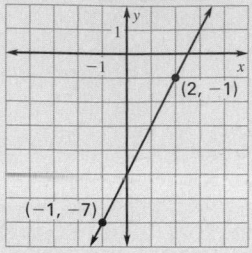

(2, −1)

(−1, −7)

$y + 7 = 2(x + 1)$ or $y + 1 = 2(x - 2)$

11. $y - 7 = -6(x - 4)$ or
$y - 1 = -6(x - 5)$

12. $y + 2 = -\dfrac{1}{3}(x - 9)$ or
$y - 2 = -\dfrac{1}{3}(x + 3)$

13. $y + 2 = -\dfrac{6}{11}(x + 3)$ or
$y + 8 = -\dfrac{6}{11}(x - 8)$

5.2 Use Linear Equations in Slope-Intercept Form
pp. 292–299

EXAMPLE

Write an equation of the line that passes through the point (−2, −6) and has a slope of 2.

STEP 1 Find the y-intercept.

$y = mx + b$ Write slope-intercept form.

$-6 = 2(-2) + b$ Substitute 2 for *m*, −2 for *x*, and −6 for *y*.

$-2 = b$ Solve for *b*.

STEP 2 Write an equation of the line.

$y = mx + b$ Write slope intercept form.

$y = 2x - 2$ Substitute 2 for *m* and −2 for *b*.

EXERCISES

EXAMPLE 1
on p. 292
for Exs. 8–10

Write an equation in slope-intercept form of the line that passes through the given point and has the given slope *m*.

8. $(-3, -1)$; $m = 4$
$y = 4x + 11$

9. $(-2, 1)$; $m = 1$
$y = x + 3$

10. $(8, -4)$; $m = -3$
$y = -3x + 20$

5.3 Write Linear Equations in Point-Slope Form
pp. 302–308

EXAMPLE

Write an equation in point-slope form of the line shown.

STEP 1 Find the slope of the line.

$$m = \frac{y_2 - y_1}{x_2 - x_1} = \frac{-8 - 4}{-1 - 3} = \frac{-12}{-4} = 3$$

STEP 2 Write an equation. Use (3, 4).

$y - y_1 = m(x - x_1)$ Write point-slope form.

$y - 4 = 3(x - 3)$ Substitute 3 for *m*, 3 for x_1, and 4 for y_1.

(3, 4)

(−1, −8)

EXERCISES

EXAMPLES 3 and 5
on pp. 303, 304
for Exs. 11–14

Write an equation in point-slope form of the line that passes through the given points. **11–13. See margin.**

11. $(4, 7), (5, 1)$

12. $(9, -2), (-3, 2)$

13. $(8, -8), (-3, -2)$

14. **BUS TRIP** A bus leaves at 10 A.M. to take students on a field trip to a historic site. At 10:25 A.M., the bus is 100 miles from the site. At 11:15 A.M., the bus is 65 miles from the site. The bus travels at a constant speed. Write an equation in point-slope form that relates the distance (in miles) from the site and the time (in minutes) after 10:00 A.M. How far is the bus from the site at 11:30 A.M.? $y - 100 = -\dfrac{7}{10}(x - 25)$ or $y - 65 = -\dfrac{7}{10}(x - 75)$; 54.5 mi

346   Chapter 5   Writing Linear Equations

5.4 Write Linear Equations in Standard Form
pp. 311–316

EXAMPLE

Write an equation in standard form of the line shown.

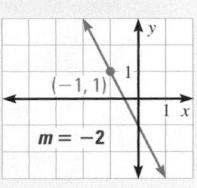

$y - y_1 = m(x - x_1)$	Write point-slope form.
$y - 1 = -2(x - (-1))$	Substitute 1 for y_1, -2 for m, and -1 for x_1.
$y - 1 = -2x - 2$	Distributive property
$2x + y = -1$	Collect variable terms on one side, constants on the other.

EXERCISES

**EXAMPLES
2 and 5**
on pp. 311, 313
for Exs. 15–17

Write an equation in standard form of the line that has the given characteristics.

15. Slope: -4; passes through $(-2, 7)$
$4x + y = -1$

16. Passes through $(-1, -5)$ and $(3, 7)$
$-3x + y = -2$

17. COSTUMES You are buying ribbon to make costumes for a school play. Organza ribbon costs \$.07 per yard. Satin ribbon costs \$.04 per yard. Write an equation to model the possible combinations of yards of organza ribbon and yards of satin ribbon you can buy for \$5. List several possible combinations. $0.07r + 0.04s = 5$. *Sample answer:* 4 organza, 118 satin; 8 organza, 111 satin; 12 organza, 104 satin

5.5 Write Equations of Parallel and Perpendicular Lines
pp. 319–324

EXAMPLE

Write an equation of the line that passes through $(-4, -2)$ and is perpendicular to the line $y = 4x - 7$.

The slope of the line $y = 4x - 7$ is 4. The slope of the perpendicular line through $(-4, -2)$ is $-\frac{1}{4}$. Find the y-intercept of the perpendicular line.

$y = mx + b$	Write slope-intercept form.
$-2 = -\frac{1}{4}(-4) + b$	Substitute $-\frac{1}{4}$ for m, -4 for x, and -2 for y.
$-3 = b$	Solve for b.

An equation of the perpendicular line through $(-4, -2)$ is $y = -\frac{1}{4}x - 3$.

EXERCISES

**EXAMPLES
1 and 4**
on pp. 319, 321
for Exs. 18–20

Write an equation of the line that passes through the given point and is (a) parallel to the given line and (b) perpendicular to the given line.

18. $(0, 2)$, $y = -4x + 6$
  a. $y = -4x + 2$
  b. $y = \frac{1}{4}x + 2$

19. $(2, -3)$, $y = -2x - 3$
  a. $y = -2x + 1$
  b. $y = \frac{1}{2}x - 4$

20. $(6, 0)$, $y = \frac{3}{4}x - \frac{1}{4}$
  a. $y = \frac{3}{4}x - 4\frac{1}{2}$; b. $y = -\frac{4}{3}x + 8$

Chapter Review **347**

Extra Example 5.4
Write an equation in standard form of the line shown. $3x + y = 4$

Extra Example 5.5
Write an equation of the line that passes through $(-2, -2)$ and is parallel to the line $y = \frac{3}{2}x - 5$.
$y = \frac{3}{2}x + 1$

Extra Example 5.6

The table shows the number of students who joined the astronomy club at a school from 1996 to 2003. Make a scatter plot of the data. *Describe* the correlation of the data.

Year	Students in the Astronomy Club
1996	8
1999	15
2000	18
2001	22
2003	24

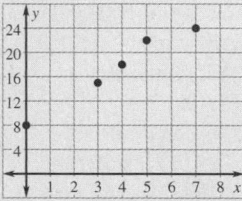

The scatter plot shows a positive correlation, which means that the number of students who joined the astronomy club tended to increase with each passing year.

Extra Example 5.7

Use the scatter plot from Extra Example 5.6 to estimate the number of students who joined the club in 1998. **About 13 students joined the astronomy club in 1998.**

21.

5.6 Fit a Line to Data
pp. 323–331

EXAMPLE

The table shows the time needed to roast turkeys of different weights. Make a scatter plot of the data. *Describe* the correlation of the data.

Weight (pounds)	6	8	12	14	18	20	24
Roast time (hours)	2.75	3.00	3.50	4.00	4.25	4.75	5.25

Treat the data as ordered pairs. Let x represent the turkey weight (in pounds), and let y represent the time (in hours) it takes to roast the turkey. Plot the ordered pairs as points in a coordinate plane.

The scatter plot shows a positive correlation, which means that heavier turkeys tend to require more time to roast.

EXERCISES

EXAMPLE 2
on p. 326
for Ex. 21

21. AIRPORTS The table shows the number of airports in the Unites States for several years during the period 1990–2001. Make a scatter plot of the data. *Describe* the correlation of the data. **See margin for art; positive correlation.**

Years	1990	1995	1998	1999	2000	2001
Airports (thousands)	17.5	18.2	18.8	19.1	19.3	19.3

5.7 Predict with Linear Models
pp. 335–341

EXAMPLE

Use the scatter plot from the example for Lesson 5.6 above to estimate the time (in hours) it takes to roast a 10 pound turkey.

Draw a line that appears to fit the points in the scatter plot closely. There should be approximately as many points above the line as below it.

Find the point on the line whose x-coordinate is 10. At that point, you can see that the y-coordinate is about 3.25.

▶ It takes about 3.25 hours to roast a 10 pound turkey.

EXERCISES

EXAMPLE 2
on p. 336
for Ex. 22

22. COOKING TIMES Use the graph in the Example above to estimate the time (in hours) it takes to roast a turkey that weighs 30 pounds. *Explain* how you found your answer. **About 5.75 h. *Sample answer:* Use the points (10, 3.25) and (8, 3) to find the slope of the line to be 0.125. Looking at the graph, you can see that the y-intercept is 2, so the equation of the line is $y = 0.125x + 2$. Substitute 30 for x to find $y = 5.75$.**

Write an equation in slope-intercept form of the line with the given slope and *y*-intercept.

1. slope: 5
   y-intercept: −7 **$y = 5x − 7$**

2. slope: $\frac{2}{5}$
   y-intercept: −2 **$y = \frac{2}{5}x − 2$**

3. slope: $−\frac{4}{3}$
   y-intercept: 1
   $y = −\frac{4}{3}x + 1$

Write an equation in slope-intercept form of the line that passes through the given point and has the given slope *m*.

4. (−2, −8); *m* = 3
   $y = 3x − 2$

5. (1, 1); *m* = −4
   $y = −4x + 5$

6. (−1, 3); *m* = −6
   $y = −6x − 3$

Write an equation in point-slope form of the line that passes through the given points. 7–9. See margin.

7. (4, 5), (2, 9)

8. (−2, 2), (8, −3)

9. (3, 4), (1, −6)

Write an equation in standard form of the line with the given characteristics.

10. Slope: 10; passes through (6, 2)
    $−10x + y = −58$

11. Passes through (−3, 2) and (6, −1)
    $\frac{1}{3}x + y = 1$

Write an equation of the line that passes through the given point and is (a) parallel to the given line and (b) perpendicular to the given line. 12–14. See margin.

12. (2, 0), $y = −5x + 3$

13. (−1, 4), $y = −x − 4$

14. (4, −9), $y = \frac{1}{4}x + 2$

Make a scatter plot of the data. Draw a line of fit. Write an equation of the line.

15, 16. See margin.

15.

x	0	1	2	3	4
y	15	35	53	74	94

16.

x	0	2	4	8	10
y	−2	6	15	38	50

17. **FIELD TRIP** Your science class is taking a field trip to an observatory. The cost of a presentation and a tour of the telescope is $60 for the group plus an additional $3 per person. Write an equation that gives the total cost *C* as a function of the number of people *p* in the group. **$C = 3p + 60$**

18. **GOLF FACILITIES** The table shows the number of golf facilities in the United States during the period 1997–2001.

    a. Make a scatter plot of the data where *x* is the number of years since 1997 and *y* is the number of golf facilities (in thousands). **See margin.**

    b. Write an equation that models the number of golf facilities (in thousands) as a function of the number of years since 1997. **Sample answer: $y = 0.28x + 14.6$**

Year	Golf facilities (thousands)
1997	14.6
1998	14.9
1999	15.2
2000	15.5
2001	15.7

    c. At about what rate did the number of golf facilities change during the period 1997–2001? **Sample answer: About 280 golf facilities per year**

    d. Use the equation from part (b) to predict the number of golf facilities in 2004. **Sample answer: About 16,560 golf facilities**

    e. Predict the year in which the number of golf facilities reached 16,000. *Explain* how you found your answer. **Sample answer: 2002; substitute 16 for *y* in the equation $y = 0.28x + 14.6$ and solve for *x*.**

Chapter Test **349**

15.

Sample answer: $y = 19.7x + 14.8$

16.

Sample answer: $y = 5.3x − 3.9$

18a.

7. $y − 5 = −2(x − 4)$ or
   $y − 9 = −2(x − 2)$

8. $y − 2 = −\frac{1}{2}(x + 2)$ or
   $y + 3 = −\frac{1}{2}(x − 8)$

9. $y − 4 = 5(x − 3)$ or
   $y + 6 = 5(x − 1)$

12a. $y = −5x + 10$

12b. $y = \frac{2}{5}x − \frac{2}{5}$

13a. $y = −x + 3$

13b. $y = x + 5$

14a. $y = \frac{1}{4}x − 10$

14b. $y = −4x + 7$

Additional Resources

Assessment Book
- Chapter Test, Levels A, B, C, pp. 63–68
- Standardized Chapter Test, pp. 69–70
- SAT/ACT Chapter Test, pp. 71–72
- Alternative Assessment, pp. 73–74

Test Generator CD-ROM

Chapter Test

Easily-readable reduced copies (with answers) of Chapter Test B, the Standardized Chapter Test, and the Alternative Assessment from the Assessment Book can be found on pp. 280F–280H.

Scoring Rubric

Full Credit
- solution is complete and correct

Partial Credit
- solution is complete but has errors,
  or
- solution is without error but incomplete

No Credit
- no solution is given,
  or
- solution makes no sense

SHORT RESPONSE QUESTIONS

PROBLEM

The average monthly cost of basic cable increased by about $1.47 each year from 1986 to 2003. In 1986 the average monthly cost of basic cable was $10.67. Write an equation that gives the monthly cost (in dollars) of basic cable as a function of the number of years since 1986. In what year was the monthly cost of basic cable $31.25? *Explain* your reasoning.

Below are sample solutions to the problem. Read each solution and the comments in blue to see why the sample represents full credit, partial credit, or no credit.

SAMPLE 1: Full credit solution

A verbal model shows how the equation is obtained.

Let y be the average monthly cost x years since 1986.

Monthly cost	=	Cost in 1986	+	Cost increase per year	·	Years since 1986
y	=	10.67	+	1.47	·	x

To find the year when the monthly cost was $31.25, substitute 31.25 for y and solve for x.

Calculations are performed correctly.

$$y = 10.67 + 1.47x$$
$$31.25 = 10.67 + 1.47x$$
$$14 = x$$

The question is answered correctly.

The monthly cost was $31.25 fourteen years after 1986, or in 2000.

SAMPLE 2: Partial credit solution

The equation is correct, and the student has explained what the variables represent.

Let y be the monthly cost. Let x be the number of years since 1986.

Monthly cost	=	Cost in 1986	+	Cost increase per year	·	Years since 1986
y	=	10.67	+	1.47	·	x

The answer is incorrect, because the student mistakenly substituted the cost for the variable that represents the years since 1986.

To find the year when the cost was $31.25, substitute 31.25 for x.

$$y = 10.67 + 1.47x$$
$$= 10.67 + 1.47(31.25) \approx 56.61$$

The cost was $31.25 about 57 years after 1986, or in 2042.

SAMPLE 3: Partial credit solution

The equation and answer are correct. There are no explanations to support the student's work.

$$y = 10.67 + 1.47x$$
$$31.25 = 10.67 + 1.47x$$
$$14 = x$$

The monthly cost was $31.25 fourteen years after 1986, or in 2000.

SAMPLE 4: No credit solution

The student's reasoning is incorrect, and the equation is incorrect. The answer is incorrect.

Year when cost is $31.25 = $31.25 ÷ 1.47
$$y = 31.25 \div 1.47 \approx 21.25$$

The year is about 21 years after 1986, or in 2007.

PRACTICE   Apply the Scoring Rubric

Score the solution to the problem below as *full credit*, *partial credit*, or *no credit*. *Explain* your reasoning. 1–3. See margin.

PROBLEM A hot air balloon is flying at an altitude of 870 feet. It descends at a rate of 15 feet per minute. Write an equation that gives the altitude (in feet) of the balloon as a function of the time (in minutes) since it began its descent. Find the time it takes the balloon to reach an altitude of 12 feet. *Explain* your reasoning.

1. Let y be the altitude (in feet) after x minutes.

Final altitude	=	Starting altitude	+	Decrease in altitude per minute	·	Minutes

$$y = 870 + (-15)x = 870 - 15(12) = 690$$
The balloon will take 690 minutes to reach an altitude of 12 feet.

2. Let y be the altitude (in feet) after x minutes.

Final altitude	=	Starting altitude	+	Decrease in altitude per minute	·	Minutes

$$y = 870 + (-15)x$$
$$12 = 870 - 15x$$
$$57.2 = x$$
The balloon will take about 57 minutes to reach an altitude of 12 feet.

3. $870 \div 15 = 58$

The balloon will take 58 minutes to reach an altitude of 12 feet.

Avoiding Common Errors

When students use a verbal model, encourage them to write the parts of the equation directly underneath the corresponding parts of the verbal model before they write the equation. This will help them avoid errors in writing the equation, such as confusing the constant with the rate.

1. Partial credit; the equation is correct, and the student has explained what the variables represent. The answer is incorrect because the student mistakenly substituted the altitude for the variable that represents the time.

2. Full credit; a verbal model shows how the equation is obtained, and the student has explained what the variables represent. The correct calculations are performed and the question is answered correctly.

3. No credit; the student's reasoning is incorrect, and the equation is incorrect. The answer is incorrect.

1. $3.5p + 5j = 50$; 14 boxes of pretzels; if you find the value of p when j is 0, $p = 14.29$. Because you cannot buy part of a box, the greatest number of boxes of pretzels you can buy is 14.

2b. The graph of this equation is a line with a negative slope because as the time increases the distance from home decreases.

3. $0.05n + 0.1d = 2.2$; 16 nickels; substitute 14 for d into the equation $0.05n + 0.1d = 2.2$ and solve for n.

4. $-\frac{1}{2}$; 2; write $x + 2y = 4$ in slope-intercept form, $y = -\frac{1}{2}x + 2$ to see that the slope of the line is $-\frac{1}{2}$. If the streets are parallel, the slopes are the same; if the streets are perpendicular then the slopes are negative reciprocals.

5a.

5b. 2010; find the equation of the line of best fit of the data, $y = 1.617x + 0.1$, substitute 20 for y and solve for x. $x = 12.4$, so 12.4 years after 1998, which is 2010, spending per person will reach $20.

7a. Because there is an initial fee for the first hour and then a constant rate for hours after the first, this situation can be modeled by a linear equation.

SHORT RESPONSE

1. You have $50 to spend on pretzels and juice drinks for a school dance. A box of pretzels costs $3.50, and a package of juice drinks costs $5.00. Write an equation in standard form that models the possible combinations of boxes of pretzels and packages of juice drinks that you can buy. What is the greatest number of boxes of pretzels you can buy? *Explain.* **See margin.**

2. You and your family are traveling home in a car at an average speed of 60 miles per hour. At noon you are 180 miles from home.

  a. Write an equation that gives your distance from home (in miles) as a function of the number of hours since noon. $d = -60t + 180$

  b. *Explain* why the graph of this equation is a line with a negative slope. **See margin.**

3. Robyn needs $2.20 to buy a bag of trail mix. Write an equation in standard form that models the possible combinations of nickels and dimes she could use to pay for the mix. How many nickels would she need if she used 14 dimes? *Explain* your reasoning. **See margin.**

4. On a street map, Main Street and Maple Street can be modeled by the equations $y = ax + 6$ and $x + 2y = 4$. For what value of a are the streets parallel? For what value of a are the streets perpendicular? *Justify* your answers. **See margin.**

5. The table shows the projected dollar amount spent per person in the U.S. on interactive television for several years during the period 1998–2006.

Year	Spending per person (dollars)
1998	0
2000	2.86
2002	6.63
2004	9.50
2006	12.85

  a. Make a scatter plot of the data. **a–b. See margin.**

  b. Predict the year in which spending per person in the U.S. on interactive television will reach $20. *Explain* how you found your answer.

6. You are mountain biking on a 10 mile trail. You biked 4 miles before stopping to take a break. After your break, you bike at a rate of 9 miles per hour.

  a. Write an equation that gives the length (in miles) of the trail you have completed as a function of the number of hours since you began. $d = 9t + 4$

  b. How much time (in hours and minutes) after your break will it take you to complete the entire trail? *Explain.* **40 min; substitute 10 for d and solve for t.**

7. A guide gives dogsled tours during the winter months. The guide charges one amount for the first hour of a tour and a different amount for each hour after the first. You paid $55 for a 2 hour dogsled tour. Your friend paid $70 for a 3 hour tour.

  a. *Explain* why this situation can be modeled by a linear equation. **See margin.**

  b. Write an equation that gives the cost (in dollars) of a dogsled tour as a function of the number of hours after the first hour of the tour. $y = 15x + 40$

8. The scatter plot shows the total carbon dioxide emissions throughout the world for several years during the period 1950–1995.

  a. Write an equation that models the carbon dioxide emissions (in billions of metric tons) as a function of the number of years since 1950. *Sample answer:* $y = 0.4x + 5.8$

  b. At about what rate did the amount of carbon dioxide emissions increase from 1950 to 1995? *Explain* how you found your answer. *Sample answer:* **0.4 billion metric tons of carbon dioxide emissions per year; the slope of the line is 0.4, which represents the rate of change.**

352 Chapter 5 Writing Linear Equations

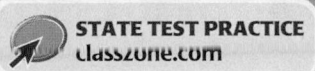

MULTIPLE CHOICE

9. Which equation represents the line that passes through (0, 8) and (2, 0)? **D**

   Ⓐ $y = 4x + 2$ **Ⓑ** $y = -4x + 2$

   Ⓒ $y = 4x + 8$ **Ⓓ** $y = -4x + 8$

10. Which equation represents the line with a slope of 5 and a y-intercept of 2? **C**

   Ⓐ $y = 2x + 5$ **Ⓑ** $y = 2x - 5$

   Ⓒ $y = 5x + 2$ **Ⓓ** $y = 5x - 2$

11. Which function has the values $f(1) = 8$ and $f(7) = -10$? **A**

   Ⓐ $f(x) = -3x + 11$ **Ⓑ** $f(x) = -2x + 10$

   Ⓒ $f(x) = -3x + 25$ **Ⓓ** $f(x) = 3x - 24$

GRIDDED ANSWER

12. What is the slope of a line that is perpendicular to the line $y = -2x - 7$? $\frac{1}{2}$

13. What is the y-intercept of the line that has a slope of $\frac{1}{2}$ and passes through (5, 4)? **1.5**

14. What is the y-intercept of the line that is parallel to the line $y = 2x - 3$ and passes through the point (6, 11)? **−1**

15. What is the zero of the function

   $f(x) = -\frac{4}{5}x + 9$? **11.25**

16. The graph of the equation $Ax + y = 2$ is a line that passes through (−2, 8). What is the value of A? **3**

17a.

17c. About 2.9 h. *Sample answer:* **The data shows that the only student to receive a grade of 93 or above studied for 3 hours and earned a 94. Therefore, to earn a grade of 93, you would need to study almost 3 hours.**

EXTENDED RESPONSE

17. The table shows the time several students spent studying for an exam and each student's grade on the exam.

Study time (hours)	1.5	0.5	0.5	1	1	3	2.5	3	0
Grade	90	60	70	72	80	88	89	94	58

  a. Make a scatter plot of the data. **See margin.**

  b. Write an equation that models a student's exam grade as a function of the time (in hours) the student spent studying for the exam. $y = 10.6x + 62.6$

  c. How many hours would you need to study in order to earn a grade of 93 on the exam? *Justify* your answer using the data above. **See margin.**

18. The scatter plot shows the number of FM radio stations in the United States for several years during the period 1994–2000.

  a. *Describe* the correlation of the data.   **positive correlation**

  b. Write an equation that models the number of FM radio stations in the United States as a function of the number of years since 1994. *Sample answer:* $y = 128x + 5144$

  c. At about what rate did the number of radio stations change during the period 1994–2000? *Sample answer:* **About 128 radio stations per year**

  d. Find the zero of the function from part (b). *Explain* what the zero means in this situation. *Sample answer:* **About −40; there were 0 radio stations 40 years before 1994, or in 1954.**

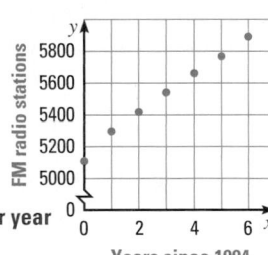

FM radio stations / Years since 1994

REGULAR SCHEDULE

Pre-AP For pacing and assignments for a Pre-AP course, see the *Algebra 1 Toolkit*.

Lesson	Les. Day	BASIC	AVERAGE	ADVANCED
6.1	Day 1	EP p. 939 Exs.12–19; pp. 359–361 Exs. 1–17, 22–25, 31–36, 40–50 even	pp. 359–361 Exs. 1–9, 14–28, 31–38, 41, 44, 47, 50	pp. 359–361 Exs. 1, 2, 4, 5, 8, 9, 14–21, 24–39*, 42, 45, 48, 51
6.2	Day 1	pp. 366–368 Exs. 1–18, 27–31, 36–40, 43–53 odd	pp. 366–368 Exs. 1, 2, 15–34, 36–41, 44–52 even	pp. 366–368 Exs. 1, 2, 17–27, 30–42*, 44–52 even
6.3	Day 1	EP p. 940 Exs. 9–14; pp. 372–374 Exs. 1–10, 17–24, 29, 30, 37–41, 44–56 even	pp. 372–374 Exs. 1, 2, 4–14 even, 15, 16, 21–27 odd, 29–34, 37–42, 44, 45–55 odd	pp. 372–374 Exs. 1, 2, 4–8 even, 13, 14, 22–28 even, 29–36*, 38–43*, 44–56 even
6.4	Day 1	pp. 384–387 Exs. 1–8, 23–27, 47–50, 55	pp. 384–387 Exs. 1–8, 23–31, 40, 55	pp. 384–387 Exs. 1, 2, 5–8, 23–32, 50, 55
	Day 2	pp. 384–387 Exs. 9–22, 37–43, 51–54	pp. 384–387 Exs. 12–22, 32, 33, 39–45, 51–54	pp. 384–387 Exs. 13–20, 33–36*, 40–46*, 52, 54
6.5	Day 1	EP p. 940 Exs. 12–20; pp. 393–395 Exs. 1–22, 51–53	pp. 393–395 Exs. 1, 2, 6–17, 37–40, 51–53	pp. 393–395 Exs. 1, 2, 6–8, 12–20, 37–41*, 54–59
	Day 2	pp. 393–395 Exs. 23–37, 42–47, 54–59	pp. 393–395 Exs. 21–36, 42–49, 54–59	pp. 393–395 Exs. 24–36, 43–50*, 54–58 even
6.6	Day 1	SRH p. 918 Exs. 1–5; pp. 401–403 Exs. 1, 2, 3–21 odd, 22–28, 35–38, 42–52 even	pp. 401–403 Exs. 1, 2, 6–20 even, 21–24, 25–31 odd, 35–40, 45–50	pp. 401–403 Exs. 1, 6–20 even, 21, 22, 26–32 even, 33*, 34*, 36–41*, 44, 47, 52
6.7	Day 1	EP p. 941 Exs. 41–44; pp. 409–412 Exs. 1–11, 15–25, 62–70 even	pp. 409–412 Exs. 1, 2, 8–16, 20–28, 44–46, 63–69 odd	pp. 409–412 Exs. 1, 10–16, 21–28, 44–46, 51*, 52*, 63–69 odd
	Day 2	pp. 409–412 Exs. 29–41, 53–58, 71–76	pp. 409–412 Exs. 29–43, 47–50, 54–59, 71–75 odd	pp. 409–412 Exs. 29–43, 47–50, 55–61*, 73, 76
Review	Day 1	pp. 415–418 Exs. 1–44	pp. 415–418 Exs. 1–44	pp. 415–418 Exs. 1–44
Assess	Day 1	Chapter 6 Test	Chapter 6 Test	Chapter 6 Test
Yearly Pacing		Chapter 6 Total – 12 days	Chapters 1–6 Total – 70 days	Remaining – 90 days

*Challenge Exercises   EP = Extra Practice   SRH = Skills Review Handbook

BLOCK SCHEDULE

DAY 1	DAY 2	DAY 3	DAY 4	DAY 5	DAY 6
6.1	6.3	6.4 (CONT.)	6.5 (CONT.)	6.7	REVIEW
pp. 359–361 Exs. 1–9, 14–28, 31–38, 41, 44, 47, 50	pp. 372–374 Exs. 1, 2, 4–14 even, 15, 16, 21–27 odd, 29–34, 37–42, 44, 45–55 odd	pp. 384–387 Exs. 12–22, 32, 33, 39–45, 51–54	pp. 393–395 Exs. 21–36, 42–49, 54–59	pp. 409–412 Exs. 1, 2, 8–16, 20–50, 54–59, 63–75 odd	pp. 415–418 Exs. 1–44
6.2	6.4	6.5	6.6		ASSESS
pp. 366–368 Exs. 1, 2, 15–34, 36–41, 44–52 even	pp. 384–387 Exs. 1–8, 23–31, 48, 55	pp. 393–395 Exs. 1, 2, 6–17, 37–40, 51–53	pp. 401–403 Exs. 1, 2, 6–20 even, 21–24, 25–31 odd, 35–40, 45–50		Chapter 6 Test
Yearly Pacing		Chapter 6 Total – 6 days	Chapters 1–6 Total – 35 days	Remaining – 45 days	

Chapter Resource Guide

6

RESOURCE MANAGER

Chapter Resource Book

CHAPTER SUPPORT

| Parents as Partners (Chapter Overview with home involvement exercises and activity) | | | | | | p. 1 | |

LESSON SUPPORT	6.1	6.2	6.3	6.4	6.5	6.6	6.7
Teaching Guide/Lesson Plan	p. 3	p. 17	p. 30	p. 43	p. 58	p. 68	p. 82
Activity Masters	p. 5					p. 70	
Technology Activities & Keystrokes				p. 45			p. 84
Activity Support Masters							p. 86
Practice (3 levels)	p. 6	p. 19	p. 32	p. 46	p. 60	p. 71	p. 87
Study Guide	p. 12	p. 25	p. 38	p. 52	p. 63	p. 77	p. 93
Catch-Up for Absent Students	p. 14	p. 27	p. 40	p. 54	p. 65	p. 79	p. 95
Problem Solving/Application	p. 15	p. 28	p. 41	p. 55	p. 66	p. 80	p. 96
Challenge Practice	p. 16	p. 29	p. 42	p. 57	p. 67	p. 81	p. 97

REVIEW

Chapter Review Games and Activities	p. 98	Cumulative Practice	p. 100
Project with Rubric	p. 99	Resource Book Answers	A1

Transparencies

Transparencies	6.1	6.2	6.3	6.4	6.5	6.6	6.7
Warm-Up/Daily Homework Quiz	✔	✔	✔	✔	✔	✔	✔
Notetaking Guide	✔	✔	✔	✔	✔	✔	✔
Teacher Support	✔	✔	✔	✔		✔	✔
Answer Transparencies	✔	✔	✔	✔	✔	✔	✔

ASSESSMENT BOOK

Quizzes	p. 75	SAT/ACT Chapter Test	p. 86
Chapter Tests (3 levels)	p. 78	Alternative Assessment with Rubric	p. 88
Standardized Chapter Test	p. 84		

TECHNOLOGY

- Easy Planner
- Test and Practice Generator
- Power Presentations
- @HomeTutor
- Activity Generator
- Animated Algebra
- Classzone.com
- eEdition Plus Online
- eWorkbook Plus Online
- Easy Grader Online

ADDITIONAL RESOURCES

- Worked-Out Solution Key
- Notetaking Guide
- Practice Wookbook
- Algebra 1 Toolkit
- Benchmark Tests
- Reteaching and Remediation
- Spanish Study Guide
- Spanish Assessment Book
- Student Resources in Spanish
- Multi-Language Visual Glossary

LESSON 6.1 Practice B
For use with pages 356–361

Write an inequality that is represented by the graph.

1.

2.

3.

4.

5.

6.

1. $x \le 4$ 2. $x > -2$ 3. $x < 3$ 4. $x \ge -7$ 5. $x < 0$ 6. $x \le -1$

Solve the inequality. Graph your solution.

7. $x + 7 > 1$ $x > -6$

8. $n - 3 \le 9$ $n \le 12$

9. $10 \ge a + 7$ $a \le 3$

10. $m - 3 < -2$ $m < 1$

11. $p - 5 > -5$ $p > 0$

12. $x + 3 \le -4.5$ $x \le -7.5$

13. $b + 9.5 \le -6.4$ $b \le -15.9$

14. $y + 2.5 < 7.3$ $y < 4.8$

15. $z - 10.2 > 18.3$ $z > 28.5$

16. $d - 8 > 2.2$ $d > 10.2$

Write the verbal sentence as an inequality. Then solve the inequality and graph your solution.

17. The sum of 15 and n is less than 8. $15 + n < 8$; $n < -7$

LESSON 6.1 Practice B continued
For use with pages 356–361

18. The difference of m and 3 is greater than or equal to 10. $m - 3 \ge 10$; $m \ge 13$

19. Twenty-four is less than or equal to the sum of 35 and x. $24 \le 35 + x$; $x \ge -11$

20. Eighty-five is greater than the difference of x and 63. $85 < x - 63$; $x > 148$

21. **Summer Reading** During the summer you want to read at least 32 books. You have read 21 books so far this summer. What are the possible numbers of books you can read to pass your goal?   11 books or more

22. **Baseball Hats** You are a big baseball fan. You have a goal of attending a baseball game in every major league stadium in the country. Every time you go to a different stadium, you buy a baseball hat. You keep your hats in a display case that holds 25 hats. You have 8 baseball hats so far. What are the possible numbers of hats you can collect without needing another display case?   17 hats or less

23. **Gift Card** You received a $25 gift card to a sporting goods store for your birthday. You are looking at skateboards and want to spend no more than $85 of your own money.
   a. Write and solve an inequality to find the prices p in dollars of skateboards you can buy. $p - 25 \le 85$; $p \le 110$
   b. What is the most expensive skateboard you can buy?   A $110 skateboard

24. **Video Games** You and your friend are having a video game competition. The person with the highest score after two games wins. The table shows your friend's first and second scores and your first score.

Game	Friend's score	Your score
1	6532	5034
2	4887	?

   a. Write and solve an inequality to find the scores s that you can earn in your second game in order to beat your friend. $6532 + 4887 < 5034 + s$; $s > 6385$
   b. Will you win if you earn 6392 points? 6385 points? 6377 points? *Justify* your answers.   Yes, because 6392 > 6385. No, because 6385 $\ngtr$ 6385; No, because 6377 $\ngtr$ 6385.

LESSON 6.2 Practice B
For use with pages 363–368

Match the verbal sentence with the inequality. Then solve the inequality.

1. The product of 3 and x is less than or equal to 18.   C; $x \le 6$ **A.** $\frac{x}{18} \ge 3$

2. The product of 18 and x is greater than or equal to 3.   B; $x \ge \frac{1}{6}$ **B.** $18x \ge 3$

3. The quotient of x and 18 is greater than or equal to 3.   A; $x \ge 54$ **C.** $3x \le 18$

Solve the inequality. Graph your solution.

4. $3y \ge 4$ $y \ge \frac{4}{3}$

5. $\frac{x}{2} < 6$ $x < 12$

6. $\frac{m}{5} > -5$ $m > -25$

7. $\frac{c}{-10} \le -2$ $c \ge 20$

8. $8n > -1$ $n > -\frac{1}{8}$

9. $42 < 6z$ $z > 7$

10. $-5p \le 2$ $p \ge -\frac{2}{5}$

11. $\frac{w}{-4} < 8$ $w > -32$

12. $-7a \ge -3$ $a \le \frac{3}{7}$

13. $52 \le -13x$ $x \le -4$

14. $0.25x > 18$ $x > 72$

15. $-2d < 3$ $d > -\frac{3}{2}$

LESSON 6.2 Practice B continued
For use with pages 363–368

Write the verbal sentence as an inequality. Then solve the inequality and graph your solution.

16. The product of 12 and y is greater than or equal to 60. $12y \ge 60$; $y \ge 5$

17. The product of 7 and b is less than -35. $7b < -35$; $b < -5$

18. The quotient of m and 2 is greater than 23. $\frac{m}{2} > 23$; $m > 46$

19. The quotient of p and 4.5 is less than or equal to 10. $\frac{p}{4.5} \le 10$; $p \le 45$

20. **Flower Beds** You are in charge of buying the flowers for the flower beds around your school. You cannot spend over $80 on flowers. The flowers cost $10.99 for a flat of flowers. What are the possible numbers of flats of flowers you can buy?   7 flats or less

21. **Pavilion Rental** You and three of your friends decide to rent a pavilion at a local park for an end-of-the-school-year party. The group budget is $80. The group decides to split the cost equally.
   a. What are the possible amounts of money that each of you can spend? $20 or less
   b. If two more of your friends decide to pitch in for the party, what are the possible amounts of money that each of you can spend if you all split the cost equally?   about $13.33 or less

22. **Waiting Tables** Restaurants typically pay wait staff an hourly wage that is lower than minimum wage. The wait staff is expected to make up the difference in tips. The minimum wage is $5.15 per hour and a restaurant pays the wait staff $4 per hour.
   a. If a waitress works an 8-hour shift, write and solve an inequality that gives the total tips t in dollars that the waitress must earn in an 8-hour shift in order to meet or exceed the minimum wage. $\frac{t}{8} \ge 1.15$; $t \ge 9.2$
   b. If the waitress makes $10.40 in tips during an 8-hour shift, will she meet or exceed the minimum wage? By how much?   yes; by $1.20
   c. If the waitress makes $9.20 in tips during an 8-hour shift, will she meet or exceed the minimum wage? By how much?   yes; by $0

Practice B
For use with pages 369–374

Solve the inequality. Graph your solution.

1. $4x - 7 \geq 1$ $x \geq 2$

2. $7p + 3 < -11$ $p < -2$

3. $8 - 2n \geq 26$ $n \leq -9$

4. $3(a - 4) \leq 33$ $a \leq 15$

5. $6(y + 1) > 6$ $y > 0$

6. $-2(c - 1) < -22$ $c > 12$

7. $8m - 7 < 4m + 5$ $m < 3$

8. $10 - 11d > -5d - 4$ $d < \frac{7}{3}$

9. $9z \leq -7z + 14$ $z \leq \frac{7}{8}$

10. $6w + 3 < 2w + 15$ $w < 3$

Solve the inequality, if possible.

11. $6y - 9 \leq 4y + 2y - 16$ no solution

12. $7p - 11p + 3 \geq 3 - 4p$ all real numbers

13. $4(c - 5) < 2(c - 10)$ $c < 0$

14. $5(a - 3) \leq 5a - 6$ all real numbers

15. $6(x - 8) > 6x - 48$ no solution

16. $2(3d - 4) < 4 + 6d - 15$ no solution

17. $4m + 14 - 2m \leq 2(m + 7)$ all real numbers

18. $-2(n - 3) \geq 1 - 2n + 5$ all real numbers

19. $4(3 - 2x) > 2(6 - 4x)$ no solution

20. $2(5 - a) > 4a + 13 - 6a$ no solution

21. $-4n + 11 < -4(n + 6)$ no solution

22. $3(5 - 6x) \leq 2(11 - 9x)$ all real numbers

23. $2m + 10 - 7m \leq 5(4 - m)$ all real numbers

24. $6(1 - 2n) \leq 5 - 12n$ no solution

Practice B continued
For use with pages 369–374

Translate the verbal phrase into an inequality. Then solve the inequality and graph your solution.

25. Six more than 5 times a number x is greater than or equal to 31. $6 + 5x \geq 31; x \geq 5$

26. Twice the sum of 4 and x is less than -16. $2(4 + x) < -16; x < -12$

27. The difference of $10x$ and $3x$ is less than or equal to the sum of $4x$ and 21. $10x - 3x \leq 4x + 21; x \leq 7$

28. The sum of $2x$ and $4x$ is greater than or equal to the sum of $3x$ and 36. $2x + 4x \geq 3x + 36; x \geq 9$

29. The difference of $2x$ and 15 is less than or equal to the sum of $4x$ and 17. $2x - 15 \leq 4x + 17; x \geq -16$

30. **Weaving** A weaver spends $420 on supplies to make wall hangings and plans to sell the wall hangings for $80 each.
   a. Write an inequality that gives the possible numbers w of wall hangings the weaver needs to sell in order for the profit to be positive. $80w - 420 > 0$
   b. What are the possible numbers of wall hangings the weaver needs to sell in order for the profit to be positive?   6 wall hangings or more

31. **School Spirit** Your club is in charge of making pins that students can buy to show their school spirit for the upcoming football game. You have made 225 pins so far, and you only have 2 hours left to make the rest of the pins. You need to make at least 400 pins.
   a. Write an inequality that gives the possible numbers p of pins you have to make per minute in order to exceed your goal. $225 + 120p \geq 400$
   b. What are the possible numbers of pins you have to make per minute in order to exceed your goal?   2 pins or more

32. **Aquarium** You are getting a larger aquarium for your neon tetra fish and you also want to add more neon tetras to the larger aquarium. The general rule is that each fish needs 2 gallons of water. You currently have 6 neon tetras. If you buy a 20-gallon aquarium, what are the possible numbers of fish you can put in your aquarium? *Explain* how you got your answer.   4 fish or less; First find the number of gallons needed by the 6 fish by finding the product of 6 and 2, which is 12. Then subtract this amount from 20 to get 8, the number of gallons left for new fish. Then solve the inequality $2f \leq 8$, where f is the number of new fish.

Practice B
For use with pages 380–387

Translate the verbal phrase into an inequality. Then graph the inequality.

1. All real numbers that are less than or equal to -3 *and* greater than or equal to -8 $-8 \leq x \leq -3$

2. All real numbers that are greater than 5 *or* less than or equal to -1 $x \leq -1$ or $x > 5$

3. All real numbers that are greater than or equal to -2.5 *and* less than 3.5 $-2.5 \leq x < 3.5$

Solve the inequality. Graph your solution.

4. $-3 < x + 1 \leq 5$ $-4 < x \leq 4$

5. $-7 < x - 8 < 2$ $1 < x < 10$

6. $-5 < -5x \leq 20$ $-4 \leq x < 1$

7. $0 \leq 2(x - 3) < 8$ $3 \leq x < 7$

8. $3x + 2 < 8$ or $-x + 3 < -2$ $x < 2$ or $x > 5$

9. $2(x + 4) < 6$ or $-x - 3 \leq -7$ $x < -1$ or $x \geq 4$

10. $5x < -30$ or $x + 10 > 7$ $x < -6$ or $x > -3$

11. $3x + 5 \leq 1$ or $8 - x < 5$ $x \leq -\frac{4}{3}$ or $x > 3$

Practice B continued
For use with pages 380–387

Write the verbal sentence as an inequality. Then solve the inequality and graph your solution.

12. Three times x is less than -6 *and* greater than -21. $-21 < 3x < -6; -7 < x < -2$

13. One less than x is less than -1 *or* 3 more than x is greater than or equal to 7. $x - 1 < -1$ or $3 + x \geq 7; x < 0$ or $x \geq 4$

14. The difference of $2x$ and 5 is greater than -3 *and* less than or equal to 11. $-3 < 2x - 5 \leq 11; 1 < x \leq 8$

15. The sum of $3x$ and 1 is greater than -5 *and* less than or equal to 10. $-5 < 3x + 1 \leq 10; -2 < x \leq 3$

16. **Temperature** The high temperature in a city last year was 95°F. The low temperature in this city last year was -5°F. Write and graph a compound inequality that represents the temperatures T throughout the year. $-5 \leq T \leq 95$

17. **Pollen Count** Weather forecasts will often give reports on the pollen count. For people suffering from allergies, the pollen count indicates the severity of their symptoms. If a pollen count is high, the severity of the symptoms are increased. The table shows ranges for high, medium, and low pollen counts. Write an inequality to find the range at which the pollen count is not medium. $x \leq 4$ or $x > 8$

Pollen Count	High	Medium	Low
Range	Greater than 8	Greater than 4 and less than or equal to 8	Less than or equal to 4

18. **Distances** You live 5 miles from work and the gym you go to is 3 miles from work.
   a. Find the minimum distance d between your home and the gym.   2 mi
   b. Find the maximum distance d between your home and the gym.   8 mi
   c. Write an inequality that describes the possible distances d between your home and the gym. $2 \leq d \leq 8$

Home is somewhere on this circle.

5 mi

Work   3 mi

The gym is somewhere on this circle.

354D

6 Lesson Practice Level B

Solve the equation.

1. $|x| = 9$ $x = -9, 9$

2. $|x| = 2.25$ $x = -2.25, 2.25$

3. $|x| = \frac{3}{2}$ $x = -\frac{3}{2}, \frac{3}{2}$

4. $|x - 6| = 14$ $x = -8, 20$

5. $|x + 1| = 8$ $x = -9, 7$

6. $|2x - 3| = 15$ $x = -6, 9$

7. $|4x + 1| = 15$ $x = -4, \frac{7}{2}$

8. $|7x + 2| = 23$ $x = -\frac{25}{7}, 3$

9. $|5 - 2x| = 9$ $x = -2, 7$

10. $3|2x - 2| = 18$ $x = -2, 4$

11. $4|5x - 1| = 36$ $x = -\frac{8}{5}, 2$

12. $2|6x + 5| - 1 = 25$ $x = -3, \frac{4}{3}$

Solve the equation, if possible. See above.

13. $|x + 3| - 4 = -1$

14. $|x - 8| - 9 = -5$

15. $|x + 3| + 2.5 = 3$

16. $-6|10 - 2x| = 24$

17. $-3|4x + 3| = -9$

18. $-4|5 + 2x| = -16$

19. $-\frac{1}{3}|1 - 8x| = 2$

20. $|3x - 8| + 0.25 = 0.75$

21. $|6x + 5| - 1.3 = -1.9$

13. $x = -6, 0$ 14. $x = 4, 12$ 15. $x = -\frac{7}{2}, -\frac{5}{2}$

16. no solution   17. $x = -\frac{3}{2}, 0$ 18. $x = -\frac{9}{2}, -\frac{1}{2}$

19. no solution   20. $x = \frac{5}{2}, \frac{17}{6}$ 21. no solution

Find the values of x that satisfy the definition of absolute value for the given value and the given absolute deviation.

22. Given value: 3; absolute deviation: 5

23. Given value: 1; absolute deviation: 7

24. Given value: −4; absolute deviation: 2

25. Given value: −2.5; absolute deviation: 8

22. $x = -2, 8$ 23. $x = -6, 8$ 24. $x = -6, -2$ 25. $x = -10.5, 5.5$

26. **Food Scale** Bakers will typically weigh out flour for recipes rather than use a measuring cup because weighing is a more accurate measure. A baker is using a scale that has an absolute error of 0.05 gram.

   a. Find the minimum and maximum possible weights if the scale is used to measure out 225 grams of flour.   224.95 g; 225.05 g

   b. Find the minimum and maximum possible weights if the scale is used to measure out 300 grams of flour.   299.95 g; 300.05 g

   c. Find the minimum and maximum possible weights if the scale is used to measure out 420 grams of flour.   419.95 g; 420.05 g

27. **Toothpaste Prices** The average price of the brand of toothpaste that you buy is $2.49 for an 8.2-ounce tube. Depending on where you shop, the prices vary by as much as $.15.

   a. Write an absolute value equation that represents the minimum and maximum prices of the toothpaste. $|x - 2.49| = 0.15$

   b. Find the minimum and maximum prices of the toothpaste. $2.34; $2.64

   c. You have a coupon for $.50 off two tubes of toothpaste. If you go to the store that has the minimum price for the toothpaste, how much will you pay for two tubes? $4.18

Solve the inequality. Graph your solution.

1. $|x| \geq 5$ $x \leq -5$ or $x \geq 5$

2. $|x| < 6.5$ $-6.5 < x < 6.5$

3. $|x| \geq \frac{3}{2}$ $x \leq -\frac{3}{2}$ or $x \geq \frac{3}{2}$

4. $|x - 6| \leq 1$ $5 \leq x \leq 7$

5. $|x + 7| > 11$ $x < -18$ or $x > 4$

6. $|10 - x| < 2$ $8 < x < 12$

7. $|-x - 5| < 1$ $-6 < x < -4$

8. $|2x + 1| \geq 5$ $x \leq -3$ or $x \geq 2$

9. $|3x - 2| \leq 7$ $-\frac{5}{3} \leq x \leq 3$

10. $|8 - 3x| \geq 7$ $x \leq \frac{1}{3}$ or $x \geq 5$

11. $|\frac{1}{2}x - 4| > 20$ $x < -32$ or $x > 48$

12. $|1 - \frac{4}{3}x| < 5$ $-3 < x < 4.5$

Write the verbal sentence as an inequality. Then solve the inequality and graph your solution.

13. The distance between x and 8 is less than 14. $|x - 8| < 14$; $-6 < x < 22$

14. The distance between x and −5 is greater than or equal to 12. $|x + 5| \geq 12$; $x \leq -17$ or $x \geq 7$

15. The distance between 9 and x is less than or equal to 8. $|9 - x| \leq 8$; $1 \leq x \leq 17$

16. The distance between 10 and $2x$ is greater than 34. $|10 - 2x| > 34$; $x < -12$ or $x > 22$

Tell whether the statement is *true* or *false*. If it is false, give a counterexample.

17. If a is a solution of $|x + 4| < 7$, then a is also a solution of $x + 4 < 7$.   true

18. If a is a solution of $|x - 6| \geq 4$, then a is also a solution of $x - 6 \leq -4$.   true

19. **DVDs** The average price of a standard DVD is $15.99 with a standard deviation of $4. Write an absolute value inequality that describes this range in prices. $|x - 15.99| = 4$

20. **Body Temperature** A canine's body temperature is considered to be normal if it is 101°F with an absolute deviation of 1.5°F. $|x - 101| = 1.5$

   a. Write an absolute value inequality that represents the normal temperature range.

   b. Solve the inequality. What is the normal temperature range?   Between 99.5°F and 102.5°F

21. **Baseball** A baseball should weigh 5.12 ounces with an absolute deviation of 0.035 ounce. The circumference of a baseball should be 9.05 inches with an absolute deviation of 0.05 inch.

   a. Write absolute value inequalities that represent the ranges for the weight and circumference of a baseball.   weight: $|x - 5.12| = 0.035$; circumference: $|x - 9.05| = 0.05$

   b. Is a ball that weighs 5.16 ounces and has a circumference of 9 inches within the ranges that it should be? *Explain* why or why not.   No, because the ball weighs too much.

   c. What are the maximum and minimum circumferences of a baseball?   9.1 in.; 9 in.

   d. What are the maximum and minimum weights of a baseball?   5.155 oz; 5.085 oz

Tell whether the ordered pair is a solution of the inequality.

1. $x + y > -9$; $(0, 0)$ yes

2. $x - y \geq 8$; $(14, 9)$ no

3. $2x - y > 4$; $(-6, -15)$ no

4. $2x + y > -5$; $(-5, 12)$ yes

5. $5x + 2y \leq 8$; $(-3, 6)$ yes

6. $4x - 3y \geq -5$; $(6, 8)$ yes

7. $0.5x + 2.5y \geq 2$; $(0, 0)$ no

8. $1.2x - 3.1y < 4$; $(3, -1)$ no

9. $0.2y - 0.5x > -1$; $(-4, -8)$ yes

Graph the inequality.

10. $y - x < 6$

11. $x - y > -4$

12. $2y - x < 2$

13. $4y \leq 6x - 2$

14. $5y \leq 10x + 15$

15. $6y + 3 \geq -18x$

16. $2(y + 3) < 4x$

17. $2y - 3x \geq -8$

18. $2(x - y) < -5$

19. $y > 7$

20. $x \leq -5$

21. $y < -4$

Write an inequality of the graph shown.

22.

$y \geq -x + 4$

23.

$y \leq 2x + 3$

24.

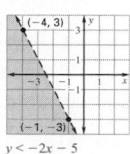

$y < -2x - 5$

25. **Clothes** You are going clothes shopping and can spend at most $130 on clothes. It costs $30 for a pair of pants and $22 for a shirt. Let x represent the number of pants you can buy. Let y represent the number of shirts you can buy.

    a. Write and graph an inequality that describes the different number of shirts and pants you can buy. $30x + 22y \leq 130$

    b. Give three possible combinations of pants and shirts that you can buy.   Answers will vary.

26. **Window** The area of the window shown is less than 42 square feet. Let x and y represent the heights of the triangular and rectangular portions of the window, respectively.

    a. Write and graph an inequality that describes the different dimensions of the window. $4y + 2x < 42$

    b. Could the height of the triangular portion be 2 feet and the height of the rectangular portion be 8 feet?   yes

CHAPTER 6 Quiz 1
For use after Lessons 6.1–6.2

Solve the inequality. Graph your solution.

1. $y - 9 < -4$

-6 -4 -2 0 2 4 6

2. $4 + m \geq 1$

-6 -4 -2 0 2 4 6

3. $k + 12 \leq 3$

-12 -9 -6 -3 0 3 6

4. $-1 > p - 8$

-6 -4 -2 0 2 4 6 8 10

5. $-15 \leq 3d$

-6 -4 -2 0 2 4 6

6. $-2t > -16$

-2 0 2 4 6 8 10

7. $\frac{b}{3} < 2$

-6 -4 -2 0 2 4 6

8. $48 \geq -4n$

-12 -9 -6 -3 0 3 6

9. $\frac{h}{-5} > 7$

-37 -35 -33 -31

10. You are buying pizzas for a neighborhood party. Each pizza costs \$9. If you have \$72, what are the possible numbers of pizzas that you can buy?

Answers

1. _____$y < 5$_____
   See left.
2. _____$m \geq -3$_____
   See left.
3. _____$k \leq -9$_____
   See left.
4. _____$p < 7$_____
   See left.
5. _____$d \geq -5$_____
   See left.
6. _____$t < 8$_____
   See left.
7. _____$b < 6$_____
   See left.
8. _____$n \geq -12$_____
   See left.
9. _____$h < -35$_____
   See left.
10. _____$p \leq 8$ pizzas_____

CHAPTER 6 Quiz 2
For use after Lessons 6.3–6.4

Solve the inequality, if possible.

1. $5x + 7 \geq 2$

2. $8x - 9 < -2x + 11$

3. $4(3x - 2) > 12(x + 1)$

4. $-3(x - 2) \leq -3x + 7$

5. $x + 3 \leq -2 \ or \ 10x - 3 > x + 15$

6. $\frac{1}{2}(x + 10) > -(x + 1)$

Answers

1. _____$x \geq -1$_____
2. _____$x < 2$_____
3. _____no solution_____
4. _____all real numbers_____
5. _____$x \leq -5 \ or \ x > 2$_____
6. _____$x > -4$_____

CHAPTER 6 Quiz 3
For use after Lessons 6.5–6.7

Solve the equation.

1. $|x| = 0.3$

2. $|x + 4| = 2$

3. $2|5x - 1| = 8$

Solve the inequality. Graph your solution.

4. $|x| \geq 5$

-6 -4 -2 0 2 4 6

5. $|3x - 2| < 2$

-3 -2 -1 0 1 2 3

6. $2|x + 3| - 1 \leq 3$

-6 -4 -2 0 2 4 6

Graph the inequality.

7. $y > 3x - 2$

8. $4x + y \leq 0$

9. $x \geq 3$

Answers

1. _____0.3 and -0.3_____
2. _____-2 and -6_____
3. _____1 and $-\frac{3}{5}$_____
4. _____$x \leq -5 \ or \ x \geq 5$_____
   See left.
5. _____$0 < x < \frac{4}{3}$_____
   See left.
6. _____$-5 \leq x \leq -1$_____
   See left.
7. _____See left._____
8. _____See left._____
9. _____See left._____

CHAPTER 6 Chapter Test B
For use after Chapter 6

Solve the inequality. Graph your solution.

1. $x + 8 > -10$

-20 -16 -12 -8 -4 0

2. $\frac{y}{-4} < -3$

6 8 10 12 14 16 18

3. $7 - 5d < -3$

-4 -2 0 2 4

4. $4a - 8 < 2a$

-4 -3 -2 -1 0 1 2 3 4

In Exercises 5 and 6, use the following information.

To be eligible for the playoffs, a baseball team cannot lose more than 40% of its remaining games. The team has 18 games remaining in the regular season.

5. Write and solve an inequality to find the number of games g that the team could lose and still be eligible for the playoffs.

6. If the baseball team loses 8 of its remaining games, will the team advance to the playoffs? Explain your answer.

Solve the inequality, if possible.

7. $2(3x - 1) > 6(x + 1)$

8. $3(2p - 5) \geq 8p - 5$

9. $5(2s + 7) - 4 > 10s - 7$

Translate the verbal statement into an inequality. Then solve the inequality.

10. Five-eighths of a number x is greater than or equal to -10.

11. The difference of 9 and $3x$ is less than or equal to -6.

In Exercises 12 and 13, use the following information.

The photography club at your school decides to publish a calendar to raise money. The initial cost for equipment and software is \$600. In addition to the initial cost, each calendar costs \$2.50 to produce. The club plans to sell the calendars for \$8 each.

12. Write and solve an inequality to find the number n of calendars that the photography club must sell in order to raise at least \$1200.

13. Will the club reach their fundraising goal if they sell 110 calendars? Explain your answer.

Answers

1. _____$x > -18$_____
   See left.
2. _____$y > 12$_____
   See left.
3. _____$d > 2$_____
   See left.
4. _____$a < 4$_____
   See left.
5. _____$\frac{g}{18} \leq 0.40; \ g \leq 7.2$_____
6. _____No, the team can lose_____
   at most 7 games.
7. _____no solution_____
8. _____$p \leq -5$_____
9. _____all real numbers_____
10. _____$\frac{5}{8}x \geq -10; \ x \geq -16$_____
11. _____$9 - 3x \leq -6; \ x \geq 5$_____
12. _____$8n - 2.50n - 600$_____
    $\geq 1200; \ n \geq \frac{3600}{11}$
13. _____No, they must sell at_____
    least 328 calendars.

Chapter Test B
For use after Chapter 6

Solve the compound inequality. Graph your solution.

14. $5 - x > 2$ or $5 \le x - 7$

15. $-10 \le 2(x - 1) < 14$

16. The water pressure p (in pounds per square inch) exerted on an object in the ocean can be given by the function $p = 15 + \frac{6}{11}d$ where d is the depth (in feet) below the surface of the water. What are the possible water pressures of an object when the depth ranges from 102 feet to 468 feet?

Solve the equation or inequality, if possible.

17. $|3x - 1| = 2$

18. $2|x| - 7 = 3$

19. $2|x + 8| + 6 = 0$

20. $|x - 2| + 6 > 9$

21. $-2|4 - x| \le -4$

22. $|2x - 8| < 0$

Graph the inequality.

23. $y > -3x - 2$

24. $x - 3y < 6$

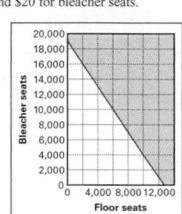

In Exercises 25 and 26, use the following information.

A concert promoter needs to take in at least \$380,000 from ticket sales. The promoter charges \$30 for floor seats and \$20 for bleacher seats.

25. Write and graph an inequality that describes his goal in terms of selling bleacher seat tickets and selling floor seat tickets.

26. Identify and interpret one of the solutions.

Answers

14.	$x < 3$ or $x > 12$
	See left.
15.	$-4 \le x < 8$
	See left.
16.	The depths are
	between 159.5 ft
	and 830.5 ft.
17.	$x = -\frac{1}{3}$; $x = 1$
18.	$x = \pm 5$
19.	no solution
20.	$x > 5$ or $x < -1$
21.	$6 \ge x \ge 2$
22.	no solution
23.	See left.
24.	See left.
25.	$30x + 20y \ge 380{,}000$
	See left.
26.	*Sample answer:*
	(10,000, 12,000); He
	could sell 10,000
	tickets for bleacher
	seats and 12,000
	tickets for floor seats.

Standardized Test
For use after Chapter 6

Multiple Choice

1. Which inequality is represented by the graph?   D

  A $x + 9 > 24$ **B** $x + 7 \ge 22$

  C $x - 5 < 10$ **D** $x - 7 \le 8$

2. Which inequality is equivalent to $3.4 \ge p - 2.3$?   B

  A $1.1 \ge p$ **B** $p \le 5.7$

  C $p \ge 1.1$ **D** $5.7 \le p$

3. Which inequality represents the sentence "The difference of r and 12 is less than or equal to 22."?   A

  A $r - 12 \le 22$ **B** $r - 12 > 22$

  C $r - 12 \ge 22$ **D** $r - 12 < 22$

4. You need to buy 5 notebooks but only have \$6 to spend. Which inequality can you use to find the possible number of notebooks that you can afford if n represents the price of one notebook?   B

  A $5n < 6$ **B** $5n \le 6$

  C $\frac{5}{n} < 6$ **D** $\frac{5}{n} \le 6$

5. Which inequality is equivalent to $\frac{m}{-8} > 7$?   D

  A $m > 56$ **B** $m < 56$

  C $m > -56$ **D** $m < -56$

6. Which inequality represents the sentence "The product of w and 12 is greater than 54."?   C

  A $\frac{w}{12} > 54$ **B** $\frac{w}{12} < 54$

  C $12w > 54$ **D** $12w < 54$

7. What is the first step in solving the inequality $5x - 12 < 18$?   B

  A Subtract 12 from each side of the inequality.

  B Add 12 to each side of the inequality.

  C Multiply each side of the inequality by 5.

  D Divide each side of the inequality by 5.

8. Which inequality is equivalent to $\frac{1}{2}f + 5 < 21$?   D

  A $f < 16$ **B** $f < 13$

  C $f < 8$ **D** $f < 32$

9. Which inequality is equivalent to $5(r - 2) \le -10r + 5$?   A

  A $r \le 1$ **B** $r \ge 1$

  C $r \le \frac{7}{15}$ **D** $r \ge \frac{7}{15}$

10. For which values of m and n are all the solutions of $mx - n > 0$ negative?   C

  A $m > 0, n > 0$ **B** $m < 0, n < 0$

  C $m > 0, n < 0$ **D** $m > 0, n = 0$

11. Which inequality is equivalent to $4 \le \frac{2}{3}(9x + 15) < 34$?   B

  A $-\frac{11}{6} \le x < \frac{19}{6}$ **B** $-1 \le x < 4$

  C $\frac{14}{6} \le x < \frac{44}{6}$ **D** $-36 \le x < 144$

12. Which inequality represents the verbal phrase "All real numbers that are greater than or equal to $-5\frac{1}{3}$ and less than $25\frac{2}{3}$"?   A

  A $-5\frac{1}{3} \le x < 25\frac{2}{3}$ **B** $-5\frac{1}{3} \ge x < 25\frac{2}{3}$

  C $-5\frac{1}{3} \ge x > 25\frac{2}{3}$ **D** $-5\frac{1}{3} \le x > 25\frac{2}{3}$

Standardized Test *continued*
For use after Chapter 6

13. Which of the following are the solutions to the equation $3|x - 8| = 132$?   D

  A $x = 44$ and $x = -44$

  B $x = 36$ and $x = -36$

  C $x = 52$ and $x = -52$

  D $x = 52$ and $x = -36$

14. A toolmaker is making a part that must have a diameter of 2.5 centimeters with an absolute error of 0.0025 centimeter. What is the minimum possible diameter that this part can have?   B

  A 0.00625 cm   **B** 2.4975 cm

  C 2.5025 cm   **D** 1000 cm

15. Which inequality is equivalent to $x < -6$ or $x > 11$?   C

  A $|x - 7| < -13$ **B** $5|x - 5| > 50$

  C $4|5 - 2x| > 68$ **D** $2|2 - 4x| > 86$

16. The graph of which inequality is shown?   D

  A $x + y < -2$

  B $x + y > -2$

  C $x + y \le -2$

  D $x + y \ge -2$

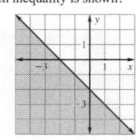

Gridded Answer

17. You will be giving a presentation in your Algebra I class. Your teacher gives you a time limit of 12 minutes with an absolute deviation of 1.5 minutes. What is the minimum possible duration (in minutes) of your presentation?

18. a. $\frac{98 + 85 + 72 + 78 + x}{5} \ge 85$; $x \ge 92$

b. No, it is not possible to earn an average of 92. A score of 100 on the last test would still only give you an average of 86.6.

Short Response

18. You earned the following scores on four English tests: 98, 85, 72, and 78. You want to have an average of at least 85 after you take the fifth test.

  a. Write and solve an inequality to find the possible scores that you can earn on your fifth test in order to meet your goal.   See above.

  b. The greatest score you can earn on a test is 100. Is it possible for you to have an average score of 92 after the fifth test? *Explain* your reasoning.   See above.

Extended Response

19. The math club at your school is selling chances to win a computer in order to help raise funds for a local tournament. Each ticket is \$2. The club has 1000 tickets to sell and must sell at least 750 to raise enough money. The table shows the number of tickets sold so far by each member.

Member	1	2	3	4	5
Tickets Sold	98	68	112	75	112

  a. Find the possible numbers a of additional tickets that the club can sell in order to meet its goal. $a \ge 285$

  b. If the club raises more than \$1500, any additional amount will be used to purchase calculators. Find the possible total numbers t of tickets that the club can sell in order to purchase at least \$100 worth of calculators. $t \ge 800$

  c. Write an inequality that describes the possible amounts c that the club can use toward the purchase of calculators. *Explain* your answer.

$c \le \$500$ or $0 \le c \le \$500$; Selling 750 tickets would raise \$1500 for the club. Anything over that amount is used to purchase calculators. After selling 750 tickets, there are 250 tickets remaining, which would total \$500. So, the maximum amount that can be used towards calculators is \$500 and the minimum amount is \$0.

Alternative Assessment and Math Journal
For use after Chapter 6

Journal

1. Explain how to solve the absolute value inequality $|ax + b| > 9$ and give a rough sketch of the graph of the resulting solution.

Multi-Step Problem

2. The Math Club has \$1500 to spend on a party. The club decides to use a portion of the money to reserve a banquet room and purchase door prizes. The banquet room costs \$125 to reserve and the door prizes each cost \$8.50.

  a. Write and solve an inequality representing the number of door prizes p that can be purchased if the club decides to use no more than \$250 to reserve the banquet room and purchase the door prizes.

  b. Graph the solution in part (a). What is the maximum number of door prizes that can be purchased?

  c. The club decides to purchase the maximum number of door prizes. Determine the amount that remains in the \$1500 budget after purchasing door prizes and reserving the banquet room.

  d. The remaining money in the budget will be used to pay for the food for the banquet. Vegetarian, beef, and chicken entrée options are available at prices of \$7, \$11, and \$9, respectively. Write an inequality representing the purchase of x beef, y chicken, and 8 vegetarian entrees that stays within the budget.

  e. Graph the inequality in part (d).

  f. Give 3 possible combinations of numbers of beef and chicken entrees.

  g. For each answer given in part (f), determine the amount of money in the budget that was not spent.

1. Complete answers should include: a discussion of the equivalent compound inequality $ax + b > 9$ or $ax + b < -9$; a discussion of how to solve each part of this compound inequality; a rough sketch of a solution consisting of two rays having open circles that point in opposite directions.

2. a. $125 + 8.5p \le 250$; $p \le 14$ **b.** ; 14 door prizes

c. \$1256   **d.** $11x + 9y + 56 \le 1256$

e.

f. *Sample answer:* 100 beef and 10 chicken; 50 beef and 70 chicken; 25 beef and 100 chicken   **g.** For sample answer in part (f): \$10, \$20, and \$25, respectively.

Main Ideas

In Chapter 6, students write, solve, and graph one-step and multi-step inequalities using addition, subtraction, multiplication, and division. They learn to reverse an inequality sign when multiplying or dividing by a negative number. Students solve and graph compound inequalities using *and* and *or*. They solve absolute value equations using *or* and they solve and graph absolute value inequalities using *and* and *or*. Finally, students graph linear inequalities in two variables.

Prerequisite Skills

- Solving equations
- Graphing equations
- Writing equations

Additional resources for reviewing prerequisite skills are:

- Skills Review Handbook, pp. 909–937
- @HomeTutor

2. No; because the solution of $7x - 4 = 10$ is $x = 2$, the two equations do not have the same solution.

16.

$y = -7x + 3$

---

6 Solving and Graphing Linear Inequalities

- **6.1** Solve Inequalities Using Addition and Subtraction
- **6.2** Solve Inequalities Using Multiplication and Division
- **6.3** Solve Multi-Step Inequalities
- **6.4** Solve Compound Inequalities
- **6.5** Solve Absolute Value Equations
- **6.6** Solve Absolute Value Inequalities
- **6.7** Graph Linear Inequalities in Two Variables

Before

In previous chapters, you learned the following skills, which you'll use in Chapter 6: solving equations, graphing equations, and writing equations.

Prerequisite Skills

VOCABULARY CHECK

1. Identify one **ordered pair** that is a solution of $8x - 5y = -2$. *Sample answer:* **(1, 2)**

2. Are $7x - 4 = 10$ and $x = 3$ **equivalent equations**? *Explain.* **See margin.**

3. The **absolute value** of a number a is the distance between a and $\underline{?}$ on a number line. **0**

SKILLS CHECK

Check whether the given number is a solution of the equation or inequality. *(Review p. 21 for 6.1–6.6.)*

4. $x - 2 = 3; 5$
   solution
5. $s + 3 = 12; 9$
   solution
6. $6y > 20; 3$
   not a solution
7. $\dfrac{p - 3}{5} \le 4; 23$
   solution

Solve the equation. Check your solution. *(Review pp. 134, 141, 148 for 6.1–6.6.)*

8. $m + 8 = -20$ **−28**
9. $-7x = 35$ **−5**
10. $-9r - 4 = 25$ **$-\dfrac{29}{9}$**
11. $4t - 7t = 9$ **−3**

For the given value of a, find $-a$ and $|a|$. *(Review p. 64 for 6.5–6.6.)*

12. $a = -3$ **3, 3**
13. $a = -5.6$ **5.6, 5.6**
14. $a = 14$ **−14, 14**
15. $a = 0$ **0, 0**

Graph the equation. *(Review p. 215 for 6.7.)* **16–19. See margin for art.**

16. $y = -7x + 3$
17. $6x + 3y = -5$
18. $x = -8$
19. $y = 4$

@HomeTutor Prerequisite skills practice at classzone.com

354

Chapter Planning Guide

Chapter 6 Resource Book
- Teaching Guide/Lesson Plan (pp. 3, 17, 30, 43, 58, 68, 82)
- Project with Rubric (p. 99)

Assessment and Intervention
- Assessment Book (pp. 75–89)
- Benchmark Tests
- Reteaching and Remediation Book

Interactive Technology
- Easy Planner
- Power Presentations CD-ROM
- Activity Generator CD-ROM
- Animated Algebra
- Test Generator CD-ROM
- Online Quizzes
- eWorkbook
- eEdition
- @HomeTutor

Resources for English Learners
- Quick Reference for English Learners
- Spanish Study Guide
- Multi-Language Visual Glossary
- Student Resources in Spanish

In Chapter 6, you will apply the big ideas listed below and reviewed in the Chapter Summary on page 414. You will also use the key vocabulary listed below.

Big Ideas

1. **Applying properties of inequality**
2. **Using statements with *and* or *or***
3. **Graphing inequalities**

KEY VOCABULARY

- graph of an inequality, *p. 356*
- equivalent inequalities, *p. 357*

- compound inequality, *p. 380*
- absolute value equation, *p. 390*
- absolute deviation, *p. 392*

- linear inequality in two variables, *p. 405*
- graph of an inequality in two variables, *p. 405*

Why?

You can use inequalities to solve problems in sound amplification. For example, you can solve an inequality to determine whether an amplifier provides enough amplification for a given number of people in an audience.

Animated Algebra

The animation illustrated below for Exercise 45 on page 387 helps you answer this question: Is a 2900 watt amplifier adequate for an audience of 350 people?

You need to decide whether the amplifier is adequate for 350 people.

Total amount of amplification provided by the amplifier: $w = 2900$ watts

Size of the audience: $p = 350$ people

$y = \dfrac{w}{p}$ $y =$

Click on the boxes to enter the appropriate values.

Animated Algebra at classzone.com

Other animations for Chapter 6: pages 358, 364, 382, 390, 391, 399, and 407

Algebra 1 Toolkit

- Reading Strategies for Chapter 6, pp. 19–20
- Differentiated Instruction Notes, pp. 65–68
- English Learners Notes, pp. 107–108
- Inclusion Notes, pp. 139–140
- Teaching Strategies with Sample Worksheets, pp. 155–178
- Using Technology in the Classroom, pp. 179–184
- Tips for New Teachers, pp. 195–196
- Math Background Notes, pp. 221–222
- Pre-AP Strategies and Copymasters, pp. 288–289, 367–383
- Teacher Survival Activities, pp. 565–566, 591–592
- Bulletin Board Idea, p. 612
- Teacher Tool Transparencies, following p. 620

17.

$6x + 3y = -5$

18.

$x = -8$

19.

$y = 4$

1 PLAN AND PREPARE

Warm-Up Exercises

🖳 **Transparency Available**

1. Is -9 a solution of $a + 7 = -2$?
   yes

2. Solve the equation $h + 12 = -8$.
   -20

3. Write an inequality that describes the number of CDs you can buy for $12 each if you have no more than $60 to spend. Can you buy 6 CDs? **$12x \le 60$; no**

Notetaking Guide

🖳 **Transparency Available**

Promotes interactive learning and notetaking skills, pp. 127–129.

Pacing

Basic: 1 day

Average: 1 day

Advanced: 1 day

Block: 0.5 block with 6.2

• See *Teaching Guide/Lesson Plan*.

2 FOCUS AND MOTIVATE

Essential Question

Big Idea 1, p. 355

How do you solve and graph inequalities using addition and subtraction? **Tell students they will learn how to answer this question by using addition and subtraction properties of inequality.**

NCTM STANDARDS

Standard 2: Represent situations using algebraic symbols; Use models to understand relationships

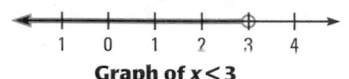 **Before** You solved equations using addition and subtraction.

 Now You will solve inequalities using addition and subtraction.

Why So you can describe desert temperatures, as in Example 1.

Key Vocabulary
• **graph of an inequality**
• **equivalent inequalities**
• **inequality**, *p. 21*
• **solution of an inequality**, *p. 22*

On a number line, the **graph of an inequality** in one variable is the set of points that represent all solutions of the inequality. To graph an inequality in one variable, use an open circle for < or > and a closed circle for ≤ or ≥. The graphs of $x < 3$ and $x \ge -1$ are shown below.

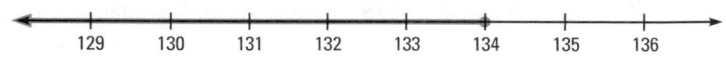

Graph of $x < 3$ Graph of $x \ge -1$

EXAMPLE 1 **Write and graph an inequality**

DEATH VALLEY The highest temperature recorded in the United States was 134°F at Death Valley, California, in 1913. Use only this fact to write and graph an inequality that describes the temperatures in the United States.

Solution

Let *T* represent a temperature (in degrees Fahrenheit) in the United States. The value of *T* must be less than or equal to 134. So, an inequality is $T \le 134$.

EXAMPLE 2 **Write inequalities from graphs**

Write an inequality represented by the graph.

a.

b.

Solution

a. The open circle means that -6.5 is not a solution of the inequality. Because the arrow points to the right, all numbers greater than -6.5 are solutions.

   ▶ An inequality represented by the graph is $x > -6.5$.

b. The closed circle means that 4 is a solution of the inequality. Because the arrow points to the left, all numbers less than 4 are solutions.

   ▶ An inequality represented by the graph is $x \le 4$.

Resource Planning Guide

Chapter Resource Book
• Teaching Guide/Lesson Plan (pp. 3–4)
• Activity Master (p. 5)
• Practice levels A, B, C (pp. 6–11)
• Study Guide (pp. 12–13)
• Catch-up for Absent Students (p. 14)
• Application (p. 15)
• Challenge (p. 16)

Workbooks
• Notetaking Guide (pp. 127–129)
• Practice Workbook (pp. 84–86)

Teaching Options
• **Power Presentations CD-ROM** provides dynamic electronic teaching resources for the classroom.
• **Activity Generator CD-ROM** provides editable activities for all ability levels.

Interactive Technology
• Easy Planner
• Power Presentations CD-ROM
• Activity Generator CD-ROM
• Animated Algebra
• Test Generator CD-ROM
• Online Quiz
• eWorkbook
• eEdition
• @HomeTutor

Resources for English Learners
• Quick Reference for English Learners
• Spanish Study Guide
• Multi-Language Visual Glossary
• Student Resources in Spanish

See also the *Algebra 1 Toolkit* for more strategies for meeting individual needs.

1. **ANTARCTICA** The lowest temperature recorded in Antarctica was −129°F at the Russian Vostok station in 1983. Use only this fact to write and graph an inequality that describes the temperatures in Antarctica.
   $x \geq -129°F$; see margin for art.

Write an inequality represented by the graph.

2.
   $x < 8$

3.
   $x \geq -2.5$

EQUIVALENT INEQUALITIES Just as you used properties of equality to produce equivalent equations, you can use properties of inequality to produce *equivalent inequalities*. **Equivalent inequalities** are inequalities that have the same solutions.

KEY CONCEPT *For Your Notebook*

Addition Property of Inequality

Words Adding the same number to each side of an inequality produces an equivalent inequality.

Algebra If $a > b$, then $a + c > b + c$.   If $a \geq b$, then $a + c \geq b + c$.

        If $a < b$, then $a + c < b + c$.   If $a \leq b$, then $a + c \leq b + c$.

EXAMPLE 3 Solve an inequality using addition

Solve $x - 5 > -3.5$. Graph your solution.

$x - 5 > -3.5$	**Write original inequality.**
$x - 5 + 5 > -3.5 + 5$	**Add 5 to each side.**
$x > 1.5$	**Simplify.**

▶ The solutions are all real numbers greater than 1.5. Check by substituting a number greater than 1.5 for x in the original inequality.

CHECK $x - 5 > -3.5$	**Write original inequality.**
$6 - 5 \overset{?}{>} -3.5$	**Substitute 6 for x.**
$1 > -3.5$ ✓	**Solution checks.**

✓ **GUIDED PRACTICE** for Example 3

Solve the inequality. Graph your solution. 4–6. See margin for art.

4. $x - 9 \leq 3$ **$x \leq 12$**

5. $p - 9.2 < -5$ **$p < 4.2$**

6. $-1 \geq m - \frac{1}{2}$ **$m \leq -\frac{1}{2}$**

Motivating the Lesson

You know that you can send no more than 50 text messages on your monthly cell phone plan without incurring additional charges. You sent 18 messages yesterday and 9 today. By knowing how to write and solve inequalities, you can find the maximum number of text messages you can send this month without additional charges.

③ TEACH

Extra Example 1

The lowest elevation recorded in the United States is −282 feet at Death Valley, California. Use this fact to write and graph an inequality that describes the elevations in the United States. **$E \geq -282$, where E is elevation in feet**

Extra Example 2

Write an inequality represented by the graph. **$x \leq -1.5$**

Key Question to Ask for Example 2

• How are the graphs in parts a and b different? **In part a, the graph points to the right and does not include the endpoint. In part b, the graph points to the left and does include the endpoint.**

Extra Example 3

Solve $m - 3.8 < -1$. Graph your solution. **all real numbers less than 2.8**

1, 4–6. See Additional Answers beginning on p. AA1.

Subtraction Property of Inequality

Words Subtracting the same number from each side of an inequality produces an equivalent inequality.

Algebra If $a > b$, then $a - c > b - c$.   If $a \geq b$, then $a - c \geq b - c$.

If $a < b$, then $a - c < b - c$.   If $a \leq b$, then $a - c \leq b - c$.

EXAMPLE 4   **Solve an inequality using subtraction**

Solve $9 \geq x + 7$. Graph your solution.

$9 \geq x + 7$	Write original inequality.
$9 - 7 \geq x + 7 - 7$	Subtract 7 from each side.
$2 \geq x$	Simplify.

▶ You can rewrite $2 \geq x$ as $x \leq 2$. The solutions are all real numbers less than or equal to 2.

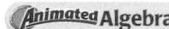 at classzone.com

---

EXAMPLE 5   **Solve a real-world problem**

READING
The phrase "no more than" indicates that you use the ≤ symbol.

LUGGAGE WEIGHTS You are checking a bag at an airport. Bags can weigh no more than 50 pounds. Your bag weighs 16.8 pounds. Find the possible weights w (in pounds) that you can add to the bag.

Solution

Write a verbal model. Then write and solve an inequality.

Weight of bag	+	Weight you can add	≤	Weight limit
⬇		⬇		⬇
16.8	**+**	w	**≤**	**50**

$16.8 + w \leq 50$	Write inequality.
$16.8 + w - 16.8 \leq 50 - 16.8$	Subtract 16.8 from each side.
$w \leq 33.2$	Simplify.

▶ You can add no more than 33.2 pounds.

 GUIDED PRACTICE   **for Examples 4 and 5**

7. Solve $y + 5.5 > 6$. Graph your solution.   **$y > 0.5$; see margin for art.**

8. **WHAT IF?** In Example 5, suppose your bag weighs 29.1 pounds. Find the possible weights (in pounds) that you can add to the bag.   **$w \leq 20.9$ lb**

HOMEWORK KEY
○ = **WORKED-OUT SOLUTIONS**
on p. WS1 for Exs. 7, 15, and 33
★ = **STANDARDIZED TEST PRACTICE**
Exs. 2, 29, 34, 35, and 38
◆ = **MULTIPLE REPRESENTATIONS**
Ex. 37

SKILL PRACTICE

[A] 1. **VOCABULARY** Copy and complete: To graph $x < -8$, you draw a(n) _?_ circle at -8, and you draw an arrow to the _?_ . **open, left of −8**

2. ★ **WRITING** Are $x + 7 \geq 18$ and $x \geq 25$ equivalent inequalities? *Explain.*
No; because the solution of $x + 7 \geq 18$ is $x \geq 11$, the two inequalities do not have the same solution.

EXAMPLE 1
on p. 356
for Exs. 3–5

WRITING AND GRAPHING INEQUALITIES Write and graph an inequality that describes the situation. **3–5. See margin for art.**

3. The speed limit on a highway is 60 miles per hour. $s \leq 60$

4. You must be at least 16 years old to go on a field trip. $a \geq 16$

5. A child must be taller than 48 inches to get on an amusement park ride. $h > 48$

EXAMPLE 2
on p. 356
for Exs. 6–9

WRITING INEQUALITIES Write an inequality represented by the graph.

6. $x \leq -4$ 7. $x < 10$

8. $x > 4$ 9. $x \geq -2$

EXAMPLES 3 and 4
on pp. 357–358
for Exs. 10–23

SOLVING INEQUALITIES Solve the inequality. Graph your solution. **10–21. See margin for art.**

10. $x + 4 < 5$
    $x < 1$

11. $-8 \leq 8 + y$
    $y \geq -16$

12. $-1\frac{1}{4} \leq m + 3$
    $m \geq -4\frac{1}{4}$

13. $n + 17 \leq 16\frac{4}{5}$ $\ n \leq -\frac{1}{5}$

14. $8.2 + v > -7.6$
    $v > -15.8$

15. $w + 14.9 > -2.7$
    $w > -17.6$

16. $r - 4 < -5$
    $r < -1$

17. $1 \leq s - 8$
    $s \geq 9$

18. $-1\frac{1}{3} \leq p - 8\frac{1}{3}$
    $p \geq 7$

19. $q - 1\frac{1}{3} > -2\frac{1}{2}$
    $q > -1\frac{1}{6}$

20. $2.1 \geq c - 6.7$
    $c \leq 8.8$

21. $d - 1.92 > -8.76$
    $d > -6.84$

22. **8 must be subtracted from both sides of the equation, not subtracted from one and added to the other; $x + 8 - 8 < -3 - 8$, $x < -11$.**

23. **The number line should be shaded to the right of −3, not the left.**

ERROR ANALYSIS *Describe* and correct the error in solving the inequality or in graphing the solution. **22, 23. See margin for art.**

22.
$x + 8 < -3$
$x + 8 - 8 < -3 + 8$
$x < 5$

23.
$-17 \leq x - 14$
$-17 + 14 \leq x - 14 + 14$
$-3 \leq x$

[B] **TRANSLATING SENTENCES** Write the verbal sentence as an inequality. Then solve the inequality and graph your solution. **24–26. See margin for art.**

24. The sum of 11 and m is greater than -23. **$11 + m > -23$; $m > -34$**

25. The difference of n and 15 is less than or equal to 37. **$n - 15 \leq 37$; $n \leq 52$**

26. The difference of c and 13 is less than -19. **$c - 13 < -19$; $c < -6$**

4 PRACTICE AND APPLY

Assignment Guide
Answer Transparencies available for all exercises

Basic:
Day 1: EP p. 939 Exs. 12–19
pp. 359–361
Exs. 1–17, 22–25, 31–36, 40–50 even

Average:
Day 1: pp. 359–361
Exs. 1–9, 14–28, 31–38, 41, 44, 47, 50

Advanced:
Day 1: pp. 359–361
Exs. 1, 2, 4, 5, 8, 9, 14–21, 24–39*, 42, 45, 48, 51

Block:
pp. 359–361
Exs. 1–9, 14–28, 31–38, 41, 44, 47, 50 (with 6.2)

Differentiated Instruction
See *Algebra 1 Best Practices Toolkit* for suggestions on addressing the needs of a diverse classroom.

Homework Check
For a quick check of student understanding of key concepts, go over the following exercises:
Basic: 3, 6, 12, 16, 31
Average: 4, 8, 14, 18, 32
Advanced: 5, 9, 15, 20, 33

Extra Practice
• Student Edition, p. 943
• Chapter 6 Resource Book: Practice levels A, B, C, pp. 6–11

Practice Worksheet
An easily-readable reduced practice page (with answers) for this lesson can be found on p. 354C.

Differentiated Instruction

Inclusion Some students may have difficulty remembering which inequality symbols to use for an open circle and which to use for a closed circle while doing **Exercises 6–9**. Stress that when the circle is open, the symbol (< or >) is an open triangle; when the circle is closed, the inequality sign (≤ or ≥) shows three lines that can be used to form a closed triangle.

See also the *Algebra 1 Toolkit* for more strategies.

3.
4.
5.
10–23. See Additional Answers beginning on p. AA1.

24.
25.
26.

GEOMETRY Write and solve an inequality to find the possible values of *x*.

27. Perimeter < 51.3 inches $x < 21.6$

14.2 in.   *x* in.
15.5 in.

28. Perimeter ≤ 18.7 feet $x \leq 3.3$

4.1 ft
4.9 ft   *x* ft
6.4 ft

29. ★ **WRITING** Is it possible to check all the numbers that are solutions of an inequality? Does checking one solution guarantee that you have solved an inequality correctly? *Explain* your answers. **See margin.**

[C] **30.** **CHALLENGE** Write and graph an inequality that represents the numbers that are *not* solutions of $x - 12 \geq 5.7$. $x < 17.7$; see margin for art.

PROBLEM SOLVING

EXAMPLE 5 [A]
on p. 358
for Exs. 31–35

31. **INTERNET** You earn points from buying items at an Internet shopping site. You would like to redeem 2350 points to get an item for free, but you want to be sure to have more than 6000 points left over. What are the possible numbers of points you can have before making a redemption?

@HomeTutor for problem solving help at classzone.com   **at least 8350 points**

32. **SPORTS RECORDS** In 1982 Wayne Gretsky set a new record for the greatest number of hockey goals in one season with 92 goals. Suppose that a hockey player has 59 goals so far in a season. What are the possible numbers of additional goals that the player can make in order to match or break Wayne Gretsky's record? **at least 33 goals**

@HomeTutor for problem solving help at classzone.com

33. **MULTI-STEP PROBLEM** In aerial ski competitions, athletes perform two acrobatic ski jumps, and the scores on both jumps are added together. The table shows your competitor's first and second scores and your first score.

Ski jump	Competitor's score	Your score
1	127.04	129.49
2	129.98	?

   a. Write and solve an inequality to find the scores *s* that you can earn in your second jump in order to beat your competitor. $s > 127.53$

   b. Will you beat your competitor if you earn 128.13 points? 126.78 points? 127.53 points? *Justify* your answers. **Yes; no; no; 128.13 > 127.53; 126.78 < 127.53; when your score is 127.53, you and your competitor will tie.**

34. ★ **MULTIPLE CHOICE** You want to buy a jacket at a clothing store, and you can spend at most $30. You have a coupon for $3 off any item at the store. Which inequality can you use to find the original prices *p* of jackets that you can buy? **C**

   (A) $3 + p \geq 30$ **(B)** $30 + p \leq 3$ **(C)** $p - 3 \leq 30$ **(D)** $p - 30 \geq 3$

35. ★ **OPEN-ENDED** *Describe* a real-world situation that can be modeled by the inequality $x + 14 \geq 17$. *Explain* what the solution of the inequality means in this situation. **See margin.**

○ = **WORKED-OUT SOLUTIONS**
on p. WS1

★ = **STANDARDIZED TEST PRACTICE**

◆ = **MULTIPLE REPRESENTATIONS**

35. *Sample answer:* You want to improve on your personal best of 16 points scored in a basketball game. In the first three quarters of the game, you scored 14 points. Write and solve an inequality to find the possible numbers of points that you can score in the fourth quarter to give yourself a new personal best; $x \geq 3$, if you score at least 3 points in the fourth quarter, you will have a new personal best.

B 36. **VEHICLE WEIGHTS** According to a state law for vehicles traveling on state roads, the maximum total weight of the vehicle and its contents depends on the number of axles the vehicle has.

Maximum Total Weights

| 2 axles | 3 axles | 4 axles | 5 axles |
| 34,000 lb | 54,000 lb | 69,000 lb | 80,000 lb |

For each type of vehicle, write and solve an inequality to find the possible weights w (in pounds) of a vehicle when its contents weigh 14,200 pounds. Can a vehicle that has 2 axles and weighs 20,000 pounds hold 14,200 pounds of contents? *Explain.* **See margin.**

37. ◆ **MULTIPLE REPRESENTATIONS** Your friend is willing to spend no more than $17,000 for a new car. The car dealership offers $3000 cash back for the purchase of a new car.

   a. **Making a Table** Make a table of values that gives the final price y of a car after the cash back offer is applied to the original price x. Use the following values for x: 19,459, 19,989, 20,549, 22,679, 23,999. **See margin.**

   b. **Writing an Inequality** Write and solve an inequality to find the original prices of the cars that your friend will consider buying.
$w - 3000 \le 17000$, $w \le \$20,000$

38. ★ **SHORT RESPONSE** A 4-member track team is trying to match or beat last year's winning time of 3 minutes 41.1 seconds for a 1600 meter relay race. The table shows the 400 meter times for the first three athletes.

Athlete	Time (sec)
1	53.34
2	56.38
3	57.46

   a. **Calculate** What are the possible times that the last athlete can run 400 meters in order for the team to match or beat last year's time? **at most 53.92 sec**

   b. **Decide** So far this season the last athlete's fastest 400 meter time is 53.18 seconds, and his average 400 meter time is 53.92 seconds. In this race the last athlete expects to run faster than his slowest time this season. Is it possible for the team to fail to meet its goal? *Explain.*

C 39. **CHALLENGE** A public television station wants to raise at least $72,000 in a pledge drive. The station raised an average of $5953 per day for the first 3 days and an average of $6153 per day for the next 3 days. What are the possible additional amounts that the station can raise to meet its goal? **at least $35,682**

MIXED REVIEW

Find the sum, difference, product, or quotient.

40. $-18 + (-27)$ *(p. 74)* **−45**   41. $15 - (-23)$ *(p. 80)* **38**   42. $7 \cdot (-9)$ *(p. 88)* **−63**

43. $-11 \cdot (-12)$ *(p. 88)* **132**   44. $-27 \div (-3)$ *(p. 103)* **9**   45. $-30 \div (-5)$ *(p. 103)* **6**

PREVIEW
Prepare for Lesson 6.2 in Exs. 46–51.

Solve the equation. *(p. 134)*

46. $6x = 48$ **8**   47. $-5y = -35$ **7**   48. $400 = -48m$ $-8\frac{1}{3}$

49. $\frac{n}{5} = 10$ **50**   50. $\frac{r}{8} = -13$ **−104**   51. $\frac{s}{-2} = -15$ **30**

Explore the Concept
- Students will solve an inequality with a negative coefficient.
- This activity leads into the study of solving inequalities in Examples 2 and 3 in Lesson 6.2.

Materials
Each student will need 11 index cards.

Recommended Time
Work activity: 10 min
Discuss results: 5 min

Grouping
Students should work individually.

② TEACH

Key Question
In Step 3, why is the number −2 a solution of −4x ≥ 8? When **x = −2** the value of −4x is (−4)(−2) = 8, and the statement 8 ≥ 8 is true.

Key Discovery
Change the direction of the inequality symbol when you multiply or divide both sides of the inequality by a negative number.

③ ASSESS AND RETEACH

Explain whether you need to change the direction of the inequality symbol to find the value of x for these inequalities: 3x > −27, −3x < 27, and −3x ≥ −27. **No for 3x > −27 because the coefficient of the variable is positive; yes for −3x < 27 and for −3x ≥ −27 because the value of each coefficient is negative.**

6.2 Inequalities with Negative Coefficients

MATERIALS · index cards

QUESTION How do you solve an inequality with a negative coefficient?

EXPLORE Check solutions of inequalities

STEP 1 *Write integers* Write the integers from −5 to 5 on index cards. Place the cards face up as shown.

| −5 | −4 | −3 | −2 | −1 | 0 | 1 | 2 | 3 | 4 | 5 |

STEP 2 *Check solutions* Determine whether each integer is a solution of $4x \geq 8$. If the integer is *not* a solution, turn over the card.

| | | | | | | | 2 | 3 | 4 | 5 |

STEP 3 *Check solutions* Turn all the cards face up. Repeat Step 2 for $-4x \geq 8$.

| −5 | −4 | −3 | −2 | | | | | | | |

DRAW CONCLUSIONS Use your observations to complete these exercises

1. State an operation that you can perform on both sides of $4x \geq 8$ to obtain the solutions found in Step 2. Then solve the inequality. **divide each side by 4; x ≥ 2**

2. Copy and complete the steps below for solving $-4x \geq 8$.

$-4x \geq 8$	Write original inequality.
_?_	Add 4x to each side. **0 ≥ 8 + 4x**
_?_	Subtract 8 from each side. **−8 ≥ 4x**
_?_	Divide each side by 4. **−2 ≥ x**
_?_	Rewrite inequality with x on the left side. **x ≤ −2**

3. Does dividing both sides of $-4x \geq 8$ by −4 give the solution found in Exercise 2? If not, what else must you do to the inequality when you divide by −4? **No; reverse the direction of the inequality symbol.**

4. Do you need to change the direction of the inequality symbol when you divide each side of an inequality by a positive number? by a negative number? **no; yes**

Solve the inequality.

5. $20x \geq 5$
   $x \geq \dfrac{1}{4}$

6. $-9x \leq 45$
   $x \geq -5$

7. $-8x > 40$
   $x < -5$

8. $7x < 21$
   $x < 3$

6.2 Solve Inequalities Using Multiplication and Division

Before	You solved inequalities using addition and subtraction.
Now	You will solve inequalities using multiplication and division.
Why?	So you can find possible distances traveled, as in Ex. 40.

Key Vocabulary
• inequality, *p. 21*
• equivalent inequalities, *p. 357*

Solving an inequality using multiplication is similar to solving an equation using multiplication, but it is different in an important way.

KEY CONCEPT
For Your Notebook

Multiplication Property of Inequality

Words Multiplying each side of an inequality by a *positive* number produces an equivalent inequality.

Multiplying each side of an inequality by a *negative* number and *reversing the direction of the inequality symbol* produces an equivalent inequality.

Algebra If $a < b$ and $c > 0$, then $ac < bc$. If $a < b$ and $c < 0$, then $ac > bc$.

If $a > b$ and $c > 0$, then $ac > bc$. If $a > b$ and $c < 0$, then $ac < bc$.

This property is also true for inequalities involving $\leq$ and $\geq$.

EXAMPLE 1 Solve an inequality using multiplication

Solve $\frac{x}{4} < 5$. Graph your solution.

$$\frac{x}{4} < 5 \qquad \text{Write original inequality.}$$

$$4 \cdot \frac{x}{4} < 4 \cdot 5 \qquad \text{Multiply each side by 4.}$$

$$x < 20 \qquad \text{Simplify.}$$

▶ The solutions are all real numbers less than 20. Check by substituting a number less than 20 in the original inequality.

 GUIDED PRACTICE for Example 1

Solve the inequality. Graph your solution. **1–3. See margin for art.**

1. $\frac{x}{3} > 8$ **$x > 24$**

2. $\frac{m}{8} \leq -2$ **$m \leq -16$**

3. $\frac{y}{2.5} \geq -4$ **$y \geq -10$**

Resource Planning Guide

Chapter Resource Book
• Teaching Guide/Lesson Plan (pp. 17–18)
• Practice levels A, B, C (pp. 19–24)
• Study Guide (pp. 25–26)
• Catch-up for Absent Students (p. 27)
• Problem Solving Workshop (p. 28)
• Challenge (p. 29)

Workbooks
• Notetaking Guide (pp. 130–133)
• Practice Workbook (pp. 87–89)

Teaching Options
• **Power Presentations CD-ROM** provides dynamic electronic teaching resources for the classroom.
• **Activity Generator CD-ROM** provides editable activities for all ability levels.

Interactive Technology
• Easy Planner
• Power Presentations CD-ROM
• Activity Generator CD-ROM
• Animated Algebra
• Test Generator CD-ROM
• Online Quiz
• eWorkbook
• eEdition
• @HomeTutor

Resources for English Learners
• Quick Reference for English Learners
• Spanish Study Guide
• Multi-Language Visual Glossary
• Student Resources in Spanish

See also the *Algebra 1 Toolkit* for more strategies for meeting individual needs.

363

---

1 PLAN AND PREPARE

Warm-Up Exercises
📄 **Transparency Available**
Check whether the given number is a solution of the inequality.

1. $\frac{x}{3} \leq 7$; 20 **yes**

2. $4m > -23$; -6 **no**

3. How long will it take a diver to ascend 36 feet if the average rate of ascent is 30 feet per minute? **1.2 min or 1 min 12 sec**

Notetaking Guide
📄 **Transparency Available**
Promotes interactive learning and notetaking skills, pp. 130–133.

Pacing
Basic: 1 day
Average: 1 day
Advanced: 1 day
Block: 0.5 block with 6.1
• See *Teaching Guide/Lesson Plan*.

2 FOCUS AND MOTIVATE

Essential Question
Big Idea 1, p. 355
How do you solve inequalities using multiplication and division? **Tell students they will learn how to answer this question by applying multiplication and division properties of inequality and by learning when to reverse the direction of the inequality symbol.**

NCTM STANDARDS
Standard 2: Understand relations; Analyze situations using algebraic symbols

Motivating the Lesson

Can you think of a time while shopping when you had to decide how many CDs, or shirts, or video games you could possibly buy with the money you had? Answering such a question involves solving an inequality.

❸ TEACH

Extra Example 1

Solve $\frac{y}{7} > -4$. Graph your solution.

all real numbers greater than or equal to −28

Extra Example 2

Solve $\frac{x}{-3} > -2$. Graph your solution.

all real numbers less than 6

Extra Example 3

Solve $-6x \le 18$. $x \ge -3$

Key Question to Ask for Example 3

• If you graph $x < -8$, would you use an open or a closed circle? **open**

Animated Algebra
classzone.com

An **Animated Algebra** activity is available on-line for **Example 3**. This activity is also available on the **Power Presentations CD-ROM**.

p. 363

1. ⟨—|—◦—|—|—|—|—|—⟩
   22 24 26 28 30

2. ⟨—|—|—|—•—|—|⟩
   −22 −20 −18 −16 −14

3. ⟨—|—|—•—|—|⟩
   −20 −10 0 10 20

EXAMPLE 2 Solve an inequality using multiplication

Solve $\frac{x}{-6} < 7$. Graph your solution.

AVOID ERRORS
Because you are multiplying by a negative number, be sure to reverse the inequality symbol.

$\frac{x}{-6} < 7$	Write original inequality.
$-6 \cdot \frac{x}{-6} > -6 \cdot 7$	Multiply each side by −6. Reverse inequality symbol.
$x > -42$	Simplify.

▶ The solutions are all real numbers greater than −42. Check by substituting a number greater than −42 in the original inequality.

⟨—|—◦—|—|—|—|—|⟩
−50 −40 −30 −20 −10 0

CHECK $\frac{x}{-6} < 7$	Write original inequality.
$\frac{0}{-6} \overset{?}{<} 7$	Substitute 0 for x.
$0 < 7$ ✓	Solution checks.

USING DIVISION The rules for solving an inequality using division are similar to the rules for solving an inequality using multiplication.

KEY CONCEPT   *For Your Notebook*

Division Property of Inequality

Words Dividing each side of an inequality by a *positive* number produces an equivalent inequality.

Dividing each side of an inequality by a *negative* number and *reversing the direction of the inequality symbol* produces an equivalent inequality.

Algebra If $a < b$ and $c > 0$, then $\frac{a}{c} < \frac{b}{c}$.   If $a < b$ and $c < 0$, then $\frac{a}{c} > \frac{b}{c}$.

If $a > b$ and $c > 0$, then $\frac{a}{c} > \frac{b}{c}$.   If $a > b$ and $c < 0$, then $\frac{a}{c} < \frac{b}{c}$.

This property is also true for inequalities involving $\le$ and $\ge$.

EXAMPLE 3 Solve an inequality using division

Solve $-3x > 24$.

$-3x > 24$	Write original inequality.
$\frac{-3x}{-3} < \frac{24}{-3}$	Divide each side by −3. Reverse inequality symbol.
$x < -8$	Simplify.

Animated Algebra at classzone.com

364   Chapter 6   Solving and Graphing Linear Inequalities

Differentiated Instruction

Visual Learners The Division Property of Inequality is equivalent to the Multiplication Property of Inequality. Write both properties on the board. Then replace c with $\frac{1}{c}$ in the Multiplication Property of Inequality to show the equivalence. See also the *Algebra 1 Toolkit* for more strategies.

Solve the inequality. Graph your solution.   4–7. See margin for art.

4. $\dfrac{x}{-4} > 12$ **5.** $\dfrac{m}{-7} < 1.6$ **6.** $5v \geq 45$ **7.** $-6n < 24$

     $x < -48$ $m > -11.2$ $v \geq 9$ $n > -4$

★ **EXAMPLE 4**   **Standardized Test Practice**

> A student pilot plans to spend 80 hours on flight training to earn a private license. The student has saved $6000 for training. Which inequality can you use to find the possible hourly rates r that the student can afford to pay for training?
>
> Ⓐ $80r \geq 6000$ Ⓑ $80r \leq 6000$ Ⓒ $6000r \geq 80$ Ⓓ $6000r \leq 80$

Solution

The total cost of training can be at most the amount of money that the student has saved. Write a verbal model for the situation. Then write an inequality.

ELIMINATE CHOICES
You need to multiply the hourly rate and the number of hours, which is 80, not 6000. So, you can eliminate choices C and D.

Training time (hours)	·	Hourly rate (dollars/hour)	≤	Amount saved (dollars)
80	·	r	≤	6000

▸ The correct answer is B. Ⓐ ⬤ Ⓒ Ⓓ

EXAMPLE 5   **Solve a real-world problem**

PILOTING In Example 4, what are the possible hourly rates that the student can afford to pay for training?

Solution

$80 \cdot r \leq 6000$ **Write inequality.**

$\dfrac{80r}{80} \leq \dfrac{6000}{80}$ **Divide each side by 80.**

$r \leq 75$ **Simplify.**

▸ The student can afford to pay at most $75 per hour for training.

✓ **GUIDED PRACTICE**   for Examples 4 and 5

8. WHAT IF? In Example 5, suppose the student plans to spend 90 hours on flight training and has saved $6300. Write and solve an inequality to find the possible hourly rates that the student can afford to pay for training.

          $90r \leq 6300,\ r \leq \$70/h$

6.2   Solve Inequalities Using Multiplication and Division   **365**

Extra Example 4

A restaurant owner plans to place identical bouquets of flowers on 35 tables for opening night. The owner wants to spend no more than $400 for all the bouquets. Which inequality can you use to find the possible amounts of money m that the owner should budget for each bouquet of flowers? **B**

Ⓐ $400 \leq 35m$ Ⓑ $400 \geq 35m$
Ⓒ $400m \geq 35$ Ⓓ $400m \leq 35$

Extra Example 5

In Extra Example 4, what are the possible amounts of money the owner should budget for each bouquet of flowers? **up to $11.42**

Closing the Lesson

Have students summarize the major points of the lesson and answer the Essential Question: How do you solve inequalities using multiplication and division?

• **The multiplication and division properties of inequality can be used to produce equivalent inequalities.**

• **Reverse the direction of the inequality symbol when multiplying or dividing by a negative number.**

Multiply or divide each side of the inequality by the same number to isolate the variable and produce an equivalent inequality. Reverse the direction of the inequality symbol if you multiply or divide by a negative number.

4.

```
        -48
 +---+---○---+---+---+
-80 -60 -40 -20   0
```

5.

```
 -11.2
 +○--+---+---+---+
-12  -8  -4   0   4
```

6.

```
            9
 +---+---+--●--+---+
 0   4   8  12  16
```

7.

```
 +---+---○---+---+---+
-6  -4  -2   0   2
```

6.2 EXERCISES

HOMEWORK KEY
○ = WORKED-OUT SOLUTIONS
on p. WS1 for Exs. 5, 9, and 39

★ = STANDARDIZED TEST PRACTICE
Exs. 2, 27, 34, and 41

◆ = MULTIPLE REPRESENTATIONS
Ex. 38

4 PRACTICE AND APPLY

Assignment Guide

⌨ Answer Transparencies available for all exercises

Basic:
Day 1: pp. 366–368
Exs. 1–18, 27–31, 36–40, 43–53 odd

Average:
Day 1: pp. 366–368
Exs. 1, 2, 15–34, 36–41, 44–52 even

Advanced:
Day 1: pp. 366–368
Exs. 1, 2, 17–27, 30–42*, 44–52 even

Block:
pp. 366–368
Exs. 1, 2, 15–34, 36–41, 44–52 even
(with 6.1)

Differentiated Instruction

See *Algebra 1 Best Practices Toolkit* for suggestions on addressing the needs of a diverse classroom.

Homework Check

For a quick check of student understanding of key concepts, go over the following exercises:

Basic: 4, 6, 10, 36, 37
Average: 16, 18, 21, 37, 38
Advanced: 20, 24, 25, 38, 39

Extra Practice

• Student Edition, p. 943
• Chapter 6 Resource Book: Practice levels A, B, C, pp. 19–24

Practice Worksheet

An easily-readable reduced practice page (with answers) for this lesson can be found on p. 354C.

3–26. See Additional Answers beginning on p. AA1.

SKILL PRACTICE

A

1. **VOCABULARY** Which property are you using when you solve $5x \geq 30$ by dividing each side by 5? **Division property of inequality**

2. ★ **WRITING** Are $\frac{x}{-4} < -9$ and $x < 36$ equivalent inequalities? *Explain* your answer. **No; when you multiply both sides of $\frac{x}{-4} < -9$ by -4 you must reverse the inequality symbol, producing the inequality $x > 36$.**

SOLVING INEQUALITIES Solve the inequality. Graph your solution. **3–26. See margin for art.**

EXAMPLES
1, 2, and 3
on pp. 363–364
for Exs. 3–29

3. $2p \geq 14$ $p \geq 7$ 4. $\frac{x}{-3} < -10$ $x > 30$ 5. $-6y < -36$ $y > 6$ 6. $40 > \frac{w}{5}$ $w < 200$

7. $\frac{q}{4} < 7$ $q < 28$ 8. $72 \leq 9r$ $r \geq 8$ 9. $\frac{g}{6} > -20$ $g > -120$ 10. $-11m \leq -22$ $m \geq 2$

11. $-90 \geq 4t$ $t \leq -22.5$ 12. $\frac{n}{3} < -9$ $n < -27$ 13. $60 \leq -12s$ $s \leq -5$ 14. $\frac{v}{-4} \geq -8$ $v \leq 32$

15. $-8.4f > 2.1$ $f < -0.25$ 16. $\frac{d}{-2} \leq 18.6$ $d \geq -37.2$ 17. $9.6 < -16c$ $c < -0.6$ 18. $0.07 \geq \frac{k}{7}$ $k \leq 0.49$

19. $-1.5 \geq 6z$ $z \leq -0.25$ 20. $\frac{x}{-5} \leq -7.5$ $x \geq 37.5$ 21. $1.02 < -3j$ $j < -0.34$ 22. $\frac{y}{-4.5} \geq -10$ $y \leq 45$

23. $\frac{r}{-30} < 1.8$ $r > -54$ 24. $1.9 \leq -5p$ $p \leq -0.38$ 25. $\frac{m}{0.6} > -40$ $m > -24$ 26. $-2t > -1.22$ $t < 0.61$

27. ★ **WRITING** How is solving $ax > b$ where $a > 0$ similar to solving $ax > b$ where $a < 0$? How is it different? **In both cases, you divide both sides of the inequality by a; when $a > 0$, you do not reverse the inequality symbol, but when $a < 0$, you do.**

ERROR ANALYSIS *Describe* and correct the error in solving the inequality.

28.

$$-15x > 45$$
$$\frac{-15x}{-15} > \frac{45}{-15}$$
$$x > -3$$

The inequality symbol was not reversed when dividing both sides by -15; $\frac{-15x}{-15} < \frac{45}{-15}$, $x < -3$.

29.

$$\frac{x}{9} \leq -7$$
$$9 \cdot \frac{x}{9} \leq 9 \cdot (-7)$$
$$x \geq -63$$

29. Both sides of the inequality were multiplied by a positive number, so the inequality symbol should not have been reversed; $x \leq -63$.

B

TRANSLATING SENTENCES In Exercises 30–33, write the verbal sentence as an inequality. Then solve the inequality and graph your solution.

30–33. See margin for art.

30. The product of 8 and x is greater than 50. $8x > 50$; $x > \frac{25}{4}$

31. The product of -15 and y is less than or equal to 90. $-15y \leq 90$; $y \geq -6$

32. The quotient of v and -9 is less than -18. $\frac{v}{-9} < -18$; $v > 162$

33. The quotient of w and 24 is greater than or equal to $-\frac{1}{6}$. $\frac{w}{24} \geq -\frac{1}{6}$; $w \geq -4$

34. ★ **OPEN-ENDED** Write an inequality in the form $ax < b$ such that the solutions are all real numbers greater than 4. *Sample answer: $-3x < -12$*

30.

31.

32.

33.

C **35. CHALLENGE** For the given values of *a* and *b*, tell whether the solution of
$ax > b$ consists of *positive numbers*, *negative numbers*, or *both*. *Explain.*   **See margin.**

     a. $a < 0, b > 0$ **b.** $a > 0, b > 0$ **c.** $a > 0, b < 0$ **d.** $a < 0, b < 0$

PROBLEM SOLVING

EXAMPLES **A**
4 and 5
on p. 365 for
Exs. 36–39

36. MUSIC You have $90 to buy CDs for your friend's party. The CDs cost
$18 each. What are the possible numbers of CDs that you can buy? **at most 5 CDs**

     @HomeTutor for problem solving help at classzone.com

37. JOB SKILLS You apply for a job that requires the ability to type 40 words
per minute. You practice typing on a keyboard for 5 minutes. The
average number of words you type per minute must at least meet the
job requirement. What are the possible numbers of words that you can
type in 5 minutes in order to meet or exceed the job requirement? **at least 200 words**

     @HomeTutor for problem solving help at classzone.com

38. ◆ **MULTIPLE REPRESENTATIONS** You are stacking books on a shelf
that has a height of 66 centimeters. Each book has a thickness of
4 centimeters.

     a. Using a Model Use a concrete model to find the possible numbers of
books that you can stack as follows: Cut strips of paper 4 centimeters
wide to represent the books. Then place the strips one above the
other until they form a column no taller than 66 centimeters. **at most 16 books**

     b. Writing an Inequality Write and solve an inequality to find the
possible numbers of books that you can stack. $4x \le 66,\ x \le 16.5,\ x \le 16$ **books**

     c. Drawing a Graph Write and graph an equation that gives the height *y*
of stacked books as a function of the number *x* of books. Then graph
$y = 66$ in the same coordinate plane. To find the possible numbers
of books that you can stack, identify the integer *x*-coordinates of the
points on the first graph that lie *on or below* the graph of $y = 66$. **See margin.**

     d. Choosing a Method Suppose the shelf has a height of 100 centimeters.
Which method would you use to find the possible numbers of books,
a concrete model, *solving an inequality*, or *drawing a graph*? *Explain.* **Answers may vary.**

39. MANUFACTURING A manufacturer of architectural moldings
recommends that the length of a piece be no more than 15 times its
minimum width *w* (in inches) in order to prevent cracking. For the
piece shown, what could the values of *w* be? **at least 3.2 in.**

B **40. RECREATION** A water-skiing instructor recommends that a boat pulling
a beginning skier have a speed less than 18 miles per hour. Write and
solve an inequality that you can use to find the possible distances *d* (in
miles) that a beginner can travel in 45 minutes of practice time. $d < 13.5$ **mi**

35a. Negative; when you divide both sides of the inequality by the
negative number *a*, the inequality symbol becomes < and $\frac{b}{a}$ is negative,
because $(+) \div (-) = (-)$. Thus, the answer is in the form $x <$ (a negative
number), so *x* itself must be negative.

35b. Positive; when you divide both sides of the inequality by the positive
number *a*, the inequality symbol stays the same and $\frac{b}{a}$ is positive,
because $(+) \div (+) = (+)$. Thus, the answer is in the form $x >$ (a positive
number), so *x* itself must be positive.

Avoiding Common Errors

Exercises 3–26 Watch for students
who do not reverse the inequality
symbol when multiplying by a negative number. Suggest that students
write the phrase "reverse the symbol" as soon as they see that an
exercise has a negative coefficient.

Reading Strategy

Exercise 34 Suggest to students
that they read this exercise carefully. Urge them to pay attention to
the inequality symbol and how it is
connected to the solutions of the
inequality.

Study Strategy

Exercise 35 Remind students that
some challenge problems may be
more manageable if they substitute
numbers for the variables and use
their observations to explain their
reasoning. Tell them that sometimes they will need to substitute
several numbers for the variables
before they see a pattern.

35c. Both; when you divide both
sides of the inequality by the
positive number *a*, the inequality
symbol stays the same and $\frac{b}{a}$ is
negative, because $(-) \div (+) = (-)$.
Thus, the answer is in the form
$x >$ (a negative number), so *x* itself
can be either positive or negative
(or 0).

35d. Both; when you divide both
sides of the inequality by the
negative number *a*, the inequality
symbol becomes < and $\frac{b}{a}$ is positive, because $(-) \div (-) = (+)$.
Thus, the answer is in the form
$x <$ (a positive number), so *x* itself
can be either positive or negative
(or 0).

38c. $y = 4x$;

0, 1, 2, 3, 4, 5, 6, 7, 8, 9, 10, 11, 12, 13,
14, 15, 16

41c. $h \leq 23$ horses; the area of the new corral is $(80 + 15)(82 + 15)$ = 9215 square feet. Find the possible numbers, h, of horses the corral can hold by solving the inequality $9215 \geq 400h$; $h \leq 23.04$.

41. ★ EXTENDED RESPONSE A state agency that offers wild horses for adoption requires that a potential owner reserve 400 square feet of land per horse in a corral.

a. Solve A farmer has a rectangular corral whose length is 80 feet and whose width is 82 feet. Write and solve an inequality to find the possible numbers h of horses that the corral can hold. **$h \leq 16$ horses**

b. Explain If the farmer increases the length and width of the corral by 20 feet each, will the corral be able to hold only 1 more horse? *Explain* your answer without calculating the new area of the corral. **See margin.**

c. Calculate The farmer decides to increase the length and width of the corral by 15 feet each. Find the possible numbers of horses that the corral can hold. Your answer should include the following:
• a calculation of the new area of the corral
• a description of your steps for solving the problem

C **42. CHALLENGE** An electronics store is selling a laptop computer for $1050. You can spend no more than $900 for the laptop, so you wait for it to go on sale. Also, you plan to use a store coupon for 5% off the sale price. For which decreases in price will you consider buying the laptop? **decreases of at least $102.63**

MIXED REVIEW

Write an expression for the situation. *(p. 15)*

43. Total cost of t movie tickets if each ticket costs $7.50 **$7.5t$**

44. Distance left to travel on a 500 mile trip if you have traveled m miles **$(500 - m)$ mi**

PREVIEW
Prepare for Lesson 6.3 in Exs. 45–50.

Solve the equation or inequality.

45. $9x + 6 = 7$ *(p. 141)* $\dfrac{1}{9}$ **46.** $3y - 8 = 5y + 2y$ *(p. 154)* **−2** **47.** $4(z + 1) = 6z$ *(p. 154)* **2**

48. $p + 8 > 10$ *(p. 356)* **$p > 2$** **49.** $q + 6 < -5$ *(p. 356)* **$q < -11$** **50.** $r - 2 \geq -9$ *(p. 356)* **$r \geq -7$**

Write an equation in slope-intercept form of the line that has the given slope and y-intercept. *(p. 283)*

51. slope: -3; y-intercept: 4 **52.** slope: -8; y-intercept: $\dfrac{1}{4}$ **53.** slope: $\dfrac{1}{5}$; y-intercept: $-\dfrac{2}{3}$

 $y = -3x + 4$ **$y = -8x + \dfrac{1}{4}$** **$y = \dfrac{1}{5}x - \dfrac{2}{3}$**

QUIZ for Lessons 6.1–6.2

Solve the inequality. Graph your solution. **1–9. See margin for art.**

1. $x + 8 \geq -5$ *(p. 356)* **$x \geq -13$** **2.** $y + 6 < 14$ *(p. 356)* **$y < 8$** **3.** $-8 \leq v - 5$ *(p. 356)* **$v \geq -3$**

4. $w - 11 > 2$ *(p. 356)* **$w > 13$** **5.** $-40 < -5r$ *(p. 363)* **$r < 8$** **6.** $-93 < 3s$ *(p. 363)* **$s > -31$**

7. $-2m \geq 26$ *(p. 363)* **$m \leq -13$** **8.** $\dfrac{n}{-4} > -7$ *(p. 363)* **$n < 28$** **9.** $\dfrac{c}{6} \leq -8$ *(p. 363)* **$c \leq -48$**

10. FOOD PREPARATION You need to make at least 150 sandwiches for a charity event. You can make 3 sandwiches per minute. How long will it take you to make the number of sandwiches you need? *(p. 363)* **at least 50 min**

EXTRA PRACTICE for Lesson 6.2, p. 943 **ONLINE QUIZ** at classzone.com

6.3 Solve Multi-Step Inequalities

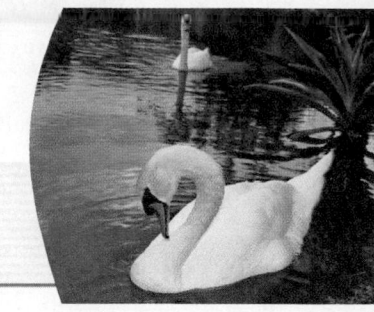

Before You solved one-step inequalities.

Now You will solve multi-step inequalities.

Why? So you can compare animal habitats, as in Ex. 39.

Key Vocabulary
• inequality, p. 21

The steps for solving two-step and multi-step equations can be applied to linear inequalities. For inequalities, be sure to reverse the inequality symbol when multiplying or dividing by a negative number.

EXAMPLE 1 **Solve a two-step inequality**

Solve $3x - 7 < 8$. Graph your solution.

$3x - 7 < 8$	Write original inequality.
$3x < 15$	Add 7 to each side.
$x < 5$	Divide each side by 3.

▶ The solutions are all real numbers less than 5. Check by substituting a number less than 5 in the original inequality.

CHECK		
	$3x - 7 < 8$	Write original inequality.
	$3(0) - 7 \overset{?}{<} 8$	Substitute 0 for x.
	$-7 < 8 ✓$	Solution checks.

EXAMPLE 2 **Solve a multi-step inequality**

Solve $-0.6(x - 5) \le 15$.

$-0.6(x - 5) \le 15$	Write original inequality.
$-0.6x + 3 \le 15$	Distributive property
$-0.6x \le 12$	Subtract 3 from each side.
$x \ge -20$	Divide each side by −0.6. Reverse inequality symbol.

 GUIDED PRACTICE for Examples 1 and 2

Solve the inequality. Graph your solution. **1–3. See margin for art.**

1. $2x - 5 \le 23$ $x \le 14$ 2. $-6y + 5 \le -16$ $y \ge 3.5$ 3. $-\frac{1}{4}(p - 12) > -2$ $p < 20$

---

① PLAN AND PREPARE

Warm-Up Exercises
📄 **Transparency Available**

1. Is 4 a solution of the inequality $2a - 1.5 \ge 6$? **yes**

2. Solve the equation $\frac{f}{4} + 8 = 7$. **−4**

3. All hats sell for the same price at a swap meet. You buy one pair of sunglasses for $7 and 2 hats. You spend $26.50. How much did each hat cost? **$9.75**

Notetaking Guide
📄 **Transparency Available**

Promotes interactive learning and notetaking skills, pp. 134–136.

Pacing
Basic: 1 day
Average: 1 day
Advanced: 1 day
Block: 0.5 block with 6.4
• See *Teaching Guide/Lesson Plan.*

② FOCUS AND MOTIVATE

Essential Question
Big Idea 1, p. 355

How do you solve multi-step inequalities? **Tell students they will learn how to answer this question by using the distributive property and the properties of inequality.**

NCTM STANDARDS

Standard 2: Analyze situations using algebraic symbols

Standard 6: Solve problems in math and other contexts

Resource Planning Guide

Chapter Resource Book
• Teaching Guide/Lesson Plan (pp. 30–31)
• Practice levels A, B, C (pp. 32–37)
• Study Guide (pp. 38–39)
• Catch-up for Absent Students (p. 40)
• Application (p. 41)
• Challenge (p. 42)

Workbooks
• Notetaking Guide (pp. 134–136)
• Practice Workbook (pp. 90–92)

Teaching Options
• **Power Presentations CD-ROM** provides dynamic electronic teaching resources for the classroom.
• **Activity Generator CD-ROM** provides editable activities for all ability levels.

Interactive Technology
• Easy Planner
• Power Presentations CD-ROM
• Activity Generator CD-ROM
• Animated Algebra
• Test Generator CD-ROM
• Online Quiz
• eWorkbook
• eEdition
• @HomeTutor

Resources for English Learners
• Quick Reference for English Learners
• Spanish Study Guide
• Multi-Language Visual Glossary
• Student Resources in Spanish

See also the *Algebra 1 Toolkit* for more strategies for meeting individual needs.

369

370

Motivating the Lesson

Ask students if the typical problems they solve in everyday life tend to be one-step or multi-step problems. Invite them to support their views by providing examples. After a short discussion, tell students that many people have trouble solving multi-step problems because they do not know where to begin. Tell them that by learning how to solve a multi-step problem, they will be able to break a problem into its parts, recognize key words, and choose from a variety of methods to solve the problem.

③ TEACH

Extra Example 1

Solve $-7x + 2 < -5$. Graph your solution. **all real numbers greater than 1**

Extra Example 2

Solve $\frac{1}{3}(3x + 6) \geq -1$. $x \geq -3$

Key Question to Ask for Example 2

• Is -21 a solution of the inequality? Explain. **No. The inequality is not true for $x = -21$ because $-21 < -20$ and the solutions are all real numbers greater than -20.**

Extra Example 3

Solve $9x + 6 \leq 6x + 21$. Graph your solution. **all real numbers less than or equal to 5**

EXAMPLE 3   Solve a multi-step inequality

ANOTHER WAY
You can also solve the inequality by subtracting 17 and $6x$ from each side, as follows:

$6x - 7 > 2x + 17$
$6x - 24 > 2x$
$\quad\quad -24 > -4x$
$\quad\quad\quad\; 6 < x$

The inequality $6 < x$ is equivalent to $x > 6$.

Solve $6x - 7 > 2x + 17$. Graph your solution.

$6x - 7 > 2x + 17$	Write original inequality.
$6x > 2x + 24$	Add 7 to each side.
$4x > 24$	Subtract $2x$ from each side.
$x > 6$	Divide each side by 4.

▶ The solutions are all real numbers greater than 6.

NUMBER OF SOLUTIONS If an inequality is equivalent to an inequality that is true, such as $-3 < 0$, then the solutions of the inequality are *all real numbers*. If an inequality is equivalent to an inequality that is false, such as $4 < -1$, then the inequality has *no solution*.

Graph of an inequality whose solutions are all real numbers

Graph of an inequality that has no solution

EXAMPLE 4   Identify the number of solutions of an inequality

Solve the inequality, if possible.

a. $14x + 5 < 7(2x - 3)$ **b.** $12x - 1 > 6(2x - 1)$

Solution

a.

$14x + 5 < 7(2x - 3)$	Write original inequality.
$14x + 5 < 14x - 21$	Distributive property
$5 < -21$	Subtract $14x$ from each side.

▶ There are no solutions because $5 < -21$ is false.

b.

$12x - 1 > 6(2x - 1)$	Write original inequality.
$12x - 1 > 12x - 6$	Distributive property
$-1 > -6$	Subtract $12x$ from each side.

▶ All real numbers are solutions because $-1 > -6$ is true.

 GUIDED PRACTICE   for Examples 3 and 4

Solve the inequality, if possible. Graph your solution. **4–6. See margin for art.**

4. $5x - 12 \leq 3x - 4$
$x \leq 4$

5. $5(m + 5) < 5m + 17$
no solution

6. $1 - 8s \leq -4(2s - 1)$
all real numbers

Differentiated Instruction

Auditory Learners While discussing **Example 3**, students follow the same steps for solving a multi-step inequality that they would use for solving a multi-step equation. Ask them if there are any differences between solving an inequality and the related equation. Stress that there is an additional step when solving an inequality; they must remember to reverse the symbol when multiplying or dividing by a negative number.

See also the *Algebra 1 Toolkit* for more strategies.

EXAMPLE 5 Solve a multi-step problem

CAR WASH Use the sign shown. A gas station charges $.10 less per gallon of gasoline if a customer also gets a car wash. What are the possible amounts (in gallons) of gasoline that you can buy if you also get a car wash and can spend at most $20?

| Gasoline | 2.09 |
| Car Wash | 8.00 |

ANOTHER WAY
For an alternative method for solving the problem in Example 5, turn to page 375 for the **Problem Solving Workshop**.

Solution

Because you are getting a car wash, you will pay $2.09 - $.10 = $1.99 per gallon of gasoline. Let g be the amount (in gallons) of gasoline that you buy.

STEP 1 Write a verbal model. Then write an inequality.

Price of gasoline (dollars/gallon)	·	Amount of gasoline (gallons)	+	Price of car wash (dollars)	≤	Maximum amount (dollars)
⬇		⬇		⬇		⬇
1.99	·	g	+	8	≤	20

STEP 2 Solve the inequality.

$1.99g + 8 \le 20$	**Write inequality.**
$1.99g \le 12$	**Subtract 8 from each side.**
$g \le 6.03015\ldots$	**Divide each side by 1.99.**

▸ You can buy up to slightly more than 6 gallons of gasoline.

CHECK You can use a table to check the reasonableness of your answer.

The table shows that you will pay $19.94 for exactly 6 gallons of gasoline. Because $19.94 is less than $20, it is reasonable to conclude that you can buy slightly more than 6 gallons of gasoline.

Gasoline (gal)	Total amount spent (dollars)
0	8.00
1	9.99
2	11.98
3	13.97
4	15.96
5	17.95
6	19.94

✓ **GUIDED PRACTICE** for Example 5

7. **WHAT IF?** In Example 5, suppose that a car wash costs $9 and gasoline regularly costs $2.19 per gallon. What are the possible amounts (in gallons) of gasoline that you can buy? $g \le$ **5.02 gal**

8. **CAMP COSTS** You are saving money for a summer camp that costs $1800. You have saved $500 so far, and you have 14 more weeks to save the total amount. What are the possible average amounts of money that you can save per week in order to have a total of at least $1800 saved? **at least $92.86/wk**

6.3 Solve Multi-Step Inequalities **371**

HOMEWORK KEY

○ = **WORKED-OUT SOLUTIONS**
on p. WS1 for Exs. 5, 19, and 39

★ = **STANDARDIZED TEST PRACTICE**
Exs. 2, 33, 39, 40, and 42

◆ = **MULTIPLE REPRESENTATIONS**
Ex. 41

4 PRACTICE AND APPLY

Assignment Guide

📖 **Answer Transparencies available for all exercises**

Basic:
Day 1: EP p. 940 Exs. 9–14
pp. 372–374
Exs. 1–10, 17–24, 29, 30, 37–41,
44–56 even

Average:
Day 1: pp. 372–374
Exs. 1, 2, 4–14 even, 15, 16,
21–27 odd, 29–34, 37–42, 44,
45–55 odd

Advanced:
Day 1: pp. 372–374
Exs. 1, 2, 4–8 even, 13, 14,
22–28 even, 29–36*, 38–43*,
44–56 even

Block:
pp. 372–374
Exs. 1, 2, 4–14 even, 15, 16,
21–27 odd, 29–34, 37–42, 44,
45–55 odd (with 6.4)

Differentiated Instruction

See *Algebra 1 Best Practices Toolkit*
for suggestions on addressing the
needs of a diverse classroom.

Homework Check

For a quick check of student understanding of key concepts, go over
the following exercises:

Basic: 3, 6, 9, 20, 37

Average: 4, 6, 12, 24, 38

Advanced: 4, 8, 13, 26, 39

Extra Practice

• Student Edition, p. 943
• Chapter 6 Resource Book:
  Practice levels A, B, C, pp. 32–37

Practice Worksheet

An easily-readable reduced
practice page (with answers)
for this lesson can be found
on p. 354C.

---

2. An inequality has no solutions if
it is equivalent to a false inequality such as 0 > 2. All real numbers
are solutions of the inequality if it
is equivalent to a true inequality
such as 0 < 2.

SKILL PRACTICE

A 1. **VOCABULARY** Copy and complete: The inequalities $3x - 1 < 11$, $3x < 12$, and $x < 4$ are called __?__. **equivalent inequalities**

2. ★ **WRITING** How do you know whether an inequality has no solutions? How do you know whether the solutions are all real numbers? **See margin.**

EXAMPLES 1, 2, and 3
on pp. 369–370
for Exs. 3–16

SOLVING INEQUALITIES Solve the inequality. Graph your solution. **3–14. See margin for art.**

3. $2x - 3 > 7$ **x > 5**

4. $5y + 9 \le 4$ **y ≤ −1**

5. $8v - 3 \ge -11$ **v ≥ −1**

6. $3(w + 12) < 0$ **w < −12**

7. $7(r - 3) \ge -13$ **r ≥ 1$\frac{1}{7}$**

8. $2(s + 4) \le 16$ **s ≤ 4**

9. $4 - 2m > 7 - 3m$ **m > 3**

10. $8n - 2 > 17n + 9$ **n < −1$\frac{2}{9}$**

11. $-10p > 6p - 8$ **p < $\frac{1}{2}$**

12. $4 - \frac{1}{2}q \le 33 - q$ **q ≤ 58**

13. $-\frac{2}{3}d - 2 < \frac{1}{3}d + 8$ **d > −10**

14. $8 - \frac{4}{5}f > -14 - 2f$ **f > −18$\frac{1}{3}$**

ERROR ANALYSIS *Describe* and correct the error in solving the inequality. **15, 16. See margin.**

15.

$$17 - 3x \ge 56$$
$$-3x \ge 39$$
$$x \ge -13$$

16.

$$-4(2x - 3) < 28$$
$$-8x - 12 < 28$$
$$-8x < 40$$
$$x > -5$$

EXAMPLE 4
on p. 370
for Exs. 17–28

SOLVING INEQUALITIES Solve the inequality, if possible.

17. $3p - 5 > 2p + p - 7$
all real numbers

18. $5d - 8d - 4 \le -4 + 3d$
d ≥ 0

19. $3(s - 4) \ge 2(s - 6)$
s ≥ 0

20. $2(t - 3) > 2t - 8$
all real numbers

21. $5(b + 9) \le 5b + 45$
all real numbers

22. $2(4c - 7) \ge 8(c - 3)$
all real numbers

23. $6(x + 3) < 5x + 18 + x$
no solution

24. $4 + 9y - 3 \ge 3(3y + 2)$
no solution

25. $2.2h + 0.4 \le 2(1.1h - 0.1)$
no solution

26. $9.5j - 6 + 5.5j \ge 3(5j - 2)$
all real numbers

27. $\frac{1}{5}(4m + 10) < \frac{4}{5}m + 2$
no solution

28. $\frac{3}{4}(8n - 4) < -3(1 - 2n)$
no solution

B **TRANSLATING PHRASES** Translate the verbal phrase into an inequality. Then solve the inequality and graph your solution. **29–32. See margin for art.**

29. Four more than the product of 3 and x is less than 40. **3x + 4 < 40; x < 12**

30. Twice the sum of x and 8 is greater than or equal to −36. **2(x + 8) ≥ −36; x ≥ −26**

31. The sum of $5x$ and $2x$ is greater than the difference of $9x$ and 4. **5x + 2x > 9x − 4; x < 2**

32. The product of 6 and the difference of $6x$ and 3 is less than or equal to the product of −2 and the sum of 4 and $8x$. **6(6x − 3) ≤ −2(4 + 8x); x ≤ $\frac{5}{26}$**

33. ★ **MULTIPLE CHOICE** For which values of a and b are all the solutions of $ax + b > 0$ positive? **C**

   Ⓐ $a > 0, b > 0$
   Ⓑ $a < 0, b < 0$
   Ⓒ $a > 0, b < 0$
   Ⓓ $a < 0, b = 0$

372   Chapter 6   Solving and Graphing Linear Inequalities

3.

4.

5.

6.

7.

8.

9.

10.

GEOMETRY Write and solve an inequality to find the possible values of *x*.

34. Area > 81 square feet $9(x + 2) > 81; x > 7$ **35.** Area ≤ 44 square centimeters

$\frac{1}{2} \cdot 8(x + 1) \le 44; x \le 10$

9 ft

$(x + 2)$ ft

8 cm

$(x + 1)$ cm

[C] **36. CHALLENGE** For which value of *a* are all the solutions of
$2(x − 5) \ge 3x + a$ less than or equal to 5? **−15**

PROBLEM SOLVING

EXAMPLE 5 [A]
on p. 371
for Exs. 37–40

37. CD BURNING A blank CD can hold 70 minutes of music. So far you have
burned 25 minutes of music onto the CD. You estimate that each song
lasts 4 minutes. What are the possible numbers of additional songs that
you can burn onto the CD? **at most 11 songs**

@HomeTutor for problem solving help at classzone.com

38. BUSINESS You spend $46 on supplies to make wooden ornaments and
plan to sell the ornaments for $8.50 each. What are the possible numbers
of ornaments that you can sell in order for your profit to be positive? **at least 6 ornaments**

@HomeTutor for problem solving help at classzone.com

39a. Up to 6
swans; the area
of the habitat is
(20 feet)(50 feet)
= 1000 square
feet. 500 square
feet are needed
for the first
two swans and
the remaining
1000 − 500 =
500 square feet
can hold up to
500 ÷ 125 = 4
more swans; so,
the maximum
number of swans
is 2 + 4 =
6 swans.

39. ★ **SHORT RESPONSE** A zookeeper is designing a rectangular habitat for
swans, as shown. The zookeeper needs to reserve 500 square feet for
the first 2 swans and 125 square feet for each additional swan.

20 ft

50 ft

a. Calculate What are the possible numbers of swans that the habitat
can hold? *Explain* how you got your answer. **See margin.**

b. Compare Suppose that the zookeeper increases both the length and
width of the habitat by 20 feet. What are the possible numbers of
additional swans that the habitat can hold? **at most 14 more swans**

40. ★ **MULTIPLE CHOICE** A gym is offering a trial membership for 3 months
by discounting the regular monthly rate by $50. You will consider joining
the gym if the total cost of the trial membership is less than $100. Which
inequality can you use to find the possible regular monthly rates that
you are willing to pay? **C**

(A) $3x − 50 < 100$

(B) $3x − 50 > 100$

(C) $3(x − 50) < 100$

(D) $3(x − 50) > 100$

Avoiding Common Errors

Exercises 3–14 Students should
always check that their written solution for an inequality matches the
graph of the solution. Specifically,
they should check that their inequality uses an open circle for < or > and
a closed circle for ≤ or ≥.

Exercises 17–28 When using the
distributive property, students who
use mental math sometimes fail to
distribute the factor to all the numbers inside the parentheses.
Encourage all students to get into
the habit of checking for this error.

Reading Strategy

Exercises 37–43 As in the previous
lessons, students should read the
problems carefully in order to determine which inequality symbol to use.
Remind them to look for key words
and phrases, such as "no more
than," "at most," and "at least."

11.

12.
58

13.

14.
$-18\frac{1}{3}$

15. The inequality symbol was not
reversed when dividing both sides
by −3; $x \le −13$.

16. The distributive property was
not used correctly, $−8x + 12 < 28$,
$−8x < 16$, $x > −2$.

29.

30.
−26

31.

32.
$\frac{5}{26}$

B **41.** ◆ **MULTIPLE REPRESENTATIONS** A baseball pitcher makes 53 pitches in the first four innings of a game and plans to pitch in the next 3 innings.

  a. Making a Table Make a table that gives the total number t of pitches made if the pitcher makes an average of p pitches per inning in the next 3 innings. Use the following values for p: 15, 16, 17, 18, 19. **See margin.**

  b. Writing an Inequality The baseball coach assigns a maximum of 105 pitches to the pitcher for the game. Write and solve an inequality to find the possible average numbers of pitches that the pitcher can make in each of the next three innings. $53 + 3p \leq 105$, $p \leq 17\frac{1}{3}$, $p \leq 17$ **pitches**

42a. 5%; the amount that was taxed was $300 − $175 = $125. To find the tax rate, solve the proportion $\frac{x}{100} = \frac{6.25}{125}$.

42. ★ **EXTENDED RESPONSE** A state imposes a sales tax on items of clothing that cost more than $175. The tax applies only to the difference of the price of the item and $175.

  a. Calculate Use the receipt shown to find the tax rate (as a percent). *Explain* how you got your answer.

  b. Apply A shopper has $400 to spend on a winter coat. Write and solve an inequality to find the prices p of coats that the shopper can afford. Assume that $p \geq 175$. $p + 0.05(p − 175) \leq 400$, $p \leq 389.29$; **up to $389.29**

  c. Compare Another state imposes a 4% sales tax on the entire price of an item of clothing. For which prices would paying the 4% tax be cheaper than paying the tax described above? Your answer should include the following:

    • writing and solving an inequality that describes the situation

    • checking the reasonableness of your answer using one of the solutions of the inequality **See margin.**

THE STYLE STORE

Item: Price: $ 300.00
Suit   Tax: $ 6.25
             Total: $306.25

C **43.** **CHALLENGE** Your scores in four bowling league tournaments are 157, 161, 149, and 172. After the next game, you want your average score to be at least 167. What are the possible scores that you can earn in your next tournament in order to meet your goal? **at least 196**

MIXED REVIEW

44. Using the positive integers less than 10, draw a Venn diagram where set A consists of factors of 30 and set B consists of odd numbers. Then tell whether this statement is *true* or *false*: "If a positive integer less than 10 is odd, then it is a factor of 30." *Explain* your reasoning. *(p. 930)*
See margin for art; false; 7 and 9 are odd numbers less than 10 that are not factors of 30.

Simplify the expression.

45. $11(−y)(−y)$ *(p. 88)* **$11y^2$**   **46.** $\frac{3}{4} \cdot (−16y)$ *(p. 88)* **−12y**   **47.** $−2(x + 1) − 7x$ *(p. 96)* **−9x − 2**

48. $5x + 4 − 3x$ *(p. 96)* **2x + 4**   **49.** $8(x + 6) − 5$ *(p. 96)* **8x + 43**   **50.** $\frac{−15x + 18}{−6}$ *(p. 103)* **$\frac{5}{2}x − 3$**

PREVIEW
Prepare for Lesson 6.4 in Exs. 51–56.

Solve the inequality. Graph your solution. **51–56. See margin for art.**

51. $x + 7 < 8$ *(p. 356)* **x < 1**   **52.** $y − 4 \geq − 2$ *(p. 356)* **y ≥ 2**   **53.** $9 \leq z + 13$ *(p. 356)* **z ≥ −4**

54. $4.8 > m − 7.4$ *(p. 356)* **m < 12.2**   **55.** $\frac{n}{4} < −1$ *(p. 363)* **n < −4**   **56.** $4p \geq 52$ *(p. 363)* **p ≥ 13**

44.

51.

52.

53.

54.

55.

56.

Using ALTERNATIVE METHODS

Another Way to Solve Example 5, page 371

MULTIPLE REPRESENTATIONS In Example 5 on page 371, you saw how to solve a problem about buying gasoline using an inequality. You can also solve the problem by working backward or by using a graph.

PROBLEM

CAR WASH Use the sign shown. A gas station charges $.10 less per gallon of gasoline if a customer also gets a car wash. What are the possible amounts (in gallons) of gasoline that you can buy if you also get a car wash and can spend at most $20?

| Gasoline | 2.09 |
| Car Wash | 8.00 |

METHOD 1

Work backward One alternative approach is to work backward.

STEP 1 **Read** the problem. It gives you the following information:
- amount you can spend: up to $20
- price of a car wash: $8
- regular price per gallon of gasoline: $2.09
- discount per gallon of gasoline when you get a car wash: $.10

Because you are getting a car wash, gasoline costs $2.09 − $.10, or $1.99, per gallon.

STEP 2 **Work** backward.
- Start with the amount you have to spend: $20.
- Subtract the cost of a car wash: $20 − $8 = $12.
- Make a table of values showing the amount of money you have left after buying various amounts of gasoline.

Gasoline (gal)	Amount of money left
0	$12.00
1	$10.01
2	$8.02
3	$6.03
4	$4.04
5	$2.05
6	$.06

− $1.99 (between each row)

▶ You can buy up to slightly more than 6 gallons of gasoline.

Alternative Strategy

Example 5 on page 371 can be solved by working backward or by using a graph. Working backward is a good strategy because the problem provides a maximum amount and a constant amount, which gives the student an immediate starting point and a quick means to a solution. A graph is a good strategy because it gives an approximate answer, which is all that is needed for this problem.

Avoiding Common Errors

In Method 1, Step 2, you may want to point out a quick way to subtract $1.99 is to subtract $2 and add $.01. This can help students avoid calculation errors and give faster results.

1. At least 9 batches; Method 1: Work backward. Begin with 100 cookies and make a table of values showing the number of cookies you have left to make after each batch of 12 cookies.

Number of batches baked	Number of cookies to bake
0	100
1	88
2	76
3	64
4	52
5	40
6	28
7	16
8	4
9	less than 0

After 9 batches you will have at least 100 cookies. Method 2: Use a graph. Write and graph an equation that gives the total number y of cookies baked as a function of the number x of batches baked: $y = 12x$. Graph $y = 100$ on the same coordinate plane.

 METHOD 2 **Using a graph** Another alternative approach is to use a graph.

STEP 1 **Write** a verbal model. Then write an equation that gives the total amount of money y (in dollars) that you spend as a function of the amount x (in gallons) of gasoline that you buy.

Total spent (dollars)	=	Price of gasoline (dollars/gallon)	·	Amount of gasoline (gallons)	+	Price of car wash (dollars)
y	=	1.99	·	x	+	8

STEP 2 **Graph** $y = 1.99x + 8$.

STEP 3 **Graph** $y = 20$ in the same coordinate plane. This equation gives the maximum amount of money that you can spend for gasoline and a car wash.

STEP 4 **Analyze** the graphs. The point of intersection shows that you can buy slightly more than 6 gallons of gasoline when you spend $20. Because you can spend *at most* $20, the solutions are the x-coordinates of the points on the graph of $y = 1.99x + 8$ that lie *on or below* the graph of $y = 20$.

▶ You can buy up to slightly more than 6 gallons of gasoline.

PRACTICE

1. **BAKING** You need to bake at least 100 cookies for a bake sale. You can bake 12 cookies per batch of dough. What are the possible numbers of batches that will allow you to bake enough cookies? Solve this problem using two different methods. **See margin.**

2. **VIDEO GAMES** A video game console costs $259, and games cost $29 each. You saved $400 to buy a console and games. What are the possible numbers of games that you can buy? Solve this problem using two different methods. **See margin.**

3. **WHAT IF?** In Exercise 2, suppose you saved $500 and decide to buy a video game console that costs $299. What are the possible numbers of games that you can buy? **at most 6 games**

4. **MONEY** You need to have at least $100 in your checking account to avoid a low balance fee. You have $247 in your account, and you make withdrawals of $20 per week. What are the possible numbers of weeks that you can withdraw money and avoid paying the fee? Solve this problem using two different methods. **See margin.**

5. **RUNNING TIMES** You are running a 10 mile race. You run the first 3 miles in 24.7 minutes. Your goal is to finish the race in less than 1 hour 20 minutes. What should your average running time (in minutes per mile) be for the remaining miles? **less than 7.9 min/mi**

376   Chapter 6 Solving and Graphing Linear Inequalities

The graphs intersect between $x = 8$ and $x = 9$. Because you must bake at least 100 cookies, the solutions are the x-coordinates of the points on the graph of $y = 12x$ that lie on or above the graph of $y = 100$. Only integer values of x make sense in this situation, so you must bake at least 9 batches.

2, 4. See Additional Answers beginning on p. AA1.

Extension
Use after Lesson 6.3

Solve Linear Inequalities by Graphing

GOAL Use graphs to solve linear inequalities.

So far in Chapter 6 you have seen how to solve linear inequalities algebraically. You can also solve linear inequalities graphically.

KEY CONCEPT *For Your Notebook*

Solving Linear Inequalities Graphically

STEP 1 **Write** the inequality in one of the following forms: $ax + b < 0$, $ax + b \le 0$, $ax + b > 0$, or $ax + b \ge 0$.

STEP 2 **Write** the related equation $y = ax + b$.

STEP 3 **Graph** the equation $y = ax + b$.

- The solutions of $ax + b > 0$ are the x-coordinates of the points on the graph of $y = ax + b$ that lie above the x-axis.

- The solutions of $ax + b < 0$ are the x-coordinates of the points on the graph of $y = ax + b$ that lie below the x-axis.

- If the inequality symbol is $\le$ or $\ge$, then the x-intercept of the graph is also a solution.

EXAMPLE 1 **Solve an inequality graphically**

Solve $3x + 2 > 8$ graphically.

Solution

STEP 1 **Write** the inequality in the form $ax + b > 0$.

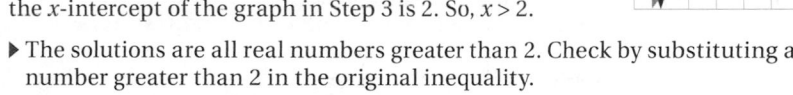

$3x + 2 > 8$ **Write original inequality.**

$3x - 6 > 0$ **Subtract 8 from each side.**

STEP 2 **Write** the related equation $y = 3x - 6$.

STEP 3 **Graph** the equation $y = 3x - 6$.

The inequality in Step 1 is in the form $ax + b > 0$, and the x-intercept of the graph in Step 3 is 2. So, $x > 2$.

▶ The solutions are all real numbers greater than 2. Check by substituting a number greater than 2 in the original inequality.

CHECK $3x + 2 > 8$ **Write original inequality.**

$3(4) + 2 \overset{?}{>} 8$ **Substitute 4 for x.**

$14 > 8 \checkmark$ **Solution checks.**

---

① PLAN AND PREPARE

Warm-Up Exercises

1. Write $4x + 2 = 5$ in the form $ax + b = 0$. Then write the related function $y = ax + b$.
$4x - 3 = 0; y = 4x - 3$

2. Solve $2x + 3 = x$ by graphing the related function $y = f(x)$. **−3**

② FOCUS AND MOTIVATE

Essential Question
Big Idea 3, p. 355

How do you use graphs to solve linear inequalities? **Tell students they will learn how to answer this question by graphing the related function and shading one of the half-planes.**

③ TEACH

Extra Example 1
Solve $2x - 1 < 5$ graphically.

all real numbers less than 3

NCTM STANDARDS

Standard 2: Use models to understand relationships

Standard 6: Solve problems in math and other contexts

EXAMPLE 2   Approximate a real-world solution

CELL PHONES Your cell phone plan costs $49.99 per month for a given number of minutes. Each additional minute or part of a minute costs $.40. You budgeted $55 per month for phone costs. What are the possible additional minutes x that you can afford each month?

Solution

STEP 1   **Write** a verbal model. Then write an inequality.

Rate for additional time (dollars/minute)	·	Additional time (minutes)	+	Cost of phone plan (dollars)	≤	Amount budgeted (dollars)
0.40	·	x	+	49.99	≤	55

Write the inequality in the form $ax + b \le 0$.

$0.40x + 49.99 \le 55$ **Write original inequality.**

$0.40x - 5.01 \le 0$ **Subtract 55 from each side.**

STEP 2   **Write** the related equation $y = 0.40x - 5.01$.

STEP 3   **Graph** the equation $y = 0.40x - 5.01$ on a graphing calculator.

Use the *trace* feature of the graphing calculator to find the x-intercept of the graph.

The inequality in Step 1 is in the form $ax + b \le 0$, and the x-intercept is about 12.5. Because a part of a minute costs $.40, round 12.5 down to 12 to be sure that you stay within your budget.

▶ You can afford up to 12 additional minutes.

Extra Example 2

Your gym membership costs $18.95 per month. Yoga classes cost $3.25 each. You budget $30 per month for gym costs. What are the possible numbers of yoga classes that you can afford each month? **no more than 3 yoga classes per month**

Closing the Lesson

Have students summarize the major points of the lesson and answer the Essential Question: How do you use graphs to solve linear inequalities?

• You can solve a linear inequality graphically by writing and graphing the related function.

Write the inequality in a form that sets it to zero. Then write the related function and graph the equation. The inequality symbol specifies whether or not the solutions contain the x-intercept and whether the solutions are to the right or to the left of the x-intercept.

④ PRACTICE AND APPLY

Avoiding Common Errors

Exercises 1–3 Some students may find the y-intercept instead of the x-intercept for these exercises. Remind these students that they are solving for x and not for y.

Study Strategy

Exercise 4 Point out that the problem in the exercise is similar to Example 2. Suggest that students closely model their solutions on the patterns shown in the steps of Example 2.

PRACTICE

**EXAMPLES
1 and 2**
on pp. 377–378
for Exs. 1–4

Solve the inequality graphically.

1. $2x + 5 > 11$ **$x > 3$**

2. $\frac{1}{2}x + 6 \le 13$ **$x \le 14$**

3. $0.2x - 15.75 < 27$ **$x < 213.75$**

4. **CABLE COSTS** Your family has a cable television package that costs $40.99 per month. Pay-per-view movies cost $3.95 each. Your family budgets $55 per month for cable television costs. What are the possible numbers of pay-per-view movies that your family can afford each month? **up to 3 movies**

6.4 Statements with *And* and *Or*

MATERIALS · paper and pencil

QUESTION What is the difference between a statement with *and* and a statement with *or*?

EXPLORE Use a Venn diagram to answer questions about a group

STEP 1 *Answer questions* Copy the questions below and write your answers beside them. **Steps 1, 2. Answers may vary.**

1. Are you taking an art class?

2. Are you taking a foreign language class?

STEP 2 *Complete a Venn diagram* Form a group with 3 or 4 classmates. Draw a Venn diagram, like the one shown below, where set A consists of students taking an art class, and set B consists of students taking a foreign language class. Then write the name of each student in the appropriate section of the diagram.

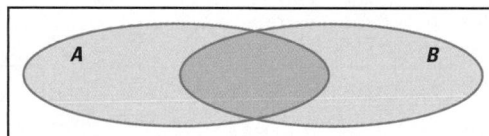

DRAW CONCLUSIONS Use your observations to complete these exercises

In Exercises 1–3, use your Venn diagram to list the students who belong in the given set. **1–6. Answers may vary.**

1. Set A
2. Set B
3. Set A *and* set B

4. The students who belong in set A *or* set B are all of the students who belong only in set A, only in set B, or in set A *and* set B. List the students in your group who belong in set A *or* set B.

5. **OPEN-ENDED** Write a statement with *and* so that the statement is true for all students in your group.

6. **OPEN-ENDED** Write a statement with *or* so that the statement is true for all students in your group.

REASONING Tell whether the statement is *true* or *false*.

7. If a student belongs in set A *and* set B, then the student belongs in set A *or* set B. **true**

8. If a student belongs in set A *or* set B, then the student belongs in set A *and* set B. **false**

---

① PLAN AND PREPARE

Explore the Concept

- Students will use a Venn diagram to explore the difference between statements with *and* and with *or*.
- This activity leads into the study of compound inequalities in Example 1 in Lesson 6.4.

Recommended Time

Work activity: 10 min

Discuss results: 5 min

Grouping

Students can work individually or in groups of 4. If students work in groups, two can ask questions and write answers and two can draw and label the Venn diagram.

② TEACH

Tips for Success

If students are not taking art or foreign language, then suggest other classes such as science or English.

Key Discovery

Statements with *and* describe the intersection of two sets, while statements with *or* describe the union of two sets.

③ ASSESS AND RETEACH

Which usually contains more students, "Set A *and* Set B" or "Set A *or* Set B"? Explain. **"Set *A* or Set *B*" includes students in either set, so it usually contains more than "Set *A* and Set *B*," for which students must be in both sets.**

6.4 Solve Compound Inequalities

Key Vocabulary
• compound inequality

A **compound inequality** consists of two separate inequalities joined by *and* or *or*.

The graph of a compound inequality with *and* is the *intersection* of the graphs of the inequalities.

The graph of a compound inequality with *or* is the *union* of the graphs of the inequalities.

 $x > -2$

$x \leq 1$

$-2 < x$ and $x \leq 1$
$-2 < x \leq 1$

$x \geq 0$

$x < -1$

$x < -1$ or $x \geq 0$

EXAMPLE 1 Write and graph compound inequalities

Translate the verbal phrase into an inequality. Then graph the inequality.

a. All real numbers that are greater than -2 *and* less than 3

Inequality: $-2 < x < 3$

Graph:

b. All real numbers that are less than 0 *or* greater than or equal to 2

Inequality: $x < 0$ or $x \geq 2$

Graph:

✓ **GUIDED PRACTICE** for Example 1

Translate the verbal phrase into an inequality. Then graph the inequality.

1–2. See margin for art.

1. All real numbers that are less than -1 *or* greater than or equal to 4 $x < -1$ or $x \geq 4$

2. All real numbers that are greater than or equal to -3 *and* less than 5 $-3 \leq x < 5$

EXAMPLE 2   Write and graph a real-world compound inequality

CAMERA CARS A crane sits on top of a camera car and faces toward the front. The crane's maximum height and minimum height above the ground are shown. Write and graph a compound inequality that describes the possible heights of the crane.

18 feet

4 feet

Solution

Let h represent the height (in feet) of the crane. All possible heights are greater than or equal to 4 feet *and* less than or equal to 18 feet. So, the inequality is $4 \leq h \leq 18$.

SOLVING COMPOUND INEQUALITIES A number is a solution of a compound inequality with *and* if the number is a solution of *both* inequalities. A number is a solution of a compound inequality with *or* if the number is a solution of *at least one* of the inequalities.

EXAMPLE 3   Solve a compound inequality with *and*

Solve $2 < x + 5 < 9$. **Graph your solution.**

Solution

Separate the compound inequality into two inequalities. Then solve each inequality separately.

$2 < x + 5$	*and*	$x + 5 < 9$	**Write two inequalities.**
$2 - 5 < x + 5 - 5$	*and*	$x + 5 - 5 < 9 - 5$	**Subtract 5 from each side.**
$-3 < x$	*and*	$x < 4$	**Simplify.**

The compound inequality can be written as $-3 < x < 4$.

▶ The solutions are all real numbers greater than -3 *and* less than 4.

✓ **GUIDED PRACTICE**   for Examples 2 and 3

3. **INVESTING** An investor buys shares of a stock and will sell them if the change c in value from the purchase price of a share is less than $-\$3.00$ or greater than $\$4.50$. Write and graph a compound inequality that describes the changes in value for which the shares will be sold.
$c < -3$ or $c > 4.5$; see margin for art.

Solve the inequality. Graph your solution. 4–6. See margin for art.

4. $-7 < x - 5 < 4$ $-2 < x < 9$ 5. $10 \leq 2y + 4 \leq 24$ $3 \leq y \leq 10$ 6. $-7 < -z - 1 < 3$
$-4 < z < 6$

6.4 Solve Compound Inequalities   **381**

Motivating the Lesson

Your veterinarian wants you to monitor your dog's weight if it dips 3 pounds below a minimum weight of 8 pounds or increases 5 pounds above a maximum weight of 12 pounds. Knowing how to solve compound inequalities will help you determine the possible weights you need to monitor.

❸ TEACH

Extra Example 1
Translate the verbal phrase into an inequality. Then graph the inequality.
a. All real numbers that are greater than or equal to -4 *and* less than 4 $-4 \leq x < 4$

b. All real numbers that are less than -1 or greater than 2
$x < -1$ *or* $x > 2$

Extra Example 2
At an auction, the lowest bid for an autographed trading card is \$20. The highest bid is \$54. Write and graph a compound inequality that describes the possible bids. **All bids b are greater than or equal to \$20 *and* less than or equal to \$54; $20 \leq b \leq 54$.**

Extra Example 3
Solve $-1 < x + 1 \leq 7$. Graph your solution. **all real numbers greater than -2 *and* less than or equal to 6**

1–6. See Additional Answers beginning on p. AA1.

Extra Example 4

Solve $1 < -2x + 3 < 19$. Graph your solution. **all real numbers greater than −8 and less than 1**

Extra Example 5

Solve $3x - 2 \leq -11$ or $2x + 8 > 16$. Graph your solution. **all real numbers less than or equal to −3 or greater than 4**

Key Questions to Ask for Example 5

• According to the graph, is 3 a solution of the compound inequality? Explain. **No; the inequality $x < 3$ is not true when x is 3.**

• Does a number have to be a solution of both inequalities to be a solution of the compound inequality? Explain. **No; a number has to be a solution of at least one of the inequalities for an *or* compound inequality.**

classzone.com

An **Animated Algebra** activity is available on-line for **Example 5**. This activity is also available on the **Power Presentations CD-ROM**.

7.

8.

9.

10.

ANOTHER WAY In Example 3, you could solve $2 < x + 5 < 9$ by subtracting 5 from 2, $x + 5$, and 9 without first separating the compound inequality into two separate inequalities. To solve a compound inequality with *and*, you perform the same operation on each expression.

EXAMPLE 4 Solve a compound inequality with *and*

Solve $-5 \leq -x - 3 \leq 2$. Graph your solution.

$-5 \leq -x - 3 \leq 2$	Write original inequality.
$-5 + 3 \leq -x - 3 + 3 \leq 2 + 3$	Add 3 to each expression.
$-2 \leq -x \leq 5$	Simplify.
$-1(-2) \geq -1(-x) \geq -1(5)$	Multiply each expression by −1 and reverse *both* inequality symbols.
$2 \geq x \geq -5$	Simplify.
$-5 \leq x \leq 2$	Rewrite in the form $a \leq x \leq b$.

▶ The solutions are all real numbers greater than or equal to −5 *and* less than or equal to 2.

EXAMPLE 5 Solve a compound inequality with *or*

Solve $2x + 3 < 9$ or $3x - 6 > 12$. Graph your solution.

Solution

Solve the two inequalities separately.

$2x + 3 < 9$	or	$3x - 6 > 12$	Write original inequality.
$2x + 3 - 3 < 9 - 3$	or	$3x - 6 + 6 > 12 + 6$	Addition or subtraction property of inequality
$2x < 6$	or	$3x > 18$	Simplify.
$\dfrac{2x}{2} < \dfrac{6}{2}$	or	$\dfrac{3x}{3} > \dfrac{18}{3}$	Division property of inequality
$x < 3$	or	$x > 6$	Simplify.

▶ The solutions are all real numbers less than 3 *or* greater than 6.

 at classzone.com

✓ **GUIDED PRACTICE** for Examples 4 and 5

Solve the inequality. Graph your solution. **7–10. See margin for art.**

7. $-14 < x - 8 < -1$ **$-6 < x < 7$**

8. $-1 \leq -5t + 2 \leq 4$ **$-\dfrac{2}{5} \leq t \leq \dfrac{3}{5}$**

9. $3h + 1 < -5$ or $2h - 5 > 7$ **$h < -2$ or $h > 6$**

10. $4c + 1 \leq -3$ or $5c - 3 > 17$ **$c \leq -1$ or $c > 4$**

Differentiated Instruction

Below Level Some students may have difficulty recognizing differences between compound inequalities with *and* and with *or*. Stress that compound inequalities with *and* have solutions that overlap. Have students graph $x \geq -5$ and $x \leq 2$ in **Example 4** on separate graphs. This may help them see that the solutions overlap. Point out that graphs of most compound inequalities with *or* have gaps, with arrows heading in opposite directions. See also the *Algebra 1 Toolkit* for more strategies.

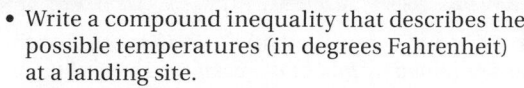

EXAMPLE 6 **Solve a multi-step problem**

ASTRONOMY The Mars Exploration Rovers *Opportunity* and *Spirit* are robots that were sent to Mars in 2003 in order to gather geological data about the planet. The temperature at the landing sites of the robots can range from −100°C to 0°C.

• Write a compound inequality that describes the possible temperatures (in degrees Fahrenheit) at a landing site.

• Solve the inequality. Then graph your solution.

• Identify three possible temperatures (in degrees Fahrenheit) at a landing site.

Solution

Let *F* represent the temperature in degrees Fahrenheit, and let *C* represent the temperature in degrees Celsius. Use the formula $C = \frac{5}{9}(F - 32)$.

STEP 1 **Write** a compound inequality. Because the temperature at a landing site ranges from −100°C to 0°C, the lowest possible temperature is −100°C, and the highest possible temperature is 0°C.

$$-100 \le C \le 0 \qquad \text{Write inequality using } C.$$

$$-100 \le \frac{5}{9}(F - 32) \le 0 \qquad \text{Substitute } \tfrac{5}{9}(F - 32) \text{ for } C.$$

STEP 2 **Solve** the inequality. Then graph your solution.

ANOTHER WAY

You can solve the compound inequality by multiplying through by 9:

$-100 \le \frac{5}{9}(F - 32) \le 0$

$-900 \le 5(F - 32) \le 0$

$-900 \le 5F - 160 \le 0$

$-740 \le 5F \le 160$

$-148 \le F \le 32$

$$-100 \le \frac{5}{9}(F - 32) \le 0 \qquad \text{Write inequality from Step 1.}$$

$$-180 \le F - 32 \le 0 \qquad \text{Multiply each expression by } \tfrac{9}{5}.$$

$$-148 \le F \le 32 \qquad \text{Add 32 to each expression.}$$

STEP 3 **Identify** three possible temperatures.

The temperature at a landing site is greater than or equal to −148°F *and* less than or equal to 32°F. Three possible temperatures are −115°F, 15°F, and 32°F.

✓ **GUIDED PRACTICE** for Example 6

11. **MARS** Mars has a maximum temperature of −7°C at the equator and a minimum temperature of −133°C at the winter pole.

• Write and solve a compound inequality that describes the possible temperatures (in degrees Fahrenheit) on Mars.

• Graph your solution. Then identify three possible temperatures (in degrees Fahrenheit) on Mars.

$-133 \le \frac{5}{9}(F - 32) \le 27$; $-207.4 \le F \le 80.6$; see margin for art.
Sample answer: −100°F, 0°F, 25°F

6.4 Solve Compound Inequalities **383**

Extra Example 6

The eggs of a Rocky Mountain Tailed frog can survive in streams where the temperature ranges from 5°C to 18°C. Write a compound inequality that describes the possible stream temperatures (in degrees Fahrenheit) for egg survival. Solve the inequality. Then graph your solution. Identify three possible stream temperatures (in degrees Fahrenheit) for egg survival.

$5 \le \frac{5}{9}(F - 32) \le 18$; $41 \le F \le 64.4$

examples: 45°F, 53°F, 61°F

Closing the Lesson

Have students summarize the major points of the lesson and answer the Essential Question: How do you solve and graph compound inequalities?

• **Compound inequalities are two inequalities joined by *and* or joined by *or*.**

• **The graph of a compound inequality with *and* is the intersection of the graphs of the inequalities. The graph of an inequality with *or* is the union of the graphs.**

Solve the two inequalities in the compound inequality separately. On the graph of a compound inequality with *and*, shade all the numbers that satisfy both inequalities together. On the graph of a compound inequality with *or*, shade the numbers that satisfy the separate inequalities.

11.

Differentiated Instruction

Advanced Have students research the Internet for astronomical or other scientific data that involve a range and a conversion, as in **Example 6**. Ask them to create a multi-step problem that uses a compound inequality with *and* or *or* and that involves a conversion. Encourage them to share their problems with the class.

See also the *Algebra 1 Toolkit* for more strategies.

383

6.4 EXERCISES

HOMEWORK KEY
○ = **WORKED-OUT SOLUTIONS**
on p. WS1 for Exs. 7, 11, and 41
★ = **STANDARDIZED TEST PRACTICE**
Exs. 2, 27, 39, and 45
◆ = **MULTIPLE REPRESENTATIONS**
Ex. 43

④ PRACTICE AND APPLY

Assignment Guide

📖 Answer Transparencies available for all exercises

Basic:
Day 1: pp. 384–387
Exs. 1–8, 23–27, 47–50, 55
Day 2: pp. 384–387
Exs. 9–22, 37–43, 51–54

Average:
Day 1: pp. 384–387
Exs. 1–8, 23–31, 48, 55
Day 2: pp. 384–387
Exs. 12–22, 32, 33, 39–45, 51–54

Advanced:
Day 1: pp. 384–387
Exs. 1, 2, 5–8, 23–32, 50, 55
Day 2: pp. 384–387
Exs. 13–20, 33–36*, 40–46*, 52, 54

Block:
pp. 384–387
Exs. 1–8, 23–31, 48, 55 (with 6.3)
pp. 384–387
Exs. 12–22, 32, 33, 39–45, 51–54
(with 6.5)

Differentiated Instruction

See *Algebra 1 Best Practices Toolkit* for suggestions on addressing the needs of a diverse classroom.

Homework Check

For a quick check of student understanding of key concepts, go over the following exercises:

Basic: 3, 7, 10, 18, 41
Average: 4, 8, 13, 19, 42
Advanced: 6, 8, 14, 20, 43

Extra Practice

• Student Edition, p. 943
• Chapter 6 Resource Book: Practice levels A, B, C, pp. 46–51

Practice Worksheet

An easily-readable reduced practice page (with answers) for this lesson can be found on p. 354C.

SKILL PRACTICE

[A] 1. **VOCABULARY** Copy and complete: A(n) _?_ is an inequality that consists of two inequalities joined by *and* or *or*. **compound inequality**

2. ★ **WRITING** *Describe* the difference between the graphs of $-6 \le x \le -4$ and $x \le -6$ *or* $x \ge -4$. **See margin.**

EXAMPLE 1
on p. 380
for Exs. 3–6

TRANSLATING VERBAL PHRASES **Translate the verbal phrase into an inequality. Then graph the inequality.** **3–6. See margin for art.**

3. All real numbers that are less than 6 *and* greater than 2 $2 < x < 6$

4. All real numbers that are less than or equal to -8 *or* greater than 12 $x \le -8$ or $x > 12$

5. All real numbers that are greater than or equal to -1.5 *and* less than 9.2 $-1.5 \le x < 9.2$

6. All real numbers that are greater than or equal to $-7\frac{1}{2}$ *or* less than or equal to -10 $x \le -10$ or $x \ge -7\frac{1}{2}$

EXAMPLE 2
on p. 381
for Exs. 7–8

WRITING AND GRAPHING INEQUALITIES **Write and graph an inequality that describes the situation.** **7, 8. See margin for art.**

⑦ The minimum speed on a highway is 40 miles per hour, and the maximum speed is 60 miles per hour. $40 \le s \le 60$

8. The temperature inside a room is uncomfortable if the temperature is lower than 60°F or higher than 75°F. $t < 60$ or $t > 75$

EXAMPLES 3, 4, and 5
on pp. 381–382
for Exs. 9–22

SOLVING COMPOUND INEQUALITIES **Solve the inequality. Graph your solution.** **9–20. See margin for art.**

9. $6 < x + 5 \le 11$ $1 < x \le 6$

10. $-7 > y - 8 \ge -12$ $-4 \le y < -1$

⑪ $-1 \le -4m \le 16$ $-4 \le m \le \frac{1}{4}$

12. $-6 < 3n + 9 < 21$ $-5 \le n < 4$

13. $-15 \le 5(3p - 2) < 20$ $-\frac{1}{3} \le p < 2$

14. $7 > \frac{2}{3}(6q + 18) \ge -9$ $-5\frac{1}{4} \le q < -1\frac{1}{4}$

15. $2r + 3 < 7$ *or* $-r + 9 \le 2$ $r < 2$ or $r \ge 7$

16. $16 < -s - 6$ *or* $2s + 5 \ge 11$ $s < -22$ or $s \ge 3$

17. $v + 13 < 8$ *or* $-8v < -40$ $v < -5$ or $v > 5$

18. $-14 > w + 3$ *or* $5w - 13 > w + 7$ $w < -17$ or $w > 5$

19. $9g - 6 > 12g + 1$ *or* $4 < -\frac{2}{5}g + 8$ $g < -2\frac{1}{3}$ or $g > 10$

20. $-2h - 7 > h + 5$ *or* $\frac{1}{4}(h + 8) \ge 9$ $h < -4$ or $h \ge 28$

ERROR ANALYSIS *Describe* and correct the error in solving the inequality or in graphing the solution. **21, 22. See margin for art.**

21.

22.

21. 3 was subtracted from only two of the three expressions of the inequality; $1 < -2x < 6$, $-\frac{1}{2} > x > -3$.

22. The graph should include the points of the number line to the left of -10 and to the right of 7, not the points between -10 and 7.

2. The graph of $-6 \le x \le -4$ consists of -6, -4, and all the points on the number line between -6 and -4. The graph of $x \le -6$ *or* $x \ge -4$ consists of -6 and all the points on the number line to the left of -6, along with -4 and all the points on the number line to the right of -4.

3.

4.

5.

6.

30. True; any solution of $x < 5$ *and* $x \ge -4$ lies between -4 and 5 on the number line, so it is to the left of 5 and is therefore a solution of $x < 5$.

385

43b.

°F	23	86	140	194	239
°C	−5	30	60	90	115

45c. 4800 watts; because each person requires at least 8 watts of amplification, and you want to be sure to provide enough amplification for 600 people, you need at least 8(600) = 4800 watts of amplification.

Quiz

1.

39. ★ MULTIPLE CHOICE The euro is the currency in several countries in Europe. In 2003, the dollar value of one euro ranged from $1.0361 to $1.2597. Which inequality represents the dollar values v that the euro was *not* worth during the year? **C**

(A) $1.0361 < v < 1.2597$ (B) $v < 1.0361 \text{ or } v > 1.2597$

(C) $1.0361 \le v \le 1.2597$ (D) $v \le 1.0361 \text{ or } v \ge 1.2597$

40. CURRENCY On October 25, 1865, the steamship *S.S. Republic* sank along with a cargo of gold and silver coins. The list gives the prices of several recovered gold coins. Use the least price and greatest price to write a compound inequality that describes the prices p of the coins. $5319 \le p \le 73{,}486$

Prices of Recovered Gold Coins

$9,098	$20,995	$9,798	$33,592	$12,597
$16,796	$9,798	$10,498	$5,319	$73,486
$11,897	$32,895	$7,349	$6,578	$29,395

41. ANIMALS A deer can eat 2% to 4% of its body weight in food per day. The percent p of the deer's body weight eaten in food is given by the equation $p = \dfrac{f}{d}$ where f is the amount (in pounds) of food eaten and d is the weight (in pounds) of the deer. Find the possible amounts of food that a 160 pound deer can eat per day. **3.2 lb ≤ f ≤ 6.4 lb**

42. SKIS A ski shop sells recreational skis with lengths ranging from 150 centimeters to 220 centimeters. The shop recommends that recreational skis be 1.16 times the skier's height (in centimeters). For which heights of skiers does the shop *not* provide recreational skis? **less than 129.31 cm or greater than 189.66 cm**

[B] **43. ◆ MULTIPLE REPRESENTATIONS** Water can exist as either a solid, a liquid, or a gas. The table shows the temperatures (in degrees Celsius) at which water can exist in each state.

State of water	Solid	Liquid	Gas
Temperatures (°C)	Less than 0	0 to 100	Greater than 100

a. **Writing an Inequality** Write and solve a compound inequality to find the temperatures (in degrees Fahrenheit) at which water is *not* a liquid. $\frac{5}{9}(F-32) < 0 \text{ or } \frac{5}{9}(F-32) > 100$, **F < 32°F or F > 212°F**

b. **Making a Table** Make a table that gives the temperature (in degrees Celsius) when the temperature (in degrees Fahrenheit) of water is 23°F, 86°F, 140°F, 194°F, and 239°F. For which temperatures in the table is water *not* a liquid? **23°F, 239°F; see margin for table.**

44. WEATHER Wind chill temperature describes how much colder it feels when the speed of the wind is combined with air temperature. At a wind speed of 20 miles per hour, the wind chill temperature w (in degrees Fahrenheit) can be given by the model $w = -22 + 1.3a$ where a is the air temperature (in degrees Fahrenheit). What are the possible air temperatures if the wind chill temperature ranges from −9°F to −2.5°F at a wind speed of 20 miles per hour? **from 10°F to 15°F**

○ = **WORKED-OUT SOLUTIONS** on p. WS1   ★ = **STANDARDIZED TEST PRACTICE**   ◆ = **MULTIPLE REPRESENTATIONS**

45a. $8 \le \dfrac{w}{300} \le 10$, $2400 \le w \le 3000$; 2400 watts to 3000 watts

45b. Yes; no; the amplification per person for 350 people is $\dfrac{2900}{350} \approx 8.3$ watts, which is between 8 watts and 10 watts, the amplification for 400 people is $\dfrac{2900}{400} = 7.25$ watts, which is not between 8 watts and 10 watts.

45. ★ **EXTENDED RESPONSE** Some musicians use audio amplifiers so that everyone in the audience can hear the performance. The amount y of amplification per person is given by the equation $y = \dfrac{w}{p}$ where w is the total amount (in watts) of amplification provided by the amplifier and p is the number of people in the audience.

   a. **Solve** Each person requires 8 watts to 10 watts of amplification. Write and solve an inequality to find the possible total amounts of amplification that an amplifier would need to provide for 300 people.

   b. **Decide** Will an amplifier that provides 2900 watts of amplification be strong enough for an audience of 350 people? 400 people? *Explain.*

   c. **Justify** Your band usually performs before an audience of 500 to 600 people. What is the least amount of amplification that your amplifier should provide? *Justify* your answer. **See margin.**

 Animated Algebra at classzone.com

[C] **46. CHALLENGE** You and three friends are planning to eat at a restaurant, and all of you agree to divide the total cost of the meals and the 15% tip equally. Each person agrees to pay at least $10 but no more than $20. How much can you spend altogether on meals before the tip is applied?
        from $34.78 up to $69.57

MIXED REVIEW

Evaluate the expression.

47. $14x$ when $x = 3$ *(p. 2)* **42**
     48. $6d^3$ when $d = 4$ *(p. 8)* **384**

49. $|m|$ when $m = -1$ *(p. 64)* **1**
     50. $-8t$ when $t = -5$ *(p. 88)* **40**

PREVIEW
Prepare for Lesson 6.5 in Exs. 51–54.

Solve the equation.

51. $8x - 14 = -16$ *(p. 134)* $-\dfrac{1}{4}$
     52. $2y + 8 + 5y = -1$ *(p. 141)* $-1\dfrac{2}{7}$

53. $4(f - 3) = -28$ *(p. 148)* **−4**
     54. $6r - 2 = 5r - 3$ *(p. 154)* **−1**

55. MUSEUMS You and some friends are taking a trip to a museum. Parking costs $15, and the price of a ticket is $14.50. Write an equation that gives the total cost C (in dollars) of the trip as a function of the number p of people who are going. *(p. 283)* $C = 14.5p + 15$

QUIZ *for Lessons 6.3–6.4*

Solve the inequality, if possible. Graph your solution. **1–8. See margin for art.**

1. $-\dfrac{1}{5}(x - 5) > x - 9$ *(p. 369)* $x < 8\dfrac{1}{3}$
     2. $\dfrac{1}{2}y - 8 \ge -2y + 3$ *(p. 369)* $y \ge 4\dfrac{2}{5}$

3. $-4r + 7 \le r + 10$ *(p. 369)* $r \ge -\dfrac{3}{5}$
     4. $-2(s + 6) \le -2s + 8$ *(p. 369)* **all real numbers**

5. $a - 4 \ge -1$ or $3a < -24$ *(p. 380)*
          $a < -8$ or $a \ge 3$
     6. $22 > -3c + 4 > 14$ *(p. 380)* $-6 < c < -3\dfrac{1}{3}$

7. $-27 \le 9m \le -18$ *(p. 380)*
          $-3 \le m \le -2$
     8. $5n + 2 > -18$ or $-3(n + 4) > 21$ *(p. 380)*
                       $n < -11$ or $n > -4$

EXTRA PRACTICE for Lesson 6.4, p. 943
     ⏺ **ONLINE QUIZ** at classzone.com
     387

6.4 Solve Compound Inequalities

QUESTION How can you use a graphing calculator to display the solutions of a compound inequality?

EXAMPLE Display the solutions of a compound inequality on a graphing calculator

Display the solutions of $12 \le 3x \le 21$ on a graphing calculator.

STEP 1 *Rewrite inequality*

Rewrite $12 \le 3x \le 21$ as two separate inequalities joined by *and*.

$12 \le 3x \le 21$	Write original inequality.
$12 \le 3x$ *and* $3x \le 21$	Write as two inequalities joined by *and*.

STEP 2 *Enter inequalities*

Press Y= and enter the two inequalities, as shown. Inequality signs can be found in the TEST menu, and *and* and *or* can be found in the LOGIC menu.

STEP 3 *Display solutions*

Press GRAPH to display the solutions of $12 \le 3x$ *and* $3x \le 21$. For each value of x that makes the inequality true, the calculator assigns a value of 1 to y and plots the point $(x, 1)$. For each value of x that makes the inequality false, the calculator assigns a value of 0 to y and plots the point $(x, 0)$.

The screen in Step 3 shows the graph of $y = 1$ over the interval $4 \le x \le 7$. This suggests that the solutions are all real numbers greater than or equal to 4 *and* less than or equal to 7.

DRAW CONCLUSIONS

1. Display the solutions of $12 < 3x < 21$ on a graphing calculator. Then compare the graph of $12 < 3x < 21$ with the graph of $12 \le 3x \le 21$. **$4 < x < 7$; the graphs are the same.**

2. When displaying the solutions of an inequality on a graphing calculator, how do you know which inequality symbols you should use in your solution?
   Use the inequality symbols from the original inequality.

Display the solutions of the inequality on a graphing calculator.

3. $9 \le 3x \le 21$ **$3 \le x \le 7$**
4. $4 < 4x < 8$ **$1 < x < 2$**
5. $2 \le \frac{1}{4}x \le 12$ **$8 \le x \le 48$**

6. $-6x > 18$ *or* $-9x < 45$
   $x < -3$ or $x > -5$
7. $4x \le 18$ *or* $5x \ge 25$
   $x \le 4\frac{1}{2}$ or $x \ge 5$
8. $8x \le 16$ *or* $3x \ge 30$
   $x \le 2$ or $x \ge 10$

Learn the Method

• Students will use a graphing calculator to solve compound inequalities.

• After the activity, students can use a graphing calculator to check their solutions in Exercises 9–20 and 33–36 in Lesson 6.4.

Keystroke Help

Keystrokes for several models of calculators are available in blackline format in the *Chapter 6 Resource Book*.

② TEACH

Tips for Success

Stress to students that the graphing calculator does not draw open or closed circles so they need to pay attention to the inequality symbols in the compound inequality.

Extra Example

Solve $-28 < -4x < 4$ using a graphing calculator. **all real numbers greater than −1 *and* less than 7**

③ ASSESS AND RETEACH

Solve $-5x \le -30$ *or* $-2x > 8$ using a graphing calculator. What inequality symbols should you use in your solution? Explain. **$\ge$ and $<$; you have to reverse both of the original inequality symbols because each solution involves dividing by a negative number.**

MIXED REVIEW of Problem Solving

Lessons 6.1–6.4

1. MULTI-STEP PROBLEM A nanotube thermometer is so tiny that it is invisible to the human eye. The thermometer can measure temperatures from 50°C to 500°C.
a–c. See margin.
   a. Write and solve a compound inequality to find the temperatures (in degrees Fahrenheit) that the thermometer can measure.

   b. Graph your solution of the inequality.

   c. Can the thermometer measure a temperature of 1000°F? *Explain.*

2. SHORT RESPONSE You earned the following scores on five science tests: 75, 82, 90, 84, and 71. You want to have an average score of at least 80 after you take the sixth test.
a–b. See margin.
   a. Write and solve an inequality to find the possible scores that you can earn on your sixth test in order to meet your goal.

   b. The greatest score that you can earn on a test is 100. Is it possible for you to have an average score of 90 after the sixth test? *Explain* your reasoning.

3. GRIDDED ANSWER You need at least 34 eggs to make enough chiffon cakes for a bake sale. Your grocery store sells cartons of eggs only by the dozen. Of all the possible numbers of cartons that you can buy, which is the least number? **3 cartons**

4. MULTI-STEP PROBLEM You have a $300 gift card to use at a sporting goods store.

   a. You want to use your card to buy 2 pairs of shoes for $85 each and several pairs of socks. Write and solve an inequality to find the possible amounts of money that you can spend on socks using your card.
   up to $130
   b. Suppose that socks cost $4.75 per pair. Write and solve an inequality to find the possible numbers of socks that you can buy using the card. **4.75$s \le$ 130;**
   up to 27 pairs of socks

5. OPEN-ENDED *Describe* a real-world situation that can be modeled by the inequality $17x \le 240$. *Explain* what the solution of the inequality means in this situation. **See margin.**

6. SHORT RESPONSE A rafting guide plans to take 6 adults on a rafting trip. The raft can hold up to 1520 pounds. The guide weighs 180 pounds and estimates that each adult will bring 10 pounds of baggage.

   a. Write and solve an inequality to find the possible average weights of an adult such that the raft will not exceed its maximum weight capacity. **at most $213\frac{1}{3}$ lb**

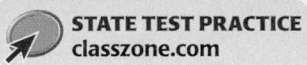

   b. Suppose that the weights of the adults range from 105 pounds to 200 pounds. Can the raft accommodate all the people and the baggage at one time? *Justify* your answer.
   See margin.

7. EXTENDED RESPONSE In 1862 the United States imposed a tax on annual income in order to pay for the expenses of the Civil War. The table shows the tax rates for different incomes.

Annual income	Tax rate
$600 to $10,000	3% of income
Greater than $10,000	3% of the first $10,000 plus 5% of income over $10,000

   a. Write a compound inequality that represents the possible taxes paid by a person whose annual income was at least $600 but not greater than $10,000. **$18 \le t \le 300$**

   b. For people whose taxes ranged from $400 to $750, tell whether their annual incomes were greater than $10,000 or less than $10,000. *Explain* how you know. Then find the possible annual incomes of those people. **See margin.**

   c. Suppose that the tax rate had been 4% of the total income for people whose annual incomes were greater than $10,000. For which incomes would paying the 4% rate have resulted in less taxes than paying the tax rate described above? *Explain.* **See margin.**

1a. from 122°F to 932°F

1b.

![number line from 0 to 1000 with points at 122 and 932]
122   932
0 200 400 600 800 1000

1c. No; the thermometer cannot measure temperatures higher than 932°F.

2a. $x \ge 78$

2b. No; with a score of 100 your average will be $\frac{402 + 100}{6} = \frac{502}{6} \approx 84$.

5. *Sample answer:* The solution $x \le 14.12$ means that the greatest number that will make the inequality true is 14.12.

6b. Yes; since the most the adults weigh is 200 pounds, and that is less than what the average weight needs to be, all the people and baggage can be accommodated on the raft.

7b. Greater than $10,000; their taxes are higher than $300, the highest tax paid by people with annual incomes of $10,000 or less; from $12,000 up to $19,000.

7c. Greater than $20,000; the inequality to describe the situation is $0.04x < 0.03(10,000) + 0.05(x - 10,000)$. Solving the inequality gives $x > \$20,000$.

1 PLAN AND PREPARE

Warm-Up Exercises

✎ Transparency Available

1. For $a = -12$, find $-a$ and $|a|$.
   12, 12

2. Evaluate $|x| - 2$ when $x = -3$. **1**

3. The change in elevation as a diver explored a reef was -0.5 feet, 1.5 feet, -2.5 feet, and 2.25 feet. Which change in elevation had the greatest absolute value? **-2.5 ft**

Notetaking Guide

✎ Transparency Available

Promotes interactive learning and notetaking skills, pp. 140–142.

Pacing

Basic: 2 days

Average: 2 days

Advanced: 2 days

Block: 0.5 block with 6.4
0.5 block with 6.6

• See *Teaching Guide/Lesson Plan*.

2 FOCUS AND MOTIVATE

Essential Question

Big Idea 2, p. 355

How do you solve absolute value equations? **Tell students they will learn how to answer this question by rewriting absolute value equations as two equations and then solving the equations.**

NCTM STANDARDS

Standard 2: Analyze situations using algebraic symbols

Standard 4: Understand the processes of measurement

Before	You solved linear equations.
Now	You will solve absolute value equations.
Why?	So you can analyze rules of a competition, as in Ex. 43.

Key Vocabulary
- **absolute value equation**
- **absolute deviation**
- **absolute value,** p. 66

The absolute value of a number a, written $|a|$, is the distance between a and 0 on a number line. An **absolute value equation**, such as $|x| = 4$, is an equation that contains an absolute value expression. The equation $|x| = 4$ means that the distance between x and 0 is 4. The solutions of the equation are 4 and -4, because they are the only numbers whose distance from 0 is 4.

EXAMPLE 1 Solve an absolute value equation

Solve $|x| = 7$.

Solution

The distance between x and 0 is 7. So, $x = 7$ or $x = -7$.

▶ The solutions are 7 and -7.

Animated Algebra at classzone.com

✓ GUIDED PRACTICE for Example 1

1. Solve (a) $|x| = 3$ and (b) $|x| = 15$.
   a. 3, -3
   b. 15, -15

SOLVING ABSOLUTE VALUE EQUATIONS In Example 1, notice that the expression inside the absolute value symbols equals 7 or the opposite of 7. This suggests the following rule for solving an absolute value equation.

KEY CONCEPT *For Your Notebook*

Solving an Absolute Value Equation

The equation $|ax + b| = c$ where $c \geq 0$ is equivalent to the statement $ax + b = c$ or $ax + b = -c$.

---

390 Chapter 6 Solving and Graphing Linear Inequalities

EXAMPLE 2   Solve an absolute value equation

Solve $|x - 3| = 8$.

Solution

Rewrite the absolute value equation as two equations. Then solve each equation separately.

$$|x - 3| = 8 \qquad \text{Write original equation.}$$
$$x - 3 = 8 \quad or \quad x - 3 = -8 \qquad \text{Rewrite as two equations.}$$
$$x = 11 \quad or \qquad x = -5 \qquad \text{Add 3 to each side.}$$

▶ The solutions are 11 and −5. Check your solutions.

CHECK	$|x - 3| = 8$	$|x - 3| = 8$	Write original inequality.
	$|11 - 3| \overset{?}{=} 8$	$|-5 - 3| \overset{?}{=} 8$	Substitute for *x*.
	$|8| \overset{?}{=} 8$	$|-8| \overset{?}{=} 8$	Subtract.
	$8 = 8 ✓$	$8 = 8 ✓$	Simplify. The solution checks.

REWRITING EQUATIONS To solve an absolute value equation, you may first need to rewrite the equation in the form $|ax + b| = c$.

EXAMPLE 3   Rewrite an absolute value equation

Solve $3|2x - 7| - 5 = 4$.

Solution

First, rewrite the equation in the form $|ax + b| = c$.

$$3|2x - 7| - 5 = 4 \qquad \text{Write original equation.}$$
$$3|2x - 7| = 9 \qquad \text{Add 5 to each side.}$$
$$|2x - 7| = 3 \qquad \text{Divide each side by 3.}$$

Next, solve the absolute value equation.

$$|2x - 7| = 3 \qquad \text{Write absolute value equation.}$$
$$2x - 7 = 3 \quad or \quad 2x - 7 = -3 \qquad \text{Rewrite as two equations.}$$
$$2x = 10 \quad or \qquad 2x = 4 \qquad \text{Add 7 to each side.}$$
$$x = 5 \quad or \qquad x = 2 \qquad \text{Divide each side by 2.}$$

▶ The solutions are 5 and 2.

 Animated Algebra at classzone.com

 GUIDED PRACTICE   for Examples 2 and 3

Solve the equation.

2. $|r - 7| = 9$ **16, −2**

3. $2|s| + 4.1 = 18.9$ **7.4, −7.4**

4. $4|t + 9| - 5 = 19$ **−3, −15**

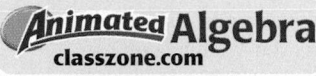

NO SOLUTIONS The absolute value of a number is never negative. So, when an absolute value expression equals a negative number, there are *no solutions*.

EXAMPLE 4 Decide if an equation has no solutions

Solve $|3x + 5| + 6 = -2$, if possible.

$|3x + 5| + 6 = -2$	Write original equation.
$|3x + 5| = -8$	Subtract 6 from each side.

▶ The absolute value of a number is never negative. So, there are no solutions.

ABSOLUTE DEVIATION The **absolute deviation** of a number x from a given value is the absolute value of the difference of x and the given value:

absolute deviation = $|x - \text{given value}|$.

EXAMPLE 5 Use absolute deviation

BASKETBALLS Before the start of a professional basketball game, a basketball must be inflated to an air pressure of 8 pounds per square inch (psi) with an absolute error of 0.5 psi. (*Absolute error* is the absolute deviation of a measured value from an accepted value.) Find the minimum and maximum acceptable air pressures for the basketball.

Solution

Let p be the air pressure (in psi) of a basketball. Write a verbal model. Then write and solve an absolute value equation.

Absolute error	=		Measured air pressure	−	Accepted air pressure	
0.5	=		p	−	8	

$0.5 = |p - 8|$	Write original equation.
$0.5 = p - 8$ or $-0.5 = p - 8$	Rewrite as two equations.
$8.5 = p$ or $7.5 = p$	Add 8 to each side.

▶ The minimum and maximum acceptable pressures are 7.5 psi and 8.5 psi.

✓ **GUIDED PRACTICE** for Examples 4 and 5

Solve the equation, if possible.

5. $2|m - 5| + 4 = 2$ **no solution**   6. $-3|n + 2| - 7 = -10$ **−1, −3**

7. The absolute deviation of x from 7.6 is 5.2. What are the values of x that satisfy this requirement?   **12.8, 2.4**

6.5 EXERCISES

SKILL PRACTICE

[A] 1. **VOCABULARY** Copy and complete: The equation $|x - 7| = 0.15$ is an example of a(n) __?__ . **absolute value equation**

2. ★ **WRITING** Given $|x - 9| = 5$, describe the relationship between x, 9, and 5 using absolute deviation. **The absolute deviation of x from 9 is 5.**

EXAMPLES 1, 2, and 3
on pp. 390–391
for Exs. 3–20

SOLVING EQUATIONS Solve the equation.

3. $|x| = 5$ **5, −5**

4. $|y| = 36$ **36, −36**

5. $|v| = 0.7$ **0.7, −0.7**

6. $|w| = 9.2$ **9.2, −9.2**

7. $|r| = \frac{1}{2}$ **$\frac{1}{2}, -\frac{1}{2}$**

8. $|s| = \frac{7}{4}$ **$\frac{7}{4}, -\frac{7}{4}$**

9. $|m + 3| = 7$ **4, −10**

10. $|4n - 5| = 18$ **$5\frac{3}{4}, -3\frac{1}{4}$**

⑪. $|3p + 7| = 4$ **$-1, -3\frac{2}{3}$**

12. $|q + 8| = 2$ **−7, −11**

13. $|2d + 7| = 11$ **2, −9**

14. $|f - 8| = 14$ **22, −6**

15. $3|13 - 2t| = 15$ **4, 9**

16. $4|b - 1| - 7 = 17$ **7, −5**

17. $\frac{1}{3}|2c - 5| + 3 = 7$ **$8\frac{1}{2}, -3\frac{1}{2}$**

18. $\frac{7}{4}|3j + 5| + 1 = 15$ **$1, -4\frac{1}{3}$**

19. $4|2k + 3| - 2 = 6$ **$-\frac{1}{2}, -2\frac{1}{2}$**

20. $-3|5g + 1| - 6 = -9$ **$0, -\frac{2}{5}$**

ERROR ANALYSIS *Describe* and correct the error in solving the absolute value equation.

21.
$$|x + 4| = 13$$
$$x + 4 = 13$$
$$x = 9$$

22.
$$|x - 6| = -2$$
$$x - 6 = -2 \text{ or } x - 6 = 2$$
$$x = 4 \quad \text{or} \quad x = 8$$

EXAMPLE 4
on p. 392
for Exs. 23–31

SOLVING EQUATIONS Solve the equation, if possible.

㉓. $|x - 1| + 5 = 2$ **no solution**

24. $|y - 4| + 8 = 6$ **no solution**

25. $|m + 5| + 1.5 = 2$ **−4.5, −5.5**

26. $-4|8 - 5n| = 13$ **no solution**

27. $-3|1 - \frac{2}{3}v| = -9$ **−3, 6**

28. $-5|\frac{4}{5}w + 6| = -10$ **−5, −10**

29. $-10|14 - r| - 2 = -7$ **$13\frac{1}{2}, 14\frac{1}{2}$**

30. $-2|\frac{1}{3}s - 5| + 3 = 8$ **no solution**

31. $-9|4p + 2| - 8 = -35$ **$\frac{1}{4}, -1\frac{1}{4}$**

32. ★ **MULTIPLE CHOICE** Which number is a solution of $|4x - 1| + 2 = 1$? **D**

Ⓐ $-\frac{1}{2}$ Ⓑ 0 Ⓒ 1 Ⓓ There is no solution.

EXAMPLE 5
on p. 392
for Exs. 33–36

USING ABSOLUTE DEVIATION Find the values of x that satisfy the definition of absolute deviation for the given value and the given absolute deviation.

33. Given value: 5;
absolute deviation: 8 **13, −3**

34. Given value: 20;
absolute deviation: 5 **25, 15**

35. Given value: −9.1;
absolute deviation: 1.6 **−7.5, −10.7**

36. Given value: −3.4;
absolute deviation: 6.7 **3.3, −10.1**

21. The absolute value symbol was removed without writing the second equation, $x + 4 = -13$; $x = 9$ or $x = -17$.

22. The absolute value of a number is never negative, so it is incorrect to rewrite this absolute value equation as two equations; there are no solutions.

Differentiated Instruction

Below Level Some students may need help in determining whether they can solve **Exercises 23–31**. Demonstrate strategies they can use to determine whether the absolute value equation is equal to a negative number and, thus, has no solution. In **Exercise 24**, point out that the right side becomes $6 - 8$, and in **Exercise 26**, point out that the right side becomes $\frac{13}{-4}$. Have students use these strategies to identify all the exercises that have no solutions.

See also the *Algebra 1 Toolkit* for more strategies.

---

④ **PRACTICE AND APPLY**

Assignment Guide

☐ **Answer Transparencies** available for all exercises

Basic:
Day 1: EP p. 940 Exs. 12–20
pp. 393–395
Exs. 1–22, 51–53
Day 2: pp. 393–395
Exs. 23–37, 42–47, 54–59

Average:
Day 1: pp. 393–395
Exs. 1, 2, 6–17, 37–40, 51–53
Day 2: pp. 393–395
Exs. 21–36, 42–49, 54–59

Advanced:
Day 1: pp. 393–395
Exs. 1, 2, 6–8, 12–20, 37–41*, 54–59
Day 2: pp. 393–395
Exs. 24–36, 43–50*, 54–58 even

Block:
pp. 393–395
Exs. 1, 2, 6–17, 37–40, 51–53
(with 6.4)
pp. 393–395
Exs. 21–36, 42–49, 54–59 (with 6.6)

Differentiated Instruction

See *Algebra 1 Best Practices Toolkit* for suggestions on addressing the needs of a diverse classroom.

Homework Check

For a quick check of student understanding of key concepts, go over the following exercises:

Basic: 4, 10, 16, 24, 42
Average: 6, 12, 18, 26, 44
Advanced: 8, 14, 20, 30, 45

Extra Practice

• Student Edition, p. 943
• Chapter 6 Resource Book:
Practice levels A, B, C, pp. 60–62

Practice Worksheet

An easily-readable reduced practice page (with answers) for this lesson can be found on p. 354C.

B **37.** **SOLVING AN EQUATION** Interpreted geometrically, the equation $|x - a| = b$ means that the distance between x and a on a number line is b. Solve $|x - 3| = 7$ both geometrically and algebraically. *Compare* your solutions. **The distance between x and 3 is 7, 10, −4; $x − 3 = 7$ or $x − 3 = −7$, 10, −4; the solutions are the same.**

TRANSLATING SENTENCES In Exercises 38 and 39, write the verbal sentence as an absolute value equation. Then solve the equation.

38. Four more than the absolute deviation of x from 3 is 8. $|x − 3| + 4 = 8$; **7, −1**

39. Five times the absolute deviation of $2x$ from $−9$ is 15. $5|2x + 9| = 15$; **−3, −6**

40. **REASONING** Is $a|x|$ equivalent to $|ax|$ when a is positive? when a is negative? when a is 0? Give examples to support your answers. **See margin.**

C **41.** **CHALLENGE** How many solutions does the equation $a|x + b| + c = d$ have if $a > 0$ and $c = d$? if $a < 0$ and $c > d$? **one, two**

PROBLEM SOLVING

EXAMPLE 5 **A**
on p. 392
for Exs. 42–46

40. Yes; no; yes;
when $a = 3$ and
$x = −2, 3|−2| =$
$3(2) = 6 =$
$|−6| = |3(−2)|$;
when $a = −3$
and $x = −2$,
$−3|−2| =$
$−3(2) = −6 \neq$
$|6| = |−3(−2)|$;
when $a = 0$ and x
$= −2, 0|−2| = 0$
$= |0| = |0(−2)|$.

42. **GUARDRAILS** A safety regulation requires that the height of a guardrail be 42 inches with an absolute deviation of 3 inches. Find the minimum and maximum heights of a guardrail. **39 in., 45 in**

@HomeTutor for problem solving help at classzone.com

43. **CHEERLEADING** A cheerleading team is preparing a dance program for a competition. The program must last 4 minutes with an absolute deviation of 5 seconds. Find the least and greatest possible times (in seconds) that the program can last. **235 sec, 245 sec**

@HomeTutor for problem solving help at classzone.com

44. ★ **MULTIPLE CHOICE** The diameter of a billiard ball must be 2.25 inches with an absolute error of 0.005 inch. What is the maximum possible diameter that a billiard ball can have? **C**

(A) 2.2 inches **(B)** 2.245 inches **(C)** 2.255 inches **(D)** 2.3 inches

45. **SPORTS** In gymnastics meets last year, the mean of your friend's least and greatest scores was 54.675 points. The absolute deviation of his least and greatest scores from the mean was 2.213 points.

a. What were the least and greatest scores that he earned? **52.462 points, 56.888 points**

b. This year the mean of his least and greatest scores is 56.738 points, and the absolute deviation of the least and greatest scores from the mean is 0.45 point. How many points more than last year's greatest score is this year's greatest score? **0.3 point**

46. **JEWELRY** A jewelry store advertisement states that a certain diamond bracelet weighs 12 carats, but the actual weight can vary by as much as 5% of the advertised weight. Find the minimum and maximum possible weights of the bracelet. **11.4 carats, 12.6 carats**

○ = **WORKED-OUT SOLUTIONS** on p. WS1   ★ = **STANDARDIZED TEST PRACTICE**

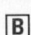

47. **CONTESTS** You currently have 450 points in an academic contest. You choose the value p of the question you want to answer. The value p represents the absolute deviation of your new score s from 450.

   a. Write an absolute value equation that gives p in terms of s. $p = |s - 450|$

   b. If you choose a question worth 150 points, what are the possible new scores that you can have after answering the question? **300 points, 600 points**

48. ★ **EXTENDED RESPONSE** The percent p of United States residents who were foreign born, or born outside of the United States, during the period 1910–2000 can be modeled by the equation $p = 0.165|t - 60| + 4.8$ where t is the number of years since 1910.

   a. **Approximate** During the period 1910–2000, in approximately what year did foreign-born residents account for 13% of all residents? **1920**

   b. **Predict** If the model holds for years after 2000, predict the year in which foreign-born residents will again account for 13% of all residents. **2019**

   c. **Decide** According to the model, did foreign-born residents account for 4% of all residents at any time during the period 1910–2000? *Explain* your answer. **No; if you substitute 4 for p in the model, the equation has no solution.**

49. ★ **SHORT RESPONSE** A stock's average price p (in dollars) during the period February 2005 to October 2005 can be modeled by the equation $p = 2.3|m - 7| + 9.57$ where m is the number of months since February 2005.

49b. Yes; make a table of values for (m, p) using integer values of m from 0 to 8. Look for the lowest value of p in the table.

   a. **Approximate** In approximately what month and year was the average price $16.15? If the model holds for months after October 2005, predict the month and year in which the average price will again be $16.15. **June 2005; November 2005**

   b. **Justify** Is it possible to use the model to estimate the stock's lowest average price during this period? *Justify* your answer.

C 50. **CHALLENGE** In a recent Olympics, swimmers in a men's 200 meter butterfly event finished with times from 1 minute 54.04 seconds to 1 minute 57.48 seconds. Let t represent the slowest or fastest time (in seconds). Write an absolute value equation that describes the situation. $|t - 115.76| \le 1.72$

MIXED REVIEW

Write an equation of the line shown. *(p. 283)*

51. $y = \frac{2}{3}x - 1$

52. $y = -\frac{1}{2}x + 2$

53. $y = -\frac{2}{3}x - \frac{5}{3}$

51.

52.

53.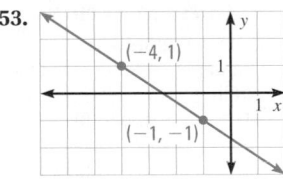

PREVIEW
Prepare for Lesson 6.6 in Exs. 54–59.

Solve the inequality. Graph your solution. 54–59. See margin for art.

54. $r + 7 \ge 28$ *(p. 356)* $r \ge 21$

55. $-\frac{1}{2}s > -8$ *(p. 363)* $s < 16$

56. $-6t + 7 \le 15$ *(p. 369)* $t \ge -1\frac{1}{3}$

57. $-5(v - 2) < -16$ *(p. 369)* $v > 5\frac{1}{5}$

58. $-14 < 1 - 5w < 12$ *(p. 380)* $-2\frac{1}{5} < w < 3$

59. $-3x > 9$ or $4x \ge 8$ *(p. 380)* $x < -3$ or $x \ge 2$

EXTRA PRACTICE for Lesson 6.5, p. 943   ⊘ **ONLINE QUIZ** at classzone.com   **395**

---

5 ASSESS AND RETEACH

Daily Homework Quiz

 Transparency Available

Solve the equation, if possible.

1. $|x - 4| = 13$ **−9, 17**

2. $|x + 2| + 7 = 3$ **no solutions**

3. $|2x - 6| + 4 = 20$ **−5, 11**

4. $-2|x - 5| + 7 = 12$ **no solutions**

5. A pattern for a 26-inch skirt allows for an absolute deviation of 1.5 inches. Find the minimum and maximum skirt lengths that can be made from the pattern. **minimum: 24.5 in.; maximum: 27.5 in.**

 Online Quiz

Available at **classzone.com**

Diagnosis/Remediation

- Practice A, B, C in Chapter 6 Resource Book, pp. 60–62
- Study Guide in Chapter 6 Resource Book, pp. 63–64
- Practice Workbook, pp. 96–97
- @HomeTutor

Challenge

Additional challenge is available in the Chapter 6 Resource Book, p. 67.

54.

55.

56.

57.

58.

59.

395

Graph Absolute Value Functions

Key Vocabulary
• absolute value, p. 66

GOAL Graph absolute value functions.

The function $f(x) = |x|$ is an example of an *absolute value function* and is the parent function for all absolute value functions. You can graph absolute value functions by using a table of values, as shown below for $f(x) = |x|$.

KEY CONCEPT   *For Your Notebook*

Graph of Parent Function for Absolute Value Functions

x	$f(x) = |x|$
−2	$|-2| = 2$
−1	$|-1| = 1$
0	$|0| = 0$
1	$|1| = 1$
2	$|2| = 2$

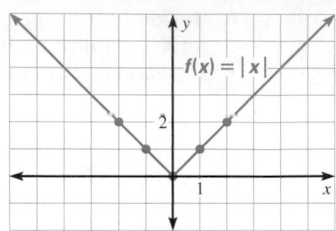

EXAMPLE 1   Graph $g(x) = |x - h|$ and $g(x) = |x| + k$

Graph each function. Compare the graph with the graph of $f(x) = |x|$.

a. $g(x) = |x - 2|$

STEP 1 Make a table of values.

x	0	1	2	3	4
$g(x)$	2	1	0	1	2

STEP 2 Graph the function.

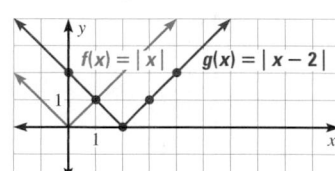

STEP 3 Compare the graphs of g and f. The graph of $g(x) = |x - 2|$ is 2 units to the right of the graph of $f(x) = |x|$.

b. $g(x) = |x| - 1$

STEP 1 Make a table of values.

x	−2	−1	0	1	2
$g(x)$	1	0	−1	0	1

STEP 2 Graph the function.

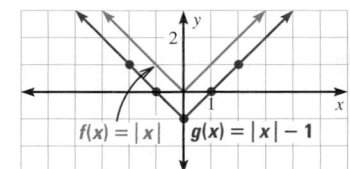

STEP 3 Compare the graphs of g and f. The graph of $g(x) = |x| - 1$ is 1 unit below the graph of $f(x) = |x|$.

APPLY TRANSFORMATIONS

The two graphs in Example 1 are translations of the graph of $f(x) = |x|$. The graph in part (a) is a horizontal translation. The graph in part (b) is a vertical translation.

EXAMPLE 2 **Graph** $g(x) = a|x|$

Graph each function. Compare the graph with the graph of $f(x) = |x|$

a. $g(x) = 4|x|$

STEP 1 **Make** a table of values.

x	−2	−1	0	1	2
g(x)	8	4	0	4	8

APPLY TRANSFORMATIONS
The graph in part (a) of Example 2 is a vertical stretch of the graph of $f(x) = |x|$. The graph in part (b) is a vertical shrink with a reflection in the x-axis of the graph of $f(x) = |x|$.

STEP 2 **Graph** the function.

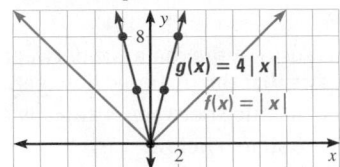

STEP 3 **Compare** the graphs of g and f. The graph of $g(x) = 4|x|$ opens up and is narrower than the graph of $f(x) = |x|$.

b. $g(x) = -0.5|x|$

STEP 1 **Make** a table of values.

x	−4	−2	0	2	4
g(x)	−2	−1	0	−1	−2

STEP 2 **Graph** the function.

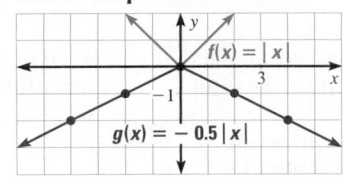

STEP 3 **Compare** the graphs of g and f. The graph of $g(x) = -0.5|x|$ opens down and is wider than the graph of $f(x) = |x|$.

KEY CONCEPT *For Your Notebook*

Comparing Graphs of Absolute Value Functions with the Graph of $f(x) = |x|$

$g(x) = |x - h|$	$g(x) = |x| + k$	$g(x) = a|x|$
If $h > 0$, the graph of g is $|h|$ units to the right of the graph of $f(x) = |x|$. If $h < 0$, the graph of g is $|h|$ units to the left of the graph of $f(x) = |x|$.	If $k > 0$, the graph of g is $|k|$ units above the graph of $f(x) = |x|$. If $k < 0$, the graph of g is $|k|$ units below the graph of $f(x) = |x|$.	If $|a| > 1$, the graph of g is narrower than the graph of $f(x) = |x|$. If $0 < |a| < 1$, the graph of g is wider. If $a > 0$, the graph of g opens up. If $a < 0$, the graph opens down.

PRACTICE

EXAMPLES 1 and 2
on pp. 396–397
for Exs. 1–6

Graph the function. *Compare* the graph with the graph of $f(x) = |x|$. 1–6. See margin.

1. $g(x) = |x + 3|$
2. $g(x) = |x| + 5$
3. $g(x) = |x| - 7$
4. $g(x) = 2|x|$
5. $g(x) = 0.6|x|$
6. $g(x) = -3|x|$

7. Make a table of values for $g(x) = 2|x - 3| + 4$. Use the following values for x: 1, 2, 3, 4, 5. Then graph the function and compare the graph with the graph of $f(x) = |x|$. **See margin.**

1–6. See Additional Answers beginning on p. AA1.

7.
x	1	2	3	4	5
g(x)	8	6	4	6	8

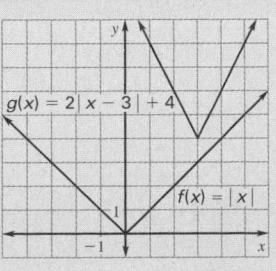

See graph at right. The graph of g is the graph of f moved 3 units right and 4 units up, and made narrower.

Extra Example 2
Graph each function. Compare the graph with the graph of $f(x) = |x|$.

a. $g(x) = -2|x|$

The graph opens down and is narrower than the graph of $f(x) = |x|$.

b. $g(x) = 0.5|x|$

The graph is wider than the graph of $f(x) = |x|$.

Closing the Lesson
Have students summarize the major points of the lesson and answer the Essential Question: How do you graph absolute value functions?

- **Absolute value functions are transformations of the parent function** $f(x) = |x|$.

Make a table of values for the function. Plot points and connect them.

④ PRACTICE AND APPLY

Avoiding Common Errors
Exercises 1–7 Some students may make a table of values for one side of the function only. Have them start in the middle of the table with an x value that gives 0 for the expression inside the absolute value symbols. Then assign x values on each side of that first value.

6.6 Solve Absolute Value Inequalities

 You solved absolute value equations.

 You will solve absolute value inequalities.

Why So you can analyze softball compression, as in Ex. 38.

Key Vocabulary
• **absolute value,** p. 66
• **equivalent inequalities,** p. 357
• **compound inequality,** p. 380
• **absolute deviation,** p. 391
• **mean,** p. 918

Recall that $|x| = 3$ means that the distance between x and 0 is 3. The inequality $|x| < 3$ means that the distance between x and 0 is *less than* 3, and $|x| > 3$ means that the distance between x and 0 is *greater than* 3. The graphs of $|x| < 3$ and $|x| > 3$ are shown below.

Graph of $|x| < 3$

Graph of $|x| > 3$

EXAMPLE 1 Solve absolute value inequalities

Solve the inequality. Graph your solution.

a. $|x| \geq 6$ **b.** $|x| \leq 0.5$

Solution

a. The distance between x and 0 is greater than or equal to 6. So, $x \leq -6$ *or* $x \geq 6$.

▶ The solutions are all real numbers less than or equal to −6 *or* greater than or equal to 6.

b. The distance between x and 0 is less than or equal to 0.5. So, $-0.5 \leq x \leq 0.5$.

▶ The solutions are all real numbers greater than or equal to −0.5 *and* less than or equal to 0.5.

✓ GUIDED PRACTICE for Example 1

Solve the inequality. Graph your solution.   **1–3. See margin for art.**

1. $|x| \leq 8$ **−8 ≤ x ≤ 8**   **2.** $|u| < 3.5$ **−3.5 < u < 3.5**   **3.** $|v| > \frac{2}{3}$ **$v < -\frac{2}{3}$ or $v > \frac{2}{3}$**

SOLVING ABSOLUTE VALUE INEQUALITIES In Example 1, the solutions of $|x| \geq 6$ and $|x| \leq 0.5$ suggest that you can rewrite an absolute value inequality as a compound inequality.

398   Chapter 6   Solving and Graphing Linear Inequalities

KEY CONCEPT   *For Your Notebook*

Solving Absolute Value Inequalities

- The inequality $|ax + b| < c$ where $c > 0$ is equivalent to the compound inequality $-c < ax + b < c$.

- The inequality $|ax + b| > c$ where $c > 0$ is equivalent to the compound inequality $ax + b < -c$ or $ax + b > c$.

In the inequalities above, $<$ can be replaced by $\le$ and $>$ can be replaced by $\ge$.

EXAMPLE 2 Solve an absolute value inequality

Solve $|x - 5| \ge 7$. Graph your solution.

$\|x - 5\| \ge 7$	Write original inequality.
$x - 5 \le -7$ *or* $x - 5 \ge 7$	Rewrite as compound inequality.
$x \le -2$ *or* $x \ge 12$	Add 5 to each side.

▶ The solutions are all real numbers less than or equal to -2 *or* greater than or equal to 12. Check several solutions in the original inequality.

EXAMPLE 3 Solve an absolute value inequality

Solve $|-4x - 5| + 3 < 9$. Graph your solution.

$\|-4x - 5\| + 3 < 9$	Write original inequality.
$\|-4x - 5\| < 6$	Subtract 3 from each side.
$-6 < -4x - 5 < 6$	Rewrite as compound inequality.
$-1 < -4x < 11$	Add 5 to each expression.
$0.25 > x > -2.75$	Divide each expression by -4. Reverse inequality symbol.
$-2.75 < x < 0.25$	Rewrite in the form $a < x < b$.

▶ The solutions are all real numbers greater than -2.75 *and* less than 0.25.

Animated Algebra at classzone.com

✓ **GUIDED PRACTICE** for Examples 2 and 3

Solve the inequality. Graph your solution. 4–6. See margin for art.

4. $|x + 3| > 8$ 　　　　**5.** $|2w - 1| < 11$ 　　　**6.** $3|5m - 6| - 8 \le 13$

$x < -11$ or $x > 5$ 　　　　$-5 < w < 6$ 　　　　　$-0.2 \le m \le 2.6$

Motivating the Lesson

Knowing how to solve absolute value inequalities can help you analyze statistical data. For example, if you know that 582 people in a poll voted for a candidate and the poll has a 2% margin of error, you can determine the least and greatest number of people who voted for the candidate.

3 TEACH

Extra Example 1

Solve the inequality. Graph your solution.

a. $|x| > 2$ **all real numbers less than -2 *or* greater than 2**

b. $|x| < 1.5$ **all real numbers greater than -1.5 *and* less than 1.5**

Extra Example 2

Solve $|x + 2| > 1$. Graph your solution. **all real numbers less than -3 *or* greater than -1**

Extra Example 3

Solve $|2x + 3| - 4 \le 5$. Graph your solution. **all real numbers greater than or equal to -6 *and* less than or equal to 3**

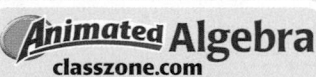
Animated Algebra
classzone.com

An **Animated Algebra** activity is available on-line for **Example 3**. This activity is also available on the **Power Presentations CD-ROM**.

1.

2.

3.

4.

5.

6.

EXAMPLE 4 Solve a multi-step problem

COMPUTERS You are buying a new computer and find 10 models in a store advertisement. The prices are $890, $750, $650, $370, $660, $670, $450, $650, $725, and $825.

- Find the mean of the computer prices.
- You are willing to pay the mean price with an absolute deviation of at most $100. How many of the computer prices meet your condition?

Solution

STEP 1 Find the mean by dividing the sum of the prices by 10.

REVIEW MEAN
For help with finding a mean, see p. 918.

$$\text{Mean} = \frac{890 + 750 + 650 + 370 + 660 + 670 + 450 + 650 + 725 + 825}{10}$$

$$= \frac{6640}{10} = 664$$

STEP 2 Write and solve an inequality. An absolute deviation of at most $100 from the mean, $664, is given by the inequality $|x - 664| \leq 100$.

$|x - 664| \leq 100$	**Write absolute value inequality.**
$-100 \leq x - 664 \leq 100$	**Write as compound inequality.**
$564 \leq x \leq 764$	**Add 664 to each expression.**

▶ The prices you will consider must be at least $564 and at most $764. Six prices meet your condition: $750, $650, $660, $670, $650, and $725.

✓ **GUIDED PRACTICE** for Example 4

7. **WHAT IF?** In Example 4, suppose that you are willing to pay the mean price with an absolute deviation of at most $75. How many of the computer prices meet this condition? **5 computer prices**

CONCEPT SUMMARY   *For Your Notebook*

Solving Inequalities

One-Step and Multi-Step Inequalities

- Follow the steps for solving an equation, but reverse the inequality symbol when multiplying or dividing by a negative number.

Compound Inequalities

- If necessary, rewrite the inequality as two separate inequalities. Then solve each inequality separately. Include *and* or *or* in the solution.

Absolute Value Inequalities

- If necessary, isolate the absolute value expression on one side of the inequality. Rewrite the absolute value inequality as a compound inequality. Then solve the compound inequality.

7.
10.
11.

12.
13.
14.

6.6 EXERCISES

HOMEWORK KEY
○ = WORKED-OUT SOLUTIONS
on p. WS1 for Exs. 9, 15, and 37

★ = STANDARDIZED TEST PRACTICE
Exs. 2, 21, 22, 37, and 40

◆ = MULTIPLE REPRESENTATIONS
Ex. 38

SKILL PRACTICE

[A] 1. **VOCABULARY** Copy and complete: The inequalities $|x| > 8$ and $x > 8 \ or \ x < -8$ are __?__. equivalent inequalities

2. ★ **WRITING** *Describe* the difference between solving $|x| \le 5$ and solving $|x| \ge 5$. Solving $|x| \le 5$ involves solving a compound inequality with *and*, while solving $|x| \ge 5$ involves solving a compound inequality with *or*.

EXAMPLES 1, 2, and 3 on pp. 398–399 for Exs. 3–24

SOLVING INEQUALITIES Solve the inequality. Graph your solution. 3–20. See margin for art.

3. $|x| < 4 \quad -4 < x < 4$

4. $|y| \ge 3 \quad y \le -3 \ or \ y \ge 3$

5. $|h| > 4.5$
$h < -4.5 \ or \ h > 4.5$

6. $|p| < 1.3 \quad -1.3 < p < 1.3$

7. $|t| \le \frac{3}{5} \quad -\frac{3}{5} \le t \le \frac{3}{5}$

8. $|j| \ge 1\frac{3}{4} \quad j \le 1\frac{3}{4} \ or \ j \ge 1\frac{3}{4}$

9. $|d + 4| \ge 3 \quad d \le -7 \ or \ d \ge -1$

10. $|b - 5| < 10 \quad -5 < b < 15$

11. $|14 - m| > 6 \quad m < -20$
or $m > 8$

12. $|2s - 7| < 1 \quad 3 < s < 4$

13. $|4c + 5| \ge 7 \quad c \le -3 \ or \ c \ge \frac{1}{2}$

14. $|9 - 4n| \le 5$
$1 \le n \le 3.5$

15. $5\left|\frac{1}{2}r + 3\right| > 5 \quad r < -8 \ or \ r > -4$

16. $\left|\frac{4}{3}s - 7\right| - 8 > 3$
$s < -3 \ or \ s > 13\frac{1}{2}$

17. $-3\left|2 - \frac{5}{4}u\right| \le -18$
$u \le -3\frac{1}{5} \ or \ u \ge 6\frac{2}{5}$

18. $2|3w + 8| - 13 < -5$
$-4 < w < -1\frac{1}{3}$

19. $2\left|\frac{1}{4}v - 5\right| - 4 > 3$
$v < 6 \ or \ v > 34$

20. $\frac{2}{7}|4f + 6| - 2 \ge 10$
$f \le -12 \ or \ f \ge 9$

21. ★ **MULTIPLE CHOICE** Which inequality is equivalent to $x < 1 \ or \ x > 5$? **B**

Ⓐ $|x + 8| - 2 > 10$

Ⓑ $3|6 - 2x| > 12$

Ⓒ $|5x + 9| < 10$

Ⓓ $|7 - 4x| - 9 < 8$

22. ★ **WRITING** How can you tell whether an absolute value inequality is equivalent to a compound inequality with *and* or to a compound inequality with *or*?

ERROR ANALYSIS *Describe* and correct the error in solving the inequality.

23.

$|x + 4| > 13$
$13 > x + 4 > -13$
$9 > x > -17$

24.
$|x - 5| < 20$
$x - 5 < 20$
$x < 25$

[B] **TRANSLATING SENTENCES** Write the verbal sentence as an inequality. Then solve the inequality and graph your solution. 25–28. See margin for art.

25. The absolute deviation of x from 6 is less than or equal to 4. $|x - 6| \le 4; 2 \le x \le 10$

26. The absolute deviation of $2x$ from -7 is greater than or equal to 15. $|2x + 7| \ge 15; x \le -11 \ or \ x \ge 4$

27. Three more than the absolute deviation of $-4x$ from 7 is greater than 10. $|-4x - 7| + 3 > 10; x < -3.5 \ or \ x > 0$

28. Four times the absolute deviation of x from 9 is less than 8. $4|x - 9| < 8; 7 < x < 11$

Margin notes (left column):

22. When the inequality has the absolute value expression isolated on the left side, the equivalent compound inequality will use *and* if the symbol is < or ≤, and it will use *or* if the symbol is > or ≥.

23. The compound inequality should use *or*: $x + 4 > 13$ or $x + 4 < -13$; $x > 9 \ or \ x < -17$.

24. Part of the compound inequality is missing; the compound inequality should be $-20 < x - 5 < 20; -15 < x < 25$.

④ PRACTICE AND APPLY

Assignment Guide
📖 Answer Transparencies available for all exercises

Basic:
Day 1: SRH p. 918 Exs. 1–5
pp. 401–403
Exs. 1, 2, 3–21 odd, 22–28, 35–38, 42–52 even

Average:
Day 1: pp. 401–403
Exs. 1, 2, 6–20 even, 21–24, 25–31 odd, 35–40, 45–50

Advanced:
Day 1: pp. 401–403
Exs. 1, 6–20 even, 21, 22, 26–32 even, 33*, 34*, 36–41*, 44, 47, 52

Block:
pp. 401–403
Exs. 1, 2, 6–20 even, 21–24, 25–31 odd, 35–40, 45–50 (with 6.5)

Differentiated Instruction
See *Algebra 1 Best Practices Toolkit* for suggestions on addressing the needs of a diverse classroom.

Homework Check
For a quick check of student understanding of key concepts, go over the following exercises:
Basic: 5, 11, 17, 25, 35
Average: 6, 10, 18, 26, 36
Advanced: 8, 12, 20, 27, 37

Extra Practice
• Student Edition, p. 943
• Chapter 6 Resource Book:
 Practice levels A, B, C, pp. 71–76

Practice Worksheet
An easily-readable reduced practice page (with answers) for this lesson can be found on p. 354C.

15.

16.

17.

18.

19.

20.

25.

26.

27.

28.

401

33. $6 < x < 7$; solve each absolute value inequality by rewriting it as a compound inequality. Graph the solutions and find the intersection of the graphs.

REASONING Tell whether the statement is *true* or *false*. If it is false, give a counterexample.

29. If *a* is a solution of $|x + 3| \le 8$, then *a* is also a solution of $x + 3 \ge -8$. **true**

30. If *a* is a solution of $|x + 3| > 8$, then *a* is also a solution of $x + 3 > 8$.
False. *Sample answer:* −20

31. If *a* is a solution of $|x + 3| \ge 8$, then *a* is also a solution of $x + 3 \le -8$.
False. *Sample answer:* 20

32. If *a* is a solution of $x + 3 \le -8$, then *a* is also a solution of $|x + 3| \ge 8$.
true

33. **CHALLENGE** Solve $|x - 3| < 4$ *and* $|x + 2| > 8$. *Describe* your steps.

34. **CHALLENGE** If $|ax + b| < c$ where $c < 0$, what is the solution of the inequality? If $|ax + b| > c$ where $c < 0$, what is the solution of the inequality? *Explain* your answers.
No solution; all real numbers; because an absolute value cannot be negative, $|ax + b|$ is never less than any negative number *c*, and is always greater than any negative number *c*.

PROBLEM SOLVING

EXAMPLE 4 **A**
on p. 400
for Exs. 35–38

35. **ESSAY CONTEST** An essay contest requires that essay entries consist of 500 words with an absolute deviation of at most 30 words. What are the possible numbers of words that the essay can have? **at least 470 words and at most 530 words**

@HomeTutor for problem solving help at classzone.com

36. **SWIMMING POOL** The saturation index for a pool measures the balance between the acid level and the amount of minerals in pool water. Balanced water has an index value of 0. Water is highly corrosive or highly scale forming if the absolute deviation of the index value from 0 is greater than 0.5. Find the index values for which pool water is highly corrosive or highly scale forming. **greater than 0.5 or less than −0.5**

@HomeTutor for problem solving help at classzone.com

37. ★ **SHORT RESPONSE** You are preheating an oven to 350°F before you bake muffins. Several minutes later, the oven thermometer reads 346°F. The measured temperature has an absolute deviation of at most 2°F. Write and solve an inequality to find the possible temperatures in the oven. Should you continue to preheat the oven, or should you start baking the muffins? *Explain* your choice. $|t - 346| \le 2$, at least 344°F and at most 348°F; continue to preheat; the temperature is still below 350°F.

38. ◆ **MULTIPLE REPRESENTATIONS** Softball compression measures the hardness of a softball and affects the distance that the softball can travel upon contact with a bat. A softball organization requires that the compression of a softball be 350 pounds but allows an absolute deviation of at most 50 pounds.

a. **Making a Table** Make a table that shows the absolute deviation from the required compression when the measured compression of a softball is *p* pounds. Use the following values for *p*: 275, 325, 375, 425, 475. **See margin.**

b. **Writing an Inequality** Write and solve an inequality to find the softball compressions that the organization will allow. Which values of *p* in the table are solutions of the inequality?
$|p - 350| \le 50$, at least 300 lb and at most 400 lb; 325, 375

○ = **WORKED-OUT SOLUTIONS**
on p. WS1

★ = **STANDARDIZED TEST PRACTICE**

◆ = **MULTIPLE REPRESENTATIONS**

402

39. MULTI-STEP PROBLEM In a physics class, 7 groups of students experimentally determine the acceleration (in meters per second per second) of an object in free fall. The table below shows the value calculated by each group.

Group	1	2	3	4	5	6	7
Calculated value (m/sec²)	10.50	9.52	9.73	9.86	9.78	10.90	9.86

a. **Calculate** Find the mean of the measured values given in the table. Round to the nearest hundredth. **10.02 m/sec²**

b. **Solve** When writing up their lab reports, the students wanted to state that the absolute deviation of each measured value x from the mean was at most d. What is the value of d in this situation? **0.88 m/sec²**

40b. $|p - 18{,}000|$ ≤ 3600; at least 14,400 antelope and at most 21,600 antelope.

40. ★ EXTENDED RESPONSE *Relative absolute deviation* of a number from a given value is the absolute deviation expressed as a percent of the given value. A wildlife biologist estimates that the number of pronghorn antelopes in Nevada is 18,000 with a relative absolute deviation of at most 20%.

a. **Calculate** Find the absolute deviation from the estimated population of pronghorn antelopes by multiplying the estimated population by the relative absolute deviation. **3600 antelope**

b. **Solve** Write and solve an inequality to find the possible numbers of pronghorn antelopes in Nevada.

c. **Explain** If the relative absolute deviation were 25%, could you conclude that the actual population is necessarily greater than if the relative absolute deviation were 20%? *Explain* your reasoning. **See margin.**

41. CHALLENGE According to the rules for a women's figure skating event, a skater should finish a routine in an ideal time of 3 minutes 30 seconds. The skater receives a 0.1 point penalty if the absolute deviation of the finishing time from the ideal time is greater than 10 seconds *and* less than or equal to 20 seconds. Write and solve an inequality to find the finishing times for which the skater receives a 0.1 penalty point.
at least 3 minutes 10 seconds and less than 3 minutes 20 seconds, more than 3 minutes 40 seconds and at most 3 minutes 50 seconds

MIXED REVIEW

PREVIEW
Prepare for Lesson 6.7 in Exs. 42–53.

Graph the equation. *(p. 215)* **42–47. See margin.**

42. $y = -5.5$

43. $x = 10$

44. $3x + y = 3$

45. $y = 2x + 7$

46. $y = -5x + 2$

47. $5 = -\frac{1}{2}x - y$

Check whether the ordered pair is a solution of the equation. *(p. 215)*

48. $x - y = 1$; $(2, 1)$
solution

49. $-x + 2y = -12$; $(3, 0)$
not a solution

50. $x = -9$; $(-9, 3)$
solution

51. $y = -1$; $(-1, 10)$
not a solution

52. $-4y - x = -1$; $(-2, -8)$
not a solution

53. $6y + 5x = 10$; $(-4, 8)$
not a solution

EXTRA PRACTICE for Lesson 6.6, p. 943   ☉ **ONLINE QUIZ** at classzone.com   **403**

42–47. See Additional Answers beginning on p. AA1.

❶ PLAN AND PREPARE

Explore the Concept

- Students will use inequalities to describe an overestimate and an underestimate.
- This activity leads into the study of linear inequalities in two variables in Example 2 in Lesson 6.7.

Materials

Each pair of students will need:
- set of tangram pieces
- 4 tangram puzzles
- stopwatch
- Activity Support Master (*Chapter 6 Resource Book*, p. 86)

Recommended Time

Work activity: 15 min
Discuss results: 5 min

Grouping

Students should work in pairs. Students can take turns conducting the experiment and recording and graphing the results.

❷ TEACH

Tips for Success

Test the stopwatch before you begin the experiment.

Key Discovery

You can write inequalities that describe points that are either above or below the graph of a line.

❸ ASSESS AND RETEACH

Does the inequality that represents an overestimate or underestimate include the points that lie on the line? Explain. **No; the points that are on the line are neither overestimates nor underestimates.**

6.7 Linear Inequalities in Two Variables

MATERIALS · set of tangram pieces   · 4 tangram puzzles   · stopwatch

QUESTION How can you use inequalities to describe an overestimate or an underestimate?

EXPLORE Conduct an experiment

To solve a tangram puzzle, you use seven pieces to create a figure. Each piece must lie flat and touch at least one other piece, and the pieces cannot overlap.

STEP 1 *Predict a time*

Have your partner give you a tangram puzzle, such as the dog shown below. Predict how long it will take you to create the figure.

**Predicted time:
50 seconds**

STEP 2 *Create figure*

Use the tangrams to create the figure. Your partner will use a stopwatch to record the actual time it takes you to finish.

**Actual time:
73 seconds**

STEP 3 *Record times*

Record the actual time *x* and the predicted time *y* in a table, as below. Repeat Steps 1–3 for three more puzzles. Then switch roles with your partner.

Figure	Actual time *x* (sec)	Predicted time *y* (sec)
1	73	50
2	67	67
3	70	88
4	90	74

STEP 4 *Plot points*

Graph $y = x$ in Quadrant I. Then plot the points (x, y) from the table.

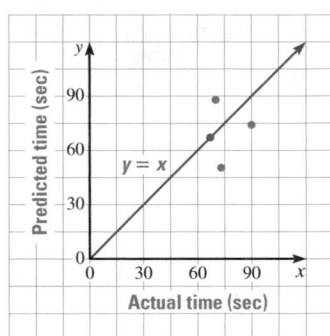

DRAW CONCLUSIONS Use your observations to complete these exercises

1. *Describe* the points that represent an *overestimate* of the actual finishing time. Then write an inequality that describes the location of the points in the coordinate plane. **points that lie above the line $y = x$; $y > x$**

2. *Describe* the points that represent an *underestimate* of the actual finishing time. Then write an inequality that describes the location of the points in the coordinate plane. **points that lie below the line $y = x$; $y < x$**

404   Chapter 6   Solving and Graphing Linear Inequalities

6.7 Graph Linear Inequalities in Two Variables

Before You graphed linear equations in two variables.

Now You will graph linear inequalities in two variables.

Why? So you can analyze a music competition, as in Ex. 56.

Key Vocabulary
• linear inequality in two variables
• graph of an inequality in two variables

A **linear inequality in two variables**, such as $x - 3y < 6$, is the result of replacing the = sign in a linear equation with <, ≤, >, or ≥. A **solution of an inequality in two variables** x and y is an ordered pair (x, y) that produces a true statement when the values of x and y are substituted into the inequality.

EXAMPLE 1 Standardized Test Practice

Which ordered pair is *not* a solution of $x - 3y \leq 6$?

(A) $(0, 0)$ (B) $(6, -1)$ (C) $(10, 3)$ (D) $(-1, 2)$

Solution

Check whether each ordered pair is a solution of the inequality.

Test (0, 0): $x - 3y \leq 6$ **Write inequality.**

$0 - 3(0) \leq 6$ **Substitute 0 for x and 0 for y.**

$0 \leq 6$ ✓ **Simplify.**

Test (6, −1): $x - 3y \leq 6$ **Write inequality.**

$6 - 3(-1) \leq 6$ **Substitute 6 for x and −1 for y.**

$9 \leq 6$ ✗ **Simplify.**

So, $(0, 0)$ is a solution of $x - 3y \leq 6$ but $(6, -1)$ is *not* a solution.

▶ The correct answer is B. (A) (B) (C) (D)

 GUIDED PRACTICE for Example 1

Tell whether the ordered pair is a solution of $-x + 2y < 8$.

1. $(0, 0)$ **solution**
2. $(0, 4)$ **not a solution**
3. $(3, 5)$ **solution**

GRAPH OF AN INEQUALITY In a coordinate plane, the **graph of an inequality in two variables** is the set of points that represent all solutions of the inequality. The *boundary line* of a linear inequality divides the coordinate plane into two **half-planes**. Only one half-plane contains the points that represent the solutions of the inequality.

---

① PLAN AND PREPARE

Warm-Up Exercises
📝 Transparency Available

Tell whether the ordered pair is a solution of the equation.

1. $x + 2y = 4$; $(2, -1)$ **no**
2. $4x + 3y = 22$; $(7, -2)$ **yes**
3. Graph the equation $y - 2x = 4$.

Notetaking Guide
📝 Transparency Available

Promotes interactive learning and notetaking skills, pp. 146–148.

Pacing
Basic: 2 days
Average: 2 days
Advanced: 2 days
Block: 1 block
• See *Teaching Guide/Lesson Plan*.

② FOCUS AND MOTIVATE

Essential Question
Big Idea 3, p. 355

How do you graph a linear inequality in two variables? **Tell students they will learn how to answer this question by graphing a boundary line and shading one half-plane.**

NCTM STANDARDS
Standard 9: Use connections among mathematical ideas

Standard 10: Use representations to solve problems

Resource Planning Guide

Chapter Resource Book
• Teaching Guide/Lesson Plan (pp. 82–83)
• Activity Master (p. 84)
• Practice levels A, B, C (pp. 87–92)
• Study Guide (pp. 93–94)
• Catch-up for Absent Students (p. 95)
• Problem Solving Workshop (p. 96)
• Challenge (p. 97)

Workbooks
• Notetaking Guide (pp. 146–148)
• Practice Workbook (pp. 101–103)

Teaching Options
• **Power Presentations CD-ROM** provides dynamic electronic teaching resources for the classroom.
• **Activity Generator CD-ROM** provides editable activities for all ability levels.

Interactive Technology
• Easy Planner
• Power Presentations CD-ROM
• Activity Generator CD-ROM
• Animated Algebra
• Test Generator CD-ROM
• Online Quiz
• eWorkbook
• eEdition
• @HomeTutor

Resources for English Learners
• Quick Reference for English Learners
• Spanish Study Guide
• Multi-Language Visual Glossary
• Student Resources in Spanish

See also the *Algebra 1 Toolkit* for more strategies for meeting individual needs.

405

Motivating the Lesson

Your two favorite rides at the State Fair are the Ferris wheel and the spinner. You need 4 tickets for the Ferris wheel and 6 tickets for the spinner. You have at least 42 tickets. If you know how to write and solve an inequality in two variables, you can determine the possible numbers of times you can go on each ride.

③ TEACH

Extra Example 1
Which point is *not* a solution of $x + 2y \geq 7$? **D**
- **(A)** $(-1, 4)$
- **(B)** $(2, 4)$
- **(C)** $(11, -2)$
- **(D)** $(8, -1)$

Extra Example 2
Graph the inequality $y \geq 3x + 1$.

Key Questions to Ask for Example 2
- Why do you test a point that is not on the boundary line? **If the point is on the boundary line, you cannot tell which half-plane should be shaded.**
- What is a point on the graph that is *not* a solution of the inequality? **any point in the unshaded region**

Extra Example 3
Graph the inequality $x + 4y < -8$.

EXAMPLE 2   Graph a linear inequality in two variables

Graph the inequality $y > 4x - 3$.

Solution

STEP 1 **Graph** the equation $y = 4x - 3$. The inequality is >, so use a dashed line.

STEP 2 **Test** $(0, 0)$ in $y > 4x - 3$.

$$0 \overset{?}{>} 4(0) - 3$$
$$0 > -3 \checkmark$$

STEP 3 **Shade** the half-plane that contains $(0, 0)$, because $(0, 0)$ is a solution of the inequality.

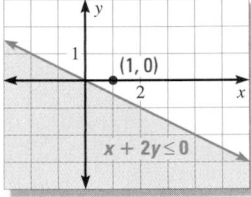

EXAMPLE 3   Graph a linear inequality in two variables

Graph the inequality $x + 2y \leq 0$.

Solution

STEP 1 **Graph** the equation $x + 2y = 0$. The inequality is ≤, so use a solid line.

> **AVOID ERRORS**
> Be sure to test a point that is not on the boundary line. In Example 3, you can't test $(0, 0)$ because it lies on the boundary line $x + 2y = 0$.

STEP 2 **Test** $(1, 0)$ in $x + 2y \leq 0$.

$$1 + 2(0) \overset{?}{\leq} 0$$
$$1 \leq 0 \; ✗$$

STEP 3 **Shade** the half-plane that does not contain $(1, 0)$, because $(1, 0)$ is *not* a solution of the inequality.

✓ **GUIDED PRACTICE**   for Examples 2 and 3

4. Graph the inequality $x + 3y \geq -1$. **See margin.**

Differentiated Instruction

Inclusion Some students may have difficulty remembering which inequality symbol to use when the graph includes a solid line, and which to use when the graph includes a dashed line. Have students make the following connection: when the graph includes a solid line, the inequality symbol has a solid line under it (≤ or ≥), and when the graph includes a dashed line, the symbol does not (< or >).

See also the *Algebra 1 Toolkit* for more strategies.

LINEAR INEQUALITIES IN ONE VARIABLE The steps for graphing a linear inequality in two variables can be used to graph a linear inequality in one variable in a coordinate plane.

The boundary line for an inequality in one variable is either vertical or horizontal. When testing a point to determine which half-plane to shade, do the following:

- If an inequality has only the variable x, substitute the x-coordinate of the test point into the inequality.

- If an inequality has only the variable y, substitute the y-coordinate of the test point into the inequality.

EXAMPLE 4   Graph a linear inequality in one variable

Graph the inequality $y \geq -3$.

Solution

STEP 1   **Graph** the equation $y = -3$.
The inequality is $\geq$, so use a solid line.

STEP 2   **Test** $(2, 0)$ in $y \geq -3$. You substitute only the y-coordinate, because the inequality does not have the variable x.

$$0 \geq -3 \checkmark$$

STEP 3   **Shade** the half-plane that contains $(2, 0)$, because $(2, 0)$ is a solution of the inequality.

EXAMPLE 5   Graph a linear inequality in one variable

Graph the inequality $x < -1$.

Solution

STEP 1   **Graph** the equation $x = -1$.
The inequality is $<$, so use a dashed line.

STEP 2   **Test** $(3, 0)$ in $x < -1$. You substitute only the x-coordinate, because the inequality does not have the variable y.

$$3 < -1 \; ✗$$

STEP 3   **Shade** the half-plane that does *not* contain $(3, 0)$, because $(3, 0)$ is not a solution of the inequality.

Animated **Algebra**   at classzone.com

✔ **GUIDED PRACTICE**   for Examples 4 and 5

Graph the inequality. 5–7. See margin.

5. $y > 1$ **6.** $y \leq 3$ **7.** $x < -2$

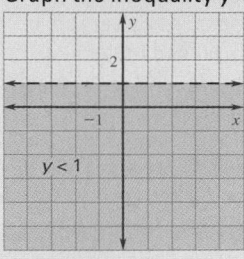

Key Questions to Ask for Example 4

- How is graphing a linear inequality in one variable different from graphing a linear inequality in two variables? **When you test a point for a linear inequality in one variable, you substitute only the variable that appears in the inequality. To test a point for a two-variable inequality, you substitute both coordinates.**

- Does it matter which point you test? **As with linear inequalities in two variables, you should test a point on the boundary line.**

Extra Example 5
Graph the inequality $x \geq 2$.

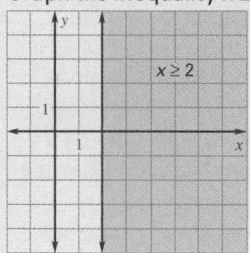

Key Question to Ask for Example 5

- Is the point $(-1, y)$ a solution of the inequality? Explain. **No; the inequality $x < -1$ is not true when x is -1.**

4.

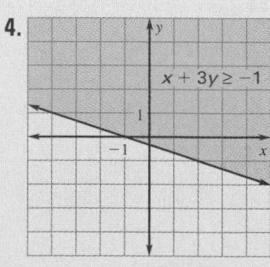

$x + 3y \geq -1$

5.

$y > 1$

6.

$y \leq 3$

7.

$x < -2$

❖ **EXAMPLE 6** **Solve a multi-step problem**

JOB EARNINGS You have two summer jobs at a youth center. You earn $8 per hour teaching basketball and $10 per hour teaching swimming. Let x represent the amount of time (in hours) you teach basketball each week, and let y represent the amount of time (in hours) you teach swimming each week. Your goal is to earn at least $200 per week.

• Write an inequality that describes your goal in terms of x and y.
• Graph the inequality.
• Give three possible combinations of hours that will allow you to meet your goal.

Solution

STEP 1 **Write** a verbal model. Then write an inequality.

Basketball pay rate (dollars/hour)	·	Basketball time (hours)	+	Swimming pay rate (dollars/hour)	·	Swimming time (hours)	≥	Total earnings (dollars)
8	·	x	+	10	·	y	≥	200

STEP 2 **Graph** the inequality $8x + 10y \geq 200$.

First, graph the equation $8x + 10y = 200$ in Quadrant I. The inequality is ≥, so use a solid line.

Next, test (5, 5) in $8x + 10y \geq 200$:

$$8(5) + 10(5) \geq 200$$

$$90 \geq 200 \ ✗$$

Finally, shade the part of Quadrant I that does not contain (5, 5), because (5, 5) is not a solution of the inequality.

STEP 3 **Choose** three points on the graph, such as (13, 12), (14, 10), and (16, 9). The table shows the total earnings for each combination of hours.

Basketball time (hours)	13	14	16
Swimming time (hours)	12	10	9
Total earnings (dollars)	224	212	218

✓ **GUIDED PRACTICE** **for Example 6**

8. **WHAT IF?** In Example 6, suppose that next summer you earn $9 per hour teaching basketball and $12.50 per hour teaching swimming. Write and graph an inequality that describes your goal. Then give three possible combinations of hours that will help you meet your goal.
$9x + 12.5y \geq 200$; see margin for art. *Sample answer:* (8, 12), (12, 10), (16, 6)

6.7 EXERCISES

HOMEWORK KEY
○ = WORKED-OUT SOLUTIONS
  on p. WS1 for Exs. 5, 19, and 57
★ = STANDARDIZED TEST PRACTICE
  Exs. 2, 15, 16, 39, 56, 59, and 60
◆ = MULTIPLE REPRESENTATIONS
  Ex. 55

SKILL PRACTICE

A 1. **VOCABULARY** Copy and complete: The ordered pair $(2, -4)$ is a(n) __?__ of $3x - y > 7$. **solution**

2. ★ **WRITING** *Describe* the difference between graphing a linear inequality in two variables and graphing a linear equation in two variables. **See margin.**

EXAMPLE 1
on p. 405
for Exs. 3–15

CHECKING SOLUTIONS Tell whether the ordered pair is a solution of the inequality.

3. $x + y < -4$; $(0, 0)$
not a solution

4. $x - y \le 5$; $(8, 3)$
solution

5.○ $y - x > -2$; $(-1, -4)$
not a solution

6. $2x + 3y \ge 14$; $(5, 2)$
solution

7. $4x - 7y > 28$; $(-2, 4)$
not a solution

8. $-3y - 2x < 12$; $(5, -6)$
solution

9. $2.8x + 4.1y \le 1$; $(0, 0)$
solution

10. $0.5y - 0.5x > 3.5$; $(6, 2)$
not a solution

11. $x \ge -3$; $(-4, 0)$
not a solution

12. $y \le 8$; $(-9, -7)$
solution

13. $\frac{3}{4}x - \frac{1}{3}y < 6$; $(-8, 12)$
solution

14. $\frac{2}{5}x + y \ge 2$; $(1, 2)$
solution

15. ★ **MULTIPLE CHOICE** Which ordered pair is *not* a solution of $x + 5y < 15$? **C**

Ⓐ $(-1, -3)$ Ⓑ $(-1, 3)$ Ⓒ $(1, 3)$ Ⓓ $(3, 2)$

EXAMPLES
2, 3, 4, and 5
on pp. 406–407
for Exs. 16–38

16. ★ **MULTIPLE CHOICE** The graph of which inequality is shown? **A**

Ⓐ $x + y \le -1$ Ⓑ $x + y \ge -1$
Ⓒ $x - y \le -1$ Ⓓ $x - y \ge -1$

GRAPHING INEQUALITIES Graph the inequality. **17–36. See margin.**

17. $y > x + 3$ 18. $y \le x - 2$ 19.○ $y < 3x + 5$ 20. $y \ge -2x + 8$

21. $x + y < -8$ 22. $x - y \le -11$ 23. $x + 8y > 16$ 24. $5x - y \ge 1$

25. $2(x + 2) > 7y$ 26. $y - 4 < x - 6$ 27. $-4y \le 16x$ 28. $6(2x) \ge -24y$

29. $y < -3$ 30. $x \ge 5$ 31. $x > -2$ 32. $y \le 4$

33. $3(x - 2) > y + 8$ 34. $x - 4 \le -2(y + 6)$ 35. $\frac{1}{2}(x + 2) + 3y < 8$ 36. $2(x + 1) \ge \frac{1}{4}y - 1$

ERROR ANALYSIS *Describe* and correct the error in graphing the inequality.

37. $2y - x > 2$ 38. $x \le -3$

37, 38. See margin for art.

The wrong half-plane is shaded.

The boundary line should be solid.

2. Graphing a linear inequality in two variables involves graphing the boundary line (as either a solid or dashed line) and then shading the appropriate half-plane. Graphing a linear equation in two variables involves only the graphing of one (solid) line.

17–38. See Additional Answers beginning on p. AA1.

④ PRACTICE AND APPLY

Assignment Guide

▢ Answer Transparencies available for all exercises

Basic:
Day 1: EP p. 941 Exs. 41–44
pp. 409–412
Exs. 1–11, 15–25, 62–70 even
Day 2: pp. 409–412
Exs. 29–41, 53–58, 71–76

Average:
Day 1: pp. 409–412
Exs. 1, 2, 8–16, 20–28, 44–46, 63–69 odd
Day 2: pp. 409–412
Exs. 29–43, 47–50, 54–59, 71–75 odd

Advanced:
Day 1: pp. 409–412
Exs. 1, 10–16, 21–28, 44–46, 51*, 52*, 63–69 odd
Day 2: pp. 409–412
Exs. 29–43, 47–50, 55–61*, 73, 76

Block:
pp. 409–412
Exs. 1, 2, 8–16, 20–50, 54–59, 63–75 odd

Differentiated Instruction

See *Algebra 1 Best Practices Toolkit* for suggestions on addressing the needs of a diverse classroom.

Homework Check

For a quick check of student understanding of key concepts, go over the following exercises:

Basic: 4, 18, 25, 30, 53
Average: 12, 20, 27, 31, 54
Advanced: 14, 22, 28, 32, 55

Extra Practice

• Student Edition, p. 943
• Chapter 6 Resource Book: Practice levels A, B, C, pp. 87–92

Practice Worksheet

An easily-readable reduced practice page (with answers) for this lesson can be found on p. 354C.

40.

$x - 4 \ge y$

41.

$-2y \le x + 6$

42.

$\frac{y}{2} > 7 - x$

39. ★ **WRITING** Can you use (0, 0) as a test point when graphing $2x > -5y$? *Explain* your reasoning. **No; (0, 0) is a point on the boundary line $2x = -5y$.**

 TRANSLATING SENTENCES Write the verbal sentence as an inequality. Then graph the inequality. 40–43. See margin for art.

40. Four less than x is greater than or equal to y. $x - 4 \ge y$

41. The product of -2 and y is less than or equal to the sum of x and 6. $-2y \le x + 6$

42. The quotient of y and 2 is greater than the difference of 7 and x. $\frac{y}{2} > 7 - x$

43. The sum of x and the product of 4 and y is less than -3. $x + 4y < -3$

USING A GRAPH Write an inequality of the graph shown.

44. $y > -\frac{5}{4}x + \frac{7}{4}$

45. $y \le \frac{5}{7}x - \frac{9}{7}$

46. $y > \frac{1}{2}x + 2$

44.

45.

46.

WRITING INEQUALITIES Write an inequality whose graph contains only the points in the given quadrants.

47. Quadrants I and II $y > 0$

48. Quadrants II and III $x < 0$

49. Quadrants III and IV $y < 0$

50. Quadrants I and IV $x > 0$

 CHALLENGE In Exercises 51 and 52, write and graph an inequality whose graph is described by the given information. **51, 52. See margin for art.**

51. The points (2, 5) and (−3, −5) lie on the boundary line. The points (6, 5) and (−2, −3) are solutions of the inequality. $y \le 2x + 1$

52. The points (−7, −16) and (1, 8) lie on the boundary line. The points (−7, 0) and (3, 14) are *not* solutions of the inequality. $y < 3x + 5$

PROBLEM SOLVING

EXAMPLE 6 A
on p. 408
for Exs. 53–57

53. **BOBSLEDS** In a two-man bobsled competition, the sum of the weight x (in pounds) of the bobsled and the combined weight y (in pounds) of the athletes must not exceed 860 pounds. Write and graph an inequality that describes the possible weights of the bobsled and the athletes. Identify and interpret one of the solutions.

@HomeTutor for problem solving help at classzone.com

See margin.

54. **ELEVATORS** The number y of passengers riding an elevator can be no greater than the elevator's maximum weight capacity x (in pounds) divided by 150. Write and graph an inequality that relates the number of passengers to the maximum weight capacity. Identify and interpret one of the solutions. **See margin.**

@HomeTutor for problem solving help at classzone.com

○ = WORKED-OUT SOLUTIONS
on p. WS1

★ = STANDARDIZED
TEST PRACTICE

◆ = MULTIPLE
REPRESENTATIONS

43.

$x + 4y < -3$

51.

$y \le 2x + 1$

52.

$y < 3x + 5$

55. ◆ **MULTIPLE REPRESENTATIONS** You tutor Spanish for $15 per hour and French for $10 per hour. You want to earn at least $100 per week.

a. **Writing an Inequality** Write an inequality that describes your goal in terms of hours spent tutoring Spanish and hours spent tutoring French. **15x + 10y ≥ 100**

b. **Drawing a Graph** Graph the inequality. Then give three possible combinations of hours that meet your goal. **See margin for art; (4, 8), (5, 3), (6, 1).**

c. **Making a Table** Make a table that gives the amount of money that you will earn for each combination of hours given in part (b). **See margin.**

56. ★ **MULTIPLE CHOICE** To compete in a piano competition, you need to perform two musical pieces whose combined duration is no greater than 15 minutes. Which inequality describes the possible durations x and y (in minutes) of the pieces? **B**

Ⓐ $x + y < 15$ Ⓑ $x + y \leq 15$ Ⓒ $x + y > 15$ Ⓓ $x + y \geq 15$

57. **MULTI-STEP PROBLEM** You are making muffins and loaves of bread for a bake sale. You need $\frac{1}{6}$ batch of batter per muffin and $\frac{1}{2}$ batch of batter per loaf of bread. You have enough ingredients to make up to 12 batches of batter. **$\frac{1}{6}m + \frac{1}{2}\ell \leq 12$; See margin for art.**

a. Write and graph an inequality that describes the possible combinations of muffins m and loaves ℓ of bread that you can make.

b. You make 4 loaves of bread. What are the possible numbers of muffins that you can make? **$m \leq 60$**

Ⓑ **58.** **NUTRITION** A nutritionist recommends that the fat calories y consumed per day should be at most 30% of the total calories x consumed per day.

a. Write and graph an inequality that relates the number of fat calories consumed to the total calories consumed. **$y \leq 0.3x$; see margin for art.**

b. Use the nutrition labels below. You normally consume 2000 calories per day. So far today you have eaten 6 crackers and 1 container of yogurt. What are the possible additional fat calories that you can consume today? **$y \leq 500$**

Nutrition Facts
Serving Size 3 crackers
Amount Per Serving
Calories 90
Calories from Fat 40

Nutrition Facts
Serving Size 1 container
Amount Per Serving
Calories 220
Calories from Fat 20

59. ★ **SHORT RESPONSE** You need to bring a duffel and a bedroll for a trip in the mountains. The sum of the weight x (in pounds) of the duffel and the weight y (in pounds) of the bedroll cannot exceed 30 pounds.

a. **Graph and Apply** Write and graph a linear inequality that describes the possible weights of the duffel and bedroll. Then give three possible combinations of weights of the duffel and bedroll. **See margin.**

b. **Interpret** Are (0, 30) and (30, 0) solutions of the inequality in part (a)? Do these ordered pairs make sense for this situation? *Explain.*

6.7   Graph Linear Inequalities in Two Variables   **411**

53, 54. See Additional Answers beginning on p. AA1.

*Margin left column:*

59a. $x + y \leq 30$, see margin for art. *Sample answer:* (20, 4), (25, 5), (26, 2)

59b. Yes; no; (0, 30) means that you do not take a duffel and have a 30 pound bedroll, while (30, 0) means you take a 30 pound duffel and do not take a bedroll. You need to bring both a duffel and a bedroll.

*Margin right column:*

Study Strategy

Exercise 55 Suggest that students review Example 6 before they begin this exercise. This will help them write a verbal model for the problem, graph the inequality, and create a table.

55b.

$15x + 10y \geq 100$

Spanish (hours)

55c. Sample answer:

Spanish time (hours)	4	5	6
French time (hours)	8	3	1
Total earnings (dollars)	140	105	100

57a.

$\frac{1}{6}m + \frac{1}{2}\ell \leq 12$

Number of muffins

58a.

$y \leq 0.3x$

Total calories

59a.

$x + y \leq 30$

Duffel weight (pounds)

Daily Homework Quiz

🖥 **Transparency Available**

Tell whether the ordered pair is a solution of the inequality.

1. $x + 4y \geq 16$; $(3, 3)$ **no**

2. $3x - 2y < 20$; $(5, -2)$ **yes**

3. For a fundraiser, students offer a basic car wash for $2 and a deluxe for $5. They want to earn at least $100 per day. Write an inequality that describes the goal. Graph the inequality. Identify and interpret one combination that meets the goal. $2x + 5y \geq 100$, where *x* represents basic washes and *y* represents deluxe washes

(40, 15); 40 basic washes and 15 deluxe washes

🔁 **Online Quiz**

Available at **classzone.com**

Diagnosis/Remediation

- Practice A, B, C in Chapter 6 Resource Book, pp. 87–92
- Study Guide in Chapter 6 Resource Book, pp. 93–94
- Practice Workbook, pp. 101–103
- @HomeTutor

Challenge

Additional challenge is available in the Chapter 6 Resource Book, p. 97.

Quiz

An easily-readable reduced copy of the quiz (with answers) on Lessons 6.5–6.7 from the Assessment Book can be found on p. 354G.

60a, 60b, 61a, Quiz 4–9. See Additional Answers beginning on p. AA1.

412

---

60. ★ **EXTENDED RESPONSE** A financial advisor suggests that if a person is an aggressive investor, the percent *y* of money that the person invests in stocks should be greater than the difference of 110 and the person's age *x*.

  a. Graph Write and graph a linear inequality that relates the percent of money invested in stocks to an aggressive investor's age. $y > 110 - x$; see margin for art.

  b. Calculate If an aggressive investor is 30 years old, what are the possible percents that the investor can invest in stocks? *Explain* your answer. **See margin.**

  c. Justify Are there any ages for which none of the solutions of the inequality makes sense for this situation? *Justify* your answer.

🅲 **61. CHALLENGE** The formula $m = dV$ gives the mass *m* of an object in terms of the object's density *d* and its volume *V*. Water has a density of 1 gram per cubic centimeter. An object immersed in water will sink if its density is greater than the density of water. An object will float in water if its density is less than the density of water.

  a. For an object that sinks, write and graph an inequality that relates its mass (in grams) to its volume (in cubic centimeters). For an object that floats, write and graph an inequality that relates its mass (in grams) to its volume (in cubic centimeters). **See margin.**

  b. A cylindrical can has a radius of 5 centimeters, a height of 10 centimeters, and a mass of 2119.5 grams. Will the can sink or float in water? *Explain* your answer.
Sink; the volume of the cylindrical can is $\pi r^2 h = \pi(25)(10) \approx 785.40$ cubic centimeters. Since the mass, 2119.5 grams, is greater than the volume, 785.40 cubic centimeters, the can will sink.

MIXED REVIEW

Solve the equation or inequality.

62. $-4a = 20$ *(p. 134)* **−5**

63. $3c + 8 = 17$ *(p. 141)* **3**

64. $6m - 5 = -8m + 2$ *(p. 154)* $\frac{1}{2}$

65. $\frac{n}{5} = \frac{n+1}{3}$ *(p. 168)* $-2\frac{1}{2}$

66. $p - 9 \geq -15$ *(p. 356)* $p \geq -6$

67. $-2s + 3 < -4$ *(p. 369)* $s > 3\frac{1}{2}$

68. $2x \geq 8$ or $5x < 10$ *(p. 380)*
$x < 2$ or $x \geq 4$

69. $-2 < 9y - 2 \leq 5$ *(p. 380)*
$0 \leq y \leq \frac{7}{9}$

70. $|g - 7| \geq 15$ *(p. 398)*
$g \leq -8$ or $g \geq 22$

PREVIEW
Prepare for Lesson 7.1 in Exs. 71–76.

Graph the equation. *(p. 225)*
71–76. See margin.

71. $x - y = 8$

72. $-6x + 2y = -12$

73. $12x + 3y = -9$

74. $y = -7x + 1$

75. $y = 5x + 2$

76. $y = 0.5x - 5$

QUIZ for Lessons 6.5–6.7

Solve the equation. *(p. 390)*

1. $|x| = 5$ **5, −5**

2. $|c - 8| = 24$ **32, −16**

3. $-2|r - 5| = -6$ **8, 2**

Solve the inequality. Graph your solution. *(p. 398)* 4–6. See margin for art.

4. $|y| > 4$ $y < -4$ or $y > 4$

5. $|2t - 5| < 3$ $1 < t < 4$

6. $4|3s + 7| - 5 \geq 7$
$s \leq -3\frac{1}{3}$ or $s \geq -1\frac{1}{3}$

Graph the inequality. *(p. 405)* 7–9. See margin.

7. $x + y \geq 3$

8. $\frac{5}{7}x < 10$

9. $2y - x \leq 8$

---

412   **EXTRA PRACTICE** for Lesson 6.7, p. 943   🔁 **ONLINE QUIZ** at classzone.com

71–76. See Additional Answers beginning on p. AA1.

MIXED REVIEW *of Problem Solving*

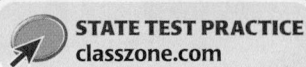
Lessons 6.5–6.7

1. **MULTI-STEP PROBLEM** You gathered 36 apples from your backyard apple tree in order to make apple pies and applesauce. You use 7 apples to make one apple pie and 5 apples to make one pint of applesauce.

   a. Write an inequality that describes the possible numbers of apple pies and pints of applesauce that you can make. $7p + 5s \le 36$

   b. Graph the inequality. **See margin.**

   c. Give three possible combinations of apple pies and pints of applesauce that you can make. *Sample answer:* **1 pie and 5 pints of applesauce, 3 pies and 3 pints of applesauce, 4 pies and 1 pint of applesauce**

2. **SHORT RESPONSE** You are scooping ice cream as part of your training at an ice cream shop. The weight of a scoop must be 4 ounces with an absolute deviation of at most 0.5 ounce.

   a. Write an inequality to find the possible weights (in ounces) of each scoop. $|x - 4| \le 0.5$

   b. You make 10 scoops. You can start working at the shop if at least 80% of the scoops meet the weight requirement. The list shows the weights (in ounces) of your scoops.

      3.8, 4.2, 3.9, 4.5, 3.7, 4.6, 4.1, 3.3, 4.3, 4.2

      Can you start working at the shop? *Explain* your reasoning. **See margin.**

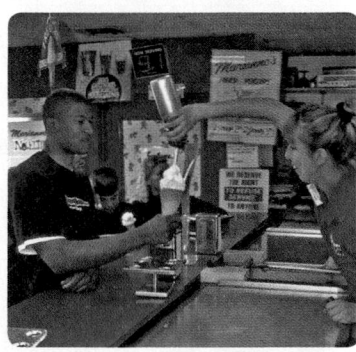

3. **GRIDDED ANSWER** You will be making a presentation in your history class. Your teacher gives you a time limit of 15 minutes with an absolute deviation of 1.5 minutes. What is the maximum possible duration (in minutes) of your presentation? **16.5 min**

4. **OPEN-ENDED** *Describe* a real-world situation that can be modeled by the equation $|x - 10| = 50$. *Explain* what the solution of the equation means in this situation.
   See margin.

5. **EXTENDED RESPONSE** A tour operator recommends that a river rafter wear a protective suit under the temperature conditions described below.

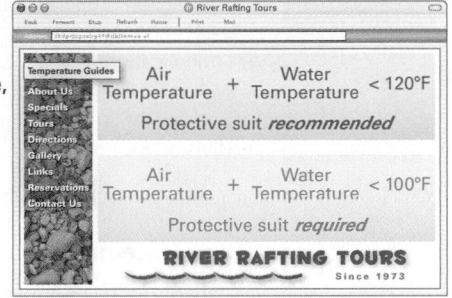

   a. Write and graph an inequality that describes the possible air temperatures and water temperatures for which a protective suit is recommended.
   $a + w < 120$; **see margin for art.**

   b. If the water temperature is 40°F, for which air temperatures is a protective suit recommended? $a < 80°F$

   c. How would you change the graph in part (a) in order to describe the situations in which a protective suit is required? *Explain* your answer. **See margin.**

6. **MULTI-STEP PROBLEM** You are buying a new cell phone and see eight phones listed on a website. The prices of the phones are shown.

   $139, $249, $229, $199, $179, $359, $199, $209

   a. Find the mean price of the phones. **$220.25**

   b. You are willing to purchase a phone that has the mean price with an absolute deviation of at most $50. Write and solve an inequality to find the prices of phones that you will consider.
   $|x - 220.25| \le 50$; **from $170.25 up to $270.25**

   c. How many of the phones on the website will you consider buying? **6 phones**

1b.

2b. Yes; the solution of the inequality from part (a) is $3.5 \le x \le 4.5$. For at least 80% of your scoops to meet the weight requirement, at least 8 scoops must weigh at least 3.5 ounces and at most 4.5 ounces. Because 8 out of 10 of your scoops are in the required range of weights, you can start working at the shop.

4. *Sample answer:* During a portion of time spent driving on the highway, your average speed is 50 miles per hour with an absolute deviation of your actual speed from your average speed of 10 miles per hour. What are your minimum and maximum speeds during this time? 40, 60; your minimum speed was 40 miles per hour and your maximum speed was 60 miles per hour.

5a.

5c. Move the line so that its *x*- and *y*-intercepts are 100 instead of 120. The linear inequality that describes the situations in which a protective suit is required is $a + w < 100$.

Additional Resources

The following resources are available to help review the materials in this chapter.

Chapter 6 Resource Book
- Chapter Review Games and Activities, p. 98
- Cumulative Practice, Chs. 1–6, pp. 100–101

Student Resources in Spanish

eWorkbook

@HomeTutor

Vocabulary Practice

Vocabulary practice is available at **classzone.com**

BIG IDEAS
For Your Notebook

Big Idea 1

Applying Properties of Inequality

You can apply the properties of inequality to solve inequalities. The properties listed below are also true for inequalities involving $\leq$ and $\geq$.

Property	If $a < b$, then ...	If $a > b$, then ...
Addition property of inequality	$a + c < b + c$.	$a + c > b + c$.
Subtraction property of inequality	$a - c < b - c$.	$a - c > b - c$.
Multiplication property of inequality	$ac < bc$ if $c > 0$. $ac > bc$ if $c < 0$.	$ac > bc$ if $c > 0$. $ac < bc$ if $c < 0$.
Division property of inequality	$\frac{a}{c} < \frac{b}{c}$ if $c > 0$. $\frac{a}{c} > \frac{b}{c}$ if $c < 0$.	$\frac{a}{c} > \frac{b}{c}$ if $c > 0$. $\frac{a}{c} < \frac{b}{c}$ if $c < 0$.

Big Idea 2

Using Statements with *And* or *Or*

An absolute value equation can be rewritten as two equations joined by *or*. An absolute value inequality can be rewritten as a compound inequality with *and* or *or*. In the statements below, $<$ can be replaced by $\leq$, and $>$ can be replaced by $\geq$.

Absolute value equation or inequality	Equivalent statement with *and* or *or*
$|ax + b| = c, c \geq 0$	$ax + b = c$ or $ax + b = -c$
$|ax + b| < c, c \geq 0$	$-c < ax + b < c$
$|ax + b| > c, c \geq 0$	$ax + b < -c$ or $ax + b > c$

Big Idea 3

Graphing Inequalities

You use a number line to graph an inequality in one variable. Similarly, you use a coordinate plane to graph a linear inequality in two variables (including cases where one of the variables has a coefficient of 0, such as $0x + y < 1$, or $y < 1$).

Graphing inequalities in one variable	Graphing linear inequalities in two variables
Graph simple inequalities: 1. Solve for the variable. 2. Draw an open circle for $<$ or $>$ and a closed circle for $\leq$ or $\geq$. Draw an arrow in the appropriate direction. Graph compound inequalities: 1. Solve the compound inequality. 2. Use the union of graphs of simple inequalities for *or*. Use the intersection for *and*.	1. Graph the boundary line. Use a solid line for $\leq$ or $\geq$ and a dashed line for $<$ or $>$. 2. Test a point that does not lie on the boundary line. 3. Shade the half-plane containing the point if the ordered pair is a solution of the inequality. Shade the other half-plane if the ordered pair is *not* a solution.

@HomeTutor
classzone.com
· Multi Language Glossary
· Vocabulary practice

REVIEW KEY VOCABULARY

- graph of an inequality, *p. 356*
- equivalent inequalities, *p. 357*
- compound inequality, *p. 380*
- absolute value equation, *p. 390*
- absolute deviation, *p. 392*
- linear inequality in two variables, *p. 405*
- solution of an inequality in two variables, *p. 405*
- graph of an inequality in two variables, half-plane, *p. 405*

VOCABULARY EXERCISES

1. Translate the verbal sentence into an absolute value equation: "The absolute deviation of x from 19 is 8." $|x - 19| = 8$

2. Identify three ordered pairs that are solutions of $2x - 3y \geq -10$.
   Sample answer: (1, 1), (−2, 1), (4, 2)

3. **WRITING** When you graph a linear inequality in two variables, how do you know whether the boundary line is a solid line or a dashed line? How do you know which half-plane to shade? **The boundary line is solid if the inequality symbol is ≤ or ≥, the boundary line is dashed if the inequality symbol is < or >; choose a test point that is not on the boundary line. If the ordered pair is a solution to the inequality, shade the half-plane that contains the test point; if it not a solution, shade the other half-plane.**

REVIEW EXAMPLES AND EXERCISES

Use the review examples and exercises below to check your understanding of the concepts you have learned in each lesson of Chapter 6.

6.1 | Solve Inequalities Using Addition and Subtraction   *pp. 356–361*

EXAMPLE

Solve $x - 2.1 \leq 1.4$. Graph your solution.

$$x - 2.1 \leq 1.4 \qquad \text{Write original inequality.}$$
$$x - 2.1 + 2.1 \leq 1.4 + 2.1 \qquad \text{Add 2.1 to each side.}$$
$$x \leq 3.5 \qquad \text{Simplify.}$$

▶ The solutions are all real numbers less than or equal to 3.5.

EXERCISES

EXAMPLES
1, 2, 3, and 4
on pp. 356–358
for Exs. 4–7

4. **GEOGRAPHY** The lowest elevation in Mexico is −10 meters at Laguna Salada. Write and graph an inequality that describes all elevations in Mexico that are greater than the lowest elevation. **$x > -10$; see margin for art.**

Solve the inequality. Graph your solution. **5–7. See margin for art.**

5. $x + 5 > -13$ **$x > -18$**   6. $m - 9 \geq -4$ **$m \geq 5$**   7. $s + 3.7 < 1$ **$s < -2.7$**

Extra Example 6.1
Solve $x + 6 > 9$. Graph your solution. **all real numbers greater than 3**

4.

5.

6.

7.

Extra Example 6.2

Solve $\frac{x}{-6} \geq 4$. Graph your solution.

all real numbers less than or equal to −24

Extra Example 6.3

Solve $-3x - 2 < 10$. Graph your solution. **all real numbers greater than −4**

8.

9.

10.

11.

13.

14.

15.

16.

17.

18.

6.2 | **Solve Inequalities Using Multiplication and Division** *pp. 363–368*

EXAMPLE

Solve $\frac{x}{-4} < 9$. Graph your solution.

$$\frac{x}{-4} < 9 \qquad \text{Write original inequality.}$$

$$-4 \cdot \frac{x}{-4} > -4 \cdot 9 \qquad \text{Multiply each side by −4. Reverse inequality symbol.}$$

$$x > -36 \qquad \text{Simplify.}$$

▶ The solutions are all real numbers greater than −36.

EXERCISES

EXAMPLES
1, 2, 3, 4, and 5
on pp. 363–365
for Exs. 8–12

Solve the inequality. Graph your solution. **8–11. See margin for art.**

8. $\frac{p}{2} \leq 5$ **$p \leq 10$** **9.** $\frac{n}{-4.5} < -8$ **$n > 36$** **10.** $-3x > 27$ **$x < -9$** **11.** $2y \geq 18$ **$y \geq 9$**

12. GYMNASTICS In men's gymnastics, an athlete competes in 6 events. Suppose that an athlete's average score per event is at most 9.7 points. Write and solve an inequality to find the possible total scores for the athlete.
$\frac{x}{6} \leq 9.7$, at most 58.2 points

6.3 | **Solve Multi-Step Inequalities** *pp. 369–374*

EXAMPLE

Solve $4x + 7 \geq -13$. Graph your solution.

$$-4x + 7 \geq -13 \qquad \text{Write original inequality.}$$

$$-4x \geq -20 \qquad \text{Subtract 7 from each side.}$$

$$x \leq 5 \qquad \text{Divide each side by −4. Reverse inequality symbol.}$$

▶ The solutions are all real numbers less than or equal to 5.

EXERCISES

EXAMPLES
1, 2, 3, and 4
on pp. 369–370
for Exs. 13–19

Solve the inequality, if possible. Graph your solution. **13–18. See margin for art.**

13. $2g + 11 < 25$ **$g < 7$** **14.** $\frac{2}{3}r - 4 \geq 1$ **$r \geq 7\frac{1}{2}$** **15.** $1 - 3x \leq -14 + 2x$ **$x \geq 3$**

16. $3(q + 1) < 3q + 7$ **all real numbers** **17.** $8(t - 1) > -8 + 8t$ **no solution** **18.** $-3(2n - 1) \geq 1 - 8n$ **$n \geq -1$**

19. TICKET PURCHASES You can order discount movie tickets from a website for $7 each. You must also pay a shipping fee of $4. You want to spend no more than $40 on movie tickets. Find the possible numbers of movie tickets that you can order. **at most 5 tickets**

416 Chapter 6 Solving and Graphing Linear Inequalities

6.4 Solve Compound Inequalities

pp. 380–387

EXAMPLE

Solve $-1 < -2x + 7 < 9$. Graph your solution.

$-1 < -2x + 7 < 9$	Write original inequality.
$-8 < -2x < 2$	Subtract 7 from each expression.
$4 > x > -1$	Divide each side by -2. Reverse both inequality symbols.
$-1 < x < 4$	Rewrite in the form $a < x < b$.

▶ The solutions are all real numbers greater than -1 *and* less than 4.

EXERCISES

EXAMPLES 3, 4, and 5
on pp. 381–382
for Exs. 20–23

Solve the inequality. Graph your solution. **20–23. See margin for art.**

20. $-6 \le 2t - 5 \le -3$ **$-\frac{1}{2} \le t \le 1$**

21. $-3 < -3x + 8 < 11$ **$-1 < x < 3\frac{2}{3}$**

22. $9s - 6 < 12 \text{ or } 3s + 1 > 13$ **$s < 2 \text{ or } s > 4$**

23. $-4w + 12 \ge 10 \text{ or } 5w - 14 > -4$
$w \le \frac{1}{2} \text{ or } w > 2$

6.5 Solve Absolute Value Equations

pp. 390–395

EXAMPLE

Solve $4|5x - 3| + 6 = 30$.

First, rewrite the equation in the form $|ax + b| = c$.

$4|5x - 3| + 6 = 30$	Write original equation.
$4|5x - 3| = 24$	Subtract 6 from each side.
$|5x - 3| = 6$	Divide each side by 4.

Next, solve the absolute value equation.

$5x - 3 = 6$	*or* $5x - 3 = -6$	Rewrite as two equations.
$5x = 9$	*or* $5x = -3$	Add 3 to each side.
$x = 1.8$	*or* $x = -0.6$	Divide each side by 5.

▶ The solutions are -0.6 and 1.8.

EXERCISES

EXAMPLES 1, 2, 3, 4, and 5
on pp. 390–392
for Exs. 24–30

Solve the equation, if possible.

24. $|r| = 7$ **$7, -7$**

25. $|a + 6| = 2$ **$-4, -8$**

26. $|2c + 5| = 21$ **$8, -13$**

27. $2|x - 3| + 1 = 5$ **$5, 1$**

28. $3|2q + 1| - 5 = 1$ **$0.5, -1.5$**

29. $4|3p - 2| + 5 = 11$ **$1\frac{1}{6}, \frac{1}{6}$**

30. BOWLING In tenpin bowling, the height of each bowling pin must be 15 inches with an absolute deviation of 0.03125 inch. Find the minimum and maximum possible heights of a bowling pin. **14.96875 in., 15.03125 in.**

Chapter Review **417**

Extra Example 6.4

Solve $2x + 3 \le 5 \text{ or } 5x + 2 > 12$. Graph your solution. **all real numbers less than or equal to 1 *or* greater than 2**

Extra Example 6.5

Solve $3|4x + 2| - 5 = 13$. **1, -2**

20.

21.

22.

23.

Extra Example 6.6

Solve $|-2x - 3| + 6 < 17$. Graph your solution. **all real numbers greater than -7 and less than 4**

Extra Example 6.7

Graph the inequality $2x + y \geq 4$.

31.

32.

33.

34.

35.

36.

41.

42.

43.

6.6 Solve Absolute Value Inequalities
pp. 398–403

EXAMPLE

Solve $3|2x + 11| + 2 \leq 17$. Graph your solution.

$3|2x + 11| + 2 \leq 17$	Write original inequality.
$3|2x + 11| \leq 15$	Subtract 2 from each side.
$|2x + 11| \leq 5$	Divide each side by 3.
$-5 \leq 2x + 11 \leq 5$	Rewrite as compound inequality.
$-16 \leq 2x \leq -6$	Subtract 11 from each expression.
$-8 \leq x \leq -3$	Divide each side by 2.

▶ The solutions are all real numbers greater than or equal to -8 *and* less than or equal to -3.

EXERCISES

EXAMPLES 1, 2, and 3 on pp. 398–399 for Exs. 31–36

Solve the inequality. Graph your solution. **31–36. See margin for art.**

31. $|m| \geq 8$ $m \geq 8$ or $m \leq -8$ **32.** $|6k + 1| \geq 2$ $k \geq \frac{1}{6}$ or $k \leq -\frac{1}{2}$ **33.** $|3g - 2| < 5$ $-1 < g < 2\frac{1}{3}$

34. $6|3x + 5| \leq 14$
$-2\frac{4}{9} \leq x \leq -\frac{8}{9}$

35. $|2j - 9| - 2 > 10$
$j < -1\frac{1}{2}$ or $j > 10\frac{1}{2}$

36. $5|d + 8| - 7 > 13$
$d < -12$ or $d > -4$

6.7 Graph Linear Inequalities in Two Variables
pp. 405–412

EXAMPLE

Graph the inequality $y < 3x - 1$.

STEP 1 Graph the equation $y = 3x - 1$. The inequality is <, so use a dashed line.

STEP 2 Test $(0, 0)$ in $y < 3x - 1$.

$0 \overset{?}{<} 3(0) - 1$

$0 < -1$ ✗

STEP 3 Shade the half-plane that does not contain $(0, 0)$, because $(0, 0)$ is *not* a solution of the inequality.

EXERCISES

EXAMPLES 1, 2, 3, 4, and 5 on pp. 405–407 for Exs. 37–44

Tell whether the ordered pair is a solution of $-3x + 2y \geq 16$.

37. $(-2, 8)$
solution

38. $(-1, -1)$
not a solution

39. $(-2, 10)$
solution

40. $(9, -5)$
not a solution

Graph the inequality. **41–44. See margin.**

41. $y > 2x + 3$ **42.** $y \leq \frac{1}{2}x - 1$ **43.** $3x - 2y < 12$ **44.** $y \geq 3$

44.

Chapter Test

1.

2.

3.

4.

5.

6.

Translate the verbal phrase into an inequality. Then graph the inequality.
1–4. See margin for art.

1. All real numbers that are less than 5 $x < 5$

2. All real numbers that are greater than or equal to -1 $x \geq -1$

3. All real numbers that are greater than -2 *and* less than or equal to 7 $-2 < x \leq 7$

4. All real numbers that are greater than 8 *or* less than -4 $x > 8 \text{ or } x < -4$

Solve the inequality, if possible. Graph your solution. 5–22. See margin for art.

5. $x - 9 \geq -5$ $x \geq 4$

6. $-2 > 5 + y$ $y < -7$

7. $-0.8 \leq z + 7.7$ $z \geq -8.5$

8. $5m \geq 35$ $m \geq 7$

9. $\dfrac{n}{6} < -1$ $n < -6$

10. $\dfrac{r}{-3} \leq 4$ $r \geq -12$

11. $-4s < 6s + 1$ $s > -0.1$

12. $4t - 7 \leq 13$ $t \leq 5$

13. $-8 > 5 - v$ $v > 13$

14. $3(5w + 4) < 12w - 11$
    $w < -7\dfrac{2}{3}$

15. $4p - 3 > 2(2p + 1)$
    no solution

16. $9q - 12 \geq 3(3q - 4)$
    all real numbers

17. $-2 \leq 4 - 3a \leq 13$
    $-3 \leq a \leq 2$

18. $-7 < 2c - 1 < 10\dfrac{1}{2}$
    $-3 < c < 5.75$

19. $-5 \leq 2 - h \text{ or } 6h + 5 \geq 71$
    $h \leq 7 \text{ or } h \geq 11$

20. $|2d + 8| > 3$
    $d < -5.5 \text{ or } d > -2.5$

21. $2|3f - 7| + 5 < 11$
    $1\dfrac{1}{3} < f < 3\dfrac{1}{3}$

22. $|j - 7| - 1 \leq 3\dfrac{5}{6}$
    $2\dfrac{1}{6} \leq j \leq 11\dfrac{5}{6}$

Solve the equation, if possible.

23. $-\dfrac{3}{4}|x - 3| = \dfrac{1}{4}$
    no solution

24. $|3y + 1| - 6 = -2$ $1, -\dfrac{2}{3}$

25. $4|2z + 5| + 9 = 5$
    no solution

Check whether the ordered pair is a solution of the inequality.

26. $2x - y < 4; (2, -1)$
    not a solution

27. $y + 3x \geq -5; (-3, -4)$
    not a solution

28. $y \leq -3; (4, -7)$
    solution

Graph the inequality. 29–31. See margin.

29. $y < x + 4$

30. $y \geq 2x - 5$

31. $y \geq -6$

32. **BUSINESS** Your friend is starting a small business baking and decorating cakes and wants to make a profit of at least $250 for the first month. The expenses for the first month are $155. What are the possible revenues that your friend can earn in order to meet the profit goal? **at least $405**

33. **BICYCLES** A manufacturer of bicycle parts requires that a bicycle chain have a width of 0.3 inch with an absolute error of at most 0.0003 inch. Find the possible widths of bicycle chains that the manufacturer will accept. **0.2997 in. up to 0.3003 in.**

34. **HORSES** You are planning to ride a horse to a campsite. The sum of your weight x (in pounds) and the combined weight y (in pounds) of your camping supplies can be at most 20% of the weight of the horse.

   a. Suppose that the horse weighs 1000 pounds. Write and graph an inequality that describes the possible combinations of your weight and the combined weight of the camping supplies. **$x + y \leq 200$; see margin for art.**

   b. Identify and interpret one of the solutions of the inequality in part (a).
   Sample answer: **(130, 60); if you weigh 130 pounds and the combined weight of your camping supplies is 60 pounds, the combined weight is 190, so you will be able to ride the horse to the campsite.**

Chapter Test **419**

Additional Resources

Assessment Book
• Chapter Test, Levels A, B, C, pp. 78–83
• Standardized Chapter Test, pp. 84–85
• SAT/ACT Chapter Test, pp. 86–87
• Alternative Assessment, pp. 88–89

Test Generator CD-ROM

Chapter Test

Easily-readable reduced copies (with answers) of Chapter Test B, the Standardized Chapter Test, and the Alternative Assessment from the Assessment Book can be found on pp. 354G–354H.

16.

17.

18.

19.

20.

21.

22.

29–31. See Additional Answers beginning on p. AA1.

34a.

7.
8.
9.

10.
11.
12.

13.
14.
15.

Scoring Rubric

Full Credit
- solution is complete and correct

Partial Credit
- solution is complete but errors are made, *or*
- solution is without error but incomplete

No Credit
- no solution is given, *or*
- solution makes no sense

EXTENDED RESPONSE QUESTIONS

PROBLEM

Your school chess club is selling chess sets for $9 each to raise funds for a regional tournament. The club wants to sell at least 100 of them. The table shows the number of chess sets sold so far by each member of the club.

Member	1	2	3	4	5	6
Chess sets sold	17	16	12	13	16	10

a. Find the possible numbers a of additional chess sets that the club can sell in order to meet its goal.

b. If the club raises more than $1000, it will donate the amount that exceeds $1000 to a charity. Find the possible total numbers t of chess sets that the club can sell in order to donate at least $100 to the charity.

c. Suppose the club has 61 chess sets left to sell. Write an inequality that describes the possible amounts that the club can donate to the charity. *Explain* your answer.

Below are sample solutions to the problem. Read each solution and the comments in blue to see why the sample represents full credit, partial credit, or no credit.

Sample 1: Full credit solution

The correct inequality is given. The solution is correct.

a. $17 + 16 + 12 + 13 + 16 + 10 + a \geq 100$

$$84 + a \geq 100$$

$$a \geq 16$$

The club will meet its goal if it sells at least 16 more chess sets.

The correct inequality is given. The student rounded correctly so that the answer makes sense.

b. $9t - 1000 \geq 100$

$$9t \geq 1100$$

$$t \geq 122.22\ldots$$

The club can donate only $9(122) - $1000 = $98 if it sells 122 sets. So, the club can donate at least $100 if it sells at least 123 sets.

The student's calculation of the least and greatest values is correct. The answer is correct.

c. If the club doesn't sell any more chess sets, it will have raised a total of $9(84) = $756. Because the club will not have raised at least $1000, its donation to the charity would be $0. If the club sells the remaining 61 chess sets, it will have raised a total of $756 + $9(61) = $1305. So, the club's donation to the charity would be $1305 - $1000 = $305. The inequality is $0 \leq d \leq 305$ where d is the donation.

Sample 2: Partial credit solution

The correct inequality is given. The solution is correct.

a. $84 + a \geq 100$

$a \geq 16$

The club must sell at least 16 chess sets.

The student solved the inequality correctly but gave the wrong answer.

b. $9t - 1000 \geq 100$

$9t \geq 1100$

$t \geq 122.22\ldots$

The club can donate at least \$100 if it sells at least 122 sets.

The reasoning doesn't make sense, and the inequality is incorrect.

c. If the club doesn't sell any more chess sets, it will raise \$0 more. So, the donation would be \$0. If the club sells the remaining 61 sets, it will raise $9(61) = \$549$ more. So, the donation would be at most \$549. The inequality is $0 \leq d \leq 549$ where d is the donation.

Sample 3: No credit solution

The inequalities in parts (a) and (b) are incorrect, and the answers are incorrect.

a. $84 + a \leq 100$

$a \leq 16$

The club will meet its goal if it sells up to 16 chess sets.

b. $9t \geq 1000$

$t \geq 111.11\ldots$

The club can donate at least \$100 if it sells at least 112 chess sets.

The student didn't consider the number of chess sets the club can sell.

c. The donation would be \$0 if the club raised up to \$1000. But the donation would be greater than \$0 if the club raised more than \$1000. The inequality is $d \geq 0$ where d is the donation.

PRACTICE Apply the Scoring Rubric

1. A student's solution to the problem on the previous page is given below. Score the solution as *full credit*, *partial credit*, or *no credit*. *Explain* your reasoning. If you choose *partial credit* or *no credit*, explain how you would change the solution so that it earns a score of full credit. **See margin.**

a. Because $a \geq 100 - 84$, the club must sell at least 16 sets to meet its goal.

b. The total amount raised is 9t. In order to donate at least \$100, the club needs to raise a total of at least \$1100.

$9t \geq 1100$, so $t \geq 122.22\ldots$

c. If the club sells the remaining 61 sets, then it will have raised $\$9(61) = \$549$ more. The inequality is $d \leq 549$ where d is the donation.

Avoiding Common Errors
Caution students to check the context of a question when rounding answers in real-world situations. A student may round a number up or down correctly in terms of method, but the context of the question may require the next or previous integer rather than the rounded value.

1. Partial credit; in part (a), show how the inequality $a \geq 16$ is arrived at. In part (c), calculate the total amount raised, not just the additional amount raised, and then subtract \$1000 from the total amount to find the largest possible donation. Also consider what the lowest possible donation is.

1c. Solve $5.5x + 7(20 - x) \geq 150$; the solution is $x \leq -6\frac{2}{3}$. Because x represents a number of hours, x cannot be a negative number, so the solution does not makes sense in this situation.

2a.

2c. Move the line so that the t-intercept is $\frac{40}{3}$ and the d-intercept is 20. The linear inequality that describes the situation in which you can spend up to \$40 is $3t + 2d < 40$.

EXTENDED RESPONSE

1. You plan to work a total of 20 hours per week at two part-time jobs. The table shows the hourly wage at each job.

Job	Working at a sandwich shop	After-school tutoring
Hourly wage (dollars)	5.50	7.00

a. You want to earn from \$100 to \$120 per week. What are the possible numbers of hours that you can work at the sandwich shop so that you can meet your earnings goal? **from $18\frac{2}{11}$ h up to 20 h**

b. Suppose you need to reduce the total number of hours you work each week to 18 hours. Can you still meet your earnings goal? If so, what are the least and greatest numbers of hours that you can work at the sandwich shop? If not, explain why not. **yes; 4 h, $17\frac{1}{3}$ h**

c. Show that it is not possible to earn more than \$150 after working 20 hours in one week by writing and solving an inequality that describes the situation and showing that the solutions do not make sense for the situation. **See margin.**

2. You plan to spend up to \$30 on flower bulbs for a garden. The table shows the prices of tulip bulbs and daffodil bulbs.

Flower bulb	Tulip	Daffodil
Price (dollars)	3	2

a. Write and graph an inequality that describes the possible combinations of tulip bulbs and daffodil bulbs that you can buy. **$3t + 2d \leq 30$; see margin for art.**

b. Give three possible combinations of tulip bulbs and daffodil bulbs that you can buy. **Sample answer:** 5 tulip bulbs and 5 daffodil bulbs, 0 tulip bulbs and 15 daffodil bulbs, 8 tulip bulbs and 2 daffodil bulbs

c. Suppose you plan to spend up to \$40 on flower bulbs. How would you change the graph in part (a) in order to describe this situation? *Explain* your answer. **See margin.**

3. The average number of hits h per day that your website received during the period January 2001 to February 2004 can be modeled by the equation $h = -16|m - 30| + 500$ where m is the number of months since January 2001.

a. In what month and year did your website receive an average of 100 hits per day? If the model holds for months after February 2004, predict the month and year in which your website will again receive an average of 100 hits per day. **June 2001; August 2005**

b. According to the model, did your website receive an average of 600 hits per day at any time during the period January 2001 to February 2004? *Explain* your answer. **No; if you substitute 600 for h in the model, the equation has no solution.**

c. Can you use the model to find the month and year in which the average number of hits per day was the greatest? *Justify* your answer. **Yes. Sample answer:** Make a table of values for (m, h) for integer values of m from 0 to 49. Look for the greatest value of h in the table.

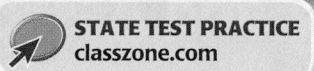

MULTIPLE CHOICE

4. In a piano competition, a pianist must perform a sonata that lasts no less than 8 minutes and no more than 10 minutes. Which inequality represents the durations d (in minutes) of sonatas that can be performed? **C**

   Ⓐ $8 < d < 10$ Ⓑ $d \le 8 \ or \ d \ge 10$

   Ⓒ $8 \le d \le 10$ Ⓓ $d < 8 \ or \ d > 10$

5. Which ordered pair is a solution of the inequality $4x - y \ge 3$? **C**

   Ⓐ $(0, 0)$ Ⓑ $(-1, 2)$

   Ⓒ $(1, 1)$ Ⓓ $(0, -2)$

6. You are designing an obstacle course for a dog agility event. The course includes a tunnel that must have a height of 24 inches with an absolute deviation of 2 inches. Which equation can you use to find the minimum and maximum heights of the tunnel? **B**

   Ⓐ $|x + 24| = 2$ Ⓑ $|x - 24| = 2$

   Ⓒ $|x + 2| = 24$ Ⓓ $|x - 2| = 24$

GRIDDED ANSWER

7. You scored the following points in four basketball games: 16, 24, 32, and 22. You want to score an average of more than 25 points per game after your fifth game. Of all the possible points you can score in your fifth game in order to meet your goal, which is the least? **31 points**

8. In men's weightlifting, the bar that holds the weights must have a length of 2.2 meters with an absolute deviation of 1 millimeter. Of all the possible lengths that the bar can have, which is the greatest length (in millimeters)? **2201 mm**

9. Of all the numbers that are solutions of the inequality $\left| -\frac{1}{3}x + 4 \right| \le 2$, which is the least number? **6**

10. The perimeter of the rectangle shown is at least 47 inches and at most 52 inches. Find the greatest value of x that satisfies the condition. **5**

$2x$ in.

$(x + 11)$ in.

SHORT RESPONSE

11. You and 4 friends each order a three course dinner at a restaurant, and all of you agree to divide the total cost equally. The table shows the range of prices for each of the three courses.

Dinner course	Appetizer	Main course	Dessert
Price range (dollars)	2–4	12–20	3–6

  a. Find the least and greatest possible total costs C (in dollars). Then write an inequality that describes the possible total costs. **$85, $150; $85 \le C \le 150$**

  b. Your share s (in dollars) of the total cost is given by $s = \frac{C}{5}$. You chose a $3 appetizer, a $15 main course, and a $4 dessert. *Explain* why your share could be greater than or less than $3 + $15 + $4 = $22. **See margin.**

12. A family is planning a vacation and is willing to spend no more than $2000 for 4 airplane tickets and 5 nights at a hotel. Write and graph an inequality that describes the combinations of prices x (in dollars) of an airplane ticket and prices y (in dollars) of a night at a hotel. If the family spends $275 per airplane ticket, is the family willing to spend $200 per night at a hotel? *Explain* your answer using the graph. **See margin.**

11b. $C = 5s$, so to find an inequality that describes the possible shares, solve $85 \le 5s \le 150$, to get $17 \le s \le 30$. Each person's share will be from $17 to $30. Your meal cost $3 + $15 + $4 = $22, so your share of the total cost could end up being either more or less than the total price of your meal.

12.

Cost of hotel per night (dollars)

$4x + 5y \le 2000$

Airplane ticket price (dollars)

No; spending $275 on airplane tickets and $200 per night at a hotel is represented by the ordered pair (275, 200). The point lies above the line of the graph, but the solutions of the graph are all the points below the line, so it is not a solution.

REGULAR SCHEDULE

Pre-AP For pacing and assignments for a Pre-AP course, see the *Algebra 1 Toolkit*.

Lesson	Les. Day	BASIC	AVERAGE	ADVANCED
7.1	Day 1	EP p. 941 Exs. 19–22; pp. 430–433 Exs. 1–17, 31–34, 38–42 even, 43–48	pp. 430–433 Exs. 1–11, 18–35, 37–41 odd, 43–48	pp. 430–433 Exs. 1, 4–7, 9, 10, 21–36*, 38–48 even
7.2	Day 1	EP p. 940 Exs. 21–26; pp. 439–441 Exs. 1–19	pp. 439–441 Exs. 1, 2, 4–18 even, 19–29 odd	pp. 439–441 Exs. 1, 6–8, 15–18, 20–28
	Day 2	pp. 439–441 Exs. 20–25, 31–35, 39–50	pp. 439–441 Exs. 31–37, 39–50	pp. 439–441 Exs. 29–38*, 42–44, 48–50
7.3	Day 1	pp. 447–450 Exs. 1, 2, 3–21 odd, 22–30, 39–43, 46–54 even	pp. 447–450 Exs. 1, 2, 6–8, 12–15, 19–24, 26–36 even, 39–44, 47–55 odd	pp. 447–450 Exs. 1, 2, 7, 8, 13–15, 19–22, 25–33 odd, 34–45*, 49, 52, 54
7.4	Day 1	SRH p. 911 Exs. 25, 26, 32, 36; pp. 454–457 Exs. 1, 2, 3–17 odd, 18–25, 37–41, 46–58 even	pp. 454–457 Exs. 1, 2, 6–8, 13–20, 21–33 odd, 34, 37–42, 45–57 odd	pp. 454–457 Exs. 1, 7, 8, 15–18, 21–36*, 39–44*, 47, 52, 58
7.5	Day 1	pp. 462–465 Exs. 1–20, 24, 25, 42–45	pp. 462–465 Exs. 1–14, 18–25, 42–45	pp. 462–465 Exs. 1–4, 11–13, 18–25, 44, 45
	Day 2	pp. 462–465 Exs. 26–30, 36–39, 46–60	pp. 462–465 Exs. 26–34, 36–40, 46–54 even, 56–61	pp. 462–465 Exs. 26–35*, 37–41*, 51, 52, 55, 59
7.6	Day 1	EP p. 943 Exs. 67–70, 72, 73; pp. 469–472 Exs. 1–8, 9–21 odd, 22–26, 36–39, 43–53 odd	pp. 469–472 Exs. 1–8, 15–23, 25–33 odd, 36–40, 42–52 even	pp. 469–472 Exs. 1, 2, 16–22, 24–41*, 47, 52
Review	Day 1	pp. 475–478 Exs. 1–31	pp. 475–478 Exs. 1–31	pp. 475–478 Exs. 1–31
Assess	Day 1	Chapter 7 Test	Chapter 7 Test	Chapter 7 Test
Yearly Pacing		Chapter 7 Total – 10 days	Chapters 1–7 Total – 80 days	Remaining – 80 days

*Challenge Exercises   EP = Extra Practice   SRH = Skills Review Handbook

BLOCK SCHEDULE

DAY 1	DAY 2	DAY 3	DAY 4	DAY 5
7.1	**7.2 (CONT.)**	**7.4**	**7.5 (CONT.)**	**REVIEW**
pp. 430–433 Exs. 1–11, 18–35, 37–41 odd, 43–48	pp. 439–441 Exs. 31–37, 39–50	pp. 454–457 Exs. 1, 2, 6–8, 13–20, 21–33 odd, 34, 37–42, 45–57 odd	pp. 462–465 Exs. 26–34, 36–40, 46–54 even, 56–61	pp. 475–478 Exs. 1–31
7.2	**7.3**	**7.5**	**7.6**	**ASSESS**
pp. 439–441 Exs. 1, 2, 4–18 even, 19–29 odd	pp. 447–450 Exs. 1, 2, 6–8, 12–15, 19–24, 26–36 even, 39–44, 47–55 odd	pp. 462–465 Exs. 1–14, 18–25, 42–45	pp. 469–472 Exs. 1–8, 15–23, 25–33 odd, 36–40, 42–52 even	Chapter 7 Test
Yearly Pacing	Chapter 7 Total – 5 days	Chapters 1–7 Total – 40 days	Remaining – 40 days	

RESOURCE MANAGER

Chapter Resource Book

CHAPTER SUPPORT

Parents as Partners (Chapter Overview with home involvement exercises and activity)				p. 1	

LESSON SUPPORT	7.1	7.2	7.3	7.4	7.5	7.6
Teaching Guide/Lesson Plan	p. 3	p. 17	p. 27	p. 38	p. 50	p. 64
Activity Masters				p. 40	p. 52	
Technology Activities & Keystrokes	p. 5					p. 66
Activity Support Masters			p. 29			
Practice (3 levels)	p. 6	p. 19	p. 30	p. 41	p. 53	p. 68
Study Guide	p. 12	p. 22	p. 33	p. 44	p. 59	p. 74
Catch-Up for Absent Students	p. 14	p. 24	p. 35	p. 46	p. 61	p. 76
Problem Solving/Application	p. 15	p. 25	p. 36	p. 47	p. 62	p. 77
Challenge Practice	p. 16	p. 26	p. 37	p. 49	p. 63	p. 78

REVIEW

Chapter Review Games and Activities	p. 79	Cumulative Practice	p. 81
Project with Rubric	p. 80	Resource Book Answers	A1

Transparencies

Transparencies	7.1	7.2	7.3	7.4	7.5	7.6
Warm-Up/Daily Homework Quiz	✔	✔	✔	✔	✔	✔
Notetaking Guide	✔	✔	✔	✔	✔	✔
Teacher Support	✔				✔	✔
Answer Transparencies	✔	✔	✔	✔	✔	✔

ASSESSMENT BOOK

Quizzes	p. 90	SAT/ACT Chapter Test	p. 101
Chapter Tests (3 levels)	p. 93	Alternative Assessment with Rubric	p. 103
Standardized Chapter Test	p. 99	Cumulative Test	p. 105

TECHNOLOGY

- Easy Planner
- Test and Practice Generator
- Power Presentations
- @HomeTutor
- Activity Generator
- Animated Algebra
- Classzone.com
- eEdition Plus Online
- eWorkbook Plus Online
- Easy Grader Online

ADDITIONAL RESOURCES

- Worked-Out Solution Key
- Notetaking Guide
- Practice Wookbook
- Algebra 1 Toolkit
- Benchmark Tests
- Reteaching and Remediation
- Spanish Study Guide
- Spanish Assessment Book
- Student Resources in Spanish
- Multi-Language Visual Glossary

LESSON 7.1 Practice B
For use with pages 427–433

Tell whether the ordered pair is a solution of the linear system.

1. $(4, 1)$; no
$x + 2y = 6$
$3x + y = 11$

2. $(-2, 1)$; yes
$5x - 2y = -12$
$x + 3y = 1$

3. $(4, -3)$; yes
$-3x + 2y = -18$
$6x - y = 27$

4. $(-4, -6)$; no
$3x - y = 6$
$-x + 2y = 8$

5. $(-4, 3)$; no
$4x + 3y = -12$
$x + 2y = -6$

6. $(-2, -5)$; yes
$-x + y = -3$
$-x + 3y = -13$

Use the graph to solve the linear system. Check your solution.

7. $x - y = 8$ $(3, -5)$
$x + y = -2$

8. $5x - y = -9$ $(-1, 4)$
$y + 2x = 2$

9. $2x + 3y = 2$ $(-2, 2)$
$-2x + y = 6$

10. $3x - 2y = 16$ $(4, -2)$
$5x + y = 18$

11. $2x - y = -13$ $(-5, 3)$
$y + 3x = -12$

12. $6x + 2y = 8$ $(0, 4)$
$3x + 4y = 16$

Solve the linear system by graphing. Check your solution.

13. $y = 3x$ $(1, 3)$
$y = 4x - 1$

14. $2x + y = -4$ $(-4, 4)$
$x - y = -8$
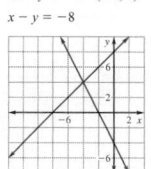

15. $-3x - y = -1$ $(2, -5)$
$2x + 4y = -16$

LESSON 7.1 Practice B
For use with pages 427–433

16. $2x + 2y = -6$ $(-3, 0)$
$-5x + y = 15$

17. $-6x + y = 33$ $(-5, 3)$
$2x - 8y = -34$

18. $-9x + 6y = -6$ $(-2, -4)$
$2x - 3y = 8$
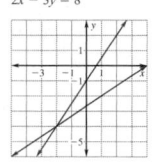

19. $3x + 2y = 3$ $(-3, 6)$
$5x + y = -9$

20. $x - y = 9$ $(4, -5)$
$3x + 2y = 2$

21. $6x + y = 19$ $(2, 7)$
$5x - 2y = -4$

22. Hanging Flower Baskets You will be making hanging flower baskets. The plants you have picked out are blooming annuals and non-blooming annuals. The blooming annuals cost $3.20 each and the non-blooming annuals cost $1.50 each. You bought a total of 24 plants for $49.60. Write a linear system of equations that you can use to find out how many of each type of plant you bought. Then graph the linear system and use the graph to find how many of each type of plant you bought.
8 blooming annuals and 16 non-blooming annuals

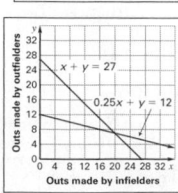

23. Baseball Outs In a game, 12 of a baseball team's 27 outs were fly balls. Twenty-five percent of the outs made by infielders and 100% of the outs made by outfielders were fly balls.

a. Write a linear system you can use to find the number of outs made by infielders and the number of outs made by outfielders. (*Hint:* Write one equation for the total number of outs and another equation for the number of fly ball outs.)

b. Graph your linear system.   **a.** $x + y = 27$ and $0.25x + y = 12$

c. How many outs were made by infielders? How many outs were made by outfielders?   infielders: 20 outs; outfielders: 7 outs

---

LESSON 7.2 Practice B
For use with pages 435–441

Solve for the indicated variable.

1. $8x + 4y = 12$; y $y = -2x + 3$

2. $3x - 4y = 12$; y $y = \frac{3}{4}x - 3$

3. $6x - 4y = 8$; x $x = \frac{2}{3}y + \frac{4}{3}$

Tell which equation you would use to isolate a variable. *Explain* your reasoning.

4. $x = 8y - 3$
$3x - 4y = 1$
Answers will vary.

5. $-4x + 5y = 11$
$y = 4x - 1$
Answers will vary.

6. $9 - 3x = y$
$3x - y = -2$
Answers will vary.

Solve the linear system by using substitution.

7. $x = 6 - 4y$ $(2, 1)$
$2x - 3y = 1$

8. $4x + 3y = 0$ $(-3, 4)$
$2x + y = -2$

9. $-x + 2y = -6$ $(4, -1)$
$8x + y = 31$

10. $6x - y = -35$ $(-5, 5)$
$5x - 2y = -35$

11. $-x + 3y = -9$ $(3, -2)$
$8x - 4y = 32$

12. $3x + 3y = -18$ $(-4, -2)$
$4x - y = -14$

13. $2x + 2y = 6$ $(6, -3)$
$-3x + 5y = -33$

14. $5x + 2y = 43$ $(7, 4)$
$-6x + 3y = -30$

15. $4x - 2y = -4$ $(3, 8)$
$7x - 5y = -19$

16. $3x + 2y = 5$ $(1, 1)$
$5x - 9y = -4$

17. $4x - 3y = 28$ $(4, -4)$
$2x + 3y = -4$

18. $8x + 8y = 24$ $(1, 2)$
$x + 5y = 11$

19. Drum Sticks A drummer is stocking up on his drum sticks and brushes. The wood sticks that he buys are $10.50 a pair and the brushes are $24 a pair. He ends up spending $90 on sticks and brushes and buys two times as many pairs of sticks as brushes. How many pairs of sticks and brushes did he buy? 4 pairs of sticks and 2 pairs of brushes

20. Mowing and Shoveling Last year you mowed grass and shoveled snow for 12 households. You earned $225 for mowing a household's lawn for the entire year and you earned $200 for shoveling a household's walk and driveway for an entire year. You earned a total of $2600 last year.

a. Let x be the number of households you mowed for and let y be the number of households you shoveled for. Write an equation in x and y that shows the total number of households you worked for. Then write an equation in x and y that shows the total amount of money you earned. $x + y = 12$; $225x + 200y = 2600$

b. How many households did you mow the lawn for and how many households did you shovel the walk and driveway for? households mowed: 8 households; households shoveled: 4 households

21. Dimensions of a Metal Sheet A rectangular hole 3 centimeters wide and x centimeters long is cut in a rectangular sheet of metal that is 4 centimeters wide and y centimeters long. The length of the hole is 1 centimeter less than the length of the metal sheet. After the hole is cut, the area of the remaining metal sheet is 20 square centimeters. Find the length of the hole and the length of the metal sheet.
length of hole: 16 cm; length of sheet: 17 cm

Practice B
7.3 For use with pages 444–450

Rewrite the linear system so that the like terms are arranged in columns.

1. $8x - y = 19$ $8x - y = 19$
$y + 3x = 7$ and $3x + y = 7$

2. $4x = y - 11$
$6y + 4x = -3$
$4x - y = -11$ and $4x + 6y = -3$

3. $9x - 2y = 5$
$2y = -11x + 8$
$9x - 2y = 5$ and
$11x + 2y = 8$

Describe the first step you would use to solve the linear system.

4. $22x - y = -4$
$y = 6x - 5$
Arrange the terms.

5. $25 = x - 7y$
$x + 12y = -8$
Arrange the terms.

6. $3x + 7 = 2y$
$-2y - 1 = 10x$
Arrange the terms.

7. $x + 9y = 2$
$14x - 9y = -4$
Add the equations.

8. $4x + 3y = -6$
$3y = -5x + 1$
Arrange the terms.

9. $4x + y = -10$
$x + y = -14$
Subtract the equations.

Solve the linear system by using elimination.

10. $x + 5y = 28$ $(3, 5)$
$-x - 2y = -13$

11. $7x - 4y = -30$ $(-2, 4)$
$3x + 4y = 10$

12. $6x + y = 39$ $(7, -3)$
$-2x + y = -17$

13. $3x = y - 20$ $(-6, 2)$
$-7x = y = 40$

14. $2x - 6y = -10$ $(10, 5)$
$4x = 10 + 6y$

15. $x - 3y = 6$ $(-9, -5)$
$2x = 3y + 33$

16. $-3x = y - 20$ $(3, 11)$
$-y = -5x + 4$

17. $x - \frac{1}{2}y = \frac{11}{2}$ $(10, 9)$
$-x + 4y = 26$

18. $-\frac{2}{3}x + 6y = 38$ $(15, 8)$
$x - 6y = -33$

19. $\frac{3}{2}x + y = -\frac{5}{2}$ $(-1, -1)$
$4x + y = -5$

20. $7x - \frac{1}{3}y = -29$ $(-4, 3)$
$2x - \frac{1}{3}y = -9$

21. $\frac{1}{2}x - \frac{3}{2}y = -\frac{29}{2}$ $\left(8, \frac{37}{3}\right)$
$-\frac{1}{2}x + 3y = 33$

22. Fishing Barge A fishing barge leaves from a dock and moves upstream (against the current) at a rate of 3.8 miles per hour until it reaches its destination. After the people on the barge are done fishing, the barge moves the same distance downstream (with the current) at a rate of 8 miles per hour until it returns to the dock. The speed of the current remains constant. Use the models below to write and solve a system of equations to find the average speed of the barge in still water and the speed of the current.   Speed of barge in still water: 5.9 mi/h; Speed of current: 2.1 mi/h

Upstream: Speed of barge in still water − Speed of current = Speed of barge

Downstream: Speed of barge in still water + Speed of current = Speed of barge

23. Floor Sander Rental A rental company charges a flat fee of x dollars for a floor sander rental plus y dollars per hour of the rental. One customer rents a floor sander for 4 hours and pays $63. Another customer rents a floor sander for 6 hours and pays $87.

a. Find the flat fee and the cost per hour for the rental.   Flat fee: $15; Hourly fee: $12

b. How much would it cost someone to rent a sander for 11 hours? $147

Practice B
7.4 For use with pages 451–457

1. *Sample answer:* Multiply the first equation by 2.
2. *Sample answer:* Multiply the second equation by -3.
3. *Sample answer:* Multiply the first equation by -3.

Describe the first step you would use to solve the linear system.

1. $3x - 4y = 7$
$5x + 8y = 10$

2. $9x + 4y = 13$
$3x + 5y = 9$

3. $5x + 7y = -3$
$15x + 4y = -5$

4. $7x - 4y = 6$ See below.
$3x - 2y = -15$

5. $7x + 9y = -6$ See below.
$-5x + 14y = 11$

6. $9x - 5y = 14$ See below.
$-6x + 8y = 13$

Solve the linear system by using elimination.

7. $x + 3y = 1$ $(4, -1)$
$-5x + 4y = -24$

8. $-3x - y = -15$ $(3, 6)$
$8x + 4y = 48$

9. $x + 7y = -37$ $(-2, -5)$
$2x - 5y = 21$

10. $8x - 4y = -76$ $(-6, 7)$
$5x + 2y = -16$

11. $-3x + 10y = 23$ $(9, 5)$
$5x + 2y = 55$

12. $9x - 4y = 26$ $(2, -2)$
$18x + 7y = 22$

13. $4x - 3y = 16$ $(10, 8)$
$16x + 10y = 240$

14. $20x + 10y = 100$ $(-1, 12)$
$-5x + 4y = 53$

15. $3x - 10y = -25$ $(5, 4)$
$5x - 20y = -55$

16. $-3x - 4y = 27$ $(-5, -3)$
$5x - 6y = -7$

17. $2x + 7y = 2$ $(15, -4)$
$5x - 2y = 83$

18. $3x - 5y = -16$ $(8, 8)$
$2x - 3y = -8$

19. Hockey Game Two families go to a hockey game. One family purchases two adult tickets and four youth tickets for $28. Another family purchases four adult tickets and five youth tickets for $45.50. Let x represent the cost in dollars of one adult ticket and let y represent the cost in dollars of one youth ticket.

a. Write a linear system that represents this situation. $2x + 4y = 28$ and $4x + 5y = 45.5$

b. Solve the linear system to find the cost of one adult and one youth ticket.   Adult: $7; Youth: $3.50

c. How much would it cost two adults and five youths to attend the game? $31.50

20. Travel Agency A travel agency offers two Chicago outings. Plan A includes hotel accommodations for three nights and two pairs of baseball tickets worth a total of $557. Plan B includes hotel accommodations for five nights and four pairs of baseball tickets worth a total of $974. Let x represent the cost in dollars of one night's hotel accommodations and let y represent the cost in dollars of one pair of baseball tickets.

a. Write a linear system you could use to find the cost of one night's hotel accommodations and the cost of one pair of baseball tickets. $3x + 2y = 557$ and $5x + 4y = 974$

b. Solve the linear system to find the cost of one night's hotel accommodations and the cost of one pair of baseball tickets.   Hotel: $140/night; Tickets: $68.50/pair

21. Highway Project There are fifteen workers employed on a highway project, some at $180 per day and some at $155 per day. The daily payroll is $2400. Let x represent the number of $180 per day workers and let y represent the number of $155 per day workers. Write and solve a linear system to find the number of workers employed at each wage. $x + y = 15$ and $180x + 155y = 2400$; $180/day: 3 workers; $155/day: 12 workers

4. *Sample answer:* Multiply the second equation by -2.
5. *Sample answer:* Multiply the first equation by -5.
6. *Sample answer:* Multiply the first equation by 2.

Practice B
7.5 For use with pages 459–465

Match the linear system with its graph. Then use the graph to tell whether the linear system has one solution, no solution, or infinitely many solutions.

1. $y + 3 = 4x$ C
$3y = 12x - 9$

2. $2x + y = 1$ A
$2x + y = 5$

3. $3x + y = 1$ B
$-2x + y = -3$

A.
B.
C.

Graph the linear system. Then use the graph to tell whether the linear system has one solution, no solution, or infinitely many solutions.

4. $-6x + 2y = -2$
$-3x + y = 2$ no solution

5. $2y - x = -4$
$2x + y = 3$ one solution
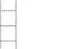

6. $4x - y = 2$
$-x + 3y = 9$ one solution
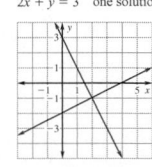

7. $x + 2y = 3$
$-x + 2y = -2$ one solution

8. $3x + y = 4$
$x + \frac{1}{3}y = 2$ no solution

9. $2x - y = 4$
$-2x + y = -4$ infinitely many solutions

Practice B continued
7.5 For use with pages 459–465

Solve the linear system by using substitution or elimination.

10. $3x - 2y = 24$ $(8, 0)$
$x + 2y = 8$

11. $3x + 2y = 4$ infinitely many solutions
$-6x - 4y = -8$

12. $x + y = 50$ $(20, 30)$
$-3x + 2y = 0$

13. $-x + 4y = -3$ $(-1, -1)$
$-3x + 2y = 1$

14. $-x + 3y = 9$ $(3, 4)$
$2x + y = 10$

15. $2x + y = 6$ no solution
$2x + y = -7$

Without solving the linear system, tell whether the linear system has one solution, no solution, or infinitely many solutions.

16. $-6x + 6y = -4$ no solution
$2x - 2y = 5$

17. $y + 2x = \frac{8}{3}$ no solution
$2x + y = -10$

18. $4x + 3y = 9$ one solution
$\frac{3}{4}x + y - 3$

19. $4x - 6y = -1$ one solution
$-\frac{3}{2}x + y = \frac{1}{4}$

20. $-\frac{2}{3}x + y = 2$ one solution
$-6x + 3y = 6$

21. $9x - 15y = 15$ one solution
$x + \frac{3}{5}y = 1$

22. $-3x + 4y = 2$
$2y = \frac{3}{2}x + 1$ infinitely many solutions

23. $3x + y = 4$ no solution
$x + \frac{1}{3}y = 2$

24. $-4x + 3y = 2$
$4 - 6y = -8x$ infinitely many solutions

25. Golf Clubs A sporting goods store stocks a "better" set of golf clubs in both left-handed and right-handed sets. The set of left-handed golf clubs sells for x dollars and the set of right-handed golf clubs sells for y dollars. In one month, the store sells 2 sets of left-handed golf clubs and 12 sets of right-handed golf clubs for a total of $1859.30. The next month, the store sells 2 sets of left-handed golf clubs and 22 sets of right-handed golf clubs for a total of $3158.80. Is there enough information to determine the cost of each kind of set? *Explain.*   Yes; Answers will vary.

26. Comedy Tickets The table below shows the tickets sales at an all-ages comedy club on a Friday night and a Saturday night.

Day	Number of adult tickets	Number of student tickets	Total sales (dollars)
Friday	30	20	910
Saturday	45	30	1365

a. Let x represent the cost (in dollars) of one adult ticket and let y represent the cost (in dollars) of one student ticket. Write a linear system that models the situation.

b. Solve the linear system.   infinitely many solutions

c. Can you determine how much each kind of ticket costs? Why or why not?   No, because one equation in the system is a multiple of the other, specific values for neither x nor y can be found.

26. a. $30x + 20y = 910$ and $45x + 30y = 1365$

LESSON 7.6 Practice B
For use with pages 466–472

Tell whether the ordered pair is a solution of the system of inequalities.

1. $(3, 0)$ yes

2. $(2, 2)$ yes

3. $(-2, 2)$ no

Match the system of inequalities with its graph.

4. $\frac{1}{2}x + y \geq 3$ B
$x > -1$

5. $y - \frac{1}{2}x \leq 3$ A
$x < -1$

6. $y \leq \frac{1}{2}x + 3$ C
$x > -1$

A.

B.

C.

Graph the system of inequalities.

7. $x > -1$
$x < 1$

8. $y \geq 2$
$y < 3$

9. $x + y > 1$
$x \leq y$

10. $x \geq y + 2$
$2x + y < 4$

11. $y \geq 2$
$x + y \leq -3$

12. $x \leq -y$
$2x - y < 4$

LESSON 7.6 Practice B *continued*
For use with pages 466–472

13. $y \geq -4$ and $y < 1$
14. $x \geq -4$ and $y < -3$
15. $y \geq x + 1$ and $x \leq 0$
16. $y \leq 4 - x$ and $y > 2$
17. $y \leq x$ and $y \leq 1 - x$
18. $x \geq 0, y \geq 0,$ and $y \leq x + 2$

Write a system of inequalities for the shaded region.

13.

14.

15.

16.

17.

18.

19. Cookout You are planning a cookout. You figure that you will need at least 5 packages of hot dogs and hamburgers. A package of hot dogs costs $1.90 and a package of hamburgers costs $5.20. You can spend a maximum of $20 on the hot dogs and hamburgers.

a. Let x represent the number of packages of hot dogs and let y represent the number of packages of hamburgers. Write a system of linear inequalities for the number of packages of each that can be bought. $x + y \geq 5$ and $1.9x + 5.2y \leq 20$

b. Graph the system of inequalities.

c. Identify two possible combinations of packages of hot dogs and hamburgers you can buy.   Answers will vary.

20. Chores You need at least 4 hours to do your chores, which is cleaning out the garage and weeding the flower beds around your house. It is 1:30 P.M. on Sunday and your friend wants you to go to the movies at 7:00 P.M.

a. How much time do you have between now and 7:00 P.M. to do your chores?   5.5 h

b. Let x represent the number of hours spent cleaning out the garage and let y represent the number of hours spent on weeding the flower beds. Write and graph a system of linear inequalities that shows the number of hours you can work on each chore if you go to the movies.

c. Identify two possible combinations of time you can spend on each chore. Answers will vary.

7 Assessment

Solve the linear system by graphing. Check your solution.

1. $x - y = 1$
$x + y = -5$

2. $x - 4y = 10$
$2x + y = 2$

3. $-5x + y = 0$
$x + y = 6$

Solve the linear system using substitution.

4. $y = 6 - 2x$
$7x - y = 3$

5. $x = y - 4$
$3x + y = 12$

6. $y - 5 = x$
$4x - y = 4$

7. $y - 2x = -6$
$5x - y = 9$

8. $3y + x = 2$
$y - x = -6$

Answers

1. $(-2, -3)$
   See left.
2. $(2, -2)$
   See left.
3. $(1, 5)$
   See left.
4. $(1, 4)$
5. $(2, 6)$
6. $(3, 8)$
7. $(1, -4)$
8. $(5, -1)$

Solve the linear system using elimination.

1. $5x + y = 4$
$6x - y = 7$

2. $-3x + 4y = 2$
$3x + y = 8$

3. $x + 3y = 14$
$x + 2y = 10$

4. $5x + 3y = 1$
$5x + y = -3$

5. $6x - y = 8$
$7x - y = 9$

6. $x - 2y = 8$
$4x + y = 5$

7. $7x + y = 11$
$4x + 2y = 12$

8. $3x + y = 10$
$5x - 2y = 13$

Answers

1. $(1, -1)$
2. $(2, 2)$
3. $(2, 4)$
4. $(-1, 2)$
5. $(1, -2)$
6. $(2, -3)$
7. $(1, 4)$
8. $(3, 1)$

Graph the linear system. Then use the graph to tell whether the linear system has *one solution, no solution,* or *infinitely many solutions.*

1. $3y - 7x = -4$
$3y - 2x = 1$

2. $-8x + 2y = -16$
$4x - y = 10$

3. $3x + y = 2$
$-9x - 3y = -6$

Graph the system of inequalities.

4. $x > 2$
$y < 3$

5. $y \le x + 2$
$y \ge 1$

6. $x \ge 0$
$y > 3x$

7. $y \le -x$
$y > 1$
$x < -1$

Answers

1. See left.
   one solution
2. See left.
   no solution
3. See left.
   infinitely many
   solutions
4. See left.
5. See left.
6. See left.
7. See left.

424F

Chapter Test B
For use after Chapter 7

Tell whether the ordered pair is a solution of the linear system.

1. $(4, -1)$
$x + 2y = 2$
$x - 2y = 6$

2. $(8, 5)$
$5x - 4y = 20$
$3y = 2x + 1$

3. $(-3, 5)$
$9x + 7y = 8$
$8x - 9y = -69$

In Exercises 4–6, use the following information.

Tickets for a school play cost $4 for adults and $2 for students. At the end of the play, the school sold a total of 105 tickets and collected $360.

4. Write a linear system. Let x be the number of adult tickets sold and let y be the number of student tickets sold.

5. Graph the linear system.

6. Find the number of adult tickets sold and the number of student tickets sold.

Solve the linear system using substitution.

7. $4x + 3y = -5$
$x = y - 3$

8. $x + 3y = -28$
$y = -5x$

9. $x + 4y = -1$
$2x - 5y = 11$

10. $3x + y = -4$
$2x + y = 0$

11. $3x - y = 13$
$2x + 5y = 20$

12. $x - 4y = -3$
$-3x + 5y = 2$

13. A hotel rents a double-occupancy room for $20 more than a single-occupancy room. One night, the hotel took in $3115 after renting 15 double-occupancy rooms and 26 single-occupancy rooms. Write and solve a linear system to find the cost of renting a double-occupancy room and the cost of renting a single-occupancy room.

Answers

1. yes
2. no
3. yes
4. $x + y = 105,$
   $4x + 2y = 360$
5. See left.
6. 75 adult tickets and
   30 student tickets
7. $(-2, 1)$
8. $(2, -10)$
9. $(3, -1)$
10. $(-4, 8)$
11. $(5, \frac{6}{5})$
12. $(1, 1)$
13. $y = x + 20,$
    $26x + 15y = 3115;$
    $65 for a single-
    occupancy room and
    $95 for a double-
    occupancy room

Chapter Test B continued
For use after Chapter 7

Solve the linear system using elimination.

14. $3x - y = 9$
$2x + y = 1$

15. $5x + 7y = 10$
$3x - 14y = 6$

16. $4x + 3y = 15$
$2x - 5y = 1$

17. $2x + 3y = 1$
$3x - 5y = -8$

18. $2x - 3y = -2$
$-2y + 3x = 12$

19. $2x + 9y = 16$
$5x = 1 - 3y$

Without solving the linear system, tell whether the linear system has one solution, no solution, or infinitely many solutions.

20. $y = 2 - 3x$
$6x + 2y = 7$

21. $y = x + 2$
$x + y = 6$

22. $2x - y = 1$
$4x - 2y = 2$

23. On Monday, the office staff at your school paid $8.77 for 4 cups of coffee and 7 bagels. On Wednesday, they paid $15.80 for 8 cups of coffee and 14 bagels. Can you determine the cost of a bagel? Explain.

Graph the system of linear inequalities.

24. $y \geq x - 3$
$y \leq -x + 2$

25. $x < 3$
$y > 1$
$y \geq -x$

26. In an academic competition, scoring is based on a written examination and an oral presentation. The written examination score cannot exceed 65 points and the oral presentation cannot exceed 35 points. Write and graph a system of inequalities for the scores a school team can receive.

Answers

14. $(2, -3)$
15. $(2, 0)$
16. $(3, 1)$
17. $(-1, 1)$
18. $(8, 6)$
19. $(-1, 2)$
20. no solution
21. one solution
22. infinitely many
    solutions
23. There is no solution,
    so you cannot
    determine the cost
    of a bagel.
24. See left.
25. See left.
26. $x \geq 0, y \geq 0,$
    $x \leq 65, y \leq 35$
    See left.

Standardized Test
For use after Chapter 7

Multiple Choice

1. Which ordered pair is a solution of the linear system $x + y = -3$ and $2x + -3y = -16$? D
Ⓐ $(-8, 5)$ Ⓑ $(-2, 4)$
Ⓒ $(-2, -1)$ Ⓓ $(-5, 2)$

2. Which ordered pair is a solution of the linear system $5x + 2y = 29$ and $8x - 8y = 80$? B
Ⓐ $(5, 2)$ Ⓑ $(7, -3)$
Ⓒ $(10, 0)$ Ⓓ $(1, 12)$

3. Which ordered pair is a solution of the linear system shown? A

Ⓐ $(-8, -7)$ Ⓑ $(7, 2)$
Ⓒ $(-7, -8)$ Ⓓ $(2, 7)$

4. Which ordered pair is a solution of the linear system $y - x = 2$ and $5x + 4y = 30.5$? B
Ⓐ $(3, 5)$ Ⓑ $(2.5, 4.5)$
Ⓒ $(5.2, 7.2)$ Ⓓ $(2.1, 5)$

5. Which ordered pair is a solution of the linear system $6x - 3y = 2$ and $2x - 9y = -2$? D
Ⓐ $\left(1, \frac{4}{3}\right)$ Ⓑ $(8, 2)$
Ⓒ $\left(\frac{10}{3}, 6\right)$ Ⓓ $\left(\frac{1}{2}, \frac{1}{3}\right)$

6. Which step below contains an error in solving the linear system $2x + y = 10$ and $5y - 6x = 2$? B

Step 1
$2x + y = 10$
$y = 10 - 2x$

Step 2
$5(10 - 2x) - 6x = 2$
$50 - 10x - 6x = 2$
$50 - 4x = 2$
$48 = 4x$
$12 = x$

Step 3
$2(12) + y = 10$
$24 + y = 10$
$y = -14$

Step 4
$(12, -14)$

Ⓐ Step 1   Ⓑ Step 2
Ⓒ Step 3   Ⓓ Step 4

7. Which ordered pair is a solution of the linear system $5x + 3y = 22$ and $4x - 3y = -4$? C
Ⓐ $(5, -1)$ Ⓑ $(-1, 0)$
Ⓒ $(2, 4)$ Ⓓ $(8, -6)$

8. Which of the linear systems has exactly one solution? A
Ⓐ $5x + 3y = -22$ Ⓑ $2x + 3y = 45$
   $4x - 5y = 12$ $2y + \frac{4}{3}x = 30$
Ⓒ $2x - 3y = -15$ Ⓓ $x + y = 2$
   $\frac{2}{3}x - y = 3$ $\frac{1}{2}x + \frac{1}{2}y = 1$

9. Which of the linear systems has no solution?
Ⓐ $5x + 3y = -22$ Ⓑ $2x + 3y = 45$ C
   $4x - 5y = 12$ $2y + \frac{4}{3}x = 30$
Ⓒ $2x - 3y = -15$ Ⓓ $x + y = 2$
   $\frac{2}{3}x - y = 3$ $\frac{1}{2}x + \frac{1}{2}y = 1$

Standardized Test continued
For use after Chapter 7

10. Which ordered pair is a solution of the system $x < 5$ and $x + 2y \geq 1$? D
Ⓐ $(4, -2)$ Ⓑ $(8, 2)$
Ⓒ $(1, -1)$ Ⓓ $(4, 5)$

11. The graph of which system of inequalities is shown? C

Ⓐ $y \leq \frac{1}{2}x$ Ⓑ $y \leq \frac{1}{2}x$
   $4x + 2y < 8$ $4x + 2y > 8$
Ⓒ $y \geq \frac{1}{2}x$ Ⓓ $y \geq \frac{1}{2}x$
   $4x + 2y < 8$ $4x + 2y > 8$

Gridded Answer

12. What is the x-coordinate of the solution of the system whose graph is shown?

Short Response

13. Use the linear system below.
$3x + 8y = 32$
$y = -\frac{3}{8}x + m$ $m = 4$

a. Find a value for m so that the linear system has infinitely many solutions.

b. Is it possible to find a value for m so that the linear system has exactly one solution? Explain.   See below.

Extended Response

14. The owner of a car wash combines x gallons of a 2% liquid soap and 98% water mix with y gallons of a 7% liquid soap and 93% water mix to make 500 gallons of a 5% liquid soap and 95% water mix.   See below.

a. Write a system of linear equations that represents the situation.

b. How many fluid ounces of the 2% liquid soap and 98% water mix and the 7% liquid soap and 93% water mix did the car wash owner combine to make 500 gallons of the 5% liquid soap and 95% water mix?

c. Suppose the car wash owner combines pure (100%) water and the 7% liquid soap and 93% water mix to make the 500 gallons of the 5% liquid soap and 95% water mix. Is more of the 7% liquid soap and 93% water mix used in this mix than in the original mix? Explain.

13. b. No; because the lines have the same slope, they are parallel. Therefore, there will never be exactly one solution.

14. a. $x + y = 500$ and $0.02x + 0.07y = 25$
b. The car wash owner would use 200 gallons of the 2% liquid soap and 98% water solution and 300 gallons of the 7% liquid soap and 93% water solution.   **c.** The car wash owner would use more of the 7% liquid soap and 93% water mix than in the original mix because in the original mix the other solution contained soap. In the new mix, there is no soap being added to the 7% liquid soap and 93% water mix.

Journal 1. There are three different categories for the number of solutions to a system of two linear equations. Name each category and describe the graph of the system for each case.

Multi-Step Problem 2. Last week a football team ran a total of 108 offensive plays. There were twice as many running plays as passing plays.

   a. Write a system of equations to represent this information given that x is the number of running plays and y is the number of passing plays.

   b. Use the graphing method to solve the system in part (a).

   c. Use the method of substitution to solve the system in part (a) and compare this answer to the one that resulted from your work in part (b). Are the solutions the same?

   d. How many offensive plays were running plays last week?

   e. The team sets some offensive goals for the next game. The first goal is to execute a total of at least 80 offensive plays, and the second goal is to gain at least 360 offensive yards. The team averages 3 yards on each running play and 7 yards on each passing play. The system of inequalities used to model this situation is

$$x + y \geq 80$$
$$3x + 7y \geq 360$$
$$x \geq 0$$
$$y \geq 0$$

   Graph this system of inequalities.

   f. Give 3 solutions to this system.

   g. Suppose the team decided to also set a goal of having more running plays than passing plays. Write an inequality to represent this new goal.

   h. Add the graph of the inequality for the new goal to the graph in part (e).

1. Complete answers should include: mention of all three categories for the number of solutions to a system of two linear equations (one solution, no solution, infinitely many solutions); a description of the graph of the system as intersecting, parallel, or coincidental lines.

2. **a.** $x + y = 108$
    $x = 2y$

b.   **c.** (72, 36) **d.** 72 running plays **e.**

f. *Sample answer:* (50, 30); (70, 25); (30, 50) **g.** $x > y$

h.

Journal Solution 1. Complete answers should include:

   • mention of all three categories for the number of solutions to a system of two linear equations (one solution, no solution, infinitely many solutions).

   • a description of the graph of the system as intersecting, parallel, or coincidental lines.

Multi-Step Problem Solution 2. **a.** $x + y = 108$
    $x = 2y$

b.

c. (72, 36)   **d.** 72 running plays

e.

f. *Sample answer:* (50, 30); (70, 25); (30, 50)

g. $x > y$

h.

Multi-Step Problem Rubric

4 The student answers all parts of the problem correctly and completely. The student shows all work. The student's work is neat.

3 The student answers all parts of the problem. The student's work may contain one or two errors in the calculations, equations, or graphs. The student shows most work. The student's work is neat.

2 The student answers all parts of the problem, but there are more than two errors in the calculations, equations, or graphs. The student shows some work. The student's work is sloppy.

1 The student does not complete all parts of the problem. The student's work has several errors in the calculations, equations, and graphs. The student's work is sloppy, or no work is shown.

PLAN AND PREPARE

Main Ideas

In Chapter 7, students use graphing, substitution, and elimination to solve systems of linear equations. When solving by the elimination method, they either add or subtract, or they multiply first and then add or subtract. Students identify linear systems as having one solution, no solution, or infinitely many solutions. Students solve systems of linear inequalities.

Prerequisite Skills

- Graphing linear equations
- Solving equations
- Determining whether lines are parallel
- Graphing linear inequalities in two variables

Additional resources for reviewing prerequisite skills are:

- Skills Review Handbook, pp. 909–937
- @HomeTutor

3–6. See p. 425.

9. Not parallel; the slope of the graph of the first equation is 2, while the slope of the graph of the second equation is −2.

10. Parallel; the 2 lines have a slope of 5, but different y-intercepts.

11. Parallel; the 2 lines have a slope of 1, but different y-intercepts.

12. Not parallel; the slope of the graph of the first equation is 6, while the slope of the graph of the second equation is 4.

13–16. See p. 425.

7 Systems of Equations and Inequalities

7.1 Solve Linear Systems by Graphing

7.2 Solve Linear Systems by Substitution

7.3 Solve Linear Systems by Adding or Subtracting

7.4 Solve Linear Systems by Multiplying First

7.5 Solve Special Types of Linear Systems

7.6 Solve Systems of Linear Inequalities

Before

In previous chapters, you learned the following skills, which you'll use in Chapter 7: graphing linear equations, solving equations, determining whether lines are parallel, and graphing linear inequalities in two variables.

Prerequisite Skills

VOCABULARY CHECK

Copy and complete the statement.

1. The least common multiple of 10 and 15 is __?__. **30**

2. Two lines in the same plane are __?__ if they do not intersect. **parallel**

SKILLS CHECK

Graph the equation. *(Review p. 225 for 7.1.)* **3–6. See margin.**

3. $x - y = 4$ 4. $6x - y = -1$ 5. $4x + 5y = 20$ 6. $3x - 2y = -12$

Solve the equation. *(Review p. 148 for 7.2–7.4.)*

7. $5m + 4 - m = 20$ **4**   8. $10(z + 5) + z = 6$ **−4**

Tell whether the graphs of the two equations are parallel lines. *Explain* your reasoning. *(Review p. 244 for 7.5.)* **9–12. See margin.**

9. $y = 2x - 3, y + 2x = -3$ 10. $y - 5x = -1, y - 5x = 1$

11. $y = x + 10, x - y = -9$ 12. $6x - y = 4, 4x - y = 6$

Graph the inequality. *(Review p. 405 for 7.6.)* **13–16. See margin.**

13. $y \le -2x + 1$ 14. $x - y < 5$ 15. $x \ge -4$ 16. $y > 3$

@HomeTutor Prerequisite skills practice at classzone.com

424

Chapter Planning Guide

Chapter 7 Resource Book
- Teaching Guide/Lesson Plan (pp. 3, 17, 27, 38, 50, 64)
- Project with Rubric (p. 80)

Assessment and Intervention
- Assessment Book (pp. 90–108)
- Benchmark Tests
- Reteaching and Remediation Book

Interactive Technology
- Easy Planner
- Power Presentations CD-ROM
- Activity Generator CD-ROM
- Animated Algebra
- Test Generator CD-ROM
- Online Quizzes
- eWorkbook
- eEdition
- @HomeTutor

Resources for English Learners
- Quick Reference for English Learners
- Spanish Study Guide
- Multi-Language Visual Glossary
- Student Resources in Spanish

In Chapter 7, you will apply the big ideas listed below and reviewed in the Chapter Summary on page 474. You will also use the key vocabulary listed below.

Big Ideas

1 Solving linear systems by graphing
2 Solving linear systems using algebra
3 Solving systems of linear inequalities

KEY VOCABULARY

- system of linear equations, *p. 427*
- solution of a system of linear equations, *p. 427*
- consistent independent system, *p. 427*

- inconsistent system, *p. 459*
- consistent dependent system, *p. 459*
- system of linear inequalities, *p. 466*

- solution of a system of linear inequalities, *p. 466*
- graph of a system of linear inequalities, *p. 466*

Why?

You can use a system of linear equations to solve problems about traveling with and against a current. For example, you can write and solve a system of linear equations to find the average speed of a kayak in still water.

Animated Algebra

The animation illustrated below for Example 4 on page 446 helps you answer this question: What is the average speed of the kayak in still water?

You have to find the speed of the kayak in still water.

Click the button that will produce an equation in one variable.

Animated Algebra at classzone.com

Other animations for Chapter 7: pages 428, 435, 441, 446, 452, 459, and 466

425

Algebra 1 Toolkit

- Reading Strategies for Chapter 7, pp. 21–22
- Differentiated Instruction Notes, pp. 65–68
- English Learners Notes, pp. 109–110
- Inclusion Notes, pp. 141–142
- Teaching Strategies with Sample Worksheets, pp. 155–178
- Using Technology in the Classroom, pp. 179–184
- Tips for New Teachers, pp. 197–198
- Math Background Notes, pp. 223–224
- Pre-AP Strategies and Copymasters, pp. 290–291, 384–399
- Teacher Survival Activities, pp. 567–568, 593–594
- Bulletin Board Idea, p. 613
- Teacher Tool Transparencies, following p. 620

6.

13.

14.

15.

16.

3.

4.

5.

1 PLAN AND PREPARE

Explore the Concept

- Students will use a table to solve a linear system.
- This activity leads into the study of solving linear systems by graphing in Example 1 in Lesson 7.1.

Recommended Time

Work activity: 15 min
Discuss results: 5 min

Grouping

Students should work individually.

2 TEACH

Tips for Success

Students may want to write the two ordered pairs in a fourth column as a visual reminder that the *x*-value is the same for both *y*-value columns.

Key Discovery

A solution of a linear system is an ordered pair that must satisfy each equation in the system.

3 ASSESS AND RETEACH

1. If Bill adds 3 books to his collection each month instead of 2, when will he and his brother have the same number of books in their collections? **after 8 mo**

2. Use a table to solve this linear system. **(−4, −16)**
$y = 5x + 4$
$y = 2x - 8$

7.1 Solving Linear Systems Using Tables

MATERIALS · pencil and paper

QUESTION   How can you use a table to solve a linear system?

A *system of linear equations*, or *linear system*, consists of two or more linear equations in the same variables. A *solution of a linear system* is an ordered pair that satisfies each equation in the system. You can use a table to find a solution to a linear system.

EXPLORE   Solve a linear system

Bill and his brother collect comic books. Bill currently has 15 books and adds 2 books to his collection every month. His brother currently has 7 books and adds 4 books to his collection every month. Use the equations below to find the number *x* of months after which Bill and his brother will have the same number *y* of comic books in their collections.

$y = 2x + 15$ **Number of comic books in Bill's collection**

$y = 4x + 7$ **Number of comic books in his brother's collection**

STEP 1 *Make a table*
Copy and complete the table of values shown.

STEP 2 *Find a solution*
Find an *x*-value that gives the same *y*-value for both equations. **4**

STEP 3 *Interpret the solution*
Use your answer to Step 2 to find the number of months after which Bill and his brother have the same number of comic books. **4 mo**

x	y = 2x + 15	y = 4x + 7
0	15	7
1	? 17	? 11
2	? 19	? 15
3	? 21	? 19
4	? 23	? 23
5	? 25	? 27

DRAW CONCLUSIONS   Use your observations to complete these exercises

1. When Bill and his brother have the same number of books in their collections, how many books will each of them have? **23 books**

2. Graph the equations above on the same coordinate plane. What do you notice about the graphs and the solution you found above?
See margin for art; the graphs intersect at (4, 23), which is a solution of both equations.

Use a table to solve the linear system.

3. $y = 2x + 3$
$y = -3x + 18$
(3, 9)

4. $y = -x + 1$
$y = 2x - 5$
(2, −1)

5. $y = -3x + 1$
$y = 5x - 31$
(4, −11)

426   Chapter 7   Systems of Equations and Inequalities

2.

7.1 Solve Linear Systems by Graphing

Before You graphed linear equations.

Now You will graph and solve systems of linear equations.

Why? So you can analyze craft fair sales, as in Ex. 33.

Key Vocabulary
- system of linear equations
- solution of a system of linear equations
- consistent independent system

A **system of linear equations,** or simply a *linear system*, consists of two or more linear equations in the same variables. An example is shown below.

$$x + 2y = 7 \quad \textbf{Equation 1}$$
$$3x - 2y = 5 \quad \textbf{Equation 2}$$

A **solution of a system of linear equations** in two variables is an ordered pair that satisfies each equation in the system.

One way to find the solution of a linear system is by graphing. If the lines intersect in a single point, then the coordinates of the point are the solution of the linear system. A solution found using graphical methods should be checked algebraically.

EXAMPLE 1 Check the intersection point

Use the graph to solve the system. Then check your solution algebraically.

$$x + 2y = 7 \quad \textbf{Equation 1}$$
$$3x - 2y = 5 \quad \textbf{Equation 2}$$

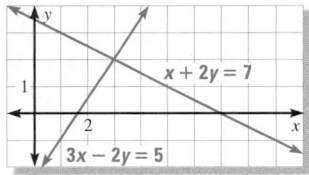

Solution

The lines appear to intersect at the point (3, 2).

CHECK Substitute 3 for x and 2 for y in each equation.

$x + 2y = 7$	$3x - 2y = 5$
$3 + 2(2) \stackrel{?}{=} 7$	$3(3) - 2(2) \stackrel{?}{=} 5$
$7 = 7 ✓$	$5 = 5 ✓$

▶ Because the ordered pair (3, 2) is a solution of each equation, it is a solution of the system.

TYPES OF LINEAR SYSTEMS In Example 1, the linear system has exactly one solution. A linear system that has exactly one solution is called a **consistent independent system** because the lines are distinct (are independent) and intersect (are consistent). You will solve consistent independent systems in Lessons 7.1–7.4. In Lesson 7.5 you will consider other types of systems.

---

① **PLAN AND PREPARE**

Warm-Up Exercises

⬦ Transparency Available

1. Graph the equation $-2x + y = 1$.

2. It takes 3 hours to mow a lawn and 2 hours to trim hedges. You spend 16 hours doing yard work. What are two possible numbers of lawns you mowed and hedges you trimmed? **2 lawns and 5 hedges, or 4 lawns and 2 hedges**

Notetaking Guide

⬦ Transparency Available

Promotes interactive learning and notetaking skills, pp. 150–152.

Pacing

Basic: 1 day

Average: 1 day

Advanced: 1 day

Block: 0.5 block with 7.2

- See *Teaching Guide/Lesson Plan.*

② **FOCUS AND MOTIVATE**

Essential Question

Big Idea 1, p. 425

How do you solve systems of linear equations by graphing? **Tell students they will learn how to answer this question by graphing the equations in the same coordinate plane.**

NCTM STANDARDS

Standard 2: Use models to understand relationships

Standard 9: Use connections among mathematical ideas

Resource Planning Guide

Chapter Resource Book
- Teaching Guide/Lesson Plan (pp. 3–4)
- Activity Master (p. 5)
- Practice levels A, B, C (pp. 6–11)
- Study Guide (pp. 12–13)
- Catch-up for Absent Students (p. 14)
- Problem Solving Workshop (p. 15)
- Challenge (p. 16)

Workbooks
- Notetaking Guide (pp. 150–152)
- Practice Workbook (pp. 104–106)

Teaching Options
- **Power Presentations CD-ROM** provides dynamic electronic teaching resources for the classroom.
- **Activity Generator CD-ROM** provides editable activities for all ability levels.

Interactive Technology
- Easy Planner
- Power Presentations CD-ROM
- Activity Generator CD-ROM
- Animated Algebra
- Test Generator CD-ROM
- Online Quiz
- eWorkbook
- eEdition
- @HomeTutor

Resources for English Learners
- Quick Reference for English Learners
- Spanish Study Guide
- Multi-Language Visual Glossary
- Student Resources in Spanish

See also the *Algebra 1 Toolkit* for more strategies for meeting individual needs.

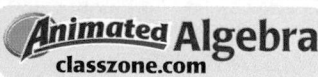

KEY CONCEPT   *For Your Notebook*

Solving a Linear System Using the Graph-and-Check Method

STEP 1 **Graph** both equations in the same coordinate plane. For ease of graphing, you may want to write each equation in slope-intercept form.

STEP 2 **Estimate** the coordinates of the point of intersection.

STEP 3 **Check** the coordinates algebraically by substituting into each equation of the original linear system.

❖ **EXAMPLE 2** **Use the graph-and-check method**

Solve the linear system: $-x + y = -7$ **Equation 1**
                             $x + 4y = -8$ **Equation 2**

Solution

STEP 1 **Graph** both equations.

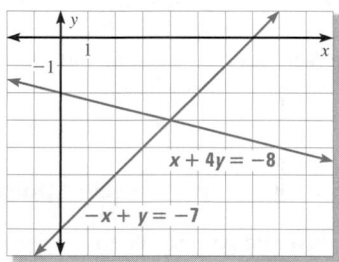

STEP 2 **Estimate** the point of intersection. The two lines appear to intersect at (4, −3).

STEP 3 **Check** whether (4, −3) is a solution by substituting 4 for x and −3 for y in each of the original equations.

Equation 1	Equation 2
$-x + y = -7$	$x + 4y = -8$
$-(4) + (-3) \stackrel{?}{=} -7$	$4 + 4(-3) \stackrel{?}{=} -8$
$-7 = -7$ ✓	$-8 = -8$ ✓

▶ Because (4, −3) is a solution of each equation, it is a solution of the linear system.

Animated Algebra at classzone.com

✓ **GUIDED PRACTICE**   for Examples 1 and 2

Solve the linear system by graphing. Check your solution.

1. $-5x + y = 0$ **(1, 5)**
   $5x + y = 10$

2. $-x + 2y = 3$ **(1, 2)**
   $2x + y = 4$

3. $x - y = 5$ **(2, −3)**
   $3x + y = 3$

Differentiated Instruction

Below Level Some students may need help graphing linear systems. In **Example 2** and **Guided Practice Exercises 1–3**, remind students that they can solve the equation for y to give the slope-intercept form of the equation. They can then plot the point for the y-intercept, use the slope to find another point, and then draw a line through the points. If they prefer, they can make a table of values for the equations, plot the points, and then draw a line through the points.

See also the *Algebra 1 Toolkit* for more strategies.

EXAMPLE 3   **Standardized Test Practice**

The parks and recreation department in your town offers a season pass for $90.

- As a season pass holder, you pay $4 per session to use the town's tennis courts.
- Without the season pass, you pay $13 per session to use the tennis courts.

Which system of equations can be used to find the number x of sessions of tennis after which the total cost y with a season pass, including the cost of the pass, is the same as the total cost without a season pass?

ELIMINATE CHOICES
You can eliminate choice A because neither of the equations include the cost of a season pass.

(A) $y = 4x$
$y = 13x$

(B) $y = 4x$
$y = 90 + 13x$

(C) $y = 13x$
$y = 90 + 4x$

(D) $y = 90 + 4x$
$y = 90 + 13x$

Solution

Write a system of equations where y is the total cost (in dollars) for x sessions.

EQUATION 1

Total cost (dollars)	=	Cost per session (dollars/session)	·	Number of sessions (sessions)
y	=	13	·	x

EQUATION 2

Total cost (dollars)	=	Cost for season pass (dollars)	+	Cost per session (dollars/session)	·	Number of sessions (sessions)
y	=	90	+	4	·	x

▸ The correct answer is C.   Ⓐ Ⓑ ⓒ Ⓓ

✓ **GUIDED PRACTICE**   for Example 3

4. Solve the linear system in Example 3 to find the number of sessions after which the total cost with a season pass, including the cost of the pass, is the same as the total cost without a season pass. **10 sessions**

5. **WHAT IF?** In Example 3, suppose a season pass costs $135. After how many sessions is the total cost with a season pass, including the cost of the pass, the same as the total cost without a season pass? **15 sessions**

7.1   Solve Linear Systems by Graphing   **429**

Extra Example 3

The cost to join an art museum is $60. If you are a member, you can take lessons at the museum for $2 each. If you are not a member, lessons cost $6 each. Which system of equations can be used to find the number x of lessons after which the total cost y of lessons with a membership is the same as the total cost of lessons without a membership? **D**

(A) $y = 2x$
$y = 6x$

(B) $y = 60x + 2$
$y = 6x$

(C) $y = 2x + 60$
$y = 6x + 60$

(D) $y = 2x + 60$
$y = 6x$

Key Questions to Ask for Example 3

- Why is it possible to eliminate choice D? Explain. **Both equations include the cost of a season pass.**
- How would a graph of the system of equations in Example 3 be different from the graph of the system of equations in Example 2? **The graph in Example 3 would be restricted to Quadrant I, since the costs would be positive numbers only.**

Differentiated Instruction

English Learners Make mathematical language easier to understand by using more common terms. In **Example 2**, tell students that the coordinates of the intersecting lines "agree" at one point. Mathematicians might say that the two lines are "consistent" at that point. In ordinary language, to be consistent means to be in agreement.

See also the *Algebra 1 Toolkit* for more strategies.

EXAMPLE 4 Solve a multi-step problem

RENTAL BUSINESS A business rents in-line skates and bicycles. During one day, the business has a total of 25 rentals and collects $450 for the rentals. Find the number of pairs of skates rented and the number of bicycles rented.

Solution

STEP 1 **Write** a linear system. Let x be the number of pairs of skates rented, and let y be the number of bicycles rented.

$x + y = 25$ **Equation for number of rentals**

$15x + 30y = 450$ **Equation for money collected from rentals**

STEP 2 **Graph** both equations.

STEP 3 **Estimate** the point of intersection. The two lines appear to intersect at (20, 5).

STEP 4 **Check** whether (20, 5) is a solution.

$$20 + 5 \stackrel{?}{=} 25 \qquad\qquad 15(20) + 30(5) \stackrel{?}{=} 450$$

$$25 = 25 \checkmark \qquad\qquad\qquad\qquad 450 = 450 \checkmark$$

▸ The business rented 20 pairs of skates and 5 bicycles.

✓ **GUIDED PRACTICE** for Example 4

6. **WHAT IF?** In Example 4, suppose the business has a total of 20 rentals and collects $420. Find the number of bicycles rented. **8 bicycles**

7.1 EXERCISES

HOMEWORK KEY

◯ = **WORKED-OUT SOLUTIONS**
on p. WS1 for Exs. 15 and 31

★ = **STANDARDIZED TEST PRACTICE**
Exs. 2, 6, 7, 27, 28, 29, and 32

◆ = **MULTIPLE REPRESENTATIONS**
Ex. 35

SKILL PRACTICE

[A]

1. **VOCABULARY** Copy and complete: A(n) __?__ of a system of linear equations in two variables is an ordered pair that satisfies each equation in the system. **solution**

2. ★ **WRITING** *Explain* how to use the graph-and-check method to solve a linear system of two equations in two variables. **See margin.**

CHECKING SOLUTIONS Tell whether the ordered pair is a solution of the linear system.

3. $(-3, 1)$; **solution**
$x + y = -2$
$x + 5y = 2$

4. $(5, 2)$; **not a solution**
$2x - 3y = 4$
$2x + 8y = 11$

5. $(-2, 1)$; **not a solution**
$6x + 5y = -7$
$x - 2y = 0$

430 Chapter 7 Systems of Equations and Inequalities

EXAMPLE 1
on p. 427
for Exs. 6–11

6. ★ **MULTIPLE CHOICE** Which ordered pair is a solution of the linear system $x + y = -2$ and $7x - 4y = 8$? **B**

    A $(-2, 0)$ **B** $(0, \ 2)$ **O** $(2, 0)$ **D** $(0, 2)$

7. ★ **MULTIPLE CHOICE** Which ordered pair is a solution of the linear system $2x + 3y = 12$ and $10x + 3y = -12$? **B**

    A $(-3, 3)$ **B** $(-3, 6)$ **C** $(3, 3)$ **D** $(3, 6)$

SOLVING SYSTEMS GRAPHICALLY Use the graph to solve the linear system. Check your solution.

8. $x - y = 4$ **(1, −1)**
$4x + y = 1$

9. $-x + y = -2$ **(4, 2)**
$2x - y = 6$

10. $x + y = 5$ **(3, 2)**
$-2x + y = -4$

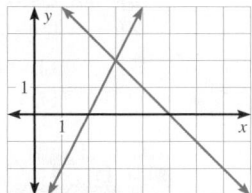

11. **ERROR ANALYSIS** *Describe* and correct the error in solving the linear system below.

$x - 3y = 6$ **Equation 1**
$2x - 3y = 3$ **Equation 2**

The solution (3, −1) does not satisfy Equation 2. The graph of Equation 2 is incorrect; if properly graphed, the lines would intersect at (−3, −3); see margin for art.

The solution is (3, −1).

EXAMPLE 2 [B]
on p. 428
for Exs. 12–26

GRAPH-AND-CHECK METHOD Solve the linear system by graphing. Check your solution.

12. $y = -x + 3$ **(1, 2)**
$y = x + 1$

13. $y = -x + 4$ **(4, 0)**
$y = 2x - 8$

14. $y = 2x + 2$ **(−2, −2)**
$y = 4x + 6$

15. $x - y = 2$ **(−3, −5)**
$x + y = -8$

16. $x + 2y = 1$ **(1.8, −0.4)**
$-2x + y = -4$

17. $3x + y = 15$ **(10, −15)**
$y = -15$

18. $2x - 3y = -1$ **(4, 3)**
$5x + 2y = 26$

19. $6x + y = 37$ **(7, −5)**
$4x + 2y = 18$

20. $7x + 5y = -3$ **(1, −2)**
$-9x + y = -11$

21. $6x + 12y = -6$ **(−5, 2)**
$2x + 5y = 0$

22. $2x + y = 9$ **(3, 3)**
$2x + 3y = 15$

23. $-5x + 3y = 3$ **(3, 6)**
$4x + 3y = 30$

24. $\frac{3}{4}x + \frac{1}{4}y = \frac{13}{2}$ **(8, 2)**
$x - \frac{3}{4}y = \frac{13}{2}$

25. $\frac{1}{5}x - \frac{2}{5}y = -\frac{8}{5}$ **(4, 6)**
$-\frac{3}{4}x + y = 3$

26. $-1.6x - 3.2y = -24$ **(5, 5)**
$2.6x + 2.6y = 26$

27. ★ **OPEN-ENDED** Find values for m and b so that the system $y = \frac{3}{5}x - 1$ and $y = mx + b$ has (5, 2) as a solution. *Sample answer: m = 0 and b = 2*

28. (0.5, 0.5).
Sample answer:
It is important
to check the
solution because
the lines do
not intersect at
integer values.

28. ★ **WRITING** Solve the linear system shown by graphing. *Explain* why it is important to check your solution.

$y = 4x - 1.5$ **Equation 1**
$y = -2x + 1.5$ **Equation 2**

④ PRACTICE AND APPLY

Assignment Guide

📑 Answer Transparencies available for all exercises

Basic:
Day 1: EP p. 941 Exs. 19–22
pp. 430–433
Exs. 1–17, 31–34, 38–42 even, 43–48

Average:
Day 1: pp. 430–433
Exs. 1–11, 18–35, 37–41 odd, 43–48

Advanced:
Day 1: pp. 430–433
Exs. 1, 4–7, 9, 10, 21–36*, 38–48 even

Block:
pp. 430–433
Exs. 1–11, 18–35, 37–41 odd, 43–48 (with 7.2)

Differentiated Instruction

See *Algebra 1 Best Practices Toolkit* for suggestions on addressing the needs of a diverse classroom.

Homework Check

For a quick check of student understanding of key concepts, go over the following exercises:
Basic: 8, 14, 16, 31, 32
Average: 9, 20, 21, 32, 33
Advanced: 10, 22, 24, 32, 33

Extra Practice

• Student Edition, p. 944
• Chapter 7 Resource Book: Practice levels A, B, C, pp. 6–11

Practice Worksheet

An easily-readable reduced practice page (with answers) for this lesson can be found on p. 424C.

11.

29d. *Sample answer:* Set each side of the equation equal to *y* to create a system of two equations. Then solve the system using the graph-and-check method.

29. **★ EXTENDED RESPONSE** Consider the equation $-\frac{1}{4}x + 6 = \frac{1}{2}x + 3$.

a. Solve the equation using algebra. **4**

b. Solve the linear system below using a graph. **4**

$$y = -\frac{1}{4}x + 6 \qquad \text{Equation 1}$$

$$y = \frac{1}{2}x + 3 \qquad \text{Equation 2}$$

c. How is the linear system in part (b) related to the original equation?
Sample answer: Each side of the equation is set equal to *y*.

d. *Explain* how to use a graph to solve the equation $-\frac{2}{5}x + 5 = \frac{1}{5}x + 2$.

$\boxed{C}$ 30. **CHALLENGE** The three lines given below form a triangle. Find the coordinates of the vertices of the triangle.

Line 1: $-3x + 2y = 1$ Line 2: $2x + y = 11$ Line 3: $x + 4y = 9$

(3, 5), (1, 2), and (5, 1)

PROBLEM SOLVING

EXAMPLES $\boxed{A}$
3 and 4
on pp. 429–430
for Exs. 31–33

(31.) **TELEVISION** The graph shows a projection, from 1990 on, of the percent of eighth graders who watch 1 hour or less of television on a weekday and the percent of eighth graders who watch more than 1 hour of television on a weekday. Use the graph to predict the year when the percent of eighth graders who watch 1 hour or less will equal the percent who watch more than 1 hour. **2040**

@HomeTutor   for problem solving help at classzone.com

32. **★ MULTIPLE CHOICE** A car dealership is offering interest-free car loans for one day only. During this day, a salesperson at the dealership sells two cars. One of his clients decides to pay off his $17,424 car in 36 monthly payments of $484. His other client decides to pay off his $15,840 car in 48 monthly payments of $330. Which system of equations can be used to determine the number *x* of months after which both clients will have the same loan balance *y*? **B**

(A) $y = -484x$
$y = -330x$

(B) $y = -484x + 17,424$
$y = -330x + 15,840$

(C) $y = -484x + 15,840$
$y = -330x + 17,424$

(D) $y = 484x + 17,424$
$y = 330x + 15,840$

@HomeTutor   for problem solving help at classzone.com

33. **CRAFTS** Kirigami is the Japanese art of making paper designs by folding and cutting paper. A student sells small and large greeting cards decorated with kirigami at a craft fair. The small cards cost $3 per card, and the large cards cost $5 per card. The student collects $95 for selling a total of 25 cards. How many of each type of card did the student sell?

15 small cards and 10 large cards

○ = **WORKED-OUT SOLUTIONS**
on p. WS1

★ = **STANDARDIZED**
TEST PRACTICE

◆ = **MULTIPLE**
REPRESENTATIONS

Side column (left)

Avoiding Common Errors

Exercises 3–10 Some students may substitute the *x*- and *y*-coordinates of a solution into one equation of the linear system only. Remind these students that a solution of a linear system must satisfy both equations of the system.

Exercises 12–26 Some students may reverse the *x*- and *y*-coordinates in their solutions. Emphasize that checking their solutions will help correct such errors.

Reading Strategy

Exercises 15, 31 Remind students that there is a worked-out solution for exercises circled in red. Point out the Homework Key at the beginning of the exercises on page 430 and at the bottom of the page on page 432.

Teaching Strategy

Exercise 36 You may want to point out that 20% off of the purchase is the same as paying 80% of the purchase.

35b.

Tickets	Cost for members	Cost for non-members
1	$20	$8
2	$25	$16
3	$30	$24
4	$35	$32
5	$40	$40
6	$45	$48

35c.

When you rent 6 or more movies.
Sample answer: The graph for a non-member is below the graph for a member up through 4 movies. For 5 movies, the cost is the same. The graph for members is lower than the graph for non-members for 6 or more movies.

Differentiated Instruction

Advanced When discussing **Exercise 27**, ask students to describe values for *b* in the equation $y = mx + b$ when the value of *m* is negative and when the value of *m* is positive. Have them support their reasoning by graphing several equations in the system $y = \frac{3}{5}x - 1$ and $y = mx + b$ with a solution of (5, 2) and then describing the pattern of graphs in the system as they relate to the values of *m* and *b*.

See also the *Algebra 1 Toolkit* for more strategies.

34. FITNESS You want to burn 225 calories while exercising at a gym. The number of calories that you burn per minute on different machines at the gym is shown below.

Stair machine	Elliptical trainer	Stationary bike
You burn 5 Cal/min.	You burn 8 Cal/min.	You burn 6 Cal/min.

34a. 25 min on the stationary bike and 15 min on the stair machine

a. Suppose you have 40 minutes to exercise at the gym and you want to use the stair machine and stationary bike. How many minutes should you spend on each machine so that you burn 225 calories?

34b. 25 min on the ellipiical trainer and 5 min on the stair machine

b. Suppose you have 30 minutes to exercise at the gym and you want to use the stair machine and the elliptical trainer. How many minutes should you spend on each machine so that you burn 225 calories?

35. ◆ **MULTIPLE REPRESENTATIONS** It costs $15 for a yearly membership to a movie club at a movie theater. A movie ticket costs $5 for club members and $8 for nonmembers.

a. Writing a System of Equations Write a system of equations that you can use to find the number x of movies viewed after which the total cost y for a club member, including the membership fee, is the same as the cost for a nonmember. **$y = 5x + 15, y = 8x$**

b. Making a Table Make a table of values that shows the total cost for a club member and a nonmember after paying to see 1, 2, 3, 4, 5, and 6 movies. **See margin.**

36. You should choose $25 off if your purchase is less than $125, and choose 20% off purchases greater than $125. *Sample answer:* For values less than $125, 20% off is less than $25 off. For values greater than $125, 20% off is greater than $25 off.

c. Drawing a Graph Use the table to graph the system of equations. Under what circumstances does it make sense to become a movie club member? *Explain* your answer by using the graph. **See margin.**

36. CHALLENGE With a minimum purchase of $25, you can open a credit account with a clothing store. The store is offering either $25 or 20% off of your purchase if you open a credit account. You decide to open a credit account. Should you choose $25 or 20% off of your purchase? *Explain.*

MIXED REVIEW

Solve the equation.

37. $x + 5 = -14$ *(p. 134)* **−19**

38. $-5x + 6 = 21$ *(p. 141)* **−3**

39. $3(x + 2) = -6$ *(p. 148)* **−4**

40. $11x + 9 = 13x - 3$ *(p. 154)* **6**

41. $3x - 8 = 11x + 12$ *(p. 154)* **−2.5**

42. $4(x + 1) = -2x - 18$ *(p. 154)* $-\frac{11}{3}$

PREVIEW

Prepare for Lesson 7.2 in Exs. 43–48.

Write the equation so that y is a function of x. *(p. 184)*

43. $5y + 25 = 3x$ $y = \frac{3}{5}x - 5$

44. $7x = y + 9$ $y = 7x - 9$

45. $4y + 11 = 3y + 4x$ $y = 4x - 11$

46. $6x + 3y = 2x + 3$ $y = -\frac{4}{3}x + 1$

47. $y + 2x + 6 = -1$ $y = -2x - 7$

48. $4x - 12 = 5x + 2y$ $y = -\frac{1}{2}x - 6$

EXTRA PRACTICE for Lesson 7.1, p. 944   🔊 **ONLINE QUIZ** at classzone.com   **433**

7.1 Solving Linear Systems by Graphing

QUESTION How can you use a graphing calculator to solve a linear system?

EXAMPLE Solve a linear system

Solve the linear system using a graphing calculator.

$$5x + 2y = 6 \quad \text{Equation 1}$$
$$x - 3y = -5 \quad \text{Equation 2}$$

STEP 1 *Rewrite equations*
Solve each equation for *y*.

Equation 1	Equation 2
$5x + 2y = 6$	$x - 3y = -5$
$2y = -5x + 6$	$-3y = -x - 5$
$y = -\frac{5}{2}x + 3$	$y = \frac{1}{3}x + \frac{5}{3}$

STEP 2 *Enter equations*
Press [Y=] and enter the equations.

STEP 3 *Display graph*
Graph the equations using a standard viewing window.

STEP 4 *Find point of intersection*
Use the *intersect* feature to find the point where the graphs intersect.

The solution is about (0.47, 1.8).

PRACTICE

Solve the linear system using a graphing calculator.

1. $y = x + 4$
$y = -3x - 2$
$(-1.5, 2.5)$

2. $5x + y = -4$
$x - y = -2$
$(-1, 1)$

3. $-0.45x - y = 1.35$
$-1.8x + y = -1.8$
$(0.2, -1.44)$

4. $-0.4x + 0.8y = -16$
$1.2x + 0.4y = 1$
$(6.43, -16.79)$

7.2 Solve Linear Systems by Substitution

Before You solved systems of linear equations by graphing.

Now You will solve systems of linear equations by substitution.

Why? So you can find tubing costs, as in Ex. 32.

Key Vocabulary
• system of linear equations, p. 427

KEY CONCEPT

For Your Notebook

Solving a Linear System Using the Substitution Method

STEP 1 **Solve** one of the equations for one of its variables. When possible, solve for a variable that has a coefficient of 1 or −1.

STEP 2 **Substitute** the expression from Step 1 into the other equation and solve for the other variable.

STEP 3 **Substitute** the value from Step 2 into the revised equation from Step 1 and solve.

EXAMPLE 1 — Use the substitution method

Solve the linear system: $y = 3x + 2$ **Equation 1**
                             $x + 2y = 11$ **Equation 2**

Solution

STEP 1 **Solve** for y. Equation 1 is already solved for y.

STEP 2 **Substitute** $3x + 2$ for y in Equation 2 and solve for x.

$$x + 2y = 11 \qquad \text{Write Equation 2.}$$
$$x + 2(3x + 2) = 11 \qquad \text{Substitute } 3x + 2 \text{ for } y.$$
$$7x + 4 = 11 \qquad \text{Simplify.}$$
$$7x = 7 \qquad \text{Subtract 4 from each side.}$$
$$x = 1 \qquad \text{Divide each side by 7.}$$

STEP 3 **Substitute** 1 for x in the original Equation 1 to find the value of y.

$$y = 3x + 2 = 3(1) + 2 = 3 + 2 = 5$$

▸ The solution is $(1, 5)$.

CHECK Substitute 1 for x and 5 for y in each of the original equations.

$y = 3x + 2$	$x + 2y = 11$
$5 \overset{?}{=} 3(1) + 2$	$1 + 2(5) \overset{?}{=} 11$
$5 = 5 ✓$	$11 = 11 ✓$

Animated Algebra at classzone.com

---

1 PLAN AND PREPARE

Warm-Up Exercises

📑 Transparency Available

Solve the equation.

1. $6a - 3 + 2a = 13$ $a = 2$
2. $4(n + 2) - n = 11$ $n = 1$
3. You burned 8 calories per minute on a treadmill and 10 calories per minute on an elliptical trainer for a total of 560 calories in 60 minutes. How many minutes did you spend on each machine? **treadmill: 20 min, elliptical trainer: 40 min**

Notetaking Guide

📑 Transparency Available

Promotes interactive learning and notetaking skills, pp. 153–154.

Pacing

Basic: 2 days
Average: 2 days
Advanced: 2 days
Block: 0.5 block with 7.1
        0.5 block with 7.3
• See *Teaching Guide/Lesson Plan.*

2 FOCUS AND MOTIVATE

Essential Question

Big Idea 2, p. 425

How do you solve systems of linear equations by substitution? **Tell students they will learn how to answer this question by substituting an expression for a variable in one equation into the other equation.**

NCTM STANDARDS

Standard 2: Analyze situations using algebraic symbols

Standard 6: Solve problems in math and other contexts

Resource Planning Guide

Chapter Resource Book
• Teaching Guide/Lesson Plan (pp. 17–18)
• Practice levels A, B, C (pp. 19–21)
• Study Guide (pp. 22–23)
• Catch-up for Absent Students (p. 24)
• Application (p. 25)
• Challenge (p. 26)

Workbooks
• Notetaking Guide (pp. 153–154)
• Practice Workbook (pp. 107–108)

Teaching Options
• **Power Presentations CD-ROM** provides dynamic electronic teaching resources for the classroom.
• **Activity Generator CD-ROM** provides editable activities for all ability levels.

Interactive Technology
• Easy Planner
• Power Presentations CD-ROM
• Activity Generator CD-ROM
• Animated Algebra
• Test Generator CD-ROM
• Online Quiz
• eWorkbook
• eEdition
• @HomeTutor

Resources for English Learners
• Quick Reference for English Learners
• Spanish Study Guide
• Multi-Language Visual Glossary
• Student Resources in Spanish

See also the *Algebra 1 Toolkit* for more strategies for meeting individual needs.

EXAMPLE 2 Use the substitution method

Solve the linear system: $x - 2y = -6$ **Equation 1**
$\qquad\qquad\qquad\qquad\qquad$ $4x + 6y = 4$ **Equation 2**

CHOOSE AN EQUATION
Equation 1 was chosen in Step 1 because *x* has a coefficient of 1. So, only one step is needed to solve Equation 1 for *x*.

Solution

STEP 1 Solve Equation 1 for *x*.

$\qquad x - 2y = -6$ **Write original Equation 1.**

$\qquad\quad x = 2y - 6$ **Revised Equation 1**

STEP 2 Substitute $2y - 6$ for *x* in Equation 2 and solve for *y*.

$\qquad\qquad\quad 4x + 6y = 4$ **Write Equation 2.**

$\qquad\quad 4(2y - 6) + 6y = 4$ **Substitute $2y - 6$ for *x*.**

$\qquad\quad 8y - 24 + 6y = 4$ **Distributive property**

$\qquad\qquad\quad 14y - 24 = 4$ **Simplify.**

$\qquad\qquad\qquad\quad 14y = 28$ **Add 24 to each side.**

$\qquad\qquad\qquad\qquad y = 2$ **Divide each side by 14.**

STEP 3 Substitute 2 for *y* in the revised Equation 1 to find the value of *x*.

$\qquad x = 2y - 6$ **Revised Equation 1**

$\qquad x = 2(2) - 6$ **Substitute 2 for *y*.**

$\qquad x = -2$ **Simplify.**

▶ The solution is $(-2, 2)$.

CHECK Substitute -2 for *x* and 2 for *y* in each of the original equations.

Equation 1	**Equation 2**
$x - 2y = -6$	$4x + 6y = 4$
$-2 - 2(2) \overset{?}{=} -6$	$4(-2) + 6(2) \overset{?}{=} 4$
$-6 = -6 \checkmark$	$4 = 4 \checkmark$

CHECK REASONABLENESS When solving a linear system using the substitution method, you can use a graph to check the reasonableness of your solution. For example, the graph at the right verifies that $(-2, 2)$ is a solution of the linear system in Example 2.

 GUIDED PRACTICE   for Examples 1 and 2

Solve the linear system using the substitution method.

1. $y = 2x + 5$ **(1, 7)**
   $3x + y = 10$

2. $x - y = 3$ **(0, −3)**
   $x + 2y = -6$

3. $3x + y = -7$ **(−2, −1)**
   $-2x + 4y = 0$

436   Chapter 7   Systems of Equations and Inequalities

EXAMPLE 3 Solve a multi-step problem

ANOTHER WAY
For an alternative method for solving the problem in Example 3, turn to page 442 for the **Problem Solving Workshop**.

WEBSITES Many businesses pay website hosting companies to store and maintain the computer files that make up their websites. Internet service providers also offer website hosting. The costs for website hosting offered by a website hosting company and an Internet service provider are shown in the table. Find the number of months after which the total cost for website hosting will be the same for both companies.

Company	Set-up fee (dollars)	Cost per month (dollars)
Internet service provider	10	21.95
Website hosting company	None	22.45

Solution

STEP 1 **Write** a system of equations. Let y be the total cost after x months.

Equation 1: Internet service provider

Total cost	=	Set-up fee	+	Cost per month	·	Number of months

$$y \;=\; 10 \;+\; 21.95 \;\cdot\; x$$

Equation 2: Website hosting company

Total cost	=	Cost per month	·	Number of months

$$y \;=\; 22.45 \;\cdot\; x$$

The system of equations is: $y = 10 + 21.95x$ **Equation 1**

$y = 22.45x$ **Equation 2**

STEP 2 **Substitute** $22.45x$ for y in Equation 1 and solve for x.

$y = 10 + 21.95x$	**Write Equation 1.**
$22.45x = 10 + 21.95x$	**Substitute $22.45x$ for y.**
$0.5x = 10$	**Subtract $21.95x$ from each side.**
$x = 20$	**Divide each side by 0.5.**

▶ The total cost will be the same for both companies after 20 months.

✓ **GUIDED PRACTICE** **for Example 3**

4. In Example 3, what is the total cost for website hosting for each company after 20 months? **$449**

5. **WHAT IF?** In Example 3, suppose the Internet service provider offers $5 off the set-up fee. After how many months will the total cost for website hosting be the same for both companies? **10 mo**

Extra Example 3
A food cooperative is a business that usually offers special prices on locally grown food and produce. Some cooperatives are clubs and others are retail stores. The weekly costs for seasonal produce offered by a club-based and a store-based food cooperative are shown in the table. Find the number of weeks at which the total cost of weekly produce will be the same.

Type of cooperative	Club fee (dollars)	Cost per week (dollars)
Club	$20	$15
Retail	None	$17.50

The total cost will be the same for both cooperatives at 8 weeks.

Key Question to Ask for Example 3
• Which company will have the greater total cost for 21 months? Explain. **The website hosting company, since its monthly cost is greater than the monthly cost for the Internet service provider.**

Avoiding Common Errors
In Step 2 of Example 3, some students may substitute 22.45 for y instead of $22.45x$. Remind these students that y is equivalent to $22.45 \cdot x$ in Equation 2.

EXAMPLE 4 **Solve a mixture problem**

ANTIFREEZE For extremely cold temperatures, an automobile manufacturer recommends that a 70% antifreeze and 30% water mix be used in the cooling system of a car. How many quarts of pure (100%) antifreeze and a 50% antifreeze and 50% water mix should be combined to make 11 quarts of a 70% antifreeze and 30% water mix?

Solution

STEP 1 **Write** an equation for the total number of quarts and an equation for the number of quarts of antifreeze. Let x be the number of quarts of 100% antifreeze, and let y be the number of quarts a 50% antifreeze and 50% water mix.

Equation 1: Total number of quarts

$$x + y = 11$$

Equation 2: Number of quarts of antifreeze

x quarts of 100% antifreeze		y quarts of 50%–50% mix		11 quarts of 70%–30% mix
$1 \cdot x$	$+$	$0.5 \cdot y$	$=$	$0.7(11)$

$$x + 0.5y = 7.7$$

DRAW A DIAGRAM
Each bar shows the liquid in each mix. The green portion shows the percent of the mix that is antifreeze.

The system of equations is: $x + y = 11$ **Equation 1**

$x + 0.5y = 7.7$ **Equation 2**

STEP 2 **Solve** Equation 1 for x.

$x + y = 11$ **Write Equation 1.**

$x = 11 - y$ **Revised Equation 1**

STEP 3 **Substitute** $11 - y$ for x in Equation 2 and solve for y.

$x + 0.5y = 7.7$ **Write Equation 2.**

$(11 - y) + 0.5y = 7.7$ **Substitute $11 - y$ for x.**

$y = 6.6$ **Solve for y.**

STEP 4 **Substitute** 6.6 for y in the revised Equation 1 to find the value of x.

$x = 11 - y = 11 - 6.6 = 4.4$

▶ Mix 4.4 quarts of 100% antifreeze and 6.6 quarts of a 50% antifreeze and 50% water mix to get 11 quarts of a 70% antifreeze and 30% water mix.

 GUIDED PRACTICE   **for Example 4**

6. **WHAT IF?** How many quarts of 100% antifreeze and a 50% antifreeze and 50% water mix should be combined to make 16 quarts of a 70% antifreeze and 30% water mix? **6.4 quarts of 100% antifreeze and 9.6 quarts of 50% antifreeze and 50% water mix**

Differentiated Instruction

Below Level Some students avoid mixture problems, such as the one in **Example 4**, because they look complicated. Tell students that following the steps in the example and using diagrams will help them learn how to break mixture problems into parts. Suggest that they solve the problem for 10 quarts of antifreeze instead of 11. This will make the computation more manageable. Break Step 3 into a stepped-out solution so students see how to get a positive value for y. Students can then solve **Guided Practice Exercise 5** for 16 quarts.

See also the *Algebra 1 Toolkit* for more strategies.

7.2 EXERCISES

HOMEWORK KEY
○ = WORKED-OUT SOLUTIONS
on p. WS1 for Exs. 13 and 33
★ = STANDARDIZED TEST PRACTICE
Exs. 2, 18, 29, 33, and 37

SKILL PRACTICE

A 1. **VOCABULARY** Give an example of a system of linear equations.
Sample answer: $y = x + 1, y = 2x + 1$

2. ★ **WRITING** If you are solving the linear system
shown using the substitution method, which
equation would you solve for which variable?
Explain. **Sample answer:** Solve Equation 2 for y; the y term does not have a coefficient.

$2x - 3y = 24$ **Equation 1**
$2x + y = 8$ **Equation 2**

EXAMPLE 1
on p. 435
for Exs. 3–8

SOLVING LINEAR SYSTEMS Solve the linear system using substitution.

3. $x = 17 - 4y$ **(5, 3)**
$y = x - 2$

4. $y = 2x - 1$ **(1, 1)**
$2x + y = 3$

5. $x = y + 3$ **(2, −1)**
$2x - y = 5$

6. $4x - 7y = 10$ **(13, 6)**
$y = x - 7$

7. $x = 16 - 4y$ **(−4, 5)**
$3x + 4y = 8$

8. $-5x + 3y = 51$ **(3, 22)**
$y = 10x - 8$

EXAMPLE 2
on p. 436
for Exs. 9–19

9. $2x = 12$ **(6, 7)**
$x - 5y = -29$

10. $2x - y = 23$ **(8, −7)**
$x - 9 = -1$

11. $x + y = 0$ **(2, −2)**
$x - 2y = 6$

12. $2x + y = 9$ **(−1, 11)**
$4x - y = -15$

13. $5x + 2y = 9$ **(5, −8)**
$x + y = -3$

14. $5x + 4y = 32$ **(4, 3)**
$9x - y = 33$

15. $11x - 7y = -14$ **(0, 2)**
$x - 2y = -4$

16. $20x - 30y = -50$ **(−1, 1)**
$x + 2y = 1$

17. $6x + y = 4$ **(1.4, −4.4)**
$x - 4y = 19$

18. ★ **MULTIPLE CHOICE** Which ordered pair is a solution of the linear system
$4x - y = 17$ and $-9x + 8y = 2$? **A**

Ⓐ (6, 7) Ⓑ (7, 6) Ⓒ (7, 11) Ⓓ (11, 7)

19. **ERROR ANALYSIS** *Describe* and correct the error in solving the linear
system $4x + 2y = 6$ and $3x + y = 9$.

Step 1	Step 2	Step 3	The solution
$3x + y = 9$	$4x + 2(9 - 3x) = 6$	$y = 9 - 3x$	is (6, 1).
$y = 9 - 3x$	$4x + 18 - 6x = 6$	$6 = 9 - 3x$	
	$-2x = -12$	$-3 = -3x$	
	$x = 6$	$1 = x$	

Sample answer: In Step 3, 6 is substituted for y instead of x; $y = 9 - 3(6)$, $y = -9$, the solution is $(6, -9)$.

B **SOLVING LINEAR SYSTEMS** Solve the linear system using substitution.

20. $4.5x + 1.5y = 24$ **(5, 1)**
$x - y = 4$

21. $35x + y = 20$ **(4, −120)**
$1.5x - 0.1y = 18$

22. $3x - 2y = 8$ **(10.5, 11.75)**
$0.5x + y = 17$

23. $0.5x + 0.6y = 5.7$ **(3, 7)**
$2x - y = -1$

24. $x - 9 = 0.5y$ **(14, 10)**
$2.2x - 3.1y = -0.2$

25. $0.2x + y = -1.8$ **(6, −3)**
$1.8y + 5.5x = 27.6$

26. $\frac{1}{2}x + \frac{1}{4}y = 5$ $\left(5\frac{1}{2}, 9\right)$
$x - \frac{1}{2}y = 1$

27. $x + \frac{1}{3}y = -2$ **(0, −6)**
$-8x - \frac{2}{3}y = 4$

28. $\frac{3}{8}x + \frac{3}{4}y = 12$ **(12, 10)**
$\frac{2}{3}x + \frac{1}{2}y = 13$

④ PRACTICE AND APPLY

Assignment Guide

📄 **Answer Transparencies**
available for all exercises

Basic:
Day 1: EP p. 940 Exs. 21–26
pp. 439–441
Exs. 1–19
Day 2: pp. 439–441
Exs. 20–25, 31–35, 39–50

Average:
Day 1: pp. 439–441
Exs. 1, 2, 4–18 even, 19–29 odd
Day 2: pp. 439–441
Exs. 31–37, 39–50

Advanced:
Day 1: pp. 439–441
Exs. 1, 6–8, 15–18, 20–28
Day 2: pp. 439–441
Exs. 29–38*, 42–44, 48–50

Block:
pp. 439–441
Exs. 1, 2, 4–18 even, 19–29 odd
(with 7.1)
pp. 439–441
Exs. 31–37, 39–50 (with 7.3)

Differentiated Instruction

See *Algebra 1 Best Practices Toolkit*
for suggestions on addressing the
needs of a diverse classroom.

Homework Check

For a quick check of student understanding of key concepts, go over
the following exercises:

Basic: 4, 10, 14, 31, 35
Average: 6, 14, 21, 32, 35
Advanced: 8, 16, 24, 33, 35

Extra Practice

• Student Edition, p. 944
• Chapter 7 Resource Book:
Practice levels A, B, C, pp. 19–21

Practice Worksheet

An easily-readable reduced
practice page (with answers)
for this lesson can be found
on p. 424C.

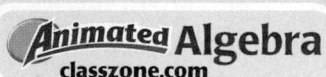
29. ★ **WRITING** Suppose you solve a linear system using substitution. *Explain* how you can use a graph to check your solution. **Sample answer: The graphs of the equations should intersect at the solution you found using the substitution method.**

C 30. **CHALLENGE** Find values of a and b so that the linear system shown has a solution of $(-9, 4)$. $ax + by = -16$ **Equation 1**
$ax - by = -56$ **Equation 2**
$a = 4, b = 5$

PROBLEM SOLVING

EXAMPLE 3 A
on p. 437
for Exs. 31–33

31. **FUNDRAISING** During a football game, the parents of the football players sell pretzels and popcorn to raise money for new uniforms. They charge $2.50 for a bag of popcorn and $2 for a pretzel. The parents collect $336 in sales during the game. They sell twice as many bags of popcorn as pretzels. How many bags of popcorn do they sell? How many pretzels do they sell? **96 bags of popcorn; 48 pretzels**

@HomeTutor for problem solving help at classzone.com

32. **TUBING COSTS** The members of an outing club take a day-long tubing trip down a river. The company that offers the tubing trip charges $15 to rent a tube for a person to use and $7.50 to rent a "cooler" tube, which is used to carry food and water in a cooler. The club members spend $360 to rent a total of 26 tubes. How many of each type of tube do they rent? **22 tubes for a person and 4 "cooler" tubes**

@HomeTutor for problem solving help at classzone.com

33. ★ **SHORT RESPONSE** In the mobile shown, objects are attached to each end of a dowel. For the dowel to balance, the following must be true:

$$x \cdot \begin{array}{c} \text{Weight hanging} \\ \text{from point } A \end{array} = y \cdot \begin{array}{c} \text{Weight hanging} \\ \text{from point } B \end{array}$$

The weight of the objects hanging from point A is 1.5 pounds, and the weight of the objects hanging from point B is 1.2 pounds. The length of the dowel is 9 inches. How far from point A should the string be placed? *Explain*.
4 in. Sample answer: (4, 5) is the solution to the appropriate linear system, so x should equal 4.

B 34. **MULTI-STEP PROBLEM** Two swimming teams are competing in a 400 meter medley relay. During the last leg of the race, the swimmer in lane 1 has a 1.2 second head start on the swimmer in lane 2, as shown.

1 — Swimming at 1.8 m/sec with a 1.2 sec head start

2 — Swimming at 1.9 m/sec

34b. Yes. *Sample answer:* After 21.6 seconds they have swam 41.04 meters, so the race is not over.

a. Let t be the time since the swimmer in lane 2 started the last leg. After how many seconds into the leg will the swimmer in lane 2 catch up to the swimmer in lane 1? **21.6 sec**

b. Does the swimmer in lane 2 catch up to the swimmer in lane 1 before the race ends? *Explain*.

○ = **WORKED-OUT SOLUTIONS**
on p. WS1

★ = **STANDARDIZED TEST PRACTICE**

EXAMPLE 4
on p. 430
for Ex. 35

35. CHEMISTRY In your chemistry lab, you have a bottle of 1% hydrochloric acid solution and a bottle of 5% hydrochloric acid solution. You need 100 milliliters of a 3% hydrochloric acid solution for an experiment. How many milliliters of each solution do you need to mix together?
50 milliliters of 1% hydrochloric acid solution and 50 milliliters of 5% hydrochloric acid solution

36. MONEY Laura has $4.50 in dimes and quarters. She has 3 more dimes than quarters. How many quarters does she have? **12 quarters**

37. ★ SHORT RESPONSE A gazelle can run 73 feet per second for several minutes. A cheetah can run 88 feet per second, but it can sustain this speed for only 20 seconds. A gazelle is 350 feet from a cheetah when both animals start running. Can the gazelle stay ahead of the cheetah? *Explain.* **Yes.** *Sample answer:* **The cheetah would have to run at 88 feet per second for 23.3 seconds to catch the gazelle.**

 Algebra at classzone.com

C 38. CHALLENGE A gardener needs 6 bushels of a potting medium of 40% peat moss and 60% vermiculite. He decides to add 100% vermiculite to his current potting medium that is 50% peat moss and 50% vermiculite. The gardener has 5 bushels of the 50% peat moss and 50% vermiculite mix. Does he have enough of the 50% peat moss and 50% vermiculite mix to make 6 bushels of the 40% peat moss and 60% vermiculite mix? *Explain.*
Yes. *Sample answer:* **The gardener needs 4.8 bushels of the 50% peat moss and 50% vermiculite mix, and the gardener had 5 bushels.**

MIXED REVIEW

Solve the proportion. Check your solution.

39. $\frac{3}{7} = \frac{x}{21}$ *(p. 162)* **9**

40. $\frac{y}{30} = \frac{9}{10}$ *(p. 162)* **27**

41. $\frac{12}{16} = \frac{3z}{4}$ *(p. 162)* **1**

42. $\frac{35}{q} = \frac{5}{3}$ *(p. 168)* **21**

43. $\frac{3}{2r} = \frac{-6}{16}$ *(p. 168)* **−4**

44. $\frac{4}{3} = \frac{s}{s-2}$ *(p. 168)* **8**

PREVIEW
Prepare for
Lesson 7.3
in Exs. 45–50.

Write two equations in standard form that are equivalent to the given equation. *(p. 311)* **45–50. Sample answers are given.**

45. $x - 4y = 0$
$2x - 8y = 0, 4x - 16y = 0$

46. $-3x + 9y = 6$
$x - 3y = -2, 3x - 9y = -6$

47. $-7x - y = 1$
$7x + y = -1, -14x - 2y = 2$

48. $5x - 10y = 5$
$x - 2y = 1, -x + 2y = -1$

49. $-2x - 12y = 8$
$-x - 6y = 4, x + 6y = -4$

50. $6x + 15y = -3$
$2x + 5y = -1, 12x + 30y = -6$

QUIZ *for Lessons 7.1–7.2*

Solve the linear system by graphing. Check your solution. *(p. 427)*

1. $x + y = -2$ **(−4, 2)**
$-x + y = 6$

2. $x - y = 0$ **(−1, −1)**
$5x + 2y = -7$

3. $x - 2y = 12$ **(−2, −7)**
$-3x + y = -1$

Solve the linear system using substitution. *(p. 435)*

4. $y = x - 4$ **(−22, −26)**
$-2x + y = 18$

5. $y = 4 - 3x$ **(3.25, −5.75)**
$5x - y = 22$

6. $x = y + 9$ **(−10, −19)**
$5x - 3y = 7$

7. $2y + x = -4$ **(2, −3)**
$y - x = -5$

8. $5x - 4y = 27$ **(−13, −23)**
$-2x + y = 3$

9. $3x - 5y = 13$ **(6, 1)**
$x + 4y = 10$

---

5 ASSESS AND RETEACH

Daily Homework Quiz

🗂 **Transparency Available**

Solve the linear system using substitution.

1. $-5x - y = 12$
$3x - 5y = 4$ **(−2, −2)**

2. $2x + 9y = -4$
$x - 2y = 11$ **(7, −2)**

3. You are making 6 quarts of fruit punch for a party. You want the punch to contain 80% fruit juice. You have bottles of 100% fruit juice and 20% fruit juice. How many quarts of 100% fruit juice and how many quarts of 20% fruit juice should you mix to make 6 quarts of 80% fruit juice?
4.5 quarts of 100% fruit juice and 1.5 quarts of 20% fruit juice

 Online Quiz

Available at **classzone.com**

Diagnosis/Remediation

• Practice A, B, C in Chapter 7 Resource Book, pp. 19–21
• Study Guide in Chapter 7 Resource Book, pp. 22–23
• Practice Workbook, pp. 107–108
• @HomeTutor

Challenge

Additional challenge is available in the Chapter 7 Resource Book, p. 26.

Quiz

An easily-readable reduced copy of the quiz (with answers) on Lessons 7.1–7.2 from the Assessment Book can be found on p. 424F.

Using ALTERNATIVE METHODS

Alternative Strategy

Example 3 on page 437 can be solved by making a table rather than by writing a system of equations. Making a table is a good alternative for students who have difficulties with algebraic representations. A table in this situation has the added benefit of showing a detailed analysis of the costs of both companies. This allows the student to reason about the benefits of choosing one company over another, which is often the goal in this type of exercise.

Avoiding Common Errors

Calculation errors are the biggest drawback in using this method. One way to avoid these errors is to make tables using a spreadsheet. After students enter the formulas in the appropriate cells, the spreadsheet will enter the correct calculations.

Another Way to Solve Example 3, page 437

MULTIPLE REPRESENTATIONS In Example 3 on page 437, you saw how to solve the problem about website hosting by solving a linear system algebraically. You can also solve the problem using a table.

PROBLEM

WEBSITES Many businesses pay website hosting companies to store and maintain the computer files that make up their websites. Internet service providers also offer website hosting. The costs for website hosting offered by a website hosting company and an Internet service provider are shown in the table. Find the number of months after which the total cost for website hosting will be the same for both companies.

Company	Set-up fee	Cost per month
Internet service provider	$10	$21.95
Website hosting company	None	$22.45

METHOD

Making a Table An alternative approach is to make a table.

STEP 1 **Make** a table for the total cost of website hosting for both companies.

> Include the set-up fee in the cost for the first month.

Months	Internet service provider	Website hosting company
1	$31.95	$22.45
2	$53.90	$44.90
3	$75.85	$67.35
⋮	⋮	⋮
19	$427.05	$426.55
20	$449.00	$449.00
21	$470.95	$471.45

STEP 2 **Look** for the month in which the total cost of the service from the Internet service provider and the website hosting company is the same. This happens after 20 months.

PRACTICE

1. **TAXIS** A taxi company charges $2.80 for the first mile and $1.60 for each additional mile. Another taxi company charges $3.20 for the first mile and $1.50 for each additional mile. After how many miles will each taxi cost the same? Use a table to solve the problem. **5 mi**

2. **SCHOOL PLAY** An adult ticket to a school play costs $5 and a student ticket costs $3. A total of $460 was collected from the sale of 120 tickets. How many student tickets were purchased? Solve the problem using algebra. Then use a table to check your answer. **70 student tickets**

7.3 Linear Systems and Elimination

MATERIALS · algebra tiles

QUESTION How can you solve a linear system using algebra tiles?

You can use the following algebra tiles to model equations.

1-tiles   x-tiles   y-tiles

EXPLORE Solve a linear system using algebra tiles.

Solve the linear system: $3x - y = 5$ **Equation 1**
                             $x + y = 3$ **Equation 2**

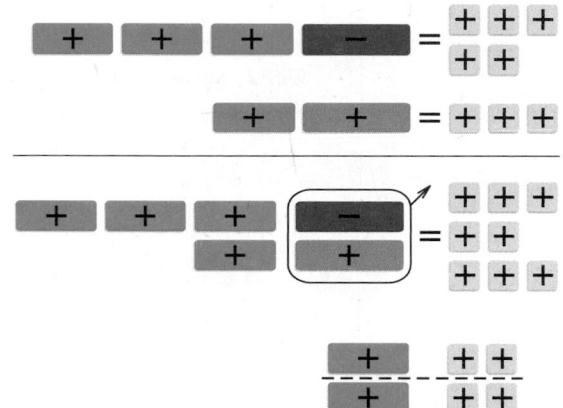

STEP 1 *Model equations*

Model each equation using algebra tiles. Arrange the algebra tiles so that one equation is directly below the other equation.

STEP 2 *Add equations*

Combine the two equations to form one equation. Notice that the new equation has one positive y-tile and one negative y-tile. The y-tiles can be removed because the pair of y-tiles has a value of 0.

STEP 3 *Solve for x*

Divide the remaining tiles into four equal groups. Each x-tile is equal to two 1-tiles. So, $x = 2$.

STEP 4 *Solve for y*

To find the value of y, use the model for Equation 2. Because $x = 2$, you can replace the x-tile with two 1-tiles. Solve the new equation for y. So $y = 1$, and the solution of the system is $(2, 1)$.

DRAW CONCLUSIONS Use your observations to complete these exercises

Use algebra tiles to model and solve the linear system.

1. $x + 3y = 8$
   $4x - 3y = 2$
   (2, 2)

2. $2x + y = 5$
   $-2x + 3y = 7$
   (1, 3)

3. $5x - 2y = -2$
   $x + 2y = 14$
   (2, 6)

4. $x + 2y = 3$
   $-x + 3y = 2$
   (1, 1)

5. **REASONING** Is it possible to solve the linear system $3x - 2y = 6$ and $2x + y = 11$ using the steps shown above? *Explain* your reasoning. **See margin.**

7.3 Solve Linear Systems by Adding or Subtracting   **443**

---

① PLAN AND PREPARE

Explore the Concept

- Students will use algebra tiles to solve a linear system.
- This activity leads into the study of solving linear systems by adding, as in Example 1 in Lesson 7.3.

Materials

Each student will need:
- algebra tiles
- Activity Support Master (*Chapter 7 Resource Book*, p. 29)

Recommended Time

Work activity: 15 min
Discuss results: 5 min

Grouping

Students should work individually.

② TEACH

Tips for Success

Make sure that the models of the equations are directly beneath each other.

Key Question

- In Step 4, why should you use the model for Equation 2? **Equation 2 is easier to solve for y because the coefficient of y is 1.**

Key Discovery

You can eliminate a variable if the coefficients are opposites.

③ ASSESS AND RETEACH

If you model the linear system $3x - 2y = 1$ and $-3x + y = 4$, which tiles can you remove when you combine the equations? **3 positive x-tiles and 3 negative x-tiles**

5. No. *Sample answer:* When you combine the two equations, the result still has 2 variables.

444

① PLAN AND PREPARE

Warm-Up Exercises

📑 Transparency Available

1. Solve the linear system using substitution.
   $2x + y = 12$
   $3x - 2y = 11$ **(5, 2)**

2. One auto repair shop charges $30 for a diagnosis and $25 per hour for labor. Another auto repair shop charges $35 per hour for labor. For how many hours are the total charges for both of the shops the same? **3 h**

Notetaking Guide

📑 Transparency Available

Promotes interactive learning and notetaking skills, pp. 155–157.

Pacing

Basic: 1 day
Average: 1 day
Advanced: 1 day
Block: 0.5 block with 7.2

• See *Teaching Guide/Lesson Plan*.

② FOCUS AND MOTIVATE

Essential Question

Big Idea 2, p. 425

How do you solve linear systems by eliminating a variable? **Tell students they will learn how to answer this question by adding or subtracting equations to eliminate one of the variables.**

NCTM STANDARDS

Standard 2: Analyze situations using algebraic symbols

Standard 7: Recognize reasoning and proof as fundamental to math

7.3 Solve Linear Systems by Adding or Subtracting

Before	You solved linear systems by graphing and using substitution.
Now	You will solve linear systems using elimination.
Why?	So you can solve a problem about arranging flowers, as in Ex. 42.

Key Vocabulary
• system of linear equations, *p. 427*

When solving a linear system, you can sometimes add or subtract the equations to obtain a new equation in one variable. This method is called *elimination*.

KEY CONCEPT *For Your Notebook*

Solving a Linear System Using the Elimination Method

STEP 1 **Add or subtract** the equations to eliminate one variable.

STEP 2 **Solve** the resulting equation for the other variable.

STEP 3 **Substitute** in either original equation to find the value of the eliminated variable.

EXAMPLE 1 Use addition to eliminate a variable

Solve the linear system: $2x + 3y = 11$ **Equation 1**
$\qquad\qquad\qquad\qquad\qquad -2x + 5y = 13$ **Equation 2**

Solution

ADD EQUATIONS
When the coefficients of one variable are opposites, add the equations to eliminate the variable.

STEP 1 **Add** the equations to eliminate one variable.

$2x + 3y = 11$
$-2x + 5y = 13$
$\overline{\qquad\qquad 8y = 24}$

STEP 2 **Solve** for y.

$y = 3$

STEP 3 **Substitute** 3 for y in either equation and solve for x.

$2x + 3y = 11$ **Write Equation 1.**
$2x + 3(3) = 11$ **Substitute 3 for y.**
$x = 1$ **Solve for x.**

▶ The solution is (1, 3).

CHECK Substitute 1 for x and 3 for y in each of the original equations.

$2x + 3y = 11$	$-2x + 5y = 13$
$2(1) + 3(3) \stackrel{?}{=} 11$	$-2(1) + 5(3) \stackrel{?}{=} 13$
$11 = 11 ✓$	$13 = 13 ✓$

Resource Planning Guide

Chapter Resource Book
• Teaching Guide/Lesson Plan (pp. 27–28)
• Practice levels A, B, C (pp. 30–32)
• Study Guide (pp. 33–34)
• Catch-up for Absent Students (p. 35)
• Problem Solving Workshop (p. 36)
• Challenge (p. 37)

Workbooks
• Notetaking Guide (pp. 155–157)
• Practice Workbook (pp. 109–110)

Teaching Options
• **Power Presentations CD-ROM** provides dynamic electronic teaching resources for the classroom.
• **Activity Generator CD-ROM** provides editable activities for all ability levels.

Interactive Technology
• Easy Planner
• Power Presentations CD-ROM
• Activity Generator CD-ROM
• Animated Algebra
• Test Generator CD-ROM
• Online Quiz
• eWorkbook
• eEdition
• @HomeTutor

Resources for English Learners
• Quick Reference for English Learners
• Spanish Study Guide
• Multi-Language Visual Glossary
• Student Resources in Spanish

See also the *Algebra 1 Toolkit* for more strategies for meeting individual needs.

EXAMPLE 2   Use subtraction to eliminate a variable

Solve the linear system: $4x + 3y = 2$ **Equation 1**
$5x + 3y = -2$ **Equation 2**

SUBTRACT EQUATIONS
When the coefficients of one variable are the same, subtract the equations to eliminate the variable.

Solution

STEP 1   **Subtract** the equations to eliminate one variable.

$$4x + 3y = 2$$
$$5x + 3y = -2$$

STEP 2   **Solve** for x.

$$-x = 4$$
$$x = -4$$

STEP 3   **Substitute** -4 for x in either equation and solve for y.

$4x + 3y = 2$ **Write Equation 1.**

$4(-4) + 3y = 2$ **Substitute -4 for x.**

$y = 6$ **Solve for y.**

▶ The solution is $(-4, 6)$.

EXAMPLE 3   **Arrange like terms**

Solve the linear system: $8x - 4y = -4$ **Equation 1**
$4y = 3x + 14$ **Equation 2**

Solution

STEP 1   **Rewrite** Equation 2 so that the like terms are arranged in columns.

$8x - 4y = -4$ $8x - 4y = -4$
$4y = 3x + 14$ ⟶ $-3x + 4y = 14$

AVOID ERRORS
Make sure that the equal signs are in the same column, just as the like terms are.

STEP 2   **Add** the equations.

$$5x = 10$$

STEP 3   **Solve** for x.

$$x = 2$$

STEP 4   **Substitute** 2 for x in either equation and solve for y.

$4y = 3x + 14$ **Write Equation 2.**

$4y = 3(2) + 14$ **Substitute 2 for x.**

$y = 5$ **Solve for y.**

▶ The solution is $(2, 5)$.

 GUIDED PRACTICE   for Examples 1, 2, and 3

Solve the linear system.

1. $4x - 3y = 5$ **(−1, −3)**
   $-2x + 3y = -7$

2. $-5x - 6y = 8$ **(2, −3)**
   $5x + 2y = 4$

3. $6x - 4y = 14$ **(5, 4)**
   $-3x + 4y = 1$

4. $7x - 2y = 5$ **(1, 1)**
   $7x - 3y = 4$

5. $3x + 4y = -6$ **(−2, 0)**
   $2y = 3x + 6$

6. $2x + 5y = 12$ **(1, 2)**
   $5y = 4x + 6$

7.3 Solve Linear Systems by Adding or Subtracting   **445**

Motivating the Lesson
You and a friend go to a county fair. Your friend pays an entrance fee and buys 8 tickets for rides, and the total cost is $16.50. You buy 6 tickets for rides and your total cost, with the entrance fee, is $14. By writing and solving a linear system, you can determine the entrance fee for the county fair and the cost per ticket for rides at the fair.

③ TEACH

Extra Example 1
Solve the linear system.
$3x + 4y = 8$
$-3x + 5y = 10$ **(0, 2)**

Extra Example 2
Solve the linear system.
$5x + 6y = 4$
$7x + 6y = 8$ **(2, −1)**

Avoiding Common Errors
When using subtraction to solve, as in Example 2, some students may add terms rather than subtract. One way to avoid this error is to use the definition of subtraction to rewrite Equation 2 with opposite signs and then add the equations.

Extra Example 3
Solve the linear system.
$9x - 3y = 18$
$3y = -7x + 30$ **(3, 3)**

Key Question to Ask for Example 3
• How do you know that you need to add the equations in Example 3? **Since the coefficients of y are opposites, you add to solve the system.**

EXAMPLE 4 **Write and solve a linear system**

KAYAKING During a kayaking trip, a kayaker travels 12 miles upstream (against the current) and 12 miles downstream (with the current), as shown. The speed of the current remained constant during the trip. Find the average speed of the kayak in still water and the speed of the current.

Upstream: 3 hours
DIRECTION OF CURRENT
Downstream: 2 hours

STEP 1 **Write** a system of equations. First find the speed of the kayak going upstream and the speed of the kayak going downstream.

Upstream: $d = rt$ | **Downstream:** $d = rt$
$$12 = r \cdot 3$$ | $$12 = r \cdot 2$$
$$4 = r$$ | $$6 = r$$

Use the speeds to write a linear system. Let x be the average speed of the kayak in still water, and let y be the speed of the current.

Equation 1: Going upstream

Speed of kayak in still water	−	Speed of current	=	Speed of kayak going upstream
x	−	y	=	4

Equation 2: Going downstream

Speed of kayak in still water	+	Speed of current	=	Speed of kayak going downstream
x	+	y	=	6

COMBINE SPEEDS
When you go upstream, the speed at which you can travel in still water is decreased by the speed of the current. The opposite is true when you go downstream.

STEP 2 **Solve** the system of equations.

$$x - y = 4$$ Write Equation 1.
$$x + y = 6$$ Write Equation 2.
$$2x = 10$$ Add equations.
$$x = 5$$ Solve for x.

Substitute 5 for x in Equation 2 and solve for y.

$$5 + y = 6$$ Substitute 5 for x in Equation 2.
$$y = 1$$ Subtract 5 from each side.

▶ The average speed of the kayak in still water is 5 miles per hour, and the speed of the current is 1 mile per hour.

Animated Algebra at classzone.com

Differentiated Instruction

English Learners When discussing **Example 4**, students may have difficulty with the meanings of "upstream" and "downstream". When you go up, you move against the force of gravity; so going upstream is going against the force of the river flow. Similarly, going down is moving with the force of gravity; so going downstream is going with the river flow.

See also the *Algebra 1 Toolkit* for more strategies.

7. **WHAT IF?** In Example 4, suppose it takes the kayaker 5 hours to travel 10 miles upstream and 2 hours to travel 10 miles downstream. The speed of the current remains constant during the trip. Find the average speed of the kayak in still water and the speed of the current.
average speed of the kayak: 3.5 mi/h, speed of the current: 1.5 mi/h

7.3 EXERCISES

HOMEWORK
KEY

○ = **WORKED-OUT SOLUTIONS**
on p. WS1 for Exs. 17 and 41

★ = **STANDARDIZED TEST PRACTICE**
Exs. 2, 15, 22, 36, and 44

◆ = **MULTIPLE REPRESENTATIONS**
Ex. 42

SKILL PRACTICE

 A

1. **VOCABULARY** Give an example of a linear system in two variables that can be solved by first adding the equations to eliminate one variable.
Sample answer: $x + y = 10$, $x - y = 5$

2. ★ **WRITING** *Explain* how to solve the linear system shown using the elimination method.
$2x - y = 2$ Equation 1
$2x + 3y = 22$ Equation 2
Sample answer: **Subtract Equation 2 from Equation 1 then solve the resulting equation for y. Then substitute the value of y and solve for x.**

EXAMPLE 1
on p. 444
for Exs. 3–8

USING ADDITION Solve the linear system using elimination.

3. $x + 2y = 13$ **(1, 6)**
$-x + y = 5$

4. $9x + y = 2$ **(−3, 29)**
$-4x - y = -17$

5. $-3x - y = 8$ **(−1, −5)**
$7x + y = -12$

6. $3x - y = 30$ **(12, 6)**
$-3x + 7y = 6$

7. $-9x + 4y = -17$ **(5, 7)**
$9x - 6y = 3$

8. $-3x - 5y = -7$ **(−1, 2)**
$-4x + 5y = 14$

EXAMPLE 2
on p. 445
for Exs. 9–15

USING SUBTRACTION Solve the linear system using elimination.

9. $x + y = 1$ **(−1, 2)**
$-2x + y = 4$

10. $x - y = -4$ **(−2, 2)**
$x + 3y = 4$

11. $2x - y = 7$ **(5, 3)**
$2x + 7y = 31$

12. $6x + y = -10$ **(0, −10)**
$5x + y = -10$

13. $5x + 6y = 50$ **(4, 5)**
$-x + 6y = 26$

14. $4x - 9y = -21$ **(−3, 1)**
$4x + 3y = -9$

15. ★ **MULTIPLE CHOICE** Which ordered pair is a solution of the linear system $4x + 9y = -2$ and $11x + 9y = 26$? **C**

   (A) $(-2, 4)$ (B) $(2, -4)$ (C) $(4, -2)$ (D) $(4, 2)$

EXAMPLE 3
on p. 445
for Exs. 16–22

ARRANGING LIKE TERMS Solve the linear system using elimination.

16. $2x - y = 32$ **(−15, −62)**
$y - 5x = 13$

17. $-8y + 6x = 36$ **(2, −3)**
$6x - y = 15$

18. $2x - y = -11$ **(−6, −1)**
$y = -2x - 13$

19. $-x - y = 14$ **(−18, 4)**
$x = 5y - 38$

20. $11y - 3x = 18$ **(5, 3)**
$-3x = -16y + 33$

21. $-5x + y = -23$ **(4, −3)**
$-y = 3x - 9$

22. ★ **MULTIPLE CHOICE** Which ordered pair is a solution of the linear system $2x + y = 10$ and $3y = 2x + 6$? **B**

   (A) $(-3, -4)$ (B) $(3, 4)$ (C) $(-4, 3)$ (D) $(4, 3)$

7.3 Solve Linear Systems by Adding or Subtracting   **447**

④ PRACTICE AND APPLY

Assignment Guide

▧ **Answer Transparencies**
available for all exercises

Basic:
Day 1: pp. 447–450
Exs. 1, 2, 3–21 odd, 22–30, 39–43, 46–54 even

Average:
Day 1: pp. 447–450
Exs. 1, 2, 6–8, 12–15, 19–24, 26–36 even, 39–44, 47–55 odd

Advanced:
Day 1: pp. 447–450
Exs. 1, 2, 7, 8, 13–15, 19–22, 25–33 odd, 34–45*, 49, 52, 54

Block:
pp. 447–450
Exs. 1, 2, 6–8, 12–15, 19–24, 26–36 even, 39–44, 47–55 odd
(with 7.2)

Differentiated Instruction

See *Algebra 1 Best Practices Toolkit* for suggestions on addressing the needs of a diverse classroom.

Homework Check

For a quick check of student understanding of key concepts, go over the following exercises:

Basic: 5, 11, 17, 19, 39
Average: 6, 12, 19, 21, 40
Advanced: 8, 14, 20, 21, 41

Extra Practice

• Student Edition, p. 944
• Chapter 7 Resource Book:
Practice levels A, B, C, pp. 30–32

Practice Worksheet

An easily-readable reduced practice page (with answers) for this lesson can be found on p. 424C.

23. Sample answer: The two equations should be subtracted rather than added; $6x = 8$, $x = \frac{4}{3}$.

24. Sample answer: When $-3x$ is moved to the other side, it should become $3x$, the equations should then be subtracted; $3x - 2y = -3$, $3x + 5y = 60$, $-7y = -63$, $y = 9$.

ERROR ANALYSIS *Describe* and correct the error in finding the value of one of the variables in the given linear system.

23. $5x - 7y = 16$
$-x - 7y = 8$

$$\begin{array}{r} 5x - 7y = 16 \\ -x - 7y = 8 \\ \hline 4x \qquad = 24 \\ x = 6 \end{array}$$ ✗

24. $3x - 2y = -3$
$5y = 60 - 3x$

$$\begin{array}{r} 3x - 2y = -3 \\ -3x + 5y = 60 \\ \hline 3y = 57 \\ y = 19 \end{array}$$ ✗

B **SOLVING LINEAR SYSTEMS** Solve the linear system using elimination.

25. $-x + \frac{1}{2}y = -19$ **(26, 14)**
$x - y = 12$

26. $\frac{1}{4}x - \frac{2}{3}y = 7$ **(4, −9)**
$\frac{1}{2}x + \frac{2}{3}y = -4$

27. $8x - \frac{1}{2}y = -38$ **(−4, 12)**
$\frac{1}{4}x - \frac{1}{2}y = -7$

28. $5.2x + 3.5y = 54$ **(5, 8)**
$-3.6x + 3.5y = 10$

29. $1.3x - 3y = -17.6$ **(−2, 5)**
$-1.3x + 4.5y = 25.1$

30. $-2.6x - 3.2y = 4.8$
$1.9x - 3.2y = -4.2$
(−2, 0.125)

31. $\frac{4}{5}x + \frac{2}{5}y = 14$ **(5, 25)**
$\frac{2}{5}y + \frac{1}{5}x = 11$

32. $2.7x + 1.5y = 36$ **(10, 6)**
$3.5y = 2.7x - 6$

33. $4 - 4.8x = 1.7y$ **(−2, 8)**
$12.8 + 1.7y = -13.2x$

34. WRITING AN EQUATION OF A LINE Use the following steps to write an equation of the line that passes through the points (1, 2) and (−4, 12).

a. Write a system of linear equations by substituting 1 for x and 2 for y in $y = mx + b$ and −4 for x and 12 for y in $y = mx + b$. **$2 = m + b$, $12 = -4m + b$**

b. Solve the system of linear equations from part (a). What is the slope of the line? What is the y-intercept? **slope: −2; y-intercept: 4**

c. Write an equation of the line that passes through (1, 2) and (−4, 12). **$y = -2x + 4$**

35. ◆ **GEOMETRY** The rectangle has a perimeter P of 14 feet, and twice its length ℓ is equal to 1 less than 4 times its width w. Write and solve a system of linear equations to find the length and the width of the rectangle. **$\ell = 4.5$ ft, $w = 2.5$ ft**

36. ★ **SHORT RESPONSE** Find the solution of the system of linear equations below. *Explain* your steps. **(−1, 3).** *Sample answer:* **First solve Equation 1 and 2 using elimination. Then check the solution for all three equations.**

$x + 3y = 8$ Equation 1
$x - 6y = -19$ Equation 2
$5x - 3y = -14$ Equation 3

C **37. CHALLENGE** For $a \neq 0$, what is the solution of the system $ax + 2y = 4$ and $ax - 3y = -6$? **(0, 2)**

38. CHALLENGE Solve for x, y, and z in the system of equations below. *Explain* your steps. **(−5, 4, 2).** *Sample answer:* **Subtract Equation 2 from Equation 1 to solve for y. Then substitute y into equation 3 to solve for x. Then substitute x and y into Equation 1 or Equation 2 to solve for z. Check solution in all three equations.**

$x + 7y + 3z = 29$ Equation 1
$3z + x - 2y = -7$ Equation 2
$5y = 10 - 2x$ Equation 3

EXAMPLE 4 A
on p. 446
for Exs. 39–41

39. ROWING During a practice, a 4 person crew team rows a rowing shell upstream (against the current) and then rows the same distance downstream (with the current). The shell moves upstream at a speed of 4.3 meters per second and downstream at a speed of 4.9 meters per second. The speed of the current remains constant. Use the models below to write and solve a system of equations to find the average speed of the shell in still water and the speed of the current.
speed in still water: 4.6 m/sec, speed of current: 0.3 m/sec

Upstream

| Speed of shell in still water | − | Speed of current | = | Speed of shell |

Downstream

| Speed of shell in still water | + | Speed of current | = | Speed of shell |

@HomeTutor for problem solving help at classzone.com

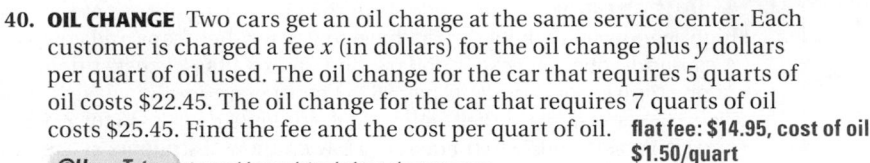

40. OIL CHANGE Two cars get an oil change at the same service center. Each customer is charged a fee x (in dollars) for the oil change plus y dollars per quart of oil used. The oil change for the car that requires 5 quarts of oil costs $22.45. The oil change for the car that requires 7 quarts of oil costs $25.45. Find the fee and the cost per quart of oil. **flat fee: $14.95, cost of oil: $1.50/quart**

@HomeTutor for problem solving help at classzone.com

(41.) PHONES Cellular phone ring tones can be monophonic or polyphonic. Monophonic ring tones play one tone at a time, and polyphonic ring tones play multiple tones at a time. The table shows the ring tones downloaded from a website by two customers. Use the information to find the cost of a monophonic ring tone and a polyphonic ring tone, assuming that all monophonic ring tones cost the same and all polyphonic ring tones cost the same. **monophonic ring tone: $1.95, polyphonic ring tone: $3.50**

Customer	Monophonic ring tones	Polyphonic ring tones	Total cost (dollars)
Julie	3	2	12.85
Tate	1	2	8.95

42a. Let x represent the number of twigs and y represent the number of flowers; $x + 3y = 15$, $x + y = 9$, 6 twigs and 3 flowers.

42. ◆ MULTIPLE REPRESENTATIONS For a floral arrangement class, Alicia has to create an arrangement of twigs and flowers that has a total of 9 objects. She has to pay for the twigs and flowers that she uses in her arrangement. Each twig costs $1, and each flower costs $3.

a. **Writing a System** Alicia spends $15 on the twigs and flowers. Write and solve a linear system to find the number of twigs and the number of flowers she used.

b. **Making a Table** Make a table showing the number of twigs in the arrangement and the total cost of the arrangement when the number of flowers purchased is 0, 1, 2, 3, 4, or 5. Use the table to check your answer to part (a). **See margin.**

7.3 Solve Linear Systems by Adding or Subtracting **449**

Avoiding Common Errors

Exercise 40 When some students use Example 4 as a model for this exercise, they may believe that they should subtract the x- and y-values for the first equation and add the x- and y-values for the second equation. Remind these students that the context of the problem determines whether they add or subtract the x- and y-values in each equation.

Study Strategy

Exercise 43 Suggest that students use Example 4 as a model for solving this problem. Point out that wind speed is comparable to current speed and that flying into the wind is comparable to going upstream, while flying with the wind is comparable to going downstream.

42b.

Flowers	Twigs	Cost
0	9	$9
1	8	$11
2	7	$13
3	6	$15
4	5	$17
5	4	$19

5 **ASSESS** AND **RETEACH**

Daily Homework Quiz

📄 **Transparency Available**

Solve the linear system using elimination.

1. $-5x + y = 18$
   $3x - y = -10$ **(−4, −2)**

2. $4x + 2y = 14$
   $4x - 3y = -11$ **(1, 5)**

3. $2x - y = -14$
   $y = 3x + 6$ **(8, 30)**

4. $x + 4y = 15$
   $2y = x - 9$ **(11, 1)**

5. A business center charges a flat fee to send faxes plus a fee per page. You send one fax with 4 pages for $5.36 and another fax with 7 pages for $7.88. Find the flat fee and the cost per page to send a fax. **flat fee: $2, price per page: $.84**

 Online Quiz

Available at **classzone.com**

Diagnosis/Remediation

• Practice A, B, C in Chapter 7 Resource Book, pp. 30–32
• Study Guide in Chapter 7 Resource Book, pp. 33–34
• Practice Workbook, pp. 109–110
• @HomeTutor

Challenge

Additional challenge is available in the Chapter 7 Resource Book, p. 37.

B **43. MULTI-STEP PROBLEM** On a typical day with light winds, the 1800 mile flight from Charlotte, North Carolina, to Phoenix, Arizona, takes longer than the return trip because the plane has to fly into the wind.

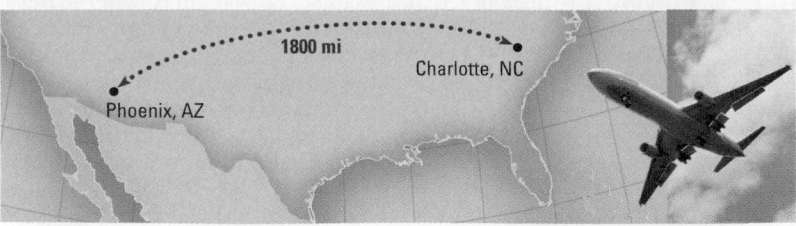

1800 mi
Charlotte, NC
Phoenix, AZ

  a. The flight from Charlotte to Phoenix is 4 hours 30 minutes long, and the flight from Phoenix to Charlotte is 4 hours long. Find the average speed (in miles per hour) of the airplane on the way to Phoenix and on the return trip to Charlotte. **flight to Phoenix: 400 mi/h, flight to Charlotte: 450 mi/h**

  b. Let s be the speed (in miles per hour) of the plane with no wind, and let w be the speed (in miles per hour) of the wind. Use your answer to part (a) to write and solve a system of equations to find the speed of the plane with no wind and the speed of the wind.
  $s + w = 450$, $s - w = 400$; plane: 425 mi/h, wind: 25 mi/h

44. ★ **SHORT RESPONSE** The students in the graduating classes at the three high schools in a school district have to pay for their caps and gowns. A cap-and-gown set costs x dollars, and an extra tassel costs y dollars. At one high school, students pay $3262 for 215 cap-and-gown sets and 72 extra tassels. At another high school, students pay $3346 for 221 cap-and-gown sets and 72 extra tassels. How much will students at the third high school pay for 218 cap-and-gown sets and 56 extra tassels? *Explain.*
$3248. *Sample answer:* **Each cap-and-gown costs $14 and each extra tassel costs $3.50.**

C **45. CHALLENGE** A clothing manufacturer makes men's dress shirts. For the production process, an ideal sleeve length x (in centimeters) for each shirt size and an allowable deviation y (in centimeters) from the ideal length are established. The deviation is expressed as $\pm y$. For a specific shirt size, the minimum allowable sleeve length is 62.2 centimeters and the maximum allowable sleeve length is 64.8 centimeters. Find the ideal sleeve length and the allowable deviation.
ideal sleeve length: 63.5 cm, allowable deviation: 1.3 cm

MIXED REVIEW

Graph the equation. 46–49. See margin.

46. $x - 5y = -12$ *(p. 225)*   **47.** $-2x + 3y = -15$ *(p. 225)*

48. $y + 9 = -(x + 2)$ *(p. 302)*   **49.** $y - 4 = \frac{2}{3}(x + 1)$ *(p. 302)*

Solve the linear system by graphing. Check your solution. *(p. 427)*

50. $y = x - 3$ **(2, −1)**   **51.** $y = 2$ **(6, 2)**   **52.** $2x + y = 6$ **(0, 6)**
   $y = -x + 1$ $2x - 3y = 6$ $6x - 2y = -12$

Find the least common multiple of the pair of numbers. *(p. 910)*

53. 9, 12 **36**   **54.** 18, 24 **72**   **55.** 15, 20 **60**

PREVIEW
Prepare for Lesson 7.4 in Exs. 53–55.

46–49. See Additional Answers beginning on p. AA1.

7.4 Solve Linear Systems by Multiplying First

Before You solved linear systems by adding or subtracting.

Now You will solve linear systems by multiplying first.

Why So you can solve a problem about preparing food, as in Ex. 39.

Key Vocabulary
• least common multiple, *p. 910*

In a linear system like the one below, neither variable can be eliminated by adding or subtracting the equations. For systems like these, you can multiply one or both of the equations by a constant so that adding or subtracting the equations will eliminate one variable.

$5x + 2y = 16$ $\times 2$ $\longrightarrow$ $10x + 4y = 32$

$3x - 4y = 20$ $\longrightarrow$ $3x - 4y = 20$

The new system is equivalent to the original system.

EXAMPLE 1 Multiply one equation, then add

Solve the linear system: $6x + 5y = 19$ **Equation 1**

$2x + 3y = 5$ **Equation 2**

Solution

STEP 1 **Multiply** Equation 2 by -3 so that the coefficients of x are opposites.

$6x + 5y = 19$ $\qquad$ $6x + 5y = 19$

$2x + 3y = 5$ $\times (-3)$ $\qquad$ $-6x - 9y = -15$

$\qquad\qquad\qquad\qquad\qquad\qquad -4y = 4$

ANOTHER WAY
You can also multiply Equation 2 by 3 and subtract the equations.

STEP 2 **Add** the equations.

STEP 3 **Solve** for y. $\qquad\qquad y = -1$

STEP 4 **Substitute** -1 for y in either of the original equations and solve for x.

$2x + 3y = 5$ **Write Equation 2.**

$2x + 3(-1) = 5$ **Substitute -1 for y.**

$2x + (-3) = 5$ **Multiply.**

$2x = 8$ **Subtract -3 from each side.**

$x = 4$ **Divide each side by 2.**

▶ The solution is $(4, -1)$.

CHECK Substitute 4 for x and -1 for y in each of the original equations.

Equation 1	**Equation 2**
$6x + 5y = 19$	$2x + 3y = 5$
$6(4) + 5(-1) \stackrel{?}{=} 19$	$2(4) + 3(-1) \stackrel{?}{=} 5$
$19 = 19 ✓$	$5 = 5 ✓$

① PLAN AND PREPARE

Warm-Up Exercises

⬛ **Transparency Available**

Solve the linear system.

1. $4x - 3y = 15$
$2x - 3y = 9$ **(3, −1)**

2. $-2x + y = -8$
$2x - 2y = 8$ **(4, 0)**

3. You row a canoe 10 miles upstream in 2.5 hours and 10 miles downstream in 2 hours. What is the average speed of the canoe in still water? **4.5 mi/h**

Notetaking Guide

⬛ **Transparency Available**

Promotes interactive learning and notetaking skills, pp. 158–159.

Pacing

Basic: 1 day

Average: 1 day

Advanced: 1 day

Block: 0.5 block with 7.5

• See *Teaching Guide/Lesson Plan*.

② FOCUS AND MOTIVATE

Essential Question

Big Idea 2, p. 425

How do you solve linear systems by multiplying first? **Tell students they will learn how to answer this question by multiplying one or both equations by a constant and then adding or subtracting to eliminate a variable.**

NCTM STANDARDS

Standard 2: Analyze situations using algebraic symbols

Standard 10: Use representations to solve problems

Resource Planning Guide

Chapter Resource Book
• Teaching Guide/Lesson Plan (pp. 38–39)
• Activity Master (p. 40)
• Practice levels A, B, C (pp. 41–43)
• Study Guide (pp. 44–45)
• Catch-up for Absent Students (p. 46)
• Problem Solving Workshop (p. 47)
• Challenge (p. 49)

Workbooks
• Notetaking Guide (pp. 158–159)
• Practice Workbook (pp. 111–112)

Teaching Options
• **Power Presentations CD-ROM** provides dynamic electronic teaching resources for the classroom.
• **Activity Generator CD-ROM** provides editable activities for all ability levels.

Interactive Technology
• Easy Planner
• Power Presentations CD-ROM
• Activity Generator CD-ROM
• Animated Algebra
• Test Generator CD-ROM
• Online Quiz
• eWorkbook
• eEdition
• @HomeTutor

Resources for English Learners
• Quick Reference for English Learners
• Spanish Study Guide
• Multi-Language Visual Glossary
• Student Resources in Spanish

See also the *Algebra 1 Toolkit* for more strategies for meeting individual needs.

451

❸ TEACH

Extra Example 1

Solve the linear system.
$2x + y = -9$
$4x + 11y = 9$ $(-6, 3)$

Key Question to Ask for Example 1

• Why do you eliminte x rather than y? **Since 6 is a multiple of 2, it is easier to eliminate x. To eliminate y, you would need to multiply by a fraction, either $\frac{5}{3}$ or $\frac{3}{5}$.**

Extra Example 2

Solve the linear system.
$2x - 3y = 6$
$4y = -7x - 8$ $(0, -2)$

Key Question to Ask for Example 2

• Is it possible to eliminate x by multiplying each equation by a constant? Explain. **You can eliminate x by multiplying Equation 1 by 3 and Equation 2 by 4.**

An **Animated Algebra** activity is available on-line for **Example 2**. This activity is also available on the **Power Presentations CD-ROM**.

MULTIPLYING BOTH EQUATIONS To eliminate one variable when adding or subtracting equations in a linear system, you may need to multiply both equations by constants. Use the least common multiple of the coefficients of one of the variables to determine the constants.

$$2x - 9y = 1 \quad \times 4 \quad \longrightarrow \quad 8x - 36y = 4$$
$$7x - 12y = 23 \quad \times 3 \quad \longrightarrow \quad 21x - 36y = 69$$

⤷ The least common multiple of −9 and −12 is −36.

EXAMPLE 2 | Multiply both equations, then subtract

Solve the linear system: $4x + 5y = 35$ **Equation 1**
                                     $2y = 3x - 9$ **Equation 2**

Solution

STEP 1   **Arrange** the equations so that like terms are in columns.

      $4x + 5y = 35$ **Write Equation 1.**

     $-3x + 2y = -9$ **Rewrite Equation 2.**

ANOTHER WAY
You can also multiply Equation 1 by 3 and Equation 2 by 4. Then add the revised equations to eliminate x.

STEP 2   **Multiply** Equation 1 by 2 and Equation 2 by 5 so that the coeffcient of y in each equation is the least common multiple of 5 and 2, or 10.

$$4x + 5y = 35 \quad \times 2 \quad \longrightarrow \quad 8x + 10y = 70$$
$$-3x + 2y = -9 \quad \times 5 \quad \longrightarrow \quad -15x + 10y = -45$$

STEP 3   **Subtract** the equations. $23x \quad\quad = 115$

STEP 4   **Solve** for x. ··▶ $x = 5$

STEP 5   **Substitute** 5 for x in either of the original equations and solve for y.

      $4x + 5y = 35$ **Write Equation 1.**

   $4(5) + 5y = 35$ **Substitute 5 for x.**

           $y = 3$ **Solve for y.**

▶ The solution is (5, 3).

CHECK   Substitute 5 for x and 3 for y in each of the original equations.

Equation 1	Equation 2
$4x + 5y = 35$	$2y = 3x - 9$
$4(5) + 5(3) \stackrel{?}{=} 35$	$2(3) \stackrel{?}{=} 3(5) - 9$
$35 = 35 ✓$	$6 = 6 ✓$

 Algebra   at classzone.com

✓ GUIDED PRACTICE   for Examples 1 and 2

Solve the linear system using elimination.

1. $6x - 2y = 1$ $(-0.5, -2)$
   $-2x + 3y = -5$

2. $2x + 5y = 3$ $(9, -3)$
   $3x + 10y = -3$

3. $3x - 7y = 5$ $(-10, -5)$
   $9y = 5x + 5$

Differentiated Instruction

English Learners   Caution students not to confuse the words "equal" and "equivalent". In **Example 2**, multiplying the first equation by 2 and the second equation by 5 produces "equivalent" equations, because the solution set is not changed. The sides of each equation are "equal".

See also the *Algebra 1 Toolkit* for more strategies.

Darlene is making a quilt that has alternating stripes of regular quilting fabric and sateen fabric. She spends $76 on a total of 16 yards of the two fabrics at a fabric store. Which system of equations can be used to find the amount x (in yards) of regular quilting fabric and the amount y (in yards) of sateen fabric she purchased?

— Sateen fabric costs $6 per yard.

— Quilting fabric costs $4 per yard.

ELIMINATE CHOICES
You can eliminate choice A because $x + y$ cannot equal both 16 and 76.

Ⓐ $x + y = 16$
   $x + y = 76$

Ⓑ $x + y = 16$
   $4x + 6y = 76$

Ⓒ $x + y = 76$
   $4x + 6y = 16$

Ⓓ $x + y = 16$
   $6x + 4y = 76$

Solution

Write a system of equations where x is the number of yards of regular quilting fabric purchased and y is the number of yards of sateen fabric purchased.

Equation 1: Amount of fabric

Amount of quilting fabric	+	Amount of sateen fabric	=	Total yards of fabric
⬇		⬇		⬇
x	+	y	=	16

Equation 2: Cost of fabric

Quilting fabric price (dollars/yd)	·	Amount of quilting fabric (yd)	+	Sateen fabric price (dollars/yd)	·	Amount of sateen fabric (yd)	=	Total cost (dollars)
⬇		⬇		⬇		⬇		⬇
4	·	x	+	6	·	y	=	76

The system of equations is: $x + y = 16$ **Equation 1**
                        $4x + 6y = 76$ **Equation 2**

▸ The correct answer is B. Ⓐ **Ⓑ** Ⓒ Ⓓ

✓ **GUIDED PRACTICE**   for Example 3

4. **SOCCER** A sports equipment store is having a sale on soccer balls. A soccer coach purchases 10 soccer balls and 2 soccer ball bags for $155. Another soccer coach purchases 12 soccer balls and 3 soccer ball bags for $189. Find the cost of a soccer ball and the cost of a soccer ball bag.
   soccer ball: $14.50, soccer ball bag: $5

Extra Example 3

Mr. Alvarado bought a total of 20 pounds of grass seed at the nursery for $168. He paid $9 per pound for Kentucky bluegrass and $6 per pound for Tall Fescue. Which system of equations can be used to find the amount x (in pounds) of Kentucky bluegrass and the amount y (in pounds) of Tall Fescue Mr. Alvarado purchased? **D**

Ⓐ $x + y = 168$
   $9x + 6y = 20$

Ⓑ $x + y = 20$
   $6x + 9y = 168$

Ⓒ $x + y = 168$
   $6x + 9y = 20$

Ⓓ $x + y = 20$
   $9x + 6y = 168$

Mathematical Reasoning

You may want to point out that choice C does not make sense mathematically because one yard each of quilting fabric and sateen cannot cost $76 if one costs $4 per yard and one costs $6 per yard.

Closing the Lesson

Have students summarize the major points of the lesson and answer the Essential Question: How do you solve linear systems by multiplying first?

• **Multiply one or both equations of a linear system by a constant or constants and then add or subtract to eliminate a variable.**

Determine whether you need to multiply one equation or both equations by constants so you can eliminate one of the variables. After multiplying, use addition or subtraction to eliminate the variable. Solve the equation and then substitute in one of the original equations to find the value of the eliminated variable.

Methods for Solving Linear Systems

Method	Example	When to Use
Table (p. 426)	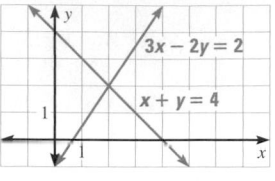	When *x*-values are integers, so that equal values can be seen in the table
Graphing (p. 427)		When you want to see the lines that the equations represent
Substitution (p. 435)	$y = 4 - 2x$ $4x + 2y = 8$	When one equation is already solved for *x* or *y*
Addition (p. 444)	$4x + 7y = 15$ $6x - 7y = 5$	When the coefficients of one variable are opposites
Subtraction (p. 445)	$3x + 5y = -13$ $3x + y = -5$	When the coefficients of one variable are the same
Multiplication (p. 451)	$9x + 2y = 38$ $3x - 5y = 7$	When no corresponding coefficients are the same or opposites

For the Table (p. 426) example:

x	y = 2x	y = 3x − 1
0	0	−1
1	2	2
2	4	5

④ PRACTICE AND APPLY

Assignment Guide

📖 **Answer Transparencies** available for all exercises

Basic:
Day 1: SRH p. 911 Exs. 25, 26, 32, 36
pp. 454–457
Exs. 1, 2, 3–17 odd, 18–25, 37–41, 46–58 even

Average:
Day 1: pp. 454–457
Exs. 1, 2, 6–8, 13–20, 21–33 odd, 34, 37–42, 45–57 odd

Advanced:
Day 1: pp. 454–457
Exs. 1, 7, 8, 15–18, 21–36*, 39–44*, 47, 52, 58

Block:
pp. 454–457
Exs. 1, 2, 6–8, 13–20, 21–33 odd, 34, 37–42, 45–57 odd (with 7.5)

Differentiated Instruction

See *Algebra 1 Best Practices Toolkit* for suggestions on addressing the needs of a diverse classroom.

Homework Check

For a quick check of student understanding of key concepts, go over the following exercises:

Basic: 5, 11, 16, 37, 38
Average: 7, 14, 21, 38, 39
Advanced: 8, 16, 28, 39, 40

Extra Practice

- Student Edition, p. 944
- Chapter 7 Resource Book: Practice levels A, B, C, pp. 41–43

Practice Worksheet

An easily-readable reduced practice page (with answers) for this lesson can be found on p. 424C.

7.4 EXERCISES

HOMEWORK KEY
○ = **WORKED-OUT SOLUTIONS** on p. WS1 for Exs. 15 and 39
★ = **STANDARDIZED TEST PRACTICE** Exs. 2, 18, 34, 41, and 42
◆ = **MULTIPLE REPRESENTATIONS** Ex. 40

SKILL PRACTICE

A 1. **VOCABULARY** What is the least common multiple of 12 and 18? **36**

2. ★ **WRITING** *Explain* how to solve the linear system using the elimination method.

$2x - 3y = -4$ **Equation 1**
$7x + 9y = -5$ **Equation 2**

Sample answer: Multiply Equation 1 by 3 and add to Equation 2. Then solve for *x* and substitute to find *y*.

EXAMPLE 1 on p. 451 for Exs. 3–8

SOLVING LINEAR SYSTEMS Solve the linear system using elimination.

3. $x + y = 2$ **(1, 1)**
   $2x + 7y = 9$

4. $3x - 2y = 3$ **(5, 6)**
   $-x + y = 1$

5. $4x + 3y = 8$ **(5, −4)**
   $x - 2y = 13$

6. $10x - 9y = 46$ **(19, 16)**
   $-2x + 3y = 10$

7. $8x - 5y = 11$ **(2, 1)**
   $4x - 3y = 5$

8. $11x - 20y = 28$ **(8, 3)**
   $3x + 4y = 36$

EXAMPLE 2

on p. 452 for
Exs. 9–20

SOLVING LINEAR SYSTEMS Solve the linear system using elimination.

9. $4x - 3y = 8$ **(−7, −12)**
   $5x - 2y = -11$

10. $-2x - 5y = 9$ **(−17, 5)**
    $3x + 11y = 4$

11. $7x - 6y = -1$ **(5, 6)**
    $5x - 4y = 1$

12. $7x + 3y = -12$ **(−6, 10)**
    $2x + 5y = 38$

13. $9x - 8y = 4$ **(4, 4)**
    $2x - 3y = -4$

14. $12x - 7y = -2$ **(1, 2)**
    $-8x + 11y = 14$

15. $9x + 2y = 39$ **(5, −3)**
    $6x + 13y = -9$

16. $-7x + 10y = 11$ **(7, 6)**
    $-8x + 15y = 34$

17. $-14x + 15y = 15$ $\left(4\frac{2}{7}, 5\right)$
    $21x - 20y = -10$

18. ★ **MULTIPLE CHOICE** Which ordered pair is a solution of the linear system
    $15x + 8y = 6$ and $25x + 12y = 14$? **D**

    (A) $(-3, -2)$ (B) $(-3, 2)$ (C) $(-2, -3)$ (D) $(2, -3)$

ERROR ANALYSIS *Describe* and correct the error when solving the linear system. 19–20. See margin.

19.
$$2x - 3y = -9 \xrightarrow{\times 2} 4x - 6y = -18$$
$$5x - 6y = -9 \qquad \underline{5x - 6y = -9}$$
$$9x \qquad = -27$$
$$x = -3$$

20.
$$9x + 8y = 11 \xrightarrow{\times 3} 27x + 24y = 11$$
$$7x + 6y = 9 \xrightarrow{\times 4} \underline{28x + 24y = 9}$$
$$-x \qquad = 2$$
$$x = -2$$

B   **SOLVING LINEAR SYSTEMS** Solve the linear system using any algebraic method.

21. $3x + 2y = 4$ **(2, −1)**
    $2y = 8 - 5x$

22. $4x - 5y = 18$ $\left(3\frac{4}{11}, -\frac{10}{11}\right)$
    $3x = y + 11$

23. $8x - 9y = -15$ $\left(-4\frac{5}{22}, -2\frac{1}{11}\right)$
    $-4x = 19 + y$

24. $0.3x + 0.1y = -0.1$ **(−1, 2)**
    $-x + y = 3$

25. $4.4x - 3.6y = 7.6$ **(5, 4)**
    $x - y = 1$

26. $3x - 2y = -20$ **(−2, 7)**
    $x + 1.2y = 6.4$

27. $0.2x - 1.5y = -1$ **(10, 2)**
    $x - 4.5y = 1$

28. $1.5x - 3.5y = -5$ **(20, 10)**
    $-1.2x + 2.5y = 1$

29. $4.9x + 2.4y = 7.4$ **(2, −1)**
    $0.7x + 3.6y = -2.2$

30. $x + y = 0$ **(2, −2)**
    $\frac{1}{2}x - \frac{1}{2}y = 2$

31. $3x + y = \frac{1}{3}$ $\left(\frac{1}{3}, -\frac{2}{3}\right)$
    $2x - 3y = \frac{8}{3}$

32. $\frac{3}{5}x - \frac{3}{4}y = -3$ **(10, 12)**
    $\frac{2}{5}x + \frac{1}{3}y = 8$

33.   **GEOMETRY** A rectangle has a perimeter of 18 inches. A new rectangle is formed by doubling the width w and tripling the length ℓ, as shown. The new rectangle has a perimeter P of 46 inches.

    a. Write and solve a system of linear equations to find the length and width of the original rectangle.
    $2\ell + 2w = 18, 6\ell + 4w = 46$

    b. Find the length and width of the new rectangle.
    length: 15 in., width: 8 in.

$P = 46$ in. $2w$

3ℓ

34. ★ **WRITING** For which values of a can you solve the linear system $ax + 3y = 2$ and $4x + 5y = 6$ without multiplying first? *Explain*.
    4 and −4. *Sample answer:* For these values, you can add or subtract to eliminate the *x* term.

C   **CHALLENGE** Find the values of a and b so that the linear system has the given solution.

$ax - by = 4$ **Equation 1**
$bx - ay = 10$ **Equation 2**

35. $(4, 2)$ $a = 3, b = 4$

36. $(2, 1)$ $a = 6, b = 8$

Margin notes (left side):

19. *Sample answer:* The two equations should be subtracted rather than added;
$-x = -9, x = 9$.

20. *Sample answer:* The right side of the equations were not multiplied;
$27x + 24y = 33$,
$28x + 24y = 36$,
$-x = -3, x = 3$.

Margin notes (right side):

Avoiding Common Errors

Exercises 9–17, 21–32 Some students may fail to subtract the equations in a linear system when the coefficients of a variable are the same. Suggest that they give the equations a second look to make sure that the coefficients of the eliminated variable are opposites.

Graphing Calculator

Exercises 24–32 Students may want to graph these linear systems to check their solutions. They should enter the equations using `y=`, and adjust the standard viewing window if necessary. The intersect feature will show the coordinates of the intersection point.

Mathematical Reasoning

Exercises 37–40 Before students begin these exercises, you may want to discuss how a system of linear equations represents a real-world situation. You could point out in Exercise 37 that one equation represents the total number of books and the other equation represents the cost of the books. In contrast, in Exercise 38, one equation represents the number of individual songs and albums and their cost for one person and the other equation represents the same information for a different person.

🔎 Internet Reference

Exercise 39 Information about the various apple varieties can be found at www.urbanext.uiuc.edu/apple.varieties.html

40b.

42. *Sample answer:* Two cars are traveling on the same route. One car leaves 30 minutes before the other car and travels at a rate of 40 miles per hour. If the other car travels 45 miles per hour, how many hours will it take for the second car to catch the first car? 4 h, the second car will have to travel 4 hours in order to catch the first car.

EXAMPLE 3 [A]
on p. 453
for Exs. 37–39

40a. Let *x* represent the number of student tickets and *y* represent the number of adult tickets; $3x + 5y = 2995$, $x + y = 729$, 325 student tickets and 404 adult tickets.

41. $16.50; a small costs $2.90, and a large costs $3.90; 3(2.90) + 2(3.90) = 16.50.

---

37. BOOK SALE A library is having a book sale to raise money. Hardcover books cost $4 each and paperback books cost $2 each. A person spends $26 for 8 books. How many hardcover books did she purchase? **5 hardcover books**

@HomeTutor for problem solving help at classzone.com

38. MUSIC A website allows users to download individual songs or an entire album. All individual songs cost the same to download, and all albums cost the same to download. Ryan pays $14.94 to download 5 individual songs and 1 album. Seth pays $22.95 to download 3 individual songs and 2 albums. How much does the website charge to download a song? an entire album?
$.99; $9.99

@HomeTutor for problem solving help at classzone.com

(39.) FARM PRODUCTS The table shows the number of apples needed to make the apple pies and applesauce sold at a farm store. During a recent apple picking at the farm, 169 Granny Smith apples and 95 Golden Delicious apples were picked. How many apple pies and batches of applesauce can be made if every apple is used? **21 pies, 16 batches of applesauce**

Type of apple	Granny Smith	Golden Delicious
Needed for a pie	5	3
Needed for a batch of applesauce	4	2

[B]

40. ◆ **MULTIPLE REPRESENTATIONS** Tickets for admission to a high school football game cost $3 for students and $5 for adults. During one game, $2995 was collected from the sale of 729 tickets.

  a. Writing a System Write and solve a system of linear equations to find the number of tickets sold to students and the number of tickets sold to adults.

  b. Drawing a Graph Graph the system of linear equations. Use the graph to determine whether your answer to part (a) is reasonable.
The answer is reasonable; see margin for art.

41. ★ **SHORT RESPONSE** A dim sum restaurant offers two sizes of dishes: small and large. All small dishes cost the same and all large dishes cost the same. The bills show the cost of the food before the tip is included. What will 3 small and 2 large dishes cost before the tip is included? *Explain.*

42. ★ **OPEN-ENDED** *Describe* a real-world problem that can be solved using a system of linear equations. Then solve the problem and explain what the solution means in this situation. **See margin.**

○ = **WORKED-OUT SOLUTIONS**
on p. WS1

★ = **STANDARDIZED TEST PRACTICE**

◆ = **MULTIPLE REPRESENTATIONS**

43. INVESTMENTS Matt invested $2000 in stocks and bonds. This year the bonds paid 8% interest, and the stocks paid 6% in dividends. Matt received a total of $144 in interest and dividends. How much money did he invest in stocks? in bonds? **$800; $1200**

44. CHALLENGE You drive a car 45 miles at an average speed r (in miles per hour) to reach your destination. Due to traffic, your average speed on the return trip is $\frac{3}{4}r$. The round trip took a total of 1 hour 45 minutes. Find the average speed for each leg of your trip. **first leg: 60 mi/h, second leg: 45 mi/h**

MIXED REVIEW

Graph the equation. *(pp. 215, 225, 244)* **45–50. See margin.**

45. $x - 8y = -10$ **46.** $-2x + 5y = -15$ **47.** $\frac{1}{4}x + \frac{1}{2}y = 8$

48. $y = \frac{2}{3}x - 1$ **49.** $y = -9x + 2$ **50.** $y - 1 = 2x - 7$

PREVIEW
Prepare for Lesson 7.5 in Exs. 51–52.

Determine which lines are parallel. *(p. 244)*

51.

b and c

52.

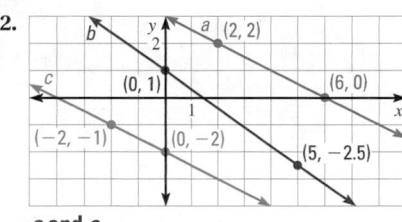

a and c

Solve the linear system using any method. *(pp. 427, 435, 444, 451)*

53. $y = 4x - 9$ **(2, −1)**   **54.** $y = -2x + 20$ **(5, 10)**   **55.** $x + 2y = 0$ **(−6, 3)**
     $y = -8x + 15$ $y = -6x + 40$ $-x = y + 3$

56. $x + 2y = 2$ **(8, −3)**   **57.** $7x - 8y = -15$ **(−1, 1)**   **58.** $8x + y = 5$ **(0.5, 1)**
     $-x + y = -11$ $5x + 8y = 3$ $-2x + y = 0$

QUIZ *for Lessons 7.3–7.4*

Solve the linear system using elimination. *(pp. 444, 451)*

1. $x + y = 4$ **(3, 1)**   **2.** $2x - y = 2$ **(−1, −4)**   **3.** $x + y = 5$ **(4, 1)**
     $-3x + y = -8$ $6x - y = -2$ $-x + y = -3$

4. $x + 3y = -10$ **(5, −5)**   **5.** $x + 3y = 10$ **(4.9, 1.7)**   **6.** $x + 7y = 10$ **(−15.2, 3.6)**
     $-x + 5y = -30$ $3x - y = 13$ $x + 2y = -8$

7. $4x - y = -2$ $\left(\frac{3}{11}, 3\frac{1}{11}\right)$ **8.** $x + 3y = 1$ **(4, −1)**   **9.** $3x + y = 21$ **(10, −9)**
     $3x + 2y = 7$ $5x + 6y = 14$ $x + y = 1$

10. $2x - 3y = -5$ **(2, 3)**   **11.** $7x + 2y = 13$ **(1, 3)**   **12.** $\frac{1}{3}x + 5y = -3$ **(6, −1)**
     $5x + 2y = 16$ $4x + 3y = 13$ $-\frac{2}{3}x + 6y = -10$

45–50. See Additional Answers beginning on p. AA1.

457

1c. speed in still air: 67.5 km/h, wind speed: 7.5 km/h

2. $12. *Sample answer:* Potato salad costs $3.25 per pound, and coleslaw costs $2.75 per pound. So 2 pounds of each costs $12.

4. *Sample answer:* You have $75 to spend on 10 items. Small items cost $5 each and large items cost $10 each. How many of each item can you buy? Linear system: $5x + 10y = 75$, $x + y = 10$. Solution: $x = 5$, $y = 5$. You can buy 5 small items and 5 large items for $75.

5. No. *Sample answer:* After 30 minutes the balloon from Newman Park remains higher than the balloon from Kirby Park.

6b. 250 milliliters of 10% acid and 90% water mix, and 250 milliliters of the 30% acid and 70% water mix

Lessons 7.1–7.4

1. MULTI-STEP PROBLEM Flying into the wind, a helicopter takes 15 minutes to travel 15 kilometers. The return flight takes 12 minutes. The wind speed remains constant during the trip.

   a. Find the helicopter's average speed (in kilometers per hour) for each leg of the trip. **first leg: 60 km/h, second leg: 75 km/h**

   b. Write a system of linear equations that represents the situation. $r - w = 60$, $r + w = 75$

   c. What is the helicopter's average speed in still air? What is the speed of the wind? **See margin.**

2. SHORT RESPONSE At a grocery store, a customer pays a total of $9.70 for 1.8 pounds of potato salad and 1.4 pounds of coleslaw. Another customer pays a total of $6.55 for 1 pound of potato salad and 1.2 pounds of coleslaw. How much do 2 pounds of potato salad and 2 pounds of coleslaw cost? *Explain.* **See margin.**

3. GRIDDED ANSWER During one day, two computers are sold at a computer store. The two customers each arrange payment plans with the salesperson. The graph shows the amount y of money (in dollars) paid for the computers after x months. After how many months will each customer have paid the same amount? **4 mo**

Months since purchase

4. OPEN-ENDED *Describe* a real-world problem that can be modeled by a linear system. Then solve the system and interpret the solution in the context of the problem. **See margin.**

5. SHORT RESPONSE A hot air balloon is launched at Kirby Park, and it ascends at a rate of 7200 feet per hour. At the same time, a second hot air balloon is launched at Newman Park, and it ascends at a rate of 4000 feet per hour. Both of the balloons stop ascending after 30 minutes. The diagram shows the altitude of each park. Are the hot air balloons ever at the same height at the same time? *Explain.* **See margin.**

Kirby Park | Newman Park

3940 ft

1705 ft

SEA LEVEL   *Not drawn to scale*

6. EXTENDED RESPONSE A chemist needs 500 milliliters of a 20% acid and 80% water mix for a chemistry experiment. The chemist combines x milliliters of a 10% acid and 90% water mix and y milliliters of a 30% acid and 70% water mix to make the 20% acid and 80% water mix.

   a. Write a linear system that represents the situation. $0.1x + 0.3y = 0.2 \cdot 500$, $x + y = 500$

   b. How many milliliters of the 10% acid and 90% water mix and the 30% acid and 70% water mix are combined to make the 20% acid and 80% water mix? **See margin.**

   c. The chemist also needs 500 milliliters of a 15% acid and 85% water mix. Does the chemist need more of the 10% acid and 90% water mix than the 30% acid and 70% water mix to make this new mix? *Explain.* **More of the 10% acid and 90% water mix.** *Sample answer:* Adding more of the 30% acid and 70% water mix would raise the percent of acid, not lower it.

7.5 Solve Special Types of Linear Systems

Before You found the solution of a linear system.

Now You will identify the number of solutions of a linear system.

Why? So you can compare distances traveled, as in Ex. 39.

Key Vocabulary
- inconsistent system
- consistent dependent system
- system of linear equations, *p. 427*
- parallel, *p. 244*

A linear system can have no solution or infinitely many solutions. A linear system has no solution when the graphs of the equations are parallel. A linear system with no solution is called an **inconsistent system**.

A linear system has infinitely many solutions when the graphs of the equations are the same line. A linear system with infinitely many solutions is called a **consistent dependent system**.

❖ **EXAMPLE 1** A linear system with no solution

Show that the linear system has no solution.

$3x + 2y = 10$ **Equation 1**
$3x + 2y = 2$ **Equation 2**

Solution

METHOD 1 Graphing

REVIEW GRAPHING
For help with graphing linear equations, see pp. 215, 225, and 244.

Graph the linear system.

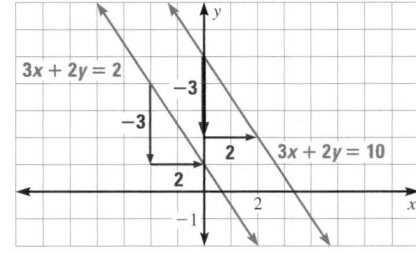

▶ The lines are parallel because they have the same slope but different y-intercepts. Parallel lines do not intersect, so the system has no solution.

METHOD 2 Elimination

Subtract the equations.

IDENTIFY TYPES OF SYSTEMS
The linear system in Example 1 is called an inconsistent system because the lines do not intersect (are not consistent).

$$3x + 2y = 10$$
$$\underline{3x + 2y = 2}$$
$$0 = 8 \longleftarrow \text{This is a false statement.}$$

▶ The variables are eliminated and you are left with a false statement regardless of the values of x and y. This tells you that the system has no solution.

 Animated Algebra at classzone.com

7.5 Solve Special Types of Linear Systems   **459**

---

① PLAN AND PREPARE

Warm-Up Exercises
📑 Transparency Available

1. Solve the linear system.
   $2x + 3y = -9$
   $x - 2y = 6$ **(0, −3)**

2. You buy 8 pencils for $8 at the bookstore. Standard pencils cost $.85 and specialty pencils cost $1.25. How many specialty pencils did you buy? **3 specialty pencils**

Notetaking Guide
📑 Transparency Available
Promotes interactive learning and notetaking skills, pp. 160–162.

Pacing
Basic: 2 days
Average: 2 days
Advanced: 2 days
Block: 0.5 block with 7.4
       0.5 block with 7.6
- See *Teaching Guide/Lesson Plan.*

② FOCUS AND MOTIVATE

Essential Question
Big Idea 1, p. 425

How can you identify the number of solutions of a linear system? **Tell students they will learn how to answer this question by graphing and solving linear systems and by looking at the slopes and the y-intercepts of the equations.**

NCTM STANDARDS
Standard 2: Analyze situations using algebraic symbols

Standard 3: Describe spatial relationships using coordinate geometry

---

Resource Planning Guide

Chapter Resource Book
- Teaching Guide/Lesson Plan (pp. 50–51)
- Activity Master (p. 52)
- Practice levels A, B, C (pp. 53–58)
- Study Guide (pp. 59–60)
- Catch-up for Absent Students (p. 61)
- Application (p. 62)
- Challenge (p. 63)

Workbooks
- Notetaking Guide (pp. 160–162)
- Practice Workbook (pp. 113–115)

Teaching Options
- **Power Presentations CD-ROM** provides dynamic electronic teaching resources for the classroom.
- **Activity Generator CD-ROM** provides editable activities for all ability levels.

Interactive Technology
- Easy Planner
- Power Presentations CD-ROM
- Activity Generator CD-ROM
- Animated Algebra
- Test Generator CD-ROM
- Online Quiz
- eWorkbook
- eEdition
- @HomeTutor

Resources for English Learners
- Quick Reference for English Learners
- Spanish Study Guide
- Multi-Language Visual Glossary
- Student Resources in Spanish

See also the *Algebra 1 Toolkit* for more strategies for meeting individual needs.

459

EXAMPLE 2 **A linear system with infinitely many solutions**

Motivating the Lesson

A group of people bought 15 bus tickets and 12 transfers for $63. Another group bought 5 bus tickets and 4 transfers for $21. You want to know the cost of one bus ticket. By knowing how to identify whether a system has one solution, no solution, or infinitely many solutions, you will be able to determine if you have enough information to find the cost of one ticket.

❸ TEACH

Extra Example 1

Show that the linear system has no solution.

$2x - 3y = 6$
$2x - 3y = -4$

The lines are parallel, so the system has no solution.

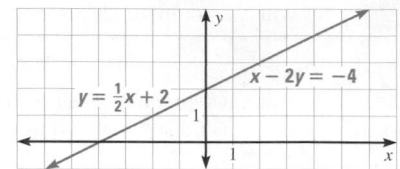
Animated Algebra
classzone.com

An **Animated Algebra** activity is available on-line for **Example 1**. This activity is also available on the **Power Presentations CD-ROM**.

Extra Example 2

Show that the linear system has infinitely many solutions.

$4x - 2y = 8$
$y = 2x - 4$

Substitute $2x - 4$ for y in the first equation.

$4x - 2(2x - 4) = 8$
$4x - 4x + 8 = 8$
$8 = 8$

The statement is true; the system has infinitely many solutions.

Show that the linear system has infinitely many solutions.

$$x - 2y = -4 \qquad \text{Equation 1}$$
$$y = \frac{1}{2}x + 2 \qquad \text{Equation 2}$$

Solution

METHOD 1 Graphing

Graph the linear system.

▸ The equations represent the same line, so any point on the line is a solution. So, the linear system has infinitely many solutions.

METHOD 2 Substitution

Substitute $\frac{1}{2}x + 2$ for y in Equation 1 and solve for x.

$$x - 2y = -4 \qquad \text{Write Equation 1.}$$
$$x - 2\left(\frac{1}{2}x + 2\right) = -4 \qquad \text{Substitute } \frac{1}{2}x + 2 \text{ for } y.$$
$$-4 = -4 \qquad \text{Simplify.}$$

▸ The variables are eliminated and you are left with a statement that is true regardless of the values of x and y. This tells you that the system has infinitely many solutions.

IDENTIFY TYPES OF SYSTEMS
The linear system in Example 2 is called a consistent dependent system because the lines intersect (are consistent) and the equations are equivalent (are dependent).

 GUIDED PRACTICE for Examples 1 and 2

1. No solution. *Sample answer:* When you solve the system you get $0 = 9$, which is a false statement.

2. Infinitely many solutions. *Sample answer:* When you solve the system you get $-12 = -12$, which is a true statement.

Tell whether the linear system has *no solution* or *infinitely many solutions*. *Explain.*

1. $5x + 3y = 6$
   $-5x - 3y = 3$

2. $y = 2x - 4$
   $-6x + 3y = -12$

IDENTIFYING THE NUMBER OF SOLUTIONS When the equations of a linear system are written in slope-intercept form, you can identify the number of solutions of the system by looking at the slopes and y-intercepts of the lines.

Number of solutions	Slopes and y-intercepts
One solution	Different slopes
No solution	Same slope Different y-intercepts
Infinitely many solutions	Same slope Same y-intercept

Differentiated Instruction

Inclusion Some students may need help understanding the concept of linear dependence. In **Example 2**, have students solve $x - 2y = 24$ for y. By doing so, students will get the second equation. This shows that the two equations are algebraically equivalent.

See also the *Algebra 1 Toolkit* for more strategies.

EXAMPLE 3 · Identify the number of solutions

Without solving the linear system, tell whether the linear system has *one solution*, *no solution*, or *infinitely many solutions*.

a. $5x + y = -2$ **Equation 1**
   $-10x - 2y = 4$ **Equation 2**

b. $6x + 2y = 3$ **Equation 1**
   $6x + 2y = -5$ **Equation 2**

Solution

a. $y = -5x - 2$ Write Equation 1 in slope-intercept form.

   $y = -5x - 2$ Write Equation 2 in slope-intercept form.

▶ Because the lines have the same slope and the same y-intercept, the system has infinitely many solutions.

b. $y = -3x + \frac{3}{2}$ Write Equation 1 in slope-intercept form.

   $y = -3x - \frac{5}{2}$ Write Equation 2 in slope-intercept form.

▶ Because the lines have the same slope but different y-intercepts, the system has no solution.

EXAMPLE 4 · Write and solve a system of linear equations

ART An artist wants to sell prints of her paintings. She orders a set of prints for each of two of her paintings. Each set contains regular prints and glossy prints, as shown in the table. Find the cost of one glossy print.

Regular	Glossy	Cost
45	30	$465
15	10	$155

Solution

STEP 1 **Write** a linear system. Let x be the cost (in dollars) of a regular print, and let y be the cost (in dollars) of a glossy print.

$45x + 30y = 465$ **Cost of prints for one painting**
$15x + 10y = 155$ **Cost of prints for other painting**

STEP 2 **Solve** the linear system using elimination.

$45x + 30y = 465$ $45x + 30y = 465$
$15x + 10y = 155$ ×(−3)→ $-45x - 30y = -465$
                          $0 = 0$

▶ There are infinitely many solutions, so you cannot determine the cost of one glossy print. You need more information.

✓ **GUIDED PRACTICE**   for Examples 3 and 4

3. Without solving the linear system, tell whether it has *one solution*, *no solution*, or *infinitely many solutions*. **one solution**

   $x - 3y = -15$ **Equation 1**
   $2x - 3y = -18$ **Equation 2**

4. **WHAT IF?** In Example 4, suppose a glossy print costs $3 more than a regular print. Find the cost of a glossy print. **$8**

7.5 Solve Special Types of Linear Systems   **461**

Key Question to Ask for Example 2

- What happens if you multiply Equation 2 by 2? **You get** $2y = x + 4$, **which is the same as Equation 1.**

Extra Example 3

Without solving the linear system, tell whether the linear system has *one solution*, *no solution*, or *infinitely many solutions*.

a. $-3x + 5y = 6$ **infinitely many**
   $6x - 10y = -12$ **solutions**

b. $9x - 5y = 12$
   $9x - 5y = 8$ **no solution**

Extra Example 4

A pizza parlor fills two pizza orders. Find the cost of one medium pizza.

Medium	Large	Cost
4	12	$168
8	24	$336

You cannot determine the cost of one medium pizza, since there are infinitely many solutions.

Closing the Lesson

Have students summarize the major points of the lesson and answer the Essential Question: How can you identify the number of solutions of a linear system?

- **Linear systems can have one solution, no solution, or infinitely many solutions.**

Systems with one solution have graphs with intersecting lines and equations with different slopes. Systems with no solution have graphs with parallel lines, equations with the same slope but different y-intercepts, and result in false statements when solved algebraically. Systems with infinitely many solutions have graphs with coinciding lines, identical equations, and result in true statements when solved algebraically.

461

Number of Solutions of a Linear System

One solution	No solution	Infinitely many solutions

The lines intersect.

The lines have different slopes.

The lines are parallel.

The lines have the same slope and different y-intercepts.

The lines coincide.

The lines have the same slope and the same y-intercept.

7.5 EXERCISES

HOMEWORK KEY

○ = **WORKED-OUT SOLUTIONS**
on p. WS1 for Exs. 11 and 37

★ = **STANDARDIZED TEST PRACTICE**
Exs. 3, 4, 24, 25, 32, 33, and 40

SKILL PRACTICE

[A] 1. **VOCABULARY** Copy and complete: A linear system with no solution is called a(n) _?_ system. **inconsistent system**

2. **VOCABULARY** Copy and complete: A linear system with infinitely many solutions is called a(n) _?_ system. **consistent dependent system**

3. ★ **WRITING** *Describe* the graph of a linear system that has no solution.
Sample answer: **The lines have the same slope but different intercepts.**

4. ★ **WRITING** *Describe* the graph of a linear system that has infinitely many solutions. *Sample answer:* **The graph would show only one line.**

INTERPRETING GRAPHS Match the linear system with its graph. Then use the graph to tell whether the linear system has *one solution*, *no solution*, or *infinitely many solutions.*

5. $x - 3y = -9$
   $x - y = -1$
   B; one solution

6. $x - y = -4$
   $-3x + 3y = 2$
   C; no solution

7. $x + 3y = -1$
   $-2x - 6y = 2$
   A; infinitely many solutions

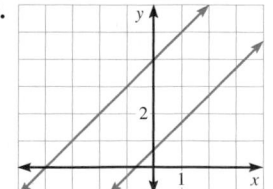

A.

B.

C.

---

4 PRACTICE AND APPLY

Assignment Guide

📄 **Answer Transparencies** available for all exercises

Basic:
Day 1: pp. 462–465
Exs. 1–20, 24, 25, 42–45
Day 2: pp. 462–465
Exs. 26–30, 36–39, 46–60

Average:
Day 1: pp. 462–465
Exs. 1–14, 18–25, 42–45
Day 2: pp. 462–465
Exs. 26–34, 36–40, 46–54 even, 56–61

Advanced:
Day 1: pp. 462–465
Exs. 1–4, 11–13, 18–25, 44, 45
Day 2: pp. 462–465
Exs. 26–35*, 37–41*, 51, 52, 55, 59

Block:
pp. 462–465
Exs. 1–14, 18–25, 42–45 (with 7.4)
pp. 462–465
Exs. 26–34, 36–40, 46–54 even, 56–61 (with 7.6)

Differentiated Instruction

See *Algebra 1 Best Practices Toolkit* for suggestions on addressing the needs of a diverse classroom.

Homework Check

For a quick check of student understanding of key concepts, go over the following exercises:

Basic: 9, 20, 26, 36, 37
Average: 13, 18, 28, 36, 38
Advanced: 12, 21, 30, 37, 38

Extra Practice

• Student Edition, p. 944
• Chapter 7 Resource Book:
  Practice levels A, B, C, pp. 53–58

Practice Worksheet

An easily-readable reduced practice page (with answers) for this lesson can be found on p. 424C.

462

INTERPRETING GRAPHS Graph the linear system. Then use the graph to tell whether the linear system has *one solution*, *no solution*, or *infinitely many solutions*.

8. $x + y = -2$
$y = -x + 5$
no solution

9. $3x - 4y = 12$
$y = \frac{3}{4}x - 3$
infinitely many solutions

10. $3x - y = -9$
$3x + 5y = -15$
one solution

(11.) $-2x + 2y = -16$
$3x - 6y = 30$
one solution

12. $-9x + 6y = 18$
$6x - 4y = -12$
infinitely many solutions

13. $-3x + 4y = 12$
$-3x + 4y = 24$
no solution

14. Sample
answer: The
lines do not
have the same
slope, so they
are not parallel
and they do have
a solution. If
the graph were
larger the lines
would intersect
at (4, 12); see
margin for art.

14. **ERROR ANALYSIS** *Describe* and correct the error in solving the linear system below.

$6x + y = 36$
$5x - y = 8$

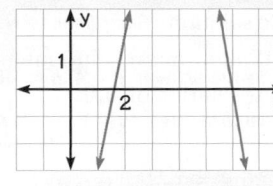

The lines do not intersect, so there is no solution.

SOLVING LINEAR SYSTEMS Solve the linear system using substitution or elimination.

15. $2x + 5y = 14$
$6x + 7y = 10$ **(−3, 4)**

16. $-16x + 2y = -2$
$y = 8x - 1$ **infinitely many solutions**

17. $3x - 2y = -5$
$4x + 5y = 47$ **(3, 7)**

18. $5x - 5y = -3$
$y = x + 0.6$ **infinitely many solutions**

19. $x - y = 0$
$5x - 2y = 6$ **(2, 2)**

20. $x - 2y = 7$
$-x + 2y = 7$ **no solution**

21. $-18x + 6y = 24$
$3x - y = -2$ **no solution**

22. $4y + 5x = 15$
$x = 8y + 3$ **(3, 0)**

23. $6x + 3y = 9$
$2x + 9y = 27$ **(0, 3)**

24. ★ **MULTIPLE CHOICE** Which of the linear systems has *exactly* one solution? **C**

(A) $-x + y = 9$
$x - y = 9$

(B) $-x + y = 9$
$x - y = -9$

(C) $-x + y = 9$
$-x - y = 9$

(D) $x - y = -9$
$-x + y = -9$

25. ★ **MULTIPLE CHOICE** Which of the linear systems has infinitely many solutions? **D**

(A) $15x + 5y = 20$
$6x - 2y = 8$

(B) $15x - 5y = 20$
$6x - 2y = -8$

(C) $15x - 5y = -20$
$6x - 2y = 8$

(D) $15x - 5y = 20$
$6x - 2y = 8$

IDENTIFYING THE NUMBER OF SOLUTIONS Without solving the linear system, tell whether the linear system has *one solution*, *no solution*, or *infinitely many solutions*.

26. $y = -6x - 2$
$12x + 2y = -6$
no solution

27. $y = 7x + 13$
$-21x + 3y = 39$
infinitely many solutions

28. $4x + 3y = 27$
$4x - 3y = -27$
one solution

29. $9x - 15y = 24$
$6x - 10y = 16$
infinitely many solutions

30. $0.3x + 0.4y = 2.4$
$0.5x - 0.6y = 0.2$
one solution

31. $0.9x - 2.1y = 12.3$
$1.5x - 3.5y = 20.5$
infinitely many solutions

7.5 Solve Special Types of Linear Systems **463**

Avoiding Common Errors
Exercises 15–23 Some students may erroneously correlate true statements with no solution and false statements with infinitely many solutions. Stress that a true statement means that all points on a line are solutions and a false statement means that none of the points on either line are solutions. To reinforce these concepts, suggest that students write the equations of these systems in slope-intercept form and then look at the slopes and *y*-intercepts to determine the number of solutions. This will also help them associate true statements with infinitely many solutions and false statements with no solution.

11.

12.

13.

14.

8.

9.

10.

463

Teaching Strategy

Exercise 37 You may want to point out to students that after they write the equations for this system, they can write the equations in slope-intercept form and then look at the slopes and y-intercepts to determine whether there is enough information to find the cost of one ticket. Note that if the slopes are different, then there is enough information to find the cost of one ticket. If the slopes are the same, then there are either infinitely many solutions or no solution, and in either case, there is not enough information to find the cost of one ticket.

Avoiding Common Errors

Exercise 38 Some students may write the equations in the system, using the first row of the table for x and the second for y. Caution students to read the description in the problem to determine what x and y should represent.

32. ★ **OPEN-ENDED** Write a linear system so that it has infinitely many solutions, and one of the equations is $y = 3x + 2$. *Sample answer: $y = 3x + 2, 2y = 6x + 4$*

33. ★ **OPEN-ENDED** Write a linear system so that it has no solution and one of the equations is $7x - 8y = -9$.
Sample answer: $7x - 8y = -9, 7x - 8y = 4$

C **34.** **REASONING** Give a counterexample for the following statement: If the graphs of the equations of a linear system have the same slope, then the linear system has no solution.
Sample answer: $y = 3x, 2y = 6x$

35. **CHALLENGE** Find values of p, q, and r that produce the solution(s).

  a. No solution *Sample answer: $p = 2, q = -3, r = 0$*

                                    $px + qy = r$ **Equation 1**

  b. Infinitely many solutions
     Sample answer: $p = 4, q = -6, r = 10$ $2x - 3y = 5$ **Equation 2**

  c. One solution of $(4, 1)$
     Sample answer: $p = 1, q = 1, r = 5$

PROBLEM SOLVING

EXAMPLE 4 A
on p. 461
for Exs. 36–38

36. **RECREATION** One admission to a roller skating rink costs x dollars and renting a pair of skates costs y dollars. A group pays $243 for admission for 36 people and 21 skate rentals. Another group pays $81 for admission for 12 people and 7 skate rentals. Is there enough information to determine the cost of one admission to the roller skating rink? *Explain.*

@HomeTutor for problem solving help at classzone.com   *No. Sample answer: There are infinitely many solutions to the resulting linear system.*

(**37.**) **TRANSPORTATION** A passenger train travels from New York City to Washington, D.C., then back to New York City. The table shows the number of coach tickets and business class tickets purchased for each leg of the trip. Is there enough information to determine the cost of one coach ticket? *Explain.* **Yes.** *Sample answer: There is one solution to the resulting linear system.*

Destination	Coach tickets	Business class tickets	Money collected (dollars)
Washington, D.C.	150	80	22,860
New York City	170	100	27,280

@HomeTutor for problem solving help at classzone.com

38a. No. *Sample answer:* There are infinitely many solutions to the resulting linear system.

38b. Yes. *Sample answer:* You can write a new equation and create a linear system that has only one solution.

38. **PHOTOGRAPHY** In addition to taking pictures on your digital camera, you can record 30 second movies. All pictures use the same amount of memory, and all 30 second movies use the same amount of memory. The number of pictures and 30 second movies on 2 memory cards is shown.

  a. Is there enough information given to determine the amount of memory used by a 30 second movie? *Explain.*

  b. Given that a 30 second movie uses 50 times the amount of memory that a digital picture uses, can you determine the amount of memory used by a 30 second movie? *Explain.*

Size of card (megabytes)	64	256
Pictures	450	1800
Movies	7	28

B | **39. MULTI-STEP PROBLEM** Two people are training for a speed ice-climbing event. During a practice climb, one climber starts 15 seconds after the first climber. The rates that the climbers ascend are shown.

Climbs 10 feet every 30 seconds   Climbs 5 feet every 15 seconds

a. Let d be the distance (in feet) traveled by a climber t seconds after the first person starts climbing. Write a linear system that models the situation. $d = \frac{t}{3}, d = \frac{t}{3} - 5$

b. Graph the linear system from part (a). Does the second climber catch up to the first climber? *Explain.*

39b. Sample answer: No, since the lines are parallel, the two climbers will never be at the same distance at the same time.

40. ★ **EXTENDED RESPONSE** Two employees at a banquet facility are given the task of folding napkins. One person starts folding napkins at a rate of 5 napkins per minute. The second person starts 10 minutes after the first person and folds napkins at a rate of 4 napkins per minute.

a. Model Let y be the number of napkins folded x minutes after the first person starts folding. Write a linear system that models the situation. $y = 5x, y = 4(x - 10)$

b. Solve Solve the linear system. $(-40, -200)$

c. Interpret Does the solution of the linear system make sense in the context of the problem? *Explain.* **No. Sample answer: x and y only make sense for positive values.**

C | **41. CHALLENGE** An airplane has an average air speed of 160 miles per hour. The airplane takes 3 hours to travel with the wind from Salem to Lancaster. The airplane has to travel against the wind on the return trip. After 3 hours into the return trip, the airplane is 120 miles from Salem. Find the distance from Salem to Lancaster. If the problem cannot be solved with the information given, *explain* why.   **540 mi**

MIXED REVIEW

Solve the equation, if possible. *(p. 154)*

42. $61 + 5c = 7 - 4c$ **−6**

43. $3m - 2 = 7m - 50 + 8m$ **4**

44. $11z + 3 = 10(2z + 3)$ **−3**

45. $-6(1 - w) = 14(w - 5)$ **8**

Solve the inequality. Then graph your solution. 46–55. See margin for art.

PREVIEW
Prepare for Lesson 7.6 in Exs. 46–61.

46. $x + 15 < 23$ *(p. 356)*   **x < 8**

47. $x - 1 \geq 10$ *(p. 356)*   **x ≥ 11**

48. $\frac{x}{4} > -2.5$ *(p. 363)*   **x > −10**

49. $-7x \leq 84$ *(p. 363)*   **x ≥ −12**

50. $2 - 5x \geq 27$ *(p. 369)*   **x ≤ −5**

51. $3x - 9 > 3(x - 3)$ *(p. 369)*   **no solution**

52. $-2 < x + 3 \leq 11$ *(p. 380)*   **−5 < x ≤ 8**

53. $-7 \leq 5 - 2x \leq 7$ *(p. 380)*   **−1 ≤ x ≤ 6**

54. $|x - 3| \geq 5$ *(p. 398)*   **x ≤ −2 or x ≥ 8**

55. $2|2x - 1| - 9 \leq 1$ *(p. 398)*   **−2 ≤ x ≤ 3**

Graph the inequality. *(p. 405)*   **56–61. See margin.**

56. $x + y < -3$

57. $x - y \geq 1$

58. $2x - y < 5$

59. $-2x - 3y \leq 9$

60. $y \leq -4$

61. $x > 6.5$

EXTRA PRACTICE for Lesson 7.5, p. 944   ⟲ **ONLINE QUIZ** at classzone.com   **465**

46–61. See Additional Answers beginning on p. AA1.

⑤ ASSESS AND RETEACH

Daily Homework Quiz

⬛ **Transparency Available**

Without solving the linear system, tell whether the linear system has *one solution*, *no solution*, or *infinitely many solutions*.

1. $4x + 2y = 12$
$y = -2x + 8$ **no solution**

2. $-2x + 5y = 5$
$y = \frac{2}{5}x + 1$ **infinitely many solutions**

3. A group of 12 students and 3 teachers pays $57 for admission to a primate research center. Another group of 14 students and 4 teachers pays $69. Find the cost of one student ticket. **$3.50**

⟲ **Online Quiz**

Available at **classzone.com**

Diagnosis/Remediation

- Practice A, B, C in Chapter 7 Resource Book, pp. 53–58
- Study Guide in Chapter 7 Resource Book, pp. 59–60
- Practice Workbook, pp. 113–115
- @HomeTutor

Challenge

Additional challenge is available in the Chapter 7 Resource Book, p. 63.

39b.

466

7.6 Solve Systems of Linear Inequalities

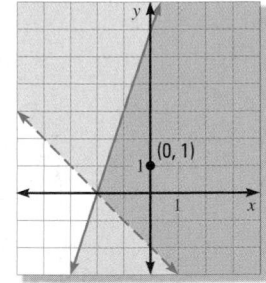

Before	You graphed linear inequalities in two variables.
Now	You will solve systems of linear inequalities in two variables.
Why	So you can find a marching band's competition score, as in Ex. 36.

① PLAN AND PREPARE

Warm-Up Exercises

Transparency Available

1. Graph $y < \frac{2}{3}x - 1$.

2. You are running one ad that costs $6 per day and another that costs $8 per day. You can spend no more than $120. Name a possible combination of days that you can run the ads. *Sample:* **16 days of the $6 ad and 3 days of the $8 ad**

Notetaking Guide

Transparency Available

Promotes interactive learning and notetaking skills, pp. 163–165.

Pacing

Basic: 1 day
Average: 1 day
Advanced: 1 day
Block: 0.5 block with 7.5

• See *Teaching Guide/Lesson Plan*.

② FOCUS AND MOTIVATE

Essential Question

Big Idea 3, p. 467

How do you solve systems of linear inequalities in two variables? **Tell students they will learn how to answer this question by graphing in the same coordinate plane.**

NCTM STANDARDS

Standard 3: Describe spatial relationships using coordinate geometry

Standard 8: Communicate thinking clearly to others

Key Vocabulary
• **system of linear inequalities**
• **solution of a system of linear inequalities**
• **graph of a system of linear inequalities**

A **system of linear inequalities** in two variables, or simply a *system of inequalities*, consists of two or more linear inequalities in the same variables. An example is shown.

$$x - y > 7 \qquad \textbf{Inequality 1}$$
$$2x + y < 8 \qquad \textbf{Inequality 2}$$

A **solution of a system of linear inequalities** is an ordered pair that is a solution of each inequality in the system. For example, (6, −5) is a solution of the system above. The **graph of a system of linear inequalities** is the graph of all solutions of the system.

KEY CONCEPT   *For Your Notebook*

Graphing a System of Linear Inequalities

STEP 1   **Graph** each inequality (as you learned to do in Lesson 6.7).

STEP 2   **Find** the intersection of the half-planes. The graph of the system is this intersection.

EXAMPLE 1   **Graph a system of two linear inequalities**

Graph the system of inequalities. $y > -x - 2$ **Inequality 1**
                                     $y \le 3x + 6$ **Inequality 2**

REVIEW GRAPHING INEQUALITIES
For help with graphing a linear inequality in two variables, see p. 405.

Solution

Graph both inequalities in the same coordinate plane. The graph of the system is the intersection of the two half-planes, which is shown as the darker shade of blue.

CHECK   Choose a point in the dark blue region, such as (**0, 1**). To check this solution, substitute 0 for x and 1 for y into each inequality.

$1 \overset{?}{>} 0 - 2$	$1 \overset{?}{\le} 0 + 6$
$1 > -2 \checkmark$	$1 \le 6 \checkmark$

Animated Algebra at classzone.com

Resource Planning Guide

Chapter Resource Book
• Teaching Guide/Lesson Plan (pp. 64–65)
• Activity Master (p. 66)
• Practice levels A, B, C (pp. 68–73)
• Study Guide (pp. 74–75)
• Catch-up for Absent Students (p. 76)
• Problem Solving Workshop (p. 77)
• Challenge (p. 78)

Workbooks
• Notetaking Guide (pp. 163–165)
• Practice Workbook (pp. 116–118)

Teaching Options
• **Power Presentations CD-ROM** provides dynamic electronic teaching resources for the classroom.
• **Activity Generator CD-ROM** provides editable activities for all ability levels.

Interactive Technology
• Easy Planner
• Power Presentations CD-ROM
• Activity Generator CD-ROM
• Animated Algebra
• Test Generator CD-ROM
• Online Quiz
• eWorkbook
• eEdition
• @HomeTutor

Resources for English Learners
• Quick Reference for English Learners
• Spanish Study Guide
• Multi-Language Visual Glossary
• Student Resources in Spanish

See also the *Algebra 1 Toolkit* for more strategies for meeting individual needs.

THE SOLUTION REGION In Example 1, the half-plane for each inequality is shaded, and the solution region is the intersection of the half-planes. From this point on, only the solution region will be shaded.

EXAMPLE 2 **Graph a system of three linear inequalities**

Graph the system of inequalities.

$y \geq -1$	Inequality 1
$x > -2$	Inequality 2
$x + 2y \leq 4$	Inequality 3

Solution

Graph all three inequalities in the same coordinate plane. The graph of the system is the triangular region shown.

The region is to the right of the line $x = -2$.

The region is on and below the line $x + 2y = 4$.

The region is on and above the line $y = -1$.

 GUIDED PRACTICE for Examples 1 and 2

Graph the system of linear inequalities. 1–3. See margin.

1. $y < x - 4$
   $y \geq -x + 3$

2. $y \geq -x + 2$
   $y < 4$
   $x < 3$

3. $y > -x$
   $y \geq x - 4$
   $y < 5$

EXAMPLE 3 **Write a system of linear inequalities**

Write a system of inequalities for the shaded region.

REVIEW EQUATIONS OF LINES
For help with writing an equation of a line, see pp. 283, 302, and 311.

Solution

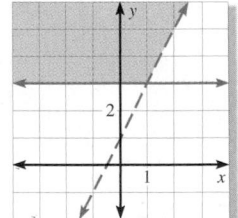

INEQUALITY 1: One boundary line for the shaded region is $y = 3$. Because the shaded region is *above* the *solid* line, the inequality is $y \geq 3$.

INEQUALITY 2: Another boundary line for the shaded region has a slope of 2 and a y-intercept of 1. So, its equation is $y = 2x + 1$. Because the shaded region is *above* the *dashed* line, the inequality is $y > 2x + 1$.

▶ The system of inequalities for the shaded region is:

$y \geq 3$	Inequality 1
$y > 2x + 1$	Inequality 2

Differentiated Instruction

Auditory Learners Tell students that the method used in **Example 1** is sometimes called the "graph-and-check" method, because students *graph* the inequalities and then *check* points in each test region. Students should get in the habit of checking their graphs by verifying that points in their solution satisfy each inequality.

See also the *Algebra 1 Toolkit* for more strategies.

EXAMPLE 4 Write and solve a system of linear inequalities

BASEBALL The National Collegiate Athletic Association (NCAA) regulates the lengths of aluminum baseball bats used by college baseball teams. The NCAA states that the length (in inches) of the bat minus the weight (in ounces) of the bat cannot exceed 3. Bats can be purchased at lengths from 26 to 34 inches.

a. Write and graph a system of linear inequalities that describes the information given above.

b. A sporting goods store sells an aluminum bat that is 31 inches long and weighs 25 ounces. Use the graph to determine if this bat can be used by a player on an NCAA team.

Solution

a. Let x be the length (in inches) of the bat, and let y be the weight (in ounces) of the bat. From the given information, you can write the following inequalities:

$x - y \leq 3$	The difference of the bat's length and weight can be at most 3.
$x \geq 26$	The length of the bat must be at least 26 inches.
$x \leq 34$	The length of the bat can be at most 34 inches.
$y \geq 0$	The weight of the bat cannot be a negative number.

WRITING SYSTEMS OF INEQUALITIES
Consider the values of the variables when writing a system of inequalities. In many real-world problems, the values cannot be negative.

Graph each inequality in the system. Then identify the region that is common to all of the graphs of the inequalities. This region is shaded in the graph shown.

b. Graph the point that represents a bat that is 31 inches long and weighs 25 ounces.

▶ Because the point falls outside the solution region, the bat cannot be used by a player on an NCAA team.

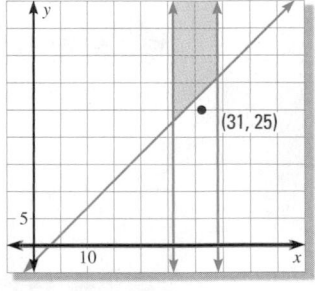

(31, 25)

✓ **GUIDED PRACTICE** for Examples 3 and 4

Write a system of inequalities that defines the shaded region.

4.
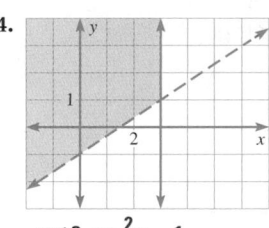

$x \leq 3$, $y > \frac{2}{3}x - 1$

5.
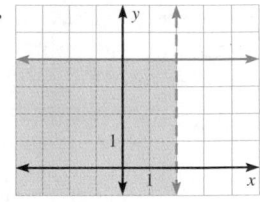

$y \leq 4$, $x < 2$

6. **WHAT IF?** In Example 4, suppose a Senior League (ages 10–14) player wants to buy the bat described in part (b). In Senior League, the length (in inches) of the bat minus the weight (in ounces) of the bat cannot exceed 8. Write and graph a system of inequalities to determine whether the described bat can be used by the Senior League player.
$x - y \leq 8$, $x \geq 26$, $x \leq 34$, $y \geq 0$, see margin for art; the bat can be used.

7.6 EXERCISES

HOMEWORK KEY
○ = WORKED-OUT SOLUTIONS
on p. WS1 for Exs. 13 and 39

★ = STANDARDIZED TEST PRACTICE
Exs. 2, 21, 22, 33, and 40

SKILL PRACTICE

[A] 1. **VOCABULARY** Copy and complete: A(n) __?__ of a system of linear inequalities is an ordered pair that is a solution of each inequality in the system. **solution**

2. Sample answer: Graph each inequality then shade the region that is the intersection of the solutions to each inequality. Then check the solution with a test point.

2. ★ **WRITING** Describe the steps you would take to graph the system of inequalities shown.
$x - y < 7$ **Inequality 1**
$y \geq 3$ **Inequality 2**

CHECKING A SOLUTION Tell whether the ordered pair is a solution of the system of inequalities.

3. (1, 1) **not a solution**

4. (0, 6) **solution**

5. (3, −1) **not a solution**

EXAMPLE 1
on p. 466
for Exs. 6–17

MATCHING SYSTEMS AND GRAPHS Match the system of inequalities with its graph.

6. $x - 4y > -8$
$x \geq 2$ **C**

7. $x - 4y \geq -8$
$x < 2$ **A**

8. $x - 4y > -8$
$y \geq 2$ **B**

A. B. C.

GRAPHING A SYSTEM Graph the system of inequalities. **9–20. See margin.**

9. $x > -5$
$x < 2$

10. $y \leq 10$
$y \geq 6$

11. $x > 3$
$y > x$

12. $y < -2x + 3$
$y \geq 4$

13. $y \geq 0$
$y < 2.5x - 1$

14. $y \geq 2x + 1$
$y < -x + 4$

15. $x < 8$
$x - 4y \leq -8$

16. $y \geq -2$
$2x + 3y > -6$

17. $y - 2x < 7$
$y + 2x > -1$

EXAMPLE 2
on p. 467
for Exs. 18–21

18. $x < 4$
$y > 1$
$y \geq -x + 1$

19. $x \geq 0$
$y \geq 0$
$6x - y < 12$

20. $x + y \leq 10$
$x - y \geq 2$
$y \geq 2$

21. ★ **MULTIPLE CHOICE** Which ordered pair is a solution of the system $2x - y \leq 5$ and $x + 2y > 2$? **D**

Ⓐ (1, −1) Ⓑ (4, 1) Ⓒ (2, 0) Ⓓ (3, 2)

7.6 Solve Systems of Linear Inequalities **469**

4 **PRACTICE AND APPLY**

Assignment Guide
⬚ Answer Transparencies available for all exercises

Basic:
Day 1: EP p. 943 Exs. 67–70, 72, 73
pp. 469–472
Exs. 1–8, 9–21 odd, 22–26, 36–39, 43–53 odd

Average:
Day 1: pp. 469–472
Exs. 1–8, 15–23, 25–33 odd, 36–40, 42–52 even

Advanced:
Day 1: pp. 469–472
Exs. 1, 2, 16–22, 24–41*, 47, 52

Block:
pp. 469–472
Exs. 1–8, 15–23, 25–33 odd, 36–40, 42–52 even (with 7.5)

Differentiated Instruction
See Algebra 1 Best Practices Toolkit for suggestions on addressing the needs of a diverse classroom.

Homework Check
For a quick check of student understanding of key concepts, go over the following exercises:
Basic: 11, 19, 21, 24, 36
Average: 16, 18, 22, 27, 37
Advanced: 16, 20, 22, 28, 38

Extra Practice
• Student Edition, p. 944
• Chapter 7 Resource Book: Practice levels A, B, C, pp. 68–73

Practice Worksheet
An easily-readable reduced practice page (with answers) for this lesson can be found on p. 424C.

9–20. See Additional Answers beginning on p. AA1.

23.

30.

31.

32.

22. ★ **MULTIPLE CHOICE** The graph of which system of inequalities is shown? **B**

Ⓐ $y < 2x$
  $2x + 3y < 6$

Ⓑ $y < 2x$
  $2x + 3y > 6$

Ⓒ $y > 2x$
  $2x + 3y < 6$

Ⓓ $y > 2x$
  $2x + 3y > 6$

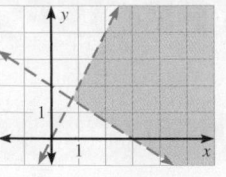

23. **ERROR ANALYSIS** *Describe* and correct the error in graphing this system of inequalities:

$x + y < 3$ Inequality 1
$x > -1$ Inequality 2
$x \le 3$ Inequality 3

The graph is shaded to include $x + y > 3$, not $x + y < 3$; see margin for art.

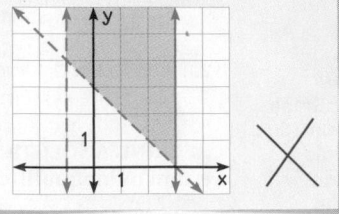

WRITING A SYSTEM Write a system of inequalities for the shaded region.

24.

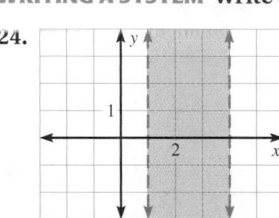

$x > 1, x < 4$

25.

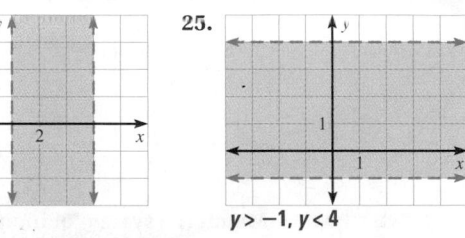

$y > -1, y < 4$

26.

$y \ge -3, y < 2$

27.

$y \le 5x + 1, y > x - 2$

28.

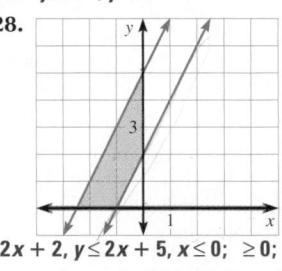

$y \ge 2x + 2, y \le 2x + 5, x \le 0; \ge 0; y \ge 0$

29.

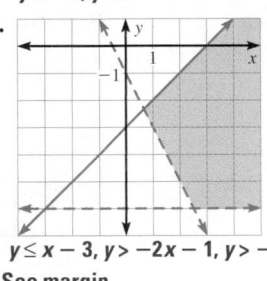

$y \le x - 3, y > -2x - 1, y > -6$

GRAPHING A SYSTEM Graph the system of inequalities. 30–32. See margin.

30. $x > 4$
  $x < 9$
  $y \le 2$
  $y > -2$

31. $x + y < 4$
  $x + y > -2$
  $x - y \le 3$
  $x - y \ge -4$

32. $x \le 10$
  $3x + 2y \ge 9$
  $x - 2y \le 6$
  $x + y \le 5$

33. ★ **SHORT RESPONSE** Does the system of inequalities have any solutions? *Explain.* **No; there are no possible values for *x* and *y* that satisfy both equations.**

$x - y > 5$ Inequality 1
$x - y < 1$ Inequality 2

Ⓒ **CHALLENGE** Write a system of inequalities for the shaded region described.

34. The shaded region is a rectangle with vertices at (2, 1), (2, 4), (6, 4), and (6, 1). $x \ge 2, x \le 6, y \ge 1, y \le 4$

35. The shaded region is a triangle with vertices at (−3, 0), (3, 2), and (0, −2). $y \le \frac{1}{3}x + 1, y \ge -\frac{2}{3}x - 2, y \ge \frac{4}{3}x - 2$

○ = **WORKED-OUT SOLUTIONS**
on p. WS1

★ = **STANDARDIZED TEST PRACTICE**

EXAMPLE 4 [A]
on p. 468
for Exs. 36–38

36. COMPETITION SCORES In a marching band competition, scoring is based on a musical evaluation and a visual evaluation. The musical evaluation score cannot exceed 60 points, the visual evaluation score cannot exceed 40 points. Write and graph a system of inequalities for the scores that a marching band can receive.

@HomeTutor for problem solving help at classzone.com

Let x represent the musical evaluation score and y represent the visual evaluation score. $x \le 60$, $y \le 40$, $x \ge 0$, $y \ge 0$, *see margin for art.*

37. NUTRITION For a hiking trip, you are making a mix of x ounces of peanuts and y ounces of chocolate pieces. You want the mix to have less than 70 grams of fat and weigh less than 8 ounces. An ounce of peanuts has 14 grams of fat, and an ounce of chocolate pieces has 7 grams of fat. Write and graph a system of inequalities that models the situation.

@HomeTutor for problem solving help at classzone.com

$14x + 7y < 70$, $x + y < 8$, $x \ge 0$, $y \ge 0$, *see margin for art.*

38. FISHING LIMITS You are fishing in a marina for surfperch and rockfish, which are two species of bottomfish. Gaming laws in the marina allow you to catch no more than 15 surfperch per day, no more than 10 rockfish per day, and no more than 15 total bottomfish per day.

a. Write and graph a system of inequalitites that models the situation.

b. Use the graph to determine whether you can catch 11 surfperch and 9 rockfish in one day. **no**

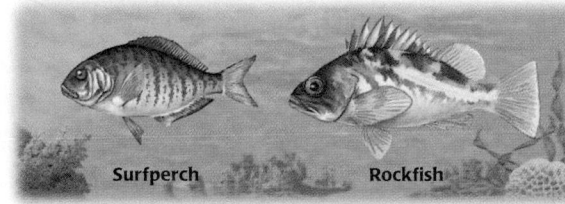

Surfperch   Rockfish

38a. Let *s* represent the number of surfperch and *r* represent the number of rockfish. $s \le 15$, $s + r \le 15$, $r \le 10$, $s \ge 0$, $r \ge 0$, see margin for art.

39a. $20 \le x \le 65$, $y \ge 154 - 0.7x$, $y \le 187 - 0.85x$, see margin for art.

39b. No. *Sample answer:* The heart rate is below 70% of the maximum heart rate.

(39.) HEALTH A person's maximum heart rate (in beats per minute) is given by $220 - x$ where x is the person's age in years ($20 \le x \le 65$). When exercising, a person should aim for a heart rate that is at least 70% of the maximum heart rate and at most 85% of the maximum heart rate.

a. Write and graph a system of inequalitites that models the situation.

b. A 40-year-old person's heart rate varies from 104 to 120 beats per minute while exercising. Does his heart rate stay in the suggested target range for his age? *Explain.*

40a. $8x + 8y \le 48$, $4x + 2y \ge 16$, $x \ge 0$, $y \ge 0$, see margin for art.

40b. Yes. *Sample answer:* It would cost $48 and give you 18 pictures.

40. ★ SHORT RESPONSE [B] A photography shop has a self-service photo center that allows you to make prints of pictures. Each sheet of printed pictures costs $8. The number of pictures that fit on each sheet is shown.

a. You want at least 16 pictures of any size, and you are willing to spend up to $48. Write and graph a system of inequalities that models the situation.

Four 3 inch by 5 inch pictures fit on one sheet.

b. Will you be able to purchase 12 pictures that are 3 inches by 5 inches and 6 pictures that are 4 inches by 6 inches? *Explain.*

Two 4 inch by 6 inch pictures fit on one sheet.

7.6 Solve Systems of Linear Inequalities **471**

39a.

40a.

36.

37.

38.

[C] 41. CHALLENGE You make necklaces and keychains to sell at a craft fair. The table shows the time that it takes to make each necklace and keychain, the cost of materials for each necklace and keychain, and the time and money that you can devote to making necklaces and keychains.

	Necklace	Keychain	Available
Time to make (hours)	0.5	0.25	20
Cost to make (dollars)	2	3	120

41a. $0.5x + 0.25y \leq 20$, $2y + 3x \leq 120$, $y \geq 0$, $x \geq 0$, see margin for art.

a. Write and graph a system of inequalities for the number x of necklaces and the number y of keychains that you can make under the given constraints.

b. Find the vertices (corner points) of the graph. **(0, 0), (40, 0), (0, 40), (30, 20)**

c. You sell each necklace for $10 and each keychain for $8. The revenue R is given by the equation $R = 10x + 8y$. Find the revenue for each ordered pair in part (b). Which vertex results in the maximum revenue? **(0, 0): $0, (40, 0): $400, (0, 40): $320, (30, 20): $460. The maximum revenue is at (30, 20), or 30 necklaces and 20 bracelets.**

MIXED REVIEW

PREVIEW
Prepare for Lesson 8.1 in Exs. 42–47.

Evaluate the expression.

42. $13x^2$ when $x = 2$ *(p. 8)* **52**

43. $64 \div z^3$ when $z = 2$ *(p. 8)* **8**

44. $-|-c| - 3^2$ when $c = 8$ *(p. 64)* **−17**

45. $-8 + 3y - 16$ when $y = -6$ *(p. 88)* **−42**

46. $\dfrac{7 - 8w}{11w}$ when $w = 5$ *(p. 103)* **$-\dfrac{3}{5}$**

47. $21 + \sqrt{x}$ when $x = 144$ *(p. 110)* **33**

Use any method to solve the linear system. *(pp. 427, 435, 444, 451)*

48. $y = 4x - 1$ **(2, 7)**
   $y = -8x + 23$

49. $y = -2x - 6$ **(−2, −2)**
   $y = -5x - 12$

50. $x + 2y = -1$ **(5, −3)**
   $-x = y - 2$

51. $4x + y = 0$ **(−1, 4)**
   $-x + y = 5$

52. $2x - y = -5$ $\left(-3\frac{1}{3}, -1\frac{2}{3}\right)$
   $y = -x - 5$

53. $3x + 2y = 2$ $\left(2\frac{2}{3}, -3\right)$
   $-3x + y = -11$

QUIZ *for Lessons 7.5–7.6*

Graph the linear system. Then use the graph to tell whether the linear system has *one solution*, *no solution*, or *infinitely many solutions*. *(p. 459)*
1–3. See margin for art.

1. $x - y = 1$ **no solution**
   $x - y = 6$

2. $6x + 2y = 16$ **one solution**
   $2x - y = 2$

3. $3x - 3y = -2$
   $-6x + 6y = 4$
   infinitely many solutions

Graph the system of linear inequalities. *(p. 466)* **4–9. See margin.**

4. $x > -3$
   $x < 7$

5. $y \leq 2$
   $y < 6x + 2$

6. $4x \geq y$
   $-x + 4y < 4$

7. $x + y < 2$
   $2x + y > -3$
   $y \geq 0$

8. $y \geq 3x - 4$
   $y \leq x$
   $y \geq -5x - 15$

9. $x > -5$
   $x < 0$
   $y \leq 2x + 7$

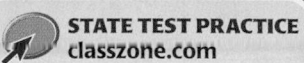
Lessons 7.5–7.6

1. MULTI-STEP PROBLEM A minimum of 600 bricks and 12 bags of sand are needed for a construction job. Each brick weighs 2 pounds, and each bag of sand weighs 50 pounds. The maximum weight that a delivery truck can carry is 3000 pounds.

a. Let x be the number of bricks, and let y be the number of bags of sand. Write a system of linear inequalities that models the situation. **$x \geq 600, y \geq 12, 2x + 50y \leq 3000$**

b. Graph the system of inequalities. **See margin.**

c. Use the graph to determine whether 700 bricks and 20 bags of sand can be delivered in one trip. **yes**

2. MULTI-STEP PROBLEM Dana decides to paint the ceiling and the walls of a room. She spends $120 on 2 gallons of paint for the ceiling and 4 gallons of paint for the walls. Then she decides to paint the ceiling and the walls of another room using the same kinds of paint. She spends $60 for 1 gallon of paint for the ceiling and 2 gallons of paint for the walls.

a. Write a system of linear equations that models the situation. **$2x + 4y = 120,$ $x + 2y = 60$**

b. Is there enough information given to determine the cost of one gallon of each type of paint? *Explain.* **See margin.**

c. A gallon of ceiling paint costs $3 more than a gallon of wall paint. What is the cost of one gallon of each type of paint? **ceiling paint: $22, wall paint: $19**

3. SHORT RESPONSE During a sale at a music and video store, all CDs are priced the same and all DVDs are priced the same. Karen buys 4 CDs and 2 DVDs for $78. The next day, while the sale is still in progress, Karen goes back and buys 2 CDs and 1 DVD for $39. Is there enough information to determine the cost of 1 CD? *Explain.* **Yes. *Sample answer:* Since the CDs and DVDs are all priced the same, the 3 items she bought on the second day cost $39 ÷ 3 = $3 each. So 1 CD costs $13.**

4. SHORT RESPONSE Two airport shuttles, bus A and bus B, take passengers to the airport from the same bus stop. The graph shows the distance d (in miles) traveled by each bus t hours after bus A leaves the station. The distance from the bus stop to the airport is 25 miles. If bus A and bus B continue at the same rates, will bus B ever catch up to bus A? *Explain.* **See margin.**

5. EXTENDED RESPONSE During the summer, you want to earn at least $200 per week. You earn $10 per hour working as a lifeguard, and you earn $8 per hour working at a retail store. You can work at most 30 hours per week.

a. Write and graph a system of linear inequalities that models the situation. **See margin.**

b. If you work 5 hours per week as a lifeguard and 15 hours per week at the retail store, will you earn at least $200 per week? *Explain.* **No; you will earn $170.**

c. You are scheduled to work 20 hours per week at the retail store. What is the range of hours you can work as a lifeguard to earn at least $200 per week? **$4 \leq x \leq 10$**

6. OPEN-ENDED *Describe* a real-world situation that can be modeled by a system of linear inequalities. Then write and graph the system of inequalities. **See margin.**

7. GRIDDED ANSWER What is the area (in square feet) of the triangular garden defined by the system of inequalities below? **90 ft²**

$$y \geq 0$$
$$x \geq 0$$
$$4x + 5y \leq 60$$

1b.

2b. No. *Sample answer:* There are infinitely many solutions to the linear system.

4. No. *Sample answer:* The lines are parallel so there is never a point when the shuttles will have traveled the same distance at the same time.

5a. Let x represent the hours working as a lifeguard, and y represent the hours working at a retail store. $10x + 8y \geq 200, x + y \leq 30, x \geq 0,$ $y \geq 0$

6. *Sample answer:* You have 80 dollars and want to buy cups at a store. Small cups are $4, and large cups are $5. The store has 10 small cups and 12 large cups. $x \geq 0, y \geq 0, x \leq 10, y \leq 12,$ $4x + 5y \leq 80$

Additional Resources

The following resources are available to help review the materials in this chapter.

Chapter 7 Resource Book
- Chapter Review Games and Activities, p. 79
- Cumulative Practice, Chs. 1–7, pp. 81–82

Student Resources in Spanish

eWorkbook

@HomeTutor

Vocabulary Practice

Vocabulary practice is available at **classzone.com**

BIG IDEAS

For Your Notebook

Big Idea 1

Solving Linear Systems by Graphing

The graph of a system of two linear equations tells you how many solutions the system has.

One solution	No solution	Infinitely many solutions

The lines intersect. The lines are parallel. The lines coincide.

Big Idea 2

Solving Linear Systems Using Algebra

You can use any of the following algebraic methods to solve a system of linear equations. Sometimes it is easier to use one method instead of another.

Method	Procedure	When to use
Substitution	Solve one equation for x or y. Substitute the expression for x or y into the other equation.	When one equation is already solved for x or y
Addition	Add the equations to eliminate x or y.	When the coefficients of one variable are opposites
Subtraction	Subtract the equations to eliminate x or y.	When the coefficients of one variable are the same
Multiplication	Multiply one or both equations by a constant so that adding or subtracting the equations will eliminate x or y.	When no corresponding coefficients are the same or opposites

Big Idea 3

Solving Systems of Linear Inequalities

The graph of a system of linear inequalities is the intersection of the half-planes of each inequality in the system. For example, the graph of the system of inequalities below is the shaded region.

$x \le 6$ **Inequality 1**
$y < 2$ **Inequality 2**
$2x + 3y \ge 6$ **Inequality 3**

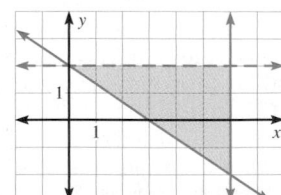

REVIEW KEY VOCABULARY

- system of linear equations, *p. 427*
- solution of a system of linear equations, *p. 427*
- consistent independent system, *p. 427*
- inconsistent system, *p. 459*
- consistent dependent system, *p. 459*
- system of linear inequalities, *p. 466*
- solution of a system of linear inequalities, *p. 466*
- graph of a system of linear inequalities, *p. 466*

VOCABULARY EXERCISES

1. Copy and complete: A(n) __?__ consists of two or more linear inequalities in the same variables. **system of linear inequalities**

2. Copy and complete: A(n) __?__ consists of two or more linear equations in the same variables. **system of linear equations**

3. *Describe* how you would graph a system of two linear inequalities. **See margin.**

4. Give an example of a consistent dependent system. *Explain* why the system is a consistent dependent system. **Sample answer: $y = 2x + 3$, $2y = 4x + 6$; the lines intersect (are consistent) and the equations are equivalent (are dependent).**

REVIEW EXAMPLES AND EXERCISES

Use the review examples and exercises below to check your understanding of the concepts you have learned in each lesson of Chapter 7.

7.1 Solve Linear Systems by Graphing   *pp. 427–433*

EXAMPLE

Solve the linear system by graphing. Check your solution.

$y = x - 2$ **Equation 1**
$y = -3x + 2$ **Equation 2**

Graph both equations. The lines appear to intersect at $(1, -1)$. Check the solution by substituting 1 for x and -1 for y in each equation.

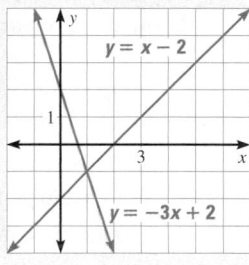

$y = x - 2$	$y = -3x + 2$
$-1 \stackrel{?}{=} 1 - 2$	$-1 \stackrel{?}{=} -3(1) + 2$
$-1 = -1 \checkmark$	$-1 = -1 \checkmark$

EXERCISES

EXAMPLES 1 and 2
on pp. 427–428
for Exs. 5–7

Solve the linear system by graphing. Check your solution.

5. $y = -3x + 1$ **(2, -5)**
   $y = x - 7$

6. $y = 3x + 4$ **(-1, 1)**
   $y = -2x - 1$

7. $x + y = 3$ **(4, -1)**
   $x - y = 5$

Extra Example 7.1
Solve the linear system by graphing. Check your solution.
$y = -x + 4$
$y = 2x - 5$ **(3, 1)**

3. Sample answer: Graph each inequality then shade the region that is the intersection of the solutions to each inequality. Then check the solution with a test point.

Extra Example 7.2
Solve the linear system using substitution.
$y + 2x = 13$
$-x + 4y = -2$ **(6, 1)**

Extra Example 7.3
Solve the linear system using elimination.
$-2x + 3y = 6$
$-2x + 5y = -6$ **(−12, −6)**

7.2 Solve Linear Systems by Substitution
pp. 435–441

EXAMPLE

Solve the linear system: $3x + y = -9$ **Equation 1**
$\qquad\qquad\qquad\qquad\qquad y = 5x + 7$ **Equation 2**

STEP 1 Substitute $5x + 7$ for y in Equation 1 and solve for x.

$\qquad 3x + y = -9$ **Write Equation 1.**

$\qquad 3x + 5x + 7 = -9$ **Substitute $5x + 7$ for y.**

$\qquad x = -2$ **Solve for x.**

STEP 2 Substitute -2 for x in Equation 2 to find the value of y.

$\qquad y = 5x + 7 = 5(-2) + 7 = -10 + 7 = -3$

▶ The solution is $(-2, -3)$. Check the solution by substituting -2 for x and -3 for y in each of the original equations.

EXERCISES

Solve the linear system using substitution.

**EXAMPLES
1, 2, and 3**
on pp. 435–437
for Exs. 8–11

8. $y = 2x - 7$ **(3, −1)**   **9.** $x + 4y = 9$ **(5, 1)**   **10.** $2x + y = -15$ **(−3, −9)**
$\quad\; x + 2y = 1$ $\qquad\;\; x - y = 4$ $\qquad\quad\; y - 5x = 6$

11. ART Kara spends \$16 on tubes of paint and disposable brushes for an art project. Each tube of paint costs \$3, and each disposable brush costs \$.50. Kara purchases twice as many brushes as tubes of paint. Find the number of brushes and the number of tubes of paint that she purchases.
4 tubes of paint, 8 brushes

7.3 Solve Linear Systems by Adding or Subtracting
pp. 444–450

EXAMPLE

Solve the linear system: $5x - y = 8$ **Equation 1**
$\qquad\qquad\qquad\qquad\quad -5x + 4y = -17$ **Equation 2**

STEP 1 **Add** the equations to $\quad 5x - y = 8$
eliminate one variable. $\quad \underline{-5x + 4y = -17}$
$\qquad\qquad\qquad\qquad\qquad\qquad\qquad 3y = -9$

STEP 2 **Solve** for y. $\qquad\qquad\qquad\quad y = -3$

STEP 3 Substitute -3 for y in either equation and solve for x.

$\qquad 5x - y = 8$ **Write Equation 1.**

$\qquad 5x - (-3) = 8$ **Substitute -3 for y.**

$\qquad x = 1$ **Solve for x.**

▶ The solution is $(1, -3)$. Check the solution by substituting 1 for x and -3 for y in each of the original equations.

Extra Example 7.4
Solve the linear system using elimination.
$3x - 2y = 5$
$2x - 3y = 5$ **(1, −1)**

EXAMPLES
1, 2, and 3
on pp. 444–445
for Exs. 12–17

EXERCISES

Solve the linear system using elimination.

12. $x + 2y = 13$ **(3, 5)**
  $x - 2y = -7$

13. $4x - 5y = 14$ **(1, −2)**
  $-4x + y = -6$

14. $x + 7y = 12$ **(−2, 2)**
  $-2x + 7y = 18$

15. $9x - 2y = 34$ **(6, 10)**
  $5x - 2y = 10$

16. $3x = y + 1$ **(−8, −25)**
  $2x - y = 9$

17. $4y = 11 - 3x$ **(−7, 8)**
  $3x + 2y = -5$

7.4 Solve Linear Systems by Multiplying First
pp. 451–457

EXAMPLE

Solve the linear system: $x - 2y = -7$ **Equation 1**
  $3x - y = 4$ **Equation 2**

STEP 1 **Multiply** the first equation by −3.

$x - 2y = -7$ × **(−3)** → $-3x + 6y = 21$
$3x - y = 4$ $\underline{3x - y = 4}$

STEP 2 **Add** the equations. $5y = 25$

STEP 3 **Solve** for y. $y = 5$

STEP 4 **Substitute** 5 for y in either of the original equations and solve for x.

$x - 2y = -7$ **Write Equation 1.**

$x - 2(5) = -7$ **Substitute 5 for y.**

$x = 3$ **Solve for x.**

▸ The solution is (3, 5).

CHECK Substitute 3 for x and 5 for y in each of the original equations.

Equation 1	**Equation 2**
$x - 2y = -7$	$3x - y = 4$
$3 - 2(5) \stackrel{?}{=} -7$	$3(3) - 5 \stackrel{?}{=} 4$
$-7 = -7$ ✓	$4 = 4$ ✓

EXERCISES

Solve the linear system using elimination.

EXAMPLES
1 and 2
on pp. 451–452
for Exs. 18–24

18. $-x + y = -4$ **(7, 3)**
  $2x - 3y = 5$

19. $x + 6y = 28$ **(−2, 5)**
  $2x - 3y = -19$

20. $3x - 5y = -7$ **(−9, −4)**
  $-4x + 7y = 8$

21. $8x - 7y = -3$ **(4, 5)**
  $6x - 5y = -1$

22. $5x = 3y - 2$ **(2, 4)**
  $3x + 2y = 14$

23. $11x = 2y - 1$ **(1, 6)**
  $3y = 10 + 8x$

24. CAR MAINTENANCE You pay $24.50 for 10 gallons of gasoline and 1 quart of oil at a gas station. Your friend pays $22 for 8 gallons of the same gasoline and 2 quarts of the same oil. Find the cost of 1 quart of oil. **$2**

Extra Example 7.5

Show that the linear system has infinitely many solutions.

$y = -2x - 4$
$6x + 3y = -12$

Substitute $-2x - 4$ for y in the equation $6x + 3y = -12$ and solve for x.

$$6x + 3y = -12$$
$$6x + 3(-2x - 4) = -12$$
$$6x - 6x - 12 = -12$$
$$-12 = -12$$

Since this is a true statement, the system has infinitely many solutions.

Extra Example 7.6

Graph the system of linear inequalities.

$y \geq x - 1$
$y < -2x$

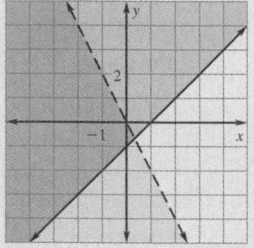

25. No solution. *Sample answer:* When the variables are eliminated, a false statement remains, which means there is no solution.

26. Infinitely many solutions. *Sample answer:* When the variables are eliminated, a true statement remains, which means there are infinitely many solutions.

27. One solution. *Sample answer:* The lines have different slopes, so there is only one solution.

28.

29.

7.5 Solve Special Types of Linear Systems
pp. 459–465

EXAMPLE

Show that the linear system has no solution.

$$-2x + y = -3 \quad \text{Equation 1}$$
$$y = 2x + 1 \quad \text{Equation 2}$$

Graph the linear system.

The lines are parallel because they have the same slope but different y-intercepts. Parallel lines do not intersect, so the system has no solution.

EXERCISES

> EXAMPLES
> 1, 2, and 3
> on pp. 459–461
> for Exs. 25–27

Tell whether the linear system has *one solution*, *no solution*, or *infinitely many solutions*. Explain. 25–27. See margin.

25. $x = 2y - 3$
    $1.5x - 3y = 0$

26. $-x + y = 8$
    $x + 8 = y$

27. $4x = 2y + 6$
    $4x + 2y = 10$

7.6 Solve Systems of Linear Inequalities
pp. 466–472

EXAMPLE

Graph the system of linear inequalities.

$$y < -2x + 3 \quad \text{Inequality 1}$$
$$y \geq x - 3 \quad \text{Inequality 2}$$

The graph of $y < -2x + 3$ is the half-plane *below* the *dashed* line $y = -2x + 3$.

The graph of $y \geq x - 3$ is the half-plane *on and above* the *solid* line $y = x - 3$.

The graph of the system is the intersection of the two half-planes shown as the darker shade of blue.

EXERCISES

> EXAMPLES
> 1, 2, 3, and 4
> on pp. 466–468
> for Exs. 28–31

Graph the system of linear inequalities. 28–30. See margin.

28. $y < x + 3$
    $y > -3x - 2$

29. $y \leq -x - 2$
    $y > 4x + 1$

30. $y \geq 0$
    $x \leq 2$
    $y < x + 4$

31. **MOVIE COSTS** You receive a $40 gift card to a movie theater. A ticket to a matinee movie costs $5, and a ticket to an evening movie costs $8. Write and graph a system of inequalities for the number of tickets you can purchase using the gift card. Let m **represent the number of matinee movies and n represent the number of evening movies.** $5m + 8n \leq 40, m \geq 0, n \geq 0$, **see margin for art.**

30.

31.

Solve the linear system by graphing. Check your solution.

1. $3x - y = -6$ **(−1, 3)**
$x + y = 2$

2. $-2x + y = 5$ **(−2, 1)**
$x + y = -1$

3. $y = 4x + 4$ $\left(\frac{4}{11}, 5\frac{5}{11}\right)$
$3x + 2y = 12$

4. $5x - 4y = 20$ **(4, 0)**
$x + 2y = 4$

5. $x + 3y = 9$ **(3, 2)**
$2x - y = 4$

6. $2x + 7y = 14$ **(−7, 4)**
$5x + 7y = -7$

Solve the linear system using substitution.

7. $y = 5x - 7$ **(6, 23)**
$-4x + y = -1$

8. $x = y - 11$ **(−17, −6)**
$x - 3y = 1$

9. $3x + y = -19$ **(−3, −10)**
$x - y = 7$

10. $15x + y = 70$ **(4, 10)**
$3x - 2y = -8$

11. $3y + x = 17$ **(3.5, 4.5)**
$x + y = 8$

12. $0.5x + y = 9$
$1.6x + 0.2y = 13$
$\left(7\frac{7}{15}, 5\frac{4}{15}\right)$

Solve the linear system using elimination.

13. $8x + 3y = -9$ **(−3, 5)**
$-8x + y = 29$

14. $x - 5y = -3$ **(7, 2)**
$3x - 5y = 11$

15. $4x + y = 17$ **(4, 1)**
$7y = 4x$ **9**

16. $3x + 2y = -5$ **(3, −7)**
$x - y = 10$

17. $3y = x + 5$ **(16, 7)**
$-3x + 8y = 8$

18. $6x - 5y = 9$ **(4, 3)**
$9x - 7y = 15$

Tell whether the linear system has *one solution*, *no solution*, or *infinitely many solutions*.

19. $15x - 3y = 12$
$y = 5x - 4$
infinitely many solutions

20. $4x - y = -4$ **no solution**
$-8x + 2y = 2$

21. $-12x + 3y = 18$
$4x + y = -6$
one solution

22. $6x - 7y = 5$
$-12x + 14y = 10$ **no solution**

23. $3x - 4y = 24$ **one solution**
$3x + 4y = 24$

24. $10x - 2y = 14$
$15x - 3y = 21$
infinitely many solutions

Graph the system of linear inequalities. 25–27. See margin.

25. $y < 2x + 2$
$y \geq -x - 1$

26. $y \leq 3x - 2$
$y > x + 4$

27. $y \leq 3$
$x > -1$
$y > 3x - 3$

28. TRUCK RENTALS Carrie and Dave each rent the same size moving truck for one day. They pay a fee of x dollars for the truck and y dollars per mile they drive. Carrie drives 150 miles and pays $215. Dave drives 120 miles and pays $176. Find the amount of the fee and the cost per mile.
flat fee: $20, cost per mile: $1.30

29. ⬡ **GEOMETRY** The rectangle has a perimeter P of 58 inches. The length ℓ is one more than 3 times the width w. Write and solve a system of linear equations to find the length and width of the rectangle.
$2\ell + 2w = 58$, $\ell = 3w + 1$, $\ell = 22$ in., $w = 7$ in.

$P = 58$ in. w

ℓ

30. COMMUNITY SERVICE A town committee has a budget of $75 to spend on snacks for the volunteers participating in a clean-up day. The committee chairperson decides to purchase granola bars and at least 50 bottles of water. Granola bars cost $.50 each, and bottles of water cost $.75 each. Write and graph a system of linear inequalities for the number of bottles of water and the number of granola bars that can be purchased. **See margin.**

Additional Resources

Assessment Book

- Chapter Test, Levels A, B, C, pp. 93–98
- Standardized Chapter Test, pp. 99–100
- SAT/ACT Chapter Test, pp. 101–102
- Alternative Assessment, pp. 103–104

Test Generator CD-ROM

Chapter Test

Easily-readable reduced copies (with answers) of Chapter Test B, the Standardized Chapter Test, and the Alternative Assessment from the Assessment Book can be found on pp. 424G–424H.

26.

27.

30. Let w represent the number of water bottles and g represent the number of granola bars; $w \geq 50$, $g \geq 0$, $0.5g + 0.75w \leq 75$.

25.

Test-Taking Strategy

When solving multiple-choice questions that have ordered pairs or pairs of numbers for answer choices, eliminate pairs that cannot possibly be the answer based on the conditions of the problem.

For example, the condition $y = \frac{1}{2}x$ in Problem 1 means both x and y must have the same sign. This eliminates choice B. In Problem 2, the condition that the sum has to be -1 means the numbers must have different signs. This eliminates choice B. Once you have eliminated one or two of the answer choices, you can substitute the remaining pairs of numbers in the original question. The fewer numbers you need to substitute in the original question, the fewer chances you have of making a mistake.

MULTIPLE CHOICE QUESTIONS

If you have difficulty solving a multiple choice problem directly, you may be able to use another approach to eliminate incorrect answer choices and obtain the correct answer.

PROBLEM 1

Which ordered pair is the solution of the linear system $y = \frac{1}{2}x$ and $2x + 3y = -7$?

(A) $(2, 1)$ **(B)** $(1, -3)$ **(C)** $(-2, -1)$ **(D)** $(4, 2)$

Method 1

SOLVE DIRECTLY Use substitution to solve the linear system.

STEP 1 Substitute $\frac{1}{2}x$ for y in the equation $2x + 3y = -7$ and solve for x.

$$2x + 3y = -7$$
$$2x + 3\left(\frac{1}{2}x\right) = -7$$
$$2x + \frac{3}{2}x = -7$$
$$\frac{7}{2}x = -7$$
$$x = -2$$

STEP 2 Substitute -2 for x in $y = \frac{1}{2}x$ to find the value of y.

$$y = \frac{1}{2}x$$
$$= \frac{1}{2}(-2)$$
$$= -1$$

The solution of the system is $(-2, -1)$.

The correct answer is C. **(A) (B) (C) (D)**

Method 2

ELIMINATE CHOICES Substitute the values given in each answer choice for x and y in both equations.

Choice A: $(2, 1)$
Substitute 2 for x and 1 for y.

$$y = \frac{1}{2}x \qquad 2x + 3y = -7$$
$$1 \overset{?}{=} \frac{1}{2}(2) \qquad 2(2) + 3(1) \overset{?}{=} -7$$
$$1 = 1 \checkmark \qquad\qquad 7 = -7 \text{ ✗}$$

Choice B: $(1, -3)$
Substitute 1 for x and -3 for y.

$$y = \frac{1}{2}x$$
$$-3 \overset{?}{=} \frac{1}{2}(1)$$
$$-3 = \frac{1}{2} \text{ ✗}$$

Choice C: $(-2, -1)$
Substitute -2 for x and -1 for y.

$$y = \frac{1}{2}x \qquad\qquad 2x + 3y = -7$$
$$-1 \overset{?}{=} \frac{1}{2}(-2) \qquad 2(-2) + 3(-1) \overset{?}{=} -7$$
$$-1 = -1 \checkmark \qquad\qquad -7 = -7 \checkmark$$

The correct answer is C. **(A) (B) (C) (D)**

The sum of two numbers is -1, and the difference of the two numbers is 5. What are the numbers?

(A) -5 and 4   (B) 1 and 6   (C) 2 and -3 (D) -2 and 3

Avoiding Common Errors

Multiple choice questions that have ordered pairs or pairs of numbers for answer choices often contain two or more choices that are inverses of one another. For example, in Problem 2, choices C and D fall into this category. If one of the pairs of numbers is the correct answer choice, double check your answer to make sure you chose the correct answer and not its inverse.

1. The sum of 9 and 18 is not -27.

2. $5(-3) + 2(-13)$ does not equal -11.

3. If 180 short-sleeve T-shirts are sold, then 261 long-sleeve T-shirts would be sold, and $261(\$25) + 180(\$15)$ does not equal $8415.

Method 1

SOLVE DIRECTLY Write and solve a system of equations for the numbers.

STEP 1 Write a system of equations. Let x and y be the numbers.

$x + y = -1$ **Equation 1**
$x - y = 5$ **Equation 2**

STEP 2 Add the equations to eliminate one variable. Then find the value of the other variable.

$x + y = -1$
$x - y = 5$
───────────
$2x = 4$, so $x = 2$

STEP 3 Substitute 2 for x in Equation 1 and solve for y.

$2 + y = -1$, so $y = -3$

The correct answer is C. (A) (B) (C) (D)

Method 2

ELIMINATE CHOICES Find the sum and difference of each pair of numbers. Because the difference is positive, be sure to subtract the lesser number from the greater number.

Choice A: -5 and 4

Sum: $-5 + 4 = 1$ ✓

Difference: $-5 - 4 = -9$ ✗

Choice B: 1 and 6

Sum: $1 + 6 = 7$ ✗

Choice C: 2 and -3

Sum: $2 + (-3) = -1$ ✓

Difference: $2 - (-3) = 5$ ✓

The correct answer is C. (A) (B) (C) (D)

PRACTICE

Explain why you can eliminate the highlighted answer choice. 1–3. See margin.

1. The sum of two numbers is –27. One number is twice the other. What are the numbers?

   (A) ✗ **9 and 18**   (B) -3 and 24   (C) -18 and -9 (D) -14 and -13

2. Which ordered pair is a solution of the linear system $5x + 2y = -11$ and $x = -\frac{1}{2}y - 4$?

   (A) $\left(-\frac{7}{6}, -\frac{17}{3}\right)$ (B) $\left(-\frac{23}{3}, \frac{1}{3}\right)$ (C) $(-3, 2)$ (D) ✗ $(-3, -13)$

3. Long-sleeve and short-sleeve T-shirts can be purchased at a concert. A long-sleeve T-shirt costs $25 and a short-sleeve T-shirt costs $15. During a concert, the T-shirt vendor collects $8415 from the sale of 441 T-shirts. How many short-sleeve T-shirts were sold?

   (A) 100   (B) ✗ **180**   (C) 261   (D) 441

MULTIPLE CHOICE

1. Which ordered pair is the solution of the linear system $y = \frac{1}{2}x + 1$ and $y = \frac{3}{2}x + 4$? **B**

  Ⓐ $\left(3, \frac{5}{2}\right)$ **Ⓑ** $\left(-3, -\frac{1}{2}\right)$

  Ⓒ $\left(\frac{3}{2}, \frac{7}{4}\right)$ **Ⓓ** $(0, 1)$

2. How many solutions does the linear system $3x + 5y = 8$ and $3x + 5y = 1$ have? **A**

  Ⓐ 0   **Ⓑ** 1

  Ⓒ 2   **Ⓓ** Infinitely many

3. The sum of two numbers is −3, and the difference of the two numbers is 11. What are the numbers? **D**

  Ⓐ 4 and 7   **Ⓑ** −3 and 8

  Ⓒ 3 and 14   **Ⓓ** −7 and 4

4. Which ordered pair is the solution of the system of linear equations whose graph is shown? **D**

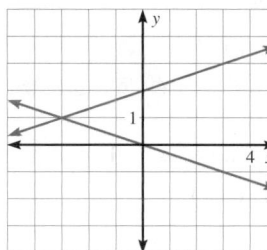

  Ⓐ $(3, -1)$ **Ⓑ** $(0, 0)$

  Ⓒ $(0, 2)$ **Ⓓ** $(-3, 1)$

5. Which ordered pair is the solution of the linear system $3x + y = -1$ and $y = -\frac{1}{2}x - \frac{7}{2}$? **B**

  Ⓐ $\left(\frac{5}{2}, -\frac{17}{2}\right)$ **Ⓑ** $(1, -4)$

  Ⓒ $(-1, -3)$ **Ⓓ** $(0, -1)$

6. Which ordered pair is a solution of the system $x + 2y \le -2$ and $y \le -3x + 4$? **D**

  Ⓐ $(0, 0)$ **Ⓑ** $(2, -2)$

  Ⓒ $(-2, 2)$ **Ⓓ** $(5, -4)$

7. How many solutions does the system of linear equations whose graph is shown have? **B**

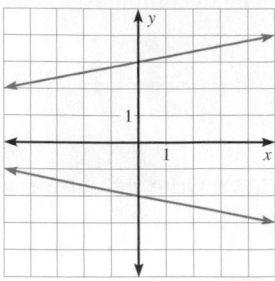

  Ⓐ 0   **Ⓑ** 1

  Ⓒ 2   **Ⓓ** Infinitely many

8. At a bakery, one customer pays $5.67 for 3 bagels and 4 muffins. Another customer pays $6.70 for 5 bagels and 3 muffins. Which system of equations can be used to determine the cost x (in dollars) of one bagel and the cost y (in dollars) of one muffin at the bakery? **D**

  Ⓐ $x + y = 7$ **Ⓑ** $y = 3x + 5.67$
         $x + y = 8$ $y = 5x + 6.7$

  Ⓒ $3x + 4y = 6.7$ **Ⓓ** $3x + 4y = 5.67$
         $5x + 3y = 5.67$ $5x + 3y = 6.7$

9. The perimeter P (in feet) of each of the two rectangles below is given. What are the values of ℓ and w? **A**

  Ⓐ $\ell = 7$ and $w = 5$

  Ⓑ $\ell = 8$ and $w = 4$

  Ⓒ $\ell = 11$ and $w = 10$

  Ⓓ $\ell = 12$ and $w = 9$

GRIDDED ANSWER

10. What is the *x*-coordinate of the solution of the system whose graph is shown? **2**

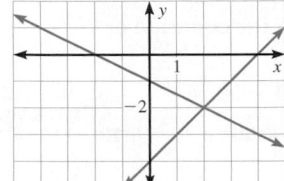

11. What is the *x*-coordinate of the solution of the system $y = \frac{1}{3}x + 8$ and $2x - y = 2$? **6**

12. A science museum charges one amount for admission for an adult and a lesser amount for admission for a student. Admission to the museum for 28 students and 5 adults costs $284. Admission for 40 students and 10 adults costs $440. What is the admission cost (in dollars) for one student? **$8**

SHORT RESPONSE

13. Is it possible to find a value for *c* so that the linear system below has exactly one solution? *Explain.* **See margin.**

$$5x + 3y = 21 \quad \text{Equation 1}$$
$$y = -\frac{5}{3}x + c \quad \text{Equation 2}$$

14. A rental car agency charges *x* dollars per day plus *y* dollars per mile to rent any of the mid-sized cars at the agency. The total costs for two customers are shown below.

Customer	Time (days)	Distance (miles)	Cost (dollars)
Jackson	3	150	217.50
Bree	2	112	148.00

How much will it cost to rent a mid-sized car for 5 days and drive 250 miles? *Explain.* **$362.50.** *Sample answer:* **The company charges $60 per day and $0.25 per mile, so 5 days and 250 miles will cost $362.50.**

EXTENDED RESPONSE

15. A baseball player's batting average is the number of hits the player has divided by the number of at-bats. At the beginning of a game, a player has a batting average of .360. During the game, the player gets 3 hits during 5 at-bats, and his batting average changes to .375.

a. Write a system of linear equations that represents the situation. $\frac{x}{y} = 0.360$, $(x + 3)/(y + 5) = 0.375$

b. How many at-bats has the player had so far this season? **80 at-bats**

c. Another player on the team has a batting average of .240 at the beginning of the same game. During the game, he gets 3 hits during 5 at-bats, and his batting average changes to .300. Has this player had more at-bats so far this season than the other player? *Explain.* **No.** *Sample answer:* **The player has had 30 at-bats, while the other player has had 80.**

16. A gardener combines *x* fluid ounces of a 20% liquid fertilizer and 80% water mix with *y* fluid ounces of a 5% liquid fertilizer and 95% water mix to make 30 fluid ounces of a 10% liquid fertilizer and 90% water mix.

a. Write a system of linear equations that represents the situation. $0.2x + 0.05y = 3$, $x + y = 30$

b. Solve the system from part (a). **10 fluid ounces of the 20% liquid fertilizer and 80% water mix and 20 fluid ounces of the 5% liquid fertilizer and 95% water mix.**

c. Suppose the gardener combines pure (100%) water and the 20% liquid fertilizer and 80% water mix to make the 30 fluid ounces of the 10% liquid fertilizer and 90% water mix. Is more of the 20% liquid fertilizer and 80% water mix used in this mix than in the original mix? *Explain.* **Yes.** *Sample answer:* **The gardener would use 15 fluid ounces of the mix, instead of 10.**

13. No. *Sample answer:* Any value of *c* other than 7 will produce an inconsistent system that has 0 solutions, and $c = 7$ will produce a consistent dependent system.

Additional Resources

The following resources are available to help review the materials in Chapters 1–7.

Chapter Resource Books

- Chapter 4 CRB, Cumulative Review, pp. 104–105
- Chapter 5 CRB, Cumulative Review, pp. 91–92
- Chapter 6 CRB, Cumulative Review, pp. 100–101
- Chapter 7 CRB, Cumulative Review, pp. 81–82

Assessment Book

- Cumulative Test, Chapters 1–7, pp. 105–108

28.

29.

30.

31.

32.

Evaluate the expression.

1. $2^5 \cdot 2 - 4 \div 2$ *(p. 8)* **62**

2. $24 \div 6 + (9 - 6)$ *(p. 8)* **7**

3. $5[(6 - 2)^2 - 5]$ *(p. 8)* **55**

4. $\sqrt{144}$ *(p. 110)* **12**

5. $-\sqrt{2500}$ *(p. 110)* **−50**

6. $\pm\sqrt{400}$ *(p. 110)* **±20**

Check whether the given number is a solution of the equation or inequality. *(p. 21)*

7. $7 + 3x = 16; 3$ **solution**

8. $21y + 1 = 1; 0$ **solution**

9. $20 - 12h = 12; 1$ **not a solution**

10. $g - 3 > 2; 5$ **not a solution**

11. $10 \geq 4 - x; 0$ **solution**

12. $30 - 4p \geq 5; 6$ **solution**

Simplify the expression.

13. $5(y - 1) + 4$ *(p. 96)* **5y − 1**

14. $12w + (w - 2)3$ *(p. 96)* **15w − 6**

15. $(g - 1)(-4) + 3g$ *(p. 96)* **−g + 4**

16. $\frac{10h - 25}{5}$ *(p. 103)* **2h − 5**

17. $\frac{21 - 4x}{-7}$ *(p. 103)* **−3 + $\frac{4}{7}$ x**

18. $\frac{32 - 20m}{2}$ *(p. 103)* **16 − 10m**

Solve the equation.

19. $x - 8 = 21$ *(p. 134)* **29**

20. $-1 = x + 3$ *(p. 134)* **−4**

21. $6x = -42$ *(p. 134)* **−7**

22. $\frac{x}{3} = 8$ *(p. 134)* **24**

23. $5 - 2x = 11$ *(p. 141)* **−3**

24. $\frac{2}{3}x - 3 = 17$ *(p. 141)* **30**

25. $3(x - 2) = -15$ *(p. 148)* **−3**

26. $3(5x - 7) = 5x - 1$ *(p. 154)* **2**

27. $-7(2x - 10) = 4x - 10$ *(p. 154)* **$4\frac{4}{9}$**

Graph the equation. **28–33. See margin.**

28. $x + 2y = -8$ *(p. 225)*

29. $-2x + 5y = -10$ *(p. 225)*

30. $3x - 4y = 12$ *(p. 225)*

31. $y = 3x - 7$ *(p. 244)*

32. $y = x + 6$ *(p. 244)*

33. $y = -\frac{1}{3}x$ *(p. 253)*

Write an equation of the line in slope-intercept form with the given slope and y-intercept. *(p. 283)*

34. slope: 5
y-intercept: −1 **y = 5x − 1**

35. slope: −1
y-intercept: 3 **y = −x + 3**

36. slope: −7
y-intercept: 0 **y = −7x**

Write an equation in point-slope form of the line that passes through the given points. *(p. 302)* **37–42. See margin.**

37. $(1, -10), (-5, 2)$

38. $(4, 7), (-4, 3)$

39. $(-9, -2), (-6, 8)$

40. $(-1, 1), (1, -3)$

41. $(2, 4), (8, 2)$

42. $(-6, 1), (3, -5)$

Solve the inequality. Then graph your solution. **43–54. See margin for art.**

43. $x - 9 < -13$ *(p. 356)* **x < −4**

44. $8 \leq x + 7$ *(p. 356)* **x ≥ 1**

45. $8x \geq 56$ *(p. 363)* **x ≥ 7**

46. $\frac{x}{-4} > 7$ *(p. 363)* **x < −28**

47. $1 - 2x < 11$ *(p. 369)* **x > −5**

48. $8 > -3x - 1$ *(p. 369)* **x > −3**

49. $4x - 10 \leq 7x + 8$ *(p. 369)* **x ≥ −6**

50. $7x - 5 < 6x - 4$ *(p. 369)* **x < 1**

51. $-4 < 3x - 1 < 5$ *(p. 380)* **−1 < x < 2**

52. $3 \leq 9 - 2x \leq 15$ *(p. 380)* **−3 ≤ x ≤ −3**

53. $|3x| < 15$ *(p. 398)* **−5 < x < 5**

54. $|4x - 2| \geq 18$ *(p. 398)* **x ≤ −4 or x ≥ 5**

33.

37. $y + 10 = -2(x - 1)$ or $y - 2 = -2(x + 5)$

38. $y - 7 = \frac{1}{2}(x - 4)$ or $y - 3 = \frac{1}{2}(x + 4)$

39. $y + 2 = \frac{10}{3}(x + 9)$ or $y - 8 = \frac{10}{3}(x + 6)$

40. $y - 1 = -2(x + 1)$ or $y + 3 = -2(x - 1)$

41. $y - 4 = -\frac{1}{3}(x - 2)$ or $y - 2 = -\frac{1}{3}(x - 8)$

42. $y - 1 = -\frac{2}{3}(x + 6)$ or $y + 5 = -\frac{2}{3}(x - 3)$

Solve the linear system using elimination. *(p. 451)*

55. $4x + y = 8$
$5x - 2y = -3$ **(1, 4)**

56. $3x - 5y = 5$
$x - 5y = -4$ **(4.5, 1.7)**

57. $12x + 7y = 3$
$8x + 5y = 1$ **(2, -3)**

58. ART PROJECT You are making a tile mosaic on the rectangular tabletop shown. A bag of porcelain tiles costs $3.95 and covers 36 square inches. How much will it cost to buy enough tiles to cover the tabletop? *(p. 28)* **$79**

24 in.

30 in.

59. FOOD The table shows the changes in the price for a dozen grade A, large eggs over 4 years. Find the average yearly change to the nearest cent in the price for a dozen grade A, large eggs during the period 1999–2002. *(p. 103)* **$.02**

Year	1999	2000	2001	2002
Change in price for a dozen grade A, large eggs (dollars)	−0.17	0.04	−0.03	0.25

60. HONEY PRODUCTION Honeybees visit about 2,000,000 flowers to make 16 ounces of honey. About how many flowers do honeybees visit to make 6 ounces of honey? *(p. 168)* **750,000 flowers**

61. MUSIC The table shows the price p (in dollars) for various lengths of speaker cable. *(p. 253)*

Length, ℓ (feet)	3	5	12	15
Price, p (dollars)	7.50	12.50	30.00	37.50

a. *Explain* why p varies directly with ℓ. **The ratio $\frac{p}{\ell}$ is always the same, so p varies directly with ℓ.**

b. Write a direct variation equation that relates ℓ and p. **$p = 2.5\ell$**

62. CURRENCY The table shows the exchange rate between the currency of Bolivia (bolivianos) and U.S. dollars from 1998 to 2003. *(p. 335)*

Year	1998	1999	2000	2001	2002	2003
Bolivianos per U.S. dollar	5.51	5.81	6.18	6.61	7.17	7.66

a. Find an equation that models the bolivianos per U.S. dollar as a function of the number of years since 1998. **See margin.**

b. If the trend continues, predict the number of bolivianos per U.S. dollar in 2010. *Sample answer:* **$10.63**

63. BATTERIES A manufacturer of nickel-cadmium batteries recommends storing the batteries at temperatures ranging from −20°C to 45°C. Use an inequality to describe the temperatures (in degrees Fahrenheit) at which the batteries can be stored. *(p. 380)* **−4 < F < 113**

43.

44.

45.

46.

47.

48.

49.

50.

51.

52.

53. See below.

54.

62a. *Sample answer:* Let x = number of years since 1998 and y = bolivianos per U.S. dollar; $y = 0.436x + 5.4$.

53.

485

REGULAR SCHEDULE

Pre-AP For pacing and assignments for a Pre-AP course, see the *Algebra 1 Toolkit*.

Lesson	Les. Day	BASIC	AVERAGE	ADVANCED
8.1	Day 1	pp. 492–494 Exs. 1, 2, 3–15 odd, 19–39 odd, 40–42, 52–57, 60–74 even	pp. 492–494 Exs. 1, 2, 4–18 even, 29–49, 53–58, 61, 64, 67, 73	pp. 492–494 Exs. 1, 2, 8–18 even, 31–38, 40–51*, 54–59*, 62, 65, 68, 74
8.2	Day 1	pp. 498–501 Exs. 1–28	pp. 498–501 Exs. 1, 2, 7–28, 38–40	pp. 498–501 Exs. 1, 2, 9–19, 21–28, 38–40, 47, 48*
	Day 2	pp. 498–501 Exs. 29–39, 49–52, 55–66	pp. 498–501 Exs. 31–37, 41–46, 49–53, 55–66	pp. 498–501 Exs. 32–37, 41–46, 49–66*
8.3	Day 1	pp. 506–508 Exs. 1, 2, 3–35 odd, 50–55, 60–68 even	pp. 506–508 Exs. 1, 2, 9–14, 21–27, 28–44 even, 45, 51–57, 60–68 even	pp. 506–508 Exs. 1, 2, 11–14, 22–26, 29–43 odd, 44, 49*, 52–68*, 59, 61, 68
8.4	Day 1	EP p. 939 Exs. 32–37; pp. 514–518 Exs. 1–28	pp. 514–518 Exs. 1, 2, 6–15, 19–28, 39–44	pp. 514–518 Exs. 1, 2, 8–15, 21–27, 39–47
	Day 2	pp. 514–518 Exs. 29–36, 39–41, 51–56, 61–74	pp. 514–518 Exs. 29–38, 45–49, 51–59, 62–74 even	pp. 514–518 Exs. 29–38, 48–60*, 64, 67, 68, 71
8.5	Day 1	SRH p. 923 Exs. 9–13; pp. 523–527 Exs. 1–21	pp. 523–527 Exs. 1–8, 11–21, 35, 60, 61	pp. 523–527 Exs. 1, 2, 4–8, 13–21, 35–37*, 60
	Day 2	pp. 523–527 Exs. 22–27, 38–43, 52–61	pp. 523–527 Exs. 22–34, 38–46, 52–58 even	pp. 523–527 Exs. 26–34, 39–51*, 54, 58
8.6	Day 1	pp. 535–538 Exs. 1–18, 63–66	pp. 535–538 Exs. 1–6, 10–18, 32–34, 63–66	pp. 535–538 Exs. 1, 4–6, 12–18, 32–37, 63–66
	Day 2	pp. 535–538 Exs. 19–35 odd, 36–40, 47–50, 54–62 even	pp. 535–538 Exs. 19, 20–30 even, 35–44, 47–52, 55, 58, 61	pp. 535–538 Exs. 19, 24–31, 38–53*, 56, 59, 62
Review	Day 1	pp. 543–546 Exs. 1–42	pp. 543–546 Exs. 1–42	pp. 543–546 Exs. 1–42
Assess	Day 1	Chapter 8 Test	Chapter 8 Test	Chapter 8 Test
Yearly Pacing		Chapter 8 Total – 12 days	Chapters 1–8 Total – 92 days	Remaining – 68 days

*Challenge Exercises   EP = Extra Practice   SRH = Skills Review Handbook

BLOCK SCHEDULE

DAY 1	DAY 2	DAY 3	DAY 4	DAY 5	DAY 6
8.1	8.2 (CONT.)	8.4	8.5	8.6	REVIEW
pp. 492–494 Exs. 1, 2, 4–18 even, 29–49, 53–58, 61, 64, 67, 73	pp. 498–501 Exs. 31–37, 41–46, 49–53, 55–66	pp. 514–518 Exs. 1, 2, 6–15, 19–49, 51–59, 62–74 even	pp. 523–527 Exs. 1–8, 11–35, 38–46, 52–58 even, 60, 61	pp. 535–538 Exs. 1–6, 10–19, 20–30 even, 32–44, 47–52, 55, 58, 61, 63–66	pp. 543–546 Exs. 1–42
8.2	8.3				ASSESS
pp. 498–501 Exs. 1, 2, 7–28, 38–40	pp. 506–508 Exs. 1, 2, 9–14, 21–27, 28–44 even, 45, 51–57, 60–68 even				Chapter 8 Test
Yearly Pacing	Chapter 8 Total – 6 days	Chapters 1–8 Total – 46 days	Remaining – 34 days		

RESOURCE MANAGER

Chapter Resource Book

CHAPTER SUPPORT

Parents as Partners (Chapter Overview with home involvement exercises and activity)				p. 1	

LESSON SUPPORT	8.1	8.2	8.3	8.4	8.5	8.6
Teaching Guide/Lesson Plan	p. 3	p. 14	p. 25	p. 36	p. 47	p. 62
Activity Masters		p. 16			p. 49	
Technology Activities & Keystrokes				p. 38	p. 50	p. 64
Activity Support Masters	p. 5					
Practice (3 levels)	p. 6	p. 17	p. 27	p. 39	p. 51	p. 66
Study Guide	p. 9	p. 20	p. 30	p. 42	p. 57	p. 72
Catch-Up for Absent Students	p. 11	p. 22	p. 32	p. 44	p. 59	p. 74
Problem Solving/Application	p. 12	p. 23	p. 33	p. 45	p. 60	p. 75
Challenge Practice	p. 13	p. 24	p. 35	p. 46	p. 61	p. 76

REVIEW

Chapter Review Games and Activities	p. 77	Cumulative Practice	p. 79
Project with Rubric	p. 78	Resource Book Answers	A1

Transparencies	8.1	8.2	8.3	8.4	8.5	8.6
Warm-Up/Daily Homework Quiz	✔	✔	✔	✔	✔	✔
Notetaking Guide	✔	✔	✔	✔	✔	✔
Teacher Support					✔	✔
Answer Transparencies	✔	✔	✔	✔	✔	✔

ASSESSMENT BOOK

Quizzes	p. 109	SAT/ACT Chapter Test	p. 120
Chapter Tests (3 levels)	p. 112	Alternative Assessment with Rubric	p. 122
Standardized Chapter Test	p. 118		

TECHNOLOGY

- Easy Planner
- Test and Practice Generator
- Power Presentations
- @HomeTutor
- Activity Generator
- Animated Algebra
- Classzone.com
- eEdition Plus Online
- eWorkbook Plus Online
- Easy Grader Online

ADDITIONAL RESOURCES

- Worked-Out Solution Key
- Notetaking Guide
- Practice Wookbook
- Algebra 1 Toolkit
- Benchmark Tests
- Reteaching and Remediation
- Spanish Study Guide
- Spanish Assessment Book
- Student Resources in Spanish
- Multi-Language Visual Glossary

8 Lesson Practice Level B

LESSON 8.1 Practice B
For use with pages 489–494

Simplify the expression. Write your answer using exponents.

1. $5^4 \cdot 5^8$ 5^{12}
2. $(-4)^7 \cdot (-4)^3$ $(-4)^{10}$
3. $(-10)^5 \cdot (-10)^2$ $(-10)^7$
4. $8^2 \cdot 8^4 \cdot 8$ 8^7
5. $2^5 \cdot 2 \cdot 2^4$ 2^{10}
6. $(3^5)^2$ 3^{10}
7. $(9^3)^7$ 9^{21}
8. $(15^2)^4$ 15^8
9. $[(-4)^5]^9$ $(-4)^{45}$
10. $(13 \cdot 19)^4$ $13^4 \cdot 19^4$
11. $(48 \cdot 27)^6$ $48^6 \cdot 27^6$
12. $(135 \cdot 8)^5$ $135^5 \cdot 8^5$

Simplify the expression.

13. $x^5 \cdot x^2$ x^7
14. $y^3 \cdot y \cdot y^4$ y^8
15. $a^{10} \cdot a^2 \cdot a^6$ a^{18}
16. $(z^5)^5$ z^{25}
17. $(b^7)^2$ b^{14}
18. $[(b+1)^2]^3$ $(b+1)^6$
19. $(-3x)^4$ $81x^4$
20. $-(3x)^4$ $-81x^4$
21. $(2ab)^5$ $32a^5b^5$
22. $(2x^3y)^6$ $64x^{18}y^6$
23. $(3m^7)^4 \cdot m^3$ $81m^{31}$
24. $4p^2 \cdot (3p^5)^2$ $36p^{12}$

Find the missing exponent.

25. $x^6 \cdot x^? = x^{12}$ 6
26. $(x^4)^? = x^{12}$ 3
27. $(3z^7)^3 = 27z^{18}$ 6

28. **Newspaper Circulation** In 1996, the newspaper circulation in the country of Algeria was approximately 10^3 times the newspaper circulation in the country of Mauritania. The newspaper circulation in Mauritania was 10^3. What was the newspaper circulation in Algeria? 10^6 newspapers

29. **Metric System** The metric system has names for very large weights.
   a. One gigaton is 10^2 times the weight of a hectaton. One hectaton is 10^2 ton. Write one gigaton in tons. 10^4 tons
   b. One teraton is 10^9 times the weight of a kiloton. One kiloton is 10^2 ton. Write one teraton in tons. 10^{11} tons
   c. One exaton is 10^6 times the weight of a teraton. Use your answer to part (b) to write one exaton in tons. 10^{17} tons

30. **Wall Mural** You are designing a wall mural that will be composed of squares of different sizes. One of the requirements of your design is that the side length of each square is itself a perfect square.
   a. If you represent the side length of a square as x^2, write an expression for the area of a mural square. x^4 square units
   b. Find the area of a mural square when $x = 5$. 625 square units
   c. Find the area of a mural square when $x = 10$. 10,000 square units

Algebra 1
Chapter 8 Resource Book   7

LESSON 8.2 Practice B
For use with pages 495–501

Simplify the expression. Write your answer using exponents.

1. $\dfrac{6^{14}}{6^8}$ 6^6
2. $\dfrac{14^5}{14^4}$ 14^1
3. $\dfrac{(-5)^7}{(-5)^2}$ $(-5)^5$
4. $\dfrac{12^5 \cdot 12^3}{12^4}$ 12^4
5. $\dfrac{8^{17}}{8^3 \cdot 8^7}$ 8^7
6. $\left(\dfrac{3}{4}\right)^5$ $\dfrac{3^5}{4^5}$
7. $\left(-\dfrac{1}{5}\right)^6$ $\dfrac{(-1)^6}{5^6}$
8. $3^8 \cdot \dfrac{1}{3^1}$ 3^7
9. $\left(\dfrac{1}{4}\right)^5 \cdot 4^{13}$ 4^8

Simplify the expression.

10. $\dfrac{1}{y^9} \cdot y^{15}$ y^6
11. $z^{16} \cdot \dfrac{1}{z^7}$ z^9
12. $\left(\dfrac{a}{b}\right)^8$ $\dfrac{a^8}{b^8}$
13. $\left(-\dfrac{6}{z}\right)^3$ $-\dfrac{216}{z^3}$
14. $\left(\dfrac{a^3}{2b^5}\right)^4$ $\dfrac{a^{12}}{16b^{20}}$
15. $\left(\dfrac{3x^4}{y^6}\right)^5$ $\dfrac{243x^{20}}{y^{30}}$
16. $\left(\dfrac{m^4}{5n^9}\right)^3$ $\dfrac{m^{12}}{125n^{27}}$
17. $\left(\dfrac{3x^7}{2y^{12}}\right)^4$ $\dfrac{81x^{28}}{16y^{48}}$
18. $\left(\dfrac{2m^5}{3n^9}\right)^5$ $\dfrac{32m^{25}}{243n^{45}}$

19. **Area** The area of New Zealand is 104,454 square miles and the area of Saint Kitts and Nevis, islands in the Caribbean Sea, is 104 square miles. Use order of magnitude to estimate how many times greater New Zealand's area is than Saint Kitts and Nevis' area. 10^4

20. **Cell Phone Subscribers** The table below shows the approximate number of cell phone subscribers in selected countries in 2001.

Country	Algeria	Dominican Republic	Poland	Solomon Islands
Number of subscribers	10^5	10^6	10^7	10^3

   a. How many times greater is the number of cell phone subscribers in Poland than in the Solomon Islands? 10^4
   b. How many times greater is the number of cell phone subscribers in the Dominican Republic than in the Solomon Islands? 10^3

21. **Glass Vase** You are taking a glass-blowing class and have created a vase in the shape of a sphere. The vase will have a hole in the top so you can put flowers in it and it will sit on a stand. The radius of your vase is $\dfrac{21}{2}$ inches. Use the formula $V = \dfrac{4}{3}\pi r^3$ to write an expression for the volume of your vase. $\dfrac{3087\pi}{2}$ in.^{3}

18   Algebra 1
Chapter 8 Resource Book

LESSON 8.3 Practice B
For use with pages 503–508

Evaluate the expression.

1. 3^{-5} $\dfrac{1}{243}$
2. 10^{-3} $\dfrac{1}{1000}$
3. $(-2)^{-6}$ $\dfrac{1}{64}$
4. 5^0 1
5. $(-6)^0$ 1
6. $\left(\dfrac{4}{3}\right)^0$ 1
7. $\left(\dfrac{5}{8}\right)^{-2}$ $\dfrac{64}{25}$
8. $\left(\dfrac{7}{4}\right)^3$ $\dfrac{343}{64}$
9. 0^{-5} undefined
10. $10^{-2} \cdot 10^{-3}$ $\dfrac{1}{100,000}$
11. $4^{-6} \cdot 4^3$ $\dfrac{1}{64}$
12. $\dfrac{1}{5^{-4}}$ 625

Simplify the expression. Write your answer using only positive exponents.

13. x^{-7} $\dfrac{1}{x^7}$
14. $6y^{-4}$ $\dfrac{6}{y^4}$
15. $(2b)^{-5}$ $\dfrac{1}{32b^5}$
16. $(-3m)^{-4}$ $\dfrac{1}{81m^4}$
17. a^2b^{-4} $\dfrac{a^2}{b^4}$
18. $3x^{-2}y^{-5}$ $\dfrac{3}{x^2y^5}$
19. $(4x^{-4}y^2)^{-3}$ $\dfrac{x^{12}}{64y^6}$
20. $(8mn^3)^0$ 1
21. $\dfrac{c^{-3}}{d^{-5}}$ $\dfrac{d^5}{c^3}$
22. $\dfrac{x^2}{y^{-4}}$ x^2y^4
23. $\dfrac{x^{-6}}{4y^5}$ $\dfrac{1}{4x^6y^5}$
24. $\dfrac{x^{-6}}{3x^{-3}y^{-7}}$ $\dfrac{x^3y^7}{3}$

25. **Paper** A sheet of 67-pound paper has a thickness of 100^{-1} inch.
   a. Write and evaluate an expression for the total thickness of 5 sheets of 67-pound paper. $\dfrac{1}{20}$ in.
   b. Write and evaluate an expression for the total thickness of 2^3 sheets of 67-pound paper. $\dfrac{2}{25}$ in.

26. **Frogs** A frog egg currently has a radius of 5^{-1} centimeter. Write an expression using positive exponents for the volume of the frog egg. Use the formula for the volume of a sphere $V = \dfrac{4}{3}\pi r^3$. $\dfrac{4\pi}{375}$ cm^3

27. **Metric System** The metric system has names for very small lengths.
   a. One micrometer is 10^3 times the length of one nanometer. One nanometer is 10^{-9} meter. Write one micrometer in meters. 10^{-6} m
   b. One femtometer is 10^3 times the length of one attometer. One attometer is 10^{-18} meter. Write one femtometer in meters. 10^{-15} m
   c. One centimeter is 10^{10} times the length of one picometer. One picometer is 10^{-12} meter. Write one centimeter in meters. 10^{-2} m

28   Algebra 1
Chapter 8 Resource Book

LESSON 8.4 Practice B
For use with pages 512–518

Write the number in scientific notation.

1. 10.4 1.04×10^1
2. 6751 6.751×10^3
3. 0.54 5.4×10^{-1}
4. 0.000103 1.03×10^{-4}
5. 415,620 4.1562×10^5
6. 0.08104 8.104×10^{-2}
7. 3,412,000 3.412×10^6
8. 525.5 5.255×10^2
9. 104.25 1.0425×10^2
10. 0.0000456 4.56×10^{-5}
11. 0.000000207 2.07×10^{-7}
12. 23,551 2.3551×10^4

Write the number in standard form.

13. 15.8×10^4 158,000
14. 3.21×10^8 321,000,000
15. 450.21×10^7 4,502,100,000
16. 8.1045×10^5 810,450
17. 17.22×10^6 17,220,000
18. 1.012×10^2 101.2
19. 8.12×10^{-4} 0.000812
20. 4.014×10^{-7} 0.0000004014
21. 8.1025×10^{-3} 0.0081025
22. 3.12056×10^{-9} 0.00000000312056
23. 1.211×10^{-2} 0.01211
24. 7.00135×10^{-5} 0.0000700135

Order the numbers from least to greatest.

25. 1.3759×10^4; 14,205; 9.287×10^3; 3.0214×10^4 9.287×10^3; 1.3759×10^4; 14,205; 3.0214×10^4
26. 0.16; 2.5×10^{-3}; 1.04×10^{-3}; 0.0985 1.04×10^{-3}; 2.5×10^{-3}; 0.0985; 0.16
27. 8.79×10^2; 1146; 1.0085×10^3; 1023 8.79×10^2; 1.0085×10^3; 1023; 1146
28. 1.2×10^{-5}; 0.001023; 1.045×10^{-3}; 0.01036 1.2×10^{-5}; 0.001023; 1.045×10^{-3}; 0.01036

Evaluate the expression. Write your answer in scientific notation.

29. $(6 \times 10^8)(5 \times 10^{-2})$ 3×10^7
30. $\dfrac{4.5 \times 10^{-5}}{9 \times 10^{-2}}$ 5×10^{-4}
31. $(2 \times 10^{-5})^5$ 3.2×10^{-24}

32. **Pixels** The images on a computer screen are made up of more than 5000 pixels, or dots, per square inch. How many pixels are on a computer screen that measures 108 square inches? Write your answer in scientific notation. 5.4×10^5 pixels

33. **Oregon** Oregon has an area of approximately 2.52×10^5 square kilometers. In 2000, the population of Oregon was approximately 3.42×10^6 people. How many people were there per square kilometer in Oregon in 2000? about 13.57 people/km^2

34. **Uranus' Moons** The table below shows the masses in kilograms of some of Uranus' moons.

Moon	Miranda	Titania	Ariel	Oberon	Umbriel
Mass (kg)	6.6×10^{19}	3.52×10^{21}	13.5×10^{20}	30.1×10^{20}	11.7×10^{20}

   a. Write the moons in order of largest mass to smallest mass. Titania, Oberon, Ariel, Umbriel, Miranda
   b. How many times larger is the moon of largest mass than the moon of smallest mass? about 53

40   Algebra 1
Chapter 8 Resource Book

486C

Practice B
For use with pages 520–527

3. domain: all real numbers; range: all positive real numbers
4. domain: all real numbers; range: all positive real numbers
5. domain: all real numbers; range: all positive real numbers

Write a rule for the function.

1.

x	−2	−1	0	1	2
y	$\frac{1}{121}$	$\frac{1}{11}$	1	11	121

$y = 11^x$

2.

x	−1	0	1	2	3
y	$\frac{1}{8}$	$\frac{1}{4}$	$\frac{1}{2}$	1	2

$y = 0.25(2)^x$

Graph the function and identify its domain and range.

3. $y = 12^x$

4. $y = (1.75)^x$

5. $y = (3.1)^x$

6. $y = \left(\frac{9}{2}\right)^x$ See below.

7. $y = -5^x$ See below.

8. $y = -\left(\frac{3}{2}\right)^x$ See below.

9. $y = 5 \cdot 2^x$ See below.

10. $y = 2 \cdot \left(\frac{4}{3}\right)^x$ See below.

11. $y = -3 \cdot 2^x$ See below.

6. domain: all real numbers; range: all positive real numbers
7. domain: all real numbers; range: all negative real numbers
8. domain: all real numbers; range: all negative real numbers
9. domain: all real numbers; range: all positive real numbers
10. domain: all real numbers; range: all positive real numbers
11. domain: all real numbers; range: all negative real numbers

---

Practice B continued
For use with pages 520–527

Graph the function. Compare the graph with the graph of $y = 6^x$.

12. $y = 2 \cdot 6^x$ vertical stretch

13. $y = -6^x$ reflection in x-axis

14. $y = \frac{1}{2} \cdot 6^x$ vertical shrink

15. $y = -3 \cdot 6^x$ See below.

16. $y = -\frac{1}{4} \cdot 6^x$ See below.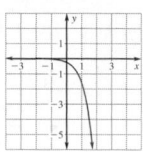

17. $y = -\frac{3}{2} \cdot 6^x$ See below.

18. **Investments** You deposit $500 in a savings account that earns 2.5% interest compounded yearly. Find the balance in the account after the given amounts of time.

 a. 1 year $512.50
 b. 5 years $565.70
 c. 20 years $819.31

19. **College Tuition** From 1995 to 2005, the tuition at a college increased by about 7% per year. Use the graph to write an exponential growth function that models the tuition over time. $y = 8000(1.07)^t$

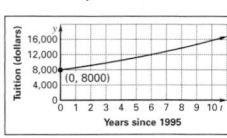

20. **Profit** A business had $10,000 profit in 2000. Then the profit increased by 8% each year for the next 10 years.

 a. Write a function that models the profit in dollars over time. $y = 10,000(1.08)^t$
 b. Use the function to predict the profit in 2009. $19,990.05

15. vertical stretch and reflection in x-axis
16. vertical shrink and reflection in x-axis
17. vertical stretch and reflection in x-axis

Practice B
For use with pages 531–538

3. domain: all real numbers; range: all positive real numbers
4. domain: all real numbers; range: all positive real numbers
5. domain: all real numbers; range: all positive real numbers

Tell whether the table represents an exponential function. If so, write a rule for the function.

1.

x	−2	−1	0	1	2
y	25	5	1	$\frac{1}{5}$	$\frac{1}{25}$

yes; $y = \left(\frac{1}{5}\right)^x$

2.

x	−1	0	1	2	3
y	1	4	7	10	13

no

Graph the function and identify its domain and range.

3. $y = \left(\frac{1}{12}\right)^x$

4. $y = \left(\frac{7}{8}\right)^x$

5. $y = \left(\frac{8}{9}\right)^x$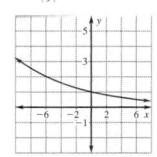

6. $y = -\left(\frac{1}{8}\right)^x$ See below.

7. $y = 2 \cdot \left(\frac{1}{5}\right)^x$ See below.

8. $y = -2 \cdot \left(\frac{2}{3}\right)^x$ See below.

9. $y = 2 \cdot (0.25)^x$ See below.

10. $y = -0.5 \cdot (0.3)^x$ See below.

11. $y = -0.2 \cdot (0.2)^x$ See below.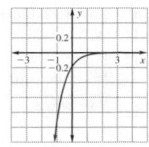

6. domain: all real numbers; range: all negative real numbers
7. domain: all real numbers; range: all positive real numbers
8. domain: all real numbers; range: all negative real numbers
9. domain: all real numbers; range: all positive real numbers
10. domain: all real numbers; range: all negative real numbers
11. domain: all real numbers; range: all negative real numbers

---

Practice B continued
For use with pages 531–538

Graph the function. Compare the graph with the graph of $y = \left(\frac{1}{8}\right)^x$.

12. $y = 2 \cdot \left(\frac{1}{8}\right)^x$ vertical stretch

13. $y = -\left(\frac{1}{8}\right)^x$ reflection in x-axis

14. $y = \frac{1}{4} \cdot \left(\frac{1}{8}\right)^x$ vertical shrink

Tell whether the graph represents exponential growth or exponential decay. Then write a rule for the function.

15.

16.

17.

exponential decay; $y = 3(0.75)^x$ exponential decay; $y = 2(0.7)^x$ exponential growth; $y = 4(2)^x$

18. **Computer Value** You buy a computer for $3000. It depreciates at the rate of 20% per year. Find the value of the computer for the given year.

 a. 1 year $2400
 b. 3 years $1536
 c. 5 years $983.04

19. **Unemployment Rate** In 2000, the unemployment rate of a city decreased by approximately 2.1% each month. In January, the unemployment rate was 7%.

 a. Use the graph at the right to write a function that models the unemployment rate of the city over time.
 b. What was the unemployment rate in December? about 5.4%   **19. a.** $y = 7(0.979)^t$

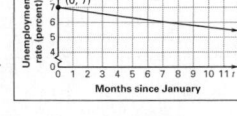

20. **Indoor Water Park** An indoor water park had a declining attendance from 2000 to 2005. The attendance in 2000 was 18,000. Each year for the next 5 years, the attendance decreased by 5.5%.

 a. Write a function that models the attendance since 2000. $y = 18,000(0.945)^t$
 b. What was the attendance in 2005? about 13,565 people

486D

CHAPTER 8 Quiz 1
For use after Lessons 8.1–8.2

Simplify the expression. Write your answer using exponents.

1. $8^2 \cdot 8^3$

2. $(-3)^4(-3)^2$

3. $(6^3)^5$

4. $[(-2)^2]^5$

5. $(16 \cdot 7)^4$

6. $4^3 \cdot 4 \cdot 4^5$

7. $\dfrac{9^{12}}{9^5}$

8. $\dfrac{2^7 \cdot 2^8}{2^3}$

Simplify the expression.

9. $x^3 \cdot x^7$

10. $-(x^7)^2$

11. $(x^2)^4(3x^5)$

12. $(3x^3)^2(2x)^3$

13. $\dfrac{1}{x^2} \cdot x^{17}$

14. $\left(-\dfrac{x^5}{2}\right)^4$

Answers

1. 8^5

2. $(-3)^6$

3. 6^{15}

4. $(-2)^{10}$

5. $16^4 \cdot 7^4$

6. 4^9

7. 9^7

8. 2^{12}

9. x^{10}

10. $-x^{14}$

11. $3x^{13}$

12. $72x^9$

13. x^{15}

14. $\dfrac{x^{20}}{16}$

CHAPTER 8 Quiz 2
For use after Lessons 8.3–8.4

Simplify the expression. Write your answer using only positive exponents.

1. $(8x)^3 \cdot 8^{-4}$

2. $2x^{-5} \cdot y^{-3}$

3. $(4x^4y^{-3})^{-2}$

4. $\dfrac{1}{(3x)^{-2}}$

Write the number in standard form.

5. 9.3×10^5

6. 7.04×10^4

7. 5.62×10^{-3}

8. 4.209×10^{-6}

9. The distance from Earth to the sun is approximately 93 million miles. Write this distance in scientific notation.

Answers

1. $\dfrac{x^3}{8}$

2. $\dfrac{2}{x^5y^3}$

3. $\dfrac{y^6}{16x^8}$

4. $9x^2$

5. $930,000$

6. $70,400$

7. 0.00562

8. 0.000004209

9. 9.3×10^7

CHAPTER 8 Quiz 3
For use after Lessons 8.5–8.6

Graph the function.

1. $y = 4$

2. $y = \left(\dfrac{1}{4}\right)^x$

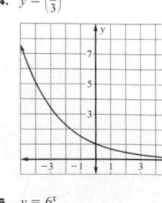

3. $y = 4 \cdot 2^x$

4. $y = \left(\dfrac{2}{3}\right)^x$

5. $y = 2 \cdot 4^x$

6. $y = 6^x$

7. A family purchased a house for $80,000. Each year the value of the house increases by 5%. Write a function that models the value of the house over time. Then find the value of the house after 6 years. Round your answer to the nearest dollar.

Answers

1. See left.

2. See left.

3. See left.

4. See left.

5. See left.

6. See left.

7. $y = 80,000(1.05)^x$;

$\$107,208$

CHAPTER 8 Chapter Test
For use after Chapter 8

Simplify the expression. Write your answer using exponents.

1. $(-7)^9(-7)^2$

2. $(5^3)^8$

3. $\dfrac{12^2 \cdot 12^4}{12^3}$

In Exercises 4 and 5, use the table.

Unit	tera	giga	mega	kilo	hecto	deka
Meters	10^{12}	10^9	10^6	10^3	10^2	10^1

4. How many hectometers are there in 1 gigameter?

5. How many kilometers are there in 1 terameter?

Simplify the expression.

6. $x^4 \cdot x$

7. $(9pq)^2$

8. $(-5m^6)^2 \cdot m^3$

9. $\dfrac{1}{y} \cdot y^{11}$

10. $\left(-\dfrac{1}{t}\right)^5$

11. $\left(\dfrac{a^8}{2b}\right)^4$

12. Write and simplify an expression for the area of the triangle.

6x⁴

Simplify the expression. Write your answer using only positive exponents.

13. $2w^{-7}$

14. $(5g)^{-3}$

15. $\dfrac{1}{8c^{-10}d^{-6}}$

Complete the statement using <, >, or =.

16. 9.27×10^{-4} __?__ 0.00927

17. $527,000,000$ __?__ 5.27×10^8

Evaluate the expression. Write your answer in scientific notation.

18. $(4 \times 10^8)^3$

19. $(4 \times 10^{13})(5 \times 10^{-9})$

20. $\dfrac{9.3 \times 10^{12}}{3.1 \times 10^{-3}}$

Answers

1. $(-7)^{11}$

2. 5^{24}

3. 12^3

4. 10^7

5. 10^9

6. x^5

7. $81p^2q^2$

8. $25m^{15}$

9. y^{10}

10. $-\dfrac{1}{t^5}$

11. $\dfrac{a^{32}}{16b^4}$

12. $A = \dfrac{1}{2}x^2(6x^4) = 3x^6$

square units

13. $\dfrac{2}{w^7}$

14. $\dfrac{1}{125g^3}$

15. $\dfrac{d^6}{8c^{10}}$

16. $<$

17. $=$

18. 6.4×10^{25}

19. 2×10^5

20. 3×10^{15}

21. In a recent year, 6.5×10^8 metric tons of wheat were produced in the world. One metric ton is equivalent to 1000 kilograms. A grain of wheat weighs about 0.000008 kilogram. Find the number of grains of wheat that were produced in the world.

Write a rule for the function.

22.

x	−2	−1	0	1	2
y	$\frac{1}{8}$	$\frac{1}{2}$	2	8	32

23.

x	−2	−1	0	1	2
y	24	12	6	3	$\frac{3}{2}$

In Exercises 24–26, use the following information.

A house was bought 20 years ago for $160,000. Due to inflation, its value has increased about 5% each year.

24. Write a function that models the value of the home over time.

25. Identify the initial value, the growth factor, and the growth rate.

26. What is the home worth today?

27. Graph the function $y = -5\left(\frac{1}{3}\right)^x$ and compare it to the graph of $y = \left(\frac{1}{3}\right)^x$. Then identify its domain and range.

Tell whether the graph represents exponential growth or exponential decay. Then write a rule for the function.

28.

(1, 12)
(0, 8)

29.

(1, 3.6)
(0, 4)

Answers

21. 8.125×10^{16}

22. $y = 2 \cdot 4^x$

23. $y = 6 \cdot \left(\frac{1}{2}\right)^x$

24. $y = 160,000(1.05)^t$

25. $160,000; 1.05; 0.05

26. $424,528

27. See left.

The graph is a vertical stretch and reflection in the x-axis of the graph of $y = \left(\frac{1}{3}\right)^x$; The domain is all real numbers and the range is all negative real numbers.

28. exponential growth; $y = 8 \cdot (1.5)^x$

29. exponential decay; $y = 4 \cdot (0.9)^x$

Multiple Choice

1. Which expression is equivalent to $(-2)^8$? B
- Ⓐ $(-2)^2(-2)^4$
- Ⓑ $(-2)(-2)^7$
- Ⓒ $[(-2)^4]^4$
- Ⓓ $[(-2)^5]^3$

2. Which expression is equivalent to $16x^{15}$? A
- Ⓐ $(4x^6)^2 \cdot x^3$
- Ⓑ $2x^5 \cdot 8x^3$
- Ⓒ $2x^5 \cdot (2x)^3$
- Ⓓ $(2x^3)^5$

3. Which expression is equivalent to $(-2a)(-4a^2b^3c)^2(-5a^4b^3c^6)^2$? D
- Ⓐ $-40a^{13}b^{12}c^{14}$
- Ⓑ $800a^{11}b^{10}c^{11}$
- Ⓒ $400a^{11}b^{10}c^{10}$
- Ⓓ $-800a^{13}b^{12}c^{14}$

4. Which expression is equivalent to 14^6? B
- Ⓐ $\frac{14^4}{14^2}$
- Ⓑ $\frac{(14^5)^3}{14^9}$
- Ⓒ $\frac{14^{12}}{14^2}$
- Ⓓ $\left(\frac{14^{11}}{14^5}\right)^3$

5. Which expression is equivalent to $\left(\frac{4x^4}{2x^3}\right)^3$? C
- Ⓐ $2x$
- Ⓑ $8x$
- Ⓒ $8x^3$
- Ⓓ $16x^{21}$

6. Which value of x makes the equation $\frac{ax \cdot a^8}{a^3} = a^6$ true? B
- Ⓐ $x = 0$
- Ⓑ $x = 1$
- Ⓒ $x = 2$
- Ⓓ $x = 3$

7. Which expression simplifies to $3x^5$? A
- Ⓐ $\frac{3}{x^{-5}}$
- Ⓑ $3x^{-5}$
- Ⓒ $\frac{1}{3x^{-5}}$
- Ⓓ $\left(\frac{1}{3x}\right)^{-5}$

8. Which expression is equivalent to $(-5 \cdot 2^2 \cdot 2^0)^{-2}$? D
- Ⓐ -80
- Ⓑ -40
- Ⓒ $-\frac{1}{40}$
- Ⓓ $-\frac{1}{400}$

9. Which of the following equations is *not* true? C
- Ⓐ $\frac{m^{-1}}{p^{-1}} = \frac{p}{m}$
- Ⓑ $\frac{2}{(5p)^{-2}} = 50p^2$
- Ⓒ $\left(\frac{p^2}{3p}\right)^{-1} = \frac{3p^2}{p}$
- Ⓓ $m^{-1} + p^{-1} = \frac{1}{m} + \frac{1}{p}$

10. Which number represents 65,006,000 in scientific notation? B
- Ⓐ 6.5006×10^{-7}
- Ⓑ 6.5006×10^7
- Ⓒ 65.006×10^{-6}
- Ⓓ 65.006×10^6

11. Which number represents 0.00007605 in scientific notation? A
- Ⓐ 7.605×10^{-5}
- Ⓑ 7.605×10^5
- Ⓒ 0.7605×10^{-4}
- Ⓓ 0.7605×10^4

12. Which number represents 8.205×10^{-4} in standard form? B
- Ⓐ 0.00008205
- Ⓑ 0.0008205
- Ⓒ $82,050$
- Ⓓ $82,050,000$

13. Which number represents 5.4289×10^{-3} in standard form? B
- Ⓐ 0.00054289
- Ⓑ 0.0054289
- Ⓒ $54,289$
- Ⓓ 5428.9

14. Which number is the value of $\frac{1.728 \times 10^6}{5.4 \times 10^8}$? C
- Ⓐ 3.2×10^3
- Ⓑ 0.32×10^{-1}
- Ⓒ 3.2×10^{-3}
- Ⓓ 3.2×10^{-2}

---

15. Which expression is written in scientific notation and equivalent to $(7.2 \times 10^{-4})(2.3 \times 10^6)$? D
- Ⓐ 16.56×10^2
- Ⓑ 16.56×10^{-2}
- Ⓒ 1.656×10
- Ⓓ 1.656×10^3

16. Which rule applies to the table below? C

x	−2	−1	0	1	2
y	1	2	4	8	16

- Ⓐ $y = 2 \cdot 4^x$
- Ⓑ $y = 2 \cdot x^4$
- Ⓒ $y = 4 \cdot 2^x$
- Ⓓ $y = 4 \cdot x^2$

17. The graph of which function is shown? A

(−1, 3)
$\left(1, \frac{1}{3}\right)$

- Ⓐ $y = \left(\frac{1}{3}\right)^x$
- Ⓑ $y = 3^x$
- Ⓒ $y = 2 \cdot \left(\frac{1}{3}\right)^x$
- Ⓓ $y = 2 \cdot 3^x$

Gridded Answer

18. The distance from the Sun to Earth is 1.5×10^8 kilometers. Mercury is 5.8×10^7 kilometers from the Sun. What is the difference between these distances in millions of kilometers?

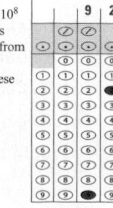

Short Response

19. The graph shows the value of a car over time. **a.** $y = 20,000 \cdot \left(\frac{37}{40}\right)^x$

(0, 20,000)
(1, 18,500)

a. Write an equation for the function whose graph is shown. See above.

b. At what rate is the car losing value? *Explain.* The car is losing value at a rate of $\frac{37}{40}$ each year.

Extended Response

20. You are saving money to buy a car. You put $2500 in a savings account that pays 4% annual interest compounded yearly.

a. Write a function that models the amount of the money in the account over time. $A = 2500(1 + 0.04)^t$

b. Graph the function. See below.

c. Suppose you want to buy a car for $3,000. Will there be enough money in the account after 5 years? *Explain.* Yes. After 5 years there will be approximately $3041.63 in the account. This is about $41.63 more than what he needs to buy the car.

20. b.

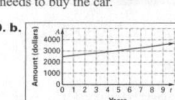

Journal **1.** Describe the difference between numbers that have positive exponents versus negative exponents when written in scientific notation. Give an example of each type of number and include both the scientific notation and the standard form for each.

Multi-Step Problem **2.** Let $L = 2^x$ be the function representing the number of layers of paper that has been folded in half x times.

a. Determine the value of L for $x = 0$. Explain the meaning of your answer.

b. Complete the table.

x	0	1	2	3	4
L	?	?	?	?	?

c. What pattern do you notice in the values in part (b)?

d. How many folds are needed to have 128 layers of paper?

e. Consider the function $T = (0.1)2^{x-4}$ where T is the thickness (in centimeters) of a piece of paper folded in half x times. Use properties of exponents to show that an equivalent function is $T = (0.00625)2^x$.

f. Graph the function $T = (0.00625)2^x$.

g. Does this graph represent exponential growth or exponential decay?

h. How thick is a piece of paper that has been folded 10 times?

1. Complete answers should include: an explanation that numbers larger than 10 will have positive exponents when written in scientific notation; an explanation that numbers between 0 and 1 will have negative exponents when written in scientific notation; an example of each case in both scientific notation and standard form.

2. a. $L = 1$; A paper folded 0 times will have 1 layer.

b.

x	0	1	2	3	4
L	1	2	4	8	16

c. Each additional fold results in twice as many layers. **d.** 7 folds

e. $T = (0.1)2^{x-4} = (0.1)\frac{2^x}{2^4} = \left(\frac{0.1}{2^4}\right)2^x = (0.00625)2^x$

f.

g. exponential growth **h.** 6.4 cm

486F

Main Ideas

In Chapter 8, students learn and use properties of exponents involving products and quotients. They learn how to apply the product of powers property, the power of a power property, the power of a product property, the quotient of powers property, and the power of a quotient property. Students also use zero and negative exponents. Students learn how to read, write, and compute with numbers in scientific notation. Students also learn how to graph and write rules for exponential functions, including exponential growth and exponential decay functions.

Prerequisite Skills

- Evaluating expressions involving exponents
- Ordering numbers
- Writing percents as decimals
- Writing function rules

Additional resources for reviewing prerequisite skills are:

- Skills Review Handbook, pp. 909–937
- @HomeTutor

8 Exponents and Exponential Functions

8.1 **Apply Exponent Properties Involving Products**

8.2 **Apply Exponent Properties Involving Quotients**

8.3 **Define and Use Zero and Negative Exponents**

8.4 **Use Scientific Notation**

8.5 **Write and Graph Exponential Growth Functions**

8.6 **Write and Graph Exponential Decay Functions**

Before

In previous chapters and courses, you learned the following skills, which you'll use in Chapter 8: evaluating expressions involving exponents, ordering numbers, writing percents as decimals, and writing function rules.

Prerequisite Skills

VOCABULARY CHECK

1. Identify the exponent and the base in the expression 13^8. **exponent: 8, base: 13**

2. Copy and complete: An expression that represents repeated multiplication of the same factor is called a(n) $\underline{\ ?\ }$. **power**

SKILLS CHECK

Evaluate the expression. *(Review p. 2 for 8.1–8.3.)*

3. x^2 when $x = 10$ 4. a^3 when $a = 3$ 5. r^2 when $r = \frac{5}{6}$ 6. z^3 when $z = \frac{1}{2}$
   100   **27**   **$\frac{25}{36}$**   **$\frac{1}{8}$**

Order the numbers from least to greatest. *(Review p. 909 for 8.4.)*

7. 6.12, 6.2, 6.01   8. 0.073, 0.101, 0.0098
   6.01, 6.12, 6.2   **0.0098, 0.073, 0.101**

Write the percent as a decimal. *(Review p. 916 for 8.5 and 8.6.)*

9. 4% **0.04**   10. 0.5% **0.005**   11. 13.8% **0.138**   12. 145% **1.45**

13. Write a rule for the function.
    (Review p. 35 for 8.5 and 8.6.)
    $f(x) = x + 2$

Input	0	1	4	6	10
Output	2	3	6	8	12

@HomeTutor Prerequisite skills practice at classzone.com

486

Chapter 8 Resource Book
- Teaching Guide/Lesson Plan (pp. 3, 14, 25, 36, 47, 62)
- Project with Rubric (p. 78)

Assessment and Intervention
- Assessment Book (pp. 109–123)
- Benchmark Tests
- Reteaching and Remediation Book

Interactive Technology
- Easy Planner
- Power Presentations CD-ROM
- Activity Generator CD-ROM
- Animated Algebra
- Test Generator CD-ROM
- Online Quizzes
- eWorkbook
- eEdition
- @HomeTutor

Resources for English Learners
- Quick Reference for English Learners
- Spanish Study Guide
- Multi-Language Visual Glossary
- Student Resources in Spanish

In Chapter 8, you will apply the big ideas listed below and reviewed in the Chapter Summary on page 542. You will also use the key vocabulary listed below.

Big Ideas

(1) Applying properties of exponents to simplify expressions
(2) Working with numbers in scientific notation
(3) Writing and graphing exponential functions

KEY VOCABULARY
- order of magnitude, *p. 491*
- scientific notation, *p. 512*
- exponential function, *p. 520*
- exponential growth, *p. 522*
- compound interest, *p. 523*
- exponential decay, *p. 533*

You can use exponents to explore exponential growth and decay. For example, you can write an exponential function to find the value of a collector car over time.

Animated Algebra

The animation illustrated below for Example 4 on page 522 helps you answer this question: If you know the growth rate of the value of a collector car over time, can you predict what the car will sell for at an auction?

Find the value of the collector car over time.

The owner of a 1953 Hudson Hornet sold the car at an auction.

Initial value of the car (a) =

Growth rate (r) =

Model: $C = a(1 + r)^t$

Click on the boxes to enter the initial value and growth rate.

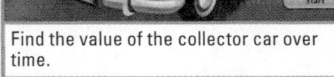

Animated Algebra at classzone.com

Other animations for Chapter 8: pages 491, 505, 512, 534, and 536

Algebra 1 Toolkit
- Reading Strategies for Chapter 8, pp. 23–24
- Differentiated Instruction Notes, pp. 69–72
- English Learners Notes, pp. 111–112
- Inclusion Notes, pp. 143–144
- Teaching Strategies with Sample Worksheets, pp. 155–178
- Using Technology in the Classroom, pp. 179–184
- Tips for New Teachers, pp. 199–200
- Math Background Notes, pp. 225–226
- Pre-AP Strategies and Copymasters, pp. 292–293, 400–419
- Teacher Survival Activities, pp. 569–570, 595–596
- Bulletin Board Idea, p. 614
- Teacher Tool Transparencies, following p. 620

① PLAN AND PREPARE

Explore the Concept

- Students will find products of powers and powers of powers.
- This activity leads into the study of using the product of powers property in Example 1 and the power of a power property in Example 2 in Lesson 8.1.

Materials

Each student will need:
- Activity Support Master (*Chapter 8 Resource Book*, p. 5)

Recommended Time

Work activity: 10 min

Discuss results: 5 min

Grouping

Students should work individually.

② TEACH

Tips for Success

In Explore 2, help students understand how a power of a power is different from a product of powers. For example, contrast the expression $(5^3)^2$, which means $5^3 \cdot 5^3$, with the expression $5^3 \cdot 5^2$.

Key Discovery

When you find a product of powers for powers that have the same base, you add the exponents. When you find a power of a power, you multiply the exponents.

③ ASSESS AND RETEACH

Does $(2x)^3 = 2x^3$? *Explain* your reasoning. **No. The expression $(2x)^3$ means $2x \cdot 2x \cdot 2x$, or $8x^3$.**

Explore 2: Step 1. $[(-6) \cdot (-6)] \cdot [(-6) \cdot (-6)] \cdot [(-6) \cdot (-6)] \cdot [(-6) \cdot (-6)]$

MATERIALS · paper and pencil

QUESTION How can you find a product of powers and a power of a power?

EXPLORE 1 Find products of powers

STEP 1 *Copy and complete* Copy and complete the table.

Expression	Expression as repeated multiplication	Number of factors	Simplified expression
$7^4 \cdot 7^5$	$(7 \cdot 7 \cdot 7 \cdot 7) \cdot (7 \cdot 7 \cdot 7 \cdot 7 \cdot 7)$	9	7^9
$(-4)^2 \cdot (-4)^3$	$[(-4) \cdot (-4)] \cdot [(-4) \cdot (-4) \cdot (-4)]$	? 5	? $(-4)^5$
$x^1 \cdot x^5$	?$(x) \cdot (x \cdot x \cdot x \cdot x \cdot x)$	? 6	? x^6

STEP 2 *Analyze results* Find a pattern that relates the exponents of the factors in the first column and the exponent of the expression in the last column. **See margin.**

EXPLORE 2 Find powers of powers

STEP 1 *Copy and complete* Copy and complete the table.

Expression	Expanded expression	Expression as repeated multiplication	Number of factors	Simplified expression
$(5^3)^2$	$(5^3) \cdot (5^3)$	$(5 \cdot 5 \cdot 5) \cdot (5 \cdot 5 \cdot 5)$	6	5^6
$[(-6)^2]^4$	$[(-6)^2] \cdot [(-6)^2] \cdot [(-6)^2] \cdot [(-6)^2]$	? **See margin.**	? 8	? $(-6)^8$
$(a^3)^3$	?	?	? 9	? a^9
	$(a^3) \cdot (a^3) \cdot (a^3)$	$(a \cdot a \cdot a) \cdot (a \cdot a \cdot a) \cdot (a \cdot a \cdot a)$		

STEP 2 *Analyze results* Find a pattern that relates the exponents of the expression in the first column and the exponent of the expression in the last column. *Sample answer:* The exponent of the simplified expression is equal to the product of the exponents in the first column.

DRAW CONCLUSIONS Use your observations to complete these exercises

Simplify the expression. Write your answer using exponents.

1. $5^2 \cdot 5^3$ $\mathbf{5^5}$
2. $(-6)^1 \cdot (-6)^4$ $\mathbf{(-6)^5}$
3. $m^6 \cdot m^4$ $\mathbf{m^{10}}$
4. $(10^3)^3$ $\mathbf{10^9}$
5. $[(-2)^3]^4$ $\mathbf{(-2)^{12}}$
6. $(c^2)^6$ $\mathbf{c^{12}}$

In Exercises 7 and 8, copy and complete the statement.

7. If a is a real number and m and n are positive integers, then $a^m \cdot a^n = \underline{\ ?\ }$. $\mathbf{a^{m+n}}$

8. If a is a real number and m and n are positive integers, then $(a^m)^n = \underline{\ ?\ }$. $\mathbf{a^{mn}}$

488 Chapter 8 Exponents and Exponential Functions

8.1 Apply Exponent Properties Involving Products

Before	You evaluated exponential expressions.
Now	You will use properties of exponents involving products.
Why?	So you can evaluate agricultural data, as in Example 5.

Key Vocabulary
- order of magnitude
- power, *p. 3*
- exponent, *p. 3*
- base, *p. 3*

Notice what happens when you multiply two powers that have the same base.

$$a^2 \cdot a^3 = \overbrace{(a \cdot a) \cdot (a \cdot a \cdot a)}^{\text{5 factors}} = a^5 = a^{2+3}$$

2 factors 3 factors

The example above suggests the following property of exponents, known as the product of powers property.

KEY CONCEPT   *For Your Notebook*

Product of Powers Property

Let a be a real number, and let m and n be positive integers.

Words To multiply powers having the same base, add the exponents.

Algebra $a^m \cdot a^n = a^{m+n}$ **Example** $5^6 \cdot 5^3 = 5^{6+3} = 5^9$

SIMPLIFY EXPRESSIONS
When simplifying powers with numerical bases only, write your answers using exponents, as in parts (a), (b), and (c).

EXAMPLE 1 Use the product of powers property

a. $7^3 \cdot 7^5 = 7^{3+5} = 7^8$

b. $9 \cdot 9^8 \cdot 9^2 = 9^1 \cdot 9^8 \cdot 9^2$
$$= 9^{1+8+2}$$
$$= 9^{11}$$

c. $(-5)(-5)^6 = (-5)^1 \cdot (-5)^6$
$$= (-5)^{1+6}$$
$$= (-5)^7$$

d. $x^4 \cdot x^3 = x^{4+3} = x^7$

✓ **GUIDED PRACTICE**   for Example 1

Simplify the expression.

1. $3^2 \cdot 3^7$ **3^9**
2. $5 \cdot 5^9$ **5^{10}**
3. $(-7)^2(-7)$ **$(-7)^3$**
4. $x^2 \cdot x^6 \cdot x$ **x^9**

---

❶ PLAN AND PREPARE

Warm-Up Exercises
📑 **Transparency Available**
Evaluate the expression.

1. x^4 when $x = 3$ **81**
2. a^2 when $a = -6$ **36**
3. m^3 when $m = -5$ **-125**
4. A food storage container is in the shape of a cube. What is the volume of the container if one side is 4 inches long? Use $V = s^3$. **64 in.³**

Notetaking Guide
📑 **Transparency Available**
Promotes interactive learning and notetaking skills, pp. 167–169.

Pacing
Basic: 1 day
Average: 1 day
Advanced: 1 day
Block: 0.5 block with 8.2
• See *Teaching Guide/Lesson Plan*.

❷ FOCUS AND MOTIVATE

Essential Question
Big Idea 1, p. 487
How do you use properties of exponents involving products?
Tell students they will learn how to answer this question by applying properties of exponents to simplify expressions.

NCTM STANDARDS
Standard 1: Understand meanings of operations
Standard 2: Understand patterns

Resource Planning Guide

Chapter Resource Book
- Teaching Guide/Lesson Plan (pp. 3–4)
- Practice levels A, B, C (pp. 6–8)
- Study Guide (pp. 9–10)
- Catch-up for Absent Students (p. 11)
- Application (p. 12)
- Challenge (p. 13)

Workbooks
- Notetaking Guide (pp. 167–169)
- Practice Workbook (pp. 119–120)

Teaching Options
- **Power Presentations CD-ROM** provides dynamic electronic teaching resources for the classroom.
- **Activity Generator CD-ROM** provides editable activities for all ability levels.

Interactive Technology
- Easy Planner
- Power Presentations CD-ROM
- Activity Generator CD-ROM
- Animated Algebra
- Test Generator CD-ROM
- Online Quiz
- eWorkbook
- eEdition
- @HomeTutor

Resources for English Learners
- Quick Reference for English Learners
- Spanish Study Guide
- Multi-Language Visual Glossary
- Student Resources in Spanish

See also the *Algebra 1 Toolkit* for more strategies for meeting individual needs.

489

POWER OF A POWER Notice what happens when you raise a power to a power.

$$(a^2)^3 = a^2 \cdot a^2 \cdot a^2 = (a \cdot a) \cdot (a \cdot a) \cdot (a \cdot a) = a^6 = a^{2 \cdot 3}$$

The example above suggests the following property of exponents, known as the power of a power property.

> **KEY CONCEPT**   *For Your Notebook*
>
> **Power of a Power Property**
>
> Let a be a real number, and let m and n be positive integers.
>
> **Words** To find a power of a power, multiply exponents.
>
> **Algebra** $(a^m)^n = a^{mn}$
>
> **Example** $(3^4)^2 = 3^{4 \cdot 2} = 3^8$

EXAMPLE 2   Use the power of a power property

AVOID ERRORS

In part (d), notice that you can write $[(y + 2)^6]^2$ as $(y + 2)^{12}$, but you cannot write $(y + 2)^{12}$ as $y^{12} + 2^{12}$.

a. $(2^5)^3 = 2^{5 \cdot 3}$

     $= 2^{15}$

c. $(x^2)^4 = x^{2 \cdot 4}$

     $= x^8$

b. $[(-6)^2]^5 = (-6)^{2 \cdot 5}$

     $= (-6)^{10}$

d. $[(y + 2)^6]^2 = (y + 2)^{6 \cdot 2}$

     $= (y + 2)^{12}$

✓ **GUIDED PRACTICE**   for Example 2

Simplify the expression.

5. $(4^2)^7$ 4^{14}

6. $[(-2)^4]^5$ $(-2)^{20}$

7. $(n^3)^6$ n^{18}

8. $[(m + 1)^5]^4$ $(m + 1)^{20}$

POWER OF A PRODUCT Notice what happens when you raise a product to a power.

$$(ab)^3 = (ab) \cdot (ab) \cdot (ab) = (a \cdot a \cdot a) \cdot (b \cdot b \cdot b) = a^3 b^3$$

The example above suggests the following property of exponents, known as the power of a product property.

> **KEY CONCEPT**   *For Your Notebook*
>
> **Power of a Product Property**
>
> Let a and b be real numbers, and let m be a positive integer.
>
> **Words** To find a power of a product, find the power of each factor and multiply.
>
> **Algebra** $(ab)^m = a^m b^m$
>
> **Example** $(23 \cdot 17)^5 = 23^5 \cdot 17^5$

> ### *Differentiated Instruction*
>
> **Inclusion** Students may have difficulty interpreting the symbols used in mathematics (such as exponents), and in memorizing complex rules. At first, it may be more instructive to allow them to write out terms like a^3 as *aaa*, rather than memorize rules like the power of a power property. Later, they should have no need of this particular technique.
>
> See also the *Algebra 1 Toolkit* for more strategies.

When simplifying
powers with numerical
and variable bases, be
sure to evaluate the
numerical power, as in
parts (b), (c), and (d).

EXAMPLE 3 **Use the power of a product property**

a. $(24 \cdot 13)^8 = 24^8 \cdot 13^8$

b. $(9xy)^2 = (9 \cdot x \cdot y)^2 = 9^2 \cdot x^2 \cdot y^2 = 81x^2y^2$

c. $(-4z)^2 = (-4 \cdot z)^2 = (-4)^2 \cdot z^2 = 16z^2$

d. $-(4z)^2 = -(4 \cdot z)^2 = -(4^2 \cdot z^2) = -16z^2$

EXAMPLE 4 **Use all three properties**

Simplify $(2x^3)^2 \cdot x^4$.

$(2x^3)^2 \cdot x^4 = 2^2 \cdot (x^3)^2 \cdot x^4$ Power of a product property

$\qquad\qquad = 4 \cdot x^6 \cdot x^4$ Power of a power property

$\qquad\qquad = 4x^{10}$ Product of powers property

Animated **Algebra** at classzone.com

ORDER OF MAGNITUDE The **order of magnitude** of a quantity can be defined
as the power of 10 nearest the quantity. Order of magnitude can be used to
estimate or perform rough calculations. For instance, there are about 91,000
species of insects in the United States. The power of 10 closest to 91,000 is 10^5,
or 100,000. So, there are about 10^5 species of insects in the United States.

EXAMPLE 5 **Solve a real-world problem**

BEES In 2003 the U.S. Department of Agriculture (USDA)
collected data on about 10^3 honeybee colonies. There
are about 10^4 bees in an average colony during honey
production season. About how many bees were in the
USDA study?

Solution

To find the total number of bees, find the product
of the number of colonies, 10^3, and the number of
bees per colony, 10^4.

$\qquad 10^3 \cdot 10^4 = 10^{3+4} = 10^7$

▶ The USDA studied about 10^7, or 10,000,000, bees.

✓ **GUIDED PRACTICE**   for Examples 3, 4, and 5

Simplify the expression.

9. $42^2 \cdot 12^2$

11. $6561m^{12}n^4$

9. $(42 \cdot 12)^2$ **10.** $(-3n)^2$ $9n^2$ **11.** $(9m^3n)^4$ **12.** $5 \cdot (5x^2)^4$ $3125x^8$

13. WHAT IF? In Example 5, 10^2 honeybee colonies in the study were located in
Idaho. About how many bees were studied in Idaho?   **about 1,000,000 bees**

8.1 EXERCISES

HOMEWORK KEY

○ = **WORKED-OUT SOLUTIONS**
on p. WS1 for Exs. 31 and 55

★ = **STANDARDIZED TEST PRACTICE**
Exs. 2, 40, 41, 50, and 58

◆ = **MULTIPLE REPRESENTATIONS**
Ex. 55

④ PRACTICE AND APPLY

Assignment Guide

📄 Answer Transparencies available for all exercises

Basic:
Day 1: pp. 492–494
Exs. 1, 2, 3–15 odd, 19–39 odd, 40–42, 52–57, 60–74 even

Average:
Day 1: pp. 492–494
Exs. 1, 2, 4–18 even, 29–49, 53–58, 61, 64, 67, 73

Advanced:
Day 1: pp. 492–494
Exs. 1, 2, 8–18 even, 31–38, 40–51*, 54–59*, 62, 65, 68, 74

Block:
pp. 492–494
Exs. 1, 2, 4–18 even, 29–49, 53–58, 61, 64, 67, 73 (with 8.2)

Differentiated Instruction

See *Algebra 1 Best Practices Toolkit* for suggestions on addressing the needs of a diverse classroom.

Homework Check

For a quick check of student understanding of key concepts, go over the following exercises:

Basic: 6, 11, 15, 27, 52
Average: 8, 12, 16, 33, 53
Advanced: 10, 14, 18, 36, 54

Extra Practice

• Student Edition, p. 945
• Chapter 8 Resource Book:
Practice levels A, B, C, pp. 6–8

Practice Worksheet

An easily-readable reduced practice page (with answers) for this lesson can be found on p. 486C.

SKILL PRACTICE

Ⓐ 1. **VOCABULARY** Copy and complete: The __?__ of the quantity 93,534,004 people is the power of 10 nearest the quantity, or 10^8 people. **order of magnitude**

2. ★ **WRITING** *Explain* when and how to use the product of powers property.
When powers have the same base, their product is the base raised to the sum of the exponents.

EXAMPLES 1, 2, 3, and 4 on pp. 489–491 for Exs. 3–41

SIMPLIFYING EXPRESSIONS Simplify the expression. Write your answer using exponents.

3. $4^2 \cdot 4^6$ **4^8**   4. $8^5 \cdot 8^2$ **8^7**   5. $3^3 \cdot 3$ **3^4**   6. $9 \cdot 9^5$ **9^6**

7. $(-7)^4(-7)^5$ **$(-7)^9$**   8. $(-6)^6(-6)$ **$(-6)^7$**   9. $2^4 \cdot 2^9 \cdot 2$ **2^{14}**   10. $(-3)^2(-3)^{11}(-3)$ **$(-3)^{14}$**

11. $(3^5)^2$ **3^{10}**   12. $(7^4)^3$ **7^{12}**   13. $[(-5)^3]^4$ **$(-5)^{12}$**   14. $[(-8)^9]^2$ **$(-8)^{18}$**

15. $(15 \cdot 29)^3$ **$15^3 \cdot 29^3$**   16. $(17 \cdot 16)^4$ **$17^4 \cdot 16^4$**   17. $(132 \cdot 9)^6$ **$132^6 \cdot 9^6$**   18. $((-14) \cdot 22)^5$ **$(-14)^5 \cdot 22^5$**

SIMPLIFYING EXPRESSIONS Simplify the expression.

19. $x^4 \cdot x^2$ **x^6**   20. $y^9 \cdot y$ **y^{10}**   21. $z^2 \cdot z \cdot z^3$ **z^6**   22. $a^4 \cdot a^3 \cdot a^{10}$ **a^{17}**

23. $(x^5)^2$ **x^{10}**   24. $(y^4)^6$ **y^{24}**   25. $[(b-2)^2]^6$ **$(b-2)^{12}$**   26. $[(d+9)^7]^3$ **$(d+9)^{21}$**

27. $(-5x)^2$ **$25x^2$**   28. $-(5x)^2$ **$-25x^2$**   29. $(7xy)^2$ **$49x^2y^2$**   30. $(5pq)^3$ **$125p^3q^3$**

⊙31. $(-10x^6)^2 \cdot x^2$ **$100x^{14}$**   32. $(-8m^4)^2 \cdot m^3$ **$64m^{11}$**   33. $6d^2 \cdot (2d^5)^4$ **$96d^{22}$**   34. $(-20x^3)^2(-x^7)$ **$-400x^{13}$**

35. $-(2p^4)^3(-1.5p^7)$ **$12p^{19}$**   36. $\left(\frac{1}{2}y^5\right)^3(2y^2)^4$ **$2y^{23}$**   37. $(3x^5)^3(2x^7)^2$ **$108x^{29}$**   38. $(-10n)^2(-4n^3)^3$ **$-6400n^{11}$**

39. **ERROR ANALYSIS** *Describe* and correct the error in simplifying $c \cdot c^4 \cdot c^5$.
Sample answer: The exponents should be added, not multiplied; $c^1 \cdot c^4 \cdot c^5 = c^{1+4+5} = c^{10}$.

$$c \cdot c^4 \cdot c^5 = c^1 \cdot c^4 \cdot c^5$$
$$= c^{1 \cdot 4 \cdot 5}$$
$$= c^{20}$$

Ⓑ 40. ★ **MULTIPLE CHOICE** Which expression is equivalent to $(-9)^6$? **B**

   Ⓐ $(-9)^2(-9)^3$ Ⓑ $(-9)(-9)^5$ Ⓒ $[(-9)^4]^2$ Ⓓ $[(-9)^3]^3$

41. ★ **MULTIPLE CHOICE** Which expression is equivalent to $36x^{12}$? **D**

   Ⓐ $(6x^3)^4$ Ⓑ $12x^4 \cdot 3x^3$ Ⓒ $3x^3 \cdot (4x^3)^3$ Ⓓ $(6x^5)^2 \cdot x^2$

SIMPLIFYING EXPRESSIONS Find the missing exponent.

42. $x^4 \cdot x^? = x^5$ **1**   43. $(y^8)^? = y^{16}$ **2**   44. $(2z^?)^3 = 8z^{15}$ **5**   45. $(3a^3)^? \cdot 2a^3 = 18a^9$ **2**

46. **POPULATION** The population of New York City in 2000 was 8,008,278. What was the order of magnitude of the population of New York City? **10^7 people**

SIMPLIFYING EXPRESSIONS Simplify the expression.

47. $(-3x^2y)^3(11x^3y^5)^2$ 48. $-(-xy^2z^3)^5(x^4yz)^2$ 49. $(-2s)(-5r^3st)^3(-2r^4st^7)^2$
     $-3267x^{12}y^{13}$ **$x^{13}y^{12}z^{17}$**   **$1000r^{17}s^6t^{17}$**

50. ★ **OPEN-ENDED** Write three expressions involving products of powers, powers of powers, or powers of products that are equivalent to $12x^8$

$$\textbf{Sample answer: } 3x^2 \cdot 4x^6, \; 12(x^4)^2, \; 3(2x^4)^2$$

51. **CHALLENGE** Show that when a and b are real numbers and n is a positive integer, $(ab)^n = a^n b^n$. **See margin.**

PROBLEM SOLVING

EXAMPLE 5 [A]
on p. 491
for Exs. 52–56

52. **ICE CREAM COMPOSITION** There are about 954,930 air bubbles in 1 cubic centimeter of ice cream. There are about 946 cubic centimeters in 1 quart. Use order of magnitude to find the approximate number of air bubbles in 1 quart of ice cream. **10^9 air bubbles**

@*HomeTutor* for problem solving help at classzone.com

53. **ASTRONOMY** The order of magnitude of the radius of our solar system is 10^{13} meters. The order of magnitude of the radius of the visible universe is 10^{13} times as great. Find the approximate radius of the visible universe. **10^{26} m**

@*HomeTutor* for problem solving help at classzone.com

54. **COASTAL LANDSLIDE** There are about 1 billion grains of sand in 1 cubic foot of sand. In 1995 a stretch of beach at Sleeping Bear Dunes National Lakeshore in Michigan slid into Lake Michigan. Scientists believe that around 35 million cubic feet of sand fell into the lake. Use order of magnitude to find about how many grains of sand slid into the lake. **10^{16} grains of sand**

(55.) ◆ **MULTIPLE REPRESENTATIONS** There are about 10^{23} atoms of gold in 1 ounce of gold.

a. **Making a Table** Copy and complete the table by finding the number of atoms of gold for the given amounts of gold (in ounces).

Gold (ounces)	10	100	1000	10,000	100,000
Number of atoms	?	?	?	?	?

10^{24} 10^{25} 10^{26} 10^{27} 10^{28}

b. **Writing an Expression** A particular mine in California extracted about 96,000 ounces of gold in 1 year. Use order of magnitude to write an expression you can use to find the approximate number of atoms of gold extracted in the mine that year. Simplify the expression. Verify your answer using the table. **$10^5 \cdot 10^{23}$; 10^{28} atoms**

56. **MULTI-STEP PROBLEM** A microscope has two lenses, the objective lens and the eyepiece, that work together to magnify an object. The total magnification of the microscope is the product of the magnification of the objective lens and the magnification of the eyepiece.

Eyepiece

Objective lens

a. Your microscope's objective lens magnifies an object 10^2 times, and the eyepiece magnifies an object 10 times. What is the total magnification of your microscope? **10^3 times**

b. You magnify an object that is 10^2 nanometers long. How long is the magnified image? **10^5 nanometers**

493

Vocabulary

Exercise 2 Encourage students to write out explanations and give specific examples for all three properties covered in this lesson.

Avoiding Common Errors

Exercises 3–38 Watch for students who fail to account for numerical or variable bases that have an exponent of 1. Remind these students that a base without an exponent is raised to the power of 1 and that they need to add 1 or multiply by 1 when simplifying expressions. Also, some students may overlook the numerical factor when simplifying powers with numerical and variable bases. Remind these students to evaluate the numerical power first.

Study Strategy

Exercise 54 You may want to suggest that students write the standard form of 1 billion and 35 million before they determine the order of magnitude. Students may want to review order of magnitude and estimation on page 491 before they begin this exercise.

51. *Sample answer:* $(ab)^n = (ab) \cdot (ab) \cdot \ldots \cdot (ab)$ so that there are n total terms (ab). By the commutative property, the n a's can be grouped as a repeated multiplication equal to a^n and the n b's can be grouped as a repeated multiplication equal to b^n. $(ab)^n$ is equal to the product of these two groups, or $a^n \cdot b^n$.

Daily Homework Quiz

 Transparency Available

Simplify the expression. Write your answer using exponents.

1. $14^5 \cdot 14^2$ **14^7**

2. $[(-8)^4]^3$ **$(-8)^{12}$**

Simplify the expression.

3. $[(m-3)^6]^4$ **$(m-3)^{24}$**

4. $-(2s)^3$ **$-8s^3$**

5. A website had about 102 hits after a week. After a year, it had about 103 times the number of hits of the first week. About how many hits did it have at the end of the year? **about 10,000 hits**

🔗 **Online Quiz**

Available at **classzone.com**

Diagnosis/Remediation

• Practice A, B, C in Chapter 8 Resource Book, pp. 6–8
• Study Guide in Chapter 8 Resource Book, pp. 9–10
• Practice Workbook, pp. 119–120
• @HomeTutor

Challenge

Additional challenge is available in the Chapter 8 Resource Book, p. 13.

494

B 57. **VOLUME OF THE SUN** The radius of the sun is about 695,000,000 meters. The formula for the volume of a sphere, such as the sun, is $V = \frac{4}{3}\pi r^3$.

Because the order of magnitude of $\frac{4}{3}\pi$ is 1, it does not contribute to the formula in a significant way. So, you can find the order of magnitude of the volume of the sun by cubing its radius. Find the order of magnitude of the volume of the sun. **10^{27}**

58. ★ **EXTENDED RESPONSE** Rock salt can be mined from large deposits of salt called salt domes. A particular salt dome is roughly cylindrical in shape. The order of magnitude of the radius of the salt dome is 10^3 feet. The order of magnitude of the height of the salt dome is about 10 times that of its radius. The formula for the volume of a cylinder is $V = \pi r^2 h$.

Salt

a. **Calculate** What is the order of magnitude of the height of the salt dome? **10^4**

b. **Calculate** What is the order of magnitude of the volume of the salt dome? **10^{10}**

58c. Increases the volume by 10^8. *Sample answer:* Since the radius is squared in the formula for volume, multiplying the radius by 10 would raise the volume by a factor of 10 · 10, or 10^2.

c. **Explain** The order of magnitude of the radius of a salt dome can be 10 times the radius of the salt dome described in this exercise. What effect does multiplying the order of magnitude of the radius of the salt dome by 10 have on the volume of the salt dome? *Explain.*

C 59. **CHALLENGE** Your school is conducting a poll that has two parts, one part that has 13 questions and a second part that has 10 questions. Students can answer the questions in either part with "agree" or "disagree." What power of 2 represents the number of ways there are to answer the questions in the first part of the poll? What power of 2 represents the number of ways there are to answer the questions in the second part of the poll? What power of 2 represents the number of ways there are to answer all of the questions on the poll? **2^{13} ways; 2^{10} ways; 2^{23} ways**

MIXED REVIEW

PREVIEW

Prepare for Lesson 8.2 in Exs. 60–65.

Find the product. *(p. 88)*

60. $\left(\frac{1}{2}\right)\left(-\frac{4}{5}\right)$ **$-\frac{2}{5}$**

61. $\left(-\frac{2}{3}\right)\left(\frac{7}{4}\right)$ **$1\frac{1}{6}$**

62. $\left(-\frac{6}{5}\right)\left(-\frac{3}{8}\right)$ **$\frac{9}{20}$**

Evaluate the expression for the given value of the variable. *(p. 2)*

63. x^4 when $x = 3$ **81**

64. x^2 when $x = -2.2$ **4.84**

65. x^3 when $x = \frac{3}{4}$ **$\frac{27}{64}$**

Graph the equation or inequality. **66–74. See margin.**

66. $y = -4$ *(p. 215)*

67. $3x - y = 15$ *(p. 225)*

68. $7x - 6y = 84$ *(p. 225)*

69. $y = -5x + 3$ *(p. 244)*

70. $y = \frac{1}{2}x - 5$ *(p. 244)*

71. $x \geq -3$ *(p. 405)*

72. $y < 1.5$ *(p. 405)*

73. $x + y \leq 7$ *(p. 405)*

74. $2x - y < 3$ *(p. 405)*

66–74. See Additional Answers beginning on p. AA1.

8.2 Apply Exponent Properties Involving Quotients

Before	You used properties of exponents involving products.
Now	You will use properties of exponents involving quotients.
Why?	So you can compare magnitudes of earthquakes, as in Ex. 53.

Key Vocabulary
• power, p. 3
• exponent, p. 3
• base, p. 3

Notice what happens when you divide powers with the same base.

$$\frac{a^5}{a^3} = \frac{a \cdot a \cdot \cancel{a} \cdot \cancel{a} \cdot \cancel{a}}{\cancel{a} \cdot \cancel{a} \cdot \cancel{a}} = a \cdot a = a^2 = a^{5-3}$$

The example above suggests the following property of exponents, known as the quotient of powers property.

> **KEY CONCEPT**   *For Your Notebook*
>
> **Quotient of Powers Property**
>
> Let a be a nonzero real number, and let m and n be positive integers such that $m > n$.
>
> **Words** To divide powers having the same base, subtract exponents.
>
> **Algebra** $\dfrac{a^m}{a^n} = a^{m-n}$, $a \neq 0$ **Example** $\dfrac{4^7}{4^2} = 4^{7-2} = 4^5$

EXAMPLE 1   Use the quotient of powers property

SIMPLIFY EXPRESSIONS
When simplifying powers with numerical bases only, write your answers using exponents, as in parts (a), (b), and (c).

a. $\dfrac{8^{10}}{8^4} = 8^{10-4}$

      $= 8^6$

b. $\dfrac{(-3)^9}{(-3)^3} = (-3)^{9-3}$

      $= (-3)^6$

c. $\dfrac{5^4 \cdot 5^8}{5^7} = \dfrac{5^{12}}{5^7}$

      $= 5^{12-7}$

      $= 5^5$

d. $\dfrac{1}{x^4} \cdot x^6 = \dfrac{x^6}{x^4}$

      $= x^{6-4}$

      $= x^2$

✓ **GUIDED PRACTICE**   for Example 1

Simplify the expression.

1. $\dfrac{6^{11}}{6^5}$ 6^6 **2.** $\dfrac{(-4)^9}{(-4)^2}$ $(-4)^7$ **3.** $\dfrac{9^4 \cdot 9^3}{9^2}$ 9^5 **4.** $\dfrac{1}{y^5} \cdot y^8$ y^3

8.2   Apply Exponent Properties Involving Quotients   **495**

---

① PLAN AND PREPARE

Warm-Up Exercises
📑 Transparency Available
Evaluate the expression.

1. q^3 when $q = \dfrac{1}{4}$ $\dfrac{1}{64}$

2. c^2 when $c = \dfrac{3}{5}$ $\dfrac{9}{25}$

3. A magazine had a circulation of 9364 in 2001. The circulation was about 125 times greater in 2006. Use order of magnitude to estimate the circulation in 2006.   **about 10^6 or 1,000,000**

Notetaking Guide
📑 Transparency Available
Promotes interactive learning and notetaking skills, pp. 170–172.

Pacing
Basic: 2 days
Average: 2 days
Advanced: 2 days
Block: 0.5 block with 8.1
• See *Teaching Guide/Lesson Plan*.

② FOCUS AND MOTIVATE

Essential Question
Big Idea 1, p. 487

How do you use properties of exponents involving quotients? Tell students they will learn how to answer this question by simplifying expressions that involve division of powers.

NCTM STANDARDS
Standard 1: Understand how operations are related

Standard 2: Understand patterns

Resource Planning Guide

Chapter Resource Book
• Teaching Guide/Lesson Plan (pp. 14–15)
• Activity Master (p. 16)
• Practice levels A, B, C (pp. 17–19)
• Study Guide (pp. 20–21)
• Catch-up for Absent Students (p. 22)
• Application (p. 23)
• Challenge (p. 24)

Workbooks
• Notetaking Guide (pp. 170–172)
• Practice Workbook (pp. 121–122)

Teaching Options
• **Power Presentations CD-ROM** provides dynamic electronic teaching resources for the classroom.
• **Activity Generator CD-ROM** provides editable activities for all ability levels.

Interactive Technology
• Easy Planner
• Power Presentations CD-ROM
• Activity Generator CD-ROM
• Animated Algebra
• Test Generator CD-ROM
• Online Quiz
• eWorkbook
• eEdition
• @HomeTutor

Resources for English Learners
• Quick Reference for English Learners
• Spanish Study Guide
• Multi-Language Visual Glossary
• Student Resources in Spanish

See also the *Algebra 1 Toolkit* for more strategies for meeting individual needs.

495

POWER OF A QUOTIENT Notice what happens when you raise a quotient to a power.

$$\left(\frac{a}{b}\right)^4 = \frac{a}{b} \cdot \frac{a}{b} \cdot \frac{a}{b} \cdot \frac{a}{b} = \frac{a \cdot a \cdot a \cdot a}{b \cdot b \cdot b \cdot b} = \frac{a^4}{b^4}$$

The example above suggests the following property of exponents, known as the power of a quotient property.

KEY CONCEPT   *For Your Notebook*

Power of a Quotient Property

Let a and b be real numbers with $b \neq 0$, and let m be a positive integer.

Words To find a power of a quotient, find the power of the numerator and the power of the denominator and divide.

Algebra $\left(\dfrac{a}{b}\right)^m = \dfrac{a^m}{b^m}$, $b \neq 0$

Example $\left(\dfrac{3}{2}\right)^7 = \dfrac{3^7}{2^7}$

EXAMPLE 2   Use the power of a quotient property

SIMPLIFY EXPRESSIONS
When simplifying powers with numerical *and* variable bases, evaluate the numerical power, as in part (b).

a. $\left(\dfrac{x}{y}\right)^3 = \dfrac{x^3}{y^3}$

b. $\left(-\dfrac{7}{x}\right)^2 = \left(\dfrac{-7}{x}\right)^2 = \dfrac{(-7)^2}{x^2} = \dfrac{49}{x^2}$

EXAMPLE 3   Use properties of exponents

a. $\left(\dfrac{4x^2}{5y}\right)^3 = \dfrac{(4x^2)^3}{(5y)^3}$ Power of a quotient property

$= \dfrac{4^3 \cdot (x^2)^3}{5^3 y^3}$ Power of a product property

$= \dfrac{64x^6}{125y^3}$ Power of a power property

b. $\left(\dfrac{a^2}{b}\right)^5 \cdot \dfrac{1}{2a^2} = \dfrac{(a^2)^5}{b^5} \cdot \dfrac{1}{2a^2}$ Power of a quotient property

$= \dfrac{a^{10}}{b^5} \cdot \dfrac{1}{2a^2}$ Power of a power property

$= \dfrac{a^{10}}{2a^2 b^5}$ Multiply fractions.

$= \dfrac{a^8}{2b^5}$ Quotient of powers property

Simplify the expression.

5. $\left(\dfrac{a}{b}\right)^2$ $\dfrac{a^2}{b^2}$

6. $\left(-\dfrac{5}{y}\right)^3$ $-\dfrac{125}{y^3}$

7. $\left(\dfrac{x^2}{4y}\right)^2$ $\dfrac{x^4}{16y^2}$

8. $\left(\dfrac{2s}{3t}\right)^3 \cdot \left(\dfrac{t^5}{16}\right)$ $\dfrac{s^3t^2}{54}$

EXAMPLE 4   **Solve a multi-step problem**

FRACTAL TREE To construct what is known as a *fractal tree*, begin with a single segment (the trunk) that is 1 unit long, as in Step 0. Add three shorter segments that are $\frac{1}{2}$ unit long to form the first set of branches, as in Step 1.

Then continue adding sets of successively shorter branches so that each new set of branches is half the length of the previous set, as in Steps 2 and 3.

Step 0   Step 1   Step 2   Step 3

a. Make a table showing the number of new branches at each step for Steps 1–4. Write the number of new branches as a power of 3.

b. How many times greater is the number of new branches added at Step 5 than the number of new branches added at Step 2?

Solution

a.

Step	Number of new branches
1	$3 = 3^1$
2	$9 = 3^2$
3	$27 = 3^3$
4	$81 = 3^4$

b. The number of new branches added at Step 5 is 3^5. The number of new branches added at Step 2 is 3^2. So, the number of new branches added at Step 5 is $\dfrac{3^5}{3^2} = 3^3 = 27$ times the number of new branches added at Step 2.

---

9. FRACTAL TREE In Example 4, add a column to the table for the length of the new branches at each step. Write the lengths of the new branches as powers of $\frac{1}{2}$. What is the length of a new branch added at Step 9?   **See margin.**

Extra Example 3

Use properties of exponents.

a. $\left(\dfrac{3a^4}{5b}\right)^3$ $\dfrac{27a^{12}}{125b^3}$

b. $\left(\dfrac{x^3}{y}\right)^7 \cdot \dfrac{1}{3x^8}$ $\dfrac{x^{13}}{3y^7}$

Extra Example 4

Construct a fractal tree that begins with a V-shaped segment, with each side of the V-shape 1 unit long. Then add a V-shaped segment on each end with each side $\frac{1}{2}$ unit long.

Continue adding sets of successively shorter branches so that each new set of branches is half the length of the previous set.

Step 0   Step 1

Step 2   Step 3

a. Make a table showing the number of new branches at each step for Steps 1–3. Write the number of new branches as a power of 2.

Step	New branches
1	$4 = 2^2$
2	$8 = 2^3$
3	$16 = 2^4$

b. How many times as great is the number of new branches at Step 6 as the number of new branches at Step 2? **16**

Key Question to Ask for Example 4

• Why do you write the number of new branches as a power of 3? **Since you add 3 segments to each set of successive branches, the steps are 3, then 3 × 3, then 3 × 3 × 3, and so on.**

9.

Step	Number of new branches	Length of new branches
1	$3 = 3^1$	$\dfrac{1}{2} = \left(\dfrac{1}{2}\right)^1$
2	$9 = 3^2$	$\dfrac{1}{4} = \left(\dfrac{1}{2}\right)^2$
3	$27 = 3^3$	$\dfrac{1}{8} = \left(\dfrac{1}{2}\right)^3$
4	$81 = 3^4$	$\dfrac{1}{16} = \left(\dfrac{1}{2}\right)^4$

$\left(\dfrac{1}{2}\right)^9 = \dfrac{1}{512}$ unit

EXAMPLE 5 Solve a real-world problem

ASTRONOMY The luminosity (in watts) of a star is the total amount of energy emitted from the star per unit of time. The order of magnitude of the luminosity of the sun is 10^{26} watts. The star Canopus is one of the brightest stars in the sky. The order of magnitude of the luminosity of Canopus is 10^{30} watts. How many times more luminous is Canopus than the sun?

Canopus

Solution

$$\frac{\text{Luminosity of Canopus (watts)}}{\text{Luminosity of the sun (watts)}} = \frac{10^{30}}{10^{26}} = 10^{30-26} = 10^4$$

▶ Canopus is about 10^4 times as luminous as the sun.

 GUIDED PRACTICE for Example 5

10. **WHAT IF?** Sirius is considered the brightest star in the sky. Sirius is less luminous than Canopus, but Sirius appears to be brighter because it is much closer to Earth. The order of magnitude of the luminosity of Sirius is 10^{28} watts. How many times more luminous is Canopus than Sirius? **10^2**

8.2 EXERCISES

HOMEWORK KEY

○ = **WORKED-OUT SOLUTIONS**
on p. WS1 for Exs. 33 and 51

★ = **STANDARDIZED TEST PRACTICE**
Exs. 2, 19, 37, 46, and 54

◆ = **MULTIPLE REPRESENTATIONS**
Ex. 49

SKILL PRACTICE

A

1. **VOCABULARY** Copy and complete: In the power 4^3, 4 is the __?__ and 3 is the __?__. **base, exponent**

2. ★ **WRITING** *Explain* when and how to use the quotient of powers property. **When powers have the same base, their quotient is the base raised to the difference of the exponents.**

SIMPLIFYING EXPRESSIONS Simplify the expression. Write your answer using exponents.

EXAMPLES 1 and 2
on pp. 495–496
for Exs. 3–20

3. $\frac{5^6}{5^2}$ **5^4**

4. $\frac{2^{11}}{2^6}$ **2^5**

5. $\frac{3^9}{3^5}$ **3^4**

6. $\frac{(-6)^8}{(-6)^5}$ **$(-6)^3$**

7. $\frac{(-4)^7}{(-4)^4}$ **$(-4)^3$**

8. $\frac{(-12)^9}{(-12)^3}$ **$(-12)^6$**

9. $\frac{10^5 \cdot 10^5}{10^4}$ **10^6**

10. $\frac{6^7 \cdot 6^4}{6^6}$ **6^5**

11. $\left(\frac{1}{3}\right)^5$ **$\frac{1}{3^5}$**

12. $\left(\frac{3}{2}\right)^4$ **$\frac{3^4}{2^4}$**

13. $\left(-\frac{5}{4}\right)^4$ **$\frac{5^4}{4^4}$**

14. $\left(-\frac{2}{5}\right)^5$ **$-\frac{2^5}{5^5}$**

15. $7^9 \cdot \frac{1}{7^2}$ **7^7**

16. $\frac{1}{9^5} \cdot 9^{11}$ **9^6**

17. $\left(\frac{1}{3}\right)^4 \cdot 3^{12}$ **3^8**

18. $4^9 \cdot \left(-\frac{1}{4}\right)^5$ **-4^4**

498 Chapter 8 Exponents and Exponential Functions

19. ★ **MULTIPLE CHOICE** Which expression is equivalent to 16^6? **C**

   A $\dfrac{16^4}{16^2}$ **B** $\dfrac{16^{12}}{16^2}$ **C** $\left(\dfrac{16^6}{16^3}\right)^2$ **D** $\left(\dfrac{16^9}{16^6}\right)^3$

20. **ERROR ANALYSIS** *Describe* and correct the error in simplifying $\dfrac{9^5 \cdot 9^3}{9^4}$. **See margin.**

$$\dfrac{9^5 \cdot 9^3}{9^4} = \dfrac{9^8}{9^4} = 9^{12} \quad \times$$

EXAMPLES 1, 2, and 3 on pp. 495–496 for Exs. 21–37

SIMPLIFYING EXPRESSIONS Simplify the expression.

21. $\dfrac{1}{y^8} \cdot y^{15}$ y^7 22. $z^8 \cdot \dfrac{1}{z^7}$ z 23. $\left(\dfrac{a}{y}\right)^9$ $\dfrac{a^9}{y^9}$ 24. $\left(\dfrac{j}{k}\right)^{11}$ $\dfrac{j^{11}}{k^{11}}$

25. $\left(\dfrac{p}{q}\right)^4$ $\dfrac{p^4}{q^4}$ 26. $\left(-\dfrac{1}{x}\right)^5$ $-\dfrac{1}{x^5}$ 27. $\left(-\dfrac{4}{x}\right)^3$ $-\dfrac{64}{x^3}$ 28. $\left(-\dfrac{a}{b}\right)^4$ $\dfrac{a^4}{b^4}$

29. $\left(\dfrac{4c}{d^2}\right)^3$ $\dfrac{64c^3}{d^6}$ 30. $\left(\dfrac{a^7}{2b}\right)^5$ $\dfrac{a^{35}}{32b^5}$ 31. $\left(\dfrac{x^2}{3y^3}\right)^2$ $\dfrac{x^4}{9y^6}$ 32. $\left(\dfrac{3x^5}{7y^2}\right)^3$ $\dfrac{27x^{15}}{343y^6}$

33. $\left(\dfrac{3x^3}{2y}\right)^2 \cdot \dfrac{1}{x^2}$ $\dfrac{9x^4}{4y^2}$ 34. $\left(\dfrac{2x^3}{y}\right)^3 \cdot \dfrac{1}{6x^3}$ $\dfrac{4x^6}{3y^3}$ 35. $\dfrac{3}{8m^5} \cdot \left(\dfrac{m^4}{n^2}\right)^3$ $\dfrac{3m^7}{8n^6}$ 36. $\left(-\dfrac{5}{x}\right)^2 \cdot \left(\dfrac{2x^4}{y^3}\right)^2$ $\dfrac{100x^6}{y^6}$

37. ★ **MULTIPLE CHOICE** Which expression is equivalent to $\left(\dfrac{7x^3}{2y^4}\right)^2$? **D**

   A $\dfrac{7x^5}{2y^6}$ **B** $\dfrac{7x^6}{2y^8}$ **C** $\dfrac{49x^5}{4y^6}$ **D** $\dfrac{49x^6}{4y^8}$

SIMPLIFYING EXPRESSIONS Find the missing exponent.

38. $\dfrac{(-8)^7}{(-8)^?} = (-8)^3$ **4**   39. $\dfrac{7^? \cdot 7^2}{7^4} = 7^6$ **8**   40. $\dfrac{1}{p^5} \cdot p^? = p^9$ **14**   41. $\left(\dfrac{2c^3}{d^2}\right)^? = \dfrac{16c^{12}}{d^8}$ **4**

SIMPLIFYING EXPRESSIONS Simplify the expression.

42. $\left(\dfrac{2f^2g^3}{3fg}\right)^4$ $\dfrac{16f^4g^8}{81}$ 43. $\dfrac{2s^3t^3}{st^2} \cdot \dfrac{(3st)^3}{s^2t}$ $54s^3t^3$ 44. $\left(\dfrac{2m^5n}{4m^2}\right)^2 \cdot \left(\dfrac{mn^4}{5n}\right)^2$ $\dfrac{m^8n^8}{100}$ 45. $\left(\dfrac{3x^3y}{x^2}\right)^3 \cdot \left(\dfrac{y^2x^4}{5y}\right)^2$ $\dfrac{27x^{11}y^5}{25}$

46. ★ **OPEN-ENDED** Write three expressions involving quotients that are equivalent to 14^7. **Sample answer:** $\dfrac{14^8}{14}, \dfrac{14^{10}}{14^3}, \dfrac{14^{14}}{14^7}$

47. **REASONING** Name the definition or property that justifies each step to show that $\dfrac{a^m}{a^n} = \dfrac{1}{a^{n-m}}$ for $m < n$.

Let $m < n$.   Given

$$\dfrac{a^m}{a^n} = \dfrac{a^m}{a^n}\left(\dfrac{\frac{1}{a^m}}{\frac{1}{a^m}}\right) \qquad \underline{\quad?\quad} \quad \text{Identity property of multiplication}$$

$$= \dfrac{1}{\frac{a^n}{a^m}} \qquad\qquad\qquad \underline{\quad?\quad} \quad \text{Multiply fractions.}$$

$$= \dfrac{1}{a^{n-m}} \qquad\qquad\qquad \underline{\quad?\quad} \quad \text{Quotient of powers property}$$

48. $x = 8$, $y = -1$. *Sample answer:* Using the quotient of a power property, write two equations for x and y: $x - y = 9$, and $x + 2 - 3y = 13$. Solve the equations.

48. **CHALLENGE** Find the values of x and y if you know that $\dfrac{b^x}{b^y} = b^9$ and $\dfrac{b^x \cdot b^2}{b^{3y}} = b^{13}$. *Explain* how you found your answer.

8.2 Apply Exponent Properties Involving Quotients   **499**

20. *Sample answer:* When using the quotient of powers property, the base is raised to the difference of the exponents, not the sum; $\dfrac{9^8}{9^4} = 9^{(8-4)} = 9^4$.

4 PRACTICE AND APPLY

Assignment Guide

📓 Answer Transparencies available for all exercises

Basic:
Day 1: pp. 498–501
Exs. 1–28
Day 2: pp. 498–501
Exs. 29–39, 49–52, 55–66

Average:
Day 1: pp. 498–501
Exs. 1, 2, 7–28, 38–40
Day 2: pp. 498–501
Exs. 31–37, 41–46, 49–53, 55–66

Advanced:
Day 1: pp. 498–501
Exs. 1, 2, 9–19, 21–28, 38–40, 47, 48*
Day 2: pp. 498–501
Exs. 32–37, 41–46, 49–66*

Block:
pp. 498–501
Exs. 1, 2, 7–28, 38–40 (with 8.1)
pp. 498–501
Exs. 31–37, 41–46, 49–53, 55–66 (with 8.3)

Differentiated Instruction

See *Algebra 1 Best Practices Toolkit* for suggestions on addressing the needs of a diverse classroom.

Homework Check

For a quick check of student understanding of key concepts, go over the following exercises:
Basic: 6, 23, 30, 49, 50
Average: 12, 24, 32, 49, 51
Advanced: 16, 27, 34, 50, 51

Extra Practice

• Student Edition, p. 945
• Chapter 8 Resource Book: Practice levels A, B, C, pp. 17–19

Practice Worksheet

An easily-readable reduced practice page (with answers) for this lesson can be found on p. 486C.

PROBLEM SOLVING

EXAMPLES A
4 and 5
on pp. 497–498
for Exs. 49–51

49. ◆ **MULTIPLE REPRESENTATIONS** Draw a square with side lengths that are 1 unit long. Divide it into four new squares with side lengths that are one half the side length of the original square, as shown in Step 1. Keep dividing the squares into new squares, as shown in Steps 2 and 3.

Step 0   Step 1   Step 2   Step 3

   a. Making a Table Make a table showing the number of new squares and the side length of a new square at each step for Steps 1–4. Write the number of new squares as a power of 4. Write the side length of a new square as a power of $\frac{1}{2}$. **See margin.**

   b. Writing an Expression Write and simplify an expression to find by how many times the number of squares increased from Step 2 to Step 4. $\frac{4^4}{4^2}$; **16 times**

   @**HomeTutor** for problem solving help at classzone.com

50. GROSS DOMESTIC PRODUCT In 2003 the gross domestic product (GDP) for the United States was about 11 trillion dollars, and the order of magnitude of the population of the U.S. was 10^8. Use order of magnitude to find the approximate per capita (per person) GDP? **about 10^5 dollars**

   @**HomeTutor** for problem solving help at classzone.com

51. **SPACE TRAVEL** Alpha Centauri is the closest star system to Earth. Alpha Centauri is about 10^{13} kilometers away from Earth. A spacecraft leaves Earth and travels at an average speed of 10^4 meters per second. About how many years would it take the spacecraft to reach Alpha Centauri?

   about 31,710 yr

B **52. ASTRONOMY** The brightness of one star relative to another star can be measured by comparing the magnitudes of the stars. For every increase in magnitude of 1, the relative brightness is diminished by a factor of 2.512. For instance, a star of magnitude 8 is 2.512 times less bright than a star of magnitude 7.

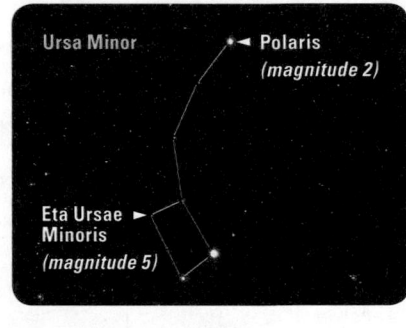

Ursa Minor

Polaris
(magnitude 2)

Eta Ursae ►
Minoris
(magnitude 5)

The constellation Ursa Minor (the Little Dipper) is shown. How many times less bright is Eta Ursae Minoris than Polaris?

   2.512^3 times

53. EARTHQUAKES The energy released by one earthquake relative to another earthquake can be measured by comparing the magnitudes (as determined by the Richter scale) of the earthquakes. For every increase of 1 in magnitude, the energy released is multiplied by a factor of about 31. How many times greater is the energy released by an earthquake of magnitude 7 than the energy released by an earthquake of magnitude 4?

   31^3 times greater

◯ = **WORKED-OUT SOLUTIONS** on p. WS1   ★ = **STANDARDIZED TEST PRACTICE**   ◆ = **MULTIPLE REPRESENTATIONS**

49a.

Step	Number of new squares	Side length of new square
1	$4 = 4^1$	$\frac{1}{2} = \left(\frac{1}{2}\right)^1$
2	$16 = 4^2$	$\frac{1}{4} = \left(\frac{1}{2}\right)^2$
3	$64 = 4^3$	$\frac{1}{8} = \left(\frac{1}{2}\right)^3$
4	$256 = 4^4$	$\frac{1}{16} = \left(\frac{1}{2}\right)^4$

C 54. ★ **EXTENDED RESPONSE** A byte is a unit used to measure computer memory. Other units are based on the number of bytes they represent. The table shows the number of bytes in certain units. For example, from the table you can calculate that 1 terabyte is equivalent to 2^{10} gigabytes.

  a. **Calculate** How many kilobytes are there in 1 terabyte? 2^{30} **kilobytes**

  b. **Calculate** How many megabytes are there in 1 petabyte? 2^{30} **megabytes**

  c. **CHALLENGE** Another unit used to measure computer memory is a bit. There are 8 bits in a byte. *Explain* how you can convert the number of bytes per unit given in the table to the number of bits per unit.

  Multiply the number of bytes in each unit by 8, or 2^3.

Unit	Number of bytes
Kilobyte	2^{10}
Megabyte	2^{20}
Gigabyte	2^{30}
Terabyte	2^{40}
Petabyte	2^{50}

MIXED REVIEW

PREVIEW
Prepare for
Lesson 8.3 in
Exs. 55–60.

Solve the equation. Check your solution. *(p. 134)*

55. $\frac{3}{4}k = 9$ **12**

56. $\frac{2}{5}t = -4$ **−10**

57. $-\frac{2}{3}v = 14$ **−21**

58. $-\frac{5}{2}y = -35$ **14**

59. $-\frac{7}{5}z = \frac{14}{3}$ **$-3\frac{1}{3}$**

60. $-\frac{3}{2}z = -\frac{3}{4}$ **$\frac{1}{2}$**

Write an equation of the line that passes through the given points. *(p. 292)*

61. $(-2, 1), (0, -5)$ **$y = -3x - 5$** 62. $(0, 3), (-4, 1)$ **$y = \frac{1}{2}x + 3$** 63. $(0, -3), (7, -3)$ **$y = -3$**

64. $(4, 3), (5, 6)$ **$y = 3x - 9$** 65. $(4, 1), (-2, 4)$ **$y = -\frac{1}{2}x + 3$** 66. $(-1, -3), (-3, 1)$ **$y = -2x - 5$**

QUIZ *for Lessons 8.1–8.2*

Simplify the expression. Write your answer using exponents.

1. $3^2 \cdot 3^6$ *(p. 489)* **3^8**

2. $(5^4)^3$ *(p. 489)* **5^{12}**

3. $(32 \cdot 14)^7$ *(p. 489)* **$32^7 \cdot 14^7$**

4. $7^2 \cdot 7^6 \cdot 7$ *(p. 489)* **7^9**

5. $(-4)(-4)^9$ *(p. 489)* **$(-4)^{10}$**

6. $\frac{7^{12}}{7^4}$ *(p. 495)* **7^8**

7. $\frac{(-9)^9}{(-9)^7}$ *(p. 495)* **$(-9)^2$**

8. $\frac{3^7 \cdot 3^4}{3^6}$ *(p. 495)* **3^5**

9. $\left(\frac{5}{4}\right)^4$ *(p. 495)* **$\frac{5^4}{4^4}$**

Simplify the expression.

10. $x^2 \cdot x^5$ *(p. 489)* **x^7**

11. $(3x^3)^2$ *(p. 489)* **$9x^6$**

12. $-(7x)^2$ *(p. 489)* **$-49x^2$**

13. $(6x^5)^3 \cdot x$ *(p. 489)* **$216x^{16}$**

14. $(2x^5)^3(7x^7)^2$ *(p. 489)* **$392x^{29}$**

15. $\frac{1}{x^9} \cdot x^{21}$ *(p. 495)* **x^{12}**

16. $\left(-\frac{4}{x}\right)^3$ *(p. 495)* **$-\frac{64}{x^3}$**

17. $\left(\frac{w}{v}\right)^6$ *(p. 495)* **$\frac{w^6}{v^6}$**

18. $\left(\frac{x^3}{4}\right)^2$ *(p. 495)* **$\frac{x^6}{16}$**

19. **MAPLE SYRUP PRODUCTION** In 2001 the order of magnitude of the number of maple syrup taps in Vermont was 10^6. The order of magnitude of the number of gallons of maple syrup produced in Vermont was 10^5. About how many gallons of syrup were produced per tap in Vermont in 2001? *(p. 495)*
   about 10^{-1} gallons per tap

EXTRA PRACTICE for Lesson 8.2, p. 945   **ONLINE QUIZ** at classzone.com   **501**

⑤ ASSESS AND **RETEACH**

Daily Homework Quiz

🗐 **Transparency Available**

1. Simplify $\frac{6^3 \cdot 6^5}{6^4}$ **6^4**

2. Simplify $10^7 \cdot \left(\frac{-1}{10}\right)^4$ **10^3**

3. Simplify $\left(\frac{s^8}{3r}\right)^3$ **$\frac{s^{24}}{27r^3}$**

4. The order of magnitude of the power output of a nuclear-powered aircraft carrier is about 10^6 watts. The order of magnitude of peak power at Hoover Dam is about 10^9 watts. How many times as great is the power output of Hoover Dam as the power output of a nuclear-powered aircraft carrier? **10^3**

 Online Quiz

Available at **classzone.com**

Diagnosis/Remediation

• Practice A, B, C in Chapter 8 Resource Book, pp. 17–19
• Study Guide in Chapter 8 Resource Book, pp. 20–21
• Practice Workbook, pp. 121–122
• @HomeTutor

Challenge

Additional challenge is available in the Chapter 8 Resource Book, p. 24.

Quiz

An easily-readable reduced copy of the quiz (with answers) on Lessons 8.1–8.2 from the Assessment Book can be found on p. 486E.

8.3 Zero and Negative Exponents

MATERIALS · paper and pencil

QUESTION   How can you simplify expressions with zero or negative exponents?

EXPLORE   Evaluate powers with zero and negative exponents

STEP 1 *Find a pattern*

Copy and complete the tables for the powers of 2 and 3.

Exponent, n	Value of 2^n
4	16
3	? **8**
2	? **4**
1	? **2**

Exponent, n	Value of 3^n
4	81
3	? **27**
2	? **9**
1	? **3**

As you read the tables from the *bottom up*, you see that each time the exponent is increased by 1, the value of the power is multiplied by the base. What can you say about the exponents and the values of the powers as you read the table from the *top down*?

STEP 2 *Extend the pattern*

Copy and complete the tables using the pattern you observed in Step 1.

Exponent, n	Power, 2^n
3	8
2	? **4**
1	? **2**
0	? **1**
−1	? $\dfrac{1}{2}$
−2	? $\dfrac{1}{4}$

Exponent, n	Power, 3^n
3	27
2	? **9**
1	? **3**
0	? **1**
−1	? $\dfrac{1}{3}$
−2	? $\dfrac{1}{9}$

DRAW CONCLUSIONS   Use your observations to complete these exercises

1. Find 2^n and 3^n for $n = -3, -4,$ and -5. $2^{-3} = \dfrac{1}{8}, 3^{-3} = \dfrac{1}{27}; 2^{-4} = \dfrac{1}{16}, 3^{-4} = \dfrac{1}{81}; 2^{-5} = \dfrac{1}{32}, 3^{-5} = \dfrac{1}{243}$

2. What appears to be the value of a^0 for any nonzero number a? **1**

3. Write each power in the tables above as a power with a positive exponent. For example, you can write 3^{-1} as $\dfrac{1}{3^1}$. **See margin.**

502   Chapter 8   Exponents and Exponential Functions

3.

Power, 2^n	Exponent
8	2^3
4	2^2
2	2^1
1	2^0
$\dfrac{1}{2}$	$\dfrac{1}{2^1}$
$\dfrac{1}{4}$	$\dfrac{1}{2^2}$

Power, 3^n	Exponent
27	3^3
9	3^2
3	3^1
1	3^0
$\dfrac{1}{3}$	$\dfrac{1}{3^1}$
$\dfrac{1}{9}$	$\dfrac{1}{3^2}$

8.3 Define and Use Zero and Negative Exponents

Before You used properties of exponents to simplify expressions.

Now You will use zero and negative exponents.

Why? So you can compare masses, as in Ex. 52.

Key Vocabulary
• reciprocal, p. 915

In the activity, you saw what happens when you raise a number to a zero or negative exponent. The activity suggests the following definitions.

KEY CONCEPT *For Your Notebook*

Definition of Zero and Negative Exponents

Words	Algebra	Example
a to the zero power is 1.	$a^0 = 1, a \neq 0$	$5^0 = 1$
a^{-n} is the reciprocal of a^n.	$a^{-n} = \dfrac{1}{a^n}, a \neq 0$	$2^{-1} = \dfrac{1}{2}$
a^n is the reciprocal of a^{-n}.	$a^n = \dfrac{1}{a^{-n}}, a \neq 0$	$2 = \dfrac{1}{2^{-1}}$

EXAMPLE 1 Use definition of zero and negative exponents

SIMPLIFY EXPRESSIONS
In this lesson, when simplifying powers with numerical bases, evaluate the numerical power.

a. $3^{-2} = \dfrac{1}{3^2}$ Definition of negative exponents

$= \dfrac{1}{9}$ Evaluate exponent.

b. $(-7)^0 = 1$ Definition of zero exponent

c. $\left(\dfrac{1}{5}\right)^{-2} = \dfrac{1}{\left(\frac{1}{5}\right)^2}$ Definition of negative exponents

$= \dfrac{1}{\frac{1}{25}}$ Evaluate exponent.

$= 25$ Simplify by multiplying numerator and denominator by 25.

d. $0^{-5} = \cancel{\dfrac{1}{0^5}}$ (Undefined) a^{-n} is defined only for a *nonzero* number a.

✓ **GUIDED PRACTICE** for Example 1

Evaluate the expression.

1. $\left(\dfrac{2}{3}\right)^0$ **1**   **2.** $(-8)^{-2}$ $\dfrac{1}{64}$ **3.** $\dfrac{1}{2^{-3}}$ **8**   **4.** $(-1)^0$ **1**

8.3 Define and Use Zero and Negative Exponents **503**

① PLAN AND PREPARE

Warm-Up Exercises
📄 Transparency Available

1. Simplify $(-3x)^2$. **$9x^2$**

2. Simplify $\left(\dfrac{a^3}{2b}\right)^5$. $\dfrac{a^5}{32b^5}$

3. The order of magnitude of Earth's mass is about 10^{27} grams. The order of magnitude of the sun's mass is about 10^{33} grams. About how many times as great is the sun's mass as Earth's mass? **about 10^6**

Notetaking Guide
📄 Transparency Available
Promotes interactive learning and notetaking skills, pp. 173–175.

Pacing
Basic: 1 day
Average: 1 day
Advanced: 1 day
Block: 0.5 block with 8.2
• See *Teaching Guide/Lesson Plan*.

② FOCUS AND MOTIVATE

Essential Question
Big Idea 1, p. 487

How do you use zero and negative exponents? **Tell students they will learn how to answer this question by using properties of exponents to simplify and evaluate expressions.**

NCTM STANDARDS
Standard 1: Understand how operations are related

Standard 8: Use the language of math to express ideas

Resource Planning Guide

Chapter Resource Book
• Teaching Guide/Lesson Plan (pp. 25–26)
• Practice levels A, B, C (pp. 27–29)
• Study Guide (pp. 30–31)
• Catch-up for Absent Students (p. 32)
• Problem Solving Workshop (p. 33)
• Challenge (p. 35)

Workbooks
• Notetaking Guide (pp. 173–175)
• Practice Workbook (pp. 123–124)

Teaching Options
• **Power Presentations CD-ROM** provides dynamic electronic teaching resources for the classroom.
• **Activity Generator CD-ROM** provides editable activities for all ability levels.

Interactive Technology
• Easy Planner
• Power Presentations CD-ROM
• Activity Generator CD-ROM
• Animated Algebra
• Test Generator CD-ROM
• Online Quiz
• eWorkbook
• eEdition
• @HomeTutor

Resources for English Learners
• Quick Reference for English Learners
• Spanish Study Guide
• Multi-Language Visual Glossary
• Student Resources in Spanish

See also the *Algebra 1 Toolkit* for more strategies for meeting individual needs.

❸ TEACH

Extra Example 1

Use the definition of zero and negative exponents.

a. 6^{-2} $\dfrac{1}{36}$

b. x^0 **1**

c. $\left(\dfrac{2}{3}\right)^{-2}$ $\dfrac{9}{4}$

d. 0^{-7} **undefined**

Key Questions to Ask for Example 1

- Why is the expression in part d undefined? **Division by zero is not defined.**

- If the base of a power is positive and the exponent is negative, is the power always positive? Explain. **Yes; the reciprocal of a positive number is positive, and the power of a positive number is positive.**

Extra Example 2

Evaluate exponential expressions.

a. $(-2)^5 \cdot (-2)^{-5}$ **1**

b. $(3^3)^{-2}$ $\dfrac{1}{729}$

c. $\dfrac{1}{8^{-2}}$ **64**

d. $\dfrac{7^3}{7^5}$ $\dfrac{1}{49}$

Key Question to Ask for Example 2

- In part (c), why is $\dfrac{1}{3^{-4}}$ equal to 3^4? 3^4 **is the reciprocal of** 3^{-4}.

> **KEY CONCEPT**   *For Your Notebook*
>
> **Properties of Exponents**
>
> Let a and b be real numbers, and let m and n be integers.
>
> $a^m \cdot a^n = a^{m+n}$ **Product of powers property**
>
> $(a^m)^n = a^{mn}$ **Power of a power property**
>
> $(ab)^m = a^m b^m$ **Power of a product property**
>
> $\dfrac{a^m}{a^n} = a^{m-n}, a \neq 0$ **Quotient of powers property**
>
> $\left(\dfrac{a}{b}\right)^m = \dfrac{a^m}{b^m}, b \neq 0$ **Power of a quotient property**

EXAMPLE 2   **Evaluate exponential expressions**

a. $6^{-4} \cdot 6^4 = 6^{-4+4}$ **Product of powers property**

$\qquad\qquad = 6^0$ **Add exponents.**

$\qquad\qquad = 1$ **Definition of zero exponent**

b. $(4^{-2})^2 = 4^{-2 \cdot 2}$ **Power of a power property**

$\qquad\qquad = 4^{-4}$ **Multiply exponents.**

$\qquad\qquad = \dfrac{1}{4^4}$ **Definition of negative exponents**

$\qquad\qquad = \dfrac{1}{256}$ **Evaluate power.**

c. $\dfrac{1}{3^{-4}} = 3^4$ **Definition of negative exponents**

$\qquad\quad = 81$ **Evaluate power.**

d. $\dfrac{5^{-1}}{5^2} = 5^{-1-2}$ **Quotient of powers property**

$\qquad\quad = 5^{-3}$ **Subtract exponents.**

$\qquad\quad = \dfrac{1}{5^3}$ **Definition of negative exponents**

$\qquad\quad = \dfrac{1}{125}$ **Evaluate power.**

✓   **GUIDED PRACTICE**   for Example 2

Evaluate the expression.

5. $\dfrac{1}{4^{-3}}$ **64**   **6.** $(5^{-3})^{-1}$ **125**   **7.** $(-3)^5 \cdot (-3)^{-5}$ **1**   **8.** $\dfrac{6^{-2}}{6^2}$ $\dfrac{1}{1296}$

Differentiated Instruction

Visual Learners Some of these examples give students a way to visualize zero and negative exponents. In **Example 2a**, 6^0 is simplified from $6^{-4} \cdot 6^4$, which by the quotient of powers property is $\dfrac{6^4}{6^4}$, or 1. In **Example 2b**, 4^{-4} is 4^{0-4}, which by the quotient of powers property is $\dfrac{4^0}{4^4}$, or $\dfrac{1}{256}$.

See also the *Algebra 1 Toolkit* for more strategies.

EXAMPLE 3 — Use properties of exponents

Simplify the expression. Write your answer using only positive exponents.

a. $(2xy^{-5})^3 = 2^3 \cdot x^3 \cdot (y^{-5})^3$ Power of a product property

$= 8 \cdot x^3 \cdot y^{-15}$ Power of a power property

$= \dfrac{8x^3}{y^{15}}$ Definition of negative exponents

b. $\dfrac{(2x)^{-2}y^5}{-4x^2y^2} = \dfrac{y^5}{(2x)^2(-4x^2y^2)}$ Definition of negative exponents

$= \dfrac{y^5}{(4x^2)(-4x^2y^2)}$ Power of a product property

$= \dfrac{y^5}{-16x^4y^2}$ Product of powers property

$= -\dfrac{y^3}{16x^4}$ Quotient of powers property

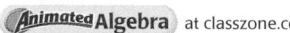 at classzone.com

---

★ EXAMPLE 4 — Standardized Test Practice

Not to scale

The order of magnitude of the mass of a polyphemus moth larva when it hatches is 10^{-3} gram. During the first 56 days of its life, the moth larva can eat about 10^5 times its own mass in food. About how many grams of food can the moth larva eat during its first 56 days?

(A) 10^{-15} gram   **(B)** 0.00000001 gram

(C) 100 grams   **(D)** 10,000,000 grams

Solution

To find the amount of food the moth larva can eat in the first 56 days of its life, multiply its original mass, 10^{-3}, by 10^5.

$10^5 \cdot 10^{-3} = 10^{5 + (-3)} = 10^2 = 100$

The moth larva can eat about 100 grams of food in the first 56 days of its life.

▸ The correct answer is C. (A) (B) (C) (D)

✓ **GUIDED PRACTICE** for Examples 3 and 4

9. Simplify the expression $\dfrac{3xy^{-3}}{9x^3y}$. Write your answer using only positive exponents. $\dfrac{1}{3x^2y^4}$

10. SCIENCE The order of magnitude of the mass of a proton is 10^4 times greater than the order of magnitude of the mass of an electron, which is 10^{-27} gram. Find the order of magnitude of the mass of a proton. 10^{-23} g

8.3   Define and Use Zero and Negative Exponents   **505**

Extra Example 3

Simplify the expression. Write your answer using only positive exponents.

a. $(3x^{-2}y^2)^3$ $\dfrac{27y^6}{x^6}$

b. $\dfrac{4x^{-2}y^4}{8xy^6}$ $\dfrac{1}{2x^3y^2}$

Key Question to Ask for Example 3

- In part a, why is the variable y in the denominator after simplifying the expression? **It has a negative exponent.**

An **Animated Algebra** activity is available on-line for **Example 3**. This activity is also available on the **Power Presentations CD-ROM**.

Extra Example 4

The order of magnitude of the radius of an atom is about 10^5 times as great as the order of magnitude of the radius of a proton, which is about 10^{-15} meters. What is the order of magnitude of the radius of an atom? **about 10^{-10} m**

Closing the Lesson

Have students summarize the major points of the lesson and answer the Essential Question: How do you use zero and negative exponents?

- **A nonzero number raised to the zero power is always 1.**
- **A power with a negative exponent is the reciprocal of the power with a positive exponent.**

To evaluate an expression, write powers with negative exponents as their reciprocals and powers with a zero exponent as 1. Use the properties of exponents to multiply and divide powers and to raise a power or a quotient to a power.

8.3 EXERCISES

HOMEWORK KEY

○ = **WORKED-OUT SOLUTIONS**
on p. WS1 for Exs. 11 and 53

★ = **STANDARDIZED TEST PRACTICE**
Exs. 2, 44, 45, 54, and 57

◆ = **MULTIPLE REPRESENTATIONS**
Ex. 55

4 PRACTICE AND APPLY

Assignment Guide

📕 **Answer Transparencies**
available for all exercises

Basic:
Day 1: pp. 506–508
Exs. 1, 2, 3–35 odd, 50–55,
60–68 even

Average:
Day 1: pp. 506–508
Exs. 1, 2, 9–14, 21–27, 28–44 even,
45, 51–57, 60–68 even

Advanced:
Day 1: pp. 506–508
Exs. 1, 2, 11–14, 22–26, 29–43 odd,
44–49*, 52–58*, 59, 61, 68

Block:
pp. 506–508
Exs. 1, 2, 9–14, 21–27, 28–44 even,
45, 51–57, 60–68 even (with 8.2)

Differentiated Instruction

See *Algebra 1 Best Practices Toolkit*
for suggestions on addressing the
needs of a diverse classroom.

Homework Check

For a quick check of student understanding of key concepts, go over
the following exercises:

Basic: 5, 19, 25, 29, 51
Average: 10, 22, 26, 34, 52
Advanced: 12, 24, 33, 42, 53

Extra Practice

• Student Edition, p. 945
• Chapter 8 Resource Book:
Practice levels A, B, C, pp. 27–29

Practice Worksheet

An easily-readable reduced
practice page (with answers)
for this lesson can be found
on p. 486C.

SKILL PRACTICE

A 1. **VOCABULARY** Which definitions or properties would you use to simplify the expression $3^5 \cdot 3^{-5}$? *Explain.* **Product of powers property and definition of zero exponent; the expression simplifies using the product of powers property to 3^0, which by definition equals 1**

2. ★ **WRITING** *Explain* why the expression 0^{-4} is undefined.
Sample answer: **The definition of negative exponents is defined only for nonzero bases.**

EXAMPLE 1
on p. 503
for Exs. 3–14

EVALUATING EXPRESSIONS Evaluate the expression.

3. 4^{-3} $\frac{1}{64}$

4. 7^{-3} $\frac{1}{343}$

5. $(-3)^{-1}$ $-\frac{1}{3}$

6. $(-2)^{-6}$ $\frac{1}{64}$

7. 2^0 1

8. $(-4)^0$ 1

9. $\left(\frac{3}{4}\right)^0$ 1

10. $\left(\frac{-9}{16}\right)^0$ 1

11. $\left(\frac{2}{7}\right)^{-2}$ $\frac{49}{4}$

12. $\left(\frac{4}{3}\right)^{-3}$ $\frac{27}{64}$

13. 0^{-3} **undefined**

14. 0^{-2} **undefined**

EXAMPLE 2
on p. 504
for Exs. 15–27

15. $2^{-2} \cdot 2^{-3}$ $\frac{1}{32}$

16. $7^{-6} \cdot 7^4$ $\frac{1}{49}$

17. $(2^{-1})^5$ $\frac{1}{32}$

18. $(3^{-2})^2$ $\frac{1}{81}$

19. $\frac{1}{3^{-3}}$ 27

20. $\frac{1}{6^{-2}}$ 36

21. $\frac{3^{-3}}{3^2}$ $\frac{1}{243}$

22. $\frac{6^{-3}}{6^{-5}}$ 36

23. $4\left(\frac{3}{2}\right)^{-1}$ $\frac{8}{3}$

24. $16\left(\frac{2^{-3}}{2^2}\right)$ $\frac{1}{2}$

25. $6^0 \cdot \left(\frac{1}{4^{-2}}\right)$ 16

26. $3^{-2} \cdot \left(\frac{5}{7^0}\right)$ $\frac{5}{9}$

27. **ERROR ANALYSIS** *Describe* and correct the error in evaluating the expression $-6 \cdot 3^0$.

3^0 **is not equivalent to 0, but to 1;**
$-6 \cdot 3^0 = -6 \cdot 1 = -6.$

$$-6 \cdot 3^0 = -6 \cdot 0$$
$$= 0$$ ✗

EXAMPLE 3 **B**
on p. 505
for Exs. 28–43

SIMPLIFYING EXPRESSIONS Simplify the expression. Write your answer using only positive exponents.

28. x^{-4} $\frac{1}{x^4}$

29. $2y^{-3}$ $\frac{2}{y^3}$

30. $(4g)^{-3}$ $\frac{1}{64g^3}$

31. $(-11h)^{-2}$ $\frac{1}{121h^2}$

32. $x^2 y^{-3}$ $\frac{x^2}{y^3}$

33. $5m^{-3}n^{-4}$ $\frac{5}{m^3 n^4}$

34. $(6x^{-2}y^3)^{-3}$ $\frac{x^6}{216y^9}$

35. $(-15fg^2)^0$ 1

36. $\frac{r^{-2}}{s^{-4}}$ $\frac{s^4}{r^2}$

37. $\frac{x^{-5}}{y^2}$ $\frac{1}{x^5 y^2}$

38. $\frac{1}{8x^{-2}y^{-6}}$ $\frac{x^2 y^6}{8}$

39. $\frac{1}{15x^{10}y^{-8}}$ $\frac{y^8}{15x^{10}}$

40. $\frac{1}{(-2z)^{-2}}$ $4z^2$

41. $\frac{9}{(3d)^{-3}}$ $243d^3$

42. $\frac{(3x)^{-3}y^4}{-x^2 y^{-6}}$ $-\frac{y^{10}}{27x^5}$

43. $\frac{12x^8 y^{-7}}{(4x^{-2}y^{-6})^2}$ $\frac{3x^{12}y^5}{4}$

44. ★ **MULTIPLE CHOICE** Which expression simplifies to $2x^4$? **D**

Ⓐ $2x^{-4}$ Ⓑ $\frac{32}{(2x)^{-4}}$ Ⓒ $\frac{1}{2x^{-4}}$ Ⓓ $\frac{8}{4x^{-4}}$

45. ★ **MULTIPLE CHOICE** Which expression is equivalent to $(-4 \cdot 2^0 \cdot 3)^{-2}$? **D**

Ⓐ -12 Ⓑ $-\frac{1}{144}$ Ⓒ 0 Ⓓ $\frac{1}{144}$

46. Not true.
Sample answer:
$\dfrac{2^{-3}}{2^{-4}} = 2$

48. Not true.
Sample answer:
$2^{-1} + 2^{-1} = 1$

C **CHALLENGE** In Exercises 46–48, tell whether the statement is true for all nonzero values of *a* and *b*. If it is not true, give a counterexample.

46. $\dfrac{a^{-3}}{a^{-4}} = \dfrac{1}{a}$

47. $\dfrac{a^{-1}}{b^{-1}} = \dfrac{b}{a}$ **true**

48. $a^{-1} + b^{-1} = \dfrac{1}{a+b}$

49. **REASONING** For $n > 0$, what happens to the value of a^{-n} as *n* increases?
Sample answer: It approaches 0.

PROBLEM SOLVING

EXAMPLE 4 A
on p. 505
for Exs. 50–54

50. **MASS** The mass of a grain of salt is about 10^{-4} gram. About how many grains of salt are in a box containing 100 grams of salt? **about 10^6 grains of salt**

@HomeTutor for problem solving help at classzone.com

51. **MASS** The mass of a grain of a certain type of rice is about 10^{-2} gram. About how many grains of rice are in a box containing 10^3 grams of rice?

@HomeTutor for problem solving help at classzone.com **about 10^5 grains of rice**

52. **BOTANY** The average mass of the fruit of the wolffia angusta plant is about 10^{-4} gram. The largest pumpkin ever recorded had a mass of about 10^4 kilograms. About how many times greater is the mass of the largest pumpkin than the mass of the fruit of the wolffia angusta plant? **about 10^8 times greater**

53. **MEDICINE** A doctor collected about 10^{-2} liter of blood from a patient to run some tests. The doctor determined that a drop of the patient's blood, or about 10^{-6} liter, contained about 10^7 red blood cells. How many red blood cells did the entire sample contain? **about 10^{11} red blood cells**

54. ★ **SHORT RESPONSE** One of the smallest plant seeds comes from an orchid, and one of the largest plant seeds comes from a giant fan palm. A seed from an orchid has a mass of 10^{-9} gram and is 10^{13} times less massive than a seed from a giant fan palm. A student says that the seed from the giant fan palm has a mass of about 1 kilogram. Is the student correct? *Explain.*
No. *Sample answer:* The giant fan palm has a mass of about 10^4 grams or 10,000 grams, which equals 10 kilograms.

Orchid   Giant fan palm

B 55. ◆ **MULTIPLE REPRESENTATIONS** Consider folding a piece of paper in half a number of times.

a. **Making a Table** Each time the paper is folded, record the number of folds and the fraction of the original area in a table like the one shown.

Number of folds	0	1	2	3
Fraction of original area	? 1	? $\frac{1}{2}$	? $\frac{1}{4}$	? $\frac{1}{8}$

b. **Writing an Expression** Write an exponential expression for the fraction of the original area of the paper using a base of $\frac{1}{2}$. $\left(\dfrac{1}{2}\right)^x$

8.3 Define and Use Zero and Negative Exponents **507**

Avoiding Common Errors

Exercises 3–26, 28–43 Students often evaluate an expression with an exponent of zero as equal to 0. Remind these students that any nonzero expression with an exponent of 0 is equal to 1.

Exercises 28–43 Caution students to distinguish between a negative number or variable in the base of an expression and a negative exponent. Remind them that they take the reciprocal when the exponent in a power is negative, not when the base is negative.

Study Strategy

Exercises 28–43 Tell students that a variety of strategies and steps can be used to solve these problems and that the best strategy overall is to take their time in simplifying the expressions. Urge them to pay attention to the sign of the exponent, to expressions in parentheses, and to whether an exponent applies to a number or variable. Remind them that they can always expand factors if necessary.

Mathematical Reasoning

Exercises 50, 51 You may want to point out to students that they can determine a reasonable answer to these exercises by asking how many grains of salt are in 1 gram of salt and how many grains of rice are in 1 gram of rice. Suggest that they first write the mass of the grains of salt and rice using positive exponents, then determine how many grains are in a gram, and finally multiply by the number of respective grams in the boxes of salt and rice.

56. SCIENCE Diffusion is the movement of molecules from one location to another. The time t (in seconds) it takes molecules to diffuse a distance of x centimeters is given by $t = \frac{x^2}{2D}$ where D is the diffusion coefficient.

  a. You can examine a cross section of a drop of ink in water to see how the ink diffuses. The diffusion coefficient for the molecules in the drop of ink is about 10^{-5} square centimeter per second. How long will it take the ink to diffuse 1 micrometer (10^{-4} centimeter)? **0.0005 sec**

  b. Check your answer to part (a) using unit analysis. $\frac{(cm)^2}{\frac{cm^2}{sec}} = cm^2 \cdot \frac{sec}{cm^2} = sec$

57. ★ EXTENDED RESPONSE The intensity of sound I (in watts per square meter) can be modeled by $I = 0.08Pd^{-2}$ where P is the power (in watts) of the sound's source and d is the distance (in meters) that you are from the source of the sound.

$I = 10^{-2}$ watts per square meter *(at hearer's ear)*

$d = 30$ meters

Not to scale

  a. What is the power (in watts) of the siren of the firetruck shown in the diagram? **112.5 watts**

  b. Using the power of the siren you found in part (a), simplify the formula for the intensity of sound from the siren. $I = 9d^{-2}$

  c. *Explain* what happens to the intensity of the siren when you double your distance from it. **The intensity is divided by 4.**

58. CHALLENGE Coal can be burned to generate energy. The heat energy in 1 pound of coal is about 10^4 BTU (British Thermal Units). Suppose you have a stereo. It takes about 10 pounds of coal to create the energy needed to power the stereo for 1 year.

  a. About how many BTUs does your stereo use in 1 year? **10^5 BTUs**

  b. Suppose the power plant that delivers energy to your home produces 10^{-1} pound of sulfur dioxide for each 10^6 BTU of energy that it creates. How much sulfur dioxide is added to the air by generating the energy needed to power your stereo for 1 year? **0.01 lb**

MIXED REVIEW

PREVIEW
Prepare for Lesson 8.4 in Exs. 59–62.

Evaluate the expression.

59. $10^3 \cdot 10^3$ *(p. 489)* **1,000,000**

60. $10^2 \cdot 10^5$ *(p. 489)* **10,000,000**

61. $\frac{10^9}{10^7}$ *(p. 495)* **100**

62. $\frac{10^6}{10^3}$ *(p. 495)* **1000**

Solve the linear system. Then check your answer. *(pp. 427, 435, 444, 451)*

63. $y = 3x - 6$ $\left(\frac{1}{2}, -4\frac{1}{2}\right)$
$y = -7x - 1$

64. $y = -2x + 12$ **(4, 4)**
$y = -5x + 24$

65. $5x + y = 40$ **(8, 0)**
$-x + y = -8$

66. $-x - 2y = -6.5$ $\left(6, \frac{1}{4}\right)$
$3x - 6y = 16.5$

67. $3x + 4y = -5$ **(1, −2)**
$x - 2y = 5$

68. $2x + 6y = 5$ $\left(-4\frac{1}{2}, 2\frac{1}{3}\right)$
$-2x - 3y = 2$

Define and Use Fractional Exponents

GOAL Use fractional exponents.

Key Vocabulary
• cube root

In Lesson 2.7, you learned to write the square root of a number using a radical sign. You can also write a square root of a number using exponents.

For any $a \geq 0$, suppose you want to write $\sqrt{a}$ as a^k. Recall that a number b (in this case, a^k) is a square root of a number a provided $b^2 = a$. Use this definition to find a value for k as follows.

$b^2 = a$	**Definition of square root**
$(a^k)^2 = a$	**Substitute a^k for b.**
$a^{2k} = a^1$	**Product of powers property**

Because the bases are the same in the equation $a^{2k} = a^1$, the exponents must be equal:

$2k = 1$	**Set exponents equal.**
$k = \dfrac{1}{2}$	**Solve for k.**

So, for a nonnegative number a, $\sqrt{a} = a^{1/2}$.

You can work with exponents of $\frac{1}{2}$ and multiples of $\frac{1}{2}$ just as you work with integer exponents.

EXAMPLE 1 **Evaluate expressions involving square roots**

a. $16^{1/2} = \sqrt{16}$
$= 4$

b. $25^{-1/2} = \dfrac{1}{25^{1/2}}$
$= \dfrac{1}{\sqrt{25}}$
$= \dfrac{1}{5}$

c. $9^{5/2} = 9^{(1/2) \cdot 5}$
$= (9^{1/2})^5$
$= (\sqrt{9})^5$
$= 3^5$
$= 243$

d. $4^{-3/2} = 4^{(1/2) \cdot (-3)}$
$= (4^{1/2})^{-3}$
$= (\sqrt{4})^{-3}$
$= 2^{-3}$
$= \dfrac{1}{2^3}$
$= \dfrac{1}{8}$

FRACTIONAL EXPONENTS You can work with other fractional exponents just as you did with $\frac{1}{2}$.

Extension: Define and Use Fractional Exponents **509**

---

① PLAN AND PREPARE

Warm-Up Exercises
Evaluate the expression.
1. $\sqrt{49}$ **7**
2. $\sqrt{121}$ **11**
3. 2^{-5} $\dfrac{1}{32}$
4. 13^2 **169**

② FOCUS AND MOTIVATE

Essential Question
Big Idea 1, p. 487
How do you evaluate expressions with fractional exponents? **Tell students they will learn how to answer this question by writing expressions as square roots and cube roots and evaluating them using the properties of exponents.**

③ TEACH

Extra Example 1
Evaluate the expression.
a. $49^{1/2}$ **7**
b. $36^{-1/2}$ $\dfrac{1}{6}$
c. $25^{3/2}$ **125**
d. $4^{-7/2}$ $\dfrac{1}{128}$

Key Questions to Ask for Example 1
• Which part of the fractional exponent is the same for all parts of the example? **denominator**
• Which part of the exponent determines the power to which the base is raised? **numerator**

NCTM STANDARDS
Standard 1: Understand meanings of operations

Standard 9: Understand how mathematical ideas build on one another

CUBE ROOTS If $b^3 = a$, then b is the **cube root** of a. For example, $2^3 = 8$, so 2 is the cube root of 8. The cube root of a can be written as $\sqrt[3]{a}$ or $a^{1/3}$.

Extra Example 2

Evaluate the expression.

a. $216^{1/3}$ **6** b. $64^{-1/3}$ $\dfrac{1}{4}$

c. $27^{2/3}$ **9** d. $8^{-5/3}$ $\dfrac{1}{32}$

Key Questions to Ask for Example 2

• How is Example 2 different from Example 1? **The denominators are 3 instead of 2 in Example 2.**

• What does the denominator 3 tell you? **take the cube root**

Extra Example 3

Use properties of exponents.

a. $8^{1/2} \cdot 8^{-5/2}$ $\dfrac{1}{64}$

b. $\dfrac{(3^{5/3} \cdot 3^0)}{3^{2/3}}$ **3**

Closing the Lesson

Have students summarize the major points of the lesson and answer the Essential Question: How do you evaluate expressions with fractional exponents?

• **The square root of a can be written as $a^{1/2}$, and the cube root of a can be written as $a^{1/3}$.**

If an exponent in an expression is $\dfrac{1}{2}$, take the square root of the base. If an exponent is $\dfrac{1}{3}$, take the cube root of the base. If the exponent is negative, take the reciprocal. If the exponent is a multiple of $\dfrac{1}{2}$ or $\dfrac{1}{3}$, use $\dfrac{1}{2}$ for the square root, $\dfrac{1}{3}$ for the cube root, and the other factor as the power. All the properties of integral exponents apply to fractional exponents.

4 PRACTICE AND APPLY

Avoiding Common Errors

Exercises 1–12 Watch for students who multiply the exponent by the base. Remind students that the denominator of the exponent tells them what root to take and the numerator what power to use.

EXAMPLE 2 **Evaluate expressions involving cube roots**

a. $27^{1/3} = \sqrt[3]{27}$

$\qquad = \sqrt[3]{3^3}$

$\qquad = 3$

b. $8^{-1/3} = \dfrac{1}{8^{1/3}}$

$\qquad = \dfrac{1}{\sqrt[3]{8}}$

$\qquad = \dfrac{1}{2}$

c. $64^{4/3} = 64^{(1/3) \cdot 4}$

$\qquad = (64^{1/3})^4$

$\qquad = (\sqrt[3]{64})^4$

$\qquad = 4^4$

$\qquad = 256$

d. $125^{-2/3} = 125^{(1/3) \cdot (-2)}$

$\qquad = (125^{1/3})^{-2}$

$\qquad = (\sqrt[3]{125})^{-2}$

$\qquad = 5^{-2}$

$\qquad = \dfrac{1}{5^2}$

$\qquad = \dfrac{1}{25}$

PROPERTIES OF EXPONENTS The properties of exponents for integer exponents also apply to fractional exponents.

EXAMPLE 3 **Use properties of exponents**

a. $12^{-1/2} \cdot 12^{5/2} = 12^{(-1/2) + (5/2)}$

$\qquad = 12^{4/2}$

$\qquad = 12^2$

$\qquad = 144$

b. $\dfrac{6^{4/3} \cdot 6}{6^{1/3}} = \dfrac{6^{(4/3) + 1}}{6^{1/3}}$

$\qquad = \dfrac{6^{7/3}}{6^{1/3}}$

$\qquad = 6^{(7/3) - (1/3)}$

$\qquad = 6^2$

$\qquad = 36$

PRACTICE

EXAMPLES
1, 2, and 3
on pp. 509–510
for Exs. 1–12

Evaluate the expression.

1. $100^{3/2}$ **1000**

2. $121^{-1/2}$ $\dfrac{1}{11}$

3. $81^{-3/2}$ $\dfrac{1}{729}$

4. $216^{2/3}$ **36**

5. $27^{-1/3}$ $\dfrac{1}{3}$

6. $343^{-2/3}$ $\dfrac{1}{49}$

7. $9^{7/2} \cdot 9^{-3/2}$ **81**

8. $\left(\dfrac{1}{16}\right)^{1/2}\left(\dfrac{1}{16}\right)^{-1/2}$ **1**

9. $36^{5/2} \cdot \dfrac{36^{-1/2}}{(36^{-1})^{-7/2}}$ $\dfrac{1}{216}$

10. $(27^{-1/3})^3$ $\dfrac{1}{27}$

11. $(-64)^{-5/3}(-64)^{4/3}$ $-\dfrac{1}{4}$

12. $(-8)^{1/3}(-8)^{-2/3}(-8)^{1/3}$ **1**

13. **REASONING** Show that the cube root of a can be written as $a^{1/3}$ using an argument similar to the one given for square roots on the previous page. **See margin.**

510 Chapter 8 Exponents and Exponential Functions

13. *Sample answer:* $b^3 = a$, substitute a^k for b to create $(a^k)^3 = a$. $a^{3k} = a^1$ by the power of a power property. Solving for k, $3k = 1$ so $k = \dfrac{1}{3}$.

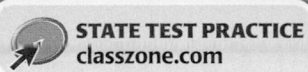
Lessons 8.1–8.3

1. GRIDDED ANSWER In 2004 the fastest computers could record about 10^9 bits per second. (A bit is the smallest unit of memory storage for computers.) Scientists believed that the speed limit at the time was about 10^{12} bits per second. About how many times more bits per second was the speed limit than the fastest computers? **1000 times**

2. MULTI-STEP PROBLEM An office supply store sells cubical containers that can be used to store paper clips, rubber bands, or other supplies.

a. One of the containers has a side length of $4\frac{1}{2}$ inches. Find the container's volume by writing the side length as an improper fraction and substituting the length into the formula for the volume of a cube. $\frac{729}{8}$ in.^{3}

b. Identify the property of exponents you used to find the volume in part (a). **Power of a quotient property**

3. SHORT RESPONSE Clouds contain millions of tiny spherical water droplets. The radius of one droplet is shown.

$r = 10^{-4}$ cm

a. Find the order of magnitude of the volume of the droplet. **10^{-12}**

b. Droplets combine to form raindrops. The radius of a raindrop is about 10^2 times greater than the droplet's radius. Find the order of magnitude of the volume of the raindrop. **10^{-6}**

c. *Explain* how you can find the number of droplets that combine to form the raindrop. Then find the number of droplets and identify any properties of exponents you used. **See margin.**

4. GRIDDED ANSWER The least intense sound that is audible to the human ear has an intensity of about 10^{-12} watt per square meter. The intensity of sound from a jet engine at a distance of 30 meters is about 10^{15} times greater than the least intense sound. Find the intensity of sound from the jet engine. **1000 watts per square meter**

5. EXTENDED RESPONSE For an experiment, a scientist dropped a spoonful, or about 10^{-1} cubic inch, of biodegradable olive oil into a pond to see how the oil would spread out over the surface of the pond. The scientist found that the oil spread until it covered an area of about 10^5 square inches.

a. About how thick was the layer of oil that spread out across the pond? Check your answer using unit analysis. **10^{-6} in.**

b. The pond has a surface area of 10^7 square inches. If the oil spreads to the same thickness as in part (a), how many cubic inches of olive oil would be needed to cover the entire surface of the pond? **10 in.^{3}**

c. *Explain* how you could find the amount of oil needed to cover a pond with a surface area of 10^x square inches. **See margin.**

6. OPEN-ENDED The table shows units of measurement of time and the durations of the units in seconds.

Name of unit	Duration (seconds)
Gigasecond	10^9
Megasecond	10^6
Millisecond	10^{-3}
Nanosecond	10^{-9}

a. Use the table to write a conversion problem that can be solved by applying a property of exponents involving products. **See margin.**

b. Use the table to write a conversion problem that can be solved by applying a property of exponents involving quotients. **Sample answer: How many megaseconds are in 1 gigasecond?**

3c. *Sample answer:* Divide the order of magnitude of the volume of the raindrop by the order of magnitude of the volume of the droplet; 10^2 droplets, Quotient of a power property.

5c. *Sample answer:* Multiply the surface area 10^x square inches by the thickness of the oil 10^{-6} inches to calculate the volume of oil in cubic inches needed. $10^x \cdot 10^{-6} = 10^{x-6}$ in.^{3}

6a. *Sample answer:* How many milliseconds are in a gigasecond?

1 PLAN AND PREPARE

Warm-Up Exercises

📄 **Transparency Available**

1. Order the numbers 0.014, 0.1, 0.01 from least to greatest. **0.01, 0.014, 0.1**

2. Find the ratio of the mass of the Milky Way galaxy, which is about 10^{44} grams, to the mass of the universe, which is about 10^{55} grams. **about $\frac{1}{10^{11}}$**

Notetaking Guide

📄 **Transparency Available**

Promotes interactive learning and notetaking skills, pp. 176–178.

Pacing

Basic: 2 days

Average: 2 days

Advanced: 2 days

Block: 1 block

• See *Teaching Guide/Lesson Plan.*

2 FOCUS AND MOTIVATE

Essential Question

Big Idea 2, p. 487

How do you write a number in scientific notation? **Tell students they will learn how to answer this question by rewriting a number as the product of a number from 1 up to 10 and a power of 10.**

NCTM STANDARDS

Standard 1: Compute fluently

Standard 2: Analyze situations using algebraic symbols

8.4 Use Scientific Notation

Before	You used properties of exponents.
Now	You will read and write numbers in scientific notation.
Why?	So you can compare lengths of insects, as in Ex. 51.

Key Vocabulary
• scientific notation

Numbers such as 1,000,000, 153,000, and 0.0009 are written in *standard form*. Another way to write a number is to use *scientific notation*.

KEY CONCEPT *For Your Notebook*

Scientific Notation

A number is written in **scientific notation** when it is of the form $c \times 10^n$ where $1 \le c < 10$ and n is an integer.

Number	Standard form	Scientific notation
Two million	2,000,000	2×10^6
Five thousandths	0.005	5×10^{-3}

EXAMPLE 1 Write numbers in scientific notation

a. $42,590,000 = 4.259 \times 10^7$ — **Move decimal point 7 places to the left. Exponent is 7.**

b. $0.0000574 = 5.74 \times 10^{-5}$ — **Move decimal point 5 places to the right. Exponent is −5.**

EXAMPLE 2 Write numbers in standard form

READING
A positive number in scientific notation is greater than 1 if the exponent is positive. A positive number in scientific notation is between 0 and 1 if the exponent is negative.

a. $2.0075 \times 10^6 = 2,007,500$ — **Exponent is 6. Move decimal point 6 places to the right.**

b. $1.685 \times 10^{-4} = 0.0001685$ — **Exponent is −4. Move decimal point 4 places to the left.**

Animated Algebra at classzone.com

✓ **GUIDED PRACTICE** for Examples 1 and 2

1. Write the number 539,000 in scientific notation. Then write the number 4.5×10^{-4} in standard form. **5.39×10^5; 0.00045**

512 Chapter 8 Exponents and Exponential Functions

EXAMPLE 3 Order numbers in scientific notation

Order 103,400,000, 7.8×10^8, and 80,760,000 from least to greatest.

Solution

STEP 1 Write each number in scientific notation, if necessary.

$103,400,000 = 1.034 \times 10^8$ $80,760,000 = 8.076 \times 10^7$

STEP 2 Order the numbers. First order the numbers with different powers of 10. Then order the numbers with the same power of 10.

Because $10^7 < 10^8$, you know that 8.076×10^7 is less than both 1.034×10^8 and 7.8×10^8. Because $\mathbf{1.034} < \mathbf{7.8}$, you know that $\mathbf{1.034} \times 10^8$ is less than $\mathbf{7.8} \times 10^8$.

So, $8.076 \times 10^7 < 1.034 \times 10^8 < 7.8 \times 10^8$.

STEP 3 Write the original numbers in order from least to greatest.

$80,760,000; 103,400,000; 7.8 \times 10^8$

EXAMPLE 4 Compute with numbers in scientific notation

Evaluate the expression. Write your answer in scientific notation.

a. $(8.5 \times 10^2)(1.7 \times 10^6)$

$= (8.5 \cdot 1.7) \times (10^2 \cdot 10^6)$	Commutative property and associative property
$= 14.45 \times 10^8$	Product of powers property
$= (1.445 \times 10^1) \times 10^8$	Write 14.45 in scientific notation.
$= 1.445 \times (10^1 \times 10^8)$	Associative property
$= 1.445 \times 10^9$	Product of powers property

b. $(1.5 \times 10^{-3})^2 = 1.5^2 \times (10^{-3})^2$ Power of a product property

$= 2.25 \times 10^{-6}$ Power of a power property

c. $\dfrac{1.2 \times 10^4}{1.6 \times 10^{-3}} = \dfrac{1.2}{1.6} \times \dfrac{10^4}{10^{-3}}$ Product rule for fractions

$= 0.75 \times 10^7$ Quotient of powers property

$= (7.5 \times 10^{-1}) \times 10^7$ Write 0.75 in scientific notation.

$= 7.5 \times (10^{-1} \times 10^7)$ Associative property

$= 7.5 \times 10^6$ Product of powers property

AVOID ERRORS
Notice that 14.45×10^8 is *not* written in scientific notation because $14.45 > 10$.

REVIEW FRACTIONS
For help with fractions, see p. 915.

✓ **GUIDED PRACTICE** for Examples 3 and 4

2. Order 2.7×10^5, 3.401×10^4, and 27,500 from least to greatest.
$27,500; 3.401 \times 10^4; 2.7 \times 10^5$

Evaluate the expression. Write your answer in scientific notation.

3. $(1.3 \times 10^{-5})^2$ 1.69×10^{-10} **4.** $\dfrac{4.5 \times 10^5}{1.5 \times 10^{-2}}$ 3×10^7 **5.** $(1.1 \times 10^7)(4.2 \times 10^2)$
4.62×10^9

Motivating the Lesson
Knowing how to write numbers in scientific notation allows you to better manage extremely large or small numbers with lots of zeros. For example, the number of electrons that pass through a 1-amp circuit every second is 625 followed by 16 zeros. It is easier to write the number in scientific notation in order to determine how many electrons pass through the circuit in 60 seconds.

❸ TEACH

Extra Example 1
Write in scientific notation.
a. 267,500,000 2.675×10^8
b. 0.000486 4.86×10^{-4}

Key Question to Ask for Example 1
• How do you know if the power of 10 is positive or negative? **If the original number is greater than 1, the power is positive. If the original number is between 0 and 1, the power is negative.**

Extra Example 2
Write in standard form.
a. 7.0234×10^5 **702,340**
b. 3.096×10^{-6} **0.000003096**

An **Animated Algebra** activity is available on-line for **Example 2**. This activity is also available on the **Power Presentations CD-ROM**.

Extra Example 3
Order 93,000,000, 9.2×10^6, and 9,028,000 from least to greatest.
9,028,000, 9.2×10^6, 93,000,000

513

514

Extra Example 4

Evaluate the expression. Write your answer in scientific notation.

a. $(5.7 \times 10^3)(2.6 \times 10^4)$
1.482×10^8

b. $(2.4 \times 10^{-4})^2$ **5.76×10^{-8}**

c. $\dfrac{2.4 \times 10^5}{2.5 \times 10^{-4}}$ **9.6×10^8**

Extra Example 5

The radius of a red blood cell is about 4.5×10^{-6} meters. The radius of *Mycoplasma* bacteria is about 1.25×10^{-8} meters.

a. Find the ratio of the radius of a red blood cell to the radius of *Mycoplasma* bacteria. What does the ratio tell you? **360; the radius of the red blood cell is about 360 times that of the *Mycoplasma* bacteria.**

b. Find the ratio of the volumes of the red blood cell and the *Mycoplasma* bacteria. What does the ratio tell you? **46,656,000; the volume of the red blood cell is about 46,656,000 times that of the *Mycoplasma* bacteria.**

Closing the Lesson

Have students summarize the major points of the lesson and answer the Essential Question: How do you write numbers in scientific notation?

• **A number written in scientific notation is in the form $c \times 10^n$, where $1 \le c < 10$.**

Write a positive number as the product of a decimal from 1 up to 10 and a power of 10. If the original number is greater than 1, the power of 10 has a positive exponent. If the number is between 0 and 1, the exponent is negative.

EXAMPLE 5 Solve a multi-step problem

BLOOD VESSELS Blood flow is partially controlled by the cross-sectional area of the blood vessel through which the blood is traveling. Three types of blood vessels are venules, capillaries, and arterioles.

Capillary	Venule	Arteriole
$r = 5.0 \times 10^{-3}$ mm	$r = 1.0 \times 10^{-2}$ mm	$r = 5.0 \times 10^{-1}$ mm

a. Let r_1 be the radius of a venule, and let r_2 be the radius of a capillary. Find the ratio of r_1 to r_2. What does the ratio tell you?

b. Let A_1 be the cross-sectional area of a venule, and let A_2 be the cross-sectional area of a capillary. Find the ratio of A_1 to A_2. What does the ratio tell you?

c. What is the relationship between the ratio of the radii of the blood vessels and the ratio of their cross-sectional areas?

Solution

a. From the diagram, you can see that the radius of the venule r_1 is 1.0×10^{-2} millimeter and the radius of the capillary r_2 is 5.0×10^{-3} millimeter.

$$\frac{r_1}{r_2} = \frac{1.0 \times 10^{-2}}{5.0 \times 10^{-3}} = \frac{1.0}{5.0} \times \frac{10^{-2}}{10^{-3}} = 0.2 \times 10^1 = 2$$

The ratio tells you that the radius of the venule is twice the radius of the capillary.

ANOTHER WAY

You can also find the ratio of the cross-sectional areas by finding the areas using the values for r_1 and r_2, setting up a ratio, and then simplifying.

b. To find the cross-sectional areas, use the formula for the area of a circle.

$$\frac{A_1}{A_2} = \frac{\pi r_1^{\,2}}{\pi r_2^{\,2}} \qquad \text{Write ratio.}$$

$$= \frac{r_1^{\,2}}{r_2^{\,2}} \qquad \text{Divide numerator and denominator by } \pi.$$

$$= \left(\frac{r_1}{r_2}\right)^2 \qquad \text{Power of a quotient property}$$

$$= 2^2 = 4 \qquad \text{Substitute and simplify.}$$

The ratio tells you that the cross-sectional area of the venule is four times the cross-sectional area of the capillary.

c. The ratio of the cross-sectional areas of the blood vessels is the square of the ratio of the radii of the blood vessels.

6. The cross-sectional area of the arteriole is 10^4 times larger than the cross-sectional area of the capillary.

 GUIDED PRACTICE for Example 5

6. WHAT IF? *Compare* the radius and cross-sectional area of an arteriole with the radius and cross-sectional area of a capillary.

514 Chapter 8 Exponents and Exponential Functions

Differentiated Instruction

Below Level Some students may need extra practice writing numbers in scientific and standard notation. Have students search the Internet for very large and very small numbers. For example, they can search for astronomical data for large numbers and cellular biology data for small numbers. Suggest that they exchange numbers with partners for more practice.

See also the *Algebra 1 Toolkit* for more strategies.

8.4 EXERCISES

○ = WORKED-OUT SOLUTIONS
on p. WS1 for Exs. 3, 17, and 53

★ = STANDARDIZED TEST PRACTICE
Exs. 2, 15, 48, 49, 54, and 59

◆ = MULTIPLE REPRESENTATIONS
Ex. 58

4 PRACTICE AND APPLY

SKILL PRACTICE

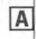 **A**

1. VOCABULARY Is 0.5×10^6 written in scientific notation? *Explain* why or why not. **No; 0.5 is not a number greater than or equal to 1.0 and less than 10.**

2. ★ WRITING Is 7.89×10^6 between 0 and 1 or greater than 1? *Explain* how you know. **Greater than 1; the exponent is positive.**

EXAMPLE 1
on p. 512
for Exs. 3–15

WRITING IN SCIENTIFIC NOTATION Write the number in scientific notation.

3. 8.5 $\mathbf{8.5 \times 10^1}$ **4.** 0.72 $\mathbf{7.2 \times 10^{-1}}$ **5.** 82.4 $\mathbf{8.24 \times 10^1}$

6. 0.005 $\mathbf{5 \times 10^{-3}}$ **7.** 72,000,000 $\mathbf{7.2 \times 10^7}$ **8.** 0.00406 $\mathbf{4.06 \times 10^{-3}}$

9. 1,065,250 $\mathbf{1.06525 \times 10^6}$ **10.** 0.000045 $\mathbf{4.5 \times 10^{-5}}$ **11.** 1,060,000,000 $\mathbf{1.06 \times 10^9}$

12. 0.00000526 $\mathbf{5.26 \times 10^{-6}}$ **13.** 900,000,000,000,000   **14.** 0.00000007008
                                                       $\mathbf{9 \times 10^{14}}$ $\mathbf{7.008 \times 10^{-8}}$

15. ★ MULTIPLE CHOICE Which number represents 54,004,000,000 written in scientific notation? **C**

     A 54004×10^6 **B** 54.004×10^9

     C 5.4004×10^{10} **D** 0.54004×10^{11}

EXAMPLE 2
on p. 512
for Exs. 16–28

WRITING IN STANDARD FORM Write the number in standard form.

16. 2.6×10^3 **2600**   **17.** 7.5×10^7 **75,000,000**   **18.** 1.11×10^2 **111**

19. 3.03×10^4 **30,300**   **20.** 4.709×10^6 **4,709,000**   **21.** 1.544×10^{10} **15,440,000,000**

22. 6.1×10^{-3} **0.0061**   **23.** 4.4×10^{-10} **0.00000000044**   **24.** 2.23×10^{-6} **0.00000223**

25. 8.52×10^{-8} **0.0000000852**   **26.** 6.4111×10^{-10}
                                                    0.00000000064111   **27.** 1.2034×10^{-6} **0.0000012034**

28. ERROR ANALYSIS *Describe* and correct the error in writing 1.24×10^{-3} in standard form. **The decimal point should be moved to the left, not the right; $1.24 \times 10^{-3} = 0.00124$.**

$1.24 \times 10^{-3} = 1240$ ✗

EXAMPLE 3 **B**
on p. 513
for Exs. 29–32

ORDERING NUMBERS Order the numbers from least to greatest.

29. 45,000; 6.7×10^3; 12,439; 2×10^4 $\mathbf{6.7 \times 10^3; 12,439; 2 \times 10^4; 45,000}$

30. 65,000,000; 6.2×10^6; 3.557×10^7; 55,004,000; 6.07×10^6

31. 0.0005; 9.8×10^{-6}; 5×10^{-3}; 0.00008; 0.04065; 8.2×10^{-3}

32. 0.0000395; 0.00010068; 2.4×10^{-5}; 5.08×10^{-6}; 0.000005
     $\mathbf{0.000005; 5.08 \times 10^{-6}; 2.4 \times 10^{-5}; 0.0000395; 0.00010068}$

30. 6.07×10^6;
6.2×10^6;
3.557×10^7;
55,004,000;
65,000,000

31. 9.8×10^{-6};
0.00008; 0.0005;
5×10^{-3};
8.2×10^{-3};
0.04065

COMPARING NUMBERS Copy and complete the statement using <, >, or =.

33. 5.6×10^3 ? 56,000   **<**   **34.** 404,000.1 ? 4.04001×10^5 **<**

35. 9.86×10^{-3} ? 0.00986   **=**   **36.** 0.003309 ? 3.309×10^{-3} **=**

37. 2.203×10^{-4} ? 0.0000203   **>**   **38.** 604,589,000 ? 6.04589×10^7 **>**

8.4 Use Scientific Notation 515

📄 Answer Transparencies available for all exercises

Basic:
Day 1: EP p. 939 Exs. 32–37
pp. 514–518
Exs. 1–28
Day 2: pp. 514–518
Exs. 29–36, 39–41, 51–56, 61–74

Average:
Day 1: pp. 514–518
Exs. 1, 2, 6–15, 19–28, 39–44
Day 2: pp. 514–518
Exs. 29–38, 45–49, 51–59, 62–74 even

Advanced:
Day 1: pp. 514–518
Exs. 1, 2, 8–15, 21–27, 39–47
Day 2: pp. 514–518
Exs. 29–38, 48–60*, 64, 67, 68, 71

Block:
pp. 514–518
Exs. 1, 2, 6–15, 19–49, 51–59, 62–74 even

Differentiated Instruction

See *Algebra 1 Best Practices Toolkit* for suggestions on addressing the needs of a diverse classroom.

Homework Check

For a quick check of student understanding of key concepts, go over the following exercises:
Basic: 8, 20, 29, 53, 54
Average: 10, 24, 42, 51, 55
Advanced: 12, 26, 45, 52, 55

Extra Practice

• Student Edition, p. 945
• Chapter 8 Resource Book: Practice levels A, B, C, pp. 39–41

Practice Worksheet

An easily-readable reduced practice page (with answers) for this lesson can be found on p. 486C.

Differentiated Instruction

Kinesthetic Learners In mathematics, a left-shift is associated with negative numbers, and a right-shift is associated with positive numbers. Another way to complete **Exercises 3–14** is as follows. To write 93,000,000 in scientific notation, place the decimal point to the right of 9 and count 7 places right to the last 0 to get 9.3×10^7. Similarly, place the decimal point to the right of 1 in 0.0017 and count 3 places to the left to the last 0 to get 1.7×10^{-3}.
See also the *Algebra 1 Toolkit* for more strategies.

EXAMPLE 4
on p. 513
for Exs. 39–48

EVALUATING EXPRESSIONS Evaluate the expression. Write your answer in scientific notation.

39. $\dfrac{(4.4 \times 10^3)(1.5 \times 10^{-7})}{6.6 \times 10^{-4}}$ 40. $\dfrac{(7.3 \times 10^{-5})(5.8 \times 10^2)}{4.234 \times 10^{-2}}$ 41. $\dfrac{(8.1 \times 10^{-4})(9 \times 10^{-6})}{7.29 \times 10^{-9}}$

42. $\dfrac{6 \times 10^{-3}}{8 \times 10^{-6}}$ **7.5 × 10²** 43. $\dfrac{5.4 \times 10^{-5}}{1.8 \times 10^{-2}}$ **3 × 10⁻³** 44. $\dfrac{4.1 \times 10^4}{8.2 \times 10^8}$ **5 × 10⁻⁵**

45. $(5 \times 10^{-8})^3$ **1.25 × 10⁻²²** 46. $(7 \times 10^{-5})^4$ **2.401 × 10⁻¹⁷** 47. $(1.4 \times 10^3)^2$ **1.96 × 10⁶**

48. ★ **MULTIPLE CHOICE** Which number is the value of $\dfrac{1.235 \times 10^4}{9.5 \times 10^7}$? **B**

   Ⓐ 0.13×10^{-4} Ⓑ 1.3×10^{-4} Ⓒ 1.3×10^{-3} Ⓓ 0.13×10^3

49. ★ **OPEN-ENDED** Write two numbers in scientific notation whose product is 2.8×10^4. Write two numbers in scientific notation whose quotient is 2.8×10^4. *Sample answer:* **2.8 × 10¹ and 1 × 10³; 11.2 × 10⁵ and 4.0 × 10¹**

Ⓒ 50. **CHALLENGE** Add the numbers 3.6×10^5 and 6.7×10^4 *without* writing the numbers in standard form. Write your answer in scientific notation. *Describe* the steps you take. **4.27 × 10⁵.** *Sample answer:* **Rewrite 6.7 × 10⁴ as 0.67 × 10⁵, then add 3.6 + 0.67 = 4.27. Since the answer is between 1 and 10, the exponent does not change, so the answer is 4.27 × 10⁵.**

PROBLEM SOLVING

EXAMPLE 3 Ⓐ
on p. 513
for Exs. 51–52
51a. 1.4 × 10⁻⁴;
2.5 × 10⁻¹;
1.67 × 10²; 555

51. **INSECT LENGTHS** The lengths of several insects are shown in the table.

   a. List the lengths of the insects in order from least to greatest.

   b. Which insects are longer than the fringed ant beetle?
   the elephant beetle and the walking stick

Insect	Length (millimeters)
Fringed ant beetle	2.5×10^{-1}
Walking stick	555
Parasitic wasp	1.4×10^{-4}
Elephant beetle	1.67×10^2

@HomeTutor for problem solving help at classzone.com

54. 14; the flow
rate of the
Amazon River is
about 14 times
faster than the
flow rate of the
Mississippi
River.

52. **ASTRONOMY** The spacecrafts *Voyager 1* and *Voyager 2* were launched in 1977 to gather data about our solar system. As of March 12, 2004, *Voyager 1* had traveled a total distance of about 9,643,000,000 miles, and *Voyager 2* had traveled a total distance of about 9.065×10^9 miles. Which spacecraft had traveled the greater distance at that time? *Voyager 1*

@HomeTutor for problem solving help at classzone.com

EXAMPLE 4
on p. 513
for Ex. 53

53. **AGRICULTURE** In 2002, about 9.7×10^8 pounds of cotton were produced in California. The cotton was planted on 6.9×10^5 acres of land. What was the average number of pounds of cotton produced per acre? Round your answer to the nearest whole number. **1406 pounds per acre**

EXAMPLE 5
on p. 514
for Exs. 54–55

54. ★ **SHORT RESPONSE** The average flow rate of the Amazon River is about 7.6×10^6 cubic feet per second. The average flow rate of the Mississippi River is about 5.53×10^5 cubic feet per second. Find the ratio of the flow rate of the Amazon to the flow rate of the Mississippi. Round to the nearest whole number. What does the ratio tell you?

○ = **WORKED-OUT SOLUTIONS**
on p. WS1

★ = **STANDARDIZED TEST PRACTICE**

◆ = **MULTIPLE REPRESENTATIONS**

Avoiding Common Errors

Exercises 3–15 Some students may write scientific notation with two or more digits to the left of the decimal point. Remind them that the decimal must be less than 10 but greater than or equal to 1. Suggest that students check their answers by expanding the scientific notation to make sure they have written the numbers correctly.

Exercises 16–28 Caution students that they need to move the decimal to the right for numbers with positive exponents and to the left for numbers with negative exponents when writing numbers in standard form.

 Internet Reference

Exercise 52 For more information about the *Voyager 1* and *Voyager 2* spacecrafts, visit NASA's website voyager.jpl.nasa.gov

Reading Strategy

Exercise 53 Encourage students to read the problem carefully for clues on what operation they should use to solve the problem. Draw their attention to the phrase "per acre."

55. ASTRONOMY The radius of Earth and the radius of the moon are shown.

Earth
$r = 6.38 \times 10^3$ km

Moon
$r = 1.74 \times 10^3$ km

a. Find the ratio of the radius of Earth to the radius of the moon. Round to the nearest hundredth. What does the ratio tell you?

b. Assume Earth and the moon are spheres. Find the ratio of the volume of Earth to the volume of the moon. Round to the nearest hundredth. What does the ratio tell you?

c. What is the relationship between the ratios of the radii and the ratios of the volumes? **The ratio of the volumes is the cube of the ratio of the radii.**

B **56. MULTI-STEP PROBLEM** In 1954, 50 swarms of locusts were observed in Kenya. The largest swarm covered an area of 200 square kilometers. The average number of locusts in a swarm is about 5×10^7 locusts per square kilometer.

a. About how many locusts were in Kenya's largest swarm? Write your answer in scientific notation. **about 1×10^{10} locusts**

b. The average mass of a desert locust is 2 grams. What was the total mass (in kilograms) of Kenya's largest swarm? Write your answer in scientific notation. **2×10^{10} kg**

57. DIGITAL PHOTOGRAPHY When a picture is taken with a digital camera, the resulting image is made up of square pixels (the smallest unit that can be displayed on a monitor). For one image, the side length of a pixel is 4×10^{-3} inch. A print of the image measures 1×10^3 pixels by 1.5×10^3 pixels. What are the dimensions of the print in inches? **4 in. by 6 in.**

58. ◆ MULTIPLE REPRESENTATIONS The speed of light is 1.863×10^5 miles per second.

a. **Writing an Expression** Assume 1 year is 365 days. Write an expression to convert the speed of light from miles per second to miles per year. **See margin.**

b. **Making a Table** Make a table that shows the distance light travels in 1, 10, 100, 1000, 10,000, and 100,000 years. Our galaxy has a diameter of about 5.875×10^{17} miles. Based on the table, about how long would it take for light to travel across our galaxy? **See margin.**

C **59. ★ EXTENDED RESPONSE** When a person is at rest, approximately 7×10^{-2} liter of blood flows through the heart with each heartbeat. The human heart beats about 70 times per minute.

a. **Calculate** About how many liters of blood flow through the heart each minute when a person is at rest? **4.9 L**

b. **Estimate** There are approximately 5.265×10^5 minutes in a year. Use your answer from part (a) to estimate the number of liters of blood that flow through the human heart in 1 year, in 10 years, and in 80 years. Write your answers in scientific notation.

c. **Explain** Are your answers to part (b) underestimates oroverestimates? *Explain.*

58a. $\dfrac{1.863 \times 10^5 \text{ mi}}{1 \text{ sec}} \cdot \dfrac{60 \text{ sec}}{1 \text{ min}} \cdot \dfrac{60 \text{ min}}{1 \text{ h}} \cdot \dfrac{24 \text{ h}}{1 \text{ day}} \cdot \dfrac{365 \text{ days}}{1 \text{ yr}} \approx 5.875 \times 10^{12} \text{ mi/yr}$

58b.

Years	1	10	100	1000	10,000	100,000
Miles traveled	5.875×10^{12}	5.875×10^{13}	5.875×10^{14}	5.875×10^{15}	5.875×10^{16}	5.875×10^{17}

100,000 yr

60. CHALLENGE A solar flare is a sudden eruption of energy in the sun's atmosphere. Solar flares are classified according to their peak X-ray intensity (in watts per meter squared) and are denoted with a capital letter and a number, as shown in the table. For example, a C4 flare has a peak intensity of 4×10^{-6} watt per square meter.

Class	Bn	Cn	Mn	Xn
Peak intensity (w/m²)	$n \times 10^{-7}$	$n \times 10^{-6}$	$n \times 10^{-5}$	$n \times 10^{-4}$

a. In November 2003, a massive X45 solar flare was observed. In April 2004, a C9 flare was observed. How many times greater was the intensity of the X45 flare than that of the C9 flare? **500 times greater**

b. A solar flare may be accompanied by a coronal mass ejection (CME), a bubble of mass ejected from the sun. A CME related to the X45 flare was estimated to be traveling at 8.2 million kilometers per hour. At that rate, how long would it take the CME to travel from the sun to Earth, a distance of about 1.5×10^{11} meters? **about 18 h**

MIXED REVIEW

PREVIEW
Prepare for Lesson 8.5 in Exs. 61–68.

Write the percent as a decimal. *(p. 916)*

61. 33% **0.33**
62. 62.7% **0.627**
63. 0.9% **0.009**
64. 0.04% **0.0004**
65. 3.95% **0.0395**
66. $\frac{1}{4}$% **0.0025**
67. $\frac{5}{2}$% **0.025**
68. 133% **1.33**

Graph the equation. **69–74. See margin.**

69. $x = -5$ *(p. 215)*
70. $y = 4$ *(p. 215)*
71. $3x - 7y = 42$ *(p. 225)*
72. $y - 2x = 12$ *(p. 225)*
73. $y = -2x + 6$ *(p. 244)*
74. $y = 1.5x - 9$ *(p. 244)*

QUIZ for Lessons 8.3–8.4

Simplify the expression. Write your answer using only positive exponents. *(p. 503)*

1. $(-4x)^4 \cdot (-4)^{-6}$ $\dfrac{x^4}{16}$
2. $(-3x^7y^{-2})^{-3}$ $-\dfrac{y^6}{27x^{21}}$
3. $\dfrac{1}{(5z)^{-3}}$ $125z^3$
4. $\dfrac{(6x)^{-2}y^5}{-x^3y^{-7}}$ $-\dfrac{y^{12}}{36x^5}$

Write the number in standard form. *(p. 512)*

5. 6.02×10^6
   6,020,000
6. 5.41×10^{11}
   541,000,000,000
7. 8.007×10^{-5}
   0.00008007
8. 9.253×10^{-7}
   0.0000009253

9a. 1.06×10^4; 29,000; 77,100; 1.36×10^5

9. **DINOSAURS** The estimated masses of several dinosaurs are shown in the table. *(p. 512)*

a. List the masses of the dinosaurs in order from least to greatest.

b. Which dinosaurs are more massive than Brachiosaurus? **Ultrasaurus**

Dinosaur	Mass (kilograms)
Brachiosaurus	77,100
Diplodocus	1.06×10^4
Apatosaurus	29,900
Ultrasaurus	1.36×10^5

EXTRA PRACTICE for Lesson 8.4, p. 945   ● **ONLINE QUIZ** at classzone.com

69–74. See Additional Answers beginning on p. AA1.

8.4 Use Scientific Notation

QUESTION How can you use a graphing calculator to solve problems that involve numbers in scientific notation?

EXAMPLE Use numbers in scientific notation

Gold is one of many trace elements dissolved in seawater. There is about 1.1×10^{-8} gram of gold per kilogram of seawater. The mass of the oceans is about 1.4×10^{21} kilograms. About how much gold is present in the oceans?

STEP 1 *Write a verbal model*

| Amount of gold present in oceans (grams) | = | Amount of gold in 1 kilogram of seawater (gram/kilogram) | • | Amount of seawater in oceans (kilograms) |

STEP 2 *Find product* The product is $(1.1 \times 10^{-8}) \cdot (1.4 \times 10^{21})$.

(1.1 × 10 ^ (-) 8) (1.4 × 10 ^ 21) ENTER

STEP 3 *Read result*

The calculator indicates that a number is in scientific notation by using "E." You can read the calculator's result 1.54E13 as 1.54×10^{13}.

There are about 1.54×10^{13} grams of gold present in the oceans.

```
(1.1*10^-8)(1.4*10
^21)
              1.54E13
```

PRACTICE

Evaluate the expression. Write the result in scientific notation.

1. $(1.5 \times 10^4)(1.8 \times 10^9)$ **2.7×10^{13}**
2. $(2.6 \times 10^{-14})(1.4 \times 10^{20})$ **3.64×10^6**
3. $(7.0 \times 10^{25}) \div (2.8 \times 10^6)$ **2.5×10^{19}**
4. $(4.5 \times 10^{15}) \div (9.0 \times 10^{-2})$ **5.0×10^{16}**
5. **GASOLINE** A scientist estimates that it takes about 4.45×10^7 grams of carbon from ancient plant matter to produce 1 gallon of gasoline. In 2002 motor vehicles in the U.S. used about 1.37×10^{11} gallons of gasoline.

   a. If all of the gasoline used in 2002 by motor vehicles in the U.S. came from carbon from ancient plant matter, how many grams of carbon were used to produce the gasoline? **about 6.10×10^{18} g**

   b. There are about 5.0×10^{22} atoms of carbon in 1 gram of carbon. How many atoms of carbon were used? **about 3.05×10^{41} atoms**

8.4 Use Scientific Notation **519**

1 PLAN AND PREPARE

Learn the Method

- Students will use a graphing calculator to solve a problem involving scientific notation.
- After the activity, students can use a graphing calculator to check their solutions in Exercises 39–48 in Lesson 8.4.

Keystroke Help

Keystrokes for several models of calculators are available in blackline format in the *Chapter 8 Resource Book*.

2 TEACH

Tips for Success

Make sure that students place parentheses around the numbers in scientific notation.

Extra Example

In 2003, about 1.35×10^6 acres of beans were harvested in the United States. The yield per acre was about 1.67×10^3 pounds of beans. About how many pounds of beans were produced in the United States in 2003? **about 2.25×10^9 lb**

3 ASSESS AND RETEACH

Evaluate the expression. Write the result in scientific notation.

1. $(3.6 \times 10^{-16})(1.8 \times 10^5)$ **6.48×10^{-11}**
2. $(2.4 \times 10^{12}) \div (1.5 \times 10^{-3})$ **1.6×10^{15}**

Before	You wrote and graphed linear models.
Now	You will write and graph exponential growth models.
Why?	So you can find the value of a collector car, as in Example 4.

Key Vocabulary
- **exponential function**
- **exponential growth**
- **compound interest**

An **exponential function** is a function of the form $y = ab^x$ where $a \neq 0$, $b > 0$, and $b \neq 1$. Exponential functions are *nonlinear* functions. Observe how an exponential function compares with a linear function.

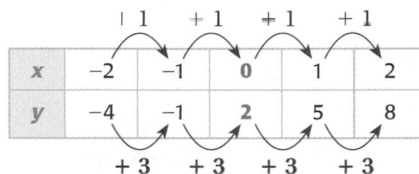

Linear function: $y = 3x + 2$

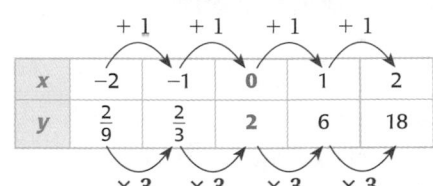

Exponential function: $y = 2 \cdot 3^x$

EXAMPLE 1 **Write a function rule**

Write a rule for the function.

x	−2	−1	0	1	2
y	2	4	8	16	32

Solution

STEP 1 **Tell** whether the function is exponential.

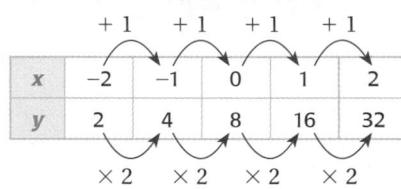

Here, the y-values are multiplied by 2 for each increase of 1 in x, so the table represents an exponential function of the form $y = ab^x$ where $b = 2$.

STEP 2 **Find** the value of a by finding the value of y when $x = 0$. When $x = 0$, $y = ab^0 = a \cdot 1 = a$. The value of y when $x = 0$ is 8, so $a = 8$.

STEP 3 **Write** the function rule. A rule for the function is $y = 8 \cdot 2^x$.

✓ **GUIDED PRACTICE** **for Example 1**

1. Write a rule for the function.

$y = 27 \cdot 3^x$

x	−2	−1	0	1	2
y	3	9	27	81	243

❖ **EXAMPLE 2** Graph an exponential function

Graph the function $y = 2^x$. Identify its domain and range.

Solution

READ A GRAPH
Notice that the graph has a *y*-intercept of 1 and that it gets closer to the negative *x*-axis as the *x*-values decrease.

STEP 1 **Make** a table by choosing a few values for x and finding the values of y. The domain is all real numbers.

x	−2	−1	0	1	2
y	$\frac{1}{4}$	$\frac{1}{2}$	1	2	4

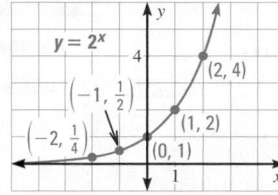

STEP 2 **Plot** the points.

STEP 3 **Draw** a smooth curve through the points. From either the table or the graph, you can see that the range is all positive real numbers.

❖ **EXAMPLE 3** Compare graphs of exponential functions

Graph the functions $y = 3 \cdot 2^x$ and $y = -3 \cdot 2^x$. Compare each graph with the graph of $y = 2^x$.

Solution

To graph each function, make a table of values, plot the points, and draw a smooth curve through the points.

x	$y = 2^x$	$y = 3 \cdot 2^x$	$y = -3 \cdot 2^x$
−2	$\frac{1}{4}$	$\frac{3}{4}$	$-\frac{3}{4}$
−1	$\frac{1}{2}$	$\frac{3}{2}$	$-\frac{3}{2}$
0	1	3	−3
1	2	6	−6
2	4	12	−12

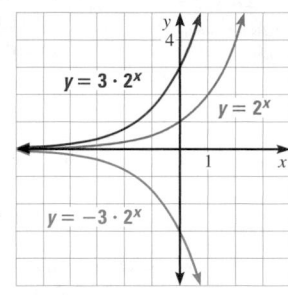

Because the *y*-values for $y = 3 \cdot 2^x$ are 3 times the corresponding *y*-values for $y = 2^x$, the graph of $y = 3 \cdot 2^x$ is a vertical stretch of the graph of $y = 2^x$.

Because the *y*-values for $y = -3 \cdot 2^x$ are −3 times the corresponding *y*-values for $y = 2^x$, the graph of $y = -3 \cdot 2^x$ is a vertical stretch with a reflection in the *x*-axis of the graph of $y = 2^x$.

✓ **GUIDED PRACTICE** for Examples 2 and 3

2–4. See margin for art.

2. Graph $y = 5^x$ and identify its domain and range.
   domain: all real numbers, range: all positive real numbers

3. Graph $y = \frac{1}{3} \cdot 2^x$. Compare the graph with the graph of $y = 2^x$.
   The graph is a vertical shrink of the graph of $y = 2^x$.

4. Graph $y = -\frac{1}{3} \cdot 2^x$. Compare the graph with the graph of $y = 2^x$.
   The graph is a vertical shrink with a reflection in the *x*–axis of the graph of $y = 2^x$.

Motivating the Lesson
You are studying population growth in your city. You know the current population is 128,256 and the annual rate of growth averages 3%. By knowing how to write and evaluate an exponential growth model, you can estimate the population in 2012.

❸ **TEACH**

Extra Example 1

Write a rule for the function.

x	−2	−1	0	1	2
y	1	4	16	64	256

$y = 16 \cdot 4^x$

Extra Example 2

Graph the function $y = 3^x$. Identify its domain and range. **Domain: all real numbers; Range: all positive real numbers**

Extra Example 3

Graph $y = \frac{1}{2} \cdot 2x$ and $y = -\frac{1}{2} \cdot 2x$. Compare each graph with the graph of $y = 2^x$.

The graph of $y = \frac{1}{2} \cdot 2^x$ is a vertical shrink of the graph of $y = 2^x$. The graph of $y = -\frac{1}{2} \cdot 2^x$ is a vertical shrink and reflection in the *x*-axis of the graph of $y = 2^x$.

2–4. See Additional Answers beginning on p. AA1.

Differentiated Instruction

Inclusion Students with fine-motor problems may find it difficult to graph exponential functions and thus get frustrated. Have these students understand the general shape of an exponential function and have them graph on a coordinate plane without grid lines. Also show how a spreadsheet program or graphing calculator can be used to generate a graph.

See also the *Algebra 1 Toolkit* for more strategies.

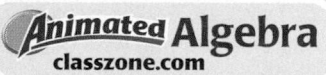
EXPONENTIAL GROWTH When $a > 0$ and $b > 1$, the function $y = ab^x$ represents **exponential growth**. When a quantity grows exponentially, it increases by the same percent over equal time periods. To find the amount to which the quantity grows after t time periods, use the following model.

KEY CONCEPT — *For Your Notebook*

Exponential Growth Model

a is the **initial amount**. — r is the **growth rate**.

$$y = a(1 + r)^t$$

$1 + r$ is the **growth factor**. — t is the **time period**.

Notice the relationship between the growth rate r and the growth factor $1 + r$. If the initial amount of a quantity is a units and the quantity is growing at a rate of r, then after one time period the new amount is:

$$\text{Initial amount} + \text{amount of increase} = a + r \cdot a = a(1 + r)$$

EXAMPLE 4 Solve a multi-step problem

ANOTHER WAY

For alternative methods for solving Example 4, turn to page 528 for the **Problem Solving Workshop**.

COLLECTOR CAR The owner of a 1953 Hudson Hornet convertible sold the car at an auction. The owner bought it in 1984 when its value was $11,000. The value of the car increased at a rate of 6.9% per year.

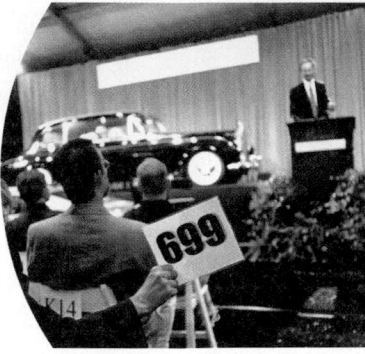

a. Write a function that models the value of the car over time.

b. The auction took place in 2004. What was the approximate value of the car at the time of the auction? Round your answer to the nearest dollar.

Solution

a. Let C be the value of the car (in dollars), and let t be the time (in years) since 1984. The initial value a is $11,000, and the growth rate r is 0.069.

$C = a(1 + r)^t$	Write exponential growth model.
$= 11,000(1 + 0.069)^t$	Substitute 11,000 for a and 0.069 for r.
$= 11,000(1.069)^t$	Simplify.

b. To find the value of the car in 2004, 20 years after 1984, substitute 20 for t.

$C = 11,000(1.069)^{20}$	Substitute 20 for t.
$\approx 41,778$	Use a calculator.

▶ In 2004 the value of the car was about $41,778.

***Animated* Algebra** at classzone.com

COMPOUND INTEREST **Compound interest** is interest earned on both an initial investment and on previously earned interest. Compounding of interest can be modeled by exponential growth where *a* is the initial investment, *r* is the annual interest rate, and *t* is the number of years the money is invested.

 EXAMPLE 5 **Standardized Test Practice**

> You put $250 in a savings account that earns 4% annual interest compounded yearly. You do not make any deposits or withdrawals. How much will your investment be worth in 5 years?
>
> (A) $300 (B) $304.16 (C) $1344.56 (D) $781,250

ESTIMATE
You can use the simple interest formula, *I = prt*, to estimate the amount of interest earned: (250)(0.04)(5) = 50. Compounding interest will result in slightly more than $50.

Solution

$$y = a(1 + r)^t$$ Write exponential growth model.

$$= 250(1 + 0.04)^5$$ Substitute 250 for *a*, 0.04 for *r*, and 5 for *t*.

$$= 250(1.04)^5$$ Simplify.

$$\approx 304.16$$ Use a calculator.

You will have $304.16 in 5 years.

▸ The correct answer is B. (A) (B) (C) (D)

 GUIDED PRACTICE for Examples 4 and 5

5. WHAT IF? In Example 4, suppose the owner of the car sold it in 1994. Find the value of the car to the nearest dollar. **$21,437**

6. WHAT IF? In Example 5, suppose the annual interest rate is 3.5%. How much will your investment be worth in 5 years? **$296.92**

8.5 EXERCISES

HOMEWORK KEY

○ = **WORKED-OUT SOLUTIONS**
  on p. WS1 for Exs. 13 and 41

★ = **STANDARDIZED TEST PRACTICE**
  Exs. 3, 8, 34, 35, 42, 43, 46, and 50

◆ = **MULTIPLE REPRESENTATIONS**
  Ex. 41

SKILL PRACTICE

1. **VOCABULARY** In the exponential growth model $y = a(1 + r)^t$, the quantity $1 + r$ is called the __?__. **growth factor**

2. **VOCABULARY** For what values of *b* does the exponential function $y = ab^x$ (where $a > 0$) represent exponential growth? **b > 1**

3. ★ **WRITING** How does the graph of $y = 2 \cdot 5^x$ compare with the graph of $y = 5^x$? *Explain.* **The graph would be a vertical stretch.** *Sample answer:* **Since the y-values of $y = 2 \cdot 5^x$ are double those of $y = 5^x$.**

Assignment Guide

📖 Answer Transparencies available for all exercises

Basic:
Day 1: SRH p. 923 Exs. 9–13
pp. 523–527
Exs. 1–21
Day 2: pp. 523–527
Exs. 22–27, 38–43, 52–61

Average:
Day 1: pp. 523–527
Exs. 1–8, 11–21, 35, 60, 61
Day 2: pp. 523–527
Exs. 22–34, 38–46, 52–58 even

Advanced:
Day 1: pp. 523–527
Exs. 1, 2, 4–8, 13–21, 35–37*, 60
Day 2: pp. 523–527
Exs. 26–34, 39–51*, 54, 58

Block:
pp. 523–527
Exs. 1–8, 11–35, 38–46,
52–58 even, 60, 61

Differentiated Instruction

See *Algebra 1 Best Practices Toolkit* for suggestions on addressing the needs of a diverse classroom.

Homework Check

For a quick check of student understanding of key concepts, go over the following exercises:
Basic: 4, 12, 24, 38, 39
Average: 5, 16, 28, 38, 40
Advanced: 6, 20, 32, 38, 41

Extra Practice

• Student Edition, p. 945
• Chapter 8 Resource Book: Practice levels A, B, C, pp. 51–56

Practice Worksheet

An easily-readable reduced practice page (with answers) for this lesson can be found on p. 486C.

EXAMPLE 1
on p. 520
for Exs. 4–8

4. $y = 4 \cdot 2^x$
5. $y = 125 \cdot 5^x$
6. $y = \frac{1}{2} \cdot 2^x$
7. $y = \frac{1}{9} \cdot 3^x$

WRITING FUNCTIONS Write a rule for the function.

4.

x	−2	−1	0	1	2
y	1	2	4	8	16

5.

x	−2	−1	0	1	2
y	5	25	125	625	3125

6.

x	−2	−1	0	1	2
y	$\frac{1}{8}$	$\frac{1}{4}$	$\frac{1}{2}$	1	2

7.

x	−2	−1	0	1	2
y	$\frac{1}{81}$	$\frac{1}{27}$	$\frac{1}{9}$	$\frac{1}{3}$	1

8. ★ **WRITING** Given a table of values, describe how can you tell if the table represents a linear function or an exponential function. **See margin.**

EXAMPLE 2
on p. 521
for Exs. 9–21

GRAPHING FUNCTIONS Graph the function and identify its domain and range.
9–20. See margin.

9. $y = 4^x$
10. $y = 7^x$
11. $y = 8^x$
12. $y = 9^x$

⑬. $y = (1.5)^x$
14. $y = (2.5)^x$
15. $y = (1.2)^x$
16. $y = (4.3)^x$

17. $y = \left(\frac{4}{3}\right)^x$
18. $y = \left(\frac{7}{2}\right)^x$
19. $y = \left(\frac{5}{3}\right)^x$
20. $y = \left(\frac{5}{4}\right)^x$

21. The percent increase was not written as a decimal;
$0.27(1 + 0.02)^3$
$= 0.27(1.02)^3 =$
$.29.

21. **ERROR ANALYSIS** The price P (in dollars) of a pound of flour was $.27 in 1999. The price has increased by about 2% each year. Let t be the number of years since 1999. *Describe* and correct the error in finding the price of a pound of flour in 2002.

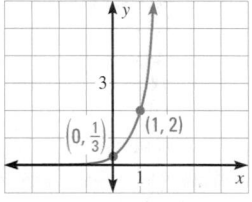

$P = a(1 + r)^t$
$= 0.27(1 + 2)^3 = 0.27(3)^3 = 7.29$

In 2002 the price of a pound of flour was $7.29.

EXAMPLE 3 [B]
on p. 521
for Exs. 22–34

COMPARING GRAPHS OF FUNCTIONS Graph the function. Compare the graph with the graph of $y = 3^x$. 22–33. See margin.

22. $y = 2 \cdot 3^x$
23. $y = 4 \cdot 3^x$
24. $y = \frac{1}{4} \cdot 3^x$
25. $y = \frac{2}{3} \cdot 3^x$

26. $y = 0.5 \cdot 3^x$
27. $y = 2.5 \cdot 3^x$
28. $y = -2 \cdot 3^x$
29. $y = -4 \cdot 3^x$

35. 200%.
Sample answer: A growth rate of 200% would create a growth factor of $1 + 2 = 3$, which would represent the tripling of the population every year.

30. $y = -\frac{1}{4} \cdot 3^x$
31. $y = -\frac{2}{3} \cdot 3^x$
32. $y = -0.5 \cdot 3^x$
33. $y = -2.5 \cdot 3^x$

34. ★ **MULTIPLE CHOICE** The graph of which function is shown? **C**

Ⓐ $f(x) = 6^x$ Ⓑ $f(x) = \left(\frac{1}{3}\right)^x$

Ⓒ $f(x) = \frac{1}{3} \cdot 6^x$ Ⓓ $f(x) = 6 \cdot \left(\frac{1}{3}\right)^x$

[graph showing curve through $\left(0, \frac{1}{3}\right)$ and $(1, 2)$]

[C]
35. ★ **WRITING** If a population triples each year, what is the population's growth rate (as a percent)? *Explain.*

36. **CHALLENGE** Write a linear function and an exponential function whose graphs pass through the points (0, 2) and (1, 6). *Sample answer: $f(x) = 4x + 2$, $f(x) = 2 \cdot 3^x$*

37. **CHALLENGE** Compare the graph of the function $f(x) = 2^{x+2}$ with the graph of the function $g(x) = 4 \cdot 2^x$. Use properties of exponents to explain your observations. *Sample answer: The graphs are the same. Since by the product of a power property $2^{x+2} = 2^x \cdot 2^2$, and $2^x \cdot 2^2$ simplifies to $4 \cdot 2^x$, $2^{x+2} = 4 \cdot 2^x$.*

○ = **WORKED-OUT SOLUTIONS** on p. WS1   ★ = **STANDARDIZED TEST PRACTICE**   ◆ = **MULTIPLE REPRESENTATIONS**

524

---

8. *Sample answer:* If the difference between successive terms is constant, the function is linear and if the ratio of successive terms is constant, the function is exponential.

9–20, 22–33. See Additional Answers beginning on p. AA1.

GRAPHING CALCULATOR You may wish to use a graphing calculator to complete the following Problem Solving exercises.

EXAMPLES [A]
4 and 5
on pp. 522–523
for Exs. 38–41

38. INVESTMENTS You deposit $125 in a savings account that earns 5% annual interest compounded yearly. Find the balance in the account after the given amounts of time.

a. 1 year **$131.25** **b.** 2 years **$137.81** **c.** 5 years **$159.54** **d.** 20 years **$331.66**

@HomeTutor for problem solving help at classzone.com

39a. Let *x* represent the number of years since 2001 and *f*(*x*) represent the number of computers (in hundreds of millions); *f*(*x*) = 6 • (1.1)ˣ.

39. MULTI-STEP PROBLEM One computer industry expert reported that there were about 600 million computers in use worldwide in 2001 and that the number was increasing at an annual rate of about 10%.

a. Write a function that models the number of computers in use over time.

b. Use the function to predict the number of computers that will be in use worldwide in 2009. **about 1,286,153,286 computers**

@HomeTutor for problem solving help at classzone.com

40a. Let *x* represent the number of years since 1985 and *f*(*x*) represent the number of grills shipped; *f*(*x*) = 3,173,000 • (1.07)ˣ.

40. MULTI-STEP PROBLEM A research association reported that 3,173,000 gas grills were shipped by various manufacturers in the U.S. in 1985. Shipments increased by about 7% per year from 1985 to 2002.

a. Write a function that models the number of gas grills shipped over time.

b. About how many gas grills were shipped in 2002? **about 10,022,921 gas grills**

41. ◆ MULTIPLE REPRESENTATIONS A tree's cross-sectional area taken at a height of 4.5 feet from the ground is called its basal area and is measured in square inches. Tree growth can be measured by the growth of the tree's basal area. The initial basal area and annual growth rate for two particular trees are shown.

Tree 1

Growth rate: 6%

Initial basal area: 154 in.²

Tree 2

Growth rate: 10%

Initial basal area: 113 in.²

a. Writing a Model Write a function that models the basal area *A* of each tree over time. **tree 1: *A* = 154 • (1.06)ᵗ, tree 2: *A* = 113 • (1.1)ᵗ**

b. Graphing a Function Use a graphing calculator to graph the functions from part (a) in the same coordinate plane. In about how many years will the trees be the same height? **See margin for art; about 8.4 yr.**

8.5 Write and Graph Exponential Growth Functions **525**

Avoiding Common Errors

Exercises 4–6 Some students may fail to find the value of *a*. Remind students that an exponential function is in the form of *y* = *abˣ* and that they can find the value of *a* by finding the value of *y* when *x* = 0.

Exercises 38–41 Watch for students who do not write percents as decimals before applying the exponential growth model.

Graphing Calculator

Exercises 9–20, 22–34 Students may want to check their graphs on a graphing calculator. They can enter the function in the Y = menu and then press **Graph**. They can press **Table** to check values. They can scroll up or down to see more values.

Reading Strategy

Exercises 38–41 Draw students' attention to the graphing calculator logo at the top of page 525. Point out that the logo appears whenever a graphing calculator is suggested for the exercises.

41b.

42. ★ **SHORT RESPONSE** A company sells advertising blimps. The table shows the costs of advertising blimps of different lengths. Does the table represent an exponential function? *Explain.*

Length, ℓ (feet)	10	15	20	25
Cost, c (dollars)	400.00	700.00	1225.00	2143.75

43. ★ **MULTIPLE CHOICE** A weblog, or blog, refers to a website that contains a personal journal. According to one analyst, over one 18 month period, the number of blogs in existence doubled about every 6 months. The analyst estimated that there were about 600,000 blogs at the beginning of the period. How many blogs were there at the end of the period? **C**

(A) 660,000   (B) 1,200,000   (C) 4,800,000   (D) 16,200,000

44. TELECOMMUNICATIONS For the period 1991–2001, the number y (in millions) of Internet users worldwide can be modeled by the function $y = 4.67(1.65)^x$ where x is the number of years since 1991.

  a. Identify the initial amount, the growth factor, and the growth rate.

  b. Graph the function. Identify its domain and range.

  c. Use the graph to estimate the year in which the number of Internet users worldwide was about 21 million. **1994**

45. GRAPHING CALCULATOR The frequency (in hertz) of a note played on a piano is a function of the position of the key that creates the note. The position of some piano keys and the frequencies of the notes created by the keys are shown below. Use the exponential regression feature on a graphing calculator to find an exponential model for the frequency of piano notes. What is the frequency of the note created by the 30th key?

46. ★ **EXTENDED RESPONSE** In 1830, the population of the United States was 12,866,020. By 1890, the population was 62,947,714.

  a. Model Assume the population growth from 1830 to 1890 was linear. Write a linear model for the U.S. population from 1830 to 1890. By about how much did the population grow per year from 1830 to 1890? $y = 834694.9x + 12,866,020$; 834694.9 people

  b. Model Assume the population growth from 1830 to 1890 was exponential. Write an exponential model for the U.S. population from 1830 to 1890. By approximately what percent did the population grow per year from 1830 to 1890? $y = 12,866,020(1.0268)^x$; about 2.68%

  c. Explain The U.S. population was 23,191,876 in 1850 and 38,558,371 in 1870. Which of the models in parts (a) and (b) is a better approximation of actual U.S. population for the time period 1850–1890? *Explain.* **See margin.**

★ = STANDARDIZED TEST PRACTICE

COMPOUND INTEREST In Exercises 47–50, use the example below to find the balance of the account compounded with the given frequency.

> **EXAMPLE** **Use the general compound interest formula**
>
> **FINANCE** You deposit $1000 in an account that pays 3% annual interest. Find the balance after 8 years if the interest is compounded monthly.
>
> **Solution**
>
> The general formula for compound interest is $A = P\left(1 + \frac{r}{n}\right)^{nt}$. In this formula, P is the initial amount, called principal, in an account that pays interest at an annual rate r and that is compounded n times per year. The amount A (in dollars) is the amount in the account after t years.
>
> Here, the interest is compounded monthly. So, $n = 12$.
>
> $$A = P\left(1 + \frac{r}{n}\right)^{nt}$$ Write compound interest formula.
>
> $$= 1000\left(1 + \frac{0.03}{12}\right)^{12(8)}$$ Substitute 1000 for *P*, 0.03 for *r*, 12 for *n*, and 8 for *t*.
>
> $$= 1000(1.0025)^{96}$$ Simplify.
>
> $$\approx 1270.868467$$ Use a calculator.
>
> ▶ The account balance after 8 years will be about $1270.87.

47. Yearly **$1266.77**　　　　**48.** Quarterly **$1270.11**　　　　**49.** Daily ($n = 365$) **$1271.24**

50. Daily; in an account compounded daily, each day you earn interest on both the principal and the interest that was accrued on the previous days.

50. ★ **WRITING** Which compounding frequency yields the highest balance in the account in the example above: monthly, yearly, quarterly, or daily? *Explain* why this is so.

51. **CHALLENGE** You invest $500 in an account that earns interest compounded monthly. Use a table or graph to find the least annual interest rate (to the nearest tenth of a percent) that the account would have to earn if you want to have a balance of $600 in 4 years. **4.6%**

MIXED REVIEW

PREVIEW
Prepare for Lesson 8.6 in Exs. 52–59.

Evaluate the expression.

52. $\left(\frac{1}{3}\right)^2$ *(p. 495)* $\frac{1}{9}$　　**53.** $\left(\frac{1}{8}\right)^2$ *(p. 495)* $\frac{1}{64}$　　**54.** $\left(\frac{1}{4}\right)^3$ *(p. 495)* $\frac{1}{64}$　　**55.** $\left(\frac{1}{2}\right)^6$ *(p. 495)* $\frac{1}{64}$

56. $\left(\frac{2}{3}\right)^{-2}$ *(p. 503)* $\frac{9}{4}$　　**57.** $\left(\frac{7}{5}\right)^{-2}$ *(p. 503)* $\frac{25}{49}$　　**58.** $\left(\frac{4}{3}\right)^{-3}$ *(p. 503)* $\frac{27}{64}$　　**59.** $\left(\frac{3}{2}\right)^{-4}$ *(p. 503)* $\frac{16}{81}$

Write an equation of the line shown. *(p. 283)*

60.

$y = \frac{4}{5}x - 3$

61.
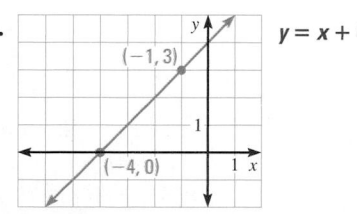
$y = x + 4$

EXTRA PRACTICE for Lesson 8.5, p. 945　　　🖉 **ONLINE QUIZ** at classzone.com　　　**527**

5 ASSESS AND RETEACH

Daily Homework Quiz
📑 Transparency Available

1. Graph $y = 1.4^x$.

2. Your family bought a house for $150,000 in 2000. The value of the house increases at an annual rate of 8%. What is the value of the house after 5 years? **about $220,399**

🖉 **Online Quiz**

Available at **classzone.com**

Diagnosis/Remediation
• Practice A, B, C in Chapter 8 Resource Book, pp. 51–56
• Study Guide in Chapter 8 Resource Book, pp. 57–58
• Practice Workbook, pp. 127–129
• @HomeTutor

Challenge
Additional challenge is available in the Chapter 8 Resource Book, p. 61.

Alternative Strategy

Example 4 on page 522 can be solved by using a spreadsheet. A spreadsheet has the advantage of showing the value of the car each year after1984. If the student wants to find the value for a different year or knows the value of the car but not the year, all the information can be readily found on the spreadsheet. Should the student want to find the value of the car in future years, using the *fill down* feature on the spreadsheet will quickly furnish the value.

Avoiding Common Errors

Watch for students who enter the formula incorrectly. Suggest that they double-check their formulas for accuracy.

Reading Strategy

Point out the note on formatting a spreadsheet. Tell students that the number of decimal places becomes unwieldy if they do not format the cells to round to 2 decimal places.

Another Way to Solve Example 4, page 522

MULTIPLE REPRESENTATIONS In Example 4 on page 522, you saw how to solve a problem about the value of a collector car over time by using an exponential model. You can also solve the problem by using a spreadsheet.

PROBLEM

COLLECTOR CAR The owner of a 1953 Hudson Hornet convertible sold the car at an auction. The owner bought it in 1984 when its value was $11,000. The value of the car increased at a rate of 6.9% per year.

a. Write a function that models the value of the car over time.

b. The auction took place in 2004. What was the approximate value of the car at the time of the auction? Round your answer to the nearest dollar.

METHOD

Using a Spreadsheet An alternative approach is to use a spreadsheet.

a. The model for the value of the car over time is $C = 11,000(1.069)^t$, as shown in Example 4 on page 522.

b. You can find the value of the car in 2004 by creating a spreadsheet.

STEP 1 Create a table showing the years since 1984 and the value of the car. Enter the car's value in 1984. To find the value in any year after 1984, multiply the car's value in the preceding year by the growth factor, as shown in cell B3 below.

FORMAT A SPREADSHEET
Format the spreadsheet so that calculations are rounded to 2 decimal places.

	A	B
1	Years since 1984, t	Value, C (dollars)
2	0	11000
3	1	=B2*1.069

STEP 2 Find the value of the car in 2004 by using the *fill down* feature until you get to the desired cell.

	A	B
1	Years since 1984, t	Value, C (dollars)
2	0	11000
3	1	11759
...	...	...
21	19	39081.31
22	20	41777.92

▶ From the spreadsheet, you can see the value of the car was about $41,778 in 2004.

PROBLEM

WHAT IF? Suppose the owner decided to sell the car when it was worth about $28,000. In what year did the owner sell the car?

METHOD

Using a Spreadsheet To solve the equation algebraically, you need to substitute 28,000 for C and solve for t, but you have not yet learned how to solve this type of equation. An alternative to the algebraic approach is using a spreadsheet.

STEP 1 **Use** the same spreadsheet as on the previous page.

STEP 2 **Find** when the value of the car is about $28,000.

	A	B
	Years since 1984, t	Value, C (dollars)
1	Years since 1984, t	Value, C (dollars)
2	0	11000
...	...	...
15	13	26188.03
16	14	27995.01

The value of the car is about $28,000 when $t = 14$.

▸ The owner sold the car in 1998.

PRACTICE

1. TRANSPORTATION In 1997 the average intercity bus fare for a particular state was $20. For the period 1997–2000, the bus fare increased at a rate of about 12% each year.

  a. Write a function that models the intercity bus fare for the period 1997–2000. **See margin.**

  b. Find the intercity bus fare in 1998. Use two different methods to solve the problem. **$22.40**

  c. In what year was the intercity bus fare $28.10? *Explain* how you found your answer. **2000.** *Sample answer:* **Make a table of values.**

2. ERROR ANALYSIS *Describe* and correct the error in writing the function for part (a) of Exercise 1.

> Let b be the bus fare (in dollars) and t be the number of years since 1997.
>
> $b = 20(0.12)^t$

The growth factor should be 1.12, not 0.12; $b = 20(1.12)^t$.

3. TECHNOLOGY A computer's Central Processing Unit (CPU) is made up of transistors. One manufacturer released a CPU in May 1997 that had 7.5 million transistors. The number of transistors in the CPUs sold by the company increased at a rate of 3.9% per month.

  a. Write a function that models the number T (in millions) of transistors in the company's CPUs t months after May 1997. **$T = 7.5(1.039)^t$**

  b. Use a spreadsheet to find the number of transistors in a CPU released by the company in November 2000. **about 37.4 million**

4. HOUSING The value of a home in 2002 was $150,000. The value of the home increased at a rate of about 6.5% per year.

  a. Write a function that models the value of the home over time. **See margin.**

  b. Use a spreadsheet to find the year in which the value of the home was about $200,000. **2007**

530

① PLAN AND PREPARE

Explore the Concept

- Students will model a situation using an exponential function.
- This activity leads into the study of writing function rules in Example 1 in Lesson 8.6.

Materials

Each student or group of students will need:

- yarn
- scissors

Recommended Time

Work activity: 10 min
Discuss results: 5 min

Grouping

Students can work individually or in pairs. If students work in pairs, one student can fold and cut the yarn and the other student can record the data in the chart.

② TEACH

Tips for Success

Make sure that students fold all the pieces of yarn in half at each stage and then cut all of the pieces.

Key Discovery

Some exponential functions model increases in value, while others model decreases.

③ ASSESS AND RETEACH

How does the function in Exercise 2 differ from the one in Exercise 1?. **The values in Exercise 2 are decreasing rather than increasing as in Exercise 1.**

1a. Yes. *Sample answer:* **Each value is twice the value of the previous stage.**

2a. Yes. *Sample answer:* **Each value is half the value of the previous stage.**

8.6 Exponential Models

MATERIALS · yarn · scissors

QUESTION How can you model a situation using an exponential function?

EXPLORE Collect data so that you can write exponential models

STEP 1 *Fold and cut* Take about 1 yard of yarn and consider it to be 1 unit long. Fold it in half and cut, as shown. You are left with two pieces of yarn, each half the length of the original piece of yarn.

STEP 2 *Copy and complete* Copy the table. Notice that the row for stage 1 has the data from Step 1. For each successive stage, fold *all* the pieces of yarn in half and cut. Then record the number of new pieces and the length of each new piece until the table is complete.

Stage	Number of pieces	Length of each new piece
1	2	$\frac{1}{2}$
2	? **4**	? $\frac{1}{4}$
3	? **8**	? $\frac{1}{8}$
4	? **16**	? $\frac{1}{16}$
5	? **32**	? $\frac{1}{32}$

DRAW CONCLUSIONS Use your observations to complete these exercises

1. Use the data in the first and second columns of the table.
   a. Do the data represent an exponential function? *Explain* how you know. **See margin.**
   b. Write a function that models the number of pieces of yarn at stage *x*. $y = 2^x$
   c. Use the function to find the number of pieces of yarn at stage 10. **1024 pieces of yarn**

2. Use the data in the first and third columns of the table.
   a. Do the data represent an exponential function? *Explain* how you know. **See margin.**
   b. Write a function that models the length of each new piece of yarn at stage *x*. $y = \left(\frac{1}{2}\right)^x$
   c. Use the function to find the length of each new piece of yarn at stage 10. $\frac{1}{1024}$ **units**

8.6 Write and Graph Exponential Decay Functions

Before	You wrote and graphed exponential growth functions.
Now	You will write and graph exponential decay functions.
Why?	So you can use a graph to solve a sports problem, as in Ex. 50.

Key Vocabulary
• exponential decay

A table of values represents an exponential function $y = ab^x$ provided successive y-values are multiplied by b each time the x-values increase by 1.

EXAMPLE 1 Write a function rule

Tell whether the table represents an exponential function. If so, write a rule for the function.

a.

The y-values are multiplied by 3 for each increase of 1 in x, so the table represents an exponential function of the form $y = ab^x$ with $b = 3$.

The value of y when $x = 0$ is $\frac{1}{3}$, so $a = \frac{1}{3}$.

The table represents the exponential function $y = \frac{1}{3} \cdot 3^x$.

b.

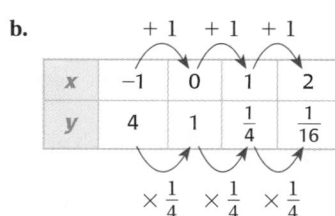

The y-values are multiplied by $\frac{1}{4}$ for each increase of 1 in x, so the table represents an exponential function of the form $y = ab^x$ with $b = \frac{1}{4}$.

The value of y when $x = 0$ is 1, so $a = 1$.

The table represents the exponential function $y = \left(\frac{1}{4}\right)^x$.

✓ **GUIDED PRACTICE** for Example 1

1. Tell whether the table represents an exponential function. If so, write a rule for the function. **yes;** $y = \left(\frac{1}{5}\right)^x$

x	−1	0	1	2
y	5	1	$\frac{1}{5}$	$\frac{1}{25}$

8.6 Write and Graph Exponential Decay Functions **531**

① PLAN AND PREPARE

Warm-Up Exercises
📄 Transparency Available

1. Evaluate $\left(\frac{1}{2}\right)^3 \cdot \frac{1}{8}$

2. Evaluate $\left(\frac{1}{4}\right)^{-2}$. **16**

3. The table shows how much money Tess owes after w weeks. Write a rule for the function.

Week, w	0	1	2	3
Owes, m	50	45	40	35

$m = 50 - 5w$

Notetaking Guide
📄 Transparency Available
Promotes interactive learning and notetaking skills, pp. 183–186.

Pacing
Basic: 2 days
Average: 2 days
Advanced: 2 days
Block: 1 block
• See *Teaching Guide/Lesson Plan.*

② FOCUS AND MOTIVATE

Essential Question
Big Idea 3, p. 487
How do you write and graph exponential decay functions?
Tell students they will learn how to answer this question by using tables, graphs, and exponential decay models.

NCTM STANDARDS
Standard 2: Understand patterns; Understand functions

Resource Planning Guide

Chapter Resource Book
• Teaching Guide/Lesson Plan (pp. 62–63)
• Activity Master (p. 64)
• Practice levels A, B, C (pp. 66–71)
• Study Guide (pp. 72–73)
• Catch-up for Absent Students (p. 74)
• Problem Solving Workshop (p. 75)
• Challenge (p. 76)

Workbooks
• Notetaking Guide (pp. 183–186)
• Practice Workbook (pp. 130–132)

Teaching Options
• **Power Presentations CD-ROM** provides dynamic electronic teaching resources for the classroom.
• **Activity Generator CD-ROM** provides editable activities for all ability levels.

Interactive Technology
• Easy Planner
• Power Presentations CD-ROM
• Activity Generator CD-ROM
• Animated Algebra
• Test Generator CD-ROM
• Online Quiz
• eWorkbook
• eEdition
• @HomeTutor

Resources for English Learners
• Quick Reference for English Learners
• Spanish Study Guide
• Multi-Language Visual Glossary
• Student Resources in Spanish

See also the *Algebra 1 Toolkit* for more strategies for meeting individual needs.

531

Motivating the Lesson

Your aunt bought a car two years ago for $12,000 and now she wants to sell it. She knows that the value of similar models has been decreasing at a rate of 17% per year. By knowing how to write and use an exponential decay model, she will be able to determine the value of the car at the time that she sells it.

❸ TEACH

Extra Example 1

Tell whether the table represents an exponential function. If so, write a rule for the function.

x	−1	0	1	2
y	$\frac{1}{8}$	$\frac{1}{2}$	2	8

yes; $y = \frac{1}{2} \cdot 4^x$

Extra Example 2

Graph the function $y = \left(\frac{1}{3}\right)^x$ and identify its domain and range.
Domain: all real numbers; Range: all positive real numbers

Key Question to Ask for Example 2

• How does the graph in Example 2 differ from a graph that represents exponential growth? **The graph in Example 2 falls from left to right and gets closer to the x-axis as x gets larger. A graph of exponential growth rises from left to right and gets closer to the x-axis as x gets smaller.**

2, 3. See Additional Answers beginning on p. AA1.

 EXAMPLE 2 Graph an exponential function

Graph the function $y = \left(\frac{1}{2}\right)^x$ and identify its domain and range.

Solution

STEP 1 **Make** a table of values. The domain is all real numbers.

x	−2	−1	0	1	2
y	4	2	1	$\frac{1}{2}$	$\frac{1}{4}$

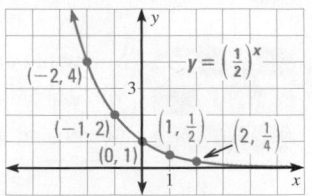

STEP 2 **Plot** the points.

STEP 3 **Draw** a smooth curve through the points. From either the table or the graph, you can see the range is all positive real numbers.

EXAMPLE 3 Compare graphs of exponential functions

Graph the functions $y = 3 \cdot \left(\frac{1}{2}\right)^x$ and $y = -\frac{1}{3} \cdot \left(\frac{1}{2}\right)^x$. Compare each graph with the graph of $y = \left(\frac{1}{2}\right)^x$.

Solution

x	$y = \left(\frac{1}{2}\right)^x$	$y = 3 \cdot \left(\frac{1}{2}\right)^x$	$y = -\frac{1}{3} \cdot \left(\frac{1}{2}\right)^x$
−2	4	12	$-\frac{4}{3}$
−1	2	6	$-\frac{2}{3}$
0	1	3	$-\frac{1}{3}$
1	$\frac{1}{2}$	$\frac{3}{2}$	$-\frac{1}{6}$
2	$\frac{1}{4}$	$\frac{3}{4}$	$-\frac{1}{12}$

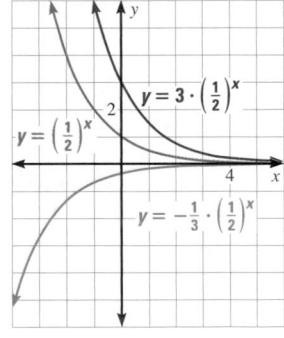

Because the y-values for $y = 3 \cdot \left(\frac{1}{2}\right)^x$ are 3 times the corresponding y-values for $y = \left(\frac{1}{2}\right)^x$, the graph of $y = 3 \cdot \left(\frac{1}{2}\right)^x$ is a vertical stretch of the graph of $y = \left(\frac{1}{2}\right)^x$.

Because the y-values for $y = -\frac{1}{3} \cdot \left(\frac{1}{2}\right)^x$ are $-\frac{1}{3}$ times the corresponding y-values for $y = \left(\frac{1}{2}\right)^x$, the graph of $y = -\frac{1}{3} \cdot \left(\frac{1}{2}\right)^x$ is a vertical shrink with reflection in the x-axis of the graph of $y = \left(\frac{1}{2}\right)^x$.

✓ **GUIDED PRACTICE** for Examples 2 and 3

2. See margin for art; domain: all real numbers, range: all positive real numbers.

2. Graph $y = (0.4)^x$ and identify its domain and range.

3. Graph $y = 5 \cdot (0.4)^x$. Compare the graph with the graph of $y = (0.4)^x$.
   See margin for art; the graph is a vertical stretch of $y = (0.4)^x$.

COMPARE GRAPHS When $a > 0$ and $0 < b < 1$, the function $y = ab^x$ represents **exponential decay**. The graph of an exponential decay function falls from left to right. In comparison, the graph of an exponential growth function $y = ab^x$ where $a > 0$ and $b > 1$ rises from the left.

EXAMPLE 4 Classify and write rules for functions

Tell whether the graph represents *exponential growth* or *exponential decay*. Then write a rule for the function.

a.

b.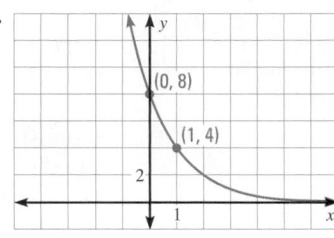

Solution

ANALYZE GRAPHS
For the function $y = ab^x$, where $x = 0$, the value of y is $y = ax^0 = a$. This means that the graph of $y = ab^x$ has a y-intercept of a.

a. The graph represents exponential growth ($y = ab^x$ where $b > 1$). The y-intercept is 10, so $a = 10$. Find the value of b by using the point $(1, 12)$ and $a = 10$.

$y = ab^x$ Write function.

$12 = 10 \cdot b^1$ Substitute.

$1.2 = b$ Solve.

A function rule is $y = 10(1.2)^x$.

b. The graph represents exponential decay ($y = ab^x$ where $0 < b < 1$). The y-intercept is 8, so $a = 8$. Find the value of b by using the point $(1, 4)$ and $a = 8$.

$y = ab^x$ Write function.

$4 = 8 \cdot b^1$ Substitute.

$0.5 = b$ Solve.

A function rule is $y = 8(0.5)^x$.

✓ **GUIDED PRACTICE** for Example 4

4. The graph of an exponential function passes through the points $(0, 10)$ and $(1, 8)$. Graph the function. Tell whether the graph represents *exponential growth* or *exponential decay*. Write a rule for the function.
See margin for art; exponential decay; $y = 10 \cdot (0.8)^x$.

CONCEPT SUMMARY   *For Your Notebook*

Exponential Growth and Decay

Exponential Growth

$y = ab^x$, $a > 0$ and $b > 1$

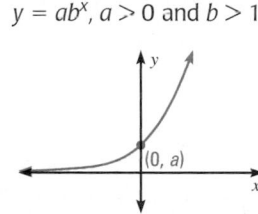

Exponential Decay

$y = ab^x$, $a > 0$ and $0 < b < 1$

8.6 Write and Graph Exponential Decay Functions   **533**

4.

533

EXPONENTIAL DECAY When a quantity decays exponentially, it decreases by the same percent over equal time periods. To find the amount of the quantity left after t time periods, use the following model.

> **KEY CONCEPT** *For Your Notebook*
>
> **Exponential Decay Model**
>
> a is the **initial amount**. ———— r is the **decay rate**.
>
> $$y = a\underbrace{(1 - r)}^t$$
>
> $1 - r$ is the **decay factor**. ———— t is the **time period**.

The relationship between the decay rate r and the decay factor $1 - r$ is similar to the relationship between the growth rate and growth factor in an exponential growth model. You will explore this relationship in Exercise 45.

EXAMPLE 5   Solve a multi-step problem

FORESTRY The number of acres of Ponderosa pine forests decreased in the western United States from 1963 to 2002 by 0.5% annually. In 1963 there were about 41 million acres of Ponderosa pine forests.

a. Write a function that models the number of acres of Ponderosa pine forests in the western United States over time.

b. To the nearest tenth, about how many million acres of Ponderosa pine forests were there in 2002?

Solution

a. Let P be the number of acres (in millions), and let t be the time (in years) since 1963. The initial value is 41, and the decay rate is 0.005.

$P = a(1 - r)^t$ **Write exponential decay model.**

$\quad = 41(1 - 0.005)^t$ **Substitute 41 for a and 0.005 for r.**

$\quad = 41(0.995)^t$ **Simplify.**

b. To find the number of acres in 2002, 39 years after 1963, substitute 39 for t.

$P = 41(0.995)^{39} \approx 33.7$ **Substitute 39 for t. Use a calculator.**

▸ There were about 33.7 million acres of Ponderosa pine forests in 2002.

Animated Algebra at classzone.com

  GUIDED PRACTICE   for Example 5

5. **WHAT IF?** In Example 5, suppose the decay rate of the forests remains the same beyond 2002. About how many acres will be left in 2010?
about 32.4 million

8.6 EXERCISES

HOMEWORK KEY

○ = WORKED-OUT SOLUTIONS
on p. WS1 for Exs. 7 and 49

★ = STANDARDIZED TEST PRACTICE
Exs. 2, 19, 36, 45, and 49

◆ = MULTIPLE REPRESENTATIONS
Ex. 50

SKILL PRACTICE

 A

1. **VOCABULARY** What is the decay factor in the exponential decay model $y = a(1 - r)^t$? **1 – r**

2. ★ **WRITING** *Explain* how you can tell if a graph represents *exponential growth* or *exponential decay*. **See margin.**

EXAMPLE 1
on p. 531
for Exs. 3–6

WRITING FUNCTIONS Tell whether the table represents an exponential function. If so, write a rule for the function.

3.

x	−1	0	1	2
y	2	8	32	128

exponential function; $y = 8 \cdot 4^x$

4.

x	−1	0	1	2
y	50	10	2	0.4

exponential function; $y = 10(0.2)^x$

5.

x	−1	0	1	2
y	6	2	$\frac{2}{3}$	$\frac{2}{9}$

exponential function; $y = 2\left(\frac{1}{3}\right)^x$

6.

x	−1	0	1	2
y	−11	−7	−3	1

not an exponential function

EXAMPLE 2
on p. 532
for Exs. 7–18

GRAPHING FUNCTIONS Graph the function and identify its domain and range.
7–18. See margin.

○ 7. $y = \left(\frac{1}{5}\right)^x$

8. $y = \left(\frac{1}{6}\right)^x$

9. $y = \left(\frac{2}{3}\right)^x$

10. $y = \left(\frac{3}{4}\right)^x$

11. $y = \left(\frac{4}{5}\right)^x$

12. $y = \left(\frac{3}{5}\right)^x$

13. $y = (0.3)^x$

14. $y = (0.5)^x$

15. $y = (0.1)^x$

16. $y = (0.9)^x$

17. $y = (0.7)^x$

18. $y = (0.25)^x$

EXAMPLE 3
on p. 532
for Exs. 19–31

19. ★ **MULTIPLE CHOICE** The graph of which function is shown? **D**

Ⓐ $y = (0.25)^x$

Ⓑ $y = (0.5)^x$

Ⓒ $y = 0.25 \cdot (0.5)^x$

Ⓓ $y = 4 \cdot (0.5)^x$

2. Sample answer: If the graph increases from left to right, then it represents growth; if it decreases from left to right, then it represents decay.

COMPARING FUNCTIONS Graph the function. Compare the graph with the graph of $y = \left(\frac{1}{4}\right)^x$. **20–31. See margin.**

20. $y = 5 \cdot \left(\frac{1}{4}\right)^x$

21. $y = 3 \cdot \left(\frac{1}{4}\right)^x$

22. $y = \frac{1}{2} \cdot \left(\frac{1}{4}\right)^x$

23. $y = \frac{1}{3} \cdot \left(\frac{1}{4}\right)^x$

24. $y = 0.2 \cdot \left(\frac{1}{4}\right)^x$

25. $y = 1.5 \cdot \left(\frac{1}{4}\right)^x$

26. $y = -5 \cdot \left(\frac{1}{4}\right)^x$

27. $y = -3 \cdot \left(\frac{1}{4}\right)^x$

28. $y = -\frac{1}{2} \cdot \left(\frac{1}{4}\right)^x$

29. $y = -\frac{1}{3} \cdot \left(\frac{1}{4}\right)^x$

30. $y = -0.2 \cdot \left(\frac{1}{4}\right)^x$

31. $y = -1.5 \cdot \left(\frac{1}{4}\right)^x$

8.6 Write and Graph Exponential Decay Functions **535**

4 PRACTICE AND APPLY

Assignment Guide

📄 **Answer Transparencies** available for all exercises

Basic:
Day 1: pp. 535–538
Exs. 1–18, 63–66
Day 2: pp. 535–538
Exs. 19–35 odd, 36–40, 47–50, 54–62 even

Average:
Day 1: pp. 535–538
Exs. 1–6, 10–18, 32–34, 63–66
Day 2: pp. 535–538
Exs. 19, 20–30 even, 35–44, 47–52, 55, 58, 61

Advanced:
Day 1: pp. 535–538
Exs. 1, 4–6, 12–18, 32–37, 63–66
Day 2: pp. 535–538
Exs. 19, 24–31, 38–53*, 56, 59, 62

Block:
pp. 535–538
Exs. 1–6, 10–19, 20–30 even, 32–44, 47–52, 55, 58, 61, 63–66

Differentiated Instruction

See *Algebra 1 Best Practices Toolkit* for suggestions on addressing the needs of a diverse classroom.

Homework Check

For a quick check of student understanding of key concepts, go over the following exercises:

Basic: 4, 8, 21, 38, 47
Average: 5, 12, 24, 39, 48
Advanced: 6, 16, 28, 40, 49

Extra Practice

• Student Edition, p. 945
• Chapter 8 Resource Book: Practice levels A, B, C, pp. 66–71

Practice Worksheet

An easily-readable reduced practice page (with answers) for this lesson can be found on p. 486C.

7–18, 20–31. See Additional Answers beginning on p. AA1.

35. initial amount: 90,000 people, decay factor: 0.975, decay rate: 2.5%; Let *P* represent the population and *t* represent the number of years. $P = 90,000(0.975)^t$

45. *Sample answer:* Since the quantity loses the same percent each time period, the amount *y* remaining after *x* time periods can be modeled using the exponential function $y = a(1 - r)^x$. After 1 time period, when *x* is 1, $y = a(1 - r)^1$, or $a(1 - r)$.

37. The decay rate, *r*, is 0.14. So the decay factor $(1 - r)$ should be 0.86, not 0.14; $y = 25,000(0.86)^t$.

EXAMPLE 4
on p. 533
for Exs. 38–40

38. exponential decay; $y = 6 \cdot 0.8^x$

41b. The graph is a vertical stretch with a reflection in the *x*-axis.

41c. The graph is a vertical shift up 1 unit.

46. *Sample answer:* The graphs are the same. By the product of powers property, $4^{x-2} = 4x \cdot 4^{-2}$, or $\frac{1}{16} \cdot 4x$.

B **MATCHING** Match the function with its graph.

32. $y = (0.2)^x$ **A**   **33.** $y = 5(0.2)^x$ **C**   **34.** $y = \frac{1}{2}(0.2)^x$ **B**

35. POPULATION A population of 90,000 decreases by 2.5% per year. Identify the initial amount, the decay factor, and the decay rate. Then write a function that models the population over time. **See margin.**

36. ★ **MULTIPLE CHOICE** What is the decay rate of the function $y = 4(0.97)^t$? **D**

(A) 4   (B) 0.97   (C) 0.3   (D) 0.03

37. ERROR ANALYSIS In 2004 a person purchased a car for $25,000. The value of the car decreased by 14% annually. *Describe* and correct the error in writing a function that models the value of the car since 2004.

RECOGNIZING EXPONENTIAL MODELS Tell whether the graph represents *exponential growth* or *exponential decay*. Then write a rule for the function.

38.   **39.**   **40.**

at classzone.com

exponential decay;
$y = 8 \cdot 0.6^x$

exponential growth;
$y = 8 \cdot 1.6^x$

41. REASONING Without graphing, explain how the graphs of the given functions are related to the graph of $f(x) = (0.5)^x$.

a. $m(x) = \frac{1}{3} \cdot (0.5)^x$ **b.** $n(x) = -4 \cdot (0.5)^x$ **c.** $p(x) = (0.5)^x + 1$

The graph is a vertical shrink.

C **CHALLENGE** Write an exponential function of the form $y = ab^x$ whose graph passes through the given points.

42. $(0, 1), \left(2, \frac{1}{4}\right)$ $y = \left(\frac{1}{2}\right)^x$ **43.** $(1, 20), (2, 4)$ $y = 100 \cdot \left(\frac{1}{5}\right)^x$ **44.** $\left(1, \frac{3}{2}\right), \left(2, \frac{3}{4}\right)$ $y = 3 \cdot \left(\frac{1}{2}\right)^x$

45. ★ **WRITING** The initial amount of a quantity is *a* units and the quantity is decaying at a rate of *r* (a percent per time period). Show that the amount of the quantity after one time period is $a(1 - r)$. *Explain* how you found your answer. **See margin.**

46. CHALLENGE Compare the graph of the function $f(x) = 4^{x-2}$ with the graph of the function $g(x) = \frac{1}{16} \cdot 4^x$. Use properties of exponents to explain your observation.

○ = **WORKED-OUT SOLUTIONS**
for on p. WS1

★ = **STANDARDIZED TEST PRACTICE**

◆ = **MULTIPLE REPRESENTATIONS**

GRAPHING CALCULATOR You may wish to use a graphing calculator to complete the following Problem Solving exercises.

EXAMPLE 5 [A]
on p. 534
for Exs. 47–50

47. **CELL PHONES** You purchase a cell phone for $125. The value of the cell phone decreases by about 20% annually. Write a function that models the value of the cell phone over time. Then find the value of the cell phone after 3 years. Round to the nearest dollar. **Let *V* represent the value of the cell phone and *t* represent the number of years since purchase, $V = 125(0.8)^t$; $64.**

@HomeTutor for problem solving help at classzone.com

48a. initial amount: 141,200; decay factor: 0.89; decay rate: 11%

48b. Let *B* represent the number of bats and *t* represent the number of years since 1983, $B = 141,200(0.89)^t$; 13,729 bats.

48. **ANIMAL POPULATION** Scientists studied the population of a species of bat in some caves in Missouri from 1983 to 2003. In 1983, there were 141,200 bats living in the caves. That number decreased by about 11% annually until 2003.

   a. Identify the initial amount, the decay factor, and the decay rate.

   b. Write a function that models the number of bats since 1983. Then find the number of bats in 2003.

   @HomeTutor for problem solving help at classzone.com

49. ★ **SHORT RESPONSE** In 2003 a family bought a boat for $4000. The boat depreciates (loses value) at a rate of 7% annually. In 2006 a person offers to buy the boat for $3000. Should the family sell the boat? *Explain*. **No. *Sample answer:* The boat's value is worth about $3217.**

50. ◆ **MULTIPLE REPRESENTATIONS** There are a total of 128 teams at the start of a citywide 3-on-3 basketball tournament. Half of the teams are eliminated after each round.

   a. **Writing a Model** Write a function for the number of teams left after *x* rounds. $f(x) = 128(0.5)^x$

   b. **Making a Table** Make a table for the function using $x = 0, 1, 2, \ldots, 7$. **See margin.**

   c. **Drawing a Graph** Use the table in part (b) to graph the function. After which round are there 4 teams left in the tournament? **See margin for art; round 5.**

[B] 51. **GUITARS** The frets on a guitar are the small metal bars that divide the fingerboard. The distance *d* (in inches) between the nut and the first fret or any two consecutive frets can be modeled by the function $d = 1.516(0.9439)^f$ where *f* is the number of the fret farthest from the nut.

51a. decay factor: 0.9439, decay rate: 5.61%

Fret   Nut

   a. Identify the decay factor and the decay rate for the model.

   b. What is the distance between the nut and the first fret? **about 1.431 in.**

   c. The distance between the 12th and 13th frets is about half the distance between the nut and the first fret. Use this fact to find the distance between the 12th and 13th frets. Use the model to verify your answer. **about 0.716 in.**

Study Strategy
Exercise 48 Suggest that students use the exponential decay model on page 534 to check their solutions to parts (a) and (b).

Vocabulary
Exercise 49 You may want to ask a student to use a dictionary or thesaurus to define the word *depreciate*. Have the student look up the word *appreciate* as an antonym to depreciate. Then ask them to discuss the relationship of these terms to exponential functions.

Internet Reference

Exercise 53 More information about maximal oxygen consumption can be found at www.nismat.org/physcor/max_o2.html

50b.

Rounds completed	Teams remaining
0	128
1	64
2	32
3	16
4	8
5	4
6	2
7	1

50c.

1. Graph $y = \left(\frac{1}{3}\right)^x$.

2. The population in a town has been declining at a rate of 2% per year since 2001. The population was 84,223 in 2001. What was the population in 2006? **about 76,130**

Online Quiz

Available at **classzone.com**

Diagnosis/Remediation

- Practice A, B, C in Chapter 8 Resource Book, pp. 66–71
- Study Guide in Chapter 8 Resource Book, pp. 72–73
- Practice Workbook, pp. 130–132
- @HomeTutor

Challenge

Additional challenge is available in the Chapter 8 Resource Book, p. 76.

Quiz

An easily-readable reduced copy of the quiz (with answers) on Lessons 8.5–8.6 from the Assessment Book can be found on p. 486E.

53b.

Quiz 1–6. See Additional Answers beginning on p. AA1.

---

52. CHALLENGE A college student finances a computer that costs $1850. The financing plan states that as long as a minimum monthly payment of 2.25% of the remaining balance is made, the student does not have to pay interest for 24 months. The student makes only the minimum monthly payments until the last payment. What is the amount of the last payment if the student buys the computer without paying interest? Round your answer to the nearest cent. **$1096.12**

Ⓒ **53. MULTI-STEP PROBLEM** Maximal oxygen consumption is the maximum volume of oxygen (in liters per minute) that the body uses during exercise. Maximal oxygen consumption varies from person to person and decreases with age by about 0.5% per year after age 25 for active adults.

   a. Model A 25-year-old female athlete has a maximal oxygen consumption of 4 liters per minute. Another 25-year-old female athlete has a maximal oxygen consumption of 3.5 liters per minute. Write a function for each athlete that models the maximal consumption each year after age 25 $y = 4(0.995)^x,$ $y = 3.5(0.995)^x$

   b. Graph Graph the models in the same coordinate plane. **See margin.**

   c. Estimate About how old will the first athlete be when her maximal oxygen consumption is equal to what the second athlete's maximal oxygen consumption is at age 25? **about 52 yr**

MIXED REVIEW

PREVIEW
Prepare for Lesson 9.1 in Exs. 54–62.

Simplify the expression. *(p. 96)*

54. $-12x + (-3x)$ **−15x**

55. $8x - 3x$ **5x**

56. $14 + x + 2x$ **14 + 3x**

57. $7(2x + 1) - 5$ **14x + 2**

58. $13x + (x - 4)5$ **18x − 20**

59. $3x + 6(x + 9)$ **9x + 54**

60. $(5 - x) + x$ **5**

61. $(3x - 4)7 + 21$ **21x − 7**

62. $-(x - 1) - x^2$ **−x² − x + 1**

Solve the equation.

63. $x + 14 = 8$ *(p. 134)* **−6**

64. $8x - 7 = 17$ *(p. 141)* **3**

65. $4x + 2x - 6 = 18$ *(p. 148)* **4**

66. $2x - 7(x + 5) = 20$ *(p. 148)* **−11**

QUIZ for Lessons 8.5–8.6

Graph the function. **1–6. See margin.**

7. Let V represent the value of the coin and t represent the number of years since purchase, $V = 25(1.08)^t$; about $53.97.

1. $y = \left(\frac{5}{2}\right)^x$ *(p. 520)*

2. $y = 3 \cdot \left(\frac{1}{4}\right)^x$ *(p. 531)*

3. $y = \frac{1}{4} \cdot 3^x$ *(p. 520)*

4. $y = (0.1)^x$ *(p. 531)*

5. $y = 10 \cdot 5^x$ *(p. 520)*

6. $y = 7(0.4)^x$ *(p. 531)*

7. COINS You purchase a coin from a coin collector for $25. Each year the value of the coin increases by 8%. Write a function that models the value of the coin over time. Then find the value of the coin after 10 years. Round to the nearest cent. *(p. 520)*

EXTRA PRACTICE for Lesson 8.6, p. 945   🌐 **ONLINE QUIZ** at classzone.com

Extension
Use after Lesson 8.6

Relate Geometric Sequences to Exponential Functions

GOAL Identify, graph, and write geometric sequences.

Key Vocabulary
• geometric sequence
• common ratio

In a **geometric sequence**, the ratio of any term to the previous term is constant. This constant ratio is called the **common ratio** and is denoted by r.

A geometric sequence with first term a_1 and common ratio r has the form a_1, $a_1 r, a_1 r^2, a_1 r^3, \ldots$. For instance, if $a_1 = 5$ and $r = 2$, the sequence $5, 5 \cdot 2, 5 \cdot 2^2$, $5 \cdot 2^3, \ldots$, or $5, 10, 20, 40, \ldots$, is geometric.

EXAMPLE 1 Identify a geometric sequence

Tell whether the sequence is *arithmetic* or *geometric*. Then write the next term of the sequence.

 a. $3, 6, 9, 12, 15, \ldots$ **b.** $128, 64, 32, 16, 8, \ldots$

Solution

a. The first term is $a_1 = 3$. Find the ratios of consecutive terms:

$$\frac{a_2}{a_1} = \frac{6}{3} = 2 \qquad \frac{a_3}{a_2} = \frac{9}{6} = 1\frac{1}{2} \qquad \frac{a_4}{a_3} = \frac{12}{9} = 1\frac{1}{3} \qquad \frac{a_5}{a_4} = \frac{15}{12} = 1\frac{1}{4}$$

> **REVIEW ARITHMETIC SEQUENCES**
> For help with identifying an arithmetic sequence and finding a common difference, see p. 309.

Because the ratios are not constant, the sequence is not geometric. To see if the sequence is arithmetic, find the differences of consecutive terms.

$$a_2 - a_1 = 6 - 3 = 3 \qquad\qquad a_3 - a_2 = 9 - 6 = 3$$
$$a_4 - a_3 = 12 - 9 = 3 \qquad\qquad a_5 - a_4 = 15 - 12 = 3$$

The common difference is 3, so the sequence is arithmetic. The next term of the sequence is $a_6 = a_5 + 3 = 18$.

b. The first term is $a_1 = 128$. Find the ratios of consecutive terms:

$$\frac{a_2}{a_1} = \frac{64}{128} = \frac{1}{2} \qquad \frac{a_3}{a_2} = \frac{32}{64} = \frac{1}{2} \qquad \frac{a_4}{a_3} = \frac{16}{32} = \frac{1}{2} \qquad \frac{a_5}{a_4} = \frac{8}{16} = \frac{1}{2}$$

Because the ratios are constant, the sequence is geometric. The common ratio is $\frac{1}{2}$. The next term of the sequence is $a_6 = a_5 \cdot \frac{1}{2} = 4$.

EXAMPLE 2 Graph a geometric sequence

> **ANALYZE A GRAPH**
> Notice that the graph in Example 2 appears to be exponential.

To graph the sequence from part (b) of Example 1, let each term's position number in the sequence be the x-value. The term is the corresponding y-value. Then make and plot the points.

Position, x	1	2	3	4	5
Term, y	128	64	32	16	8

---

① PLAN AND PREPARE

Warm-Up Exercises
1. Write the next term in the pattern $1, 2, 4, 7, 11, \ldots$. **16**
2. Bill earns \$16 in 2 hours, \$32 in 4 hours, and \$48 in 6 hours. What does he earn in 12 hours? **\$96**

② FOCUS AND MOTIVATE

Essential Question
Big Idea 3, p. 487
How do you identify and write geometric sequences? **Tell students they will learn how to answer this question by examining patterns and writing rules.**

③ TEACH

Extra Example 1
Tell whether the sequence is *arithmetic* or *geometric*. Then write the next term of the sequence.
a. $81, 77, 73, 69, 65, \ldots$ **arithmetic; 61**
b. $3, 6, 12, 24, 48, \ldots$ **geometric; 96**

Extra Example 2
Graph the geometric sequence from part b of Extra Example 1.

NCTM STANDARDS
Standard 2: Analyze situations using algebraic symbols
Standard 9: Grasp how mathematical ideas interconnect

Position, n	1	2	3	4	...	n
Term, a_n	a_1	$a_1 r$	$a_1 r^2$	$a_1 r^3$	...	$a_1 r^{n-1}$

For the nth term, you multiply a_1 by r $(n-1)$ times.

Extra Example 3

Write a rule for the nth term of the geometric sequence in Extra Example 1. Then find a_{10}.
$a_n = 3 \cdot 2^{n-1}$; $a_{10} = 5136$

Key Question to Ask for Example 3

• Can you substitute any term in the sequence for a_1? Explain. **No; the correct terms would not be generated if a term other than a_1 were substituted.**

Closing the Lesson

Have students summarize the major points of the lesson and answer the Essential Question: How do you identify and write geometric sequences?

• **In a geometric sequence, the ratio of any term to the previous term is constant.**

• **To find the nth term of a geometric sequence, use the general rule $a_n = a_1 r^{n-1}$.**

To identify a geometric sequence, find the ratios of consecutive terms. If the ratios are constant, the sequence is geometric. Use the general rule for a geometric sequence to write a specific rule by substituting the first term in the sequence for a_1, and the ratio for r. Substitute the position in the sequence for n to find the nth term.

4 PRACTICE AND APPLY

Avoiding Common Errors

Exercises 1–6 Some students may only look for a common difference between terms of a sequence and fail to see that a sequence is geometric. Remind students to check the ratios of consecutive terms and then determine if the ratios are constant.

1–6. See Additional Answers beginning on p. AA1.

540

KEY CONCEPT   *For Your Notebook*

General Rule for a Geometric Sequence

The nth term of a geometric sequence with first term a_1 and common ratio r is given by: $a_n = a_1 r^{n-1}$.

EXAMPLE 3   Write a rule for a geometric sequence

Write a rule for the nth term of the geometric sequence in Example 1. Then find a_{10}.

Solution

To write a rule for the nth term of the sequence, substitute the values for a_1 and r in the general rule $a_n = a_1 r^{n-1}$. Because $a_1 = 128$ and $r = \frac{1}{2}$,

$a_n = 128 \cdot \left(\frac{1}{2}\right)^{n-1}$. The 10th term of the sequence is $a_{10} = 128 \cdot \left(\frac{1}{2}\right)^{10-1} = \frac{1}{4}$.

PRACTICE

EXAMPLES 1, 2, and 3
on pp. 539–540 for Exs. 1–10

Tell whether the sequence is *arithmetic* or *geometric*. Then graph the sequence. 1–6. See margin for art.

1. 3, 12, 48, 192, . . .
   geometric
2. 7, 16, 25, 34, . . .
   arithmetic
3. 34, 28, 22, 16, . . .
   arithmetic
4. 1024, 128, 16, 2, . . .
   geometric
5. 9, −18, 36, −72, . . .
   geometric
6. 29, 43, 57, 71, . . .
   arithmetic

Write a rule for the nth term of the geometric sequence. Then find a_7.

7. 1, −5, 25, −125, . . .
   $a_n = (-5)^{n-1}$; **15,625**
8. 13, 26, 52, 104, . . .
   $a_n = 13 \cdot 2^{n-1}$; **832**
9. 432, 72, 12, 2, . . .
   $a_n = 432\left(\frac{1}{6}\right)^{n-1}$; $\frac{1}{108}$

10. **E-MAIL** A chain e-mail instructs the recipient to forward the e-mail to four more people. The table shows the number of rounds of sending the e-mail and the number of new e-mails generated. Write a rule for the nth term of the sequence. Then graph the first six terms of the sequence. $a_n = 4^{n-1}$; see margin for art.

Number of rounds sending e-mail, n	1	2	3	4
Number of new e-mails generated, a_n	1	4	16	64

540   Chapter 8   Exponents and Exponential Functions

10.

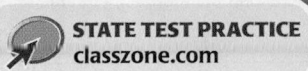
Lessons 8.4–8.6

1. MULTI-STEP PROBLEM The radius of the sun is about 96,600,000 kilometers. The radius of Earth is about 6370 kilometers. **a–c. See margin.**

a. Write each radius in scientific notation.

b. The surface area S of a sphere with radius r is given by $S = 4\pi r^2$. Assume the sun and Earth are perfect spheres. Find their surface areas. Write your answers in scientific notation.

c. What is the ratio of the surface area of the sun to the surface area of Earth? What does the ratio tell you?

2. SHORT RESPONSE The graph shows the value of a truck over time.

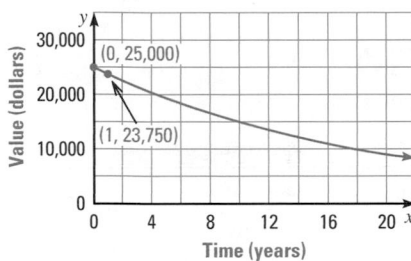

a. Write an equation for the function whose graph is shown. $y = 25{,}000(0.95)^x$

b. At what rate is the truck losing value? *Explain.* **5%; the decay rate for the truck is 0.05, or 5%.**

3. GRIDDED ANSWER A new laptop computer costs $2000. The value of the computer decreases over time. The value V (in dollars) of the computer after t years is given by the function $V = 2000(0.82)^t$. What is the decay rate, written as a decimal, of the value of the computer? **0.18**

4. OPEN-ENDED The value of a house in Iowa increased, on average, at a rate of about 4% per quarter from the first quarter in 2001 to the last quarter in 2004. Write a function that models the value of the house over time. Choose an initial value of the house and a quarter such that the value of the house is about $275,000. **See margin.**

5. EXTENDED RESPONSE A musician is saving money to buy a new snare drum. The musician puts $100 in a savings account that pays 3% annual interest compounded yearly. **a–c. See margin.**

a. Write a function that models the amount of money in the account over time.

b. Graph the function.

c. The musician wants a drum that costs $149.95. Will there be enough in the account after 3 years? *Explain.*

6. MULTI-STEP PROBLEM The graph shows the value of a business over time.

a. Does the graph represent *exponential growth* or *exponential decay*? **exponential growth**

b. Write a function that models the value of the business over time. $y = 15{,}000(1.3)^x$

c. How much is the business worth after 4 years? **$42,841.50**

7. MULTI-STEP PROBLEM The half-life of a medication is the time it takes for the medication to reduce to half of its original amount in a patient's bloodstream. A certain antibiotic has a half-life of about 8 hours.

a. A patient is administered 500 milligrams of the medication. Write a function that models the amount of the medication in the patient's bloodstream over time. **See margin.**

b. How much of the 500 milligram dose will be in the patient's bloodstream after 24 hours? **62.5 mg**

1a. Sun: 9.66×10^7 km, Earth: 6.37×10^3 km

1b. Sun: about 1.17×10^{17} km, Earth: about 5.10×10^8 km

1c. about 2.23×10^8; *Sample answer:* The Sun's surface area is 223,000,000 times larger than the Earth's.

4. Let V represent the value of the house and t represent the number of quarters since 2001; $V = 200{,}000(1.04)^t$. *Sample answer:* A house with a value of $200,000 at the end of 2002 would have a value of about $275,000 at the end of 2004.

5a. Let y represent the amount of money in the account and x represent the number of years since the $100 was deposited. $y = 100(1.03)^x$.

5b.

5c. No. *Sample answer:* There will only be $109.27 in the account in 3 years.

7a. Let M represent the amount of medication in patient's bloodstream (in milligrams) and let t represent the number of 8 hour periods since the medication was taken. $M = 500\left(\dfrac{1}{2}\right)^t$.

BIG IDEAS
For Your Notebook

Big Idea 1 — Applying Properties of Exponents to Simplify Expressions

You can use the properties of exponents to simplify expressions. For the properties listed below, a and b are real numbers, and m and n are integers.

Expression	Property
$a^m \cdot a^n = a^{m+n}$	Product of powers property
$(a^m)^n = a^{mn}$	Power of a power property
$(ab)^m = a^m b^m$	Power of a product property
$\dfrac{a^m}{a^n} = a^{m-n},\ a \neq 0$	Quotient of powers property
$\left(\dfrac{a}{b}\right)^m = \dfrac{a^m}{b^m},\ b \neq 0$	Power of a quotient property

Big Idea 2 — Working with Numbers in Scientific Notation

You can write numbers in scientific notation.

Number	Standard form	Scientific notation
Four billion	4,000,000,000	4×10^9
Thirty-two thousandths	0.032	3.2×10^{-2}

You can also compute with numbers in scientific notation. For example:

$$(4 \times 10^9) \times (3.2 \times 10^{-2}) = 12.8 \times 10^7 = 1.28 \times 10^8, \text{ or } 128,000,000$$

Big Idea 3 — Writing and Graphing Exponential Functions

You can write and graph exponential growth and decay functions. You can also model real-world situations involving exponential growth and exponential decay.

Exponential growth	Exponential decay
Function $y = ab^x$, $a > 0$ and $b > 1$	**Function** $y = ab^x$, $a > 0$ and $0 < b < 1$
Graph $(0, a)$	**Graph** $(0, a)$
Model $y = a(1 + r)^t$	**Model** $y = a(1 - r)^t$

REVIEW KEY VOCABULARY

- order of magnitude, *p. 491*
- zero exponent, *p. 503*
- negative exponent, *p. 503*
- scientific notation, *p. 512*
- exponential function, *p. 520*
- exponential growth, *p. 522*
- growth factor, growth rate, *p. 522*
- compound interest, *p. 523*
- exponential decay, *p. 533*
- decay factor, decay rate, *p. 534*

VOCABULARY EXERCISES

1. Copy and complete: The function $y = 1200(0.3)^t$ is an exponential _?_ function, and the base 0.3 is called the _?_. **decay, decay factor**

2. **WRITING** *Explain* how you can tell whether a table represents a linear function or an exponential function. **See margin.**

Tell whether the function represents exponential growth or exponential decay. *Explain.* **3–5. See margin.**

3. $y = 3(0.85)^x$ 4. $y = \frac{1}{2}(1.01)^x$ 5. $y = 2(2.1)^x$

REVIEW EXAMPLES AND EXERCISES

Use the review examples and exercises below to check your understanding of the concepts you have learned in each lesson of Chapter 8.

8.1 Apply Exponent Properties Involving Products   *pp. 489–494*

EXAMPLE

Simplify $(3y^3)^4 \cdot y^5$.

$(3y^3)^4 \cdot y^5 = 3^4 \cdot (y^3)^4 \cdot y^5$ Power of a product property

$= 81 \cdot y^{12} \cdot y^5$ Power of a power property

$= 81y^{17}$ Product of powers property

EXERCISES

EXAMPLES 1, 2, 3, 4, and 5 on pp. 489–491 for Exs. 6–15

Simplify the expression.

6. $4^4 \cdot 4^3$ **4^7**   7. $(-3)^7(-3)$ **$(-3)^8$**   8. $z^3 \cdot z^5 \cdot z^5$ **z^{13}**

9. $(y^4)^5$ **y^{20}**   10. $[(-7)^4]^4$ **$(-7)^{16}$**   11. $[(b+2)^8]^3$ **$(b+2)^{24}$**

12. $(6^4 \cdot 31)^5$ **$6^{20} \cdot 31^5$**   13. $-(8xy)^2$ **$-64x^2y^2$**   14. $(2x^2)^4 \cdot x^5$ **$16x^{13}$**

15. **EARTH SCIENCE** The order of magnitude of the mass of Earth's atmosphere is 10^{18} kilograms. The order of magnitude of the mass of Earth's oceans is 10^3 times greater. What is the order of magnitude of the mass of Earth's oceans? **10^{21}**

8.2 Apply Exponent Properties Involving Quotients *pp. 495–501*

EXAMPLE

Simplify $\left(\dfrac{x^3}{y}\right)^4 \cdot \dfrac{2}{x^5}$.

$\left(\dfrac{x^3}{y}\right)^4 \cdot \dfrac{2}{x^5} = \dfrac{(x^3)^4}{y^4} \cdot \dfrac{2}{x^5}$ **Power of a quotient property**

$= \dfrac{x^{12}}{y^4} \cdot \dfrac{2}{x^5}$ **Power of a power property**

$= \dfrac{2x^{12}}{y^4 x^5}$ **Multiply fractions.**

$= \dfrac{2x^7}{y^4}$ **Quotient of powers property**

EXERCISES

EXAMPLES
1, 2, and 3
on pp. 495–496
for Exs. 16–24

Simplify the expression.

16. $\dfrac{(-3)^7}{(-3)^3}$ $(-3)^4$ **17.** $\dfrac{5^2 \cdot 5^4}{5^3}$ 5^3 **18.** $\left(\dfrac{m}{n}\right)^3$ $\dfrac{m^3}{n^3}$ **19.** $\dfrac{17^{12}}{17^8}$ 17^4

20. $\left(-\dfrac{1}{x}\right)^4$ $\dfrac{1}{x^4}$ **21.** $\left(\dfrac{7x^5}{y^2}\right)^2$ $\dfrac{49x^{10}}{y^4}$ **22.** $\dfrac{1}{p^2} \cdot p^6$ p^4 **23.** $\dfrac{6}{7r^{10}} \cdot \left(\dfrac{r^5}{s}\right)^5$ $\dfrac{6r^{15}}{7s^5}$

24. PER CAPITA INCOME The order of magnitude of the population of Montana in 2003 was 10^6 people. The order of magnitude of the total personal income (in dollars) for Montana in 2003 was 10^{10}. What was the order of magnitude of the mean personal income in Montana in 2003? 10^4

8.3 Define and Use Zero and Negative Exponents *pp. 503–508*

EXAMPLE

Evaluate $(2x^0y^{-5})^3$.

$(2x^0y^{-5})^3 = 2^3 \cdot x^0 \cdot y^{-15}$ **Power of a power property**

$= 8 \cdot 1 \cdot y^{-15}$ **Definition of zero exponent**

$= \dfrac{8}{y^{15}}$ **Definition of negative exponents**

EXERCISES

EXAMPLES
1, 2, and 4
on pp. 503–505
for Exs. 25–29

Evaluate the expression.

25. 14^0 1 **26.** 3^{-4} $\dfrac{1}{81}$ **27.** $\left(\dfrac{2}{3}\right)^{-3}$ $\dfrac{27}{8}$ **28.** $7^{-5} \cdot 7^5$ 1

29. UNITS OF MEASURE Use the fact that 1 femtogram = 10^{-18} kilogram and 1 nanogram = 10^{-12} kilogram to complete the following statement: 1 nanogram = $\underline{?}$ femtogram(s). 10^6

8.4 Use Scientific Notation
pp. 512–518

EXAMPLE

Write the number in scientific notation.

a. $2097 = 2.097 \times 10^3$ Move decimal point left 3 places. Exponent is 3.

b. $0.00032 = 3.2 \times 10^{-4}$ Move decimal point right 4 places. Exponent is −4.

Write the number in standard form.

a. $4.3201 \times 10^2 = 432.01$ Exponent is 2. Move decimal point right 2 places.

b. $2.068 \times 10^{-3} = 0.002068$ Exponent is −3. Move decimal point left 3 places.

EXERCISES

EXAMPLES
1, 2, 4, and 5
on pp. 512–514
for Exs. 30–34

30. Write 78,120 in scientific notation.
7.812×10^4

31. Write 7.5×10^{-5} in standard form.
0.000075

Evaluate the expression. Write your answer in scientific notation.

32. $(6.3 \times 10^3)(1.9 \times 10^{-5})$ 1.197×10^{-1}

33. $\dfrac{6.5 \times 10^9}{1.6 \times 10^{-4}}$ 4.0625×10^{13}

34. **MASS** The mass m_1 of a gate of the Thames Barrier in London is about 1.5×10^6 kilograms. The mass m_2 of the Great Pyramid of Giza is about 6×10^9 kilograms. Find the ratio of m_1 to m_2. What does the ratio tell you?
2.5×10^{-4}; the pyramid has a mass 25,000 times the mass of the gate.

8.5 Write and Graph Exponential Growth Functions
pp. 520–527

EXAMPLE

Graph the function $y = 4^x$ and identify its domain and range.

STEP 1 Make a table. The domain is all real numbers.

x	−1	0	1	2
y	$\frac{1}{4}$	1	4	16

STEP 2 Plot the points.

STEP 3 Draw a smooth curve through the points.

STEP 4 Identify the range. As you can see from the graph, the range is all positive real numbers.

EXERCISES

EXAMPLES
2 and 3
on p. 521
for Exs. 35–39

Graph the function and identify its domain and range. **35–38. See margin.**

35. $y = 6^x$

36. $y = (1.1)^x$

37. $y = (3.5)^x$

38. $y = \left(\dfrac{5}{2}\right)^x$

39. Graph the function $y = -5 \cdot 2^x$. Compare the graph with the graph of $y = 2^x$. **See margin.**

Chapter Review   **545**

Extra Example 8.4
Write the number in scientific notation.
a. 463,250 4.6325×10^5
b. 0.3457 3.457×10^{-1}
Write the number in standard form.
a. 5.23×10^4 **52,300**
b. 9.021×10^{-6} **0.000009021**

Extra Example 8.5
Graph the function $y = \left(\dfrac{5}{2}\right)^x$ and identify its domain and range.

domain: all real numbers;
range: all positive real numbers

38.

domain: all real numbers,
range: all positive real numbers

39.

The graph is a vertical stretch with a reflection in the x-axis.

35.

domain: all real numbers,
range: all positive real numbers

36.

domain: all real numbers,
range: all positive real numbers

37.

domain: all real numbers,
range: all positive real numbers

Extra Examples 8.6

1. Tell whether the graph represents exponential growth or exponential decay. Then write a rule for the function.

The graph represents exponential growth. A function rule is $y = 3(2)^x$.

2. A high school issued a report that enrollment in physical education classes at their school has been declining at a rate of 6% per year since 1984. For all grades at the high school, enrollment in physical education classes was 2864 in 1984. Write a function that models the enrollment over time. Find the approximate number of students enrolled in physical education in 2006. $y = 2864(1 - 0.06)^t$; There were about 734 students enrolled in physical education classes at the high school in 2006.

42. Let V represent the value of the car (in dollars) and x represent the number of years since the initial value. $V = 13,000(0.85)^x$; about $6786.

8.6 Write and Graph Exponential Decay Functions *pp. 531–538*

EXAMPLE 1

Tell whether the graph represents _exponential growth_ or _exponential decay_. Then write a rule for the function.

The graph represents exponential decay ($y = ab^x$ where $0 < b < 1$). The y-intercept is 2, so $a = 2$. Find the value of b by using the point (1, 0.5) and $a = 2$.

$$y = ab^x \qquad \text{Write function.}$$
$$0.5 = 2 \cdot b^1 \qquad \text{Substitute.}$$
$$0.25 = b \qquad \text{Solve for } b.$$

A function rule is $y = 2(0.25)^x$.

EXAMPLE 2

CAR VALUE A family purchases a car for $11,000. The car depreciates (loses value) at a rate of about 16% annually. Write a function that models the value of the car over time. Find the approximate value of the car in 4 years.

Let V represent the value (in dollars) of the car, and let t represent the time (in years since the car was purchased). The initial value is 11,000, and the decay rate is 0.16.

$$V = a(1 - r)^t \qquad \text{Write exponential decay model.}$$
$$= 11,000(1 - 0.16)^t \qquad \text{Substitute 11,000 for } a \text{ and 0.16 for } r.$$
$$= 11,000(0.84)^t \qquad \text{Simplify.}$$

To find the approximate value of the car in 4 years, substitute 4 for t.

$$V = 11,000(0.84)^t = 11,000(0.84)^4 \approx \$5477$$

The approximate value of the car in 4 years is $5477.

EXERCISES

EXAMPLES 4 and 5
on pp. 533–534
for Exs. 40–42

Tell whether the graph represents _exponential growth_ or _exponential decay_. Then write a rule for the function.

40.

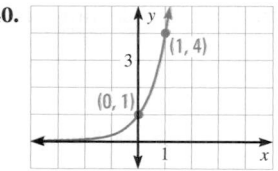

exponential growth; $y = 4x$

41.

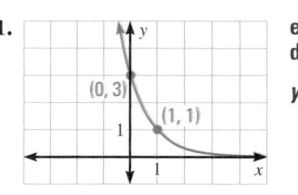

exponential decay; $y = 3 \cdot \left(\dfrac{1}{3}\right)^x$

42. CAR VALUE The value of a car is $13,000. The car depreciates (loses value) at a rate of about 15% annually. Write an exponential decay model for the value of the car. Find the approximate value of the car in 4 years. **See margin.**

CHAPTER TEST

Simplify the expression. Write your answer using exponents.

1. $(62 \cdot 17)^4$ **$62^4 \cdot 17^4$**
2. $(-3)(-3)^6$ **$(-3)^7$**
3. $\dfrac{8^4 \cdot 8^5}{8^3}$ **8^6**
4. $(8^4)^3$ **8^{12}**

5. $\dfrac{2^{15}}{2^8}$ **2^7**
6. $5^3 \cdot 5^0 \cdot 5^5$ **5^8**
7. $[(-4^3)]^2$ **$(-4)^6$**
8. $\dfrac{(-5)^{10}}{(-5)^3}$ **$(-5)^7$**

Simplify the expression.

9. $t^2 \cdot t^6$ **t^8**
10. $\left(\dfrac{s}{t}\right)^6$ **$\dfrac{s^6}{t^6}$**
11. $\dfrac{1}{9^{-2}}$ **81**
12. $-(6p)^2$ **$-36p^2$**

13. $(5xy)^2$ **$25x^2y^2$**
14. $\dfrac{1}{z^7} \cdot z^9$ **z^2**
15. $(x^5)^3$ **x^{15}**
16. $\left(-\dfrac{4}{c}\right)^2$ **$\dfrac{16}{c^2}$**

Simplify the expression. Write your answer using only positive exponents.

17. $\left(\dfrac{a^{-3}}{3b}\right)^4$ **$\dfrac{1}{81a^{12}b^4}$**
18. $\dfrac{3}{4d} \cdot \dfrac{(2d)^4}{c^3}$ **$\dfrac{12d^3}{c^3}$**
19. $y^0 \cdot (8x^6y^{-3})^{-2}$ **$\dfrac{y^6}{64x^{12}}$**
20. $(5r^5)^3 \cdot r^{-2}$ **$125r^{13}$**

Write the number in scientific notation.

21. 423.6
4.236×10^2
22. 7,194,548
7.194548×10^6
23. 500.32
5.0032×10^2
24. 71.23884
7.123884×10^1

25. 0.562
5.62×10^{-1}
26. 0.0348
3.48×10^{-2}
27. 0.000123
1.23×10^{-4}
28. 0.5603002
5.603002×10^{-1}

Write the number in standard form.

29. 4.02×10^5
402,000
30. 5.3121×10^4
53,121
31. 9.354×10^8
935,400,000
32. 1.307×10^{19}
See margin.

33. 1.3×10^{-3}
0.0013
34. 3.32×10^{-4}
0.000332
35. 7.506×10^{-5}
0.00007506
36. 9.3119×10^{-7}
0.00000093119

37. Graph the function $y = 4^x$. Identify its domain and range. **See margin.**

38. Graph the function $y = \dfrac{1}{2} \cdot 4^x$. Compare the graph with the graph of $y = 4^x$. **See margin.**

39. **ANIMATION** About 1.2×10^7 bytes of data make up a single frame of an animated film. There are 24 frames in 1 second of a film. About how many bytes of data are there in 1 hour of an animated film? **about 1.04×10^{12} bytes**

40. **SALARY** A recent college graduate accepts a job at a law firm. The job has a salary of $32,000 per year. The law firm guarantees an annual pay increase of 3% of the employee's salary.

   a. Write a function that models the employee's salary over time. Assume that the employee receives only the guaranteed pay increase. **See margin.**

   b. Use the function to find the employee's salary after 5 years. **$37,096.77**

41. **SCIENCE** At sea level, Earth's atmosphere exerts a pressure of 1 atmosphere. Atmospheric pressure P (in atmospheres) decreases with altitude and can be modeled by $P = (0.99987)^a$ where a is the altitude (in meters).

   a. Identify the initial amount, decay factor, and decay rate. **initial amount: 1, decay factor: 0.99987, decay rate: 0.013%**

   b. Use a graphing calculator to graph the function. **See margin.**

   c. Estimate the altitude at which the atmospheric pressure is about half of what it is at sea level. **about 5332 m**

Chapter Test **547**

37.

domain: all real numbers,
range: all positive real numbers

25.

The graph is a vertical shrink of $y = 4^x$.

40a. Let y represent the yearly salary and x represent the number of years since accepting the job.
$y = 32,000(1.03)^x$.

41b.

When students are developing a plan to solve a problem, encourage them to use what they know to find a solution. Sometimes they will know what is required, such as a formula, but they may not remember the formula. Their plan should therefore focus on alternative methods to solve the problem. For example, if the problem is based on a pattern and they can extend the pattern in a table without using a formula, or they can tell from a diagram how to reach a solution, then they should go ahead without the formula. Sometimes a careful examination of tables and diagrams will trigger the memory of a formula or rule that will help solve the problem.

CONTEXT-BASED MULTIPLE CHOICE QUESTIONS

Some of the information you need to solve a context-based multiple choice question may appear in a table, a diagram, or a graph.

PROBLEM 1

A scientist monitors bacteria cell growth in an experiment. The scientist records the number of bacteria cells in a petri dish every 20 minutes, as shown in the table.

Number of 20 minute time periods, t	0	1	2	3	4
Number of bacteria cells, c	15	30	60	120	240

How many bacteria cells will there be after 3 hours?

(A) 7.69×10^{10} **(B)** 7680 **(C)** 270 **(D)** 120

Plan

INTERPRET THE TABLE Determine whether the table represents a linear or an exponential function. Use the information in the table to write a function. Then use the function to find the number of bacteria cells after 3 hours.

STEP 1
Determine whether the function is exponential.

Solution

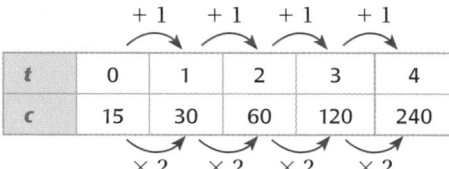

Because the c-values are multiplied by 2 for each increase of 1 in t, the table represents an exponential function of the form $c = ab^t$ where $b = 2$.

STEP 2
Write the function rule.

The value of c when $t = 0$ is 15, as shown in the table, so $a = 15$. Substitute the values of a and b in the function $c = ab^t$.

A function rule is $c = 15 \cdot 2^t$.

STEP 3
Find the number of cells after 3 hours.

There are 180 minutes in 3 hours. So there are nine 20 minute periods in 3 hours. Substitute 9 for t in the function rule you wrote in Step 2.

$c = 15 \cdot 2^t$

$ = 15 \cdot 2^9$

$ = 7680$

There are 7680 bacteria cells in the petri dish after 3 hours.

The correct answer is B. **(A)** **(B)** **(C)** **(D)**

548   Chapter 8   Exponents and Exponential Functions

PROBLEM 2

A fish tank is a rectangular prism and is partially filled with sand, as shown. The dimensions of the fish tank are given. The order of magnitude of the number of grains of sand in 1 cubic inch is 10^3. Find the order of magnitude of the total number of grains of sand in the fish tank.

A 10^2 grains   **B** 10^3 grains   **C** 10^5 grains   **D** 10^6 grains

Plan

INTERPRET THE DIAGRAM Use the information in the diagram to find the order of magnitude of the volume of sand in the fish tank. Multiply the volume by the order of magnitude of the number of grains of sand in 1 cubic inch.

Solution

STEP 1
..................➤ Use the formula for the volume of a rectangular prism.

Find the order of magnitude of the volume of sand in the fish tank.

$V = lwh$ **Write formula for volume of rectangular prism.**

$= 30 \cdot 12 \cdot 3$ **Substitute given values.**

$= 1080$ **Multiply.**

The order of magnitude of the volume of sand is 10^3 cubic inches.

STEP 2
..................➤ Multiply the order of magnitude of the volume of sand in the fish tank by the order of magnitude of the grains of sand in 1 cubic inch.

Find the order of magnitude of the number of grains of sand in the fish tank.

$$10^3 \cdot 10^3 = 10^{3+3} = 10^6$$

The order of magnitude of the total number of grains of sand in the fish tank is 10^6.

The correct answer is D. **A** **B** **C** **D**

PRACTICE

1. In Problem 2, consider the section of the fish tank occupied by water only. The order of magnitude of the weight of water per cubic inch is 10^{-2} pound. The tank is filled to the top. What is the order of magnitude of the weight of the water in the fish tank? **C**

   A 10^{-8} pound   **B** 10^{-6} pound   **C** 10^2 pounds   **D** 10^6 pounds

2. What is the volume of the cylinder shown? **A**

   A $9\pi x^3$ **B** $3\pi x^3$

   C $9\pi x^2$ **D** $3\pi x^2$

Standardized Test Preparation   **549**

MULTIPLE CHOICE

1. The table represents which function? **A**

x	−2	−1	0	1	2
y	$\frac{1}{75}$	$\frac{1}{15}$	$\frac{1}{3}$	$\frac{5}{3}$	$\frac{25}{3}$

   (A) $y = \frac{1}{3} \cdot 5^x$ **(B)** $y = -\frac{1}{3} \cdot 5^x$

   (C) $y = 3 \cdot 5^x$ **(D)** $y = -3 \cdot 5^x$

2. What is the volume of the cube? **D**

   (A) $4x^3$ **(B)** $12x^3$

   (C) $16x^2$ **(D)** $64x^3$

In Exercises 3 and 4, use the table below.

3. List the elements in order from least concentration to greatest concentration. **D**

Element in Seawater	Concentration (parts per million)
Sulfur	904
Chloride	1.95×10^4
Magnesium	1.29×10^3
Sodium	10,770

   (A) Sulfur, sodium, magnesium, chloride

   (B) Chloride, sodium, magnesium, sulfur

   (C) Sulfur, chloride, magnesium, sodium

   (D) Sulfur, magnesium, sodium, chloride

4. About how many times greater is the concentration of chloride than the concentration of magnesium? **D**

   (A) 0.066 **(B)** 0.66

   (C) 1.5 **(D)** 15

In Exercises 5–7, use the table below.

Unit	Number of meters
Kilometer	10^3
Centimeter	10^{-2}
Millimeter	10^{-3}
Nanometer	10^{-9}

5. How many millimeters are in 1 kilometer? **D**

   (A) 1 **(B)** 10

   (C) 10^3 **(D)** 10^6

6. How many nanometers are in a centimeter? **B**

   (A) 10^{-11} **(B)** 10^{-7}

   (C) 10^7 **(D)** 10^{18}

7. A micrometer is 10^3 times greater than a nanometer. How many meters are in a micrometer? **C**

   (A) 10^{-27} **(B)** 10^{-12}

   (C) 10^{-6} **(D)** 10^6

In Exercises 8 and 9, use the graph below.

8. The graph of which exponential function is shown? **D**

   (A) $y = 3^x$ **(B)** $y = -3^x$

   (C) $y = -2 \cdot 3^x$ **(D)** $y = 2 \cdot 3^x$

9. How does the graph compare with the graph of $y = 3^x$? **A**

   (A) It is a vertical stretch.

   (B) It is a vertical shrink.

   (C) It is a reflection in the x-axis.

   (D) It is the same graph.

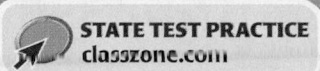

GRIDDED ANSWER

10. If $\left(\dfrac{x^{-6}}{x^{-5}}\right)^{-3} = x^n$ and $x \neq 0$, what is the value of n? **3**

11. Write the number 7.8×10^{-1} in standard form. **0.78**

12. What power of 10 is used when you write 12,560,000 in scientific notation? **7**

13. The table shows the values for an exponential function.

x	-2	-1	0	1	2
y	$\dfrac{3}{25}$	$\dfrac{3}{5}$	3	15	$?$

What is the missing value in the table? **75**

14. An initial investment of $200 is losing value at a rate of 1.5% per year. What is the value of the investment (in dollars) after 3 years? Round your answer to the nearest cent. **$191.13**

15. What is the value of $(2x)^3 \cdot x^2$ when $x = \frac{1}{2}$? Write your answer as a fraction. **$\frac{1}{4}$**

EXTENDED RESPONSE

19. Europa, one of Jupiter's moons, is roughly spherical. The equatorial radius of Europa is 1.569×10^6 meters.

   a. Find the volume of Europa. Write your answer in scientific notation. **about 1.618×10^{19} m³**

   b. Find the average density d (in kilograms per cubic meters) of Europa by using the formula $d = \dfrac{m}{V}$ where m is the mass of Europa (about 4.8×10^{22} kilograms) and V is the volume you calculated in part (a). **about 2.97×10^3 kg/m³**

   c. *Explain* how you could have used order of magnitude to approximate the density of Europa. How would the approximation compare with the density you calculated in part (b)? **See margin.**

20. A gardener is growing a water lily plant. The plant starts out with 4 lily pads and the number of lily pads increases at a rate of about 6.5% per day for the first 20 days. **a–c. See margin.**

   a. Write a function that models the number of lily pads the plant has over the first 20 days.

   b. Graph the model and identify its domain and range.

   c. On about what day did the plant have 10 lily pads? *Explain* how you found your answer.

SHORT RESPONSE

16. A female sockeye salmon lays about 10^3 eggs in one season.

   a. About how many eggs will 10^4 female sockeyes lay? **10^7 eggs**

   b. Suppose about 10^6 of the eggs survive to become young salmon. What percent of eggs survive? *Explain* how you found your answer. **See margin.**

17. You deposit $75 in a bank account that pays 3% annual interest compounded yearly. If you do not make any deposits or withdrawals, how much will your investment be worth in 3 years? *Explain.* **See margin.**

18. Membership in an after-school athletic club declined at a rate of 5% per year for the period 2000–2005. There were 54 members in 2000.

   a. Identify the initial amount, the decay rate, and the decay factor. **See margin.**

   b. In what year did the club have 45 members? *Explain.*
   2003. *Sample answer:* Make a table of values to find that 45 members occurred 3 years after 2000, which is 2003.

16b. 10%. *Sample answer:* Divide 10^6 by 10^7: $10^{-1} = 0.1 = 10\%$.

17. $81.95. *Sample answer:* Substitute 3 for t in the formula $75(1.03)^t$ and solve.

18a. initial amount: 54 members, decay rate: 5%, decay factor: 0.95

19c. *Sample answer:* Divide 10^{22} by 10^{19}: 10^3. This approximation would underestimate the result by about 2×10^3.

20a. Let ℓ represent the number of lily pads and d represent the number of days since the start; $\ell = 4 \cdot (1.065)^d$, $0 \leq d \leq 20$.

20b.

domain: $0 \leq d \leq 20$,
range: $4 \leq \ell \leq 14$

20c. About 15 days. *Sample answer:* By making a table of values and choosing the day with the value closest to 10.

REGULAR SCHEDULE

Pre-AP For pacing and assignments for a Pre-AP course, see the *Algebra 1 Toolkit*.

Lesson	Les. Day	BASIC	AVERAGE	ADVANCED
9.1	Day 1	pp. 557–559 Exs. 1, 2, 3–7 odd, 9, 10, 11–25 odd, 27–31, 37–40, 43–53 odd	pp. 557–559 Exs. 1, 2, 6–10, 12–26 even, 27–34, 37–41, 44, 47, 50, 53	pp. 557–559 Exs. 1, 2, 7–10, 14–16, 18–26 even, 29–42*, 48, 51, 54
9.2	Day 1	pp. 565–568 Exs. 1, 2, 4–14 even, 15, 16, 17–39 odd, 49–52, 56–66 even	pp. 565–568 Exs. 1, 2, 3–43 odd, 45, 46, 49–53, 56, 59, 62, 65	pp. 565–568 Exs. 1, 2, 7, 8, 14, 21–26, 30–32, 33–41 odd, 43–54*, 60, 63, 66
9.3	Day 1	SRH p. 917 Exs. 1–9 odd; pp. 572–574 Exs. 1, 2, 4–8 even, 9–13, 17–22, 24–34 even, 40–43, 46–56 even	pp. 572–574 Exs. 1, 2, 4–22, 24–34 even, 35–37, 40–44, 48, 52, 54, 56	pp. 572–574 Exs. 1, 2, 6–8, 14–18, 19–33 odd, 35–45*, 53, 57
9.4	Day 1	SRH p. 911 Exs. 13–23 odd; pp. 578–580 Exs. 2, 3–15 odd, 16–26, 72–74	pp. 578–580 Exs. 2, 9–16, 18–26 even, 40–45, 72–74	pp. 578–580 Exs. 2, 10–15, 22–26, 40–45, 72–74
	Day 2	pp. 578–580 Exs. 1, 27–42, 51–56, 60–70 even	pp. 578–580 Exs. 1, 31–39, 46–49, 51–58, 61–71 odd	pp. 578–580 Exs. 1, 32–39, 46–50*, 52–59*, 60–70 even
9.5	Day 1	SRH p. 911 Exs. 1–11 odd; pp. 586–589 Exs. 1–19, 66–73	pp. 586–589 Exs. 1, 2, 3–17 odd, 18, 19, 47–55, 66–72 even	pp. 586–589 Exs. 1, 2, 12–17, 47–58*, 66–72 even
	Day 2	pp. 586–589 Exs. 20–28 even, 29, 30–43, 59–62, 74–80 even	pp. 586–589 Exs. 21–29 odd, 33–46, 59–64, 74, 78	pp. 586–589 Exs. 24–29, 34–46, 60–65*, 76, 80
9.6	Day 1	pp. 596–599 Exs. 1–22, 64–72 even	pp. 596–599 Exs. 1–3, 8–21, 52–55, 65–71 odd	pp. 596–599 Exs. 1–3, 12–21, 52–57*, 65–71 odd
	Day 2	pp. 596–599 Exs. 23–37 odd, 38–45, 58–62, 73–81 odd	pp. 596–599 Exs. 26–38 even, 39–51, 58–62, 74, 77, 80	pp. 596–599 Exs. 30–37, 40–51, 58–63*, 75, 78, 81
9.7	Day 1	pp. 603–605 Exs. 1, 2, 3–21 odd, 22–30, 46–50, 53–75 odd	pp. 603–605 Exs. 1, 2, 6–8, 12–24, 25–39 odd, 46–51, 54–76 even	pp. 603–605 Exs. 1, 2, 6–9, 12–20, 23, 24, 26–38 even, 40–52*, 61, 70, 76
9.8	Day 1	SRH p. 928 Exs. 1, 2, 4, 6, 10; pp. 610–613 Exs. 1–22, 87–89	pp. 610–613 Exs. 1–12, 14–22 even, 61–66, 87–89	pp. 610–613 Exs. 1, 6–12, 16–21, 61–67*, 87–89
	Day 2	pp. 610–613 Exs. 23–41 odd, 42–50, 68–72, 76–86 even	pp. 610–613 Exs. 32–60, 68–73, 76, 80, 84	pp. 610–613 Exs. 34–42, 48–60, 68–74*, 78, 82, 86
Review	Day 1	pp. 616–620 Exs. 1–66	pp. 616–620 Exs. 1–66	pp. 616–620 Exs. 1–66
Assess	Day 1	Chapter 9 Test	Chapter 9 Test	Chapter 9 Test
Yearly Pacing		Chapter 9 Total – 14 days	Chapters 1–9 Total – 106 days	Remaining – 54 days

*Challenge Exercises   EP = Extra Practice   SRH = Skills Review Handbook

BLOCK SCHEDULE

DAY 1	DAY 2	DAY 3	DAY 4	DAY 5	DAY 6	DAY 7
9.1	9.3	9.4 (CONT.)	9.5 (CONT.)	9.6 (CONT.)	9.8	REVIEW
pp. 557–559 Exs. 1, 2, 6–10, 12–26 even, 27–34, 37–41, 44, 47, 50, 53	pp. 572–574 Exs. 1, 2, 4–22, 24–34 even, 35–37, 40–44, 48, 52, 54, 56	pp. 578–580 Exs. 1, 31–39, 46–49, 51–58, 61–71 odd	pp. 586–589 Exs. 21–29 odd, 33–46, 59–64, 74, 78	pp. 596–599 Exs. 26–38 even, 39–51, 58–62, 74, 77, 80	pp. 610–613 Exs. 1–12, 14–22 even, 32–66, 68–73, 76, 80, 84, 87–89	pp. 616–620 Exs. 1–66
9.2	9.4	9.5	9.6	9.7		ASSESS
pp. 565–568 Exs. 1, 2, 3–43 odd, 45, 46, 49–53, 56, 59, 62, 65	pp. 578–580 Exs. 2, 9–16, 18–26 even, 40–45, 72–74	pp. 586–589 Exs. 1, 2, 3–17 odd, 18, 19, 47–55, 66–72 even	pp. 596–599 Exs. 1–3, 8–21, 52–55, 65–71 odd	pp. 603–605 Exs. 1, 2, 6–8, 12–24, 25–39 odd, 46–51, 54–76 even		Chapter 9 Test
Yearly Pacing		Chapter 9 Total – 7 days	Chapters 1–9 Total – 53 days	Remaining – 27 days		

RESOURCE MANAGER

Chapter Resource Book

CHAPTER SUPPORT

Parents as Partners (Chapter Overview with home involvement exercises and activity)							p. 1	

LESSON SUPPORT	9.1	9.2	9.3	9.4	9.5	9.6	9.7	9.8
Teaching Guide/Lesson Plan	p. 3	p. 15	p. 26	p. 36	p. 50	p. 61	p. 72	p. 82
Activity Masters	p. 5			p. 38				
Technology Activities & Keystrokes	p. 6			p. 39				
Activity Support Masters		p. 17			p. 52	p. 63		
Practice (3 levels)	p. 7	p. 18	p. 28	p. 41	p. 53	p. 64	p. 74	p. 84
Study Guide	p. 10	p. 21	p. 31	p. 44	p. 56	p. 67	p. 77	p. 87
Catch-Up for Absent Students	p. 12	p. 23	p. 33	p. 46	p. 58	p. 69	p. 79	p. 89
Problem Solving/Application	p. 13	p. 24	p. 34	p. 47	p. 59	p. 70	p. 80	p. 90
Challenge Practice	p. 14	p. 25	p. 35	p. 49	p. 60	p. 71	p. 81	p. 91

REVIEW

Chapter Review Games and Activities	p. 92	Cumulative Practice	p. 94
Project with Rubric	p. 93	Resource Book Answers	A1

Transparencies	9.1	9.2	9.3	9.4	9.5	9.6	9.7	9.8
Warm-Up/Daily Homework Quiz	✔	✔	✔	✔	✔	✔	✔	✔
Notetaking Guide	✔	✔	✔	✔	✔	✔	✔	✔
Teacher Support		✔			✔	✔		
Answer Transparencies	✔	✔	✔	✔	✔	✔	✔	✔

ASSESSMENT BOOK

Quizzes	p. 124	SAT/ACT Chapter Test	p. 135
Chapter Tests (3 levels)	p. 127	Alternative Assessment with Rubric	p. 137
Standardized Chapter Test	p. 133		

TECHNOLOGY

- Easy Planner
- Test and Practice Generator
- Power Presentations
- @HomeTutor
- Activity Generator
- Animated Algebra
- Classzone.com
- eEdition Plus Online
- eWorkbook Plus Online
- Easy Grader Online

ADDITIONAL RESOURCES

- Worked-Out Solution Key
- Notetaking Guide
- Practice Wookbook
- Algebra 1 Toolkit
- Benchmark Tests
- Reteaching and Remediation
- Spanish Study Guide
- Spanish Assessment Book
- Student Resources in Spanish
- Multi-Language Visual Glossary

9 Lesson Practice Level B

LESSON 9.1 Practice B
For use with pages 554–559

Answer key (top right):
1. $4n^5$; degree: 5; leading coefficient: 4
2. $-2x^2 + 4x + 3$; degree: 2; leading coefficient: -2
3. $4y^4 + 6y^3 - 2y^2 - 5$; degree: 4; leading coefficient: 4

Write the polynomial so that the exponents decrease from left to right. Identify the degree and leading coefficient of the polynomial.

1. $4n^5$
2. $4x - 2x^2 + 3$
3. $6y^3 - 2y^2 + 4y^4 - 5$

Tell whether the expression is a polynomial. If it is a polynomial, find its degree and classify it by the number of its terms. Otherwise, tell why it is not a polynomial.

4. 10^x
not a polynomial

5. $-6n^2 - n^3 + 4$
polynomial; degree: 3; trinomial

6. $w^{-3} + 5$
not a polynomial

Find the sum or difference.

7. $(3z^2 + z - 4) + (2z^2 + 2z - 3)$ $5z^2 + 3z - 7$
8. $(8c^2 - 4c + 1) + (-3c^2 + c + 5)$
9. $(2x^2 + 5x - 1) + (x^2 - 5x + 7)$ $3x^2 + 6$
10. $(10b^2 - 3b + 2) - (4b^2 + 5b + 1)$
11. $(-4m^2 + 3m - 1) - (m + 2)$
12. $(3m + 4) - (2m^2 - 6m + 5) - 2m^2 + 9m - 1$

8. $5c^2 - 3c + 6$ 10. $6b^2 - 8b + 1$ 11. $-4m^2 + 2m - 3$

Write a polynomial that represents the perimeter of the figure.

13.

$10x + 2$

14.
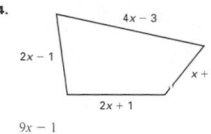
$9x - 1$

15. **Floor Plan** The first floor of a home has the floor plan shown. Find the area of the first floor.

Area: $\frac{17}{4}x^2 + 8x - 32$

16. **Profit** For 1995 through 2005, the revenue R (in dollars) and the cost C (in dollars) of producing a product can be modeled by
$$R = \frac{1}{4}t^2 + \frac{21}{4}t + 400 \quad \text{and} \quad C = \frac{1}{12}t^2 + \frac{13}{4}t + 200$$
where t is the number of years since 1995. Write an equation for the profit earned from 1995 to 2005. (*Hint:* Profit = Revenue − Cost)

$$P = \frac{1}{6}t^2 + 2t + 200$$

Algebra 1
Chapter 9 Resource Book **8**

LESSON 9.2 Practice B
For use with pages 562–568

Answer key (top right):
1. $6x^4 - 3x^3 - x^2$
2. $-20a^7 + 15a^4 - 5a^3$
3. $-8d^5 + 20d^4 - 24d^3 + 8d^2$
4. $6x^2 - 13x - 5$
5. $2y^2 - 7y - 15$
6. $24a^2 - 18a + 3$
7. $5b^2 - 42b + 16$
8. $16m^2 + 38m + 21$

Find the product.

1. $x^2(6x^2 - 3x - 1)$
2. $-5a^3(4a^4 - 3a + 1)$
3. $4d^2(-2d^3 + 5d^2 - 6d + 2)$
4. $(3x + 1)(2x - 5)$
5. $(2y + 3)(y - 5)$
6. $(6a - 3)(4a - 1)$
7. $(b - 8)(5b - 2)$
8. $(8m + 7)(2m + 3)$
9. $(-p + 2)(3p^2 + 1)$
10. $(2z - 7)(-z + 3)$
11. $(-3d + 10)(2d - 1)$
12. $(n + 1)(n^2 + 4n + 5)$
13. $(w - 3)(w^2 + 8w + 1)$
14. $(2s + 5)(s^2 + 3s - 1)$
15. $(x^2 - 4xy + y^2)(5xy)$

Simplify the expression.

16. $a(3a + 1) + (a + 1)(a - 1)$ $4a^2 + a - 1$
17. $(x + 2)(x + 5) - x(4x - 1)$ $-3x^2 - 2x - 10$
18. $(m + 7)(m - 3) + (m - 4)(m + 5)$ $2m^2 + 5m - 41$

9. $-3p^3 + 6p^2 - p + 2$
10. $-2z^2 + 13z - 21$
11. $-6d^2 + 23d - 10$
12. $n^3 + 5n^2 + 9n + 5$
13. $w^3 + 5w^2 - 23w - 3$
14. $2s^3 + 11s^2 + 13s - 5$
15. $5x^3y - 20x^2y^2 + 5xy^3$

Write a polynomial for the area of the shaded region.

19.

$3x^2 + 15x$

20.

$x^2 + 6x + 8$

21. **Flower Bed** You are designing a rectangular flower bed that you will border using brick pavers. The width of the border around the bed will be the same on every side, as shown.

   a. Write a polynomial that represents the total area of the flower bed and the border. $A = 4x^2 + 22x + 30$
   b. Find the total area of the flower bed and border when the width of the border is 1.5 feet. 72 ft^2

22. **School Enrollment** During the period 1995–2002, the number S of students (in thousands) enrolled in school in the U.S. and the percent P (in decimal form) of this amount that are between 7 and 13 years old can be modeled by
$$S = 32.6t^3 - 376.45t^2 + 1624.2t + 66{,}939$$
and
$$P = 0.000005t^4 - 0.0003t^3 + 0.003t^2 - 0.007t + 0.4$$
where t is the number of years since 1995.

   a. Find the values of S and P for $t = 0$. What does the product $S \cdot P$ mean for $t = 0$ in the context of this problem? S: 66,939 students; P: 40%; $A \cdot P$ indicates the number of students that are between 7 and 13
   b. Write an equation that models the number of students (in thousands) that are between 7 and 13 years old as a function of the number of years since 1995.
   c. How many students between 7 and 13 years old were enrolled in 1995?   about 26,776

22. b. $A \cdot P = 0.000163t^7 - 0.01166225t^6 + 0.218856t^5 - 1.510115t^4 + 0.46605t^3 + 38.8676t^2 + 181.107t + 26{,}775.6$

Algebra 1
Chapter 9 Resource Book **19**

LESSON 9.3 Practice B
For use with pages 569–574

Find the product of the square of the binomial.

1. $(x - 9)^2$ $x^2 - 18x + 81$
2. $(m + 11)^2$ $m^2 + 22m + 121$
3. $(5s + 2)^2$ $25s^2 + 20s + 4$
4. $(3m + 7)^2$ $9m^2 + 42m + 49$
5. $(4p - 5)^2$ $16p^2 - 40p + 25$
6. $(7a - 6)^2$ $49a^2 - 84a + 36$
7. $(10z - 3)^2$ $100z^2 - 60z + 9$
8. $(2x + y)^2$ $4x^2 + 4xy + y^2$
9. $(3y - x)^2$ $9y^2 - 6xy + x^2$

Find the product of the sum and difference.

10. $(a - 9)(a + 9)$ $a^2 - 81$
11. $(z - 20)(z + 20)$ $z^2 - 400$
12. $(5r + 1)(5r - 1)$ $25r^2 - 1$
13. $(6m + 10)(6m - 10)$
14. $(7p - 2)(7p + 2)$ $49p^2 - 4$
15. $(9c - 1)(9c + 1)$ $81c^2 - 1$
16. $(4x + 3)(4x - 3)$ $16x^2 - 9$
17. $(4 - w)(4 + w)$ $-w^2 + 16$
18. $(5 - 2y)(5 + 2y)$ $-4y^2 + 25$

13. $36m^2 - 100$

Describe how you can use mental math to find the product.

19. $15 \cdot 25$ Find the product $(20 - 5)(20 + 5)$.
20. $43 \cdot 57$ Find the product $(50 - 7)(50 + 7)$.
21. 18^2 Find the product $(20 - 2)^2$.

Perform the indicated operation using the functions $f(x) = 4x + 0.5$ and $g(x) = 4x - 0.5$.

22. $f(x) \cdot g(x)$ $16x^2 - 0.25$
23. $(f(x))^2$ $16x^2 + 4x + 0.25$
24. $(g(x))^2$ $16x^2 - 4x + 0.25$

25. **Pea Plants** In pea plants, the gene S is for spherical seed shape, and the gene s is for wrinkled seed shape. Any gene combination with an S results in a spherical seed shape. Suppose two pea plants have the same gene combination Ss.
   a. Make a Punnett square that shows the possible gene combinations of an offspring pea plant and the resulting seed shape.   See below.
   b. Write a polynomial that models the possible gene combinations of an offspring pea plant. $0.25S^2 + 0.5Ss + 0.25s^2$
   c. What percent of the possible gene combinations of the offspring results in a wrinkled seed shape?   25%

26. **Basketball Statistics** You are on the basketball team and you want to figure out some statistics about foul shots. The area model shows the possible outcomes of two attempted foul shots.

   a. What percent of the two possible outcomes of two attempted foul shots results in you making at least one foul shot? *Explain* how you found your answer using the table.   75%; Three of the four squares in the area model represent at least one foul shot being made.
   b. Show how you could use polynomials to model the possible results of two attempted foul shots. The chance of making a foul shot is 50% and the chance of not making a foul shot is 50%. So the polynomial $(0.5C + 0.5I)^2 = 0.25C^2 + 0.5CI + 0.25I^2$ represents this situation where C represents a foul shot made and I represents a foul shot missed.

25. a.

	S	s
S	SS	Ss
s	sS	ss

Algebra 1
Chapter 9 Resource Book **29**

LESSON 9.4 Practice B
For use with pages 575–580

Solve the equation.

1. $(x + 14)(x - 3) = 0$ $-14, 3$
2. $(m - 12)(m + 5) = 0$ $-5, 12$
3. $(p + 15)(p + 24) = 0$ $-24, -15$
4. $(n - 8)(n - 9) = 0$ $8, 9$
5. $(d + 8)\left(d - \frac{1}{2}\right) = 0$ $-8, \frac{1}{2}$
6. $\left(c + \frac{3}{4}\right)(c - 6) = 0$ $-\frac{3}{4}, 6$
7. $(2z - 8)(z + 5) = 0$ $-5, 4$
8. $(y - 3)(5y + 10) = 0$ $-2, 3$
9. $(6b - 4)(b - 8) = 0$ $\frac{2}{3}, 8$
10. $(8x + 4)(6x - 3) = 0$ $-\frac{1}{2}, \frac{1}{2}$
11. $(3x + 9)(6x - 3) = 0$ $-3, \frac{1}{2}$
12. $(4x + 5)(4x - 5) = 0$ $-\frac{5}{4}, \frac{5}{4}$

Factor out the greatest common monomial factor.

13. $10x - 10y$ $10(x - y)$
14. $8x^2 + 20y$ $4(2x^2 + 5y)$
15. $18a^2 - 6b$ $6(3a^2 - b)$
16. $4x^2 - 4x$ $4x(x - 1)$
17. $r^2 + 2rs$ $r(r + 2s)$
18. $2m^2 + 6mn$ $2m(m + 3n)$
19. $5p^2q + 10q$ $5q(p^2 + 2)$
20. $9a^5 + a^3$ $a^3(9a^2 + 1)$
21. $6w^3 - 14w^2$ $2w^2(3w - 7)$

Solve the equation.

22. $m^2 - 10m = 0$ $0, 10$
23. $b^2 + 14b = 0$ $-14, 0$
24. $5w^2 - 5w = 0$ $0, 1$
25. $24k^2 + 24k = 0$ $-1, 0$
26. $8r^2 - 24r = 0$ $0, 3$
27. $9p^2 + 18p = 0$ $-2, 0$
28. $6n^2 - 15n = 0$ $0, \frac{5}{2}$
29. $-8y^2 - 10y = 0$ $-\frac{5}{4}, 0$
30. $-10b^2 + 25b = 0$ $0, \frac{5}{2}$
31. $8c^2 = 4c$ $0, \frac{1}{2}$
32. $30r^2 = -15r$ $-\frac{1}{2}, 0$
33. $-24y^2 = 9y$ $-\frac{3}{8}, 0$

34. **Diving Board** A diver jumps from a diving board that is 24 feet above the water. The height of the diver is given by
$$h = -16(t - 1.5)(t + 1)$$
where the height h is measured in feet, and the time t is measured in seconds. When will the diver hit the water? Can you see a quick way to find the answer? *Explain.*   1.5 sec; Yes. From the equation, you can see that the factor $t - 1.5$ will be zero when $t = 1.5$.

35. **Dog** A dog leaps into the air to catch a frisbee with an initial velocity of 14 feet per second.
   a. Write a model for the height of the dog above the ground. $h = -16t^2 + 14t$
   b. After how many seconds does the dog land on the ground? $\frac{7}{8}$ sec

36. **Desktop Areas** You have two components to the desktop where you do your homework that fit together into an L shape. The two components have the same area.
   a. Write an equation that relates the areas of the desktop components. $w(w + 3) = w(7 - w)$
   b. Find the value of w.   2 ft
   c. What is the combined area of the desktop components?   20 ft²

Algebra 1
Chapter 9 Resource Book **42**

Practice B
For use with pages 583–589

Factor the trinomial.

1. $x^2 + 8x + 7$ $(x + 7)(x + 1)$
2. $b^2 - 7b + 10$ $(b - 5)(b - 2)$
3. $w^2 - 12w - 13$
4. $p^2 + 10p + 25$ $(p + 5)^2$
5. $m^2 - 10m + 24$
6. $y^2 - 5y - 24$ $(y - 8)(y + 3)$
7. $a^2 + 13a + 36$ $(a + 9)(a + 4)$
8. $n^2 + 2n - 48$ $(n - 6)(n + 8)$
9. $z^2 - 14z + 40$ $(z - 10)(z - 4)$

   3. $(w - 13)(w + 1)$ 5. $(m - 6)(m - 4)$

Solve the equation.

10. $y^2 + 17y + 72 = 0$ $-9, -8$
11. $a^2 - 9a - 36 = 0$ $-3, 12$
12. $w^2 - 13w + 42 = 0$ $6, 7$
13. $m^2 - 5m - 14 = 0$ $-2, 7$
14. $x^2 + 11x + 24 = 0$
15. $n^2 - 12n + 27 = 0$ $3, 9$
16. $d^2 + 5d - 50 = 0$ $-10, 5$
17. $p^2 + 16p + 48 = 0$
18. $z^2 - z - 30 = 0$ $-5, 6$

   14. $-8, -3$ 17. $-12, -4$

Find the zeros of the polynomial function.

19. $f(x) = x^2 - 5x - 36$
20. $g(x) = x^2 + 8x - 20$
21. $h(x) = x^2 - 11x + 24$ $3, 8$
22. $f(x) = x^2 + 11x + 28$
23. $g(x) = x^2 + 11x - 12$
24. $h(x) = x^2 + 3x - 18$ $-6, 3$

   19. $-4, 9$ 20. $-10, 2$
   22. $-7, -4$ 23. $-12, 1$

Solve the equation.

25. $x(x + 17) = -60$ $-12, -5$
26. $p(p - 4) = 32$ $-4, 8$
27. $w(w + 8) = -15$ $-5, -3$
28. $n(n + 6) = 7$ $-7, 1$
29. $s^2 - 3(s + 2) = 4$ $-2, 5$
30. $d^2 + 18(d + 4) = -9$ -9

31. **Patio Area** A community center is building a patio area along two sides of its pool. The pool is rectangular with a width of 50 feet and a length of 100 feet. The patio area will have the same width on each side of the pool.

   a. Write a polynomial that represents the combined area of the pool and the patio area. $x^2 + 150x + 5000$
   b. The combined area of the pool and patio area should be 8400 square feet. How wide should the patio area be? 20 ft

32. **Area Rug** You are creating your own area rug from a square piece of remnant carpeting. You plan on cutting 4 inches from the length and 3 inches from the width. The area of the resulting area rug is 1056 square inches.

   a. Write a polynomial that represents the area of your area rug. $x^2 - 7x + 12$
   b. What is the perimeter of the original piece of remnant carpeting? 144 in.

Practice B
For use with pages 593–599

1. $(-x + 4)(x + 7)$
2. $(-p + 2)(p - 6)$
3. $(-m - 8)(m + 5)$
4. $(2y + 1)(y + 7)$
5. $(3a - 1)(a - 4)$
6. $(5d + 2)(d - 4)$
7. $(3c + 2)(2c + 1)$
8. $(2n - 3)(n - 2)$
9. $(2w + 3)(6w - 5)$
10. $(b + 4)(-2b + 3)$
11. $(r + 5)(-3r - 2)$
12. $(s - 2)(-4s - 2)$

Factor the trinomial.

1. $-x^2 - 3x + 28$
2. $-p^2 + 8p - 12$
3. $-m^2 - 13m - 40$
4. $2y^2 + 15y + 7$
5. $3a^2 - 13a + 4$
6. $5d^2 - 18d - 8$
7. $6c^2 + 7c + 2$
8. $10n^2 - 26n + 12$
9. $12w^2 + 8w - 15$
10. $-2b^2 - 5b + 12$
11. $-3r^2 - 17r - 10$
12. $-4s^2 + 6s + 4$

Solve the equation. See below.

13. $-x^2 + x + 20 = 0$
14. $-m^2 - 10m - 16 = 0$
15. $-p^2 + 13p - 42 = 0$
16. $2c^2 - 11c + 5 = 0$
17. $2y^2 + y - 10 = 0$
18. $16r^2 + 18r + 5 = 0$
19. $3w^2 + 19w + 6 = 0$
20. $12n^2 - 11n + 2 = 0$
21. $15a^2 - 2a - 8 = 0$
22. $-2x^2 - 9x - 4 = 0$
23. $-3s^2 - s + 10 = 0$
24. $8d^2 - 6d - 5 = 0$

Find the zeros of the polynomial function. See below.

25. $f(x) = -x^2 + 6x + 27$
26. $f(x) = 6x^2 + 45x - 24$
27. $f(x) = -3x^2 - 14x + 24$
28. $f(x) = -2x^2 + 2x + 4$
29. $f(x) = 3x^2 - 17x + 20$
30. $f(x) = 8x^2 + 53x - 21$
31. $f(x) = 4x^2 + 29x + 30$
32. $f(x) = -2x^2 - 17x + 30$
33. $f(x) = 10x^2 + 5x - 5$

34. **Summer Business** Your weekly revenue R (in dollars) from your tie-dye T-shirt business can be modeled by
   $$R = -2t^2 + 87t + 90$$
   where t represents the number of weeks since the first week you started selling T-shirts. How much did you make your first week? $90

35. **Cliff Diving** A cliff diver jumps from a ledge 96 feet above the ocean with an initial upward velocity of 16 feet per second. How long will it take until the diver enters the water? 3 sec

36. **Wall Mirror** You plan on making a wall hanging that contains two small mirrors as shown. $4x^2 + 24x + 32$

   a. Write a polynomial that represents the area of the wall hanging.
   b. The area of the wall hanging will be 480 square inches. Find the length and width of the mirrors you will use. 8 in. by 16 in.

13. $-4, 5$ 14. $-8, -2$ 15. $6, 7$
16. $\frac{1}{2}, 5$ 17. $-\frac{5}{2}, 2$ 18. $-\frac{5}{8}, -\frac{1}{2}$
19. $-6, -\frac{1}{3}$ 20. $\frac{1}{4}, \frac{2}{3}$ 21. $-\frac{4}{3}, \frac{4}{5}$
22. $-4, -\frac{1}{2}$ 23. $-2, \frac{5}{3}$ 24. $-\frac{1}{2}, \frac{5}{4}$
25. $-3, 9$ 26. $-8, \frac{1}{2}$ 27. $-6, \frac{4}{3}$
28. $-1, 2$ 29. $\frac{5}{3}, 4$ 30. $-7, \frac{3}{8}$
31. $-6, -\frac{5}{4}$ 32. $-10, \frac{3}{2}$ 33. $-1, \frac{1}{2}$

Practice B
For use with pages 600–605

2. $(5p - 12)(5p + 12)$
3. $(2b - 10)(2b + 10)$
5. $-2(x - 4)(x + 4)$
6. $-4(r - 5s)(r + 5s)$
7. $(y + 12)^2$
8. $(3c + 4)^2$

Factor the polynomial.

1. $x^2 - 36$ $(x - 6)(x + 6)$
2. $25p^2 - 144$
3. $4b^2 - 100$
4. $36m^2 - 81$ $(6m - 9)(6m + 9)$
5. $-2x^2 + 32$
6. $-4r^2 + 100s^2$
7. $y^2 + 24y + 144$
8. $9c^2 + 24c + 16$
9. $25w^2 - 20w + 4$ $(5w - 2)^2$
10. $16n^2 - 56n + 49$ $(4n - 7)^2$
11. $-18a^2 - 12a - 2$ $-2(3a + 1)^2$
12. $20z^2 - 140z + 245$ $5(2z - 7)^2$

Solve the equation.

13. $x^2 + 14x + 49 = 0$ -7
14. $8w^2 = 50$ $-\frac{5}{2}, \frac{5}{2}$
15. $64p^2 - 16p + 1 = 0$ $\frac{1}{8}$
16. $8a^2 - 72 = 0$ $-3, 3$
17. $3m^2 + 30m + 75 = 0$ -5
18. $-4y^2 + 32y - 64 = 0$ 4
19. $-5x^2 + 125 = 0$ $-5, 5$
20. $-7r^2 + 140r - 700 = 0$ 10
21. $24w^2 - 24w + 6 = 0$ $\frac{1}{2}$
22. $18n^2 + 60n + 50 = 0$ $-\frac{5}{3}$
23. $\frac{25}{2}x^2 + 15x + \frac{9}{2} = 0$ $-\frac{3}{5}$
24. $4x^2 = \frac{9}{16}$ $-\frac{3}{8}, \frac{3}{8}$

Find the value of x in the geometric shape.

25. Area $= 144\pi$ cm^2 8

$(x + 4)$ cm

26. Area $= 225$ in.^{2} 3

$(4x + 3)$ in.

27. **Measuring Tape** A measuring tape drops from a roof that is 16 feet above the ground. After how many seconds does the measuring tape land on the ground? 1 sec

28. **Playground** A curved ladder that children can climb on can be modeled by the equation
   $$y = -\frac{1}{20}x^2 + x$$
   where x and y are measured in feet.

   a. Make a table of values that shows the height of the ladder for $x = 0, 5, 10, 15,$ and 20 feet from the left end. 0; 3.75; 5; 3.75; 0
   b. For what additional values of x does the equation make sense? *Explain.*
   c. Plot the ordered pairs in the table from part (a) as points in the coordinate plane. Connect the points with a smooth curve.
   d. At approximately what distance from the left end does the ladder reach a height of 5 feet? Check your answer algebraically. 10 ft

   b. Any other values between 0 and 20 because the ladder is on the ground at $x = 0$ and meets the ground again at $x = 20$.

Height (feet) / Distance from left end (feet)

Practice B
For use with pages 606–813

14. $4m(m - 2)(m + 2)$
19. $5(m^2 + 4m + 8)$
20. $6(x + 5)(x - 4)$
21. $4z(z - 2)(z + 1)$
22. $9(x^3 + 4x^2 + 4)$
23. $(x^2 + 5)(x + 1)$
24. $(d^2 + 5)(d + 4)$

Factor the expression.

1. $4x(x + 5) - 3(x + 5)$ $(4x - 3)(x + 5)$
2. $12(a - 3) - 2a(a - 3)$ $(12 - 2a)(a - 3)$
3. $w^2(w + 8) - 5(w + 8)$ $(w^2 - 5)(w + 8)$
4. $2b^2(b + 6) + 3(b + 6)$ $(2b^2 + 3)(b + 6)$
5. $y(15 + x) - (x + 15)$ $(y - 1)(x + 15)$
6. $3x(4 + y) - 6(4 + y)$ $(3x - 6)(y + 4)$

Factor the polynomial by grouping.

7. $x^3 + x^2 + 5x + 5$ $(x^2 + 5)(x + 1)$
8. $y^3 - 14y^2 + y - 14$ $(y^2 + 1)(y - 14)$
9. $m^3 - 6m^2 + 2m - 12$ $(m^2 + 2)(m - 6)$
10. $p^3 + 9p^2 + 4p + 36$ $(p^2 + 4)(p + 9)$
11. $t^3 + 12t^2 - 2t - 24$ $(t^2 - 2)(t + 12)$
12. $3n^3 - 3n^2 + n - 1$ $(3n^2 + 1)(n - 1)$

Factor the polynomial completely.

13. $7x^3 + 28x^2$ $7x^2(x + 4)$
14. $4m^3 - 16m$ See above.
15. $-16p^3 - 2p$ $-2p(8p^2 + 1)$
16. $48r^3 - 30r^2$ $6r^2(8r - 5)$
17. $15y - 60y^2$ $15y(1 - 4y)$
18. $18xy - 24x^2$ $6x(3y - 4x)$
19. $5m^2 + 20m + 40$ See above.
20. $6x^2 + 6x - 120$ See above.
21. $4z^3 - 4z^2 - 8z$ See above.
22. $9x^3 + 36x^2 + 36$ See above.
23. $x^3 + x^2 + 5x + 5$ See above.
24. $d^3 + 4d^2 + 5d + 20$ See above.

Solve the equation.

25. $3x^2 + 18x + 24 = 0$
26. $10x^2 = 250$ $-5, 5$
27. $4m^2 - 28m + 49 = 0$ $\frac{7}{2}$
28. $12x^2 + 18x + 6 = 0$
29. $18x^2 - 48x + 32 = 0$ $\frac{4}{3}$
30. $-18x^2 - 60x - 50 = 0$ $-\frac{5}{3}$

   25. $-4, -2$ 28. $-\frac{1}{2}, -1$

31. **Countertop** A countertop will have a hole drilled in it to hold a cylindrical container that will function as a utensil holder. The area of the entire countertop is given by $5x^2 + 12x + 7$. The area of the hole is given by $x^2 + 2x + 1$. Write an expression for the area in factored form of the countertop that is left after the hole is drilled. $2(2x + 3)(x + 1)$

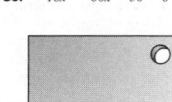

32. **Film Canister** A film canister in the shape of a cylinder has a height of 8 centimeters and a volume of 32π cubic centimeters.

   a. Write an equation for the volume of the film canister. $8\pi r^2 - 32\pi = 0$
   b. What is the radius of the film canister? 2 cm

33. **Badminton** You hit a badminton birdie upward with a racket from a height of 2 feet with an initial velocity of 8 feet per second.

   a. Write an equation that models this situation. $-16t^2 + 8t + 2$
   b. How high is the birdie at 0.1 second? 2.64 ft
   c. How high is the birdie at 0.25 second? 3 ft
   d. How long will it take the birdie to reach the ground? about 0.7 sec

9 Assessment

CHAPTER 9 Quiz 1
For use after Lessons 9.1–9.3

Find the sum, difference, or product.

1. $(-3x^2 - 8x + 5) + (x^2 - 6x + 2)$

2. $(q^3 - 7q^2 - 3q) - (q^3 + 10q^2 - 4)$

3. $-5k^2(k^4 - 3k^3)$

4. $(y + 2)(y^2 + y - 1)$

5. $(4z + 9)(z - 2)$

6. $(p - 7)(p + 1)$

7. $(8m + 3)^2$

8. $(5y - 6)^2$

9. A flower garden is 4 feet longer that its width w. Write a polynomial that represents the area of the garden.

Answers

1. $-2x^2 - 14x + 7$

2. $-17q^2 - 3q + 4$

3. $-5k^6 + 15k^4$

4. $y^3 + 3y^2 + y - 2$

5. $4z^2 + z - 18$

6. $p^2 - 6p - 7$

7. $64m^2 + 48m + 9$

8. $25y^2 - 60y + 36$

9. $w^2 + 4w$

CHAPTER 9 Quiz 2
For use after Lessons 9.4–9.6

Factor out the greatest common monomial factor.

1. $12x^2 + 3xy$ **2.** $21ab^2 + 35ab$

3. $9z^2 - 18z^3$ **4.** $4p - 8p^2$

Factor the trinomial.

5. $w^2 + 15w + 14$ **6.** $m^2 - 12m + 20$

7. $2k^2 + 5k - 3$ **8.** $3b^2 - 20b - 7$

9. $8y^2 + 26y + 15$ **10.** $-2d^2 - 7d - 5$

Solve the equation.

11. $(h + 6)(h - 4) = 0$ **12.** $21d^2 - 7d = 0$

13. $s^2 - 7s + 14 = 2$ **14.** $-5z^2 - 10z = 0$

15. $2g^2 - 14g = -20$ **16.** $-r^2 - 5r - 6 = 0$

Answers

1. $3x(4x + y)$

2. $7ab(3b + 5)$

3. $9z^2(1 - 2z)$

4. $4p(1 - 2p)$

5. $(w + 1)(w + 14)$

6. $(m - 10)(m - 2)$

7. $(2k - 1)(k + 3)$

8. $(3b + 1)(b - 7)$

9. $(2y + 5)(4y + 3)$

10. $-(2d + 5)(d + 1)$

11. $-6, 4$

12. $0, \frac{1}{3}$

13. $3, 4$

14. $-2, 0$

15. $2, 5$

16. $-3, -2$

CHAPTER 9 Quiz 3
For use after Lessons 9.7–9.8

Factor the polynomial.

1. $x^2 - 81$ **2.** $9z^2 - 121$

3. $100m^2 - 49n^2$ **4.** $h^2 + 14h + 49$

5. $64t^2 - 16t + 1$ **6.** $4a^2 + 4b^2$

Factor the polynomial completely.

7. $6x^2 - 6y^2$ **8.** $5m^2 - 20n^2$

9. $x^3 - 3x^2 - 10x$ **10.** $3z^2 + 30z + 75$

11. $2k^3 - 36k^2 + 162k$ **12.** $x^2 + 2x + xy + 2y$

Solve the equation.

13. $d^2 + 10d + 25 = 0$ **14.** $20 - 5s^2 = 0$

15. $y^3 - 49y = 0$ **16.** $6x^3 - 36x^2 + 30x = 0$

17. A box of crackers has a volume of 96 cubic inches. The box has a height of x inches, a width of $(x - 6)$ inches, and a length of $(x - 2)$ inches. Find the dimensions of the box.

Answers

1. $(x + 9)(x - 9)$

2. $(3z + 11)(3z - 11)$

3. $(10m + 7n) \cdot$ $(10m - 7n)$

4. $(h + 7)^2$

5. $(8t - 1)^2$

6. $4(a^2 + b^2)$

7. $6(x + y)(x - y)$

8. $5(m + 2n)(m - 2n)$

9. $x(x - 5)(x + 2)$

10. $3(z + 5)^2$

11. $2k(k - 9)^2$

12. $(x + y)(x + 2)$

13. -5

14. $-2, 2$

15. $-7, 0, 7$

16. $0, 1, 5$

17. 6 in. long by 2 in. wide by 8 in. high

CHAPTER 9 Chapter Test B
For use after Chapter 9

Find the sum or difference.

1. $(4a^3 - 2a + 1) - (a^3 - 2a + 3)$

2. $(3x^3 + 4x + 14) + (-4x^2 + 21)$

3. $(3d - 5d^3 + 2d^2) - (8d^3 + 6d - 1)$

4. $(-3n + 7n) + (4n^3 - 2n^2 + 12)$

In Exercises 5 and 6, use the following information.

During the period 1985–2012, the projected enrollment B (in thousands of students) in public schools and the projected enrollment R (in thousands of students) in private schools can be modeled by

$B = -18.53t^2 + 975.8t + 48,140$ and $R = 80.8t + 8049$

where t is the number of years since 1985.

5. Write an equation that models the difference in the projected enrollments for public schools and private schools as a function of the number of years since 1985.

6. Find the difference in projected enrollments for public schools and private schools in 2005.

Find the product.

7. $-4c(-9c^2 + 5c + 8)$ **8.** $(y + 4)(5y - 3)$

9. $(s^2 + 6s - 5)(5s + 2)$ **10.** $(4p + 1)(4p - 1)$

11. $(w - 5)^2$ **12.** $(2b + 3)^2$

In Exercises 13 and 14, use the following information.

You are making an open box from a rectangular sheet of cardboard by cutting squares 2 inches in length from each corner and folding up the sides. The length of the sheet of cardboard is 8 inches more than the width.

2 in.
2 in.

13. Write a polynomial that represents the total volume of the open box.

14. Find the volume of the open box when the width of the sheet of cardboard is 6 inches.

Answers

1. $3a^3 - 2$

2. $3x^3 - 4x^2 + 4x + 35$

3. $-13d^3 + 2d^2 - 3d + 1$

4. $4n^3 - 2n^2 + 4n + 12$

5. $D = -18.53t^2 - 895t + 40,091$

6. 14,779,000 students

7. $36c^3 - 20c^2 - 32c$

8. $5y^2 + 7y - 12$

9. $5s^3 + 32s^2 - 13s - 10$

10. $16p^2 - 1$

11. $w^2 - 10w + 25$

12. $4b^2 + 12b + 9$

13. $V = 2x(x + 8)$ $= 2x^2 + 16x$

14. 168 in.^{3}

Solve the equation.

15. $(h - 7)(2h + 1) = 0$

16. $4g^2 - 32g = 0$

17. $3m^2 = -6m$

In Exercises 18 and 19, use the following information.

The room and the hallway shown in the floor plan below have different dimensions but the same area.

18. Write an equation that relates the areas of the rooms.

19. Find the value of w.

Factor the trinomial.

20. $n^2 - 14n - 72$ 21. $-x^2 + 14x - 45$ 22. $6k^2 - k - 12$

In Exercises 23 and 24, use the following information.

A juggler throws a ball from an initial height of 4 feet with an initial vertical velocity of 30 feet per second. The height h (in feet) of the ball can be modeled by $h = -16t^2 + vt + s$ where t is the time (in seconds) the ball has been in the air, v is the initial vertical velocity (in feet per second), and s is the initial height.

23. Write an equation that gives the height (in feet) of the ball as a function of the time (in seconds) since it left the juggler's hand.

24. If the juggler misses the ball, after how many seconds does it hit the ground?

Factor the polynomial completely.

25. $x^6 - x^3$ 26. $5a(a - 3) - 7(a - 3)$

27. $9t^4 + 30t^3 + 25t^2$ 28. $b^3 + 5b^2 - 3b - 15$

Solve the equation.

29. $x^2 + 8x + 15 = 0$ 30. $7y - 2 = 5y^2$

31. $72 = 32q^2$ 32. $u^3 + 6u^2 = 4u + 24$

Answers

15. $-\frac{1}{2}, 7$

16. $0, 8$

17. $-2, 0$

18. $3w(w - 2)$
   $= w(w + 1)$

19. $\frac{7}{2}$

20. $(n - 18)(n + 4)$

21. $-(x - 9)(x - 5)$

22. $(3k + 4)(2k - 3)$

23. $h = -16t^2$
   $+ 30t + 4$

24. 2 sec

25. $x^3(x + 1)(x - 1)$

26. $(a - 3)(5a - 7)$

27. $t^2(3t + 5)^2$

28. $(b - 5)(b^2 - 3)$

29. $-5, -3$

30. $1, \frac{2}{5}$

31. $\pm\frac{3}{2}$

32. $-6, \pm 2$

Multiple Choice

1. What is the degree of $-5a^2b + 4a^2 - 2b + 5$? C
   (A) -5 (B) 2 (C) 3 (D) 4

2. Which expression is *not* a monomial? D
   (A) $-2n$ (B) $\frac{m}{2}$ (C) r^2 (D) $3p^{-3}$

3. What is the sum of $6m^2 - 5m + 4$ and $7m^2 + 2m - 5$? B
   (A) $13m^2 - 7m - 9$
   (B) $13m^2 - 3m - 1$
   (C) $13m^2 + 3m - 1$
   (D) $13m^2 - 3m + 1$

4. What is $(12s^2 + 8s - 6) - (9s^2 - 2s + 5)$ in simplest form? B
   (A) $3s^2 + 6s - 1$ (B) $3s^2 + 10s - 11$
   (C) $3s^2 + 10s + 11$ (D) $3s^2 + 6s - 11$

5. What is the product of $x + 5$ and $3x - 2$? A
   (A) $3x^2 + 13x - 10$ (B) $3x^2 - 10$
   (C) $3x^2 + 17x - 10$ (D) $3x^2 - 13x - 10$

6. Which polynomial represents $f(x) \cdot g(x)$ if $f(x) = -4x^2$ and $g(x) = x^3 + 2x^2 - 5x + 3$? C
   (A) $-4x^5 + 8x^4 - 20x^3 - 12x^2$
   (B) $-4x^5 - 8x^3 - 20x^3 - 12x^2$
   (C) $-4x^5 - 8x^4 + 20x^3 - 12x^2$
   (D) $-4x^5 + 8x^4 + 20x^3 - 12x^2$

7. What is the simplest form of $(5x + 2)(5x - 2)$? A
   (A) $25x^2 - 4$ (B) $10x^2$
   (C) $25x^2 + 10x - 4$ (D) $25x^2 - 20x - 4$

8. What is the simplest form of $(2n + 3)^2$? D
   (A) $4n^2 + 12n + 6$ (B) $4n^2 + 6n + 9$
   (C) $4n^2 + 9$ (D) $4n^2 + 12n + 9$

9. Which of the following are the roots of the equation $(y - 3)(y + 2) = 0$? B
   (A) 2 and 3 (B) -2 and 3
   (C) -3 and 2 (D) -3 and -2

10. What is the greatest monomial factor of $32x^5 - 12x^2$? A
    (A) $4x^2$ (B) $32x^5$
    (C) $12x^2$ (D) $20x^3$

11. What are the roots of the equation $5x^2 = x$? C
    (A) -5 and 0 (B) 0 and $-\frac{1}{5}$
    (C) 0 and $\frac{1}{5}$ (D) 0 and 5

12. Which of the following is the correct factorization of $x^2 - 15x + 56$? A
    (A) $(x - 7)(x - 8)$
    (B) $(x + 7)(x - 8)$
    (C) $(x - 7)(x + 8)$
    (D) $(x + 7)(x + 8)$

13. What are the roots of the equation $x^2 + 30x = 1000$? D
    (A) 20 and 50 (B) -50 and -20
    (C) -20 and 50 (D) -50 and 20

14. Which of the following is the correct factorization of $6x^2 - 2x - 20$? B
    (A) $(3x - 5)(2x + 4)$
    (B) $(3x + 5)(2x - 4)$
    (C) $(6x - 10)(x + 2)$
    (D) $(6x + 2)(x - 10)$

---

15. Which of the following is the correct factorization of $-y^2 + y + 6$? C
    (A) $(-y + 3)(y - 2)$
    (B) $-(y + 6)(y + 1)$
    (C) $-(y + 2)(y - 3)$
    (D) $-(y + 2)(y + 3)$

16. What are the roots of the equation $1.5x^2 - 4.5x = -3$? C
    (A) -2 and -1 (B) -1 and 1
    (C) 1 and 2 (D) 2 and 3

17. Which of the following is the correct factorization of $-60m^2 + 15n^2$? D
    (A) $15(2m + n)^2$
    (B) $15(2m - n)(2m + n)$
    (C) $-15(2m - n)^2$
    (D) $-15(2m - n)(2m + n)$

18. Which of the following is the correct factorization of $3x^3 + 24x^2 - 27x$? A
    (A) $3x(x + 9)(x - 1)$
    (B) $3x(x - 9)(x + 1)$
    (C) $3x(x - 9)(x - 1)$
    (D) $3x(x + 9)(x + 1)$

19. What is the completely factored form of $4x^5 - 256x^3$? B
    (A) $4x^3(x - 8)^2$
    (B) $4x^3(x + 8)(x - 8)$
    (C) $4x^3(x^2 - 64)$
    (D) $4x^3(x + 8)^2$

Gridded Answer

20. The square of the binomial $x - 4$ has the form $x^2 - ax + 16$. What is the value of a?

   [gridded answer: 8]

Short Response

21. You made a square card to send to a friend. The card did not fit in the envelope so you had to trim the card. You trimmed 4 inches from the length and 5 inches from the width. The area of the resulting card is 20 square inches.

    a. What were the original dimensions of the card? 9 in. × 9 in.

    b. What was the perimeter of the original card? 36 in.

    c. What is the difference in the areas of the original and trimmed cards? 61 in.²

Extended Response

22. The length of a box is 2 centimeters less than its height. The width of the box is 7 centimeters more than its height.

    a. Draw a diagram of the box and label its dimensions in terms of the height h. See left.

    b. Write a polynomial that represents the volume of the box. $h^3 + 5h^2 - 14h$

    c. If the box has a volume of 180 cubic centimeters, what is its surface area? *Explain*. See left.

22. a.

22. c. 222 cm²; If you set the polynomial in part (b) equal to 180 and solve for h, you will find that the height is 5 centimeters. From there, you find the area of each side and add to find the total surface area.

Journal

1. Explain the four steps that you should try when factoring a polynomial completely.

Multi-Step Problem

2. The diagram below represents a picture frame that is being built.

    a. Write a polynomial expression to represent each dimension of the inner rectangle.

    b. A gold ribbon is to be placed around the outside of each rectangle of the frame. Write a polynomial expression to represent the amount of ribbon needed.

    c. How much gold ribbon is needed if the value of x is 1.5 inches?

    d. Write a polynomial expression to represent the area of the interior portion of the picture frame.

    e. What is the interior area of the picture frame if the value of x is 1.5 inches?

    f. Write and solve a polynomial equation to determine the value of x that will make the interior area of the picture frame measure 63 square inches.

    g. Write a polynomial expression to represent the area of the shaded portion of the frame.

    h. Write and solve a polynomial equation to determine the value of x that will make the shaded area of the picture frame measure 38.75 square inches.

1. Complete answers should include: a brief description of the four steps of factoring a polynomial completely:
1. Factor out the greatest common monomial factor.
2. Look for a difference of two squares or a perfect square trinomial.
3. Factor a trinomial of the form $ax^2 + bx + c$ into a product of binomial factors.
4. Factor a polynomial with four terms by grouping; mention that some of the steps may not work for the polynomial that is being factored.

2. **a.** $10 - 2x$; $8 - 2x$ **b.** $72 - 8x$ **c.** 60 in. **d.** $4x^2 - 36x + 80$ **e.** 35 in.²
f. $\frac{1}{2}$ in. **g.** $-4x^2 + 36x$ **h.** 1.25 in.

Polynomials and Factoring

9.1 Add and Subtract Polynomials

9.2 Multiply Polynomials

9.3 Find Special Products of Polynomials

9.4 Solve Polynomial Equations in Factored Form

9.5 Factor $x^2 + bx + c$

9.6 Factor $ax^2 + bx + c$

9.7 Factor Special Products

9.8 Factor Polynomials Completely

Before

In previous chapters, you learned the following skills, which you'll use in Chapter 9: using the distributive property, combining like terms, and using the properties of exponents.

Prerequisite Skills

VOCABULARY CHECK

Copy and complete the statement.

1. Terms that have the same variable part are called __?__. **like terms**

2. For a function $f(x)$, a(n) __?__ is an x-value for which $f(x) = 0$. **zero**

SKILLS CHECK

Find the greatest common factor of the pair of numbers. *(Review p. 910 for 9.4.)*

3. $121, 77$ **11**   4. $96, 32$ **32**   5. $81, 42$ **3**   6. $12, 56$ **4**

Simplify the expression. *(Review p. 96 for 9.1–9.8.)*

7. $3x + (-6x)$ **$-3x$**   8. $5 + 4x + 2$ **$4x + 7$**   9. $4(2x - 1) + x$ **$9x - 4$**   10. $-(x + 4) - 6x$ **$-7x - 4$**

Simplify the expression. *(Review p. 489 for 9.2–9.8.)*

11. $(3xy)^3$ **$27x^3y^3$**   12. $xy^2 \cdot xy^3$ **x^2y^5**   13. $(x^5)^3$ **x^{15}**   14. $(-x)^3$ **$-x^3$**

@HomeTutor Prerequisite skills practice at classzone.com

552

In Chapter 9, you will apply the big ideas listed below and reviewed in the Chapter Summary on page 615. You will also use the key vocabulary listed below.

Big Ideas

① Adding, subtracting, and multiplying polynomials
② Factoring polynomials
③ Writing and solving polynomial equations to solve problems

KEY VOCABULARY
- monomial, *p. 554*
- degree, *p. 554*
- polynomial, *p. 554*
- leading coefficient, *p. 554*
- binomial, *p. 555*

- trinomial, *p. 555*
- roots, *p. 575*
- vertical motion model, *p. 577*

- perfect square trinomial, *p. 601*
- factor by grouping, *p. 606*
- factor completely, *p. 607*

Why?

You can use a polynomial function to model vertical motion. For example, you can use a polynomial function to model the height of a jumping animal as a function of time.

Animated Algebra

The animation illustrated below for Exercise 62 on page 598 helps you to answer this question: How does changing the initial vertical velocity of a serval, an African cat, affect its jumping height?

Your goal is to find the height of the serval at different times.

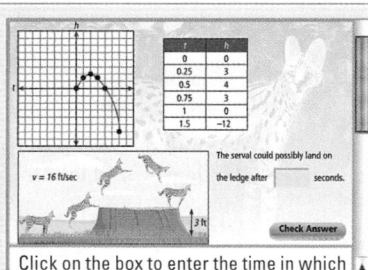
Click on the box to enter the time in which the serval lands on the ledge.

Animated Algebra at classzone.com

Other animations for Chapter 9: pages 555, 582, 592, and 601

1 PLAN AND PREPARE

Warm-Up Exercises

📄 **Transparency Available**

Simplify the expression.

1. $5x + 4(2x + 7)$ **$13x + 28$**

2. $9x - 6(x + 2) + 3$ **$3x - 9$**

3. Imported square tiles used for a kitchen floor measure 18 centimeters on one side. What is the area of a floor composed of 50 tiles? Use $A = s^2$ for the area of a tile. **16,200 cm²**

Notetaking Guide

📄 **Transparency Available**

Promotes interactive learning and notetaking skills, pp. 188–190.

Pacing

Basic: 1 day

Average: 1 day

Advanced: 1 day

Block: 0.5 block with 9.2

• See *Teaching Guide/Lesson Plan.*

2 FOCUS AND MOTIVATE

Essential Question

Big Idea 1, p. 553

How do you add and subtract polynomials? **Tell students they will learn how to answer this question by using vertical and horizontal formats to find sums and differences of polynomials.**

NCTM STANDARDS

Standard 2: Represent situations using algebraic symbols

Standard 10: Use representations to communicate mathematical ideas

9.1 Add and Subtract Polynomials

Before You added and subtracted integers.

Now You will add and subtract polynomials.

Why? So you can model trends in recreation, as in Ex. 37.

Key Vocabulary
• monomial
• degree
• polynomial
• leading coefficient
• binomial
• trinomial

A **monomial** is a number, a variable, or the product of a number and one or more variables with whole number exponents. The **degree of a monomial** is the sum of the exponents of the variables in the monomial. The degree of a nonzero constant term is 0. The constant 0 does not have a degree.

Monomial	Degree		Not a monomial	Reason
10	0		$5 + x$	A sum is not a monomial.
$3x$	1		$\frac{2}{n}$	A monomial cannot have a variable in the denominator.
$\frac{1}{2}ab^2$	$1 + 2 = 3$		4^a	A monomial cannot have a variable exponent.
$-1.8m^5$	5		x^{-1}	The variable must have a whole number exponent.

A **polynomial** is a monomial or a sum of monomials, each called a *term* of the polynomial. The **degree of a polynomial** is the greatest degree of its terms.

When a polynomial is written so that the exponents of a variable decrease from left to right, the coefficient of the first term is called the **leading coefficient**.

$$2x^3 + x^2 - 5x + 12$$

EXAMPLE 1 Rewrite a polynomial

Write $15x - x^3 + 3$ so that the exponents decrease from left to right. Identify the degree and leading coefficient of the polynomial.

Solution

Consider the degree of each of the polynomial's terms.

Degree is 1.   Degree is 3.   Degree is 0.

$$15x - x^3 + 3$$

The polynomial can be written as $-x^3 + 15x + 3$. The greatest degree is 3, so the degree of the polynomial is 3, and the leading coefficient is -1.

Resource Planning Guide

Chapter Resource Book
• Teaching Guide/Lesson Plan (pp. 3–4)
• Activity Master (p. 5)
• Practice levels A, B, C (pp. 7–9)
• Study Guide (pp. 10–11)
• Catch-up for Absent Students (p. 12)
• Problem Solving Workshop (p. 13)
• Challenge (p. 14)

Workbooks
• Notetaking Guide (pp. 188–190)
• Practice Workbook (pp. 133–134)

Teaching Options
• **Power Presentations CD-ROM**
  provides dynamic electronic teaching resources for the classroom.
• **Activity Generator CD-ROM** provides editable activities for all ability levels.

Interactive Technology
• Easy Planner
• Power Presentations CD-ROM
• Activity Generator CD-ROM
• Animated Algebra
• Test Generator CD-ROM
• Online Quiz
• eWorkbook
• eEdition
• @HomeTutor

Resources for English Learners
• Quick Reference for English Learners
• Spanish Study Guide
• Multi-Language Visual Glossary
• Student Resources in Spanish

See also the *Algebra 1 Toolkit* for more strategies for meeting individual needs.

BINOMIALS AND TRINOMIALS A polynomial with two terms is called a **binomial**. A polynomial with three terms is called a **trinomial**.

EXAMPLE 2 **Identify and classify polynomials**

Tell whether the expression is a polynomial. If it is a polynomial, find its degree and classify it by the number of its terms. Otherwise, tell why it is not a polynomial.

	Expression	Is it a polynomial?	Classify by degree and number of terms
a.	9	Yes	0 degree monomial
b.	$2x^2 + x - 5$	Yes	2nd degree trinomial
c.	$6n^4 - 8^n$	No; variable exponent	
d.	$n^{-2} - 3$	No; negative exponent	
e.	$7bc^3 + 4b^4c$	Yes	5th degree binomial

ADDING POLYNOMIALS To add polynomials, add like terms. You can use a vertical or a horizontal format.

EXAMPLE 3 **Add polynomials**

Find the sum.

a. $(2x^3 - 5x^2 + x) + (2x^2 + x^3 - 1)$ b. $(3x^2 + x - 6) + (x^2 + 4x + 10)$

Solution

> **ALIGN TERMS**
> If a particular power of the variable appears in one polynomial but not the other, leave a space in that column, or write the term with a coefficient of 0.

a. **Vertical format:** Align like terms in vertical columns.

$$\begin{array}{r} 2x^3 - 5x^2 + x \\ +\quad x^3 + 2x^2 \qquad - 1 \\ \hline 3x^3 - 3x^2 + x - 1 \end{array}$$

b. **Horizontal format:** Group like terms and simplify.

$(3x^2 + x - 6) + (x^2 + 4x + 10) = (3x^2 + x^2) + (x + 4x) + (-6 + 10)$

$= 4x^2 + 5x + 4$

Animated Algebra at classzone.com

✓ **GUIDED PRACTICE** for Examples 1, 2, and 3

1. Write $5y - 2y^2 + 9$ so that the exponents decrease from left to right. Identify the degree and leading coefficient of the polynomial.
   $-2y^2 + 5y + 9; 2, -2$

2. Tell whether $y^3 - 4y + 3$ is a polynomial. If it is a polynomial, find its degree and classify it by the number of its terms. Otherwise, tell why it is not a polynomial. **polynomial; 3, trinomial**

3. Find the sum $(5x^3 + 4x - 2x) + (4x^2 + 3x^3 - 6)$. $8x^3 + 4x^2 + 2x - 6$

9.1   Add and Subtract Polynomials   **555**

Differentiated Instruction

Below Level To help students gain confidence in recognizing polynomials, have them work with partners to write examples of 1st degree through 6th degree monomials, binomials, and trinomials. Suggest that they create a table to organize their work. Encourage students to write some polynomials with more than one variable per term. Have partners exchange their polynomials so that other partners can check that the polynomials fit the descriptions.

See also the *Algebra 1 Toolkit* for more strategies.

555

Extra Example 4
Find the difference.
a. $(2c^2 - 8) - (3c^2 - 4c + 1)$
$-c^2 + 4c - 9$
b. $(5y^2 + 2y - 4) - (-y^2 + 4y - 3)$
$6y^2 - 2y - 1$

Key Question to Ask for Example 4

• How do you group terms in the horizontal format for part (a)? $(4n^2 - (-2n^2)) + (-2n) + (5 - (-4))$

Extra Example 5
During the period 1999–2005, the number of hours an individual person watched broadcast television B and cable and satellite television C can be modeled by $B = 2.8t^2 - 35t + 879$ and $C = -5t^2 + 80t + 712$ where t is the number of years since 1999. About how many hours did people watch television in 2002? **about 1706 h**

Closing the Lesson
Have students summarize the major points of the lesson and answer the Essential Question: How do you add and subtract polynomials?

• A polynomial is a monomial or the sum of monomials. The degree of a polynomial is the greatest degree of its terms.

• Use a vertical or horizontal format to add and subtract polynomials.

To use a vertical format, align like terms in columns. To use a horizontal format, group like terms and simplify. To add, add the terms. To subtract, add the opposite of each term of the subtracted polynomial.

SUBTRACTING POLYNOMIALS To subtract a polynomial, add its opposite. To find the opposite of a polynomial, multiply each of its terms by −1.

EXAMPLE 4 Subtract polynomials

Find the difference.

a. $(4n^2 + 5) - (-2n^2 + 2n - 4)$ b. $(4x^2 - 3x + 5) - (3x^2 - x - 8)$

Solution

AVOID ERRORS
Remember to multiply *each* term in the polynomial by −1 when you write the subtraction as addition.

a.
$$
\begin{array}{r}
(4n^2 \quad\;\; + 5) \\
-(-2n^2 + 2n - 4)
\end{array}
$$

$$
\begin{array}{r}
4n^2 \quad\;\; + 5 \\
+ 2n^2 - 2n + 4 \\
\hline
6n^2 - 2n + 9
\end{array}
$$

b. $(4x^2 - 3x + 5) - (3x^2 - x - 8) = 4x^2 - 3x + 5 - 3x^2 + x + 8$
$$= (4x^2 - 3x^2) + (-3x + x) + (5 + 8)$$
$$= x^2 - 2x + 13$$

EXAMPLE 5 Solve a multi-step problem

BASEBALL ATTENDANCE Major League Baseball teams are divided into two leagues. During the period 1995–2001, the attendance N and A (in thousands) at National and American League baseball games, respectively, can be modeled by

$N = -488t^2 + 5430t + 24{,}700$ and

$A = -318t^2 + 3040t + 25{,}600$

where t is the number of years since 1995. About how many people attended Major League Baseball games in 2001?

Solution

STEP 1 **Add** the models for the attendance in each league to find a model for M, the total attendance (in thousands).

$$M = (-488t^2 + 5430t + 24{,}700) + (-318t^2 + 3040t + 25{,}600)$$
$$= (-488t^2 - 318t^2) + (5430t + 3040t) + (24{,}700 + 25{,}600)$$
$$= -806t^2 + 8470t + 50{,}300$$

AVOID ERRORS
Because a value of M represents *thousands* of people, $M \approx 72{,}100$ represents 72,100,000 people.

STEP 2 **Substitute** 6 for t in the model, because 2001 is 6 years after 1995.

$$M = -806(6)^2 + 8470(6) + 50{,}300 \approx 72{,}100$$

▶ About 72,100,000 people attended Major League Baseball games in 2001.

 GUIDED PRACTICE   for Examples 4 and 5

4. Find the difference $(4x^2 - 7x) - (5x^2 + 4x - 9)$. $-x^2 - 11x + 9$

5. about 7,320,000 people

5. **BASEBALL ATTENDANCE** Look back at Example 5. Find the difference in attendance at National and American League baseball games in 2001.

Differentiated Instruction

Advanced Have students use the online U.S. Statistical Abstract to research a favorite sport or activity. Have them create a problem similar to **Example 5** using data that appear nonlinear. If necessary, they can review the Activity on page 342 on using the Abstract. They can enter data on a graphing calculator and use the quadratic and cubic regression option to find a best-fit equation. Students can discuss which equations best fit the data and exchange and solve each other's problems.

See also the *Algebra 1 Toolkit* for more strategies.

SKILL PRACTICE

[A] 1. **VOCABULARY** Copy and complete: A number, a variable, or the product of one or more variables is called a(n) __?__ . **monomial**

2. ★ **WRITING** Is 6 a polynomial? *Explain* why or why not. **Yes; a polynomial is a monomial or a sum of monomials, since 6 is a monomial, it is also a polynomial.**

EXAMPLE 1
on p. 554
for Exs. 3–9

REWRITING POLYNOMIALS Write the polynomial so that the exponents decrease from left to right. Identify the degree and leading coefficient of the polynomial.

3. $9m^5$ $9m^5$; 5, 9   4. $2 - 6y$ $-6y + 2$; 1, -6 5. $2x^2y^2 - 8xy$
                                                                    $2x^2y^2 - 8xy$; 4, 2

6. $5n^3 + 2n - 7$ 7. $5z + 2z^3 - z^2 + 3z^4$ 8. $-2h^2 + 2h^4 - h^6$
  $5n^3 + 2n - 7$; 3, 5 $3z^4 + 2z^3 - z^2 + 5z$; 4, 3 $-h^6 + 2h^4 - 2h^2$; 6, -1

9. ★ **MULTIPLE CHOICE** What is the degree of $-4x^3 + 6x^4 - 1$? **C**

   Ⓐ -4 Ⓑ 3   Ⓒ 4   Ⓓ 6

EXAMPLE 2
on p. 555
for Exs. 10–16

10. ★ **MULTIPLE CHOICE** Which expression is *not* a monomial? **D**

   Ⓐ $-5x^2$ Ⓑ $0.2y^4$ Ⓒ $3mn$ Ⓓ $3s^{-2}$

IDENTIFYING AND CLASSIFYING POLYNOMIALS Tell whether the expression is a polynomial. If it is a polynomial, find its degree and classify it by the number of its terms. Otherwise, tell why it is not a polynomial.

11. -4^x **not a polynomial; variable exponent**   12. $w^{-3} + 1$ **not a polynomial; negative exponent**   13. $3x - 5$ **1 polynomial, binomial**

14. $\frac{4}{5}f^2 - \frac{1}{2}f + \frac{2}{3}$ 15. $6 - n^2 + 5n^3$ 16. $10y^4 - 3y^2 + 11$
  polynomial; 2, trinomial   **polynomial; 3, trinomial**   **polynomial; 4, trinomial**

EXAMPLES 3 and 4
on pp. 555–556
for Exs. 17–28

ADDING AND SUBTRACTING POLYNOMIALS Find the sum or difference.

17. $(5a^2 - 3) + (8a^2 - 1)$ $13a^2 - 4$ 18. $(h^2 + 4h - 4) + (5h^2 - 8h + 2)$
                                                                $6h^2 - 4h - 2$

19. $(4m^2 - m + 2) + (-3m^2 + 10m + 7)$ 20. $(7k^2 + 2k - 6) + (3k^2 - 11k - 8)$
                   $m^2 + 9m + 9$ $10k^2 - 9k - 14$

⦿21. $(6c^2 + 3c + 9) - (3c - 5)$ 22. $(3x^2 - 8) - (4x^3 + x^2 - 15x + 1)$
                 $6c^2 + 14$ $-4x^3 + 2x^2 + 15x - 9$

23. $(-n^2 + 2n) - (2n^3 - n^2 + n + 12)$ 24. $(9b^3 - 13b^2 + b) - (-13b^2 - 5b + 14)$
                   $-2n^3 + n - 12$ $9b^3 + 6b - 14$

25. $(4d - 6d^3 + 3d^2) - (9d^3 + 7d - 2)$ 26. $(9p^2 - 6p^3 + 3 - 11p) + (7p^3 - 3p^2 + 4)$
                 $-15d^3 + 3d^2 - 3d + 2$ $p^3 + 6p^2 - 11p + 7$

27. **Two unlike terms, $-4x^2$ and $8x$, were combined; $-2x^3 - 4x^2 + 8x + 1$.**

28. **When the subtraction was rewritten as addition, the last two terms of the second polynomial were not multiplied by -1; $(6x^2 - 2x^2) + (-5x - 3x) + 2, 4x^2 - 8x + 2$.**

ERROR ANALYSIS *Describe* and correct the error in finding the sum or difference of the polynomials.

27.
$$x^3 - 4x^2 + 3$$
$$+ \quad -3x^3 + 8x - 2$$
$$\overline{-2x^3 + 4x^2 + 1}$$
   ✗

28.
$$(6x^2 - 5x) - (2x^2 + 3x - 2)$$
$$= (6x^2 - 2x^2) + (-5x + 3x) - 2$$
$$= 4x^2 - 2x - 2$$
   ✗

[B] 29. **POLYNOMIAL FUNCTIONS** Find the sum $f(x) + g(x)$ and the difference $f(x) - g(x)$ for the functions $f(x) = 3x^2 + x - 7$ and $g(x) = -x^2 + 5x - 2$. $2x^2 + 6x - 9$, $4x^2 - 4x - 5$

9.1   Add and Subtract Polynomials   **557**

---

4 PRACTICE AND APPLY

Assignment Guide

📘 **Answer Transparencies** available for all exercises

Basic:
Day 1: pp. 557–559
Exs. 1, 2, 3–7 odd, 9, 10, 11–25 odd, 27–31, 37–40, 43–53 odd

Average:
Day 1: pp. 557–559
Exs. 1, 2, 6–10, 12–26 even, 27–34, 37–41, 44, 47, 50, 53

Advanced:
Day 1: pp. 557–559
Exs. 1, 2, 7–10, 14–16, 18–26 even, 29–42*, 48, 51, 54

Block:
pp. 557–559
Exs. 1, 2, 6–10, 12–26 even, 27–34, 37–41, 44, 47, 50, 53 (with 9.2)

Differentiated Instruction

See *Algebra 1 Best Practices Toolkit* for suggestions on addressing the needs of a diverse classroom.

Homework Check

For a quick check of student understanding of key concepts, go over the following exercises:

Basic: 4, 13, 17, 23, 37
Average: 6, 14, 18, 24, 38
Advanced: 8, 16, 20, 25, 39

Extra Practice

• Student Edition, p. 946
• Chapter 9 Resource Book:
Practice levels A, B, C, pp. 7–9

Practice Worksheet

An easily-readable reduced practice page (with answers) for this lesson can be found on p. 552C.

Differentiated Instruction

English Learners Prefixes such as *mono-*, *bi-*, *tri-*, and *poly-* occur often in English. For example, the word *monotonous* means "one tone" and the word *bisect* means "cut into two." For some English learners, these prefixes do not occur in their native language, so the meanings of the terms *monomial*, *binomial*, *trinomial*, and *polynomial* may not be familiar. Try using more common language such as saying "one term" instead of monomial in classifying various polynomials.

See also the *Algebra 1 Toolkit* for more strategies.

GEOMETRY Write a polynomial that represents the perimeter of the figure.

30.
$2x + 6$ $12x + 8$
$x + 8$
$9x - 6$

31.
$3x - 2$ $12x - 3$
$2x$ $2x + 1$
$5x - 2$

ADDING AND SUBTRACTING POLYNOMIALS Find the sum or difference.

32. $(3r^2s + 5rs + 3) + (-8rs^2 - 9rs - 12)$
$3r^2s - 8rs^2 - 4rs - 9$

33. $(x^2 + 11xy - 3y^2) + (-2x^2 - xy + 4y^2)$
$-x^2 + 10xy + y^2$

34. $(5mn + 3m - 9n) - (13mn + 2m)$
$-8mn + m - 9n$

35. $(8a^2b - 6a) - (2a^2b - 4b + 19)$
$6a^2b - 6a + 4b - 19$

C **36. CHALLENGE** Consider any integer x. The next consecutive integer can be represented by the binomial $(x + 1)$.

    a. Write a polynomial for the sum of any two consecutive integers. $2x + 1$

    b. *Explain* how you can be sure that the sum of two consecutive integers is always odd. Use the polynomial from part (a) in your explanation. **The sum of any two consecutive integers can be written in the form $2x + 1$ where x is an integer. Since x is an integer, $2x$ is an integer with a factor of 2, so $2x$ must be even. Then $2x + 1$ must be odd.**

 PROBLEM SOLVING

EXAMPLE 5 **A**
on p. 556
for Exs. 37–39

37. BACKPACKING AND CAMPING During the period 1992–2002, the participation B (in millions of people) in backpacking and the participation C (in millions of people) in camping can be modeled by

$$B = -0.0262t^3 + 0.376t^2 - 0.574t + 9.67 \text{ and}$$
$$C = -0.0182t^3 + 0.522t^2 - 2.59t + 47$$
about 39,800,000 people

where t is the number of years since 1992. About how many more people camped than backpacked in 2002?

@HomeTutor for problem solving help at classzone.com

39b. 1998; substitute $t = 0$ into the equation for T to find the number of books shipped in 1998 to get 860 million books. Substitute 4 into the equation for T to find the number of books shipped in 2002 to get 820 million books. More books were shipped in 1998.

38. CAR COSTS During the period 1990–2002, the average costs D (in dollars) for a new domestic car and the average costs I (in dollars) for a new imported car can be modeled by

$$D = 442.14t + 14{,}433 \quad \text{and} \quad I = -137.63t^2 + 2705.2t + 15{,}111$$

where t is the number of years since 1990. Find the difference in average costs (in dollars) for a new imported car and a new domestic car in 2002. **\$8016**

@HomeTutor for problem solving help at classzone.com

39. ★ **SHORT RESPONSE** During the period 1998–2002, the number A (in millions) of books for adults and the number J (in millions) of books for juveniles sold can be modeled by

$$A = 9.5t^3 - 58t^2 + 66t + 500 \quad \text{and} \quad J = -15t^2 + 64t + 360$$

where t is the number of years since 1998.

    a. Write an equation that gives the total number (in millions) of books for adults and for juveniles sold as a function of the number of years since 1998. $T = 9.5t^3 - 73t^2 + 130t + 860$

    b. Were more books sold in 1998 or in 2002? *Explain* your answer.

41c. about 61%; Cy Young's career lasted 1911 − 1890 = 21 years. To find the number of wins in his career, find the value of *W* when *t* = 21; about 525 wins. From part (b), we know that the total number of decisions in his career is about 855, so to find the percent of the decisions that were wins, find 525 ÷ 855 ≈ 0.614, or about 61%.

B **40. SCHOOL ENROLLMENT** During the period 1985–2012, the projected enrollment *B* (in thousands of students) in public schools and the projected enrollment *R* (in thousands of students) in private schools can be modeled by

$$B = -18.53t^2 + 975.8t + 48{,}140 \quad \text{and} \quad R = 80.8t + 8049$$

where *t* is the number of years since 1985. Write an equation that models the total school enrollment (in thousands of students) as a function of the number of years since 1985. What percent of all students is expected to be enrolled in public schools in 2012? $T = -18.53t^2 + 1056.6t + 56{,}189$; **about 86%**

41. ★ EXTENDED RESPONSE The award for the best pitchers in baseball is named after the pitcher Cy Young. During the period 1890–1911, the total number of Cy Young's wins *W* and losses *L* can be modeled by

$$W = -0.44t^2 + 34t + 4.7 \quad \text{and} \quad L = 15t + 15$$

where *t* is the number of years since 1890.

Cy Young Award

a. A game credited to a pitcher as a win or a loss is called a decision. Write an equation that models the number of decisions for Cy Young as a function of the number of years since 1890. $D = -0.44t^2 + 49t + 19.7$

b. Cy Young's career in Major League Baseball lasted from 1890 to 1911. Approximately how many total decisions did Cy Young have during his career? **about 855 decisions**

c. About what percent of the decisions in Cy Young's career were wins? *Explain* how you found your answer.

C **42. CHALLENGE** In 1970 the United States produced 63.5 quadrillion BTU (British Thermal Units) of energy and consumed 67.86 quadrillion BTU. From 1970 through 2001, the total U.S. energy production increased by about 0.2813 quadrillion BTU per year, and the total U.S. energy consumption increased by about 0.912 quadrillion BTU per year.

a. Write two equations that model the total U.S. energy production and consumption (in quadrillion BTU) as functions of the number of years since 1970. $P = 0.2813t + 63.5$, $C = 0.912t + 67.86$

b. How much more energy was consumed than produced in the U.S. in 1970 and in 2001? What was the change in the amount of energy consumed from 1970 to 2001? **4.36 quadrillion BTU, about 23.91 quadrillion BTU; 28.272 quadrillion BTU**

MIXED REVIEW

PREVIEW
Prepare for Lesson 9.2 in Exs. 43–48.

Simplify the expression.

43. $0.6(3 - x)$ *(p. 96)* **1.8 − 0.6x**   **44.** $4(y + 6)$ *(p. 96)* **4y + 24**   **45.** $4(1 - b) - 5b$ *(p. 96)* **4 − 9b**

46. $-4(16c - 8)$ *(p. 96)* **−64c + 32**   **47.** $(6t^7)^2$ *(p. 489)* **36t¹⁴**   **48.** $n(2m^2n)$ *(p. 489)* **2m²n²**

Graph the equation or inequality. **49–54. See margin.**

49. $y = -8$ *(p. 215)*   **50.** $x - 3y = 15$ *(p. 215)*   **51.** $y = -5x - 14$ *(p. 215)*

52. $x \geq -3$ *(p. 405)*   **53.** $x + y \leq 9$ *(p. 405)*   **54.** $2x - y < 7$ *(p. 405)*

49–54. See Additional Answers beginning on p. AA1.

⑤ ASSESS AND RETEACH

Daily Homework Quiz
📄 **Transparency Available**

If the expression is a polynomial, find its degree and classify it by the number of terms. Otherwise, tell why it is not a polynomial.

1. $m^3 + n^4m^2 + m^{-2}$ **No; one exponent is not a whole number.**

2. $-3b^3c^4 - 4b^2c + c^8$ **8th degree trinomial**

Find the sum or difference.

3. $(3m^2 - 2m + 9) + (m^2 + 2m - 4)$ **4m² + 5**

4. $(-4a^2 + 3a - 1) - (a^2 + 2a - 6)$ **−5a² + a + 5**

5. The number of dog adoptions *D* and cat adoptions *C* can be modeled by $D = 1.35t^2 - 9.8t + 131$ and $C = 0.1t^2 - 3t + 79$ where *t* represents the years since 1998. About how many dogs and cats were adopted in 2004? **about 185 dogs and cats**

Online Quiz

Available at **classzone.com**

Diagnosis/Remediation
- Practice A, B, C in Chapter 9 Resource Book, pp. 7–9
- Study Guide in Chapter 9 Resource Book, pp. 10–11
- Practice Workbook, pp. 133–134
- @HomeTutor

Challenge
Additional challenge is available in the Chapter 9 Resource Book, p. 14.

9.1 Graph Polynomial Functions

QUESTION How can you use a graph to check your work with polynomials?

EXAMPLE Check a sum or difference of polynomials

Tell whether the sum or difference is correct.

a. $(x^2 - 2x + 3) + (2x^2 + 4x - 5) \stackrel{?}{=} 3x^2 + 2x - 2$

b. $(x^3 + x + 1) - (5x^3 - 2x + 7) \stackrel{?}{=} -4x^3 - x - 6$

STEP 1 Enter expressions	*STEP 2* Graph expressions
Let y_1 equal the original expression. Let y_2 equal the sum.	For y_1, choose a normal graph style. For y_2, choose a thicker graph style.

a.

a.

b.

b.

STEP 3 Analyze graphs

a. The thick curve coincides with the thin curve, so the sum is correct.

b. The thick curve deviates from the thin curve, so the difference is incorrect.

PRACTICE

Find the sum or difference. Use a graphing calculator to check your answer.

1. $(6x^2 + 4x - 1) + (x^2 - 2x + 2)$ **2.** $(3x^2 - 2x + 1) - (4x^2 - 5x + 1)$ $-x^2 + 3x$
$7x^2 + 2x + 1$

Tell whether the sum or difference is correct. Correct any incorrect answers.

3. $(3x^2 - 2x + 4) + (-x^2 + 3x + 2) \stackrel{?}{=} 2x^2 + x + 6$ **correct**

4. $(-4x^2 - 5x - 1) - (-5x^2 + 6x + 3) \stackrel{?}{=} -9x^2 + x + 2$ **not correct; $x^2 - 11x - 4$**

9.2 Multiplication with Algebra Tiles

MATERIALS · algebra tiles

QUESTION How can you multiply binomials using algebra tiles?

You can use the following algebra tiles to model polynomials. Notice that the value of each tile is the same as its area.

 1-tile

 x-tile

 x^2-tile

EXPLORE Multiply binomials

Find the product $(x + 3)(2x + 1)$.

STEP 1 *Model the rectangle's dimensions*
Model each binomial with algebra tiles. Arrange the first binomial vertically and the second horizontally, as shown. These polynomials model the length and width of a rectangle.

STEP 2 *Fill in the area*
Fill in the rectangle with the appropriate algebra tiles.

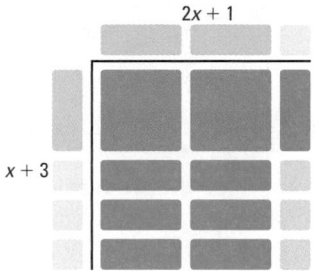

STEP 3 *Find the product*
The rectangle you created represents the polynomial $2x^2 + 7x + 3$.
So, $(x + 3)(2x + 1) = 2x^2 + 7x + 3$.

DRAW CONCLUSIONS Use your observations to complete these exercises

Use algebra tiles to find the product. Include a drawing of your model. 1–6. See margin for art.

1. $(x + 1)(x + 3)$
   $x^2 + 4x + 3$
2. $(x + 5)(x + 4)$
   $x^2 + 9x + 20$
3. $(2x + 1)(x + 2)$ $2x^2 + 5x + 2$
4. $(3x + 2)(x + 1)$
   $3x^2 + 5x + 2$
5. $(3x + 2)(2x + 1)$
   $6x^2 + 7x + 2$
6. $(4x + 1)(2x + 3)$ $8x^2 + 14x + 3$
7. **REASONING** Find the product $x(2x + 1)$ and the product $3(2x + 1)$. What is the sum of these two products? What do your answers suggest you can do to find the product $(x + 3)(2x + 1)$? **See margin.**

9.2 Multiply Polynomials **561**

① PLAN AND PREPARE

Explore the Concept
• Students will use algebra tiles to multiply binomials.
• This activity leads into the study of multiplying polynomials using a table of products in Example 2 of Lesson 9.2.

Materials
Each student will need:
• algebra tiles
• Activity Support Master (*Chapter 9 Resource Book*, p. 17)

Recommended Time
Work activity: 10 min
Discuss results: 5 min

Grouping
Students should work individually.

② TEACH

Key Question
• How do you know which are appropriate algebra tiles to fill in the rectangle? **The length and width of each tile matches the tiles at the left of and above the rectangle.**

Key Discovery
Multiplying binomials is based on the distributive property.

③ ASSESS AND RETEACH

If you use algebra tiles to multiply $(3x + 1)(3x + 4)$, how many x^2-tiles will you need to fill in the rectangle? Explain. **9, since you need to fill in 3 columns and 3 rows of tiles where both dimensions are determined by x-tiles.**

1–6. See Additional Answers beginning on p. AA1.
7. $2x^2 + x, 6x + 3; 2x^2 + 7x + 3$; multiply $(2x + 1)$ by each term of $(x + 3)$ and then add the products.

Before	You added and subtracted polynomials.
Now	You will multiply polynomials.
Why?	So you can determine areas, as in Example 7.

Key Vocabulary
• polynomial, *p. 554*
• binomial, *p. 555*

The diagram shows that a rectangle with width x and length $2x + 3$ has an area of $2x^2 + 3x$. You can also find this product by using the distributive property.

$$x(2x + 3) = x(2x) + x(3) = 2x^2 + 3x$$

In this lesson, you will learn several methods for multiplying polynomials. Each method is based on the distributive property.

EXAMPLE 1 Multiply a monomial and a polynomial

Find the product $2x^3(x^3 + 3x^2 - 2x + 5)$.

$2x^3(x^3 + 3x^2 - 2x + 5)$	Write product.
$= 2x^3(x^3) + 2x^3(3x^2) - 2x^3(2x) + 2x^3(5)$	Distributive property
$= 2x^6 + 6x^5 - 4x^4 + 10x^3$	Product of powers property

REVIEW PROPERTIES OF EXPONENTS
For help with using the properties of exponents, see p. 489.

EXAMPLE 2 Multiply polynomials using a table

Find the product $(x - 4)(3x + 2)$.

Solution

STEP 1 Write subtraction as addition in each polynomial.

$$(x - 4)(3x + 2) = [x + (-4)](3x + 2)$$

STEP 2 Make a table of products.

	$3x$	2
x	$3x^2$	
-4		

	$3x$	2
x	$3x^2$	$2x$
-4	$-12x$	-8

▶ The product is $3x^2 + 2x - 12x - 8$, or $3x^2 - 10x - 8$.

 GUIDED PRACTICE for Examples 1 and 2

Find the product.

1. $x(7x^2 + 4)$ **$7x^3 + 4x$**
2. $(a + 3)(2a + 1)$ **$2a^2 + 7a + 3$**
3. $(4n - 1)(n + 5)$ **$4n^2 + 19n - 5$**

EXAMPLE 3 Multiply polynomials vertically

Find the product $(b^2 + 6b - 7)(3b - 4)$.

Solution

AVOID ERRORS
Remember that the terms of $(3b - 4)$ are $3b$ and -4. They are *not* $3b$ and 4.

STEP 1 Multipy by -4.

$$\begin{array}{r} b^2 + 6b - 7 \\ \times \quad\quad 3b - 4 \\ \hline -4b^2 - 24b + 28 \end{array}$$

STEP 2 Multiply by $3b$.

$$\begin{array}{r} b^2 + 6b - 7 \\ \times \quad\quad 3b - 4 \\ \hline -4b^2 - 24b + 28 \\ 3b^3 + 18b^2 - 21b \end{array}$$

STEP 3 Add products.

$$\begin{array}{r} b^2 + 6b - 7 \\ \times \quad\quad 3b - 4 \\ \hline -4b^2 - 24b + 28 \\ 3b^3 + 18b^2 - 21b \\ \hline 3b^3 + 14b^2 - 45b + 28 \end{array}$$

EXAMPLE 4 Multiply polynomials horizontally

Find the product $(2x^2 + 5x - 1)(4x - 3)$.

$(2x^2 + 5x - 1)(4x - 3)$ Write product.

$= 2x^2(4x - 3) + 5x(4x - 3) - 1(4x - 3)$ Distributive property

$= 8x^3 - 6x^2 + 20x^2 - 15x - 4x + 3$ Distributive property

$= 8x^3 + 14x^2 - 19x + 3$ Combine like terms.

FOIL PATTERN The letters of the word FOIL can help you to remember how to use the distributive property to multiply binomials. The letters should remind you of the words First, Outer, Inner, and Last.

$$(2x + 3)(4x + 1) = 8x^2 + 2x + 12x + 3$$

EXAMPLE 5 Multiply binomials using the FOIL pattern

Find the product $(3a + 4)(a - 2)$.

$(3a + 4)(a - 2)$

$= (3a)(a) + (3a)(-2) + (4)(a) + (4)(-2)$ Write products of terms.

$= 3a^2 + (-6a) + 4a + (-8)$ Multiply.

$= 3a^2 - 2a - 8$ Combine like terms.

✓ **GUIDED PRACTICE** for Examples 3, 4, and 5

Find the product.

4. $(x^2 + 2x + 1)(x + 2)$
$x^3 + 4x^2 + 5x + 2$

5. $(3y^2 - y + 5)(2y - 3)$
$6y^3 - 11y^2 + 13y - 15$

6. $(4b - 5)(b - 2)$
$4b^2 - 13b + 10$

9.2 Multiply Polynomials   **563**

Motivating the Lesson
You want to know how much wall space you need for a poster surrounded by different borders. If you know the length and width of the poster, you can write an expression that models the total area of the poster and its border. You can then evaluate the expression to determine how much wall space you need.

❸ TEACH

Extra Example 1
Find the product $3x^2(2x^3 - x^2 + 4x - 3)$.
$6x^5 - 3x^4 + 12x^3 - 9x^2$

Key Question to Ask for Example 1
• How do you multiply powers that have the same base? **Write the base, add the exponents.**

Extra Example 2
Find the product $(x + 4)(2x - 1)$.
$2x^2 + 7x - 4$

Extra Example 3
Find the product $(a^2 + 3a - 4)(2a + 3)$.
$2a^3 + 9a^2 + a - 12$

Extra Example 4
Find the product $(2x^2 - x - 2)(3x - 1)$.
$6x^3 - 5x^2 - 5x + 2$

Extra Example 5
Find the product $(4a + 3)(a + 2)$.
$4a^2 + 11a + 6$

Differentiated Instruction

Below Level Some students may find the FOIL pattern confusing. To help these students, you may want to use algebra tiles to show how the filled-in rectangle corresponds to each letter of the FOIL pattern. After they have a better understanding of the pattern, encourage them to use notecards to write out each step of the pattern. Suggest that they write an example at the top of the card, such as $(4x + 2)(3x - 1)$, and then First, Outer, Inner, and Last, each on one line of the card. They should show the step next to each word and explain the step in words.

See also the *Algebra 1 Toolkit* for more strategies.

EXAMPLE 6 **Standardized Test Practice**

The dimensions of a rectangle are $x + 3$ and $x + 2$. Which expression represents the area of the rectangle?

(A) $x^2 + 6$ (B) $x^2 + 5x + 6$ (C) $x^2 + 6x + 6$ (D) $x^2 + 6x$

Solution

$$\begin{aligned}
\text{Area} &= \text{length} \cdot \text{width} & \text{Formula for area of a rectangle} \\
&= (x + 3)(x + 2) & \text{Substitute for length and width.} \\
&= x^2 + 2x + 3x + 6 & \text{Multiply binomials.} \\
&= x^2 + 5x + 6 & \text{Combine like terms.}
\end{aligned}$$

▶ The correct answer is B. (A) (B) (C) (D)

CHECK You can use a graph to check your answer. Use a graphing calculator to display the graphs of $y_1 = (x + 3)(x + 2)$ and $y_2 = x^2 + 5x + 6$ in the same viewing window. Because the graphs coincide, you know that the product of $x + 3$ and $x + 2$ is $x^2 + 5x + 6$.

EXAMPLE 7 **Solve a multi-step problem**

SKATEBOARDING You are designing a rectangular skateboard park on a lot that is on the corner of a city block. The park will have a walkway along two sides. The dimensions of the lot and the walkway are shown in the diagram.

- Write a polynomial that represents the area of the skateboard park.

- What is the area of the park if the walkway is 3 feet wide?

Not drawn to scale

Solution

STEP 1 **Write** a polynomial using the formula for the area of a rectangle. The length is $45 - x$. The width is $33 - x$.

$$\begin{aligned}
\text{Area} &= \text{length} \cdot \text{width} & \text{Formula for area of a rectangle} \\
&= (45 - x)(33 - x) & \text{Substitute for length and width.} \\
&= 1485 - 45x - 33x + x^2 & \text{Multiply binomials.} \\
&= 1485 - 78x + x^2 & \text{Combine like terms.}
\end{aligned}$$

STEP 2 **Substitute** 3 for x and evaluate.

$$\text{Area} = 1485 - 78(3) + (3)^2 = 1260$$

▶ The area of the park is 1260 square feet.

7. The dimensions of a rectangle are $x + 5$ and $x + 9$. Which expression represents the area of the rectangle? **C**

(A) $x^2 + 45x$

(B) $x^2 + 45$

(C) $x^2 + 14x + 45$

(D) $x^2 + 45x + 45$

8. GARDEN DESIGN You are planning to build a walkway that surrounds a rectangular garden, as shown. The width of the walkway around the garden is the same on every side.

10 ft
9 ft
x ft
x ft

a. Write a polynomial that represents the combined area of the garden and the walkway. $4x^2 + 38x + 90$

b. Find the combined area when the width of the walkway is 4 feet. 306 ft^2

9.2 EXERCISES

HOMEWORK KEY

○ = WORKED-OUT SOLUTIONS
on p. WS1 for Exs. 23 and 51

★ = STANDARDIZED TEST PRACTICE
Exs. 2, 26, 44, 52, and 53

SKILL PRACTICE

[A] **1. VOCABULARY** Copy and complete: The FOIL pattern can be used to multiply any two __?__. **binomials**

2. ★ **WRITING** *Explain* how the letters of the word FOIL can help you multiply polynomials. **See margin.**

EXAMPLE 1
on p. 562
for Exs. 3–8

MULTIPLYING POLYNOMIALS Find the product.

$4z^6 + z^5 - 11z^4 - 6z^2$

3. $x(2x^2 - 3x + 9)$
$2x^3 - 3x^2 + 9x$

4. $4y(-y^3 - 2y - 1)$
$-4y^4 - 8y^2 - 4y$

5. $z^2(4z^4 + z^3 - 11z^2 - 6)$

6. $3c^3(8c^4 - c^2 - 3c + 5)$
$24c^7 - 3c^5 - 9c^4 + 15c^3$

7. $-a^5(-9a^2 + 5a + 13)$
$9a^7 - 5a^6 - 13a^5$

8. $-5b^3(4b^5 - 2b^3 + b - 11)$
$-20b^8 + 10b^6 - 5b^4 + 55b^3$

EXAMPLE 2
on p. 562
for Exs. 9–15

USING TABLES Use a table to find the product.

9. $(x + 2)(x - 3)$ $x^2 - x - 6$

10. $(y - 5)(2y + 3)$
$2y^2 - 7y - 15$

11. $(4b - 3)(b - 7)$
$4b^2 - 31b + 21$

12. $(5s + 2)(s + 8)$
$5s^2 + 42s + 16$

13. $(3k - 1)(4k + 9)$
$12k^2 + 23k - 9$

14. $(8n - 5)(3n - 6)$
$24n^2 - 63n + 30$

EXAMPLES
3 and 4
on p. 563
for Exs. 16–26

ERROR ANALYSIS *Describe* and correct the error in finding the product of the polynomials.

15. The second term of the first binomial is −5, not 5, so the entries in the second row of the diagram should be −15x and −5; $3x^2 - 14x - 5$.

15.

$(x - 5)(3x + 1)$

	3x	1
x	$3x^2$	x
5	15x	5

$(x - 5)(3x + 1) = 3x^2 + 16x + 5$

16.

$$\begin{array}{r} 2x^2 - 3x - 4 \\ \times \quad\quad x + 7 \\ \hline 14x^2 - 21x - 28 \\ 2x^3 - 3x^2 - 4x \quad\quad \\ \hline 2x^3 + 11x^4 - 25x^2 - 28 \end{array}$$

When combining like terms, the exponents on the variables should stay the same, rather than being added together; $2x^3 + 11x^2 - 25x - 28$.

4 PRACTICE AND APPLY

Assignment Guide

📑 **Answer Transparencies** available for all exercises

Basic:
Day 1: pp. 565–568
Exs. 1, 2, 4–14 even, 15, 16, 17–39 odd, 49–52, 56–66 even

Average:
Day 1: pp. 565–568
Exs. 1, 2, 3–43 odd, 45, 46, 49–53, 56, 59, 62, 65

Advanced:
Day 1: pp. 565–568
Exs. 1, 2, 7, 8, 14, 21–26, 30–32, 33–41 odd, 43–54*, 60, 63, 66

Block:
pp. 565–568
Exs. 1, 2, 3–43 odd, 45, 46, 49–53, 56, 59, 62, 65 (with 9.1)

Differentiated Instruction

See *Algebra 1 Best Practices Toolkit* for suggestions on addressing the needs of a diverse classroom.

Homework Check

For a quick check of student understanding of key concepts, go over the following exercises:

Basic: 6, 19, 28, 38, 49

Average: 11, 22, 30, 40, 50

Advanced: 14, 24, 31, 41, 50

Extra Practice

• Student Edition, p. 946
• Chapter 9 Resource Book: Practice levels A, B, C, pp. 18–20

Practice Worksheet

An easily-readable reduced practice page (with answers) for this lesson can be found on p. 552C.

2. The letters of the word **FOIL** remind you to find the sum of the products of these terms: First terms of each binomial, Outer terms of each binomial, Inner terms of each binomial, Last terms of each binomial.

MULTIPLYING POLYNOMIALS Use a vertical or a horizontal format to find the product.

17. $(y + 6)(y - 5)$ $y^2 + y - 30$
18. $(5x - 8)(2x - 5)$ $10x^2 - 41x + 40$
19. $(7w + 5)(11w - 3)$ $77w^2 + 34w - 15$

20. $(b - 2)(b^2 - b + 1)$ $b^3 - 3b^2 + 3b - 2$
21. $(s + 4)(s^2 + 6s - 5)$ $s^3 + 10s^2 + 19s - 20$
22. $(-r + 7)(2r^2 - r - 9)$ $-2r^3 + 15r^2 + 2r - 63$

23. $(5x + 2)(-3x^2 + 4x - 1)$ $-15x^3 + 14x^2 + 3x - 2$
24. $(y^2 + 8y - 6)(4y - 3)$ $4y^3 + 29y^2 - 48y + 18$
25. $(6z^2 + z - 1)(9z - 5)$ $54z^3 - 21z^2 - 14z + 5$

26. ★ **MULTIPLE CHOICE** What is the product of $2x - 9$ and $4x + 1$? **B**

Ⓐ $8x^2 - 38x - 9$ 　　　　Ⓑ $8x^2 - 34x - 9$

Ⓒ $8x^2 + 34x - 9$ 　　　　Ⓓ $8x^2 + 38x - 9$

EXAMPLE 5
on p. 563
for Exs. 27–32

USING THE FOIL PATTERN Use the FOIL pattern to find the product.

27. $(2r - 1)(5r + 3)$ $10r^2 + r - 3$
28. $(7a - 2)(3a - 4)$ $21a^2 - 34a + 8$
29. $(4m + 9)(2m + 7)$ $8m^2 + 46m + 63$

30. $(8t + 11)(6t - 1)$ $48t^2 + 58t - 11$
31. $(4x - 5)(12x - 7)$ $48x^2 - 88x + 35$
32. $(8z + 3)(5z + 4)$ $40z^2 + 47z + 12$

B **SIMPLIFYING EXPRESSIONS** Simplify the expression.

33. $p(2p - 3) + (p - 3)(p + 3)$ $3p^2 - 3p - 9$
34. $x^2(7x + 5) - (2x + 6)(x - 1)$ $7x^3 + 3x^2 - 4x + 6$

35. $-3c^2(c + 11) - (4c - 5)(3c - 2)$ $-3c^3 - 45c^2 + 23c - 10$
36. $2w^3(2w^3 - 7w - 1) + w(5w^2 + 2w)$ $4w^6 - 14w^4 + 3w^3 + 2w^2$

GEOMETRY Write a polynomial that represents the area of the shaded region.

37. $2x^2 + x - 45$

38. $2x^2 + 12x$

39. $x^2 + 8x + 15$

40. 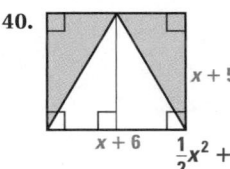 $\frac{1}{2}x^2 + \frac{11}{2}x + 15$

41. $80 - 6x^2$

42. $x^2 - 3x + 36$

43. **POLYNOMIAL FUNCTIONS** Find the product $f(x) \cdot g(x)$ for the functions $f(x) = x - 11$ and $g(x) = 2x + 12$. $2x^2 - 10x - 132$

44. ★ **MULTIPLE CHOICE** Which polynomial represents $f(x) \cdot g(x)$ if $f(x) = -2x^2$ and $g(x) = x^3 - 5x^2 + 2x - 1$? **C**

Ⓐ $-2x^5 - 10x^4 + 4x^3 - 2x^2$ 　　　Ⓑ $-2x^5 + 10x^4 - 4x^3 - 2x^2$

Ⓒ $-2x^5 + 10x^4 - 4x^3 + 2x^2$ 　　　Ⓓ $2x^5 - 10x^4 + 4x^3 - 2x^2$

45. **REASONING** Find the product $(x^2 - 7x)(2x^2 + 3x + 1)$. Show that the product is correct by using a graphing calculator. *Explain* your reasoning.

C **CHALLENGE** Find the product.

46. $(x - y)(3x + 4y)$ $3x^2 + xy - 4y^2$

47. $(x^2y + 9y)(2x + 3y)$ $2x^3y + 3x^2y^2 + 18xy + 27y^2$

48. $(x^2 - 5xy + y^2)(4xy)$ $4x^3y - 20x^2y^2 + 4xy^3$

45. $2x^4 - 11x^3 - 20x^2 - 7x$; graph $Y_1 = (x^2 - 7x)(2x^2 + 3x + 1)$ and $Y_2 = 2x^4 - 11x^3 - 20x^2 - 7x$ in the same viewing window. Because the graphs coincide, the expressions for Y_1 and Y_2 must be equivalent.

○ = **WORKED-OUT SOLUTIONS**
p. WS1

★ = **STANDARDIZED TEST PRACTICE**

EXAMPLES 6 and 7
on p. 564
for Exs. 37–42

EXAMPLE 7 Ⓐ
on p. 564
for Exs. 49–50

49. PICTURE FRAME You are designing a frame to surround a rectangular picture. The width of the frame around the picture is the same on every side, as shown.

   a. Write a polynomial that represents the total area of the picture and the frame. $4x^2 + 84x + 440$

   b. Find the combined area of the picture and the frame when the width of the frame is 4 inches. 840 in.^{2}

   @HomeTutor for problem solving help at classzone.com

50. SWIMMING POOL A rectangular swimming pool is bordered on one side by a deck. A contractor is hired to build a walkway along the remaining three sides of the pool. The width of the walkway is the same on every side, as shown.

   a. Write a polynomial that represents the total area of the pool and the walkway. $2x^2 + 100x + 800$

   b. Find the combined area of the pool and the walkway when the width of the walkway is 5 feet. 1350 ft^2

   @HomeTutor for problem solving help at classzone.com

51a. $12,300 million, 0.171; for $t = 0$, the amount of money (in millions of dollars) people between 15 and 19 years old spent on sound recordings in the U.S. in 1997.

(51.) SOUND RECORDINGS During the period 1997–2002, the amount of money R (in millions of dollars) spent on sound recordings in the U.S. and the percent P (in decimal form) of this amount spent by people who are between 15 and 19 years old can be modeled by

$$R = -336t^2 + 1730t + 12{,}300 \text{ and } P = 0.00351t^2 - 0.0249t + 0.171$$

where t is the number of years since 1997.

   a. Find the values of R and P for $t = 0$. What does the product $R \cdot P$ mean for $t = 0$ in this situation?

   b. Write an equation that models the amount spent on sound recordings by people who are between 15 and 19 years old as a function of the number of years since 1997.
   $R \cdot P = -1.18t^4 + 14.4t^3 - 57.4t^2 - 10.4t + 2100.$

   c. How much money did people between 15 and 19 years old spend on sound recordings in 2002? **about $1680 million**

52a. $H \cdot P = 2t^2 + 263t + 8366$; find the product $H \cdot P$, because the number of housing units times the percent of housing units that were vacant will give the number of vacant housing units.

52. ★ SHORT RESPONSE During the period 1980–2002, the number H (in thousands) of housing units in the U.S. and the percent P (in decimal form) of housing units that were vacant can be modeled by

$$H = 1570t + 89{,}000 \text{ and } P = 0.0013t + 0.094$$

where t is the number of years since 1980.

   a. Write an equation that models the number (in thousands) of vacant housing units as a function of the number of years since 1980. *Explain* how you found this equation.

   b. How many housing units were vacant in 2002? **about 15,120 housing units**

Mathematical Reasoning

Exercise 49 You may want to discuss the usefulness of using a variable to represent the width of the frame. Lead students to see that the ease of manipulating a variable at the design stage allows them to consider the impact of various widths.

Reading Strategy

Exercises 51–52 You may want to point out that Exercise 51 has a worked-out solution and that Exercise 52 uses the same concepts. Exercise 52 is also an example of a short response question, so the worked-out solution for Exercise 51 can provide useful strategies for this type of test question. Suggest that students carefully read Exercise 51 so they understand the problem before they attempt a solution.

⑤ ASSESS AND RETEACH

Daily Homework Quiz

📄 Transparency Available

Find the product.

1. $3x(x^3 - 3x^2 + 2x - 4)$
$3x^4 - 9x^3 + 6x^2 - 12x$

2. $(y - 4)(2y + 5)$ $2y^2 - 3y - 20$

3. $(4x + 3)(3x - 2)$ $12x^2 + x - 6$

4. $(b^2 - 2b - 1)(3b - 5)$
$3b^3 - 11b^2 + 7b + 5$

5. The dimensions of a rectangle are $x + 4$ and $3x - 1$. Write an expression to represent the area of the rectangle. $3x^2 + 11x - 4$

🌐 **Online Quiz**

Available at **classzone.com**

Diagnosis/Remediation

• Practice A, B, C in Chapter 9 Resource Book, pp. 18–20
• Study Guide in Chapter 9 Resource Book, pp. 21–22
• Practice Workbook, pp. 135–136
• @HomeTutor

Challenge

Additional challenge is available in the Chapter 9 Resource Book, p. 25.

53a. *Sample answer: $T = t + 90$; use the data points from 1995–1999: (5, 95), (6, 96), (7, 97), (8, 98), (9, 99). All these points lie on a line with slope $m = 1$; use any one of the points to find the y-intercept $b = 90$. The other data points, (0, 92), (10, 101), and (11, 102), lie close to the line $T = t + 90$.*

B **53.** ★ **EXTENDED RESPONSE** The bar graph shows the number of households with a television for various years during the period 1990–2001.

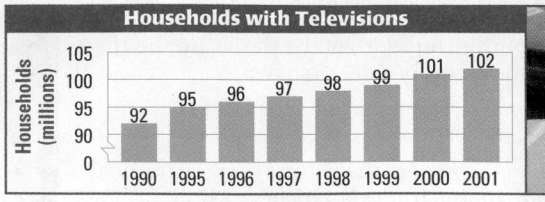

Households with Televisions

a. Find a linear equation that models the number of households T (in millions) with a television as a function of the number of years since 1990. *Explain* how you found your model.

b. During the period 1990–2001, the percent P (in decimal form) of television households that also have a VCR can be modeled by

$$P = -0.0015t^2 + 0.032t + 0.069$$

where t is the number of years since 1990. Write an equation that models the number of households V (in millions) with a VCR and a television as a function of the number of years since 1990.
$V = -0.0015t^3 - 0.103t^2 + 2.949t + 6.21$

c. Use the equation from part (b) to predict the number of households that had a VCR and a television in 2002 and in 2005. **about 24.2 million households, about 22.2 million households**

C **54.** **CHALLENGE** For the period 1990–2001, the total United States energy consumption C (in quadrillion British Thermal Units, or BTU) and the percent P of the total energy that was consumed in the United States for industrial purposes can be modeled by

$$C = 1.5t + 84$$
$$P = -0.05t^2 + 0.25t + 38$$

where t is the number of years since 1990.

a. Find the percent of total energy that was consumed in the United States for industrial purposes in 2000. **35.5%**

b. Write an equation that gives the total energy (in quadrillion BTU) consumed in the United States for industrial purposes as a function of the number of years since 1990. To write the equation, you may need to rewrite one of the given equations.
$C \cdot 0.01P = -0.00075t^3 - 0.03825t^2 + 0.78t + 31.92$

MIXED REVIEW

PREVIEW
Prepare for Lesson 9.3 in Exs. 55–60.

Simplify the expression. *(p. 96)*

55. $5(2x - 7) + 5x$ $15x - 35$

56. $2x + 3(4x - 1)$ $14x - 3$

57. $15x - 7(x + 3)$ $8x - 21$

58. $-2x(x + 1) + 2x$ $-2x^2$

59. $x(x - 4) - 9x$ $x^2 - 13x$

60. $11x + (x - 1)(8x)$ $8x^2 + 3x$

Solve the system.

61. $2x + y = -5$ **(7, −19)**
$y = -3x + 2$ *(p. 435)*

62. $x - 2y = -7$ **(3, 5)**
$x + 2y = 13$ *(p. 444)*

63. $-2x + 4y = -2$ **no solution**
$x - 2y = -1$ *(p. 451)*

64. $-6x + 4y = 40$
$-3x + 2y = 20$ *(p. 451)*
all real numbers

65. $x \geq -3$ **See margin.**
$y < 5$ *(p. 466)*

66. $y \leq 2x - 5$ **See margin.**
$y > -3x + 1$ *(p. 466)*

65.

66.

9.3 Find Special Products of Polynomials

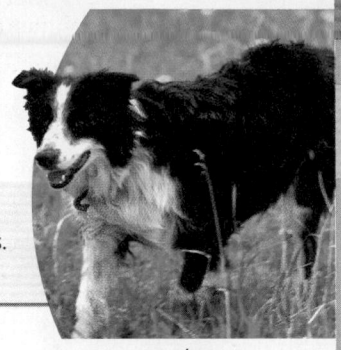

Before	You multiplied polynomials.
Now	You will use special product patterns to multiply polynomials.
Why?	So you can make a scientific prediction, as in Example 4.

Key Vocabulary
• binomial, *p. 555*
• trinomial, *p. 555*

The diagram shows a square with a side length of $(a + b)$ units. You can see that the area of the square is

$$(a + b)^2 = a^2 + 2ab + b^2.$$

This is one version of a pattern called the square of a binomial. To find another version of this pattern, use algebra: replace b with $-b$.

$(a + (-b))^2 = a^2 + 2a(-b) + (-b)^2$ **Replace b with $-b$ in the pattern above.**

$(a - b)^2 = a^2 - 2ab + b^2$ **Simplify.**

	a	b
a	a^2	ab
b	ab	b^2

KEY CONCEPT   *For Your Notebook*

Square of a Binomial Pattern

Algebra

$(a + b)^2 = a^2 + 2ab + b^2$

$(a - b)^2 = a^2 - 2ab + b^2$

Example

$(x + 5)^2 = x^2 + 10x + 25$

$(2x - 3)^2 = 4x^2 - 12x + 9$

EXAMPLE 1   Use the square of a binomial pattern

USE PATTERNS
When you use special product patterns, remember that a and b can be numbers, variables, or variable expressions.

Find the product.

a. $(3x + 4)^2 = (3x)^2 + 2(3x)(4) + 4^2$ **Square of a binomial pattern**

$= 9x^2 + 24x + 16$ **Simplify.**

b. $(5x - 2y)^2 = (5x)^2 - 2(5x)(2y) + (2y)^2$ **Square of a binomial pattern**

$= 25x^2 - 20xy + 4y^2$ **Simplify.**

✓ **GUIDED PRACTICE**   for Example 1

Find the product.

1. $(x + 3)^2$ **2.** $(2x + 1)^2$ **3.** $(4x - y)^2$ **4.** $(3m + n)^2$

    $x^2 + 6x + 9$ $4x^2 + 4x + 1$ $16x^2 - 8xy + y^2$ $9m^2 + 6mn + n^2$

9.3 Find Special Products of Polynomials   **569**

① PLAN AND PREPARE

Warm-Up Exercises
📄 Transparency Available
Find the product.
1. $(x + 7)(x + 2)$ $x^2 + 9x + 14$
2. $(3x - 1)(3x + 2)$ $9x^2 + 3x - 2$

3. The dimensions of a rectangular playground can be represented by $3x + 8$ and $5x + 2$. Write a polynomial that represents the area of the playground. What is the area of the playground if x is 8 meters? $15x^2 + 46x + 16$; 1344 m^2

Notetaking Guide
📄 Transparency Available
Promotes interactive learning and notetaking skills, pp. 195–198.

Pacing
Basic: 1 day
Average: 1 day
Advanced: 1 day
Block: 0.5 block with 9.4
• See *Teaching Guide/Lesson Plan.*

② FOCUS AND MOTIVATE

Essential Question
Big Idea 1, p. 553

How do you use special product patterns to multiply binomials? **Tell students they will learn how to answer this question by using patterns to write products of binomials.**

NCTM STANDARDS
Standard 2: Understand patterns; Use models to understand relationships

Resource Planning Guide

Chapter Resource Book
• Teaching Guide/Lesson Plan (pp. 26–27)
• Practice levels A, B, C (pp. 28–30)
• Study Guide (pp. 31–32)
• Catch-up for Absent Students (p. 33)
• Application (p. 34)
• Challenge (p. 35)

Workbooks
• Notetaking Guide (pp. 195–198)
• Practice Workbook (pp. 137–138)

Teaching Options
• **Power Presentations CD-ROM** provides dynamic electronic teaching resources for the classroom.
• **Activity Generator CD-ROM** provides editable activities for all ability levels.

Interactive Technology
• Easy Planner
• Power Presentations CD-ROM
• Activity Generator CD-ROM
• Animated Algebra
• Test Generator CD-ROM
• Online Quiz
• eWorkbook
• eEdition
• @HomeTutor

Resources for English Learners
• Quick Reference for English Learners
• Spanish Study Guide
• Multi-Language Visual Glossary
• Student Resources in Spanish

See also the *Algebra 1 Toolkit* for more strategies for meeting individual needs.

569

Motivating the Lesson

If both parents have brown eyes, it is possible for one child to have brown eyes while another child has blue eyes. By using a special pattern to multiply binomials, you can calculate the likelihood of such an occurrence.

❸ TEACH

Extra Example 1
Find the product.
a. $(2x + 5)^2$ $4x^2 + 20x + 25$
b. $(3x - y)^2$ $9x^2 - 6xy + y^2$

Key Question to Ask for Example 1
• How would the product $(3x - 4)^2$ be different from the product in part (a)? **The middle term would be negative rather than positive.**

Extra Example 2
Find the product.
a. $(r + 3)(r - 3)$ $r^2 - 9$
b. $(4x + y)(4x - y)$ $16x^2 - y^2$

Key Question to Ask for Example 2
• What happens to the middle terms when you find the product using the sum and difference pattern? **The sum of the two middle terms is zero.**

Extra Example 3
Use special products to find the product $18 \cdot 22$. **396**

SUM AND DIFFERENCE PATTERN To find the product $(x + 2)(x - 2)$, you can multiply the two binomials using the FOIL pattern.

$$(x + 2)(x - 2) = x^2 - 2x + 2x - 4 \qquad \text{Use FOIL pattern.}$$
$$= x^2 - 4 \qquad \text{Combine like terms.}$$

This suggests a pattern for the product of the sum and difference of two terms.

KEY CONCEPT *For Your Notebook*

Sum and Difference Pattern

Algebra   **Example**

$(a + b)(a - b) = a^2 - b^2$ $(x + 3)(x - 3) = x^2 - 9$

EXAMPLE 2   **Use the sum and difference pattern**

Find the product.

a. $(t + 5)(t - 5) = t^2 - 5^2$ **Sum and difference pattern**
$$= t^2 - 25 \qquad \text{Simplify.}$$

b. $(3x + y)(3x - y) = (3x)^2 - y^2$ **Sum and difference pattern**
$$= 9x^2 - y^2 \qquad \text{Simplify.}$$

✓ **GUIDED PRACTICE**   for Example 2

Find the product.

5. $(x + 10)(x - 10)$ 6. $(2x + 1)(2x - 1)$ 7. $(x + 3y)(x - 3y)$
    $x^2 - 100$ $4x^2 - 1$ $x^2 - 9y^2$

SPECIAL PRODUCTS AND MENTAL MATH The special product patterns can help you use mental math to find certain products of numbers.

EXAMPLE 3   **Use special products and mental math**

Use special products to find the product $26 \cdot 34$.

Solution

Notice that 26 is 4 less than 30 while 34 is 4 more than 30.

$26 \cdot 34 = (30 - 4)(30 + 4)$ **Write as product of difference and sum.**
$$= 30^2 - 4^2 \qquad \text{Sum and difference pattern}$$
$$= 900 - 16 \qquad \text{Evaluate powers.}$$
$$= 884 \qquad \text{Simplify.}$$

Differentiated Instruction

Visual Learners Students sometimes forget the coefficient of the linear term ab in the square of a binomial, or they misplace the minus sign. In addition to the colored tiles shown on page 569, another way to remember the formulas is to apply the FOIL method to the product of two binomials using mental math. See also the *Algebra 1 Toolkit* for more strategies.

EXAMPLE 4   **Solve a multi-step problem**

BORDER COLLIES The color of the dark patches of a border collie's coat is determined by a combination of two genes. An offspring inherits one patch color gene from each parent. Each parent has two color genes, and the offspring has an equal chance of inheriting either one.

The gene B is for black patches, and the gene r is for red patches. Any gene combination with a B results in black patches. Suppose each parent has the same gene combination Br. The Punnett square shows the possible gene combinations of the offspring and the resulting patch color.

- What percent of the possible gene combinations of the offspring result in black patches?

- Show how you could use a polynomial to model the possible gene combinations of the offspring.

Solution

STEP 1   **Notice** that the Punnett square shows 4 possible gene combinations of the offspring. Of these combinations, 3 result in black patches.

▸ 75% of the possible gene combinations result in black patches.

STEP 2   **Model** the gene from each parent with $0.5B + 0.5r$. There is an equal chance that the collie inherits a black or red gene from each parent.

The possible genes of the offspring can be modeled by $(0.5B + 0.5r)^2$. Notice that this product also represents the area of the Punnett square.

Expand the product to find the possible patch colors of the offspring.

$$(0.5B + 0.5r)^2 = (0.5B)^2 + 2(0.5B)(0.5r) + (0.5r)^2$$
$$= 0.25B^2 + 0.5Br + 0.25r^2$$

Consider the coefficients in the polynomial.

$$0.25B^2 + 0.5Br + 0.25r^2$$

25% *BB*,   50% *Br*,   25% *rr*,
black patches   black patches   red patches

The coefficients show that 25% + 50% = 75% of the possible gene combinations will result in black patches.

✓   **GUIDED PRACTICE**   **for Examples 3 and 4**

8. *Describe* how you can use special products to find 21^2.
   Use the square of a binomial pattern to find the product $(20 + 1)^2$.
9. **BORDER COLLIES** Look back at Example 4. What percent of the possible gene combinations of the offspring result in red patches? **25%**

Extra Example 4

In dogs, the gene E is for erect ears and the gene e is for droopy ears. Any gene combination with an E results in erect ears. The Punnett square shows the possible gene combinations of the offspring and the resulting type of ear.

	E	e
E	EE erect	Ee erect
e	Ee erect	ee droopy

- What percent of the possible gene combinations of the offspring result in droopy ears? **25%**
- Show how you could use a polynomial to model the possible gene combinations of the offspring. **Use $(0.5E + 0.5e)^2$ to model the possible genes of the offspring. Expand the product to find the possible gene combinations: $0.25E^2 + 0.5Ee + 0.25e^2$. The coefficient of e^2 shows that 25% of the possible gene combinations will result in droopy ears.**

Closing the Lesson

Have students summarize the major points of the lesson and answer the Essential Question: How do you use special product patterns to multiply binomials?

- **The square of a binomial pattern is for $(a + b)^2$ or $(a - b)^2$.**

- **The sum and difference pattern is for $(a + b)(a - b)$.**

To find $(a + b)^2$ or $(a - b)^2$, square a, add (or subtract) twice the product ab, and add the square of c. The product $(a + b)(a - b)$ is $a^2 - b^2$.

9.3 EXERCISES

HOMEWORK KEY

○ = WORKED-OUT SOLUTIONS
on p. WS1 for Exs. 11 and 41

★ = STANDARDIZED TEST PRACTICE
Exs. 2, 17, 18, 42, and 44

◆ = MULTIPLE REPRESENTATIONS
Ex. 41

SKILL PRACTICE

[A] **1. VOCABULARY** Give an example of two binomials whose product you can find using the sum and difference pattern. *Sample answer: x − 5, x + 5*

2. ★ WRITING *Explain* how to use the square of a binomial pattern. **See margin.**

EXAMPLE 1
on p. 569
for Exs. 3–10, 18

SQUARE OF A BINOMIAL Find the product.

3. $(x + 8)^2$ $x^2 + 16x + 64$ 4. $(a + 6)^2$ $a^2 + 12a + 36$ 5. $(2y + 5)^2$ $4y^2 + 20y + 25$

6. $(t − 7)^2$ $t^2 − 14t + 49$ 7. $(n − 11)^2$ $n^2 − 22n + 121$ 8. $(6b − 1)^2$ $36b^2 − 12b + 1$

ERROR ANALYSIS *Describe* and correct the error in multiplying. **9, 10. See margin.**

9.
$$(s − 3)^2 = s^2 + 9$$ ✗

10.
$$(2d − 10)^2 = 4d^2 − 20d + 100$$ ✗

EXAMPLE 2
on p. 570
for Exs. 11–17

SUM AND DIFFERENCE PATTERN Find the product.

⑪ $(t + 4)(t − 4)$ $t^2 − 16$ 12. $(m − 6)(m + 6)$ $m^2 − 36$ 13. $(2x + 1)(2x − 1)$ $4x^2 − 1$

14. $(3x − 1)(3x + 1)$ $9x^2 − 1$ 15. $(7 + w)(7 − w)$ $49 − w^2$ 16. $(3s − 8)(3s + 8)$ $9s^2 − 64$

17. **★ MULTIPLE CHOICE** Find the product $(7x + 3)(7x − 3)$. **B**

Ⓐ $7x^2 − 9$ Ⓑ $49x^2 − 9$ Ⓒ $49x^2 − 21x − 9$ Ⓓ $49x^2 − 42x − 9$

18. **★ MULTIPLE CHOICE** Find the product $(5n − 3)^2$. **D**

Ⓐ $5n^2 − 9$ Ⓑ $25n^2 − 9$ Ⓒ $25n^2 − 15n + 9$ Ⓓ $25n^2 − 30n + 9$

EXAMPLE 3
on p. 570
for Exs. 19–22

MENTAL MATH *Describe* how you can use mental math to find the product.
19–22. See margin.

19. $16 \cdot 24$ 20. $28 \cdot 32$ 21. 17^2 22. 44^2

SPECIAL PRODUCT PATTERNS Find the product.

23. $(r + 9s)^2$
$r^2 + 18rs + 81s^2$
24. $(6x + 5)^2$
$36x^2 + 60x + 25$
25. $(3m + 11n)(3m − 11n)$
$9m^2 − 121n^2$
26. $(7a + 8b)(7a − 8b)$
$49a^2 − 64b^2$
27. $(3m − 7n)^2$
$9m^2 − 42mn + 49n^2$
28. $(13 − 2x)^2$
$169 − 52x + 4x^2$
29. $(3f − 9)(3f + 9)$
$9f^2 − 81$
30. $(9 − 4t)(9 + 4t)$
$81 − 16t^2$
31. $(3x + 8y)^2$
$9x^2 + 48xy + 64y^2$
32. $(−x − 2y)^2$
$x^2 + 4xy + 4y^2$
33. $(2a − 5b)(2a + 5b)$
$4a^2 − 25b^2$
34. $(6x + y)(6x − y)$
$36x^2 − y^2$

[B] **MULTIPLYING FUNCTIONS** Perform the indicated operation using the functions $f(x) = 3x + 0.5$ and $g(x) = 3x − 0.5$.

35. $f(x) \cdot g(x)$ $9x^2 − 0.25$ 36. $(f(x))^2$ $9x^2 + 3x + 0.25$ 37. $(g(x))^2$ $9x^2 − 3x + 0.25$.

[C] **38. CHALLENGE** Write two binomials that have the product $x^2 − 121$. *Explain.* **See margin.**

39. CHALLENGE Write a pattern for the cube of a binomial $(a + b)^3$. $a^3 + 3a^2b + 3ab^2 + b^3$

9. The middle term of the products, $2(s)(−3)$ was left out; $s^2 − 6s + 9$.

10. The middle term of the products should be twice the product of the terms of the binomial; $4d^2 − 40d + 100$.

19. Use the sum and difference pattern to find the product $(20 − 4)(20 + 4)$.

20. Use the sum and difference pattern to find the product $(30 − 2)(30 + 2)$.

21. Use the square of a binomial pattern to find the product $(20 − 3)^2$.

22. Use the square of a binomial pattern to find the product $(40 + 4)^2$.

38. $x − 11$, $x + 11$; since $x^2 − 121 = x^2 − 11^2$ is in the form $a^2 − b^2$, you can use the sum and difference pattern in reverse to find the binomials $a − b = x − 11$ and $a + b = x + 11$.

EXAMPLE 4 [A]
on p. 571
for Exs. 40–42

40. PEA PLANTS In pea plants, the gene *G* is for green pods, and the gene *y* is for yellow pods. Any gene combination with a *G* results in a green pod. Suppose two pea plants have the same gene combination *Gy*. The Punnett square shows the possible gene combinations of an offspring pea plant and the resulting pod color.

   a. What percent of possible gene combinations of the offspring plant result in a yellow pod? **25%**

   b. Show how you could use a polynomial to model the possible gene combinations of the offspring. **See margin.**

   @HomeTutor for problem solving help at classzone.com

(41.) ♦ **MULTIPLE REPRESENTATIONS** In humans, the gene *s* is for straight thumbs, and the gene *C* is for curved thumbs. Any gene combination with a *C* results in a curved thumb. Suppose each parent has the same gene combination *Cs*.

   a. Making a Diagram Make a Punnet square that shows the possible gene combinations inherited by a child. **See margin.**

   b. Writing a Model Write a polynomial that models the possible gene combinations of the child. $0.25C^2 + 0.5Cs + 0.25s^2$

   c. Interpreting a Model What percent of the possible gene combinations of the child result in a curved thumb? **75%**

   @HomeTutor for problem solving help at classzone.com

42. ★ **SHORT RESPONSE** In ball pythons, the gene *N* is for normal coloring, and the gene *a* is for no coloring, or albino. Any gene combination with an *N* results in normal coloring. Suppose one parent python has the gene combination *Na* and the other parent python has the gene combination *aa*. What percent of the possible gene combinations of the offspring result in an albino python? *Explain* how you found your answer. **See margin.**

[B] **43. FOOTBALL STATISTICS** During the 2004 regular season, the San Diego Chargers' quarterback Drew Brees completed 65.5% of the passes he attempted. The area model shows the possible outcomes of two attempted passes. **a, b. See margin.**

   a. What percent of the possible outcomes of two attempted passes results in Drew Brees's throwing at least one complete pass? *Explain* how you found your answer using the area model.

   b. Show how you could use a polynomial to model the possible results of two attempted passes.

	First Pass Attempt	
	Complete 65.5%	Incomplete 34.5%
Complete 65.5%	2 complete	1 complete 1 incomplete
Second Pass Attempt		
Incomplete 34.5%	1 complete 1 incomplete	2 incomplete

9.3 Find Special Products of Polynomials **573**

Avoiding Common Errors

Exercises 23–34 Students often use an incorrect pattern when finding products of binomials. Suggest that students go through all of the exercises before finding the products to determine which pattern they should use for each exercise. If the square of a binomial pattern is appropriate, encourage them to indicate whether the middle term is positive or negative.

Teaching Strategy

Exercise 42 It may be useful to have students make Punnet squares for several other possible combinations of genes, such as *NN* and *aa* or *NN* and *Na*, so they can see the range of possible combinations. They may find it interesting to compare the Punnett squares. Ask students to determine the percent of each of the possible gene combinations for each of the Punnett squares. You may want to challenge students to write offspring polynomials for each of the possible parent combinations.

🌐 **Internet Reference**

Exercises 40–42 To learn more about Mendel and his pea plant experiment, visit anthro.palomar.edu/mendel/mendel_1.htm

42. 50%; the gene from one parent is modeled by $0.5N + 0.5a$ and the gene from the other parent in modeled by $0.5a + 0.5a = a$, so the possible gene combinations of the offspring are modeled by $a(0.5N + 0.5a) = 0.5Na + 0.5a^2$. Because any gene combination with an *N* results in normal coloring, only the second term, $0.5a^2$, represents albino offspring. The coefficient of a^2, 0.5, shows that 50% of the offspring will be albino.

43a–b. See Additional Answers beginning on p. AA1.

40b. The gene from each parent is modeled by $0.5G + 0.5y$. The possible genes of the offspring are modeled by $(0.5G + 0.5y)^2 = 0.25G^2 + 0.5Gy + 0.25y^2$. Because any gene combination with a *G* results in a green pod, the coefficients of the first two terms show that 25% + 50% = 75% of the offspring will have green pods, and the coefficient of the last term shows that 25% of the offspring will have yellow pods.

41a.

44. ★ **EXTENDED RESPONSE** The iris of an eye surrounds the pupil. It regulates the amount of light entering the eye by opening and closing the pupil. For parts (a)–(c) below, leave your answers in terms of π.

 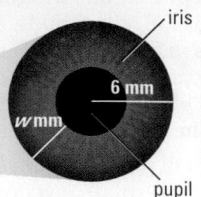

iris

pupil

The iris of a human eye has a width w that varies from 0.5 millimeter to 4 millimeters.

a. Write a polynomial that represents the pupil's radius. **6 − w**

b. Write a polynomial that represents the pupil's area. $\pi w^2 - 12\pi w + 36\pi$

c. What is the least possible area and the greatest possible area of the pupil? *Explain* how you found your answers. **See margin.**

ⓒ **45. CHALLENGE** You use 100 feet of fencing to form a square with a side length of 25 feet. You want to change the dimensions of the enclosed region. For every 1 foot you increase the width, you must decrease the length by 1 foot. Write a polynomial that gives the area of the rectangle after you increase the width by x feet and decrease the length by x feet. *Explain* why *any* change in dimensions results in an area less than that of the original square. $625 - x^2$; the area of the original square is $25^2 = 625$ square feet, and the area of a square when the dimensions are changed is $(25 - x)(25 + x) = 625 - x^2$ square feet; since x^2 is always positive, the area of the new square will be less than 625 square feet.

MIXED REVIEW

PREVIEW Prepare for Lesson 9.4 in Exs. 46–53.

Find the greatest common factor of the pair of numbers. *(p. 910)*

46. 25, 30 **5**   **47.** 36, 54 **18**   **48.** 14, 21 **7**   **49.** 36, 50 **2**

50. 65, 39 **13**   **51.** 13, 20 **1**   **52.** 77, 143 **11**   **53.** 24, 162 **6**

Solve the equation. Check your solution.

54. $x + 11 = 6$ *(p. 134)* **−5**

55. $11x + 8 = -14$ *(p. 141)* **−2**

56. $2x - 5(x - 13) = 35$ *(p. 148)* **10**

57. $9x + 4 - 4x = 6x + 7$ *(p. 154)* **−3**

QUIZ for Lessons 9.1–9.3

Find the sum, difference, or product.

1. $(x^2 - 3x + 5) + (-2x^2 + 11x + 1)$ *(p. 554)*
$-x^2 + 8x + 6$

2. $(8y^3 - 7y^2 + y) - (9y^2 - 5y + 7)$ *(p. 554)*
$8y^3 - 16y^2 + 6y - 7$

3. $(2r + 11)(r - 6)$ *(p. 562)*
$2r^2 - r - 66$

4. $(m + 3)(-2m^2 + 5m - 1)$ *(p. 562)*
$-2m^3 - m^2 + 14m - 3$

5. $(2 + 8p)(2 - 10p)$ *(p. 562)*
$4 - 4p - 80p^2$

6. $(15 - 2s)^2$ *(p. 569)*
$225 - 60s + 4s^2$

7. $(5w + 9z)^2$ *(p. 569)*
$25w^2 + 90wz + 81z^2$

8. $(5x - 4y)(5x + 4y)$ *(p. 569)*
$25x^2 - 16y^2$

9. **AREA** The length of a rectangular rug is 2 times its width. The rug is centered in a rectangular room. Each edge is 3 feet from the nearest wall. Write a polynomial that represents the area of the room. *(p. 564)* $2w^2 + 18w + 36$

9.4 Solve Polynomial Equations in Factored Form

Before You solved linear equations.

Now You will solve polynomial equations.

Why So you can analyze vertical motion, as in Ex. 55.

Key Vocabulary
• roots
• vertical motion model

In Lesson 2.4, you learned the property of zero: For any real number a, $a \cdot 0 = 0$. This is equivalent to saying:

For real numbers a and b, if $a = 0$ or $b = 0$, then $ab = 0$.

The converse of this statement is also true (as shown in Exercise 49), and it is called the zero-product property.

KEY CONCEPT   *For Your Notebook*

Zero-Product Property

Let a and b be real numbers. If $ab = 0$, then $a = 0$ or $b = 0$.

The zero-product property is used to solve an equation when one side is zero and the other side is a product of polynomial factors. The solutions of such an equation are also called **roots**.

EXAMPLE 1 Use the zero-product property

Solve $(x - 4)(x + 2) = 0$.

$$(x - 4)(x + 2) = 0 \qquad \text{Write original equation.}$$

$$x - 4 = 0 \quad or \quad x + 2 = 0 \qquad \text{Zero-product property}$$

$$x = 4 \quad or \qquad x = -2 \qquad \text{Solve for } x.$$

▶ The solutions of the equation are 4 and −2.

CHECK Substitute each solution into the original equation to check.

$$(4 - 4)(4 + 2) \stackrel{?}{=} 0 \qquad (-2 - 4)(-2 + 2) \stackrel{?}{=} 0$$

$$0 \cdot 6 \stackrel{?}{=} 0 \qquad\qquad -6 \cdot 0 \stackrel{?}{=} 0$$

$$0 = 0 \checkmark \qquad\qquad 0 = 0 \checkmark$$

 GUIDED PRACTICE for Example 1

1. Solve the equation $(x - 5)(x - 1) = 0$. **5, 1**

---

① PLAN AND PREPARE

Warm-Up Exercises
⬛ Transparency Available
1. Find the GCF of 12 and 28. **4**
2. Find the GCF of 18 and 42. **6**
3. The number (in hundreds) of sunscreen and sun tanning products sold at a pharmacy from 1999–2005 can be modeled by $-0.8t^2 + 0.3x + 107$, where t is the number of years since 1999. About how many products were sold in 2002? **about 10,070**

Notetaking Guide
⬛ Transparency Available
Promotes interactive learning and notetaking skills, pp. 199–202.

Pacing
Basic: 2 days
Average: 2 days
Advanced: 2 days
Block: 0.5 block with 9.3
0.5 block with 9.5
• See *Teaching Guide/Lesson Plan*.

② FOCUS AND MOTIVATE

Essential Question
Big Idea 3, p. 553

How do you solve polynomial equations in factored form? **Tell students they will learn how to answer this question by using the zero-product property.**

NCTM STANDARDS

Standard 2: Analyze situations using algebraic symbols

Standard 6: Solve problems in math and other contexts

Resource Planning Guide

Chapter Resource Book
• Teaching Guide/Lesson Plan (pp. 36–37)
• Activity Master (p. 38)
• Practice levels A, B, C (pp. 41–43)
• Study Guide (pp. 44–45)
• Catch-up for Absent Students (p. 46)
• Problem Solving Workshop (p. 47)
• Challenge (p. 49)

Workbooks
• Notetaking Guide (pp. 199–202)
• Practice Workbook (pp. 139–140)

Teaching Options
• **Power Presentations CD-ROM** provides dynamic electronic teaching resources for the classroom.
• **Activity Generator CD-ROM** provides editable activities for all ability levels.

Interactive Technology
• Easy Planner
• Power Presentations CD-ROM
• Activity Generator CD-ROM
• Animated Algebra
• Test Generator CD-ROM
• Online Quiz
• eWorkbook
• eEdition
• @HomeTutor

Resources for English Learners
• Quick Reference for English Learners
• Spanish Study Guide
• Multi-Language Visual Glossary
• Student Resources in Spanish

See also the *Algebra 1 Toolkit* for more strategies for meeting individual needs.

575

REVIEW GCF
For help with finding the GCF, see p. 910.

FACTORING To solve a polynomial equation using the zero-product property, you may need to *factor* the polynomial, or write it as a product of other polynomials. Look for the *greatest common factor* (GCF) of the polynomial's terms. This is a monomial with an integer coefficient that divides evenly into each term.

EXAMPLE 2 Find the greatest common monomial factor

Factor out the greatest common monomial factor.

a. $12x + 42y$ **b.** $4x^4 + 24x^3$

Solution

a. The GCF of 12 and 42 is 6. The variables x and y have no common factor. So, the greatest common monomial factor of the terms is 6.

▸ $12x + 42y = 6(2x + 7y)$

b. The GCF of 4 and 24 is 4. The GCF of x^4 and x^3 is x^3. So, the greatest common monomial factor of the terms is $4x^3$.

▸ $4x^4 + 24x^3 = 4x^3(x + 6)$

✓ **GUIDED PRACTICE** for Example 2

2. Factor out the greatest common monomial factor from $14m + 35n$. $7(2m + 5n)$

EXAMPLE 3 Solve an equation by factoring

Solve $2x^2 + 8x = 0$.

$2x^2 + 8x = 0$	**Write original equation.**
$2x(x + 4) = 0$	**Factor left side.**
$2x = 0$ *or* $x + 4 = 0$	**Zero-product property**
$x = 0$ *or* $x = -4$	**Solve for x.**

▸ The solutions of the equation are 0 and -4.

EXAMPLE 4 Solve an equation by factoring

Solve $6n^2 = 15n$.

AVOID ERRORS
To use the zero-product property, you must write the equation so that one side is 0. For this reason, $15n$ must be subtracted from each side.

$6n^2 - 15n = 0$	**Subtract 15n from each side.**
$3n(2n - 5) = 0$	**Factor left side.**
$3n = 0$ *or* $2n - 5 = 0$	**Zero-product property**
$n = 0$ *or* $n = \dfrac{5}{2}$	**Solve for n.**

▸ The solutions of the equation are 0 and $\dfrac{5}{2}$.

576   Chapter 9 Polynomials and Factoring

---

❸ TEACH

Extra Example 1
Solve $(x + 3)(x - 5) = 0$. $-3, 5$

Key Question to Ask for Example 1
• Why does this type of equation have two solutions? **The left side of the equation is the product of two quantities. By the zero-product property, either of them could be zero. This allows for the equation to have two solutions.**

Extra Example 2
Factor out the greatest common monomial factor.
a. $8x + 12y$ $4(2x + 3y)$
b. $14y^2 + 21y$ $7y(2y + 3)$

Key Question to Ask for Example 2
• In part (b), how do you know x^3 is a factor of x^3 and x^4?
$\dfrac{x^4}{x^3} = x^{4-3}$ or x and
$\dfrac{x^3}{x^3} = x^{3-3} = x^0$ or 1

Extra Example 3
Solve $3x^2 + 18x = 0$ $-6, 0$

Extra Example 4
Solve $4s^2 = 14s$. $0, \dfrac{7}{2}$

Solve the equation.

3. $a^2 + 5a = 0$ **0, −5**   4. $3s^2 − 9s = 0$ **0, 3**   5. $4x^2 = 2x$ **0, $\frac{1}{2}$**

VERTICAL MOTION A *projectile* is an object that is propelled into the air but has no power to keep itself in the air. A thrown ball is a projectile, but an airplane is not. The height of a projectile can be described by the **vertical motion model**.

KEY CONCEPT   *For Your Notebook*

Vertical Motion Model

The height h (in feet) of a projectile can be modeled by

$$h = −16t^2 + vt + s$$

where t is the time (in seconds) the object has been in the air, v is the initial vertical velocity (in feet per second), and s is the initial height (in feet).

UNDERSTAND THE MODEL
The vertical motion model takes into account the effect of gravity but ignores other, less significant, factors such as air resistance.

EXAMPLE 5   **Solve a multi-step problem**

ARMADILLO A startled armadillo jumps straight into the air with an initial vertical velocity of 14 feet per second. After how many seconds does it land on the ground?

Solution

STEP 1   **Write** a model for the armadillo's height above the ground.

$h = −16t^2 + vt + s$ Vertical motion model

$h = −16t^2 + 14t + 0$ Substitute 14 for *v* and 0 for *s*.

$h = −16t^2 + 14t$ Simplify.

STEP 2   **Substitute** 0 for h. When the armadillo lands, its height above the ground is 0 feet. Solve for t.

$0 = −16t^2 + 14t$ Substitute 0 for *h*.

$0 = 2t(−8t + 7)$ Factor right side.

$2t = 0$ or $−8t + 7 = 0$ Zero-product property

$t = 0$ or $t = 0.875$ Solve for *t*.

AVOID ERRORS
The solution $t = 0$ means that before the armadillo jumps, its height above the ground is 0 feet.

▶ The armadillo lands on the ground 0.875 second after the armadillo jumps.

✓ **GUIDED PRACTICE**   for Example 5

6. **WHAT IF?** In Example 5, suppose the initial vertical velocity is 12 feet per second. After how many seconds does the armadillo land on the ground?
   0.75 sec

9.4   Solve Polynomial Equations in Factored Form   **577**

Extra Example 5
A dolphin jumped out of the water with an initial velocity of 32 feet per second. After how many seconds did the dolphin enter the water?
2 sec

Key Questions to Ask for Example 5
• Can you use the vertical motion model to calculate when a hot air balloon will return to the ground? Explain. **No, a hot air balloon is not a projectile.**
• What steps can you use to solve $8t + 7 = 0$? **Subtract 7 from both sides of the equation and then divide both sides of the equation by −8.**

Closing the Lesson
Have students summarize the major points of the lesson and answer the Essential Question: How do you solve polynomial equations in factored form?
• **The zero-product property can be used to solve a polynomial equation in factored form.**
• **If a polynomial expression can be factored, rewrite it in factored form before solving the equation.**
If necessary, rewrite the equation so one side is 0 and factor out any monomial factor. Then use the zero-product property to set each factor equal to 0 and find the solutions.

9.4 **EXERCISES**

HOMEWORK
KEY

○ = **WORKED-OUT SOLUTIONS**
on p. WS1 for Exs. 3 and 55

★ = **STANDARDIZED TEST PRACTICE**
Exs. 2, 15, 39, 53, and 56

◆ = **MULTIPLE REPRESENTATIONS**
Ex. 58

④ PRACTICE AND APPLY

Assignment Guide

📑 **Answer Transparencies**
available for all exercises

Basic:
Day 1: SRH p. 911 Exs. 13–23 odd
pp. 578–580
Exs. 2, 3–15 odd, 16–26, 72–74
Day 2: pp. 578–580
Exs. 1, 27–42, 51–56, 60–70 even

Average:
Day 1: pp. 578–580
Exs. 2, 9–16, 18–26 even, 40–45,
72–74
Day 2: pp. 578–580
Exs. 1, 31–39, 46–49, 51–58,
61–71 odd

Advanced:
Day 1: pp. 578–580
Exs. 2, 10–15, 22–26, 40–45, 72–74
Day 2: pp. 578–580
Exs. 1, 32–39, 46–50*, 52–59*,
60–70 even

Block:
pp. 578–580
Exs. 2, 9–16, 18–26 even, 40–45,
72–74 (with 9.3)
pp. 578–580
Exs. 1, 31–39, 46–49, 51–58,
61–71 odd (with 9.5)

Differentiated Instruction

See *Algebra 1 Best Practices Toolkit*
for suggestions on addressing the
needs of a diverse classroom.

Homework Check

For a quick check of student understanding of key concepts, go over
the following exercises:

Basic: 5, 18, 28, 34, 51
Average: 10, 22, 31, 36, 52
Advanced: 12, 24, 32, 38, 53

Extra Practice

• Student Edition, p. 946
• Chapter 9 Resource Book:
Practice levels A, B, C, pp. 41–43

Practice Worksheet

An easily-readable reduced
practice page (with answers)
for this lesson can be found
on p. 552C.

SKILL PRACTICE

A 1. **VOCABULARY** What is the vertical motion model and what does each variable in the model represent? **See margin.**

2. ★ **WRITING** *Explain* how to use the zero-product property to find the solutions of the equation $3x(x - 7) = 0$. **Set each of the two polynomial factors, 3x and x − 7, equal to zero and then solve each equation for x.**

EXAMPLE 1
on p. 575
for Exs. 3–16

ZERO-PRODUCT PROPERTY Solve the equation.

③. $(x - 5)(x + 3) = 0$ **5, −3**   4. $(y + 9)(y - 1) = 0$ **−9, 1**   5. $(z - 13)(z - 14) = 0$ **13, 14**

6. $(c + 6)(c + 8) = 0$ **−6, −8**   7. $(d - 7)\left(d + \frac{4}{3}\right) = 0$ **7, −$\frac{4}{3}$**   8. $\left(g - \frac{1}{8}\right)(g + 18) = 0$ **$\frac{1}{8}$, −18**

9. $(m - 3)(4m + 12) = 0$ **±3** 10. $(2n - 14)(3n + 9) = 0$ **7, −3** 11. $(3n + 11)(n + 1) = 0$ **−$\frac{11}{3}$, −1**

12. $(3x + 1)(x + 6) = 0$ **−$\frac{1}{3}$, −6** 13. $(2y + 5)(7y - 5) = 0$ **−$\frac{5}{2}$, $\frac{5}{7}$** 14. $(8z - 6)(12z + 14) = 0$ **$\frac{3}{4}$, −$\frac{7}{6}$**

15. ★ **MULTIPLE CHOICE** What are the solutions of the equation $(y - 12)(y + 6) = 0$? **C**

   Ⓐ −12 and −6   Ⓑ −12 and 6   Ⓒ −6 and 12   Ⓓ 6 and 12

16. **ERROR ANALYSIS** *Describe* and correct the error in solving $(z - 15)(z + 21) = 0$. **The step of setting each factor equal to zero was left out; z − 15 = 0 or z + 21 = 0, z = 15 or z = −21.**

$(z - 15)(z + 21) = 0$
$z = -15 \text{ or } z = 21$

EXAMPLE 2
on p. 576
for Exs. 17–26

FACTORING EXPRESSIONS Factor out the greatest common monomial factor.

17. $2x + 2y$ **2(x + y)**   18. $6x^2 - 15y$ **3(2x² − 5y)**   19. $3s^4 + 16s$ **s(3s³ + 16)**

20. $5d^6 + 2d^5$ **d⁵(5d + 2)**   21. $7w^5 - 35w^2$ **7w²(w³ − 5)**   22. $9m^7 - 3m^2$ **3m²(3m⁵ − 1)**

23. $15n^3 + 25n$ **5n(3n² + 5)**   24. $12a^5 + 8a$ **4a(3a⁴ + 2)**   25. $\frac{5}{2}x^6 - \frac{1}{2}x^4$ **$\frac{1}{2}$x⁴(5x² − 1)**

26. **ERROR ANALYSIS** *Describe* and correct the error in factoring out the greatest common monomial factor of $18x^8 - 9x^4 - 6x^3$. **See margin.**

$18x^8 - 9x^4 - 6x^3 = 3x(6x^7 - 3x^3 - 2x^2)$

26. A common
monomial factor,
3x, was factored
out, but not the
greatest
common factor,
which is $3x^3$;
$3x^3(6x^5 - 3x - 2)$.

EXAMPLES 3 and 4
on p. 576
for Exs. 27–39

SOLVING EQUATIONS Solve the equation.

27. $b^2 + 6b = 0$ **0, −6**   28. $5w^2 - 5w = 0$ **0, 1**   29. $-10n^2 + 35n = 0$ **0, $\frac{7}{2}$**

30. $2x^2 + 15x = 0$ **0, −$\frac{15}{2}$**   31. $18c^2 + 6c = 0$ **0, −$\frac{1}{3}$**   32. $-32y^2 - 24y = 0$ **0, −$\frac{3}{4}$**

33. $3k^2 = 6k$ **0, 2**   34. $6h^2 = 3h$ **0, $\frac{1}{2}$**   35. $4s^2 = 10s$ **0, $\frac{5}{2}$**

36. $-42z^2 = 14z$ **0, −$\frac{1}{3}$**   37. $28m^2 = -8m$ **0, −$\frac{2}{7}$**   38. $-12p^2 = -30p$ **0, $\frac{5}{2}$**

39. ★ **MULTIPLE CHOICE** What are the solutions of $4x^2 = x$? **C**

   Ⓐ −4 and 0   Ⓑ −$\frac{1}{4}$ and 0   Ⓒ 0 and $\frac{1}{4}$ Ⓓ 0 and 4

---

1. The vertical motion model is the equation $h = -16t^2 + vt + s$, where h is the height (in feet) of a projectile after t seconds in the air, given an initial velocity of v feet per second and an initial height of s feet.

B **FACTORING EXPRESSIONS** Factor out the greatest common monomial factor.

40. $20x^2y^2 - 4xy$ **$4xy(5xy - 1)$** **41.** $8a^2b - 6ab^2$ **$2ab(4a - 3b)$** **42.** $18s^2t^5 - 2s^3t$ **$2s^2t(9t^4 - s)$**

43. $v^3 - 5v^2 + 9v$ **44.** $-2g^4 + 14g^2 + 6g$ **45.** $6q^5 - 21q^4 - 15q^2$
  $v(v^2 - 5v + 9)$ **$-2g(g^3 - 7g - 3)$**   **$3q^2(2q^3 - 7q^2)$**

FINDING ZEROS OF FUNCTIONS Find the zeros of the function.

46. $f(x) = x^2 - 15x$ **0, 15**   **47.** $f(x) = -2x^2 + x$ **$0, \frac{1}{2}$**   **48.** $f(x) = 3x^2 - 27x$ **0, 9**

C **49.** **CHALLENGE** Consider the equation $ab = 0$. Assume that $a \neq 0$ and solve the equation for b. Then assume that $b \neq 0$ and solve the equation for a. What conclusion can you draw about the values of a and b?
0; 0; at least one of them must be 0.

50. **CHALLENGE** Consider the equation $z = x^2 - xy$. For what values of x and y does $z = 0$? **for $x = 0$ and y any real number, or for all real numbers x and y where $x = y$**

HINT
For help with finding zeros of functions, see p. 335.

PROBLEM SOLVING

EXAMPLE 5 **A**
on p. 577
for Exs. 51–53

51. **MOTION** A cat leaps from the ground into the air with an initial vertical velocity of 11 feet per second. After how many seconds does the cat land on the ground? **about 0.69 sec**

@HomeTutor for problem solving help at classzone.com

52. **SPITTLEBUG** A spittlebug jumps into the air with an initial vertical velocity of 10 feet per second.

a. Write an equation that gives the height of the spittlebug as a function of the time (in seconds) since it left the ground. $h = -16t^2 + 10t$

b. The spittlebug reaches its maximum height after 0.3125 second. How high can it jump?

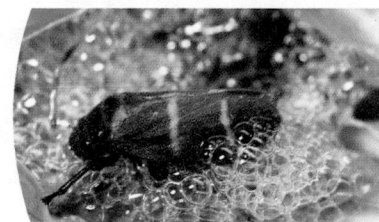

52b. about 1.563 ft

@HomeTutor for problem solving help at classzone.com

53. ★ **SHORT RESPONSE** A penguin jumps out of the water while swimming. This action is called porpoising. The height h (in feet) of the porpoising penguin can be modeled by $h = -16t^2 + 4.5t$ where t is the time (in seconds) since the penguin jumped out of the water. Find the zeros of the function. *Explain* what the zeros mean in this situation. **See margin.**

VERTICAL MOTION In Exercises 54 and 55, use the information below.

The height h (in meters) of a projectile can be modeled by $h = -4.9t^2 + vt + s$ where t is the time (in seconds) the object has been in the air, v is the initial vertical velocity (in meters per second), and s is the initial height (in meters).

54. **SOCCER** A soccer ball is kicked upward from the ground with an initial vertical velocity of 3.6 meters per second. After how many seconds does it land? **about 0.73 sec**

55. **RABBIT HIGH JUMP** A rabbit in a high jump competition leaves the ground with an initial vertical velocity of 4.9 meters per second.

a. Write an equation that gives the height of the rabbit as a function of the time (in seconds) since it left the ground. $h = -4.9t^2 + 4.9t$

b. What is a reasonable domain for the function? *Explain* your answer. **See margin.**

Avoiding Common Errors

Exercises 3–14, 27–38 Urge students to pay attention to the sign of each solution. Remind them that they must use properties of equality to solve an equation.

Exercises 17–25 Watch for students who factor a common factor that is not the greatest common monomial factor. Suggest to all students that they check each non-monomial factor to see if the terms still have a common factor.

Graphing Calculator

Exercise 58 Students can check their graphs by graphing $y = -2x^2 + 8x$ on a graphing calculator using the $y=$ key. They can use the trace feature to check the value of y for the given x-values.

53. 0, about 0.28; the zero $t = 0$ seconds means that the penguin begins at a height of 0 feet in the air as it leaves the water; the zero $t \approx 0.28$ second means that the penguin lands back in the water (at a height of 0 feet in the air) after about 0.28 second.

55b. $0 \leq t \leq 1$; a reasonable domain for the function will cover the time from when the rabbit leaves the ground until the rabbit lands back on the ground; these times t are the zeros of the function, 0 seconds and 1 second.

56. ★ **MULTIPLE CHOICE** Two rectangular rooms in a building's floor plan have different dimensions but the same area. The dimensions (in meters) are shown. What is the value of w? **B**

(A) 3 m (B) 4 m (C) 6 m (D) 8 m

57. TABLETOP AREAS A display in your school library sits on top of two rectangular tables arranged in an L shape, as shown. The tabletops have the same area.

a. Write an equation that relates the areas of the tabletops. $w(w + 2) = w(10 - w)$

b. Find the value of w. **4**

c. What is the combined area of the tabletops? **48 ft²**

58. ◆ **MULTIPLE REPRESENTATIONS** An arch frames the entrance to a garden. The shape of the arch is modeled by the graph of the equation $y = -2x^2 + 8x$ where x and y are measured in feet. On a coordinate plane, the ground is represented by the x-axis.

a. **Making a Table** Make a table of values that shows the height of the arch for $x = 0, 1, 2, 3,$ and 4 feet. **See margin.**

b. **Drawing a Graph** Plot the ordered pairs in the table as points in a coordinate plane. Connect the points with a smooth curve that represents the arch. **See margin.**

c. **Interpreting a Graph** How wide is the base of the arch? **4 ft**

59. CHALLENGE The shape of an arched doorway is modeled by the graph of the function $y = -0.5x(x - 8)$ where x and y are measured in feet. On a coordinate plane, the floor is represented by the x-axis. **a, b. See margin.**

a. How wide is the doorway at its base? *Justify* your answer using the zeros of the function.

b. The doorway's highest point occurs above the center of its base. How high is the highest point of the arched doorway? *Explain* how you found your answer.

MIXED REVIEW

PREVIEW
Prepare for Lesson 9.5 in Exs. 60–71.

Find the product.

60. $45(\frac{-}{5}x)(-x)$ *(p. 88)*
$45x^2$

61. $-9a(-6a)(-a)$ *(p. 88)*
$-54a^3$

62. $-7(8n)(-4)$ *(p. 88)*
$224n$

63. $(y - 1)(y + 7)$ *(p. 562)*
$y^2 + 6y - 7$

64. $(m - 5)(m - 13)$ *(p. 562)*
$m^2 - 18m + 65$

65. $(2b + 5)(b + 3)$ *(p. 562)*
$2b^2 + 11b + 15$

66. $(3p + 8)(4p - 1)$ *(p. 562)*
$12p^2 + 29p - 8$

67. $(5z - 2)(5z - 4)$ *(p. 562)*
$25z^2 - 30z + 8$

68. $(9t + 7)(4t + 5)$ *(p. 562)*
$36t^2 + 73t + 35$

69. $(2c + 7)^2$ *(p. 569)*
$4c^2 + 28c + 49$

70. $(9 - 5w)^2$ *(p. 569)*
$81 - 90w + 25w^2$

71. $(3g - 4h)^2$ *(p. 569)*
$9g^2 - 24gh + 16h^2$

Graph the system of linear inequalities. *(p. 466)* **72–74. See margin.**

72. $x > -3$
$x \leq 3$

73. $x \geq 0$
$-3x + y < -1$
$y \geq 0$

74. $x < 6$
$y > -4$
$y < 2$
$y \leq x$

72.

73.

74.

Lessons 9.1–9.4

1. **MULTI-STEP PROBLEM** You are making a blanket with a fringe border of equal width on each edge, as shown.

72 in.

48 in.

x in.

x in.

a. Write a polynomial that represents the total area of the blanket with the fringe. **$4x^2 + 240x + 3456$**

b. Find the total area of the blanket with fringe when the width of the fringe is 4 inches. **4480 in.²**

2. **OPEN-ENDED** A horse with pinto coloring has white fur with patches of color. The gene *P* is for pinto coloring, and the gene *s* is for solid coloring. Any gene combination with a *P* results in pinto coloring.

a. Suppose a male horse has the gene combination *Ps*. Choose a color gene combination for a female horse. Create a Punnett square to show the possible gene combinations of the two horses' offspring. **See margin.**

b. What percent of the possible gene combinations of the offspring result in pinto coloring? *Sample answer:* **100%**

c. Show how you could use a polynomial to model the possible color gene combinations of the offspring. **See margin.**

3. **SHORT RESPONSE** One football is kicked into the air with an initial vertical velocity of 44 feet per second. Another football is kicked into the air with an initial vertical velocity of 40 feet per second. **a, b. See margin.**

a. Which football is in the air for more time?

b. *Justify* your answer to part (a).

4. **GRIDDED ANSWER** During the period 1996–2000, the total value *T* (in millions of dollars) of toys imported to the United States can be modeled by

$$T = 82.9t^3 - 848t^2 + 3030t + 9610$$

where *t* is the number of years since 1996. What is the degree of the polynomial that represents *T*? **3**

5. **EXTENDED RESPONSE** During the period 1992–2000, the number *C* (in millions) of people participating in cross-country skiing and the number *S* (in millions) of people participating in snowboarding can be modeled by

$$C = 0.067t^3 - 0.107t^2 + 0.27t + 3.5$$

$$S = 0.416t + 1.24$$

where *t* is the number of years since 1992.

a. Write an equation that models the total number of people *T* (in millions) participating in cross-country skiing and snowboarding as a function of the number of years since 1992.
$$T = 0.067t^3 - 0.107t^2 + 0.686t + 4.74$$

b. Find the total participation in these activities in 1992 and 2000. **about 4.74 million people, about 37.7 million people**

c. What was the average rate of change in total participation from 1992 to 2000? *Explain* how you found this rate. **See margin.**

6. **SHORT RESPONSE**
A circular rug has an interior circle and two rings around the circle, as shown.

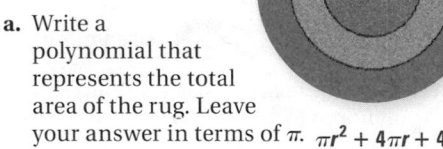

1 ft

1 ft

r ft

a. Write a polynomial that represents the total area of the rug. Leave your answer in terms of π. **$\pi r^2 + 4\pi r + 4\pi$**

b. The interior circle of the rug has a diameter of 3 feet. What is the area of the rug? Leave your answer in terms of π. *Explain* how you found your answer. **See margin.**

2a. *Sample:*

PP

P   P

P   PP   PP

Ps

s   Ps   Ps

2c. The gene from the father is modeled by $0.5P + 0.5s$ and the gene from the mother in modeled by $0.5P + 0.5P = P$, so the possible gene combinations of the offspring are modeled by $P(0.5P + 0.5s) = 0.5P^2 + 0.5Ps$. Because any gene combination with a *P* results in pinto coloring, both terms represent pinto offspring. The sum of the coefficients, $0.5 + 0.5 = 1$, shows that 100% of the offspring will be pinto.

3a. The football with the initial vertical velocity of 44 ft/sec

3b. The height of the football with the initial vertical velocity of 44 feet per second is modeled by the equation $h = -16t^2 + 44t$, which has zeros $h = 0$ seconds and $h = 2.75$ seconds. The height of the football with the initial vertical velocity of 40 feet per second is modeled by the equation $h = -16t^2 + 40t$, which has zeros $h = 0$ seconds and $h = 2.5$ seconds. The first football stays in the air $2.75 - 2.5 = 0.25$ second longer than the second football.

5c. About 4.12 million people per year; to find the average rate of change, divide the total change in participation from 1992 to 2000 by the number of years from 1992 to 2000: $\dfrac{(37.7 - 4.74)\text{ million people}}{(2000 - 1992)\text{ years}} = \dfrac{32.96\text{ million people}}{8\text{ years}} \approx 4.12$ million people per year.

6b. 12.25π ft²; evaluate the polynomial from part (a) when $r = 1.5$: $\pi(1.5^2) + 4\pi(1.5) + 4\pi = 2.25\pi + 6\pi + 4\pi = 12.25\pi$ square feet.

9.5 Factorization with Algebra Tiles

MATERIALS · algebra tiles

QUESTION How can you factor a trinomial using algebra tiles?

You have seen that algebra tiles can be used to model polynomials and to multiply binomials. Now, you will use algebra tiles to factor trinomials.

EXPLORE Factor the trinomial $x^2 + 6x + 8$

STEP 1 *Make a rectangle*

Model the trinomial with algebra tiles. You will need one x^2-tile, six x-tiles, and eight 1-tiles. Arrange all of the tiles to form a rectangle. There can be no gaps or leftover tiles. The area of the rectangle represents the trinomial.

There is a gap. Try again.

Correct arrangement

STEP 2 *Find the side lengths*

The side lengths of the rectangle represent the polynomials $x + 2$ and $x + 4$. So, $x^2 + 6x + 8 = (x + 2)(x + 4)$.

$x + 4$

$x + 2$

DRAW CONCLUSIONS Use your observations to complete these exercises

1. Use multiplication to show that $x + 4$ and $x + 2$ are factors of the polynomial $x^2 + 6x + 8$. $(x + 4)(x + 2) = x^2 + 2x + 4x + 8 = x^2 + 6x + 8$

Use algebra tiles to factor the trinomial. Include a drawing of your model. 2–7. See margin for art.

2. $x^2 + 6x + 5$
   $(x + 5)(x + 1)$

3. $x^2 + 9x + 14$
   $(x + 7)(x + 2)$

4. $x^2 + 5x + 6$
   $(x + 3)(x + 2)$

5. $x^2 + 8x + 16$
   $(x + 4)^2$

6. $x^2 + 5x + 4$
   $(x + 4)(x + 1)$

7. $x^2 + 8x + 12$
   $(x + 6)(x + 2)$

8. **REASONING** The factors of the trinomial $x^2 + 6x + 8$ have the form $x + p$ and $x + q$, as shown above. How are p and q related to 6 and 8? $p + q = 6, pq = 8$

2–7. See Additional Answers beginning on p. AA1.

9.5 Factor $x^2 + bx + c$

Before You factored out the greatest common monomial factor.
Now You will factor trinomials of the form $x^2 + bx + c$.
Why So you can find the dimensions of figures, as in Ex. 61.

Key Vocabulary
• zero of a function, p. 337

From Lesson 9.2, you know that

$(x + 3)(x + 4) = x^2 + (4 + 3)x + 4 \cdot 3 = x^2 + 7x + 12$.

You will reverse this process to factor trinomials of the form $x^2 + bx + c$.

KEY CONCEPT *For Your Notebook*

Factoring $x^2 + bx + c$

Algebra $x^2 + bx + c = (x + p)(x + q)$ provided $p + q = b$ and $pq = c$.

Example $x^2 + 5x + 6 = (x + 3)(x + 2)$ because $3 + 2 = 5$ and $3 \cdot 2 = 6$.

EXAMPLE 1 **Factor when *b* and *c* are positive**

Factor $x^2 + 11x + 18$.

Solution

Find two positive factors of 18 whose sum is 11. Make an organized list.

Factors of 18	Sum of factors	
18, 1	$18 + 1 = 19$	✗
9, 2	$9 + 2 = \mathbf{11}$	← Correct sum
6, 3	$6 + 3 = 9$	✗

The factors 9 and 2 have a sum of 11, so they are the correct values of p and q.

▸ $x^2 + 11x + 18 = (x + 9)(x + 2)$

CHECK $(x + 9)(x + 2) = x^2 + 2x + 9x + 18$ **Multiply binomials.**

$= x^2 + 11x + 18$ ✓   **Simplify.**

 GUIDED PRACTICE for Example 1

Factor the trinomial.

1. $x^2 + 3x + 2$
$(x + 2)(x + 1)$

2. $a^2 + 7a + 10$
$(a + 5)(a + 2)$

3. $t^2 + 9t + 14$
$(t + 7)(t + 2)$

9.5 Factor $x^2 + bx + c$ **583**

---

① PLAN AND PREPARE

Warm-Up Exercises

📄 Transparency Available

Find the product.
1. $(x + 6)(x - 4)$ $x^2 + 2x - 24$
2. $(2y + 3)(y + 5)$ $2y^2 + 13y + 15$
3. The dimensions of a rectangular print can be represented by $x - 2$ and $2x + 1$. Write an expression that models the area of the print. What is its area if x is 4 inches? $2x^2 - 3x - 2$; 18 in.²

Notetaking Guide

📄 Transparency Available

Promotes interactive learning and notetaking skills, pp. 203–206.

Pacing

Basic: 2 days
Average: 2 days
Advanced: 2 days
Block: 0.5 block with 9.4
0.5 block with 9.6
• See *Teaching Guide/Lesson Plan*.

② FOCUS AND MOTIVATE

Essential Question

Big Idea 2, p. 553

How do you factor trinomials of the form $x^2 + bx + c$? **Tell students they will learn how to answer this question by making lists of the possible factors.**

NCTM STANDARDS

Standard 2: Analyze situations using algebraic symbols

Standard 6: Solve problems in math and other contexts

Resource Planning Guide

Chapter Resource Book
• Teaching Guide/Lesson Plan (pp. 50–51)
• Practice levels A, B, C (pp. 53–55)
• Study Guide (pp. 56–57)
• Catch-up for Absent Students (p. 58)
• Application (p. 59)
• Challenge (p. 60)

Workbooks
• Notetaking Guide (pp. 203–206)
• Practice Workbook (pp. 141–142)

Teaching Options
• **Power Presentations CD-ROM** provides dynamic electronic teaching resources for the classroom.
• **Activity Generator CD-ROM** provides editable activities for all ability levels.

Interactive Technology
• Easy Planner
• Power Presentations CD-ROM
• Activity Generator CD-ROM
• Animated Algebra
• Test Generator CD-ROM
• Online Quiz
• eWorkbook
• eEdition
• @HomeTutor

Resources for English Learners
• Quick Reference for English Learners
• Spanish Study Guide
• Multi-Language Visual Glossary
• Student Resources in Spanish

See also the *Algebra 1 Toolkit* for more strategies for meeting individual needs.

③ TEACH

FACTORING When factoring a trinomial, first consider the signs of p and q.

$(x + p)(x + q)$	$x^2 + bx + c$	Signs of b and c
$(x + 2)(x + 3)$	$x^2 + 5x + 6$	b is positive; c is positive.
$(x + 2)(x + (-3))$	$x^2 - x - 6$	b is negative; c is negative.
$(x + (-2))(x + 3)$	$x^2 + x - 6$	b is positive; c is negative.
$(x + (-2))(x + (-3))$	$x^2 - 5x + 6$	b is negative; c is positive.

By observing the signs of b and c in the table, you can see that:

• b and c are positive when both p and q are positive.

• b is negative and c is positive when both p and q are negative.

• c is negative when p and q have different signs.

EXAMPLE 2 Factor when b is negative and c is positive

Factor $n^2 - 6n + 8$.

Because b is negative and c is positive, p and q must both be negative.

Factors of 8	Sum of factors	
$-8, -1$	$-8 + (-1) = -9$	✗
$-4, -2$	$-4 + (-2) = -6$	← Correct sum

▶ $n^2 - 6n + 8 = (n - 4)(n - 2)$

EXAMPLE 3 Factor when b is positive and c is negative

Factor $y^2 + 2y - 15$.

Because c is negative, p and q must have different signs.

Factors of −15	Sum of factors	
$-15, 1$	$-15 + 1 = -14$	✗
$15, -1$	$15 + (-1) = 14$	✗
$-5, 3$	$-5 + 3 = -2$	✗
$5, -3$	$5 + (-3) = 2$	← Correct sum

▶ $y^2 + 2y - 15 = (y + 5)(y - 3)$

✓ **GUIDED PRACTICE** for Examples 2 and 3

Factor the trinomial.

4. $x^2 - 4x + 3$
$(x - 3)(x - 1)$

5. $t^2 - 8t + 12$
$(t - 6)(t - 2)$

6. $m^2 + m - 20$
$(m + 5)(m - 4)$

7. $w^2 + 6w - 16$
$(w + 8)(w - 2)$

EXAMPLE 4   Solve a polynomial equation

Solve the equation $x^2 + 3x = 18$.

$x^2 + 3x = 18$	Write original equation.
$x^2 + 3x - 18 = 0$	Subtract 18 from each side.
$(x + 6)(x - 3) = 0$	Factor left side.
$x + 6 = 0$ *or* $x - 3 = 0$	Zero-product property
$x = -6$ *or* $x = 3$	Solve for *x*.

▶ The solutions of the equation are −6 and 3.

 GUIDED PRACTICE   for Example 4

8. Solve the equation $s^2 - 2s = 24$.   **−4, 6**

 EXAMPLE 5   Solve a multi-step problem

BANNER DIMENSIONS You are making banners to hang during school spirit week. Each banner requires 16.5 square feet of felt and will be cut as shown. Find the width of one banner.

ANOTHER WAY
For alternative methods for solving Example 5, turn to page 590 for the **Problem Solving Workshop**.

Solution

STEP 1 **Draw** a diagram of two banners together.

STEP 2 **Write** an equation using the fact that the area of 2 banners is $2(16.5) = 33$ square feet. Solve the equation for *w*.

$A = \ell \cdot w$	Formula for area of a rectangle
$33 = (4 + w + 4) \cdot w$	Substitute 33 for *A* and $(4 + w + 4)$ for ℓ.
$0 = w^2 + 8w - 33$	Simplify and subtract 33 from each side.
$0 = (w + 11)(w - 3)$	Factor right side.
$w + 11 = 0$ *or* $w - 3 = 0$	Zero-product property
$w = -11$ *or* $w = 3$	Solve for *w*.

▶ The banner cannot have a negative width, so the width is 3 feet.

 GUIDED PRACTICE   for Example 5

9. **WHAT IF?** In Example 5, suppose the area of a banner is to be 10 square feet. What is the width of one banner? **2 ft**

9.5   Factor $x^2 + bx + c$ **585**

Extra Example 4
Solve the equation $x^2 - 3x = 28$.
−4, 7

Extra Example 5
You are designing a flag for the school football team with the dimensions shown in the diagram. The shaded region will show the team name. The flag requires 117 square inches of fabric. Find the width *w* of the flag. **9 in.**

Key Question to Ask for Example 5

• In Step 2, why do you subtract 33 from both sides of the equation? **One side of the equation must be 0 to use the zero-product property.**

Closing the Lesson

Have students summarize the major points of the lesson and answer the Essential Question: How do you factor trinomials of the form $x^2 + bx + c$?

• To factor $x^2 + bx + c$, find factors of the form $(x + p)(x + q)$ where $p + q = b$ and $pq = c$.

Find factors of *c* whose sum $p + q$ is *b*. When *b* and *c* are positive, *p* and *q* are positive. When *b* is negative and *c* is positive, *p* and *q* are negative. When *c* is negative, *p* and *q* have different signs.

Differentiated Instruction

Advanced Some students may be interested in learning about Descartes' Rule of Signs. Tell them they can use this rule to determine the maximum number of positive and negative real roots of a polynomial. Suggest that students research the rule and then test it on polynomials in the lesson or on ones they create for their classmates.

See also the *Algebra 1 Toolkit* for more strategies.

585

HOMEWORK KEY

○ = **WORKED-OUT SOLUTIONS**
on p. WS1 for Exs. 7 and 61

★ = **STANDARDIZED TEST PRACTICE**
Exs. 2, 29, 42, 61, 62, and 63

◆ = **MULTIPLE REPRESENTATIONS**
Ex. 64

④ PRACTICE AND APPLY

Assignment Guide

📑 Answer Transparencies
available for all exercises

Basic:
Day 1: SRH p. 911 Exs. 1–11 odd
pp. 586–589
Exs. 1–19, 66–73
Day 2: pp. 586–589
Exs. 20–28 even, 29, 30–43, 59–62,
74–80 even

Average:
Day 1: pp. 586–589
Exs. 1, 2, 3–17 odd, 18, 19, 47–55,
66–72 even
Day 2: pp. 586–589
Exs. 21–29 odd, 33–46, 59–64, 74, 78

Advanced:
Day 1: pp. 586–589
Exs. 1, 2, 12–17, 47–58*, 66–72 even
Day 2: pp. 586–589
Exs. 24–29, 34–46, 60–65*, 76, 80

Block:
pp. 586–589
Exs. 1, 2, 3–17 odd, 18, 19, 47–55,
66–72 even (with 9.4)
pp. 586–589
Exs. 21–29 odd, 33–46, 59–64, 74, 78
(with 9.6)

Differentiated Instruction

See *Algebra 1 Best Practices Toolkit*
for suggestions on addressing the
needs of a diverse classroom.

Homework Check

For a quick check of student understanding of key concepts, go over
the following exercises:

Basic: 4, 10, 13, 22, 59

Average: 5, 11, 15, 25, 60

Advanced: 13, 14, 17, 27, 61

Extra Practice

• Student Edition, p. 946
• Chapter 9 Resource Book:
 Practice levels A, B, C, pp. 53–55

SKILL PRACTICE

A

1. **VOCABULARY** Copy and complete: The __?__ of $t^2 + 2t + 3$ are $t + 2$ and $t + 1$. **factors**

2. ★ **WRITING** If $x^2 - 8x + 12 = (x + p)(x + q)$, what are the signs of p and q? *Justify* your answer. **See margin.**

EXAMPLES 1, 2, and 3
on pp. 583–584
for Exs. 3–19

FACTORING TRINOMIALS Factor the trinomial.

3. $x^2 + 4x + 3$
$(x + 3)(x + 1)$

4. $a^2 + 6a + 8$
$(a + 4)(a + 2)$

5. $b^2 - 17b + 72$
$(b - 9)(b - 8)$

6. $s^2 - 10s + 16$
$(s - 8)(s - 2)$

7. $z^2 + 8z - 48$
$(z + 12)(z - 4)$

8. $w^2 + 18w + 56$
$(w + 14)(w + 4)$

9. $y^2 - 7y - 18$
$(y - 9)(y + 2)$

10. $n^2 - 9n + 14$
$(n - 7)(n - 2)$

11. $x^2 + 3x - 70$
$(x + 10)(x - 7)$

12. $f^2 + 4f - 32$
$(f + 8)(f - 4)$

13. $m^2 - 7m - 120$
$(m - 15)(m + 8)$

14. $d^2 - 20d + 99$
$(d - 11)(d - 9)$

15. $p^2 + 20p + 64$
$(p + 16)(p + 4)$

16. $x^2 + 6x - 72$
$(x + 12)(x - 6)$

17. $c^2 + 15c + 44$
$(c + 11)(c + 4)$

ERROR ANALYSIS *Describe* and correct the error in factoring the trinomial.

18. In order to
have a product
of −60, p and q
cannot both be
negative;
$(s - 20)(s + 3)$.

18.
$$s^2 - 17s - 60 = (s - 5)(s - 12)$$

19.
$$m^2 - 10m + 24 = (m - 12)(m + 2)$$

In order to have a product of +24, p and q
must have the same sign; $(m - 6)(m - 4)$.

EXAMPLE 4
on p. 585
for Exs. 20–29

SOLVING EQUATIONS Solve the equation.

20. $x^2 - 10x + 21 = 0$ **7, 3**

21. $n^2 - 7n - 30 = 0$ **10, −3**

22. $w^2 - 15w + 44 = 0$ **11, 4**

23. $a^2 + 5a = 50$ **−10, 5**

24. $r^2 + 2r = 24$ **−6, 4**

25. $t^2 + 9t = -20$ **−5, −4**

26. $y^2 - 2y - 8 = 7$ **5, −3**

27. $m^2 + 22 = -23m$ **−22, −1**

28. $b^2 + 5 = 8b - 10$ **5, 3**

29. ★ **MULTIPLE CHOICE** What are the solutions of the equation $x^2 - 8x = 240$? **C**

Ⓐ −20 and −12

Ⓑ −20 and 12

Ⓒ 20 and −12

Ⓓ 12 and 20

B **FINDING ZEROS OF FUNCTIONS** Find the zeros of the polynomial function.

30. $f(x) = x^2 + 11x + 18$
−9, −2

31. $g(x) = x^2 + 5x + 6$
−3, −2

32. $h(x) = x^2 - 18x + 32$
16, 2

33. $f(x) = x^2 - 14x + 45$
9, 5

34. $h(x) = x^2 - 5x - 24$
8, −3

35. $g(x) = x^2 - 14x - 51$
17, −3

36. $g(x) = x^2 + 10x - 39$
−13, 3

37. $f(x) = -x^2 + 16x - 28$
14, 2

38. $f(x) = -x^2 + 24x + 180$
30, −6

SOLVING EQUATIONS Solve the equation.

39. $s(s + 1) = 72$ **−9, 8**

40. $x^2 - 10(x - 1) = -11$ **7, 3**

41. $q(q + 19) = -34$ **−17, −2**

2. p and q are both negative; $pq = 12$, so the product pq is positive,
which means p and q are either both positive or both negative. Also,
$p + q = -8$. In order for p and q to have the same sign and have a
negative sum, both p and q must be negative.

42. ★ SHORT RESPONSE Write an equation of the form $x^2 + bx + c = 0$ that has the solutions -4 and 6. *Explain* how you found your answer. **See margin.**

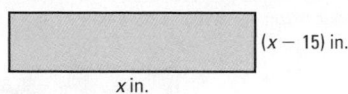 **GEOMETRY** Find the dimensions of the rectangle or triangle that has the given area.

43. Area: 100 square inches **20 in., 5 in.**

$(x - 15)$ in.

x in.

44. Area: 34 square meters **17 m, 2 m**

$(x - 4)$ m

$(x + 11)$ m

45. Area: 78 square yards **26 yd, 6 yd**

x yd

$(x + 20)$ yd

46. Area: 119 square feet **17 ft, 14 ft**

$(x + 3)$ ft

$(x + 6)$ ft

FACTORING TRINOMIALS In Exercises 47–55, use the example below to factor the trinomial.

EXAMPLE **Factor a trinomial in two variables**

Factor $x^2 + 9xy + 14y^2$.

Solution

To factor the trinomial, you must find factors of the form $x + py$ and $x + qy$.

First, consider the signs of the factors needed. In this example, b is 9, and c is 14. Because both b and c are positive, you must find two positive factors of 14 that have a sum of 9.

Factors of 14	Sum of factors	
14, 1	$14 + 1 = 15$	✗
7, 2	$7 + 2 = 9$	← Correct sum

The factors 7 and 2 have a sum of 9, so 7 and 2 are the correct values of p and q.

▶ $x^2 + 9xy + 14y^2 = (x + 7y)(x + 2y)$

---

47. $x^2 - 4xy + 4y^2$
$(x - 2y)^2$
48. $y^2 - 6yz + 5z^2$
$(y - 5z)(y - z)$
49. $c^2 + 13cd + 36d^2$
$(c + 9d)(c + 4d)$

50. $r^2 + 15rs + 50s^2$
$(r + 10s)(r + 5s)$
51. $a^2 + 2ab - 15b^2$
$(a + 5b)(a - 3b)$
52. $x^2 + 8xy - 65y^2$
$(x + 13y)(x - 5y)$

53. $m^2 - mn - 42n^2$
$(m - 7n)(m + 6n)$
54. $u^2 - 3uv - 108v^2$
$(u - 12v)(u + 9v)$
55. $g^2 + 4gh - 60h^2$
$(g + 10h)(g - 6h)$

C **CHALLENGE** Find all integer values of b for which the trinomial has factors of the form $x + p$ and $x + q$ where p and q are integers.

56. $x^2 + bx + 15$
±8, ±16
57. $x^2 - bx + 21$
±10, ±22
58. $x^2 + bx - 42$
±1, ±11, ±19, ±41

Teaching Strategy

Exercise 59 If students do not see how to start a solution, tell them that they can use Step 2 in Example 5 as a model for finding the dimensions of the white part of the card.

61. 40 in.; the side lengths of the trimmed photo can be represented by $x - 5$ and $x - 6$; the area of the trimmed photo is 20 square inches, so to find the side length x of the original square photo, solve the equation $(x - 5)(x - 6) = 20$. The equation has two solutions, 10 and 1, but when $x = 1$ inch, both $x - 5$ and $x - 6$ are negative, which does not make sense in this situation. So, $x = 10$ inches, and the perimeter of the original square photo was $4(10) = 40$ inches.

EXAMPLE 5 [A]
on p. 585
for Exs. 59–61

62c. 625 feet does not make sense as a path width in this problem situation because it is wider than the length of either path. In the diagram w is also the side length of the overlapping square. If $w = 625$ feet, the square is larger than either part of the path. Only the solution $w = 5$ feet makes sense as a path width.

59. CARD DESIGN You are designing a gift card that has a border along one side, as shown. The area of the white part of the card is 30 square centimeters. What is the area of the border? **10 cm²**

@**HomeTutor** for problem solving help at classzone.com

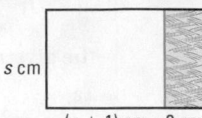
s cm

$(s + 1)$ cm 2 cm

60. CONSTRUCTION A contractor is building a porch along two sides of a house. The house is rectangular with a width of 32 feet and a length of 50 feet. The porch will have the same width on each side of the house.

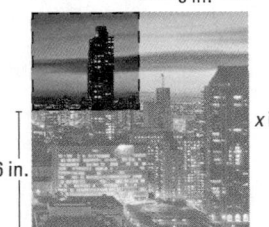
50 ft x ft
32 ft
x ft

a. Write a polynomial that represents the combined area of the first floor of the house and the porch. $x^2 + 82x + 1600$

b. The owners want the combined area of the first floor and the porch to be 2320 square feet. How wide should the contractor build the porch? **8 ft**

@**HomeTutor** for problem solving help at classzone.com

61. ★ **SHORT RESPONSE** You trimmed a large square picture so that you could fit it into a frame. You trimmed 6 inches from the length and 5 inches from the width. The area of the resulting picture is 20 square inches. What was the perimeter of the original large square picture? *Explain* how you found your answer. **See margin.**

← 5 in. →
x in.
6 in.
x in.

[B] **62.** ★ **EXTENDED RESPONSE** A town has a rectangular park. The parks department is planning to install two brick paths that will intersect at right angles. One path will be 130 feet long, and the other path will be 500 feet long. The paths will have the same width.

130 ft
500 ft
w ft
w ft
Not drawn to scale

HINT
Add the path areas, but subtract the overlap, so that it is not counted twice.

a. Write a polynomial that represents the combined area of the two paths. $630w - w^2$

b. The parks department can afford brick for 3125 square feet of path. Write and solve an equation to find the width of the paths. $630w - w^2 = 3125$; 625, 5; 5 ft

c. In part (b) you used one solution of the equation to find your answer. *Explain* how you chose which solution to use. **See margin.**

○ **= WORKED-OUT SOLUTIONS**
on p. WS1

★ **= STANDARDIZED TEST PRACTICE**

◆ **= MULTIPLE REPRESENTATIONS**

588

64a.

x (feet)	y (feet)
2	17
4	21
6	17
8	0

64b.

(4, 21)
(2, 17)   (6, 17)
(8, 5)

63. ★ **MULTIPLE CHOICE** A square quilt has a border that is 1 foot wide on each side. The quilt has an area of 25 square feet. What is the side length of the quilt without the border? **B**

   Ⓐ 2 feet   Ⓑ 3 feet   Ⓒ 4 feet   Ⓓ 5 feet

64. ◆ **MULTIPLE REPRESENTATIONS** You toss a set of keys to a friend who is standing at a window 20 feet above the ground in a building that is 5 feet away from where you are standing. The path of the keys can be modeled by the graph of the equation $y = -x^2 + 8x + 5$ where x and y are measured in feet. On a coordinate plane, the ground is represented by the x-axis, and you are standing at the origin. **a–d. See margin.**

   a. Making a Table Make a table of values that shows the height of the keys for $x = 2, 4, 6,$ and 8 feet.

   b. Drawing a Graph Plot the ordered pairs in the table as points in a coordinate plane. Connect the points with a smooth curve.

   c. Interpreting a Graph Based on your graph, do you expect the keys to reach your friend? *Explain* your answer.

   d. Using an Equation Find the value of x when $y = 20$. (You may need to factor out a -1 in order to factor the trinomial.) What do you notice? *Explain* how the x-value justifies your answer from part (c).

C **65. CHALLENGE** A rectangular stage is positioned in the center of a rectangular room, as shown. The area of the stage is 120 square feet.

   a. Use the dimensions given in the diagram to find the length and width of the stage. **10 ft, 12 ft**

   b. The combined area of the stage and the surrounding floor is 360 square feet. Find the length and width of the room. **20 ft, 18 ft**

MIXED REVIEW

Solve the equation.

66. $x + 12 = 4$ *(p. 134)* **−8**

67. $5y - 2 = 13$ *(p. 141)* **3**

68. $6n + 4 = -14$ *(p. 141)* **−3**

69. $3a - 5a + 12 = -6$ *(p. 148)* **9**

70. $3 - 2(w + 7) = -1$ *(p. 148)* **−5**

71. $-6 + 2(d - 9) = 8d$ *(p. 154)* **−4**

72. $(x - 8)(x + 3) = 0$ *(p. 575)* **8, −3**

73. $(3t + 5)(t + 2) = 0$ *(p. 575)* $-\frac{5}{3}, -2$

Find the product.

74. $(3x + 7)(x - 5)$ *(p. 562)* $3x^2 - 8x - 35$

75. $(3a - 4)(2a - 9)$ *(p. 562)* $6a^2 - 35a + 36$

76. $(c + 2)(c^2 + c - 4)$ *(p. 562)* $c^3 + 3c^2 - 2c - 8$

77. $(7 + 3y)(7 - 5y)$ *(p. 562)* $49 - 14y - 15y^2$

78. $(2k - 8)(2k + 8)$ *(p. 569)* $4k^2 - 64$

79. $(14 - 2n)^2$ *(p. 569)* $196 - 56n + 4n^2$

80. $(5x + 16y)^2$ *(p. 569)* $25x^2 + 160xy + 256y^2$

81. $(3x - 6y)(3x + 6y)$ *(p. 569)* $9x^2 - 36y^2$

PREVIEW
Prepare for Lesson 9.6 in Exs. 74–81.

Using ALTERNATIVE METHODS

Alternative Strategy

Example 5 on page 585 can be solved using a table or a graph. Both methods work well for students who prefer to use one of the figures to determine the width of the banner rather than combining the two complex figures. Though both alternative methods require a few more steps to determine an area formula for the figure, many students find it easier to break a figure into its component parts, determine an appropriate formula for each, and then combine the formulas. The table method aids students by using the familiar guess and check strategy in an organized way. The graphing method aids students who prefer visual solutions to problems.

Avoiding Common Errors

Because both the base and height of the triangle are w, some students may write the formula for the area of a triangle as $A = \frac{1}{2}w$. Remind these students to substitute into the area formula $A = \frac{1}{2}bh$ to get $A = \frac{1}{2} \cdot w \cdot w$ or $A = \frac{1}{2}w^2$.

1. 2 ft; Method 1: Use a table. Write the area of the countertop as the sum of the areas of the two triangles and the rectangle: $A = \left(\frac{1}{2}w^2\right) + 4w = w^2 + 4w$. Make a table showing the total area A for various values of w and look for the value of w that gives a total area of 12 square feet.

w	Total area ($A = w^2 + 4w$)
1	5
2	12

The total area is 12 square feet when $w = 2$ feet. **Method 2: Use a graph.** Write the area of the countertop as the sum of the areas of the two triangles and the rectangle: $A = \left(\frac{1}{2}w^2\right) + 4w = w^2 + 4w$. Graph the equations $A = w^2 + 4w$ and $A = 12$ on the same coordinate plane.

Another Way to Solve Example 5, page 585

MULTIPLE REPRESENTATIONS In Example 5 on page 585, you saw how to solve the problem about a school banner by solving an equation. You can also solve the problem using a table or a graph.

PROBLEM

BANNER DIMENSIONS You are making banners to hang during school spirit week. Each banner requires 16.5 square feet of felt and will be cut as shown. Find the width of one banner.

METHOD 1

Using a Table Consider the separate geometric figures that form one banner and find their areas in terms of w. Then find the total area of the banner for different values of w until you find a value that gives a total area of 16.5 square feet. Use a table to organize your work.

STEP 1 **Write** equations for the area of the pieces and the total area.

$A = \frac{1}{2}w^2$ $A = 4w$ $A = \frac{1}{2}w^2 + 4w$

STEP 2 **Organize** your work in a table.

w	Triangle's area $\left(\frac{1}{2}w^2\right)$	Rectangle's area $(4w)$	Total area $\left(\frac{1}{2}w^2 + 4w\right)$	
1	0.5	4	4.5	$4.5 < 16.5$, so try a greater value of w.
2	2	8	10	$10 < 16.5$, so try a greater value of w.
3	4.5	12	16.5	Correct area

▶ The width of the banner is 3 feet.

To use a graphing calculator, enter the equations as $y = x^2 + 4x$ and $y = 12$ in the same viewing window. To find the w-value for which $A = 12$ square feet, use the calculator's *intersect* feature to find that the graphs intersect at $(2, 12)$.

The total area is 12 square feet when the width is 2 feet.

2. The signs are reversed in the factorization of $w^2 + 4w - 12$; $(w + 2)(w - 6)$ gives a middle term of $-4w$ instead of $+4w$. The correct factorization is $(w - 2)(w + 6)$, which leads to solutions of 2 and -6. The width cannot be negative, so the width is 2 feet.

METHOD 2 **Using a Graph** Another approach is to use a graph.

STEP 1 **Write** an equation for the area of the banner. The area of the banner can be thought of as the area of a triangle plus the area of a rectangle.

> Area of banner = Area of triangle + Area of rectangle
>
> $A = \frac{1}{2}w^2 + 4w$

STEP 2 **Graph** the equation for the area of the banner using a graphing calculator. Graph $y_1 = 0.5x^2 + 4x$. Because you are looking for the value of x that gives an area of 16.5 square feet, you should display the graph of $y_2 = 16.5$ in the same viewing window.

STEP 3 **Find** the intersection of the graphs by using the *intersect* feature on your calculator. The graphs intersect at (3, 16.5).

▸ The width of the banner is 3 feet.

PRACTICE

1–4. See margin.

1. **COUNTER DESIGN** A contractor is building a counter in a kitchen using the diagram shown. The countertop will have an area of 12 square feet. How wide should it be? Solve this problem using two different methods.

2. **ERROR ANALYSIS** *Describe* and correct the error in using an equation to solve the problem in Exercise 1.

> $12 = 4w + \frac{1}{2}w^2 + \frac{1}{2}w^2$
>
> $0 = w^2 + 4w - 12$
>
> $0 = (w + 2)(w - 6)$ ✕
>
> $w + 2 = 0$ or $w - 6 = 0$
>
> $w = -2$ or $w = 6$
>
> The width is 6 feet.

3. **FOUNTAIN DESIGN** A square fountain in a city plaza is surrounded by brick patios as shown. The combined area of the fountain and brick patios is 205 square feet. What is the side length of the fountain? Solve this problem using two different methods.

4. **WHAT IF?** You want to make a larger banner using the same pattern shown in the problem on page 585. The new banner will have an area of 24 square feet. Find the width of the new banner. *Describe* the method you used to find your answer.

Using Alternative Methods   **591**

(Exercise 3 continued)
The combined area is 205 square feet when $x = 9$ feet. Method 2: Use a graph. Write the combined area of the fountain and the brick patios as the sum of the areas of the rectangles minus the area of the fountain (so that the fountain's area is not counted twice): $A = 2(13)(11) - x^2$, or $A = 286 - x^2$. Graph the equations $A = 286 - x^2$ and $A = 205$ on the same coordinate plane. To use a graphing calculator, enter the equations as $y = 286 - x^2$ and $y = 205$ in the same viewing window. To find the x-value for which $A = 205$ square feet, use the calculator's *intersect* feature to find that the graphs intersect at (9, 205).

The combined area is 205 square feet when the side length of the fountain is 9 feet.

4. 4 ft. *Sample answer:* Use a graph. Write the area of the banner as the sum of the area of the triangle and the rectangle: $A = \frac{1}{2}w^2 + 4w$. Graph the equations $A = \frac{1}{2}w^2 + 4w$ and $A = 24$ on the same coordinate plane. To use a graphing calculator, enter the equations as $y = 0.5x^2 + 4x$ and $y = 24$ in the same viewing window. To find the w-value for which $A = 24$ square feet, use the calculator's *intersect* feature to find the x-value of the intersection point of the graphs.

---

3. 9 ft; Method 1: Use a table. To write a polynomial that represents the combined area of the fountain and the brick patios, find the sum of the areas of the rectangles and subtract the area of the fountain (so that the fountain's area is not counted twice): $A = 2(13)(11) - x^2$, or $A = 286 - x^2$. Make a table showing the combined area A for various values of x and look for the value of x that gives a combined area of 205 square feet.

x	Combined area ($A = 286 - x^2$)
5	261
6	250
7	237
8	222
9	205

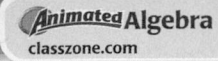
9.6 More Factorization with Algebra Tiles

MATERIALS · algebra tiles

QUESTION How can you factor a trinomial using algebra tiles?

EXPLORE Factor the trinomial $2x^2 + 7x + 3$

STEP 1 *Make a rectangle*

Model the trinomial with algebra tiles. Arrange all of the tiles to form a rectangle. You may have to try a few arrangements to make the rectangle. There can be no gaps or leftover tiles.

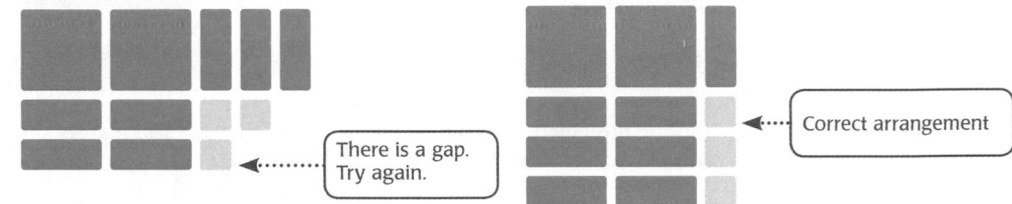

There is a gap. Try again.

Correct arrangement

STEP 2 *Find the side lengths*

The side lengths of the rectangle represent the polynomials $x + 3$ and $2x + 1$. So $2x^2 + 7x + 3 = (x + 3)(2x + 1)$.

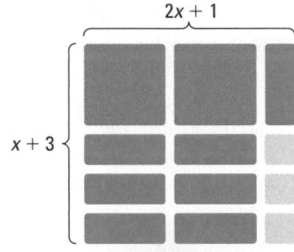

$2x + 1$

$x + 3$

DRAW CONCLUSIONS Use your observations to complete these exercises

1. Use multiplication to show that $x + 3$ and $2x + 1$ are factors of the polynomial $2x^2 + 7x + 3$. **$(x + 3)(2x + 1) = 2x^2 + x + 6x + 3 = 2x^2 + 7x + 3$**

Use algebra tiles to factor the trinomial. Include a drawing of your model. **2–7. See margin for art.**

2. $2x^2 + 5x + 3$
   $(x + 1)(2x + 3)$
3. $3x^2 + 5x + 2$
   $(x + 1)(3x + 2)$
4. $4x^2 + 9x + 2$
   $(x + 2)(4x + 1)$
5. $3x^2 + 13x + 4$
   $(x + 4)(3x + 1)$
6. $4x^2 + 11x + 6$
   $(x + 2)(4x + 3)$
7. $4x^2 + 8x + 3$
   $(2x + 1)(2x + 3)$
8. **REASONING** Factor the trinomial $2x^2 + 11x + 5$ into two binomials. How is the leading coefficient of the trinomial related to the leading coefficients of its binomial factors? **$(x + 5)(2x + 1)$; the leading coefficient of the trinomial is the product of the leading coefficients of its binomial factors.**

592   Chapter 9   Polynomials and Factoring

2–7. See Additional Answers beginning on p. AA1.

9.6 Factor $ax^2 + bx + c$

Before	You factored trinomials of the form $x^2 + bx + c$.
Now	You will factor trinomials of the form $ax^2 + bx + c$.
Why?	So you can find the dimensions of a building, as in Ex. 61.

Key Vocabulary
• trinomial, *p. 555*

When factoring a trinomial of the form $ax^2 + bx + c$, first consider the signs of b and c, as in Lesson 9.5. This approach works when a is positive.

EXAMPLE 1 Factor when *b* is negative and *c* is positive

Factor $2x^2 - 7x + 3$.

Solution

REVIEW FACTORING
For help with determining the signs of the factors of a trinomial, see p. 584.

Because b is negative and c is positive, both factors of c must be negative. Make a table to organize your work.

You must consider the order of the factors of 3, because the x-terms of the possible factorizations are different.

Factors of 2	Factors of 3	Possible factorization	Middle term when multiplied	
1, 2	−1, −3	$(x - 1)(2x - 3)$	$-3x - 2x = -5x$	✗
1, 2	−3, −1	$(x - 3)(2x - 1)$	$-x - 6x = -7x$	← Correct

▶ $2x^2 - 7x + 3 = (x - 3)(2x - 1)$

EXAMPLE 2 Factor when *b* is positive and *c* is negative

Factor $3n^2 + 14n - 5$.

Solution

Because b is positive and c is negative, the factors of c have different signs.

Factors of 3	Factors of −5	Possible factorization	Middle term when multiplied	
1, 3	1, −5	$(n + 1)(3n - 5)$	$-5n + 3n = -2n$	✗
1, 3	−1, 5	$(n - 1)(3n + 5)$	$5n - 3n = 2n$	✗
1, 3	5, −1	$(n + 5)(3n - 1)$	$-n + 15n = 14n$	← Correct
1, 3	−5, 1	$(n - 5)(3n + 1)$	$n - 15n = -14n$	✗

▶ $3n^2 + 14n - 5 = (n + 5)(3n - 1)$

Motivating the Lesson

Engage students in a discussion about football, baseball, or soccer. Remark that when a ball is kicked, thrown, or hit in the air, sometimes the ball's starting position is some distance above the ground. Tell students that if they know the initial velocity of the ball and the height at which it was kicked or thrown, they can calculate when it will hit the ground.

❸ TEACH

Extra Example 1

Factor $2x^2 - 13x + 6$.
$(x - 6)(2x - 1)$

Key Question to Ask for Example 1

• Which terms of the binomial factors do you multiply to find the middle term? **the two outer terms, the two inner terms**

Extra Example 2

Factor $4n^2 + 11n - 3$.
$(n + 3)(4n - 1)$

Extra Example 3

Factor $-3x^2 - 13x - 4$.
$-(3x + 1)(x + 4)$

Key Question to Ask for Example 3

• What are the possible first terms for the binomial factors? What are the possible second terms? **4 and −1, −4 and 1, 2 and −2; 1 and 7; −1 and −7**

 GUIDED PRACTICE for Examples 1 and 2

Factor the trinomial.

1. $3t^2 + 8t + 4$
$(t + 2)(3t + 2)$

2. $4s^2 - 9s + 5$
$(s - 1)(4s - 5)$

3. $2h^2 + 13h - 7$
$(h + 7)(2h - 1)$

FACTORING WHEN a IS NEGATIVE To factor a trinomial of the form $ax^2 + bx + c$ when a is negative, first factor -1 from each term of the trinomial. Then factor the resulting trinomial as in the previous examples.

❖ EXAMPLE 3 Factor when a is negative

Factor $-4x^2 + 12x + 7$.

Solution

STEP 1 **Factor** -1 from each term of the trinomial.

$$-4x^2 + 12x + 7 = -(4x^2 - 12x - 7)$$

STEP 2 **Factor** the trinomial $4x^2 - 12x - 7$. Because b and c are both negative, the factors of c must have different signs. As in the previous examples, use a table to organize information about the factors of a and c.

Factors of 4	Factors of −7	Possible factorization	Middle term when multiplied	
1, 4	1, −7	$(x + 1)(4x - 7)$	$-7x + 4x = -3x$	✗
1, 4	7, −1	$(x + 7)(4x - 1)$	$-x + 28x = 27x$	✗
1, 4	−1, 7	$(x - 1)(4x + 7)$	$7x - 4x = 3x$	✗
1, 4	−7, 1	$(x - 7)(4x + 1)$	$x - 28x = -27x$	✗
2, 2	1, −7	$(2x + 1)(2x - 7)$	$-14x + 2x = -12x$	← Correct
2, 2	−1, 7	$(2x - 1)(2x + 7)$	$14x - 2x = 12x$	✗

AVOID ERRORS
Remember to include the −1 that you factored out in Step 1.

▶ $-4x^2 + 12x + 7 = -(2x + 1)(2x - 7)$

CHECK You can check your factorization using a graphing calculator. Graph $y_1 = -4x^2 + 12x + 7$ and $y_2 = -(2x + 1)(2x - 7)$. Because the graphs coincide, you know that your factorization is correct.

 GUIDED PRACTICE for Example 3

Factor the trinomial.

4. $-2y^2 - 5y - 3$
$-(y + 1)(2y + 3)$

5. $-5m^2 + 6m - 1$
$-(m - 1)(5m - 1)$

6. $-3x^2 - x + 2$
$-(x + 1)(3x - 2)$

594 Chapter 9 Polynomials and Factoring

Differentiated Instruction

Inclusion Organizing a table may be difficult for some students. When discussing **Example 3**, consider adding an additional column for the factors of a and c. Start the table as follows.

Factors of 4		Factors of −7		Possible factorization	Middle term when multiplied
1	4	1	−7	$(x + 1)(4x - 7)$	$-7x + 4x = -3x$

See also the *Algebra 1 Toolkit* for more strategies.

FINDING A COMMON FACTOR In Lesson 9.4, you learned to factor out the greatest common monomial factor from the terms of a polynomial. Sometimes you may need to do this before finding two binomial factors of a trinomial.

EXAMPLE 4   **Write and solve a polynomial equation**

DISCUS An athlete throws a discus from an initial height of 6 feet and with an initial vertical velocity of 46 feet per second.

a. Write an equation that gives the height (in feet) of the discus as a function of the time (in seconds) since it left the athlete's hand.

b. After how many seconds does the discus hit the ground?

Solution

USE VERTICAL MOTION MODEL
For help with using the vertical motion model, see p. 575.

a. Use the vertical motion model to write an equation for the height h (in feet) of the discus. In this case, $v = 46$ and $s = 6$.

$h = -16t^2 + vt + s$ **Vertical motion model**

$h = -16t^2 + 46t + 6$ **Substitute 46 for *v* and 6 for *s*.**

b. To find the number of seconds that pass before the discus lands, find the value of t for which the height of the discus is 0. Substitute 0 for h and solve the equation for t.

$0 = -16t^2 + 46t + 6$ **Substitute 0 for *h*.**

$0 = -2(8t^2 - 23t - 3)$ **Factor out −2.**

$0 = -2(8t + 1)(t - 3)$ **Factor the trinomial. Find factors of 8 and −3 that produce a middle term with a coefficient of −23.**

$8t + 1 = 0 \quad or \ t - 3 = 0$ **Zero-product property**

$t = -\dfrac{1}{8} \ or \qquad t = 3$ **Solve for *t*.**

The solutions of the equation are $-\dfrac{1}{8}$ and 3. A negative solution does not

make sense in this situation, so disregard $-\dfrac{1}{8}$.

▶ The discus hits the ground after 3 seconds.

✓   **GUIDED PRACTICE**   **for Example 4**

7. WHAT IF? In Example 4, suppose another athlete throws the discus with an initial vertical velocity of 38 feet per second and releases it from a height of 5 feet. After how many seconds does the discus hit the ground? **2.5 sec**

8. SHOT PUT In a shot put event, an athlete throws the shot put from an initial height of 6 feet and with an initial vertical velocity of 29 feet per second. After how many seconds does the shot put hit the ground? **2 sec**

Extra Example 4
A soccer goalie throws a ball into the air at an initial height of 8 feet and an initial vertical velocity of 28 feet per second.

a. Write an equation that gives the height (in feet) of the soccer ball as a function of the time (in seconds) since it left the goalie's hand. $h = -16t^2 + 28t + 8$

b. After how many seconds does it hit the ground? **2 sec**

Key Questions to Ask for Example 4

• Why do you substitute 0 for h in the vertical motion model? $h = 0$ **means that the discus is at 0 height or ground level. You use 0 because you want to find the number of seconds it takes the discus to reach the ground.**

• How could you use the model if you want to know how long it takes the discus to reach a height of 6 feet on the way down? **Substitute 6 for *h*, get 0 on one side of the equation, and solve.**

• Can you use the model if the vertical motion is given in miles per hour or meters per second? Explain. **No, for this model the motion must be measured in feet per second. You can convert miles per hour to feet per second and then use the model. A different model is used for metric units.**

596

EXAMPLE 5   Standardized Test Practice

A rectangle's length is 13 meters more than 3 times its width. The area is 10 square meters. What is the width?

Ⓐ $\frac{2}{3}$ m   Ⓑ 3 m   Ⓒ 5 m   Ⓓ 10 m

$w(3w + 13) = 10$	Write an equation to model area.
$3w^2 + 13w - 10 = 0$	Simplify and subtract 10 from each side.
$(w + 5)(3w - 2) = 0$	Factor left side.
$w + 5 = 0 \quad or \quad 3w - 2 = 0$	Zero-product property
$w = -5 \quad or \qquad w = \frac{2}{3}$	Solve for w.

Reject the negative width.

▸ The correct answer is A. Ⓐ Ⓑ Ⓒ Ⓓ

 GUIDED PRACTICE   for Example 5

9. A rectangle's length is 1 inch more than twice its width. The area is 6 square inches. What is the width? **B**

Ⓐ $\frac{1}{2}$ in.   Ⓑ $\frac{3}{2}$ in.   Ⓒ 2 in.   Ⓓ $\frac{5}{2}$ in.

9.6 EXERCISES

HOMEWORK KEY

○ = **WORKED-OUT SOLUTIONS**
on p. WS1 for Exs. 5, 25, and 61

★ = **STANDARDIZED TEST PRACTICE**
Exs. 2, 3, 22, 41, 51, and 61

◆ = **MULTIPLE REPRESENTATIONS**
Ex. 62

SKILL PRACTICE

Ⓐ 1. **VOCABULARY** What is another word for the solutions of $x^2 + 2x + 1 = 0$? **roots**

2. ★ **WRITING** *Explain* how you can use a graph to check a factorization. **See margin.**

3. ★ **WRITING** *Compare* factoring $6x^2 - x - 2$ with factoring $x^2 - x - 2$. **See margin.**

EXAMPLES 1, 2, and 3
on pp. 593–594
for Exs. 4–22

FACTORING TRINOMIALS Factor the trinomial.

4. $-x^2 + x + 20$
$-(x - 5)(x + 4)$

5. $-y^2 + 2y + 8$
$-(y - 4)(y + 2)$

6. $-a^2 + 12a - 27$
$-(a - 3)(a - 9)$

7. $5w^2 - 6w + 1$
$(5w - 1)(w - 1)$

8. $-3p^2 - 10p - 3$
$-(3p + 1)(p + 3)$

9. $6s^2 - s - 5$
$(6s + 5)(s - 1)$

10. $2t^2 + 5t - 63$
$(2t - 9)(t + 7)$

11. $2c^2 - 7c + 3$
$(2c - 1)(c - 3)$

12. $3n^2 - 17n + 10$
$(3n - 2)(n - 5)$

13. $-2h^2 + 5h + 3$
$-(2h + 1)(h - 3)$

14. $-6k^2 - 13k - 6$
$-(2k + 3)(3k + 2)$

15. $10x^2 - 3x - 27$
$(2x + 3)(5x - 9)$

16. $4m^2 + 9m + 5$
$(4m + 5)(m + 1)$

17. $3z^2 + z - 14$
$(3z + 7)(z - 2)$

18. $4a^2 + 9a - 9$
$(4a - 3)(a + 3)$

19. $4n^2 + 16n + 15$
$(2n + 3)(2n + 51)$

20. $-5b^2 + 7b - 2$
$-(5b - 2)(b - 1)$

21. $6y^2 - 5y - 4$
$(3y - 4)(2y + 1)$

596   Chapter 9   Polynomials and Factoring

---

38. In order to solve an equation by factoring and using the zero-product property, the equation must first be put in the form $ax^2 + bx + c = 0$. The left side of the equation should not be factored until 4 is subtracted from each side, making the right side of the equation zero; $5x^2 + x - 4 = 0$,

$(5x - 4)(x + 1) = 0$, $5x - 4 = 0$ or $x + 1 = 0$, $x = \frac{4}{5}$ or $x = -1$; $\frac{4}{5}, -1$.

22. ★ **MULTIPLE CHOICE** What is the correct factorization of $8x^2 - 10x + 3$? **B**

    A $(2x - 3)(4x - 1)$ **B** $(2x - 1)(4x - 3)$

    C $(4x + 1)(2x - 3)$ **D** $(8x - 3)(x - 1)$

EXAMPLES
4 and 5
on pp. 595–596
for Exs. 23–39

SOLVING EQUATIONS Solve the equation.

23. $2x^2 - 3x - 35 = 0$ $-\frac{7}{2}, 5$ **24.** $3w^2 + 22w + 7 = 0$ $-\frac{1}{3}, -7$ **25.** $4s^2 + 11s - 3 = 0$ $\frac{1}{4}, -3$

26. $7a^2 + 2a = 5$ $\frac{5}{7}, -1$ **27.** $8t^2 - 2t = 3$ $\frac{3}{4}, -\frac{1}{2}$ **28.** $6m^2 - 5m = 14$ $-\frac{7}{6}, 2$

29. $b(20b - 3) - 2 = 0$ $-\frac{1}{4}, \frac{2}{5}$ **30.** $4(3y^2 - 7y + 4) = 1$ $\frac{5}{6}, \frac{3}{2}$ **31.** $p(3p + 14) = 5$ $\frac{1}{3}, -5$

32. $4n^2 - 2n - 90 = 0$ $-\frac{9}{2}, 5$ **33.** $10c^2 - 14c + 4 = 0$ $\frac{2}{5}, 1$ **34.** $-16k^2 + 8k + 24 = 0$ $\frac{3}{2}, -1$

35. $6r^2 - 15r = 99$ $\frac{11}{2}, -3$ **36.** $56z^2 + 2 = 22z$ $\frac{1}{7}, \frac{1}{4}$ **37.** $30x^2 + 25x = 20$ $-\frac{4}{3}, \frac{1}{2}$

39. The
factorization of
the polynomial
should be
$(3x + 2)(4x - 1)$
instead of
$(3x - 1)(4x + 2)$;
$-\frac{2}{3}, \frac{1}{4}$.

ERROR ANALYSIS *Describe* and correct the error in solving the equation.

38.

$$5x^2 + x = 4$$
$$x(5x + 1) = 4$$
$$x = 4 \text{ or } 5x + 1 = 4$$
$$x = 4 \text{ or } \qquad x = \frac{3}{5}$$
See margin.

39.
$$12x^2 + 5x - 2 = 0$$
$$(3x - 1)(4x + 2) = 0$$
$$3x - 1 = 0 \text{ or } 4x + 2 = 0$$
$$x = \frac{1}{3} \text{ or } \qquad x = -\frac{1}{2}$$

40. ✏ **GEOMETRY** The length of a rectangle is 7 inches more than 5 times its width. The area of the rectangle is 6 square inches. What is the width? $\frac{3}{5}$ in.

41. ★ **SHORT RESPONSE** The length of a rectangle is 1 inch more than 4 times its width. The area of the rectangle is 3 square inches. What is the perimeter of the rectangle? *Explain* how you found your answer. **See margin.**

B **FINDING ZEROS OF FUNCTIONS** Find the zeros of the polynomial function.

42. $g(x) = 2x^2 + x - 1$ $\frac{1}{2}, -1$ **43.** $f(x) = -x^2 + 12x - 35$ $5, 7$ **44.** $h(x) = -3x^2 + 2x + 5$ $\frac{5}{3}, -1$

45. $f(x) = 3x^2 + x - 14$ $-\frac{7}{3}, 2$ **46.** $g(x) = 8x^2 - 6x - 14$ $\frac{7}{4}, -1$ **47.** $f(x) = 12x^2 - 24x - 63$ $\frac{7}{2}, -\frac{3}{2}$

SOLVING EQUATIONS Multiply each side of the equation by an appropriate power of 10 to obtain integer coefficients. Then solve the equation.

48. $0.3x^2 - 0.7x - 4.0 = 0$ $-\frac{8}{3}, 5$ **49.** $0.8x^2 - 1.8x - 0.5 = 0$ $-\frac{1}{4}, \frac{5}{2}$ **50.** $0.4x^2 - 0.4x = 9.9$ $-\frac{9}{2}, \frac{11}{2}$

51. ★ **MULTIPLE CHOICE** What are the solutions of the equation $0.4x^2 - 1.1x = 2$? **C**

    A -12.5 AND 40 **B** -4 AND 1.25 **C** -1.25 AND 4 **D** -0.125 AND 0.4

WRITING EQUATIONS Write a polynomial equation that has the given solutions. The equation must have integer coefficients. *Explain* your reasoning. **52–54. See margin.**

52. -3 and 2 **53.** $-\frac{1}{2}$ and 5 **54.** $-\frac{3}{4}$ and $-\frac{1}{3}$

C **CHALLENGE** Factor the trinomial.

55. $2x^2 - 11xy + 5y^2$ **56.** $3x^2 + 2xy - 8y^2$ **57.** $6x^3 - 10x^2y - 56xy^2$
$(2x - y)(x - 5y)$ $(3x - 4y)(x + 2y)$ $2x(3x + 7y)(x - 4y)$

                                             9.6   Factor $ax^2 + bx + c$ **597**

41. $9\frac{1}{2}$ in.; to find the width, solve the equation $w(4w + 1) = 3$ to get

$w = \frac{3}{4}$ or $w = -1$. The width cannot be negative, so the width is $\frac{3}{4}$ inch.

Then the length is $4\left(\frac{3}{4}\right) + 1 = 4$ inches, and the perimeter is

$2\left(\frac{3}{4}\right) + 2(4) = 9\frac{1}{2}$ inches.

52–54. See Additional Answers beginning on p. AA1.

④ PRACTICE AND APPLY

Assignment Guide

📖 **Answer Transparencies**
   available for all exercises

Basic:
Day 1: pp. 596–599
Exs. 1–22, 64–72 even
Day 2: pp. 596–599
Exs. 23–37 odd, 38–45, 58–62,
73–81 odd

Average:
Day 1: pp. 596–599
Exs. 1–3, 8–21, 52–55, 65–71 odd
Day 2: pp. 596–599
Exs. 26–38 even, 39–51, 58–62, 74,
77, 80

Advanced:
Day 1: pp. 596–599
Exs. 1–3, 12–21, 52–57*, 65–71 odd
Day 2: pp. 596–599
Exs. 30–37, 40–51, 58–63*, 75, 78, 81

Block:
pp. 596–599
Exs. 1–3, 8–21, 52–55, 65–71 odd
(with 9.5)
pp. 596–599
Exs. 26–38 even, 39–51, 58–62, 74,
77, 80 (with 9.7)

Differentiated Instruction

See *Algebra 1 Best Practices Toolkit*
for suggestions on addressing the
needs of a diverse classroom.

Homework Check

For a quick check of student under-
standing of key concepts, go over
the following exercises:
Basic: 7, 10, 13, 27, 59
Average: 12, 14, 18, 30, 60
Advanced: 17, 20, 21, 58, 61

Extra Practice
• Student Edition, p. 946
• Chapter 9 Resource Book:
  Practice levels A, B, C, pp. 64–66

Practice Worksheet

An easily-readable reduced
practice page (with answers)
for this lesson can be found
on p. 552C.

Avoiding Common Errors

Exercises 4–21 Remind students to factor out −1 before they factor trinomials with a negative leading coefficient. Remind them to include it after they have factored the trinomial.

 Graphing Calculator

Exercises 4–21 Have students use a graphing calculator to check their factorizations. They can graph the trinomial and the factorization in the same viewing window using a thin line and a thick line. If the graphs do not coincide, they can try different factors.

Vocabulary

Exercises 58 Some students may not know what "center of gravity" means. Explain that *center of gravity* generally means the point on which a person or object will balance.

An **Animated Algebra** activity is available on-line for **Exercise 62**. This activity is also available on the **Power Presentations CD-ROM**.

 Internet Reference

Exercise 62 For more information about serval cats, visit the African Wildlife Foundation's website www.awf.org/wildlives/185

60. 2 sec; the ball's height (in feet) is modeled by the equation $h = -16t^2 + 31t + 6$, where t is the time (in seconds) since you threw it. To find when the height is 4 feet, substitute 4 for h. Solve the equation $4 = -16t^2 + 31t + 6$, or $16t^2 - 31t - 2 = 0$. The roots of this equation are $-\frac{1}{16}$ and 2. The time t cannot be negative, so disregard the root $-\frac{1}{16}$; the ball reaches a height of 4 feet after 2 seconds.

EXAMPLE 4 $\boxed{A}$
on p. 595
for Exs. 58, 60

58. DIVING You dive from a platform when your center of gravity is 32 feet above the surface of a swimming pool. Your initial vertical velocity leaving the platform is 28 feet per second. After how many seconds does your center of gravity enter the water? **about 2.54 sec**

@HomeTutor for problem solving help at classzone.com

EXAMPLE 5
on p. 596
for Exs. 59, 61

59. SCRAPBOOK DESIGN You plan to make a scrapbook. On the cover, you want to show three pictures with space between them, as shown. Each of the pictures is twice as long as it is wide.

  a. Write a polynomial that represents the area of the scrapbook cover. $24x^2 + 48x + 24$

  b. The area of the cover will be 96 square centimeters. Find the length and width of the pictures you will use. **4 in., 2 in.**

  @HomeTutor for problem solving help at classzone.com

60. ★ SHORT RESPONSE You throw a ball into the air with an initial vertical velocity of 31 feet per second. The ball leaves your hand when it is 6 feet above the ground. You catch the ball when it reaches a height of 4 feet. After how many seconds do you catch the ball? *Explain* how you can use the solutions of an equation to find your answer. **See margin.**

61. PARTHENON The Parthenon in Athens, Greece, is an ancient structure that has a rectangular base. The length of the Parthenon's base is 8 meters more than twice its width. The area of the base is about 2170 square meters. Find the length and width of the Parthenon's base. **31 m, 70 m**

$\boxed{B}$ **62. ◆ MULTIPLE REPRESENTATIONS** An African cat called a serval leaps from the ground in an attempt to catch a bird. The serval's initial vertical velocity is 24 feet per second.

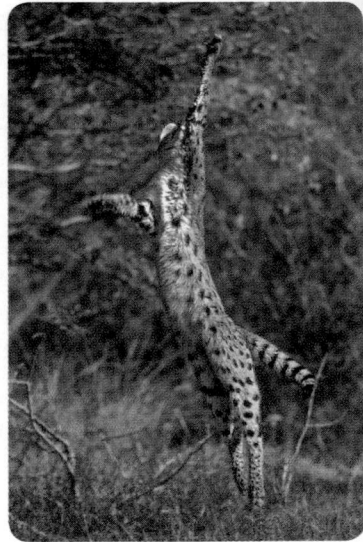

  a. Writing an Equation Write an equation that gives the serval's height (in feet) as a function of the time (in seconds) since it left the ground. $h = -16t^2 + 24t$

  b. Making a Table Use the equation from part (a) to make a table that shows the height of the serval for $t = 0, 0.3, 0.6, 0.9, 1.2$, and 1.5 seconds. **See margin.**

  c. Drawing a Graph Plot the ordered pairs in the table as points in a coordinate plane. Connect the points with a smooth curve. After how many seconds does the serval reach a height of 9 feet? *Justify* your answer using the equation from part (a).

  Animated Algebra at classzone.com

See margin for art; 0.75 sec; substitute $h = 9$ feet into the equation $h = -16t^2 + 24t$ and solve for t, $t = 0.75$ second.

○ = WORKED-OUT SOLUTIONS   ★ = STANDARDIZED   ◆ = MULTIPLE
on p. WS1   TEST PRACTICE   REPRESENTATIONS

62b.

x (feet)	y (feet)
0	0
0.3	5.76
0.6	8.64
0.9	8.64
1.2	5.76
1.5	0

62c.

C 63. **CHALLENGE** A bush cricket jumps from the ground into the air with an initial vertical velocity of 4 feet per second.

    a. Write an equation that gives the cricket's height (in feet) as a function of the time (in seconds) since it left the ground. $h = -16t^2 + 4t$

    b. After how many seconds is the cricket 3 inches off the ground? **0.125 sec**

    c. Does the cricket jump higher than 3 inches? *Explain* your reasoning using your answer from part (b). **See margin.**

MIXED REVIEW

Check whether the given number is a solution of the equation or inequality.

64. $b - 9 = 18$; 3 *(p. 21)*
    not a solution

65. $8 - 3h = 2$; 2 *(p. 21)*
    solution

66. $\dfrac{28 - 2x}{x} < 5$; 4 *(p. 21)*
    not a solution

67. $6t + 18 = 0$; -3 *(p. 21)*
    solution

68. $6c = 3c$; 2 *(p. 21)*
    not a solution

69. $|x + 3| = 2$; -5 *(p. 64)*
    solution

70. $|y - 2| + 6 = 5$; 1 *(p. 64)*
    not a solution

71. $|3n - 11| < 1$; 2 *(p. 64)*
    not a solution

72. $4|3a - 8| > 2$; 3 *(p. 64)*
    solution

PREVIEW
Prepare for Lesson 9.7 in Exs. 73–81.

Find the product. *(p. 569)*

73. $(a - 9)^2$ $a^2 - 18a + 81$

74. $(k + 12)^2$ $k^2 + 24k + 144$

75. $(3x - 2)^2$ $9x^2 - 12x + 4$

76. $(m + 4)(m - 4)$ $m^2 - 16$

77. $(2c + 1)(2c - 1)$ $4c^2 - 1$

78. $(5n - 3)(5n + 3)$ $25n^2 - 9$

79. $(8 - 3y)^2$ $64 - 48y + 9y^2$

80. $(2s - 5t)^2$ $4s^2 - 20st + 25t^2$

81. $(x + 2y)(x - 2y)$ $x^2 - 4y^2$

QUIZ *for Lessons 9.4–9.6*

Factor out the greatest common monomial factor. *(p. 575)*

1. $16a^2 - 40b$
    $8(2a^2 - 5b)$

2. $9xy^2 + 6x^2y$
    $3xy(3y + 2x)$

3. $4n^4 - 22n^3 - 8n^2$
    $2n^2(2n^2 - 11n - 4)$

4. $3x^2 + 6xy - 3y^2$
    $3(x^2 + 2xy - y^2)$

5. $12abc^2 - 6a^2c$
    $6ac(2bc - a)$

6. $-36s^3 + 18s^2 - 54s$
    $-6s(6s^2 - 3s + 9)$

Factor the trinomial.

7. $r^2 + 15r + 56$ *(p. 583)*
    $(r + 7)(r + 8)$

8. $s^2 - 6s + 5$ *(p. 583)*
    $(s - 5)(s - 1)$

9. $w^2 + 6w - 40$ *(p. 583)*
    $(w + 10)(w - 4)$

10. $-a^2 + 9a + 22$ *(p. 593)*
    $-(a - 11)(a + 2)$

11. $2x^2 - 9x + 4$ *(p. 593)*
    $(2x - 1)(x - 4)$

12. $5m^2 + m - 6$ *(p. 593)*
    $(5m + 6)(m - 1)$

13. $6h^2 - 19h + 3$ *(p. 593)*
    $(6h - 1)(h - 3)$

14. $-7y^2 - 23y - 6$ *(p. 593)*
    $-(7y + 2)(y + 3)$

15. $18c^2 + 12c - 6$ *(p. 593)*
    $6(3c - 1)(c + 1)$

Solve the equation.

16. $\dfrac{7}{4}, -5$

16. $(4p - 7)(p + 5) = 0$ *(p. 575)*

17. $-8u^2 + 28u = 0$ *(p. 575)* $0, \dfrac{7}{2}$

18. $51x^2 = -17x$ *(p. 575)* $0, -\dfrac{1}{3}$

19. $b^2 - 11b = -24$ *(p. 583)*
    3, 8

20. $m^2 + 12m = -35$ *(p. 583)*
    −7, −5

21. $q^2 + 19 = -20q$ *(p. 583)*
    −19, −1

22. $3t^2 - 11t + 10 = 0$ *(p. 593)*
    $\dfrac{5}{3}, 2$

23. $4y^2 + 31y = 8$ *(p. 593)*
    $\dfrac{1}{4}, -8$

24. $14s^2 + 12s = 2$ *(p. 593)*
    $\dfrac{1}{7}, -1$

25. BASEBALL A baseball player hits a baseball into the air with an initial vertical velocity of 72 feet per second. The player hits the ball from a height of 3 feet. *(p. 593)*

    a. Write an equation that gives the baseball's height as a function of the time (in seconds) after it is hit. $h = -16t^2 + 72t + 3$

    b. After how many seconds is the baseball 84 feet above the ground? **2.25 sec**

EXTRA PRACTICE for Lesson 9.6, p. 946   **ONLINE QUIZ** at classzone.com   **599**

5 ASSESS AND **RETEACH**

Daily Homework Quiz
 Transparency Available

Factor the trinomial.

1. $-x^2 + x + 30$ $-(x + 5)(x - 6)$

2. $5b^2 + 3b - 14$ $(b + 2)(5b - 7)$

3. $6y^2 - 13y - 5$ $(3y + 1)(2y - 5)$

4. Solve $2x^2 + 7x = -3$. $-\dfrac{1}{2}, -3$

5. A baseball is hit into the air at an initial height of 4 feet and an initial velocity of 30 feet per second. For how many seconds is it in the air? **2 sec**

🌐 **Online Quiz**

Available at **classzone.com**

Diagnosis/Remediation
• Practice A, B, C in Chapter 9 Resource Book, pp. 64–66
• Study Guide in Chapter 9 Resource Book, pp. 67–68
• Practice Workbook, pp. 143–144
• @HomeTutor

Challenge
Additional challenge is available in the Chapter 9 Resource Book, p. 71.

Quiz

An easily-readable reduced copy of the quiz (with answers) on Lessons 9.4–9.6 from the Assessment Book can be found on p. 552E.

63c. No; $t = 0.125$ is the only solution of the equation $\dfrac{1}{4} = -16t^2 + 4t$, so the cricket is 3 inches off the ground only once. This happens only at the highest point of the cricket's jump; all other heights are reached twice, once on the way up and once on the way down.

Before	You factored polynomials of the form $ax^2 + bx + c$.
Now	You will factor special products.
Why?	So you can use a scientific model, as in Ex. 48.

Key Vocabulary
• perfect square trinomial

You can use the special product patterns you studied in Lesson 9.3 to factor polynomials, such as the difference of two squares.

KEY CONCEPT *For Your Notebook*

Difference of Two Squares Pattern

Algebra

$a^2 - b^2 = (a + b)(a - b)$

Example

$4x^2 - 9 = (2x)^2 - 3^2 = (2x + 3)(2x - 3)$

EXAMPLE 1 **Factor the difference of two squares**

Factor the polynomial.

a. $y^2 - 16 = y^2 - 4^2$ Write as $a^2 - b^2$.

$ = (y + 4)(y - 4)$ Difference of two squares pattern

b. $25m^2 - 36 = (5m)^2 - 6^2$ Write as $a^2 - b^2$.

$ = (5m + 6)(5m - 6)$ Difference of two squares pattern

c. $x^2 - 49y^2 = x^2 - (7y)^2$ Write as $a^2 - b^2$.

$ = (x + 7y)(x - 7y)$ Difference of two squares pattern

EXAMPLE 2 **Factor the difference of two squares**

Factor the polynomial $8 - 18n^2$.

$8 - 18n^2 = 2(4 - 9n^2)$ Factor out common factor.

$ = 2[2^2 - (3n)^2]$ Write $4 - 9n^2$ as $a^2 - b^2$.

$ = 2(2 + 3n)(2 - 3n)$ Difference of two squares pattern

 GUIDED PRACTICE for Examples 1 and 2

1. Factor the polynomial $4y^2 - 64$. **$(2y + 8)(2y - 8)$**

Resource Planning Guide

Chapter Resource Book
• Teaching Guide/Lesson Plan (pp. 72–73)
• Practice levels A, B, C (pp. 74–76)
• Study Guide (pp. 77–78)
• Catch-up for Absent Students (p. 79)
• Application (p. 80)
• Challenge (p. 81)

Workbooks
• Notetaking Guide (pp. 210–213)
• Practice Workbook (pp. 145–146)

Teaching Options
• **Power Presentations CD-ROM** provides dynamic electronic teaching resources for the classroom.
• **Activity Generator CD-ROM** provides editable activities for all ability levels.

Interactive Technology
• Easy Planner
• Power Presentations CD-ROM
• Activity Generator CD-ROM
• Animated Algebra
• Test Generator CD-ROM
• Online Quiz
• eWorkbook
• eEdition
• @HomeTutor

Resources for English Learners
• Quick Reference for English Learners
• Spanish Study Guide
• Multi-Language Visual Glossary
• Student Resources in Spanish

See also the *Algebra 1 Toolkit* for more strategies for meeting individual needs.

PERFECT SQUARE TRINOMIALS The pattern for finding the square of a binomial gives you the pattern for factoring trinomials of the form $a^2 + 2ab + b^2$ and $a^2 - 2ab + b^2$. These are called **perfect square trinomials**.

KEY CONCEPT *For Your Notebook*

Perfect Square Trinomial Pattern

Algebra

$a^2 + 2ab + b^2 = (a + b)^2$

$a^2 - 2ab + b^2 = (a - b)^2$

Example

$x^2 + 6x + 9 = x^2 + 2(x \cdot 3) + 3^2 = (x + 3)^2$

$x^2 - 10x + 25 = x^2 - 2(x \cdot 5) + 5^2 = (x - 5)^2$

EXAMPLE 3 **Factor perfect square trinomials**

Factor the polynomial.

a. $n^2 - 12n + 36 = n^2 - 2(n \cdot 6) + 6^2$ Write as $a^2 - 2ab + b^2$.

$= (n - 6)^2$ Perfect square trinomial pattern

b. $9x^2 - 12x + 4 = (3x)^2 - 2(3x \cdot 2) + 2^2$ Write as $a^2 - 2ab + b^2$.

$= (3x - 2)^2$ Perfect square trinomial pattern

c. $4s^2 + 4st + t^2 = (2s)^2 + 2(2s \cdot t) + t^2$ Write as $a^2 + 2ab + b^2$.

$= (2s + t)^2$ Perfect square trinomial pattern

Animated **Algebra** at classzone.com

EXAMPLE 4 **Factor a perfect square trinomial**

Factor the polynomial $-3y^2 + 36y - 108$.

$-3y^2 + 36y - 108 = -3(y^2 - 12y + 36)$ Factor out -3.

$= -3[y^2 - 2(y \cdot 6) + 6^2]$ Write $y^2 - 12y + 36$ as $a^2 - 2ab + b^2$.

$= -3(y - 6)^2$ Perfect square trinomial pattern

CHECK Check your factorization using a graphing calculator. Graph $y_1 = -3x^2 + 36x - 108$ and $y_2 = -3(x - 6)^2$. Because the graphs coincide, you know that your factorization is correct.

✓ **GUIDED PRACTICE** for Examples 3 and 4

Factor the polynomial.

2. $h^2 + 4h + 4$ $(h + 2)^2$ **3.** $2y^2 - 20y + 50$ $2(y - 5)^2$ **4.** $3x^2 + 6xy + 3y^2$ $3(x + y)^2$

9.7 Factor Special Products   **601**

Motivating the Lesson

Ask students to discuss how long it takes objects to fall from different heights. Tell them that if they know the height from which an object is dropped, they can calculate the time it takes the object to reach the ground.

③ TEACH

Extra Example 1

Factor the polynomial.

a. $y^2 - 9$ $(y + 3)(y - 3)$

b. $64c^2 - 16$ $(8c + 4)(8c - 4)$

c. $x^2 - 81y^2$ $(x + 9y)(x - 9y)$

Extra Example 2

Factor the polynomial $12 - 48m^2$.

$3(2 + 4m)(2 - 4m)$

Extra Example 3

Factor the polynomial.

a. $a^2 + 6a + 9$ $(a + 3)^2$

b. $4n^2 + 20n + 25$ $(2n + 5)^2$

c. $9c^2 - 6cd + d^2$ $(3c - d)^2$

Animated **Algebra**

classzone.com

An **Animated Algebra** activity is available on-line for **Example 3**. This activity is also available on the **Power Presentations CD-ROM**.

Extra Example 4

Factor the polynomial $-2x^2 - 16x - 32$. $-2(x + 4)^2$

Key Question to Ask for Example 4

• How can you check the factorization other than by graphing? **Use FOIL and then multiply each term by -3.**

EXAMPLE 5 Solve a polynomial equation

Solve the equation $x^2 + \frac{2}{3}x + \frac{1}{9} = 0$.

$x^2 + \frac{2}{3}x + \frac{1}{9} = 0$	Write original equation.
$9x^2 + 6x + 1 = 0$	Multiply each side by 9.
$(3x)^2 + 2(3x \cdot 1) + (1)^2 = 0$	Write left side as $a^2 + 2ab + b^2$.
$(3x + 1)^2 = 0$	Perfect square trinomial pattern
$3x + 1 = 0$	Zero-product property
$x = -\frac{1}{3}$	Solve for x.

FIND SOLUTIONS
This equation has two identical solutions, because it has two identical factors.

▶ The solution of the equation is $-\frac{1}{3}$.

EXAMPLE 6 Solve a vertical motion problem

FALLING OBJECT A window washer drops a wet sponge from a height of 64 feet. After how many seconds does the sponge land on the ground?

Solution

Use the vertical motion model to write an equation for the height h (in feet) of the sponge as a function of the time t (in seconds) after it is dropped.

The sponge was dropped, so it has no initial vertical velocity. Find the value of t for which the height is 0.

$h = -16t^2 + vt + s$	Vertical motion model
$0 = -16t^2 + (0)t + 64$	Substitute 0 for h, 0 for v, and 64 for s.
$0 = -16(t^2 - 4)$	Factor out −16.
$0 = -16(t - 2)(t + 2)$	Difference of two squares pattern
$t - 2 = 0$ or $t + 2 = 0$	Zero-product property
$t = 2$ or $t = -2$	Solve for t.

Disregard the negative solution of the equation.

▶ The sponge lands on the ground 2 seconds after it is dropped.

 GUIDED PRACTICE   for Examples 5 and 6

Solve the equation.

5. $a^2 + 6a + 9 = 0$ **−3**   6. $w^2 - 14w + 49 = 0$ **7**   7. $n^2 - 81 = 0$ **±9**

8. **WHAT IF?** In Example 6, suppose the sponge is dropped from a height of 16 feet. After how many seconds does it land on the ground? **1 sec**

9.7 EXERCISES

SKILL PRACTICE

[A] 1. **VOCABULARY** Copy and complete: The polynomial $9n^2 + 6n + 1$ is called a(n) __?__ trinomial. **perfect square**

2. ★ **WRITING** *Explain* how to factor the difference of two squares. **Write the binomial in the form $a^2 - b^2$ and then factor it as $(a + b)(a - b)$, the sum and difference of a and b.**

EXAMPLES 1 and 2
on p. 600
for Exs. 3–8

DIFFERENCE OF TWO SQUARES Factor the polynomial.

3. $x^2 - 25$ $(x + 5)(x - 5)$

4. $n^2 - 64$ $(n + 8)(n - 8)$

5. $81c^2 - 4$ $(9c + 2)(9c - 2)$

6. $49 - 121p^2$
$(7 + 11p)(7 - 11p)$

7. $-3m^2 + 48n^2$
$-3(m + 4n)(m - 4n)$

8. $225x^2 - 144y^2$
$9(5x + 4y)(5x - 4y)$

EXAMPLES 3 and 4
on p. 601
for Exs. 9–14

PERFECT SQUARE TRINOMIALS Factor the polynomial.

9. $x^2 - 4x + 4$ $(x - 2)^2$

10. $y^2 - 10y + 25$ $(y - 5)^2$

11. $49a^2 + 14a + 1$ $(7a + 1)^2$

12. $9t^2 - 12t + 4$ $(3t - 2)^2$

13. $m^2 + m + \frac{1}{4}$ $\left(m + \frac{1}{2}\right)^2$

14. $2x^2 + 12xy + 18y^2$
$2(x + 3y)^2$

EXAMPLES 1, 2, 3, and 4
on pp. 600–601
for Exs. 15–24

FACTORING POLYNOMIALS Factor the polynomial.

15. $4c^2 - 400$ $4(c + 10)(c - 10)$

16. $4f^2 - 36f + 81$ $(2f - 9)^2$

17. $-9r^2 + 4s^2$
$(2s + 3r)(2s - 3r)$

18. $z^2 + 12z + 36$ $(z + 6)^2$

19. $72 - 32y^2$
$8(3 + 2y)(3 - 2y)$

20. $45r^2 - 120rs + 80s^2$
$5(3r - 4s)^2$

ERROR ANALYSIS *Describe* and correct the error in factoring. **21, 22. See margin.**

21.

$$36x^2 - 81 = 9(4x^2 - 9)$$
$$= 9((2x)^2 - 3^2) \quad ✗$$
$$= 9(2x - 3)^2$$

22.

$$y^2 - 6y + 9 = y^2 - 2(y \cdot 3) + 3^2$$
$$= (y - 3)(y + 3) \quad ✗$$

23. ★ **MULTIPLE CHOICE** Which is the correct factorization of $-45x^2 + 20y^2$? **C**

  Ⓐ $-5(3x + 2y)^2$

  Ⓑ $5(3x - 2y)^2$

  Ⓒ $-5(3x + 2y)(3x - 2y)$

  Ⓓ $5(3x + 2y)(3x - 2y)$

24. ★ **MULTIPLE CHOICE** Which is the correct factorization of $16m^2 - 8mn + n^2$? **A**

  Ⓐ $(4m - n)^2$

  Ⓑ $(4m + n)^2$

  Ⓒ $(8m - n)^2$

  Ⓓ $(4m - n)(4m + n)$

EXAMPLE 5 [B]
on p. 602
for Exs. 25–39

SOLVING EQUATIONS Solve the equation.

25. $x^2 + 8x + 16 = 0$ -4

26. $16a^2 - 8a + 1 = 0$ $\frac{1}{4}$

27. $4w^2 - 36 = 0$ ± 3

28. $32 - 18m^2 = 0$ $\pm\frac{4}{3}$

29. $27c^2 + 108c + 108 = 0$ -2

30. $-2h^2 - 28h - 98 = 0$ -7

31. $6p^2 = 864$ ± 12

32. $-3t^2 = -108$ ± 6

33. $8k^2 = 98$ $\pm\frac{7}{2}$

34. $-\frac{4}{3}x + \frac{4}{9} = -x^2$ $\frac{2}{9}$

35. $y^2 - \frac{5}{3}y = -\frac{25}{36}$ $\frac{5}{6}$

36. $\frac{2}{9} = 8n^2$ $\pm\frac{1}{6}$

37. $-9c^2 = -16$ $\pm\frac{4}{3}$

38. $-20s - 3 = 25s^2 + 1$ $-\frac{2}{5}$

39. $y^4 - 2y^3 + y^2 = 0$ $0, 1$

21. $(2x)^2 - 3^2$ is in the form $a^2 - b^2$, so it must be factored using the difference of two squares pattern, not the perfect square trinomial pattern; $9(2x + 3)(2x - 3)$.

22. $y^2 - 2(y \cdot 3) + 3^2$ is in the form $a^2 - 2ab + b^2$, so it must be factored using the perfect square trinomial pattern, not the difference of two squares pattern; $(y - 3)^2$.

---

④ PRACTICE AND APPLY

Assignment Guide

📖 Answer Transparencies available for all exercises

Basic:
Day 1: pp. 603–605
Exs. 1, 2, 3–21 odd, 22–30, 46–50, 53–75 odd

Average:
Day 1: pp. 603–605
Exs. 1, 2, 6–8, 12–24, 25–39 odd, 46–51, 54–76 even

Advanced:
Day 1: pp. 603–605
Exs. 1, 2, 6–9, 12–20, 23, 24, 26–38 even, 40–52*, 61, 70, 76

Block:
pp. 603–605
Exs. 1, 2, 6–8, 12–24, 25–39 odd, 46–51, 54–76 even (with 9.6)

Differentiated Instruction

See *Algebra 1 Best Practices Toolkit* for suggestions on addressing the needs of a diverse classroom.

Homework Check

For a quick check of student understanding of key concepts, go over the following exercises:

Basic: 5, 9, 17, 26, 46
Average: 6, 12, 19, 29, 47
Advanced: 8, 14, 20, 38, 48

Extra Practice

• Student Edition, p. 946
• Chapter 9 Resource Book: Practice levels A, B, C, pp. 74–76

Practice Worksheet

An easily-readable reduced practice page (with answers) for this lesson can be found on p. 552C.

C **CHALLENGE** Determine the value(s) of k for which the expression is a perfect square trinomial.

40. $x^2 + kx + 36$ **±12** **41.** $4x^2 + kx + 9$ **±12** **42.** $16x^2 + kx + 4$ **±16**

43. $25x^2 + 10x + k$ **1** **44.** $49x^2 - 84x + k$ **36** **45.** $4x^2 - 48x + k$ **144**

PROBLEM SOLVING

EXAMPLE 6 **A**
on p. 602
for Exs. 46–48

46. **FALLING BRUSH** While standing on a ladder, you drop a paintbrush from a height of 25 feet. After how many seconds does the paintbrush land on the ground? **1.25 sec**

@HomeTutor for problem solving help at classzone.com

47. **FALLING OBJECT** A hickory nut falls from a branch that is 100 feet above the ground. After how many seconds does the hickory nut land on the ground? **2.5 sec**

@HomeTutor for problem solving help at classzone.com

48. **GRASSHOPPER** A grasshopper jumps straight up from the ground with an initial vertical velocity of 8 feet per second.

a. Write an equation that gives the height (in feet) of the grasshopper as a function of the time (in seconds) since it leaves the ground. $h = -16t^2 + 8t$

b. After how many seconds is the grasshopper 1 foot off the ground? **0.25 sec**

49. ★ **SHORT RESPONSE** A ball is thrown up into the air from a height of 5 feet with an initial vertical velocity of 56 feet per second. How many times does the ball reach a height of 54 feet? *Explain* your answer. **See margin.**

B **50.** ★ **EXTENDED RESPONSE** An arch of balloons decorates the stage at a high school graduation. The balloons are tied to a frame. The shape of the frame can be modeled by the graph of the equation $y = -\frac{1}{4}x^2 + 3x$ where x and y are measured in feet.

a. Make a table of values that shows the height of the balloon arch for $x = 0, 2, 5, 8,$ and 11 feet. **See margin.**

b. For what additional values of x does the equation make sense? *Explain.* **See margin.**

c. At approximately what distance from the left end does the arch reach a height of 9 feet? Check your answer algebraically. **6 ft**

○ = **WORKED-OUT SOLUTIONS** on p. WS1   ★ = **STANDARDIZED TEST PRACTICE**

51. FRAMING A square mirror is framed with stained glass as shown. Each corner of the frame began as a square with a side length of d inches before it was cut to fit the mirror. The mirror has a side length of 3 inches. The area of the stained glass frame is 91 square inches.

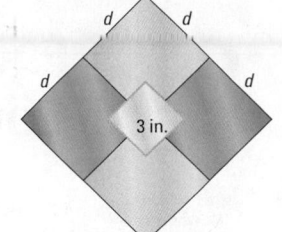

3 in.

a. Write a polynomial that represents the area of the stained glass frame. **$4d^2 - 9$**

b. What is the side length of the frame? **10 in.**

C **52. CHALLENGE** You have 120 folding chairs to set up in a park for an outdoor play. You want each row to have an odd number of chairs. You also want each row after the first to have 2 more chairs than the row in front of it. The first row will have 15 chairs.

a. Copy and complete the table below.

n	nth odd integer	Sum of first n odd integers	Sum as a power
1	1	1	1^2
2	3	$1 + 3 = 4$	2^2
3	5	$1 + 3 + 5 = 9$	?
4	7	? **$1 + 3 + 5 + 7 = 16$**	**? 4^2**
5	9	?	**? 5^2**

$1 + 3 + 5 + 7 + 9 = 16$

b. *Describe* the relationship between n and the sum of the first n odd integers. Then find the sum of the first 10 odd integers.
The sum of the first n odd integers is n^2; 100.

c. *Explain* how to find the sum of the odd integers from 11 to 21. **See margin.**

d. How many rows of chairs will you need for the outdoor play? *Explain* your thinking. **See margin.**

MIXED REVIEW

PREVIEW
Prepare for Lesson 9.8 in Exs. 53–61.

Solve the equation.

53. $a + 6 = 3$ *(p. 134)* **−3**
54. $5y - 2 = -32$ *(p. 141)* **−6**
55. $8m + 4 = 20$ *(p. 141)* **2**

56. $5b - 3b + 6 = 4$ *(p. 148)* **−1**
57. $(x - 9)(x + 1) = 0$ *(p. 575)* **−1, 9**
58. $x^2 + 17x = -66$ *(p. 583)* **−11, −6**

59. $x^2 = -12x + 45$ *(p. 583)* **−15, 3**
60. $2y^2 + y = 15$ *(p. 593)* **$-3, \frac{5}{2}$**
61. $22z - 35 = 3z^2$ *(p. 593)* **$\frac{7}{3}, 5$**

Graph the linear equation. 62–70. See margin.

62. $y = -6$ *(p. 215)*
63. $x = 14$ *(p. 215)*
64. $2x + y = 8$ *(p. 225)*

65. $-4x + 5y = -20$ *(p. 225)*
66. $0.6x + 0.2y = 3.6$ *(p. 225)*
67. $y = -\frac{3}{2}x - 9$ *(p. 225)*

68. $y = \frac{5}{2}x$ *(p. 244)*
69. $y = -12x + 3$ *(p. 244)*
70. $y = \frac{4}{3}x + 2$ *(p. 244)*

Find the product.

71. $(2a - 3)(5a - 2)$ *(p. 562)* **$10a^2 - 19a + 6$**
72. $(2x^2 + x + 3)(x - 1)$ *(p. 562)* **$2x^3 - x^2 + 2x - 3$**
73. $(c + 3)(c + 5)$ *(p. 562)* **$c^2 + 8c + 15$**

74. $(3x - 4)(2x - 7)$ *(p. 562)* **$6x^2 - 29x + 28$**
75. $(2k - 11)(2k + 11)$ *(p. 569)* **$4k^2 - 121$**
76. $(y - 7)^2$ *(p. 569)* **$y^2 - 14y + 49$**

EXTRA PRACTICE for Lesson 9.7, p. 946   **ONLINE QUIZ** at classzone.com   **605**

62–70. See Additional Answers beginning on p. AA1.

Before	You factored polynomials.
Now	You will factor polynomials completely.
Why?	So you can model the height of a projectile, as in Ex. 71.

---

1 PLAN AND PREPARE

Warm-Up Exercises
Transparency Available

1. Solve $2x^2 + 11x = 21$. $\frac{3}{2}, -7$

2. Factor $4x^2 + 10x + 4$.
   $(2x + 4)(2x + 1)$

3. A replacement piece of sod for a lawn has an area of 112 square inches. The width is w and the length is $2w - 2$. What are the dimensions of the sod?
   width: 8 in., length: 14 in.

Notetaking Guide
Transparency Available

Promotes interactive learning and notetaking skills, pp. 214–218.

Pacing
Basic: 2 days
Average: 2 days
Advanced: 2 days
Block: 1 block
• See *Teaching Guide/Lesson Plan.*

---

2 FOCUS AND MOTIVATE

Essential Question
Big Idea 3, p. 553

How do you factor polynomials completely? **Tell students they will learn how to answer this question by grouping terms and factoring out binomials.**

NCTM STANDARDS

Standard 2: Analyze situations using algebraic symbols

Standard 6: Solve problems in math and other contexts

Key Vocabulary
• factor by grouping
• factor completely

You have used the distributive property to factor a greatest common monomial from a polynomial. Sometimes, you can factor out a common binomial.

EXAMPLE 1 Factor out a common binomial

Factor the expression.

a. $2x(x + 4) - 3(x + 4)$ b. $3y^2(y - 2) + 5(2 - y)$

Solution

a. $2x(x + 4) - 3(x + 4) = (x + 4)(2x - 3)$

b. The binomials $y - 2$ and $2 - y$ are opposites. Factor -1 from $2 - y$ to obtain a common binomial factor.

$3y^2(y - 2) + 5(2 - y) = 3y^2(y - 2) - 5(y - 2)$ **Factor -1 from $(2 - y)$.**

$= (y - 2)(3y^2 - 5)$ **Distributive property**

GROUPING You may be able to use the distributive property to factor polynomials with four terms. Factor a common monomial from pairs of terms, then look for a common binomial factor. This is called **factor by grouping**.

EXAMPLE 2 Factor by grouping

Factor the polynomial.

a. $x^3 + 3x^2 + 5x + 15$ b. $y^2 + y + yx + x$

Solution

> **CHECK WORK**
> Remember that you can check a factorization by multiplying the factors.

a. $x^3 + 3x^2 + 5x + 15 = (x^3 + 3x^2) + (5x + 15)$ **Group terms.**

$= x^2(x + 3) + 5(x + 3)$ **Factor each group.**

$= (x + 3)(x^2 + 5)$ **Distributive property**

b. $y^2 + y + yx + x = (y^2 + y) + (yx + x)$ **Group terms.**

$= y(y + 1) + x(y + 1)$ **Factor each group.**

$= (y + 1)(y + x)$ **Distributive property**

Resource Planning Guide

Chapter Resource Book
• Teaching Guide/Lesson Plan (pp. 82–83)
• Practice levels A, B, C (pp. 84–86)
• Study Guide (pp. 87–88)
• Catch-up for Absent Students (p. 89)
• Problem Solving Workshop (p. 90)
• Challenge (p. 91)

Workbooks
• Notetaking Guide (pp. 214–218)
• Practice Workbook (pp. 147–148)

Teaching Options
• **Power Presentations CD-ROM** provides dynamic electronic teaching resources for the classroom.
• **Activity Generator CD-ROM** provides editable activities for all ability levels.

Interactive Technology
• Easy Planner
• Power Presentations CD-ROM
• Activity Generator CD-ROM
• Animated Algebra
• Test Generator CD-ROM
• Online Quiz
• eWorkbook
• eEdition
• @HomeTutor

Resources for English Learners
• Quick Reference for English Learners
• Spanish Study Guide
• Multi-Language Visual Glossary
• Student Resources in Spanish

See also the *Algebra 1 Toolkit* for more strategies for meeting individual needs.

EXAMPLE 3 Factor by grouping

Factor $x^3 - 6 + 2x - 3x^2$.

Solution

The terms x^2 and -6 have no common factor. Use the commutative property to rearrange the terms so that you can group terms with a common factor.

$$x^3 - 6 + 2x - 3x^2 = x^3 - 3x^2 + 2x - 6 \qquad \text{Rearrange terms.}$$
$$= (x^3 - 3x^2) + (2x - 6) \qquad \text{Group terms.}$$
$$= x^2(x - 3) + 2(x - 3) \qquad \text{Factor each group.}$$
$$= (x - 3)(x^2 + 2) \qquad \text{Distributive property}$$

CHECK Check your factorization using a graphing calculator. Graph $y_1 = x^3 - 6 + 2x - 3x^2$ and $y_2 = (x - 3)(x^2 + 2)$. Because the graphs coincide, you know that your factorization is correct.

✓ **GUIDED PRACTICE** for Examples 1, 2, and 3

Factor the expression.

1. $x(x - 2) + (x - 2)$
   $(x - 2)(x + 1)$

2. $a^3 + 3a^2 + a + 3$
   $(a + 3)(a^2 + 1)$

3. $y^2 + 2x + yx + 2y$
   $(y + 2)(y + x)$

READING

If a polynomial has two or more terms and is unfactorable, it is called a *prime polynomial*.

FACTORING COMPLETELY You have seen that the polynomial $x^2 - 1$ can be factored as $(x + 1)(x - 1)$. This polynomial is factorable. Notice that the polynomial $x^2 + 1$ cannot be written as the product of polynomials with integer coefficients. This polynomial is unfactorable. A factorable polynomial with integer coefficients is **factored completely** if it is written as a product of unfactorable polynomials with integer coefficients.

CONCEPT SUMMARY   *For Your Notebook*

Guidelines for Factoring Polynomials Completely

To factor a polynomial completely, you should try each of these steps.

1. Factor out the greatest common monomial factor.
   (Lesson 9.4) $3x^2 + 6x = 3x(x + 2)$

2. Look for a difference of two squares or a perfect
   square trinomial. *(Lesson 9.7)* $x^2 + 4x + 4 = (x + 2)^2$

3. Factor a trinomial of the form $ax^2 + bx + c$ into a product $3x^2 - 5x - 2 = (3x + 1)(x - 2)$
   of binomial factors. *(Lessons 9.5 and 9.6)*

4. Factor a polynomial with four terms by grouping. $x^3 + x - 4x^2 - 4 = (x^2 + 1)(x - 4)$
   (Lesson 9.8)

9.8 Factor Polynomials Completely **607**

Differentiated Instruction

Visual Learners Some students may see that the grouping method is not unique. Show the following for **Example 3**.

$$x^3 - 6 + 2x - 3x^2 = x^3 + 2x - 6 - 3x^2$$
$$= (x^3 + 2x) - (6 + 3x^2)$$
$$= x(x^2 + 2) - 3(2 + x^2)$$
$$= x(x^2 + 2) - 3(x^2 + 2)$$
$$= (x - 3)(x^2 + 2)$$

See also the *Algebra 1 Toolkit* for more strategies.

Motivating the Lesson

Food packagers often know what the volume of a package must be and have to decide what the package's dimensions can be. If they know how the dimensions are related, they can use factoring to find the dimensions.

❸ TEACH

Extra Example 1

Factor the expression.

a. $4x(x - 3) + 5(x - 3)$
   $(x - 3)(4x + 5)$

b. $2y^2(y - 5) - 3(5 - y)$
   $(y - 5)(2y^2 + 3)$

Key Questions to Ask for Example 1

- In part (b), why is one of the factors $3y^2 - 5$ instead of $3y^2 + 5$?
  When you factor out -1 to obtain the common binomial factor $y - 2$, you are left with the factor $-1 \cdot 5$, or -5.

- In part (b), if the binomials were $(y + 2)(2 + y)$, how would you obtain a common binomial? **Use the commutative property to change $2 + y$ to $y + 2$.**

Extra Example 2

Factor the polynomial.

a. $x^3 + 2x^2 + 8x + 16$
   $(x + 2)(x^2 + 8)$

b. $r^2 + 4r + rs + 4s$ $(r + 4)(r + s)$

Extra Example 3

Factor $x^3 - 10 - 5x + 2x^2$.
$(x + 2)(x^2 - 5)$

607

EXAMPLE 4 Factor completely

Factor the polynomial completely.

a. $n^2 + 2n - 1$ b. $4x^3 - 44x^2 + 96x$ c. $50h^4 - 2h^2$

Solution

a. The terms of the polynomial have no common monomial factor. Also, there are no factors of -1 that have a sum of 2. This polynomial cannot be factored.

b. $4x^3 - 44x^2 + 96x = 4x(x^2 - 11x + 24)$ **Factor out 4x.**

$= 4x(x - 3)(x - 8)$ **Find two negative factors of 24 that have a sum of -11.**

c. $50h^4 - 2h^2 = 2h^2(25h^2 - 1)$ **Factor out $2h^2$.**

$= 2h^2(5h - 1)(5h + 1)$ **Difference of two squares pattern**

✓ **GUIDED PRACTICE** for Example 4

Factor the polynomial completely.

4. $3x^3 - 12x$ 5. $2y^3 - 12y^2 + 18y$ 6. $m^3 - 2m^2 - 8m$
   $3x(x - 2)(x + 2)$ $2y(y - 3)^2$ $m(m - 4)(m + 2)$

EXAMPLE 5 Solve a polynomial equation

Solve $3x^3 + 18x^2 = -24x$.

$3x^3 + 18x^2 = -24x$ **Write original equation.**

$3x^3 + 18x^2 + 24x = 0$ **Add 24x to each side.**

$3x(x^2 + 6x + 8) = 0$ **Factor out 3x.**

$3x(x + 2)(x + 4) = 0$ **Factor trinomial.**

$3x = 0$ or $x + 2 = 0$ or $x + 4 = 0$ **Zero-product property**

$x = 0$ $x = -2$ $x = -4$ **Solve for x.**

▶ The solutions of the equation are 0, -2, and -4.

CHECK   Check each solution by substituting it for x in the equation. One check is shown here.

$3(-2)^3 + 18(-2)^2 \overset{?}{=} -24(-2)$

$-24 + 72 \overset{?}{=} 48$

$48 = 48$ ✓

✓ **GUIDED PRACTICE** for Example 5

Solve the equation.

7. $w^3 - 8w^2 + 16w = 0$ **0, 4**   8. $x^3 - 25x = 0$ **0, ±5**   9. $c^3 - 7c^2 + 12c = 0$
                                                            0, 3, 4

EXAMPLE 6 **Solve a multi-step problem**

TERRARIUM A terrarium in the shape of a rectangular prism has a volume of 4608 cubic inches. Its length is more than 10 inches. The dimensions of the terrarium are shown. Find the length, width, and height of the terrarium.

$(w + 4)$ in.

$(36 - w)$ in. w in.

Solution

STEP 1 **Write** a verbal model. Then write an equation.

Volume (cubic inches)	=	Length (inches)	·	Width (inches)	·	Height (inches)

4608	=	$(36 - w)$	·	w	·	$(w + 4)$

STEP 2 **Solve** the equation for w.

$4608 = (36 - w)(w)(w + 4)$ Write equation.

$0 = 32w^2 + 144w - w^3 - 4608$ Multiply. Subtract 4608 from each side.

$0 = (-w^3 + 32w^2) + (144w - 4608)$ Group terms.

$0 = -w^2(w - 32) + 144(w - 32)$ Factor each group.

$0 = (w - 32)(-w^2 + 144)$ Distributive property

$0 = -1(w - 32)(w^2 - 144)$ Factor −1 from $-w^2 + 144$.

$0 = -1(w - 32)(w - 12)(w + 12)$ Difference of two squares pattern

$w - 32 = 0$ *or* $w - 12 = 0$ *or* $w + 12 = 0$ Zero-product property

$w = 32$ $w = 12$ $w = -12$ Solve for w.

STEP 3 **Choose** the solution of the equation that is the correct value of w. Disregard $w = -12$, because the width cannot be negative.

You know that the length is more than 10 inches. Test the solutions 12 and 32 in the expression for the length.

Length = 36 − 12 = 24 ✓   *or*   Length = 36 − 32 = 4 ✗

The solution 12 gives a length of 24 inches, so 12 is the correct value of w.

STEP 4 **Find** the height.

Height = $w + 4 = 12 + 4 = 16$

▶ The width is 12 inches, the length is 24 inches, and the height is 16 inches.

✓ **GUIDED PRACTICE**   for Example 6

10. 3 ft long by 2 ft wide by 12 ft high

10. DIMENSIONS OF A BOX A box in the shape of a rectangular prism has a volume of 72 cubic feet. The box has a length of x feet, a width of $(x - 1)$ feet, and a height of $(x + 9)$ feet. Find the dimensions of the box.

9.8 **EXERCISES**

HOMEWORK KEY
○ = WORKED-OUT SOLUTIONS on p. WS1 for Exs. 13, 23, and 71
★ = STANDARDIZED TEST PRACTICE Exs. 2, 12, 41, 55, 71, and 73

④ PRACTICE AND APPLY

Assignment Guide

📑 Answer Transparencies available for all exercises

Basic:
Day 1: SRH p. 928 Exs. 1, 2, 4, 6, 10
pp. 610–613
Exs. 1–22, 87–89
Day 2: pp. 610–613
Exs. 23–41 odd, 42–50, 68–72, 76–86 even

Average:
Day 1: pp. 610–613
Exs. 1–12, 14–22 even, 61–66, 87–89
Day 2: pp. 610–613
Exs. 32–60, 68–73, 76, 80, 84

Advanced:
Day 1: pp. 610–613
Exs. 1, 6–12, 16–21, 61–67*, 87–89
Day 2: pp. 610–613
Exs. 34–42, 48–60, 68–74*, 78, 82, 86

Block:
pp. 610–613
Exs. 1–12, 14–22 even, 32–66, 68–73, 76, 80, 84, 87–89

Differentiated Instruction

See *Algebra 1 Best Practices Toolkit* for suggestions on addressing the needs of a diverse classroom.

Homework Check

For a quick check of student understanding of key concepts, go over the following exercises:
Basic: 6, 15, 29, 44, 68
Average: 8, 18, 34, 50, 69
Advanced: 10, 20, 37, 53, 70

Extra Practice

• Student Edition, p. 946
• Chapter 9 Resource Book: Practice levels A, B, C, pp. 84–86

Practice Worksheet

An easily-readable reduced practice page (with answers) for this lesson can be found on p. 552C.

SKILL PRACTICE

Ⓐ 1. **VOCABULARY** What does it mean for a polynomial to be factored completely? **The polynomial is written as a monomial or as a product of a monomial and one or more prime polynomials.**

2. ★ **WRITING** *Explain* how you know if a polynomial is unfactorable. **See margin.**

EXAMPLE 1
on p. 606
for Exs. 3–12

BINOMIAL FACTORS Factor the expression.

3. $x(x - 8) + (x - 8)$
$(x - 8)(x + 1)$

4. $5y(y + 3) - 2(y + 3)$
$(y + 3)(5y - 2)$

5. $6z(z - 4) - 7(z - 4)$
$(z - 4)(6z - 7)$

6. $10(a - 6) - 3a(a - 6)$
$(a - 6)(10 - 3a)$

7. $b^2(b + 5) - 3(b + 5)$
$(b + 5)(b^2 - 3)$

8. $7c^2(c + 9) + 2(c + 9)$
$(c + 9)(7c^2 + 2)$

9. $x(13 + x) - (x + 13)$
$(x + 13)(x - 1)$

10. $y^2(y - 4) + 5(4 - y)$
$(y - 4)(y^2 - 5)$

11. $12(z - 1) - 5z^2(1 - z)$
$(z - 1)(12 + 5z^2)$

12. ★ **MULTIPLE CHOICE** Which is the correct factorization of $x^2(x - 8) + 5(8 - x)$? **C**

Ⓐ $(x^2 + 5)(x - 8)$

Ⓑ $(x^2 + 5)(8 - x)$

Ⓒ $(x^2 - 5)(x - 8)$

Ⓓ $(x^2 - 5)(8 - x)$

EXAMPLES 2 and 3
on pp. 606–607
for Exs. 13–22

FACTORING BY GROUPING Factor the polynomial. **13–21. See margin.**

⑬ $x^3 + x^2 + 2x + 2$

14. $y^3 - 9y^2 + y - 9$

15. $z^3 - 4z^2 + 3z - 12$

16. $c^3 + 7c^2 + 5c + 35$

17. $a^3 + 13a^2 - 5a - 65$

18. $2s^3 - 3s^2 + 18s - 27$

19. $5n^3 - 4n^2 + 25n - 20$

20. $x^2 + 8x - xy - 8y$

21. $y^2 + y + 5xy + 5x$

22. **ERROR ANALYSIS** *Describe* and correct the error in factoring. **See margin.**

$$a^3 + 8a^2 - 6a - 48 = a^2(a + 8) + 6(a + 8)$$
$$= (a + 8)(a^2 + 6)$$ ✗

EXAMPLE 4
on p. 608
for Exs. 23–42

FACTORING COMPLETELY Factor the polynomial completely.

⑬ $x^4 - x^2$ $x^2(x - 1)(x + 1)$

24. $36a^4 - 4a^2$
$4a^2(3a - 1)(3a + 1)$

25. $3n^5 - 48n^3$ $3n^3(n - 4)(n + 4)$

26. $4y^6 - 16y^4$ $4y^4(y - 2)(y + 2)$

27. $75c^9 - 3c^7$
$3c^7(5c - 1)(5c + 1)$

28. $72p - 2p^3$ $2p(6 - p)(6 + p)$

29. $32s^4 - 8s^2$
$8s^2(2s - 1)(2s + 1)$

30. $80z^8 - 45z^6$
$5z^6(4z - 3)(4z + 3)$

31. $m^2 - 5m - 35$
cannot be factored

32. $6g^3 - 24g^2 + 24g$
$6g(g - 2)^2$

33. $3w^4 + 24w^3 + 48w^2$
$3w^2(w + 4)^2$

34. $3r^5 + 3r^4 - 90r^3$
$3r^3(r + 6)(r$

35. $b^3 - 5b^2 - 4b + 20$
$(b - 5)(b - 2)(b + 2)$

36. $h^3 + 4h^2 - 25h - 100$
$(h + 4)(h - 5)(h + 5)$

37. $9t^3 + 18t - t^2 - 2$
$(9t - 1)(t^2 + 2)$

38. $2x^5y - 162x^3y$
$2x^3y(x - 9)(x + 9)$

39. $7a^3b^3 - 63ab^3$
$7ab^3(a - 3)(a + 3)$

40. $-4s^3t^3 + 24s^2t^2 - 36st$
$-4st(st - 3)^2$

42. The factorization is correct, but the polynomial has not been factored completely. The binomial factor $(x^2 - 9)$ can be factored using the difference of two squares patterns; $(x - 6)(x - 3)$ $(x + 3)$.

41. ★ **MULTIPLE CHOICE** What is the completely factored form of $3x^6 - 75x^4$? **D**

Ⓐ $3x^4(x^2 - 25)$ Ⓑ $3x^4(x - 5)^2$ Ⓒ $3x^4(x + 5)^2$ Ⓓ $3x^4(x - 5)(x + 5)$

Ⓑ 42. **ERROR ANALYSIS** *Describe* and correct the error in factoring the polynomial completely.

$$x^3 - 6x^2 - 9x + 54 = x^2(x - 6) - 9(x - 6)$$
$$= (x - 6)(x^2 - 9)$$ ✗

610   Chapter 9   Polynomials and Factoring

---

2. A polynomial with integer coefficients is not factorable if it cannot be written as the product of polynomials of lesser degree using only integer coefficients and constants, and if the only common factors of its terms are 1 and −1.

13. $(x + 1)(x^2 + 2)$

14. $(y - 9)(y^2 + 1)$

15. $(z - 4)(z^2 + 3)$

16. $(c + 7)(c^2 + 5)$

17. $(a + 13)(a^2 - 5)$

18. $(2s - 3)(s^2 + 9)$

19. $(5n - 4)(n^2 + 5)$

20. $(x + 8)(x - y)$

21. $(y + 1)(y + 5x)$

22. −6, not +6, was the common monomial factored out of the third and fourth terms of the polynomial, so the sign between the two groups of factors should be − not +; $(a + 8)(a^2 - 6)$.

EXAMPLE 5
on p. 608
for Exs. 43–54

SOLVING EQUATIONS Solve the equation.

43. $r^3 + r^2 - 4r - 4 = 0$
-1, ±2

44. $a^3 - 11a^2 - 9a + 99 = 0$
11, ±3

45. $4y^3 - 7y^2 - 16y + 28 = 0$

$\frac{7}{4}$, ±2

46. $5n^3 - 30n^2 + 40n = 0$
0, 2, 4

47. $3b^3 + 24b^2 + 45b = 0$
0, -5, -3

48. $2t^5 + 2t^4 - 144t^3 = 0$
0, -9, 8

49. $z^3 - 81z = 0$
0, ±9

50. $c^4 - 100c^2 = 0$
0, ±10

51. $12s - 3s^3 = 0$
0, ±2

52. $2x^3 - 10x^2 + 40 = 8x$
5, ±2

53. $3p + 1 = p^2 + 3p^3$
$-\frac{1}{3}$, ±1

54. $m^3 - 3m^2 = 4m - 12$
3, ±2

55. ★ **WRITING** Is it possible to find three solutions of the equation $x^3 + 2x^2 + 3x + 6 = 0$? *Explain* why or why not. **See margin.**

GEOMETRY Find the length, width, and height of the rectangular prism with the given volume.

56. Volume = 12 cubic inches **6 in., 1 in., 2 in.** **57.** Volume = 96 cubic feet **12 ft, 4 ft, 2 ft**

x in.
$(x + 4)$ in. $(x - 1)$ in.

$(x - 2)$ ft
x ft
$(x + 8)$ ft

FACTORING COMPLETELY Factor the polynomial completely.

58. $x^3 + 2x^2y - x - 2y$
$(x + 2y)(x - 1)(x + 1)$

59. $8b^3 - 4b^2a - 18b + 9a$
$(2b - a)(2b - 3)(2b + 3)$

60. $4s^2 - s + 12st - 3t$
$(4s - 1)(s + 3t)$

FACTOR BY GROUPING In Exercises 61–66, use the example below to factor the trinomial by grouping.

EXAMPLE **Factor a trinomial by grouping**

Factor $8x^2 + 10x - 3$ by grouping.

Solution

Notice that the polynomial is in the form $ax^2 + bx + c$.

STEP 1 **Write** the product ac as the product of two factors that have a sum of b. In this case, the product ac is $8(-3) = -24$. Find two factors of -24 that have a sum of 10.

$-24 = 12 \cdot (-2)$ and $12 + (-2) = 10$

STEP 2 **Rewrite** the middle term as two terms with coefficients 12 and -2.

$8x^2 + 10x - 3 = 8x^2 + 12x - 2x - 3$

STEP 3 **Factor** by grouping.

$8x^2 + 12x - 2x - 3 = (8x^2 + 12x) + (-2x - 3)$ **Group terms.**

$= 4x(2x + 3) - (2x + 3)$ **Factor each group.**

$= (2x + 3)(4x - 1)$ **Distributive property**

---

61. $6x^2 + 5x - 4$
$(3x + 4)(2x - 1)$

62. $10s^2 + 19s + 6$
$(2s + 3)(5s + 2)$

63. $12n^2 - 13n + 3$
$(4n - 3)(3n - 1)$

64. $16a^2 + 14a + 3$
$(8a + 3)(2a + 1)$

65. $21w^2 + 8w - 4$
$(3w + 2)(7w - 2)$

66. $15y^2 - 31y + 10$
$(3y - 5)(5y - 2)$

C **67.** **CHALLENGE** Use factoring by grouping to show that a trinomial of the form $a^2 + 2ab + b^2$ can be factored as $(a + b)^2$. *Justify* your steps. **See margin.**

Avoiding Common Errors

Exercises 10–11 Watch for students who identify and rewrite opposite binomial factors but who do not multiply the rest of the term by -1.

Exercises 43–54 Remind students that 3rd degree or higher degree polynomials may have 3 or more roots. Encourage students to examine their solutions to make sure they have not missed one of the solutions.

Study Strategy

Exercises 23–40 Students may find it easier to factor completely if they follow a systematic plan for factoring. Suggest that they develop a set of steps in which they look for common monomial factors, grouping, and so on. Suggest that they write the steps on notecards for reference.

55. No; when the polynomial is factored completely, the equation becomes $(x + 2)(x^2 + 3) = 0$. When the factor $x^2 + 3$ is set equal to zero, the resulting equation, $x^2 + 3 = 0$, or $x^2 = -3$, has no real number solutions because x^2 cannot be negative.

67. First, rewrite the middle term as $ab + ab$ and group the terms: $a^2 + 2ab + b^2 = (a^2 + ab) + (ab + b^2)$. Factor each group and then use the distributive property to factor out the common binomial: $(a^2 + ab) + (ab + b^2) = a(a + b) + b(a + b) = (a + b)(a + b) = (a + b)^2$.

Study Strategy

Exercises 69–70 You may want to point out that in Exercise 69, part (a) corresponds to Step 1 in Example 6 and that part (b) corresponds to Steps 2–4. Suggest that students write a stepped-out solution to Exercise 70 using Example 6 as a model.

 Internet Reference

Exercise 71 Additional information about the game of bocce can be found on the Bocce Standards Association's website at www.boccestandardsassociation.org

72b. 3 ft; to find how far the robot has traveled horizontally when it lands back on the ground, find the non-zero *x*-value that makes the height *y* equal to zero. Solve $0 = -10x^2 + 30x$; the roots are $x = 0$ feet (which is the starting point of the jump) and $x = 3$ feet (which is the ending point of the jump).

EXAMPLE 6
on p. 609
for Exs. 68–70

69b. 4 in. long by 4 in. wide by 8 in. high

71b. The zero $t \approx -0.2$ has no meaning because *t*, which represents time in seconds, cannot be negative in this situation. The zero $t = 1$ means that the ball hits the ground 1 second after you throw it. **B**

68. CYLINDRICAL VASE A vase in the shape of a cylinder has a height of 6 inches and a volume of 24π cubic inches. What is the radius of the vase? **2 in.**

@HomeTutor for problem solving help at classzone.com

69. CARPENTRY You are building a birdhouse that will have a volume of 128 cubic inches. The birdhouse will have the dimensions shown.

a. Write a polynomial that represents the volume of the birdhouse. $4w^2 + 16w$

b. What are the dimensions of the birdhouse?

@HomeTutor for problem solving help at classzone.com

$(w + 4)$ in.
w in. 4 in.

70. BAG SIZE A gift bag is shaped like a rectangular prism and has a volume of 1152 cubic inches. The dimensions of the gift bag are shown. The height is greater than the width. What are the dimensions of the gift bag? **16 in. long by 6 in. wide by 12 in. high**

$(18 - w)$ in.
w in.
$(2w + 4)$ in.

71. ★ **SHORT RESPONSE** A pallino is the small target ball that is tossed in the air at the beginning of a game of bocce. The height *h* (in meters) of the pallino after you throw it can be modeled by $h = -4.9t^2 + 3.9t + 1$ where *t* is the time (in seconds) since you released it.

a. Find the zeros of the function. **1, about −0.2**

b. Do the zeros of the function have any meaning in this situation? *Explain* your reasoning.

72. JUMPING ROBOT The path of a jumping robot can be modeled by the graph of the equation $y = -10x^2 + 30x$ where *x* and *y* are both measured in feet. On a coordinate plane, the ground is represented by the *x*-axis, and the robot's starting position is the origin.

a. The robot's maximum height is 22.5 feet. What is the robot's horizontal distance from its starting point when its height is 22.5 feet? **1.5 ft**

b. How far has the robot traveled horizontally when it lands on the ground? *Explain* your answer. **See margin.**

73. ★ **EXTENDED RESPONSE** The width of a box is 4 inches more than the height *h*. The length is the difference of 9 inches and the height.

a. Write a polynomial that represents the volume of the box. $-h^3 + 5h^2 + 36h$

b. The volume of the box is 180 cubic inches. What are all the possible dimensions of the box? **4 in. long by 9 in. wide by 5 in. high, 3 in. long by 10 in. wide by 6 in. high**

c. Which dimensions result in a box with the smallest possible surface area? *Explain* your reasoning.
4 in. long by 9 in. wide by 5 in. high; the 4-inch long box has a surface area of 202 square inches and the 3-inch long box has a surface area of 216 square inches.

○ = **WORKED-OUT SOLUTIONS** on p. WS1   ★ = **STANDARDIZED TEST PRACTICE**

74. CHALLENGE A plastic cube is used to display an autographed baseball. The cube has an outer surface area of 54 square inches.

   a. What is the length of an outer edge of the cube? **3 in.**

   b. What is the greatest volume the cube can possibly have? *Explain* why the actual volume inside of the cube may be less than the greatest possible volume. **27 in.³; the thickness of the plastic used to make the sides of the box will make the edge length of the interior of the cube be less than 3 inches, so the volume of the interior will be less than 27 cubic inches.**

MIXED REVIEW

PREVIEW

Prepare for Lesson 10.1 in Exs. 75–86.

Graph the equation. *(p. 244)* **75–86. See margin.**

75. $y - 2x = 0$ **76.** $y + 2x = 3$ **77.** $y + 5x = 2$ **78.** $2y - 6x = 6$

79. $-3y + 4x = 12$ **80.** $-4x + 2y = 8$ **81.** $x - 4y = 2$ **82.** $x - 2y = -10$

83. $y = 5$ **84.** $y = 0$ **85.** $x = -4$ **86.** $x = 2$

Write an equation of the line shown.

87.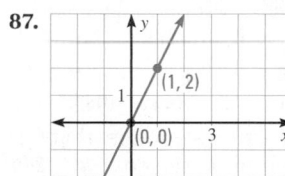

(p. 283) $y = 2x$

88.

(p. 283) $y = \dfrac{5}{3}x$

89.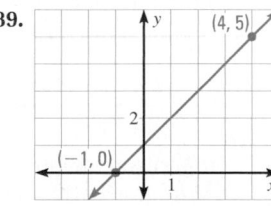

(p. 283) $y = x + 1$

QUIZ for Lessons 9.7–9.8

Factor the polynomial. *(p. 600)*

1. $x^2 - 400$ **(x − 20)(x + 20)**   **2.** $18 - 32z^2$ **2(3 − 4z)(3 + 4z)**   **3.** $169x^2 - 25y^2$
(13x − 5y)(13x + 5y)

4. $n^2 - 6n + 9$ **(n − 3)²**   **5.** $100a^2 + 20a + 1$ **(10a + 1)²**   **6.** $8r^2 - 40rs + 50s^2$
2(2r − 5s)²

Factor the polynomial completely. *(p. 606)*
3x²y(x − 10)(x + 10)

7. $3x^5 - 75x^3$ **3x³(x − 5)(x + 5)** **8.** $72s^4 - 8s^2$ **8s²(3s − 1)(3s + 1)** **9.** $3x^4y - 300x^2y$

10. $a^3 - 4a^2 - 21a$
a(a − 7)(a + 3)   **11.** $2h^4 + 28h^3 + 98h^2$
2h²(h + 7)²   **12.** $z^3 - 4z^2 - 16z + 64$
(z + 4)(z − 4)²

Solve the equation.

13. $x^2 + 10x + 25 = 0$ *(p. 600)* **−5**   **14.** $48 - 27m^2 = 0$ *(p. 600)* **±$\dfrac{4}{3}$**

15. $w^3 - w^2 - 4w + 4 = 0$ *(p. 606)* **1, ±2**   **16.** $4x^3 - 28x^2 + 40x = 0$ *(p. 606)* **0, 2, 5**

17. $3x^5 - 6x^4 - 45x^3 = 0$ *(p. 606)* **0, −3, 5**   **18.** $x^3 - 121x = 0$ *(p. 606)* **0, ±11**

19. VOLUME The cylinder shown has a volume of 72π cubic inches. *(p. 600)*

   a. Write a polynomial that represents the volume of the cylinder. Leave your answer in terms of π. **8πr^2**

   b. Find the radius of the cylinder. **3 in.**

8 in.

EXTRA PRACTICE for Lesson 9.8, p. 946   **ONLINE QUIZ** at classzone.com   **613**

75–86. See Additional Answers beginning on p. AA1.

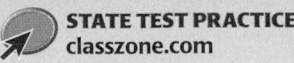
3b. 196 in.²; set the area polynomial from part (a) equal to 100 and solve for *x*. There are two solutions, $x = 14$ and $x = -6$. Because *x* represents a length in this situation, *x* cannot be negative, so disregard the solution $x = -6$. The length of a side of the original piece of wood is 14 inches, so its area is $14^2 = 196$ square inches.

4. *Sample answer:* A ball is kicked from the ground with an initial vertical velocity of 48 feet per second; 0, 3; the starting time is 0, the ball lands back on the ground after 3 seconds.

5c. Yes; to find the values of *t* for which the height is 99 feet, solve the equation $99 = -16t^2 + 80t + 3$. The equation has two solutions, $t = 2$ and $t = 3$, so the ball reaches the height of 99 feet twice, after 2 seconds and after 3 seconds.

6a.

(h + 25) in. | h in. | (h − 1) in.

6c. 120 in.²; to find the height *h* of the box, set the volume polynomial from part (b) equal to 600 and solve for *h*; the only positive solution is $h = 5$ inches, so the length and width of the top of the box are $h + 25 = 5 + 25 = 30$ inches and $h - 1 = 5 - 1 = 4$ inches. So the area of the top of the box is $30(4) = 120$ square inches.

7. No; we are not given the initial height from which the ball is hit. We do not know the value of *s* in the vertical motion model $h = -16t^2 + vt + s$.

9. 100 ft. *Sample answer:* Replacing *y* in the equation $y = -0.005x^2 + 0.6x$ with 10 and solving for *x* gives $x = 20$ and $x = 100$. The lesser value is the distance from the kicker while the ball is on its way up and the greater value is the distance while the ball is on its way down. So the kicker is 100 feet from the goal post.

Lessons 9.5–9.8

1. MULTI-STEP PROBLEM A rectangular room has the dimensions shown.

w ft
(*w* + 5) ft

a. Write a polynomial that represents the area of the room. $w^2 + 5w$

b. The room has an area of 150 square feet. What are the length and width of the room? **15 ft, 10 ft**

2. MULTI-STEP PROBLEM A block of clay has the dimensions shown.

(*x* − 4) in.
x in.
(*x* + 9) in.

a. Write a polynomial that represents the volume of the clay. $x^3 + 5x^2 - 36x$

b. The clay has a volume of 180 cubic inches. What are the length, width, and height of the block? **15 in., 6 in., 2 in.**

3. MULTI-STEP PROBLEM You are making a wooden game board. You cut a square piece of wood, as shown.

x in.
extra wood 4 in.
x in.
game board
4 in.

a. Write a polynomial that represents the area of the game board. $x^2 - 8x + 16$

b. The area of the game board is 100 square inches. What was the area of the original piece of wood? *Explain* how you found your answer. **See margin.**

4. OPEN-ENDED *Describe* a situation that can be modeled using the vertical motion model $h = -16t^2 + 48t$. Then find the value of *t* when $h = 0$. *Explain* what this value of *t* means in this situation. **See margin.**

5. EXTENDED RESPONSE You hit a baseball straight up into the air. The baseball is hit with an initial vertical velocity of 80 feet per second when it is 3 feet off the ground.

a. Write an equation that gives the height (in feet) of the baseball as a function of the time (in seconds) since it was hit. $h = -16t^2 + 80t + 3$

b. After how many seconds does the ball reach a height of 99 feet? **2 sec**

c. Does the ball reach a height of 99 feet more than once? *Justify* your answer. **See margin.**

6. EXTENDED RESPONSE The length of a box is 25 inches more than its height. The width of the box is 1 inch less than its height.

a. Draw a diagram of the box. Label its dimensions in terms of the height *h*. **See margin.**

b. Write a polynomial that represents the volume of the box. $h^3 + 24h^2 - 25h$

c. The box has a volume of 600 cubic inches. What is the area of its top? *Explain.* **See margin.**

7. SHORT RESPONSE A tennis player hits a ball with an initial vertical velocity of 63 feet per second. Can you find the number of seconds the tennis ball is in the air? *Explain* why not or find the number of seconds. **See margin.**

8. GRIDDED ANSWER During an experiment in physics class, you drop a ball from a height of 144 feet. After how many seconds does the ball hit the ground? **3 sec**

9. SHORT RESPONSE A football is kicked toward a goal post that is 10 feet high. The path of the football is modeled by the graph of $y = -0.005x^2 + 0.6x$ where *x* and *y* are measured in feet. On a coordinate plane, the *x*-axis represents the ground, and the ball leaves the ground at the origin. The ball hits the goal post on the way down. How far from the goal post is the kicker? *Explain.* **See margin.**

Additional Resources

The following resources are available to help review the materials in this chapter.

BIG IDEAS *For Your Notebook*

Big Idea 1

Adding, Subtracting, and Multiplying Polynomials

You can perform operations with polynomials using the steps below.

Operation	Steps
Add	Group like terms and add.
Subtract	First, rewrite subtraction as addition. Second, group like terms and add.
Multiply	First, multiply terms using the distributive property. Second, combine like terms.

Big Idea 2

Factoring Polynomials

When factoring a polynomial, you should use the following checklist so that you can be sure you have factored the polynomial completely.

STEP 1 **Factor** out the greatest common monomial factor.

STEP 2 **Look** for special products to factor.

STEP 3 **Factor** a trinomial into a pair of binomials, if possible.

STEP 4 **Factor** a polynomial with four terms by grouping, if possible.

Big Idea 3

Writing and Solving Polynomial Equations to Solve Problems

You can write polynomials that model real-world situations in order to solve problems. For example, you can use the vertical motion model.

Height (in feet) of a projectile: $h = -16t^2 + vt + s$ where t is the time (in seconds) the object has been in the air, v is the initial vertical velocity (in feet per second), and s is the initial height (in feet).

The height of the ball can be modeled by $h = -16t^2 + 30t + 4$.

$v = 30$ ft/sec

When the ball lands on the ground, $h = 0$.

Additional Resources

Chapter 9 Resource Book
- Chapter Review Games and Activities, p. 92
- Cumulative Practice, Chs. 1–9, pp. 94–95

Student Resources in Spanish

eWorkbook

@HomeTutor

Vocabulary Practice

Vocabulary practice is available at **classzone.com**

@HomeTutor
classzone.com
• Multi-Language Glossary
• Vocabulary practice

Extra Example 9.1
Find the sum
$(3x^3 - x^2 + 6) + (-x^3 + 3x^2 + x)$.
$2x^3 + 2x^2 + x + 6$

3. A factorable polynomial with integer coefficients is factored completely if it is written as a product of unfactorable polynomials with integer coefficients.
Sample answer: $3x(x - 4)(2x + 1)$

REVIEW KEY VOCABULARY

- monomial, *p. 554*
- degree of a monomial, *p. 554*
- polynomial, *p. 554*
- degree of a polynomial, *p. 554*
- leading coefficient, *p. 554*
- binomial, *p. 555*
- trinomial, *p. 555*
- roots, *p. 575*
- vertical motion model, *p. 577*
- perfect square trinomial, *p. 601*
- factor by grouping, *p. 606*
- factor completely, *p. 607*

VOCABULARY EXERCISES

1. Copy and complete: The greatest degree of the terms in a polynomial is called the __?__. **degree of the polynomial**

2. **WRITING** Is $2x^{-1}$ a monomial? *Explain* why or why not.
   No; a monomial cannot have a negative exponent.

3. **WRITING** What does it mean for a polynomial to be factored completely? Give an example of a polynomial that has been factored completely. **See margin.**

In Exercises 4–6, match the polynomial with its classification.

4. $5x - 22$ **B**

5. $-11x^3$ **A**

6. $x^2 + x + 1$ **C**

A. Monomial

B. Binomial

C. Trinomial

REVIEW EXAMPLES AND EXERCISES

Use the review examples and exercises below to check your understanding of the concepts you have learned in each lesson of Chapter 9.

9.1 Add and Subtract Polynomials
pp. 554–559

EXAMPLE

Find the difference $(3x^2 + 2) - (4x^2 - x - 9)$.

Use a vertical format.

$$\begin{array}{r} 3x^2 \quad\quad + 2 \\ - \quad (4x^2 - x - 9) \end{array} \longrightarrow \begin{array}{r} 3x^2 \quad\quad + 2 \\ + \quad -4x^2 + x + 9 \\ \hline -x^2 + x + 11 \end{array}$$

EXERCISES

EXAMPLES
3 and 4
on pp. 555–556
for Exs. 7–12

Find the sum or difference.

7. $(9x + 6x^3 - 8x^2) + (-5x^3 + 6x)$
   $x^3 - 8x^2 + 15x$

8. $(7a^3 - 4a^2 - 2a + 1) + (a^3 - 1)$
   $8a^3 - 4a^2 - 2a$

9. $(11y^5 + 3y^2 - 4) + (y^2 - y + 1)$
   $11y^5 + 4y^2 - y - 3$

10. $(3n^2 - 4n + 1) - (8n^2 - 4n + 17)$
    $-5n^2 - 16$

11. $(2s^3 + 8) - (-3s^3 + 7s - 5)$
    $5s^3 - 7s + 13$

12. $(-k^2 + 7k + 5) - (2k^4 - 3k^3 - 6)$
    $-2k^4 + 3k^3 - k^2 + 7k + 11$

9.2 Multiply Polynomials

pp. 562–568

EXAMPLE

Find the product.

a. $(x^2 + 4x - 5)(2x - 1)$

b. $(5y + 6)(y - 3)$

Solution

a. Use a horizontal format.

$(x^2 + 4x - 5)(2x - 1)$ Write product.

$= x^2(2x - 1) + 4x(2x - 1) - 5(2x - 1)$ Distributive property

$= 2x^3 - x^2 + 8x^2 - 4x - 10x + 5$ Distributive property

$= 2x^3 + 7x^2 - 14x + 5$ Combine like terms.

b. Use a vertical format.

STEP 1 **Multiply** by −3.   *STEP 2* **Multiply** by y.   *STEP 3* **Add** products.

$$
\begin{array}{r}
5y + 6 \\
\times \quad y - 3 \\
\hline
-15y - 18
\end{array}
\qquad
\begin{array}{r}
5y + 6 \\
\times \quad y - 3 \\
\hline
-15y - 18 \\
5y^2 + 6y
\end{array}
\qquad
\begin{array}{r}
5y + 6 \\
\times \quad y - 3 \\
\hline
-15y - 18 \\
5y^2 + 6y \\
\hline
5y^2 - 9y - 18
\end{array}
$$

EXERCISES

EXAMPLES
1, 2, 3, and 4
on pp. 562–563
for Exs. 13–21

Find the product.

13. $(x^2 - 2x + 1)(x - 3)$
$x^3 - 5x^2 + 7x - 3$

14. $(y^2 + 5y + 4)(3y + 2)$
$3y^3 + 17y^2 + 22y + 8$

15. $(x - 4)(x + 2)$
$x^2 - 2x - 8$

16. $(5b^2 - b - 7)(b + 6)$
$5b^3 + 29b^2 - 13b - 42$

17. $(z + 8)(z - 11)$
$z^2 - 3z - 88$

18. $(2a - 1)(a - 3)$
$2a^2 - 7a + 3$

19. $(6n + 7)(3n + 1)$
$18n^2 + 27n + 7$

20. $(4n - 5)(7n - 3)$
$28n^2 - 47n + 15$

21. $(3x - 2)(x + 4)$
$3x^2 + 10x - 8$

9.3 Find Special Products of Polynomials

pp. 569–574

EXAMPLE

Find the product $(3x + 2)(3x - 2)$.

$(3x + 2)(3x - 2) = (3x)^2 - 2^2$ Sum and difference pattern

$= 9x^2 - 4$ Simplify.

EXERCISES

EXAMPLES
1 and 2
on pp. 569–570
for Exs. 22–27

Find the product.

22. $(x + 11)^2$ $x^2 + 22x + 121$

23. $(6y + 1)^2$ $36y^2 + 12y + 1$

24. $(2x - y)^2$ $4x^2 - 4xy + y^2$

25. $(4a - 3)^2$ $16a^2 - 24a + 9$

26. $(k + 7)(k - 7)$ $k^2 - 49$

27. $(3s + 5)(3s - 5)$ $9s^2 - 25$

Extra Example 9.2
Find the product.
a. $(5y + 4)(y - 2)$ $5y^2 - 6y - 8$
b. $(s^2 + 3s - 6)(4s - 2)$
   $4s^3 + 10s^2 - 30s + 12$

Extra Example 9.3
Find the product $(4x + 3)^2$.
$16x^2 + 24x + 9$

Chapter Review   **617**

Extra Example 9.4

Solve $4x^2 = 18x$. $0, \dfrac{9}{2}$

Extra Example 9.5

Factor $x^2 - 3x - 54$.
$(x + 6)(x - 9)$

9.4 Solve Polynomial Equations in Factored Form

pp. 575–580

EXAMPLE

Solve $6x^2 + 42x = 0$.

$$6x^2 + 42x = 0 \qquad \text{Write original equation.}$$

$$6x(x + 7) = 0 \qquad \text{Factor left side.}$$

$$6x = 0 \quad or \quad x + 7 = 0 \qquad \text{Zero-product property}$$

$$x = 0 \quad or \qquad x = -7 \qquad \text{Solve for } x.$$

▶ The solutions of the equation are 0 and -7.

EXERCISES

EXAMPLES 3 and 4
on p. 576
for Exs. 28–33

Solve the equation.

28. $2a^2 + 26a = 0$ **0, −13**

29. $3t^2 - 33t = 0$ **0, 11**

30. $8x^2 - 4x = 0$ **0, $\dfrac{1}{2}$**

31. $m^2 = 9m$ **0, 9**

32. $5y^2 = -50y$ **0, −10**

33. $21h^2 = 7h$ **0, $\dfrac{1}{3}$**

9.5 Factor $x^2 + bx + c$

pp. 583–589

EXAMPLE

Factor $x^2 + 2x - 63$.

Find two factors of -63 whose sum is 2. One factor will be positive, and the other will be negative. Make an organized list of factors.

Factors of −63	Sum of factors	
1, −63	$1 + (-63) = -62$	✗
−1, 63	$-1 + 63 = 62$	✗
3, −21	$3 + (-21) = -18$	✗
−3, 21	$-3 + 21 = 18$	✗
9, −7	$9 + (-7) = 2$	← Correct sum
−9, 7	$-9 + 7 = -2$	✗

▶ $x^2 + 2x - 63 = (x + 9)(x - 7)$

EXERCISES

EXAMPLES 1, 2 and 3
on pp. 583–584
for Exs. 34–42

Factor the trinomial.

34. $n^2 + 15n + 26$
$(n + 13)(n + 2)$

35. $s^2 + 10s - 11$
$(s + 11)(s - 1)$

36. $b^2 - 5b - 14$
$(b - 7)(b + 2)$

37. $a^2 + 5a - 84$
$(a + 12)(a - 7)$

38. $t^2 - 24t + 135$
$(t - 9)(t - 15)$

39. $x^2 + 4x - 32$
$(x + 8)(x - 4)$

40. $p^2 + 9p + 14$
$(p + 7)(p + 2)$

41. $c^2 + 8c + 15$
$(c + 5)(c + 3)$

42. $y^2 - 10y + 21$
$(y - 7)(y - 3)$

9.6 Factor $ax^2 + bx + c$

pp. 593–599

EXAMPLE

THROWN BALL You throw a ball up into the air. At 4 feet above the ground, the ball leaves your hand with an initial vertical velocity of 30 feet per second.

  a. Write an equation that gives the height (in feet) of the ball as a function of the time (in seconds) since it left your hand.

  b. After how many seconds does the ball land on the ground?

Solution

  a. Use the vertical motion model $h = -16t^2 + vt + s$ to write an equation for the height h (in feet) of the ball as a function of the time t (in seconds). In this case, $v = 30$ and $s = 4$.

$h = -16t^2 + vt + s$ **Vertical motion model**

$h = -16t^2 + 30t + 4$ **Substitute 30 for v and 4 for s.**

  b. When the ball lands on the ground, its height is 0 feet. Substitute 0 for h and solve the equation for t.

$0 = -16t^2 + 30t + 4$ **Substitute 0 for h.**

$0 = -2(8t^2 - 15t - 2)$ **Factor out −2.**

$0 = -2(8t + 1)(t - 2)$ **Factor the trinomial. Find factors of 8 and −2 that produce a middle term with a coefficient of −15.**

$8t + 1 = 0$ or $t - 2 = 0$ **Zero-product property**

$t = -\dfrac{1}{8}$ or $t = 2$ **Solve for t.**

The solutions of the equation are $-\dfrac{1}{8}$ and 2. A negative solution does not make sense in this situation, so disregard $-\dfrac{1}{8}$.

▶ The ball lands on the ground after 2 seconds.

EXERCISES

EXAMPLES
1, 2, 3, and 4
on pp. 593–595
for Exs. 43–50

Solve the equation.

43. $7x^2 - 8x = -1$ $\dfrac{1}{7}, 1$ **44.** $4n^2 + 3 = 7n$ $\dfrac{3}{4}, 1$ **45.** $3s^2 + 4s + 4 = 8$ $\dfrac{2}{3}, -2$

46. $6z^2 + 13z = 5$ $\dfrac{1}{3}, -\dfrac{5}{2}$ **47.** $-4r^2 = 18r + 18$ $-\dfrac{3}{2}, -3$ **48.** $9a^2 = 6a + 24$ $-\dfrac{4}{3}, 2$

49. THROWN BALL You throw a ball up into the air with an initial vertical velocity of 46 feet per second. The ball leaves your hand when it is 6 feet above the ground. After how many seconds does the ball land on the ground? **3 sec**

50. ⊕ **GEOMETRY** The length of a rectangle is 1 inch less than twice the width. The area of the rectangle is 21 square inches. What is the length of the rectangle? **6 in.**

Extra Example 9.6

You throw a ball up into the air with an initial velocity of 38 feet per second. The ball leaves your hand at 5 feet above the ground.

a. Write an equation that gives the height (in feet) of the ball as a function of the time (in seconds) since it left your hand.
$h = -16t^2 + 38t + 5$

b. After how many seconds does the ball land on the ground?
2.5 sec

Extra Example 9.7

Factor the polynomial.

a. $a^2 - 36y^2$ $(a - 6y)(a + 6y)$

b. $9x^2 + 12x + 4$ $(3x + 2)^2$

Extra Example 9.8

Factor the polynomial completely.

a. $c^3 - 7c^2 + 3c - 21$
$(c - 7)(c^2 + 3)$

b. $4y^3 + 24y^2 + 36y$ $4y(y + 3)^2$

9.7 Factor Special Products

pp. 600–605

EXAMPLE

Factor the polynomial.

a. $100x^2 - y^2$

b. $4x^2 - 36x + 81$

Solution

a. $100x^2 - y^2 = (10x)^2 - y^2$ Write as $a^2 - b^2$.

$= (10x + y)(10x - y)$ Difference of two squares pattern

b. $4x^2 - 36x + 81 = (2x)^2 - 2(2x \cdot 9) + 9^2$ Write as $a^2 - 2ab + b^2$.

$= (2x - 9)^2$ Perfect square trinomial pattern

EXERCISES

**EXAMPLES
1, 2, 3, 4, and 6**
on pp. 600–602
for Exs. 51–57

Factor the polynomial.

51. $z^2 - 225$ $(z - 15)(z + 15)$ 52. $a^2 - 16y^2$ $(a - 4y)(a + 4y)$ 53. $12 - 48n^2$
$12(1 - 2n)(1 + 2n)$

54. $x^2 + 20x + 100$ 55. $16p^2 - 8p + 1$ 56. $-2y^2 + 32y - 128$
$(x + 10)^2$ $(4p - 1)^2$ $-2(y - 8)^2$

57. **DROPPED OBJECT** You drop a penny from a height of 16 feet. After how many seconds does the penny land on the ground? **1 sec**

9.8 Factor Polynomials Completely

pp. 606–613

EXAMPLE

Factor the polynomial completely.

a. $y^3 - 4y^2 + 8y - 32$

b. $5x^3 - 40x^2 + 80x$

Solution

a. $y^3 - 4y^2 + 8y - 32 = (y^3 - 4y^2) + (8y - 32)$ Group terms.

$= y^2(y - 4) + 8(y - 4)$ Factor each group.

$= (y - 4)(y^2 + 8)$ Distributive property

b. $5x^3 - 40x^2 + 80x = 5x(x^2 - 8x + 16)$ Factor out $5x$.

$= 5x(x - 4)^2$ Perfect square trinomial pattern

EXERCISES

EXAMPLE 4
on pp. 606–608
for Exs. 58–66

Factor the polynomial completely.

58. $a^3 + 6a - 5a^2 - 30$
$(a^2 + 6)(a - 5)$
61. $5s^4 - 125s^2$
$5s^2(s - 5)(s + 5)$
64. $x^3 + 5x^2 - x - 5$
$(x + 5)(x + 1)(x - 1)$

59. $y^2 + 3y + yx + 3x$
$(y + 3)(y + x)$
62. $147n^5 - 3n^3$
$3n^3(7n - 1)(7n + 1)$
65. $2b^3 + 3b^2 - 8b - 12$
$(2b + 3)(b - 2)(b + 2)$

60. $x^3 - 11x^2 - x + 11$
$(x - 11)(x - 1)(x + 1)$
63. $2z^3 + 2z^2 - 60z$
$2z(z + 6)(z - 5)$
66. $x^3 + x^2 - 6x - 6$
$(x + 1)(x^2 - 6)$

CHAPTER TEST

Find the sum or difference.

1. $(a^2 - 4a + 6) + (-3a^2 + 13a + 1)$
   $-2a^2 + 9a + 7$

2. $(5x^2 - 2) + (8x^3 + 2x^2 - x + 9)$
   $8x^3 + 7x^2 - x + 7$

3. $(15n^2 + 7n - 1) - (4n^2 - 3n - 8)$
   $11n^2 + 10n + 7$

4. $(9c^3 - 11c^2 + 2c) - (-6c^2 - 3c + 11)$
   $9c^3 - 5c^2 + 5c - 11$

Find the product.

5. $(2z + 9)(z - 7)$
   $2z^2 - 5z - 63$

6. $(5m - 8)(5m - 7)$
   $25m^2 - 75m + 56$

7. $(b + 2)(-b^2 + 4b - 3)$
   $-b^3 + 2b^2 + 5b - 6$

8. $(5 + 7y)(1 - 9y)$
   $5 - 38y - 63y^2$

9. $(2x^2 - 3x + 5)(x - 4)$
   $2x^3 - 11x^2 + 17x - 20$

10. $(5p - 6)(5p + 6)$
    $25p^2 - 36$

11. $(12 - 3g)^2$
    $144 - 72g + 9g^2$

12. $(2s + 9t)^2$
    $4s^2 + 36st + 81t^2$

13. $(11a - 4b)(11a + 4b)$
    $121a^2 - 16b^2$

Factor the polynomial.

14. $x^2 + 8x + 7$
    $(x + 7)(x + 1)$

15. $2n^2 - 11n + 15$
    $(2n - 5)(n - 3)$

16. $-12r^2 + 5r + 3$
    $-(3r + 1)(4r - 3)$

17. $t^2 - 10t + 25$
    $(t - 5)^2$

18. $-3n^2 + 75$
    $-3(n - 5)(n + 5)$

19. $3x^2 + 29x - 44$
    $(3x - 4)(x + 11)$

20. $x^2 - 49$
    $(x - 7)(x + 7)$

21. $2a^4 + 21a^3 + 49a^2$
    $a^2(2a + 7)(a + 7)$

22. $y^3 + 2y^2 - 81y - 162$
    $(y + 2)(y - 9)(y + 9)$

Solve the equation.

23. $25a = 10a^2$ $0, \dfrac{5}{2}$

24. $21z^2 + 85z - 26 = 0$ $-\dfrac{13}{3}, \dfrac{2}{7}$

25. $x^2 - 22x = -121$ 11

26. $a^2 - 11a + 24 = 0$ $3, 8$

27. $t^2 + 7t = 60$ $-12, 5$

28. $4x^2 = 22x + 42$ $-\dfrac{3}{2}, 7$

29. $56b^2 + b = 1$ $\dfrac{1}{8}, -\dfrac{1}{7}$

30. $n^3 - 121n = 0$ $0, \pm 11$

31. $a^3 + a^2 = 64a + 64$
    $-1, \pm 8$

32. **VERTICAL MOTION** A cricket jumps off the ground with an initial vertical velocity of 4 feet per second.

   a. Write an equation that gives the height (in feet) of the cricket as a function of the time (in seconds) since it jumps. $h = -16t^2 + 4t$

   b. After how many seconds does the cricket land on the ground? **0.25 sec**

33. **POSTER AREA** Two posters have the lengths and widths shown. The posters have the same area.

   a. Write an equation that relates the areas of the two posters. $3w^2 = 2w(w + 2)$

   b. Find the length and width of each poster. **12 ft, 4 ft; 8 ft, 6 ft**

 w ft
$3w$ ft

 $(w + 2)$ ft
$2w$ ft

34. **CONSTRUCTION** A construction worker is working on the roof of a building. A drop of paint falls from a rafter that is 225 feet above the ground. After how many seconds does the paint hit the ground? **3.75 sec**

35. **BOX DIMENSIONS** A cardboard box that is a rectangular prism has the dimensions shown.

   a. Write a polynomial that represents the volume of the box. $x^3 + 3x^2 - 16x + 12$

   b. The volume of the box is 60 cubic inches. What are the length, width, and height of the box? **10 in., 2 in., 3 in.**

 $(x - 1)$ in.
$(x + 6)$ in. $(x - 2)$ in.

Additional Resources

Assessment Book
- Chapter Test, Levels A, B, C, pp. 127–132
- Standardized Chapter Test, pp. 133–134
- SAT/ACT Chapter Test, pp. 135–136
- Alternative Assessment, pp. 137–138

Test Generator CD-ROM

Chapter Test

Easily-readable reduced copies (with answers) of Chapter Test B, the Standardized Chapter Test, and the Alternative Assessment from the Assessment Book can be found on pp. 552E–552F.

Using Rubrics

The rubric given on the pupil page is a sample of a three-level rubric. Other rubrics may contain four, five, or six levels. For more information on rubrics, see the *Algebra 1 Toolkit*.

Test-Taking Strategy

Encourage students to draw diagrams or models to help them visualize and solve problems. This is a useful strategy for a range of problems, including problems that involve area, perimeter, volume, patterns, and counting techniques. Diagrams often support an answer, so stress to students that a diagram should be understandable, it should have labels, and it should clearly show what its relationship is to the test question.

Avoiding Common Errors

Remind students that as equations become more complex, it becomes more important to write legibly to avoid calculation errors and loss of credit because the calculations appear incorrect. Caution students to write powers in superscript and to distinguish between the multiplication symbol $\times$ and the variable x.

Scoring Rubric

Full Credit
- solution is complete and correct

Partial Credit
- solution is complete but errors are made,

or
- solution is without error but incomplete

No Credit
- no solution is given,

or
- solution makes no sense

SHORT RESPONSE QUESTIONS

PROBLEM

A rectangular photo has an area of 24 square inches. You trim the photo so that it fits into a square frame. You trim 3 inches from the length and 1 inch from the width of the photo. Write and solve an equation to find the side length of the resulting square photo. *Explain* how you chose one solution of the equation to find the side length.

Below are sample solutions to the problem. Read each solution and the comments in blue to see why the sample represents full credit, partial credit, or no credit.

SAMPLE 1: Full credit solution

> A diagram shows how the equation is obtained.

Draw a diagram. Use the formula for the area of a rectangle.

$$A = \ell \cdot w$$
$$= (x + 3)(x + 1)$$
$$= x^2 + 4x + 3$$

> The correct calculations are performed.

Substitute 24 for A and solve.

$$24 = x^2 + 4x + 3$$
$$0 = x^2 + 4x - 21$$
$$0 = (x - 3)(x + 7)$$
$$0 = x - 3 \quad or \quad 0 = x + 7$$
$$x = 3 \quad or \quad x = -7$$

> The question is answered correctly and includes an explanation.

A solution represents the side length of the square photo. A negative side length does not make sense, so choose $x = 3$. The side length is 3 inches.

SAMPLE 2: Partial credit solution

The length of the rectangular photo is $x + 3$. The width is $x + 1$.

> The equation is correct, and the student has explained how it was obtained.

$$A = (x + 3)(x + 1)$$
$$24 = x^2 + 4x + 3$$
$$0 = x^2 + 4x - 21$$
$$0 = (x - 3)(x + 7)$$

> The question is answered correctly but does not include an explanation.

$$x = 3 \ or \ x = -7$$

The side length of the square photo is 3 inches.

---

622 Chapter 9 Polynomials and Factoring

SAMPLE 3: Partial credit solution

The equation and its solutions are correct, but the student found the length and width of the original photo instead of the trimmed photo.

$24 = (x + 3)(x + 1)$
$0 = x^2 + 4x - 21$
$0 = (x - 3)(x + 7)$
$x = 3$ *or* $x = -7$

A negative solution does not make sense in the situation. The length is $3 + 3 = 6$ inches, and the width is $3 + 1 = 4$ inches.

SAMPLE 4: No credit solution

The student's reasoning is incorrect, and the equation is incorrect. The answer is incorrect.

$(x - 3)(x - 1) = 24$
$x^2 - 4x - 21 = 0$
$(x - 3)(x + 7) = 0$

$x = -3$ or 7, so the side length of the square is 7 inches.

PRACTICE   Apply the Scoring Rubric

Score the solution to the problem below as *full credit*, *partial credit*, or *no credit*. *Explain* your reasoning.

> **PROBLEM** You are making a banner for a surprise birthday party. The banner will have the dimensions shown in the diagram. Its area will be 6 square feet. Write and solve an equation to find the length and width of the banner. *Explain* your reasoning.
>
> *Happy Birthday* $(x - 7)$ ft
>
> $(x - 2)$ ft

1, 2. See margin.

1. $6 = (x - 2)(x - 7)$
   $6 = x^2 - 9x + 14$
   $0 = x^2 - 9x + 8$
   $0 = (x - 8)(x - 1)$
   $x = 8$ or $x = 1$

   In this problem, the solutions of the equation are 8 and 1. If $x = 1$, then the width of the banner is $x - 7 = -6$. A width cannot be negative, so disregard the solution $x = 1$.

   The length of the banner is $8 - 2 = 6$ feet, and the width is $8 - 7 = 1$ foot.

2. $6 = (x - 2)(x - 7)$
   $6 = x^2 - 2x - 7x + 14$
   $0 = x^2 - 9x + 20$
   $0 = (x - 5)(x - 4)$
   $x = 5$ or $x = 4$

   The equation has two solutions. They are 5 and 4. So, the width of the banner is 5 feet, and the length of the banner is 4 feet.

1b. $0, \frac{5}{8}$; the zero $t = 0$ seconds means that the cat is on the ground at the start of its jump, and the zero $t = \frac{5}{8}$ second means that the cat lands back on the ground after $\frac{5}{8}$ second.

2b. 12 in., 6 in., 8 in.; to find the width of the tank, set the volume polynomial from part (a) equal to 576 (the given volume of the tank) and solve for w. The solutions are $w = 16$, $w = 6$, and $w = -6$. The length and width cannot be negative, so disregard the solution $w = -6$ because it makes the width negative, and disregard the solution $w = 16$ because it makes the length $18 - w$ less than 10. The width is 6 inches, so the length is $18 - 6 = 12$ inches and the height is $6 + 2 = 8$ inches.

3b. Twice; to find the times(s) at which the ball reaches a height of 25 feet, substitute 25 for h in the equation from part (a) and solve for t; the solutions are $t = 1$ and $t = \frac{5}{4}$. The ball reaches the height of 25 feet two times, after 1 second and after $\frac{5}{4}$ seconds.

4a. 0 ft/sec; the pencil has no initial vertical velocity because it falls from a position of rest.

5a. $S \cdot P = 0.22x^3 + 6.55x^2 - 13.7x + 4166.4$; the number of public school students in the United States enrolled in a foreign language class is the number of students multiplied by the percent of those students who are enrolled in a foreign language class.

6b. The solution $x = 20$ feet does not make sense in this situation because if the path was 20 feet wide, it would be wider than the whole garden. Only a path width of 4 feet makes sense for a garden that is 16 feet long and 8 feet wide.

7. 20 ft; substitute 0 for y in the equation $y = -0.2x(x - 20)$ and solve for x: $0 = -0.2x(x - 20)$, $x = 0$ and $x = 20$, which are the points where the tunnel touches the ground. The distance between 0 and 20 feet is 20 feet.

SHORT RESPONSE

1. A cat jumps straight up from the ground with an initial vertical velocity of 10 feet per second.

  a. Write an equation that gives the height of the cat (in feet) as a function of the time (in seconds) since it left the ground. $h = -16t^2 + 10t$

  b. Find the zeros of the function from part (a). *Explain* what the zeros mean in this situation. **See margin.**

2. A fish tank is shaped like a rectangular prism with a volume of 576 cubic inches. Its length is greater than 10 inches. The dimensions of the tank are shown in the diagram.

$(w + 2)$ in.

w in.

$(18 - w)$ in.

  a. Write a polynomial that represents the volume of the fish tank. $-w^3 + 16w^2 + 36w$

  b. Find the length, width, and height of the fish tank. *Explain* your reasoning using the solutions of the equation from part (a). **See margin.**

3. You throw a ball from an initial height of 5 feet and with an initial vertical velocity of 36 feet per second.

  a. Write an equation that gives the height of the ball (in feet) as a function of the time (in seconds) since it left your hand. $h = -16t^2 + 36t + 5$

  b. How many times does the ball reach a height of 25 feet? *Explain* your reasoning using the function from part (a). **See margin.**

4. A pencil falls off a shelf with a height of 4 feet.

  a. What is the initial vertical velocity of the pencil? *Explain* your answer. **See margin.**

  b. After how many seconds does the pencil hit the ground? **0.5 sec**

5. During the period 1985–2000, the number S (in thousands) of students enrolled in public school in the United States and the percent p (in decimal form) of the students enrolled in public school who are also enrolled in a foreign language class can be modeled by

$$S = 27.5x^2 - 336x + 12,400 \text{ and}$$
$$p = 0.008x + 0.336$$

where x is the number of years since 1985.

  a. Write an equation that models the number (in thousands) of public school students in the United States enrolled in a foreign language class as a function of the number of years since 1985. *Explain* how you found this equation. **See margin.**

  b. How many public school students in the United States were enrolled in a foreign language class in 2000? **about 6,178,000 students**

6. Students in an environmental club are planning a garden with four rectangular plots of land separated by stone paths, as shown. The stone paths will have the same width.

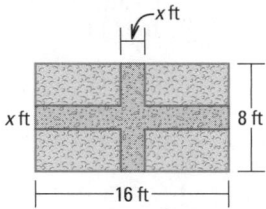

x ft

x ft

8 ft

16 ft

  a. The students plan to cover 80 square feet of path with stone. Write and solve an equation to find the width of the paths. $24x - x^2 = 80$; 4, 20; 4 ft

  b. In part (a) you used one solution of an equation to find your answer. *Explain* how you chose which solution to use. **See margin.**

7. The shape of an entrance to a tunnel can be modeled by the graph of the equation $y = -0.2x(x - 20)$ where x and y are measured in feet. On a coordinate plane, the ground is represented by the x-axis. How wide is the tunnel at its base? *Explain* how you found your answer. **See margin.**

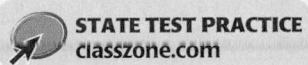

MULTIPLE CHOICE

8. Which is the correct factorization of $25x^2 - 144$? **D**

Ⓐ $(5x + 9)(5x - 16)$

Ⓑ $(5x - 12)^2$

Ⓒ $(5x + 18)(5x - 8)$

Ⓓ $(5x - 12)(5x + 12)$

9. What are the solutions of the equation $(x + 4)(x - 12) = 0$? **D**

Ⓐ 4 and −12   Ⓑ 4 and 12

Ⓒ −4 and −12   Ⓓ −4 and 12

10. What are the solutions of the equation $x^2 - 26 = 11x$? **A**

Ⓐ −2 and 13   Ⓑ 2 and 13

Ⓒ −2 and −13   Ⓓ 2 and −13

GRIDDED ANSWER

11. The equation $x^2 - 20x + 100 = 0$ has two identical solutions. What is the solution of the equation? **10**

12. The square of the binomial $x + 3$ has the form $x^2 + bx + 9$. What is the value of b? **6**

13. What is the degree of the polynomial $6x^4 - 3x^2 + 10x$? **4**

14. The function $f(x) = 4x^2 - 36$ has two zeros. What is the greater of the two zeros? **3**

15. The area of a rectangle is 28 square inches. The length of the rectangle is 3 inches more than its width. What is the width (in inches) of the rectangle? **4 in.**

16. A pine cone falls from a tree branch that is 144 feet above the ground. After how many seconds does the pine cone land on the ground? **3 sec**

EXTENDED RESPONSE

17. The shape of a stone arch in a park can be modeled by the graph of the equation $y = -x^2 + 6x$ where x and y are measured in feet. On a coordinate plane, the ground is represented by the x-axis.   **a–d. See margin.**

a. Make a table of values that shows the height of the stone arch for $x = 0, 1, 2, 3, 4,$ and 5 feet.

b. Plot the ordered pairs in the table from part (a) as points in a coordinate plane. Connect the points with a smooth curve.

c. How wide is the base of the arch? *Justify* your answer using the zeros of the given function.

d. At how many points does the arch reach a height of 9 feet? *Justify* your answer algebraically.

18. A box is a rectangular prism with a volume of 768 cubic inches. The length of the box is 4 inches more than its height. Its width is the difference of 16 and its height.

a. Draw a diagram of the box and label its dimensions in terms of its height. **See margin.**

b. Write a polynomial that represents the volume of the box. $h^3 + 12h^2 - 64h$

c. Use the polynomial from part (b) to find two sets of possible dimensions of the box. **8 in. by 8 in. by 12 in., 4 in. by 12 in. by 16 in.**

d. Which set of dimensions results in a box with the least possible surface area? *Explain* your reasoning.
8 in. by 8 in. by 12 in. *Sample answer:* The surface area of the 8-8-12 prism is 512 square inches, while the surface area of the 4-12-16 prism is 608 square inches.

17a.

x (feet)	y (feet)
0	0
1	5
2	8
3	9
4	8
5	5

17b.

17c. 6 ft; the zeros of the function $y = -x^2 + 6x$ are the solutions of the equation $0 = -x^2 + 6x$, $x = 0$ and $x = 6$. These two x-values are the ends of the base of the arch, because at these x-values, the height y of the arch is 0. So, the arch is $6 - 0 = 6$ feet wide at the base.

17d. One; to find any points at which the arch reaches a height of 9 feet, substitute 9 for y in the equation $y = -x^2 + 6x$ and solve for x; the equation $9 = -x^2 + 6x$ becomes the equation $x^2 - 6x + 9 = 0$, or $(x - 3)^2 = 0$, an equation with one (double) root. So there is only one point at which the arch reaches a height of 9 feet.

18a.

h in.

$(16 - h)$ in.

$(h + 4)$ in.

REGULAR SCHEDULE

Pre-AP For pacing and assignments for a Pre-AP course, see the *Algebra 1 Toolkit*.

Lesson	Les. Day	BASIC	AVERAGE	ADVANCED
10.1	Day 1	EP p. 941 Exs. 56–59; pp. 632–634 Exs. 1–23	pp. 632–634 Exs. 1–5, 10–23, 52–57	pp. 632–634 Exs. 1–5, 12–23, 45*, 52–57
	Day 2	pp. 632–634 Exs. 24–35, 40–42, 46–57	pp. 632–634 Exs. 26–36, 40–44, 46–51	pp. 632–634 Exs. 28–44*, 46–51
10.2	Day 1	pp. 638–640 Exs. 1, 2, 3–11 odd, 12–20, 27–32, 37, 40–43, 46, 49, 51, 55	pp. 638–640 Exs. 1, 2, 6–14 even, 20–27, 31–38, 40–44, 47, 52, 56	pp. 638–640 Exs. 1, 8–12, 20–27, 32–45*, 48, 53, 54, 58
10.3	Day 1	EP p. 944 Exs. 1–4; pp. 647–649 Exs. 1–21	pp. 647–649 Exs. 1, 2, 5–21, 47, 48, 59–63 odd	pp. 647–649 Exs. 1, 2, 6–20, 47–49*, 60–64 even
	Day 2	pp. 647–649 Exs. 22–36 even, 37–41, 50–53, 56–64	pp. 647–649 Exs. 24–46, 50–54, 56–58	pp. 647–649 Exs. 25–46, 50–56*, 58
10.4	Day 1	pp. 655–658 Exs. 1–11, 15–25, 29	pp. 655–658 Exs. 1, 2, 7–16, 21–29, 47–49	pp. 655–658 Exs. 1, 2, 8–16, 23–29, 47–52
	Day 2	pp. 655–658 Exs. 30–46, 56–60, 64–73	pp. 655–658 Exs. 30–46, 50–52, 56–62, 64–72 even	pp. 655–658 Exs. 32–46, 53–63*, 66, 70, 73
10.5	Day 1	EP p. 946 Exs. 13–18; pp. 666–668 Exs. 1–23	pp. 666–668 Exs. 1, 2, 5–11, 15–23, 28–33	pp. 666–668 Exs. 1, 7–11, 18–25, 28–36
	Day 2	pp. 666–668 Exs. 24–33, 45–48, 52–64 even	pp. 666–668 Exs. 24–27, 34–42, 45–50, 55–58, 62	pp. 666–668 Exs. 37–51*, 56, 57, 60, 63, 64
10.6	Day 1	pp. 674–676 Exs. 1–8, 12–21, 25–27	pp. 674–676 Exs. 1, 2, 6–12, 16–27	pp. 674–676 Exs. 1, 2, 6–12, 16–25
	Day 2	pp. 674–676 Exs. 28–38, 46–49, 52–61	pp. 674–676 Exs. 28–44, 46–50, 52–60 even	pp. 674–676 Exs. 28–51*, 53–61 odd
10.7	Day 1	pp. 681–683 Exs. 1–11, 18–26, 31–35, 45–48, 51, 54, 57, 60, 63	pp. 681–683 Exs. 1, 2, 11–21, 27–41, 45–49, 52, 58, 64	pp. 681–683 Exs. 1, 2, 13–19, 28–50*, 56, 62, 65
10.8	Day 1	pp. 688–691 Exs. 1–11, 35–43	pp. 688–691 Exs. 1–11, 35–43	pp. 688–691 Exs. 1–11, 35–43
	Day 2	pp. 688–691 Exs. 12–20, 23–26, 29–34	pp. 688–691 Exs. 14–21, 23–27, 29–34	pp. 688–691 Exs. 15–18, 20–34*
Review	Day 1	pp. 696–700 Exs. 1–38	pp. 696–700 Exs. 1–38	pp. 696–700 Exs. 1–38
Assess	Day 1	Chapter 10 Test	Chapter 10 Test	Chapter 10 Test
Yearly Pacing		Chapter 10 Total – 16 days	Chapters 1–10 Total – 122 days	Remaining – 38 days

*Challenge Exercises   EP = Extra Practice   SRH = Skills Review Handbook

BLOCK SCHEDULE

DAY 1	DAY 2	DAY 3	DAY 4	DAY 5	DAY 6	DAY 7	DAY 8
10.1	10.2	10.3 (CONT.)	10.4 (CONT.)	10.5 (CONT.)	10.6 (CONT.)	10.8	REVIEW
pp. 632–634 Exs. 1–5, 10–23, 26–37, 40–44, 46–57	pp. 638–640 Exs. 1, 2, 6–14 even, 20–27, 31–38, 40–44, 47, 52, 56	pp. 647–649 Exs. 24–46, 50–54, 56–58	pp. 655–658 Exs. 30–46, 50–52, 56–62, 64–72 even	pp. 666–668 Exs. 24–27, 34–42, 45–50, 55–58, 62	pp. 674–676 Exs. 28–44, 46–50, 52–60 even	pp. 688–691 Exs. 1–11, 14–21, 23–27, 29–43	pp. 696–700 Exs. 1–38
	10.3	10.4	10.5	10.6	10.7		ASSESS
	pp. 647–649 Exs. 1, 2, 5–21, 47, 48, 59–63 odd	pp. 655–658 Exs. 1, 2, 7–16, 21–29, 47–49	pp. 666–668 Exs. 1, 2, 5–11, 15–23, 28–33	pp. 674–676 Exs. 1, 2, 6–12, 16–27	pp. 681–683 Exs. 1, 2, 11–21, 27–41, 45–49, 52, 58, 64		Chapter 10 Test
Yearly Pacing		Chapter 10 Total – 8 days		Chapters 1–10 Total – 61 days		Remaining – 19 days	

RESOURCE MANAGER

Chapter Resource Book

CHAPTER SUPPORT

Parents as Partners (Chapter Overview with home involvement exercises and activity)							p. 1	
LESSON SUPPORT	**10.1**	**10.2**	**10.3**	**10.4**	**10.5**	**10.6**	**10.7**	**10.8**
Teaching Guide/Lesson Plan	p. 3	p. 17	p. 32	p. 46	p. 58	p. 69	p. 79	p. 89
Activity Masters	p. 5			p. 48				
Technology Activities & Keystrokes		p. 19	p. 34					p. 91
Activity Support Masters					p. 60			
Practice (3 levels)	p. 6	p. 21	p. 35	p. 49	p. 61	p. 71	p. 81	p. 92
Study Guide	p. 12	p. 27	p. 41	p. 52	p. 64	p. 74	p. 84	p. 98
Catch-Up for Absent Students	p. 14	p. 29	p. 43	p. 54	p. 66	p. 76	p. 86	p. 100
Problem Solving/Application	p. 15	p. 30	p. 44	p. 55	p. 67	p. 77	p. 87	p. 101
Challenge Practice	p. 16	p. 31	p. 45	p. 57	p. 68	p. 78	p. 88	p. 102

REVIEW

Chapter Review Games and Activities	p. 103	Cumulative Practice	p. 105
Project with Rubric	p. 104	Resource Book Answers	A1

Transparencies

	10.1	**10.2**	**10.3**	**10.4**	**10.5**	**10.6**	**10.7**	**10.8**
Warm-Up/Daily Homework Quiz	✔	✔	✔	✔	✔	✔	✔	✔
Notetaking Guide	✔	✔	✔	✔	✔	✔	✔	✔
Teacher Support	✔	✔	✔		✔			✔
Answer Transparencies	✔	✔	✔	✔	✔	✔	✔	✔

ASSESSMENT BOOK

Quizzes	p. 139	SAT/ACT Chapter Test	p. 150
Chapter Tests (3 levels)	p. 142	Alternative Assessment with Rubric	p. 152
Standardized Chapter Test	p. 148		

TECHNOLOGY

- Easy Planner
- Test and Practice Generator
- Power Presentations
- @HomeTutor
- Activity Generator
- Animated Algebra
- Classzone.com
- eEdition Plus Online
- eWorkbook Plus Online
- Easy Grader Online

ADDITIONAL RESOURCES

- Worked-Out Solution Key
- Notetaking Guide
- Practice Wookbook
- Algebra 1 Toolkit
- Benchmark Tests
- Reteaching and Remediation
- Spanish Study Guide
- Spanish Assessment Book
- Student Resources in Spanish
- Multi-Language Visual Glossary

10 Lesson Practice Level B

Top-left panel

13. shift the graph 8 units down
14. shift the graph 4 units up and reflect over x-axis
15. stretch vertically by a factor of 2 and shift 3 units up

Use the quadratic function to complete the table of values.

1. $y = 9x^2$

x	−2	−1	0	1	2
y	36	9	0	9	36

2. $y = -5x^2$

x	−2	−1	0	1	2
y	−20	−5	0	−5	−20

3. $y = \frac{5}{2}x^2 + 1$

x	−4	−2	0	2	4
y	41	11	1	11	41

4. $y = -\frac{1}{8}x^2 - 2$

x	−16	−8	0	8	16
y	−34	−10	−2	−10	−34

5. $y = -4x^2 + 3$

x	−2	−1	0	1	2
y	−13	−1	3	−1	−13

6. $y = 6x^2 - 5$

x	−2	−1	0	1	2
y	19	1	−5	1	19

16. stretch vertically by a factor of 5, reflect in x-axis, and shift 1 unit up

Match the function with its graph.

7. $y = -4x^2 + 3$ F
8. $y = 3x^2 + 4$ A
9. $y = \frac{1}{3}x^2 - 4$ D
10. $y = \frac{1}{4}x^2 - 3$ B
11. $y = -3x^2 + 4$ C
12. $y = 4x^2 + 3$ E

A. B. C.

D. E. F.

Describe how you can use the graph of $y = x^2$ to graph the given function.

13. $y = x^2 - 8$ See above.
14. $y = -\frac{1}{2}x^2 + 4$ See above.
15. $y = 2x^2 + 3$ See above.
16. $y = -5x^2 + 1$ See above.
17. $y = \frac{1}{2}x^2 - 2$
18. $y = -\frac{3}{4}x^2 + 5$

17. shrink vertically by a factor of $\frac{1}{2}$ and shift 2 units down
18. shrink vertically by a factor of $\frac{3}{4}$, reflect over x-axis, and shift 5 units up

Top-right panel

19. domain: all reals; range: $y \geq 9$; vertical shift 9 units up
20. domain: all reals; range: $y \leq 0$; vertical shrink by a factor of $\frac{1}{5}$ and reflection in x-axis

Graph the function and identify its domain and range. Compare the graph with the graph of $y = x^2$.

19. $y = x^2 + 9$ See above.
20. $y = -\frac{1}{5}x^2$ See above.
21. $y = -\frac{3}{2}x^2$ See below.

22. $y = x^2 - 3.5$ See below.
23. $y = 2x^2 - 9$ See below.
24. $y = -5x^2 + 2$ See below.

25. **Serving Plate** The top view of a freeform serving plate you made in a ceramics class is shown in the graph. One edge of the plate can be modeled by the graph of the function $y = -\frac{5}{81}x^2 + 20$ where x and y are measured in inches.
   a. Find the domain of the function in this situation. $-18 \leq x \leq 18$
   b. Find the range of the function in this situation. $-4 \leq y \leq 20$

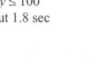

26. **Roof Shingle** A roof shingle is dropped from a rooftop that is 100 feet above the ground. The height y (in feet) of the dropped roof shingle is given by the function $y = -16t^2 + 100$ where t is the time (in seconds) since the shingle is dropped.
   a. Graph the function.
   b. Identify the domain and range of the function in this situation.
   c. Use the graph to estimate the shingle's height at 1 second. 84 ft
   d. Use the graph to estimate when the shingle is at a height of 50 feet.
   e. Use the graph to estimate when the shingle is at a height of 0 feet. 2.5 sec

26. b. $0 \leq t \leq 2.5$; $0 \leq y \leq 100$
   d. about 1.8 sec

21. domain: all reals; range: $y \leq 0$; vertical stretch by a factor of $\frac{3}{2}$ and reflection in x-axis
22. domain: all reals; range: $y \geq -3.5$; vertical shift 3.5 units down
23. domain: all reals; range: $y \geq -9$; vertical stretch by a factor of 2 and shift 9 units down
24. domain: all reals; range: $y \leq 2$; vertical stretch by a factor of 5, reflection in x-axis, and vertical shift 2 units up

Bottom-left panel

1. $a = 6, b = 3, c = 5$
2. $a = \frac{3}{2}, b = -1, c = 8$
3. $a = 7, b = -3, c = -1$
4. $a = -2, b = 9, c = 0$
5. $a = \frac{3}{4}, b = 0, c = -10$
6. $a = -8, b = 3, c = -7$

Identify the values of a, b, and c in the quadratic function.

1. $y = 6x^2 + 3x + 5$
2. $y = \frac{3}{2}x^2 - x + 8$
3. $y = 7x^2 - 3x - 1$
4. $y = -2x^2 + 9x$
5. $y = \frac{3}{4}x^2 - 10$
6. $y = -8x^2 + 3x - 7$

Tell whether the graph opens upward or downward. Then find the axis of symmetry and vertex of the graph of the function. See below.

7. $y = x^2 - 5$
8. $y = -x^2 + 9$
9. $y = -2x^2 + 6x + 7$
10. $y = 3x^2 - 12x + 1$
11. $y = 3x^2 + 6x - 2$
12. $y = -2x^2 + 7x - 21$
13. $y = \frac{1}{2}x^2 + 5x - 4$
14. $y = -\frac{1}{4}x^2 - 24$
15. $y = -3x^2 + 9x - 8$
16. $y = 3x^2 - 2x + 3$
17. $y = -2x^2 + 7x + 1$
18. $y = 3x^2 + 2x - 5$

Find the vertex of the graph of the function. Make a table of values using x-values to the left and right of the vertex.

19. $y = x^2 - 10x + 3$

x	3	4	5	6	7
y	−18	−21	−22	−21	−18

20. $y = -x^2 + 6x - 2$

x	1	2	3	4	5
y	3	6	7	6	3

21. $y = \frac{1}{2}x^2 - x + 7$

x	−1	0	1	2	3
y	$\frac{17}{2}$	7	$\frac{13}{2}$	7	$\frac{17}{2}$

22. $y = \frac{1}{3}x^2 - 2x + 3$

x	1	2	3	4	5
y	$\frac{4}{3}$	$\frac{1}{3}$	0	$\frac{1}{3}$	$\frac{4}{3}$

Graph the function. Label the vertex and axis of symmetry.

23. $y = -x^2 - 10$
24. $y = 2x^2 + 3$
25. $y = -2x^2 + 2x + 1$

7. upward; $x = 0$; $(0, -5)$
8. downward; $x = 0$; $(0, 9)$
9. downward; $x = \frac{3}{2}$; $\left(\frac{3}{2}, \frac{23}{2}\right)$
10. upward; $x = 2$; $(2, -11)$
11. upward; $x = -1$; $(-1, -5)$
12. downward; $x = \frac{7}{4}$; $\left(\frac{7}{4}, -\frac{119}{8}\right)$
13. upward; $x = -5$; $\left(-5, -\frac{33}{2}\right)$
14. downward; $x = 0$; $(0, -24)$
15. downward; $x = \frac{3}{2}$; $\left(\frac{3}{2}, -\frac{5}{4}\right)$
16. upward; $x = \frac{1}{3}$; $\left(\frac{1}{3}, \frac{8}{3}\right)$
17. downward; $x = \frac{7}{4}$; $\left(\frac{7}{4}, \frac{57}{8}\right)$
18. upward; $x = -\frac{1}{3}$; $\left(-\frac{1}{3}, -\frac{16}{3}\right)$

Bottom-right panel

26. $y = 5x^2 + 2x$
27. $y = -2x^2 + x - 4$
28. $y = x^2 - 8x + 5$

$\left(-\frac{1}{5}, -\frac{1}{5}\right)$

$\left(\frac{1}{4}, -\frac{31}{8}\right)$

$(4, -11)$

29. $y = -\frac{1}{2}x^2 - 8x + 3$
30. $y = \frac{1}{4}x^2 + 3x - 1$
31. $y = -\frac{3}{4}x^2 - 2x + 2$

Tell whether the function has a minimum value or a maximum value. Then find the minimum or maximum value.

32. $f(x) = 8x^2 - 40$ minimum; $(0, -40)$
33. $f(x) = -5x^2 + 10x - 2$ maximum; $(1, 3)$
34. $f(x) = 8x^2 - 4x + 4$ minimum; $\left(\frac{1}{4}, \frac{7}{2}\right)$

35. **Storage Building** The storage building shown can be modeled by the graph of the function $y = -0.12x^2 + 2.4x$ where x and y are measured in feet. What is the height h at the highest point of the building as shown in the diagram? 12 ft

36. **Velvet Rope** A parabola is formed by a piece of velvet rope found around a museum display as shown. This parabola can be modeled by the graph of the function $y = \frac{4}{225}x^2 - \frac{16}{15}x + 40$ where x and y are measured in inches and y represents the number of inches the parabola is above the ground. How far above the ground is the lowest point on the rope? 24 in.

626C

LESSON 10.3 — Practice B
For use with pages 643–649

Determine whether the given value is a solution of the equation.

1. $x^2 - 2x + 15 = 0$; 3
2. $x^2 - 4x - 12 = 0$; 2
3. $-x^2 - 5x - 6 = 0$; 3
4. $x^2 + 3x - 4 = 0$; 1
5. $2x^2 + 9x - 5 = 0$; -2
6. $3x^2 - 5x - 2 = 0$; 2

1. not a solution 2. not a solution 3. not a solution 4. solution 5. not a solution 6. solution

Use the graph to find the solutions of the given equation.

7. $x^2 + 8x + 16 = 0$ -4
8. $-x^2 + 36 = 0$ $-6, 6$
9. $x^2 + 5x - 24 = 0$ $-8, 3$

10. $x^2 + 11x + 30 = 0$ $-6, -5$
11. $x^2 - 25 = 0$ $-5, 5$
12. $x^2 + 7 = 0$ no solution

Solve the equation by graphing.

13. $-x^2 - 6x = 0$ $-6, 0$
14. $2x^2 = 2$ $-1, 1$
15. $x^2 - 7x + 10 = 0$ 2, 5

  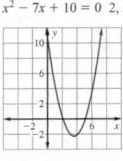

16. $x^2 = 10x$ 0, 10
17. $x^2 - 6x + 9 = 0$ 3
18. $-x^2 + 9x = 18$ 3, 6

LESSON 10.3

LESSON 10.3 — Practice B
For use with pages 643–649

Find the zeros of the function by graphing.

19. $f(x) = -x^2 - 5x - 10$ no zeros
20. $f(x) = x^2 + 12x + 36$ -6
21. $f(x) = 2x^2 + 24x$ $-12, 0$

22. $f(x) = x^2 - 49$ $-7, 7$
23. $f(x) = -x^2 + 1$ $-1, 1$
24. $f(x) = 3x^2 + 12x$ $-4, 0$

25. **Stunt Double** A movie stunt double jumps from the top of a building 50 feet above the ground onto a pad on the ground below. The stunt double jumps with an initial vertical velocity of 10 feet per second.
   a. Write and graph a function that models the height h (in feet) of the stunt double t seconds after she jumps.
   b. How long does it take the stunt double to reach the ground? about 2.1 sec

26. **Wastebasket** You throw a wad of used paper towards a wastebasket from a height of about 1.3 feet above the floor with an initial vertical velocity of 3 feet per second.
   a. Write and graph a function that models the height h (in feet) of the paper t seconds after it is thrown.
   b. If you miss the wastebasket and the paper hits the floor, how long does it take for the ball of paper to reach the floor? about 0.4 sec
   c. If the ball of paper hits the rim of the wastebasket one-half foot above the ground, how long was the ball in the air? about 0.34 sec

LESSON 10.3

LESSON 10.4 — Practice B
For use with pages 652–658

LESSON 10.4

Solve the equation.

1. $6x^2 - 24 = 0$ $-2, 2$
2. $8x^2 - 128 = 0$ $-4, 4$
3. $x^2 - 13 = 23$ $-6, 6$
4. $3x^2 - 60 = 87$ $-7, 7$
5. $2x^2 - 33 = 17$ $-5, 5$
6. $5x^2 - 200 = 205$ $-9, 9$
7. $4x^2 - 125 = -25$ $-5, 5$
8. $7x^2 - 50 = 13$ $-3, 3$
9. $\frac{1}{2}x^2 - \frac{1}{2} = 0$ $-1, 1$

Solve the equation. Round the solutions to the nearest hundredth.

10. $x^2 + 15 = 23$ $-2.83, 2.83$
11. $x^2 - 16 = -13$ $-1.73, 1.73$
12. $12 - x^2 = 17$ no solution
13. $3x^2 - 8 = 7$ $-2.24, 2.24$
14. $9 - x^2 = 9$ 0
15. $4 + 5x^2 = 34$ $-2.45, 2.45$
16. $48 = 14 + 2x^2$ $-4.12, 4.12$
17. $8x^2 = 50$ $-2.5, 2.5$
18. $3x^2 + 23 = 18$ no solution
19. $(x - 3)^2 = 5$ 0.76, 5.24
20. $(x + 2)^2 = 10$ $-5.16, 1.16$
21. $3(x - 4)^2 = 18$ 1.55, 6.45

Use the given area A of the circle to find the radius r or the diameter d of the circle. Round the answer to the nearest hundredth, if necessary.

22. $A = 169\pi$ m^2 13 m
23. $A = 38\pi$ in.^{2} about 6.16 in.
24. $A = 45\pi$ cm^2 about 13.42 cm

25. **Flower Seed** A manufacturer is making a cylindrical can that will hold and dispense flower seeds through small holes in the top of the can. The manufacturer wants the can to have a volume of 42 cubic inches and be 6 inches tall. What should the diameter of the can be? (*Hint:* Use the formula for volume, $V = \pi r^2 h$, where V is the volume, r is the radius, and h is the height.) Round your answer to the nearest inch. about 3 in.

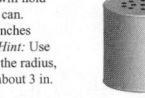
6 in.

26. **Stockpile** You can find the diameter D (in feet) of a conical pile of sand, dirt, etc. by using the formula $V = 0.2618hD^2$ where h is the height of the pile (in feet) and V is the volume of the pile (in cubic feet). Find the diameter of each stockpile in the table. Round your answers to the nearest foot. 5 ft, 8 ft, 10 ft

Stockpile	Height (ft)	Diameter (ft)	Volume (ft³)
A	10	?	68
B	15	?	230
C	20	?	545

LESSON 10.5 — Practice B
For use with pages 663–668

Find the value of c that makes the expression a perfect square trinomial. Then write the expression as a square of a binomial.

1. $x^2 + 12x + c$ 36; $(x + 6)^2$
2. $x^2 + 50x + c$ 625; $(x + 25)^2$
3. $x^2 - 26x + c$ 169; $(x - 13)^2$
4. $x^2 - 18x + c$ 81; $(x - 9)^2$
5. $x^2 + 13x + c$ $\frac{169}{4}$; $\left(x + \frac{13}{2}\right)^2$
6. $x^2 - 9x + c$ $\frac{81}{4}$; $\left(x - \frac{9}{2}\right)^2$
7. $x^2 - 11x + c$ $\frac{121}{4}$; $\left(x - \frac{11}{2}\right)^2$
8. $x^2 + \frac{1}{2}x + c$ $\frac{1}{16}$; $\left(x + \frac{1}{4}\right)^2$
9. $x^2 - \frac{6}{5}x + c$ $\frac{9}{25}$; $\left(x - \frac{3}{5}\right)^2$

Solve the equation by completing the square. Round your solutions to the nearest hundredth, if necessary.

10. $x^2 + 6x = 1$ $-6.16, 0.16$
11. $x^2 + 4x = 13$ $-6.12, 2.12$
12. $x^2 - 10x = 15$ $-1.32, 11.32$
13. $x^2 + 8x = 10$ $-9.10, 1.10$
14. $x^2 - 2x - 7 = 0$
15. $x^2 - 12x - 21 = 0$
16. $x^2 + 3x - 2 = 0$
17. $x^2 + 5x - 3 = 0$
18. $x^2 - x = 1$ $-0.62, 1.62$

14. $-1.83, 3.83$ 15. $-1.55, 13.55$ 16. $-3.56, 0.56$ 17. $-5.54, 0.54$

Find the value of x. Round your answer to the nearest hundredth, if necessary.

19. Area of triangle = 30 ft^2 6
20. Area of rectangle = 140 in.^{2} 5

x ft
$(x + 4)$ ft

$2x$ in.
$(3x - 1)$ in.

21. **Colorado** The state of Colorado is almost perfectly rectangular, with its north border is 111 miles longer than its west border. If the state encompasses 104,000 square miles, estimate the dimensions of Colorado. Round your answer to the nearest mile. about 272 mi by about 383 mi

22. **Baseball** After a baseball is hit, the height h (in feet) of the ball above the ground t seconds after it is hit can be approximated by the equation $h = -16t^2 + 65t + 3$. Determine how long it will take for the ball to hit the ground. Round your answer to the nearest hundredth. about 4.11 sec

23. **Fenced-In Yard** You have 60 feet of fencing to fence in part of your backyard for your dog. You want to make sure that your dog has 400 square feet of space to run around in. The back of your house will be used as one side of the enclosure as shown.
   a. Write equations for the perimeter and area of the enclosure.
   b. Use substitution to solve the system of equations from part (a). What are the possible lengths and widths of the enclosure? 20 ft by 20 ft, 40 ft by 10 ft

House

23. a. $\ell + 2w = 60$; $\ell w = 400$

LESSON 10.5

626D

Practice B
For use with pages 671–676

13. *Sample answer:* Use finding square roots because the equation can be written in the form $x^2 = d$.

14. *Sample answer:* Use finding square roots because the equation can be written in the form $x^2 = d$.

Use the quadratic formula to solve the equation. Round your solutions to the nearest hundredth, if necessary.

1. $x^2 + 7x - 80 = 0$ $-13.10, 6.10$ **2.** $3x^2 - x - 16 = 0$ $-2.15, 2.48$

3. $8x^2 - 2x - 30 = 0$ $-1.82, 2.07$ **4.** $x^2 + 4x + 1 = 0$ $-3.73, -0.27$

5. $-x^2 + x + 12 = 0$ $-3, 4$ **6.** $-3x^2 - 4x + 10 = 0$ $-2.61, 1.28$

7. $5x^2 + 30x + 32 = 0$ $-4.61, -1.39$ **8.** $x^2 + 6x - 100 = 0$ $-13.44, 7.44$

9. $4x^2 - x - 20 = 0$ $-2.11, 2.36$ **10.** $5x^2 + x - 9 = 0$ $-1.45, 1.25$

11. $6x^2 + 7x - 3 = 0$ $-\frac{3}{2}, \frac{1}{3}$ **12.** $10x^2 - 7x + 5 = 0$ no solution

Tell which method(s) you would use to solve the quadratic equation. *Explain* your choice(s).

13. $6x^2 - 216 = 0$ See above.   **14.** $8x^2 = 56$ See above.   **15.** $5x^2 - 10x = 0$ See below.

16. $x^2 + 8x + 7 = 0$ See below.   **17.** $x^2 - 6x + 1 = 0$ See below.   **18.** $-9x^2 + 10x = 5$ See below.

Solve the quadratic equation using any method. Round your solutions to the nearest hundredth, if necessary.

19. $-10x^2 = -50$ $-2.24, 2.24$ **20.** $x^2 - 16x = -64$ 8 **21.** $x^2 + 3x - 8 = 0$ $-4.70, 1.70$

22. $x^2 - 14x = 49$ 7 **23.** $x^2 + 6x = 14$ $-7.80, 1.80$ **24.** $-5x^2 + x = 13$ no solution

15. *Sample answer:* Use factoring because the equation is easily factored.

16. *Sample answer:* Use factoring because the equation is easily factored.

25. Pasta For the period 1990–2003, the amount of biscuits, pasta, and noodles y (in thousands of metric tons) imported into the United States can be modeled by the function $y = 1.36x^2 + 27.8x + 304$ where x is the number of years since 1990.

   a. Write and solve an equation that you can use to approximate the year in which 500 million pounds of biscuits, pasta, and noodles were imported. See below.

   b. Write and solve an equation that you can use to approximate the year in which 575 million pounds of biscuits, pasta, and noodles were imported. See below.

26. Eggs For the period 1997–2003, the number of eggs y (in billions) produced in the United States can be modeled by the function $y = -0.27x^2 + 3.3x + 77$ where x is the number of years since 1997.

   a. Write and solve an equation that you can use to approximate the year(s) in which 80 billion eggs were produced. $80 = -0.27x^2 + 3.3x + 77$; 1998

   b. Graph the function on a graphing calculator. Use the *trace* feature to find the year when 80 billion eggs were produced. Use the graph to check your answer from part (a).

17. *Sample answer:* Use the quadratic formula because it cannot be factored easily.

18. *Sample answer:* Use the quadratic formula because it cannot be factored easily.

25. a. $500 = 1.36x^2 + 27.8x + 304$; between 1995 and 1996

b. $575 = 1.36x^2 + 27.8x + 304$; 1997

Practice B
For use with pages 678–683

2. two solutions   **3.** two solutions
4. no solution   **5.** two solutions

Tell whether the equation has *two solutions, one solution,* or *no solution*.

1. $x^2 + x + 3 = 0$ no solution   **2.** $2x^2 - 4x - 5 = 0$ **3.** $-2x^2 + 10x - 5 = 0$

4. $3x^2 - 9x + 8 = 0$ **5.** $10x^2 - 8x + 1 = 0$ **6.** $-4x^2 + 9 = 0$ two solutions

7. $36x^2 - 9x = 0$ two solutions   **8.** $3x^2 + 2 = 4x$ no solution   **9.** $12 = x^2 - 6x$ two solutions

10. $\frac{1}{6}x^2 + 3 = x$ no solution   **11.** $-8x^2 - 9x = \frac{2}{3}$ two solutions   **12.** $8x^2 + 12x + 2 = 4x$ one solution

Find the number of *x*-intercepts that the graph of the function has.

13. $y = x^2 - 6x - 3$ two   **14.** $y = 5x^2 - x - 1$ two   **15.** $y = 6x^2 - 6x + 1$ two

16. $y = x^2 + x + 6$ none   **17.** $y = -4x^2 + x + 1$ two   **18.** $y = 4x^2 + 5x - 1$ two

19. $y = 2x^2 - 4x + 2$ one   **20.** $y = 10x^2 - 5x + 1$ none   **21.** $y = 8x^2 + x + 4$ none

22. $y = -15x^2 + 3x + 5$ two   **23.** $y = \frac{1}{2}x^2 - 4x + 8$ one   **24.** $y = \frac{2}{3}x^2 - 5x + 2$ two

Give a value of c for which the equation has (a) two solutions, (b) one solution, and (c) no solution.

25. $x^2 + 10x + c = 0$ **26.** $x^2 - 4x + c = 0$ **27.** $25x^2 + 10x + c = 0$

28. $49x^2 - 14x + c = 0$ **29.** $2x^2 + 4x + c = 0$ **30.** $3x^2 - 18x + c = 0$

25–30. Answers will vary.

31. Playhouse You want to build a playhouse for your sister in your backyard. You have blueprints which show that the playhouse is 12 feet long and 13 feet wide. You want to change the dimensions as shown. The new area can be modeled by the function $y = -x^2 + x + 156$.

   a. Write an equation that you can use to determine if there is a value of x that gives an area of 150 square feet.

   b. Use the discriminant of your equation from part (a) to show that it is possible to find a value of x for which the area is 150 square feet.   discriminant: $25 > 0$

   31. a. $150 = -x^2 + x + 156$

   c. Find the value(s) of x for which the area is 150 square feet. 3

32. Tennis You and your friend are walking around the exterior of a tennis court that has a 12-foot high fence around it. You pick up a ball and try to throw it from a height of 5 feet over the fence. You throw it with an initial vertical velocity of 20 feet per second. Did the ball make it over the fence?   no

LESSON 10.8 — Practice B
For use with pages 684–691

Match the function with the graph it represents.

1. Linear function   B   **2.** Exponential function   C   **3.** Quadratic function   A

A.   **B.**   **C.**

Use a graph to tell whether the ordered pairs represent a *linear function*, an *exponential function*, or a *quadratic function*.

4. (−2, 16), (−1, 8), (0, 4), (1, 2), (2, 1)

 exponential

5. (−3, 4), (−2, 0), (−1, −2), (0, −2), (1, 0)

 quadratic

6. (−4, 17), (−2, 11), (0, 5), (2, −1), (4, −7)

 linear

7. (−9, −1), (−6, −2), (−3, −3), (0, −4), (3, −5)

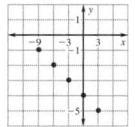 linear

8. $\left(-2, \frac{1}{9}\right), \left(-1, \frac{1}{3}\right), (0, 1), (1, 3), (2, 9)$

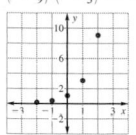 exponential

9. (2, 5), (3, 2), (4, 1), (5, 2), (6, 5)

 quadratic

LESSON 10.8 — Practice B *continued*
For use with pages 684–691

Tell whether the table of values represents a *linear function*, an *exponential function*, or a *quadratic function*.

10. exponential

x	0	1	2	3	4
y	1	5	25	125	625

11. linear

x	−2	−1	0	1	2
y	−10	−7	−4	−1	2

12. quadratic

x	−1	0	1	2	3
y	4	1	0	1	4

13. linear

x	−10	−5	0	5	10
y	4	3.5	3	2.5	2

14. exponential

x	−2	−1	0	1	2
y	32	8	2	$\frac{1}{2}$	$\frac{1}{8}$

15. quadratic

x	−4	−3	−2	−1	0
y	−3	0	1	0	−3

16. linear

x	−2	−1	0	1	2
y	1	3	5	7	9

17. exponential

x	−3	−2	−1	0	1
y	27	9	3	1	$\frac{1}{3}$

18. Use the graph shown.

   a. Which function does the graph represent, an *exponential function* or a *quadratic function*? *Explain* your reasoning.   exponential; The graph rises quickly.

   b. Make a table of values for the points on the graph. Then use differences or ratios to check your answer in part (a).

   c. Write an equation for the function that the table of values from part (b) represents. $y = 4^x$

   b.

x	0	1	2	3	4
y	1	4	16	64	256

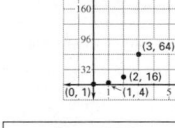

(4, 256)
(3, 64)
(2, 16)
(1, 4)
(0, 1)

19. **Pleasure Boats** The graph shows total amount of sales (in millions of dollars) of pleasure boats in the United States for the period 1990–2002. Tell whether the data should be modeled by a *linear function*, an *exponential function*, or a *quadratic function*. *Explain* your reasoning.   Answers will vary.

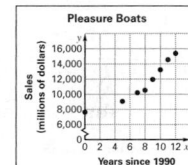

Pleasure Boats

20. **Computer Value** The value V of a computer between 1999 and 2003 is given in the table. Tell whether the data should be modeled by a *linear function*, an *exponential function*, or a *quadratic function*. Then write an equation for the function.   linear; $V = −75t + 800$

Years since 1999, t	0	1	2	3	4
Value, V (dollars)	800	725	650	575	500

Graph the function. Compare the graph with the graph of $y = x^2$.

1. $y = \frac{2}{5}x^2$

2. $y = -3x^2 + 2$

Graph the function. Label the vertex and axis of symmetry.

3. $y = x^2 + 2x + 3$

4. $y = -2x^2 + 8x - 5$

Solve the equation by graphing.

5. $x^2 - 5x + 6 = 0$

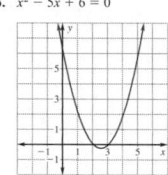

6. $x^2 - 8x = -12$

Find the zeros of the function.

7. $y = x^2 - 7x + 12$

8. $y = -x^2 - 6x - 5$

Answers

1. _See left._

The graph of $y = \frac{2}{5}x^2$

is a vertical shrink

$\left(\text{by a factor of } \frac{2}{5}\right)$ of

the graph of $y = x^2$.

2. _See left._

The graph of

$y = -3x^2 + 2$ is a

reflection in the

x-axis and a vertical

translation (of 2 units

up) of the graph of

$y = x^2$.

3. _See left._

4. _See left._

5. _See left._

2, 3

6. _See left._

2, 6

7. _3, 4_

8. _-5, -1_

Solve the equation using square roots.

1. $5x^2 = 45$

2. $x^2 - 3 = 4$

Solve the equation by completing the square.

3. $x^2 + 4x - 5 = 0$

4. $x^2 - 10x + 24 = 0$

5. $x^2 - 8x + 12 = 0$

6. $x^2 - 2x = 10$

7. $x^2 + 6x + 2 = 0$

8. $x^2 + 8x = -4$

Solve the equation by using the quadratic formula.

9. $3x^2 - 5x - 2 = 0$

10. $x^2 - 2x - 15 = 0$

11. $x^2 + 6x + 9 = 0$

12. $2x^2 - 7x = -3$

Answers

1. _-3, 3_

2. _$-\sqrt{7}, \sqrt{7}$_

3. _-5, 1_

4. _4, 6_

5. _2, 6_

6. _$1 - \sqrt{11}, 1 + \sqrt{11}$_

7. _$-3 - \sqrt{7}, -3 + \sqrt{7}$_

8. _$-4 - 2\sqrt{3},$_
$-4 + 2\sqrt{3}$

9. _$-\frac{1}{3}, 2$_

10. _-3, 5_

11. _-3_

12. _$\frac{1}{2}, 3$_

Tell whether the equation has _two solutions_, _one solution_, or _no solution_.

1. $2x^2 + x + 2 = 0$

2. $3x^2 - 4x + 1 = 0$

Find the number of _x_-intercepts of the graph of the function.

3. $y = 4x^2 - 12x + 9$

4. $y = x^2 + x - 20$

Tell whether the table of values represents a _linear function_, an _exponential function_, or a _quadratic function_. Then write an equation for the function.

5.

x	-2	-1	0	1	2
y	-5	-3	-1	1	3

6.

x	-2	-1	0	1	2
y	-3	0	1	0	-3

Answers

1. _no solution_

2. _two solutions_

3. _one x-intercept_

4. _two x-intercepts_

5. _linear function_
_$y = 2x - 1$_

6. _quadratic function_
_$y = 2x^2 + 1$_

Graph the function. Compare the graph with the graph of $y = x^2$.

1. $y = \frac{1}{4}x^2 - 1$

2. $y = -x^2 + 5$

3. A cross section of the parabolic glass mirror of the Hubble space telescope shown can be modeled by the graph of the function $y = 0.0043x^2$ where x and y are measured in meters. Find the domain and range of the function in this situation.

Find the axis of symmetry and the vertex of the graph of the function. Then tell whether the function has a _maximum value_ or a _minimum value_.

4. $y = -2x^2 + 8x + 3$

5. $y = \frac{1}{2}x^2 - 2x + 5$

6. $y = 6x^2 + 7$

7. An arch of balloons decorates the entrance to a high school prom. The balloons are tied to a frame. The shape of the frame can be modeled by the graph of the equation $y = -\frac{1}{4}x^2 + 3x$ where x and y are measured in feet. What is the maximum height of the arch of balloons?

Solve the equation by graphing.

8. $x^2 + 5x - 14 = 0$

9. $-x^2 + 3x + 4 = 0$

Answers

1. _See left._

The graph is a

vertical shrink and

downward translation

of the graph of

$y = x^2$.

2. _See left._

The graph is a

reflection in the

x-axis and an upward

translation of the

graph of $y = x^2$.

3. _$-1.2 \le x \le 1.2$_
_$0 \le y \le 0.006$_

4. _$x = 2; (2, 11)$_
maximum value

5. _$x = 2; (2, 3)$_
minimum value

6. _$x = 0; (0, 7)$_
minimum value

7. _6 ft_

8. _See left._
_-7, 2_

9. _See left._
_-1, 4_

Solve the equation. Round the solutions to the nearest hundredth, if necessary.

10. $16t^2 - 9 = 0$ **11.** $2(x - 6)^2 = 24$ **12.** $4n^2 - 13 = -20$

13. Sailors need to consider the speed of the wind when adjusting the sails on their boat. The force F (in pounds per square foot) on a sail when the wind is blowing perpendicular to the sail can be modeled by the function $F = 0.004v^2$ where v is the wind speed (in knots). Find the wind speed that will produce a force of 2.5 pounds per square foot on a sail.

14. Complete the steps to solve the equation $x^2 - 8x - 3 = 0$ by completing the square.

$$x^2 - 8x = \underline{\ ?\ }$$
$$x^2 - 8x + \underline{\ ?\ } = 19$$
$$(x - \underline{\ ?\ })^2 = 19$$
$$x - \underline{\ ?\ } = \underline{\ ?\ }$$
$$x = \underline{\ ?\ }$$

Use the quadratic formula to solve the equation. Round the solutions to the nearest hundredth, if necessary.

15. $p^2 + 8p - 15 = 0$ **16.** $2y^2 - 7y = 10$ **17.** $9z^2 + 12z + 4 = 0$

18. During the period 1998–2002, the number y (in millions) of juvenile books shipped to bookstores can be modeled by the equation $y = -15x^2 + 64x + 360$ where x is the number of years since 1998. In what year were there 400 million juvenile books shipped to bookstores?

Find the number of *x*-intercepts that the graph of the function has.

19. $f(x) = 3x^2 - 3x + 4$

20. $f(x) = 4x^2 - 2x - 1$

21. $f(x) = 4x^2 + 12x + 9$

Tell whether the ordered pairs represent a *linear function*, an *exponential function*, or a *quadratic function*.

22. $(-2, -13), (-1, -8), (0, -3), (1, 2), (2, 7)$

23. $(-2, 0), (-1, -3), (0, -4), (1, -3), (2, 0)$

24. $\left(-2, \frac{1}{9}\right), \left(-1, \frac{1}{3}\right), (0, 1), (1, 3), (2, 9)$

Answers

10. ± 0.75
11. $2.54, 9.46$
12. no solution
13. 25 knots
14. $3; 16; 4; 4; \pm\sqrt{19}$
    $4 \pm \sqrt{19}$
15. $-9.57, 1.57$
16. $-1.09, 4.59$
17. -0.67
18. 2001
19. none
20. two
21. one
22. linear function
23. quadratic function
24. exponential function

Multiple Choice

1. What is the vertex of the graph of the function $y = -\frac{2}{3}x^2 + 5$?   A

(A) $(0, 5)$ (B) $(5, 0)$
(C) $(0, -5)$ (D) $(-5, 0)$

2. How would the graph of the function $y = x^2 - 3$ be affected if the function were changed to $y = x^2 + 2$?   B

(A) The graph would shift 2 units up.
(B) The graph would shift 5 units up.
(C) The graph would shift 2 units to the right.
(D) The graph would shift 5 unit down.

3. What is the vertex of the graph of the function $y = -2x^2 + 16x - 15$?   D

(A) $(-4, -111)$ (B) $(-4, -81)$
(C) $(4, -47)$ (D) $(4, 17)$

4. What is the axis of symmetry of the function $y = -x^2 + 6x - 8$?   B

(A) $x = -3$ (B) $x = 3$
(C) $x = -8$ (D) $x = 8$

5. What are the solutions of the equation shown?   C

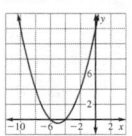

(A) 4 and 6   (B) 4 and -6
(C) -4 and -6 (D) -4 and 6

6. Which function has a zero between 7 and 8?   C

(A) $f(x) = \frac{1}{2}x^2 + 5x + 12$
(B) $f(x) = -4x^2 + 6x + 5$
(C) $f(x) = 3x^2 - 24x + 12$
(D) $f(x) = \frac{1}{2}x^2 + 12$

7. What are the approximate zeros of the function $y = -x^2 - 5x + 5$ to the nearest tenth?   D

(A) 1.4 and 3.6   (B) -0.9 and 5.9
(C) -3.6 and -1.4 (D) -5.9 and 0.9

8. Which of the following is a solution of the equation $107 - 5x^2 = -18$?   B

(A) -25 (B) -5 (C) 15   (D) 25

9. Which of the following is a solution of the equation $2x^2 - 5 = -4\frac{1}{2}$?   A

(A) $-\frac{1}{2}$ (B) $-\frac{1}{4}$ (C) 1   (D) $\frac{3}{4}$

10. What are the solutions of $4x^2 + 40x = -91$?   A

(A) $-\frac{13}{2}, -\frac{7}{2}$ (B) $-\frac{13}{2}, \frac{7}{2}$
(C) $\frac{13}{2}, -\frac{7}{2}$ (D) $\frac{13}{2}, \frac{7}{2}$

11. What are the solutions of $4x^2 + 48x + 20 = 0$?   D

(A) $6 \pm \sqrt{41}$ (B) $6 \pm \sqrt{31}$
(C) $-6 \pm \sqrt{41}$ (D) $-6 \pm \sqrt{31}$

12. What are the solutions of $4x^2 - 16x = 16x - 39$?   D

(A) $-\frac{13}{2}, -\frac{3}{2}$ (B) $-\frac{13}{2}, \frac{3}{2}$
(C) $\frac{13}{2}, -\frac{3}{2}$ (D) $\frac{13}{2}, \frac{3}{2}$

---

13. What is the value of the discriminant of the equation $6x^2 - 5x - 3 = 0$?   C

(A) -47 (B) 24   (C) 97   (D) 115

14. How many solutions does $5x^2 - 2x + 3$ have?   A

(A) None   (B) One
(C) Two   (D) Three

15. Which function is represented by the following ordered pairs: $(-5, 50), (-2, 8), (0, 0), (1, 2), (3, 18)$?   C

(A) $y = 2^x$ (B) $y = 2x$
(C) $y = 2x^2$ (D) $y = 0.5x^2$

16. The graph represents what kind of function?   B

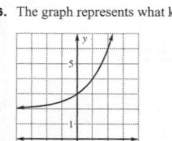

(A) absolute value function
(B) exponential function
(C) linear function
(D) quadratic function

Gridded Answer

17. The value of the discriminant of the equation $2x^2 - x - c = 2$ is 49. What is the value of c?

Short Response

18. The science club wants to have fliers made to advertise their upcoming science fair. The table shows the cost y (in dollars) for x fliers.

Fliers, x	75	125	175	225
Cost (dollars), y	17	23	29	35

  a. Tell whether the data can be modeled by a *linear function*, an *exponential function*, or a *quadratic function*. Then write an equation for the function.

  b. If the number of fliers printed is tripled, does the price triple? *Explain.*
    See below.

Extended Response

19. The Art Club is selling scrapbooks to raise money for supplies. Last year, when the students charged $10 per scrapbook, they sold 250 scrapbooks. The students want to increase the cost per scrapbook. They estimate that they will lose 5 sales for each $1 increase in the cost per package. The revenue R (in dollars) generated by selling the scrapbooks is given by the function $R = (10 + n)(250 - 5n)$ where n is the number of $1 increases.

  a. Write the function in standard form.

  b. Find the maximum value of the function.   4500   See below.

  c. At what price should the scrapbooks be sold to generate the most revenue? *Explain* your reasoning. $30; According to the function, the maximum amount of revenue is $4500. The maximum amount of revenue is made when n is 20. This means they can increase their price by $20 to make their maximum amount of revenue. So, the new selling price would be $30.

18. a. Linear function; $y = \frac{3}{25}x + 8$ **b.** No, if the number of fliers printed is tripled, the price is not tripled. The price increases exponentially.

19. a. $R = -5n^2 + 200n + 2500$

Journal

1. Discuss the behavior of successive y-values for linear, exponential, and quadratic functions given that the increments between successive x-values are all equal. Give an example of an equation for each type of function.

Multi-Step Problem

2. During a halftime show, a baton twirler releases her baton from a point 4 feet above the ground with an initial vertical velocity of 25 feet per second.

  a. Use the vertical motion model to write a function for the height h (in feet) of the baton after t seconds.

  b. Graph the function in part (a). Label the vertex of the graph.

  c. How high does the baton go? Round your answer to the nearest tenth.

  d. How long after the baton is released does it reach its maximum height?

  e. At what moments is the baton at a height of 10 feet? Round your answer to the nearest hundredth.

  f. How much time does the twirler have if she plans to catch the baton on its way down at a height of 5 feet? Round your answer to the nearest hundredth.

1. Complete answers should include: an explanation that the differences in successive y-values will be equal for linear functions; an explanation that the ratios in successive y-values will be equal for exponential functions; an explanation that the differences in successive first differences in y-values will be equal for quadratic functions; an example of an equation for each type of function.

2. a. $h = -16t^2 + 25t + 4$

b.

c. 13.8 ft   **d.** 0.78125 sec   **e.** 0.30 sec and 1.27 sec after release   **f.** 1.52 sec

626H

PLAN AND PREPARE

Main Ideas

In Chapter 10, students graph quadratic functions and compare them to the parent graph. They find the axis of symmetry, the vertex, and minimum or maximum values. They solve quadratic equations by factoring, graphing, using square roots, completing the square, and using the quadratic formula. Students use the discriminant to determine the number and type of solutions of a quadratic equation. Finally, students determine whether a linear, exponential, or quadratic function best models a set of data.

Prerequisite Skills

- Reflecting points in a line
- Finding square roots

Additional resources for reviewing prerequisite skills are:
- Skills Review Handbook, pp.909–937
- @HomeTutor

10 Quadratic Equations and Functions

10.1 Graph $y = ax^2 + c$

10.2 Graph $y = ax^2 + bx + c$

10.3 Solve Quadratic Equations by Graphing

10.4 Use Square Roots to Solve Quadratic Equations

10.5 Solve Quadratic Equations by Completing the Square

10.6 Solve Quadratic Equations by the Quadratic Formula

10.7 Interpret the Discriminant

10.8 Compare Linear, Exponential, and Quadratic Models

Before

In previous chapters, you learned the following skills, which you'll use in Chapter 10: reflecting points in a line and finding square roots.

Prerequisite Skills

VOCABULARY CHECK

Copy and complete the statement.

1. The x-coordinate of a point where a graph crosses the x-axis is a(n) __?__ .
   x-intercept

2. A(n) __?__ is a function of the form $y = a \cdot b^x$ where $a \neq 0$, $b > 0$, and $b \neq 1$.
   exponential function

SKILLS CHECK

Draw the blue figure. Then draw its image after a reflection in the red line.
(Review p. 922 for 10.1–10.3.) **3–5. See margin.**

3.

4.

5.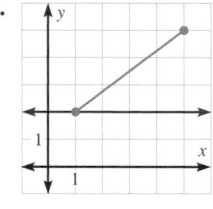

Evaluate the expression. *(Review p. 110 for 10.4–10.6.)*

6. $\sqrt{81}$ **9**

7. $-\sqrt{25}$ **−5**

8. $\sqrt{1}$ **1**

9. $\pm\sqrt{64}$ **±8**

@HomeTutor Prerequisite skills practice at classzone.com

626

Chapter Planning Guide

Chapter 10 Resource Book
- Teaching Guide/Lesson Plan (pp. 3, 17, 32, 46, 58, 69, 79, 89)
- Project with Rubric (p. 104)

Assessment and Intervention
- Assessment Book (pp. 139–153)
- Benchmark Tests
- Reteaching and Remediation Book

Interactive Technology
- Easy Planner
- Power Presentations CD-ROM
- Activity Generator CD-ROM
- Animated Algebra
- Test Generator CD-ROM
- Online Quizzes
- eWorkbook
- eEdition
- @HomeTutor

Resources for English Learners
- Quick Reference for English Learners
- Spanish Study Guide
- Multi-Language Visual Glossary
- Student Resources in Spanish

Now

In Chapter 10, you will apply the big ideas listed below and reviewed in the Chapter Summary on page 695. You will also use the key vocabulary listed below.

Big Ideas

① Graphing quadratic functions
② Solving quadratic equations
③ Comparing linear, exponential, and quadratic models

KEY VOCABULARY
- quadratic function, *p. 628*
- parabola, *p. 628*
- parent quadratic function, *p. 628*
- vertex, *p. 628*
- axis of symmetry, *p. 628*
- minimum value, *p. 636*
- maximum value, *p. 636*
- quadratic equation, *p. 643*
- completing the square, *p. 663*
- quadratic formula, *p. 671*
- discriminant, *p. 678*

Why?

You can use a quadratic model for real-world situations involving vertical motion. For example, you can write and solve a quadratic equation to find the time a snowboarder is in the air during a jump.

Animated Algebra

The animation illustrated below for Exercise 50 on page 668 helps you answer this question: How many seconds is the snowboarder in the air during a jump?

You need to find the time that the snowboarder is in the air.

Now solve for t by completing the square. Use the buttons below to perform operations on both sides of the equation.
First, simplify all of the terms.

$$13.2 = -16\,t^2 + 24t + 16.4$$

Add   Subtract   Multiply   Divide   Sqrt

Check Answer

Click the buttons and enter expressions to solve the equation.

Animated Algebra at classzone.com

Other animations for Chapter 10: pages 634, 636, 642, 662, 668, 672, 684, and 695

Algebra 1 Toolkit
- Reading Strategies for Chapter 10, pp. 27–28
- Differentiated Instruction Notes, pp. 77–80
- English Learners Notes, pp. 115–116
- Inclusion Notes, pp. 147–148
- Teaching Strategies with Sample Worksheets, pp. 155–178
- Using Technology in the Classroom, pp. 179–184
- Tips for New Teachers, pp. 203–204
- Math Background Notes, pp. 229–230
- Pre-AP Strategies and Copymasters, pp. 296–297, 427–452
- Teacher Survival Activities, pp. 573–574, 599–600
- Bulletin Board Idea, p. 616
- Teacher Tool Transparencies, following p.620

627

3.

4.

5.

Before	You graphed linear and exponential functions.	
Now	You will graph simple quadratic functions.	
Why?	So you can solve a problem involving an antenna, as in Ex. 40.	

Key Vocabulary
• quadratic function
• parabola
• parent quadratic function
• vertex
• axis of symmetry

A **quadratic function** is a nonlinear function that can be written in the **standard form** $y = ax^2 + bx + c$ where $a \neq 0$. Every quadratic function has a U-shaped graph called a **parabola**. In this lesson, you will graph quadratic functions where $b = 0$.

KEY CONCEPT   *For Your Notebook*

Parent Quadratic Function

The most basic quadratic function in the family of quadratic functions, called the **parent quadratic function**, is $y = x^2$. The graph of $y = x^2$ is shown below.

The lowest or highest point on a parabola is the **vertex**. The vertex of the graph of $y = x^2$ is (0, 0).

The line that passes through the vertex and divides the parabola into two symmetric parts is called the **axis of symmetry**. The axis of symmetry for the graph of $y = x^2$ is the y-axis, $x = 0$.

EXAMPLE 1   Graph $y = ax^2$ where $|a| > 1$

STEP 1 **Make** a table of values for $y = 3x^2$.

x	−2	−1	0	1	2
y	12	3	0	3	12

STEP 2 **Plot** the points from the table.

STEP 3 **Draw** a smooth curve through the points.

STEP 4 **Compare** the graphs of $y = 3x^2$ and $y = x^2$. Both graphs open up and have the same vertex, (0, 0), and axis of symmetry, $x = 0$. The graph of $y = 3x^2$ is narrower than the graph of $y = x^2$ because the graph of $y = 3x^2$ is a vertical stretch (by a factor of 3) of the graph of $y = x^2$.

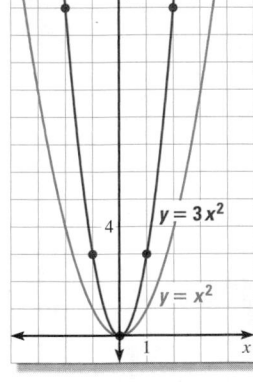

PLOT ADDITIONAL POINTS

If you are having difficulty seeing the shape of the parabola, plot additional points.

EXAMPLE 2 Graph $y = ax^2$ where $|a| < 1$

Graph $y = -\frac{1}{4}x^2$. Compare the graph with the graph of $y = x^2$.

STEP 1 Make a table of values for $y = -\frac{1}{4}x^2$.

MAKE A TABLE
To make the calculations easier, choose values of x that are multiples of 2.

x	−4	−2	0	2	4
y	−4	−1	0	−1	−4

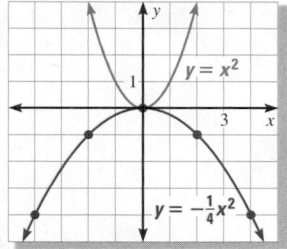

STEP 2 Plot the points from the table.

STEP 3 Draw a smooth curve through the points.

STEP 4 Compare the graphs of $y = -\frac{1}{4}x^2$ and $y = x^2$. Both graphs have the same vertex $(0, 0)$, and the same axis of symmetry, $x = 0$. However, the graph of $y = -\frac{1}{4}x^2$ is wider than the graph of $y = x^2$ and it opens down. This is because the graph of $y = -\frac{1}{4}x^2$ is a vertical shrink $\left(\text{by a factor of } \frac{1}{4}\right)$ with a reflection in the x-axis of the graph of $y = x^2$.

GRAPHING QUADRATIC FUNCTIONS Examples 1 and 2 suggest the following general result: a parabola opens up when the coefficient of x^2 is positive and opens down when the coefficient of x^2 is negative.

EXAMPLE 3 Graph $y = x^2 + c$

Graph $y = x^2 + 5$. Compare the graph with the graph of $y = x^2$.

STEP 1 Make a table of values for $y = x^2 + 5$.

x	−2	−1	0	1	2
y	9	6	5	6	9

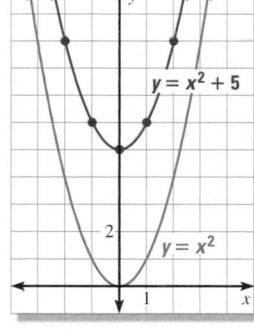

STEP 2 Plot the points from the table.

STEP 3 Draw a smooth curve through the points.

STEP 4 Compare the graphs of $y = x^2 + 5$ and $y = x^2$. Both graphs open up and have the same axis of symmetry, $x = 0$. However, the vertex of the graph of $y = x^2 + 5$, $(0, 5)$, is different than the vertex of the graph of $y = x^2$, $(0, 0)$, because the graph of $y = x^2 + 5$ is a vertical translation (of 5 units up) of the graph of $y = x^2$.

✓ **GUIDED PRACTICE** for Examples 1, 2, and 3

Graph the function. Compare the graph with the graph of $y = x^2$. 1–3. See margin.

1. $y = -4x^2$ 2. $y = \frac{1}{3}x^2$ 3. $y = x^2 + 2$

Motivating the Lesson

You see that your neighbors have a satellite dish on the roof of their house. You notice that the face of the dish is curved. In this lesson you will learn about that curve, called a parabola, and learn how to solve problems involving parabolas.

❸ TEACH

Extra Example 1

Graph $y = 2x^2$. Compare the graph with the graph of $y = x^2$.

Both graphs open up and have the same vertex, $(0, 0)$, and the same axis of symmetry, $x = 0$. The graph of $y = 2x^2$ is narrower than the graph of $y = x^2$ because it is a vertical stretch (by a factor of 2) of the parent graph.

Extra Example 2

Graph $y = -\frac{1}{2}x^2$. Compare the graph with the graph of $y = x^2$.

Both graphs have the same vertex, $(0, 0)$, and the same axis of symmetry, $x = 0$. The graph of $y = -\frac{1}{2}x^2$ opens down. Also, the graph of $y = -\frac{1}{2}x^2$ is a reflection in the x-axis of $y = x^2$ and it is wider because it is a vertical shrink $\left(\text{by a factor of } \frac{1}{2}\right)$.

1–3. See Additional Answers beginning on p. AA1.

Differentiated Instruction

English Learners The parent quadratic function $y = x^2$ produces the family of quadratic functions $y = ax^2 + bx + c$. Students may notice the analogy with a parent linear function producing a family of linear functions (Section 4.7).

See also the *Algebra 1 Toolkit* for more strategies.

630

Extra Example 3

Graph $y = x^2 + 1$. Compare the graph with the graph of $y = x^2$.

Both graphs open up and have the same axis of symmetry, $x = 0$. The vertex of the graph of $y = x^2 + 1$, which is $(0, 1)$, is different that the vertex of the graph of $y = x^2$, which is $(0, 0)$, because the graph of $y = x^2 + 1$ is a vertical translation (of 1 unit up) of the graph of $y = x^2$.

Key Questions to Ask for Example 3

• Why does the parabola open up? **The coefficient of x^2 is positive.**

• How can you tell that the parabola is shifted a positive number of units? **The value of c in $y = x^2 + c$ is positive.**

Extra Example 4

Graph $y = \frac{3}{2}x^2 - 2$. Compare the graph with the graph of $y = x^2$.

Both graphs open up and have the same axis of symmetry, $x = 0$. The graph of $y = \frac{3}{2}x^2 - 2$ is narrower and has a lower vertex than the graph of $y = x^2$ because it is a vertical stretch and a vertical translation of the graph of $y = x^2$.

4.

EXAMPLE 4 **Graph $y = ax^2 + c$**

Graph $y = \frac{1}{2}x^2 - 4$. Compare the graph with the graph of $y = x^2$.

STEP 1 **Make** a table of values for $y = \frac{1}{2}x^2 - 4$.

x	-4	-2	0	2	4
y	4	-2	-4	-2	4

STEP 2 **Plot** the points from the table.

STEP 3 **Draw** a smooth curve through the points.

STEP 4 **Compare** the graphs of $y = \frac{1}{2}x^2 - 4$ and $y = x^2$. Both graphs open up and have the same axis of symmetry, $x = 0$. However, the graph of $y = \frac{1}{2}x^2 - 4$ is wider and has a lower vertex than the graph of $y = x^2$ because the graph of $y = \frac{1}{2}x^2 - 4$ is a vertical shrink and a vertical translation of the graph of $y = x^2$.

✓ **GUIDED PRACTICE** **for Example 4**

Graph the function. Compare the graph with the graph of $y = x^2$. 4–6. See margin.

4. $y = 3x^2 - 6$ 5. $y = -5x^2 + 1$ 6. $y = \frac{3}{4}x^2 - 2$

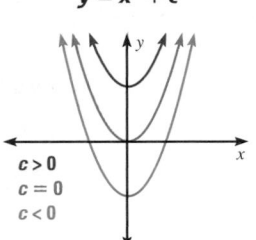

KEY CONCEPT *For Your Notebook*

$y = ax^2, a > 0$	$y = ax^2, a < 0$	$y = x^2 + c$
$a > 1$ $a = 1$ $0 < a < 1$	$a < -1$ $a = -1$ $-1 < a < 0$	$c > 0$ $c = 0$ $c < 0$
Compared with the graph of $y = x^2$, the graph of $y = ax^2$ is: • a vertical stretch if $a > 1$, • a vertical shrink if $0 < a < 1$.	Compared with the graph of $y = x^2$, the graph of $y = ax^2$ is: • a vertical stretch with a reflection in the x-axis if $a < -1$, • a vertical shrink with a reflection in the x-axis if $-1 < a < 0$.	Compared with the graph of $y = x^2$, the graph of $y = x^2 + c$ is: • an upward vertical translation if $c > 0$, • a downward vertical translation if $c < 0$.

630 Chapter 10 Quadratic Equations and Functions

4.

The graph is a vertical stretch (by a factor of 3) with a vertical translation (of 6 units down) of the graph of $y = x^2$.

5.

The graph is a vertical stretch (by a factor of 5) with a vertical translation (of 1 unit up) and a reflection in the x-axis of the graph of $y = x^2$.

EXAMPLE 5 Standardized Test Practice

How would the graph of the function $y = x^2 + 6$ be affected if the function were changed to $y = x^2 + 2$?

Ⓐ The graph would shift 2 units up.

Ⓑ The graph would shift 4 units up.

Ⓒ The graph would shift 4 units down.

Ⓓ The graph would shift 4 units to the left.

ELIMINATE CHOICES
You can eliminate choice D because changing the value of c in a function of the form $y = x^2 + c$ translates the graph up or down.

Solution

The vertex of the graph of $y = x^2 + 6$ is 6 units above the origin, or (0, 6). The vertex of the graph of $y = x^2 + 2$ is 2 units above the origin, or (0, 2). Moving the vertex from (0, 6) to (0, 2) translates the graph 4 units down.

▶ The correct answer is C. Ⓐ Ⓑ Ⓒ Ⓓ

EXAMPLE 6 Use a graph

SOLAR ENERGY A solar trough has a reflective parabolic surface that is used to collect solar energy. The sun's rays are reflected from the surface toward a pipe that carries water. The heated water produces steam that is used to produce electricity.

The graph of the function $y = 0.09x^2$ models the cross section of the reflective surface where x and y are measured in meters. Use the graph to find the domain and range of the function in this situation.

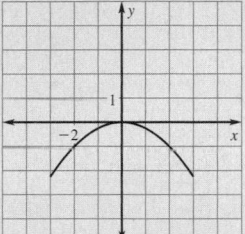

Solution

STEP 1 **Find** the domain. In the graph, the reflective surface extends 5 meters on either side of the origin. So, the domain is $-5 \le x \le 5$.

STEP 2 **Find** the range using the fact that the lowest point on the reflective surface is (0, 0) and the highest point, 5, occurs at each end.

$$y = 0.09(5)^2 = 2.25 \quad \text{Substitute 5 for } x. \text{ Then simplify.}$$

The range is $0 \le y \le 2.25$.

✓ **GUIDED PRACTICE** for Examples 5 and 6

7. *Describe* how the graph of the function $y = x^2 + 2$ would be affected if the function were changed to $y = x^2 - 2$.
The graph would be translated 4 units down.

8. **WHAT IF?** In Example 6, suppose the reflective surface extends just 4 meters on either side of the origin. Find the domain and range of the function in this situation. $-4 \le x \le 4, 0 \le y \le 1.44$

10.1 Graph $y = ax^2 + c$ **631**

6.

The graph is a vertical shrink $\left(\text{by a factor of } \frac{3}{4}\right)$ **with a vertical translation (of 2 units down) of the graph of** $y = x^2$.

631

Extra Example 5
How would the graph of the function $y = x^2 - 3$ be affected if the function were changed to $y = x^2 - 2$? **B**
Ⓐ The graph would shift 2 units up.
Ⓑ The graph would shift 1 unit up.
Ⓒ The graph would shift 1 unit down.
Ⓓ The graph would shift 2 units down.

Extra Example 6
This graph shows a large parabolic umbrella. The graph of the function $y = -0.25x^2$ models the cross section of the surface, where x and y are measured in meters. Use the graph to find the domain and range of the function.

domain: $-3 \le x \le 3$
range: $-2.25 \le y \le 0$

Closing the Lesson
Have students summarize the major points of the lesson and answer the Essential Question: How do you graph a quadratic function?

• The parent quadratic function is $y = x^2$.

• The vertex is the lowest or highest point on parabola. The axis of symmetry passes through the vertex.

Make a table of values for the function. Since a parabola is U-shaped, include values to the left and right of the vertex. Plot the points from the table and then draw a smooth curve through the points.

10.1 EXERCISES

HOMEWORK KEY

○ = WORKED-OUT SOLUTIONS
on p. WS1 for Exs. 7 and 41

★ = STANDARDIZED TEST PRACTICE
Exs. 2, 22, 33, 43, and 44

4 PRACTICE AND APPLY

Assignment Guide

📑 Answer Transparencies
available for all exercises

Basic:
Day 1: EP p. 941 Exs. 56–59
pp. 632–634
Exs. 1–23
Day 2: pp. 632–634
Exs. 24–35, 40–42, 46–57

Average:
Day 1: pp. 632–634
Exs. 1–5, 10–23, 52–57
Day 2: pp. 632–634
Exs. 26–36, 40–44, 46–51

Advanced:
Day 1: pp. 632–634
Exs. 1–5, 12–23, 45*, 52–57
Day 2: pp. 632–634
Exs. 28–44*, 46–51

Block:
pp. 632–634
Exs. 1–5, 10–23, 26–37, 40–44,
46–57

Differentiated Instruction

See *Algebra 1 Best Practices Toolkit*
for suggestions on addressing the
needs of a diverse classroom.

Homework Check

For a quick check of student understanding of key concepts, go over
the following exercises:

Basic: 8, 16, 26, 34, 40
Average: 12, 18, 28, 35, 40
Advanced: 15, 20, 31, 36, 41

Extra Practice

• Student Edition, p. 947
• Chapter 10 Resource Book:
  Practice levels A, B, C, pp. 6–11

Practice Worksheet

An easily-readable reduced
practice page (with answers)
for this lesson can be found
on p. 626C.

6–21. See Additional Answers
beginning on p. AA1.

632

SKILL PRACTICE

A 1. **VOCABULARY** Copy and complete: Every quadratic function has a
U-shaped graph called a(n) __?__. **parabola**

2. ★ **WRITING** *Explain* how you can tell whether the graph of a quadratic
function opens up or down. **The graph of the quadratic function $y = ax^2 + bx + c$ opens up if
$a > 0$ and opens down if $a < 0$.**

MATCHING Match the quadratic function with its graph.

3. $y = \frac{1}{2}x^2 - 4$ **C**

4. $y = \frac{1}{2}x^2 - 2$ **A**

5. $y = -\frac{1}{2}x^2 + 2$ **B**

A.

B.

C.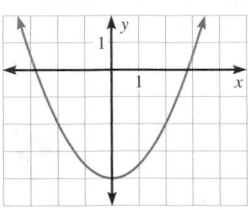

EXAMPLES 1, 2, and 3
on pp. 628–629
for Exs. 6–23

GRAPHING QUADRATIC FUNCTIONS Graph the function. Compare the graph
with the graph of $y = x^2$. **6–21. See margin.**

6. $y = 8x^2$

⑦. $y = -2x^2$

8. $y = -3x^2$

9. $y = 5x^2$

10. $y = \frac{11}{2}x^2$

11. $y = \frac{2}{3}x^2$

12. $y = -\frac{3}{4}x^2$

13. $y = -\frac{1}{9}x^2$

14. $y = \frac{3}{8}x^2$

15. $y = -\frac{1}{5}x^2$

16. $y = x^2 - 7$

17. $y = x^2 + 9$

18. $y = x^2 + 6$

19. $y = x^2 - 4$

20. $y = x^2 - 1$

21. $y = x^2 + \frac{7}{4}$

22. ★ **MULTIPLE CHOICE** What is the vertex of the graph of the function
$y = -\frac{3}{4}x^2 + 7$? **C**

Ⓐ $(-7, 0)$

Ⓑ $(0, -7)$

Ⓒ $(0, 7)$

Ⓓ $(7, 0)$

23. **ERROR ANALYSIS** *Describe* and correct the error in drawing and
comparing the graphs of $y = x^2$ and $y = x^2 - 2$.

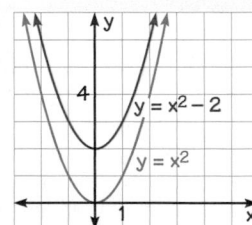

Both graphs open up and have the
same axis of symmetry. However,
the vertex of the graph of $y = x^2 - 2$,
$(0, 2)$, is 2 units above the vertex of
the graph of $y = x^2$, $(0, 0)$.

The graph of $y = x^2 - 2$ should be
shifted 2 units down,
not 2 units up. The
vertex should be at
$(0, -2)$; see margin
for art.

632 Chapter 10 Quadratic Equations and Functions

23.

EXAMPLE 4
on p. 630
for Exs. 24–32

GRAPHING QUADRATIC FUNCTIONS Graph the function. Compare the graph with the graph of $y = x^2$. 24–32. See margin.

24. $y = 7x^2 + 7$ 25. $y = -x^2 + 5$ 26. $y = 2x^2 - 12$

27. $y = -2x^2 - 1$ 28. $y = -3x^2 - 2$ 29. $y = \frac{3}{4}x^2 - 3$

30. $y = \frac{1}{5}x^2 + 10$ 31. $y = \frac{1}{2}x^2 - 5$ 32. $y = -\frac{2}{3}x^2 + 9$

EXAMPLE 5
on p. 631
for Exs. 33–36

33. ★ **MULTIPLE CHOICE** How would the graph of the function $y = x^2 + 3$ be affected if the function were changed to $y = x^2 + 9$? **B**

  (A) The graph would shift 9 units to the right.

  (B) The graph would shift 6 units up.

  (C) The graph would shift 9 units up.

  (D) The graph would shift 6 units down.

B **COMPARING GRAPHS** Tell how you can obtain the graph of g from the graph of f using transformations. 34–36. See margin.

34. $f(x) = x^2 - 5$ 35. $f(x) = 3x^2 - 11$ 36. $f(x) = 4x^2$
     $g(x) = x^2 + 8$ $g(x) = 3x^2 - 16$ $g(x) = 2x^2$

C **CHALLENGE** Write a function of the form $y = ax^2 + c$ whose graph passes through the two given points.

37. $(-1, 9)$, $(0, 3)$ 38. $(2, 1)$, $(5, -20)$ 39. $(-2, -16.5)$, $(1, 4.5)$
     $y = 6x^2 + 3$ $y = -x^2 + 5$ $y = -7x^2 + 11.5$

PROBLEM SOLVING

GRAPHING CALCULATOR You may wish to use a graphing calculator to complete the following Problem Solving exercises.

EXAMPLE 6 A
on p. 631
for Exs. 40–41

40. **ASTRONOMY** A cross section of the parabolic surface of the antenna shown can be modeled by the graph of the function $y = 0.012x^2$ where x and y are measured in meters.

  a. Find the domain of the function in this situation. $-32 \le x \le 32$

  b. Find the range of the function in this situation. $0 \le y \le 12.288$

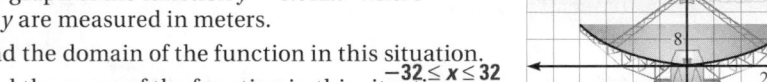

  @HomeTutor for problem solving help at classzone.com

41. **SAILING** Sailors need to consider the speed of the wind when adjusting the sails on their boat. The force F (in pounds per square foot) on a sail when the wind is blowing perpendicular to the sail can be modeled by the function $F = 0.004v^2$ where v is the wind speed (in knots).

  a. Graph the function for wind speeds from 0 knots to 50 knots. **See margin for art.**

  b. Use the graph to estimate the wind speed that will produce a force of 1 pound per square foot on a sail. **about 16 knots**

  c. Estimate the wind speed that will produce a force of 5 pounds per square foot on a sail. **about 35 knots**

  @HomeTutor for problem solving help at classzone.com

Avoiding Common Errors
Exercises 6–21, 24–32 Watch for students who do not graph points on both side of the vertex of the parabola. Remind these students that a parabola is U-shaped and symmetric, and they can use that symmetry to locate points on both sides of the vertex.

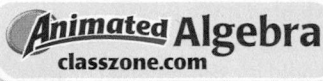

Graphing Calculator
Exercises 40–45 A graphing calculator will help students find approximate values for these exercises. Tell students to use the same steps to graph quadratic functions as they use to graph any other function.

Animated Algebra
classzone.com

An **Animated Algebra** activity is available on-line for **Exercise 44**. This activity is also available on the **Power Presentations CD-ROM**.

24–32. See Additional Answers beginning on p. AA1.

34. Translate the graph of f 13 units up.

35. Translate the graph of f 5 units down.

36. Shrink the graph of f by a factor of $\frac{1}{2}$.

41a.

633

Daily Homework Quiz

📃 Transparency Available

1. Graph $y = -0.5x^2 + 2$.

2. How would the graph of the function $y = -2x^2 + 3$ be affected if the function were changed to $y = -2x^2 - 3$? **It would be shifted down 6 units.**

3. A pinecone falls about 50 feet from the branch of a pine tree. Its height (in feet) can be modeled by the function $h(t) = -16t^2 + 50$, where t is the time in seconds. How long does it take to land on the ground? **about 1.8 sec**

 Online Quiz

Available at **classzone.com**

Diagnosis/Remediation

- Practice A, B, C in Chapter 10 Resource Book, pp. 6–11
- Study Guide in Chapter 10 Resource Book, pp. 12–13
- Practice Workbook, pp. 149–151
- @HomeTutor

Challenge

Additional challenge is available in the Chapter 10 Resource Book, p. 16.

43a–b, 44a–c. See Additional Answers beginning on p. AA1.

45.

⋮ **REVIEW**
⋮ **VERTICAL**
⋮ **MOTION**
⋯⋯⋯⋯⋯⋯⋯
For help with the vertical motion model, see p. 575.

42b. Sample answer: The graph of $h = -16t^2 + 45$ is a vertical translation (of 13 units up) of the graph of $h = -16t^2 + 32$.

Ⓑ **42. FALLING OBJECTS** Two acorns drop from an oak tree. One falls 45 feet, while the other falls 32 feet.

a. For each acorn, write an equation that gives the height h (in feet) of the acorn as a function of the time t (in seconds) it has fallen. $h = -16t^2 + 45$, $h = -16t^2 + 32$

b. *Describe* how the graphs of the two equations are related.

43. ★ **SHORT RESPONSE** The breaking strength w (in pounds) of a manila rope can be modeled by the function $w = 8900d^2$ where d is the diameter (in inches) of the rope.

a. Graph the function. **a–b. See margin.**

b. If a manila rope has 4 times the breaking strength of another manila rope, does the rope have 4 times the diameter of the other rope? *Explain.*

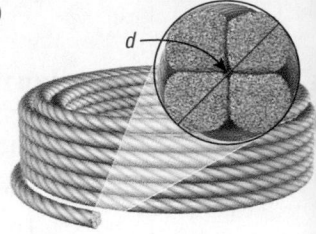

44. ★ **EXTENDED RESPONSE** For an engineering contest, you have to create a container for an egg so that the container can be dropped from a height of 30 feet without breaking the egg.

a. The distance y (in feet) that the container falls is given by the function $y = 16t^2$ where t is the time (in seconds) the container has fallen. Graph the function. **a–c. See margin.**

b. The height y (in feet) of the dropped container is given by the function $y = -16t^2 + 30$ where t is the time (in seconds) since the container is dropped. Graph the function.

c. How are the graphs from part (a) and part (b) related? *Explain* how you can use each graph to find the number of seconds after which the container has fallen 10 feet.

🄰nimated Algebra at classzone.com

Ⓒ **45. CHALLENGE** The kinetic energy E (in joules) of an object in motion is given by $E = \frac{1}{2}mv^2$ where m is the object's mass (in kilograms) and v is the object's velocity (in meters per second). Suppose a baseball has 918.75 joules of energy when traveling 35 meters per second. Use this information to write and graph an equation that gives the energy E of the baseball as a function of its velocity v. $E = 0.75v^2$; see margin for art.

MIXED REVIEW

⋮ **PREVIEW**
⋮⋯⋯⋯⋯⋯⋯
⋮ Prepare for
⋮ Lesson 10.2 in
⋮ Exs. 46–51.

Evaluate the expression. *(p. 8)*

46. $x^2 + 5$ when $x = 2$ **9**
47. $4y^2 + 1$ when $y = 0$ **1**
48. $16 + 3m^2$ when $m = 5$ **91**

49. $5b^2 + 11$ when $b = 10$ **511**
50. $20 - 8w^2$ when $w = 1$ **12**
51. $7z^2 - 22$ when $z = 3$ **41**

Solve the linear system using substitution. *(p. 435)*

52. $x = 20 - 3y$
$2x - y = -4$ $\left(1\frac{1}{7}, 6\frac{2}{7}\right)$

53. $y = 2x - 10$
$11 = 3x - 2y$ **(9, 8)**

54. $x = 11y + 4$
$2x - 17y = 13$ **(15, 1)**

Use the FOIL pattern to find the product. *(p. 562)*

55. $(2p + 3)(p + 2)$
$2p^2 + 7p + 6$

56. $(7x + 5)(3x - 1)$
$21x^2 + 8x - 5$

57. $(5n - 10)(5n - 9)$
$25n^2 - 95n + 90$

EXTRA PRACTICE for Lesson 10.1, p. 947   **ONLINE QUIZ** at classzone.com

10.2 Graph $y = ax^2 + bx + c$

Before	You graphed simple quadratic functions.
Now	You will graph general quadratic functions.
Why?	So you can investigate a cable's height, as in Example 4.

Key Vocabulary
• minimum value
• maximum value

You can use the properties below to graph any quadratic function. You will justify the formula for the axis of symmetry in Exercise 38 on page 639.

KEY CONCEPT
For Your Notebook

Properties of the Graph of a Quadratic Function

The graph of $y = ax^2 + bx + c$ is a parabola that:

• opens up if $a > 0$ and opens down if $a < 0$.

• is narrower than the graph of $y = x^2$ if $|a| > 1$ and wider if $|a| < 1$.

• has an axis of symmetry of $x = -\dfrac{b}{2a}$.

• has a vertex with an x-coordinate of $-\dfrac{b}{2a}$.

• has a y-intercept of c. So, the point $(0, c)$ is on the parabola.

$y = ax^2 + bx + c, a > 0$

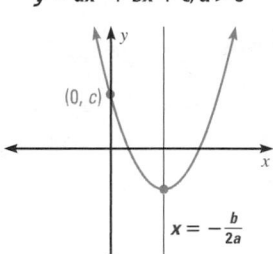

EXAMPLE 1 Find the axis of symmetry and the vertex

Consider the function $y = -2x^2 + 12x - 7$.

a. Find the axis of symmetry of the graph of the function.

b. Find the vertex of the graph of the function.

Solution

a. For the function $y = -2x^2 + 12x - 7$, $a = -2$ and $b = 12$.

$$x = -\frac{b}{2a} = -\frac{12}{2(-2)} = 3 \quad \text{Substitute } -2 \text{ for } a \text{ and } 12 \text{ for } b. \text{ Then simplify.}$$

IDENTIFY THE VERTEX
Because the vertex lies on the axis of symmetry, $x = 3$, the x-coordinate of the vertex is 3.

b. The x-coordinate of the vertex is $-\dfrac{b}{2a}$, or 3.

To find the y-coordinate, substitute 3 for x in the function and find y.

$$y = -2(3)^2 + 12(3) - 7 = 11 \quad \text{Substitute 3 for } x. \text{ Then simplify.}$$

▶ The vertex is $(3, 11)$.

---

① PLAN AND PREPARE

Warm-Up Exercises
📑 Transparency Available
Evaluate the expression.

1. $x^2 - 2$ when $x = 3$ **7**

2. $2x^2 + 9$ when $x = 2$ **17**

3. Martin is replacing a square patch of counter top. The area of the patch is represented by $A = s^2$. What is the area of the patch if the side length is 2.5 inches? **6.25 in.^{2}**

Notetaking Guide
📑 Transparency Available
Promotes interactive learning and notetaking skills, pp. 224–226.

Pacing
Basic: 1 day
Average: 1 day
Advanced: 1 day
Block: 0.5 block with 10.3
• See *Teaching Guide/Lesson Plan.*

② FOCUS AND MOTIVATE

Essential Question
Big Idea 1, p. 627

How do you graph a quadratic function of the form $y = ax^2 + bx + c$? Tell students they will learn how to answer this question by finding the axis of symmetry, finding the vertex, and using symmetry to plot several points.

NCTM STANDARDS
Standard 3: Describe spatial relationships using coordinate geometry

Standard 10: Use representations to communicate mathematical ideas

---

EXAMPLE 2   Graph $y = ax^2 + bx + c$

Graph $y = 3x^2 - 6x + 2$.

STEP 1   **Determine** whether the parabola opens up or down. Because $a > 0$, the parabola opens up.

STEP 2   **Find** and draw the axis of symmetry: $x = -\dfrac{b}{2a} = -\dfrac{-6}{2(3)} = 1$.

STEP 3   **Find** and plot the vertex.

The x-coordinate of the vertex is $-\dfrac{b}{2a}$, or 1.

To find the y-coordinate, substitute 1 for x in the function and simplify.

$y = 3(1)^2 - 6(1) + 2 = -1$

So, the vertex is $(1, -1)$.

STEP 4   **Plot** two points. Choose two x-values less than the x-coordinate of the vertex. Then find the corresponding y-values.

x	0	−1
y	2	11

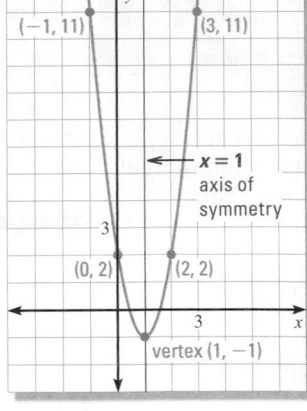

STEP 5   **Reflect** the points plotted in Step 4 in the axis of symmetry.

STEP 6   **Draw** a parabola through the plotted points.

Animated Algebra at classzone.com

✓ **GUIDED PRACTICE**   for Examples 1 and 2

1. Find the axis of symmetry and the vertex of the graph of the function $y = x^2 - 2x - 3$. **$x = 1$, $(1, -4)$**

2. Graph the function $y = 3x^2 + 12x - 1$. Label the vertex and axis of symmetry. **See margin.**

KEY CONCEPT   *For Your Notebook*

Minimum and Maximum Values

For $y = ax^2 + bx + c$, the y-coordinate of the vertex is the **minimum value** of the function if $a > 0$ or the **maximum value** of the function if $a < 0$.

$y = ax^2 + bx + c, a > 0$ $y = ax^2 + bx + c, a < 0$

---

636   Chapter 10   Quadratic Equations and Functions

Tell whether the function $f(x) = -3x^2 - 12x + 10$ has a *minimum value* or a *maximum value*. Then find the minimum or maximum value.

Solution

Because $a = -3$ and $-3 < 0$, the parabola opens down and the function has a maximum value. To find the maximum value, find the vertex.

$$x = -\frac{b}{2a} = -\frac{-12}{2(-3)} = -2 \qquad \text{The } x\text{-coordinate is } -\frac{b}{2a}.$$

$$f(-2) = -3(-2)^2 - 12(-2) + 10 = 22 \qquad \text{Substitute } -2 \text{ for } x. \text{ Then simplify.}$$

▶ The maximum value of the function is $f(-2) = 22$.

EXAMPLE 4 Find the minimum value of a function

SUSPENSION BRIDGES The suspension cables between the two towers of the Mackinac Bridge in Michigan form a parabola that can be modeled by the graph of $y = 0.000097x^2 - 0.37x + 549$ where x and y are measured in feet. What is the height of the cable above the water at its lowest point?

Solution

The lowest point of the cable is at the vertex of the parabola. Find the x-coordinate of the vertex. Use $a = 0.000097$ and $b = -0.37$.

$$x = -\frac{b}{2a} = -\frac{-0.37}{2(0.000097)} \approx 1910 \qquad \text{Use a calculator.}$$

Substitute 1910 for x in the equation to find the y-coordinate of the vertex.

$$y \approx 0.000097(1910)^2 - 0.37(1910) + 549 \approx 196$$

▶ The cable is about 196 feet above the water at its lowest point.

✓ **GUIDED PRACTICE** for Examples 3 and 4

3. minimum value; $-\frac{1}{2}$

3. Tell whether the function $f(x) = 6x^2 + 18x + 13$ has a *minimum value* or a *maximum value*. Then find the minimum or maximum value.

4. **SUSPENSION BRIDGES** The cables between the two towers of the Takoma Narrows Bridge form a parabola that can be modeled by the graph of the equation $y = 0.00014x^2 - 0.4x + 507$ where x and y are measured in feet. What is the height of the cable above the water at its lowest point? Round your answer to the nearest foot. **221 ft**

2.

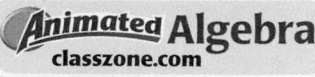
Extra Example 3

Tell whether the function $f(x) = 2x^2 - 16x + 4$ has a *minimum value* or a *maximum value*. Then find the minimum or maximum value. **The graph opens up, so it has a minimum value. The minimum value is $f(4) = -28$.**

Extra Example 4

The cables between two telephone poles can be modeled by the equation $y = 0.0024x^2 - 0.1x + 24$, where x and y are measured in feet. To the nearest foot, what is the height of the cable above the ground at its lowest point? **23 ft**

Closing the Lesson

Have students summarize the major points of the lesson and answer the Essential Question: How do you graph a quadratic function of the form $y = ax^2 + bx + c$?

- **The graph of a quadratic function is a parabola that opens up if $a > 0$ and opens down if $a < 0$.**

- **An equation for the axis of symmetry of a quadratic function is $x = -\frac{b}{2a}$.**

- **The x-coordinate of the vertex is $-\frac{b}{2a}$.**

Determine whether the graph opens up or opens down. Then find and draw the axis of symmetry by substituting values for a and b in the equation $x = -\frac{b}{2a}$. Substitute that x-value into the function and simplify to find the y-coordinate of the vertex. Choose two x-values less than the x-coordinate of the vertex and plot the points. Reflect the points in the axis of symmetry. Draw a parabola through the points.

10.2 EXERCISES

HOMEWORK
KEY

◯ = **WORKED-OUT SOLUTIONS**
on p. WS1 for Exs. 9 and 41

★ = **STANDARDIZED TEST PRACTICE**
Exs. 2, 12, 27, 37, 42, and 44

4 PRACTICE AND APPLY

Assignment Guide

📄 **Answer Transparencies**
available for all exercises

Basic:
Day 1: pp. 638–640
Exs. 1, 2, 3–11 odd, 12–20, 27–32, 37, 40–43, 46, 49, 51, 55

Average:
Day 1: pp. 638–640
Exs. 1, 2, 6–14 even, 20–27, 31–38, 40–44, 47, 52, 56

Advanced:
Day 1: pp. 638–640
Exs. 1, 8–12, 20–27, 32–45*, 48, 53, 54, 58

Block:
pp. 638–640
Exs. 1, 2, 6–14 even, 20–27, 31–38, 40–44, 47, 52, 56 (with 10.3)

Differentiated Instruction

See *Algebra 1 Best Practices Toolkit* for suggestions on addressing the needs of a diverse classroom.

Homework Check

For a quick check of student understanding of key concepts, go over the following exercises:

Basic: 5, 17, 20, 30, 40

Average: 8, 22, 24, 33, 41

Advanced: 10, 24, 25, 35, 42

Extra Practice

• Student Edition, p. 947
• Chapter 10 Resource Book: Practice levels A, B, C, pp. 21–26

Practice Worksheet

An easily-readable reduced practice page (with answers) for this lesson can be found on p. 626C.

SKILL PRACTICE

A 1. **VOCABULARY** *Explain* how you can tell whether a quadratic function has a maximum value or minimum value without graphing the function. **See margin.**

2. ★ **WRITING** *Describe* the steps you would take to graph a quadratic function in standard form. **See margin.**

EXAMPLE 1
on p. 635
for Exs. 3–14

3. $x = 2$, $(2, -2)$
4. $x = 3$, $(3, 2)$
5. $x = 4$, $(4, 26)$
6. $x = -5$, $(-5, 25)$
7. $x = -\frac{1}{2}$, $\left(-\frac{1}{2}, -\frac{3}{2}\right)$
8. $x = 0$, $(0, 7)$
9. $x = 0$, $(0, -1)$
10. $x = -8$, $(-8, -41)$
11. $x = 6$, $(6, 7)$

FINDING AXIS OF SYMMETRY AND VERTEX Find the axis of symmetry and the vertex of the graph of the function.

3. $y = 2x^2 - 8x + 6$
4. $y = x^2 - 6x + 11$
5. $y = -3x^2 + 24x - 22$
6. $y = -x^2 - 10x$
7. $y = 6x^2 + 6x$
8. $y = 4r^2 + 7$
9. $y = -\frac{2}{3}x^2 - 1$
10. $y = \frac{1}{2}x^2 + 8x - 9$
11. $y = -\frac{1}{4}x^2 + 3x - 2$

12. ★ **MULTIPLE CHOICE** What is the vertex of the graph of the function $y = -3x^2 + 18x - 13$? **D**

 A $(-3, -94)$ **B** $(-3, -14)$ **C** $(3, -13)$ **D** $(3, 14)$

ERROR ANALYSIS *Describe* and correct the error in finding the axis of symmetry of the graph of the given function. **13, 14. See margin.**

13. $y = 2x^2 + 16x - 1$

14. $y = -\frac{3}{2}x^2 + 18x - 5$

$$x = \frac{b}{2a} = \frac{16}{2(2)} = 4$$
The axis of symmetry is x = 4.

$$x = -\frac{b}{2a} = -\frac{18}{2\left(\frac{3}{2}\right)} = -6$$
The axis of symmetry is x = -6.

EXAMPLE 2
on p. 636
for Exs. 15–27

13. The equation of the axis of symmetry is $x = -\frac{b}{2a}$, not $x = \frac{b}{2a}$;
$x = -\frac{b}{2a} = -\frac{16}{2(2)}$,
$x = -4$.

14. $-\frac{3}{2}$ should be substituted for a;
$x = -\frac{18}{2\left(-\frac{3}{2}\right)}$,
$x = 6$.

GRAPHING QUADRATIC FUNCTIONS Graph the function. Label the vertex and axis of symmetry. **15–26. See margin for art.**

15. $y = x^2 + 6x + 2$
16. $y = x^2 + 4x + 8$
17. $y = 2x^2 + 7x + 21$
18. $y = 5x^2 + 10x - 3$
19. $y = 4x^2 + x - 32$
20. $y = -4x^2 + 4x + 8$
21. $y = -3x^2 - 2x - 5$
22. $y = -8x^2 - 12x + 1$
23. $y = -x^2 + \frac{1}{4}x + \frac{1}{2}$
24. $y = \frac{1}{3}x^2 + 6x - 9$
25. $y = -\frac{1}{2}x^2 + 6x + 3$
26. $y = -\frac{1}{4}x^2 - x + 1$

27. ★ **MULTIPLE CHOICE** Which function has the graph shown? **B**

 A $y = -2x^2 + 8x + 3$
 B $y = -\frac{1}{2}x^2 + 2x + 3$
 C $y = \frac{1}{2}x^2 + 2x + 3$
 D $y = 2x^2 + 8x + 3$

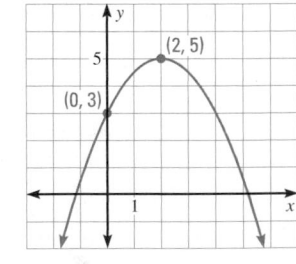

638 Chapter 10 Quadratic Equations and Functions

---

1. When the function is in standard form, $y = ax^2 + bx + c$, it will have a minimum value if $a > 0$ and a maximum value if $a < 0$.

2. Use the sign of a to tell if the parabola opens up or down. Find the axis of symmetry, $x = -\frac{b}{2a}$, which also gives the x-coordinate of the vertex.

Substitute $-\frac{b}{2a}$ for x in the function to find the y-coordinate of the vertex.

Calculate y-values for two x-values on one side of the vertex. Plot the vertex and the two points; then reflect the two points through the axis of symmetry to locate two more points. Draw a parabola through the plotted points.

15–26. See Additional Answers beginning on p. AA1.

EXAMPLE 3
on p. 637
for Exs. 28–36

MAXIMUM AND MINIMUM VALUES Tell whether the function has a *minimum value* or a *maximum value*. Then find the minimum or maximum value.

28. $f(x) = x^2 - 6$

29. $f(x) = -5x^2 + 7$

30. $f(x) = 4x^2 + 32x$

31. $f(x) = -3x^2 + 12x - 20$

32. $f(x) = x^2 + 7x + 8$

33. $f(x) = -2x^2 - x + 10$

34. $f(x) = \frac{1}{2}x^2 - 2x + 5$

35. $f(x) = -\frac{3}{8}x^2 + 9x$

36. $f(x) = \frac{1}{4}x^2 + 7x + 11$

B **37.** ★ **WRITING** Compare the graph of $y = x^2 + 4x + 1$ with the graph of $y = x^2 - 4x + 1$. **The graph of $y = x^2 + 4 = x + 1$ is a horizontal translation (of 4 units left) of the graph $y = x^2 - 4x + 1$.**

38. **REASONING** Follow the steps below to justify the equation for the axis of symmetry for the graph of $y = ax^2 + bx + c$. Because the graph of $y = ax^2 + bx + c$ is a vertical translation of the graph of $y = ax^2 + bx$, the two graphs have the same axis of symmetry. Use the function $y = ax^2 + bx$ in place of $y = ax^2 + bx + c$.

  a. Find the x-intercepts of the graph of $y = ax^2 + bx$. (You can do this by finding the zeros of the function $y = ax^2 + bx$ using factoring.) **$0, -\frac{b}{a}$**

  b. Because a parabola is symmetric about its axis of symmetry, the axis of symmetry passes through a point halfway between the x-intercepts of the parabola. Find the x-coordinate of this point. What is an equation of the vertical line through this point? **$-\frac{b}{2a}; x = -\frac{b}{2a}$**

C **39.** **CHALLENGE** Write a function of the form $y = ax^2 + bx$ whose graph contains the points $(1, 6)$ and $(3, 6)$. **Sample answer: $y = -2x^2 + 8x$**

PROBLEM SOLVING

 GRAPHING CALCULATOR You may wish to use a graphing calculator to complete the following Problem Solving exercises.

EXAMPLE 4 **A**
on p. 637
for Exs. 40–42

40. **SPIDERS** Fishing spiders can propel themselves across water and leap vertically from the surface of the water. During a vertical jump, the height of the body of the spider can be modeled by the function $y = -4500x^2 + 820x + 43$ where x is the duration (in seconds) of the jump and y is the height (in millimeters) of the spider above the surface of the water. After how many seconds does the spider's body reach its maximum height? What is the maximum height? **about 0.091 sec; about 80 mm**

@HomeTutor for problem solving help at classzone.com

41. **ARCHITECTURE** The parabolic arches that support the roof of the Dallas Convention Center can be modeled by the graph of the equation $y = -0.0019x^2 + 0.71x$ where x and y are measured in feet. What is the height h at the highest point of the arch as shown in the diagram? **about 66 ft**

@HomeTutor for problem solving help at classzone.com

ASSESS AND RETEACH

Daily Homework Quiz

Transparency Available

1. Find the axis of symmetry and the vertex of the graph of the function $y = -4x^2 + 8x - 9$.
   $x = 1$; $(1, -5)$

2. Graph $y = -2x^2 + 4x + 1$.

3. An arch to the entrance of the library can be modeled by $y = -0.13x^2 + 2.5x$, where x and y are measured in feet. To the nearest foot, what is the height of the highest point of the arch?
   12 ft

Online Quiz

Available at classzone.com

Diagnosis/Remediation

- Practice A, B, C in Chapter 10 Resource Book, pp. 21–26
- Study Guide in Chapter 10 Resource Book, pp. 27–28
- Practice Workbook, pp. 152–154
- @HomeTutor

Challenge

Additional challenge is available in the Chapter 10 Resource Book, p. 31.

43. See Additional Answers beginning on p. AA1.

44. No; the maximum value of the function $S = 332 + 132t - 10.4t^2$ occurs when $t = -\dfrac{132}{2(-10.4)} \approx 6.35$. Because the function S makes sense only for integer values of t, the maximum value of S occurs at either $t = 6$ or $t = 7$. These t-values correspond to 1996 and 1997, so the greatest number of tickets for Broadway tours was sold after 1995.

42c. $10; the maximum value of $1000 occurs when $n = 5$, so the students should charge 5 $1 increases, or $5 + $5 = $10 in order to generate the most sales revenue.

42. ★ **EXTENDED RESPONSE** Students are selling packages of flower bulbs to raise money for a class trip. Last year, when the students charged $5 per package, they sold 150 packages. The students want to increase the cost per package. They estimate that they will lose 10 sales for each $1 increase in the cost per package. The sales revenue R (in dollars) generated by selling the packages is given by the function $R = (5 + n)(150 - 10n)$ where n is the number of $1 increases.

   a. Write the function in standard form. $R = -10n^2 + 100n + 750$

   b. Find the maximum value of the function. **$1000**

   c. At what price should the packages be sold to generate the most sales revenue? *Explain* your reasoning.

B **43.** **AIRCRAFT** An aircraft hangar is a large building where planes are stored. The opening of one airport hangar is a parabolic arch that can be modeled by the graph of the equation $y = -0.007x^2 + 1.7x$ where x and y are measured in feet. Graph the function. Use the graph to determine how wide the hangar is at its base.
See margin for art; about 243 ft.

44. ★ **SHORT RESPONSE** The casts of some Broadway shows go on tour, performing their shows in cities across the United States. For the period 1990–2001, the number of tickets sold S (in millions) for Broadway road tours can be modeled by the function $S = 332 + 132t - 10.4t^2$ where t is the number of years since 1990. Was the greatest number of tickets for Broadway road tours sold in 1995? *Explain.* **See margin.**

C **45.** **CHALLENGE** During an archery competition, an archer shoots an arrow from 1.5 meters off of the ground. The arrow follows the parabolic path shown and hits the ground in front of the target 90 meters away. Use the y-intercept and the points on the graph to write an equation for the graph that models the path of the arrow.
$y = -0.00031x^2 + 0.011x + 1.5$

MIXED REVIEW

Graph the equation. *(pp. 215, 225, 244)* **46–48. See margin for art.**

46. $y = 3$ **47.** $x - 5y = 15$ **48.** $y = -\dfrac{2}{3}x - 6$

Simplify.

49. $-3(4 - 2x) - 9$ *(p. 96)*   **50.** $2(1 - a) - 5a$ *(p. 96)*   **51.** $\dfrac{12y - 4}{-4}$ *(p. 103)* $-3y + 1$
$6x - 21$ $2 - 7a$

52. $(-2mn)^4$ *(p. 489)*   **53.** $5 \cdot (7w^7)^2$ *(p. 489)*   **54.** $\dfrac{6u^3}{v} \cdot \dfrac{uv^2}{36}$ *(p. 495)* $\dfrac{u^4v}{6}$
$16m^4n^4$ $245w^{14}$

PREVIEW

Prepare for Lesson 10.3 in Exs. 55–58.

Find the zeros of the polynomial function.

55. $f(x) = x^2 - 4x - 21$ *(p. 583)* $-3, 7$ **56.** $f(x) = x^2 + 10x + 24$ *(p. 583)* $-6, -4$

57. $f(x) = 5x^2 + 18x + 9$ *(p. 593)* $-3, -\dfrac{3}{5}$ **58.** $f(x) = 2x^2 + 4x - 6$ *(p. 593)* $-3, 1$

46.

47.

48.

Graph Quadratic Functions in Intercept Form

GOAL Graph quadratic functions in intercept form.

Key Vocabulary
• intercept form

In Lesson 10.2 you graphed quadratic functions written in standard form. Quadratic functions can also be written in **intercept form**, $y = a(x - p)(x - q)$ where $a \neq 0$. In this form, the x-intercepts of the graph can easily be determined.

> **KEY CONCEPT** *For Your Notebook*
>
> **Graph of Intercept Form $y = a(x - p)(x - q)$**
>
> Characteristics of the graph of $y = a(x - p)(x - q)$:
>
> • The x-intercepts are p and q.
>
> • The axis of symmetry is halfway between $(p, 0)$ and $(q, 0)$. So, the axis of symmetry is $x = \frac{p + q}{2}$.
>
> • The parabola opens up if $a > 0$ and opens down if $a < 0$.
>
>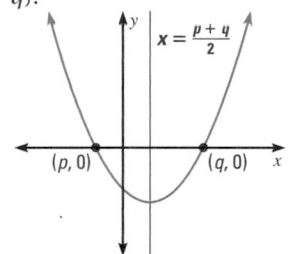

EXAMPLE 1 **Graph a quadratic function in intercept form**

Graph $y = -(x + 1)(x - 5)$.

FIND ZEROS OF A FUNCTION
Notice that the x-intercepts of the graph are also the zeros of the function:
$0 = -(x + 1)(x - 5)$
$x + 1 = 0$ *or* $x - 5 = 0$
$x = -1$ *or* $x = 5$

Solution

STEP 1 **Identify** and plot the x-intercepts. Because $p = -1$ and $q = 5$, the x-intercepts occur at the points $(-1, 0)$ and $(5, 0)$.

STEP 2 **Find** and draw the axis of symmetry.

$$x = \frac{p + q}{2} = \frac{-1 + 5}{2} = 2$$

STEP 3 **Find** and plot the vertex.

The x-coordinate of the vertex is 2.

To find the y-coordinate of the vertex, substitute 2 for x and simplify.

$$y = -(2 + 1)(2 - 5) = 9$$

So, the vertex is $(2, 9)$.

STEP 4 **Draw** a parabola through the vertex and the points where the x-intercepts occur.

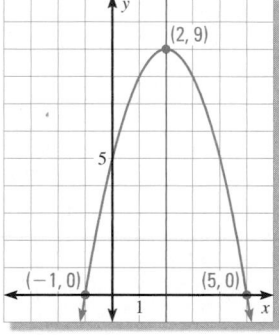

---

① PLAN AND PREPARE

Warm-Up Exercises

1. Find the axis of symmetry and the vertex of the graph of the function $y = x^2 + 2x - 15$.
   $x = -1$; $(-1, -16)$

2. Graph $y = 3x^2 - 6x + 1$.

② FOCUS AND MOTIVATE

Essential Question
Big Idea 1, p. 627

How do you graph a quadratic function in intercept form? Tell students they will learn how to answer this question by identifying and plotting the x-intercepts, the axis of symmetry, and the vertex of the function.

③ TEACH

Extra Example 1
Graph $y = (x + 1)(x - 3)$.

NCTM STANDARDS

Standard 2: Analyze situations using algebraic symbols

Standard 3: Use symmetry to analyze math situations

EXAMPLE 2 Graph a quadratic function

Graph $y = 2x^2 - 8$.

Solution

STEP 1 **Rewrite** the quadratic function in intercept form.

$$y = 2x^2 - 8 \qquad \text{Write original function.}$$
$$= 2(x^2 - 4) \qquad \text{Factor out common factor.}$$
$$= 2(x + 2)(x - 2) \qquad \text{Difference of two squares pattern}$$

STEP 2 **Identify** and plot the x-intercepts. Because $p = -2$ and $q = 2$, the x-intercepts occur at the points $(-2, 0)$ and $(2, 0)$.

STEP 3 **Find** and draw the axis of symmetry.

$$x = \frac{p + q}{2} = \frac{-2 + 2}{2} = 0$$

STEP 4 **Find** and plot the vertex.

The x-coordinate of the vertex is 0.

The y-coordinate of the vertex is:

$$y = 2(0)^2 - 8 = -8$$

So, the vertex is $(0, -8)$.

STEP 5 **Draw** a parabola through the vertex and the points where the x-intercepts occur.

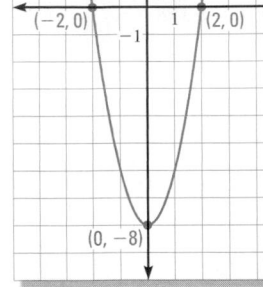

Animated Algebra at classzone.com

PRACTICE

EXAMPLE 1
on p. 641 for
Exs. 1–9

Graph the quadratic function. Label the vertex, axis of symmetry, and x-intercepts. 1–15. See margin for art.

1. $y = (x + 2)(x - 3)$
2. $y = (x + 5)(x + 2)$
3. $y = (x + 9)^2$

4. $y = -2(x - 5)(x + 1)$
5. $y = -5(x + 7)(x + 2)$
6. $y = 3(x - 6)(x - 3)$

7. $y = -\dfrac{1}{2}(x + 4)(x - 2)$
8. $y = (x - 7)(2x - 3)$
9. $y = 2(x + 10)(x - 3)$

EXAMPLE 2
on p. 642 for
Exs. 10–15

10. $y = -x^2 + 8x - 16$
11. $y = -x^2 - 9x - 18$
12. $y = 12x^2 - 48$

13. $y = -6x^2 + 294$
14. $y = 3x^2 - 24x + 36$
15. $y = 20x^2 - 6x - 2$

16. Follow the steps below to write an equation of the parabola shown.

  a. Find the x-intercepts. **−3, 5**

  b. Use the values of p and q and the coordinates of the vertex to find the value of a in the equation $y = a(x - p)(x - q)$. **$-\dfrac{3}{8}$**

  c. Write a quadratic equation in intercept form. **$y = -\dfrac{3}{8}(x + 3)(x - 5)$**

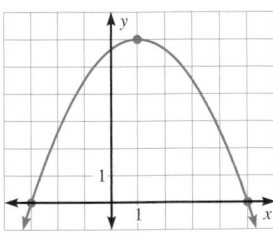

1–15. See Additional Answers beginning on p. AA1.

10.3 Solve Quadratic Equations by Graphing

Before You solved quadratic equations by factoring.

Now You will solve quadratic equations by graphing.

Why? So you can solve a problem about sports, as in Example 6.

Key Vocabulary
- quadratic equation
- x-intercept, p. 225
- roots, p. 575
- zero of a function, p. 337

A **quadratic equation** is an equation that can be written in the **standard form** $ax^2 + bx + c = 0$ where $a \neq 0$.

In Chapter 9, you used factoring to solve a quadratic equation. You can also use graphing to solve a quadratic equation. Notice that the solutions of the equation $ax^2 + bx + c = 0$ are the x-intercepts of the graph of the related function $y = ax^2 + bx + c$.

Solve by Factoring	Solve by Graphing
$x^2 - 6x + 5 = 0$	To solve $x^2 - 6x + 5 = 0$, graph $y = x^2 - 6x + 5$. From the graph you can see that the x-intercepts are 1 and 5.
$(x - 1)(x - 5) = 0$	
$x = 1 \ or \ x = 5$	

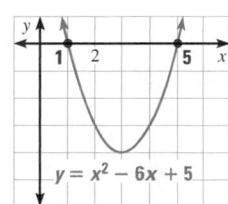
$y = x^2 - 6x + 5$

READING
In this course, *solutions* refers to real-number solutions.

To solve a quadratic equation by graphing, first write the equation in standard form, $ax^2 + bx + c = 0$. Then graph the related function $y = ax^2 + bx + c$. The x-intercepts of the graph are the solutions, or roots, of $ax^2 + bx + c = 0$.

EXAMPLE 1 Solve a quadratic equation having two solutions

Solve $x^2 - 2x = 3$ by graphing.

Solution

STEP 1 Write the equation in standard form.

$x^2 - 2x = 3$ **Write original equation.**

$x^2 - 2x - 3 = 0$ **Subtract 3 from each side.**

STEP 2 Graph the function $y = x^2 - 2x - 3$.
The x-intercepts are -1 and 3.

▶ The solutions of the equation $x^2 - 2x = 3$ are -1 and 3.

$y = x^2 - 2x - 3$

CHECK You can check -1 and 3 in the original equation.

$x^2 - 2x = 3$	$x^2 - 2x = 3$	**Write original equation.**
$(-1)^2 - 2(-1) \stackrel{?}{=} 3$	$(3)^2 - 2(3) \stackrel{?}{=} 3$	**Substitute for x.**
$3 = 3 ✓$	$3 = 3 ✓$	**Simplify. Each solution checks.**

10.3 Solve Quadratic Equations by Graphing   **643**

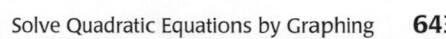

Motivating the Lesson

In soccer, the path of the ball depends on the velocity of the kick and the height of the ball when it is kicked. In this lesson, you will learn how to use the vertical motion model to determine how high and how far a kicked soccer ball will go.

③ TEACH

Extra Example 1

Solve $x^2 + 4x = 5$ by graphing. $-5, 1$

$y = x^2 + 4x - 5$

Extra Example 2

Solve $-x^2 - 6x = 9$ by graphing. -3

$y = -x^2 - 6x - 9$

Extra Example 3

Solve $x^2 + 4x = -6$ by graphing. no solutions

$y = x^2 + 4x + 6$

EXAMPLE 2 Solve a quadratic equation having one solution

Solve $-x^2 + 2x = 1$ by graphing.

Solution

STEP 1 Write the equation in standard form.

$$-x^2 + 2x = 1 \qquad \text{Write original equation.}$$

$$-x^2 + 2x - 1 = 0 \qquad \text{Subtract 1 from each side.}$$

STEP 2 Graph the function $y = -x^2 + 2x - 1$. The x-intercept is 1.

▶ The solution of the equation $-x^2 + 2x = 1$ is 1.

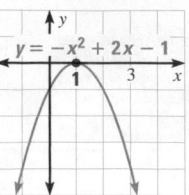

$y = -x^2 + 2x - 1$

EXAMPLE 3 Solve a quadratic equation having no solution

Solve $x^2 + 7 = 4x$ by graphing.

AVOID ERRORS
Do not confuse y-intercepts and x-intercepts. Although the graph has a y-intercept, it does not have any x-intercepts.

Solution

STEP 1 Write the equation in standard form.

$$x^2 + 7 = 4x \qquad \text{Write original equation.}$$

$$x^2 - 4x + 7 = 0 \qquad \text{Subtract } 4x \text{ from each side.}$$

STEP 2 Graph the function $y = x^2 - 4x + 7$. The graph has no x-intercepts.

▶ The equation $x^2 + 7 = 4x$ has no solution.

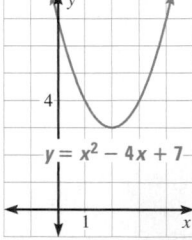

$y = x^2 - 4x + 7$

✓ **GUIDED PRACTICE** for Examples 1, 2, and 3

Solve the equation by graphing.

1. $x^2 - 6x + 8 = 0$ **2, 4**   2. $x^2 + x = -1$ **no solution**   3. $-x^2 + 6x = 9$ **3**

KEY CONCEPT _For Your Notebook_

Number of Solutions of a Quadratic Equation

        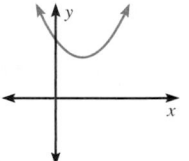

A quadratic equation has **two solutions** if the graph of its related function has **two x-intercepts**.

A quadratic equation has **one solution** if the graph of its related function has **one x-intercept**.

A quadratic equation has **no real solution** if the graph of its related function has **no x-intercepts**.

FINDING ZEROS Because a zero of a function is an x-intercept of the function's graph, you can use the function's graph to find the zeros of a function.

EXAMPLE 4 Find the zeros of a quadratic function

Find the zeros of $f(x) = x^2 + 6x - 7$.

ANOTHER WAY

You can find the zeros of a function by factoring:

$f(x) = x^2 + 6x - 7$

$0 = x^2 + 6x - 7$

$0 = (x + 7)(x - 1)$

$x = -7$ or $x = 1$

Solution

Graph the function $f(x) = x^2 + 6x - 7$. The x-intercepts are -7 and 1.

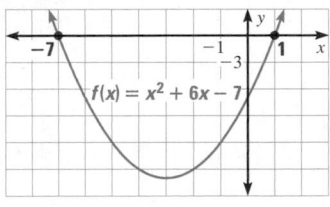

▶ The zeros of the function are -7 and 1.

CHECK Substitute -7 and 1 in the original function.

$f(-7) = (-7)^2 + 6(-7) - 7 = 0$ ✓

$f(1) = (1)^2 + 6(1) - 7 = 0$ ✓

APPROXIMATING ZEROS The zeros of a function are not necessarily integers. To approximate zeros, look at the signs of the function values. If two function values have opposite signs, then a zero falls between the x-values that correspond to the function values.

❖ EXAMPLE 5 Approximate the zeros of a quadratic function

Approximate the zeros of $f(x) = x^2 + 4x + 1$ to the nearest tenth.

Solution

STEP 1 Graph the function $f(x) = x^2 + 4x + 1$. There are two x-intercepts: one between -4 and -3 and another between -1 and 0.

STEP 2 Make a table of values for x-values between -4 and -3 and between -1 and 0 using an increment of 0.1. Look for a change in the signs of the function values.

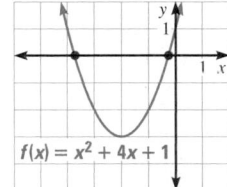

INTERPRET FUNCTION VALUES

The function value that is closest to 0 indicates the x-value that best approximates a zero of the function.

x	-3.9	-3.8	$\mathbf{-3.7}$	-3.6	-3.5	-3.4	-3.3	-3.2	-3.1
$f(x)$	0.61	0.24	$\mathbf{-0.11}$	-0.44	-0.75	-1.04	-1.31	-1.56	-1.79

x	-0.9	-0.8	-0.7	-0.6	-0.5	-0.4	$\mathbf{-0.3}$	-0.2	-0.1
$f(x)$	-1.79	-1.56	-1.31	-1.04	-0.75	-0.44	$\mathbf{-0.11}$	0.24	0.61

▶ In each table, the function value closest to 0 is -0.11. So, the zeros of $f(x) = x^2 + 4x + 1$ are about -3.7 and about -0.3.

✓ **GUIDED PRACTICE** for Examples 4 and 5

4. Find the zeros of $f(x) = x^2 + x - 6$. **$-3, 2$**

5. Approximate the zeros of $f(x) = -x^2 + 2x + 2$ to the nearest tenth. **$-0.7, 2.7$**

10.3 Solve Quadratic Equations by Graphing **645**

Differentiated Instruction

Below Level Have students work in pairs to approximate the zeros of the function in **Guided Practice Exercise 5**. Suggest that they use a step-by-step process and have you confirm that they have completed each step correctly. Check that their graphs are correct, that the calculations in their tables are correct, and that they have chosen the values in the tables for which $f(x)$ is closest to 0. After they have successfully worked through the example, have them write a summary of the steps they used.

See also the *Algebra 1 Toolkit* for more strategies.

EXAMPLE 6 Solve a multi-step problem

SPORTS An athlete throws a shot put with an initial vertical velocity of 40 feet per second as shown.

a. Write an equation that models the height h (in feet) of the shot put as a function of the time t (in seconds) after it is thrown.

b. Use the equation to find the time that the shot put is in the air.

6.5 ft

Solution

a. Use the initial vertical velocity and the release height to write a vertical motion model.

$$h = -16t^2 + vt + s \qquad \text{Vertical motion model}$$

$$h = -16t^2 + 40t + 6.5 \qquad \text{Substitute 40 for } v \text{ and 6.5 for } s.$$

b. The shot put lands when $h = 0$. To find the time t when $h = 0$, solve $0 = -16t^2 + 40t + 6.5$ for t.

To solve the equation, graph the related function $h = -16t^2 + 40t + 6.5$ on a graphing calculator. Use the *trace* feature to find the t-intercepts.

▸ There is only one positive t-intercept. The shot put is in the air for about 2.6 seconds.

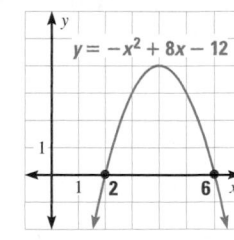

Trace
X=2.648936 Y=.1864148

✓ **GUIDED PRACTICE** for Example 6

6. **WHAT IF?** In Example 6, suppose the initial vertical velocity is 30 feet per second. Find the time that the shot put is in the air. **about 2.1 sec**

CONCEPT SUMMARY   *For Your Notebook*

Relating Solutions of Equations, x-Intercepts of Graphs, and Zeros of Functions

Solutions of an Equation
The solutions of the equation $-x^2 + 8x - 12 = 0$ are 2 and 6.

x-Intercepts of a Graph
The x-intercepts of the graph of $y = -x^2 + 8x - 12$ occur where $y = 0$, so the x-intercepts are 2 and 6, as shown.

Zeros of a Function
The zeros of the function $f(x) = -x^2 + 8x - 12$ are the values of x for which $f(x) = 0$, so the zeros are 2 and 6.

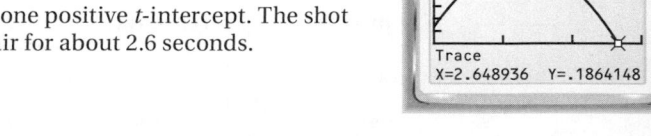

$y = -x^2 + 8x - 12$

10.3 EXERCISES

HOMEWORK KEY
○ = WORKED-OUT SOLUTIONS
on p. WS1 for Exs. 5 and 51

★ = STANDARDIZED TEST PRACTICE
Exs. 2, 46, 53, and 54

SKILL PRACTICE

A 1. **VOCABULARY** Write $2x^2 + 11 = 9x$ in standard form. **$2x^2 - 9x + 11 = 0$**

2. ★ **WRITING** Is $3x^2 - 2 = 0$ a quadratic equation? *Explain.*

SOLVING EQUATIONS Solve the equation by graphing.

> **EXAMPLES 1, 2, and 3**
> on pp. 643–644
> for Exs. 3–21
>
> 2. Yes; $3x^2 - 2 = 0$ is a quadratic equation in the standard form $ax^2 + bx + c = 0$, where $a = 3$, $b = 0$, and $c = -2$: $3x^2 + 0x + (-2) = 0$ or $3x^2 - 2 = 0$.

3. $x^2 - 5x + 4 = 0$ **4, 1**

4. $x^2 + 5x + 6 = 0$ **−3, −2**

5. $x^2 + 6x = -8$ **−4, −2**

6. $x^2 - 4x = 5$ **5, −1**

7. $x^2 - 16 = 6x$ **8, −2**

8. $x^2 - 12x = -35$ **7, 5**

9. $x^2 - 6x + 9 = 0$ **3**

10. $x^2 + 8x + 16 = 0$ **−4**

11. $x^2 + 10x = -25$ **−5**

12. $x^2 + 81 = 18x$ **9**

13. $-x^2 - 14x = 49$ **−7**

14. $-x^2 + 16x = 64$ **8**

15. $x^2 - 5x + 7 = 0$ **no solution**

16. $x^2 - 2x + 3 = 0$ **no solution**

17. $x^2 + x = -2$ **no solution**

18. $\frac{1}{5}x^2 - 5 = 0$ **±5**

19. $\frac{1}{2}x^2 + 2x = 6$ **−6, 2**

20. $-\frac{1}{4}x^2 - 8 = x$ **no solution**

21. **ERROR ANALYSIS** The graph of the function related to the equation $0 = x^2 - 4x + 4$ is shown. *Describe* and correct the error in solving the equation. **See margin.**

The only solution of the equation $0 = x^2 - 4x + 4$ is 4.

> **EXAMPLE 4**
> on p. 645
> for Exs. 22–30

FINDING ZEROS Find the zeros of the function.

22. $f(x) = x^2 + 4x - 5$ **−5, 1**

23. $f(x) = x^2 - x - 12$ **−3, 4**

24. $f(x) = x^2 - 5x - 6$ **−1, 6**

25. $f(x) = x^2 + 3x - 10$ **−5, 2**

26. $f(x) = -x^2 + 8x + 9$ **−1, 9**

27. $f(x) = x^2 + x - 20$ **−5, 4**

28. $f(x) = -x^2 - 7x + 8$ **−8, 1**

29. $f(x) = x^2 - 12x + 11$ **1, 11**

30. $f(x) = -x^2 + 4x + 12$ **−2, 6**

B **SOLVING EQUATIONS** Solve the equation by graphing.

31. $2x^2 + x = 3$ **$-1\frac{1}{2}, 1$**

32. $4x^2 - 5 = 8x$ **$-\frac{1}{2}, 2\frac{1}{2}$**

33. $4x^2 - 4x + 1 = 0$ **$\frac{1}{2}$**

34. $x^2 + x = -\frac{1}{4}$ **$-\frac{1}{2}$**

35. $3x^2 + 1 = 2x$ **no solution**

36. $5x^2 + x + 3 = 0$ **no solution**

> **EXAMPLE 5**
> on p. 645
> for Exs. 37–46
>
> 40. −3.8, 0.8
> 41. 0.8, 6.2
> 42. −4.6, −0.4

APPROXIMATING ZEROS Approximate the zeros of the function to the nearest tenth. **37–45. See margin.**

37. $f(x) = x^2 + 4x + 2$ **−3.4, −0.6**

38. $f(x) = x^2 - 5x + 3$ **0.7, 4.3**

39. $f(x) = x^2 - 2x - 5$ **−1.4, 3.4**

40. $f(x) = -x^2 - 3x + 3$

41. $f(x) = -x^2 + 7x - 5$

42. $f(x) = -x^2 - 5x - 2$

43. $f(x) = 2x^2 + x - 2$ **−1.3, 0.8**

44. $f(x) = -3x^2 + 8x - 2$ **0.3, 2.4**

45. $f(x) = 5x^2 + 30x + 30$ **−4.7, −1.3**

46. ★ **MULTIPLE CHOICE** Which function has a zero between −3 and −2? **C**

Ⓐ $f(x) = -3x^2 + 4x + 11$

Ⓑ $f(x) = 4x^2 - 3x - 11$

Ⓒ $f(x) = 3x^2 + 4x - 11$

Ⓓ $f(x) = 3x^2 + 11$

10.3 Solve Quadratic Equations by Graphing **647**

21. Any solution of a quadratic equation is an *x*-intercept of the graph of the related quadratic function. The *x*-intercept of the function shown in the graph is 2, not 4; the only solution of the equation is 2.

④ PRACTICE AND APPLY

Assignment Guide

📑 Answer Transparencies available for all exercises

Basic:
Day 1: EP p. 944 Exs. 1–4
pp. 647–649
Exs. 1–21
Day 2: pp. 647–649
Exs. 22–36 even, 37–41, 50–53, 56–64

Average:
Day 1: pp. 647–649
Exs. 1, 2, 5–21, 47, 48, 59–63 odd
Day 2: pp. 647–649
Exs. 24–46, 50–54, 56–58

Advanced:
Day 1: pp. 647–649
Exs. 1, 2, 6–20, 47–49*, 60–64 even
Day 2: pp. 647–649
Exs. 25–46, 50–56*, 58

Block:
pp. 647–649
Exs. 1, 2, 5–21, 47, 48, 59–63 odd
(with 10.2)
pp. 647–649
Exs. 24–46, 50–54, 56–58
(with 10.4)

Differentiated Instruction

See *Algebra 1 Best Practices Toolkit* for suggestions on addressing the needs of a diverse classroom.

Homework Check

For a quick check of student understanding of key concepts, go over the following exercises:

Basic: 6, 9, 24, 38, 50
Average: 10, 16, 26, 41, 51
Advanced: 12, 17, 29, 44, 52

Extra Practice

• Student Edition, p. 947
• Chapter 10 Resource Book: Practice levels A, B, C, pp. 35–40

Practice Worksheet

An easily-readable reduced practice page (with answers) for this lesson can be found on p. 626C.

CHALLENGE Use the given surface area S of the cylinder to find the radius r to the nearest tenth. (Use 3.14 for π.)

47. $S = 251 \text{ ft}^2$ **3.7 ft**   48. $S = 716 \text{ m}^2$ **4.2 m**   49. $S = 1074 \text{ cm}^2$ **5.8 cm**

PROBLEM SOLVING

GRAPHING CALCULATOR You may wish to use a graphing calculator to complete the following Problem Solving exercises.

EXAMPLE 6 A
on p. 646
for Exs. 50–52

50. **SOCCER** The height y (in feet) of a soccer ball after it is kicked can be modeled by the graph of the equation $y = -0.04x^2 + 1.2x$ where x is the horizontal distance (in feet) that the ball travels. The ball is not touched, and it lands on the ground. Find the distance that the ball was kicked. **30 ft**

@HomeTutor for problem solving help at classzone.com

(51.) **SURVEYING** To keep water off a road, the road's surface is shaped like a parabola as in the cross section below. The surface of the road can be modeled by the graph of $y = -0.0017x^2 + 0.041x$ where x and y are measured in feet. Find the width of the road to the nearest tenth of a foot. **24.1 ft**

@HomeTutor for problem solving help at classzone.com

52. **DIVING** During a cliff diving competition, a diver begins a dive with his center of gravity 70 feet above the water. The initial vertical velocity of his dive is 8 feet per second.

   a. Write an equation that models the height h (in feet) of the diver's center of gravity as a function of time t (in seconds). $h = -16t^2 + 8t + 70$

   b. How long after the diver begins his dive does his center of gravity reach the water? **about 2.4 sec**

B   53. ★ **SHORT RESPONSE** An arc of water sprayed from the nozzle of a fountain can be modeled by the graph of $y = -0.75x^2 + 6x$ where x is the horizontal distance (in feet) from the nozzle and y is the vertical distance (in feet). The diameter of the circle formed by the arcs on the surface of the water is called the display diameter. Find the display diameter of the fountain. *Explain* your reasoning. **See margin.**

Display diameter

○ = **WORKED-OUT SOLUTIONS**
on p. WS1

★ = **STANDARDIZED**
TEST PRACTICE

Side margin

Avoiding Common Errors

Exercises 5–20 Some students may attempt to graph an equation without first writing it in standard form. Suggest that students go through the exercises and write each of the equations in standard form before they solve the equations by graphing.

Mathematical Reasoning

Exercises 50–52 To help students make a connection between the real life situations in these problems and visual and algebraic representations of them, you may want to discuss how the values of x and y in these exercises are similar to the variable values in Example 6, and how they are different.

Study Strategy

Exercise 54 Point out to students that they must solve part (a) of the problem before they can solve parts (b) or (c). If students are confused by part (c), ask how many times the ball reaches a height of 5.5 feet. Then suggest that they examine the graph in terms of x and y to determine which point they should use to solve part (c).

53. 16 ft; the distance from the nozzle to the circle is the distance between the x-intercepts of $y = -0.75x^2 + 6x$. Substitute 0 for y and solve for x: $0 = -0.75x^2 + 6x$ has solutions 0 and 8. The radius of the display circle is 8 feet, so the diameter is 16 feet.

54c. 2.5 sec; the two points on the graph of $h = -16t^2 + 40t + 5.5$ that correspond to a height of 5.5 feet are the two points with h-coordinate 5.5. These points are reflections of each other in the parabola's axis of symmetry, $t = 1.25$. Because one point with h-coordinate 5.5 is (0, 5.5), the t-coordinate of the other point with h-coordinate 5.5 is 2(1.25) = 2.5. So, after 2.5 seconds, the ball is again at a height of 5.5 feet.

54. ★ **EXTENDED RESPONSE** Two softball players are practicing catching fly balls. One player throws a ball to the other. She throws the ball upward from a height of 5.5 feet with an initial vertical velocity of 40 feet per second for her teammate to catch.

   a. Write an equation that models the height h (in feet) of the ball as a function of time t (in seconds) after it is thrown. $h = -16t^2 + 40t + 5.5$

   b. If her teammate misses the ball and it lands on the ground, how long was the ball in the air? **about 2.6 sec**

   c. If her teammate catches the ball at a height of 5.5 feet, how long was the ball in the air? *Explain* your reasoning. **See margin.**

C **55. CHALLENGE** A stream of water from a fire hose can be modeled by the graph of $y = -0.003x^2 + 0.58x + 3$ where x and y are measured in feet. A firefighter is holding the hose 3 feet above the ground, 137 feet from a building. Will the stream of water pass through a window if the top of the window is 26 feet above the ground? *Explain.* **No; the height of the water at the point 137 feet from the firefighter is $-0.003(137)^2 + 0.58(137) + 3 \approx 26.2$ feet. The water will hit the building just above the window.**

MIXED REVIEW

PREVIEW
Prepare for
Lesson 10.4 in
Exs. 56–58.

Evaluate the expression. *(p. 110)*

56. $-\sqrt{25}$ **−5**   **57.** $\sqrt{400}$ **20**   **58.** $\pm\sqrt{625}$ **±25**

Simplify the expression. *(p. 495)*

59. $\dfrac{(-8)^{10}}{(-8)^7}$ **−512**   **60.** $\dfrac{9^2 \cdot 9^6}{9^4}$ **6561**   **61.** $\left(-\dfrac{1}{2}\right)^3$ **$-\dfrac{1}{8}$**

Write the number in standard form. *(p. 512)*

62. 4.4×10^{-6} **0.0000044**   **63.** 1.7×10^5 **170,000**   **64.** 6.804×10^8 **680,400,000**

QUIZ for Lessons 10.1–10.3

Graph the function. Compare the graph with the graph of $y = x^2$. *(p. 628)* **1–3. See margin.**

  1. $y = -\dfrac{1}{2}x^2$ **2.** $y = 2x^2 - 5$ **3.** $y = -x^2 + 3$

Graph the function. Label the vertex and axis of symmetry. **4–9. See margin.**

  4. $y = x^2 + 5$ *(p. 628)*   **5.** $y = -5x^2 + 1$ *(p. 628)*

  6. $y = x^2 + 4x - 2$ *(p. 635)*   **7.** $y = 2x^2 - 12x + 5$ *(p. 635)*

  8. $y = -\dfrac{1}{2}x^2 + 2x - 5$ *(p. 635)*   **9.** $y = -4x^2 - 10x + 2$ *(p. 635)*

Solve the equation by graphing. *(p. 643)*

  10. $x^2 - 7x = 8$ **−1, 8**   **11.** $x^2 + 6x + 9 = 0$ **−3**   **12.** $x^2 + 10x = 11$ **−11, 1**

  13. $x^2 - 7 = -6x$ **−7, 1**   **14.** $-x^2 + x - 1 = 0$ **no solution**   **15.** $x^2 - 4x + 9 = 0$ **no solution**

Find the zeros of the function. *(p. 643)*

  16. $f(x) = x^2 + 3x - 10$ **−5, 2**   **17.** $f(x) = x^2 - 8x + 12$ **2, 6**   **18.** $f(x) = -x^2 + 5x + 14$ **−2, 7**

650

① PLAN AND PREPARE

Learn the Method

- Students will find the maximum or minimum value and approximate the zeros of a quadratic function using their graphing calculators.
- After the activity, students can use a graphing calculator to check their solutions in Lesson 10.3, Exercises 3–46.

Keystroke Help

Keystrokes for several models of calculators are available in blackline format in the *Chapter 10 Resource Book.*

② TEACH

Tips for Success

In Example 1, point out to students that the lower right calculator screen indicates the maximum value of the function: Y = 11.5. In Example 2, make sure that students understand that they will need to give lower and upper bounds on one of the zeros at a time, not both. For the lower bound they need a number to the left of the *x*-intercept, and for the upper bound they need a number to the right of the *x*-intercept.

Extra Example 1

Find the minimum value of $y = 3x^2 + 9x - 2$. **−8.75**

10.3 Find Minimum and Maximum Values and Zeros

QUESTION How can you find the minumum or maximum value and the zeros of a quadratic function using a graphing calculator?

EXAMPLE 1 Find the maximum value of a function

Find the maximum value of the function $y = -2x^2 - 6x + 7$.

STEP 1 *Enter the function*
Press [Y=] and enter the function
$y = -2x^2 - 6x + 7$.

STEP 2 *Adjust the window*
Display the graph. Adjust the viewing window as needed so that the vertex of the parabola is visible.

STEP 3 *Use the maximum feature*
The *maximum* feature is located under the CALCULATE menu.

STEP 4 *Find the maximum value*
Follow the graphing calculator's procedure to find the maximum of the function.

▶ The maximum value of the function $y = -2x^2 - 6x + 7$ is 11.5.

PRACTICE

Find the maximum or minimum value of the function.

1. $y = 3x^2 - 8x + 7$ $1\frac{2}{3}$

2. $y = -x^2 + 3x + 10$ **12.25**

3. $y = -4x^2 - 6x - 6$ **−3.75**

4. $y = 5x^2 + 10x - 8$ **−13**

5. $y = -1.4x^2 + 3.8x - 6.1$
   about **−3.5**

6. $y = 2.57x^2 - 8.45x - 5.04$ **about −12**

@HomeTutor
classzone.com
Keystrokes

EXAMPLE 2 Approximate the zeros of a function

Approximate the zeros of the function $y = 3x^2 + 2x - 4$.

STEP 1 *Enter the function*
Press **Y=** and enter the function
$y = 3x^2 + 2x - 4$.

STEP 2 *Adjust the window*
Display the graph. Adjust the viewing window as needed so that the x-intercepts of the parabola are visible.

STEP 3 *Use the zero feature*
The *zero* feature is under the CALCULATE menu.

STEP 4 *Find the zeros*
Follow the graphing calculator's procedure to find a zero of the function. Then repeat the process to find the other zero.

▶ The zeros are about -1.54 and about 0.87.

PRACTICE

Approximate the zeros of the quadratic function to the nearest hundredth.

7. $y = 2x^2 - 5x - 8$ **−1.11, 3.61**

8. $y = -3x^2 + 6x - 2$ **0.42, 1.58**

9. $y = -x^2 + 4x + 9$ **−1.61, 5.61**

10. $y = 4x^2 - 7x + 1$ **0.16, 1.59**

11. $y = -2.5x^2 + 7.7x - 4.9$ **0.90, 2.18**

12. $y = 1.56x^2 - 5.19x - 2.25$ **−0.39, 3.72**

13. $y = -0.82x^2 - 4x + 12.4$
    −7.03, 2.15

14. $y = 5.36x^2 + 17x + 2.67$
    −3.01, −0.17

DRAW CONCLUSIONS

15. If a quadratic function has only one zero, what is the maximum or minimum value of the function? *Explain.* **See margin.**

16. If a quadratic function has a maximum value that is greater than 0, how many zeros does the function have? *Explain.* **See margin.**

Extra Example 2
Approximate the zeros of the function $y = -2x^2 + 5x + 6$.   **−0.89, 3.39**

3 ASSESS AND RETEACH

1. If a quadratic function has a minimum value less than 0, how many zeros does the function have? Explain. **Two zeros; a minimum value means the parabola opens upward, and if it opens upward from a negative y-value, it must cross the x-axis in two points.**

2. If a quadratic function has a minimum value greater than 0, how many zeros does the function have? Explain. **No zeros; a minimum value means the parabola opens upward, and if it opens upward from a positive y-value, it does not cross the x-axis.**

15. 0; the maximum or minimum value of a quadratic function occurs at the vertex of the parabola that is the graph of the function. When a quadratic function has only one zero, its graph has only one x-intercept, which must also be the x-coordinate of the vertex of the parabola. Then the y-coordinate of the vertex is 0, so the maximum or minimum value of the function is 0.

16. 2; the graph of a quadratic function with a maximum value must open down. Because the maximum is greater than 0, the vertex of the parabola is above the x-axis; then, because the parabola opens down, it must cross the x-axis in two points. The two x-intercepts are the two zeros of the function.

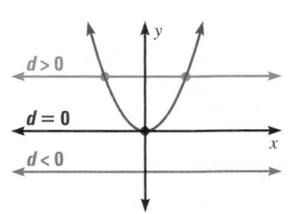

10.4 Use Square Roots to Solve Quadratic Equations

Before You solved a quadratic equation by graphing.

Now You will solve a quadratic equation by finding square roots.

Why? So you can solve a problem about a falling object, as in Example 5.

Key Vocabulary
• square root, p. 110
• perfect square, p. 111

To use square roots to solve a quadratic equation of the form $ax^2 + c = 0$, first isolate x^2 on one side to obtain $x^2 = d$. Then use the following information about the solutions of $x^2 = d$ to solve the equation.

READING
Recall that in this course, *solutions* refers to real-number solutions.

> **KEY CONCEPT** *For Your Notebook*
>
> **Solving $x^2 = d$ by Taking Square Roots**
>
> • If $d > 0$, then $x^2 = d$ has two solutions: $x = \pm\sqrt{d}$.
>
> • If $d = 0$, then $x^2 = d$ has one solution: $x = 0$.
>
> • If $d < 0$, then $x^2 = d$ has no solution.

EXAMPLE 1 Solve quadratic equations

Solve the equation.

a. $2x^2 = 8$ **b.** $m^2 - 18 = -18$ **c.** $b^2 + 12 = 5$

Solution

ANOTHER WAY
You can also use factoring to solve $2x^2 - 8 = 0$:
$$2x^2 - 8 = 0$$
$$2(x^2 - 4) = 0$$
$$2(x - 2)(x + 2) = 0$$
$$x = 2 \ or \ x = -2$$

a.
$2x^2 = 8$	Write original equation.
$x^2 = 4$	Divide each side by 2.
$x = \pm\sqrt{4} = \pm 2$	Take square roots of each side. Simplify.

▸ The solutions are −2 and 2.

b.
$m^2 - 18 = -18$	Write original equation.
$m^2 = 0$	Add 18 to each side.
$m = 0$	The square root of 0 is 0.

▸ The solution is 0.

c.
$b^2 + 12 = 5$	Write original equation.
$b^2 = -7$	Subtract 12 from each side.

▸ Negative real numbers do not have real square roots. So, there is no solution.

Resource Planning Guide

Chapter Resource Book
• Teaching Guide/Lesson Plan (pp. 46–47)
• Activity Master (p. 48)
• Practice levels A, B, C (pp. 49–51)
• Study Guide (pp. 52–53)
• Catch-up for Absent Students (p. 54)
• Problem Solving Workshop (p. 55)
• Challenge (p. 57)

Workbooks
• Notetaking Guide (pp. 230–232)
• Practice Workbook (pp. 158–159)

Teaching Options
• **Power Presentations CD-ROM** provides dynamic electronic teaching resources for the classroom.
• **Activity Generator CD-ROM** provides editable activities for all ability levels.

Interactive Technology
• Easy Planner
• Power Presentations CD-ROM
• Activity Generator CD-ROM
• Animated Algebra
• Test Generator CD-ROM
• Online Quiz
• eWorkbook
• eEdition
• @HomeTutor

Resources for English Learners
• Quick Reference for English Learners
• Spanish Study Guide
• Multi-Language Visual Glossary
• Student Resources in Spanish

See also the *Algebra 1 Toolkit* for more strategies for meeting individual needs.

SIMPLIFYING SQUARE ROOTS In cases where you need to take the square root of a fraction whose numerator and denominator are perfect squares, the radical can be written as a fraction. For example, $\sqrt{\frac{16}{25}}$ can be written as $\frac{4}{5}$ because $\left(\frac{4}{5}\right)^2 = \frac{16}{25}$.

EXAMPLE 2 Take square roots of a fraction

Solve $4z^2 = 9$.

Solution

$4z^2 = 9$	Write original equation.
$z^2 = \frac{9}{4}$	Divide each side by 4.
$z = \pm\sqrt{\frac{9}{4}}$	Take square roots of each side.
$z = \pm\frac{3}{2}$	Simplify.

▶ The solutions are $-\frac{3}{2}$ and $\frac{3}{2}$.

APPROXIMATING SQUARE ROOTS In cases where d in the equation $x^2 = d$ is not a perfect square or a fraction whose numerator and denominator are not perfect squares, you need to approximate the square root. A calculator can be used to find an approximation.

EXAMPLE 3 Approximate solutions of a quadratic equation

Solve $3x^2 - 11 = 7$. Round the solutions to the nearest hundredth.

Solution

$3x^2 - 11 = 7$	Write original equation.
$3x^2 = 18$	Add 11 to each side.
$x^2 = 6$	Divide each side by 3.
$x = \pm\sqrt{6}$	Take square roots of each side.
$x \approx \pm 2.45$	Use a calculator. Round to the nearest hundredth.

▶ The solutions are about -2.45 and about 2.45.

 GUIDED PRACTICE   for Examples 1, 2, and 3

Solve the equation.

1. $c^2 - 25 = 0$ ± 5
2. $5w^2 + 12 = -8$ **no solution**
3. $2x^2 + 11 = 11$ **0**
4. $25x^2 = 16$ $\pm\frac{4}{5}$
5. $9m^2 = 100$ $\pm\frac{10}{3}$
6. $49b^2 + 64 = 0$ **no solution**

Solve the equation. Round the solutions to the nearest hundredth.

7. $x^2 + 4 = 14$ ± 3.16
8. $3k^2 - 1 = 0$ ± 0.58
9. $2p^2 - 7 = 2$ ± 2.12

EXAMPLE 4 Solve a quadratic equation

Solve $6(x - 4)^2 = 42$. Round the solutions to the nearest hundredth.

$6(x - 4)^2 = 42$	Write original equation.
$(x - 4)^2 = 7$	Divide each side by 6.
$x - 4 = \pm\sqrt{7}$	Take square roots of each side.
$x = 4 \pm \sqrt{7}$	Add 4 to each side.

▶ The solutions are $4 + \sqrt{7} \approx 6.65$ and $4 - \sqrt{7} \approx 1.35$.

CHECK To check the solutions, first write the equation so that 0 is on one side as follows: $6(x - 4)^2 - 42 = 0$. Then graph the related function $y = 6(x - 4)^2 - 42$. The x-intercepts appear to be about 6.6 and about 1.3. So, each solution checks.

EXAMPLE 5 Solve a multi-step problem

ANOTHER WAY
For alternative methods for solving the problem in Example 5, turn to page 659 for the **Problem Solving Workshop**.

SPORTS EVENT During an ice hockey game, a remote-controlled blimp flies above the crowd and drops a numbered table-tennis ball. The number on the ball corresponds to a prize. Use the information in the diagram to find the amount of time that the ball is in the air.

45 ft

17 ft

Not drawn to scale

Solution

STEP 1 Use the vertical motion model to write an equation for the height h (in feet) of the ball as a function of time t (in seconds).

DETERMINE VELOCITY
When an object is dropped, it has an initial vertical velocity of 0 feet per second.

$h = -16t^2 + vt + s$	Vertical motion model
$h = -16t^2 + 0t + 45$	Substitute for v and s.

STEP 2 Find the amount of time the ball is in the air by substituting 17 for h and solving for t.

$h = -16t^2 + 45$	Write model.
$17 = -16t^2 + 45$	Substitute 17 for h.
$-28 = -16t^2$	Subtract 45 from each side.
$\dfrac{28}{16} = t^2$	Divide each side by -16.
$\sqrt{\dfrac{28}{16}} = t$	Take positive square root.
$1.32 \approx t$	Use a calculator.

INTERPRET SOLUTION
Because the time cannot be a negative number, ignore the negative square root.

▶ The ball is in the air for about 1.32 seconds.

Solve the equation. Round the solutions to the nearest hundredth, if necessary.

10. $2(x - 2)^2 = 18$ **−1, 5**   **11.** $4(q - 3)^2 = 28$ **0.35, 5.65**   **12.** $3(t + 5)^2 = 24$ **−7.83, −2.17**

13. WHAT IF? In Example 5, suppose the table-tennis ball is released 58 feet above the ground and is caught 12 feet above the ground. Find the amount of time that the ball is in the air. Round your answer to the nearest hundredth of a second. **1.70 sec**

10.4 **EXERCISES**

HOMEWORK KEY
○ = **WORKED-OUT SOLUTIONS**
on p. WS1 for Exs. 25 and 59

★ = **STANDARDIZED TEST PRACTICE**
Exs. 2, 15, 16, 29, 51, 52, 57, and 60

◆ = **MULTIPLE REPRESENTATIONS**
Ex. 62

SKILL PRACTICE

1. **VOCABULARY** Copy and complete: If $b^2 = a$, then b is a(n) __?__ of a. **square root**

2. ★ **WRITING** *Describe* two methods for solving a quadratic equation of the form $ax^2 + c = 0$. **(1) Graph the parabola $y = ax^2 + c$ and find its x-intercepts. (2) Write the equation in the form $x^2 = -\frac{c}{a}$ and take the square roots of each side.**

EXAMPLES 1 and 2
on pp. 652–653
for Exs. 3–16

SOLVING EQUATIONS Solve the equation.

3. $3x^2 - 3 = 0$ **±1**
4. $2x^2 - 32 = 0$ **±4**
5. $4x^2 - 400 = 0$ **±10**

6. $2m^2 - 42 = 8$ **±5**
7. $15d^2 = 0$ **0**
8. $a^2 + 8 = 3$ **no solution**

9. $4g^2 + 10 = 11$ **±$\frac{1}{2}$**
10. $2w^2 + 13 = 11$ **no solution**
11. $9q^2 - 35 = 14$ **±$\frac{7}{3}$**

12. $25b^2 + 11 = 15$ **±$\frac{2}{5}$**
13. $3z^2 - 18 = -18$ **0**
14. $5n^2 - 17 = -19$ **no solution**

15. ★ **MULTIPLE CHOICE** Which of the following is a solution of the equation $61 - 3n^2 = -14$? **A**

(A) 5   (B) 10   (C) 25   (D) 625

16. ★ **MULTIPLE CHOICE** Which of the following is a solution of the equation $13 - 36x^2 = -12$? **C**

(A) $-\frac{6}{5}$ (B) $\frac{1}{6}$ (C) $\frac{5}{6}$ (D) 5

EXAMPLE 3
on p. 653
for Exs. 17–29

APPROXIMATING SQUARE ROOTS Solve the equation. Round the solutions to the nearest hundredth.

17. $x^2 + 6 = 13$ **±2.65**
18. $x^2 + 11 = 24$ **±3.61**
19. $14 - x^2 = 17$ **no solution**

20. $2a^2 - 9 = 11$ **±3.16**
21. $4 - k^2 - 4$ **0**
22. $5 + 3p^2 = 38$ **±3.32**

23. $53 = 8 + 9m^2$ **±2.24**
24. $-21 = 15 - 2z^2$ **±4.24**
25. $7c^2 = 100$ **±3.78**

26. $5d^2 + 2 = 6$ **±0.89**
27. $4b^2 - 5 = 2$ **±1.32**
28. $9n^2 - 14 = -3$ **±1.11**

29. ★ **MULTIPLE CHOICE** The equation $17 - \frac{1}{4}x^2 = 12$ has a solution between which two integers? **D**

(A) 1 and 2   (B) 2 and 3   (C) 3 and 4   (D) 4 and 5

④ **PRACTICE AND APPLY**

Assignment Guide
◢ Answer Transparencies available for all exercises

Basic:
Day 1: pp. 655–658
Exs. 1–11, 15–25, 29
Day 2: pp. 655–658
Exs. 30–46, 56–60, 64–73

Average:
Day 1: pp. 655–658
Exs. 1, 2, 7–16, 21–29, 47–49
Day 2: pp. 655–658
Exs. 30–46, 50–52, 56–62, 64–72 even

Advanced:
Day 1: pp. 655–658
Exs. 1, 2, 8–16, 23–29, 47–52
Day 2: pp. 655–658
Exs. 32–46, 53–63*, 66, 70, 73

Block:
pp. 655–658
Exs. 1, 2, 7–16, 21–29, 47–49
(with 10.3)
pp. 655–658
Exs. 30–46, 50–52, 56–62, 64–72 even (with 10.5)

Differentiated Instruction
See *Algebra 1 Best Practices Toolkit* for suggestions on addressing the needs of a diverse classroom.

Homework Check
For a quick check of student understanding of key concepts, go over the following exercises:
Basic: 6, 11, 20, 33, 56
Average: 7, 12, 24, 36, 56
Advanced: 8, 13, 27, 38, 57

Extra Practice
• Student Edition, p. 947
• Chapter 10 Resource Book: Practice levels A, B, C, pp. 49–51

Practice Worksheet
An easily-readable reduced practice page (with answers) for this lesson can be found on p. 626C.

ERROR ANALYSIS *Describe* and correct the error in solving the equation.

30. $2x^2 - 54 = 18$

$$2x^2 - 54 = 18$$
$$2x^2 = 72$$
$$x^2 = 36$$
$$x = \sqrt{36}$$
$$x = 6$$

The solution is 6.

31. $7d^2 - 6 = -17$

$$7d^2 - 6 = -17$$
$$7d^2 = -11$$
$$d^2 = -\frac{11}{7}$$
$$d \approx \pm1.25$$

The solutions are about −1.25 and about 1.25.

SOLVING EQUATIONS Solve the equation. Round the solutions to the nearest hundredth.

32. $(x - 7)^2 = 6$ **4.55, 9.45**   **33.** $7(x - 3)^2 = 35$ **0.76, 5.24**   **34.** $6(x + 4)^2 = 18$ **−5.73, −2.27**

35. $20 = 2(m + 5)^2$ **−8.16, −1.84**   **36.** $5(a - 2)^2 = 70$ **−1.74, 5.74**   **37.** $21 = 3(z + 14)^2$ **−16.65, −11.**

38. $\frac{1}{2}(c - 8)^2 = 3$ **5.55, 10.45**   **39.** $\frac{3}{2}(n + 1)^2 = 33$ **−5.69, 3.69**   **40.** $\frac{4}{3}(k - 6)^2 = 20$ **2.13, 9.87**

B **SOLVING EQUATIONS** Solve the equation. Round the solutions to the nearest hundredth, if necessary.

41. $3x^2 - 35 = 45 - 2x^2$ **±4**   **42.** $42 = 3(x^2 + 5)$ **±3**   **43.** $11x^2 + 3 = 5(4x^2 - 3)$ **±1.41**

44. $\left(\frac{t - 5}{3}\right)^2 = 49$ **−16, 26**   **45.** $11\left(\frac{w - 7}{2}\right)^2 - 20 = 101$ **0.37, 13.63**   **46.** $(4m^2 - 6)^2 = 81$ **±1.94**

GEOMETRY Use the given area A of the circle to find the radius r or the diameter d to the nearest hundredth.

47. $A = 144\pi$ in.^{2} **12 in.**

48. $A = 21\pi$ m^2 **4.58 m**

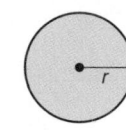

49. $A = 34\pi$ ft^2 **11.66 ft**

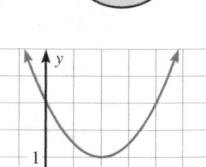

50. REASONING An equation of the graph shown is $y = \frac{1}{2}(x - 2)^2 + 1$. Two points on the parabola have y-coordinates of 9. Find the x-coordinates of these points. **−2, 6**

51. ★ **SHORT RESPONSE** Solve $x^2 = 1.44$ without using a calculator. *Explain* your reasoning. **See margin.**

52. ★ **OPEN-ENDED** Give values for a and c so that $ax^2 + c = 0$ has (a) two solutions, (b) one solution, and (c) no solution.
Sample answers are given. (a) 5, −1; (b) 3, 0; (c) 2, 4

C **CHALLENGE** Solve the equation without graphing.

53. $x^2 - 12x + 36 = 64$
−2, 14

54. $x^2 + 14x + 49 = 16$
−11, −3

55. $x^2 + 18x + 81 = 25$
−4, −14

EXAMPLE 5 [A]
on p. 654
for Exs. 56–57

56. **FALLING OBJECT** Fenway Park is a Major League Baseball park in Boston, Massachusetts. The park offers seats on top of the left field wall. A person sitting in one of these seats accidentally drops his sunglasses on the field. The height h (in feet) of the sunglasses can be modeled by the function $h = -16t^2 + 38$ where t is the time (in seconds) since the sunglasses were dropped. Find the time it takes for the sunglasses to reach the field. Round your answer to the nearest hundredth of a second. **1.54 sec**

@HomeTutor for problem solving help at classzone.com

57. ★ **MULTIPLE CHOICE** Which equation can be used to find the time it takes for an object to hit the ground after it was dropped from a height of 68 feet? **C**

Ⓐ $-16t^2 = 0$　　Ⓑ $-16t^2 - 68 = 0$　Ⓒ $-16t^2 + 68 = 0$　Ⓓ $-16t^2 = 68$

@HomeTutor for problem solving help at classzone.com

58. **INTERNET USAGE** For the period 1995–2001, the number y (in thousands) of Internet users worldwide can be modeled by the function $y = 12,697x^2 + 55,722$ where x is the number of years since 1995. Between which two years did the number of Internet users worldwide reach 100,000,000? **1996 and 1997**

59. **GEMOLOGY** To find the weight w (in carats) of round faceted gems, gemologists use the formula $w = 0.0018D^2 ds$ where D is the diameter (in millimeters) of the gem, d is the depth (in millimeters) of the gem, and s is the specific gravity of the gem. Find the diameter to the nearest tenth of a millimeter of each round faceted gem in the table.

	Gem	Weight (carats)	Depth (mm)	Specific gravity	Diameter (mm)	
a.	Amethyst	1	4.5	2.65	?	6.8 mm
b.	Diamond	1	4.5	3.52	?	5.9 mm
c.	Ruby	1	4.5	4.00	?	5.6 mm

[B] **60.** ★ **SHORT RESPONSE** In deep water, the speed s (in meters per second) of a series of waves and the wavelength L (in meters) of the waves are related by the equation $2\pi s^2 = 9.8L$.

Crest　　　　Crest
The wavelength L is the distance between one crest and the next.

a. Find the speed to the nearest hundredth of a meter per second of a series of waves with the following wavelengths: 6 meters, 10 meters, and 25 meters. (Use 3.14 for π.) **3.06 m/sec, 3.95 m/sec, 6.25 m/sec**

b. Does the speed of a series of waves increase or decrease as the wavelength of the waves increases? *Explain.* **Increase; as the wavelength in part (a) increased, respective speeds increased.**

10.4　Use Square Roots to Solve Quadratic Equations　**657**

 Internet Reference

Exercise 56 Additional information about Fenway Park can be found at redsox.mlb.com/NASApp/mlb/bos/ballpark/bos_ballpark_history.jsp

Teaching Strategy

Exercises 56–57 Before assigning these exercises, you may want to discuss how they are similar. Ask students to identify the value of h in Exercise 56 and explain what "+ 38" represents in the function. Then have them identify similar values in Exercise 57. Ask students how they can use these similarities to identify the correct solution to Exercise 57.

61. MULTI-STEP PROBLEM The Doyle log rule is a formula used to estimate the amount of lumber that can be sawn from logs of various sizes. The amount of lumber V (in board feet) is given by $V = \dfrac{L(D-4)^2}{16}$ where L is the length (in feet) of a log and D is the small-end diameter (in inches) of the log.

Diameter
Boards

a. Solve the formula for D. $D = 4 \pm \sqrt{\dfrac{16V}{L}}$

b. Use the rewritten formula to find the diameters, to the nearest tenth of a foot, of logs that will yield 50 board feet and have the following lengths: 16 feet, 18 feet, 20 feet, and 22 feet.   **11.1 ft, 10.7 ft, 10.3 ft, 10.0 ft**

62. ◆ MULTIPLE REPRESENTATIONS A ride at an amusement park lifts seated riders 250 feet above the ground. Then the riders are dropped. They experience free fall until the brakes are activated at 105 feet above the ground.

a. Writing an Equation Use the vertical motion model to write an equation for the height h (in feet) of the riders as a function of the time t (in seconds) into the free fall. $h = -16t^2 + 250$

b. Making a Table Make a table that shows the height of the riders after 0, 1, 2, 3, and 4 seconds. Use the table to estimate the amount of time the riders experience free fall.   **See margin for table; about 3 sec.**

c. Solving an Equation Use the equation to find the amount of time, to the nearest tenth of a second, that the riders experience free fall.   **3.0 sec**

Ⓒ **63. CHALLENGE** The height h (in feet) of a dropped object on any planet can be modeled by $h = -\dfrac{g}{2}t^2 + s$ where g is the acceleration (in feet per second per second) due to the planet's gravity, t is the time (in seconds) after the object is dropped, and s is the initial height (in feet) of the object. Suppose the same object is dropped from the same height on Earth and Mars. Given that g is 32 feet per second per second on Earth and 12 feet per second per second on Mars, on which planet will the object hit the ground first? *Explain.*   **See margin.**

MIXED REVIEW

PREVIEW
Prepare for Lesson 10.5 in Exs. 64–67.

Evaluate the power. *(p. 2)*

64. $\left(\dfrac{5}{2}\right)^2$ $\dfrac{25}{4}$ **65.** $\left(\dfrac{9}{5}\right)^2$ $\dfrac{81}{25}$ **66.** $\left(\dfrac{3}{4}\right)^2$ $\dfrac{9}{16}$ **67.** $\left(\dfrac{7}{2}\right)^2$ $\dfrac{49}{4}$

Write an equation of the line with the given slope and y-intercept. *(p. 283)*

68. slope: -9
y-intercept: 11
$y = -9x + 11$

69. slope: 7
y-intercept: -7
$y = 7x - 7$

70. slope: 3
y-intercept: -2
$y = 3x - 2$

Write an equation of the line that passes through the given point and is perpendicular to the given line. *(p. 319)*

71. $(1, -1)$, $y = 2x$
$y = -\dfrac{1}{2}x - \dfrac{1}{2}$

72. $(0, 8)$, $y = 4x + 1$
$y = -\dfrac{1}{4}x + 8$

73. $(-9, -4)$, $y = -3x + 6$
$y = \dfrac{1}{3}x - 1$

Using ALTERNATIVE METHODS

Another Way to Solve Example 5, page 654

MULTIPLE REPRESENTATIONS In Example 5 on page 654, you saw how to solve a problem about a dropped table-tennis ball by using a square root. You can also solve the problem by using factoring or by using a table.

PROBLEM

SPORTS EVENT During an ice hockey game, a remote-controlled blimp flies above the crowd and drops a numbered table-tennis ball. The number on the ball corresponds to a prize. Use the information in the diagram to find the amount of time that the ball is in the air.

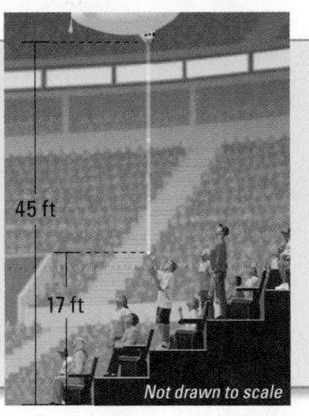

45 ft

17 ft

Not drawn to scale

METHOD 1

Using Factoring One alternative approach is to use factoring.

STEP 1 **Write** an equation for the height h (in feet) of the ball as a function of time t (in seconds) after it is dropped using the vertical motion model.

$h = -16t^2 + vt + s$ **Vertical motion model**

$h = -16t^2 + 0t + 45$ **Substitute 0 for v and 45 for s.**

STEP 2 **Substitute** 17 for h to find the time it takes the ball to reach a height of 17 feet. Then write the equation so that 0 is on one side.

$17 = -16t^2 + 45$ **Substitute 17 for h.**

$0 = -16t^2 + 28$ **Subtract 17 from each side.**

STEP 3 **Solve** the equation by factoring. Replace 28 with the closest perfect square, 25, so that the right side of the equation is factorable as a difference of two squares.

> **USE AN APPROXIMATION**
> By replacing 28 with 25, you will obtain an answer that is an approximation of the amount of time that the ball is in the air.

$0 = -16t^2 + 25$ **Use 25 as an approximation for 28.**

$0 = -(16t^2 - 25)$ **Factor out -1.**

$0 = -(4t - 5)(4t + 5)$ **Difference of two squares pattern**

$4t - 5 = 0 \ \ or \ \ 4t + 5 = 0$ **Zero-product property**

$t = \dfrac{5}{4} \ \ or \ \ t = -\dfrac{5}{4}$ **Solve for t.**

▶ The ball is in the air about $\dfrac{5}{4}$, or 1.25, seconds.

Alternative Strategy

Example 5 on page 654 can be solved by using factoring or by using a table. You may want to point out that these alternative strategies do not give the same exact result as the vertical motion model, though the results are close for all three methods. Stress that all three methods give an approximation, and that they all round to 1.3 seconds. Point out that each strategy can be used to check a solution found by using a different strategy.

Avoiding Common Errors

In Method 1, watch for students who use a perfect square that is not closest to 28. Suggest that students list the perfect squares on each side of 28 to make sure they choose the closest one.

p. 658

63. Earth; on Earth the fraction $-\dfrac{g}{2}$ is $-\dfrac{32}{2} = -16$, and on Mars the fraction $-\dfrac{g}{2}$ is $-\dfrac{12}{2} = -6$; so, on Earth the height of the object is modeled by $h = -16t^2 + s$ and on Mars the height of the object is modeled by $h = -6t^2 + s$. To compare how long it takes the same object dropped from the same height s to hit the ground on each planet, substitute 0 for h in each equation and solve for t in terms of s (disregard any negative solutions). Earth's equation:

$0 = -16t^2 + s; 16t^2 = s; t^2 = \dfrac{s}{16}$;

$t = \sqrt{\dfrac{s}{16}} = \dfrac{\sqrt{s}}{\sqrt{16}}$, or $t = \dfrac{\sqrt{s}}{4}$. Mars's

equation: $0 = -6t^2 + s; 6t^2 = s$;

$t^2 = \dfrac{s}{6}; t = \sqrt{\dfrac{s}{6}} = \dfrac{\sqrt{s}}{\sqrt{6}}$, or $t \approx \dfrac{\sqrt{s}}{2.45}$.

Because $4 > 2.45$, $\dfrac{1}{4} < \dfrac{1}{2.45}$, and

$\dfrac{\sqrt{s}}{4} < \dfrac{\sqrt{s}}{2.45}$; thus, it takes less time for the object to hit the ground on Earth than on Mars.

METHOD 2   **Using a Table** Another approach is to make and use a table.

STEP 1 **Make** a table that shows the height h (in feet) of the ball by substituting values for time t (in seconds) in the function $h = -16t^2 + 45$. Use increments of 1 second.

Time t (seconds)	Height h (feet)
0	45
1	29
2	−19

STEP 2 **Identify** the time interval in which the height of the ball is 17 feet. This happens between 1 and 2 seconds.

STEP 3 **Make** a second table using increments of 0.1 second to get a closer approximation.

Time t (seconds)	Height h (feet)
1.0	29.00
1.1	25.64
1.2	21.96
1.3	**17.96**
1.4	13.64

▸ The ball is in the air about 1.3 seconds.

PRACTICE

1. **WHAT IF?** In the problem on page 659, suppose the ball is caught at a height of 10 feet. For how many seconds is the ball in the air? Solve this problem using two different methods. **See margin.**

2. **OPEN-ENDED** *Describe* a problem about a dropped object. Then solve the problem and explain what your solution means in this situation. **See margin.**

3. **GEOMETRY** The box below is a rectangular prism with the dimensions shown.

a. Write an equation that gives the volume V (in cubic inches) of the box as a function of x. $V = 25x^2$

b. The volume of the box is 83 cubic inches. Find the dimensions of the box. Use factoring to solve the problem.   **b–c. See margin.**

c. Make a table to check your answer from part (b).

4. **TRAPEZE** You are learning how to perform on a trapeze. While hanging from a still trapeze bar, your shoe comes loose and falls to a safety net that is 6 feet off the ground. If your shoe falls from a height of 54 feet, how long does it take your shoe to hit the net? Choose any method for solving the problem. Show your steps. **See margin.**

5. **ERROR ANALYSIS** A student solved the problem in Exercise 4 as shown below. *Describe* and correct the error. **See margin.**

> Let t be the time (in seconds) that the shoe is in the air.
>
> $6 = -16t^2 + 54$
> $0 = -16t^2 + 60$
>
> Replace 60 with the closest perfect square, 64.
>
> $0 = -16t^2 + 64$
> $0 = -16(t - 2)(t + 2)$
> $t = 2$ or $t = -2$
>
> It takes about 2 seconds.

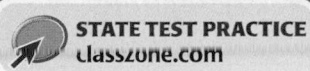
Lessons 10.1–10.4

1. **MULTI-STEP PROBLEM** A company's yearly profits from 1996 to 2006 can be modeled by the function $y = x^2 - 8x + 80$ where y is the profit (in thousands of dollars) and x is the number of years since 1996.

   a. In what year did the company experience its lowest yearly profit? **2000**

   b. What was the lowest yearly profit? **$64,000**

2. **MULTI-STEP PROBLEM** Use the rectangle below.

   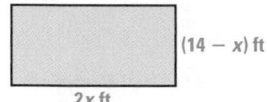

   (14 − x) ft

   2x ft

   a. Find the value of x that gives the greatest possible area of the rectangle. **7**

   b. What is the greatest possible area of the rectangle? **98 ft²**

3. **EXTENDED RESPONSE** You throw a lacrosse ball twice using a lacrosse stick. **a–c. See margin.**

   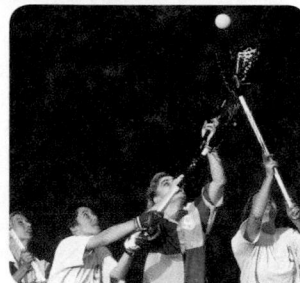

   a. For your first throw, the ball is released 8 feet above the ground with an initial vertical velocity of 35 feet per second. Use the vertical motion model to write an equation for the height h (in feet) of the ball as a function of time t (in seconds).

   b. For your second throw, the ball is released 7 feet above the ground with an initial vertical velocity of 45 feet per second. Use the vertical motion model to write an equation for the height h (in feet) of the ball as a function of time t (in seconds).

   c. If no one catches either throw, for which throw is the ball in the air longer? *Explain*.

4. **OPEN-ENDED** Describe a real-world situation of an object being dropped. Then write an equation that models the height of the object as a function of time. Use the equation to determine the time it takes the object to hit the ground. **See margin.**

5. **SHORT RESPONSE** A football player is attempting a field goal. The path of the kicked football can be modeled by the graph of $y = -0.03x^2 + 1.8x$ where x is the horizontal distance (in yards) traveled by the football and y is the corresponding height (in feet) of the football. Will the football pass over the goal post that is 10 feet above the ground and 45 yards away? *Explain*. **See margin.**

6. **GRIDDED ANSWER** The force F (in newtons) a rider feels while a train goes around a curve is given by $F = \dfrac{mv^2}{r}$ where m is the mass (in kilograms) of the rider, v is the velocity (in meters per second) of the train, and r is the radius (in meters) of the curve. A rider with a mass of 75 kilograms experiences a force of 18,150 newtons, while going around a curve that has a radius of 8 meters. Find the velocity (in meters per second) the train travels around the curve. **44 m/sec**

7. **SHORT RESPONSE** The opening of the tunnel shown can be modeled by the graph of the equation $y = -0.18x^2 + 4.4x - 12$ where x and y are measured in feet. **a, b. See margin.**

   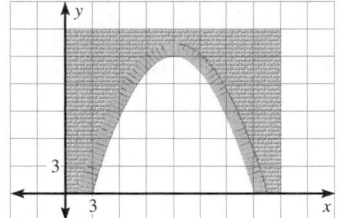

   a. Find the maximum height of the tunnel.

   b. A semi trailer is 7.5 feet wide, and the top of the trailer is 10.5 feet above the ground. Given that traffic travels one way on one lane through the center of the tunnel, will the semi trailer fit through the opening of the tunnel? *Explain*.

3a. $h = -16t^2 + 35t + 8$

3b. $h = -16t^2 + 45t + 7$

3c. The second throw; when the ball lands back on the ground, $h = 0$. To find the time t when $h = 0$ for the first throw, solve $0 = -16t^2 + 35t + 8$; $t \approx 2.40$ seconds (disregard the negative solution). To find the time t when $h = 0$ for the second throw, solve $0 = -16t^2 + 45t + 7$; $t \approx 2.96$ seconds (disregard the negative solution). The second throw is in the air longer.

4. *Sample answer:* **A pine cone hanging on a branch 20 feet above the ground drops off the branch; $h = -16t^2 + 20$; $t =$ about 1.1 seconds.**

5. Yes; to find the height of the football 45 yards from where it was kicked, find the value of y when $x = 45$: $y = -0.03(45^2) + 1.8(45) = 20.25$ feet. The ball will be above the 10-foot high goal post.

7a. about 15 ft

7b. Yes; since the trailer is 7.5 feet wide, the height of the tunnel must be at least 10.5 feet high 3.75 units to the left and right of the axis of symmetry, $x = 12\frac{2}{9}$. Find the height of the tunnel at these points to be about 12.4 feet, which is higher than the height of the truck, so the truck will fit.

1 PLAN AND PREPARE

Explore the Concept

- Students will use algebra tiles to complete the square.
- This activity leads into the study of completing the square in Lesson 10.5, Example 1.

Materials

Each student will need:
- algebra tiles
- Activity Support Master (*Chapter 10 Resource Book*, p. 60)

Recommended Time

Work activity: 10 min

Discuss results: 5 min

Grouping

Students should work individually.

2 TEACH

Tips for Success

Make sure that the tiles in Step 2 are arranged to form a square.

An **Animated Algebra** activity is available on-line. This activity is also available on the **Power Presentations CD-ROM**.

Key Discovery

You can complete the square for an expression in the form of $x^2 + bx$ by adding the square of one-half the value of b.

3 ASSESS AND RETEACH

Predict the number of 1-tiles needed to complete the square for each expression.

1. $x^2 + 2x$ **1**

2. $x^2 + 12x$ **36**

10.5 Completing the Square Using Algebra Tiles

MATERIALS · algebra tiles

QUESTION How can you use algebra tiles to complete the square?

For an expression of the form $x^2 + bx$, you can add a constant c to the expression so that the expression $x^2 + bx + c$ is a perfect square trinomial. This process is called *completing the square*.

EXPLORE Complete the square

Find the value of c that makes $x^2 + 4x + c$ a perfect square trinomial.

STEP 1 *Model expression*	STEP 2 *Rearrange tiles*	STEP 3 *Complete the square*
Use algebra tiles to model the expression $x^2 + 4x$. You will need one x^2-tile and four x-tiles for this expression.	Arrange the tiles to form a square. The arrangement will be incomplete in one of the corners.	Determine the number of 1-tiles needed to complete the square. The number of 1-tiles is the value of c. So, the perfect square trinomial is $x^2 + 4x + 4$ or $(x + 2)^2$.

DRAW CONCLUSIONS Use your observations to complete these exercises

1. Copy and complete the table using algebra tiles.

Expression	Number of 1-tiles needed to complete the square	Expression written as a square
$x^2 + 4x$	4	$x^2 + 4x + 4 = (x + 2)^2$
$x^2 + 6x$	? **9**	?
$x^2 + 8x$	? **16**	?
$x^2 + 10x$	? **25**	?

$x^2 + 6x + 9 = (x + 3)^2$

$x^2 + 8x + 16 = (x + 4)^2$

$x^2 + 10x + 25 = (x + 5)^2$

2. In the statement $x^2 + bx + c = (x + d)^2$, how are b and d related? How are c and d related? **$b = 2d$; $c = d^2$**

3. Use your answer to Exercise 2 to predict the number of 1-tiles you would need to add to complete the square for the expression $x^2 + 18x$. **81 1–tiles**

10.5 Solve Quadratic Equations by Completing the Square

Before	You solved quadratic equations by finding square roots.
Now	You will solve quadratic equations by completing the square.
Why?	So you can solve a problem about snowboarding, as in Ex. 50.

Key Vocabulary
- **completing the square**
- **perfect square trinomial**, *p. 601*

For an expression of the form $x^2 + bx$, you can add a constant c to the expression so that the expression $x^2 + bx + c$ is a perfect square trinomial. This process is called **completing the square**.

KEY CONCEPT   *For Your Notebook*

Completing the Square

Words To complete the square for the expression $x^2 + bx$, add the square of half the coefficient of the term bx.

Algebra $x^2 + bx + \left(\dfrac{b}{2}\right)^2 = \left(x + \dfrac{b}{2}\right)^2$

EXAMPLE 1   **Complete the square**

Find the value of c that makes the expression $x^2 + 5x + c$ a perfect square trinomial. Then write the expression as the square of a binomial.

STEP 1 **Find** the value of c. For the expression to be a perfect square trinomial, c needs to be the square of half the coefficient of bx.

$$c = \left(\frac{5}{2}\right)^2 = \frac{25}{4}$$ Find the square of half the coefficient of *bx*.

STEP 2 **Write** the expression as a perfect square trinomial. Then write the expression as the square of a binomial.

$$x^2 + 5x + c = x^2 + 5x + \frac{25}{4}$$ Substitute $\frac{25}{4}$ for *c*.

$$= \left(x + \frac{5}{2}\right)^2$$ Square of a binomial

 GUIDED PRACTICE   for Example 1

Find the value of c that makes the expression a perfect square trinomial. Then write the expression as the square of a binomial.

1. $x^2 + 8x + c$
   $16; (x + 4)^2$

2. $x^2 - 12x + c$
   $36; (x - 6)^2$

3. $x^2 + 3x + c$
   $\frac{9}{4}; \left(x + \frac{3}{2}\right)^2$

① PLAN AND PREPARE

Warm-Up Exercises

🗏 **Transparency Available**

Evaluate the expression.

1. $\left(\dfrac{2}{3}\right)^2$ $\dfrac{4}{9}$

2. $\left(\dfrac{7}{5}\right)^2$ $\dfrac{49}{25}$

3. An acorn falls to the ground from a height of 25 feet. How long was the acorn in the air? **1.25 sec**

Notetaking Guide

🗏 **Transparency Available**

Promotes interactive learning and notetaking skills, pp. 233–235.

Pacing

Basic: 2 days
Average: 2 days
Advanced: 2 days
Block: 0.5 block with 10.4
         0.5 block with 10.6
- See *Teaching Guide/Lesson Plan*.

② FOCUS AND MOTIVATE

Essential Question

Big Idea 2, p. 627

How do you solve a quadratic equation by completing the square? **Tell students they will learn how to answer this question by adding a value to each side of the equation so one side is a perfect square trinomial.**

NCTM STANDARDS

Standard 2: Understand patterns; Analyze situations using algebraic symbols

Resource Planning Guide

Chapter Resource Book
- Teaching Guide/Lesson Plan (pp. 58–59)
- Practice levels A, B, C (pp. 61–63)
- Study Guide (pp. 64–65)
- Catch-up for Absent Students (p. 66)
- Application (p. 67)
- Challenge (p. 68)

Workbooks
- Notetaking Guide (pp. 233–235)
- Practice Workbook (pp. 160–161)

Teaching Options
- **Power Presentations CD-ROM** provides dynamic electronic teaching resources for the classroom.
- **Activity Generator CD-ROM** provides editable activities for all ability levels.

Interactive Technology
- Easy Planner
- Power Presentations CD-ROM
- Activity Generator CD-ROM
- Animated Algebra
- Test Generator CD-ROM
- Online Quiz
- eWorkbook
- eEdition
- @HomeTutor

Resources for English Learners
- Quick Reference for English Learners
- Spanish Study Guide
- Multi-Language Visual Glossary
- Student Resources in Spanish

See also the *Algebra 1 Toolkit* for more strategies for meeting individual needs.

Motivating the Lesson

You want to put a mat frame around a photograph. You know the outside dimensions of the mat and you know the area of the photograph. You can write an equation to model this situation, and solve it to find the width of the mat frame.

❸ TEACH

Extra Example 1

Find the value of c that makes the expression $x^2 + 7x + c$ a perfect square trinomial. Then write the expression as the square of a binomial. $\frac{49}{4}; \left(x + \frac{7}{2}\right)^2$

Key Question to Ask for Example 1

• What is a perfect square trinomial? **A perfect square trinomial can be written in the form of $(a + b)^2$ or $(a - b)^2$.**

Extra Example 2

Solve $x^2 + 6x = 7$ by completing the square. $(x + 3)^2 = 16; -7, 1$

Key Question to Ask for Example 2

• What is the value of $\left(\frac{b}{2}\right)^2$? **64**

Extra Example 3

Solve $3x^2 + 12x - 18 = 0$ by completing the square. $(x + 2)^2 = 10;$ $-2 + \sqrt{10} \approx 1.16, -2 - \sqrt{10} \approx -5.16$

EXAMPLE 2 Solve a quadratic equation

Solve $x^2 - 16x = -15$ by completing the square.

Solution

AVOID ERRORS
When completing the square to solve an equation, be sure you add the term $\left(\frac{b}{2}\right)^2$ to both sides of the equation.

$x^2 - 16x = -15$	Write original equation.
$x^2 - 16x + (-8)^2 = -15 + (-8)^2$	Add $\left(\frac{-16}{2}\right)^2$, or $(-8)^2$, to each side.
$(x - 8)^2 = -15 + (-8)^2$	Write left side as the square of a binomial.
$(x - 8)^2 = 49$	Simplify the right side.
$x - 8 = \pm 7$	Take square roots of each side.
$x = 8 \pm 7$	Add 8 to each side.

▶ The solutions of the equation are $8 + 7 = 15$ and $8 - 7 = 1$.

CHECK You can check the solutions in the original equation.

If $x = 15$:	If $x = 1$:
$(15)^2 - 16(15) \overset{?}{=} -15$	$(1)^2 - 16(1) \overset{?}{=} -15$
$-15 = -15$ ✓	$-15 = -15$ ✓

EXAMPLE 3 Solve a quadratic equation in standard form

Solve $2x^2 + 20x - 8 = 0$ by completing the square.

Solution

AVOID ERRORS
Be sure that the coefficient of x^2 is 1 before you complete the square.

$2x^2 + 20x - 8 = 0$	Write original equation.
$2x^2 + 20x = 8$	Add 8 to each side.
$x^2 + 10x = 4$	Divide each side by 2.
$x^2 + 10x + 5^2 = 4 + 5^2$	Add $\left(\frac{10}{2}\right)^2$, or 5^2, to each side.
$(x + 5)^2 = 29$	Write left side as the square of a binomial.
$x + 5 = \pm\sqrt{29}$	Take square roots of each side.
$x = -5 \pm \sqrt{29}$	Subtract 5 from each side.

▶ The solutions are $-5 + \sqrt{29} \approx 0.39$ and $-5 - \sqrt{29} \approx -10.39$.

✓ **GUIDED PRACTICE** for Examples 2 and 3

Solve the equation by completing the square. Round your solutions to the nearest hundredth, if necessary.

4. $x^2 - 2x = 3$ **−1, 3**

5. $m^2 + 10m = -8$ **−9.12, −0.88**

6. $3g^2 - 24g + 27 = 0$ **1.35, 6.65**

664   Chapter 10   Quadratic Equations and Functions

Differentiated Instruction

Below Level The exercises in this lesson provides numerous places where students can make calculation errors, so encourage them to use their graphing calculators to check their solutions. After they enter and graph an equation, have them check the x-intercepts or the zeros of the function. If the solutions do not check, have them go over their calculations to discover and correct the error. Encourage students to think of their graphing calculators as a way to check their answers and to find and correct errors.

See also the *Algebra 1 Toolkit* for more strategies.

EXAMPLE 4   **Solve a multi-step problem**

CRAFTS You decide to use chalkboard paint to create a chalkboard on a door. You want the chalkboard to have a uniform border as shown. You have enough chalkboard paint to cover 6 square feet. Find the width of the border to the nearest inch.

Width of border, x ft

7 ft

Chalkboard

3 ft

Solution

STEP 1   **Write** a verbal model. Then write an equation. Let x be the width (in feet) of the border.

Area of chalkboard (square feet)	=	Length of chalkboard (feet)	·	Width of chalkboard (feet)
6	=	$(7 - 2x)$	·	$(3 - 2x)$

WRITE EQUATION
The width of the border is subtracted twice because it is at the top and the bottom of the door, as well as at the left and the right.

STEP 2   **Solve** the equation.

$6 = (7 - 2x)(3 - 2x)$	Write equation.
$6 = 21 - 20x + 4x^2$	Multiply binomials.
$-15 = 4x^2 - 20x$	Subtract 21 from each side.
$-\dfrac{15}{4} = x^2 - 5x$	Divide each side by 4.
$-\dfrac{15}{4} + \dfrac{25}{4} = x^2 - 5x + \dfrac{25}{4}$	Add $\left(-\dfrac{5}{2}\right)^2$, or $\dfrac{25}{4}$, to each side.
$-\dfrac{15}{4} + \dfrac{25}{4} = \left(x - \dfrac{5}{2}\right)^2$	Write right side as the square of a binomial.
$\dfrac{5}{2} = \left(x - \dfrac{5}{2}\right)^2$	Simplify left side.
$\pm\sqrt{\dfrac{5}{2}} = x - \dfrac{5}{2}$	Take square roots of each side.
$\dfrac{5}{2} \pm \sqrt{\dfrac{5}{2}} = x$	Add $\dfrac{5}{2}$ to each side.

The solutions of the equation are $\dfrac{5}{2} + \sqrt{\dfrac{5}{2}} \approx 4.08$ and $\dfrac{5}{2} - \sqrt{\dfrac{5}{2}} \approx 0.92$.

It is not possible for the width of the border to be 4.08 feet because the width of the door is 3 feet. So, the width of the border is 0.92 foot. Convert 0.92 foot to inches.

$$0.92 \text{ ft} \cdot \frac{12 \text{ in.}}{1 \text{ ft}} = 11.04 \text{ in.}\qquad \textbf{Multiply by conversion factor.}$$

▶ The width of the border should be about 11 inches.

✓   **GUIDED PRACTICE**   for Example 4

7. **WHAT IF?** In Example 4, suppose you have enough chalkboard paint to cover 4 square feet. Find the width of the border to the nearest inch. **13 in.**

10.5   Solve Quadratic Equations by Completing the Square   **665**

Differentiated Instruction

Kinesthetic Learners As you begin **Example 4**, have students sketch scale models of the chalkboard using 1 inch equal to 1 foot. Then have them vary the width of the border and calculate the corresponding areas. This will help students get an idea of what the width of the border should be.

See also the *Algebra 1 Toolkit* for more strategies.

Extra Example 4
You are designing an herb garden with a uniform border of ornamental grass around it as shown. Your design includes 10 square feet for the herb garden. Find the width of the grass border to the nearest inch. **20 in.**

x

x 10 ft^2 x 6 ft

x

7 ft

Key Questions to Ask for Example 4
• Why do you divide each side of the equation by 4? **You want the leading coefficient to be 1.**
• How can you check that your solution is correct? **You can substitute the solution for x in the original equation.**

Closing the Lesson
Have students summarize the major points of the lesson and answer the Essential Question: How do you solve a quadratic equation by completing the square?
• Starting with an expression in the form $x^2 + bx$, you can add a constant $c = \left(\dfrac{b}{2}\right)^2$ to the expression so that $x^2 + bx + c$ is a perfect square trinomial.
To complete the square, write the equation in the form $x^2 + bx = d$. Add $\left(\dfrac{b}{2}\right)^2$ to each side so that one side is $x^2 + bx + \left(\dfrac{b}{2}\right)^2$ or $\left(x + \dfrac{b}{2}\right)^2$. Then take the square root of each side and solve for x.

665

HOMEWORK KEY

○ = **WORKED-OUT SOLUTIONS**
on p. WS1 for Exs. 19 and 47

★ = **STANDARDIZED TEST PRACTICE**
Exs. 2, 24, 25, 42, and 49

◆ = **MULTIPLE REPRESENTATIONS**
Ex. 47

4 PRACTICE AND APPLY

Assignment Guide

📄 Answer Transparencies available for all exercises

Basic:
Day 1: EP p. 946 Exs. 13–18
pp. 666–668
Exs. 1–23
Day 2: pp. 666–668
Exs. 24–33, 45–48, 52–64 even

Average:
Day 1: pp. 666–668
Exs. 1, 2, 5–11, 15–23, 28–33
Day 2: pp. 666–668
Exs. 24–27, 34–42, 45–50, 55–58, 62

Advanced:
Day 1: pp. 666–668
Exs. 1, 7–11, 18–25, 28–36
Day 2: pp. 666–668
Exs. 37–51*, 56, 57, 60, 63, 64

Block:
pp. 666–668
Exs. 1, 2, 5–11, 15–23, 28–33
(with 10.4)
pp. 666–668
Exs. 24–27, 34–42, 45–50, 55–58, 62 (with 10.6)

Differentiated Instruction

See *Algebra 1 Best Practices Toolkit* for suggestions on addressing the needs of a diverse classroom.

Homework Check

For a quick check of student understanding of key concepts, go over the following exercises:
Basic: 6, 14, 17, 28, 45
Average: 8, 18, 21, 34, 46
Advanced: 10, 20, 22, 38, 46

Extra Practice

• Student Edition, p. 947
• Chapter 10 Resource Book:
Practice levels A, B, C, pp. 61–63

Practice Worksheet

An easily-readable reduced practice page (with answers) for this lesson can be found on p. 626C.

SKILL PRACTICE

A 1. **VOCABULARY** Copy and complete: The process of writing an expression of the form $x^2 + bx$ as a perfect square trinomial is called __?__. **completing the square**

2. ★ **WRITING** Give an example of an expression that is a perfect square trinomial. *Explain* why the expression is a perfect square trinomial.
Sample answer: $x^2 + 14x + 49$; 49 is half of 14 squared, which makes it a perfect square trinomial.

EXAMPLE 1
on p. 663
for Exs. 3–11

COMPLETING THE SQUARE Find the value of c that makes the expression a perfect square trinomial. Then write the expression as the square of a binomial.

3. $x^2 + 6x + c$ **9; $(x + 3)^2$**　　4. $x^2 + 12x + c$ **36; $(x + 6)^2$**　　5. $x^2 - 4x + c$ **4; $(x - 2)^2$**

6. $x^2 - 8x + c$ **16; $(x - 4)^2$**　　7. $x^2 - 3x + c$ **$\frac{9}{4}$; $\left(x - \frac{3}{2}\right)^2$**　　8. $x^2 + 5x + c$ **$\frac{25}{4}$, $\left(x + \frac{5}{2}\right)^2$**

9. $x^2 + 2.4x + c$ **1.44; $(x + 1.2)^2$** 10. $x^2 - \frac{1}{2}x + c$ **$\frac{1}{16}$; $\left(x - \frac{1}{4}\right)^2$** 11. $x^2 - \frac{4}{3}x + c$ **$\frac{4}{9}$; $\left(x - \frac{2}{3}\right)^2$**

EXAMPLES 2 and 3
on p. 664
for Exs. 12–27

SOLVING EQUATIONS Solve the equation by completing the square. Round your solutions to the nearest hundredth, if necessary.

12. $x^2 + 2x = 3$ **−3, 1**　　13. $x^2 + 10x = 24$ **−12, 2**　　14. $c^2 - 14c = 15$ **−1, 15**

15. $n^2 - 6n = 72$ **−6, 12**　　16. $a^2 - 8a + 15 = 0$ **3, 5**　　17. $y^2 + 4y - 21 = 0$ **−7, 3**

18. $w^2 - 5w = \frac{11}{4}$ **−0.5, 5.5** ⑲ $z^2 + 11z = -\frac{21}{4}$ **−10.5, −0.5** 20. $g^2 - \frac{2}{3}g = 7$ **−2.33, 3**

21. $k^2 - 8k - 7 = 0$ **−0.80, 8.80**　　22. $v^2 - 7v + 1 = 0$ **0.15, 6.85**　　23. $m^2 + 3m + \frac{5}{4} = 0$ **−2.5, −0.5**

24. ★ **MULTIPLE CHOICE** What are the solutions of $4x^2 + 16x = 9$? **C**

　　Ⓐ $-\frac{1}{2}, -\frac{9}{2}$　　　Ⓑ $-\frac{1}{2}, \frac{9}{2}$　　　Ⓒ $\frac{1}{2}, -\frac{9}{2}$　　　Ⓓ $\frac{1}{2}, \frac{9}{2}$

25. ★ **MULTIPLE CHOICE** What are the solutions of $x^2 + 12x + 10 = 0$? **B**

　　Ⓐ $-6 \pm \sqrt{46}$　　　Ⓑ $-6 \pm \sqrt{26}$　　　Ⓒ $6 \pm \sqrt{26}$　　　Ⓓ $6 \pm \sqrt{46}$

ERROR ANALYSIS *Describe* and correct the error in solving the given equation. **26, 27. See margin.**

26. $x^2 - 14x = 11$

$$x^2 - 14x = 11$$
$$x^2 - 14x + 49 = 11$$
$$(x - 7)^2 = 11$$
$$x - 7 = \pm\sqrt{11}$$
$$x = 7 \pm \sqrt{11}$$
✗

27. $x^2 - 2x - 4 = 0$

$$x^2 - 2x - 4 = 0$$
$$x^2 - 2x = 4$$
$$x^2 - 2x + 1 = 4 + 1$$
$$(x + 1)^2 = 5$$
$$x + 1 = \pm\sqrt{5}$$
$$x = 1 \pm \sqrt{5}$$
✗

26. When completing the square, you must add the same number to each side of the equation, not just to the side of the equation for which you complete the square; $x^2 - 14x + 49 = 11 + 49$, $(x - 7)^2 = 60$, $x - 7 = \pm\sqrt{60}$, $x = 7 \pm \sqrt{60}$.

27. The perfect square trinomial $x^2 - 2x + 1$ factors as $(x - 1)^2$ not $(x + 1)^2$; $(x - 1)^2 = 5$, $x - 1 = \pm\sqrt{5}$, $x = 1 \pm \sqrt{5}$.

31. 1.01, 0.01

32. −3.67, −0.33

33. −0.96, 6.96

34. −0.30, 12.30

35. −0.79, 2.21

36. −0.65, 4.65

[B] **SOLVING EQUATIONS** Solve the equation by completing the square. Round your solutions to the nearest hundredth, if necessary.

28. $2x^2 - 8x - 14 = 0$ −1.32, 5.32

29. $2x^2 + 24x + 10 = 0$ −11.57, −0.43

30. $3x^2 - 48x + 39 = 0$ 0.86, 15.14

31. $4y^2 + 4y - 7 = 0$

32. $9n^2 + 36n + 11 = 0$

33. $3w^2 - 18w - 20 = 0$

34. $3p^2 - 30p - 11 = 6p$

35. $3a^2 - 12a + 3 = -a^2 - 4$

36. $15c^2 - 51c - 30 = 9c + 15$

37. $7m^2 + 24m - 2 = m^2 - 9$ −3.68, −0.32

38. $g^2 + 2g + 0.4 = 0.9g^2 + g$ −9.58, −0.42

39. $11z^2 - 10z - 3 = -9z^2 + \frac{3}{4}$ −0.25, 0.75

GEOMETRY Find the value of x. Round your answer to the nearest hundredth, if necessary.

40. Area of triangle $= 108$ m^2 **12**

x m

$(x + 6)$ m

41. Area of rectangle $= 288$ in.^{2} **4.87**

$3x$ in.

$(2x + 10)$ in.

42. ★ **WRITING** How many solutions does $x^2 + bx = c$ have if $c < -\left(\frac{b}{2}\right)^2$? *Explain.* See margin.

[C] **43.** **CHALLENGE** The product of two consecutive negative integers is 210. Find the integers. **−15, −14**

44. **CHALLENGE** The product of two consecutive positive even integers is 288. Find the integers. **16, 18**

PROBLEM SOLVING

EXAMPLE 4 [A]
on p. 665
for Exs. 45–46

45. **LANDSCAPING** You are building a rectangular brick patio surrounded by crushed stone in a rectangular courtyard as shown. The crushed stone border has a uniform width x (in feet). You have enough money in your budget to purchase patio bricks to cover 140 square feet. Solve the equation $140 = (20 - 2x)(16 - 2x)$ to find the width of the border. **3 ft**

@HomeTutor for problem solving help at classzone.com

16 ft
x ft
20 ft

46. **TRAFFIC ENGINEERING** The distance d (in feet) that it takes a car to come to a complete stop on dry asphalt can be modeled by $d = 0.05s^2 + 1.1s$ where s is the speed of the car (in miles per hour). A car has 78 feet to come to a complete stop. Find the maximum speed at which the car can travel. **30 mi/h**

@HomeTutor for problem solving help at classzone.com

47. ◆ **MULTIPLE REPRESENTATIONS** For the period 1985–2001, the average salary y (in thousands of dollars) per season of a Major League Baseball player can be modeled by $y = 7x^2 - 4x + 392$ where x is the number of years since 1985.

   a. Solving an Equation Write and solve an equation to find the year when the average salary was $1,904,000. **1904 = 7x² − 4x + 392, 2000**

   b. Drawing a Graph Use a graph to check your solution to part (a). **See margin.**

Avoiding Common Errors

Exercises 12–25, 28–39 Watch for students who add the term $\left(\frac{b}{2}\right)^2$ to one side of the equation only. Stress to students that they must add the term to each side in order to write an equivalent equation.

Animated Algebra
classzone.com

An **Animated Algebra** activity is available on-line for **Exercise 50**. This activity is also available on the **Power Presentations CD-ROM**.

Study Strategy

Exercise 51 Suggest to students that they draw a diagram to help them visualize the solution to this problem.

42. Zero; $\left(\frac{b}{2}\right)^2$ is always positive, so if $c < -\left(\frac{b}{2}\right)^2$, c must be a negative number whose absolute value is greater than $\left(\frac{b}{2}\right)^2$. Then $c + \left(\frac{b}{2}\right)^2$ will simplify to a negative number, implying that $\left(x + \frac{b}{2}\right)^2 = c + \left(\frac{b}{2}\right)^2$ has no solution.

47b.

Salary (thousands of dollars)
$y = 7x^2 - 4x + 392$
Years since 1985

When $y \approx 1904$, the value of x is about 15. So, the year 2000 (1985 + 15) found in part (a) is correct.

B **48. MULTI-STEP PROBLEM** You have 80 feet of fencing to make a rectangular horse pasture that covers 750 square feet. A barn will be used as one side of the pasture as shown.

a. Write equations for the perimeter and area of the pasture. $\ell + 2w = 80 + \ell$, $\ell w = 750$

b. Use substitution to solve the system of equations from part (a). What are the possible dimensions of the pasture? **length: 50 ft, width: 15 ft; length: 30 ft, width: 25 ft**

49. ★ SHORT RESPONSE You purchase stock for $16 per share, and you sell the stock 30 days later for $23.50 per share. The price y (in dollars) of a share during the 30 day period can be modeled by $y = -0.025x^2 + x + 16$ where x is the number of days after the stock is purchased. Could you have sold the stock earlier for $23.50 per share? *Explain*. **See margin.**

50. SNOWBOARDING During a "big air" competition, snowboarders launch themselves from a half pipe, perform tricks in the air, and land back in the half pipe.

a. Model Use the vertical motion model to write an equation that models the height h (in feet) of a snowboarder as a function of the time t (in seconds) she is in the air. $h = -16t^2 + 24t + 16.4$

b. Apply How long is the snowboarder in the air if she lands 13.2 feet above the base of the half pipe? Round your answer to the nearest tenth of a second. **about 1.6 sec**

Cross section of a half pipe

Animated **Algebra** at classzone.com

C **51. CHALLENGE** You are knitting a rectangular scarf. The pattern you have created will result in a scarf that has a length of 60 inches and a width of 4 inches. However, you happen to have enough yarn to cover an area of 480 square inches. You decide to increase the dimensions of the scarf so that all of your yarn will be used. If the increase in the length is 10 times the increase in the width, what will the dimensions of the scarf be? **length: 80 in., width: 6 in.**

MIXED REVIEW

PREVIEW

Prepare for Lesson 10.6 in Exs. 52–57.

Evaluate the expression for the given value of *x*. *(p. 74)*

52. $3 + x - 6$; $x = 8$ **5**

53. $11 - (-x) + 15$; $x = -1$ **25**

54. $-x + 18 - 20$; $x = -10$ **8**

55. $32 - x - 5$; $x = 5$ **22**

56. $x + 14.7 - 16.2$; $x = 2.3$ **0.8**

57. $-9.2 - (-11.4) - x$; $x = -4.5$ **6.7**

Solve the proportion. *(p. 168)*

58. $\dfrac{8}{m-3} = \dfrac{4}{3}$ **9**

59. $\dfrac{3}{a} = \dfrac{5}{a+5}$ **15/2**

60. $\dfrac{c+2}{6} = \dfrac{2c-3}{5}$ **4**

Solve the equation.

61. $(x - 4)(x + 9) = 0$ *(p. 575)* **−9, 4**

62. $x^2 - 15x + 26 = 0$ *(p. 583)* **2, 13**

63. $3x^2 + 10x + 7 = 0$ *(p. 593)* **$-2\frac{1}{3}$, −1**

64. $4x^2 - 20x + 25 = 0$ *(p. 600)* **$2\frac{1}{2}$**

Extension
Use after Lesson 10.5

Graph Quadratic Functions In Vertex Form

GOAL Graph quadratic functions in vertex form.

Key Vocabulary
• vertex form

In Lesson 10.2, you graphed quadratic functions in standard form. Quadratic functions can also be written in **vertex form**, $y = a(x - h)^2 + k$ where $a \neq 0$. In this form, the vertex of the graph can be easily determined.

KEY CONCEPT
For Your Notebook

Graph of Vertex Form $y = a(x - h)^2 + k$

The graph of $y = a(x - h)^2 + k$ is the graph of $y = ax^2$ translated h units horizontally and k units vertically.

Characteristics of the graph of $y = a(x - h)^2 + k$:

• The vertex is (h, k).

• The axis of symmetry is $x = h$.

• The graph opens up if $a > 0$, and the graph opens down if $a < 0$.

EXAMPLE 1 Graph a quadratic function in vertex form

Graph $y = -(x + 2)^2 + 3$.

Solution

STEP 1 **Identify** the values of a, h, and k: $a = -1$, $h = -2$, and $k = 3$. Because $a < 0$, the parabola opens down.

STEP 2 **Draw** the axis of symmetry, $x = -2$.

STEP 3 **Plot** the vertex $(h, k) = (-2, 3)$.

STEP 4 **Plot** four points. Evaluate the function for two x-values less than the x-coordinate of the vertex.

$x = -3$: $y = -(-3 + 2)^2 + 3 = 2$

$x = -5$: $y = -(-5 + 2)^2 + 3 = -6$

Plot the points $(-3, 2)$ and $(-5, -6)$ and their reflections, $(-1, 2)$ and $(1, -6)$, in the axis of symmetry.

STEP 5 **Draw** a parabola through the plotted points.

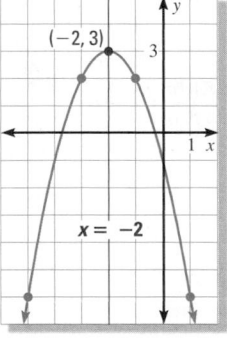

Extension: Graph Quadratic Functions in Vertex Form **669**

---

① PLAN AND PREPARE

Warm-Up Exercises

1. Find the axis of symmetry and vertex of the graph of $y = -x^2 + 2x + 1$. $x = 1$; (1, 2)

2. Graph $y = -2x^2 + 4x + 1$.

---

② FOCUS AND MOTIVATE

Essential Question

Big Idea 1, p. 627

How do you graph a quadratic function in vertex form? **Tell** students they will learn how to answer this question by using the vertex form of a quadratic to identify the axis of symmetry, the vertex, and other points.

---

③ TEACH

Extra Example 1

Graph $y = (x + 1)^2 - 1$.

NCTM STANDARDS

Standard 2: Analyze situations using algebraic symbols

Standard 3: Use symmetry to analyze math situations

EXAMPLE 2   **Graph a quadratic function**

Graph $y = x^2 - 8x + 11$.

Solution

STEP 1   **Write** the function in vertex form by completing the square.

$y = x^2 - 8x + 11$	Write original function.
$y + \square = (x^2 - 8x + \square) + 11$	Prepare to complete the square.
$y + 16 = (x^2 - 8x + 16) + 11$	Add $\left(\dfrac{-8}{2}\right)^2 = (-4)^2 = 16$ to each side.
$y + 16 = (x - 4)^2 + 11$	Write $x^2 - 8x + 16$ as a square of a binomial.
$y = (x - 4)^2 - 5$	Subtract 16 from each side.

STEP 2   **Identify** the values of a, h, and k: $a = 1$, $h = 4$, and $k = -5$. Because $a > 0$, the parabola opens up.

STEP 3   **Draw** the axis of symmetry, $x = 4$.

STEP 4   **Plot** the vertex $(h, k) = (4, -5)$.

STEP 5   **Plot** four more points. Evaluate the function for two x-values less than the x-coordinate of the vertex.

$x = 3$: $y = (3 - 4)^2 - 5 = -4$
$x = 1$: $y = (1 - 4)^2 - 5 = 4$

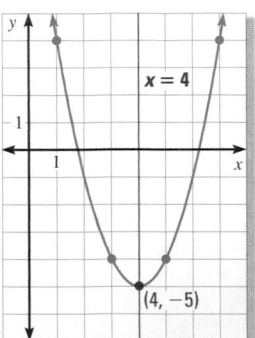

Plot the points $(3, -4)$ and $(1, 4)$ and their reflections, $(5, -4)$ and $(7, 4)$, in the axis of symmetry.

STEP 6   **Draw** a parabola through the plotted points.

PRACTICE

EXAMPLE 1
on p. 669
for Exs. 1–6

Graph the quadratic function. Label the vertex and axis of symmetry.   **1–6. See margin.**

1. $y = (x + 2)^2 - 5$ **2.** $y = -(x - 4)^2 + 1$ **3.** $y = x^2 + 3$

4. $y = 3(x - 1)^2 - 2$ **5.** $y = -2(x + 5)^2 - 2$ **6.** $y = -\dfrac{1}{2}(x + 4)^2 + 4$

EXAMPLE 2
on p. 670
for Exs. 7–12

Write the function in vertex form, then graph the function. Label the vertex and axis of symmetry.   **7–12. See margin.**

7. $y = x^2 - 12x + 36$ **8.** $y = x^2 + 8x + 15$ **9.** $y = -x^2 + 10x - 21$

10. $y = 2x^2 - 12x + 19$ **11.** $y = -3x^2 - 6x - 1$ **12.** $y = -\dfrac{1}{2}x^2 - 6x - 21$

13. Write an equation in vertex form of the parabola shown. Use the coordinates of the vertex and the coordinates of a point on the graph to write the equation.
$y = \dfrac{1}{4}(x + 6)^2 + 1$

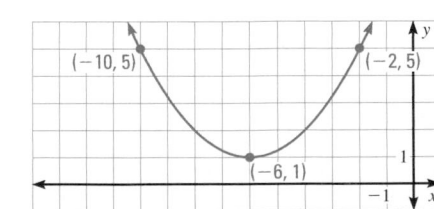

Extra Example 2

Graph $y = x^2 - 6x + 5$ by writing it in vertex form. $y = (x - 3)^2 - 4$

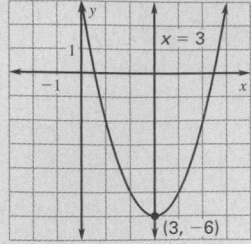

Key Question to Ask for Example 2

• Why is $h = 4$? Why is $k = 5$? Comparing $y = (x - h)^2 + k$ and $y = (x - 4)^2 - 5$, you get $h = 4$ and $k = -5$.

Closing the Lesson

Have students summarize the major points of the lesson and answer the Essential Question: How do you graph a quadratic function in intercept form?

• The vertex form of a quadratic function is $y = a(x - h)^2 + k$. The vertex is (h, k). The axis of symmetry is $x = h$.

If necessary, use the method of completing the square to write the function in vertex form. Determine whether the parabola opens up or down. Use the value of h to draw the axis of symmetry, and use the values of h and k to plot the vertex. Evaluate the function for two x-values to the left of the vertex, and use symmetry to find corresponding points to the right of the vertex. Draw a parabola through the points.

④ PRACTICE AND APPLY

Avoiding Common Errors

Exercises 1–12 Some students forget to use the sign of the leading coefficient. Remind students that if $a < 0$ the parabola opens down, and if $a > 0$ the parabola opens up.

1–12. See Additional Answers beginning on p. AA1.

10.6 Solve Quadratic Equations by the Quadratic Formula

Before You solved quadratic equations by completing the square.

Now You will solve quadratic equations using the quadratic formula.

Why? So you can solve a problem about film production, as in Example 3.

Key Vocabulary
• quadratic formula

By completing the square for the quadratic equation $ax^2 + bx + c = 0$, you can develop a formula that gives the solutions of any quadratic equation in standard form. This formula is called the **quadratic formula**. (The quadratic formula is developed on page 727.)

KEY CONCEPT
For Your Notebook

The Quadratic Formula

The solutions of the quadratic equation $ax^2 + bx + c = 0$ are

$$x = \frac{-b \pm \sqrt{b^2 - 4ac}}{2a}$$ where $a \neq 0$ and $b^2 - 4ac \geq 0$.

EXAMPLE 1 Standardized Test Practice

What are the solutions of $3x^2 + 5x = 8$?

(A) -1 and $-\dfrac{8}{3}$ (B) -1 and $\dfrac{8}{3}$ (C) 1 and $-\dfrac{8}{3}$ (D) 1 and $\dfrac{8}{3}$

ANOTHER WAY
Instead of solving the equation, you can check the answer choices in the equation.

Solution

$3x^2 + 5x = 8$	Write original equation.
$3x^2 + 5x - 8 = 0$	Write in standard form.
$x = \dfrac{-b \pm \sqrt{b^2 - 4ac}}{2a}$	Quadratic formula
$x = \dfrac{-5 \pm \sqrt{5^2 - 4(3)(-8)}}{2(3)}$	Substitute values in the quadratic formula: $a = 3$, $b = 5$, and $c = -8$.
$= \dfrac{-5 \pm \sqrt{121}}{6}$	Simplify.
$= \dfrac{-5 \pm 11}{6}$	Simplify the square root.

The solutions of the equation are $\dfrac{-5 + 11}{6} = 1$ and $\dfrac{-5 - 11}{6} = -\dfrac{8}{3}$.

▸ The correct answer is C. (A) (B) (C) (D)

---

1 PLAN AND PREPARE

Warm-Up Exercises
🗊 Transparency Available

Evaluate the expression for the given value of x.

1. $15 - (-x) + 9$; $x = -2$ **22**

2. $14 - x + 3$; $x = 8$ **9**

3. A basketball is thrown in the air from a height of 6 feet with an initial velocity of 40 feet per second. What is the height (in feet) of the ball after 2 seconds? **22 ft**

Notetaking Guide
🗊 Transparency Available

Promotes interactive learning and notetaking skills, pp. 236–238.

Pacing

Basic: 2 days
Average: 2 days
Advanced: 2 days
Block: 0.5 block with 10.5
       0.5 block with 10.7

• See *Teaching Guide/Lesson Plan*.

2 FOCUS AND MOTIVATE

Essential Question
Big Idea 2, p. 627

How do you solve a quadratic equation using the quadratic formula? **Tell students they will learn how to answer this question by substituting values in the quadratic formula and then simplifying.**

NCTM STANDARDS

Standard 2: Analyze situations using algebraic symbols

Standard 8: Use the language of math to express ideas

Resource Planning Guide

Chapter Resource Book
• Teaching Guide/Lesson Plan (pp. 69–70)
• Practice levels A, B, C (pp. 71–73)
• Study Guide (pp. 74–75)
• Catch-up for Absent Students (p. 76)
• Problem Solving Workshop (p. 77)
• Challenge (p. 78)

Workbooks
• Notetaking Guide (pp. 236–238)
• Practice Workbook (pp. 162–163)

Teaching Options
• **Power Presentations CD-ROM** provides dynamic electronic teaching resources for the classroom.
• **Activity Generator CD-ROM** provides editable activities for all ability levels.

Interactive Technology
• Easy Planner
• Power Presentations CD-ROM
• Activity Generator CD-ROM
• Animated Algebra
• Test Generator CD-ROM
• Online Quiz
• eWorkbook
• eEdition
• @HomeTutor

Resources for English Learners
• Quick Reference for English Learners
• Spanish Study Guide
• Multi-Language Visual Glossary
• Student Resources in Spanish

See also the *Algebra 1 Toolkit* for more strategies for meeting individual needs.

671

Motivating the Lesson

Ask students how they would solve a quadratic equation such as $0.5x^2 - 1.25x - 7.5 = 0$. Tell them that in this lesson they will learn how to use a formula to solve *any* quadratic equation.

3 TEACH

Extra Example 1

What are the solutions of $2x^2 + 7x = 9$? **B**

Ⓐ -1 and $-\dfrac{9}{2}$ Ⓑ 1 and $-\dfrac{9}{2}$

Ⓒ -1 and $\dfrac{9}{2}$ Ⓓ 1 and $\dfrac{9}{2}$

Extra Example 2

Use the quadratic formula to solve $3x^2 - 1 = x$. $a = 3, b = -1, c = -1$; $\dfrac{1 + \sqrt{13}}{6} \approx 0.77, \dfrac{1 - \sqrt{13}}{6} \approx -0.43$

An **Animated Algebra** activity is available on-line for **Example 2**. This activity is also available on the **Power Presentations CD-ROM**.

Extra Example 3

For the period 1990–2003, the number of book titles published by a small publishing company can be modeled by the function $y = 0.5x^2 + 4x + 19$, where x is the number of years since 1990. In what year did the company publish 80 books? **almost 8 years after 1990, or during 1997**

EXAMPLE 2 **Solve a quadratic equation**

Solve $2x^2 - 7 = x$.

$2x^2 - 7 = x$ Write original equation.

$2x^2 - x - 7 = 0$ Write in standard form.

$x = \dfrac{-b \pm \sqrt{b^2 - 4ac}}{2a}$ Quadratic formula

$= \dfrac{-(-1) \pm \sqrt{(-1)^2 - 4(2)(-7)}}{2(2)}$ Substitute values in the quadratic formula: $a = 2, b = -1,$ and $c = -7$.

$= \dfrac{1 \pm \sqrt{57}}{4}$ Simplify.

▶ The solutions are $\dfrac{1 + \sqrt{57}}{4} \approx 2.14$ and $\dfrac{1 - \sqrt{57}}{4} \approx -1.64$.

Animated Algebra at classzone.com

CHECK Write the equation in standard form, $2x^2 - x - 7 = 0$. Then graph the related function $y = 2x^2 - x - 7$. The x-intercepts are about -1.6 and 2.1. So, each solution checks.

✓ **GUIDED PRACTICE** for Examples 1 and 2

Use the quadratic formula to solve the equation. Round your solutions to the nearest hundredth, if necessary.

1. $x^2 - 8x + 16 = 0$ **4**
2. $3n^2 - 5n = -1$ **0.23, 1.43**
3. $4z^2 = 7z + 2$ **−0.25, 2**

EXAMPLE 3 **Use the quadratic formula**

FILM PRODUCTION For the period 1971–2001, the number y of films produced in the world can be modeled by the function $y = 10x^2 - 94x + 3900$ where x is the number of years since 1971. In what year were 4200 films produced?

Solution

$y = 10x^2 - 94x + 3900$ Write function.

$4200 = 10x^2 - 94x + 3900$ Substitute 4200 for y.

$0 = 10x^2 - 94x - 300$ Write in standard form.

$x = \dfrac{-(-94) \pm \sqrt{(-94)^2 - 4(10)(-300)}}{2(10)}$ Substitute values in the quadratic formula: $a = 10, b = -94,$ and $c = -300$.

$= \dfrac{94 \pm \sqrt{20{,}836}}{20}$ Simplify.

INTERPRET SOLUTIONS
The solution -3 can be ignored because -3 represents the year 1968, which is not in the given time period.

The solutions of the equation are $\dfrac{94 + \sqrt{20{,}836}}{20} \approx 12$ and $\dfrac{94 - \sqrt{20{,}836}}{20} \approx -3$.

▶ There were 4200 films produced about 12 years after 1971, or in 1983.

672 Chapter 10 Quadratic Equations and Functions

Differentiated Instruction

Visual Learners Students may find the quadratic formula easier to memorize by visualizing the graph of the quadratic function $y = ax^2 + bx + c$. Write the quadratic formula as $x = -\dfrac{b}{2a} \pm \dfrac{\sqrt{b^2 - 4ac}}{2a}$. Point out that $x = -\dfrac{b}{2a}$ is the axis of symmetry for the function $y = ax^2 + bx + c$ and the x-intercepts of the function are $\dfrac{\sqrt{b^2 - 4ac}}{2a}$ units to the left and right of the axis of symmetry.

See also the *Algebra 1 Toolkit* for more strategies.

4. **WHAT IF?** In Example 3, find the year when 4750 films were produced. **1986**

CONCEPT SUMMARY   *For Your Notebook*

Methods for Solving Quadratic Equations

Method	Lesson(s)	When to Use
Factoring	9.4–9.8	Use when a quadratic equation can be factored easily.
Graphing	10.3	Use when approximate solutions are adequate.
Finding square roots	10.4	Use when solving an equation that can be written in the form $x^2 = d$.
Completing the square	10.5	Can be used for *any* quadratic equation $ax^2 + bx + c = 0$ but is simplest to apply when $a = 1$ and b is an even number.
Quadratic formula	10.6	Can be used for *any* quadratic equation.

EXAMPLE 4   **Choose a solution method**

Tell what method you would use to solve the quadratic equation. *Explain* your choice(s).

    a. $10x^2 - 7 = 0$ **b.** $x^2 + 4x = 0$ **c.** $5x^2 + 9x - 4 = 0$

Solution

   a. The quadratic equation can be solved using square roots because the equation can be written in the form $x^2 = d$.

   b. The equation can be solved by factoring because the expression $x^2 + 4x$ can be factored easily. Also, the equation can be solved by completing the square because the equation is of the form $ax^2 + bx + c = 0$ where $a = 1$ and b is an even number.

   c. The quadratic equation cannot be factored easily, and completing the square will result in many fractions. So, the equation can be solved using the quadratic formula.

✓ **GUIDED PRACTICE**   for Example 4

Tell what method you would use to solve the quadratic equation. *Explain* your choice(s). **5–7. See margin.**

   5. $x^2 + x - 6 = 0$ **6.** $x^2 - 9 = 0$ **7.** $x^2 + 6x = 5$

---

5. *Sample answer:* Factoring, the expression $x^2 + x - 6$ factors easily.

6. *Sample answer:* Factoring, the expression $x^2 - 9$ factors easily; or using square roots, the equation can be written in the form $x^2 = d$.

7. *Sample answer:* Completing the square, the equation is of the form $ax^2 + bx = c$ where $a = 1$ and b is an even number; or quadratic formula, the equation does not factor easily.

Key Question to Ask for Example 3

• Can you use the model to approximate the number of films for any particular year? Explain. **The model is based on data from 1971 through 2001. It may not be accurate for years prior to 1971 or after 2001.**

Extra Example 4

Tell what method you would use to solve the quadratic equation. *Explain* your choice(s).

a. $3x^2 + 14x + 13 = 0$

b. $9x^2 - 3 = 0$

c. $x^2 + 8x = 0$

a. The quadratic formula is best since the equation cannot be factored easily and completing the square would result in too many fractions.

b. The equation can be written in the form $x^2 = d$, so the easiest method is finding square roots.

c. You could use factoring because it can be factored easily, or you can use completing the square since *a* is 1 and *b* is even.

Closing the Lesson

Have students summarize the major points of the lesson and answer the Essential Question: How do you solve a quadratic equation using the quadratic formula?

• For the general quadratic equation $ax^2 + bx + c = 0$, the quadratic formula is

$$x = \frac{-b \pm \sqrt{b^2 - 4ac}}{2a}.$$

Substitute values for *a*, *b*, and *c* into the quadratic formula, and then simplify.

10.6 **EXERCISES**

HOMEWORK KEY

○ = **WORKED-OUT SOLUTIONS**
on p. WS1 for Exs. 19 and 47

★ = **STANDARDIZED TEST PRACTICE**
Exs. 2, 12, 25, and 50

◆ = **MULTIPLE REPRESENTATIONS**
Ex. 49

④ PRACTICE AND APPLY

Assignment Guide

📖 **Answer Transparencies**
available for all exercises

Basic:
Day 1: pp. 674–676
Exs. 1–8, 12–21, 25–27
Day 2: pp. 674–676
Exs. 28–38, 46–49, 52–61

Average:
Day 1: pp. 674–676
Exs. 1, 2, 6–12, 16–27
Day 2: pp. 674–676
Exs. 28–44, 46–50, 52–60 even

Advanced:
Day 1: pp. 674–676
Exs. 1, 2, 6–12, 16–25
Day 2: pp. 674–676
Exs. 28–51*, 53–61 odd

Block:
pp. 674–676
Exs. 1, 2, 6–12, 16–27 (with 10.5)
pp. 674–676
Exs. 28–44, 46–50, 52–60 even
(with 10.7)

Differentiated Instruction

See *Algebra 1 Best Practices Toolkit*
for suggestions on addressing the
needs of a diverse classroom.

Homework Check

For a quick check of student under-
standing of key concepts, go over
the following exercises:
Basic: 8, 12, 28, 32, 46
Average: 12, 16, 31, 36, 46
Advanced: 20, 25, 33, 40, 47

Extra Practice

• Student Edition, p. 947
• Chapter 10 Resource Book:
Practice levels A, B, C, pp. 71–73

Practice Worksheet

An easily-readable reduced
practice page (with answers)
for this lesson can be found
on p. 626C.

SKILL PRACTICE

A 1. **VOCABULARY** What formula can be used to solve any quadratic equation? **quadratic formula**

2. ★ **WRITING** What method(s) would you use to solve $-x^2 + 8x = 1$? *Explain* your choice(s). **See margin.**

EXAMPLES 1 and 2
on pp. 671–672
for Exs. 3–27

2. *Sample answer:* Completing the square, the equation can be put in the form $ax^2 + bx = c$ where $a = 1$ and b is an even number; or quadratic formula, the equation does not factor easily.

SOLVING QUADRATIC EQUATIONS Use the quadratic formula to solve the equation. Round your solutions to the nearest hundredth, if necessary.

3. $x^2 + 5x - 104 = 0$ **−13, 8**
4. $4x^2 - x - 18 = 0$ **−2, 2.25**
5. $6x^2 - 2x - 28 = 0$ **−2, 2.33**

6. $m^2 + 3m + 1 = 0$ **−2.62, −0.38**
7. $-z^2 + z + 14 = 0$ **−3.27, 4.27**
8. $-2n^2 - 5n + 16 = 0$ **−4.34, 1.84**

9. $4w^2 + 20w + 25 = 0$ **−2.5**
10. $2t^2 + 3t - 11 = 0$ **−3.21, 1.71**
11. $-6g^2 + 9g + 8 = 0$ **−0.63, 2.13**

12. ★ **MULTIPLE CHOICE** What are the solutions of $10x^2 - 3x - 1 = 0$? **B**

Ⓐ $-\frac{1}{5}$ and $-\frac{1}{2}$
Ⓑ $-\frac{1}{5}$ and $\frac{1}{2}$
Ⓒ $\frac{1}{5}$ and $-\frac{1}{2}$
Ⓓ $\frac{1}{5}$ and $\frac{1}{2}$

SOLVING QUADRATIC EQUATIONS Use the quadratic formula to solve the equation. Round your solutions to the nearest hundredth, if necessary.

13. $x^2 - 5x = 14$ **−2, 7**
14. $3x^2 - 4 = 11x$ **−0.33, 4**
15. $9 = 7x^2 - 2x$ **−1, 1.29**

16. $2m^2 + 9m + 7 = 3$ **−4, −0.5**
17. $-10 = r^2 - 10r + 12$ **3.27, 6.73**
18. $3g^2 - 6g - 14 = 3g$ **−1.13, 4.13**

⑲ $6z^2 = 2z^2 + 7z + 5$ **−0.54, 2.29**
20. $8h^2 + 8 = 6 - 9h$ **−0.82, −0.30**
21. $4t^2 - 3t = 5 - 3t^2$ **−0.66, 1.09**

22. $-4y^2 - 3y + 3 = 2y + 4$ **−1, −0.25**
23. $7n + 5 = -3n^2 + 2$ **−1.77, −0.57**
24. $5w^2 + 4 = w + 6$ **−0.54, 0.74**

25. ★ **MULTIPLE CHOICE** What are the solutions of $x^2 + 14x = 2x - 11$? **B**

Ⓐ −2 and −22
Ⓑ −1 and −11
Ⓒ 1 and 11
Ⓓ 2 and 22

ERROR ANALYSIS *Describe* and correct the error in solving the equation. **26–27. See margin.**

26. $7x^2 - 5x - 1 = 0$

$$x = \frac{-5 \pm \sqrt{(-5)^2 - 4(7)(-1)}}{2(7)}$$

$$= \frac{-5 \pm \sqrt{53}}{14}$$

$x \approx -0.88$ and $x \approx 0.16$ ✗

27. $-2x^2 + 3x = 1$

$$x = \frac{-3 \pm \sqrt{3^2 - 4(-2)(1)}}{2(-2)}$$

$$= \frac{-3 \pm \sqrt{17}}{-4}$$

$x \approx -0.28$ and $x \approx 1.78$ ✗

EXAMPLE 4
on p. 673
for Exs. 28–33

CHOOSING A METHOD Tell what method(s) you would use to solve the quadratic equation. *Explain* your choice(s). **28–33. See margin.**

28. $3x^2 - 27 = 0$
29. $5x^2 = 25$
30. $2x^2 - 12x = 0$

31. $m^2 + 5m + 6 = 0$
32. $z^2 - 4z + 1 = 0$
33. $-10g^2 + 13g = 4$

---

26. The first term of the numerator of the quadratic formula is $-b$, so the first term of the numerator of the answer should be $-(-5) = 5$;
$x = \dfrac{5 \pm \sqrt{(-5)^2 - 4(7)(-1)}}{2(7)}$, $x = \dfrac{5 \pm \sqrt{53}}{14}$, $x \approx -0.16$ and $x \approx 0.88$.

27. Before identifying the values of a, b, and c, the equation must be written in standard form $ax^2 + bx + c = 0$; $-2x^2 + 3x - 1 = 0$, so $c = -1$, not 1; $x = \dfrac{-3 \pm \sqrt{3^2 - 4(-2)(-1)}}{2(-2)}$, $x = \dfrac{-3 \pm \sqrt{1}}{-4}$, $x = \dfrac{1}{2}$ and $x = 1$.

B **SOLVING QUADRATIC EQUATIONS** Solve the quadratic equation using any method. Round your solutions to the nearest hundredth, if necessary.

34. $-2x^2 = -32$ **±4**
35. $x^2 - 8x = -16$ **4**
36. $x^2 + 2x - 6 = 0$ **−3.65, 1.65**

37. $x^2 = 12x - 36$ **6**
38. $x^2 + 4x = 9$ **−5.61, 1.61**
39. $-4x^2 + x = -17$ **−1.94, 2.19**

40. $11x^2 - 1 = 6x^2 + 2$ **±0.77**
41. $-2x^2 + 5 = 3x^2 - 10x$
−0.41, 2.41
42. $(x + 13)^2 = 25$ **−18, −8**

GEOMETRY Use the given area A of the rectangle to find the value of x. Then give the dimensions of the rectangle.

43. $A = 91$ m^2 **5; 13 m by 7 m**

$(x + 2)$ m
$(2x + 3)$ m

44. $A = 209$ ft^2 **4; 19 ft by 11 ft**
$(4x - 5)$ ft
$(4x + 3)$ ft

C **45. CHALLENGE** The solutions of the quadratic equation $ax^2 + bx + c = 0$ are $x = \dfrac{-b + \sqrt{b^2 - 4ac}}{2a}$ and $x = \dfrac{-b - \sqrt{b^2 - 4ac}}{2a}$. Find the mean of the solutions. How is the mean of the solutions related to the graph of $y = ax^2 + bx + c$? *Explain.* **See margin.**

PROBLEM SOLVING

EXAMPLE 3 **A**
on p. 672
for Exs. 46–47

46. ADVERTISING For the period 1990−2000, the amount of money y (in billions of dollars) spent on advertising in the U.S. can be modeled by the function $y = 0.93x^2 + 2.2x + 130$ where x is the number of years since 1990. In what year was 164 billion dollars spent on advertising? **1995**

@HomeTutor for problem solving help at classzone.com

47. CELL PHONES For the period 1985−2001, the number y (in millions) of cell phone service subscribers in the U.S. can be modeled by the function $y = 0.7x^2 - 4.3x + 5.5$ where x is the number of years since 1985. In what year were there 16,000,000 cell phone service subscribers? **1993**

@HomeTutor for problem solving help at classzone.com

48. MULTI-STEP PROBLEM A football is punted from a height of 2.5 feet above the ground and with an initial vertical velocity of 45 feet per second.

Not drawn to scale
5.5 ft
2.5 ft

a. Use the vertical motion model to write an equation that gives the height h (in feet) of the football as a function of the time t (in seconds) after it has been punted. $h = -16t^2 + 45t + 2.5$

b. The football is caught 5.5 feet above the ground as shown in the diagram. Find the amount of time that the football is in the air. **about 2.7 sec**

10.6 Solve Quadratic Equations by the Quadratic Formula **675**

Avoiding Common Errors
Exercises 3–25 Students often make calculation errors when using the quadratic formula, especially when substituting values with negative signs. For each exercise, prior to doing any calculations they should write the values of a, b, and c and then rewrite the formula using those values.

Graphing Calculator
Exercises 3–25 Suggest that students use their graphing calculators to check their solutions.

Study Strategy
Exercises 47 Point out to students that this exercise has a worked-out solution. Recommend that they attempt a solution first. Then they can the worked-out solution to check their results and compare solution methods.

Internet Reference
Exercise 50 For additional information about NASA's weightless environment, visit liftoff.msfc. nasa.gov/academy/astronauts/training.html

32. Completing the square, the equation is in the form $ax^2 + bx + c = 0$ where $a = 1$ and b is an even number; or quadratic formula, the equation does not factor easily.

33. Quadratic formula, the equation does not factor easily.

45. $-\dfrac{b}{2a}$; $x = -\dfrac{b}{2a}$ is the equation of the axis of symmetry of the parabola $y = ax^2 + bx + c$, and $-\dfrac{b}{2a}$ is the x-coordinate of the vertex of the parabola; the axis of symmetry of $y = ax^2 + bx + c$ is located half-way between the x-intercepts, and the x-intercepts are the solutions of $ax^2 + bx + c = 0$, so the mean of the solutions is the equation of the axis of symmetry; the equation of the axis of symmetry gives the x-coordinate of the vertex of the parabola.

28–33. Sample answers are given.

28. Factoring, the expression $3x^2 - 27$ factors easily; or using square roots, the equation can be written in the form $x^2 = d$.

29. Using square roots, the equation can be written in the form $x^2 = d$.

30. Factoring, the expression $2x^2 - 12x$ factors easily; or using square roots, the equation can be written in the form $x^2 = d$; completing the square, the equation is of the form $ax^2 + bx = c$ where $a = 1$ and b is an even number.

31. Factoring, the expression $m^2 + 5m + 6$ factors easily.

Use the quadratic formula to solve the equation. Round your solutions to the nearest hundredth, if necessary.

1. $6x^2 - 6 = -5x$ $-\frac{3}{2}, \frac{2}{3}$

2. $2x^2 + 3x - 8 = 0$ $-2.87, 1.39$

3. $3m^2 - m + 9 = 12$ $-0.85, 1.18$

4. You have seen that the function $y = 10x^2 - 94x + 3900$ models the number y of films produced in the world, where x is the number of years since 1971. In what year were 10,000 films produced? **about 29.8 years after 1971, or during the year 2000**

🌐 **Online Quiz**

Available at **classzone.com**

Diagnosis/Remediation

• Practice A, B, C in Chapter 10 Resource Book, pp. 71–73
• Study Guide in Chapter 10 Resource Book, pp. 74–75
• Practice Workbook, pp. 162–163
• @HomeTutor

Challenge

Additional challenge is available in the Chapter 10 Resource Book, p. 78.

Quiz

An easily-readable reduced copy of the quiz (with answers) on Lessons 10.4–10.6 from the Assessment Book can be found on p. 626G.

49b.

49. ◆ **MULTIPLE REPRESENTATIONS** For the period 1997–2002, the number y (in thousands) of 16- and 17-year-olds employed in the United States can be modeled by the function $y = -46.7x^2 + 169x + 2650$ where x is the number of years since 1997.

a. Solving an Equation Write and solve an equation to find the year during which 2,500,000 16- and 17-year-olds were employed. **2001**

b. Drawing a Graph Graph the function on a graphing calculator. Use the *trace* feature to find the year when 2,500,000 16- and 17-year-olds were employed. Use the graph to check your answer from part (a). **See margin.**

50. ★ **SHORT RESPONSE** NASA creates a weightless environment by flying a plane in a series of parabolic paths. The height h (in feet) of a plane after t seconds in a parabolic flight path can be modeled by the graph of $h = -11t^2 + 700t + 21,000$. The passengers experience a weightless environment when the height of the plane is greater than or equal to 30,800 feet. Find the period of weightlessness on such a flight. *Explain.* **about 22 sec**

51. **CHALLENGE** Mineral deposits have formed a uniform coating that is 4 millimeters thick on the inside of a water pipe. The cross-sectional area of the pipe has decreased by 10%. What was the original diameter of the pipe (to the nearest tenth of a millimeter)? **about 156.0 mm**

MIXED REVIEW

PREVIEW

Prepare for Lesson 10.7 in Exs. 52–55.

Evaluate the expression.

52. $9x^2$ when $x = 2$ *(p. 8)* **36**

53. $\frac{6 - 5w}{2w}$ when $w = 10$ *(p. 103)* $-2\frac{1}{5}$

54. $2 + \sqrt{x}$ when $x = 121$ *(p. 110)* **13**

55. $8 - \sqrt{x}$ when $x = 49$ *(p. 110)* **1**

Graph the equation. **56–61. See margin.**

56. $x = 8$ *(p. 215)*

57. $3x - y = 2$ *(p. 225)*

58. $y = -\frac{2}{5}x - 6$ *(p. 244)*

59. $y = -7x^2$ *(p. 628)*

60. $y = 8x^2 - 2$ *(p. 628)*

61. $y = -x^2 - 6x + 5$ *(p. 635)*

QUIZ *for Lessons 10.4–10.6*

Solve the equation using square roots. *(p. 652)*

1. $3x^2 - 48 = 0$ ± 4

2. $-6x^2 = -24$ ± 2

3. $x^2 + 5 = 16$ **about** ± 3.32

Solve the equation by completing the square. *(p. 663)*

4. $x^2 + 2x + 6 = 0$ **no solution**

5. $x^2 + 10x - 12 = 0$ $-11.08, 1.08$

6. $x^2 - 8x = -6$ $0.84, 7.16$

7. $x^2 - 12x = 30$ $-2.12, 14.12$

8. $x^2 - 5x = -\frac{9}{4}$ $0.5, 4.5$

9. $x^2 + x = -7.75$ **no solution**

Solve the equation using the quadratic formula. *(p. 671)*

10. $x^2 + 4x + 1 = 0$ $-3.73, -0.27$

11. $-3x^2 + 3x = -1$ $-0.26, 1.26$

12. $4x^2 - 11x = 3$ $-0.25, 3$

EXTRA PRACTICE for Lesson 10.6, p. 947   🌐 **ONLINE QUIZ** at classzone.com

56–61. See Additional Answers beginning on p. AA1.

10.7 The Discriminant

QUESTION How can you determine the number of solutions of a quadratic equation?

In the quadratic formula, $x = \dfrac{-b \pm \sqrt{b^2 - 4ac}}{2a}$, the expression $b^2 - 4ac$ is called the *discriminant*.

EXPLORE Determine how the discriminant is related to the number of solutions of a quadratic equation

STEP 1 *Find the number of solutions* See Step 3.
Find the number of solutions of the equations below by finding the number of x-intercepts of the graphs of the related functions.

$$0 = x^2 - 6x - 7$$
$$0 = x^2 - 6x + 9$$
$$0 = x^2 - 6x + 12$$

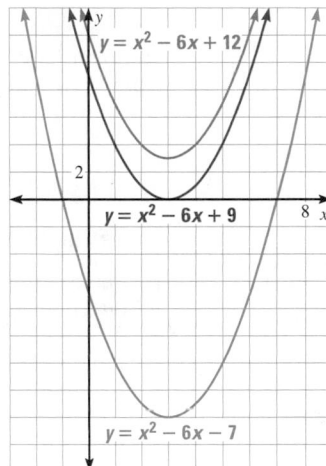

STEP 2 *Find the value of $b^2 - 4ac$* See Step 3.
For each equation in Step 1, determine whether the value of $b^2 - 4ac$ is positive, negative, or zero.

STEP 3 *Make a table*
Organize your results from Steps 1 and 2 in a table as shown.

Equation	Number of solutions	Value of $b^2 - 4ac$
$0 = x^2 - 6x - 7$	? 2	? 64
$0 = x^2 - 6x + 9$	? 1	? 0
$0 = x^2 - 6x + 12$	? 0	? −12

STEP 4 *Make a conjecture*
Make a generalization about the value of the discriminant and the number of solutions of a quadratic equation.
The number of solutions of a quadratic equation $ax^2 + bx + c = 0$ is 2 if $b^2 - 4ac > 0$, is 1 if $b^2 - 4ac = 0$, and is 0 if $b^2 - 4ac < 0$.

DRAW CONCLUSIONS Use your observations to complete these exercises
1, 2. See margin.

1. Repeat Steps 1–3 using the following equations: $x^2 + 4x - 5 = 0$, $x^2 + 4x + 4 = 0$, and $x^2 + 4x + 6 = 0$. Is your conjecture still true?

2. Notice that the expression $b^2 - 4ac$ is under the radical sign in the quadratic formula. Use this observation to explain why the value of $b^2 - 4ac$ determines the number of solutions of a quadratic equation.

10.7 Interpret the Discriminant **677**

① PLAN AND PREPARE

Explore the Concept
- Students will determine how the discriminant is related to the number of solutions of a quadratic formula.
- This activity leads into the study of using the discriminant in Lesson 10.7, Example 1.

Recommended Time
Work activity: 10 min
Discuss results: 5 min

Grouping
Students should work individually.

② TEACH

Tips for Success
Caution students to make sure that they are using the correct graphs to find the number of x-intercepts and record the number of solutions. Remind students that the number of solutions is the same as the number of x-intercepts.

Key Discovery
If the value of the discriminant is positive, there are two solutions. If the value is 0, there is one solution. If the value is negative, there is no real-number solution.

③ ASSESS AND RETEACH

Use the discriminant to find the number of x-intercepts of the graph of $5x^2 + 14x = 7$.
$b^2 - 4ac = 14^2 - 4(5)(-7) = 336$; $336 > 0$, so there are 2 x-intercepts.

1.

Equation	Number of solutions	Value of $b^2 - 4ac$
$x^2 + 4x - 5 = 0$	2	36
$x^2 + 4x + 4 = 0$	1	0
$x^2 + 4x + 6 = 0$	0	−8

yes

2. See Additional Answers beginning on p. AA1.

Evaluate the expression.

1. $8x^2$ when $x = 4$ **128**

2. $-4 + \sqrt{x}$ when $x = 9$ **−1**

3. A ball is kicked into the air from a height of 4.5 feet with an initial velocity of 30 feet per second. What is the height of the ball after 1 second? **18.5 ft**

Notetaking Guide

⬚ Transparency Available

Promotes interactive learning and notetaking skills, pp. 239–241.

Pacing

Basic: 1 day

Average: 1 day

Advanced: 1 day

Block: 0.5 block with 10.6

• See *Teaching Guide/Lesson Plan.*

2 FOCUS AND MOTIVATE

Essential Question

Big Idea 2, p. 627

How do you use the value of the discriminant? **Tell students they will learn how to answer this question by using the discriminant to find the number of solutions of a quadratic equation.**

NCTM STANDARDS

Standard 2: Analyze situations using algebraic symbols

Standard 8: Communicate thinking clearly to others

10.7 Interpret the Discriminant

Before	You used the quadratic formula.
Now	You will use the value of the discriminant.
Why?	So you can solve a problem about gymnastics, as in Ex. 49.

Key Vocabulary
• discriminant

In the quadratic formula, the expression $b^2 - 4ac$ is called the **discriminant** of the associated equation $ax^2 + bx + c = 0$.

$$x = \frac{-b \pm \sqrt{b^2 - 4ac}}{2a} \longleftarrow \text{discriminant}$$

Because the discriminant is under the radical symbol, the value of the discriminant can be used to determine the number of solutions of a quadratic equation and the number of x-intercepts of the graph of the related function.

READING
Recall that in this course, *solutions* refers to real-number solutions.

KEY CONCEPT — *For Your Notebook*

Using the Discriminant of $ax^2 + bx + c = 0$

Value of the discriminant	$b^2 - 4ac > 0$	$b^2 - 4ac = 0$	$b^2 - 4ac < 0$
Number of solutions	Two solutions	One solution	No solution
Graph of $y = ax^2 + bx + c$	Two x-intercepts	One x-intercept	No x-intercept

---

EXAMPLE 1 Use the discriminant

Equation $ax^2 + bx + c = 0$	Discriminant $b^2 - 4ac$	Number of solutions
a. $2x^2 + 6x + 5 = 0$	$6^2 - 4(2)(5) = -4$	No solution
b. $x^2 - 7 = 0$	$0^2 - 4(1)(-7) = 28$	Two solutions
c. $4x^2 - 12x + 9 = 0$	$(-12)^2 - 4(4)(9) = 0$	One solution

Resource Planning Guide

Chapter Resource Book
• Teaching Guide/Lesson Plan (pp. 79–80)
• Practice levels A, B, C (pp. 81–83)
• Study Guide (pp. 84–85)
• Catch-up for Absent Students (p. 86)
• Application (p. 87)
• Challenge (p. 88)

Workbooks
• Notetaking Guide (pp. 239–241)
• Practice Workbook (pp. 164–165)

Teaching Options
• **Power Presentations CD-ROM** provides dynamic electronic teaching resources for the classroom.
• **Activity Generator CD-ROM** provides editable activities for all ability levels.

Interactive Technology
• Easy Planner
• Power Presentations CD-ROM
• Activity Generator CD-ROM
• Animated Algebra
• Test Generator CD-ROM
• Online Quiz
• eWorkbook
• eEdition
• @HomeTutor

Resources for English Learners
• Quick Reference for English Learners
• Spanish Study Guide
• Multi-Language Visual Glossary
• Student Resources in Spanish

See also the *Algebra 1 Toolkit* for more strategies for meeting individual needs.

EXAMPLE 2 Find the number of solutions

Tell whether the equation $3x^2 - 7 = 2x$ has *two solutions, one solution,* or *no solution.*

Solution

STEP 1 **Write** the equation in standard form.

$$3x^2 - 7 = 2x \qquad \text{Write equation.}$$

$$3x^2 - 2x - 7 = 0 \qquad \text{Subtract } 2x \text{ from each side.}$$

STEP 2 **Find** the value of the discriminant.

$$b^2 - 4ac = (-2)^2 - 4(3)(-7) \qquad \text{Substitute 3 for } a, -2 \text{ for } b, \text{ and } -7 \text{ for } c.$$

$$= 88 \qquad \text{Simplify.}$$

▶ The discriminant is positive, so the equation has two solutions.

 GUIDED PRACTICE for Examples 1 and 2

Tell whether the equation has *two solutions, one solution,* or *no solution.*

1. $x^2 + 4x + 3 = 0$ 2. $2x^2 - 5x + 6 = 0$ 3. $-x^2 + 2x = 1$
    two solutions   no solution   one solution

EXAMPLE 3 Find the number of *x*-intercepts

Find the number of *x*-intercepts of the graph of $y = x^2 + 5x + 8$.

Solution

Find the number of solutions of the equation $0 = x^2 + 5x + 8$.

$$b^2 - 4ac = (5)^2 - 4(1)(8) \qquad \text{Substitute 1 for } a, 5 \text{ for } b, \text{ and 8 for } c.$$

$$= -7 \qquad \text{Simplify.}$$

▶ The discriminant is negative, so the equation has no solution. This means that the graph of $y = x^2 + 5x + 8$ has no *x*-intercepts.

CHECK You can use a graphing calculator to check the answer. Notice that the graph of $y = x^2 + 5x + 8$ has no *x*-intercepts.

 GUIDED PRACTICE for Example 3

Find the number of *x*-intercepts of the graph of the function.

4. $y = x^2 + 10x + 25$ **1**   5. $y = x^2 - 9x$ **2**   6. $y = -x^2 + 2x - 4$ **0**

Motivating the Lesson

You are helping a friend's family move to a new house. On the drive to the new house, the truck has to pass under an overpass that has an arch in the shape of a parabola. You can model the situation with a quadratic equation and then use the discriminant to determine whether the truck will fit under the overpass.

❸ TEACH

Extra Example 1

Use the discriminant to find the number of solutions of each equation.

a. $3x^2 + 8x + 7 = 0$ **Discriminant is −20; no solution**

b. $x^2 + 2x - 3 = 0$ **Discriminant is 16; two solutions**

c. $4x^2 + 20x + 25 = 0$ **Discriminant is 0; one solution**

Key Question to Ask for Example 1

• Can you tell how many *x*-intercepts each of the equations has? Explain. **Each *x*-intercept of the graph of the equation represents a solution of the equation, so the number of *x*-intercepts of the graph is the same as the number of solutions of the equation.**

Extra Example 2

Use the discriminant to tell whether the equation $4x^2 + 1 = -4x$ has *two solutions, one solution,* or *no solution.* **Discriminant is 0; one solution**

Extra Example 3

Use the discriminant to find the number of *x*-intercepts of the graph of $y = x^2 + 7x - 2$. **Discriminant is 57; that is positive, so the graph has two *x*-intercepts.**

Differentiated Instruction

Inclusion Students who have difficulty memorizing the rules for the discriminant should think of how the square root of the discriminant is used in the quadratic formula. For a positive discriminant, the square root has two real values; for a zero discriminant, the square root has one real value; and for a negative discriminant, the square root has no real values.

See also the *Algebra 1 Toolkit* for more strategies.

EXAMPLE 4 Solve a multi-step problem

FOUNTAINS The Centennial Fountain in Chicago shoots a water arc that can be modeled by the graph of the equation $y = -0.006x^2 + 1.2x + 10$ where x is the horizontal distance (in feet) from the river's north shore and y is the height (in feet) above the river. Does the water arc reach a height of 50 feet? If so, about how far from the north shore is the water arc 50 feet above the water?

Solution

STEP 1 Write a quadratic equation. You want to know whether the water arc reaches a height of 50 feet, so let $y = 50$. Then write the quadratic equation in standard form.

$$y = -0.006x^2 + 1.2x + 10 \qquad \text{Write given equation.}$$
$$50 = -0.006x^2 + 1.2x + 10 \qquad \text{Substitute 50 for } y.$$
$$0 = -0.006x^2 + 1.2x - 40 \qquad \text{Subtract 50 from each side.}$$

STEP 2 Find the value of the discriminant of $0 = -0.006x^2 + 1.2x - 40$.

$$b^2 - 4ac = (1.2)^2 - 4(-0.006)(-40) \qquad a = -0.006, b = 1.2, c = -40$$
$$= 0.48 \qquad \text{Simplify.}$$

STEP 3 Interpret the discriminant. Because the discriminant is positive, the equation has two solutions. So, the water arc reaches a height of 50 feet at two points on the water arc.

STEP 4 Solve the equation $0 = -0.006x^2 + 1.2x - 40$ to find the distance from the north shore where the water arc is 50 feet above the water.

$$x = \frac{-b \pm \sqrt{b^2 - 4ac}}{2a} \qquad \text{Quadratic formula}$$

> **USE A SHORTCUT**
> Because the value of $b^2 - 4ac$ was calculated in Step 2, you can substitute 0.48 for $b^2 - 4ac$.

$$= \frac{-1.2 \pm \sqrt{0.48}}{2(-0.006)} \qquad \text{Substitute values in the quadratic formula.}$$
$$x \approx 42 \ \text{or} \ x \approx 158 \qquad \text{Use a calculator.}$$

▶ The water arc is 50 feet above the water about 42 feet from the north shore and about 158 feet from the north shore.

✓ **GUIDED PRACTICE** for Example 4

7. **WHAT IF?** In Example 4, does the water arc reach a height of 70 feet? If so, about how far from the north shore is the water arc 70 feet above the water? **yes; 100 ft**

The arc of a baseball hit into the outfield can be modeled by the function $y = -0.005x^2 + 1.2x + 3$, where x is the horizontal distance (in feet) that the baseball travels and y is the height of the baseball. Does the baseball reach a height of 50 feet? If it does, about how far has it traveled horizontally from the hitter? **The ball reaches a height of 50 feet twice. The first time it reaches a height of 50 feet (on its way up), it is at a horizontal distance of 49 feet from the hitter. The second time (on its way down), it is at a horizontal distance of 191 feet from the hitter.**

Closing the Lesson

Have students summarize the major points of the lesson and answer the Essential Question: How do you use the value of the discriminant?

• The discriminant is $b^2 - 4ac$, where a, b, and c are the values when the equation is written in the form $ax^2 + bx + c = 0$.

If the value of the discriminant is positive, there are two solutions. If the value is negative, there are no real-number solutions. If the value is 0, there is one solution.

Differentiated Instruction

Below Level Have students, working with partners, look at Example 4 and determine whether the water arc reaches a height of 100 feet. (It does not.) Then challenge the students to determine the greatest height of the arc. (It is 70 feet.) Have them check their results by graphing the function on their graphing calculators. Then have them write a brief summary of what they discovered.

See also the *Algebra 1 Toolkit* for more strategies.

10.7 **EXERCISES**

HOMEWORK KEY
○ = **WORKED-OUT SOLUTIONS**
on p. WS1 for Exs. 9 and 47

★ = **STANDARDIZED TEST PRACTICE**
Exs. 2, 18, 19, 40, 41, and 47

SKILL PRACTICE

[A]

1. **VOCABULARY** Write the quadratic formula and circle the expression that represents the discriminant. $x = \dfrac{-b \pm \sqrt{b^2 - 4ac}}{2a}$, $b^2 - 4ac$ should be circled.

2. ★ **WRITING** *Explain* how the discriminant of $ax^2 + bx + c = 0$ is related to the graph of $y = ax^2 + bx + c$. **See margin.**

EXAMPLES 1 and 2
on pp. 678–679
for Exs. 3–21

USING THE DISCRIMINANT Tell whether the equation has *two solutions*, *one solution*, or *no solution*.

3. $x^2 + x + 1 = 0$
no solution

4. $2x^2 - 5x - 6 = 0$
two solutions

5. $-2x^2 + 8x - 4 = 0$
two solutions

6. $3m^2 - 6m + 7 = 0$
no solution

7. $9v^2 - 6v + 1 = 0$
one solution

8. $-3q^2 + 8 = 0$
two solutions

○9. $25p^2 - 16p = 0$
two solutions

10. $2h^2 + 3 = 4h$
no solution

11. $10 = x^2 - 5x$
two solutions

12. $\frac{1}{4}z^2 + 2 = z$
no solution

13. $-3g^2 - 4g = \frac{4}{3}$
one solution

14. $8r^2 + 10r - 1 = 4r$
two solutions

15. $3n^2 + 3 = 10n - 3n^2$
two solutions

16. $8x^2 + 9 = 4x^2 - 4x + 8$
one solution

17. $w^2 - 7w + 29 = 4 - 7w$
no solution

18. ★ **MULTIPLE CHOICE** What is the value of the discriminant of the equation $5x^2 - 7x - 2 = 0$? **D**

Ⓐ -9 Ⓑ 9 Ⓒ 59 Ⓓ 89

19. ★ **MULTIPLE CHOICE** How many solutions does $-x^2 + 4x = 8$ have? **A**

Ⓐ None   Ⓑ One   Ⓒ Two   Ⓓ Three

ERROR ANALYSIS *Describe* and correct the error in finding the number of solutions of the equation. **20–21. See margin.**

20. $4x^2 + 12x + 9 = 0$

$b^2 - 4ac = 12^2 - 4(4)(9)$

$= 144 - 144$

$= 0$

The equation has two solutions. ✕

21. $3x^2 - 7x - 4 = -9$

$b^2 - 4ac = (-7)^2 - 4(3)(-4)$

$= 49 - (-48)$

$= 97$

The equation has two solutions. ✕

EXAMPLE 3
on p. 679
for Exs. 22–30

FINDING THE NUMBER OF x-INTERCEPTS Find the number of x-intercepts of the graph of the function.

22. $y = x^2 - 2x - 4$ **2**

23. $y = 2x^2 - x - 1$ **2**

24. $y = 4x^2 + 4x + 1$ **1**

25. $y = 2x^2 - 5x + 5$ **0**

26. $y = x^2 - 6x + 9$ **1**

27. $y = 6x^2 + x + 2$ **0**

28. $y = -13x^2 + 2x + 6$ **2**

29. $y = \frac{1}{4}x^2 - 3x + 9$ **1**

30. $y = \frac{2}{3}x^2 - 5x + 12$

[B]

REASONING Give a value of c for which the equation has (a) two solutions, (b) one solution, and (c) no solution. **31–33. Sample answers are given for parts (a) and (c).**

31. $x^2 - 2x + c = 0$
(a) 0, (b) 1, (c) 2

32. $x^2 - 8x + c = 0$
(a) 15, (b) 16, (c) 17

33. $4x^2 + 12x + c = 0$
(a) 8, (b) 9, (c) 10

10.7 Interpret the Discriminant   **681**

---

2. The value of the discriminant (positive, zero, or negative) determines the number of solutions of the equation $ax^2 + bx + c = 0$, which is the same as the number of x-intercepts of the graph of $y = ax^2 + bx + c$.

20. The discriminant, 0, was interpreted incorrectly; the equation has one solution.

21. Before calculating the discriminant, the equation must be written in standard form: $3x^2 - 7x + 5$. Thus, c is 5, not 9, so $b^2 - 4ac = (-7)^2 - 4(3)(5) = 49 - 60 = -11$, the equation has no solution.

4 **PRACTICE AND APPLY**

Assignment Guide

📄 **Answer Transparencies** available for all exercises

Basic:
Day 1: pp. 681–683
Exs. 1–11, 18–26, 31–35, 45–48, 51, 54, 57, 60, 63

Average:
Day 1: pp. 681–683
Exs. 1, 2, 11–21, 27–41, 45–49, 52, 58, 64

Advanced:
Day 1: pp. 681–683
Exs. 1, 2, 13–19, 28–50*, 56, 62, 65

Block:
pp. 681–683
Exs. 1, 2, 11–21, 27–41, 45–49, 52, 58, 64 (with 10.6)

Differentiated Instruction

See *Algebra 1 Best Practices Toolkit* for suggestions on addressing the needs of a diverse classroom.

Homework Check

For a quick check of student understanding of key concepts, go over the following exercises:
Basic: 6, 10, 23, 26, 45
Average: 12, 14, 28, 31, 45
Advanced: 15, 17, 30, 32, 46

Extra Practice

• Student Edition, p. 947
• Chapter 10 Resource Book:
  Practice levels A, B, C, pp. 81–83

Practice Worksheet

An easily-readable reduced practice page (with answers) for this lesson can be found on p. 626C.

34. $y = x^2 - 3x + 2$ **35.** $y = 3x^2 - 6x + 3$ **36.** $y = 6x^2 - 2x + 4$

37. $y = -15x^2 + 10x - 25$ **38.** $y = -3x^2 - 4x + 8$ **39.** $y = 9x^2 - 24x + 16$

40. ★ **OPEN-ENDED** Write a function of the form $y = ax^2 + bx + c$ whose
graph has one *x*-intercept. ***Sample answer: $y = x^2 + 14x + 49$***

41. ★ **EXTENDED RESPONSE** Use the rectangular prism shown.

   a. The surface area of the prism is 314 square meters. Write
an equation that you can solve to find the value of *w*.
$314 = 2w^2 + 40w + 64$

   b. Use the discriminant to determine the number of values of
w in the equation from part (a). **2**

   c. Solve the equation. Do the value(s) of *w* make sense in the
context of the problem? *Explain.*

8 m

w m

$(w + 4)$ m

[C] **CHALLENGE** Find all values of *k* for which the equation has (a) two solutions,
(b) one solution, and (c) no solution. **See margin.**

42. $2x^2 + x + 3k = 0$ **43.** $x^2 - 4kx + 36 = 0$ **44.** $kx^2 + 5x - 16 = 0$

PROBLEM SOLVING

EXAMPLE 4 [A]
on p. 680
for Exs. 45–46

45. BIOLOGY The amount *y* (in milliliters per gram of body mass per hour)
of oxygen consumed by a parakeet during flight can be modeled by the
function $y = 0.06x^2 - 4x + 87$ where *x* is the speed (in kilometers per
hour) of the parakeet.

   a. Use the discriminant to show that it is possible for a parakeet to
consume 25 milliliters of oxygen per gram of body mass per hour. **See margin.**

   b. Find the speed(s) at which the parakeet consumes 25 milliliters of
oxygen per gram of body mass per hour. Round your solution(s) to
the nearest tenth. **24.5 km/h and 42.2 km/h**

@HomeTutor for problem solving help at classzone.com

46. FOOD For the period 1950–1999, the average amount *y* (in pounds per
person per year) of butter consumed in the United States can be modeled
by $y = 0.0051x^2 - 0.37x + 11$ where *x* is the number of years since 1950.
According to the model, did the butter consumption in the United States
ever reach 5 pounds per person per year? If so, in what year(s)? **yes; 1974 and 1988**

@HomeTutor for problem solving help at classzone.com

(47.) ★ **SHORT RESPONSE** The frame of the tent shown is
defined by a rectangular base and two parabolic arches
that connect the opposite corners of the base. The graph
of $y = -0.18x^2 + 1.6x$ models the height *y* (in feet) of one
of the arches *x* feet along the diagonal of the base. Can
a child that is 4 feet tall walk under one of the arches
without having to bend over? *Explain.* **See margin.**

○ = **WORKED-OUT SOLUTIONS**
on p. WS1

★ = **STANDARDIZED
TEST PRACTICE**

Avoiding Common Errors

Exercises 3–19, 22–30 A common
error students make is equating a
discriminant of 0 with no solution.
Remind these students that when
the discriminant is zero, then the
quadratic formula simplifies to

$x = \dfrac{-b \pm \sqrt{0}}{2a} = -\dfrac{b}{2a}$, so there is

one solution to the quadratic
equation.

Mathematical Reasoning

Exercises 34–39 Before students
attempt these exercises, you may
want to ask them to describe when
the graph of an opening-upward
parabola has and does not have
solutions, and when the graph of
an opening-downward parabola
has and does not have solutions.

Internet Reference

Exercise 49 For more information
about trampoline competitions,
visit the USA Gymnastics' site at
www.usa-gymnastics.org/tt/
about-tt.html

34. Below; $a > 0$, so the graph
opens up. The value of the discriminant is $(-3)^2 - 4(1)(2) = 1 > 0$, so
the graph has two *x*-intercepts;
a parabola that opens up and has
two *x*-intercepts must have its
vertex below the *x*-axis.

35. On; the value of the discriminant is $(-6)^2 - 4(3)(3) = 0$, so the
graph has exactly one *x*-intercept.
A parabola that has exactly one
x-intercept must have its vertex on
the *x*-axis.

36. Above; $a > 0$, so the graph
opens up. The value of the discriminant is $(-2)^2 - 4(6)(4) = -60 < 0$,
so the graph has no *x*-intercepts;
a parabola that opens up and has
no *x*-intercepts must have its
vertex above the *x*-axis.

37. Below; $a < 0$, so the graph
opens down. The value of the discriminant is $(10)^2 - 4(-15)(-25)$
$= -1400 < 0$, so the graph has no
x-intercepts; a parabola that
opens down and has no *x*-inter-
cepts must have its vertex below
the *x*-axis.

38. Above; $a < 0$, so the graph opens down. The value of the discriminant
is $(-4)^2 - 4(-3)(8) = 112 > 0$, so the graph has two *x*-intercepts; a
parabola that opens down and has two *x*-intercepts must have its vertex
above the *x*-axis.

39. On; the value of the discriminant is $(-24)^2 - 4(9)(16) = 0$, so the
graph has exactly one *x*-intercept; a parabola that has exactly one
x-intercept must have its vertex on the *x*-axis.

41c, 42–44, 45a, 47. See Additional Answers beginning on p. AA1.

48. SCIENCE Between the months of April and September, the number y of hours of daylight per day in Seattle, Washington, can be modeled by $y = -0.00046x^2 + 0.076x + 13$ where x is the number of days since April 1.

   a. Do any of the days between April and September in Seattle have 17 hours of daylight? If so, how many? **no**

   b. Do any of the days between April and September in Seattle have 14 hours of daylight? If so, how many? **yes; 2**

49. MULTI-STEP PROBLEM During a trampoline competition, a trampolinist leaves the mat when her center of gravity is 6 feet above the ground. She has an initial vertical velocity of 32 feet per second.

   a. Use the vertical motion model to write an equation that models the height h (in feet) of the center of gravity of the trampolinist as a function of the time t (in seconds) into her jump. $h = -16t^2 + 32t + 6$

   b. Does her center of gravity reach a height of 24 feet during the jump? If so, at what time(s)? **no**

   c. On another jump, the trampolinist leaves the mat when her center of gravity is 6 feet above the ground and with an initial vertical velocity of 35 feet per second. Does her center of gravity reach a height of 24 feet on this jump? If so, at what time(s)?
   yes; about 0.8 sec and about 1.4 sec

50. CHALLENGE Last year, a manufacturer sold backpacks for $24 each. At this price, the manufacturer sold about 1000 backpacks per week. A marketing analyst predicts that for every $1 reduction in the price of the backpack, the manufacturer will sell 100 more backpacks per week.

   a. Write a function that models the weekly revenue R (in dollars) that the manufacturer will receive for x reductions of $1 in the price of the backpack. $R = -100x^2 + 1400x + 24{,}000$

   b. Is it possible for the manufacturer to receive a weekly revenue of $28,000? $30,000? What is the maximum weekly revenue that the manufacturer can receive? *Explain* your answers using the discriminants of quadratic equations. **See margin.**

MIXED REVIEW

PREVIEW
Prepare for
Lesson 10.8 in
Exs. 51–56.

Graph the function. **51–56. See margin.**

51. $y = 5x - 10$ *(p. 225)* **52.** $y = \frac{1}{4}x$ *(p. 244)* **53.** $y = \frac{3}{4}x - 5$ *(p. 244)*

54. $y = 5^x$ *(p. 520)* **55.** $y = (0.2)^x$ *(p. 531)* **56.** $y = 6x^2 - 3$ *(p. 628)*

Solve the equation.

57. $a + 5 = 2$ *(p. 134)* **−3** **58.** $f - 6 = 13$ *(p. 134)* **19** **59.** $4z - 3 = -7$ *(p. 141)* **−1**

60. $9w + 4 = -41$ *(p. 141)* **−5** **61.** $2b - b - 6 = 8$ *(p. 148)* **14** **62.** $5 + 2(x - 4) = 9$ *(p. 148)* **6**

Solve the equation by factoring. *(p. 593)*

63. $2x^2 - 3x - 5 = 0$ **−1, $2\frac{1}{2}$** **64.** $4n^2 + 2n - 6 = 0$ **−1$\frac{1}{2}$, 1** **65.** $5a^2 + 21a + 4 = 0$ **−4, −$\frac{1}{5}$**

EXTRA PRACTICE for Lesson 10.7, p. 947   **ONLINE QUIZ** at classzone.com   **683**

51–56. See Additional Answers beginning on p. AA1.

---

1. Graph $y = 3^x$.

2. Tell whether the ordered pairs (0, 0), (1, 2), (2, 4), and (3, 6) represent a linear function. **yes**

3. For $y = x^2 - 3x - 5$, find corresponding y-values for the x-values -2, 1, and 3. **5, -7, -5**

Notetaking Guide

📄 Transparency Available

Promotes interactive learning and notetaking skills, pp. 242–244.

Pacing

Basic: 2 days

Average: 2 days

Advanced: 2 days

Block: 1 block

• See *Teaching Guide/Lesson Plan.*

2 FOCUS AND MOTIVATE

Essential Question

Big Idea 3, p. 627

How do you decide whether a linear, exponential, or quadratic model best represents data? **Tell students they will learn how to answer this question by making comparisons between the models.**

NCTM STANDARDS

Standard 2: Understand patterns; Understand functions

10.8 Compare Linear, Exponential, and Quadratic Models

Before	You graphed linear, exponential, and quadratic functions.
Now	You will compare linear, exponential, and quadratic models.
Why?	So you can solve a problem about biology, as in Ex. 23.

Key Vocabulary
• **linear function,** *p. 217*
• **exponential function,** *p. 520*
• **quadratic function,** *p. 628*

So far you have studied linear functions, exponential functions, and quadratic functions. You can use these functions to model data.

> **KEY CONCEPT** *For Your Notebook*
>
> **Linear, Exponential, and Quadratic Functions**
>
> | Linear Function | Exponential Function | Quadratic Function |
> |---|---|---|
> | $y = mx + b$ | $y = ab^x$ | $y = ax^2 + bx + c$ |
>
>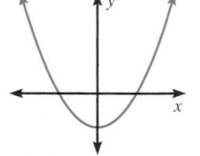

EXAMPLE 1 Choose functions using sets of ordered pairs

Use a graph to tell whether the ordered pairs represent a *linear function*, an *exponential function*, or a *quadratic function*.

a. $\left(-4, \frac{1}{32}\right), \left(-2, \frac{1}{8}\right), \left(0, \frac{1}{2}\right), (2, 2), (4, 8)$

b. $(-4, 1), (-2, 2), (0, 3), (2, 4), (4, 5)$

c. $(-4, 5), (-2, 2), (0, 1), (2, 2), (4, 5)$

Solution

a.
b.
c.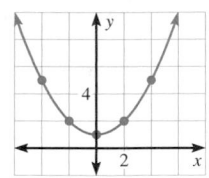

Exponential function　　Linear function　　Quadratic function

Animated Algebra at classzone.com

684 Chapter 10 Quadratic Equations and Functions

Resource Planning Guide

Chapter Resource Book
• Teaching Guide/Lesson Plan (pp. 89–90)
• Practice levels A, B, C (pp. 92–97)
• Study Guide (pp. 98–99)
• Catch-up for Absent Students (p. 100)
• Problem Solving Workshop (p. 101)
• Challenge (p. 102)

Workbooks
• Notetaking Guide (pp. 242–244)
• Practice Workbook (pp. 166–168)

Teaching Options
• **Power Presentations CD-ROM** provides dynamic electronic teaching resources for the classroom.
• **Activity Generator CD-ROM** provides editable activities for all ability levels.

Interactive Technology
• Easy Planner
• Power Presentations CD-ROM
• Activity Generator CD-ROM
• Animated Algebra
• Test Generator CD-ROM
• Online Quiz
• eWorkbook
• eEdition
• @HomeTutor

Resources for English Learners
• Quick Reference for English Learners
• Spanish Study Guide
• Multi-Language Visual Glossary
• Student Resources in Spanish

See also the *Algebra 1 Toolkit* for more strategies for meeting individual needs.

DIFFERENCES AND RATIOS A table of values represents a linear function if the *differences* of successive *y*-values are all equal. A table of values represents an exponential function if the *ratios* of successive *y*-values are all equal. In both cases, the increments between successive *x*-values need to be equal.

Linear function: $y = 3x + 5$

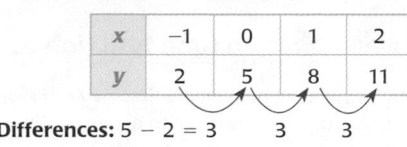

Differences: $5 - 2 = 3$ 3   3

Exponential function: $y = 0.5(2)^x$

Ratios: $\frac{0.5}{0.25} = 2$ 2   2

You can use differences to tell whether a table of values represents a quadratic function, as shown.

Quadratic function: $y = x^2 - 2x + 2$

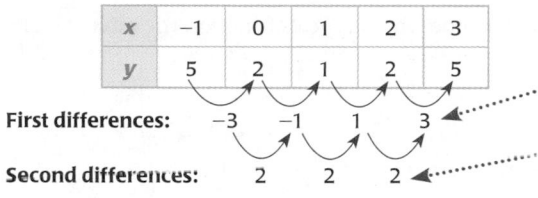

First differences: −3   −1   1   3 ◀····· First find the differences of successive *y*-values, or *first differences*.

Second differences: 2   2   2 ◀····· Then find the differences of successive first differences, or *second differences*.

The table of values represents a quadratic function if the second differences are all equal.

CHECK VALUES OF *x*
When deciding what function is represented by a table of values, be sure that the values of *x* are increasing by the same amount.

EXAMPLE 2 **Identify functions using differences or ratios**

Use differences or ratios to tell whether the table of values represents a *linear function*, an *exponential function*, or a *quadratic function*.

a.

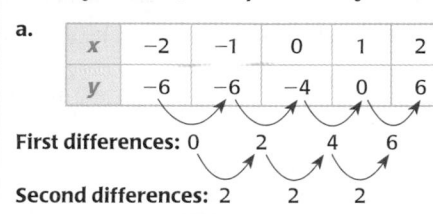

First differences: 0   2   4   6

Second differences: 2   2   2

▶ The table of values represents a quadratic function.

b.

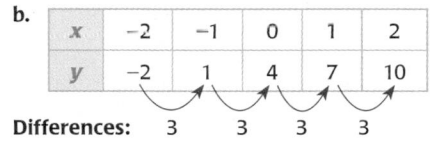

Differences: 3   3   3   3

▶ The table of values represents a linear function.

✓ **GUIDED PRACTICE**   for Examples 1 and 2

1. Tell whether the ordered pairs represent a *linear function*, an *exponential function*, or a *quadratic function*: (0, −1.5), (1, −0.5), (2, 2.5), (3, 7.5).
quadratic function

2. Tell whether the table of values represents a *linear function*, an *exponential function*, or a *quadratic function*. **exponential function**

x	−2	−1	0	1
y	0.08	0.4	2	10

Differentiated Instruction

Inclusion Some students may find a table of differences difficult to write because the alignment of the columns must be precise. One method is to align a page of ruled notebook paper so that the lines are vertical. Each ordered pair (*x*, *y*) occupies one column.

See also the *Algebra 1 Toolkit* for more strategies.

Motivating the Lesson
You create T-shirts with designs and slogans. You want to examine your sales for the past year to determine whether you should increase the price of the T-shirts, decrease the price, or keep the price the same. By knowing how to choose a linear, exponential, or quadratic model that fits the data, you can model the situation and determine the best price for your T-shirts.

❸ TEACH

Extra Example 1
Use a graph to tell whether the ordered pairs represent a *linear function*, an *exponential function*, or a *quadratic function*.

a. $\left(-2, \frac{1}{4}\right), \left(-1, \frac{1}{2}\right), (0, 1), (1, 2), (2, 4)$

exponential function

b. $(-2, -1), (-1, 0), (0, 1), (1, 2), (2, 3)$

linear function

c. $(-2, 5), (-1, 2), (0, 1), (1, 2), (2, 5)$

quadratic function

Animated Algebra
classzone.com

An **Animated Algebra** activity is available on-line for **Example 1**. This activity is also available on the **Power Presentations CD-ROM**.

685

WRITING AN EQUATION When you decide that a set of ordered pairs represents a linear, an exponential, or a quadratic function, you can write an equation for the function. In this lesson, when you write an equation for a quadratic function, the equation will have the form $y = ax^2$.

EXAMPLE 3 Write an equation for a function

Tell whether the table of values represents a *linear function*, an *exponential function*, or a *quadratic function*. Then write an equation for the function.

x	−2	−1	0	1	2
y	2	0.5	0	0.5	2

Solution

STEP 1 Determine which type of function the table of values represents.

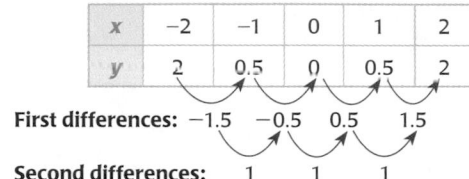

x	−2	−1	0	1	2
y	2	0.5	0	0.5	2

First differences: −1.5 −0.5 0.5 1.5

Second differences: 1 1 1

The table of values represents a quadratic function because the second differences are equal.

STEP 2 Write an equation for the quadratic function. The equation has the form $y = ax^2$. Find the value of *a* by using the coordinates of a point that lies on the graph, such as (1, 0.5).

$y = ax^2$ Write equation for quadratic function.

$0.5 = a(1)^2$ Substitute 1 for *x* and 0.5 for *y*.

$0.5 = a$ Solve for *a*.

▶ The equation is $y = 0.5x^2$.

AVOID ERRORS
In Example 3, do not use (0, 0) to find the value of *a*, even though (0, 0) lies on the graph of $y = ax^2$. If you do, you will obtain an undefined value for *a*.

CHECK Plot the ordered pairs from the table. Then graph $y = 0.5x^2$ to see that the graph passes through the plotted points.

✓ GUIDED PRACTICE for Example 3

Tell whether the table of values represents a *linear function*, an *exponential function*, or a *quadratic function*. Then write an equation for the function.

3.

x	−3	−2	−1	0	1
y	−7	−5	−3	−1	1

4.

x	−2	−1	0	1	2
y	8	2	0	2	8

3, 4. See margin.

EXAMPLE 4 **Solve a multi-step problem**

CYCLING The table shows the breathing rate y (in liters of air per minute) of a cyclist traveling at different speeds x (in miles per hour). Tell whether the data can be modeled by a *linear function*, an *exponential function*, or a *quadratic function*. Then write an equation for the function.

Speed of cyclist, x (mi/h)	20	21	22	23	24	25
Breathing rate, y (L/min)	51.4	57.1	63.3	70.3	78.0	86.6

Solution

STEP 1 **Graph** the data. The graph has a slight curve. So, a linear function does not appear to model the data.

STEP 2 **Decide** which function models the data. In the table below, notice that $\frac{57.1}{51.4} \approx 1.11$, $\frac{63.3}{57.1} \approx 1.11$, $\frac{70.3}{63.3} \approx 1.11$, $\frac{78.0}{70.3} \approx 1.11$, and $\frac{86.6}{78.0} \approx 1.11$. So, the ratios are all approximately equal. An exponential function models the data.

Speed of cyclist (mi/h)

Speed of cyclist, x (mi/h)	20	21	22	23	24	25
Breathing rate, y (L/min)	51.4	57.1	63.3	70.3	78.0	86.6

Ratios: 1.11 1.11 1.11 1.11 1.11

STEP 3 **Write** an equation for the exponential function. The breathing rate increases by a factor of 1.11 liters per minute, so $b = 1.11$. Find the value of a by using one of the data pairs, such as (20, 51.4).

REVIEW EXPONENTIAL FUNCTIONS
For help with writing an equation for an exponential function, see p. 520.

$y = ab^x$ **Write equation for exponential function.**

$51.4 = a(1.11)^{20}$ **Substitute 1.11 for b, 20 for x, and 51.4 for y.**

$\dfrac{51.4}{(1.11)^{20}} = a$ **Solve for a.**

$6.38 \approx a$ **Use a calculator.**

▸ The equation is $y = 6.38(1.11)^x$.

✓ **GUIDED PRACTICE** **for Example 4**

5. In Example 4, suppose the cyclist is traveling at 15 miles per hour. Find the breathing rate of the cyclist at this speed. **about 30.5 liters of air per minute**

10.8 Compare Linear, Exponential, and Quadratic Models **687**

HOMEWORK KEY

○ = **WORKED-OUT SOLUTIONS**
on p. WS1 for Exs. 7, 13, and 25

★ = **STANDARDIZED TEST PRACTICE**
Exs. 2, 18, 26, and 27

◆ = **MULTIPLE REPRESENTATIONS**
Ex. 25

PRACTICE AND APPLY

4

Assignment Guide

📖 **Answer Transparencies available for all exercises**

Basic:
Day 1: pp. 688–691
Exs. 1–11, 35–43
Day 2: pp. 688–691
Exs. 12–20, 23–26, 29–34

Average:
Day 1: pp. 688–691
Exs. 1–11, 35–43
Day 2: pp. 688–691
Exs. 14–21, 23–27, 29–34

Advanced:
Day 1: pp. 688–691
Exs. 1–11, 35–43
Day 2: pp. 688–691
Exs. 15–18, 20–34*

Block:
pp. 688–691
Exs. 1–11, 14–21, 23–27, 29–43

Differentiated Instruction

See *Algebra 1 Best Practices Toolkit* for suggestions on addressing the needs of a diverse classroom.

Homework Check

For a quick check of student understanding of key concepts, go over the following exercises:

Basic: 4, 6, 12, 15, 23
Average: 3, 8, 15, 20, 24
Advanced: 10, 16, 20, 25, 26

Extra Practice

• Student Edition, p. 947
• Chapter 10 Resource Book: Practice levels A, B, C, pp. 92–97

Practice Worksheet

An easily-readable reduced practice page (with answers) for this lesson can be found on p. 626C.

SKILL PRACTICE

A 1. **VOCABULARY** Copy and complete: A function that is of the form $y = ab^x$ is a(n) __?__ . **exponential function**

2. ★ **WRITING** *Describe* how you can tell whether a table of values represents a quadratic function. **See margin.**

EXAMPLE 1
on p. 684
for Exs. 3–11

MATCHING Match the function with the graph that the function represents.

3. Linear function **B**   4. Exponential function **C**   5. Quadratic function **A**

A.

B.

C.
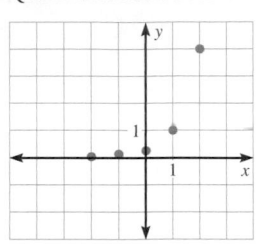

USING A GRAPH Use a graph to tell whether the ordered pairs represent a *linear function*, an *exponential function*, or a *quadratic function*.

6. $(-4, -7), (-2, -1), (0, 1), (2, -1), (4, -7)$
   quadratic function

7. $(-5, -1), (-3, 0), (-1, 1), (1, 2), (3, 3)$
   linear function

8. $\left(-1, \frac{1}{16}\right), \left(0, \frac{1}{4}\right), (1, 1), (2, 4), (3, 16)$
   exponential function

9. $(-1, 8), (1, 2), \left(3, \frac{1}{2}\right), \left(5, \frac{1}{8}\right), \left(7, \frac{1}{32}\right)$
   exponential function

10. $(-4, -4), (-2, -3.5), (0, -3), (2, -2.5)$
    linear function

11. $(-1, 0.5), (0, -0.5), (1, 0.5), (2, 3.5)$
    quadratic function

EXAMPLES 2 and 3
on p. 685–686
for Exs. 12–19

USING DIFFERENCES AND RATIOS Tell whether the table of values represents a *linear function*, an *exponential function*, or a *quadratic function*. Then write an equation for the function.

12.

x	0	1	2	3	4
y	1	0	−1	−2	−3

linear function; $y = -x + 1$

13.

x	−2	−1	0	1	2
y	−4	−1	0	−1	−4

quadratic function; $y = -x^2$

14.
x	−3	−2	−1	0	1
y	13.5	6	1.5	0	1.5

quadratic function; $y = 1.5x^2$

15.

x	−2	−1	0	1	2
y	−5	−2	1	4	7

linear function; $y = 3x + 1$

16.
x	−2	−1	0	1	2
y	$\frac{1}{9}$	$\frac{1}{3}$	1	3	9

exponential function; $y = 3^x$

17.
x	−1	0	1	2	3
y	16	4	1	$\frac{1}{4}$	$\frac{1}{16}$

exponential function; $y = 4\left(\frac{1}{4}\right)^x$

18. ★ **MULTIPLE CHOICE** Which function is represented by the following ordered pairs: $(-1, 4), (0, 0), (1, 4), (2, 16), (3, 36)$? **C**

A $y = 0.25x^2$ **B** $y = 4^x$ **C** $y = 4x^2$ **D** $y = 4x$

---

2. Find the differences of successive *y*-values, called the first differences. If they are not equal, then find the differences of successive first differences, called second differences. If the second differences are equal, then the table of values represents a quadratic function.

19. ERROR ANALYSIS *Describe* and correct the error in writing an equation for the function represented by the ordered pairs. **See margin.**

$(0, 0), (1, 2.5), (2, 10), (3, 22.5), (4, 40)$

x	0	1	2	3	4
y	0	2.5	10	22.5	40

First differences: 2.5   7.5   12.5   17.5

Second differences: 5   5   5

The ordered pairs represent a quadratic function.

$y = ax^2$

$2 = a(10)^2$

$0.02 = a$

So, the equation is $y = 0.02x^2$.

B **20. REASONING** Use the graph shown.

a. Tell whether the graph represents an *exponential function* or a *quadratic function* by looking at the graph. **exponential function**

b. Make a table of values for the points on the graph. Then use differences or ratios to check your answer in part (a). **See margin.**

c. Write an equation for the function that the table of values from part (b) represents. $y = 2^x$

21. ⬡ **GEOMETRY** The table shows the area A (in square centimeters) of an equilateral triangle for various side lengths s (in centimeters). Write an equation for the function that the table of values represents. Then find the area of an equilateral triangle that has a side length of 10 centimeters.

Side length, s (cm)	1	2	3	4	5
Area, A (cm²)	$0.25\sqrt{3}$	$\sqrt{3}$	$2.25\sqrt{3}$	$4\sqrt{3}$	$6.25\sqrt{3}$

$A = \left(\dfrac{\sqrt{3}}{4}\right)s^2; 25\sqrt{3}$ cm²

C **22. CHALLENGE** In the ordered pairs below, the y-values are given in terms of m. Tell whether the ordered pairs represent a *linear function*, an *exponential function*, or a *quadratic function*.

$(1, 3m - 1), (2, 10m + 2), (3, 24m), (4, 40m + 8), (5, 67m - 1)$ **quadratic function**

PROBLEM SOLVING

EXAMPLE 4 **A**
on p. 687
for Exs. 23–25

23. LIZARDS The table shows the body temperature B (in degrees Celsius) of a desert spiny lizard at various air temperatures A (in degrees Celsius). Tell whether the data can be modeled by a *linear function*, an *exponential function*, or a *quadratic function*. Then write an equation for the function.

Air temperature, A (°C)	26	27	28	29	30
Body temperature, B (°C)	33.44	33.78	34.12	34.46	34.80

@HomeTutor for problem solving help at classzone.com

linear function; $y = 0.34x + 24.6$

10.8 Compare Linear, Exponential, and Quadratic Models **689**

19. The *x*- and *y*-values were reversed when substituting the coordinates of the ordered pair (2, 10) into the equation $y = ax^2$. Substituting 2 for *x* and 10 for *y* gives $10 = a(2)^2$, $a = 2.5$; so, the equation is $y = 2.5x^2$.

20b.

x	1	2	3	4
y	2	4	8	16
Ratios of successive y-values	$\frac{2}{1} = 2$	$\frac{4}{2} = 2$	$\frac{8}{4} = 2$	$\frac{16}{8} = 2$

The ratios are the same, so the table of values and the graph represent an exponential function.

Avoiding Common Errors
Exercises 6–11, 12–17 A common error arises out of trying to identify a function by looking at a table of values or ordered pairs without graphing the ordered pairs or checking for differences or ratios in the table of values. Encourage students to plot points and calculate differences and ratios.

Graphing Calculator
Exercises 12–17 Encourage students to use their graphing calculators to check their equations.

Internet Reference

Exercise 23 More information about desert spiny lizards can be found at www.werc.usgs.gov/fieldguide/scma.htm

24. NAUTILUS A chambered nautilus is a marine animal that lives in the outermost chamber of its shell. When the nautilus outgrows a chamber, it adds a new, larger chamber to its shell. The table shows the volumes (in cubic centimeters) of consecutive chambers of a nautilus. Tell whether the data can be modeled by a *linear function*, an *exponential function*, or a *quadratic function*. Then write an equation for the function. **exponential function; $y = 0.791(1.06)^x$**

Chamber	1	2	3	4	5	6
Volume (cm³)	0.837	0.889	0.945	1.005	1.068	1.135

@HomeTutor for problem solving help at classzone.com

25. ◆ **MULTIPLE REPRESENTATIONS** Fold a rectangular piece of paper in half. Open the paper and record the number of folds and the number of sections created. Repeat by increasing the number of folds by 1 fold each time.

  a. Making a Table Copy and complete the table.

Folds	1	2	3	4	5
Sections	? **2**	? **4**	? **8**	? **16**	? **32**

  b. Drawing a Graph Graph the data in part (a). Use the graph and the table to tell whether the data can be modeled by a *linear function*, an *exponential function*, or a *quadratic function*. **See margin for art; exponential function.**

  c. Writing a Model Write an equation for the function that models the data. Then find the number of sections that are created by 7 folds. **$y = 2^x$; 128 sections**

26. ★ **MULTIPLE CHOICE** The table shows the cost of a custom circular rug for various diameters (in feet). What is the approximate cost of a custom circular rug that has a diameter of 8 feet? **C**

Diameter (ft)	2	3	4	5	6
Cost (dollars)	28.40	63.90	113.60	177.50	255.60

  A $333.70   **B** $411.80   **C** $454.40   **D** $908.80

27. ★ **EXTENDED RESPONSE** The time it takes for a clock's pendulum to swing from one side to the other and back again, as shown in the back view of the clock, is called the pendulum's period. The table shows the period t (in seconds) of a pendulum of length ℓ (in feet).

Period, t (sec)	1	2	3	4	5
Length, ℓ (ft)	0.82	3.28	7.38	13.12	20.5

  a. Model Tell whether the data can be modeled by a *linear function*, an *exponential function*, or a *quadratic function*. Then write an equation for the function. **quadratic function; $d = 0.82t^2$**

  b. Apply Find the length of a pendulum that has a period of 0.5 second. **0.205 ft**

  c. Analyze How does decreasing the length of the pendulum by 50% change the period? *Justify* your answer using several examples. **See margin.**

○ = WORKED-OUT SOLUTIONS on p. WS1   ★ = STANDARDIZED TEST PRACTICE   ◆ = MULTIPLE REPRESENTATIONS

28. CHALLENGE The table shows the height h (in feet) that a pole vaulter's center of gravity reaches for various running speeds s (in feet per second) at the moment the pole vaulter launches himself into the air.

Running speed, s (ft/sec)	30	31	32	33	34
Height of center of gravity, h (ft)	$14\frac{1}{16}$	$15\frac{1}{64}$	16	$17\frac{1}{64}$	$18\frac{1}{16}$

  a. A pole vaulter is running at $31\frac{1}{2}$ feet per second when he launches himself into the air. Find the height that the pole vaulter's center of gravity reaches. **about 15.5 ft**

  b. Find the speed at which the pole vaulter needs to be running when he launches himself into the air in order for his center of gravity to reach a height of 19 feet. Round your answer to the nearest foot per second. **about 35 ft/sec**

MIXED REVIEW

PREVIEW
Prepare for
Lesson 11.1 in
Exs. 29–43.

Approximate the square root to the nearest integer. *(p. 110)*

29. $\sqrt{32}$ **6**   **30.** $\sqrt{45}$ **7**   **31.** $-\sqrt{10}$ **−3**

32. $-\sqrt{60}$ **−8**   **33.** $-\sqrt{79}$ **−9**   **34.** $\sqrt{57}$ **8**

Graph the function. Compare the graph with the graph of $f(x) = x$. *(p. 262)*
35–40. See margin.

35. $g(x) = x - 4$ **36.** $g(x) = x + 1$ **37.** $g(x) = 8x$

38. $g(x) = -x$ **39.** $g(x) = \frac{1}{4}x$ **40.** $g(x) = -\frac{1}{2}x$

Graph the function. Compare the graph with the graph of $y = x^2$. *(p. 628)*
41–43. See margin.

41. $y = 7x^2$ **42.** $y = -\frac{1}{5}x^2$ **43.** $y = 2x^2 + 3$

QUIZ *for Lessons 10.7–10.8*

Tell whether the equation has *two solutions*, *one solution*, or *no solution*. *(p. 678)*

  1. $x^2 + x + 5 = 0$ **no solution**   **2.** $5x^2 + 4x - 1 = 0$ **two solutions**

Find the number of x-intercepts of the graph of the function. *(p. 678)*

  3. $y = -3x^2 + 4x - 2$ **0**   **4.** $y = \frac{4}{9}x^2 + 4x + 9$ **1**

Tell whether the table of values represents a *linear function*, an *exponential function*, or a *quadratic function*. Then write an equation for the function.
(p. 684) **quadratic function;** $y = -0.25x^2$ **exponential function;** $y = 25\left(\frac{1}{5}\right)^x$

5.

x	−6	−3	0	3	6
y	−9	−2.25	0	−2.25	−9

6.

x	1	2	3	4	5
y	5	1	$\frac{1}{5}$	$\frac{1}{25}$	$\frac{1}{125}$

35–43. See Additional Answers beginning on p. AA1.

10.8 Perform Regressions

QUESTION How can you use a graphing calculator to find models for data?

On page 335, you used a graphing calculator to perform linear regression on data to find a linear model for the data. A graphing calculator can also be used to perform exponential regression and quadratic regression.

EXAMPLE 1 Use exponential regression to find a model

The table shows the sales (in millions of dollars) of organic milk, organic half and half, and organic cream in the U.S. each year for the period 1996–2000. Find an exponential model for the data.

Year	1996	1997	1998	1999	2000
Sales (millions of dollars)	15.8	30.7	46	75.7	104

STEP 1 *Enter data*

Enter the data into two lists. Let $x = 0$ represent 1996.

STEP 2 *Make scatter plot*

Make a scatter plot of the data. Notice that the points show an exponential trend.

STEP 3 *Perform regression*

Use the exponential regression feature to obtain the model $y = 17.5(1.6)^x$.

```
ExpReg
 y=a*b^x
 a=17.50630541
 b=1.595405191
 r²=.9855757858
 r=.9927616964
```

STEP 4 *Check model*

Check how well the model fits the data by graphing the model and the data.

PRACTICE

1. The table shows the value (in dollars) of a car over time. Find an exponential model for the data in the table. $y = 15,600(0.866)^x$

Age of car (years)	0	1	2	3	4	5
Value (dollars)	15,600	13,510	11,700	10,132	8774	7598

EXAMPLE 2 | Use quadratic regression to find a model

In September 2001, the first U.S. digital satellite radio station was launched. The table shows the number of subscribers of the service for various months after its launch. Find a quadratic model for the data.

Months after launch	0	3	6	9	12	15
Subscribers	500	31,000	76,000	135,500	201,500	360,000

STEP 1 Make scatter plot
Enter the data into two lists and make a scatter plot of the data. Notice that the points show a quadratic trend.

STEP 2 Perform regression
Use the quadratic regression feature to obtain the model $y = 1440x^2 + 1010x + 8000$.

STEP 3 Check model
Check how well the model fits the data by graphing the model and the data.

PRACTICE

2. The table shows the maximum weight (in pounds) that can be supported by a 16 foot floor beam of different depths. Find a quadratic model for the data. $y = 10.2x^2 - 96.8x + 285.4$

Depth (inches)	6	7.5	9	10.5	12	13.5
Weight (pounds)	68	137	242	389	586	838

DRAW CONCLUSIONS

3. The table shows the temperature (in degrees Fahrenheit) of a cup of hot chocolate over time. Find an exponential model and a quadratic model for the data. Make a scatter plot of the data and graph both models. Which model fits the data better? *Explain.* **See margin.**

Time (minutes)	0	10	20	30	40	50	60
Temperature (°F)	200	157	128	109	99	92	90

@*HomeTutor*
classzone.com
Keystrokes

Extra Example 2

The table shows the number (in thousands) of basic cable television subscribers in the U.S. from 1997–2002. Find a quadratic model for the data.

Year	Number of Subscribers (in hundred thousands)
1997	636
1998	646.5
1999	855
2000	862.5
2001	667.32
2002	664.72

$y = -1.4x^2 + 13.3x + 635$

③ ASSESS AND RETEACH

The table shows the time it takes Nikki to keyboard 200 words each week with practice. Find an exponential and a quadratic model for the data. Does an exponential or the quadratic model fit the data better? *Explain.*

Week	Number of Minutes to Keyboard 200 Words
1	6
2	5.7
3	4.7
4	4.5
5	3.9
6	3.7

The quadratic model is $y = 0.038x^2 - 0.68x + 6.1$ and the exponential model is $y = 6.05(0.9)^x$. Both models fits the data, so one model is not better than the other.

---

3. $y = 179(0.987)^x$, $y = 0.040x^2 - 4.13x + 197$

The exponential model; although the quadratic model appears to fit the given data points more closely than the exponential model does, the graph shows that after the last data point, (60, 90), the quadratic model implies increasing temperatures as time goes on, while the exponential model shows gradually decreasing temperatures as time goes on; the exponential model is a more accurate model of what will happen as the hot chocolate continues to cool.

Lessons 10.5–10.8

Left margin column (answers):

3. No; substitute 20 for *h* in the equation from part (a) to find the time at which the flyer's center of gravity reaches a height of 20 feet: $20 = -16t^2 + 30t + 4.5$, or $16t^2 - 30t + 15.5 = 0$. The discriminant is -92. Since the discriminant is negative, the equation has no solution, and the flyer's center of gravity never reaches a height of 20 feet.

4. *Sample answer:* 37 ft/sec; to show that $25 = -16t^2 + 37t + 4.5$ has at least one solution, first write the equation in standard form, $16t^2 - 37t + 20.5 = 0$; find the discriminant to be 57. Since the discriminant is positive, the equation has two solutions.

5b. Yes; using the value of the discriminant, 1.44, evaluate the quadratic formula for the equation $-0.05x^2 + 2.2x - 17 = 0$;

$x = \dfrac{-2.2 \pm \sqrt{1.44}}{(2)(-0.05)}$; $x = 10 \text{ or } x = 34$.

$x = 10$ corresponds to the year $1990 + 10 = 2000$, which is in the given period of 1990–2000. $x = 34$ corresponds to the year $1990 + 34 = 2024$, which is not in the given period of 1990–2000.

7. No; let *x* be the length of the rectangular dog pen of perimeter 24 feet. Then $12 - x$ is the width of the dog pen and its area is represented by the expression $x(12 - x)$. To find the value of *x* for which the area will be 150 square feet, solve the equation $150 = x(12 - x)$. Write the equation in standard form, $x^2 - 12x + 150 = 0$; find the value of the discriminant, -456. Since the discriminant is negative, the equation has no solution, and the 24 feet of fencing cannot enclose an area of 150 square feet.

8c. Because *x* represents a length, *x* cannot be a negative number.

Main content:

1. **MULTI-STEP PROBLEM** Different masses (in kilograms) are hung from a spring. The distances (in centimeters) that the spring stretches are shown in the table.

Mass (kilograms)	Distance (centimeters)
1	2.6
2	5.2
3	7.8
4	10.4
5	13.0

   a. Tell whether the data can be modeled by a *linear function*, an *exponential function*, or a *quadratic function*. **linear function**

   b. Write an equation for the function. $y = 2.6x$

2. **MULTI-STEP PROBLEM** In slow-pitch softball, the ball is pitched in an underhand motion. A batter in a softball game is pitched a ball that has an initial height of 2 feet above the ground and an initial vertical velocity of 35 feet per second.

   a. Write an equation for the height *h* (in feet) of the ball as a function of the time *t* (in seconds) after it is pitched. $h = -16t^2 + 35t + 2$

   b. The batter hits the ball when it is 2.5 feet above the ground. How long after the ball is pitched is the ball hit? Round your answer to the nearest tenth of a second. **2.2 sec**

3. **SHORT RESPONSE** Part of a cheerleading routine involves throwing a flyer straight up into the air and catching her on the way down. The flyer begins this stunt with her center of gravity 4.5 feet above the ground, and she is thrown with an initial vertical velocity of 30 feet per second. Will her center of gravity reach a height of 20 feet? *Explain.* **See margin.**

4. **OPEN-ENDED** In Exercise 3, suppose the flyer wants to have her center of gravity reach a height of at least 25 feet above the ground. Give an initial vertical velocity that will accomplish this. Use the discriminant to show that your answer is correct. **See margin.**

5. **SHORT RESPONSE** For the period 1990–2000, the sales *y* (in billions of dollars) of computers, computer accessories, and computer software can be modeled by the function $y = -0.05x^2 + 2.2x + 7$ where *x* is the number of years since 1990.

   a. Use the discriminant to determine the number of values of *x* that correspond to $y = 24$. **2**

   b. Were there any years during the period 1990–2000 in which the sales reached 24 billion dollars? *Explain.* See margin.

6. **GRIDDED ANSWER** The trapezoid below has an area of 54 square inches. What is the value of *x*? **5**

7. **SHORT RESPONSE** You have 24 feet of fencing that you are using to make a rectangular dog pen. You want the dog pen to enclose 150 square feet. Is it possible for the 24 feet of fencing to enclose a rectangular area of 150 square feet? *Explain.* **See margin.**

8. **EXTENDED RESPONSE** You are making a tiled tabletop with a uniform mosaic tile border as shown.

   a. Write an equation for the area *A* (in square inches) of the border. $A = 4x^2 + 56x$

   b. You have enough mosaic tiles to cover 130 square inches. What should the width of the border be? Round your answer to the nearest inch. **about 2 in.**

   c. *Explain* why you could ignore one of the values of *x* in part (b). **See margin.**

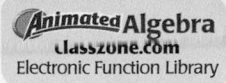

Animated Algebra
classzone.com
Electronic Function Library

BIG IDEAS
For Your Notebook

Big Idea 1

Graphing Quadratic Functions

You can use the properties below to graph any quadratic function.

The graph of $y = ax^2 + bx + c$ is a parabola that:

- opens up if $a > 0$ and opens down if $a < 0$.

- is narrower than the graph of $y = x^2$ if $|a| > 1$ and wider if $|a| < 1$.

- has an axis of symmetry of $x = -\dfrac{b}{2a}$.

- has a vertex with an x-coordinate of $-\dfrac{b}{2a}$.

- has a y-intercept of c. So, the point $(0, c)$ is on the parabola.

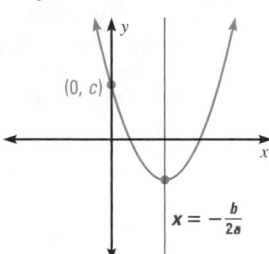

$y = ax^2 + bx + c, a > 0$

$(0, c)$

$x = -\dfrac{b}{2a}$

Big Idea 2

Solving Quadratic Equations

You can use the following methods to solve a quadratic equation. Sometimes it is easier to use one method instead of another.

Method	Lesson	When to use
Graphing	10.3	Use when approximate solutions are adequate.
Finding square roots	10.4	Use when solving an equation that can be written in the form $x^2 = d$.
Completing the square	10.5	Can be used for *any* quadratic equation $y = ax^2 + bx + c$ but is simplest to apply when $a = 1$ and b is an even number.
Quadratic formula	10.6	Can be used for *any* quadratic equation

Big Idea 3

Comparing Linear, Exponential, and Quadratic Models

You can use linear, exponential, and quadratic functions to model data.

Function	Example	*x*- and *y*-values
Linear	$y = 5x + 1$	If the increments between successive *x*-values are equal, the differences of successive *y*-values are all equal.
Exponential	$y = 3(2)^x$	If the increments between successive *x*-values are equal, the ratios of successive *y*-values are all equal.
Quadratic	$y = x^2 - 4x + 6$	If the increments between successive *x*-values are equal, the differences of successive first differences of *y*-values are all equal.

Chapter Summary **695**

Additional Resources

The following resources are available to help review the materials in this chapter.

Chapter 10 Resource Book
- Chapter Review Games and Activities, p. 103
- Cumulative Practice, Chs. 1–10, pp. 105–106

Student Resources in Spanish

eWorkbook

@HomeTutor

Vocabulary Practice

Vocabulary practice is available at **classzone.com**

10 CHAPTER REVIEW

Extra Example 10.1

Graph $y = -x^2 + 1$. Compare the graph with the graph of $y = x^2$.

Both graphs have the same line of symmetry, $x = 0$. The graph of $y = -x^2 + 1$ is a reflection in the x-axis of $y = x^2$ and then a vertical translation (of 1 unit up).

5.

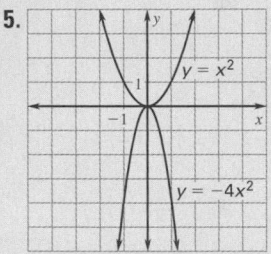

The graph is a vertical stretch (by a factor of 4) with a reflection in the x-axis of the graph of $y = x^2$.

6.

The graph is a vertical shrink $\left(\text{by a factor of } \frac{1}{3}\right)$ of the graph of $y = x^2$.

7.

The graph is a vertical stretch (by a factor of 2) with a vertical translation (of 1 unit down) of the graph of $y = x^2$.

REVIEW KEY VOCABULARY

• quadratic function, *p. 628*
• standard form of a quadratic function, *p. 628*
• parabola, *p. 628*
• parent quadratic function, *p. 628*
• vertex of a parabola, *p. 628*
• axis of symmetry, *p. 628*

• minimum value, *p. 636*
• maximum value, *p. 636*
• intercept form of a quadratic function, *p. 641*
• quadratic equation, *p. 643*
• standard form of a quadratic equation, *p. 643*

• completing the square, *p. 663*
• vertex form of a quadratic function, *p. 669*
• quadratic formula, *p. 671*
• discriminant, *p. 678*

VOCABULARY EXERCISES

1. Copy and complete: The line that passes through the vertex and divides a parabola into two symmetric parts is called the __?__. **axis of symmetry**

Tell whether the function has a *minimum value* or a *maximum value*.

2. $f(x) = 5x^2 - 4x$

minimum

3. $f(x) = -x^2 + 6x + 2$

maximum

4. $f(x) = 0.3x^2 - 7.7x + 1.8$

minimum

REVIEW EXAMPLES AND EXERCISES

Use the review examples and exercises below to check your understanding of the concepts you have learned in each lesson of Chapter 10.

10.1 **Graph $y = ax^2 + c$**

pp. 628–634

EXAMPLE

Graph $y = -x^2 + 3$. Compare the graph with the graph of $y = x^2$.

Make a table of values for $y = -x^2 + 3$. Then plot the points from the table and draw a smooth curve through the points.

x	−2	−1	0	1	2
y	−1	2	3	2	−1

Both graphs have the same axis of symmetry, $x = 0$. However, the graph of $y = -x^2 + 3$ has a different vertex than the graph of $y = x^2$, and it opens down. This is because the graph of $y = -x^2 + 3$ is a vertical translation (of 3 units up) and a reflection in the x-axis of the graph of $y = x^2$.

EXAMPLES
1, 2, and 4
on pp. 628–630
for Exs. 5–7

EXERCISES

Graph the function. Compare the graph with the graph of $y = x^2$. 5–7. See margin.

5. $y = -4x^2$

6. $y = \frac{1}{3}x^2$

7. $y = 2x^2 - 1$

10.2 Graph $y = ax^2 + bx + c$

pp. 635–640

EXAMPLE

Graph $y = -x^2 + 2x + 1$.

STEP 1 **Determine** whether the parabola opens up or down. Because $a < 0$, the parabola opens down.

STEP 2 **Find** and draw the axis of symmetry:

$$x = -\frac{b}{2a} = -\frac{2}{2(-1)} = 1$$

STEP 3 **Find** and plot the vertex. The x-coordinate of the vertex is $-\frac{b}{2a}$, or 1. The y-coordinate of the vertex is $y = -(1)^2 + 2(1) + 1 = 2$.

STEP 4 **Plot** four more points. Evaluating the function for $x = 0$ and $x = -1$ gives the points (0, 1) and (−1, −2). Plot these points and their reflections in the axis of symmetry.

STEP 5 **Draw** a parabola through the plotted points.

EXERCISES

Graph the function. Label the vertex and axis of symmetry. **8–10. See margin.**

EXAMPLE 2
on p. 636
for Exs. 8–10

8. $y = x^2 + 4x + 1$ **9.** $y = 2x^2 - 4x - 3$ **10.** $y = -2x^2 + 8x + 5$

10.3 Solve Quadratic Equations by Graphing

pp. 643–649

EXAMPLE

Solve $x^2 - 7x = -12$ by graphing.

STEP 1 **Write** the equation in standard form.

$x^2 - 7x = -12$ **Write original equation.**

$x^2 - 7x + 12 = 0$ **Add 12 to each side.**

STEP 2 **Graph** the related function $y = x^2 - 7x + 12$. The x-intercepts of the graph are 3 and 4.

▶ The solutions of the equation $x^2 - 7x + 12 = 0$ are 3 and 4.

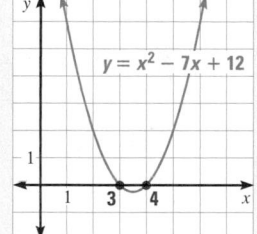

EXERCISES

EXAMPLES
1, 2, and 3
on pp. 643–644
for Exs. 11–13

Solve the equation by graphing.

11. $4x^2 + x + 3 = 0$ **no solution**   **12.** $x^2 + 2x = -1$ **−1**   **13.** $-x^2 + 8 = 7x$ **−8, 1**

Chapter Review   **697**

Extra Example 10.2
Graph $y = x^2 + 4x + 4$.

Extra Example 10.3
Solve $x^2 - 5x = -4$ by graphing.   **1, 4**

8.

9.

10.

10.4 Use Square Roots to Solve Quadratic Equations
pp. 652–658

EXAMPLE

Solve $5(x - 6)^2 = 30$. Round the solutions to the nearest hundredth.

$5(x - 6)^2 = 30$ **Write original equation.**

$(x - 6)^2 = 6$ **Divide each side by 5.**

$x - 6 = \pm\sqrt{6}$ **Take square roots of each side.**

$x = 6 \pm \sqrt{6}$ -**Add 6 to each side.**

▶ The roots of the equation are $6 + \sqrt{6} \approx 8.45$ and $6 - \sqrt{6} \approx 3.55$.

CHECK   To check the solutions, first rewrite the equation so that 0 is on the one side as follows: $5(x - 6)^2 - 30 = 0$. Then graph the related function $y = 5(x - 6)^2 - 30$. The x-intercepts are about 8.4 and about 3.5. So, each solution checks.

EXERCISES

Solve the equation. Round your solutions to the nearest hundredth, if necessary.

EXAMPLES
1–4
on p. 652–654
for Exs. 14–19

14. $6x^2 - 54 = 0$ ± 3

15. $3x^2 + 7 = 4$ **no solution**

16. $g^2 + 11 = 24$ ± 3.61

17. $7n^2 + 5 = 9$ ± 0.76

18. $2(a + 7)^2 = 34$
    $-11.12, -2.88$

19. $3(w - 4)^2 = 5$ $2.71, 5.29$

10.5 Solve Quadratic Equations by Completing the Square
pp. 663–668

EXAMPLE

Solve $3x^2 + 12x = 18$ by completing the square.

$3x^2 + 12x = 18$ **Write original equation.**

$x^2 + 4x = 6$ **Divide each side by 3.**

$x^2 + 4x + 2^2 = 6 + 2^2$ **Add $\left(\frac{4}{2}\right)^2$, or 2^2, to each side.**

$(x + 2)^2 = 10$ **Write left side as the square of a binomial.**

$x + 2 = \pm\sqrt{10}$ **Take square roots of each side.**

$x = -2 \pm \sqrt{10}$ **Subtract 2 from each side.**

▶ The solutions of the equation are $-2 + \sqrt{10} \approx 1.16$ and $-2 - \sqrt{10} \approx -5.16$.

EXAMPLES
2 and 3
on p. 664
for Exs. 20–23

EXERCISES

Solve the equation by completing the square. Round your solutions to the nearest hundredth, if necessary.

20. $x^2 - 14x = 51$ **−3, 17**

21. $2a^2 + 12a - 4 = 0$ **0.32, −6.32**

22. $2n^2 + 4n + 1 = 10n + 9$ **−1, 4**

23. $5g^2 - 3g + 6 = 2g^2 + 9$ **−0.62, 1.62**

10.6 Solve Quadratic Equations by the Quadratic Formula *pp. 671–676*

EXAMPLE

Solve $4x^2 + 3x = 1$.

$4x^2 + 3x = 1$ Write original equation.

$4x^2 + 3x - 1 = 0$ Write in standard form.

$x = \dfrac{-b + \sqrt{b^2 - 4ac}}{2a}$ Quadratic formula

$= \dfrac{-3 \pm \sqrt{3^2 - 4(4)(-1)}}{2(4)}$ Substitute values in the quadratic formula: $a = 4$, $b = 3$, and $c = -1$.

$= \dfrac{-3 \pm \sqrt{25}}{8}$ Simplify.

$= \dfrac{-3 \pm 5}{8}$ Simplify the square root.

▶ The solutions of the equation are $\dfrac{-3 + 5}{8} = \dfrac{1}{4}$ and $\dfrac{-3 - 5}{8} = -1$.

CHECK You can check the solutions in the original equation.

If $x = \dfrac{1}{4}$:   If $x = -1$:

$4x^2 + 3x = 1$ $4x^2 + 3x = 1$

$4\left(\dfrac{1}{4}\right)^2 + 3\left(\dfrac{1}{4}\right) \stackrel{?}{=} 1$ $4(-1)^2 + 3(-1) \stackrel{?}{=} 1$

$1 = 1 \checkmark$ $1 = 1 \checkmark$

EXERCISES

EXAMPLES
1, 2, and 3
on p. 671–672
for Exs. 24–30

Use the quadratic formula to solve the equation. Round your solutions to the nearest hundredth, if necessary.

24. $x^2 - 2x - 15 = 0$ **−3, 5**

25. $2m^2 + 7m - 3 = 0$ **−3.89, 0.39**

26. $-w^2 + 5w = 3$ **0.70, 4.30**

27. $5n^2 - 7n = -1$ **0.16, 1.24**

28. $t^2 - 4 = 6t + 8$ **−1.58, 7.58**

29. $2h - 1 = 10 - 9h^2$ **−1.22, 1**

30. The area A of the rectangle shown is 500 square meters. Find the value of x. Then give the dimensions of the rectangle. **7; 25 m by 20 m**

$(2x + 6)$ m

$(4x - 3)$ m

Chapter Review   **699**

Extra Example 10.6
Use the quadratic formula to solve $x^2 + 11x = -30$. $a = 1$, $b = 11$, $c = 30$; $\dfrac{-11 + 1}{2} = -5$, $\dfrac{-11 - 1}{2} = -6$

Extra Example 10.7

Use the discriminant to find the number of solutions for each equation.

a. $4x^2 + 12x + 9 = 0$ **one solution**

b. $8x^2 + 2x + 2 = 0$ **no solution**

c. $x^2 + 5x = 0$ **two solutions**

Extra Example 10.8

Use differences or ratios to tell whether the table of values represents a *linear function*, an *exponential function*, or a *quadratic function*.

a.

x	−1	0	1	2	3
y	2	6	12	20	30

Second differences are constant; quadratic function.

b.

x	−1	0	1	2	3
y	8	4	2	1	0.5

Ratios of successive *y*-values are equal; exponential function.

10.7 Interpret the Discriminant

pp. 678–683

EXAMPLE

Equation $ax^2 + bx + c = 0$	Discriminant $b^2 - 4ac$	Number of solutions
a. $-16x^2 + 8x - 1 = 0$	$8^2 - 4(-16)(-1) = 0$	One solution
b. $4x^2 - 5x + 2 = 0$	$(-5)^2 - 4(4)(2) = -7$	No solution
c. $x^2 + 3x = 0$	$3^2 - 4(1)(0) = 9$	Two solutions

EXERCISES

EXAMPLES 1 and 2
on pp. 678–679
for Exs. 31–36

Tell whether the equation has *two solutions*, *one solution*, or *no solution*.

31. $x^2 - 2x + 2 = 0$
no solution

32. $4g^2 + 12g + 9 = 0$
one solution

33. $5w^2 - 4w - 1 = 0$
two solutions

34. $\frac{1}{8}v^2 - 6 = 0$
two solutions

35. $n^2 - 3n = 4 - 2n^2$
two solutions

36. $2q^2 + 1 = 3q - 5$
no solution

10.8 Compare Linear, Exponential, and Quadratic Models

pp. 684–691

EXAMPLE

Use differences or ratios to tell whether the table of values represents a *linear function*, an *exponential function*, or a *quadratic function*.

a.

x	−1	0	1	2
y	5	3	1	−1

Differences: −2 −2 −2

▶ The table of values represents a linear function.

b.

x	−1	0	1	2
y	4	5	4	1

First differences: 1 −1 −3

Second differences: −2 −2

▶ The table of values represents a quadratic function.

EXERCISES

EXAMPLE 2
on pp. 685
for Exs. 37–38

Tell whether the table of values represents a *linear function*, an *exponential function*, or a *quadratic function*.

37.

x	1	2	3	4	5	6
y	1	2	4	8	16	32

exponential function

38.

x	−2	−1	0	1	2	3
y	0	3	6	9	12	15

linear function

Match the quadratic function with its graph.

1. $y = x^2 - 2$ **C**

2. $y = x^2 + 2$ **A**

3. $y = -2x^2$ **B**

A.

B.

C.

Graph the function. Label the vertex and axis of symmetry. 4–6. See margin.

4. $y = 2x^2 + 6x - 5$

5. $y = -4x^2 - 8x + 25$

6. $y = \frac{1}{4}x^2 - x - 7$

Approximate the zeros of the function to the nearest tenth.

7. $f(x) = x^2 + 5x + 1$
−4.8, −0.2

8. $f(x) = x^2 - 8x + 3$ 0.4, 7.6

9. $f(x) = -3x^2 - 2x + 5$
−1.7, 1

Solve the equation. Round your solutions to the nearest hundredth, if necessary.

10. $3x^2 = 108$ ±6

11. $-5w^2 + 51 = 6$ ±3

12. $-p^2 + 2p + 3 = 0$ −1, 3

13. $-2t^2 + 6t + 9 = 0$ −1.10, 4.10

14. $5m^2 - m = 5$ −0.90, 1.10

15. $2x^2 - 12x - 1 = -7x + 6$
−1, 3.5

Tell whether the equation has *two solutions*, *one solution*, or *no solution*.

16. $3x^2 - 4x + 9 = 0$
no solution

17. $4g^2 - 12g + 11 = 0$
no solution

18. $-2n^2 + 7n - 1 = 0$
two solutions

19. $-m^2 - 17m = 0$
two solutions

20. $-6x^2 - x - 5 = 0$
no solutions

21. $10x^2 - 13 = 0$
two solutions

Tell whether the table of values represents a *linear function*, an *exponential function*, or a *quadratic function*. Then write an equation for the function.

22.

x	−3	−2	−1	0	1	2
y	18	8	2	0	2	8

quadratic function; $y = 2x^2$

23.

x	−4	0	4	8	12	16
y	1	2	3	4	5	6

linear function; $y = \frac{1}{4}x + 2$

24. **TENNIS** You are playing tennis with a friend. The path of the tennis ball after you hit the ball can be modeled by the graph of the equation $y = -0.005x^2 + 0.17x + 3$ where x is the horizontal distance (in feet) from where you hit the ball and y is the height of the ball (in feet) above the court.

   a. What is the maximum height reached by the tennis ball? Round your answer to the nearest tenth of a foot. **4.4 ft**

   b. Suppose you are standing 30 feet from the net, which has a height of 3 feet. Will the ball clear the net? *Explain* your reasoning. **See margin.**

   c. If your friend does not hit the ball back to you, how far from you does the ball strike the ground? **about 47 ft**

Additional Resources

Assessment Book
• Chapter Test, Levels A, B, C, pp. 142–147
• Standardized Chapter Test, pp. 148–149
• SAT/ACT Chapter Test, pp. 150–151
• Alternative Assessment, pp. 152–153

Test Generator CD-ROM

Chapter Test

Easily-readable reduced copies (with answers) of Chapter Test B, the Standardized Chapter Test, and the Alternative Assessment from the Assessment Book can be found on pp. 626G–626H.

4.

5.

6.
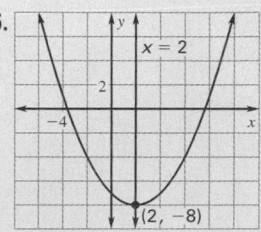

24b. Yes; to find the height of the ball 30 feet from where you hit it, evaluate y when x is 30: $y = -0.005(30)^2 + 0.17(30) + 3 = 3.6$ feet. The height of the ball is greater than the height of the net, so the ball will go over the net.

Using Rubrics

The rubric given on the pupil page is a sample of a three-level rubric. Other rubrics may contain four, five, or six levels. For more information on rubrics, see the *Algebra 1 Toolkit*.

Test-Taking Strategy

Encourage students to give a detailed, clear explanation when an extended response question asks them to explain their reasoning. Tell them that a reviewer wants to see that they grasp the basic concepts in the problem and that they see how their calculations and conclusions are connected. Emphasize that the explanations can be brief, but should include one or two details that relate calculations, graphs, or diagrams to conclusions.

Study Strategy

Point out to students that it is a good idea to get into the habit of labeling each part of the problem, as in Sample 1. Labeling the parts makes it easier for reviewers to find the answers, and it also serves as a check to the students that they have answered all the parts of the problem. Note also that it is a good idea in test-taking situations for students to show all of the steps of a problem even if they can perform some of the steps mentally.

Scoring Rubric

Full Credit
- solution is complete and correct

Partial Credit
- solution is complete but errors are made, *or*
- solution is without error but is incomplete

No Credit
- no solution is given, *or*
- solution makes no sense

EXTENDED RESPONSE QUESTIONS

PROBLEM

A skateboarder in a half pipe launches himself from the half pipe, performs a trick in the air, and lands back in the half pipe. The top of the half pipe is 12 feet above the base of the half pipe as shown.

a. During his first run, the skateboarder leaves the half pipe with an initial vertical velocity of 17 feet per second. Write an equation that models the height h (in feet) of a skateboarder as a function of the time t (in seconds) after leaving the half pipe.

b. How long is the skateboarder in the air if he lands 5 feet above the base of the half pipe? Round your answer to the nearest hundredth of a second.

c. During his second run, the skateboarder leaves the half pipe with an initial vertical velocity that is greater than his initial vertical velocity during his first run. He again lands 5 feet above the base of the half pipe. During which run is his time spent in the air greater? *Explain.*

Below are sample solutions to the problem. Read each solution and the comments in blue to see why the sample represents full credit, partial credit, or no credit.

SAMPLE 1: Full credit solution

The correct equation is given.

a. $h = -16t^2 + 17t + 12$

b. $5 = -16t^2 + 17t + 12$

$0 = -16t^2 + 17t + 7$

$t = \dfrac{-17 \pm \sqrt{17^2 - 4(-16)(7)}}{2(-16)} \approx -0.32 \text{ or } 1.38$

The correct equation is given, and the answer that makes sense is given.

The skateboarder is in the air for about 1.38 seconds.

c. $5 = -16t^2 + 18t + 12$ $5 = -16t^2 + 20t + 12$

$0 = -16t^2 + 18t + 7$ $0 = -16t^2 + 20t + 7$

$t = \dfrac{-18 \pm \sqrt{18^2 - 4(-16)(7)}}{2(-16)}$ $t = \dfrac{-20 \pm \sqrt{20^2 - 4(-16)(7)}}{2(-16)}$

$t \approx -0.31$ or $t \approx 1.43$ $t \approx -0.29$ or $t \approx 1.54$

The answer is correct, and it includes an explanation.

The examples above show that the time the skateboarder spends in the air increases as the initial vertical velocity increases and the landing height remains constant. So, the skateboarder spends more time in the air during his second run.

702   Chapter 10   Quadratic Equations and Functions

SAMPLE 2: Partial credit solution

The correct equation is given.

a. $h = -16t^2 + 17t + 12$

b. $0 = -16t^2 + 17t + 7$

$$t = \frac{-17 \pm \sqrt{17^2 - 4(-16)(7)}}{2(-16)} \approx -1.38 \text{ or } 0.32$$

The skateboarder is in the air for about 0.32 second.

In parts (b) and (c), the reasoning is correct but errors are made in calculating the values of t. So, the answers are incorrect.

c. $0 = -16t^2 + 19t + 7$

$$t = \frac{-19 \pm \sqrt{19^2 - 4(-16)(7)}}{2(-16)} \approx -1.48 \text{ or } 0.3$$

With an initial vertical velocity of 19 feet per second, the skateboarder is in the air for about 0.3 second, which is less than 0.32 second. So, the skateboarder spends more time in the air during his first run.

SAMPLE 3: No credit solution

The equation is incorrect.

a. $h = -16t^2 + 12t + 17$

b. $0 = -16t^2 + 12t + 17$

$$t = \frac{-12 \pm \sqrt{12^2 - 4(-16)(17)}}{2(-16)} \approx -0.72 \text{ or } 1.47$$

In parts (b) and (c), the incorrect equations are solved, and no answers are given.

c. $0 = -16t^2 + 15t + 17$

$$t = \frac{-15 \pm \sqrt{15^2 - 4(-16)(17)}}{2(-16)} \approx -0.66 \text{ or } 1.6$$

PRACTICE   Apply Scoring Rubric

1. A student's solution to the problem on the previous page is given below. Score the solution as *full credit*, *partial credit*, or *no credit*. *Explain* your reasoning. If you choose *partial credit* or *no credit*, explain how you would change the solution so that it earns a score of full credit.   **See margin.**

a. $h = -16t^2 + 17t + 12$

b. $0 = -16t^2 + 17t + 7$

$$t = \frac{-17 \pm \sqrt{17^2 - 4(-16)(7)}}{2(-16)} \approx 0.32$$

The skateboarder is in the air for about 0.32 second.

c. A greater initial vertical velocity means that the skateboarder will go higher. This means that he will be in the air longer. So, the skateboarder will be in the air longer during his second run.

Avoiding Common Errors

Remind students that calculation errors are frequent when calculations are complex. Encourage students to write values for a, b, and c, and then rewrite the quadratic formula in full using those values. Also encourage students to check their answers by using substitution in the original equation, a different method, or even the same method again.

1. Partial credit; the correct equations are given in parts (a) and (b). The student substituted correctly into the quadratic formula in part (b), but did not evaluate the expression correctly. The correct values of t are −0.32 and 1.38. Disregard the negative solution, so the skateboarder is in the air about 1.38 seconds. The student's reasoning in part (c) is not valid. Even though the skateboarder goes higher, we cannot necessarily conclude that he is in the air longer; he is also moving faster, so perhaps his air time will decrease. We must check by finding landing times for one or more initial vertical velocities that are greater than 17 feet per second.

1b. 10 plots; to find the maximum number of plots, substitute 4000 for A in the equation from part (a) and solve for x: $4000 = 20x^2 + 200x$, or $0 = 20x^2 + 200x - 4000$; $x = -20$ *or* $x = 10$. Only the positive solution makes sense in this situation, so the maximum number of plots is 10.

1c. 1.5 ft; Since there are 10 plots, each plot is 20 feet wide, so the area of each plot is $20(20) = 400$ square feet. If w is the width of the wildflower border, then the area of the resident's plot without the border is $(20 - 2w)(20 - 2w)$. To find the value of w that gives a border area of 111 square feet, solve the equation $400 - 111 = (20 - 2w)(20 - 2w)$, or $289 = (20 - 2w)^2$; $w = 1.5$ feet.

2b. *Sample answer:* 10 ft; when the ball is 10 feet from the player, its height is $y = -0.018(10^2) + 0.25(10) + 0.7 = 1.4$ feet. The ball is lower than the crossbar, so it will go into the goal if the player is 10 feet from the goal.

2c. Distances of 16 ft or less; from part (a), the maximum height of the ball is about 1.6 feet, so the ball is always lower than the crossbar. The ball will land back in the water when $y = 0$, so solve the equation $0 = -0.018x^2 + 0.25x + 0.7$ for x to determine the distance of the ball from the player when the ball hits the water; $x \approx 16$ feet. As long as the player is within 16 feet of the goal, the ball will go into the goal.

3c. Yes; if the farmer drives the trailer, the cost of each planter for each field would be reduced by the same amount, $.82 per acre, so the 12 row planter will still cost the least per acre to operate.

EXTENDED RESPONSE

1. A community garden is being planned in the town-owned field behind the housing development where you live. The rectangular garden will border the development and extend into the field. Each household that joins the project will have a rectangular plot that is 20 feet wide. The town has already permitted the plots to extend 10 feet into the field, and promised another foot for every household that reserves a plot.

Field

$20x$ ft

Garden

$(x + 10)$ ft

   a. Write an equation that gives the area A (in square feet) of the community garden as a function of the number x of households that reserve a plot. $A = 20x^2 + 200x$

   b. The housing association decides that the entire area of the garden cannot exceed 4000 square feet. What is the maximum number of plots there can be? *Explain* **b, c. See margin.**

   c. The maximum number of plots is used. One of the residents decides to plant a uniform border of wildflowers around all four sides of her plot. She has enough wildflower seeds to cover 111 square feet. How wide should the border be? *Explain.*

2. During a water-polo practice, a player positioned directly in front of the goal throws the ball at the goal. The ball follows a parabolic path that can be modeled by the graph of the equation $y = -0.018x^2 + 0.25x + 0.7$ where y is the height (in feet) of the ball above the surface of the water x feet from the player.

   a. What is the maximum height of the ball to the nearest tenth of a foot? **1.6 ft**

   b. The ball goes into the goal. The goal is bounded by the surface of the water and a crossbar that is 3 feet high above the surface of the water. Give a possible distance that the player is from the goal. *Explain.* **b, c. See margin.**

   c. Describe all possible distances that the player can be from the goal in order for the ball to go into the goal. *Explain.*

3. A farm machine called a planter plants multiple rows of seeds while being pulled by a tractor. Planters can be purchased in various sizes. The operation costs of a 6 row, 8 row, 12 row, 16 row, and 24 row planter are analyzed. The operation cost y (in dollars per acre) for a planter that plants x rows at once for two different sizes of fields is shown in the table.

   a. Which planter costs the least per acre to operate for planting 400 acres? **8 row planter**

   b. Which planter costs the least per acre to operate for planting 800 acres? **12 row planter**

Acres planted	Operation cost (dollars per acre), y
400	$y = 0.071x^2 - 1.1x + 17$
800	$y = 0.062x^2 - 1.6x + 20$

   c. A farmer who is planting 800 acres uses the planter that costs the least per acre to operate. The operation cost function takes into account that a tractor operator is paid $.82 per acre to drive the tractor pulling the planter. The farmer drives the tractor, so he doesn't have to pay for labor. Does his planter still cost the least per acre to operate? *Explain.* **See margin.**

704 Chapter 10 Quadratic Equations and Functions

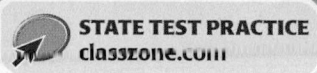
MULTIPLE CHOICE

4. How would the graph of the function $y = -3x^2 + 6$ be affected if the function were changed to $y = -3x^2 - 1$? **D**

   Ⓐ The graph would shift 5 units up.

   Ⓑ The graph would shift 5 units down.

   Ⓒ The graph would shift 7 units up.

   Ⓓ The graph would shift 7 units down.

5. A volleyball player serves the ball from a height of 6.5 feet above the ground with an initial vertical velocity of 21 feet per second. Which function models the height h (in feet) of the ball t seconds after it is served? **D**

   Ⓐ $h = 21t - t^2 + 6.5$

   Ⓑ $h = -16t^2 + 6.5$

   Ⓒ $h = 16t^2 + 21t + 6.5$

   Ⓓ $h = 6.5 + 21t - 16t^2$

GRIDDED ANSWER

6. The value of the discriminant of the equation $7x^2 - 8x + c = 6$ is -20. What is the value of c? **9**

7. The area of the rectangle below is 170 square meters. What is the value of x? **6**

$(x + 4)$ m

$(3x - 1)$ m

8. A cross section of the glass lamp shade below can be modeled by the graph of the equation $y = -0.625x^2 + 5x$ where x and y are measured in inches. How tall (in inches) is the shade? **10 in.**

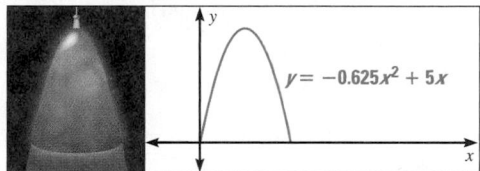

$y = -0.625x^2 + 5x$

SHORT RESPONSE

9. From January to May in 2003, the monthly snowfall y (in inches) recorded at the observatory at Mount Washington in New Hampshire can be modeled by the function $y = -5.34x^2 + 17.4x + 21.2$ where x is the number of months since January. Did the greatest monthly snowfall during the given time period occur in January? *Explain.*

No. *Sample answer:* A table of values for the function shows that the greatest monthly snowfall, 34.6 inches, occurred in March.

10. You throw a tennis ball upward from a height of 4 feet with an initial vertical velocity of 36 feet per second.

  a. Write an equation that models the height h (in feet) of the tennis ball as a function of the time t (in seconds) after it is thrown. **$h = -16t^2 + 36t + 4$**

  b. Does the ball reach a height of 30 feet? *Explain.* **See margin.**

11. A band wants to have customized stickers printed. The table shows the cost y (in dollars) for x customized stickers.

Stickers, x	1000	2000	3000	4000
Cost (dollars), y	199	239	279	319

  a. Tell whether the data can be modeled by a *linear function*, an *exponential function*, or a *quadratic function*. Then write an equation for the function. **linear function; $y = 0.04x + 159$**

  b. If the number of stickers printed is doubled, does the price double? *Explain.* **See margin.**

10b. No; substitute 30 for h in the equation from part (a): $30 = -16t^2 + 36t + 4$. Write the equation in standard form $0 = -16t^2 + 36t - 26$; find the discriminant to be -368. The discriminant is negative, so the equation has no solution and the ball cannot reach a height of 30 feet.

11b. No; the cost for n stickers is $0.04n + 159$ dollars, and the cost for $2n$ stickers is $0.04(2n) + 159 = 0.08n + 159$ dollars, which is not the same as twice the cost of n stickers. Twice the cost of n stickers would be $2(0.04n + 159) = 0.08n + 318$ dollars, or \$159 more than the cost of $2n$ stickers.

Additional Resources

The following resources are available to help review the materials in Chapters 1–10.

Chapter Resource Books

• Chapter 8 CRB, Cumulative Review, pp. 79–80
• Chapter 9 CRB, Cumulative Review, pp. 94–95
• Chapter 10 CRB, Cumulative Review, pp. 105–106

7.

8.

9.

10.

11.

12.

706

Evaluate the expression for the given value of *x*. (p. 64)

1. $-|x| + 9$ when $x = -6$ **3**
2. $|-x| + 2.6$ when $x = 2$ **4.6**
3. $0.7 - |x|$ when $x = -0.5$ **0.2**

Solve the equation.

4. $5 - 2a = 13$ *(p. 141)* **−4**
5. $13y + 16 - y = 4$ *(p. 148)* **−1**
6. $-(w + 1) = w + 3$ *(p. 154)* **−2**

Graph the equation. (pp. 215, 225, 244, 253) 7–14. See margin.

7. $x = -6$
8. $y = -3x$
9. $y = 6.5x$
10. $y = \frac{4}{3}x - 8$

11. $y = -3x + 9$
12. $y + x = 8$
13. $2y - x = 2$
14. $2x + 5y = -40$

Write an equation of the line that passes through the given point and is perpendicular to the given line. (p. 319)

15. $(0, 3)$, $y = -5x + 2$
  $y = \frac{1}{5}x + 3$
16. $(2, 2)$, $y = -x - 7$ **$y = x$**
17. $(8, 3)$, $y = \frac{1}{2}x + 2$
  $y = -2x + 19$

Solve the inequality. Then graph the solution.
18–23. See margin for art.

18. $m - 8 < -15$ *(p. 356)*
  $m < -7$
19. $\frac{x}{-3} > 12$ *(p. 363)*
  $x < -36$
20. $1 - 4n < -11$ *(p. 369)*
  $n > 3$

21. $5b - 7 \le 7b - 5$ *(p. 369)*
  $b \ge -1$
22. $12 < z + 9 \le 16$ *(p. 380)*
  $3 < z \le 7$
23. $4 \le 2c + 7 \le 21$ *(p. 380)*
  $-\frac{3}{2} \le c \le 7$

Solve the linear system. (pp. 427, 435, 444, 451, 459)

24. $y = 5x - 4$
  $-4x + y = -2$
  (2, 6)
25. $x - 4y = -44$
  $-3x + 12y = 132$
  all real numbers
26. $-4x + 7y = -33$
  $-3x + 2y = -15$
  (3, −3)

Simplify the expression.

27. $(-9r)^3$ *(p. 489)* **$-729r^3$**
28. $(2p^4)^3 \cdot p^7$ *(p. 489)* **$8p^{19}$**
29. $\frac{(3x)^4 y}{xy^3}$ *(p. 495)* **$\frac{81x^3}{y^2}$**

Graph the function.   30–32. See margin.

30. $y = (2.5)^x$ *(p. 520)*
31. $y = (0.8)^x$ *(p. 531)*
32. $y = \frac{1}{2} \cdot \left(\frac{1}{4}\right)^x$ *(p. 531)*

Find the sum or difference. (p. 554)

33. $(x^2 - 3x + 8) + (-2x^2 + 15x + 4)$
  $-x^2 + 12x + 12$
34. $(5m^2 - 6) - (8m^3 + m^2 - 2m + 11)$
  $-8m^3 + 4m^2 + 2m - 17$

Find the product.

35. $(z + 9)(2z - 7)$ *(p. 562)* $2z^2 + 11z - 63$
36. $(5b - 2)(8b - 7)$ *(p. 562)* $40b^2 - 51b + 14$

37. $(q + 2)(-3q^2 + 6q - 1)$ *(p. 562)*
  $-3q^3 + 11q - 2$
38. $(7 + y)^2$ *(p. 569)* $49 + 14y + y^2$
39. $(2k - 11)^2$ *(p. 569)* $4k^2 - 44k + 121$
40. $(12w - 5)(12w + 5)$ *(p. 569)* $144w^2 - 25$

Factor the expression.

41. $x^2 + 6x - 72$ *(p. 583)* $(x + 12)(x - 6)$
42. $2m^2 - 5mn - 3n^2$ *(p. 593)* $(2m + 1n)(m - 3n)$
43. $25d^2 + 60d + 36$ *(p. 600)* $(5d + 6)^2$
44. $-2a^2 + 50b^2$ *(p. 600)* $-2(a + 5b)(a - 5b)$
45. $z^2(z - 6) + 4(6 - z)$ *(p. 606)*
  $(z - 6)(z + 2)(z - 2)$
46. $y^3 + 8y^2 - 9y - 72$ *(p. 606)*
  $(y + 8)(y + 3)(y - 3)$

13.

14.

18–23. See Additional Answers beginning on p. AA1.

Graph the function. Label the vertex and axis of symmetry. *(p. 635)* **47–49. See margin.**

47. $y = x^2 - 4x + 1$ **48.** $y = 3x^2 + 6x + 4$ **49.** $y = -x^2 - 4x + 10$

Solve the equation. Round your solutions to the nearest hundredth, if necessary. *(pp. 643, 652, 663, 671)*

50. $5x^2 = 720$ **±12** **51.** $-x^2 + 12 = 1$ **±3.32** **52.** $x^2 + 6x - 13 = 0$
−7.69, 1.69

53. $-2x^2 + 7x - 3 = 0$ **0.5, 3** **54.** $4x^2 - 9x = 9$ **−0.75, 3** **55.** $-7x^2 + 7x + 3 = 4x - 1$
−0.57, 1

56. SPORTS The Pan American Games is a sports event that is held every four years. Athletes from countries in North America, Central America, and South America compete in the games. The table shows the number c of countries that participated in each Pan American Games as a function of the time t (in years) since 1951. Graph the function. *(p. 43)* **See margin.**

Years since 1951, t	0	4	8	12	16	20	24	28	32
Countries, c	21	22	25	22	29	32	33	34	36

57. INCOME A salesperson earns a 5% commission on the sales of computers. If the salesperson's computer sales total $9500, how much is the commission? *(p. 176)* **$475**

58. CUSTOM PRINTING You create a design for a T-shirt. The table shows the cost for printing your design on T-shirts at a printing company. The printing company requires that your design be printed on a minimum of 6 T-shirts. *(p. 302)*

T-shirts	6	7	8	9	10
Cost (dollars)	78	81	84	87	90

   a. *Explain* why the situation can be modeled by a linear equation. **See margin.**

   b. Write an equation in point-slope form that gives the cost of the T-shirts as a function of the number of T-shirts printed.
                      Sample answer: $y - 78 = 3(x - 6)$

59. ⊕ **GEOMETRY** A rectangle has a perimeter of 54 inches. Its length is 3 more than twice its width. Find the dimensions of the rectangle. *(p. 435)* **length 19 in., width: 8 in.**

60. SCHOOL ENROLLMENT In 1990, 5000 students were enrolled at a school. The number of students enrolled at the school increased by about 2% per year from 1990 to 2005. Write a model for the number of students enrolled at the school over time. According to the model, how many students were enrolled at the school in 2005? *(p. 520)*
$y = 5000(1.02)^x$; **about 6730 students**

61. LANDSCAPING An arc of water sprayed from a lawn sprinkler can be modeled by the graph of the equation $y = -0.05x^2 + 0.9x$ where x is the distance (in feet) from the sprinkler and y is the height (in feet) of the arc.

   a. Graph the function. Label the vertex and axis of symmetry. *(p. 635)* **See margin.**

   b. How far from the sprinkler does the water hit the ground? *(p. 643)* **18 ft**

47.

48.

49.

56.

58a. Each time the number of T-shirts increases by 1, the cost increases by $3, so the rate of change is $3 per T-shirt.

61a.

30.

31.

32.

REGULAR SCHEDULE

Pre-AP For pacing and assignments for a Pre-AP course, see the *Algebra 1 Toolkit*.

Lesson	Les. Day	BASIC	AVERAGE	ADVANCED
11.1	Day 1	EP p. 947 Exs. 1–7 odd; pp. 713–716 Exs. 1–22	pp. 713–716 Exs. 1, 2, 5–22, 41	pp. 713–716 Exs. 1, 2, 6–22, 41, 42*
	Day 2	pp. 713–716 Exs. 23–34, 43–46, 50–66 even	pp. 713–716 Exs. 25–40, 43–47, 51–67 odd	pp. 713–716 Exs. 26–40, 43–49*, 50–66 even
11.2	Day 1	EP p. 946 Exs. 7–12; pp. 723–726 Exs. 1–25	pp. 723–726 Exs. 1, 2, 4–22 even, 23–32, 55–58	pp. 723–726 Exs. 1, 15–23, 25–33, 55–62
	Day 2	pp. 723–726 Exs. 26–50 even, 67–70, 73–93 odd	pp. 723–726 Exs. 35–53 odd, 59–63, 67–71, 74, 77, 80, 82, 84, 87, 90, 93	pp. 723–726 Exs. 34–54 even, 59–72*, 78, 81, 88, 94
11.3	Day 1	EP p. 946 Exs. 19–24; pp. 732–734 Exs. 1–21	pp. 732–734 Exs. 1, 2, 5–21, 31, 32	pp. 732–734 Exs. 1, 6–21, 31–34
	Day 2	pp. 732–734 Exs. 22–26, 36–39, 42–49	pp. 732–734 Exs. 22–30, 36–40, 42–48 even	pp. 732–734 Exs. 22–30, 35–41*, 43–47 odd
11.4	Day 1	pp. 740–742 Exs. 1, 2, 3–15 odd, 16–30, 33–36, 39–49 odd	pp. 740–742 Exs. 1, 2, 9–22, 26–31, 33–37, 40–50 even	pp. 740–742 Exs. 1, 10–15, 17–22, 26–32*, 34–38*, 44–46, 48, 50
11.5	Day 1	pp. 747–750 Exs. 1, 2, 3–33 odd, 34–38, 47–50, 53–63 odd	pp. 747–750 Exs. 1, 2, 10–15, 19–21, 30–44, 48–51, 54–64 even	pp. 747–750 Exs. 1, 11–15, 20, 21, 31–46*, 49–52*, 56, 58, 62, 64
Review	Day 1	pp. 754–756 Exs. 1–36	pp. 754–756 Exs. 1–36	pp. 754–756 Exs. 1–36
Assess	Day 1	Chapter 11 Test	Chapter 11 Test	Chapter 11 Test
Yearly Pacing		Chapter 11 Total – 10 days	Chapters 1–11 Total – 132 days	Remaining – 28 days

*Challenge Exercises   EP = Extra Practice   SRH = Skills Review Handbook

BLOCK SCHEDULE

DAY 1	DAY 2	DAY 3	DAY 4	DAY 5
11.1	**11.2**	**11.3**	**11.4**	**Review**
pp. 713–716 Exs. 1, 2, 5–22, 25–41, 43–47, 51–67 odd	pp. 723–726 Exs. 1, 2, 4–22 even, 23–32, 35–53 odd, 55–63, 67–71, 74, 77, 80, 82, 84, 87, 90, 93	pp. 732–734 Exs. 1, 2, 5–32, 36–40, 42–48 even	pp. 740–742 Exs. 1, 2, 9–22, 26–31, 33–37, 40–50 even	pp. 754–756 Exs. 1–36
			11.5	**Assess**
			pp. 747–750 Exs. 1, 2, 10–15, 19–21, 30–44, 48–51, 54–64 even	Chapter 11 Test
Yearly Pacing	Chapter 11 Total – 5 days	Chapters 1–11 Total – 66 days	Remaining – 14 days	

RESOURCE MANAGER

Chapter Resource Book

CHAPTER SUPPORT

Parents as Partners (Chapter Overview with home involvement exercises and activity)					p. 1
LESSON SUPPORT	**11.1**	**11.2**	**11.3**	**11.4**	**11.5**
Teaching Guide/Lesson Plan	p. 3	p. 18	p. 29	p. 42	p. 52
Activity Masters	p. 5				
Technology Activities & Keystrokes	p. 6		p. 31		
Activity Support Masters		p. 20			
Practice (3 levels)	p. 7	p. 21	p. 33	p. 44	p. 54
Study Guide	p. 13	p. 24	p. 36	p. 47	p. 57
Catch-Up for Absent Students	p. 15	p. 26	p. 38	p. 49	p. 59
Problem Solving/Application	p. 16	p. 27	p. 39	p. 50	p. 60
Challenge Practice	p. 17	p. 28	p. 41	p. 51	p. 61

REVIEW

Chapter Review Games and Activities	p. 62	Cumulative Practice	p. 64
Project with Rubric	p. 63	Resource Book Answers	A1

Transparencies	**11.1**	**11.2**	**11.3**	**11.4**	**11.5**
Warm-Up/Daily Homework Quiz	✔	✔	✔	✔	✔
Notetaking Guide	✔	✔	✔	✔	✔
Teacher Support	✔				
Answer Transparencies	✔	✔	✔	✔	✔

ASSESSMENT BOOK

Quizzes	p. 154	SAT/ACT Chapter Test	p. 164
Chapter Tests (3 levels)	p. 156	Alternative Assessment with Rubric	p. 166
Standardized Chapter Test	p. 162		

TECHNOLOGY

- Easy Planner
- Test and Practice Generator
- Power Presentations
- @HomeTutor
- Activity Generator
- Animated Algebra
- Classzone.com
- eEdition Plus Online
- eWorkbook Plus Online
- Easy Grader Online

ADDITIONAL RESOURCES

- Worked-Out Solution Key
- Notetaking Guide
- Practice Wookbook
- Algebra 1 Toolkit
- Benchmark Tests
- Reteaching and Remediation
- Spanish Study Guide
- Spanish Assessment Book
- Student Resources in Spanish
- Multi-Language Visual Glossary

11 Lesson Practice Level B

1. domain: $x \geq 0$; range: $y \geq 0$; vertical stretch by a factor of 7
2. domain: $x \geq 0$; range: $y \geq 0$; vertical shrink by a factor of $\frac{1}{5}$
3. domain: $x \geq 0$; range: $y \leq 0$; vertical stretch by a factor of 4 and reflection in x-axis

Graph the function and identify its domain and range. Compare the graph with the graph of $y = \sqrt{x}$.

1. $y = 7\sqrt{x}$

2. $y = \frac{1}{5}\sqrt{x}$

3. $y = -4\sqrt{x}$

Describe how you would graph the function by using the graph of $y = \sqrt{x}$.

4. $y = \sqrt{x} - 8$
5. $y = \sqrt{x} + 3$
6. $y = \sqrt{x + 7}$
7. $y = \sqrt{x} - 5$
8. $y = \sqrt{x} + 3.5$
9. $y = \sqrt{x - \frac{1}{2}}$

4. translate graph of $y = \sqrt{x}$ horizontally 8 units right 5. translate graph of $y = \sqrt{x}$ vertically 3 units up

Match the function with its graph.

10. $y = \sqrt{x + 4} - 3$ E
11. $y = \sqrt{x - 3} + 4$ C
12. $y = \sqrt{x - 4} + 3$ A
13. $y = \sqrt{x - 4} - 3$ F
14. $y = \sqrt{x + 3} - 4$ B
15. $y = \sqrt{x + 3} + 3$ D

A.

B.

C.

D.

E.

F.

6. translate graph of $y = \sqrt{x}$ horizontally 7 units left
7. translate graph of $y = \sqrt{x}$ vertically 5 units down
8. translate graph of $y = \sqrt{x}$ vertically 3.5 units up
9. translate graph of $y = \sqrt{x}$ horizontally $\frac{1}{2}$ unit right

---

16. domain: $x \geq -4$; range: $y \geq -4$; vertical translation 4 units down and horizontal translation 4 units left
17. domain: $x \geq -5$; range: $y \geq 1$; vertical translation 1 unit up and horizontal translation 5 units left

Graph the function and identify its domain and range. Compare the graph with the graph of $y = \sqrt{x}$.

16. $y = \sqrt{x + 4} - 4$

17. $y = \sqrt{x + 5} + 1$

18. $y = \sqrt{x - 6} + 4$ See below.

19. $y = \sqrt{x - 5} - 7$ See below.
20. $y = \sqrt{x - 1} + 2$ See below.
21. $y = \sqrt{x + 5} - 4$ See below.

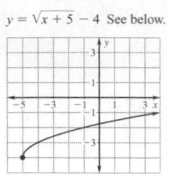

18. domain: $x \geq 6$; range: $y \geq 4$;
vertical translation 4 units up and horizontal translation 6 units right

19. domain: $x \geq 5$; range: $y \geq -7$; vertical translation 7 units down and horizontal translation 5 units right
20. domain: $x \geq 1$; range: $y \geq 2$; vertical translation 2 units up and horizontal translation 1 unit right

22. **Box Design** You are designing a box with a square base that will hold popcorn. The box must be 9 inches tall. The side length x (in inches) of the box is given by the function $x = \frac{1}{3}\sqrt{V}$ where V is the volume (in cubic inches) of the box.   domain: $V > 0$; range: $x > 0$
   a. Graph the function and identify its domain and range.
   b. What is the volume of a box with a side length of 5 inches?   225 in.³
   c. What is the volume of a box with a side length of 8 inches?   576 in.³

23. **Steel Pipe** The inside diameter d of a steel pipe (in inches) and the weight w of water in the pipe (in pounds) are related by the function $d = 1.71\sqrt{w}$.   domain: $w \geq 0$; range: $d \geq 0$
   a. Graph the function and identify its domain and range.
   b. What does the water weigh in a pipe with an inside diameter of 17 inches? Round your answer to the nearest pound.   about 99 lb
   c. What does the water weigh in a pipe with an inside diameter of 3.5 inches? Round your answer to the nearest pound.   about 4 lb

21. domain: $x \geq -5$; range: $y \geq -4$; vertical translation 4 units down and horizontal translation 5 units left

---

Simplify the expression.

1. $\sqrt{200}$ $10\sqrt{2}$
2. $\sqrt{45}$ $3\sqrt{5}$
3. $\sqrt{112}$ $4\sqrt{7}$
4. $\sqrt{400d}$ $20\sqrt{d}$
5. $\sqrt{9y^2}$ $3|y|$
6. $\sqrt{25n^3}$ $5|n|\sqrt{n}$
7. $\sqrt{3} \cdot \sqrt{21}$ $3\sqrt{7}$
8. $\sqrt{20} \cdot \sqrt{15}$ $10\sqrt{3}$
9. $\sqrt{10x} \cdot \sqrt{2x}$ $2|x|\sqrt{5}$
10. $\sqrt{\frac{16}{81}}$ $\frac{4}{9}$
11. $\sqrt{\frac{5}{49}}$ $\frac{\sqrt{5}}{7}$
12. $\sqrt{\frac{x^2}{144}}$ $\frac{|x|}{12}$

Simplify the expression by rationalizing the denominator.

13. $\frac{4}{\sqrt{5}}$ $\frac{4\sqrt{5}}{5}$
14. $\sqrt{\frac{3}{50}}$ $\frac{\sqrt{6}}{10}$
15. $\sqrt{\frac{9}{75}}$ $\frac{\sqrt{3}}{5}$
16. $\frac{2}{\sqrt{p}}$ $\frac{2\sqrt{p}}{|p|}$
17. $\frac{1}{\sqrt{3y}}$ $\frac{\sqrt{3y}}{3|y|}$
18. $\frac{9}{\sqrt{2x}}$ $\frac{9\sqrt{2x}}{2|x|}$

Simplify the expression.

19. $10\sqrt{7} + 3\sqrt{7}$ $13\sqrt{7}$
20. $4\sqrt{5} - 7\sqrt{5}$ $-3\sqrt{5}$
21. $\sqrt{7}(4 - \sqrt{7})$ $-7 + 4\sqrt{7}$
22. $\sqrt{5}(8\sqrt{10} + 1)$ $40\sqrt{2} + \sqrt{5}$
23. $(2\sqrt{3} + 5)^2$ $37 + 20\sqrt{3}$
24. $(6 + \sqrt{3})(6 - \sqrt{3})$ 33

25. **Water Flow** You can measure the speed of water by using an L-shaped tube. The speed V of the water (in miles per hour) is given by the function $V = \sqrt{\frac{5}{2}h}$ where h is the height of the column of water above the surface (in inches).

   a. If you use the tube in a river and find that h is 6 inches, what is the speed of the water? Round your answer to the nearest hundredth.   about 3.87 mi/h
   b. If you use the tube in a river and find that h is 8.5 inches, what is the speed of the water? Round your answer to the nearest hundredth.   about 4.61 mi/h

26. **Walking Speed** The maximum walking speed S (in feet per second) of an animal is given by the function $S = \sqrt{gL}$ where g is 32 feet per second squared and L is the length of the animal's leg (in feet).
   a. How fast can an animal whose legs are 9 inches long walk? Round your answer to the nearest hundredth.   about 4.90 fps
   b. How fast can an animal whose legs are 3 feet long walk? Round your answer to the nearest hundredth.   about 9.80 fps

---

7. Add 5 to each side, then square each side, subtract 3 from each side, and divide each side by 7.
8. Add 3 to each side, divide each side by 6, square each side and solve the linear equation for x.

Determine whether the given value is a solution of the equation.

1. $4\sqrt{2x} - 3 = 12$; 2   not a solution
2. $2\sqrt{9x} - 1 = 20$; 7   not a solution
3. $\sqrt{4x + 8} = \sqrt{6 + 2x}$; -1 solution
4. $\sqrt{7x} - 2 = \sqrt{8 - 3x}$; -1 not a solution
5. $x = \sqrt{4x - 3}$; 3   solution
6. $\sqrt{4x - 3} = x - 2$; 7   solution

Describe the steps you would use to solve the equation. Do not solve the equation.

9. Square each side and solve the resulting linear equation for x.

10. Divide each side by 2, square each side, and solve the resulting linear equation for x.

7. $\sqrt{7x + 3} - 5 = 2$
8. $6\sqrt{4 - x} - 3 = 1$
9. $\sqrt{12x - 7} = \sqrt{9x + 3}$
10. $10\sqrt{6 - x} = 2\sqrt{x + 4}$
11. $\sqrt{5x - 3} - \sqrt{10 - 4x} = 0$ See below.
12. $\sqrt{9x + 1} - 2 = x$ See below.

Solve the equation. Check for extraneous solutions.

13. $8\sqrt{x} - 32 = 0$ 16
14. $\sqrt{5x} - 4 = 16$ 80
15. $\sqrt{x + 3} + 8 = 15$ 46
16. $\sqrt{x - 6} - 2 = 4$ 42
17. $\sqrt{x + 9} - 5 = 2$ 40
18. $\sqrt{8 - 3x} + 5 = 6$ $\frac{7}{3}$
19. $\sqrt{5x + 4} - 12 = -6$ $\frac{32}{5}$
20. $3\sqrt{x + 5} - 3 = 6$ 4
21. $4\sqrt{2x + 1} - 7 = 1$ $\frac{3}{2}$
22. $\sqrt{x} = \sqrt{5x - 1}$ $\frac{1}{4}$
23. $\sqrt{7x - 6} = \sqrt{x}$ 1
24. $\sqrt{6x - 8} = \sqrt{4x - 10}$
25. $\sqrt{7x - 5} = \sqrt{3x + 19}$ 6
26. $\sqrt{x - 15} - \sqrt{x - 7} = 0$
27. $\sqrt{10x - 3} - \sqrt{8x - 11} = 0$
28. $\sqrt{3x - 6} = x$ 2, 3
29. $x = \sqrt{2x + 24}$ 6
30. $\sqrt{2x - 15} = x$ no solution

24. no solution   26. no solution   27. no solution

31. **Market Research** A marketing department determines that the price of a magazine subscription and the demand to subscribe are related by the function $P = 40 - \sqrt{0.0004x + 1}$ where P is the price per subscription and x is the number of subscriptions sold.
   a. If the subscription price is set at $25, how many subscriptions would be sold? Round your answer to the nearest whole subscription.   about 560,000 subscriptions
   b. If the subscription price is set at $30, how many more subscriptions are sold in part (a) than when the price is $30. Round your answer to the nearest whole subscription.   312,500 subscriptions

32. **Awning** The area A of a portion of a circle bounded by two radii r and angle t of a sector of a circle are related by the function
$$r = \sqrt{\frac{2A}{t}}.$$
The length of a side (radius) of the top view of the awning shown at the right is 6 feet and the angle that is formed by the awning is $\frac{5\pi}{3}$. Find the area of the awning. Round your answer to the nearest hundredth.   about 94.25 ft

11. Add the second radical expression to each side, square each side, and solve the resulting linear equation for x.
12. Add 2 to each side, square each side, and then solve the resulting quadratic equation for x.

708C

Let a and b represent the lengths of the legs of a right triangle, and let c represent the length of the hypotenuse. Find the unknown length.

1. $a = 1, b = 5$ $\sqrt{26}$
2. $b = 4, c = 9$ $\sqrt{65}$
3. $a = 6, b = 6$ $6\sqrt{2}$

4. $b = 7, c = 12$ $\sqrt{95}$
5. $a = 2, b = 8$ $2\sqrt{17}$
6. $a = 6, b = 30$ $6\sqrt{26}$

7. $a = 4, b = 15$ $\sqrt{241}$
8. $b = 7, c = 11$ $6\sqrt{2}$
9. $a = 10, b = 20$ $10\sqrt{5}$

10. $a = 30, b = 40$ 50
11. $a = 15, c = 25$ 20
12. $a = 11, b = 22$ $11\sqrt{5}$

Find the unknown lengths.

13.
2, 8

14.
12, 16, 20

15.
9, 12, 15 or 15, 36, 39

16. A right triangle has one leg that is 3 inches longer than the other leg. The hypotenuse is $\sqrt{65}$ inches. Find the lengths of the legs.   4 in., 7 in.

Tell whether the triangle with the given side lengths is a right triangle.

17. 4, 5, 6   not a right triangle
18. 15, 20, 25   right triangle
19. 9, 15, 20   not a right triangle

20. **Shuffleboard** The playing bed of a shuffleboard table is in the shape of a rectangle. If the playing bed measures 154 inches by 20 inches, what is the length of the diagonal from one corner of the playing bed to the opposite corner? Round your answer to the nearest inch.   about 155 in.

21. **Indirect Measurement** You are trying to determine the distance across a pond. You put posts into the ground at A, B, and C so that angle B is a right angle. You measure and find that the length of AB is 18 feet and the length of CB is 28 feet. How wide is the pond from A to C? Round your answer to the nearest foot.   about 33 ft

22. **Badminton** You are setting up a badminton net. To keep each pole standing straight, you use two ropes and two stakes as shown. How long is each piece of rope? Round your answer to the nearest tenth. about 9.2 ft

Find the distance between the two points.

1. $(8, 3), (10, 4)$ $\sqrt{5}$
2. $(2, 7), (5, 6)$ $\sqrt{10}$
3. $(9, 6), (4, 1)$ $5\sqrt{2}$

4. $(0, 4), (8, -2)$ 10
5. $(-5, 3), (1, 2)$ $\sqrt{37}$
6. $(1, -6), (-2, 4)$ $\sqrt{109}$

7. $(8, -7), (4, -3)$ $4\sqrt{2}$
8. $(-10, -2), (6, 5)$ $\sqrt{305}$
9. $(-1, -8), (-5, -2)$ $2\sqrt{13}$

The distance d between two points is given. Find the value of b.

10. $(b, 4), (2, -1); d = 5$ 2
11. $(-3, 2), (7, b); d = 10$ 2
12. $(3, 2), (b, -9); d = 11$ 3

13. $(4, 1), (5, b); d = \sqrt{17}$ $-3, 5$
14. $(b, 2), (3, -1); d = \sqrt{58}$ $-4, 10$
15. $(-4, b), (5, -2); d = \sqrt{106}$ $-7, 3$

Find the midpoint of the line segment with the given endpoints.

16. $(2, 5), (4, 12)$ $\left(3, \frac{17}{2}\right)$
17. $(-7, 2), (-10, 14)$ $\left(-\frac{17}{2}, 8\right)$
18. $(-9, -5), (7, -14)$ $\left(-1, -\frac{19}{2}\right)$

19. $(8, -8), (3, 5)$ $\left(\frac{11}{2}, -\frac{3}{2}\right)$
20. $(20, 5), (30, -5)$ $(25, 0)$
21. $(-11, 7), (8, -3)$ $\left(-\frac{3}{2}, 2\right)$

Use the distance formula and the converse of the Pythagorean theorem to determine whether the points are vertices of a right triangle.   See below.

22. $(1, 1), (4, 4), (1, 4)$
23. $(6, 0), (6, 4), (2, 4)$
24. $(-2, 1), (3, 5), (6, -2)$

25. $(6, 4), (-1, -2), (-4, 3)$
26. $(5, 3), (4, -2), (10, 2)$
27. $(2, -4), (2, -3), (6, 1)$

28. **Walking Trail** A walking trail follows the path shown on the map. The distance between consecutive grid lines is 1 mile. Find the total distance of the trail from start to finish. Round your answer to the nearest mile.   15 mi

22. right triangle   23. right triangle   24. not a right triangle
25. not a right triangle   26. right triangle   27. not a right triangle

29. **Amusement Park** An amusement park designer wants to place a Ferris wheel midway between the two largest coasters. The distance between consecutive grid lines is 500 feet.   (1750, 2000)

   a. Determine the coordinates of where the Ferris wheel should be.

   b. How far will the Ferris wheel be from each of the coasters? Round your answer to the nearest foot.   1953 ft

30. **Reading** You have 30 days left to read the books on your summer reading list. As of today, you have read 5 books. By the end of the 30 days, you have to have read 12 books. Assume that the books are all approximately the same length and you read at a relatively constant pace. After 15 days, how many books should you have read?   8.5 books

CHAPTER 11 Quiz 1
For use after Lessons 11.1–11.3

1. Graph the function $y = \sqrt{x - 2}$ and identify its domain and range. Compare the graph with the graph of $y = \sqrt{x}$.

Simplify the expression.

2. $\sqrt{90}$

3. $\sqrt{12} \cdot \sqrt{3y^2}$

4. $(\sqrt{3} + 4)(\sqrt{3} - 1)$

5. $\dfrac{10}{\sqrt{5}}$

6. $\sqrt{\dfrac{125}{x^4}}$

7. $\sqrt{\dfrac{72k^6}{6g^2}}$

Solve the equation. Check for extraneous solutions.

8. $\sqrt{x} - 9 = 0$

9. $\sqrt{4x + 3} - \sqrt{3x + 4}$

10. $\sqrt{4x - 3} = x$

11. $\sqrt{x - 6} + 4 = 9$

Answers

1. _____ See left.

The domain is

$x \geq 2$. The range is

$y \geq 0$. The graph of

$y = \sqrt{x - 2}$ is a

horizontal translation

(of 2 units to the

right) of the graph

of $y = \sqrt{x}$.

2. _____ $3\sqrt{10}$

3. _____ $6y$

4. _____ $3\sqrt{3} - 1$

5. _____ $2\sqrt{5}$

6. _____ $\dfrac{5\sqrt{5}}{x^2}$

7. _____ $\dfrac{2\sqrt{3}k^3}{g}$

8. _____ 81

9. _____ 1

10. _____ $1, 3$

11. _____ 31

CHAPTER 11 Quiz 2
For use after Lessons 11.4–11.5

Let a and b represent the lengths of the legs of a right triangle, and let c represent the length of the hypotenuse. Find the unknown length.

1. $a = 8, b = 15$

2. $b = 3, c = 7$

3. $a = 5, c = 10$

4. $a = 6, b = 6$

Find the unknown lengths.

5.

6.

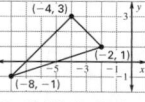

Find the distance between the two points.

7. $(4, -5), (0, -5)$

8. $(3, 2), (3, -4)$

Find the midpoint of the line segment with the given endpoints.

9. $(0, 4), (14, 2)$

10. $(6, -2), (4, -8)$

Answers

1. _____ $c = 17$

2. _____ $a = 2\sqrt{10}$

3. _____ $b = 5\sqrt{3}$

4. _____ $c = 6\sqrt{2}$

5. _____ $x = 3, 3x = 9$

6. _____ $x = 8, x - 2 = 6,$ $x + 2 = 10$

7. _____ 4

8. _____ 6

9. _____ $(7, 3)$

10. _____ $(5, -5)$

CHAPTER 11 Chapter Test B
For use after Chapter 11

Graph the function and identify the domain and range. Then compare the graph with the graph of $y = \sqrt{x}$.

1. $y = \frac{1}{2}\sqrt{x} - 3$

2. $y = -\sqrt{x} + 2$

Simplify the expression.

3. $\sqrt{72a^5}$

4. $5\sqrt{2} - 3\sqrt{2} + 12\sqrt{2}$

5. $3\sqrt{12} - 5\sqrt{27}$

6. $\dfrac{6}{\sqrt{3b}}$

7. $\sqrt{\dfrac{4p^2}{q^6}}$

8. $(2\sqrt{7} + 4)^2$

In Exercises 9 and 10, use the following information.

The time t (in seconds) it takes an object dropped from a height h (in feet) to reach the ground is given by the equation $t = \sqrt{\dfrac{h}{16}}$.

9. Write the equation in simplified form.

10. Find the exact time it takes a stone to reach the ground if it is dropped from a bridge that is 200 feet high.

Solve the equation. Check for extraneous solutions.

11. $\sqrt{4x + 5} = 2$

12. $\sqrt{3x + 4} = \sqrt{12x - 14}$

13. $\sqrt{6x + 7} + 3 = x + 5$

Answers

1. _____ See left.

domain: $x \geq 0$; range:

$y \geq -3$; The graph

is a vertical shrink and

a shift 3 units down

from the graph of

$y = \sqrt{x}$.

2. _____ See left.

domain: $x \geq -2$;

range: $y \leq 0$; The

graph is a reflection in

the x-axis and a shift

2 units to the left of

the graph of $y = \sqrt{x}$.

3. _____ $6a^2\sqrt{2a}$

4. _____ $14\sqrt{2}$

5. _____ $-9\sqrt{3}$

6. _____ $\dfrac{2\sqrt{3b}}{b}$

7. _____ $\dfrac{2p}{q^3}$

8. _____ $44 + 16\sqrt{7}$

9. _____ $t = \dfrac{\sqrt{h}}{4}$

10. _____ $\dfrac{5\sqrt{2}}{2}$ sec

11. _____ no solution

12. _____ 2

13. _____ $-1, 3$

CHAPTER 11 Chapter Test B continued
For use after Chapter 11

14. A person's maximum running speed s (in meters per second) can be approximated by the function $s = \pi\sqrt{\dfrac{9.8\ell}{6}}$ where ℓ is the person's leg length (in meters). To the nearest tenth of a meter, what is the leg length of a person whose maximum running speed is about 3.4 meters per second?

Find the unknown lengths.

15. A right triangle has one leg that is twice as long as the other leg. The hypotenuse is $2\sqrt{5}$ inches.

16. A right triangle has a hypotenuse that is 3 feet longer than one leg. The other leg is 4 feet.

Find the midpoint of the line segment with the given endpoints.

17. $(5, 4), (1, 1)$

18. $(-1, 1), (-4, -3)$

19. $(9, -2), (3, -2)$

In Exercises 20 and 21, use the following graph.

20. Find the length of each line segment.

21. Use the converse of the Pythagorean theorem to determine whether the points are the vertices of a right triangle.

The distance d between two points is given. Find the value of b.

22. $(b, -2), (6, 1); d = 5$

23. $(5, 1), (0, b); d = \sqrt{29}$

24. A fire is sighted in the forest from a helicopter. The forest ranger can send a crew from one of the two towers, as shown on the map. The distance between consecutive grid lines represents 0.5 mile. Which tower is closer to the fire?

Answers

14. _____ 0.7 m

15. _____ 4 in., 2 in.

16. _____ $\dfrac{7}{6}$ ft, $\dfrac{25}{6}$ ft

17. _____ $\left(3, \dfrac{5}{2}\right)$

18. _____ $\left(-\dfrac{5}{2}, -1\right)$

19. _____ $(6, -2)$

20. _____ $2\sqrt{2}, 2\sqrt{10}, 4\sqrt{2}$

21. _____ yes

22. _____ 2 or 10

23. _____ 3 or -1

24. _____ Tower A

Multiple Choice

1. The graph of which function is a vertical stretch of the graph $y = \sqrt{x}$?   C

Ⓐ $y = \frac{1}{2}\sqrt{x}$ Ⓑ $y = 5 + \sqrt{x}$

Ⓒ $y = 4\sqrt{x}$ Ⓓ $y = \sqrt{x + 3}$

2. The graph of which function is a horizontal translation of 2 units to the left of the graph $y = \sqrt{x}$?   D

Ⓐ $y = \sqrt{x} - 2$ Ⓑ $y = \sqrt{x} + 2$

Ⓒ $y = \sqrt{x - 2}$ Ⓓ $y = \sqrt{x + 2}$

3. The graph of which function is shown?   A

Ⓐ $y = -\sqrt{x - 3} - 6$

Ⓑ $y = -\sqrt{x + 3} + 6$

Ⓒ $y = -\sqrt{x - 3} + 6$

Ⓓ $y = -\sqrt{x + 3} - 6$

4. How is the graph of $f(x) = \sqrt{x} + 5$ related to the graph of $g(x) = \sqrt{x} - 5$?   B

Ⓐ It is a vertical translation of 5 units down of the graph of g.

Ⓑ It is a vertical translation of 10 units down of the graph of g.

Ⓒ It is a horizontal translation of 5 units to the right of the graph of g.

Ⓓ It is a horizontal translation of 10 units to the right of the graph of g.

5. Which expression is equivalent to $\sqrt{72}$?   B

Ⓐ $\sqrt{70} + \sqrt{2}$ Ⓑ $6\sqrt{2}$

Ⓒ 12   Ⓓ 36

6. Which expression is equivalent to $\sqrt{24} \cdot \sqrt{2}$ in its simplest form?   A

Ⓐ $4\sqrt{3}$ Ⓑ $16\sqrt{3}$

Ⓒ $2\sqrt{12}$ Ⓓ $12\sqrt{2}$

7. Which expression is equivalent to $\sqrt{\frac{16x}{49}}$?   C

Ⓐ $\frac{4x}{7}$ Ⓑ $\frac{4\sqrt{x}}{49}$

Ⓒ $\frac{4\sqrt{x}}{7}$ Ⓓ $\frac{\sqrt{4x}}{7}$

8. Which expression is equivalent to $\sqrt{\frac{9}{32}}$ in its simplest form?   D

Ⓐ $\frac{3}{\sqrt{32}}$ Ⓑ $\frac{3}{4\sqrt{2}}$

Ⓒ $\frac{3\sqrt{2}}{4}$ Ⓓ $\frac{3\sqrt{2}}{8}$

9. Which expression is equivalent to $\sqrt{\frac{5x^2}{6}}$ in its simplest form?   D

Ⓐ $\frac{x\sqrt{5}}{\sqrt{6}}$ Ⓑ $\frac{30\sqrt{x}}{6}$

Ⓒ $\frac{x\sqrt{5}}{6}$ Ⓓ $\frac{x\sqrt{30}}{6}$

10. Which expression is equivalent to $\sqrt{24} + 5\sqrt{6} - \sqrt{54}$?   B

Ⓐ $10\sqrt{2}$ Ⓑ $4\sqrt{6}$

Ⓒ $5 - \sqrt{24}$ Ⓓ $10\sqrt{6}$

11. Which expression is equivalent to $(3\sqrt{5} - 2)^2$?   A

Ⓐ $49 - 12\sqrt{5}$ Ⓑ $4 - 3\sqrt{5}$

Ⓒ $30 - 12\sqrt{5}$ Ⓓ $-4 - 3\sqrt{5}$

---

12. Which expression is equivalent to $\frac{5r}{\sqrt{r}} - \frac{2}{\sqrt{r}}$ in its simplest form?   C

Ⓐ $\frac{3r}{r}$ Ⓑ $\frac{5r - 2}{r^2}$

Ⓒ $\frac{3\sqrt{r}}{r}$ Ⓓ $\frac{3}{\sqrt{r}}$

13. Which expression is equivalent to $\frac{15}{\sqrt{6} - \sqrt{3}}$ in its simplest form?   B

Ⓐ $-\frac{15\sqrt{9}}{3}$ Ⓑ $5\sqrt{6} + 5\sqrt{3}$

Ⓒ $-\frac{15\sqrt{6} + 15\sqrt{3}}{3}$ Ⓓ $15\sqrt{3}$

14. What is the solution of the equation $6\sqrt{x + 2} + 5 = 35$?   C

Ⓐ $\sqrt{3}$ Ⓑ 3   Ⓒ 23   Ⓓ 25

15. Given a right triangle with side lengths 7 and 24, what is the length of the hypotenuse?   A

Ⓐ 25   Ⓑ 31   Ⓒ 62   Ⓓ 625

16. Which of the triangles with the given side lengths is *not* a right triangle?   D

Ⓐ 3, 4, 5   Ⓑ 11, 60, 61

Ⓒ 15, 20, 25   Ⓓ 9, 39, 41

17. What is the midpoint of the line segment with endpoints $(-3, -2)$ and $(5, -4)$?   A

Ⓐ $(1, -3)$ Ⓑ $(-4, -1)$

Ⓒ $(-1, 3)$ Ⓓ $(4, 1)$

18. What is the distance between $(5, 3.5)$ and $(-2, -2.5)$?   C

Ⓐ 2   Ⓑ $\sqrt{13}$

Ⓒ $\sqrt{85}$ Ⓓ 13

21. a. Twenty-four steps are needed. The height from floor to ceiling is 12 feet or 144 inches. If the riser of each step is 6 inches, you would need 24 steps to reach the second floor. **b.** 24 ft; Each step has a tread of 12 inches and there are 24 steps, so the linear distance would be 288 inches or 24 feet. **c.** A 322 inch rail is needed.

Gridded Answer

19. What is the value of x in the equation $4\sqrt{x + 5} + 2 = 18$?

20. You would meet at the fountain. The midpoint between the two locations is the point $(4, 3)$. The two locations closest to this point are the school and the library. You can use either the distance formula or your knowledge of right triangles to determine that the fountain is closest.

Short Response

20. A map of your town is shown.   See above.

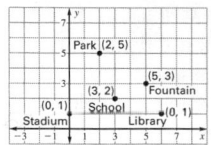

You are at the library. Your friend is at the park. You want to meet at the place that is closest to the midpoint of your locations. At which location should you meet? *Explain.*

Extended Response

21. The vertical distance from the first floor of a house to the second floor is 12 feet. The tread of each step is 12 inches and the riser is 6 inches.   See left.

a. How many steps are needed? *Explain.*

b. What is the linear distance (in feet) needed for the staircase? *Explain.*

c. If a railing is installed from the edge of the bottom step to the edge of the top step, how long of a rail is needed? Round your answer to the nearest inch.

Journal   **1.** State and explain the product and quotient properties of radicals for $a \geq 0$ and $b \geq 0$. Use examples to illustrate why there are not sum or difference properties of radicals.

Multi-Step Problem   **2.** The function $t = \frac{1}{4}\sqrt{36 - h}$ represents the time t (in seconds) it takes an object to fall to a height h (in feet) after being dropped from an initial height of 36 feet.

a. Graph the function and state the domain.

b. Identify the intercepts of this function and explain what each conveys about the position of the object.

c. Determine the distance between the intercepts. Round your answer to the nearest hundredth.

d. What is the height of the object after $\frac{1}{2}$ second?

e. What is the height of the object after 1 second?

f. How long does it take for the object to travel halfway to the ground? Round your answer to the nearest hundredth.

g. Does the second half of the object's fall take more or less time than the first half? Explain your reasoning.

1. Complete answers should include: an explanation of each property of radicals; an example illustrating why there is no sum property of radicals; an example illustrating why there is no difference property of radicals.

2. a.

Domain: $0 \leq h \leq 36$

b. $(1.5, 0)$, $(0, 36)$; 1.5 seconds after the object is dropped it has a height of 0 feet; the object is at a height of 36 feet right before it is released.
c. 36.03 units **d.** 32 ft **e.** 20 ft **f.** 1.06 sec
g. Less time; The object is in the air for a total of 1.5 seconds, and it takes just over 1 second to fall the first 18 feet, which means it takes less than 0.5 second to fall the second 18 feet.

Journal Solution   **1.** Complete answers should include:

• an explanation of each property of radicals.

• an example illustrating why there is no sum property of radicals.

• an example illustrating why there is no difference property of radicals.

Multi-Step Problem Solution   **2. a.**

Domain: $0 \leq h \leq 36$

b. x-intercept: $(1.5, 0)$, y-intercept: $(0, 36)$; 1.5 seconds after the object is dropped it has a height of 0 feet; the object is at a height of 36 feet right before it is released.

c. 36.03 units

d. 32 feet

e. 20 feet

f. 1.06 seconds

g. Less time; The object is in the air for a total of 1.5 seconds, and it takes just over 1 second to fall the first 18 feet, which means it takes less than 0.5 second to fall the second 18 feet.

Multi-Step Problem Rubric

4   The student answers all parts of the problem correctly and completely. The student shows all work. The student's work is neat.

3   The student answers all parts of the problem. The student's work may contain one or two errors in the calculations, graph, or equations. The student shows most work. The student's work is neat.

2   The student answers all parts of the problem, but there are more than two errors in the calculations, graph, or equations. The student shows some work. The student's work is sloppy.

1   The student does not complete all parts of the problem. The student's work has several errors in the calculations, graph, and equations. The student's work is sloppy, or no work is shown.

708F

Radicals and Geometry Connections

11.1 **Graph Square Root Functions**

11.2 **Simplify Radical Expressions**

11.3 **Solve Radical Equations**

11.4 **Apply the Pythagorean Theorem and Its Converse**

11.5 **Apply the Distance and Midpoint Formulas**

Before

In previous chapters, you learned the following skills, which you'll use in Chapter 11: comparing the graphs of functions with the graphs of parent functions, evaluating square roots, using the distributive property, factoring trinomials, and evaluating expressions.

Prerequisite Skills

VOCABULARY CHECK

Copy and complete the statement.

1. The number or expression inside a radical symbol is called the __?__. **radicand**

2. If $b^2 = a$, then b is a(n) __?__ of a. **square root**

SKILLS CHECK

3. Graph $y = 3 \cdot 2^x$. Compare the graph with the graph of $y = 2^x$.
   (Review p. 520 for 11.1.) **See margin for art; the graph is a vertical stretch of $y = 2^x$.**

Evaluate the expression. *(Review p. 110 for 11.2.)*

4. $\sqrt{81}$ **9**   5. $-\sqrt{64}$ **−8**   6. $\pm\sqrt{100}$ **±10**   7. $-\sqrt{121}$ **−11**

Use the distributive property to write an equivalent expression.
(Review p. 96 for 11.2.)

8. $4(y - 3)$
   $4y - 12$
9. $2(x - 2)$
   $2x - 4$
10. $-x(x + 11)$
    $-x^2 - 11x$
11. $4x(x - 9)$
    $4x^2 - 36x$

Factor the trinomial. *(Review p. 583 for 11.3.)*

12. $x^2 + 4x + 4$
    $(x + 2)^2$
13. $m^2 + 9m + 8$
    $(m + 8)(m + 1)$
14. $r^2 + 8r + 7$
    $(r + 7)(r + 1)$
15. $b^2 + 10b + 16$
    $(b + 8)(b + 2)$

16. Evaluate a^2 when $a = 7$. *(Review p. 2 for 11.4–11.5.)* **49**

@HomeTutor Prerequisite skills practice at classzone.com

In Chapter 11, you will apply the big ideas listed below and reviewed in the Chapter Summary on page 753. You will also use the key vocabulary listed below.

Big Ideas

1 Graphing square root functions

2 Using properties of radicals in expressions and equations

3 Working with radicals in geometry

KEY VOCABULARY

- radical expression, *p. 710*
- radical function, *p. 710*
- square root function, *p. 710*
- parent square root function, *p. 710*
- simplest form of a radical expression, *p. 719*

- rationalizing the denominator, *p. 721*
- radical equation, *p. 729*
- extraneous solution, *p. 730*
- hypotenuse, *p. 737*
- legs of a right triangle, *p. 737*

- Pythagorean theorem, *p. 737*
- distance formula, *p. 744*
- midpoint, *p. 745*
- midpoint formula, *p. 745*

Why?

You can use radical equations to solve real-world problems. For example, you can find the length of a sailboat's waterline given the hull speed of the sailboat.

Animated Algebra

The animation illustrated below for Example 5 on page 731 helps you answer this question: What is the length of a sailboat's waterline if the sailboat has a hull speed of 8 nautical miles per hour?

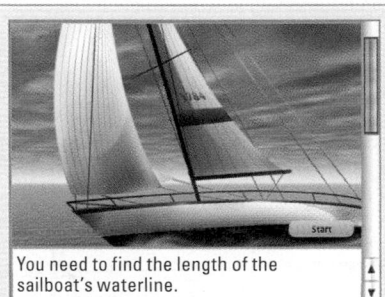

You need to find the length of the sailboat's waterline.

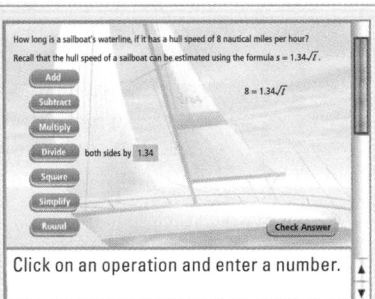

How long is a sailboat's waterline, if it has a hull speed of 8 nautical miles per hour? Recall that the hull speed of a sailboat can be estimated using the formula $s = 1.34\sqrt{l}$.

$8 = 1.34\sqrt{l}$

Add
Subtract
Multiply
Divide — both sides by 1.34
Square
Simplify
Round

Check Answer

Click on an operation and enter a number.

Animated Algebra at classzone.com

Other animations for Chapter 11: pages 711, 719, 722, 737, 746, and 753

709

Algebra 1 Toolkit

- Reading Strategies for Chapter 11, pp. 29–30
- Differentiated Instruction Notes, pp. 81–84
- English Learners Notes, pp. 117–118
- Inclusion Notes, pp. 149–150
- Teaching Strategies with Sample Worksheets, pp. 155–178
- Using Technology in the Classroom, pp. 179–184
- Tips for New Teachers, pp. 205–206
- Math Background Notes, pp. 231–232
- Pre-AP Strategies and Copymasters, pp. 298–299, 453–481
- Teacher Survival Activities, pp. 575–576, 601–602
- Bulletin Board Idea, p. 617
- Teacher Tool Transparencies, following p. 620

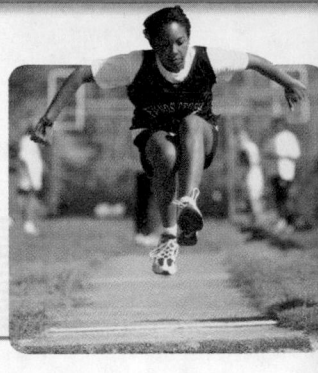

❶ PLAN AND PREPARE

Warm-Up Exercises
📄 **Transparency Available**

1. Graph the function $y = 2^x$.

2. Evaluate $3\sqrt{x}$ when $x = 4$. **6**

3. Evaluate $\sqrt{x + 5}$ when $x = 11$. **4**

Notetaking Guide
📄 **Transparency Available**

Promotes interactive learning and notetaking skills, pp. 274–250.

Pacing
Basic: 2 days
Average: 2 days
Advanced: 2 days
Block: 1 block
• See *Teaching Guide/Lesson Plan.*

❷ FOCUS AND MOTIVATE

Essential Question
Big Idea 1, p. 709

How do you graph square root functions? **Tell students they will learn how to answer this question by making tables, plotting points, and then connecting the points.**

NCTM STANDARDS
Standard 2: Understand functions

Standard 3: Apply transformations to math situations

11.1 Graph Square Root Functions

Before	You graphed linear, exponential, and quadratic functions.
Now	You will graph square root functions.
Why?	So you can analyze the speed of an athlete, as in Ex. 45.

Key Vocabulary
• **radical expression**
• **radical function**
• **square root function**
• **parent square root function**

A **radical expression** is an expression that contains a radical, such as a square root, cube root, or other root. A **radical function** contains a radical expression with the independent variable in the radicand. For example, $y = \sqrt[3]{2x}$ and $y = \sqrt{x + 2}$ are radical functions. If the radical is a square root, then the function is called a **square root function**.

> **KEY CONCEPT**   *For Your Notebook*
>
> **Parent Function for Square Root Functions**
>
> The most basic square root function in the family of all square root functions, called the **parent square root function**, is:
>
> $$y = \sqrt{x}$$
>
> The graph of the parent square root function is shown.
>
>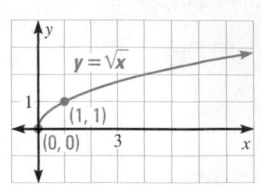

❖ **EXAMPLE 1** **Graph a function of the form $y = a\sqrt{x}$**

Graph the function $y = 3\sqrt{x}$ and identify its domain and range. Compare the graph with the graph of $y = \sqrt{x}$.

REVIEW SQUARE ROOTS
For help with square roots, see p. 110.

Solution

STEP 1 **Make** a table. Because the square root of a negative number is undefined, x must be nonnegative. So, the domain is $x \geq 0$.

x	0	1	2	3	4
y	0	3	4.2	5.2	6

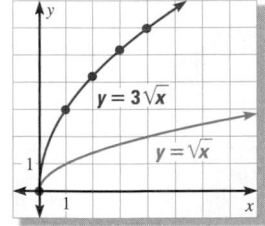

STEP 2 **Plot** the points.

STEP 3 **Draw** a smooth curve through the points. From either the table or the graph, you can see the range of the function is $y \geq 0$.

STEP 4 **Compare** the graph with the graph of $y = \sqrt{x}$. The graph of $y = 3\sqrt{x}$ is a vertical stretch (by a factor of 3) of the graph of $y = \sqrt{x}$.

710 Chapter 11 Radicals and Geometry Connections

Resource Planning Guide

Chapter Resource Book
• Teaching Guide/Lesson Plan (pp. 3–4)
• Activity Master (p. 5)
• Practice levels A, B, C (pp. 7–12)
• Study Guide (pp. 13–14)
• Catch-up for Absent Students (p. 15)
• Problem Solving Workshop (p. 16)
• Challenge (p. 17)

710

Workbooks
• Notetaking Guide (pp. 247–250)
• Practice Workbook (pp. 169–171)

Teaching Options
• **Power Presentations CD-ROM** provides dynamic electronic teaching resources for the classroom.
• **Activity Generator CD-ROM** provides editable activities for all ability levels.

Interactive Technology
• Easy Planner
• Power Presentations CD-ROM
• Activity Generator CD-ROM
• Animated Algebra
• Test Generator CD-ROM
• Online Quiz
• eWorkbook
• eEdition
• @HomeTutor

Resources for English Learners
• Quick Reference for English Learners
• Spanish Study Guide
• Multi-Language Visual Glossary
• Student Resources in Spanish

See also the *Algebra 1 Toolkit* for more strategies for meeting individual needs.

EXAMPLE 2 · Graph a function of the form $y = a\sqrt{x}$

Graph the function $y = -0.5\sqrt{x}$ and identify its domain and range. Compare the graph with the graph of $y = \sqrt{x}$.

Solution

To graph the function, make a table, plot the points, and draw a smooth curve through the points. The domain is $x \geq 0$.

x	0	1	2	3	4
y	0	−0.5	−0.7	−0.9	−1

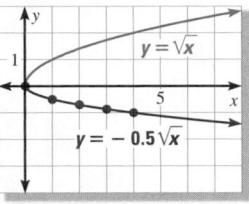

The range is $y \leq 0$. The graph of $y = -0.5\sqrt{x}$ is a vertical shrink (by a factor of 0.5) with a reflection in the x-axis of the graph of $y = \sqrt{x}$.

GRAPHS OF SQUARE ROOT FUNCTIONS Examples 1 and 2 illustrate the following:

- When $|a| > 1$, the graph of $y = a\sqrt{x}$ is a vertical stretch of the graph of $y = \sqrt{x}$. When $0 < |a| < 1$, the graph of $y = a\sqrt{x}$ is a vertical shrink of the graph of $y = \sqrt{x}$.

- When $a < 0$, the graph of $y = a\sqrt{x}$ is the reflection in the x-axis of the graph of $y = |a|\sqrt{x}$.

EXAMPLE 3 · Graph a function of the form $y = \sqrt{x} + k$

Graph the function $y = \sqrt{x} + 2$ and identify its domain and range. Compare the graph with the graph of $y = \sqrt{x}$.

Solution

To graph the function, make a table, then plot and connect the points. The domain is $x \geq 0$.

x	0	1	2	3	4
y	2	3	3.4	3.7	4

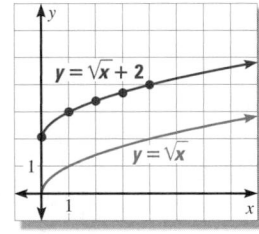

The range is $y \geq 2$. The graph of $y = \sqrt{x} + 2$ is a vertical translation (of 2 units up) of the graph of $y = \sqrt{x}$.

Animated Algebra at classzone.com

 GUIDED PRACTICE for Examples 1, 2, and 3

Graph the function and identify its domain and range. Compare the graph with the graph of $y = \sqrt{x}$. 1–4. See margin.

1. $y = 2\sqrt{x}$ 2. $y = -2\sqrt{x}$ 3. $y = \sqrt{x} - 1$ 4. $y = \sqrt{x} + 3$

Motivating the Lesson

Tell students that if they know how long two skydivers are in freefall and they know how to use a square root function, they can determine how far the skydivers fall before they open their parachutes.

③ TEACH

Extra Example 1

Graph the function $y = 0.5\sqrt{x}$ and identify its domain and range. Compare the graph with the graph of $y = \sqrt{x}$.

Domain: $x \geq 0$; range: $y \geq 0$; the graph is a vertical shrink (by a factor of 0.5) of the graph of $y = \sqrt{x}$.

Extra Example 2

Graph the function $y = -1.5\sqrt{x}$ and identify its domain and range. Compare the graph with the graph of $y = \sqrt{x}$.

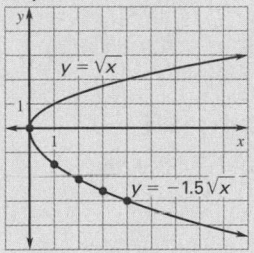

Domain: $x \geq 0$; range: $y \leq 0$; the graph is a vertical stretch (by a factor of 1.5) and a reflection in the x-axis of the graph of $y = \sqrt{x}$.

1–4. See Additional Answers beginning on p. AA1.

Differentiated Instruction

Below Level Some students may find it easier to graph the parent function and to compare graphs if they first make a table for $y = \sqrt{x}$. Suggest that they use five x-values to help them draw a smooth curve. Show students they can check the factor of the vertical stretch or shrink in Examples 1 and 2 by multiplying the y-value of the parent graph by the factor of the stretch or shrink. Compare this to Example 3 where they check that the translation is 2 units up by adding 2 to the y-value of the parent graph, rather than multiplying.

See also the *Algebra 1 Toolkit* for more strategies.

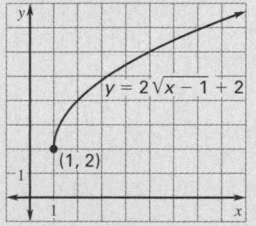
EXAMPLE 4 Graph a function of the form $y = \sqrt{x - h}$

Graph the function $y = \sqrt{x - 4}$ and identify its domain and range. Compare the graph with the graph of $y = \sqrt{x}$.

Solution

To graph the function, make a table, then plot and connect the points. To find the domain, find the values of x for which the radicand, $x - 4$, is nonnegative. The domain is $x \geq 4$.

x	4	5	6	7	8
y	0	1	1.4	1.7	2

The range is $y \geq 0$. The graph of $y = \sqrt{x - 4}$ is a horizontal translation (of 4 units to the right) of the graph of $y = \sqrt{x}$.

KEY CONCEPT *For Your Notebook*

Graphs of Square Root Functions

To graph a function of the form $y = a\sqrt{x - h} + k$, you can follow these steps.

STEP 1 **Sketch** the graph of $y = a\sqrt{x}$. The graph of $y = a\sqrt{x}$ starts at the origin and passes through the point $(1, a)$.

STEP 2 **Shift** the graph $|h|$ units horizontally (to the right if h is positive and to the left if h is negative) and $|k|$ units vertically (up if k is positive and down if k is negative).

EXAMPLE 5 Graph a function of the form $y = a\sqrt{x - h} + k$

Graph the function $y = 2\sqrt{x + 4} - 1$.

STEP 1 **Sketch** the graph of $y = 2\sqrt{x}$.

STEP 2 **Shift** the graph $|h|$ units horizontally and $|k|$ units vertically. Notice that

$$y = 2\sqrt{x + 4} - 1 = 2\sqrt{x - (-4)} + (-1).$$

So, $h = -4$ and $k = -1$. Shift the graph left 4 units and down 1 unit.

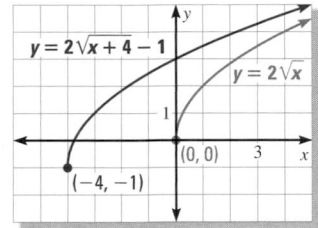

✓ **GUIDED PRACTICE** for Examples 4 and 5

5. Graph the function $y = \sqrt{x + 3}$ and identify its domain and range. Compare the graph with the graph of $y = \sqrt{x}$.
   See margin for art; domain: $x \geq -3$, range: $y \geq 0$; horizontal translation 3 units to the left.

6. Identify the domain and range of the function in Example 5.
   domain: $x \geq -4$, range: $y \geq -1$

5.

Differentiated Instruction

Visual Learners Some students may notice that the graph of the parent function $y = \sqrt{x}$ is the right half of the graph of $y = x^2$ flipped onto its side. Explain that such a transformation of a graph is a result of switching the variables x and y. That is, switching x and y in $y = x^2$ gives $x = y^2$. Taking the square root of both sides gives $\sqrt{x} = y$, or $y = \sqrt{x}$.

See also the *Algebra 1 Toolkit* for more strategies.

EXAMPLE 6 Solve a real-world problem

MICROPHONE SALES For the period 1988–2002, the amount of sales y (in millions of dollars) of microphones in the United States can be modeled by the function $y = 93\sqrt{x} + 2.2$ where x is the number of years since 1988. Graph the function on a graphing calculator. In what year were microphone sales about $325 million?

Solution

The graph of the function is shown.

Using the *trace* feature, you can see that $y \approx 325$ when $x = 10$. So, microphone sales were about $325 million 10 years after 1988, or in 1998.

Trace
X=10   Y=324.8350

✓ **GUIDED PRACTICE** for Example 6

7. **MICROPHONE SALES** Use the function in Example 6 to find the year in which microphone sales were about $250 million. **1993**

11.1 EXERCISES

HOMEWORK KEY

○ = **WORKED-OUT SOLUTIONS**
on p. WS1 for Exs. 7, 23, and 45

★ = **STANDARDIZED TEST PRACTICE**
Exs. 2, 15, 16, 29, 39, 41, and 48

SKILL PRACTICE

Ⓐ **1. VOCABULARY** Copy and complete: A function containing a radical expression with the independent variable in the radicand is called a(n) __?__. **radical function**

2. ★ WRITING Is the graph of $y = 1.25\sqrt{x}$ a vertical stretch or a vertical shrink of the graph of $y = \sqrt{x}$? *Explain* your answer.
Vertical stretch. *Sample answer:* Since $|1.25| > 1$, the graph is a vertical stretch.

GRAPHING FUNCTIONS Graph the function and identify its domain and range. Compare the graph with the graph of $y = \sqrt{x}$. **3–14. See margin.**

**EXAMPLES
1 and 2**
on pp. 710–711
for Exs. 3–16

3. $y = 4\sqrt{x}$

4. $y = 5\sqrt{x}$

5. $y = 0.5\sqrt{x}$

6. $y = 0.25\sqrt{x}$

7. $y = \dfrac{3}{2}\sqrt{x}$

8. $y = \dfrac{1}{3}\sqrt{x}$

9. $y = -3\sqrt{x}$

10. $y = -6\sqrt{x}$

11. $y = -0.8\sqrt{x}$

12. $y = -0.75\sqrt{x}$

13. $y = -\dfrac{1}{4}\sqrt{x}$

14. $y = -\dfrac{5}{2}\sqrt{x}$

15. ★ MULTIPLE CHOICE The graph of which function is a vertical shrink of the graph of $y = \sqrt{x}$? **C**

Ⓐ $y = -5\sqrt{x}$ Ⓑ $y = -\sqrt{x}$ Ⓒ $y = \dfrac{1}{2}\sqrt{x}$ Ⓓ $y = 8\sqrt{x}$

16. ★ WRITING The range of the function $y = a\sqrt{x}$ is $y \le 0$. What can you conclude about the value of a? How do you know? **See margin.**

714

4 PRACTICE AND APPLY

Assignment Guide

📖 Answer Transparencies available for all exercises

Basic:
Day 1: EP p. 947 Exs. 1–7 odd
pp. 713–716
Exs. 1–22
Day 2: pp. 713–716
Exs. 23–34, 43–46, 50–66 even

Average:
Day 1: pp. 713–716
Exs. 1, 2, 5–22, 41
Day 2: pp. 713–716
Exs. 25–40, 43–47, 51–67 odd

Advanced:
Day 1: pp. 713–716
Exs. 1, 2, 6–22, 41, 42*
Day 2: pp. 713–716
Exs. 26–40, 43–49*, 50–66 even

Block:
pp. 713–716
Exs. 1, 2, 5–22, 25–41, 43–47,
51–67 odd

Differentiated Instruction

See *Algebra 1 Best Practices Toolkit* for suggestions on addressing the needs of a diverse classroom.

Homework Check

For a quick check of student understanding of key concepts, go over the following exercises:
Basic: 6, 18, 24, 31, 43
Average: 10, 20, 25, 34, 44
Advanced: 13, 21, 26, 36, 45

Extra Practice

• Student Edition, p. 948
• Chapter 11 Resource Book:
  Practice levels A, B, C, pp. 7–12

Practice Worksheet

An easily-readable reduced practice page (with answers) for this lesson can be found on p.708C.

17–28, 30–38. See Additional Answers beginning on p. AA1.

EXAMPLES 3 and 4
on pp. 711–712
for Exs. 17–29

GRAPHING FUNCTIONS Graph the function and identify its domain and range. Compare the graph with the graph of $y = \sqrt{x}$. **17–28. See margin.**

17. $y = \sqrt{x} + 1$
18. $y = \sqrt{x} + 5$
19. $y = \sqrt{x} - 3$
20. $y = \sqrt{x} - 4$
21. $y = \sqrt{x} + \frac{3}{4}$
22. $y = \sqrt{x} - 4.5$
23. $y = \sqrt{x - 1}$
24. $y = \sqrt{x - 6}$
25. $y = \sqrt{x + 2}$
26. $y = \sqrt{x + 4}$
27. $y = \sqrt{x + 1.5}$
28. $y = \sqrt{x - \frac{1}{2}}$

29. ★ **MULTIPLE CHOICE** The graph of which function is a horizontal translation of 3 units to the right of the graph of $y = \sqrt{x}$? **D**

  (A) $y = \sqrt{x} + 3$ (B) $y = \sqrt{x} - 3$

  (C) $y = \sqrt{x + 3}$ (D) $y = \sqrt{x - 3}$

EXAMPLE 5 B
on p. 712
for Exs. 30–39

GRAPHING FUNCTIONS Graph the function. **30–38. See margin.**

30. $y - \sqrt{x + 3} - 2$
31. $y = \sqrt{x - 2} + 5$
32. $y = 2\sqrt{x} + 1$
33. $y = -\sqrt{x + 1} + 2$
34. $y = -3\sqrt{x + 2} - 6$
35. $y = 4\sqrt{x + 4} - 4$
36. $y = \frac{1}{2}\sqrt{x - 5} - 3$
37. $y = -\frac{3}{2}\sqrt{x - 1} - 5$
38. $y = -\frac{3}{4}\sqrt{x + 8} - 3$

39. ★ **MULTIPLE CHOICE** The graph of which function is shown? **A**

  (A) $y = \sqrt{x + 1} + 2$

  (B) $y = \sqrt{x - 1} + 2$

  (C) $y = \sqrt{x + 1} - 2$

  (D) $y = \sqrt{x - 1} - 2$

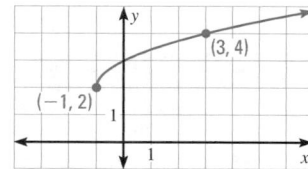

40. **ERROR ANALYSIS** *Describe* and correct the error in explaining how to graph the function $y = -5\sqrt{x - 9} - 10$.
The discussion about shifting the graph is incorrect. It should say "Then shift the graph 9 units to the right and 10 units down."

To graph $y = -5\sqrt{x - 9} - 10$, sketch the graph of $y = -5\sqrt{x}$. Then shift the graph 9 units to the left and 10 units down.

C 41. ★ **MULTIPLE CHOICE** How is the graph of $g(x) = 4\sqrt{x} - 3$ related to the graph of $h(x) = 4\sqrt{x} + 3$? **C**

  (A) It is a vertical stretch by a factor of 3 of the graph of h.

  (B) It is a vertical translation of 3 units down of the graph of h.

  (C) It is a vertical translation of 6 units down of the graph of h.

  (D) It is a horizontal translation of 6 units to the left of the graph of h.

42. **CHALLENGE** Write a rule for a radical function that has a domain of all real numbers greater than or equal to -5 and a range of all real numbers less than or equal to 3. $y = -\sqrt{x + 5} + 3$

○ = **WORKED-OUT SOLUTIONS** on p. WS1   ★ = **STANDARDIZED TEST PRACTICE**

EXAMPLE 6 A
on p. 713
for Exs. 43–45

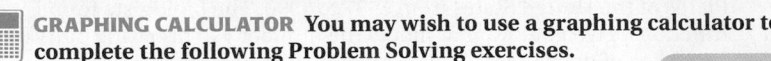 **GRAPHING CALCULATOR** You may wish to use a graphing calculator to complete the following Problem Solving exercises.

43. **SUSPENSION BRIDGE** The time t (in seconds) it takes an object dropped from a height h (in feet) to reach the ground is given by the function $t = \frac{1}{4}\sqrt{h}$.

   a. Graph the function and identify its domain and range.
   See margin for art; domain: $x \geq 0$, range: $y \geq 0$.
   b. The Royal Gorge Bridge in Canyon City, Colorado, is the world's highest suspension bridge. It takes about 8 seconds for a stone dropped from the bridge to reach the gorge below. About how high is the bridge?

43b. about 1024 ft

@HomeTutor for problem solving help at classzone.com

44. **OCEANOGRAPHY** Ocean waves can be shallow water, intermediate depth, or deep water waves. The speed s (in meters per second) of a shallow water wave can be modeled by the function $s = 3.13\sqrt{d}$ where d is the depth (in meters) of the water over which the wave is traveling.

   a. Graph the function and identify its domain and range.
   See margin for art; domain: $x \geq 0$, range: $y \geq 0$.
   b. A tsunami is a type of shallow water wave. Suppose a tsunami has a speed of 200 meters per second. Over approximately what depth of water is the tsunami traveling? **about 1021 m**

@HomeTutor for problem solving help at classzone.com

45. **LONG JUMP** A function for the speed at which a long jumper is running before jumping is $s = 10.9\sqrt{h}$ where s and h are defined in the diagram. Graph the function and identify its domain and range. To the nearest tenth, approximate the maximum height reached when the long jumper's speed before jumping is 10.25 meters per second.
See margin for art; domain: $x \geq 0$, range: $y \geq 0$; about 0.9 m.

h = maximum height (in meters)

s = speed (in meters per second)

46. **MULTI-STEP PROBLEM** The reading age of written materials is the age at which an average person can read and understand the materials. A function that is sometimes used to identify the reading age r (in years) of written materials is $r = \sqrt{w} + 8$ where w is the average number of words with 3 or more syllables in samples taken from the written materials.

   a. Graph the function and identify its domain and range.
   See margin for art; domain: $x \geq 0$, range: $y \geq 8$.
   b. What is the average number of words with 3 or more syllables in samples taken from material that can be read and understood by a 10-year-old? **4 words**

11.1 Graph Square Root Functions **715**

Avoiding Common Errors

Exercises 17–22 Watch for students who treat a number added to the radical expression as part of the radicand. You may want to remind these students that the graphs in these exercises are vertical translations.

Study Strategy

Exercises 30–38 Tell students that it may be helpful to go through each of the functions before they begin to graph them to determine the general form of the graph of the function. This will help them to start focusing on whether the graph is a vertical stretch or shrink, a reflection, or a translation of the parent function. Suggest that they make short notes next to the exercises and then check their graphs against these notes to see whether they have a good grasp of the concepts.

Mathematical Reasoning

Exercises 23–28, 30–31, 33–38 Some students may wonder why the radicand must be a nonnegative number. You may want to ask what would be the square root of -9, leading students to see that square root functions are limited to real numbers and therefore the radicand cannot be a negative number.

Internet Reference

Exercise 44 For more information about tsunamis, visit the National Oceanic and Atmospheric Administration website at www.tsunami.noaa.gov/tsunami_story.html

43a.

44a.

45.

46a.

Daily Homework Quiz

📄 Transparency Available

1. Graph the function $y = 2\sqrt{x} + 1$.

2. Graph the function
$y = \frac{1}{2}\sqrt{x - 2} + 1$.

3. Use the function $t = \frac{1}{4}\sqrt{h}$, where
t is time (in seconds) and h is
distance (in feet) to model a
sky diver's freefall. How many
feet did a sky diver freefall if the
freefall lasted 9 seconds?
1296 ft

🌐 **Online Quiz**

Available at **classzone.com**

Diagnosis/Remediation

• Practice A, B, C in Chapter 11
  Resource Book, pp. 7–12
• Study Guide in Chapter 11
  Resource Book, pp. 13–14
• Practice Workbook, pp. 169–171
• @HomeTutor

Challenge

Additional challenge is available
in the Chapter 11 Resource Book,
p. 17.

47a, 48a, 48c. See Additional
Answers beginning on p. AA1.

Ⓑ **47. BIOLOGY** Biologists studied two types of duck in the northern Great Plains of the United States from 1987 to 1990. The biologists found functions, given below, that model the number y of breeding pairs of each type of duck in wetlands with area x (in hectares).

Blue-winged teal: $y = 0.7\sqrt{x}$

Northern pintail: $y = 0.2\sqrt{x}$

  a. Graph the functions in the same coordinate plane. Identify the domain and range of each function. **See margin.**

  b. Find the area (to the nearest hectare) for 1 breeding pair of each type of duck. **blue-winged teal: about 2 hectares, northern pintail: 25 hectares**

Ⓒ **48. ★ EXTENDED RESPONSE** The amount of mozzarella cheese y (in pounds per person) consumed in the United States for the period 1980–2001 can be modeled by $y = 2\sqrt{x + 1}$ where x is the number of years since 1980.

  a. Graph Graph the function and identify its domain and range. **See margin for art; domain: $x \geq -1$, range: $y \geq 0$.**

  b. Apply In what year was the amount of mozzarella cheese consumed equal to 2 pounds per person? **1980**

  c. Explain In what year was the amount of mozzarella cheese consumed per person double the amount consumed per person in 1980? *Explain.* **See margin.**

49. CHALLENGE The flow rate r (in gallons per minute) of water through a high-pressure water hose is given by $r = 29.7d^2\sqrt{p}$ where d is the nozzle diameter (in inches) and p is the nozzle pressure (in pounds per square inch). For what value of d would the graph of the function be identical to the graph of the parent square root function? For what values of d would the graph be a vertical stretch? a vertical shrink?

$$\frac{1}{\sqrt{29.7}}; \ d > \frac{1}{\sqrt{29.7}}; \ d < \frac{1}{\sqrt{29.7}}$$

MIXED REVIEW

Write the prime factorization of the number if it is not a prime number. If the number is prime, write *prime*. *(p. 910)*

50. 7 **prime**   **51.** 14 **2 · 7**   **52.** 18 **3^2 · 2**   **53.** 9 **3^2**

54. 24 **2^3 · 3**   **55.** 13 **prime**   **56.** 53 **prime**   **57.** 72 **2^3 · 3^2**

PREVIEW
Prepare for
Lesson 11.2
in Exs. 58–61.

Evaluate the expression. *(p. 110)*

58. $\sqrt{16}$ **4**   **59.** $\sqrt{64}$ **8**   **60.** $\sqrt{144}$ **12**   **61.** $\sqrt{900}$ **30**

Factor the expression.

62. $x^2 - 31x + 58$ *(p. 583)* **$(x - 29)(x - 2)$**   **63.** $2x^2 - 7x + 6$ *(p. 593)* **$(2x - 3)(x - 2)$**

64. $7x^2 + 9x + 2$ *(p. 593)* **$(7x + 2)(x + 1)$**   **65.** $6x^2 - 11x - 35$ *(p. 593)* **$(2x - 7)(3x + 5)$**

66. $400x^2 - 9y^2$ *(p. 600)* **$(20x - 3y)(20x + 3y)$**   **67.** $25x^2 + 20xy + 4y^2$ *(p. 600)* **$(5x + 2y)^2$**

11.1 Graph Square Root Functions

QUESTION How can you use a graphing calculator to graph square root functions?

EXAMPLE Graph the function $y = \sqrt{2x + 3}$ and describe its domain and range

STEP 1 *Enter the function*
Enter the function into a graphing calculator. Use parentheses around the radicand.

STEP 2 *Graph the function*
Graph the function. Adjust the viewing window if necessary.

STEP 3 *Describe the domain and range*
From the graph, you can see that the domain is all real numbers greater than or equal to −1.5, or $x \geq -1.5$. The range is all nonnegative numbers, or $y \geq 0$.

PRACTICE

Graph the function using a graphing calculator. Then describe the domain and range of the function. **1–12. See margin.**

1. $y = \sqrt{4x}$
2. $y = \sqrt{9x}$
3. $y = \sqrt{7x}$
4. $y = -\sqrt{10x}$
5. $y = -3\sqrt{x}$
6. $y = 1.5\sqrt{3x}$
7. $y = 4.4\sqrt{8x}$
8. $y = \sqrt{2x + 8}$
9. $y = \sqrt{3x + 4}$
10. $y = -\sqrt{2x - 5}$
11. $y = -\sqrt{4x - 6}$
12. $y = \frac{1}{2}\sqrt{6 - 5x}$

13. **ROLLER COASTER** If friction is ignored, the velocity v (in meters per second) of a roller coaster when it reaches the bottom of a hill can be calculated using the formula $v = \sqrt{19.6h}$ where h (in meters) is the height of the hill.

   a. Graph the function and describe its domain and range. **See margin for art; domain: $x \geq 0$, range: $y \geq 0$.**

   b. Use the graph to find the height of a hill if the velocity of the roller coaster at the bottom of the hill is 55 meters per second. **about 154.3 m**

11.1 Graph Square Root Functions **717**

1–12. See Additional Answers beginning on p. AA1.
13a.

---

1 PLAN AND PREPARE

Learn the Method
- Students will graph square root functions.
- After the activity, students can use a graphing calculator to check their solutions in Exercises 3–14, 17–28, and 30–38 in Lesson 11.1.

Keystroke Help
Keystrokes for several models of calculators are available in blackline format in the *Chapter 11 Resource Book*.

2 TEACH

Tips for Success
In Step 3, students can use the *trace* feature if they are unsure of the domain.

Extra Example
Graph the function $y = \sqrt{2x - 5}$ and describe its domain and range.
Domain: $x \geq 2.5$, Range: $y \geq 0$.

3 ASSESS AND RETEACH

The velocity v (in feet per second) of an object dropped from a height can be found using the formula $v = \sqrt{64d}$, where d (in feet) is the distance the object is dropped. Explain how to use your graphing calculator to find the velocity of an object that that has fallen 80 feet. **Graph the function using x for distance and y for velocity. Use the trace feature to find the value of y when $x = 80$.**

11.2 Properties of Radicals

MATERIALS · calculator

QUESTION How can you simplify products and quotients of square roots?

EXPLORE Simplify products and quotients of square roots

STEP 1 *Find products of square roots*

Copy and complete the table without using a calculator. Compare the values in the second and third columns.

Values of a and b	Value of $\sqrt{a} \cdot \sqrt{b}$	Value of $\sqrt{ab}$
$a = 4, b = 9$	? 6	? 6
$a = 9, b = 16$	? 12	? 12
$a = 25, b = 4$	? 10	? 10
$a = 16, b = 36$	? 24	? 24

STEP 2 *Find products of square roots*

Use a calculator to copy and complete the table. Compare the values in the second and third columns.

Values of a and b	Value of $\sqrt{a} \cdot \sqrt{b}$	Value of $\sqrt{ab}$
$a = 2, b = 3$	? 2.45	? 2.45
$a = 10, b = 5$	? 7.07	? 7.07
$a = 7, b = 11$	? 8.77	? 8.77
$a = 13, b = 6$	? 8.83	? 8.83

STEP 3 *Find quotients of square roots*

Copy and complete the table without using a calculator. Compare the values in the second and third columns.

Values of a and b	Value of $\dfrac{\sqrt{a}}{\sqrt{b}}$	Value of $\sqrt{\dfrac{a}{b}}$
$a = 4, b = 16$	? $\frac{1}{2}$	? $\frac{1}{2}$
$a = 9, b = 25$	? $\frac{3}{5}$	? $\frac{3}{5}$
$a = 36, b = 4$	? 3	? 3
$a = 4, b = 49$	? $\frac{2}{7}$	? $\frac{2}{7}$

STEP 4 *Find quotients of square roots*

Use a calculator to copy and complete the table. Compare the values in the second and third columns.

Values of a and b	Value of $\dfrac{\sqrt{a}}{\sqrt{b}}$	Value of $\sqrt{\dfrac{a}{b}}$
$a = 1, b = 2$	? 0.71	? 0.71
$a = 3, b = 8$	? 0.61	? 0.61
$a = 12, b = 7$	? 1.31	? 1.31
$a = 6, b = 11$	? 0.74	? 0.74

DRAW CONCLUSIONS Use your observations to complete these exercises

In Exercises 1 and 2, copy and complete the statement.

1. The product of two square roots is equal to __?__ . the square root of the product of the radicands

2. The quotient of two square roots is equal to __?__ . the square root of the quotient of the radicands

3. **REASONING** Do you think that $\sqrt{a} + \sqrt{b} = \sqrt{a + b}$ for any $a \ge 0$ and any $b \ge 0$? *Justify* your answer. **No.** *Sample answer:* If $a = 1$ and $b = 4$, then $\sqrt{a} + \sqrt{b} = 1 + 2 = 3$, which does not equal $\sqrt{a + b} = \sqrt{1 + 2} = \sqrt{3}$.

718 Chapter 11 Radicals and Geometry Connections

---

❶ PLAN AND PREPARE

Explore the Concept

- Students will simplify products and quotients of square roots.
- This activity leads into the study of using the product property of radicals in Example 1 in Lesson 11.2.

Materials

Each student will need:
- calculator
- Activity Support Master (*Chapter 11 Resource Book*, p. 20)

Recommended Time

Work activity: 10 min
Discuss results: 5 min

Grouping

Students should work individually.

❷ TEACH

Key Question

- How are the examples in Step 1 different from those in Step 2? **The factors are perfect squares in Step 1 but not in Step 2.**

Key Discovery

The square root of a product is equal to the product of the square roots of the factors. The square root of a quotient is equal to the quotient of the square roots of the numerator and denominator.

❸ ASSESS AND RETEACH

1. Write an equivalent expression for $\sqrt{6b}$. $\sqrt{6} \cdot \sqrt{b}$

2. Write an equivalent expression for $\sqrt{\dfrac{7}{a}}$. $\dfrac{\sqrt{7}}{\sqrt{a}}$

11.2 Simplify Radical Expressions

Before	You found square roots.
Now	You will simplify radical expressions.
Why?	So you can find the distance to the horizon, as in Ex. 68.

Key Vocabulary
• simplest form of a radical expression
• rationalizing the denominator

A radical expression is in **simplest form** if the following conditions are true:

• No perfect square factors other than 1 are in the radicand.

• No fractions are in the radicand.

• No radicals appear in the denominator of a fraction.

You can use the following property to simplify radical expressions.

KEY CONCEPT　　　　　　　　　　　　*For Your Notebook*

Product Property of Radicals

Words The square root of a product equals the product of the square roots of the factors.

Algebra $\sqrt{ab} = \sqrt{a} \cdot \sqrt{b}$　　　**Example** $\sqrt{4x} = \sqrt{4} \cdot \sqrt{x} = 2\sqrt{x}$
where $a \geq 0$ and $b \geq 0$

You can also use the fact that $\sqrt{a^2} = a$, where $a \geq 0$, to simplify radical expressions. In this lesson, whenever a variable appears in the radicand *assume that it has only nonnegative values.*

REVIEW SQUARE ROOTS
For help finding square roots of perfect squares, see p. 110.

EXAMPLE 1 Use the product property of radicals

a.　$\sqrt{32} = \sqrt{16 \cdot 2}$　　　**Factor using perfect square factor.**

　　　　$= \sqrt{16} \cdot \sqrt{2}$　　　**Product property of radicals**

　　　　$= 4\sqrt{2}$　　　**Simplify.**

b.　$\sqrt{9x^3} = \sqrt{9 \cdot x^2 \cdot x}$　　　**Factor using perfect square factors.**

　　　　$= \sqrt{9} \cdot \sqrt{x^2} \cdot \sqrt{x}$　　　**Product property of radicals**

　　　　$= 3x\sqrt{x}$　　　**Simplify.**

Animated **Algebra** at classzone.com

✓ **GUIDED PRACTICE** **for Example 1**

1. Simplify (**a**) $\sqrt{24}$ and (**b**) $\sqrt{25x^2}$. (**a**) $2\sqrt{6}$; (**b**) $5x$

11.2 Simplify Radical Expressions　**719**

---

① PLAN AND PREPARE

Warm-Up Exercises
📑 **Transparency Available**
Use the distributive property to write an equivalent expression.

1. $2(x + 6)$ $2x + 12$

2. $x(x^2 + 2)$ $x^3 + 2x$

3. $(x + x^2)(-3)$ $-3x - 3x^2$

4. $0.1(6 + 10x)$ $0.6 + x$

5. The area of a square field is 148 square meters. What is the side length of the field? **about 12.2 m**

Notetaking Guide
📑 **Transparency Available**
Promotes interactive learning and notetaking skills, pp. 251–255.

Pacing
Basic: 2 days
Average: 2 days
Advanced: 2 days
Block: 1 block
• See *Teaching Guide/Lesson Plan.*

② FOCUS AND MOTIVATE

Essential Question
Big Idea 2, p. 709
How do you simplify radical expressions? **Tell students they will learn how to answer this question by using properties of radicals.**

NCTM STANDARDS
Standard 2: Analyze situations using algebraic symbols
Standard 4: Apply proper techniques to find measures

Resource Planning Guide

Chapter Resource Book
• Teaching Guide/Lesson Plan (pp. 18–19)
• Practice levels A, B, C (pp. 21–23)
• Study Guide (pp. 24–25)
• Catch-up for Absent Students (p. 26)
• Application (p. 27)
• Challenge (p. 28)

Workbooks
• Notetaking Guide (pp. 251–255)
• Practice Workbook (pp. 172–173)

Teaching Options
• **Power Presentations CD-ROM**
  provides dynamic electronic teaching resources for the classroom.
• **Activity Generator CD-ROM** provides editable activities for all ability levels.

Interactive Technology
• Easy Planner
• Power Presentations CD-ROM
• Activity Generator CD-ROM
• Animated Algebra
• Test Generator CD-ROM
• Online Quiz
• eWorkbook
• eEdition
• @HomeTutor

Resources for English Learners
• Quick Reference for English Learners
• Spanish Study Guide
• Multi-Language Visual Glossary
• Student Resources in Spanish

See also the *Algebra 1 Toolkit* for more strategies for meeting individual needs.

EXAMPLE 2 Multiply radicals

a.
$$\sqrt{6} \cdot \sqrt{6} = \sqrt{6 \cdot 6}$$ Product property of radicals
$$= \sqrt{36}$$ Multiply.
$$= 6$$ Simplify.

b.
$$\sqrt{3x} \cdot 4\sqrt{x} = 4\sqrt{3x \cdot x}$$ Product property of radicals
$$= 4\sqrt{3x^2}$$ Multiply.
$$= 4 \cdot \sqrt{3} \cdot \sqrt{x^2}$$ Product property of radicals
$$= 4x\sqrt{3}$$ Simplify.

WRITE RADICALS
When writing a product involving a radical, write the radical last to avoid confusion. For instance, if you write the product of x and $\sqrt{2}$ as $\sqrt{2}x$, it might be read as $\sqrt{2x}$.

c.
$$\sqrt{7xy^2} \cdot 3\sqrt{x} = 3\sqrt{7xy^2 \cdot x}$$ Product property of radicals
$$= 3\sqrt{7x^2y^2}$$ Multiply.
$$= 3 \cdot \sqrt{7} \cdot \sqrt{x^2} \cdot \sqrt{y^2}$$ Product property of radicals
$$= 3xy\sqrt{7}$$ Simplify.

KEY CONCEPT   *For Your Notebook*

Quotient Property of Radicals

Words The square root of a quotient equals the quotient of the square roots of the numerator and denominator.

Algebra $\sqrt{\dfrac{a}{b}} = \dfrac{\sqrt{a}}{\sqrt{b}}$ where $a \geq 0$ and $b > 0$

Example $\sqrt{\dfrac{16}{25}} = \dfrac{\sqrt{16}}{\sqrt{25}} = \dfrac{4}{5}$

EXAMPLE 3 Use the quotient property of radicals

a.
$$\sqrt{\dfrac{13}{100}} = \dfrac{\sqrt{13}}{\sqrt{100}}$$ Quotient property of radicals
$$= \dfrac{\sqrt{13}}{10}$$ Simplify.

b.
$$\sqrt{\dfrac{7}{x^2}} = \dfrac{\sqrt{7}}{\sqrt{x^2}}$$ Quotient property of radicals
$$= \dfrac{\sqrt{7}}{x}$$ Simplify.

✓ **GUIDED PRACTICE** for Examples 2 and 3

2. Simplify (a) $\sqrt{2x^3} \cdot \sqrt{x}$ and (b) $\sqrt{\dfrac{1}{y^2}}$. (a) $x^2\sqrt{2}$; (b) $\dfrac{1}{y}$

720   Chapter 11 Radicals and Geometry Connections

RATIONALIZING THE DENOMINATOR Example 4 shows how to eliminate a radical from the denominator of a radical expression by multiplying the expression by an appropriate value of 1. The process of eliminating a radical from an expression's denominator is called **rationalizing the denominator.**

EXAMPLE 4 Rationalize the denominator

MULTIPLY BY 1
In part (a), notice that $\frac{\sqrt{7}}{\sqrt{7}}$ is equal to 1, so multiplying by it does not change the value of the expression.

a. $\dfrac{5}{\sqrt{7}} = \dfrac{5}{\sqrt{7}} \cdot \dfrac{\sqrt{7}}{\sqrt{7}}$ Multiply by $\dfrac{\sqrt{7}}{\sqrt{7}}$.

$= \dfrac{5\sqrt{7}}{\sqrt{49}}$ Product property of radicals

$= \dfrac{5\sqrt{7}}{7}$ Simplify.

b. $\dfrac{\sqrt{2}}{\sqrt{3b}} = \dfrac{\sqrt{2}}{\sqrt{3b}} \cdot \dfrac{\sqrt{3b}}{\sqrt{3b}}$ Multiply by $\dfrac{\sqrt{3b}}{\sqrt{3b}}$.

$= \dfrac{\sqrt{6b}}{\sqrt{9b^2}}$ Product property of radicals

$= \dfrac{\sqrt{6b}}{\sqrt{9} \cdot \sqrt{b^2}}$ Product property of radicals

$= \dfrac{\sqrt{6b}}{3b}$ Simplify.

SUMS AND DIFFERENCES You can use the distributive property to simplify sums and differences of radical expressions when the expressions have the same radicand.

EXAMPLE 5 Add and subtract radicals

a. $4\sqrt{10} + \sqrt{13} - 9\sqrt{10} = 4\sqrt{10} - 9\sqrt{10} + \sqrt{13}$ Commutative property

$= (4 - 9)\sqrt{10} + \sqrt{13}$ Distributive property

$= -5\sqrt{10} + \sqrt{13}$ Simplify.

b. $5\sqrt{3} + \sqrt{48} = 5\sqrt{3} + \sqrt{16 \cdot 3}$ Factor using perfect square factor.

$= 5\sqrt{3} + \sqrt{16} \cdot \sqrt{3}$ Product property of radicals

$= 5\sqrt{3} + 4\sqrt{3}$ Simplify.

$= (5 + 4)\sqrt{3}$ Distributive property

$= 9\sqrt{3}$ Simplify.

✓ **GUIDED PRACTICE**   for Examples 4 and 5

Simplify the expression.

3. $\dfrac{1}{\sqrt{3}}$ $\dfrac{\sqrt{3}}{3}$ **4.** $\dfrac{1}{\sqrt{x}}$ $\dfrac{\sqrt{x}}{x}$ **5.** $\dfrac{3}{\sqrt{2x}}$ $\dfrac{3\sqrt{2x}}{2x}$ **6.** $2\sqrt{7} + 3\sqrt{63}$ $11\sqrt{7}$

Extra Example 4
Rationalize the denomimator
a. $\dfrac{7}{\sqrt{6}}$ $\dfrac{7\sqrt{6}}{6}$
b. $\dfrac{\sqrt{3}}{\sqrt{5a}}$ $\dfrac{\sqrt{15a}}{5a}$

Key Question to Ask for Example 4
• Could you multiply the expression in part a by $\dfrac{5}{\sqrt{7}}$ to rationalize the denominator? Explain.
No; it would change the value of the expression.

Extra Example 5
Add and subtract radicals.
a. $7\sqrt{14} + \sqrt{21} - 4\sqrt{14}$ $3\sqrt{14} + \sqrt{21}$
b. $2\sqrt{7} + \sqrt{28}$ $4\sqrt{7}$

Key Question to Ask for Example 5
• Why do you use the commutative property in part a? **You want to arrange the terms so that you can combine like terms.**

Differentiated Instruction

Auditory Learners Phrases which have parallel structure are easier to learn for some students. The product property of radicals, when abridged slightly to read, "The square root of a product is the product of the square roots", has a parallel structure which is easy for students to remember. Show students that the quotient property of radicals follows from the product property by changing b to $\dfrac{1}{b}$.

See also the *Algebra 1 Toolkit* for more strategies.

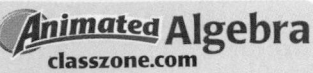

EXAMPLE 6 Multiply radical expressions

a. $\sqrt{5}(4 - \sqrt{20}) = 4\sqrt{5} - \sqrt{5} \cdot \sqrt{20}$ **Distributive property**

$= 4\sqrt{5} - \sqrt{100}$ **Product property of radicals**

$= 4\sqrt{5} - 10$ **Simplify.**

b. $(\sqrt{7} + \sqrt{2})(\sqrt{7} - 3\sqrt{2})$

REVIEW FOIL METHOD
For help with the FOIL method, see p. 562.

$= (\sqrt{7})^2 + \sqrt{7}(-3\sqrt{2}) + \sqrt{2} \cdot \sqrt{7} + \sqrt{2}(-3\sqrt{2})$ **Multiply.**

$= 7 - 3\sqrt{7 \cdot 2} + \sqrt{7 \cdot 2} - 3(\sqrt{2})^2$ **Product property of radicals**

$= 7 - 3\sqrt{14} + \sqrt{14} - 6$ **Simplify.**

$= 1 - 2\sqrt{14}$ **Simplify.**

Animated Algebra at classzone.com

EXAMPLE 7 Solve a real-world problem

ASTRONOMY The orbital period of a planet is the time that it takes the planet to travel around the sun. You can find the orbital period P (in Earth years) using the formula $P = \sqrt{d^3}$ where d is the average distance (in astronomical units, abbreviated AU) of the planet from the sun.

a. Simplify the formula.

b. Jupiter's average distance from the sun is shown in the diagram. What is Jupiter's orbital period?

Not drawn to scale

Solution

a. $P = \sqrt{d^3}$ **Write formula.**

$= \sqrt{d^2 \cdot d}$ **Factor using perfect square factor.**

$= \sqrt{d^2} \cdot \sqrt{d}$ **Product property of radicals**

$= d\sqrt{d}$ **Simplify.**

b. Substitute 5.2 for d in the simplified formula.
$P = d\sqrt{d} = 5.2\sqrt{5.2}$

▶ The orbital period of Jupiter is $5.2\sqrt{5.2}$, or about 11.9, Earth years.

✓ **GUIDED PRACTICE** for Examples 6 and 7

7. Simplify the expression $(4 - \sqrt{5})(1 - \sqrt{5})$. **$9 - 5\sqrt{5}$**

8. **ASTRONOMY** Neptune's average distance from the sun is about 6 times Jupiter's average distance from the sun. Is the orbital period of Neptune 6 times the orbital period of Jupiter? *Explain.* **See margin.**

11.2 EXERCISES

HOMEWORK KEY
○ = WORKED-OUT SOLUTIONS
on p. WS1 for Exs. 9, 37, and 69

★ = STANDARDIZED TEST PRACTICE
Exs. 2, 23, 25, 64, and 71

◆ = MULTIPLE REPRESENTATIONS
Ex. 70

SKILL PRACTICE

[A]

1. **VOCABULARY** Copy and complete: The process of eliminating a radical from the denominator of a radical expression is called __?__. **rationalizing the denominator**

2. ★ **WRITING** Is the expression $\sqrt{\frac{2x}{9}}$ written in simplest form? *Explain* why or why not.
No. *Sample answer*: An expression is not in simplest form if there is a fraction in the radicand.

EXAMPLES 1, 2, and 3
on pp. 719–720
for Exs. 3–25

USING PRODUCT AND QUOTIENT PROPERTIES Simplify the expression.

3. $\sqrt{20}$ $2\sqrt{5}$
4. $\sqrt{48}$ $4\sqrt{3}$
5. $\sqrt{96}$ $4\sqrt{6}$
6. $\sqrt{72}$ $6\sqrt{2}$

7. $\sqrt{125b}$ $5\sqrt{5b}$
8. $\sqrt{4x^2}$ $2x$
9. $\sqrt{81m^3}$ $9m\sqrt{m}$
10. $\sqrt{32m^5}$ $4m^2\sqrt{2m}$

11. $\sqrt{5} \cdot \sqrt{30}$ $5\sqrt{6}$
12. $\sqrt{50} \cdot \sqrt{18}$ 30
13. $\sqrt{14x} \cdot \sqrt{2x}$ $2x\sqrt{7}$
14. $\sqrt{3b^3} \cdot \sqrt{18b}$ $3b^2\sqrt{6}$

15. $2\sqrt{a^4b^5}$ $2a^2b^2\sqrt{b}$
16. $\sqrt{64s^4t^3}$ $8s^2t\sqrt{t}$
17. $\sqrt{m^2n} \cdot \sqrt{n}$ mn
18. $\sqrt{75xy} \cdot \sqrt{2x^3}$ $5x^2\sqrt{6y}$

19. $\sqrt{\frac{4}{49}}$ $\frac{2}{7}$
20. $\sqrt{\frac{7}{81}}$ $\frac{\sqrt{7}}{9}$
21. $\sqrt{\frac{a^3}{121}}$ $\frac{a\sqrt{a}}{11}$
22. $\sqrt{\frac{100}{4x^2}}$ $\frac{5}{x}$

23. ★ **MULTIPLE CHOICE** Which expression is equivalent to $\sqrt{\frac{9x}{16}}$? **B**

   Ⓐ $\frac{\sqrt{3x}}{4}$
   Ⓑ $\frac{3\sqrt{x}}{4}$
   Ⓒ $\frac{3\sqrt{x}}{16}$
   Ⓓ $\frac{3x}{4}$

24. **ERROR ANALYSIS** *Describe* and correct the error in simplifying the expression $\sqrt{72}$.
Sample answer: The answer is not simplified completely. $2\sqrt{18}$ can be written as $2\sqrt{2} \cdot \sqrt{9} = 6\sqrt{2}$.

$$\sqrt{72} = \sqrt{4} \cdot \sqrt{18}$$
$$= 2\sqrt{18}$$

25. ★ **WRITING** *Describe* two different sequences of steps you could take to simplify the expression $\sqrt{45} \cdot \sqrt{5}$. *Sample answer*: Simplify $\sqrt{45}$ to $\sqrt{9} \cdot \sqrt{5} = 3\sqrt{5}$. Then multiply $3\sqrt{5} \cdot \sqrt{5} = 3 \cdot 5 = 15$. Or, combine the expressions to create $\sqrt{45 \cdot 5} = \sqrt{225} = 15$.

EXAMPLE 4
on p. 721
for Exs. 26–33

RATIONALIZING THE DENOMINATOR Simplify the expression.

26. $\frac{2}{\sqrt{2}}$ $\sqrt{2}$
27. $\frac{4}{\sqrt{3}}$ $\frac{4\sqrt{3}}{3}$
28. $\sqrt{\frac{5}{48}}$ $\frac{\sqrt{15}}{12}$
29. $\sqrt{\frac{4}{52}}$ $\frac{\sqrt{13}}{13}$

30. $\frac{3}{\sqrt{a}}$ $\frac{3\sqrt{a}}{a}$
31. $\frac{1}{\sqrt{2x}}$ $\frac{\sqrt{2x}}{2x}$
32. $\sqrt{\frac{2x^2}{5}}$ $\frac{x\sqrt{10}}{5}$
33. $\sqrt{\frac{8}{3n^3}}$ $\frac{2\sqrt{6n}}{3n^2}$

EXAMPLES 5 and 6
on pp. 721–722
for Exs. 34–45

38. $8\sqrt{3} + 2\sqrt{6}$
39. $7\sqrt{7} - 5\sqrt{14}$

PERFORMING OPERATIONS ON RADICALS Simplify the expression.

34. $2\sqrt{2} + 6\sqrt{2}$ $8\sqrt{2}$
35. $\sqrt{5} - 6\sqrt{5}$ $-5\sqrt{5}$
36. $2\sqrt{6} - 5\sqrt{54}$ $-13\sqrt{6}$

37. $9\sqrt{32} + \sqrt{2}$ $37\sqrt{2}$
38. $\sqrt{12} + 6\sqrt{3} + 2\sqrt{6}$
39. $3\sqrt{7} - 5\sqrt{14} + 2\sqrt{28}$

40. $\sqrt{5}(5 - \sqrt{5})$ $5\sqrt{5} - 5$
41. $\sqrt{6}(7\sqrt{3} + 6)$ $21\sqrt{2} + 6\sqrt{6}$
42. $\sqrt{3}(6\sqrt{2} - 4\sqrt{3})$ $6\sqrt{6} - 12$

43. $(4 - \sqrt{2})(5 + \sqrt{2})$ $18 - \sqrt{2}$
44. $(2\sqrt{5} + 7)^2$ $69 + 28\sqrt{5}$
45. $(\sqrt{7} + \sqrt{3})(6 + \sqrt{8})$
    $6\sqrt{7} + 6\sqrt{3} + 2\sqrt{14} + 2\sqrt{6}$

11.2 Simplify Radical Expressions **723**

④ PRACTICE AND APPLY

Assignment Guide

Answer Transparencies available for all exercises

Basic:
Day 1: EP p. 946 Exs. 7–12
pp. 723–726
Exs. 1–25
Day 2: pp. 723–726
Exs. 26–50 even, 67–70, 73–93 odd

Average:
Day 1: pp. 723–726
Exs. 1, 2, 4–22 even, 23–32, 55–58
Day 2: pp. 723–726
Exs. 35–53 odd, 59–63, 67–71, 74, 77, 80, 82, 84, 87, 90, 93

Advanced:
Day 1: pp. 723–726
Exs. 1, 15–23, 25–33, 55–62
Day 2: pp. 723–726
Exs. 34–54 even, 59–72*, 78, 81, 88, 94

Block:
pp. 723–726
Exs. 1, 2, 4–22 even, 23–25, 26–32, 35–53 odd, 55–63, 67–71, 74, 77, 80, 82, 84, 87, 90, 93

Differentiated Instruction

See *Algebra 1 Best Practices Toolkit* for suggestions on addressing the needs of a diverse classroom.

Homework Check

For a quick check of student understanding of key concepts, go over the following exercises:
Basic: 14, 28, 36, 42, 67
Average: 18, 30, 35, 43, 67
Advanced: 21, 32, 38, 44, 68

Extra Practice

• Student Edition, p. 948
• Chapter 11 Resource Book:
  Practice levels A, B, C, pp. 21–23

Practice Worksheet

An easily-readable reduced practice page (with answers) for this lesson can be found on p. 708C.

B **SIMPLIFYING RADICAL EXPRESSIONS** Simplify the expression.

46. $\sqrt{75m^2np^4}$ $5mp^2\sqrt{3n}$

47. $\sqrt{512rs^6}\cdot\sqrt{t^3}$ $16s^3t\sqrt{2rt}$

48. $\sqrt{\dfrac{600a}{4b^3}}$ $\dfrac{5\sqrt{6ab}}{b^2}$

49. $\sqrt{\dfrac{50gh^2}{125f^3}}$ $\dfrac{h\sqrt{10gf}}{5f^2}$

50. $\dfrac{4}{\sqrt3}+\dfrac{7}{\sqrt{12}}$ $\dfrac{5\sqrt3}{2}$

51. $\dfrac{2\sqrt6}{\sqrt{30}}-\dfrac{3}{\sqrt{20}}$ $\dfrac{\sqrt5}{10}$

52. $\dfrac{7}{\sqrt x}+\dfrac{3}{2\sqrt x}$ $\dfrac{17\sqrt x}{2x}$

53. $\dfrac{3}{\sqrt{x^3}}+\dfrac{4}{\sqrt x}$ $\dfrac{3\sqrt x+4x\sqrt x}{x^2}$

54. $\dfrac{6m}{\sqrt{m^3}}-\dfrac{8}{\sqrt m}$ $\dfrac{-2\sqrt m}{m}$

CONJUGATES In Exercises 55–62, use the example to simplify the expression.

EXAMPLE Rationalize the denominator using conjugates

Simplify $\dfrac{9}{2-\sqrt3}$.

Solution

The binomials $a\sqrt b+c\sqrt d$ and $a\sqrt b-c\sqrt d$ are called *conjugates*. They differ only by the sign of one term. The product of two conjugates $a\sqrt b+c\sqrt d$ and $a\sqrt b-c\sqrt d$ does not contain a radical: $(2+\sqrt3)(2-\sqrt3)=2^2-(\sqrt3)^2=4-3=1$. You can use conjugates to simplify the expression.

$\dfrac{9}{2-\sqrt3}=\dfrac{9}{2-\sqrt3}\cdot\dfrac{2+\sqrt3}{2+\sqrt3}$ Multiply the numerator and denominator by the conjugate of the denominator.

$=\dfrac{9(2+\sqrt3)}{(2-\sqrt3)(2+\sqrt3)}$ Multiply fractions.

$=\dfrac{18+9\sqrt3}{4-3}$ Simplify numerator and denominator.

$=18+9\sqrt3$ Simplify.

---

55. $\dfrac{1}{\sqrt7+1}$ $\dfrac{\sqrt7-1}{6}$

56. $\dfrac{2}{5-\sqrt3}$ $\dfrac{5+\sqrt3}{11}$

57. $\dfrac{\sqrt{10}}{7-\sqrt2}$ $\dfrac{7\sqrt{10}+2\sqrt5}{47}$

58. $\dfrac{\sqrt5}{6+\sqrt5}$ $\dfrac{6\sqrt5-5}{31}$

59. $\dfrac{3}{\sqrt7+\sqrt6}$ $3\sqrt7-3\sqrt6$

60. $\dfrac{11}{\sqrt{11}-\sqrt7}$ $\dfrac{11\sqrt{11}+11\sqrt7}{4}$

61. $\dfrac{\sqrt6}{\sqrt2-\sqrt3}$ $-2\sqrt3-3\sqrt2$

62. $\dfrac{\sqrt7+1}{\sqrt7+\sqrt2}$ $\dfrac{7+\sqrt7-\sqrt{14}-\sqrt2}{5}$

C **63. REASONING** Multiply the binomials $a\sqrt b+c\sqrt d$ and $a\sqrt b-c\sqrt d$ to show that the product does not contain a radical.
$(a\sqrt b+c\sqrt d)(a\sqrt b-c\sqrt d)=a^2b-ac\sqrt{bd}+ac\sqrt{bd}-c^2d=a^2b-c^2d$

64. ★ **WRITING** According to the definition of square root, a number b is a square root of a number a if $b^2=a$. How can you use the definition to show that $\sqrt{x^2}=x$? *Explain.* *Sample answer:* The expression $\sqrt{x^2}=x$ is true if x is a square root of x^2. You know x is a square root of x^2 because the square of $x=x^2$.

65. MULTIPLYING FUNCTIONS Let $f(x)=\sqrt x-\sqrt{4x}$, and let $g(x)=\sqrt x$. Find $h(x)=f(x)\cdot g(x)$. $-x$

66. CHALLENGE Consider the expression $\sqrt{2^m}$. Assume m is a positive integer. For what values of m will the expression contain a radical when simplified? For what values of m will the expression contain no radical when simplified? *Explain.* **See margin.**

EXAMPLE 7 [A]
on p. 722
for Exs. 67, 68

67. FINANCE You invest $225 in a savings account for two years. The account has an annual interest rate that changes from year to year. You can find the average annual interest rate r that the account earned over two years using the formula $r = \sqrt{\dfrac{V_2}{V_0}} - 1$ where V_0 is the initial investment and V_2 is the amount in the account after two years. At the end of two years, you have $270 in the account. What was the average annual interest rate (written as a percent) the account earned over two years? **about 9.54%**

@**HomeTutor** for problem solving help at classzone.com

68. DISTANCE TO THE HORIZON The distance d (in miles) that a person can see to the horizon is given by the formula $d = \sqrt{\dfrac{3h}{2}}$ where h is the person's eye level (in feet) above the water. To the nearest mile, find the distance that the person shown can see to the horizon. **12 mi**

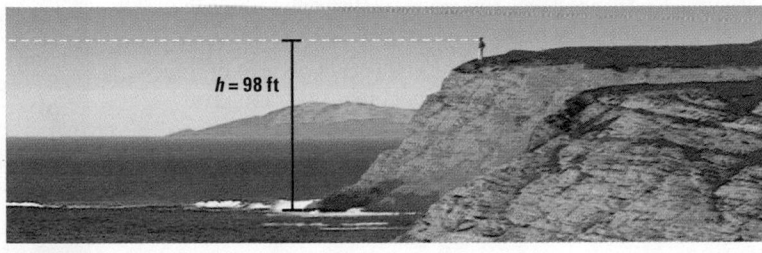

$h = 98$ ft

@**HomeTutor** for problem solving help at classzone.com

(69.) MULTI-STEP PROBLEM You are making a cube-shaped footrest. You want to cover the footrest with fabric. At a fabric store, you choose fabric that costs $6 per square yard.

a. You have $30 to spend on fabric. How much fabric can you buy? **5 yd²**

b. The edge length s (in yards) of the largest footrest you can cover can be found using the formula $s = \sqrt{\dfrac{S}{6}}$ where S is the surface area of the footrest (in square yards). Use unit analysis to check the units in the formula. **The side length s is in yd, and $\sqrt{\dfrac{S}{6}}$ is $\sqrt{\text{yd}^2}$ = yd.**

c. Find the edge length of the largest footrest you can cover to the nearest tenth of a yard. **0.9 yd**

[B] **70.** ◆ **MULTIPLE REPRESENTATIONS** The velocity v (in feet per second) of an object that has been dropped can be found using the equation $v = \sqrt{64d}$ where d is the distance the object falls (in feet) before hitting the ground.

a. **Writing an Equation** Write the equation in simplified form. $v = 8\sqrt{d}$

b. **Drawing a Graph** Graph the equation. For what value of d is the velocity about 16 feet per second? **See margin for art; 4 ft.**

c. **Solving an Equation** Use the equation from part (a) to find the exact value of d when the velocity is 16 feet per second. **4 ft**

11.2 Simplify Radical Expressions **725**

⑤ ASSESS AND RETEACH

Daily Homework Quiz

📄 Transparency Available

Simplify the expression.

1. $\sqrt{56a^2}$ $2a\sqrt{14}$

2. $\sqrt{\dfrac{b}{64}}$ $\dfrac{\sqrt{b}}{8}$

3. $5\sqrt{2} - 2\sqrt{8} + \sqrt{6}$ $\sqrt{2} + \sqrt{6}$

4. A person is standing on a cliff, with an eye level at 60 feet, looking out across the ocean. Use the formula $d = \sqrt{\dfrac{3h}{2}}$ where d (in miles) is the distance a person can see to the horizon and h (in feet) is the person's eye level above the water to find the number of miles the person can see to the horizon. **about 9.5 mi**

🔗 **Online Quiz**

Available at **classzone.com**

Diagnosis/Remediation

• Practice A, B, C in Chapter 11 Resource Book, pp. 21–23
• Study Guide in Chapter 11 Resource Book, pp. 24–25
• Practice Workbook, pp. 172–173
• @HomeTutor

Challenge

Additional challenge is available in the Chapter 11 Resource Book, p. 28.

---

71. ★ **SHORT RESPONSE** Physicians can calculate the body surface area S (in square meters) of an adult using the formula $S = \sqrt{\dfrac{hw}{3600}}$ where h is the adult's height (in centimeters) and w is the adult's mass (in kilograms).

  a. Simplify the formula. $S = \dfrac{\sqrt{hw}}{60}$

  b. Does an adult who is 1.7 meters tall and has a mass of 70 kilograms have a greater body surface area than an adult who is 1.5 meters tall and has a mass of 70 kilograms? *Explain* what effect height has on surface area if two people have the same mass.   **Yes.** *Sample answer*: **If the mass stays the same, then the greater the height the greater the body surface area will be.**

© 72. **CHALLENGE** The speed s (in miles per hour) at which a vehicle is traveling before an accident is given by $s = \sqrt{30df}$ where d is the length of the skid mark (in feet) and f is the coefficient of friction. The coefficient of friction varies depending on the type of road surface and on the road conditions.

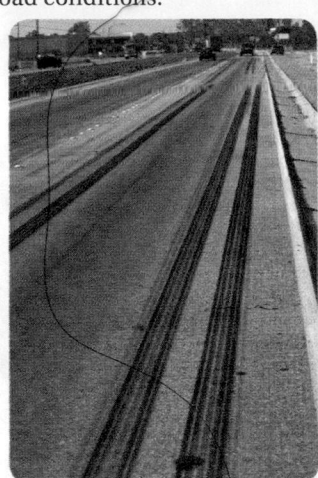

  a. A driver is traveling on a newly paved road with a coefficient of friction of 0.80. The driver sees a hazard in the road and is forced to brake. The car skids to a halt leaving a skid mark that is 100 feet long. At what speed was the car traveling when the driver applied the brakes?   **about 49.0 mi/h**

  b. A perception-reaction time is the amount of time it takes for a person to react to a situation after perceiving it, such as applying the brakes after seeing a hazard in the road. The driver in part (a) has a perception-reaction time of 1.5 seconds. How many feet does the car travel before the driver applies the brakes? *Explain* how you found your answer.

  c. What is the total distance (in feet) traveled from the time the driver in part (a) sees the hazard until the time the car skids to a halt?   **207.8 ft**

72b. about 107.8 ft. *Sample answer*: **First, convert 49 miles per hour from part (a) to feet per second** $\dfrac{49 \cdot 5280}{60 \cdot 60} =$ **71.0867 feet per second. Then multiply by 1.5 seconds.**

MIXED REVIEW

Graph the function and identify its domain and range.   **73–81. See margin.**

73. $y = -6$ for $x \ge 0$ *(p. 215)*
74. $y = -\dfrac{1}{3}x$ *(p. 215)*
75. $5x + y = 3$ *(p. 244)*

76. $y = 0.4x - 7$ *(p. 244)*
77. $y = 4^x$ *(p. 520)*
78. $y = (0.4)^x$ *(p. 531)*

79. $y = -7x^2$ *(p. 628)*
80. $y = 5x^2 + 2$ *(p. 628)*
81. $y = 3x^2 - 10x - 8$ *(p. 635)*

82. Write the equation of the line that passes through $(1, 2)$ and is perpendicular to the line $y = \dfrac{1}{2}x + 3$. *(p. 319)* $y = -2x + 4$

PREVIEW

Prepare for Lesson 11.3 in Exs. 83–94.

89. $\dfrac{-5 \pm \sqrt{67}}{2}$

Solve the equation. *(pp. 575, 583, 593, and 600)*

83. $(a - 3)(a + 8) = 0$ $-8, 3$
84. $(2y + 3)(2y + 5) = 0$ $-\dfrac{5}{2}, -\dfrac{3}{2}$
85. $-12m^2 + 48 = 0$ $-2, 2$

86. $x^2 - 8x + 16 = 0$ **4**
87. $d^2 + 8d = -2$ $-4 \pm \sqrt{14}$
88. $x^2 - 2x = 24$ $-4, 6$

89. $10z - 21 = -2z^2$
90. $5x^2 + 13x + 6 = 0$ $-2, -\dfrac{3}{5}$
91. $4x^2 - 11x - 3 = 0$ $-\dfrac{1}{4}, 3$

92. $8x^2 - 64 = 0$ $\pm 2\sqrt{2}$
93. $4z^2 = 36$ $-3, 3$
94. $b^2 + 12b + 36 = 0$ -6

73–81. See Additional Answers beginning on p. AA1.

Derive the Quadratic Formula

GOAL Solve quadratic equations and check solutions.

In Lesson 10.6, you learned how to find solutions of quadratic equations using the quadratic formula. You can use the method of completing the square and the quotient property of radicals to derive the quadratic formula.

$ax^2 + bx + c = 0$ — Write standard form of a quadratic equation.

$ax^2 + bx = -c$ — Subtract c from each side.

$x^2 + \dfrac{b}{a}x = -\dfrac{c}{a}$ — Divide each side by a, $a \neq 0$.

$x^2 + \dfrac{b}{a}x + \left(\dfrac{b}{2a}\right)^2 = -\dfrac{c}{a} + \left(\dfrac{b}{2a}\right)^2$ — Add $\left(\dfrac{b}{2a}\right)^2$ to each side to complete the square.

$\left(x + \dfrac{b}{2a}\right)^2 = -\dfrac{c}{a} + \dfrac{b^2}{4a^2}$ — Write left side as the square of a binomial.

$\left(x + \dfrac{b}{2a}\right)^2 = \dfrac{b^2 - 4ac}{4a^2}$ — Simplify right side.

$x + \dfrac{b}{2a} = \pm\sqrt{\dfrac{b^2 - 4ac}{4a^2}}$ — Take square roots of each side.

$x + \dfrac{b}{2a} = \dfrac{\pm\sqrt{b^2 - 4ac}}{2a}$ — Quotient property of radicals

$x = \dfrac{-b \pm \sqrt{b^2 - 4ac}}{2a}$ — Subtract $\dfrac{b}{2a}$ from each side.

SOLVING QUADRATIC EQUATIONS You can use the quadratic formula and properties of radicals to solve quadratic equations.

EXAMPLE 1 Solve an equation

Solve $x^2 - 6x + 3 = 0$.

Solution

$x^2 - 6x + 3 = 0$ — Identify $a = 1$, $b = -6$, and $c = 3$.

$x = \dfrac{-(-6) \pm \sqrt{(-6)^2 - 4(1)(3)}}{2(1)}$ — Substitute values in the quadratic formula.

$= \dfrac{6 \pm \sqrt{24}}{2}$ — Simplify.

$= \dfrac{6 \pm \sqrt{4 \cdot 6}}{2}$ — Product property of radicals

$= \dfrac{6 \pm 2\sqrt{6}}{2} = 3 \pm \sqrt{6}$ — Simplify.

▶ The solutions of the equation are $3 + \sqrt{6}$ and $3 - \sqrt{6}$.

Extension: Derive the Quadratic Formula   **727**

EXAMPLE 2 Check the solutions of an equation

Check the solutions of the equation from Example 1.

Solution

The solutions of $x^2 - 6x + 3 = 0$ are $3 + \sqrt{6}$ and $3 - \sqrt{6}$. You can check each solution by substituting it into the original equation.

Check $x = 3 + \sqrt{6}$:

$$x^2 - 6x + 3 = 0 \qquad \text{Write original equation.}$$
$$\left(3 + \sqrt{6}\right)^2 - 6\left(3 + \sqrt{6}\right) + 3 \overset{?}{=} 0 \qquad \text{Substitute } 3 + \sqrt{6} \text{ for } x.$$
$$9 + 6\sqrt{6} + 6 - 18 - 6\sqrt{6} + 3 \overset{?}{=} 0 \qquad \text{Multiply.}$$
$$0 = 0 \checkmark \qquad \text{Solution checks.}$$

Check $x = 3 - \sqrt{6}$:

$$x^2 - 6x + 3 = 0 \qquad \text{Write original equation.}$$
$$\left(3 - \sqrt{6}\right)^2 - 6\left(3 - \sqrt{6}\right) + 3 \overset{?}{=} 0 \qquad \text{Substitute } 3 - \sqrt{6} \text{ for } x.$$
$$9 - 6\sqrt{6} + 6 - 18 + 6\sqrt{6} + 3 \overset{?}{=} 0 \qquad \text{Multiply.}$$
$$0 = 0 \checkmark \qquad \text{Solution checks.}$$

Extra Example 2

Check the solutions of the equation from Extra Example 1. **The solutions check when you substitute them into the original equation.**

Closing the Lesson

Have students summarize the major points of the lesson and answer the Essential Question: How do you solve quadratic equations?

• The quadratic formula is
$x = \dfrac{-b \pm \sqrt{b^2 - 4ac}}{2a}$.
When using the quadratic formula, first identify the values of *a*, *b*, and *c*. Then substitute the values into the formula and simplify. Check the solutions by substituting each into the original equation.

④ PRACTICE AND APPLY

Avoiding Common Errors

Exercises 1–18 Urge students to use caution when substituting values into the quadratic formula to avoid calculation errors. Places to be especially careful include replacing *b* with a negative number and remembering that the denominator is 2 · *a*, not 2 or *a*.

🖩 Graphing Calculator

Exercises 1–18 Students may want to check their solutions by graphing the equations. They can use the *zero* feature to check the solutions.

PRACTICE

EXAMPLES
1 and 2
on pp. 727–728
for Exs. 1–18

Solve the equation using the quadratic formula. Check the solution. 1–18. See margin.

1. $x^2 + 4x + 2 = 0$
2. $x^2 + 6x - 1 = 0$
3. $x^2 + 8x + 8 = 0$
4. $x^2 - 7x + 1 = 0$
5. $3x^2 + 6x - 1 = 0$
6. $2x^2 - 4x - 3 = 0$
7. $5x^2 - 2x - 2 = 0$
8. $4x^2 + 10x + 3 = 0$
9. $x^2 - x - 3 = 0$
10. $x^2 - 2x - 8 = 0$
11. $-x^2 + 7x + 3 = 0$
12. $x^2 + 3x - 9 = 0$
13. $-\dfrac{5}{2}x^2 + 10x - 5 = 0$
14. $\dfrac{1}{2}x^2 + 3x - 9 = 0$
15. $3x^2 - 2 = 0$
16. $-2x^2 - 7x = 0$
17. $3x^2 + x = 6$
18. $x^2 - 4x = -2$

19. Show that $\dfrac{-b + \sqrt{b^2 - 4ac}}{2a}$ and $\dfrac{-b - \sqrt{b^2 - 4ac}}{2a}$ are solutions of $ax^2 + bx + c = 0$ by substituting. **See margin.**

20. Derive a formula to find solutions of equations that have the form $ax^2 + x + c = 0$. Use your formula to find solutions of $-2x^2 + x + 8 = 0$. **See margin.**

21. Find the sum and product of $\dfrac{-b + \sqrt{b^2 - 4ac}}{2a}$ and $\dfrac{-b - \sqrt{b^2 - 4ac}}{2a}$. Write a quadratic expression whose solutions have a sum of 2 and a product of $\dfrac{1}{2}$. **See margin.**

22. What values can *a* have in the equation $ax^2 + 12x + 3 = 0$ in order for the equation to have one or two real solutions? *Explain.* **See margin.**

---

1. $-2 - \sqrt{2}, -2 + \sqrt{2}$
2. $-3 - \sqrt{10}, -3 + \sqrt{10}$
3. $-4 - 2\sqrt{2}, -4 + 2\sqrt{2}$
4. $\dfrac{7}{2} - \dfrac{5\sqrt{5}}{2}, \dfrac{7}{2} + \dfrac{5\sqrt{5}}{2}$
5. $-1 - \dfrac{2\sqrt{3}}{3}, -1 + \dfrac{2\sqrt{3}}{3}$
6. $1 - \dfrac{\sqrt{10}}{2}, 1 + \dfrac{\sqrt{10}}{2}$
7. $\dfrac{1}{5} - \dfrac{\sqrt{11}}{5}, \dfrac{1}{5} + \dfrac{\sqrt{11}}{5}$
8. $-\dfrac{5}{4} - \dfrac{\sqrt{13}}{4}, -\dfrac{5}{4} + \dfrac{\sqrt{13}}{4}$
9. $\dfrac{1}{2} - \dfrac{\sqrt{13}}{2}, \dfrac{1}{2} + \dfrac{\sqrt{13}}{2}$
10. $4, -2$
11. $\dfrac{7}{2} - \dfrac{\sqrt{61}}{2}, \dfrac{7}{2} + \dfrac{\sqrt{61}}{2}$
12. $-\dfrac{3}{2} - \dfrac{3\sqrt{5}}{2}, -\dfrac{3}{2} + \dfrac{3\sqrt{5}}{2}$
13. $2 - \sqrt{2}, 2 + \sqrt{2}$
14. $-3 - 3\sqrt{3}, -3 + 3\sqrt{3}$
15. $-\dfrac{\sqrt{6}}{3}, \dfrac{\sqrt{6}}{3}$
16. $-\dfrac{7}{4} - \sqrt{57}, -\dfrac{7}{4} + \sqrt{57}$
17. $-\dfrac{1}{6} - \dfrac{\sqrt{73}}{6}, -\dfrac{1}{6} + \dfrac{\sqrt{73}}{6},$
18. $2 - \sqrt{2}, 2 + \sqrt{2}$

19. See Additional Answers beginning on p. AA1.

20. $\dfrac{-1 \pm \sqrt{1 - 4ac}}{2a}; \dfrac{1}{4} \pm \dfrac{\sqrt{65}}{4}$

21. Sum: $-\dfrac{b}{a}$. product: $\dfrac{c}{a}$.
Sample answer: $y = 2x^2 - 4x + 1$

22. See Additional Answers beginning on p. AA1.

11.3 Solve Radical Equations

Before You solved linear, quadratic, and exponential equations.

Now You will solve radical equations.

Why? So you can use scientific formulas to study animals, as in Ex. 39.

Key Vocabulary
- radical equation
- extraneous solution

An equation that contains a radical expression with a variable in the radicand is a **radical equation.** To solve a radical equation, you need to isolate the radical on one side and then square both sides of the equation.

KEY CONCEPT
For Your Notebook

Squaring Both Sides of an Equation

Words If two expressions are equal, then their squares are equal.

Algebra If $a = b$, then $a^2 = b^2$.   **Example** If $\sqrt{x} = 3$, then $(\sqrt{x})^2 = 3^2$.

EXAMPLE 1   Solve a radical equation

Solve $2\sqrt{x} - 8 = 0$.

Solution

$2\sqrt{x} - 8 = 0$	Write original equation.
$2\sqrt{x} = 8$	Add 8 to each side.
$\sqrt{x} = 4$	Divide each side by 2.
$(\sqrt{x})^2 = 4^2$	Square each side.
$x = 16$	Simplify.

▶ The solution is 16.

CHECK Check the solution by substituting it in the original equation.

$2\sqrt{x} - 8 = 0$	Write original equation.
$2\sqrt{16} - 8 \stackrel{?}{=} 0$	Substitute 16 for *x*.
$2 \cdot 4 - 8 \stackrel{?}{=} 0$	Simplify.
$0 = 0$ ✓	Solution checks.

✓ **GUIDED PRACTICE**   for Example 1

1. Solve **(a)** $\sqrt{x} - 7 = 0$ and **(b)** $12\sqrt{x} - 3 = 0$. **a.** 49 **b.** $\frac{1}{16}$

① PLAN AND PREPARE

Warm-Up Exercises
📓 Transparency Available
Solve the equation.
1. $2x + 3 = 13$ **x = 5**
2. $3x - 8 = 16$ **x = 8**
3. $4x^2 - 16 = 0$ **x = −2, x = 2**
4. $x^2 - x = 12$ **x = −3, x = 4**

5. You put $250 in a savings account that earns 3% interest compounded yearly. If you make no deposits and no withdrawals, how much will your savings be worth in 5 years? **about $290**

Notetaking Guide
📓 Transparency Available
Promotes interactive learning and notetaking skills, pp. 256–258.

Pacing
Basic: 2 days
Average: 2 days
Advanced: 2 days
Block: 1 block
- See *Teaching Guide/Lesson Plan.*

② FOCUS AND MOTIVATE

Essential Question
Big Idea 2, p. 709
How do you solve radical equations? **Tell students they will learn how to answer this question by squaring both sides of the equation and checking for extraneous solutions.**

NCTM STANDARDS
Standard 2: Represent situations using algebraic symbols; Analyze situations using algebraic symbols

Resource Planning Guide

Chapter Resource Book
- Teaching Guide/Lesson Plan (pp. 29–30)
- Activity Master (p. 31)
- Practice levels A, B, C (pp. 33–35)
- Study Guide (pp. 36–37)
- Catch-up for Absent Students (p. 38)
- Problem Solving Workshop (p. 39)
- Challenge (p. 41)

Workbooks
- Notetaking Guide (pp. 256–258)
- Practice Workbook (pp. 174–175)

Teaching Options
- **Power Presentations CD-ROM** provides dynamic electronic teaching resources for the classroom.
- **Activity Generator CD-ROM** provides editable activities for all ability levels.

Interactive Technology
- Easy Planner
- Power Presentations CD-ROM
- Activity Generator CD-ROM
- Animated Algebra
- Test Generator CD-ROM
- Online Quiz
- eWorkbook
- eEdition
- @HomeTutor

Resources for English Learners
- Quick Reference for English Learners
- Spanish Study Guide
- Multi-Language Visual Glossary
- Student Resources in Spanish

See also the *Algebra 1 Toolkit* for more strategies for meeting individual needs.

729

Motivating the Lesson

Ask students to describe some of their favorite rides at recreational parks. Tell them that solving radical equations will give them information about rides, such as the speeds of roller coasters or the forces acting on rides that spin.

③ TEACH

Extra Example 1

Solve $3\sqrt{x} - 6 = 0$. $x = 4$

Key Question to Ask for Example 1

• What is the first step in solving a radical equation? **Isolate the radical.**

• What is the next step? **Square each side of the equation.**

Extra Example 2

Solve $2\sqrt{x+6} + 9 = 21$. $x = 30$

Extra Example 3

Solve $\sqrt{4x-12} = \sqrt{x+3}$. $x = 5$

Key Question to Ask for Example 3

• How is Example 3 different from Examples 1 and 2? **In the previous examples, you isolate the radical and then square each side. In this example, you square each side first since each side contains a radical, and then you isolate the variable.**

EXAMPLE 2 Solve a radical equation

Solve $4\sqrt{x - 7} + 12 = 28$.

Solution

$4\sqrt{x - 7} + 12 = 28$	Write original equation.
$4\sqrt{x - 7} = 16$	Subtract 12 from each side.
$\sqrt{x - 7} = 4$	Divide each side by 4.
$\left(\sqrt{x - 7}\right)^2 = 4^2$	Square each side.
$x - 7 = 16$	Simplify.
$x = 23$	Add 7 to each side.

▸ The solution is 23.

CHECK To check the solution using a graphing calculator, first rewrite the equation so that one side is 0: $4\sqrt{x - 7} - 16 = 0$. Then graph the related equation $y = 4\sqrt{x - 7} - 16$. You can see that the graph crosses the x-axis at $x = 23$.

Trace
X=23   Y=0

EXAMPLE 3 Solve an equation with radicals on both sides

Solve $\sqrt{3x - 17} = \sqrt{x + 21}$.

Solution

SOLVE EQUATIONS
To solve a radical equation that contains two radical expressions, be sure that each side of the equation has only one radical expression before squaring each side.

$\sqrt{3x - 17} = \sqrt{x + 21}$	Write original equation.
$\left(\sqrt{3x - 17}\right)^2 = \left(\sqrt{x + 21}\right)^2$	Square each side.
$3x - 17 = x + 21$	Simplify.
$2x - 17 = 21$	Subtract x from each side.
$2x = 38$	Add 17 to each side.
$x = 19$	Divide each side by 2.

▸ The solution is 19. Check the solution.

✓ **GUIDED PRACTICE** for Examples 2 and 3

Solve the equation.

2. $\sqrt{x - 5} + 7 = 12$ **30**   **3.** $\sqrt{x + 4} = \sqrt{2x - 1}$ **5**   **4.** $\sqrt{4x - 3} - \sqrt{x} = 0$ **1**

EXTRANEOUS SOLUTIONS Squaring both sides of the equation $a = b$ can result in a solution of $a^2 = b^2$ that is *not* a solution of the original equation. Such a solution is called an **extraneous solution.** When you square both sides of an equation, check each solution in the original equation to be sure there are no extraneous solutions.

Differentiated Instruction

English Learners The vocabulary of mathematics can sometimes be more difficult than the mathematics itself. Explain that an extraneous solution as an *extra* solution which is to be discarded. Point out that in words such as *extracurricular* or *extraordinary*, the prefix "extra-" means *outside*. Suggest that students remember the term extraneous solution as meaning outside of the set of solutions.

See also the *Algebra 1 Toolkit* for more strategies.

EXAMPLE 4 Solve an equation with an extraneous solution

Solve $\sqrt{6-x} = x$.

$\sqrt{6-x} = x$	Write original equation.
$(\sqrt{6-x})^2 = x^2$	Square each side.
$6 - x = x^2$	Simplify.
$0 = x^2 + x - 6$	Write in standard form.
$0 = (x-2)(x+3)$	Factor.
$x - 2 = 0 \ or \ x + 3 = 0$	Zero-product property
$x = 2 \ or \ \ \ \ \ x = -3$	Solve for x.

CHECK Check 2 and −3 in the original equation.

If $x = 2$: $\sqrt{6-2} \stackrel{?}{=} 2$ If $x = -3$: $\sqrt{6-(-3)} \stackrel{?}{=} -3$

             $2 = 2$ ✓ $3 = -3$ ✗

▶ Because −3 does not check in the original equation, it is an extraneous solution. The only solution of the equation is 2.

 at classzone.com

> **REVIEW FACTORING**
> For help with factoring, see pp. 583, 593, 600, and 606.

EXAMPLE 5 Solve a real-world problem

SAILING The hull speed s (in nautical miles per hour) of a sailboat can be estimated using the formula $s = 1.34\sqrt{\ell}$ where ℓ is the length (in feet) of the sailboat's waterline, as shown. Find the length (to the nearest foot) of the sailboat's waterline if it has a hull speed of 8 nautical miles per hour.

Solution

$s = 1.34\sqrt{\ell}$	Write original equation.
$8 = 1.34\sqrt{\ell}$	Substitute 8 for s.
$\dfrac{8}{1.34} = \sqrt{\ell}$	Divide each side by 1.34.
$\left(\dfrac{8}{1.34}\right)^2 = (\sqrt{\ell})^2$	Square each side.
$35.6 \approx \ell$	Simplify.

▶ The sailboat has a waterline length of about 36 feet.

 at classzone.com

✓ **GUIDED PRACTICE** for Examples 4 and 5

5. Solve $\sqrt{3x+4} = x$. **4**

6. **WHAT IF?** In Example 5, suppose the sailboat's hull speed is 6.5 nautical miles per hour. Find the sailboat's waterline length to the nearest foot. **24 ft**

11.3 Solve Radical Equations   **731**

---

④ PRACTICE AND APPLY

Assignment Guide

📑 **Answer Transparencies** available for all exercises

Basic:
Day 1: EP p. 946 Exs. 19–24
pp. 732–734
Exs. 1–21
Day 2: pp. 732–734
Exs. 22–26, 36–39, 42–49

Average:
Day 1: pp. 732–734
Exs. 1, 2, 5–21, 31, 32
Day 2: pp. 732–734
Exs. 22–30, 36–40, 42–48 even

Advanced:
Day 1: pp. 732–734
Exs. 1, 6–21, 31–34
Day 2: pp. 732–734
Exs. 22–30, 35–41*, 43–47 odd

Block:
pp. 732–734
Exs. 1, 2, 5–32, 36–40, 42–48 even

Differentiated Instruction

See *Algebra 1 Best Practices Toolkit* for suggestions on addressing the needs of a diverse classroom.

Homework Check

For a quick check of student understanding of key concepts, go over the following exercises:
Basic: 4, 10, 14, 22, 36
Average: 5, 12, 16, 24, 37
Advanced: 6, 13, 18, 26, 38

Extra Practice

• Student Edition, p. 948
• Chapter 11 Resource Book: Practice levels A, B, C, pp. 33–35

Practice Worksheet

An easily-readable reduced practice page (with answers) for this lesson can be found on p.708C.

SKILL PRACTICE

A 1. **VOCABULARY** Copy and complete: To find the solution of $\sqrt{12-x}=x$, you square both sides of the equation and solve. The solutions of $(\sqrt{12-x})^2=x^2$ are -4 and 3, but -4 is a(n) __?__ of $\sqrt{12-x}=x$. **extraneous solution**

2. ★ **WRITING** Is $x+x\sqrt{2}=4$ a radical equation? *Explain* why or why not. **No.** *Sample answer:* **It does not contain a variable in a radicand.**

EXAMPLES 1, 2, and 3
on pp. 729–730
for Exs. 3–21, 28

SOLVING EQUATIONS Solve the equation. Check for extraneous solutions.

3. $3\sqrt{x}-6=0$ **4**

4. $2\sqrt{x}-9=0$ **$\frac{81}{4}$**

5. $\sqrt{3x}+4=16$ **48**

6. $\sqrt{5x}+5=0$ **no real solutions**

7. $\sqrt{x+7}+5=11$ **29**

8. $\sqrt{x-8}-4=-2$ **12**

9. $2\sqrt{x-4}-2=2$ **8**

10. $3\sqrt{x-1}-5=5$ **$\frac{109}{9}$**

⑪ $\sqrt{6-2x}+12=21$ **$-\frac{75}{2}$**

12. $5\sqrt{x-3}+4=14$ **7**

13. $2\sqrt{x-11}-8=4$ **47**

14. $\sqrt{3x-2}=\sqrt{x}$ **1**

15. $\sqrt{7-2x}=\sqrt{9-x}$ **−2**

16. $\sqrt{3x+8}=\sqrt{x+4}$ **−2**

17. $\sqrt{9x-30}=\sqrt{4x+5}$ **7**

18. $\sqrt{21-x}-\sqrt{1-x}=0$ **no real solutions**

19. $\sqrt{x-12}-\sqrt{x-8}=0$ **no real solutions**

20. $\sqrt{\frac{1}{2}x-2}-\sqrt{x-8}=0$ **12**

21. ★ **MULTIPLE CHOICE** Which is the solution of the equation $10\sqrt{x+3}+3=18$? **B**

Ⓐ $-\frac{3}{2}$　　Ⓑ $-\frac{3}{4}$　　Ⓒ $\frac{3}{4}$　　Ⓓ $\frac{3}{2}$

EXAMPLE 4 **B**
on p. 731
for Exs. 22–27, 29

SOLVING EQUATIONS Solve the equation. Check for extraneous solutions.

22. $x=\sqrt{42-x}$ **6**

23. $\sqrt{4-3x}=x$ **1**

24. $\sqrt{11x-24}=x$ **3, 8**

25. $\sqrt{14x-3}=4x$ **$\frac{3}{8},\frac{1}{2}$**

26. $2x=\sqrt{1-3x}$ **$\frac{1}{4}$**

27. $\sqrt{2-x}=x+4$ **−2**

ERROR ANALYSIS *Describe* and correct the error in solving the equation.

29. *Sample answer:* The solution $x=-9$ does not check in the original equation, so it is an extraneous solution. The only real solution is $x=2$.

28.

$$\sqrt{3x}+9=0$$
$$\sqrt{3x}=-9$$
$$3x=81$$
$$x=27 \quad ✗$$

Sample answer: The solution $x=27$ does not check in the original equation, so it is an extraneous solution. There are no real solutions to this equation.

29.

$$x=\sqrt{18-7x}$$
$$x^2=18-7x$$
$$x^2+7x-18=0$$
$$(x-2)(x+9)=0$$
$$x-2=0 \text{ or } x+9=0$$
$$x=2 \text{ or } \quad x=-9 \quad ✗$$

30. ⊘ **GEOMETRY** The formula for the slant height s (in inches) of a cone is $s=\sqrt{h^2+r^2}$ where h is the height of the cone (in inches) and r is the radius of its base (in inches), as shown. Find the height of the cone if you know the slant height is 4 inches and the radius is 2 inches. **$2\sqrt{3}$ in. or about 3.5 in.**

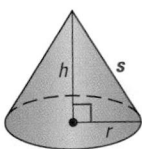

SOLVING EQUATIONS Solve the equation. Check for extraneous solutions.

31. $\sqrt{x + 2} = \sqrt{x - 1}$
no real solutions

32. $2 - \sqrt{x + 1} = \sqrt{x + 3}$ $-\dfrac{3}{4}$

33. $\sqrt{5x + 9} + \sqrt{5x} = 9$ $\dfrac{16}{5}$

34. ★ **WRITING** A student solves the equation $\sqrt{x + 2} = x$ and finds that $x = 2$ or $x = -1$. Without checking by substituting into the equation, which is the extraneous solution, 2 or -1? How do you know? **-1; since in the equation x is equal to a radical expression, x cannot be a negative number.**

35. **CHALLENGE** Write a radical equation that has 3 and 4 as solutions.
Sample answer: $\sqrt{7x - 12} = x$

PROBLEM SOLVING

EXAMPLE 5 A
on p. 731
for Exs. 36–38

36. **FORESTS** The dark green areas on the image shown represent regions with heavy foliage. In Texas, the area of land y (in millions of acres) that was covered by forest during the period 1907–2002 can be modeled by the function $y = 2.5\sqrt{143 - x}$ where x is the number of years since 1907. In what year were about 20 million acres of land covered by forest in Texas? **1986**

Texas in 2002

@HomeTutor for problem solving help at classzone.com

37. **PER CAPITA CONSUMPTION** The annual banana consumption y (in pounds per person) in the United States for the period 1970–2000 can be modeled by the function $y = \sqrt{18x + 272}$ where x is the number of years since 1970. In what year were about 20 pounds of bananas consumed per person? **1977**

@HomeTutor for problem solving help at classzone.com

38. **MULTI-STEP PROBLEM** The velocity v (in meters per second) at which a trapeze performer swings can be modeled by the function $v = \sqrt{19.6d}$ where d is the difference (in meters) between the highest and lowest position of the performer's center of gravity during the swing.

a. A trapeze performer swings at a velocity of 5 meters per second. What is the value of d? **about 1.28 m**

b. Suppose the performer jumps straight up off the starting board, increasing the velocity of the swing by 0.4 meter per second. By how many meters does the value of d increase? **about 0.21 m**

B 39. **BIOLOGY** A bushbaby is a small animal that can perform standing jumps of over 2 meters. Scientists found that the time t (in seconds) in which a bushbaby must extend its legs in order to jump to a height h (in meters) is given by the function $t = 0.45\ell\sqrt{\dfrac{1}{h}}$ where ℓ is the length of the bushbaby's legs (in meters). A particular bushbaby has a leg length of 0.16 meter. The bushbaby can extend its legs in 0.05 second. About how high does the bushbaby jump? Round your answer to the nearest tenth of a meter. **2.1 m**

11.3 Solve Radical Equations **733**

Avoiding Common Errors

Exercises 3–13 Students often fail to isolate the radical before they square both sides. Remind students that they first use properties of equality to isolate the radical on one side of the equation in the same way that they isolate the variable on one side of a linear equation.

Study Strategy

Exercise 35 Suggest to students that they use a strategy of working backward to solve this challenge. They could start by asking what two binomials they would need to multiply to get solutions of 3 and 4.

Graphing Calculator

Exercises 36–41 Students may want to use their calculators for these problems so they can concentrate on problem-solving strategies rather than calculations.

Internet Reference

Exercise 39 Additional information about bushbabies can be found at the African Wildlife Foundation website at www.awf.org/wildlives/7

40b. Increase. *Sample answer*: The greater the value of ℓ, the greater the value of the radicand, and the greater the value of t.

40. ★ **SHORT RESPONSE** The amount of time t (in seconds) it takes a simple pendulum to complete one full swing is called the period of the pendulum and is given by $t = 2\pi\sqrt{\dfrac{\ell}{32}}$ where ℓ is the length of the pendulum (in feet).

a. Apply A visitor at a museum notices that a pendulum on display has a period of about 11 seconds. About how long is the pendulum? Use 3.14 for π and round your answer to the nearest foot. **98 ft**

b. Explain Does increasing the length of a pendulum increase or decrease its period? *Explain.*

C **41. CHALLENGE** The frequency f (in cycles per second) of a string of an electric guitar is given by the equation $f = \dfrac{1}{2\ell}\sqrt{\dfrac{T}{m}}$ where ℓ is the length of the string (in meters), T is the string's tension (in newtons), and m is the string's mass per unit length (in kilograms per meter). The high E string of a particular electric guitar is 0.64 meter long with a mass per unit length of 0.000401 kilogram per meter. How much tension is required to produce a frequency of about 330 cycles per second? Would you need more or less tension if you want to create the same frequency on a string with greater mass per unit length? *Explain.* **About 71.5 N; more. *Sample answer*: If the mass increased then the tension would have to increase to create the same value in the radicand. If the radicand has the same value and the length is constant, the frequency will stay the same.**

MIXED REVIEW

Make a scatter plot of the data. *Describe* the correlation of the data. If possible, fit a line to the data and write an equation for the line. *(p. 325)*

42, 43. See margin for art.

42.

x	0	1	2	3	4
y	−5	−2	2	4	7

positive; $y = 3x - 4.8$

43.

x	2	4	6	8	10
y	0	11	24	31	44

positive; $y = 5.4x - 10.4$

PREVIEW Prepare for Lesson 11.4 in Exs. 44–49.

Solve the equation.

44. $x^2 + 21x + 20 = 0$ *(p. 583)* **−20, −1**

45. $x^2 - 21x + 38 = 0$ *(p. 583)* **2, 19**

46. $x^2 - 8x - 9 = 0$ *(p. 583)* **−1, 9**

47. $11x^2 - 11 = 0$ *(p. 600)* **−1, 1**

48. $5x^2 - 125 = 0$ *(p. 600)* **−5, 5**

49. $8x^2 - 32 = 0$ *(p. 600)* **−2, 2**

QUIZ for Lessons 11.1–11.3

1. Graph the function $y = \sqrt{x-3}$ and identify its domain and range. Compare the graph with the graph of $y = \sqrt{x}$. *(p. 710)* **See margin for art; domain: $x \geq 3$, range: $y \geq 0$; the graph is a horizontal translation 3 units to the right.**

Simplify the expression. *(p. 719)*

2. $\sqrt{150}$ **$5\sqrt{6}$**

3. $\sqrt{2c^2} \cdot \sqrt{8c}$ **$4c\sqrt{c}$**

4. $(7 + \sqrt{5})(2 - \sqrt{5})$ **$9 - 5\sqrt{5}$**

5. $\dfrac{14}{\sqrt{2}}$ **$7\sqrt{2}$**

6. $\sqrt{\dfrac{98}{x^6}}$ **$\dfrac{7\sqrt{2}}{x^3}$**

7. $\sqrt{\dfrac{80x^3}{5y}}$ **$\dfrac{4x\sqrt{xy}}{y}$**

Solve the equation. Check for extraneous solutions. *(p. 729)*

8. $\sqrt{x} - 15 = 0$ **225**

9. $\sqrt{4x-7} = \sqrt{2x+19}$ **13**

10. $\sqrt{6x-5} = x$ **1, 5**

42.

43.

Lessons 11.1–11.3

1. OPEN-ENDED The velocity v (in meters per second) of a car moving in a circular path that has radius r (in meters) is given by $v = \sqrt{\dfrac{Fr}{m}}$ where F is the force (in newtons) pulling the car toward the center of the circular path and m is the mass of the car (in kilograms).

A 1200 kilogram car is traveling at a constant velocity of 20 meters per second in a circular path of radius r meters where $r \geq 100$. Choose two different values of r to show how the force, F, acting on the car changes as the radius increases. **See margin.**

2. MULTI-STEP PROBLEM The number y of companies listed on the New York Stock Exchange for the period 1999–2002 can be modeled by the function $y = 3018 - 146\sqrt{x}$ where x is the number of years since 1999.

a. Graph the function. **See margin.**

b. How many companies were listed on the New York Stock Exchange in 1999? **3018 companies**

c. In what year were there about 220 companies fewer than the number of companies listed on the New York Stock Exchange in 1999? **2001**

3. GRIDDED ANSWER The voltage V (in volts) of an amplifier is given by the function $V = \sqrt{PR}$ where P is the power (in watts) and R is the resistance (in ohms). A particular amplifier produces 10 volts and has a resistance of 4 ohms. How many watts are produced by the amplifier? **25 watts**

4. MULTI-STEP PROBLEM For the period 1994–2001, the annual consumption of corn products y (in pounds per person) in the United States can be modeled by the function $y = 6.1\sqrt{x} + 15.8$ where x is the number of years since 1994.

a. Graph the function. **See margin.**

b. In what year were about 25 pounds of corn products consumed per person? **1995**

5. EXTENDED RESPONSE Competitors in a ski mountaineering race must climb a mountain and ski down it as quickly as possible. The race begins with the firing of a starting gun. Near Earth's surface, the speed of sound s (in meters per second) through air is given by $s = 20\sqrt{T + 273}$ where T is the air temperature (in degrees Celsius). **a–c. See margin.**

a. A typical temperature at the start of a race is $-5°C$. What is the speed of sound at this temperature?

b. The person firing the starting gun is standing 50 meters away from the racers. How long will it take for the racers to hear the starting gun?

c. What happens to the time it takes for the racers to hear the starting gun if the temperature at the start of the race is lower? *Explain.*

6. SHORT RESPONSE A person's maximum running speed s (in meters per second) can be approximated by the function $s = \pi\sqrt{\dfrac{9.8\ell}{6}}$ where ℓ is the person's leg length (in meters).

a. To the nearest tenth of a meter, what is the leg length of a person whose maximum running speed is about 3.8 meters per second? **about 0.9 m**

b. What happens to running speed as leg length increases? *Explain.*
It increases. *Sample answer*: As ℓ increases, the radicand increases as does the radical.

1. *Sample answer:* If $r = 100$, $F = 4800$. If $r = 400$, $F = 1200$. As r increases, F decreases, so that the product $Fr = 480{,}000$.

2a.

4a.

5a. about 327.4 m/sec

5b. about 0.15 sec

5c. It increases. *Sample answer:* As the temperature gets colder, the speed decreases and the time needed to cover the distance increases.

11.4 The Pythagorean Theorem

MATERIALS · graph paper · scissors

QUESTION   How are the lengths of the sides of a right trangle related to each other?

EXPLORE   Examine the relationship among the lengths of the sides of a right triangle

STEP 1 *Make right triangles*

Cut a right triangle out of graph paper. Make three copies of it.

STEP 2 *Arrange as a square*

Arrange the right triangles to form a square within a square, as shown.

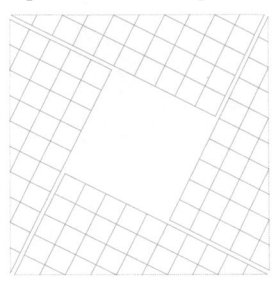

DRAW CONCLUSIONS   Use your observations to complete these exercises

1. How are the areas of the triangles and inner square related to the area of the outer square? **The sum of the areas of the triangles and the inner square is equal to the area of the outer square.**

In Exercises 2–4, let a, b, and c be the lengths of the sides of a right triangle with $a < b < c$, as shown. Write an expression for the area of the figure described below.

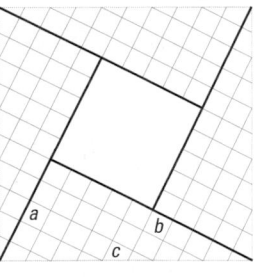

2. One of the right triangles in terms of a and b $\frac{1}{2}ab$

3. The outer square in terms of c c^2

4. The inner square in terms of a and b $(b - a)^2$

5. Use the relationship you determined in Exercise 1 and your results from Exercises 2–4 to write an equation that relates a, b, and c. Simplify the equation. $c^2 = 4 \cdot \frac{1}{2} \cdot ab + (b - a)^2 = 2ab + b^2 - 2ab + a^2 = b^2 + a^2$

6. **REASONING** The triangle shown is a right triangle. Find the value of x. *Explain* how you found your answer. **26. *Sample answer*: Use the equation found in Exercise 5, and let $a = 10$, $b = 24$, and $c = x$. Solve for x.**

736   Chapter 11   Radicals and Geometry Connections

11.4 Apply the Pythagorean Theorem and Its Converse

Before You solved radical equations.
Now You will use the Pythagorean theorem and its converse.
Why? So you can examine angles in architecture, as in Ex. 35.

Key Vocabulary
• hypotenuse
• legs of a right triangle
• Pythagorean theorem

The **hypotenuse** of a right triangle is the side opposite the right angle. It is the longest side of a right triangle. The **legs** are the two sides that form the right angle.

A *theorem* is a statement that can be proved true. The **Pythagorean theorem** states the relationship among the lengths of the sides of a right triangle.

KEY CONCEPT *For Your Notebook*

The Pythagorean Theorem

Words If a triangle is a right triangle, then the sum of the squares of the lengths of the legs equals the square of the length of the hypotenuse.

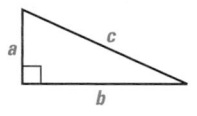

Algebra $a^2 + b^2 = c^2$

EXAMPLE 1 Use the Pythagorean theorem

Find the unknown length for the triangle shown.

Solution

$a^2 + b^2 = c^2$ **Pythagorean theorem**

$a^2 + 6^2 = 7^2$ **Substitute 6 for b and 7 for c.**

$a^2 + 36 = 49$ **Simplify.**

$a^2 = 13$ **Subtract 36 from each side.**

$a = \sqrt{13}$ **Take positive square root of each side.**

▶ The side length a is $\sqrt{13}$.

> **REVIEW QUADRATIC EQUATIONS**
> For help with solving quadratic equations by using square roots, see p. 652.

 Animated Algebra at classzone.com

✓ **GUIDED PRACTICE** for Example 1

1. The lengths of the legs of a right triangle are $a = 5$ and $b = 12$. Find c. **13**

---

① PLAN AND PREPARE

Warm-Up Exercises
📑 **Transparency Available**
Solve the equation.
1. $\sqrt{x-5} + 2 = 7$ $x = 30$
2. $2\sqrt{x} + 9 = 9$ $x = 0$
3. $\sqrt{x+11} - 3 = 5$ $x = 53$
4. Use the equation $v = \sqrt{64d}$, where v is velocity (in feet per second) and d is the distance (in feet) an object falls to find how far an object has dropped when its velocity is about 24 feet per second. **9 ft**

Notetaking Guide
📑 **Transparency Available**
Promotes interactive learning and notetaking skills, pp. 259–261.

Pacing
Basic: 1 day
Average: 1 day
Advanced: 1 day
Block: 0.5 block with 11.5
• See *Teaching Guide/Lesson Plan.*

② FOCUS AND MOTIVATE

Essential Question
Big Idea 3, p. 709

How do you use the Pythagorean theorem and its converse? **Tell students they will learn how to answer this question by using known side lengths of right triangles to find unknown lengths.**

NCTM STANDARDS
Standard 3: Analyze properties of 2-D shapes

Standard 6: Solve problems in math and other contexts

Resource Planning Guide

Chapter Resource Book
• Teaching Guide/Lesson Plan (pp. 42–43)
• Practice levels A, B, C (pp. 44–46)
• Study Guide (pp. 47–48)
• Catch-up for Absent Students (p. 49)
• Application (p. 50)
• Challenge (p. 51)

Workbooks
• Notetaking Guide (pp. 259–261)
• Practice Workbook (pp. 176–177)

Teaching Options
• **Power Presentations CD-ROM** provides dynamic electronic teaching resources for the classroom.
• **Activity Generator CD-ROM** provides editable activities for all ability levels.

Interactive Technology
• Easy Planner
• Power Presentations CD-ROM
• Activity Generator CD-ROM
• Animated Algebra
• Test Generator CD-ROM
• Online Quiz
• eWorkbook
• eEdition
• @HomeTutor

Resources for English Learners
• Quick Reference for English Learners
• Spanish Study Guide
• Multi-Language Visual Glossary
• Student Resources in Spanish

See also the *Algebra 1 Toolkit* for more strategies for meeting individual needs.

737

Motivating the Lesson

You are shopping for an entertainment center and you find one that you like. If you know the dimensions of the entertainment center and the size of your television screen, you can use the Pythagorean theorem to determine whether your television set will fit in the entertainment center.

❸ TEACH

Extra Example 1

Find the unknown length for the triangle shown. $\sqrt{65}$

$a = 4$, $c = 9$, b

classzone.com

An **Animated Algebra** activity is available on-line for **Example 1**. This activity is also available on the **Power Presentations CD-ROM**.

Extra Example 2

A right triangle has one leg that is 1 foot longer than the other leg. The hypotenuse is $\sqrt{13}$ feet. Find the unknown lengths. **2 ft and 3 ft**

Extra Example 3

A person at A in the diagram throws a flying disc to a person at C. To the nearest foot, how far does the person throw the flying disc? **D**

A
18 feet
B — 20 feet — C

(A) 6 feet (B) 19 feet
(C) 22 feet (D) 27 feet

EXAMPLE 2 Use the Pythagorean theorem

A right triangle has one leg that is 2 inches longer than the other leg. The length of the hypotenuse is $\sqrt{10}$ inches. Find the unknown lengths.

Solution

Sketch a right triangle and label the sides with their lengths. Let x be the length of the shorter leg.

$a^2 + b^2 = c^2$	**Pythagorean theorem**
$x^2 + (x + 2)^2 = \left(\sqrt{10}\right)^2$	**Substitute.**
$x^2 + x^2 + 4x + 4 = 10$	**Simplify.**
$2x^2 + 4x - 6 = 0$	**Write in standard form.**
$2(x - 1)(x + 3) = 0$	**Factor.**
$x - 1 = 0 \; or \; x + 3 = 0$	**Zero-product property**
$x = 1 \; or \quad x = -3$	**Solve for x.**

$x + 2$, $\sqrt{10}$, x

▸ Because length is nonnegative, the solution $x = -3$ does not make sense. The legs have lengths of 1 inch and $1 + 2 = 3$ inches.

 ## EXAMPLE 3 Standardized Test Practice

ELIMINATE CHOICES The hypotenuse is the longest side of the triangle, so the length must be greater than 40 yards. Eliminate choices A and B.

A soccer player makes a corner kick to another player, as shown. To the nearest yard, how far does the player kick the ball?

40 yd
12 yd

(A) 7 yards (B) 38 yards
(C) 42 yards (D) 52 yards

Solution

The path of the kicked ball is the hypotenuse of a right triangle. The length of one leg is 12 yards, and the length of the other leg is 40 yards.

$c^2 = a^2 + b^2$	**Pythagorean theorem**
$c^2 = 12^2 + 40^2$	**Substitute 12 for a and 40 for b.**
$c^2 = 1744$	**Simplify.**
$c = \sqrt{1744} \approx 42$	**Take positive square root of each side.**

▸ The correct answer is C. (A) (B) (C) (D)

✓ **GUIDED PRACTICE** for Examples 2 and 3

2. A right triangle has one leg that is 3 inches longer than the other leg. The length of the hypotenuse is 15 inches. Find the unknown lengths. **9 in. and 12 in.**

3. **SWIMMING** A rectangular pool is 30 feet wide and 60 feet long. You swim diagonally across the pool. To the nearest foot, how far do you swim? **67 ft**

Differentiated Instruction

English Learners The word *hypotenuse* comes from the Greek *hypo* meaning under and *teinein* meaning tension. Thus, the word could be translated as "under tension." Looking at a triangle such as the one in **Example 2**, the hypotenuse can be envisioned as a wire stretched from one side of the triangle to the other, with the wire being under tension.

See also the *Algebra 1 Toolkit* for more strategies.

REVIEW REASONING
For help with if-then statements and converses, see pp. 64, 110, and 319.

CONVERSE OF THE PYTHAGOREAN THEOREM Recall that when you reverse the hypothesis and conclusion of an if-then statement, the new statement is called the converse. Although not all converses of true statements are true, the converse of the Pythagorean theorem is true.

KEY CONCEPT *For Your Notebook*

Converse of the Pythagorean Theorem

If a triangle has side lengths a, b, and c such that $a^2 + b^2 = c^2$, then the triangle is a right triangle.

EXAMPLE 4 **Determine right triangles**

Tell whether the triangle with the given side lengths is a right triangle.

a. 8, 15, 17

$8^2 + 15^2 \stackrel{?}{=} 17^2$

$64 + 225 \stackrel{?}{=} 289$

$289 = 289 \checkmark$

▶ The triangle is a right triangle.

b. 5, 8, 9

$5^2 + 8^2 \stackrel{?}{=} 9^2$

$25 + 64 \stackrel{?}{=} 81$

$89 = 81 ✗$

▶ The triangle is *not* a right triangle.

EXAMPLE 5 **Use the converse of the Pythagorean theorem**

CONSTRUCTION A construction worker is making sure one corner of the foundation of a house is a right angle. To do this, the worker makes a mark 8 feet from the corner along one wall and another mark 6 feet from the same corner along the other wall. The worker then measures the distance between the two marks and finds the distance to be 10 feet. Is the corner a right angle?

Solution

$8^2 + 6^2 \stackrel{?}{=} 10^2$ Check to see if $a^2 + b^2 = c^2$ when $a = 8$, $b = 6$, and $c = 10$.

$64 + 36 \stackrel{?}{=} 100$ Simplify.

$100 = 100 \checkmark$ Add.

▶ Because the sides that the construction worker measured form a right triangle, the corner of the foundation is a right angle.

 GUIDED PRACTICE   for Examples 4 and 5

Tell whether the triangle with the given side lengths is a right triangle.

4. 7, 11, 13 **not a right triangle**   **5.** 15, 36, 39 **right triangle**   **6.** 15, 112, 113 **right triangle**

7. No. *Sample answer:* $120^2 + 120^2 \neq 180^2$, so it cannot be a right triangle.

7. WINDOW DESIGN A window has the shape of a triangle with side lengths of 120 centimeters, 120 centimeters, and 180 centimeters. Is the window a right triangle? *Explain.*

Extra Example 4

Tell whether the triangle with the given side lengths is a right triangle.

a. 7, 23, 24   no

b. 5, 12, 13   yes

Key Question to Ask for Example 4

• Which side length in part a is the hypotenuse of the triangle?   **17**

Extra Example 5

A real estate lot is in the shape of a triangle. The side lengths are 48 feet, 55 feet, and 73 feet. The real estate agent told a potential buyer that one of the corners forms a right angle. Is the real estate agent correct?   **yes**

Closing the Lesson

Have students summarize the major points of the lesson and answer the Essential Question: How do you use the Pythagorean theorem and its converse?

• **The Pythagorean theorem is $a^2 + b^2 = c^2$, where a and b are leg lengths of a right triangle and c is the length of the hypotenuse.**

To find an unknown length in a right triangle, use the Pythagorean theorem and substitute values for either the hypotenuse and one leg or both legs, and solve by isolating the variable and then taking the positive square root of each side. The hypotenuse is always side with length c. Use the converse of the Pythagorean theorem to determine whether a triangle is a right triangle by checking to see if the sum of the squares of the leg lengths is equal to the square of length of the hypotenuse.

④ PRACTICE AND APPLY

Assignment Guide

📖 Answer Transparencies available for all exercises

Basic:
Day 1: pp. 740–742
Exs. 1, 2, 3–15 odd, 16–30, 33–36, 39–49 odd

Average:
Day 1: pp. 740–742
Exs. 1, 2, 9–22, 26–31, 33–37, 40–50 even

Advanced:
Day 1: pp. 740–742
Exs. 1, 10–15, 17–22, 26–32*, 34–38*, 44–46, 48, 50

Block:
pp. 740–742
Exs. 1, 2, 9–22, 26–31, 33–37, 40–50 even (with 11.5)

Differentiated Instruction

See *Algebra 1 Best Practices Toolkit* for suggestions on addressing the needs of a diverse classroom.

Homework Check

For a quick check of student understanding of key concepts, go over the following exercises:
Basic: 7, 18, 24, 33, 34
Average: 11, 20, 26, 33, 35
Advanced: 14, 22, 28, 34, 35

Extra Practice

• Student Edition, p. 948
• Chapter 11 Resource Book:
  Practice levels A, B, C, pp. 44–46

Practice Worksheet

An easily-readable reduced practice page (with answers) for this lesson can be found on p.708C.

SKILL PRACTICE

Ⓐ 1. **VOCABULARY** Copy and complete: In a right triangle, the side opposite the right angle is called the __?__. **hypotenuse**

2. ★ **WRITING** *Explain* how you can tell whether a triangle with side lengths of 9, 12, and 15 is a right triangle. **If the sum of 9 squared and 12 squared is 15 squared, then it is a right triangle. If they are not equal, then it is not a right triangle.**

EXAMPLE 1
on p. 737
for Exs. 3–16

USING THE PYTHAGOREAN THEOREM Let a and b represent the lengths of the legs of a right triangle, and let c represent the length of the hypotenuse. Find the unknown length.

3. $a = 3, c = 5$ **$b = 4$**   4. $b = 3, c = 7$ **$a = 2\sqrt{10}$**   5. $a = 5, b = 6$ **$c = \sqrt{61}$**

6. $b = 5, c = 10$ **$a = 5\sqrt{3}$**   7. $a = 8, b = 8$ **$c = 8\sqrt{2}$**   8. $a = 5, b = 12$ **$c = 13$**

⑨. $a = 8, b = 12$ **$c = 4\sqrt{13}$**   10. $a = 7, c = 25$ **$b = 24$**   11. $b = 15, c = 17$ **$a = 8$**

12. $a = 9, c = 41$ **$b = 40$**   13. $b = 3, c = 3.4$ **$a = 1.6$**   14. $a = 1.2, c = 3.7$ **$b = 3.5$**

15. ★ **MULTIPLE CHOICE** A tennis court is 36 feet by 78 feet. What is the length of a diagonal? Round your answer to the nearest tenth of a foot. **C**

Ⓐ 42.0 feet   Ⓑ 69.2 feet   Ⓒ 85.9 feet   Ⓓ 114.0 feet

16. **ERROR ANALYSIS** *Describe* and correct the error in finding the unknown length.

$$18^2 + 30^2 = x^2$$
$$1224 = x^2$$
$$6\sqrt{34} = x$$

The side with length 30 is the hypotenuse, and should be substituted for c in the Pythagorean theorem, not b; $18^2 + x^2 = 30^2$, $324 + x^2 = 900$, $x^2 = 576$, $x = 24$.

EXAMPLE 2
on p. 738
for Exs. 17–22

USING THE PYTHAGOREAN THEOREM Find the unknown lengths.

17.
$x + 1$, $2\sqrt{5}$, $x + 3$
2, 4

18.
x, $2x - 3$, $2x + 3$
24, 45, 51

19.

$5x$, $x + 2$, $5x - 1$
3, 4, 5, or 7, 24, 25

20. A right triangle has one leg that is 2 inches longer than the other leg. The length of the hypotenuse is $\sqrt{130}$ inches. Find the lengths of the legs. **7 in., 9 in.**

21. A right triangle has one leg that is 3 times as long as the other leg. The length of the hypotenuse is $\sqrt{40}$ inches. Find the lengths of the legs. **2 in., 6 in.**

22. A right triangle has one leg that is $\frac{1}{2}$ of the length of the other leg. The length of the hypotenuse is $6\sqrt{5}$ inches. Find the lengths of the legs. **6 in., 12 in.**

EXAMPLE 4
on p. 739
for Exs. 23–28

DETERMINING RIGHT TRIANGLES Tell whether the triangle with the given side lengths is a right triangle.

㉓ 2, 3, 4 **not a right triangle**   24. 9, 12, 15 **right triangle**   25. 8, 16, 18 **not a right triangle**

26. 9, 21, 24 **not a right triangle**   27. 11, 60, 61 **right triangle**   28. 24, 143, 145 **right triangle**

---

740   Chapter 11 Radicals and Geometry Connections

29. ★ **MULTIPLE CHOICE** What is the area of the largest square in the coordinate plane shown? **A**

   Ⓐ 100 square units

   Ⓑ 64 square units

   Ⓒ 36 square units

   Ⓓ 25 square units

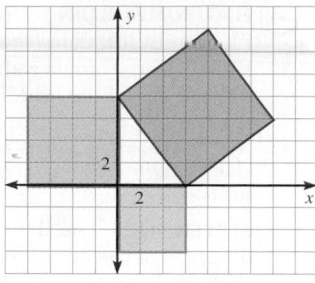

30. No.
Sample answer:
The unknown
side might be the
hypotenuse, or
it might be a leg
of the traingle.
Each case would
give a different
answer.

|B| **30.** ★ **WRITING** Given that two side lengths of a right triangle are 11 inches and 6 inches, is it possible to find the length of the third side? *Explain.*

31. **REASONING** A *Pythagorean triple* is a group of integers a, b, and c that represent the side lengths of a right triangle. For example, the integers 3, 4, and 5 form a Pythagorean triple. Choose any two positive integers m and n such that $m < n$. Then find a, b, and c as follows: $a = n^2 - m^2$, $b = 2mn$, and $c = n^2 + m^2$. Show that the numbers you generated form a Pythagorean triple. Then use the converse of the Pythagorean theorem to show that the equations for a, b, and c always generate Pythagorean triples. **See margin.**

|C| **32.** **CHALLENGE** The edge length of the cube is 7 inches.

   a. Find the value of x. $7\sqrt{2}$

   b. Find the value of y. $7\sqrt{3}$

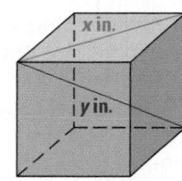

PROBLEM SOLVING

EXAMPLES |A|
3 and 5
on pp. 738–739
for Exs. 33–35

33. **ARCHITECTURE** An earthquake-resistant building has dampers built into its structure to help minimize damage caused by an earthquake. A section of the structural frame of such a building is shown. What is the length of the damper? Round your answer to the nearest foot. **16 ft**

10 ft

Damper

12 ft

@HomeTutor for problem solving help at classzone.com

34. No; the sum
of the squares
of the two
shorter sides is
not equal to the
square of the
longer side.

34. **SAILS** A sail has the shape of a triangle. The side lengths are 146 inches, 131 inches, and 84 inches. Is the sail a right triangle? *Explain.* **See margin.**

@HomeTutor for problem solving help at classzone.com

11.4 Apply the Pythagorean Theorem and Its Converse   **741**

Avoiding Common Errors

Exercises 3–14 Some students may forget to take the square of both sides when finding a leg or hypotenuse length. Suggest that students substitute the side lengths into the Pythagorean theorem to make sure that their answers make sense.

Mathematical Reasoning

Exercises 17–22 Point out to students that if they find that one or both of the legs of the triangle are longer than the hypotenuse, given that the hypotenuse is the longest side of the triangle, then they know that they need to recalculate the side lengths of the triangle.

Reading Strategy

Exercise 29 Draw students' attention to the diagram and note that the 2 on the grid indicates the length of one unit on the grid, not the length of the sides of the squares.

🔎 Internet Reference

Exercise 33 For more information about earthquake-resistant structures, visit the United States Geological Survey website at quake.wr.usgs.gov/prepare/factsheets/SaferStructures

31. *Sample answer:* Let $m = 3$ and $n = 6$. Then $a = 6^2 - 3^2 = 27$, $b = 2(3)(6) = 36$, $c = 6^2 + 3^2 = 45$; substitute the values from the equation for a, b, and c in the Pythagorean theorem: $(n^2 - m^2)^2 + (2mn)^2 = (n^2 + m^2)^2$. Simplify to $n^4 - 2m^2n^2 + m^4 + 4m^2n^2 = n^4 + 2m^2n^2 + m^4$; $-2m^2n^2 + 4m^2n^2 = 2m^2n^2$; $2 = 2$. The equations are equal, so by the converse of the Pythagorean theorem, the lengths a, b, and c are a Pythagorean triple.

Daily Homework Quiz

Transparency Available

Let a and b represent the lengths of the legs of a right triangle, and let c represent the length of the hypotenuse. Find the unknown length.

1. $a = 4$, $c = 8$ **$b = \sqrt{48}$ or $4\sqrt{3}$**
2. $a = 5$, $b = 7$ **$c = \sqrt{74}$**
3. $b = 15$, $c = 21$ **$a = \sqrt{216}$ or $6\sqrt{6}$**
4. $a = 3$, $c = 11$ **$b = \sqrt{112}$ or $4\sqrt{7}$**

5. A triangular garden has side lengths of 5 feet, 12 feet, and 14 feet. Is the garden in the shape of a right triangle? **no**

Online Quiz

Available at **classzone.com**

Diagnosis/Remediation

- Practice A, B, C in Chapter 11 Resource Book, pp. 44–46
- Study Guide in Chapter 11 Resource Book, pp. 47–48
- Practice Workbook, pp. 176–177
- @HomeTutor

Challenge

Additional challenge is available in the Chapter 11 Resource Book, p. 51.

35. **FLATIRON BUILDING** A top view of the Flatiron Building in New York City is shown. The triangle indicates the basic shape of the building's roof. Is the triangle a right triangle? *Explain.* **No; the sum of the squares of the two shorter sides is not equal to the square of the longer side.**

B **36.** **SCREEN SIZES** The size of a television is indicated by the length of a diagonal of the television screen. The aspect ratio of a television screen is the ratio of the length of the screen to the width of the screen. The size of a particular television is 30 inches, and its aspect ratio is 4 : 3. What are the width and the length of the television screen? **18 in., 24 in.**

37. ★ **EXTENDED RESPONSE** The *Wheel of Theodorus* is a figure formed by a chain of right triangles with consecutive triangles sharing a common side. The hypotenuse of one triangle becomes a leg of the next, as shown.

a. **Calculate** What is the length of the longest hypotenuse in the diagram? **$\sqrt{6}$**

b. **Extend** Extend the diagram to include two more triangles. What is the length of the longest hypotenuse in the new diagram? **$\sqrt{8}$**

c. **Analyze** Find a formula for the length of the hypotenuse of the nth triangle. *Explain* how you found your answer. **$c_n = \sqrt{n + 1}$; *Sample answer*: A list of the hypotenuse's for the first few triangles is $\sqrt{2}, \sqrt{3}, \sqrt{4}, \sqrt{5}, \ldots$. A general formula for this series is $c_n = \sqrt{n + 1}$.**

C **38.** **CHALLENGE** A baseball diamond has the shape of a square with side lengths of 90 feet. A catcher wants to get a player running from first base to second base out, so the catcher must throw the ball to second base before the runner reaches second base.

a. The catcher is 5 feet behind home plate. How far does the catcher have to throw the ball to reach second base? Round your answer to the nearest foot. **132 ft**

b. The catcher throws the ball at a rate of 90 feet per second when the player is 30 feet away from second base. Will the catcher get the player out if the player is running at a rate of 22 feet per second? *Explain.*

No. *Sample answer*: **The ball will take about 1.47 seconds to reach second base, and the player will reach the base in about 1.36 seconds.**

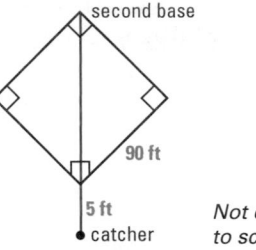

MIXED REVIEW

PREVIEW
Prepare for Lesson 11.5 in Exs. 39–46.

Plot the point in a coordinate plane. *Describe* the location of the point. *(p. 206)*

39–46. See margin for art.

39. $(5, 4)$ **Quadrant I**
40. $(-2, 6)$ **Quadrant II**
41. $(-1, -3)$ **Quadrant III**
42. $(0, 5)$ **y-axis**
43. $(0, 0)$ **origin**
44. $(-8, -2)$ **Quadrant III**
45. $(-1.5, 0)$ **x-axis**
46. $(3.25, -2.5)$ **Quadrant IV**

Evaluate the expression.

47. $5x^2$ when $x = 3$ *(p. 8)* **45**
48. $-|x| - 8$ when $x = -2$ *(p. 64)* **−10**
49. $\sqrt{x - y}$ when $x = 9$, $y = -7$ *(p. 110)* **4**
50. $\sqrt{xy}$ when $x = 27$, $y = 3$ *(p. 110)* **9**

39–46. See Additional Answers beginning on p. AA1.

11.5 Distance in The Coordinate Plane

MATERIALS · graph paper

QUESTION How can you find the distance between two points?

EXPLORE Find the distance between points $A(-3, -2)$ and $B(4, -2)$

STEP 1 *Plot points*

Plot the points $A(-3, -2)$ and $B(4, -2)$ in the same coordinate plane.

STEP 2 *Find distance*

Find the distance between the points by counting the grid lines between them. **7 units**

STEP 3 *Find distance*

Find the distance by subtracting the x-coordinate of point A from the x-coordinate of point B. **7 units**

STEP 4 *Compare results*

How does your result from Step 2 compare with your result from Step 3? **They are the same.**

DRAW CONCLUSIONS Use your observations to complete these exercises

1. Subtract the x-coordinate of point B from the x-coordinate of point A. How is the value different from the values found in Steps 2 and 3 above? How could you make them the same? **−7; it is the opposite of the value in Step 2 and 3; take the absolute value.**

2. Assume points $C(x_1, y_1)$ and $D(x_2, y_2)$ lie on the same horizontal line. Write an expression that can be used to find the distance between the points. $|x^2 - x^1|$ **or** $|x^1 - x^2|$

3. Assume points $C(x_1, y_1)$ and $D(x_2, y_2)$ lie on the same vertical line. Write an expression that can be used to find the distance between the points. Check your expression using $(-2, 4)$ and $(-2, -3)$. $|y^2 - y^1|$ **or** $|y^1 - y^2|$; **7**

In Exercises 4–12, find the distance between the two points.

4. $(2, 3)$, $(-5, 3)$ **7**   5. $(0, -4)$, $(7, -4)$ **7**   6. $(-1, 5)$, $(2, 5)$ **3**

7. $(4, -6)$, $(6, -6)$ **2**   8. $(-5, -4)$, $(-2, -4)$ **3**   9. $(2, 8)$, $(2, 3)$ **5**

10. $(5, -6)$, $(5, -2)$ **4**   11. $(0, -4)$, $(0, 2)$ **6**   12. $(-3, 0)$, $(-3, 6)$ **6**

13. **REASONING** Plot the points $A(6, 5)$, $B(2, 5)$, and $C(6, 2)$. Find the distance between points A and B. Find the distance between points A and C. Use the distances and the Pythagorean theorem to find the distance between points B and C. **See margin for art; 4; 3; 5.**

11.5 Apply the Distance and Midpoint Formulas   **743**

11.5 Apply the Distance and Midpoint Formulas

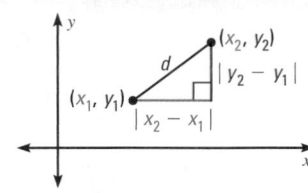

Before	You used the Pythagorean theorem and its converse.
Now	You will use the distance and midpoint formulas.
Why?	So you can calculate distances traveled, as in Ex. 47.

Key Vocabulary
- **distance formula**
- **midpoint**
- **midpoint formula**

To find the distance between the points $A(-2, -1)$ and $B(3, 2)$, draw a right triangle, as shown. The lengths of the legs of the right triangle are as follows.

$$AC = |3 - (-2)| = 5$$
$$BC = |-1 - 2| = 3$$

You can use the Pythagorean theorem to find AB, the length of the hypotenuse of the right triangle.

$(AB)^2 = (AC)^2 + (BC)^2$	**Pythagorean theorem**
$AB = \sqrt{(AC)^2 + (BC)^2}$	**Take positive square root of each side.**
$AB = \sqrt{5^2 + 3^2} = \sqrt{34}$	**Substitute 5 for AC and 3 for BC and simplify.**

This example suggests that you can find the distance between two points in a coordinate plane using the following formula, called the **distance formula**.

KEY CONCEPT
For Your Notebook

The Distance Formula

The distance d between any two points (x_1, y_1) and (x_2, y_2) is

$$d = \sqrt{(x_2 - x_1)^2 + (y_2 - y_1)^2}.$$

EXAMPLE 1 Find the distance between two points

Find the distance between $(-1, 3)$ and $(5, 2)$.

Let $(x_1, y_1) = (-1, 3)$ and $(x_2, y_2) = (5, 2)$.

$d = \sqrt{(x_2 - x_1)^2 + (y_2 - y_1)^2}$	**Distance formula**
$= \sqrt{(5 - (-1))^2 + (2 - 3)^2}$	**Substitute.**
$= \sqrt{6^2 + (-1)^2} = \sqrt{37}$	**Simplify.**

▶ The distance between the points is $\sqrt{37}$ units.

---

① PLAN AND PREPARE

Warm-Up Exercises

🗒 Transparency Available

1. Is a triangle with side lengths 9, 40, 41 a right triangle? **yes**
2. A triangular window is 14 inches wide and 18 inches high. The length and width of the window meet at a right angle. What is the length of the other side to the nearest whole number? **23 in.**

Notetaking Guide

🗒 Transparency Available

Promotes interactive learning and notetaking skills, pp. 262–264.

Pacing

Basic: 1 day
Average: 1 day
Advanced: 1 day
Block: 0.5 block with 11.4
- See *Teaching Guide/Lesson Plan*.

② FOCUS AND MOTIVATE

Essential Question

Big Idea 3, p. 709

How do you use the distance and midpoint formulas? **Tell students they will learn how to answer this question by using coordinates to find the distance between two points and the midpoint of two points.**

NCTM STANDARDS

Standard 3: Analyze properties of 2-D shapes; Describe spatial relationships using coordinate geometry

---

Resource Planning Guide

Chapter Resource Book
- Teaching Guide/Lesson Plan (pp. 52–53)
- Practice levels A, B, C (pp. 54–56)
- Study Guide (pp. 57–58)
- Catch-up for Absent Students (p. 59)
- Problem Solving Workshop (p. 60)
- Challenge (p. 61)

Workbooks
- Notetaking Guide (pp. 262–264)
- Practice Workbook (pp. 178–179)

Teaching Options
- **Power Presentations CD-ROM** provides dynamic electronic teaching resources for the classroom.
- **Activity Generator CD-ROM** provides editable activities for all ability levels.

Interactive Technology
- Easy Planner
- Power Presentations CD-ROM
- Activity Generator CD-ROM
- Animated Algebra
- Test Generator CD-ROM
- Online Quiz
- eWorkbook
- eEdition
- @HomeTutor

Resources for English Learners
- Quick Reference for English Learners
- Spanish Study Guide
- Multi-Language Visual Glossary
- Student Resources in Spanish

See also the *Algebra 1 Toolkit* for more strategies for meeting individual needs.

EXAMPLE 2 Find a missing coordinate

The distance between $(3, -5)$ and $(7, b)$ is 5 units. Find the value of b.

Solution

Use the distance formula with $d = 5$. Let $(x_1, y_1) = (3, -5)$ and $(x_2, y_2) = (7, b)$. Then solve for b.

$$d = \sqrt{(x_2 - x_1)^2 + (y_2 - y_1)^2}$$ **Distance formula**

$$5 = \sqrt{(7 - 3)^2 + (b - (-5))^2}$$ **Substitute.**

$$5 = \sqrt{16 + b^2 + 10b + 25}$$ **Multiply.**

$$5 = \sqrt{b^2 + 10b + 41}$$ **Simplify.**

$$25 = b^2 + 10b + 41$$ **Square each side.**

$$0 = b^2 + 10b + 16$$ **Write in standard form.**

$$0 = (b + 2)(b + 8)$$ **Factor.**

$$b + 2 = 0 \quad or \quad b + 8 = 0$$ **Zero-product property**

$$b = -2 \quad or \quad b = -8$$ **Solve for b.**

▶ The value of b is -2 or -8.

INTERPRET GEOMETRICALLY
The point $(7, b)$ lies on the line $x = 7$. If you let the point $(3, -5)$ be the center of a circle with radius 5, you will see that the circle crosses the line at $(7, -2)$ and $(7, -8)$.

✓ **GUIDED PRACTICE**   for Examples 1 and 2

Find the distance between the points.

1. $(3, 0)$, $(3, 6)$ **6**
2. $(-2, 1)$, $(2, 5)$ $4\sqrt{2}$
3. $(6, -2)$, $(-4, 7)$ $\sqrt{181}$

4. The distance between $(1, a)$ and $(4, 2)$ is 3 units. Find the value of a.   **2**

MIDPOINT The **midpoint** of a line segment is the point on the segment that is equidistant from the endpoints. You can find the coordinates of the midpoint of a line segment using the following formula, called the **midpoint formula**.

KEY CONCEPT   *For Your Notebook*

The Midpoint Formula

The midpoint M of the line segment with endpoints $A(x_1, y_1)$ and $B(x_2, y_2)$ is

$$M\left(\frac{x_1 + x_2}{2}, \frac{y_1 + y_2}{2}\right).$$

Motivating the Lesson
You are trying to find a place to meet a friend who lives in a different part of the city. By superimposing a coordinate grid over a map, you can use coordinates and the midpoint formula to find a meeting place that is about halfway for both of you.

❸ TEACH

Extra Example 1
Find the distance between $(-3, 1)$ and $(2, 3)$. $\sqrt{29}$ **units**

Key Questions to Ask for Example 1
- Can either addend in the radicand be negative? Explain. **No; if you obtain a negative value by subtracting two coordinates, the value is squared and a squared value is always positive.**
- Does it matter which ordered pair is first when using the distance formula? Explain. **No, either ordered pair can be first since the distance between the two points is the same no matter the order.**
- Is the distance between the two points one of the legs of the right triangle or the hypotenuse?. **The distance between the points represents the hypotenuse of the triangle.**

Extra Example 2
The distance between $(4, a)$ and $(1, 6)$ is 5 units. Find the value of a. **The value of a is 2 or 10.**

Differentiated Instruction

Kinesthetic Learners Students may learn the distance formula more easily by first doing a few examples involving plotting two points, drawing a related right triangle, and applying the properties of a right triangle. For **Example 1**, students would construct a triangle with side lengths 6 and 1 and then apply the Pythagorean theorem. This should help students see the relationship between the horizontal and vertical distances between the two points and the side lengths of the right triangle.

See also the *Algebra 1 Toolkit* for more strategies.

EXAMPLE 3   Standardized Test Practice

> **What is the midpoint of the line segment with endpoints $(-1, -2)$ and $(3, -4)$?**
>
> Ⓐ $(2, -1)$ Ⓑ $(1, -3)$ Ⓒ $(-2, 1)$ Ⓓ $(-3, 1)$

ELIMINATE CHOICES
The y-coordinate of the midpoint has to be negative because it is an average of the y-coordinates of the endpoints of the line segment. Eliminate choices C and D.

Solution

Let $(x_1, y_1) = (-1, -2)$ and $(x_2, y_2) = (3, -4)$.

$\left(\dfrac{x_1 + x_2}{2}, \dfrac{y_1 + y_2}{2}\right) = \dfrac{-1 + 3}{2}, \dfrac{-2 + (-4)}{2}$ **Substitute.**

$\qquad\qquad = (1, -3)$ **Simplify.**

▶ The correct answer is B. Ⓐ **Ⓑ** Ⓒ Ⓓ

Animated Algebra at classzone.com

EXAMPLE 4   Solve a real-world problem

ANOTHER WAY
For alternative methods for solving Example 4, turn to page 751 for the **Problem Solving Workshop**.

SIGHTSEEING You and a friend are sightseeing in Washington, D.C. You are at the National Gallery of Art, and your friend is at the Washington Monument, as shown on the map. You want to meet at the landmark that is closest to the midpoint of your locations. At which landmark should you meet?

SIGHTS IN WASHINGTON, D.C.

A) White House
B) Washington Monument
C) Natural History Museum
D) Smithsonian Institution
E) National Portrait Gallery
F) National Gallery of Art

Solution

Your coordinates are $(11, 3)$, and your friend's coordinates are $(2, 2)$. First, find the midpoint of your locations, which is

$\left(\dfrac{x_1 + x_2}{2}, \dfrac{y_1 + y_2}{2}\right) = \left(\dfrac{11 + 2}{2}, \dfrac{3 + 2}{2}\right) = (6.5, 2.5)$.

Next, find the distance from the midpoint to the Smithsonian Institution, located at $(7, 1)$, and to the Natural History Museum, located at $(7, 3)$.

Distance to Smithsonian Institution: $d = \sqrt{(6.5 - 7)^2 + (2.5 - 1)^2} \approx 1.58$ units

Distance to Natural History Museum: $d = \sqrt{(6.5 - 7)^2 + (2.5 - 3)^2} \approx 0.71$ unit

▶ You should meet at the Natural History Museum.

5. Find the midpoint of the line segment with endpoints (4, 3) and (2, 5). **(3, 4)**

6. **WHAT IF?** In Example 4, suppose you are at the Smithsonian and your friend is at the National Portrait Gallery. Which landmark on the map is closest to the midpoint of your locations? **Natural History Museum**

11.5 EXERCISES

HOMEWORK KEY
◯ = **WORKED-OUT SOLUTIONS** on p. WS1 for Exs. 7, 23, and 49
★ = **STANDARDIZED TEST PRACTICE** Exs. 2, 15, 34, 37, 45, and 50

SKILL PRACTICE

1. **VOCABULARY** Copy and complete: The point on a line segment that is equidistant from its endpoints is called the __?__ of the line segment. **midpoint**

2. ★ **WRITING** You want to know the distance between the points (3, 2) and (6, 8). Does it matter which point represents (x_1, y_1) and which point represents (x_2, y_2)? *Explain*. **No.** *Sample answer:* **Since the absolute value is taken, the points can be interchanged without affecting the distance.**

EXAMPLE 1
on p. 744
for Exs. 3–15

FINDING DISTANCE Find the distance between the two points.

3. (4, 8), (4, 7) **1**   4. (5, −9), (8, −9) **3**   5. (2, −2), (6, 1) **5**   6. (5, 1), (0, 3) $\sqrt{29}$

7. (−4, 1), (3, −1) $\sqrt{53}$ 8. (2, 4), (−5, 0) $\sqrt{65}$ 9. (−6, 7), (2, 9) $2\sqrt{17}$ 10. (−10, 8), (2, −3) $\sqrt{265}$

11. (7, 5), (−12, −1) $\sqrt{397}$ 12. (4, 2.5), (2.5, −3) $\sqrt{32.5}$ 13. $\left(5, -\frac{1}{2}\right), \left(-3, \frac{5}{2}\right)$ $\sqrt{73}$ 14. $\left(-\frac{3}{4}, \frac{7}{2}\right), \left(\frac{5}{4}, \frac{1}{4}\right)$ $\frac{\sqrt{233}}{4}$

15. ★ **MULTIPLE CHOICE** What is the distance between (4.5, 1) and (−2.5, −5)? **D**

Ⓐ $\sqrt{13}$ Ⓑ $\sqrt{24}$ Ⓒ $\sqrt{68.5}$ Ⓓ $\sqrt{85}$

EXAMPLE 2
on p. 745
for Exs. 16–21

FINDING MISSING COORDINATES The distance d between two points is given. Find the value of b.

16. (0, b), (3, 1); d = 5 **−3, 5**   17. (13, −3), (b, 2); d = 13 **1, 25**   18. (−9, −2), (b, 5); d = 7 **−9**

19. (b, −6), (−5, 2); d = 10 **−11, 1**   20. (−6, 8), (−1, b); d = $\sqrt{29}$ **6, 10**   21. (b, −4), (4, 7); d = $11\sqrt{2}$ **−7, 15**

EXAMPLE 3
on p. 746
for Exs. 22–34

FINDING THE MIDPOINT Find the midpoint of the line segment with the given endpoints.

27. **(−11, −6)**

22. (0, 1), (8, 3) **(4, 2)**   23. (6, −3), (4, −7) **(5, −5)**   24. (−5, 0), (1, 14) **(−2, 7)**

25. (11, −4), (−9, −4) **(1, −4)**   26. (−6, 6), (4, −4) **(−1, 1)**   27. (−17, −8), (5, −4)

28. (2, 7), (5, 3) **(3.5, 5)**   29. (−2, 3), (−2, −3) **(−2, 0)**   30. (12, −5), (−12, 4) **(0, −0.5)**

31. (−15, −8), (−1, −1) **(−8, −4.5)**   32. (18, −17), (12, −7) **(15, −12)**   33. (50, −75), (8, 9) **(−21, −33)**

34. ★ **MULTIPLE CHOICE** What is the midpoint of the line segment with endpoints (2, 1) and (4, 7)? **C**

Ⓐ (1, 3)   Ⓑ (1.5, 5.5)   Ⓒ (3, 4)   Ⓓ (4, 3)

11.5 Apply the Distance and Midpoint Formulas **747**

④ PRACTICE AND APPLY

Assignment Guide
▱ Answer Transparencies available for all exercises

Basic:
Day 1: pp. 747–750
Exs. 1, 2, 3–33 odd, 34–38, 47–50, 53–63 odd

Average:
Day 1: pp. 747–750
Exs. 1, 2, 10–15, 19–21, 30–44, 48–51, 54–64 even

Advanced:
Day 1: pp. 747–750
Exs. 1, 11–15, 20, 21, 31–46*, 49–52*, 56, 58, 62, 64

Block:
pp. 747–750
Exs. 1, 2, 10–15, 19–21, 30–44, 48–51, 54–64 even (with 11.4)

Differentiated Instruction
See *Algebra 1 Best Practices Toolkit* for suggestions on addressing the needs of a diverse classroom.

Homework Check
For a quick check of student understanding of key concepts, go over the following exercises:
Basic: 9, 17, 27, 47, 48
Average: 12, 20, 29, 48, 49
Advanced: 14, 21, 32, 49, 50

Extra Practice
• Student Edition, p. 948
• Chapter 11 Resource Book: Practice levels A, B, C, pp. 54–56

Practice Worksheet
An easily-readable reduced practice page (with answers) for this lesson can be found on p. 708C.

B **ERROR ANALYSIS** *Describe* and correct the error in finding the distance between (−17, −2) and (3, 8), and the midpoint of the line segment with endpoints (−17, −2) and (3, 8). 35, 36. See margin.

35.

Distance:

$d = \sqrt{(3 - (-17))^2 - (8 - (-2))^2}$

$= \sqrt{400 - 100}$

$= \sqrt{300} = 10\sqrt{3}$

36.

Midpoint:

$\left(\frac{3 - (-17)}{2}, \frac{8 - (-2)}{2}\right) = \left(\frac{20}{2}, \frac{10}{2}\right)$

$= (10, 5)$

37. ★ **MULTIPLE CHOICE** What is the distance between point *A* and the midpoint of the line segment that joins points *A* and *B*? **A**

Ⓐ $\sqrt{17}$ units   Ⓑ $3\sqrt{5}$ units

Ⓒ $2\sqrt{17}$ units   Ⓓ $\sqrt{117}$ units

FINDING ENDPOINTS The midpoint and an endpoint of a line segment are given. Find the other endpoint.

38. endpoint: (1, 2)
midpoint: (−6, 4)
(−13, 6)

39. endpoint: (−2, −4)
midpoint: (3, −3)
(8, −2)

40. endpoint: (7, 5)
midpoint: (1, 0.5)
(−5, −4)

RIGHT TRIANGLES Use the distance formula and the converse of the Pythagorean theorem to determine whether the points are vertices of a right triangle.

41. (3, 5), (3, −1), (−2, −1) **right triangle**   **42.** (3, −1), (1, 4), (−3, 0) **not a right triangle**

43. (−5, −2), (0, −4), (−2, 3) **not a right triangle** **44.** (−2, 1), (−4, 3), (−8, −1) **right triangle**

C **45.** ★ **WRITING** *Explain* how you can use the distance formula to verify that the midpoint of a line segment is equidistant from its endpoints.

46. **CHALLENGE** The midpoint of a line segment is (0, 0). The line segment has a length of 2 units. Give three possible sets of endpoints for the line segment. *Explain* how you found your answer. **See margin.**

PROBLEM SOLVING

EXAMPLE 4 **A**
on p. 746
for Exs. 47–50

47. **MULTI-STEP PROBLEM** A rescue helicopter and an ambulance are both traveling from the dispatch center to the scene of an accident. The distance between consecutive grid lines represents 1 mile.

a. Find the distance that the ambulance traveled (red route).

47b. $\sqrt{2}$ times greater

b. How many times greater is the distance that the ambulance traveled than the distance that the helicopter traveled (blue route)?

@HomeTutor for problem solving help at classzone.com

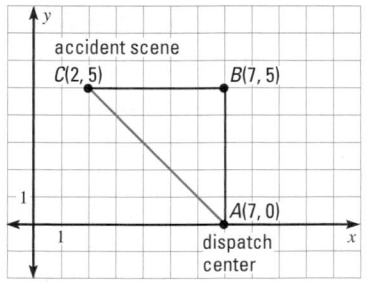

748

○ = **WORKED-OUT SOLUTIONS**
on p. WS1

★ = **STANDARDIZED TEST PRACTICE**

48. SUBWAY A student is taking the subway to the public library. The student can get off the subway at one of two stops, as shown in the map. The distance between consecutive grid lines represents 0.25 mile. Which stop is closer to the library? **stop 2**

@*HomeTutor* for problem solving help at classzone.com

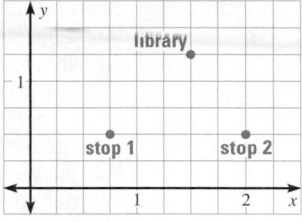

49. **ARCHAEOLOGY** Underwater archaeologists sometimes lay survey grids of the site they are studying. A sample survey grid is shown. The distance between consecutive grid lines represents 50 feet.

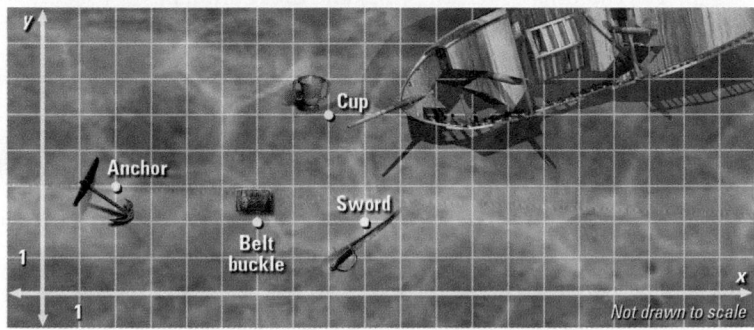

a. Which is shorter, the distance between the anchor and the sword or the distance between the anchor and the cup? **the anchor and the cup**

b. Which two objects are closest together? Which two objects are farthest apart? **the belt buckle and the sword; the anchor and the sword**

B **50.** ★ **SHORT RESPONSE** The point of no return in aviation is the farthest point to which a plane can fly and still have enough fuel to return to its starting place or to fly to an alternative landing destination. After a plane passes the point of no return, it must fly to its planned destination. The distance between consecutive grid lines represents 50 nautical miles.

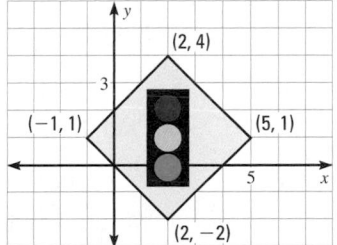

a. The flight path of a plane is from airport A to airport B. The plane is currently at the midpoint of the flight path. How far away is the plane from airport A? Round your answer to the nearest nautical mile. **168 mi**

b. The plane's point of no return is calculated to be 200 nautical miles. Has the plane reached its point of no return? *Explain.*
No. *Sample answer*: The plane has only traveled about 168 miles.

REVIEW GEOMETRY
For help with classifying quadrilaterals, see p. 919.

51. ROAD SIGN Describe the quadrilateral formed by the sides of the road sign shown by answering the following questions.

• Are opposite sides parallel? **yes**

• Do the sides form right angles? **yes**

• Which sides, if any, are congruent? **all of them**
The quadrilateral is a square.

11.5 Apply the Distance and Midpoint Formulas **749**

C 52. CHALLENGE A computer programmer is creating a baseball player's strike zone for a video game, as shown. The strike zone is a rectangular region over home plate through which a ball must pass to be called a strike. In the animation, $\overline{AB}$ is the top of the strike zone and lies on a horizontal line that passes through the midpoint of $\overline{XY}$. The distance between grid lines represents 1 foot.

a. If the coordinates of X are $(4, 5.5)$ and the coordinates of Y are $(4, 3.5)$, what is the midpoint of $\overline{XY}$? **(4, 4.5)**

b. The coordinates of C are $(7, 2)$ and the coordinates of D are $(8.5, 2)$. Find the coordinates of point A and point B. **A: (7, 4.5), B: (8.5, 4.5)**

c. What is the area of the strike zone in the animation? **3.75 ft²**

MIXED REVIEW

PREVIEW
Prepare for Lesson 12.1 in Exs. 53–58.

Given that y varies directly with x, use the specified values to write a direct variation equation that relates x and y. *(p. 253)*

53. $x = 10, y = 30$ $y = 3x$ **54.** $x = 81, y = 27$ $y = \frac{x}{3}$ **55.** $x = -6, y = -9$ $y = \frac{3x}{2}$

56. $x = 12, y = -1.5$ $y = -\frac{x}{8}$ **57.** $x = -11, y = -11$ $y = x$ **58.** $x = \frac{2}{3}, y = 6$ $y = 9x$

Graph the function.   **59–64. See margin.**

59. $y = 4^x$ *(p. 520)*   **60.** $y = 3 \cdot 4^x$ *(p. 520)*   **61.** $y = (0.5)^x$ *(p. 531)*

62. $y = 2 \cdot (0.5)^x$ *(p. 531)*   **63.** $y = x^2 - 6$ *(p. 628)*   **64.** $y = 2x^2 - x + 8$ *(p. 635)*

QUIZ *for Lessons 11.4–11.5*

Let a and b represent the lengths of the legs of a right triangle, and let c represent the length of the hypotenuse. Find the unknown length. *(p. 737)*

1. $a = 6, c = 10$ $b = 8$ **2.** $b = 2, c = 6$ $a = 4\sqrt{2}$ **3.** $a = 4, b = 7$ $c = \sqrt{65}$

Find the unknown lengths. *(p. 737)*

4.   **5.**   **6.**

3, 5   **2, 4**   **5, 12, 13**

Find the distance between the two points. *(p. 744)*

7. $(7, 2), (7, 5)$ **3**   **8.** $(-1, -3), (4, -3)$ **5**   **9.** $(0, 0), (-6, 9)$ $3\sqrt{13}$

Find the midpoint of the line segment with the given endpoints. *(p. 744)*

10. $(0, 5), (-6, 3)$ **$(-3, 4)$**   **11.** $(8, -1), (2, -7)$ **$(5, -4)$**   **12.** $(-5, -3), (5, -3)$ **$(0, -3)$**

13. $(0, 6), (1.5, 4)$ **$(0.75, 5)$**   **14.** $(2.5, -3), (0.5, 6)$ **$(1.5, 1.5)$**   **15.** $\left(-\frac{1}{4}, \frac{3}{4}\right), \left(\frac{1}{4}, \frac{5}{4}\right)$ **$(0, 1)$**

59–64. See Additional Answers beginning on p. AA1.

Using ALTERNATIVE METHODS

Another Way to Solve Example 4, page 746

MULTIPLE REPRESENTATIONS In Example 4 on page 746, you saw how to solve a problem about finding a meeting place by using the midpoint and distance formulas. You can also solve the problem by folding a map and using a compass.

PROBLEM

SIGHTSEEING You and a friend are sightseeing in Washington, D.C. You are at the National Gallery of Art, and your friend is at the Washington Monument, as shown on the map. You want to meet at the landmark that is closest to the midpoint of your locations. At which landmark should you meet?

METHOD 1

Folding a map and using a compass An alternative approach is to fold a map and use a compass. First, draw a line connecting your location to your friend's location. Then fold the map so that your locations coincide. The point where the line connecting your locations is folded represents the midpoint. Place the point of your compass at the midpoint. Adjust the opening of the compass to match the distance between the midpoint and the apparent closest landmark. Swing the compass to see if the other landmark is closer.

SIGHTS IN WASHINGTON, D.C.

A) White House
B) Washington Monument
C) Natural History Museum
D) Smithsonian Institution
E) National Portrait Gallery
F) National Gallery of Art

▶ Because the Smithsonian lies outside the circle, the Natural History Museum is closer to the midpoint of your locations.

PRACTICE

1. **WHAT IF?** In the problem above, suppose your friend is at the White House.

   a. At which landmark should you meet?
      Natural History Museum
   b. Suppose you can walk directly to the landmark in part (a). If the distance between consecutive grid lines represents 0.06 mile, how far do you have to walk?
      0.24 mi

2. **MAPS** A student makes a map of a town in which the student's house is located at (1, 2) and a friend's house is located at (8, 5). A grocery store is located at (5, 3), and a shoe store is located at (3, 4). The student and the friend want to meet at the store that is closer to the midpoint between their houses. At which store should they meet? Solve this problem using two methods. **grocery store**

Using Alternative Methods **751**

Alternative Strategy

Example 4 on page 746 can be solved by folding a map and using a compass. This strategy will appeal to students who prefer a hands-on approach to solving problems. It is also a good method to use in the field when coordinate grids are scarce. Even if students do not have a compass handy when using a map, they can still fold the map to find a midpoint.

Avoiding Common Errors

Students should make sure that the locations coincide when they fold their maps or the midpoint will be off. Students should also make sure that their compasses are stable so that when they swing the compass, it does not change calibration.

4. The library. *Sample answer:* The midpoint between the school and the stadium is at (3, 3.5). Using the distance formula, you can find that the midpoint is closer to the library than any other point.

6c. 2 h 20 min after the ferries first leave. *Sample answer:* The red ferry takes 40 minutes to return to the city and leaves the city every 50 minutes. The blue ferry takes 65 minutes to return to the city and leaves the city every 75 minutes. The red ferry will return to Shore City from its third trip after 2 hours 20 minutes. The blue ferry will return to Shore City from its second trip after 2 hours 20 minutes.

Lessons 11.4–11.5

1. SHORT RESPONSE Construction workers are building a staircase for a house. Use the drawing of the staircase to answer the following questions. Round each answer to the nearest inch.

a. Find the distance *d* between the edges of two consecutive steps. **14 in.**

b. Suppose the workers install a handrail that is as long as the distance between the front edge of the bottom step and the front edge of the top step. How long is the handrail? *Explain.* **42 in.; there are 3 steps, so you can multiply the distance from part (a) by 3.**

2. MULTI-STEP PROBLEM At the start of a football game, the kicker on one team must kick the ball to the opposing team. To position himself for the starting kick, the kicker places a football on a tee, walks 8 yards behind the tee, then 6 yards to his left.

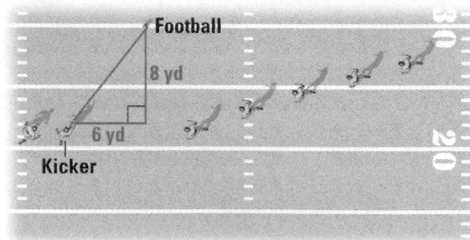

a. What is the kicker's distance (in yards) from the football? **10 yd**

b. The kicker takes 11 strides to kick the ball. What is his average stride length? Round your answer to the nearest tenth of a foot. **2.7 ft**

3. GRIDDED ANSWER You go on a hiking trip. You walk 2 miles directly east and then 4 miles directly north. If you could walk in a straight path back to your starting point, how far would you have to walk? Round your answer to the nearest tenth of a mile. **4.5 mi**

4. SHORT RESPONSE A map of a town is shown. A student is at the school. The student's friend is at the stadium. They want to meet at the place that is closest to the midpoint of their locations. At which location should they meet? *Explain* how you found your answer. **See margin.**

5. OPEN-ENDED City planners want to build a rectangular park. They want the park to have a straight path that is 2500 feet long and connects opposite corners of the park. What are three possibilities for the length and width of the park? *Sample answer*: **2000 ft by 1500 ft, 500√21 ft by 1000 ft, 2400 ft by 700 ft**

6. EXTENDED RESPONSE One ferry makes round trips shown in red. A second ferry makes round trips shown in blue. The distance between consecutive grid lines represents 1 mile.

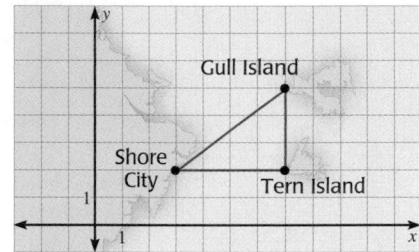

a. Find the distance (in miles) of a round trip for the first ferry. **10 mi**

b. Find the distance (in miles) of a round trip for the second ferry. **12 mi**

c. Each stop the ferries make takes 10 minutes. The first ferry travels at 20 miles per hour, and the second ferry travels at 16 miles per hour. The ferries leave Shore City at the same time each day. When will they be back at the city at the same time? *Explain.* **See margin.**

Animated Algebra
classzone.com
Electronic Function Library

Additional Resources

The following resources are available to help review the materials in this chapter.

Chapter 11 Resource Book
- Chapter Review Games and Activities, p. 62
- Cumulative Practice, Chs. 1–11, pp. 64–65

Student Resources in Spanish

eWorkbook

@HomeTutor

Vocabulary Practice

Vocabulary practice is available at **classzone.com**

BIG IDEAS
For Your Notebook

 Big Idea 1

Graphing Square Root Functions

You can graph a square root function $y = a\sqrt{x - h} + k$ and compare its graph with the graph of the parent function, $y = \sqrt{x}$, based on the constants a, h, and k.

Constant	Comparison of graphs
a	• When $a > 0$, the graph is a vertical stretch or shrink of the parent graph. • When $a < 0$, the graph is a vertical stretch or shrink with a reflection in the x-axis of the parent graph.
h	The graph is a horizontal translation of the parent graph.
k	The graph is a vertical translation of the parent graph.

 Big Idea 2

Using Properties of Radicals in Expressions and Equations

You can use the properties of radicals to simplify radical expressions and to solve radical equations.

Product property of radicals	$\sqrt{ab} = \sqrt{a} \cdot \sqrt{b}$ where $a \geq 0$ and $b \geq 0$
Quotient property of radicals	$\sqrt{\dfrac{a}{b}} = \dfrac{\sqrt{a}}{\sqrt{b}}$ where $a \geq 0$ and $b > 0$

 Big Idea 3

Working with Radicals in Geometry

You can use radicals to solve problems involving the following geometric theorems and formulas.

Pythagorean theorem	If a triangle is a right triangle, then the sum of the squares of the lengths of the legs, a and b, equals the square of the length of the hypotenuse c. $a^2 + b^2 = c^2$
Converse of Pythagorean theorem	If a triangle has side lengths a, b, and c such that $a^2 + b^2 = c^2$, then the triangle is a right triangle.
Distance formula	$d = \sqrt{(x_2 - x_1)^2 + (y_2 - y_1)^2}$
Midpoint formula	$M\left(\dfrac{x_1 + x_2}{2}, \dfrac{y_1 + y_2}{2}\right)$

Chapter Summary   **753**

Extra Example 11.1

Graph the function $3\sqrt{x} + 1$ and identify its domain and range. Compare the graph with the graph of $y = \sqrt{x}$.

Domain: $x \geq 0$, range: $y \geq 1$; the graph of $y = 3\sqrt{x} + 1$ is a vertical stretch (by a factor of 3) and a translation 1 unit up of the graph of $y = \sqrt{x}$.

2. **Sample answer:** To rationalize the denominator of a radical expression, multiply the fraction by the denominator over itself. This will not change the value of the expression and will remove the radical from the denominator. If the denominator is a binomial that contains a radical, multiply by the conjugate of the binomial over itself.

5.

domain: $x \geq 0$, range: $y \leq 0$; vertical stretch by a factor of 2 with a reflection in the x-axis

6.

domain: $x \geq 0$, range: $y \geq 7$; vertical translation of 7 units up

REVIEW KEY VOCABULARY

- radical expression, *p. 710*
- radical function, *p. 710*
- square root function, *p. 710*
- parent square root function, *p. 710*
- simplest form of a radical expression, *p. 719*
- rationalizing the denominator, *p. 721*
- radical equation, *p. 729*
- extraneous solution, *p. 730*
- hypotenuse, legs of a right triangle, *p. 737*
- Pythagorean theorem, *p. 737*
- distance formula, *p. 744*
- midpoint, midpoint formula, *p. 745*

VOCABULARY EXERCISES

1. *Describe* how the graph of the function $y = 3\sqrt{x}$ compares with the graph of the parent square root function. **It is a vertical stretch by a factor of 3.**

2. *Describe* the steps you would take to rationalize the denominator of a radical expression. **See margin.**

Tell which theorem or formula you would use to complete the exercise.

3. Tell whether a triangle with side lengths 2, 4, and 6 is a right triangle. **converse of the Pythagorean theorem**

4. The point $(b, 4)$ is 10 units away from the point $(5, 10)$. Find b. **distance formula**

REVIEW EXAMPLES AND EXERCISES

Use the review examples and exercises below to check your understanding of the concepts you have learned in each lesson of Chapter 11.

11.1 Graph Square Root Functions
pp. 710–716

EXAMPLE

Graph the function $y = \sqrt{x - 3}$ and identify its domain and range. Compare the graph with the graph of $y = \sqrt{x}$.

To graph the function, make a table, plot the points, and draw a smooth curve through the points. The domain is $x \geq 3$.

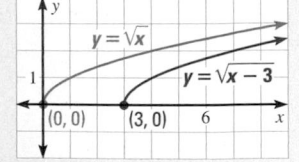

x	3	4	5	6
y	0	1	1.4	1.7

The range is $y \geq 0$. The graph of $y = \sqrt{x - 3}$ is a horizontal translation (of 3 units to the right) of the graph of $y = \sqrt{x}$.

EXERCISES

EXAMPLES 2, 3, and 4
on pp. 711–712
for Exs. 5–7

Graph the function and identify its domain and range. Compare the graph with the graph of $y = \sqrt{x}$. **5–7. See margin.**

5. $y = -2\sqrt{x}$

6. $y = \sqrt{x} + 7$

7. $y = \sqrt{x + 7}$

754   Chapter 11 Radicals and Geometry Connections

7.

domain: $x \geq -7$, range: $y \geq 0$;
horizontal translation of 7 units to the left

Extra Example 11.2
Simplify $6\sqrt{7} + \sqrt{28}$. **$8\sqrt{7}$**

Extra Example 11.3
Solve $\sqrt{6x} + 5 = 11$. **6**

11.2 Simplify Radical Expressions

pp. 719–726

> **EXAMPLE**
>
> Simplify $7\sqrt{5} - \sqrt{45}$.
>
> $7\sqrt{5} - \sqrt{45} = 7\sqrt{5} - \sqrt{9 \cdot 5}$ **Factor using perfect square factor.**
>
> $\phantom{7\sqrt{5} - \sqrt{45}} = 7\sqrt{5} - \sqrt{9} \cdot \sqrt{5}$ **Product property of radicals**
>
> $\phantom{7\sqrt{5} - \sqrt{45}} = 7\sqrt{5} - 3\sqrt{5}$ **Simplify.**
>
> $\phantom{7\sqrt{5} - \sqrt{45}} = (7 - 3)\sqrt{5}$ **Distributive property**
>
> $\phantom{7\sqrt{5} - \sqrt{45}} = 4\sqrt{5}$ **Simplify.**

EXERCISES

**EXAMPLES
1–7**
on pp. 719–722
for Exs. 8–16

Simplify the expression.

8. $\sqrt{98}$ **$7\sqrt{2}$**
        9. $\sqrt{121x^3}$ **$11x\sqrt{x}$**
        10. $\sqrt{7} \cdot \sqrt{21}$ **$7\sqrt{3}$**
        11. $\sqrt{7x} \cdot 7\sqrt{x}$ **$7x\sqrt{7}$**

12. $\sqrt{\dfrac{5}{x^2}}$ **$\dfrac{\sqrt{5}}{x}$**
        13. $\dfrac{2}{\sqrt{5}}$ **$\dfrac{2\sqrt{5}}{5}$**
        14. $3\sqrt{2} - \sqrt{128}$
          $-5\sqrt{2}$
        15. $\sqrt{2}(7 - \sqrt{6})$
          $7\sqrt{2} - 2\sqrt{3}$

16. GEOMETRY The lateral surface area L of a square pyramid with height h
and base length ℓ is given by $L = 2\ell\sqrt{0.25\ell^2 + h^2}$. Find L (in square feet)
for a square pyramid that has a height of 4 feet and a base length of 4 feet. **$16\sqrt{5}$ ft^2**

11.3 Solve Radical Equations

pp. 729–734

> **EXAMPLE**
>
> Solve $\sqrt{x + 90} = x$.
>
> $\sqrt{x + 90} = x$ **Write original equation.**
>
> $\left(\sqrt{x + 90}\right)^2 = x^2$ **Square each side.**
>
> $x + 90 = x^2$ **Simplify.**
>
> $0 = x^2 - x - 90$ **Write in standard form.**
>
> $0 = (x - 10)(x + 9)$ **Factor.**
>
> $x - 10 = 0$ *or* $x + 9 = 0$ **Zero-product property**
>
> $x = 10$ *or* $x = -9$ **Solve for x.**
>
> ▶ Checking 10 and −9 in the original equation shows that −9 is an extraneous
> solution. The only solution of the equation is 10.

EXERCISES

**EXAMPLES
1, 2, 3, and 4**
on pp. 729–731
for Exs. 17–22

Solve the equation. Check for extraneous solutions.

17. $\sqrt{x} - 28 = 0$ **784**
        18. $8\sqrt{x - 5} + 34 = 58$ **14**
        19. $\sqrt{5x - 3} = \sqrt{x + 17}$ **5**

20. $\sqrt{5x} + 6 = 5$
     no real solutions
        21. $\sqrt{x} + 36 = 0$
          no real solutions
        22. $x = \sqrt{2 - x}$ **1**

Extra Example 11.4

Find the unknown length.

$a = 9$ $c = 13$

b

$\sqrt{88}$ or $2\sqrt{22}$

Extra Example 11.5

Find the midpoint of the line segment with endpoints $(-2, 7)$ and $(4, -5)$.
(1, 1)

11.4 Apply the Pythagorean Theorem and Its Converse   *pp. 737–742*

EXAMPLE

Find the unknown length for the triangle shown.

$a^2 + b^2 = c^2$	**Pythagorean theorem**
$6^2 + b^2 = 11^2$	**Substitute 6 for a and 11 for c.**
$36 + b^2 = 121$	**Simplify.**
$b^2 = 85$	**Subtract 36 from each side.**
$b = \sqrt{85}$	**Take positive square root of each side.**

$a = 6$ $c = 11$

b

EXERCISES

**EXAMPLES
1 and 4**
on pp. 737, 739
for Exs. 23–29

Let a and b represent the lengths of the legs of a right triangle, and let c represent the length of the hypotenuse. Find the unknown length.

23. $a = 7$, $b = 13$ $\boldsymbol{c = \sqrt{218}}$ **24.** $a = 10$, $c = 21$ $\boldsymbol{b = \sqrt{341}}$ **25.** $a = 8$, $c = 11$ $\boldsymbol{b = \sqrt{57}}$

26. $a = 9$, $b = 17$ $\boldsymbol{c = \sqrt{370}}$ **27.** $b = 4$, $c = 15$ $\boldsymbol{a = \sqrt{209}}$ **28.** $b = 6$, $c = 6.5$ $\boldsymbol{a = 2.5}$

29. REFLECTING POOL The Reflecting Pool in front of the Lincoln Memorial in Washington, D.C., is rectangular with a length of 2029 feet and a width of 167 feet. To the nearest foot, what is the length of a diagonal of the Reflecting Pool? **2036 ft**

11.5 Apply the Distance and Midpoint Formulas   *pp. 744–750*

EXAMPLE

Find the distance between $(-3, 8)$ and $(5, -12)$.

Let $(x_1, y_1) = (-3, 8)$ and $(x_2, y_2) = (5, -12)$.

$d = \sqrt{(x_2 - x_1)^2 + (y_2 - y_1)^2}$	**Distance formula**
$= \sqrt{(5 - (-3))^2 + (-12 - 8)^2}$	**Substitute.**
$= \sqrt{464} = 4\sqrt{29}$	**Simplify.**

EXERCISES

**EXAMPLES
1, 3, and 4**
on pp. 744, 746
for Exs. 30–36

Find the distance between the two points.

30. $(-1, -3)$, $(9, -13)$ $\boldsymbol{10\sqrt{2}}$ **31.** $(-8, -4)$, $(0, 2)$ **10**   **32.** $(7, 1)$, $(4, -0.25)$ **3.25**

Find the midpoint of the line segment with the given endpoints.

33. $(-2, -4)$, $(9, -4)$ **(3.5, -4)**   **34.** $(-8, 0)$, $(-8, 2)$ **(-8, 1)**   **35.** $(6, 1)$, $(4, -5)$ **(5, -2)**

36. ISLANDS On a coordinate grid, an island is located at $(1, 6)$. Another island is located at $(4, 9)$. What is the distance between the islands if the distance between consecutive grid lines represents 2 miles? $\boldsymbol{6\sqrt{2}}$ **mi**

Graph the function and identify its domain and range. Compare the graph with the graph of $y = \sqrt{x}$. 1–4. See margin.

1. $y = 3\sqrt{x}$
2. $y = -\sqrt{x}$
3. $y = \sqrt{x - 5}$
4. $y = -\sqrt{x - 1} + 4$

Simplify the expression.

5. $\sqrt{72m^6}$ $6m^3\sqrt{2}$
6. $\sqrt{8z^3} \cdot \sqrt{6z^3}$ $4z^3\sqrt{3}$
7. $\sqrt{\dfrac{20}{3n^3}} \div \dfrac{\sqrt{15n}}{3n^2}$ 2

8. $7\sqrt{6} - 2\sqrt{12} + \sqrt{24}$
   $9\sqrt{6} - 4\sqrt{3}$
9. $\sqrt{3}(7 - \sqrt{15})$
   $7\sqrt{3} - 3\sqrt{5}$
10. $(8 - \sqrt{7})(1 + \sqrt{7})$
    $1 + 7\sqrt{7}$

Solve the equation. Check for extraneous solutions.

11. $\sqrt{x} = 8$ **64**
12. $\sqrt{x + 5} - 6 = -2$ **11**
13. $-4\sqrt{3x} - 6 = 30$
    no real solutions
14. $\sqrt{5x - 11} = \sqrt{x}$ $\dfrac{11}{4}$
15. $\sqrt{x + 7} = \sqrt{2x - 3}$ **10**
16. $x = \sqrt{12 - x}$ **3**

Find the unknown lengths.

17.
3, 7

18.
15, 20, 25

19.
5, 5, 5√2

Tell whether the triangle with the given side lengths is a right triangle.

20. 8, 16, 32 **not a right triangle**
21. 11, 60, 61 **right triangle**
22. 7.5, 10, 12.5 **right triangle**

Find the distance between the given points. Then find the midpoint of the line segment whose endpoints are the given points.

23. $(6, 6)$, $(9, 10)$ **5; (7.5, 8)**
24. $(-8, 7)$, $(4, 3)$ $4\sqrt{10}$; **(−2, 5)**
25. $\left(5, -\dfrac{3}{2}\right), \left(-2, \dfrac{9}{2}\right)$ $\sqrt{85}$; $\left(1\dfrac{1}{2}, 1\dfrac{1}{2}\right)$

26. **LADDERS** A ladder that is 25 feet long is placed against a house. The bottom of the ladder is 10 feet from the base of the house. How far up the house does the ladder reach? Round your answer to the nearest tenth of a foot. **22.9 ft**

27. **BIRD HOUSES** The front view of a bird house is shown. Find the height of the house to the nearest tenth of a foot. **1.9 ft**

2.6 ft   2.6 ft
1.8 ft

28. **LACROSSE** Two lacrosse players are playing on a field, as shown. The distance between consecutive grid lines represents 2 meters.
    player A: 8.2 m; player B: 10.8 m
    a. How far is each player from the ball? Round your answer to the nearest tenth of a meter.
    b. Both players start running toward the ball. Player A can run at a rate of 6 meters per second. Player B can run at a rate of 7 meters per second. Who will reach the ball first? **player A**

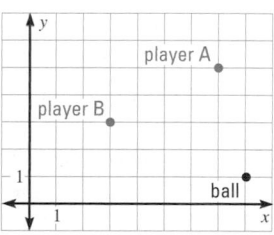
player A
player B
ball

2.
domain: $x \geq 0$, range: $y \leq 0$;
reflection in the *x*-axis

3.
domain: $x \geq 5$, range: $y \geq 0$;
horizontal translation of 5 units to the right

4.
domain: $x \geq 1$, range: $y \leq 4$;
horizontal translation of 1 unit to the right with a reflection in the *x*-axis and a translation vertically 4 units up

1.
domain: $x \geq 0$, range: $y \geq 0$;
vertical stretch by a factor of 3

MULTIPLE CHOICE QUESTIONS

If you have difficulty solving a multiple choice problem directly, you may be able to use another approach to eliminate incorrect answer choices and obtain the correct answer.

PROBLEM 1

What is the solution of the equation $\sqrt{3-x} = 2x$?

A $1, -\frac{3}{4}$ **B** $-1, \frac{3}{4}$ **C** -1 **D** $\frac{3}{4}$

METHOD 1

SOLVE DIRECTLY Solve the radical equation and check for extraneous solutions.

STEP 1 **Solve** the radical equation.

$$\sqrt{3-x} = 2x$$
$$3 - x = 4x^2$$
$$0 = 4x^2 + x - 3$$
$$0 = (4x - 3)(x + 1)$$
$$4x - 3 = 0 \ or \ x + 1 = 0$$
$$x = \frac{3}{4} \ or \qquad x = -1$$

STEP 2 **Check** $\frac{3}{4}$ and -1 in the original equation.

Check $\frac{3}{4}$: $\sqrt{3 - \frac{3}{4}} \overset{?}{=} 2\left(\frac{3}{4}\right)$

$$\frac{3}{2} = \frac{3}{2} \ \checkmark$$

Solution checks.

Check -1: $\sqrt{3 - (-1)} \overset{?}{=} 2(-1)$

$$2 = -2 \ \mathsf{X}$$

Solution does not check.

The only solution is $\frac{3}{4}$.

The correct answer is D. **A** **B** **C** **Ⓓ**

METHOD 2

ELIMINATE CHOICES Substitute the values given in each answer choice for x in the equation.

Choice A: $1, -\frac{3}{4}$

$$\sqrt{3 - 1} \overset{?}{=} 2(1) \qquad \bigg| \qquad \sqrt{3 - \left(-\frac{3}{4}\right)} \overset{?}{=} -\frac{3}{4}$$

$$\sqrt{2} = 2 \ \mathsf{X} \qquad \bigg| \qquad \frac{\sqrt{15}}{2} = -\frac{3}{4} \ \mathsf{X}$$

The values do not check, so choice A can be eliminated.

Choice B: $-1, \frac{3}{4}$

$$\sqrt{3 - (-1)} \overset{?}{=} 2(-1) \qquad \bigg| \qquad \sqrt{3 - \frac{3}{4}} \overset{?}{=} 2\left(\frac{3}{4}\right)$$

$$2 = -2 \ \mathsf{X} \qquad \bigg| \qquad \frac{3}{2} = \frac{3}{2} \ \checkmark$$

Because -1 does not check, both choice B and choice C can be eliminated.

Choice D: $\frac{3}{4}$

You know that $\frac{3}{4}$ is a solution from checking the values in choice B.

The only solution is $\frac{3}{4}$.

The correct answer is D. **A** **B** **C** **Ⓓ**

PROBLEM 2

A carpenter is building a wooden bench and wants to be sure that the back and the seat make a right angle. The back is 24 inches tall, and the seat is 18 inches deep. What should the distance from the front of the seat to the top of the back be?

(A) 6 inches   (B) 15.9 inches   (C) 30 inches   (D) 42 inches

METHOD 1

SOLVE DIRECTLY Use the Pythagorean theorem to find the unknown distance.

STEP 1 Identify the known values by drawing a diagram.

STEP 2 Substitute the values of a and b and solve for c.

$$a^2 + b^2 = c^2$$
$$18^2 + 24^2 = c^2$$
$$900 = c^2$$
$$\sqrt{900} = c$$
$$30 = c$$

The distance from the front of the seat to the top of the back should be 30 inches.

The correct answer is C. (A) (B) ⓒ (D)

METHOD 2

ELIMINATE CHOICES You can eliminate choices by using the converse of the Pythagorean theorem. Check to see if the value given in each answer choice could represent the length of the hypotenuse of a right triangle with leg lengths of 18 and 24.

Choice A: 6 inches

$$18^2 + 24^2 \overset{?}{=} 6^2$$
$$900 = 36 \; ✗$$

Choice B: 15.9 inches

$$18^2 + 24^2 \overset{?}{=} 15.9^2$$
$$900 = 252.81 \; ✗$$

Choice C: 30 inches

$$18^2 + 24^2 \overset{?}{=} 30^2$$
$$900 = 900 \; ✓$$

The correct answer is C. (A) (B) ⓒ (D)

PRACTICE

Explain why you can eliminate the highlighted answer choice. **1–3. See margin.**

1. What is the solution of the equation $\sqrt{20 - x} = x$?

   (A) 4, −5   (B) −4, 5   (C) ✗ −5   (D) 4

2. Which of the following represents the side lengths of a right triangle?

   (A) 1, 2, 3   (B) ✗ 6, 8, 14   (C) 12, 13, 15   (D) 8, 15, 17

3. A side view of a wheelchair ramp can be represented by the hypotenuse of a right triangle. The triangle has a length of 24 feet and a height of 2 feet. To the nearest tenth, how long is the ramp?

   (A) ✗ 22 feet   (B) 23.9 feet   (C) 24.1 feet   (D) 26 feet

Study Strategy

Stress to students that the Pythagorean theorem and its converse are used so extensively that they should commit the theorem to memory. Suggest that they use notecards until they are familiar with the theorem and its converse. The notecards should include a diagram that shows that the hypotenuse is opposite the right angle of the triangle and is the longest side.

1. *Sample answer:* The answer $x = -5$ does not check in the original equation, so you can eliminate both A and C as answer choices.

2. *Sample answer:* $6^2 + 8^2 \neq 14^2$, so you can eliminate choice B.

3. *Sample answer:* The square of the length of the ramp should equal the sum of the squares of 24 and 2; $24^2 + 2^2 = 580$. Since $22^2 \neq 580$, you can eliminate choice A.

MULTIPLE CHOICE

1. What is the solution of the equation $\sqrt{2x + 8} = x$? **D**

   (A) $-2, 4$ (B) $24, 2$

   (C) -2 (D) 4

2. Which expression is equivalent to $\sqrt{4x^2 y} \cdot \sqrt{y}$? **B**

   (A) $4xy$ (B) $2xy$

   (C) $2x\sqrt{y}$ (D) $4x\sqrt{y}$

3. The graph of which function is shown? **B**

   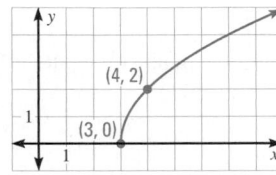

   (A) $y = \sqrt{x} - 3$ (B) $y = 2\sqrt{x - 3}$

   (C) $y = 2\sqrt{x + 3}$ (D) $y = 2\sqrt{x} - 3$

4. How does the graph of $y = \sqrt{x} + 3$ compare with the graph of $y = \sqrt{x}$? **B**

   (A) It is a vertical stretch by a factor of 3 of the graph of $y = \sqrt{x}$.

   (B) It is a vertical translation of 3 units up of the graph of $y = \sqrt{x}$.

   (C) It is a vertical translation of 3 units down of the graph of $y = \sqrt{x}$.

   (D) It is a horizontal translation of 3 units to the right of the graph of $y = \sqrt{x}$.

5. Which expression represents the length of a diagonal of the rectangle? **C**

   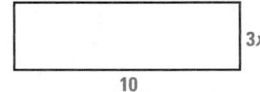

   (A) $3x^2 + 100$

   (B) $9x^2 + 100$

   (C) $\sqrt{9x^2 + 100}$

   (D) $\sqrt{3x^2 + 100}$

6. What is the solution of the equation $\sqrt{x + 3} = x - 9$? **C**

   (A) $-13, -6$ (B) $13, 6$

   (C) 13 (D) 6

7. The table below represents which function? **A**

x	4	5	8	13
y	5	8	11	14

   (A) $y = 3\sqrt{x - 4} + 5$

   (B) $y = 3\sqrt{x - 3} + 8$

   (C) $y = 3\sqrt{x - 4} + 8$

   (D) $y = 3\sqrt{x - 3} + 5$

In Exercises 8 and 9, use the map of the college campus shown.

8. Which of the following pairs of buildings are closest together? **C**

   (A) Dorm A and the library

   (B) Dorm B and the gym

   (C) The gym and the library

   (D) Dorm B and the library

9. A student who lives in dorm A forgets a book at the library. The student jogs at a rate of 6 miles per hour from the dorm straight to the library and back. The distance between consecutive grid lines represents 0.1 mile. To the nearest tenth of an hour, how long does it take the student to jog to the library and back? **B**

   (A) 0.1 hour   (B) 0.2 hour

   (C) 0.3 hour   (D) 0.4 hour

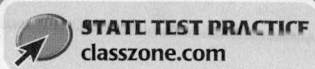
GRIDDED ANSWER

10. A line segment has endpoints (8, 0) and (14, 8). What is the distance from either endpoint to the midpoint? **5**

11. A right triangle has a hypotenuse of 18 centimeters. The length of one leg is 8 centimeters. To the nearest tenth of a centimeter, how long is the other leg? **16.1 cm**

12. The leg lengths of a triangle are shown.

To the nearest tenth, what is the length of the hypotenuse when $x = 3$? **7.3**

13. A rectangular table is 7 feet long and 3.5 feet wide. To the nearest tenth of a foot, what is the length of a diagonal of the table? **7.8 ft**

14. What is the solution of the equation $2\sqrt{x} = 3\sqrt{8} - \sqrt{2}$? Write your answer as a decimal. **12.5**

EXTENDED RESPONSE

17. For the period 1900–2000, the life expectancy at birth e (in years) for people born in the United States can be modeled by the function $e = 3.66\sqrt{t} + 40.6$ where t is the number of years since 1900. **a–c. See margin.**

a. Graph the function and identify its domain and range.

b. In what year was the life expectancy at birth about 75 years? *Explain.*

c. During which decade (1900–1909, 1910–1919, and so on) did life expectancy increase the most? *Explain.*

18. A planet's mean radius r (in meters) is given by $r = \sqrt{\dfrac{(6.67 \times 10^{-11})M}{a}}$ where

a is the planet's acceleration due to gravity (in meters per second squared) and M is the planet's mass (in kilograms).

a. For Earth, the value of a is about 9.8 meters per second squared, and the value of M is about 5.98×10^{24} kilograms. Find the value of r. **about 6.38×10^6 m**

b. For Jupiter, the value of a is about 24.8 meters per second squared, and the value of M is about 1.9×10^{27} kilograms. Find the value of r. **about 7.15×10^7 m**

c. Jupiter's mass is abouut 300 times Earth's mass, and Jupiter's acceleration due to gravity is about 2.5 times that of Earth's. If you multiply M by 300 and a by 2.5, what happens to the value of r? *Compare* your answer with your results from parts (a) and (b). **See margin.**

SHORT RESPONSE

15. A person lives in Glenville. The person's friend lives in Newport.

The friends decide to meet at the city that is closer to the midpoint of their locations. In which city should they meet? *Explain.*
See margin.

16. The front view of a shed is shown. Roofers are going to replace the tin roof of the shed.

If the depth of the shed is 20 feet, how many square feet of tin will the roofers need? *Explain.* **See margin.**

15. Riverside. *Sample answer:* The midpoint between Newport and Glenville is at (4, 2). Riverside is only 1 unit away, while Fairview is $\sqrt{2}$ units away.

16. 260 ft². *Sample answer:* Subtract 10 from 15 to find the height the roof rises, then use the Pythagorean theorem to find the length of the hypotenuse, which is one side of the roof: $12^2 + 5^2 = 169$. The length of the roof is 13, which is multiplied by a depth of 20 to give the area of the roof, 260 square feet.

17a.

domain: $x \geq 0$, range: $y \geq 40.6$

17b. In 1988. *Sample answer:* Substituting 75 for e into the equation gives a value of about 88.3, or 1988.

17c. During 1900–1910. *Sample answer:* The graph of life expectancy is modeled on the parent graph $y = \sqrt{x}$, which increases less steeply as x increases. So, in the first decade the graph increased the most.

18c. r will increase by a factor of $\sqrt{\dfrac{300}{2.5}} = \sqrt{120} \approx 10.95$. *Sample answer:* The r value for Jupiter is close to 10.95 times the r value of Earth.

REGULAR SCHEDULE

Pre-AP For pacing and assignments for a Pre-AP course, see the *Algebra 1 Toolkit*.

Lesson	Les. Day	BASIC	AVERAGE	ADVANCED
12.1	Day 1	pp. 769–772 Exs. 1–26	pp. 769–772 Exs. 1, 2, 6–26, 49–51	pp. 769–772 Exs. 1, 2, 7–26, 49–51
	Day 2	pp. 769–772 Exs. 27–43 odd, 44–49, 54–59, 62–74 even	pp. 769–772 Exs. 27, 35–48, 54–60, 63–73 odd	pp. 769–772 Exs. 37–48, 52–61*, 62–74 even
12.2	Day 1	EP p. 948 Exs. 1–9 odd; pp. 779–782 Exs. 1–17, 52–60	pp. 779–782 Exs. 1, 2, 6–17, 37, 52–60	pp. 779–782 Exs. 1, 6–17, 37, 52–60
	Day 2	pp. 779–782 Exs. 18–33, 39–43, 46–51	pp. 779–782 Exs. 18–28 even, 29–36, 39–44, 46–51	pp. 779–782 Exs. 18, 24–36, 38–45*, 46–50 even
12.3	Day 1	EP p. 946 Exs. 3–6; pp. 788–791 Exs. 1–12, 19–21, 51–59	pp. 788–791 Exs. 1, 2, 5–12, 19–21, 35–37, 51–59	pp. 788–791 Exs. 1, 2, 4–12 even, 19, 35–41*, 51–59
	Day 2	pp. 788–791 Exs. 13–18, 23–29 odd, 31–34, 42–47, 60–65	pp. 788–791 Exs. 13–18, 22–30 even, 31–34, 38, 42–49, 60–64 even	pp. 788–791 Exs. 13–18, 22–30 even, 31–34, 42–50*, 60–64 even
12.4	Day 1	EP p. 946 Exs. 25–30; pp. 797–800 Exs. 1–12, 13–33 odd, 34–36, 40–44, 48, 52, 55, 58	pp. 797–800 Exs. 1, 2, 7–12, 14–32 even, 33–38, 40–45, 49, 53, 56, 59	pp. 797–800 Exs. 1, 8–11, 14–32 even, 33–46*, 50, 54, 57, 60
12.5	Day 1	EP p. 946 Exs. 49–57 odd; pp. 806–809 Exs. 1–10, 12, 22, 23, 47–52	pp. 806–809 Exs. 1, 2, 4–10, 12, 22, 23, 29, 47–52	pp. 806–809 Exs. 1, 4–10, 22, 23, 29–31*, 47–52
	Day 2	pp. 806–809 Exs. 11, 13–21, 24–26, 33–36, 39–46	pp. 806–809 Exs. 11, 13–21, 24–28, 30, 33–37, 39–45 odd	pp. 806–809 Exs. 13–21, 24–28, 32–38*, 40–46 even
12.6	Day 1	pp. 816–819 Exs. 1–17, 19–21, 25, 26, 58–62	pp. 816–819 Exs. 1, 2, 7–17, 19–21, 25, 26, 29, 30, 35, 36, 58–62	pp. 816–819 Exs. 1, 2, 7–17, 19–21, 25, 26, 35, 36, 58–62
	Day 2	pp. 816–819 Exs. 18, 22–24, 27–35, 42–47, 50–57	pp. 816–819 Exs. 18, 22–24, 27–34, 37–40, 42–48, 50–56 even	pp. 816–819 Exs. 22–24, 27, 28, 31–34, 37, 41–49*, 51–57 odd
12.7	Day 1	EP p. 946 Exs. 43–48; pp. 823–826 Exs. 1–8, 12–19, 24–26, 31–35, 39–53 odd	pp. 823–826 Exs. 1, 2, 7–13, 19–29, 31–37, 40–52 even	pp. 823–826 Exs. 1, 2, 8–11, 20–38*, 40–52 even
Review	Day 1	pp. 831–834 Exs. 1–31	pp. 831–834 Exs. 1–31	pp. 831–834 Exs. 1–31
Assess	Day 1	Chapter 12 Test	Chapter 12 Test	Chapter 12 Test
Yearly Pacing		Chapter 12 Total – 14 days	Chapters 1–12 Total – 146 days	Remaining – 14 days

*Challenge Exercises   EP = Extra Practice   SRH = Skills Review Handbook

BLOCK SCHEDULE

DAY 1	DAY 2	DAY 3	DAY 4	DAY 5	DAY 6	DAY 7
12.1	**12.2**	**12.3**	**12.4**	**12.5 (CONT.)**	**12.6 (CONT.)**	**REVIEW**
pp. 769–772 Exs. 1, 2, 6–27, 35–51, 54–60, 63–73 odd	pp. 779–782 Exs. 1, 2, 6–17, 18–28 even, 29–37, 39–44, 46–60	pp. 788–791 Exs. 1, 2, 5–21, 22–30 even, 31–38, 42–49, 51–59, 60–64 even	pp. 797–800 Exs. 1, 2, 7–12, 14–32 even, 33–38, 40–45, 49, 53, 56, 59	pp. 806–809 Exs. 11, 13–21, 24–28, 30, 33–37, 39–45 odd	pp. 816–819 Exs. 18, 22–24, 27–34, 37–40, 42–48, 50–56 even	pp. 831–834 Exs. 1–31
			12.5	**12.6**	**12.7**	**ASSESS**
			pp. 806–809 Exs. 1, 2, 4–10, 12, 22, 23, 29, 47–52	pp. 816–819 Exs. 1, 2, 7–17, 19–21, 25, 26, 29, 30, 35, 36, 58–62	pp. 823–826 Exs. 1, 2, 7–13, 19–29, 31–37, 40–52 even	Chapter 12 Test
Yearly Pacing		Chapter 12 Total – 7 days	Chapters 1–12 Total – 73 days	Remaining – 7 days		

RESOURCE MANAGER

Chapter Resource Book

CHAPTER SUPPORT

Parents as Partners (Chapter Overview with home involvement exercises and activity)						p. 1	
LESSON SUPPORT	**12.1**	**12.2**	**12.3**	**12.4**	**12.5**	**12.6**	**12.7**
Teaching Guide/Lesson Plan	p. 3	p. 17	p. 30	p. 42	p. 54	p. 66	p. 77
Activity Masters				p. 44		p. 68	
Technology Activities & Keystrokes			p. 33		p. 56		
Activity Support Masters	p. 5		p. 32				
Practice (3 levels)	p. 6	p. 19	p. 34	p. 45	p. 58	p. 69	p. 79
Study Guide	p. 12	p. 25	p. 37	p. 48	p. 61	p. 72	p. 82
Catch-Up for Absent Students	p. 14	p. 27	p. 39	p. 50	p. 63	p. 74	p. 84
Problem Solving/Application	p. 15	p. 28	p. 40	p. 51	p. 64	p. 75	p. 85
Challenge Practice	p. 16	p. 29	p. 41	p. 53	p. 65	p. 76	p. 86

REVIEW

Chapter Review Games and Activities	p. 87	Cumulative Practice	p. 89
Project with Rubric	p. 88	Resource Book Answers	A1

Transparencies

	12.1	**12.2**	**12.3**	**12.4**	**12.5**	**12.6**	**12.7**
Warm-Up/Daily Homework Quiz	✔	✔	✔	✔	✔	✔	✔
Notetaking Guide	✔	✔	✔	✔	✔	✔	✔
Teacher Support	✔	✔	✔				
Answer Transparencies	✔	✔	✔	✔	✔	✔	✔

ASSESSMENT BOOK

Quizzes	p. 168	SAT/ACT Chapter Test	p. 179
Chapter Tests (3 levels)	p. 171	Alternative Assessment with Rubric	p. 181
Standardized Chapter Test	p. 177		

TECHNOLOGY

- Easy Planner
- Test and Practice Generator
- Power Presentations
- @HomeTutor
- Activity Generator
- Animated Algebra
- Classzone.com
- eEdition Plus Online
- eWorkbook Plus Online
- Easy Grader Online

ADDITIONAL RESOURCES

- Worked-Out Solution Key
- Notetaking Guide
- Practice Wookbook
- Algebra 1 Toolkit
- Benchmark Tests
- Reteaching and Remediation
- Spanish Study Guide
- Spanish Assessment Book
- Student Resources in Spanish
- Multi-Language Visual Glossary

12 Lesson Practice Level B

LESSON 12.1 Practice B
For use with pages 765–772

Tell whether the equation represents *direct variation*, *inverse variation*, or *neither*.

1. $y = -11x$ **direct variation**
2. $xy = -5$ **inverse variation**
3. $y = x - 4$ **neither**

4. $x = \dfrac{-8}{y}$ **inverse variation**
5. $xy = 14$ **inverse variation**
6. $\dfrac{y}{x} = 13$ **direct variation**

7. $2x + y = 8$ **neither**
8. $3y = \dfrac{9}{x}$ **inverse variation**
9. $4x - 4y = 0$ **direct variation**

Graph the inverse variation equation.

10. $xy = 12$
11. $xy = -6$
12. $xy = 7$

13. $y = \dfrac{-8}{x}$
14. $y = \dfrac{15}{x}$
15. $y = \dfrac{14}{x}$

16. $y = \dfrac{-9}{x}$
17. $y = \dfrac{-12}{x}$
18. $y = \dfrac{5}{x}$

Algebra 1
Chapter 12 Resource Book
8

LESSON 12.1 Practice B *continued*
For use with pages 765–772

22. $y = \dfrac{-11}{x}, -\dfrac{11}{2}$
23. $y = \dfrac{144}{x}, 72$
26. $y = \dfrac{-28}{x} - 14$
28. $y = \dfrac{-36}{x}, -18$
29. $y = \dfrac{-200}{x}, -100$

Given that y varies inversely with x, use the specified values to write an inverse variation equation that relates x and y. Then find the value of y when $x = 2$.

19. $x = 7, y = 2$ $y = \dfrac{14}{x}; 7$
20. $x = 3, y = 9$ $y = \dfrac{27}{x}; \dfrac{27}{2}$
21. $x = -3, y = 1$ $y = \dfrac{-3}{x}, -\dfrac{3}{2}$

22. $x = 11, y = -1$
23. $x = -12, y = -12$
24. $x = -18, y = -4$ $y = \dfrac{72}{x}; 36$

25. $x = 10, y = 5$ $y = \dfrac{50}{x}; 25$
26. $x = 7, y = -4$
27. $x = 6, y = 6$ $y = \dfrac{36}{x}; 18$

28. $x = -3, y = 12$
29. $x = -5, y = 40$
30. $x = -5, y = -11$ $y = \dfrac{55}{x}, \dfrac{55}{2}$

Tell whether the table represents inverse variation. If so, write the inverse variation equation.

31.

x	2	4	6	8	10
y	11	21	31	41	51

no

32.

x	−5	−4	1	2	10
y	−4	−5	20	10	2

yes; $y = \dfrac{20}{x}$

33.

x	10	23	25	28	50
y	160	368	400	448	800

no

34.

x	−10	−9	−6	−5	−4
y	−1.8	−2	−3	3.6	4.5

yes; $y = \dfrac{18}{x}$

35. **Catalog Orders** A clothing company allows customers to place orders on the Internet or by phone. The orders must be entered into the computer inventory system. The number of orders n entered into the system varies inversely with the number p of people working. The company estimates that 10 people working during a shift can get 960 orders entered.

   a. Write an inverse variation equation that relates n and p. $n = \dfrac{9600}{p}$

   b. Find the number of orders entered during a shift if 20 people are working. 480 orders

   c. Find the number of orders entered during a shift if 8 people are working. 1200 orders

36. **Volume and Pressure** The volume V of a gas at a constant temperature varies inversely with the pressure P. When the volume is 125 cubic inches, the pressure is 20 pounds per cubic inch.

   a. Write the inverse variation equation that relates P and V. $V = \dfrac{2500}{P}$

   b. Find the pressure of a gas with a volume of 250 cubic inches. 10 pounds per in.^{3}

37. **Running** Every other day, weather permitting, you run 5 miles. Write and graph an equation that relates your average running speed s (in miles per hour) and the time t (in hours) that it takes for you to complete the run. Is the equation an inverse variation equation? *Explain.* yes; Answers will vary.

Algebra 1
Chapter 12 Resource Book
9

LESSON 12.2 Practice B
For use with pages 775–782

1. domain: all reals except 3; range: all reals except 1
2. domain: all reals except 4; range: all reals except 3
3. domain: all reals except −6; range: all reals except −4
4. domain: all reals except −6; range: all reals except −8

Identify the domain and range of the function from its graph.

1.
2.
3.

4.
5.
6.

Graph the function and identify its domain and range. Then compare the graph with the graph of $y = \dfrac{1}{x}$.

5. domain: all reals except −3; range: all reals except 3
6. domain: all reals except 3; range: all reals except −2

7. $y = \dfrac{8}{x}$
8. $y = \dfrac{1}{6x}$
9. $y = \dfrac{-3}{2x}$

10. $y = \dfrac{1}{x} - 7$
11. $y = \dfrac{1}{x} + 10$
12. $y = \dfrac{1}{x - 4}$

7. domain: all reals except 0; range: all reals except 0; vertical stretch
8. domain: all reals except 0; range: all reals except 0; vertical shrink
9. domain: all reals except 0; range: all reals except 0; vertical stretch and reflection in x-axis
10. domain: all reals except 0; range: all reals except −7; vertical translation 7 units down
11. domain: all reals except 0; range: all reals except 10; vertical translation 10 units up
12. domain: all reals except 4; range: all reals except 0; horizontal translation 4 units right

Algebra 1
Chapter 12 Resource Book **21**

LESSON 12.2 Practice B *continued*
For use with pages 775–782

13. $x = 6, y = 4$
14. $x = -5, y = -6$
15. $x = 3, y = -8$
16. $x = -7, y = 7$
17. $x = 8, y = 12$
18. $x = -5, y = 10$

Determine the asymptotes of the graph of the function.

13. $y = \dfrac{10}{x - 6} + 4$
14. $y = \dfrac{-8}{x + 5} - 6$
15. $y = \dfrac{14}{x - 3} - 8$

16. $y = \dfrac{12}{x + 7} + 7$
17. $y = \dfrac{-4}{x - 8} + 12$
18. $y = \dfrac{9}{x + 5} + 10$

19. $y = \dfrac{14}{x - 14} + 1$ $x = 14, y = 1$
20. $y = \dfrac{-12}{x + 12} - 3$ $x = -12, y = -3$
21. $y = \dfrac{7}{x - 5} - 14$ $x = 5, y = -14$

Graph the function.

22. $y = \dfrac{2}{x} + 5$
23. $y = \dfrac{1}{x - 4} + 2$
24. $y = \dfrac{-3}{x + 6} - 1$

25. **Baseball Hall of Fame** Your baseball team is planning a bus trip to the National Baseball Hall of Fame. The cost for renting a bus is $515, and the cost will be divided equally among the people who are going on the trip. One admission costs $14.50.

   a. Write an equation that gives the cost C (in dollars per person) of the trip as a function of the number p of people going on the trip. $C = \dfrac{515}{p} + 14.5$

   b. Graph the equation.

   c. What would the cost per person be if 20 people go on the trip? $40.25

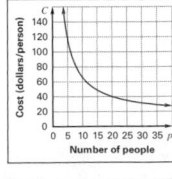

26. **Fundraiser** A pizza shop makes pizzas that organizations sell for fundraisers. One organization has placed an order for 450 pizzas. Currently, 4 people are scheduled to put together the pizzas. The owner of the shop hopes to call in some extra workers to complete all of the pizzas.

   a. Write an equation that gives the average number n of pizzas made per person as a function of the number p of extra workers that can come in and help complete the work. $n = \dfrac{450}{4 + p}$

   b. Graph the equation.

   c. If 2 people come in to help out, what is the average number of pizzas made person? 75 pizzas

Algebra 1
22 Chapter 12 Resource Book

Divide.

1. $(18x^3 - 24x^2 + 12x) \div 6x$ $3x^2 - 4x + 2$
2. $(-5x^3 + 15x^2 - 30x) \div (-5x)$ $x^2 - 3x + 6$
3. $(22x^4 - 18x^2 + 6x) \div (-2x)$ $-11x^3 + 9x - 3$
4. $(x^2 + 6x + 5) \div (x + 5)$ $x + 1$
5. $(5x^2 + 7x - 6) \div (x + 2)$ $5x - 3$
6. $(4x^2 + x - 5) \div (x - 1)$ $4x + 5$
7. $(6x^2 + 22x - 8) \div (x + 4)$ $6x - 2$
8. $(4x^2 + x - 8) \div (x - 2)$ $4x + 9 + \dfrac{10}{x - 2}$
9. $(9x^2 + 5x - 6) \div (x + 1)$ $9x - 4 - \dfrac{2}{x + 1}$
10. $(3x^2 - 7x + 14) \div (3x + 2)$ $x - 3 + \dfrac{20}{3x + 2}$

Graph the function.

11. $y = \dfrac{x + 8}{x}$

12. $y = \dfrac{3x - 5}{x}$

13. $y = \dfrac{x + 5}{x - 2}$

14. **Scootcar Rental** A resort area offers rentals of scootcars (a cross between a scooter and a small car) for $40 per hour plus a $4.50 gasoline fill-up fee.
   a. Write an equation that gives the average cost C per hour as a function of the number h of hours the scootcar is rented.
   b. Graph the equation. $C = \dfrac{40h + 4.5}{h}$

15. **Juice Bar** Between 1995 and 2004, the number D of drinks (in thousands) sold at a juice bar can be modeled by $D = 4t + 18$ where t is the number of years since 1995. The number F of drinks (in thousands) made from fruit juice rather than vegetable juice can be modeled by $F = 2t + 32$.
   a. Use long division to find a model for the ratio R of the number of fruit drinks sold to the total number of drinks sold. $R = \dfrac{1}{2} + \dfrac{23}{2(2t + 9)}$
   b. Graph the model.

Find the excluded values, if any, of the expression.

1. $\dfrac{14}{3x}$ $x = 0$
2. $\dfrac{-8}{x - 5}$ $x = 5$
3. $\dfrac{5x}{x + 10}$ $x = -10$
4. $\dfrac{-x}{4x - 8}$ $x = 2$
5. $\dfrac{3x}{7x + 21}$ $x = -3$
6. $\dfrac{x + 1}{3x + 7}$ $x = -\dfrac{7}{3}$
7. $\dfrac{x + 6}{x^2 - 2x + 1}$ $x = 1$
8. $\dfrac{8}{x^2 + 4x - 12}$ $x = -6, 2$
9. $\dfrac{7x}{x^2 - 25}$ $x = -5, 5$

Simplify the rational expression, if possible. Find the excluded values.

10. $\dfrac{-36x^2}{18x}$ $-2x; x = 0$
11. $\dfrac{6x - 24}{x - 4}$ $6; x = 4$
12. $\dfrac{4x - 12}{3 - x}$ $-4; x = 3$
13. $\dfrac{x + 11}{x^2 - 121}$ $\dfrac{1}{x - 11}; x = -11, 11$
14. $\dfrac{x + 3}{x^2 + 10x + 21}$ $\dfrac{1}{x + 7}; x = -3, -7$
15. $\dfrac{x - 4}{x^2 + 11x + 24}$ in simplest form; $x = -3, -8$

Write and simplify a rational expression for the ratio of the perimeter to the area of the given figure.

16. Square $\dfrac{1}{2x}$

17. Rectangle $\dfrac{3x + 5}{x(x + 5)}$
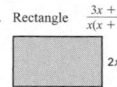

18. Triangle $\dfrac{3x + 2}{x(x + 1)}$

19. **Zoo Exhibit** The directors of a zoo have drawn up preliminary plans for a rectangular exhibit. They have decided on dimensions that are related as shown.
   a. Write a rational expression for the ratio of the perimeter to the area of the exhibit.
   b. Simplify your expression from part (a). $\dfrac{8x + 1}{(4x + 3)(2x - 1)}$
   19. a. $\dfrac{2(4x + 3) + 2(4x - 2)}{(4x + 3)(4x - 2)}$

20. **Materials Used** The material consumed M (in thousands of pounds) by a plastic injection molding machine per year between 1995 and 2004 can be modeled by
$$M = \dfrac{8t^2 + 66t + 70}{(3 - 0.2t + 0.1t^2)(t + 7)}$$
where t is the number of years since 1995. Simplify the model and approximate the number of pounds consumed in 2000.
$\dfrac{2(4t + 5)}{0.1t^2 - 0.2t + 3}$; about 11 thousand pounds

---

5. $\dfrac{1}{2(x + 5)}$ 7. $\dfrac{x(x + 3)}{3(2x - 1)}$ 9. $3(x + 5)$

Find the product.

1. $\dfrac{4x^2}{15} \cdot \dfrac{5}{8x^5}$ $\dfrac{1}{6x^3}$
2. $\dfrac{24}{7x^2} \cdot \dfrac{14x^6}{40}$ $\dfrac{6x^4}{5}$
3. $\dfrac{21}{2x + 12} \cdot \dfrac{4x + 24}{15}$ $\dfrac{14}{5}$
4. $\dfrac{5x + 10}{2x - 6} \cdot \dfrac{x - 3}{10x + 20}$ $\dfrac{1}{4}$
5. $\dfrac{x - 3}{2x + 8} \cdot \dfrac{x + 4}{x^2 + 2x - 15}$
6. $\dfrac{x^2 + 4x - 12}{x^2 + 7x + 10} \cdot \dfrac{x + 5}{2x - 4}$ $\dfrac{x + 6}{2(x + 2)}$
7. $\dfrac{6x}{4x^2 - 1} \cdot \dfrac{2x^2 + 7x + 3}{18}$
8. $\dfrac{x^4}{x^4 + 5x^3} \cdot (x + 5)$ x
9. $\dfrac{3x - 6}{x^2 - x - 2} \cdot (x^2 + 6x + 5)$

Find the quotient.

10. $\dfrac{24}{5x^3} \div \dfrac{6}{25x^2}$ $\dfrac{20}{x}$
11. $\dfrac{11x^4}{18} \div \dfrac{22}{9x^2}$ $\dfrac{x^6}{4}$
12. $\dfrac{7x + 21}{30} \div \dfrac{21x + 63}{20}$ $\dfrac{2}{9}$
13. $\dfrac{4x - 24}{3x + 15} \div \dfrac{12x - 72}{x + 5}$ $\dfrac{1}{9}$
14. $\dfrac{x + 2}{3x - 3} \div \dfrac{x^2 + 11x + 18}{x - 1}$ $\dfrac{1}{3(x + 9)}$
15. $\dfrac{x^2 + 4x}{4x} \div \dfrac{x^2 + x - 12}{x - 3}$ $\dfrac{1}{4}$
16. $\dfrac{2x + 10}{x^2 - 25} \div \dfrac{4x^2}{2x^2 - 10x}$ $\dfrac{1}{x}$
17. $\dfrac{2x - 14}{x^2 - 4x - 21} \div (x + 3)$ $\dfrac{2}{(x + 3)^2}$

18. **Wall Art** You want to create a rectangular picture from 2-inch by 3-inch tiles. You want the picture's dimensions to be related as shown.
   a. Write and simplify an expression that you can use to determine the number of 2-inch by 3-inch tiles that will be needed for the picture. $4x^2$
   b. If $x = 5$, how many tiles will you need? 100 tiles

19. **Profit** The total profit P (in millions of dollars) earned by a company from 1995 to 2004 can be modeled by
$$P = \dfrac{3500 + 500t}{98 - t}$$
where t is the number of years since 1995. The number N (in hundreds of thousands) of units sold can be modeled by
$$N = \dfrac{(t + 7)(3000 - 20t)}{490 - 5t}$$
where t is the number of years since 1995. Write a model that gives the profit earned per unit per year. Then approximate the profit per unit in 2002.
$\dfrac{125}{150 - t}$; about $8.74 per unit

LESSON 12.6 — Practice B
For use with pages 812–819

Find the sum or difference.

1. $\dfrac{8}{x+5} + \dfrac{x}{x+5}$ $\dfrac{x+8}{x+5}$

2. $\dfrac{10x}{x-4} - \dfrac{6x}{x-4}$ $\dfrac{4x}{x-4}$

3. $\dfrac{x+3}{x-9} + \dfrac{5x}{x-9}$ $\dfrac{3(2x+1)}{x-9}$

4. $\dfrac{x-5}{x+2} - \dfrac{x+6}{x+2}$ $\dfrac{-11}{x+2}$

5. $\dfrac{3x-4}{x^2-9} + \dfrac{7x-3}{x^2-9}$ $\dfrac{10x-7}{x^2-9}$

6. $\dfrac{2x+4}{3x^2} - \dfrac{x-1}{3x^2}$ $\dfrac{x+5}{3x^2}$

Find the LCD of the rational expressions.

7. $\dfrac{6}{5x^3}, \dfrac{7}{15x}$ $15x^3$

8. $\dfrac{10}{x}, \dfrac{9x}{x+7}$ $x(x+7)$

9. $\dfrac{3x+1}{x-4}, \dfrac{x-4}{x+6}$ $(x-4)(x+6)$

10. $\dfrac{x+5}{2x-4}, \dfrac{4x}{x-2}$ $2(x-2)$

11. $\dfrac{1}{x^2-5x}, \dfrac{8}{x^2-3x-10}$ $x(x-5)(x+2)$

12. $\dfrac{3}{x^2+5x+4}, \dfrac{4x}{x^2+2x+1}$ $(x+1)^2(x+4)$

Find the sum or difference.

13. $\dfrac{11}{2x} + \dfrac{4}{7x}$ $\dfrac{85}{14x}$

14. $\dfrac{8}{3x^3} - \dfrac{5}{12x}$ $\dfrac{32-5x^2}{12x^3}$

15. $\dfrac{8x}{x-5} - \dfrac{3x}{x+2}$ $\dfrac{x(5x+31)}{(x-5)(x+2)}$

10. $\dfrac{x}{6x-5} + \dfrac{1}{5x-3}$

17. $\dfrac{4}{x^2-7x} - \dfrac{3}{x}$ $\dfrac{25-3x}{x(x-7)}$

18. $\dfrac{5}{x^2} + \dfrac{x+3}{x-1}$ $\dfrac{x^3+3x^2+5x-5}{x^2(x-1)}$

19. $\dfrac{x+3}{x-1} + \dfrac{x+2}{x+1}$ $\dfrac{2x^2+5x+1}{(x-1)(x+1)}$

20. $\dfrac{2x}{x^2-3x} + \dfrac{x+4}{x-3}$ $\dfrac{x(x+6)}{x(x-3)}$

16. $\dfrac{5x^2+3x-5}{(6x-5)(5x-3)}$

21. $\dfrac{1}{x^2+5x+4} - \dfrac{1}{x^2-16}$ $\dfrac{-5}{(x+1)(x+4)(x-4)}$

22. **Paddle Boat** You paddle boat 8 miles upstream (against the current) and 8 miles downstream (with the current). The speed of the current is 1 mile per hour.

   a. Write an equation that gives the total travel time t (in hours) as a function of your average speed r (in miles per hour) in still water. $t = \dfrac{8}{r-1} + \dfrac{8}{r+1}$

   b. Find your total travel time if your average speed in still water is 3 miles per hour.   6 h

   c. How much faster is your total travel time if you increased your average speed in still water to 3.5 miles per hour? Round your answer to the nearest tenth.   about 1 h

23. **Bike Ride** You bike 50 miles from home. On your way back home, your average speed increases by 3 miles per hour.

   a. Write an equation that gives the total biking time t (in hours) as a function of your average speed r (in miles per hour) when you are biking away from home. $t = \dfrac{50}{r} + \dfrac{50}{r+3}$

   b. Find the total biking time if you bike away from your home at an average speed of 15 miles per hour. Round your answer to the nearest tenth.   about 6.1 h

   c. How much longer is your total biking time if you bike away from your home at an average speed of 12 miles per hour?   about 1.4 h

---

LESSON 12.7 — Practice B
For use with pages 820–826

Solve the equation. Check your solution.

1. $\dfrac{x}{27} = \dfrac{3}{x}$ $-9, 9$

2. $\dfrac{3}{x} = \dfrac{2}{x+4}$ -12

3. $\dfrac{4}{x-7} = \dfrac{2}{x}$ -7

4. $\dfrac{10}{x+4} = \dfrac{7}{x+2}$ 18

5. $\dfrac{-5}{x+4} = \dfrac{x}{x+4}$ -5

6. $\dfrac{8}{x+8} = \dfrac{x}{x+2}$ $-4, 4$

7. $\dfrac{-1}{x+2} = \dfrac{x}{x+2}$ -1

8. $\dfrac{2}{3x} = \dfrac{x+3}{2x-5}$ no solution

9. $\dfrac{6x}{x+2} = \dfrac{-2}{x+2}$ $-\dfrac{1}{3}$

Find the LCD of the rational expressions in the equation.

10. $\dfrac{7x}{x-3} + 4 = \dfrac{x+1}{x-3}$ $x-3$

11. $\dfrac{3}{2x-2} + 4 = \dfrac{7x}{x-1}$ $2(x-1)$

12. $\dfrac{7}{x-2} + 1 = \dfrac{4}{x-3}$ $(x-2)(x-3)$

Solve the equation. Check your solution.

13. $\dfrac{3x}{x+4} - 3 = \dfrac{-12}{x+4}$ 0

14. $\dfrac{3}{x+2} + 5 = \dfrac{4}{x+2}$ $-\dfrac{9}{5}$

15. $\dfrac{2x}{x-1} + 2 = \dfrac{10}{x+2}$ no solution

16. $\dfrac{x-1}{x+5} + 6 = \dfrac{-2}{x+2}$ $-4, -\dfrac{17}{7}$

17. $\dfrac{4x}{x-5} + 1 = \dfrac{9}{x-1}$ no solution

18. $\dfrac{x}{x-4} - \dfrac{5x}{x-2} = \dfrac{-18}{x-2}$ $3, 6$

19. **Stain Mixing** You are staining a coffee table you just made. After testing some sample pieces of wood, you decide that you want a mix of a yellow stain and a red stain. You estimate that you want a mix that contains 75% of the yellow stain. You only have 1-pint that is made up of equal parts of the stain. How many pints of the yellow stain do you have to add to the current mixture?   1 pt

20. **Wallpaper** Working together an expert wallpaper hanger and an assistant can hang the wallpaper in a room in 3 hours. The assistant can hang the wallpaper in one and one-half times the time it takes the expert wallpaper hanger to hang the wallpaper alone. Let x represent the time (in hours) that the assistant can hang the wallpaper alone.

   a. Copy and complete the table.

Person	Fraction of room papered each hour	Time (hours)	Fraction of room papered
Assistant	$\dfrac{1}{x}$	3	$\dfrac{3}{x}$
Expert	$\dfrac{3}{2x}$	3	$\dfrac{9}{2x}$

   b. *Explain* why the sum of the expressions in the last column must be 1.   Answers will vary.

   c. Write a rational equation that you can use to find the amount of time it takes the assistant to wallpaper the room alone. Then solve the equation. $\dfrac{3}{x} + \dfrac{9}{2x} = 1$; 7.5 h

762E

12 Assessment

Tell whether the equation represents *direct variation*, *inverse variation*, **or** *neither*.

1. $y = 3x$

2. $xy = -2$

3. $2x + y = 7$

Given that y varies inversely with x, use the specified values to write an inverse equation that relates x and y. Then find the value of y when $x = 2$.

4. $x = 7, y = 5$

5. $x = 3, y = -8$

6. $x = \frac{1}{2}, y = 14$

Graph the function and identify its domain and range.

7. $y = \frac{7}{x}$

8. $y = \frac{-1}{x}$

9. $y = \frac{-2}{x + 1}$

Answers

1. direct variation

2. inverse variation

3. neither

4. $y = \frac{35}{x}; \frac{35}{2}$

5. $y = \frac{-24}{x}; -12$

6. $y = \frac{7}{x}; \frac{7}{2}$

7. See left. The domain and range are all nonzero real numbers.

8. See left. The domain and range are all nonzero real numbers.

9. See left. The domain is all real numbers except $x = -1$. The range is all real numbers except $y = 0$.

Divide.

1. $(x^2 - 8x + 15) \div (x - 5)$

2. $(x^2 + 7x - 18) \div (x - 2)$

Graph the function.

3. $y = \frac{x + 5}{x - 6}$

4. $y = \frac{3x + 4}{x + 3}$

Simplify the rational expression, if possible. Find the excluded values.

5. $\frac{x - 1}{x^2 - 1}$

6. $\frac{4x^3 - 12x^2}{8x^2}$

7. $\frac{132x^4}{55x}$

8. $\frac{x^2 - 2x - 15}{x^2 - 9}$

Answers

1. $x - 3$

2. $x + 9$

3. See left.

4. See left.

5. $\frac{1}{x + 1}$; The excluded values are -1 and 1.

6. $\frac{x - 3}{2}$; The excluded value is 0.

7. $\frac{12x^3}{5}$; The excluded value is 0.

8. $\frac{x - 5}{x - 3}$; The excluded values are -3 and 3.

Find the product or quotient.

1. $\frac{6x^3}{5} \cdot \frac{7}{18x^4}$

2. $\frac{20 - 4x}{25 - x^2} \div \frac{x}{5 + x}$

Find the sum or difference.

3. $\frac{3x + 5}{x} - \frac{x - 4}{x - 6}$

4. $\frac{x}{x^2 + 9x + 8} + \frac{7}{x + 8}$

Solve the equation. Check your solution.

5. $\frac{3x}{x + 4} = \frac{x}{x - 2}$

6. $\frac{3}{x + 1} + \frac{1}{x - 1} = 2$

7. Jeremy and Paul can plant a garden in 4 hours if they work together. If each worked alone, it would take Jeremy 6 hours longer than Paul to plant the garden. How long would it take Jeremy to plant the garden if he worked alone?

Answers

1. $\frac{7}{15x}$

2. $\frac{4}{x}$

3. $\frac{2x + 9}{x - 6}$

4. $\frac{8x + 7}{(x + 8)(x + 1)}$

5. 0 and 5

6. 0 and 2

7. 12 h

Chapter Test B

Tell whether the table represents inverse variation. If so, write the inverse variation equation.

1.

x	−10	−5	5	10	15
y	−40	−20	20	40	60

2.

x	−8	−1	12	32	64
y	−6	−48	4	1.5	0.5

In Exercises 3 and 4, use the following information.

In chemistry, Boyle's law states that at a constant temperature, the volume V of a gas varies inversely with the pressure P. For a certain gas, the pressure is 5 when the volume is 20.

3. Write the inverse variation equation that relates V and P.

4. Find the volume of the gas when the pressure is 10.

Graph the function and identify its domain and range. Then compare the graph with the graph of $y = \frac{1}{x}$.

5. $y = \frac{2}{x + 3}$

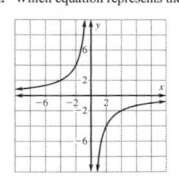

6. $y = \frac{-1}{x} + 2$

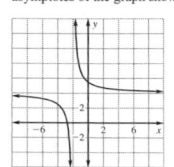

Write a function whose graph is a hyperbola that has the asymptotes and passes through the point.

7. $x = 5$, $y = 6$; $(4, 2)$

8. $x = -1$, $y = -3$; $(1, -2)$

Divide.

9. $(x^2 + 3x - 6) \div (x + 1)$

10. $(6x^2 - 3x + 5) \div (2x - 3)$

Simplify the expression, if possible. Find the excluded values.

11. $\frac{-35x^6}{25x^2}$

12. $\frac{2x - 18}{9 - x}$

13. $\frac{2x^2 - x - 15}{x^2 + x - 12}$

14. Write and simplify a rational expression for the ratio of the surface area to the volume of the rectangular solid.

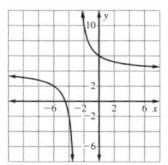

Answers

1. ___no___

2. yes; $y = \frac{48}{x}$

3. $V = \frac{100}{P}$

4. ___10___

5. See left. domain: all real numbers except −3; range: all real numbers except 0; The graph is a vertical stretch and horizontal shift (of 3 units to the left) of the graph of $y = \frac{1}{x}$.

6. See left. domain: all real numbers except 0; range: all real numbers except 2; The graph is a reflection in the x-axis and a vertical shift (of 2 units up) of the graph of $y = \frac{1}{x}$.

7. $y = \frac{4}{x - 5} + 6$

8. $y = \frac{2}{x + 1} - 3$

9. $x + 2 + \frac{-8}{x + 1}$

10. $3x + 3 + \frac{14}{2x - 3}$

11. $\frac{-7x^4}{5}$; 0

12. −2; 9

13. $\frac{2x + 5}{x + 4}$; −4, 5

14. $\frac{2(7x + 8)}{3x(x + 2)}$

Chapter Test B continued

15. The percent p of salt in a saltwater solution can be modeled by $p = \frac{100x + 100}{x + 10}$ where x is the number of grams of salt that are added to the solution. Write the model in the form $y = \frac{a}{x - h} + k$. Then graph the equation.

Find the product or quotient.

16. $\frac{18x^4}{25x^2} \cdot \frac{50x^5}{27x^6}$

17. $\frac{20}{x^3} \div \frac{30}{x^5}$

18. $\frac{x^2 - 9}{x + 3} \cdot \frac{1}{6 - 2x}$

19. $\frac{x^2 - 25}{x^2 - 4x - 5} \div \frac{2x + 10}{x^2 - 1}$

In Exercises 20 and 21, use the following information.

For the period of 1990-2002, the number Y of rushing yards gained by Emmitt Smith can be modeled by $Y = \frac{860 + 1800x}{1 + 0.024x}$ where x is the number of years since 1990.

20. Rewrite the model so that it has only whole number coefficients. Then simplify the model.

21. Approximate the number of rushing yards Smith gained in 1999.

Find the sum or difference.

22. $\frac{x - 2}{x + 3} + \frac{x + 8}{x + 3}$

23. $\frac{1}{3x^2} - \frac{2}{9x}$

24. $\frac{x}{x - 1} + \frac{2x + 3}{x^2 - 1}$

Solve the equation. Check your solutions.

25. $\frac{8}{x + 3} = \frac{4}{x}$

26. $\frac{3x}{x - 4} = 5 + \frac{12}{x - 4}$

27. The body mass index expresses the relationship between a person's height and weight by the equation $B = \frac{705W}{H^2}$ where H is the height (in inches) and W is the weight (in pounds). A woman weighs 160 pounds and is 5 feet 4 inches tall. How many pounds must the woman lose to lower her BMI to 25?

Answers

15. $y = \frac{-900}{x + 10} + 100$

See left.

16. $\frac{4x}{3}$

17. $\frac{2x^2}{3}$

18. $-\frac{1}{2}$

19. $\frac{x - 1}{2}$

20. $Y = \frac{860,000 + 1,800,000x}{1000 + 24x}$

$Y = \frac{107,500 + 225,000x}{125 + 24x}$

21. 14,030 yd

22. ___2___

23. $\frac{3 - 2x}{9x^2}$

24. $\frac{x^2 + 3x + 3}{(x - 1)(x + 1)}$

25. ___3___

26. no solution

27. about 15 pounds

Standardized Test

Multiple Choice

1. Suppose that y varies inversely with x, and $y = 8$ when $x = 9$. What is the constant of variation?   C

Ⓐ $\frac{9}{8}$ Ⓑ 8   Ⓒ 9   Ⓓ 72

2. Which equation represents the given graph?   D

Ⓐ $y = \frac{2}{x}$ Ⓑ $y = -\frac{2}{x}$

Ⓒ $y = \frac{8}{x}$ Ⓓ $y = -\frac{8}{x}$

3. What are the vertical and horizontal asymptotes of the graph shown?   B

Ⓐ $x = 4$, $y = -2$ Ⓑ $x = -2$, $y = 4$

Ⓒ $x = -4$, $y = 2$ Ⓓ $x = 2$, $y = -4$

4. What is the range of the equation $y = \frac{a}{x - 2} - 5$?   B

Ⓐ All real numbers except $y = 5$

Ⓑ All real numbers except $y = -5$

Ⓒ All real numbers except $x = 2$

Ⓓ All real numbers except $x = -2$

5. Which equation represents the given graph?   C

Ⓐ $y = \frac{6}{x + 3} - 4$ Ⓑ $y = \frac{6}{x - 3} - 4$

Ⓒ $y = \frac{6}{x + 3} + 4$ Ⓓ $y = \frac{6}{x - 3} + 4$

6. What is the remainder when you divide $5x^2 + 4x - 40$ by $x - 4$?   D

Ⓐ $\frac{15}{x - 4}$ Ⓑ $\frac{24}{x - 4}$

Ⓒ $\frac{24}{x - 4}$ Ⓓ $\frac{56}{x - 4}$

7. What is the vertical asymptote of the graph of $y = \frac{bx + c}{x} + k$?   A

Ⓐ $y = b$ Ⓑ $y = c$

Ⓒ $y = k$ Ⓓ $y = 0$

Standardized Test continued

8. The expression $\frac{a}{x^2 - 9x + 20}$ simplifies to $\frac{x + 2}{x - 4}$. What is the value of a?   C

Ⓐ $x^2 + 5x - 6$ Ⓑ $x^2 - 8x + 15$

Ⓒ $x^2 - 3x - 10$ Ⓓ $x^2 + 7x + 12$

9. What is the quotient $\frac{x^2 - 9}{-(x + 3)} \div (x - 3)$?   A

Ⓐ -1 Ⓑ 0

Ⓒ 1 Ⓓ $-(x^2 - 9)$

10. Which is a factor of the LCD of $\frac{x - 5}{x^2 + 8x + 15}$ and $\frac{x - 2}{x^2 - 4x - 21}$?   D

Ⓐ $x - 5$ Ⓑ $x - 2$

Ⓒ $x + 7$ Ⓓ $x - 7$

11. What is the solution of $\frac{4}{x - 5} = \frac{2}{x + 5} + \frac{20}{x^2 - 25}$?   B

Ⓐ -10 Ⓑ -5 Ⓒ 0 Ⓓ 5

12. If the solution to the equation $\frac{6}{x - n} = \frac{10}{x + n} - \frac{4}{x^2 - n^2}$ is 9, what is the value of n?   C

Ⓐ -2 Ⓑ 0 Ⓒ 2 Ⓓ 4

Gridded Answer

13. What value of x makes the expression $\frac{6}{x - 5} - 8$ undefined?

14. a. $t = \frac{300}{r} + 0.75$;

b. The graph shifts 5 units to the right and 0.25 unit down.

Short Response

14. Your aunt is driving 300 miles to your house. On her way, she takes a 45 minute lunch break.   See below.

a. Write and graph an equation that gives the total time t (in hours) of your aunt's trip as a function of her average driving speed r (in miles per hour).

b. Your aunt drives to your house again. This time her average speed is 5 miles per hour less than her average driving speed in part (a), and she takes a 30 minute lunch break. *Explain* how the graph would change.

Extended Response

15. A gift wrap company offers you the opportunity to sell its gift wrap packages, but you must pay the company a one-time fee of $350 plus $3 for each package that you plan to sell.

a. Write an equation that gives the average cost C per package (including the fee) as a function of the number of packages p that you plan to sell.

b. You want to sell enough gift wrap packages so that the average cost C per package (including the fee) decreases to $4. Write and solve an equation to find the number of packages you need to sell.

c. Is it possible for you to sell enough packages so that the average cost per package drops to $2.25? *Explain* your answer.   No; If you were to substitute $2.25 for C in the equation, you would get a negative answer for p. It is not possible to sell a negative number of packages.

15. a. $C = \frac{350 + 3p}{p}$ **b.** $p = \frac{350}{C - 3}$;

You would need to sell 350 packages to reduce the cost of each package to $4.

Journal 1. Explain and show how to add, subtract, multiply, and divide the rational expressions $\dfrac{5+x}{x^2+1}$ and $\dfrac{4}{x-3}$.

Multi-Step Problem

2. Your family is planning a big reunion picnic at a local park. The cost to reserve a pavilion for a day is $400. It is a potluck-style picnic, but your family has agreed to purchase all of the beverages and accessories (i.e., plates, napkins, cups) for the entire group. It has been determined that the cost for these items is $4.75 per person.

   a. Write a function C for the average cost (including pavilion) per person attending the picnic.

   b. Graph the function in part (a).

   c. If 50 people attend the picnic, what is the average cost per person?

   d. How many people need to attend to get the average cost per person below $6?

   e. What is the domain of this function? What is the range?

   f. Describe the values for the average cost per person as the number of people increases.

   g. Will the average cost per person ever go below $4.75? Explain.

1. Complete answers should include: work showing each operation being carried out; explanations of the steps being used to carry out each operation.

2. a. $C = \dfrac{400 + 4.75x}{x}$

   b.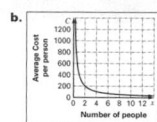

   c. $12.75 d. over 320 people e. $x > 0$; $C > 4.75$ f. The average cost per person decreases toward 4.75 as the number of people increases. The decreases are rapid at first, but become more gradual. g. No, the average cost per person cannot go below $4.75. This value is a horizontal asymptote for the function. Because the extra items cost $4.75 per person and a portion of the pavilion cost will be added to this amount, the average cost per person will never drop below this amount.

Journal Solution

1. Complete answers should include:
   • work showing each operation being carried out.
   • explanations of the steps being used to carry out each operation.

Multi-Step Problem Solution

2. a. $C = \dfrac{400 + 4.75x}{x}$

   b.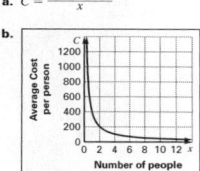

   c. $12.75

   d. over 320 people

   e. $x > 0$; $C > 4.75$

   f. The average cost per person decreases toward 4.75 as the number of people increases. The decreases are rapid at first, but become more gradual.

   g. No, the average cost per person cannot go below $4.75. This value is a horizontal asymptote for the function. Because the extra items cost $4.75 per person and a portion of the pavilion cost will be added to this amount, the average cost per person will never drop below this amount.

Multi-Step Problem Rubric

4 The student answers all parts of the problem correctly and completely. The student shows all work. The student's work is neat.

3 The student answers all parts of the problem. The student's work may contain one or two errors in the calculations, graph, or equation. The student shows most work. The student's work is neat.

2 The student answers all parts of the problem, but there are more than two errors in the calculations, graph, or equation. The student shows some work. The student's work is sloppy.

1 The student does not complete all parts of the problem. The student's work has several errors in the calculations, graph, and equation. The student's work is sloppy, or no work is shown.

Main Ideas

In Chapter 12, students model inverse variation by writing and graphing inverse equations. Students graph rational equations and compare them to the parent function. They divide polynomials and then use this skill to graph rational functions. Students simplify rational expressions, stating any excluded values. They multiply, divide, add, and subtract rational expressions and then use these operations to solve rational equations.

Prerequisite Skills

• Performing operations on numerical fractions
• Solving equations
• Factoring polynomials

Additional resources for reviewing prerequisite skills are:

• Skills Review Handbook, pp. 909–937
• @HomeTutor

12 Rational Equations and Functions

12.1 Model Inverse Variation

12.2 Graph Rational Functions

12.3 Divide Polynomials

12.4 Simplify Rational Expressions

12.5 Multiply and Divide Rational Expressions

12.6 Add and Subtract Rational Expressions

12.7 Solve Rational Equations

Before

In previous chapters and courses, you learned the following skills, which you'll use in Chapter 12: performing operations on numerical fractions, solving equations, and factoring polynomials.

Prerequisite Skills

VOCABULARY CHECK

1. What is the **least common denominator** of $\frac{3}{8}$ and $\frac{7}{10}$? **40**

2. Which equation is a **direct variation** equation, $\frac{y}{5} = x$ or $\frac{5}{y} = x$? $\frac{y}{5} = x$

3. What is the **degree** of the polynomial $4x - 2 + 5x^2$? **2**

4. Identify the **extraneous solution** when solving $\sqrt{x + 2} = x$. **−1**

SKILLS CHECK

Factor the polynomial. *(Review pp. 583, 600, 606 for 12.4–12.6.)*

5. $x^2 - 2x - 15$ 6. $2x^2 - 8x + 6$ 7. $9x^2 - 25$ 8. $3x^3 - 48x$
$(x - 5)(x + 3)$ $2(x - 3)(x - 1)$ $(3x^2 + 5)(3x^2 - 5)$ $3x(x + 4)(x - 4)$

Add, subtract, multiply, or divide. *(Review pp. 914, 915 for 12.5–12.6.)*

9. $\frac{1}{3} + \frac{3}{4}$ $1\frac{1}{12}$ 10. $\frac{7}{8} - \frac{2}{5}$ $\frac{19}{40}$ 11. $\frac{5}{9} \times \frac{3}{5}$ $\frac{1}{3}$ 12. $\frac{3}{10} \div \frac{6}{25}$ $1\frac{1}{4}$

Solve the equation or proportion. *(Review pp. 134, 162, 583, 729 for 12.7.)*

13. $4x = 9$ $\frac{9}{4}$ 14. $\frac{x}{10} = \frac{3}{5}$ **6**   15. $x^2 + x = 6$ 16. $\sqrt{x - 9} = 2$ **13**
                                                    −3, 2

@HomeTutor Prerequisite skills practice at classzone.com

Chapter 12 Resource Book

• Teaching Guide/Lesson Plan (pp. 3, 17, 30, 42, 54, 66, 77)
• Project with Rubric (p. 88)

Assessment and Intervention

• Assessment Book (pp. 168–182)
• Benchmark Tests
• Reteaching and Remediation Book

Interactive Technology

• Easy Planner
• Power Presentations CD-ROM
• Activity Generator CD-ROM
• Animated Algebra
• Test Generator CD-ROM
• Online Quizzes
• eWorkbook
• eEdition
• @HomeTutor

Resources for English Learners

• Quick Reference for English Learners
• Spanish Study Guide
• Multi-Language Visual Glossary
• Student Resources in Spanish

In Chapter 12, you will apply the big ideas listed below and reviewed in the Chapter Summary on page 830. You will also use the key vocabulary listed below.

Big Ideas

① Graphing rational functions

② Performing operations on rational expressions

③ Solving rational equations

KEY VOCABULARY

- inverse variation, *p. 765*
- constant of variation, *p. 765*
- hyperbola, *p. 767*
- branches, asymptotes of a hyperbola, *p. 767*

- rational function, *p. 775*
- rational expression, *p. 794*
- excluded value, *p. 794*
- simplest form of a rational expression, *p. 795*

- least common denominator (LCD) of rational expressions, *p. 813*
- rational equation, *p. 820*

You can use rational functions to solve problems in biology. For example, you can graph a rational function to describe how a microorganism's efficiency at performing metabolic tasks changes as its dimensions change.

Animated Algebra

The animation illustrated below for Exercise 49 on page 791 helps you answer this question: How does changing one dimension of a cylindrical microorganism change the ratio of the cylinder's surface area to its volume?

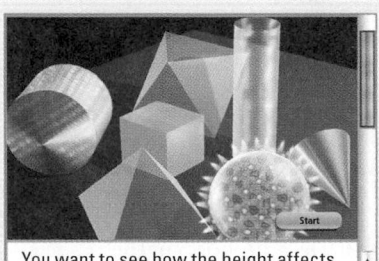

You want to see how the height affects the ratio of surface area to volume.

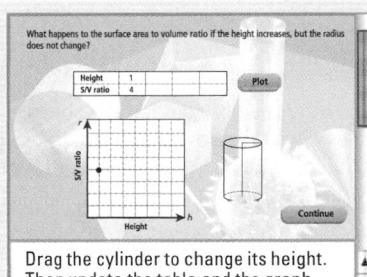

Drag the cylinder to change its height. Then update the table and the graph.

Animated Algebra at classzone.com

Other animations for Chapter 12: pages 766, 777, 783, 804, 814, and 830

Algebra 1 Toolkit

- Reading Strategies for Chapter 12, pp. 31–32
- Differentiated Instruction Notes, pp. 85–88
- English Learners Notes, pp. 119–120
- Inclusion Notes, pp. 151–152
- Teaching Strategies with Sample Worksheets, pp. 155–178
- Using Technology in the Classroom, pp. 179–184
- Tips for New Teachers, pp. 207–208
- Math Background Notes, pp. 233–234
- Pre-AP Strategies and Copymasters, pp. 300–301, 482–511
- Teacher Survival Activities, pp. 577–578, 603–604
- Bulletin Board Idea, p. 618
- Teacher Tool Transparencies, following p. 620

12.1 Relationships Between Dimensions of a Rectangle

MATERIALS · 12 square tiles

QUESTION Given a rectangle with a fixed area, how is one dimension related to the other?

EXPLORE Graph the relationship between the dimensions of a rectangle

STEP 1 *Form rectangle*

Draw the x- and y-axes on a sheet of paper as shown. Use all of the tiles to form a rectangle in Quadrant I with the lower left vertex on the origin. Then label the upper right vertex with the coordinates (x, y) where x is the horizontal length of the rectangle and y is the vertical length.

STEP 2 *Draw curve*

Repeat Step 1 for all possible rectangles that can be formed with the tiles. Then connect the points by drawing a smooth curve through them.

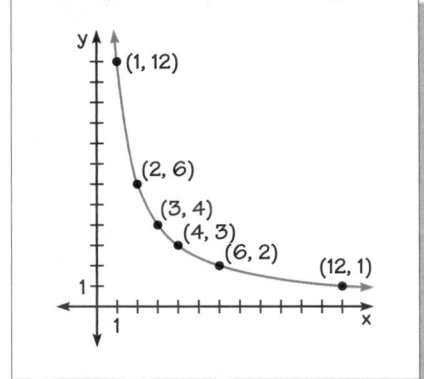

DRAW CONCLUSIONS Use your observations to complete these exercises

1. *Describe* how the vertical length changes as the horizontal length increases. *Describe* how the vertical length changes as the horizontal length decreases. **The vertical length decreases; the vertical length increases.**

2. Does the graph cross the axes? *Explain* your reasoning. **No; for the graph to cross an axis, one coordinate would have to be zero, but neither x nor y can be zero if their product is 12.**

3. Write an equation that gives the vertical length y as a function of the horizontal length x. $y = \frac{12}{x}$

4. Let A represent the area of a rectangle. For A = 40, write an equation that gives y as a function of x. Then graph the equation. $y = \frac{40}{x}$; see margin for art.

5. *Compare* the graph of the equation that you wrote in Exercise 4 with the graph of the equation that you wrote in Exercise 3. **See margin.**

4.

5. **The two graphs have the same general shape: a wide curve in the first quadrant; the curve approaches both axes, but does not cross them.**

12.1 Model Inverse Variation

Before You wrote and graphed direct variation equations.

Now You will write and graph inverse variation equations.

Why? So you can find a person's work time, as in Example 6.

Key Vocabulary
• inverse variation
• constant of variation
• hyperbola
• branches of a hyperbola
• asymptotes of a hyperbola

Recall that two variables x and y show direct variation if $y = ax$ and $a \neq 0$. The variables x and y show **inverse variation** if $y = \frac{a}{x}$ and $a \neq 0$. The nonzero number a is the **constant of variation**, and y is said to *vary inversely* with x.

EXAMPLE 1 Identify direct and inverse variation

Tell whether the equation represents *direct variation*, *inverse variation*, or *neither*.

a. $xy = 4$ **b.** $\dfrac{y}{2} = x$ **c.** $y = 2x + 3$

Solution

a. $xy = 4$ **Write original equation.**

    $y = \dfrac{4}{x}$ **Divide each side by *x*.**

Because $xy = 4$ can be written in the form $y = \frac{a}{x}$, $xy = 4$ represents inverse variation. The constant of variation is 4.

b. $\dfrac{y}{2} = x$ **Write original equation.**

    $y = 2x$ **Multiply each side by 2.**

Because $\frac{y}{2} = x$ can be written in the form $y = ax$, $\frac{y}{2} = x$ represents direct variation.

c. Because $y = 2x + 3$ cannot be written in the form $y = \frac{a}{x}$ or $y = ax$, $y = 2x + 3$ does not represent either direct variation or inverse variation.

✓ **GUIDED PRACTICE**   for Example 1

Tell whether the equation represents *direct variation*, *inverse variation*, or *neither*.

1. $y = \dfrac{2}{x}$ **2.** $4y = 3x$ **3.** $5x - y = 3$ **4.** $xy = \dfrac{1}{2}$

   inverse variation   direct variation   neither   inverse variation

---

Motivating the Lesson

You are part of a crew that is cleaning up after a football game. By knowing how to write and solve an inverse variation equation, you can determine how long it will take to clean the grounds depending on whether there are 2, 3, 4 or more students in the cleaning crew.

❸ TEACH

Extra Example 1

Tell whether the equation represents *direct variation*, *inverse variation*, or *neither*.

a. $xy = 7$ **inverse variation**

b. $\frac{x}{y} = 2$ **direct variation**

c. $3x - y = 5$ **neither**

Extra Example 2

Graph $y = \frac{2}{x}$.

Key Question to Ask for Example 2

• How is the graph of an inverse variation equation different from the graph of a direct variation equation? **The graph of an inverse variation equation is a two-part curve and it does not cross the x- or y-axis. The graph of a direct variation equation is a line and it passes through the origin.**

EXAMPLE 2 Graph an inverse variation equation

Graph $y = \frac{4}{x}$.

Solution

STEP 1 **Make** a table by choosing several integer values of x and finding the values of y. Then plot the points. To see how the function behaves for values of x very close to 0 and very far from 0, make a second table for such values and plot the points.

AVOID ERRORS
Note that y is undefined when $x = 0$. There is no point $(0, y)$ on the graph of $y = \frac{4}{x}$.

x	y
−4	−1
−2	−2
−1	−4
0	undefined
1	4
2	2
4	1

x	y
−10	−0.4
−5	−0.8
−0.5	−8
−0.4	−10
0.4	10
0.5	8
5	0.8
10	0.4

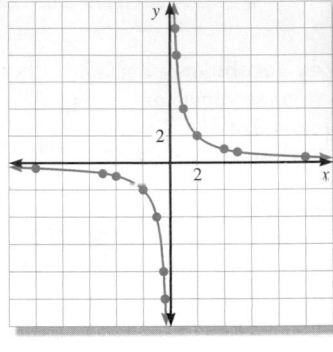

STEP 2 **Connect** the points in Quadrant I by drawing a smooth curve through them. Repeat for the points in Quadrant III.

GRAPHS OF INVERSE VARIATION As shown in Example 2, as you move away from the origin along the x-axis, the graph of an inverse variation equation approaches the x-axis without crossing it. As you move away from the origin along the y-axis, the graph approaches the y-axis without crossing it.

EXAMPLE 3 Graph an inverse variation equation

Graph $y = \frac{-4}{x}$.

Solution

COMPARE GRAPHS
The graph of an inverse variation equation lies in Quadrants I and III if $a > 0$, and the graph lies in Quadrants II and IV if $a < 0$.

Notice that $y = \frac{-4}{x} = -1 \cdot \frac{4}{x}$. So, for every nonzero value of x, the value of y in $y = \frac{-4}{x}$ is the opposite of the value of y in $y = \frac{4}{x}$. You can graph $y = \frac{-4}{x}$ by reflecting the graph of $y = \frac{4}{x}$ (see Example 2) in the x-axis.

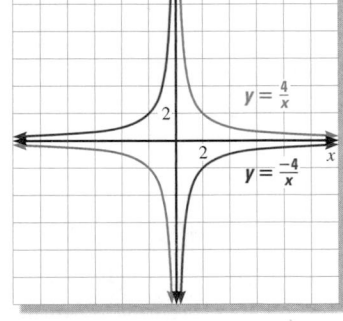

Animated Algebra at classzone.com

For Your Notebook

Graphs of Direct Variation and Inverse Variation Equations

Direct variation		Inverse variation	
$y = ax, a > 0$	$y = ax, a < 0$	$y = \dfrac{a}{x}, a > 0$	$y = \dfrac{a}{x}, a < 0$

HYPERBOLAS The graph of the inverse variation equation $y = \dfrac{a}{x}$ ($a \neq 0$) is a **hyperbola**. The two symmetrical parts of a hyperbola are called the **branches of the hyperbola**. The lines that the hyperbola approaches but doesn't intersect are called the **asymptotes of the hyperbola**. The asymptotes of the graph of $y = \dfrac{a}{x}$ are the x-axis and the y-axis.

EXAMPLE 4 Use an inverse variation equation

The variables x and y vary inversely, and $y = 6$ when $x = -3$.

a. Write an inverse variation equation that relates x and y.

b. Find the value of y when $x = 4$.

Solution

a. Because y varies inversely with x, the equation has the form $y = \dfrac{a}{x}$.

Use the fact that $x = -3$ and $y = 6$ to find the value of a.

$y = \dfrac{a}{x}$	**Write inverse variation equation.**
$6 = \dfrac{a}{-3}$	**Substitute −3 for x and 6 for y.**
$-18 = a$	**Multiply each side by −3.**

An equation that relates x and y is $y = \dfrac{-18}{x}$.

b. When $x = 4$, $y = \dfrac{-18}{4} = -\dfrac{9}{2}$.

✓ **GUIDED PRACTICE** for Examples 2, 3, and 4

5. Graph **(a)** $y = \dfrac{3}{x}$ and **(b)** $y = \dfrac{-3}{x}$. **See margin.**

6. The variables x and y vary inversely, and $y = -2$ when $x = 12$. Write an inverse variation equation that relates x and y. Then find the value of y when $x = -3$. $y = \dfrac{-24}{x}$; 8

12.1 Model Inverse Variation **767**

Differentiated Instruction

Inclusion Some students may confuse direct and inverse variation. For problems similar to **Example 4**, give additional practice by having students find the direct variation equation under the same conditions. Then have students graph both the inverse variation and direct variation equations on the same graph.

See also the *Algebra 1 Toolkit* for more strategies.

5a.

5b.

PRODUCTS By multiplying both sides of $y = \dfrac{a}{x}$ by x, you can write the equation as $xy = a$. This means that a set of ordered pairs (x, y) shows inverse variation if all the products xy are constant.

EXAMPLE 5 Write an inverse variation equation

Tell whether the table represents inverse variation. If so, write the inverse variation equation.

x	−5	−3	4	8	24
y	2.4	4	−3	−1.5	−0.5

Solution

Find the products xy for all pairs (x, y):

$-5(2.4) = -12 \quad -3(4) = -12 \quad 4(-3) = -12 \quad 8(-1.5) = -12 \quad 24(-0.5) = -12$

The products are equal to the same number, −12. So, y varies inversely with x.

▶ The inverse variation equation is $xy = -12$, or $y = \dfrac{-12}{x}$.

EXAMPLE 6 Solve a multi-step problem

THEATER A theater company plans to hire people to build a stage set. The work time t (in hours per person) varies inversely with the number p of people hired. The company estimates that 25 people working for 300 hours each can complete the job. Find the work time per person if the company hires 30 people.

Solution

STEP 1 Write the inverse variation equation that relates p and t.

$$t = \frac{a}{p} \qquad \text{Write inverse variation equation.}$$

$$300 = \frac{a}{25} \qquad \text{Substitute 25 for } p \text{ and 300 for } t.$$

$$7500 = a \qquad \text{Multiply each side by 25.}$$

The inverse variation equation is $t = \dfrac{7500}{p}$.

STEP 2 Find t when $p = 30$: $t = \dfrac{7500}{p} = \dfrac{7500}{30} = 250$.

▶ If 30 people are hired, the work time per person is 250 hours.

✓ GUIDED PRACTICE for Examples 5 and 6

7. Tell whether the ordered pairs $(-5, 2)$, $(-4, 2.5)$, $(8, -1.25)$, and $(20, -0.5)$ represent inverse variation. If so, write the inverse variation equation. **inverse variation; $y = \dfrac{-10}{x}$**

8. **WHAT IF?** In Example 6, suppose the theater company estimates that 20 people working for 270 hours each can complete the job. Find the work time per person if the company hires 30 people. **180 hours per person**

15–26. See Additional Answers beginning on p. AA1.

28. $y = \dfrac{10}{x}$; 5

29. $y = \dfrac{21}{x}$; 10.5

30. $y = \dfrac{-20}{x}$; −10

12.1 EXERCISES

HOMEWORK KEY

○ = WORKED-OUT SOLUTIONS
on p. WS1 for Exs. 17, 33, and 57

★ = STANDARDIZED TEST PRACTICE
Exs. 2, 43, 59, and 60

◆ = MULTIPLE REPRESENTATIONS
Ex. 58

SKILL PRACTICE

[A] **1. VOCABULARY** Identify the constant of variation in the equation $y = \frac{-3}{x}$. **−3**

2. ★ WRITING *Describe* the difference between a direct variation equation and an inverse variation equation. **In direct variation, *y* is the product of *x* and the constant of variation; in indirect variation, *y* is the quotient of the constant of variation and *x*.**

EXAMPLE 1
on p. 765
for Exs. 3–14,
43

DESCRIBING EQUATIONS Tell whether the equation represents *direct variation*, *inverse variation*, or *neither*.

3. $y = -2x$
direct variation

4. $xy = 1$
inverse variation

5. $y = x + 5$
neither

6. $x = \frac{-1}{y}$
inverse variation

7. $xy = 5$
inverse variation

8. $\frac{y}{x} = 4$
direct variation

9. $x = 7y$
direct variation

10. $2x + y = 6$
neither

11. $2x = \frac{8}{y}$
inverse variation

12. $x = -7$
neither

13. $3x - 3y = 0$
direct variation

14. $3xy = 20$
inverse variation

EXAMPLES 2 and 3
on p. 766
for Exs. 15–26

GRAPHING EQUATIONS Graph the inverse variation equation. **15–26. See margin.**

15. $y = \frac{2}{x}$

16. $y = \frac{-1}{x}$

17. $y = \frac{-7}{x}$

18. $y = \frac{10}{x}$

19. $y = \frac{-5}{x}$

20. $y = \frac{18}{x}$

21. $y = \frac{9}{x}$

22. $y = \frac{-2}{x}$

23. $y = \frac{15}{x}$

24. $y = \frac{6}{x}$

25. $y = \frac{-12}{x}$

26. $y = \frac{-8}{x}$

EXAMPLE 4
on p. 767
for Exs. 27–42

27. An inverse variation equation has the form $y = \frac{a}{x}$, not $y = ax$; $8 = \frac{a}{2}$, $16 = a$, so $y = \frac{16}{x}$.

27. ERROR ANALYSIS The variables x and y vary inversely, and $y = 8$ when $x = 2$. *Describe* and correct the error in writing an inverse variation equation that relates x and y.

$y = ax$
$8 = a(2)$
$4 = a$
So, $y = 4x$.

USE INVERSE VARIATION Given that y varies inversely with x, use the specified values to write an inverse variation equation that relates x and y. Then find the value of y when $x = 2$. **28–42. See margin.**

28. $x = 5, y = 2$

29. $x = 3, y = 7$

30. $x = -5, y = 4$

31. $x = 13, y = -1$

32. $x = -15, y = -15$

33. $x = -22, y = -6$

34. $x = 8, y = 3$

35. $x = 9, y = -2$

36. $x = 3, y = 3$

37. $x = -2, y = -10$

38. $x = -3, y = 40$

39. $x = -7, y = -10$

40. $x = -17, y = 8$

41. $x = 6, y = 11$

42. $x = -12, y = -13$

43. ★ MULTIPLE CHOICE The variables x and y vary inversely, and $y = 6$ when $x = 4$. What is the constant of variation? **D**

Ⓐ 1.5   Ⓑ 4   Ⓒ 6   Ⓓ 24

12.1 Model Inverse Variation   **769**

31. $y = \frac{-13}{x}$; −6.5

32. $y = \frac{225}{x}$; 112.5

33. $y = \frac{132}{x}$; 66

34. $y = \frac{27}{x}$; 12

35. $y = \frac{-18}{x}$; −9

36. $y = \frac{9}{x}$; 4.5

37. $y = \frac{20}{x}$; 10

38. $y = \frac{-120}{x}$; −60

39. $y = \frac{70}{x}$; 35

40. $y = \frac{-136}{x}$; −68

41. $y = \frac{66}{x}$; 33

42. $y = \frac{156}{x}$; 78

4 PRACTICE AND APPLY

Assignment Guide
📖 Answer Transparencies available for all exercises

Basic:
Day 1: pp. 769–772
Exs. 1–26
Day 2: pp. 769–772
Exs. 27–43 odd, 44–49, 54–59, 62–74 even

Average:
Day 1: pp. 769–772
Exs. 1, 2, 6–26, 49–51
Day 2: pp. 769–772
Exs. 27, 35–48, 54–60, 63–73 odd

Advanced:
Day 1: pp. 769–772
Exs. 1, 2, 7–26, 49–51
Day 2: pp. 769–772
Exs. 37–48, 52–61*, 62–74 even

Block:
pp. 769–772
Exs. 1, 2, 6–27, 35–51, 54–60, 63–73 odd

Differentiated Instruction
See *Algebra 1 Best Practices Toolkit* for suggestions on addressing the needs of a diverse classroom.

Homework Check
For a quick check of student understanding of key concepts, go over the following exercises:
Basic: 8, 18, 31, 44, 55
Average: 11, 22, 38, 54, 55
Advanced: 13, 23, 40, 56, 57

Extra Practice
• Student Edition, p. 946
• Chapter 12 Resource Book:
Practice levels A, B, C, pp. 6–11

Practice Worksheet
An easily-readable reduced practice page (with answers) for this lesson can be found on p. 762C.

EXAMPLE 5
on p. 768
for Exs. 44–47

WRITING EQUATIONS Tell whether the table represents inverse variation. If so, write the inverse variation equation.

44.

x	4	8	12	16	20
y	1	2	3	4	5

not inverse variation

45.

x	−20	−5	14	32	50
y	−80	−20	56	128	200

not inverse variation

46.

x	−10	−5	15	20	40
y	−30	−60	20	15	7.5

inverse variation; $y = \dfrac{300}{x}$

47.

x	−12	−10	−8	−5	−4
y	2	2.4	3	4.8	6

inverse variation; $y = \dfrac{-24}{x}$

B **48. REASONING** The variables x and y vary inversely. How does the value of y change if the value of x is doubled? tripled? Give examples. **See margin.**

GEOMETRY Translate the verbal sentence into an equation using the appropriate geometric formula. Then tell whether the equation represents *direct variation*, *inverse variation*, or *neither*.

49. The circumference of a circle with radius r units is C units. $2\pi r = C$; direct variation

50. The perimeter of a rectangle with length ℓ units and width w units is 27 units. $2\ell + 2w = 27$; neither

51. The volume of a rectangular prism with base B square units and height h units is 400 cubic units. $Bh = 400$; inverse variation

C **52. CHALLENGE** The variables x and y vary inversely with constant of variation a. The variables y and z vary inversely with constant of variation b. Write an equation that gives z as a function of x. Then tell whether x and z vary *directly* or *inversely*. $z = \dfrac{b}{a} \cdot x$; directly

53. CHALLENGE The points $(3, a^2 - 7a + 10)$ and $(3a + 1, a + 2)$ lie on the graph of an inverse variation equation. Find the coordinates of the points. **(3, 4), (4, 3)**

PROBLEM SOLVING

EXAMPLE 5 **A**
on p. 768
for Exs. 54, 57

54. BICYCLES The table shows the bicycle speed s (in miles per hour) for various pedaling speeds p (in pedal rotations per mile). Tell whether the table represents inverse variation. If so, write the inverse variation equation that relates p and s.

54. inverse variation; $s = \dfrac{3600}{p}$

Pedaling speed, p (pedal rotations/mi)	831	612	420	305
Bicycle speed, s (mi/h)	4.33	5.88	8.57	11.8

@HomeTutor for problem solving help at classzone.com

EXAMPLE 6
on p. 768
for Exs. 55–56, 58

55. ECONOMICS The owner of an electronics store determines that the monthly demand d (in units) for a computer varies inversely with the price p (in dollars) of the computer. When the price is \$700, the monthly demand is 250 units. Write the inverse variation equation that relates p and d. Then find the monthly demand when the price is \$500. $d = \dfrac{175,000}{p}$; 350 units

@HomeTutor for problem solving help at classzone.com

○ = WORKED-OUT SOLUTIONS on p. WS1   ★ = STANDARDIZED TEST PRACTICE   ◆ = MULTIPLE REPRESENTATIONS

56. SPORTS An athlete is running a 200 meter dash. Write and graph an equation that relates the athlete's average running speed r (in meters per second) and the time t (in seconds) that the athlete will take to finish the race. Is the equation an inverse variation equation? *Explain*. **See margin.**

57. **MULTI-STEP PROBLEM** The table shows the vibration frequencies f (in hertz) for various lengths ℓ (in centimeters) of strings on a stringed instrument.

Length of string, ℓ (cm)	42.1	37.5	33.4	31.5
Frequency, f (Hz)	523	587	659	698

a. **Decide** Tell whether an inverse variation equation can be used to model the data. If so, write and graph the inverse variation equation.

b. **Calculate** Find the frequency of a string with a length of 29.4 centimeters. **about 748 Hz**

c. **Describe** *Describe* the change in the frequency as the length of the string decreases. Does your answer in part (b) support your description? **The frequency increases; yes.**

58. ◆ **MULTIPLE REPRESENTATIONS** You plan to save the same amount of money each month to pay for a summer sports camp that costs $1200.

a. **Making a Table** Let a represent the amount (in dollars) that you plan to save each month. Make a table that shows the number m of months that you need to save money for the following values of a: 75, 100, 120, 150, 200, and 240. *Describe* how the number of months changes as the amount of money that you save each month increases. **a, b. See margin.**

b. **Drawing a Graph** Use the values in the table to draw a graph of the situation. Does the graph suggest a situation that represents *direct variation* or *inverse variation*? *Explain* your choice.

c. **Writing an Equation** Write the equation that relates a and m. $m = \dfrac{1200}{a}$

B **59.** ★ **SHORT RESPONSE** As shown in the diagram, the focal length of a camera lens is the distance between the lens and the point at which light rays meet after passing through the aperture, or opening, in the lens. The f-stop s is the ratio of the focal length f (in millimeters) to the diameter a (in millimeters) of the aperture.

Object   Camera lens

a

Image

Not drawn to scale f

a. **Model** A photographer has a camera with a focal length of 35 millimeters. Write and graph an equation that relates a and s. Tell whether the equation represents inverse variation.

b. **Compare** The greater the diameter of the aperture, the more light that passes through the aperture. For the camera in part (a), does more light pass through the aperture when the f-stop is 4 or when the f-stop is 8? *Explain*.

12.1 Model Inverse Variation   **771**

57a. Yes;
$f = \dfrac{22,000}{\ell}$; see margin for art.

59a. $s = \dfrac{35}{a}$, see margin for art, inverse variation.

59b. 4; when $s = 4$, the diameter of the aperture is $a = \dfrac{35}{4} =$ 8.75 millimeters, and when $s = 8$, the diameter of the aperture is $a = \dfrac{35}{8} =$ 4.375 millimeters.

58b.

Inverse variation; the points (a, m) appear to lie on a hyperbola.

59a.

58a.

Amount of money, a (dollars)	75	100	120	150	200	240
Number of months, m	16	12	10	8	6	5

The number of months decreases.

Daily Homework Quiz

📑 Transparency Available

1. Graph $y = \dfrac{-6}{x}$.

Given that *y* varies with *x*, use the specified values to write an inverse variation equation that relates *x* and *y*. Then find the value of *y* when *x* = 3.

2. $x = -6, y = 5$ $y = -\dfrac{30}{x}; -10$

3. $x = 12, y = 7$ $y = \dfrac{84}{x}; 28$

 Online Quiz

Available at **classzone.com**

Diagnosis/Remediation

• Practice A, B, C in Chapter 12 Resource Book, pp. 6–11
• Study Guide in Chapter 12 Resource Book, pp. 12–13
• Practice Workbook, pp. 180–182
• @HomeTutor

Challenge

Additional challenge is available in the Chapter 12 Resource Book, p. 16.

60c. $0 < c < 6$; substituting $\dfrac{20}{3}$ for *r* and 40 for *s* in the formula $r = \dfrac{s}{c}$ gives a value of *c* = 6 feet for the chord of a wing of the Wright brothers' airplane. The aspect ratio $r = \dfrac{40}{c}$ gets larger when the denominator *c* gets smaller; so, $0 < c < 6$ are the values of *c* for which the plane would have glided more easily.

---

60. ★ **EXTENDED RESPONSE** The photo below shows a replica of an airplane designed by Orville and Wilbur Wright, who were aviation pioneers in the early 20th century. The aspect ratio *r* of a wing from similar airplanes is given by the formula $r = \dfrac{s^2}{A}$ where *s* is the span, or the distance (in feet) between the wing tips, and *A* is the area (in square feet) of the wing.

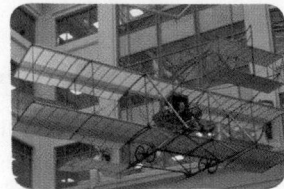

a. Model The length *c* of the chord of a wing is the distance (in feet) between the front and the back of the wing. For the rectangular wing shown, rewrite the formula for *r* in terms of *c* and *s*. $r = \dfrac{s}{c}$

b. Analyze How does the value of *r* change when *s* is constant and *c* increases? when *c* is constant and *s* increases?   *r* decreases; *r* increases.

c. Interpret The greater the aspect ratio, the easier it is for an airplane to glide. Orville and Wilbur Wright designed an airplane with two rectangular wings that each had an aspect ratio of $\dfrac{20}{3}$ and a span of 40 feet. For what values of *c* would the airplane have glided more easily? *Explain.* **See margin.**

Ⓒ **61. CHALLENGE** A fulcrum is placed under the center of a board. In order for two objects to balance on the board, the distance (in feet) of each object from the center of the board must vary inversely with its weight (in pounds). In the diagram shown, what is the distance of each animal from the center of the board? **The dog is 1.875 feet from the fulcrum and the cat is 3.125 feet from the fulcrum.**

MIXED REVIEW

62. MOVIES You buy discount movie tickets from a website. Tickets cost $3.60 each. You pay a shipping fee of $3 per order. Write an equation that gives the total cost *C* (in dollars) of the tickets as a function of the number *t* of tickets bought. Then find the total cost of 8 tickets. *(p. 283)*
$C = 3.6t + 3; \$31.80$

PREVIEW
Prepare for Lesson 12.2 in Exs. 63–68.

Graph the function. Identify its domain and range.   63–68. See margin.

63. $y = 5^x$ *(p. 520)* **64.** $y = 0.4^x$ *(p. 531)* **65.** $y = x^2 + 5$ *(p. 628)*

66. $y = x^2 + 6x - 20$ *(p. 635)* **67.** $y = -\sqrt{x}$ *(p. 710)* **68.** $y = 2\sqrt{x - 1} + 1$ *(p. 710)*

Solve the equation. Check for extraneous solutions. *(p. 729)*

69. $\sqrt{x} = 10$ **100** **70.** $\sqrt{x + 6} - 4 = 8$ **138** **71.** $\sqrt{x - 2} = -10$ **no solution**

72. $2\sqrt{x} - 5 = 23$ **196** **73.** $\sqrt{4x - 3} = \sqrt{2x + 7}$ **5** **74.** $x = \sqrt{x + 30}$ **6**

63–68. See Additional Answers beginning on p. AA1.

12.2 Graphing $y = \dfrac{a}{x - h} + k$

MATERIALS · graph paper · graphing calculator

QUESTION What characteristics does the graph of $y = \dfrac{a}{x-h} + k$ have?

EXPLORE 1 Use tables to graph a function

Graph $y = \dfrac{2}{x-3} + 4$ using a table.

STEP 1 *Use a table*

Make a table of values for $y = \dfrac{2}{x-3} + 4$ by choosing several integer values of x. Round the values of y, if necessary. Then plot the points.

x	0	1	2	3	4	5	6
y	3.3	3	2	undefined	6	5	4.7

STEP 2 *Check close to and far from 3*

To see how the function behaves for values of x closer to 3 and farther from 3, make tables for such values and plot the points.

x	2.2	2.4	2.6	2.8	3.2	3.4	3.6
y	1.5	0.7	−1	−6	14	9	7.3

x	−4	−3	−2	−1	7	8	9
y	3.71	3.66	3.6	3.5	4.5	4.4	4.3

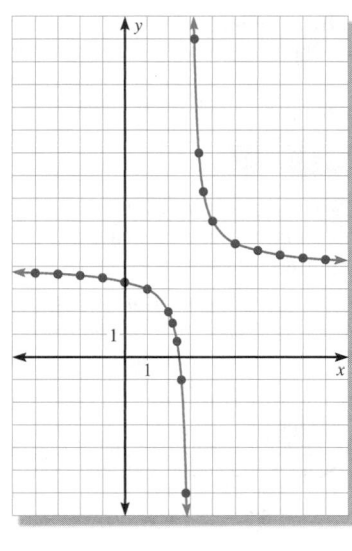

STEP 3 *Draw a graph*

Draw a smooth curve through the points (x, y) where $x > 3$. Repeat for the points (x, y) where $x < 3$.

PRACTICE

1. *Describe* how the values of y change as the values of x get close to 3. What is the equation of the vertical asymptote? **See margin.**

2. *Describe* how the values of y change as the values of x get far from 3. What is the equation of the horizontal asymptote? **As the absolute value of x becomes larger and larger, the value of y approaches 4; $y = 4$.**

Graph the function using a table.
3–5. See margin.

3. $y = \dfrac{5}{x-4} - 6$ 4. $y = \dfrac{-10}{x+3} - 1$ 5. $y = \dfrac{-11}{x+13} + 9$

PLAN AND PREPARE

① PLAN AND PREPARE

Explore the Concept
- Students will use tables and a graphing calculator to graph functions.
- This activity leads into the discussion in Lesson 12.2, Example 4, of how to transform the graph of $y = \dfrac{1}{x}$ into the graph of $y = \dfrac{a}{x-h} + k$.

Materials
Each student will need:
- graph paper
- graphing calculator

Recommended Time
Work activity: 15 min
Discuss results: 5 min

Grouping
Students should work individually.

② TEACH

Key Questions
- In Explore 1, why is the value of y undefined when $x = 3$? **The expression $x - 3$ appears in a denominator of the equation. If $x = 3$ the denominator is zero, and division by zero is undefined.**
- In Explore 2, why do you think that the vertical line connecting the two branches of the hyperbola is $x = -1.7$? **The expression $x + 1.7$ appears in a denominator, so the line at $x = -1.7$, which would make the denominator equal zero, is the vertical asymptote.**

Key Discovery
In the graph of $y = \dfrac{a}{x-h} + k$, the horizontal asymptote is $y = k$ and the vertical asymptote is $x = h$.

1. As the value of x approaches 3 through numbers less than 3, the value of y becomes a smaller and smaller negative number (larger and larger in absolute value); as the value of x approaches 3 through numbers greater than 3, the value of y becomes a larger and larger positive number; $x = 3$.

3.

4.

5.

1. Identify the horizontal and vertical asymptotes of the graph of $y = \frac{-8}{x+5} - 3$. **The horizontal asymptote is $y = -3$ and the vertical asymptote is $x = -5$.**

2. Using the form of $y = \frac{a}{x-h} + k$, write an equation of a graph that has a horizontal asymptote of $y = 3$ and a vertical asymptote of $x = 2$. *Sample answer:* $y = \frac{2}{x-2} + 3$

6. As the value of x approaches -1.7 through numbers less than -1.7, the value of y becomes a smaller and smaller negative number (larger and larger in absolute value); as the value of x approaches -1.7 through numbers greater than -1.7, the value of y becomes a larger and larger positive number; $x = -1.7$.

8.

9.

10.

EXPLORE 2   Use a graphing calculator to graph a function

Graph $y = \frac{-3.4}{x+1.7} - 2.8$ using a graphing calculator.

Enter $y_1 = \frac{-3.4}{x+1.7} - 2.8$ into your graphing calculator. Press **MODE** and select either connected mode or dot mode. Then graph the function.

Connected mode	Dot mode

In connected mode, the screen appears to show the line $x = -1.7$. This line is *not* part of the graph. The calculator is instead connecting the two branches of the hyperbola. In dot mode, the screen does not show the line, but the points that are plotted are not connected by a smooth curve.

PRACTICE

6. *Describe* how the value of y changes as the value of x gets closer to -1.7. Use the *trace* feature of the graphing calculator to find the equation of the vertical asymptote.   **See margin.**

7. *Describe* how the value of y changes as the value of x gets farther from -1.7. Use the *trace* feature of the graphing calculator to find the equation of the horizontal asymptote.   **As the absolute value of x becomes larger and larger, the value of y approaches -2.8; $y = -2.8$.**

Graph the function using a graphing calculator.
8–10. See margin.

8. $y = \frac{5.3}{x-4.6} - 1.2$

9. $y = \frac{-7.1}{x-3.2} + 4.5$

10. $y = \frac{-10.2}{x+12.4} + 9.8$

DRAW CONCLUSIONS   Use your observations to complete these exercises

11. How are the constants in the equations of the asymptotes in Exercises 1 and 2 related to the constants in the function $y = \frac{2}{x-3} + 4$? **See margin.**

12. How are the constants in the equations of the asymptotes in Exercises 6 and 7 related to the constants in the function $y = \frac{-3.4}{x+1.7} - 2.8$? **See margin.**

13. **CONJECTURE** Copy and complete: The graph of $y = \frac{a}{x-h} + k$ has a vertical asymptote of $x = \underline{}$ and a horizontal asymptote of $y = \underline{}$. **h, k**

11. The constant in the equation of the vertical asymptote is the same as the constant that is subtracted from x in the function. The constant in the equation of the horizontal asymptote is the same as the constant term of the function.

12. The constant in the equation of the vertical asymptote is the opposite of the constant that is added to x in the function. The constant in the equation of the horizontal asymptote is the same as the constant term of the function.

12.2 Graph Rational Functions

Before	You graphed inverse variation equations.
Now	You will graph rational functions.
Why?	So you can find the cost of a group trip, as in Ex. 39.

Key Vocabulary
- **rational function**
- **hyperbola**, *p. 767*
- **branches of a hyperbola**, *p. 767*
- **asymptotes of a hyperbola**, *p. 767*

The inverse variation equation $y = \frac{a}{x}$ ($a \neq 0$) is a type of *rational function*.

A **rational function** has a rule given by a fraction whose numerator and denominator are polynomials and whose denominator is not 0.

KEY CONCEPT — *For Your Notebook*

Parent Rational Function

The function $y = \frac{1}{x}$ is the parent function for any rational function whose numerator has degree 0 or 1 and whose denominator has degree 1. The function and its graph have the following characteristics:

- The domain and range are all nonzero real numbers.

- The horizontal asymptote is the *x*-axis. The vertical asymptote is the *y*-axis.

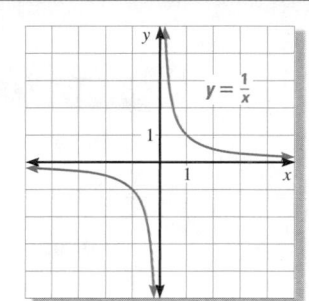

EXAMPLE 1 Compare graph of $y = \frac{a}{x}$ with graph of $y = \frac{1}{x}$

REWRITE FUNCTION

In the function $y = \frac{1}{3x}$, the value of a is $\frac{1}{3}$ as shown:

$y = \frac{1}{3x} = \frac{1}{3} \cdot \frac{1}{x}$

$\quad = \frac{\frac{1}{3}}{x}$

a. The graph of $y = \frac{-2}{x}$ is a vertical stretch with a reflection in the *x*-axis of the graph of $y = \frac{1}{x}$.

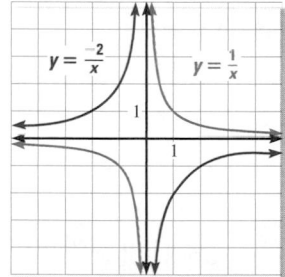

b. The graph of $y = \frac{1}{3x}$ is a vertical shrink of the graph of $y = \frac{1}{x}$.

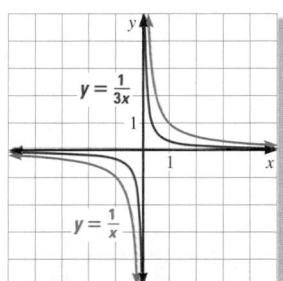

12.2 Graph Rational Functions **775**

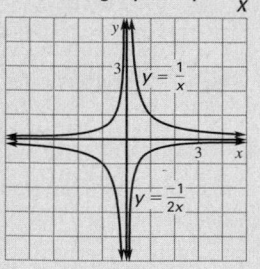
776

EXAMPLE 2 Graph $y = \dfrac{1}{x} + k$

Graph $y = \dfrac{1}{x} + 3$ and identify its domain and range. Compare the graph with the graph of $y = \dfrac{1}{x}$.

Solution

Graph the function using a table of values.

The domain is all real numbers except 0. The range is all real numbers except 3.

The graph of $y = \dfrac{1}{x} + 3$ is a vertical translation (of 3 units up) of the graph of $y = \dfrac{1}{x}$.

x	y
−2	2.5
−1	2
−0.5	1
0	undefined
0.5	5
1	4
2	3.5

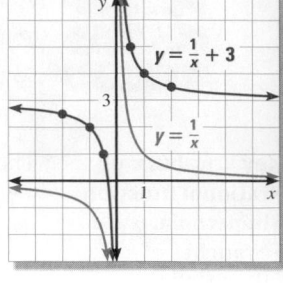

EXAMPLE 3 Graph $y = \dfrac{1}{x - h}$

Graph $y = \dfrac{1}{x - 2}$ and identify its domain and range. Compare the graph with the graph of $y = \dfrac{1}{x}$.

Solution

Graph the function using a table of values.

The domain is all real numbers except 2. The range is all real numbers except 0.

The graph of $y = \dfrac{1}{x - 2}$ is a horizontal translation (of 2 units to the right) of the graph of $y = \dfrac{1}{x}$.

x	y
0	−0.5
1	−1
1.5	−2
2	undefined
2.5	2
3	1
4	0.5

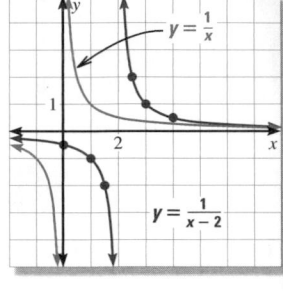

✓ **GUIDED PRACTICE** for Examples 1, 2, and 3

Graph the function and identify its domain and range. *Compare* the graph with the graph of $y = \dfrac{1}{x}$. 1–3. See margin.

1. $y = \dfrac{-4}{x}$ **2.** $y = \dfrac{1}{x} - 4$ **3.** $y = \dfrac{1}{x + 5}$

4. *Describe* how the graph of $y = \dfrac{1}{x + 3}$ is related to the graph of $y = \dfrac{1}{x}$.
See margin.

GRAPHING RATIONAL FUNCTIONS You can graph a rational function of the form $y = \frac{a}{x - h} + k$ ($a \neq 0$) by using the values of a, k, and h.

KEY CONCEPT   *For Your Notebook*

Graph of $y = \dfrac{a}{x - h} + k$

The graph of $y = \dfrac{a}{x - h} + k$ is a hyperbola that has the following characteristics:

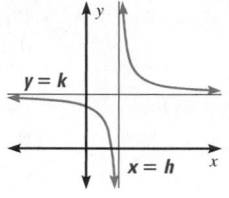

- If $|a| > 1$, the graph is a vertical stretch of the graph of $y = \frac{1}{x}$. If $0 < |a| < 1$, the graph is a vertical shrink of the graph of $y = \frac{1}{x}$. If $a < 0$, the graph is a reflection in the x-axis of the graph of $y = \frac{1}{x}$.

- The horizontal asymptote is $y = k$. The vertical asymptote is $x = h$.

The domain of the function is all real numbers except $x = h$. The range is all real numbers except $y = k$.

EXAMPLE 4   **Graph $y = \dfrac{a}{x - h} + k$**

Graph $y = \dfrac{2}{x + 1} - 3$.

Solution

AVOID ERRORS
The asymptotes are used to help you draw a hyperbola. They are *not* part of the hyperbola.

STEP 1 **Identify** the asymptotes of the graph. The vertical asymptote is $x = -1$. The horizontal asymptote is $y = -3$.

STEP 2 **Plot** several points on each side of the vertical asymptote.

STEP 3 **Graph** two branches that pass through the plotted points and approach the asymptotes.

Animated **Algebra** at classzone.com

✓ **GUIDED PRACTICE**   for Example 4

5. Graph $y = \dfrac{4}{x - 5} + 6$. **See margin.**

6. For which function is the domain all real numbers except -3 and the range all real numbers except 7? **C**

   (A) $y = \dfrac{2}{x - 3} + 7$ **(B)** $y = \dfrac{2}{x - 3} - 7$ **(C)** $y = \dfrac{2}{x + 3} + 7$ **(D)** $y = \dfrac{2}{x + 3} - 7$

12.2 Graph Rational Functions **777**

5.

Extra Example 2

Graph $y = \dfrac{1}{x} - 1$ and identify its domain and range. Compare the graph with the graph of $y = \frac{1}{x}$.

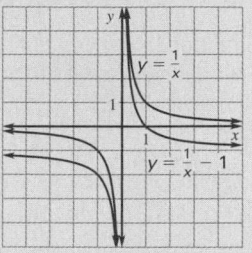

Domain: all real numbers except 0; range: all real numbers except -1; vertical translation of $y = \frac{1}{x}$, 1 unit down

Extra Example 3

Graph $y = \dfrac{1}{x + 2}$ and identify its domain and range. Compare the graph with the graph of $y = \frac{1}{x}$.

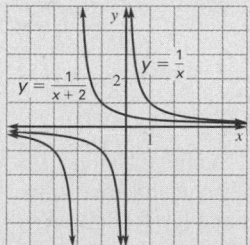

Domain: all real numbers except -2; range: all real numbers except 0; the graph of $y = \frac{1}{x + 2}$ is a horizontal translation of $y = \frac{1}{x}$, 2 units left.

Extra Example 4

Graph $y = \dfrac{3}{x + 2} + 1$.

Animated **Algebra**
classzone.com

An **Animated Algebra** activity is available on-line for **Example 4.** This activity is also available on the **Power Presentations CD-ROM.**

777

EXAMPLE 5 **Solve a multi-step problem**

TRIP EXPENSES Your art club is planning a bus trip to an art museum. The cost for renting a bus is $495, and the cost will be divided equally among the people who are going on the trip. A museum ticket costs $12.50 per person.

• Write an equation that gives the cost C (in dollars per person) of the trip as a function of the number p of people going on the trip.

• Graph the equation. *Describe* the change in the cost as the number of people increases.

• Use the graph to approximate the number of people who need to go on the trip so that the cost is about $25 per person.

San Francisco Art Museum

Solution

STEP 1 **Write** a verbal model. Then write an equation.

STEP 2 **Graph** $C = \frac{495}{p} + 12.50$ on a graphing calculator. The vertical asymptote is $p = 0$. The horizontal asymptote is $C = 12.5$. As the number of people increases, the cost decreases.

STEP 3 **Approximate** the number of people needed in order for the cost to be about $25. When $C \approx 25$, the value of p is about 40. So, if about 40 people go on the trip, each person will pay about $25.

✓ **GUIDED PRACTICE** **for Example 5**

7. **WHAT IF?** In Example 5, suppose the club rents a larger bus for $610. Write and graph an equation that gives the cost C (in dollars per person) of the trip as a function of the number p of people going on the trip. Then approximate the number of people who need to go on the trip so that the cost is about $25 per person. $C = \frac{610}{p} + 12.50$; see margin for art; 49 people.

7.

12.2 EXERCISES

HOMEWORK KEY
○ = **WORKED-OUT SOLUTIONS**
on p. WS1 for Exs. 7, 21, and 41

★ = **STANDARDIZED TEST PRACTICE**
Exs. 2, 18, 28, 29, 36, 42, and 44

◆ = **MULTIPLE REPRESENTATIONS**
Ex. 41

SKILL PRACTICE

A

1. **VOCABULARY** Identify the vertical asymptote and horizontal asymptote of the graph of $y = \dfrac{1}{x-3} - 6$. $x = 3, y = -6$

2. ★ **WRITING** *Describe* the difference between the graph of $y = \dfrac{1}{x+2}$ and the graph of $y = \dfrac{1}{x}$. **The graph of $y = \dfrac{1}{x+2}$ is the graph of $y = \dfrac{1}{x}$ translated 2 units to the left.**

EXAMPLES 1, 2, and 3
on pp. 775–776
for Exs. 3–17

GRAPHING FUNCTIONS Graph the function and identify its domain and range. *Compare* the graph with the graph of $y = \dfrac{1}{x}$.   **3–17. See margin.**

3. $y = \dfrac{3}{x}$

4. $y = \dfrac{1}{2x}$

5. $y = \dfrac{-3}{x}$

6. $y = \dfrac{-2}{3x}$

(7.) $y = \dfrac{-1}{4x}$

8. $y = \dfrac{1}{x} + 7$

9. $y = \dfrac{1}{x} - 5$

10. $y = \dfrac{1}{x} + 4$

11. $y = \dfrac{1}{x} + 8$

12. $y = \dfrac{1}{x} - 6$

13. $y = \dfrac{1}{x+3}$

14. $y = \dfrac{1}{x-7}$

15. $y = \dfrac{1}{x+8}$

16. $y = \dfrac{1}{x-1}$

17. $y = \dfrac{1}{x-6}$

EXAMPLE 4
on p. 777
for Exs. 18–31

18. ★ **MULTIPLE CHOICE** For which function is the domain all real numbers except -5 and the range all real numbers except 0? **C**

(A) $y = \dfrac{5}{x}$

(B) $y = \dfrac{5}{x-5}$

(C) $y = \dfrac{5}{x+5}$

(D) $y = \dfrac{-5}{x-5}$

GRAPHING FUNCTIONS Graph the function.   **19–27. See margin.**

19. $y = \dfrac{1}{x-2} - 8$

20. $y = \dfrac{2}{x-6} + 3$

(21.) $y = \dfrac{4}{x+7} + 5$

22. $y = \dfrac{-3}{x+3} - 4$

23. $y = \dfrac{-1}{x+5} + 6$

24. $y = \dfrac{2}{x-1} + 2$

25. $y = \dfrac{1}{x-4} + 2$

26. $y = \dfrac{4}{x-3} - 1$

27. $y = \dfrac{-5}{x-1} - 4$

28. ★ **MULTIPLE CHOICE** The graph of which function has the same horizontal asymptote as the graph of $y = \dfrac{1}{x}$? **C**

(A) $y = \dfrac{2}{x} + 3$

(B) $y = \dfrac{1}{x} - 1$

(C) $y = \dfrac{-10}{x}$

(D) $y = \dfrac{-10}{x-1} + 1$

29. ★ **OPEN-ENDED**   Write an equation whose graph is a hyperbola that has the following characteristics: ***Sample answer:*** $y = \dfrac{1}{x+1} + 2$
   - The vertical asymptote is $x = -1$.
   - The horizontal asymptote is $y = 2$.

12.2 Graph Rational Functions   **779**

3–17, 19–27. See Additional Answers beginning on p. AA1.

---

④ PRACTICE AND APPLY

Assignment Guide

📖 **Answer Transparencies available for all exercises**

Basic:
Day 1: EP p. 948 Exs. 1–9 odd
pp. 779–782
Exs. 1–17, 52–60
Day 2: pp. 779–782
Exs. 18–33, 39–43, 46–51

Average:
Day 1: pp. 779–782
Exs. 1, 2, 6–17, 37, 52–60
Day 2: pp. 779–782
Exs. 18–28 even, 29–36, 39–44, 46–51

Advanced:
Day 1: pp. 779–782
Exs. 1, 6–17, 37, 52–60
Day 2: pp. 779–782
Exs. 18, 24–36, 38–45*, 46–50 even

Block:
pp. 779–782
Exs. 1, 2, 6–17, 18–28 even, 29–37, 39–44, 46–60

Differentiated Instruction

See *Algebra 1 Best Practices Toolkit* for suggestions on addressing the needs of a diverse classroom.

Homework Check

For a quick check of student understanding of key concepts, go over the following exercises:

Basic: 4, 10, 14, 22, 39
Average: 6, 11, 15, 24, 40
Advanced: 7, 12, 16, 26, 41

Extra Practice

- Student Edition, p. 946
- Chapter 12 Resource Book: Practice levels A, B, C, pp. 19–24

Practice Worksheet

An easily-readable reduced practice page (with answers) for this lesson can be found on p. 762C.

ERROR ANALYSIS *Describe* and correct the error in identifying the asymptotes of the graph of the given rational function. **30–31. See margin.**

30. $y = \dfrac{3}{x + 1} - 4$

Vertical asymptote: x = 1 ✕
Horizontal asymptote: y = −4

31. $y = \dfrac{-2}{x - 6} + 7$

Vertical asymptote: x = 6 ✕
Horizontal asymptote: y = −7

B **WRITING EQUATIONS** Write an equation whose graph is a hyperbola that has the given asymptotes and passes through the given point.

32. $x = 7, y = 8;\ (-6, 0)$ $y = \dfrac{104}{x - 7} + 8$

33. $x = -2, y = 5;\ (0, -9)$ $y = \dfrac{-28}{x + 2} + 5$

34. $x = 3, y = -2;\ (5, -1)$ $y = \dfrac{2}{x - 3} - 2$

35. $x = -4, y = -4;\ (-8, 3)$ $y = \dfrac{-28}{x + 4} - 4$

36. ★ **WRITING** Let f be a function of the form $f(x) = \dfrac{a}{x - h} + k$. Can you graph f if you know only two points on the graph? *Explain.* **No; two points do not provide enough information to determine the three unknown values, *a*, *h*, and *k*.**

37. **GEOMETRY** The height h of a trapezoid is given by the formula

$$h = \frac{2A}{b_1 + b_2}$$

where A is the area and b_1 and b_2 are the bases.

a. Let $A = 50$ and $b_1 = 4$. Write h as a function of b_2. Then graph the function and identify its domain and range. **See margin.**

b. Use the graph to approximate the value of b_2 when $h = 6$. **about 13**

C **38.** **CHALLENGE** *Describe* how to find the asymptotes of the graph of

$$g(x) = \frac{3}{2x - 4} + 8.$$

Then graph the function. **See margin.**

PROBLEM SOLVING

GRAPHING CALCULATOR You may wish to use a graphing calculator to complete the following Problem Solving exercises.

EXAMPLE 5 A
on p. 778
for Exs. 39–42

39. $C = \dfrac{900}{p} + 400;$ see margin for art.

39. **TEAM SPORTS** A figure skating troupe is planning an out-of-town trip. The expenses for the trip are shown in the flyer. Write an equation that gives the cost C (in dollars per person) as a function of the number p of people going on the trip. Then graph the equation.

@HomeTutor for problem solving help at classzone.com

40. **CHARITY EVENTS** A committee of 5 people is responsible for making 500 sandwiches for a charity picnic. The committee hopes to recruit extra people for the task. Write an equation that gives the average number s of sandwiches made per person as a function of the number p of extra people recruited for the task. Then graph the equation. $s = \dfrac{500}{5 + p}$; see margin for art.

@HomeTutor for problem solving help at classzone.com

Trip Expenses

Bus rental $900
Food and lodging
(per person) $400

○ = **WORKED-OUT SOLUTIONS**
on p. WS1

★ = **STANDARDIZED**
TEST PRACTICE

◆ = **MULTIPLE**
REPRESENTATIONS

780

38. To write the equation in the form $y = \dfrac{a}{x - h} + k$, divide the numerator and denominator of $\dfrac{3}{2x - 4}$ by 2: $y = \dfrac{\frac{3}{2}}{x - 2} + 8$; so, the asymptotes are $x = 2$ and $y = 8$.

[graph showing hyperbola with asymptotes x = 2 and y = 8]

41. ◆ **MULTIPLE REPRESENTATIONS** Your movie rental membership lets you rent any number of movies for $22 per month. You rent at least 2 movies per month.

   a. Writing an Equation Write an equation that gives the average cost C (in dollars per rental) as a function of the number r of additional rentals beyond 2 rentals. $C = \dfrac{22}{r + 2}$

   b. Drawing a Graph Graph the equation from part (a). Then use the graph to approximate the number of additional rentals needed per month so that the average cost is $1.50 per rental.
   See margin for art; 13 additional rentals.

42. ★ SHORT RESPONSE The Mount Washington Auto Road in New Hampshire is a 7.6 mile uphill road that leads to the mountain's 6288 foot peak. The year's fastest time t (in seconds) for driving up the road during the period 1904–1998 can be modeled by

$$t = \frac{56,000}{x + 40}$$

where x is the number of years since 1904. Graph the function. *Describe* how the fastest times changed during the period. Was the *change* in the fastest time from year to year *increasing* or *decreasing*? *Explain.* **See margin.**

B **43. DIVING DEPTHS** The percent p (in decimal form) of time that an elephant seal spends gliding through the water while diving can be modeled by

$$p = \frac{-28.2}{d} + 0.859$$

where d is the depth (in meters) of the dive. Graph the equation and identify its domain and range. *Describe* how the percent of time gliding changes as the depth increases.

44. ★ EXTENDED RESPONSE Oxygen cost is a measure of a person's walking efficiency. The models below give the oxygen cost c (in millimeters per kilogram of body mass per meter) as a function of the walking speed v (in meters per minute) for various age groups.

Ages 6–12   **Ages 13–19**   **Ages 20–59**

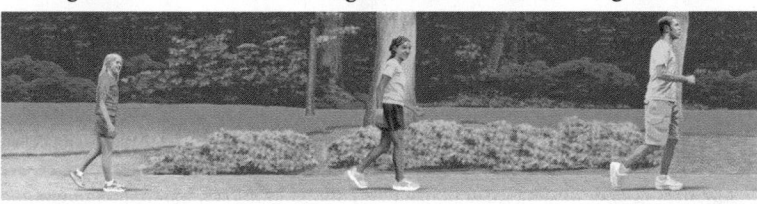

$c = \dfrac{2.61}{v} + 0.188$ $c = \dfrac{1.68}{v} + 0.147$ $c = \dfrac{2.60}{v} + 0.129$

   a. Graph Normal walking speeds range from 40 meters per minute to 100 meters per minute. Graph the models in the same coordinate plane. Use the domain $40 \le v \le 100$. **See margin.**

   b. Interpret The greater the oxygen cost, the less efficient the person is while walking. Use the graphs to tell whether a person is *more efficient* or *less efficient* while walking as the person's speed increases. **more efficient**

   c. Compare Which age group has the least efficient walkers at the speeds given in part (a)? *Justify* your choice.

---

43. See margin for art; domain: $d \ge 32.8$, range: $0 \ge p < 0.859$; the percent of time gliding increases.

44c. Ages 6–12; the graph for the 6–12 year old age group is above the graphs for the other two age groups for all values of v in the given domain. This means the oxygen cost c is greater for the 6–12 year old age group for all values of v in the given domain.

Avoiding Common Errors

Exercises 42–44 Some students confuse variables when discussing inverse relations. Caution students to make sure that their descriptions, explanations, and justifications refer to the correct relationship between specific variables.

  Internet Reference

Exercise 43 Addition information about elephant seals can be found at www.marinemammalcenter.org/learning/education/pinnipeds/noelephseal.asp

42.

The fastest time decreased. The change in the fastest time was decreasing; the graph is steeper for the years near the beginning of the time period and then gradually becomes less steep, implying that the p-value changed more between two successive years near the beginning of the time period than it changed between two successive years near the end of the time period.

43.

44a.

39.

40.

41b.

1. Graph $y = \dfrac{1}{x+3} + 2$.

2. The cost per person C for a chartered boat can be modeled by $C = \dfrac{850}{p} + 12$, where p is the number of people who charter the boat. Find the least number of people who need to charter the boat so the cost is less than $80 per person. **13 people**

 Online Quiz

Available at **classzone.com**

Diagnosis/Remediation

- Practice A, B, C in Chapter 12 Resource Book, pp. 19–24
- Study Guide in Chapter 12 Resource Book, pp. 25–26
- Practice Workbook, pp. 183–185
- @HomeTutor

Challenge

Additional challenge is available in the Chapter 12 Resource Book, p. 29.

Quiz

An easily-readable reduced copy of the quiz (with answers) on Lessons 12.1–12.2 from the Assessment Book can be found on p. 762F.

45a, Quiz 7–9. See Additional Answers beginning on p. AA1.

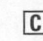 **45. CHALLENGE** To decide whether a person qualifies for a loan to buy a house, a lender uses the ratio r of the person's expected monthly housing expenses to monthly income. Suppose the person has a monthly income of $4150 and expects to pay $1200 per month in housing expenses. The person also expects to receive a raise of x dollars this month.

  a. Write and graph an equation that gives r as a function of x. $\ r = \dfrac{1200}{4150 + x};$ see margin for art.

  b. The person will qualify for a loan if the ratio is 0.28. What must the amount of the raise be in order for the person to qualify for a loan? **about $136**

MIXED REVIEW

PREVIEW
Prepare for Lesson 12.3 in Exs. 46–51.

Write the mixed number as an improper fraction, or write the improper fraction as a mixed number. *(p. 913)*

46. $1\frac{4}{7}$ $\frac{11}{7}$ **47.** $2\frac{3}{8}$ $\frac{19}{8}$ **48.** $5\frac{1}{9}$ $\frac{46}{9}$

49. $\frac{8}{5}$ $1\frac{3}{5}$ **50.** $\frac{13}{6}$ $2\frac{1}{6}$ **51.** $\frac{15}{4}$ $3\frac{3}{4}$

Find the surface area and volume of the solid. For spheres and cylinders, give your answers in terms of π and as decimals rounded to the nearest tenth. *(p. 927)*

52. surface area: 230 π cm², 722.2 cm², **volume:** 450 π cm³, 1413 cm³

53. surface area: 64 π in.², 201.0 in.², **volume:** $\frac{256\pi}{3}$ in.³, 267.9 in.³

52. 5 cm, 18 cm

53. 4 in.

54. 6 ft, 3 ft, 4 ft   **108 ft²; 72 ft³**

Simplify the expression.

55. $5x + 7 - 14x - 8$ *(p. 96)* $-9x - 1$

56. $15x - (7 - 2x)$ *(p. 96)* $17x - 7$

57. $\dfrac{12x - 4}{2}$ *(p. 103)* $6x - 2$

58. $\dfrac{-32x + 4}{-8}$ *(p. 103)* $4x - \dfrac{1}{2}$

59. $\sqrt{81x^2}$ *(p. 719)* $9x$

60. $\sqrt{100x^3y^2}$ *(p. 719)* $10xy\sqrt{x}$

QUIZ *for Lessons 12.1–12.2*

Tell whether the equation represents *direct variation*, *inverse variation*, or *neither*. *(p. 765)*

  1. $\frac{1}{5}xy = 1$ **inverse variation**   **2.** $y = -9x$ **direct variation**   **3.** $5x + y = 3$ **neither**

Given that y varies inversely with x, use the specified values to write an inverse variation equation that relates x and y. Then find the value of y when $x = 3$. *(p. 765)*

  4. $x = 6, y = 4$ $\ y = \dfrac{24}{x}; 8$ **5.** $x = -3, y = 7$ $\ y = \dfrac{-21}{x}; -7$ **6.** $x = \dfrac{5}{2}, y = 2$ $\ y = \dfrac{5}{x}; \dfrac{5}{3}$

Graph the function. Identify its domain and range. *(p. 775)* **7–9. See margin.**

  7. $y = \dfrac{4}{x}$ **8.** $y = \dfrac{-2}{x - 6}$ **9.** $y = \dfrac{3}{x + 2} - 5$

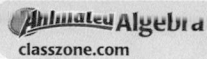

12.3 Dividing Polynomials Using Algebra Tiles

MATERIALS · algebra tiles

QUESTION How can you divide polynomials using algebra tiles?

In the equation $36 \div 5 = 7\frac{1}{5}$, the dividend is 36, the divisor is 5, the quotient is 7, and the remainder is 1. This equation illustrates the following rule:

$$\text{Dividend} \div \text{Divisor} = \text{Quotient} + \frac{\text{Remainder}}{\text{Divisor}}$$

This rule can also be applied when dividing polynomials.

EXPLORE Divide polynomials

Divide $2x^2 + 3x + 5$ by $x + 1$.

STEP 1 *Model using algebra tiles*

Think of $2x^2 + 3x + 5$ as the area of a figure. Try to arrange the tiles to form a rectangle with $x + 1$ as one of the side lengths.

Notice that the other side length is $2x + 1$, but there are four 1-tiles remaining.

STEP 2 *Write equation*

The divisor is $x + 1$, the quotient is $2x + 1$, and the remainder is 4.

So, $(2x^2 + 3x + 5) \div (x + 1) = 2x + 1 + \dfrac{4}{x + 1}$.

DRAW CONCLUSIONS Use your observations to complete these exercises

1. To check that $36 \div 5 = 7\frac{1}{5}$, you can evaluate $5 \cdot 7 + 1$ to obtain 36.

   Use this method to check the division equation in Step 2 above.
   $(x + 1)(2x + 1) + 4 = 2x^2 + 3x + 1 + 4 = 2x^2 + 3x + 5$

Use algebra tiles to divide the polynomials. Include a drawing of your model. 2–7. See margin.

2. $(2x^2 + 7x + 6) \div (x + 2)$ 3. $(2x^2 + 9x + 10) \div (x + 3)$

4. $(4x^2 + 4x + 5) \div (2x + 1)$ 5. $(2x^2 + 5x + 7) \div (2x + 3)$

6. $(3x^2 + 7x + 3) \div (x + 2)$ 7. $(4x^2 + 6x + 5) \div (x + 1)$

8. **REASONING** For which of the division problems in Exercises 2–7 is the divisor a factor of the dividend? How do you know? **Exercise 2; the remainder is zero so it is a factor.**

2–7. See Additional Answers beginning on p. AA1.

783

---

① PLAN AND PREPARE

Explore the Concept

- Students will divide polynomials using algebra tiles.
- This activity leads into the study of dividing a polynomial by a binomial in Lesson 12.3, Example 2.

Materials

Each student will need:
- algebra tiles
- Activity Support Master (*Chapter 12 Resource Book*, p. 32)

Recommended Time

Work activity: 10 min
Discuss results: 5 min

Grouping

Students should work individually.

② TEACH

Tips for Success

Encourage students to use the divisor as the length of one side of the rectangle.

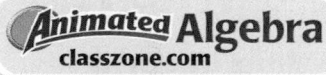

An **Animated Algebra** activity is available on-line. This activity is also available on the **Power Presentations CD-ROM**.

Key Discovery

When dividing polynomials, represent the remainder as a fraction, using the divisor as the denominator of the fraction.

③ ASSESS AND RETEACH

Explain how to check the division equation $(2x^2 + 10x + 12) \div (x + 4) = 2x + 2 + \dfrac{4}{x + 2}$. Find the product of the divisor and the quotient. Add the numerator of the fraction to the product, and compare the result with the original dividend.

Before	You multiplied polynomials.
Now	You will divide polynomials.
Why?	So you can describe an average cost, as in Ex. 43.

Key Vocabulary
• **monomial,** *p. 554*
• **polynomial,** *p. 554*
• **binomial,** *p. 555*
• **rational function,** *p. 775*

Just as you can find the product of two polynomials, you can divide the product by one of the polynomials to obtain the other polynomial. For example, $x^2 + 5x + 6 = (x + 2)(x + 3)$ is equivalent to $\dfrac{x^2 + 5x + 6}{x + 2} = x + 3$.

EXAMPLE 1 Divide a polynomial by a monomial

Divide $4x^3 + 8x^2 + 10x$ by $2x$.

Solution

Method 1: Write the division as a fraction.

$$(4x^3 + 8x^2 + 10x) \div 2x = \frac{4x^3 + 8x^2 + 10x}{2x} \quad \text{Write as fraction.}$$

$$= \frac{4x^3}{2x} + \frac{8x^2}{2x} + \frac{10x}{2x} \quad \text{Divide each term by } 2x.$$

$$= 2x^2 + 4x + 5 \quad \text{Simplify.}$$

Method 2: Use long division.

Think: $4x^3 \div 2x = ?$ Think: $8x^2 \div 2x = ?$ Think: $10x \div 2x = ?$

$$\begin{array}{r} 2x^2 + 4x + 5 \\ 2x\overline{)4x^3 + 8x^2 + 10x} \end{array}$$

▶ $(4x^3 + 8x^2 + 10x) \div 2x = 2x^2 + 4x + 5$

CHECK
$$2x(2x^2 + 4x + 5) \stackrel{?}{=} 4x^3 + 8x^2 + 10x$$
$$2x(2x^2) + 2x(4x) + 2x(5) \stackrel{?}{=} 4x^3 + 8x^2 + 10x$$
$$4x^3 + 8x^2 + 10x = 4x^3 + 8x^2 + 10x ✓$$

 GUIDED PRACTICE for Example 1

Divide.

1. $(6x^3 + 3x^2 - 12x) \div 3x$ $2x^2 + x - 4$
2. $(12y^4 - 16y^3 + 20y^2) \div 4y$
   $3y^3 - 4y^2 + 5y$

DIVIDING BY A BINOMIAL As shown in Example 1, you can use two methods when dividing a polynomial by a monomial. To divide a polynomial by a binomial, use long division.

EXAMPLE 2 Divide a polynomial by a binomial

Divide $x^2 + 2x - 3$ by $x - 1$.

Solution

STEP 1 **Divide** the first term of $x^2 + 2x - 3$ by the first term of $x - 1$.

$$
\begin{array}{r}
x \\
x - 1 \overline{) x^2 + 2x - 3} \\
\underline{x^2 - x} \\
3x
\end{array}
$$

Think: $x^2 \div x = ?$

Multiply x and $x - 1$.

Subtract $x^2 - x$ from $x^2 + 2x$.

AVOID ERRORS
Be sure to *subtract* $x^2 - x$ from $x^2 + 2x$ in order to obtain $3x$. Do *not* add the expressions.

STEP 2 **Bring** down -3. Then divide the first term of $3x - 3$ by the first term of $x - 1$.

$$
\begin{array}{r}
x + 3 \\
x - 1 \overline{) x^2 + 2x - 3} \\
\underline{x^2 - x} \\
3x - 3 \\
\underline{3x - 3} \\
0
\end{array}
$$

Think: $3x \div x = ?$

Multiply 3 and $x - 1$.

Subtract $3x - 3$ from $3x - 3$.

▶ $(x^2 + 2x - 3) \div (x - 1) = x + 3$

NONZERO REMAINDERS In Example 2, if the dividend had been $x^2 + 2x - 2$, the remainder would have been 1. When you obtain a nonzero remainder, you can apply the following rule: Dividend ÷ Divisor = Quotient + $\dfrac{\text{Remainder}}{\text{Divisor}}$.

EXAMPLE 3 Divide a polynomial by a binomial

Divide $2x^2 + 11x - 9$ by $2x - 3$.

$$
\begin{array}{r}
x + 7 \\
2x - 3 \overline{) 2x^2 + 11x - 9} \\
\underline{2x^2 - 3x} \\
14x - 9 \\
\underline{14x - 21} \\
12
\end{array}
$$

Multiply x and $2x - 3$.

Subtract $2x^2 - 3x$. Bring down -9.

Multiply 7 and $2x - 3$.

Subtract $14x - 21$.

CHECK DIVISION
To check your answer, multiply the quotient by the divisor, then add the remainder to the product.

▶ $(2x^2 + 11x - 9) \div (2x - 3) = x + 7 + \dfrac{12}{2x - 3}$

✓ **GUIDED PRACTICE** for Examples 2 and 3

3. Divide: $(a^2 + 3a - 4) \div (a + 1)$
$a + 2 + \dfrac{-6}{a + 1}$

4. Divide: $(9b^2 + 6b + 8) \div (3b - 4)$
$3b + 6 + \dfrac{32}{3b - 4}$

12.3 Divide Polynomials **785**

Motivating the Lesson
Before you join a teen bowling league, you want to know what your costs will be. If you know the cost to join the league and the cost per game, you can write an equation that models the situation and gives your total cost as a function of the number of games that you bowl.

3 TEACH

Extra Example 1
Divide $6x^3 - 12x^2 + 9x$ by $3x$.
$2x^2 - 4x + 3$

Key Question to Ask for Example 1
• In Method 2, how can you check each step as you solve the problem? **Multiply each term in the quotient by the divisor to see if you get each term in the dividend.**

Extra Example 2
Divide $x^2 - x + 6$ by $x + 3$. $x - 2$

Key Questions to Ask for Example 2
• In Step 1, why do you place the quotient term x over the dividend term $2x$? **When you multiply x and $x - 1$, each term in the product will be aligned over the like term in the dividend.**
• How do you subtract $x^2 - x$ from $x^2 + 2x$? **For each term in $x^2 - x$, add its opposite by multiplying that term by -1.**

Extra Example 3
Divide $3x^2 + 17x + 13$ by $3x + 2$.
$x + 5 + \dfrac{3}{3x + 2}$

Extra Example 4

Divide $-3n + n^2 - 21$ by $3 + n$.

$n - 6 + \dfrac{-3}{n + 3}$

Key Questions to Ask for Example 4

- How can you check your answer? **Find the product of the divisor and the quotient. Then add the numerator of the fraction. The result should be the original dividend.**
- What is the remainder? What is the entire quotient? $-2, y + 3 + \dfrac{-2}{y + 2}$

Extra Example 5

Divide $-12 + 4y^2$ by $-1 + 2y$.

$2y + 1 + \dfrac{-11}{2y - 1}$ \

Key Questions to Ask for Example 5

- Why do you insert missing terms using zero coefficients? **The dividend has no m-term, and the long-division process requires a place for m-terms.**
- What is the purpose of inserting missing terms? **Missing terms, with 0 coefficients, serve as placeholders in the long-division process.**

Extra Example 6

Graph $y = \dfrac{2x + 1}{x - 1}$.

REWRITING POLYNOMIALS When dividing polynomials, you may first need to rewrite the polynomials so that the exponents decrease from left to right. When rewriting polynomials, insert any missing terms using zero coefficients. For example, $8 + 3x^2$ should be rewritten as $3x^2 + 0x + 8$.

EXAMPLE 4 Rewrite polynomials

Divide $5y + y^2 + 4$ by $2 + y$.

REVIEW POLYNOMIALS
For help with rewriting a polynomial, see p. 554.

$$
\begin{array}{r}
y + 3 \\
y + 2 \overline{)\; y^2 + 5y + 4} \\
\underline{y^2 + 2y} \\
3y + 4 \\
\underline{3y + 6} \\
-2
\end{array}
$$

Rewrite polynomials.
Multiply y and $y + 2$.
Subtract $y^2 + 2y$. Bring down 4.
Multiply 3 and $y + 2$.
Subtract $3y + 6$.

▶ $(5y + y^2 + 4) \div (2 + y) = y + 3 + \dfrac{-2}{y + 2}$

EXAMPLE 5 Insert missing terms

Divide $13 + 4m^2$ by $-1 + 2m$.

$$
\begin{array}{r}
2m + 1 \\
2m - 1 \overline{)\; 4m^2 + 0m + 13} \\
\underline{4m^2 - 2m} \\
2m + 13 \\
\underline{2m - 1} \\
14
\end{array}
$$

Rewrite polynomials. Insert missing term.
Multiply $2m$ and $2m - 1$.
Subtract $4m^2 - 2m$. Bring down 13.
Multiply 1 and $2m - 1$.
Subtract $2m - 1$.

▶ $(13 + 4m^2) \div (-1 + 2m) = 2m + 1 + \dfrac{14}{2m - 1}$

EXAMPLE 6 Rewrite and graph a rational function

Graph $y = \dfrac{2x - 1}{x - 2}$.

Solution

USE ASYMPTOTES
Use the graphing technique in Lesson 12.2 to graph the function. For instance, the lines $x = 2$ and $y = 2$ are asymptotes of the graph.

STEP 1 Rewrite the rational function in the form $y = \dfrac{a}{x - h} + k$.

$$
\begin{array}{r}
2 \\
x - 2 \overline{)\; 2x - 1} \\
\underline{2x - 4} \\
3
\end{array}
$$

So, $y = \dfrac{3}{x - 2} + 2$.

STEP 2 Graph the function.

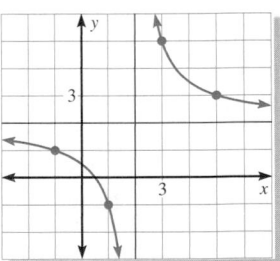

7.

$y = \dfrac{3x + 1}{x + 1}$

8.

Average cost (dollars) vs Brochures printed

$C = \dfrac{20}{b} + 0.8$

Differentiated Instruction

Inclusion Students may forget to organize the exponents in descending order before performing the long division as shown in **Examples 4 and 5**. It may help to show them the similarity to long division done in arithmetic. When they divide $23\overline{)648}$ for example, the highest powers (of 10) also appear first.

$$2.3 \times 10^1 + 3 \times 10^0 \overline{)\; 6 \times 10^2 + 4 \times 10^1 + 8 \times 10^0}$$

See also the *Algebra 1 Toolkit* for more strategies.

5. Divide: $(8m - 7 + 4m^2) \div (5 + 2m)$ **6.** Divide: $(n^2 - 6) \div (-3 + n)$

$2m - 1 + \dfrac{-2}{2m + 5}$

$n + 3 + \dfrac{3}{n - 3}$

7. Graph $y = \dfrac{3x + 1}{x + 1}$.

See margin.

❖ **EXAMPLE 7** Solve a multi-step problem

PRINTING COSTS You are creating brochures that promote your school's sports events. You pay $20 for computer time. The cost of printing a brochure is $.60. Write and graph an equation that gives the average cost C (in dollars per brochure) as a function of the number b of brochures printed.

Solution

STEP 1 **Write** a verbal model. Then write an equation.

$$\frac{\text{Average cost}}{(\text{dollars/brochure})} = \frac{\dfrac{\text{Cost of computer}}{\text{time (dollars)}} + \dfrac{\text{Printing cost}}{(\text{dollars/brochure})} \cdot \dfrac{\text{Number printed}}{(\text{brochures})}}{\dfrac{\text{Number printed}}{(\text{brochures})}}$$

$$C = \frac{20 + 0.6b}{b}$$

STEP 2 **Rewrite** the rational function.   **STEP 3** **Graph** the function.

$$C = \frac{20 + 0.6b}{b}$$

$$= \frac{20}{b} + \frac{0.6b}{b}$$

$$= \frac{20}{b} + 0.6$$

8. $C = \dfrac{20}{b} + 0.8$, see margin for art.

9. $C = \dfrac{100}{m} + 45$, see margin for art.

8. WHAT IF? In Example 7, suppose the cost of printing a brochure is $.80. Write and graph an equation that gives the average cost C (in dollars per brochure) as a function of the number b of brochures printed.

9. INTERNET COSTS A cable Internet service provider charges an installation fee of $100 and a monthly service charge of $45. Write and graph an equation that gives the average cost C (in dollars per month) as a function of the number m of months of Internet service.

12.3 Divide Polynomials **787**

Differentiated Instruction

Below Level For **Example 7**, have students find the cost to print 5, 15, 25, 70, and 80 brochures. Ask them to find those costs two ways: by substituting values for b in the equation, and by using the graph. Then ask them to compare and contrast the two methods.

Advanced For **Example 7**, have students research several local printing stores to find what they charge for computer time and for printing brochures. Ask them to do a comparison analysis of the costs by writing equations for all of the stores and then graphing them in the same coordinate plane.

See also the *Algebra 1 Toolkit* for more strategies.

12.3 EXERCISES

HOMEWORK KEY

◯ = **WORKED-OUT SOLUTIONS**
on p. WS1 for Exs. 7, 25, and 45

★ = **STANDARDIZED TEST PRACTICE**
Exs. 2, 19, 33, 34, 38, 47, 48, and 49

◆ = **MULTIPLE REPRESENTATIONS**
Ex. 46

④ PRACTICE AND APPLY

Assignment Guide

📄 Answer Transparencies available for all exercises

Basic:
Day 1: EP p. 946 Exs. 3–6
pp. 788–791
Exs. 1–12, 19–21, 51–59
Day 2: pp. 788–791
Exs. 13–18, 23–29 odd, 31–34, 42–47, 60–65

Average:
Day 1: pp. 788–791
Exs. 1, 2, 5–12, 19–21, 35–37, 51–59
Day 2: pp. 788–791
Exs. 13–18, 22–30 even, 31–34, 38, 42–49, 60–64 even

Advanced:
Day 1: pp. 788–791
Exs. 1, 2, 4–12 even, 19, 35–41*, 51–59
Day 2: pp. 788–791
Exs. 13–18, 22–30 even, 31–34, 42–50*, 60–64 even

Block:
pp. 788–791
Exs. 1, 2, 5–21, 22–30 even, 31–38, 42–49, 51–59, 60–64 even

Differentiated Instruction

See *Algebra 1 Best Practices Toolkit* for suggestions on addressing the needs of a diverse classroom.

Homework Check

For a quick check of student understanding of key concepts, go over the following exercises:
Basic: 6, 9, 17, 24, 42
Average: 8, 10, 18, 26, 43
Advanced: 11, 16, 18, 28, 44

Extra Practice

• Student Edition, p. 946
• Chapter 12 Resource Book:
Practice levels A, B, C, pp. 34–36

Practice Worksheet

An easily-readable reduced practice page (with answers) for this lesson can be found on p. 762C.

SKILL PRACTICE

A 1. **VOCABULARY** Copy and complete: To divide a polynomial by a(n) __?__, you can either write the division as a fraction or use long division. **monomial**

2. ★ **WRITING** *Describe* the steps you would take in graphing the rational function $f(x) = \dfrac{3x-2}{x+6}$. **See margin.**

EXAMPLES 1, 2, 3, 4, and 5
on pp. 784–786
for Exs. 3–21

DIVIDING POLYNOMIALS Divide.

3. $(8x^3 - 12x^2 + 16x) \div 4x$ **$2x^2 - 3x + 4$**

4. $(10y^3 + 20y^2 + 55y) \div 5y$ **$2y^2 + 4y + 11$**

5. $(12r^4 - 30r^2 - 72r) \div (-6r)$ **$-2r^3 + 5r + 12$**

6. $(21s^4 + 49s^3 - 35s^2) \div (-7s)$

6. $-3s^3 - 7s^2 + 5s$

7. $(3v^2 - v - 10) \div (v - 2)$ **$3v + 5$**

8. $(7w^2 + 3w - 4) \div (w + 1)$ **$7w - 4$**

9. $(2m^2 - 5m - 12) \div (2m + 3)$ **$m - 4$**

10. $(6n^2 + 7n - 3) \div (3n - 1)$ **$2n + 3$**

11. $(a^2 - 5a + 3) \div (a - 1)$ **$a - 4 + \dfrac{-1}{a-1}$**

12. $(c^2 - 2c - 4) \div (c + 4)$ **$c - 6 + \dfrac{20}{c+4}$**

13. $3p - 13 + \dfrac{18}{3+p}$

13. $(-21 - 4p + 3p^2) \div (3 + p)$

14. $(8q + q^2 + 7) \div (7 + q)$ **$q + 1$**

15. $(9x + x^2 + 6) \div (6 + x)$ **$x + 3 + \dfrac{-12}{6+x}$**

16. $(4y^2 - 5) \div (2y + 5)$ **$2y - 5 + \dfrac{20}{2y+5}$**

17. $(5 - t^2) \div (t - 3)$ **$-t - 3 + \dfrac{-4}{t-3}$**

18. $(7 - 8x^2) \div (3 + 2x)$

$-4x + 6 + \dfrac{-11}{3+2x}$

19. ★ **MULTIPLE CHOICE** What is the remainder when you divide $x^2 + 4x + 9$ by $x - 4$? **B**

Ⓐ $x - 4$ Ⓑ 41 Ⓒ $x + 8$ Ⓓ $\dfrac{41}{x-4}$

ERROR ANALYSIS *Describe* and correct the error in dividing the polynomials. **20, 21. See margin.**

20. $(5x + 6) \div (x + 2)$

21. $(8x - 9) \div (x - 3)$

$$\begin{array}{r} 5 \\ x+2\overline{\smash{)}5x+6} \\ \underline{5x+10} \\ -4 \end{array}$$

$(5x + 6) \div (x + 2) = 5 + \dfrac{-4}{5x+6}$ ✗

$$\begin{array}{r} 8 \\ x-3\overline{\smash{)}8x-9} \\ \underline{8x-24} \\ -33 \end{array}$$

$(8x - 9) \div (x - 3) = 8 + \dfrac{-33}{x-3}$ ✗

EXAMPLE 6
on p. 786
for Exs. 22–30

GRAPHING FUNCTIONS Graph the function. **22–30. See margin.**

22. $y = \dfrac{x + 10}{x}$

23. $y = \dfrac{2x - 7}{x}$

24. $y = \dfrac{x + 4}{x - 3}$

25. $y = \dfrac{2x - 4}{x - 1}$

26. $y = \dfrac{5x + 2}{x + 3}$

27. $y = \dfrac{6x - 4}{x + 5}$

28. $y = \dfrac{2 - x}{x + 9}$

29. $y = \dfrac{2 + 4x}{x - 3}$

30. $y = \dfrac{7 - 10x}{x + 7}$

2. *Sample answer:* Use long division to divide $3x - 2$ by $x + 6$, thus rewriting the function in the form $f(x) = \dfrac{a}{x - h} + k$. Then identify the asymptotes of the function, plot several points on each side of the vertical asymptote, and sketch the hyperbola.

20. The remainder, -4, should be placed over the divisor, $x + 2$, the dividend, $5x + 6$; $(5x + 6) \div (x + 2) = 5 + \dfrac{-4}{x + 2}$.

GEOMETRY Divide the surface area of the rectangular prism by its volume.

31.

$$\frac{7}{6} + \frac{2}{\ell}$$

32.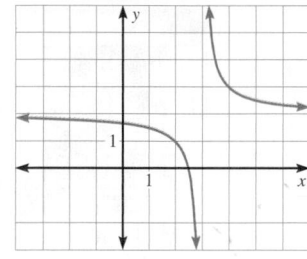

$$\frac{9}{7} + \frac{2}{w}$$

33. ★ **MULTIPLE CHOICE** What is the horizontal asymptote of the graph of

$$y = \frac{bx + c}{x - d}?\quad \mathbf{A}$$

  (A) $y = b$ (B) $y = c$ (C) $y = d$ (D) $y = 0$

34. ★ **MULTIPLE CHOICE** The graph of which function is shown? **C**

  (A) $y = \dfrac{2x + 5}{x - 3}$ (B) $y = \dfrac{2x + 5}{x + 3}$

  (C) $y = \dfrac{2x - 5}{x - 3}$ (D) $y = \dfrac{2x - 5}{x + 3}$

REASONING In Exercises 35–37, find the value of k using the given information.

35. When $8x^2 + 26x + k$ is divided by $x + 3$, the remainder is 4. **10**

36. When $100x^2 + k$ is divided by $5x + 2$, the remainder is 0. **−16**

37. The graph of $y = \dfrac{kx + 4}{x - 6}$ has $y = -5$ as its horizontal asymptote. **−5**

38. ★ **OPEN-ENDED** Write a function of the form $f(x) = \dfrac{bx + c}{x - h}$ such that the graph of the function has $x = 4$ and $y = 6$ as its asymptotes. **Sample answer:** $\dfrac{6x + 1}{x - 4}$

C **CHALLENGE** Graph the function. **39–41. See margin.**

39. $y = \dfrac{6x + 10}{3x + 6}$ **40.** $y = \dfrac{12x - 7}{4x - 8}$ **41.** $y = \dfrac{10x + 3}{2x - 6}$

PROBLEM SOLVING

EXAMPLE 7 A
on p. 787
for Exs. 42–45

42. MOVIE RENTALS You order movie rental coupons from a website for $3 each. The total cost of your order includes a $4 shipping fee. Write an equation that gives the average cost C (in dollars per coupon) as a function of the number r of coupons ordered. Then graph the function.

@HomeTutor for problem solving help at classzone.com $C = \dfrac{4 + 3r}{r}$; see margin for art.

43. MEMBERSHIP FEES You pay $80 for an annual membership to a dance club and pay $3 per dance class. Write an equation that gives the average cost C (in dollars per class) as a function of the number d of dance classes that you take. Then graph the function. $C = \dfrac{80 + 3d}{d}$; see margin for art.

@HomeTutor for problem solving help at classzone.com

12.3 Divide Polynomials   **789**

Avoiding Common Errors
Exercises 3–18 Some students may write the remainder fraction using the dividend as the fraction's denominator, rather than the divisor. Suggest that students write the following rule on a notecard and use it to check the form of their answers: Dividend ÷ Divisor = Quotient + $\dfrac{\text{Remainder}}{\text{Divisor}}$.

Teaching Strategy
Exercises 22–30 Before students graph the functions, ask for one or two volunteers to rewrite each function in the form $y = \dfrac{a}{x - h} + k$ on the chalkboard. Ask students to identify the asymptotes for each example and to explain how the asymptotes are related to the graph of the function.

41.

$$y = \frac{10x + 3}{2x - 6}$$

42.

$$C = \frac{4 + 3r}{r}$$

43.

$$C = \frac{80 + 3d}{d}$$

21. When subtracting $8x - 24$ from $8x - 9$, the result is $-9 - (-24) = -9 + 24 = 15$;

$(8x - 9) \div (x - 3) = 8 + \dfrac{15}{x - 3}$.

22–30. See Additional Answers beginning on p. AA1.

39.

$$y = \frac{6x + 10}{3x + 6}$$

40.

$$y = \frac{12x - 7}{4x - 8}$$

44a.

45b.

46a.

46c.

---

44. INVESTING An investor plans to purchase shares of a stock through a brokerage company. Each share costs $10, and the company charges a transaction fee of $20.

a. **Model** Write and graph an equation that gives the average cost C (in dollars per share) as a function of the number s of shares that the investor purchases. $C = \frac{10s + 20}{s}$; see margin for art.

b. **Approximate** Use the graph to approximate the number of shares purchased if the average cost is $12 per share. **10 shares**

45. CELL PHONE PLAN You are thinking about subscribing to the cell phone plan described in the advertisement below.

1000 Minute Plan
$40.00 per month for first 1000 minutes
$.40 for each additional minute
SPECIAL OFFER CLICK HERE

a. **Model** Write an equation that gives the average cost C (in dollars per minute) as a function of the time t (in minutes) of cell phone use for 1000 or more minutes. $C = \frac{0.4t - 360}{t}$

45b. See margin for art; the average cost increases.

b. **Describe** Graph the function. *Describe* how the average cost per minute changes as time increases.

c. **Approximate** Use the graph to approximate the number of minutes used if the average cost is $.05 per minute. **about 1030 min**

46. ◆ MULTIPLE REPRESENTATIONS The table shows several restaurant bills and their corresponding tips.

Bill, b (dollars)	15.42	26.75	42.18	58.66	63.48	75.89	97.14
Tip, t (dollars)	3.00	5.00	7.50	10.00	10.15	11.50	13.60

a. **Writing an Equation** Make a scatter plot of the data. Then write a linear equation that models the tip t as a function of the bill b. $t = 0.13b + 1.62$; see margin for art.

b. **Writing an Equation** Write an equation that gives the percent tip p (in decimal form) as a function of the bill b. $p = \frac{0.13b + 1.62}{b}$

c. **Drawing Graphs** Draw the graphs of both equations in the same coordinate plane. *Compare* how the tip changes with how the percent tip changes as the bill increases.
See margin for art; the tip increases, but the percent tip decreases.

47. ★ SHORT RESPONSE The number y (in millions) of households that owned VCRs during the period 1984–2000 can be modeled by

$$y = \frac{60 + 120x}{7 + x}$$

where x is the number of years since 1984.

47a. See margin for art; the number of households with VCRs increased.

a. **Describe** Graph the model. *Describe* how the number of households that owned VCRs changed during this period.

b. **Justify** Do you expect that the number of households that own VCRs will ever exceed 150 million? *Justify* your answer. **See margin.**

47a.

47b. No; as x increases, the graph of the function approaches its horizontal asymptote y = 120 from below, so the value of y will never exceed 120 million if this model applies to years beyond 2000.

48. ★ **MULTIPLE CHOICE** A building's ratio y of surface area to volume is a measure of how well the building minimizes heat loss. A company plans to build a store in the shape of a rectangular prism. The store will have a length of 500 feet and a width of 300 feet, but the company hasn't decided on a height h (in feet). Which equation gives the ratio y as a function of the height h? **A**

(A) $y = \dfrac{4}{375} + \dfrac{2}{h}$

(B) $y = 1600 + \dfrac{1}{150{,}000h}$

(C) $y = 1600 + \dfrac{2}{h}$

(D) $y = 300 + \dfrac{500}{h}$

49. ★ **EXTENDED RESPONSE** The ratio of a microorganism's surface area to its volume is a measure of how efficiently the microorganism can perform certain metabolic tasks. Suppose a microorganism is shaped approximately like a cylinder and grows by increasing its length but not its radius.

a–c. See margin.

a. Model and Graph Write an equation that gives the ratio y of surface area to volume in terms of the length ℓ (in micrometers) and the radius r (in micrometers). Then graph the equation for a microorganism whose radius is 50 micrometers.

b. Interpret The greater the ratio, the less efficiently a microorganism performs metabolic tasks. As the microorganism's length increases, is the microorganism *more efficient* or *less efficient* at performing metabolic tasks? *Explain* your choice.

c. Explain How would the microorganism's efficiency change if the length remained constant but the radius increased? *Explain*.

 Animated Algebra at classzone.com

50. No; the effective tax rate e for total income I is given by the function $e(I) = \dfrac{-600}{I} + 0.6$. As seen in the graph, the value of $e(I)$ approaches 0.6 from below but never actually takes on the value 0.6; see margin for art.

50. **CHALLENGE** The effective tax rate is the percent of total income that a worker pays in taxes. Suppose that a worker doesn't pay taxes on income up to $10,000 and pays taxes on 6% of total income that exceeds $10,000. Will the effective tax rate be 6% for any amount of total income? *Justify* your answer graphically.

MIXED REVIEW

Write the fraction in simplest form. *(p. 912)*

51. $\dfrac{8}{12}$ **$\dfrac{2}{3}$**

52. $\dfrac{9}{45}$ **$\dfrac{1}{5}$**

53. $\dfrac{18}{30}$ **$\dfrac{3}{5}$**

Simplify the expression.

54. $4x^4 \cdot (2x^3)^4$ *(p. 489)* **$64x^{16}$**

55. $z^6 \cdot \dfrac{1}{z^2}$ *(p. 495)* **z^4**

56. $\dfrac{4a^3}{b^4} \cdot \left(\dfrac{b}{a^2}\right)^{-3}$ *(p. 495)* **$\dfrac{4a^9}{b^7}$**

57. $\sqrt{150}$ *(p. 719)* **$5\sqrt{6}$**

58. $\dfrac{4}{\sqrt{3}}$ *(p. 719)* **$\dfrac{4\sqrt{3}}{3}$**

59. $\dfrac{3}{\sqrt{15}}$ *(p. 719)* **$\dfrac{\sqrt{15}}{5}$**

PREVIEW
Prepare for Lesson 12.4 in Exs. 60–65.

Factor the polynomial.

60. $14x - 8x^2$ *(p. 575)*
$2x(7 - 4x)$

61. $x^2 - 13x + 40$ *(p. 583)*
$(x - 5)(x - 8)$

62. $-x^2 + 11x - 28$ *(p. 593)*
$-(x - 7)(x - 4)$

63. $12x^2 - 13x + 1$ *(p. 593)*
$(12x - 1)(x - 1)$

64. $-2x^2 - 3x + 20$ *(p. 593)*
$-(2x - 5)(x + 4)$

65. $5x^4 - 5x^2$ *(p. 600)*
$5x^2(x - 1)(x + 1)$

---

⑤ ASSESS AND RETEACH

Daily Homework Quiz

▢ **Transparency Available**

Divide.

1. $(6x^3 - 4x^2 + 18x) \div 2x$
   $3x^2 - 2x + 9$

2. $(3x^2 - x - 2) \div (x - 1)$ $3x + 2$

3. $(-20 + 4x^2) \div (5 + 2x)$
   $2x - 5 + \dfrac{5}{2x + 5}$

4. A print shop charges $15 plus $.12 per page to copy and bind reports. Write an equation that gives the average cost C per page as a function of the number of pages p that are copied.
   $C = \dfrac{15}{p} + 0.12$

🌐 **Online Quiz**

Available at **classzone.com**

Diagnosis/Remediation

• Practice A, B, C in Chapter 12 Resource Book, pp. 34–36
• Study Guide in Chapter 12 Resource Book, pp. 37–38
• Practice Workbook, pp. 186–187
• @HomeTutor

Challenge

Additional challenge is available in the Chapter 12 Resource Book, p. 41.

49a–c. See Additional Answers beginning on p. AA1.

50.

12.3 Find Asymptotes of Graphs

QUESTION How can you find the asymptotes of the graph of a rational function?

EXAMPLE 1 Graph a rational function

Graph $y = \dfrac{2x+1}{3x^2 - 4x + 5}$ using a graphing calculator. Identify any vertical or horizontal asymptotes.

STEP 1 *Enter function*
Press **Y=** and enter the function as shown.

STEP 2 *Identify asymptotes*
Graph the function. Use the *trace* feature to identify the asymptotes.

The graph doesn't approach a vertical line. So, the graph doesn't have a vertical asymptote. The graph approaches the *x*-axis. So, $y = 0$ is a horizontal asymptote.

PRACTICE

Graph the function using a graphing calculator. Identify any vertical or horizontal asymptotes. 1–6. See margin.

1. $y = \dfrac{8}{x-2}$

2. $y = \dfrac{4}{6x-7}$

3. $y = \dfrac{x-9}{x^2+1}$

4. $y = \dfrac{x+5}{x^2+4x+4}$

5. $y = \dfrac{x+1}{4x^2-36}$

6. $y = \dfrac{5}{10x^2+9}$

7. Make a table that shows the following information for each function in Exercises 1–6: **See margin.**

- vertical asymptotes, if any
- values, if any, of x that make the function undefined
- horizontal asymptotes, if any
- degree of numerator
- degree of denominator

792   Chapter 12 Rational Equations and Functions

1.

vertical: $x = 2$, horizontal: $y = 0$

2.

vertical: $x = \frac{7}{6}$, horizontal: $y = 0$

3.

vertical: none, horizontal: $y = 0$

4.

vertical: $x = -2$, horizontal: $y = 0$

EXAMPLE 2 Graph a rational function

Graph $y = \dfrac{2x^2 + 1}{x^2 - 9}$ using a graphing calculator. Identify any vertical or

horizontal asymptotes.

STEP 1 *Enter function*
Press Y= and enter the function as shown.

STEP 2 *Identify asymptotes*
Graph the function. Use the *trace* feature to identify the asymptotes.

The graph approaches one of two vertical lines, $x = -3$ and $x = 3$. So, $x = -3$ and $x = 3$ are vertical asymptotes. The graph also approaches the line $y = 2$. So, $y = 2$ is a horizontal asymptote.

PRACTICE

Graph the function using a graphing calculator. Identify any vertical or horizontal asymptotes. **8–13. See margin.**

8. $y = \dfrac{-6x}{x + 9}$

9. $y = \dfrac{5x - 12}{x - 1}$

10. $y = \dfrac{10x}{2x - 9}$

11. $y = \dfrac{12x^2 - 7}{4x^2 + 2}$

12. $y = \dfrac{27x^2 - x}{9x^2 - 16}$

13. $y = \dfrac{18x^2 - 1}{6x^2 - 6}$

14. Repeat Exercise 7 for the functions in Exercises 8–13. For each function, include in your table the quotient of the leading coefficient of the numerator and the leading coefficient of the denominator. **See margin.**

DRAW CONCLUSIONS

15. What vertical asymptotes, if any, does the graph of a rational function whose numerator and denominator do not have any common factors have?
Vertical lines $x = a$, where a is an x-value that makes the denominator of the rational function equal to 0.

16. If the degree of the numerator of a rational function is less than the degree of the denominator, what is a horizontal asymptote of the graph? **$y = 0$**

17. If the degree of the numerator of a rational function equals the degree of the denominator, what is a horizontal asymptote of the graph? **$y = a$, where a is the quotient of the leading coefficient of the numerator and the leading coefficient of the denominator.**

18. **CONJECTURE** Suppose the degree of the numerator of a rational function is greater than the degree of the denominator. Does the graph of the function have a horizontal asymptote? Give examples. **See margin.**

5.

vertical: $x = -3$, $x = 3$,
horizontal: $y = 0$

6.

1.0
0.8
0.6
0.4
0.2
0
−0.2

vertical: none,
horizontal: $y = 0$

7–14. See Additional Answers beginning on p. AA1.

Extra Example 2

Graph $y = \dfrac{x^2 + 4}{x^2 - 1}$ using a graphing calculator. Identify any vertical or horizontal asymptotes.

$y = 1$ is a horizontal asymptote and $x = 1$ and $x = -1$ are vertical asymptotes.

3 ASSESS AND RETEACH

Without graphing the following functions, explain whether they have a horizontal asymptote.

1. $y = \dfrac{x + 2}{x^2 + 6x + 8}$ There is a horizontal asymptote (it is $y = 0$) since the degree of the denominator is greater than the degree of the numerator.

2. $y = \dfrac{x + 4}{2x + 1}$ There is a horizontal asymptote $\left(\text{it is } y = \dfrac{1}{2}\right)$ since the degree of the denominator and the degree of the numerator are the same.

18. No. *Sample answer:* For example, a linear equation, such as $y = 2x$, can be written as a rational equation, $y = \dfrac{2x}{1}$, where the degree of the numerator is 1 and the degree of the denominator is 0. The graph of a linear equation is a straight line, which has no horizontal asymptote. A quadratic equation, such as $y = x^2$, can also be written as a rational equation, $y = \dfrac{x^2}{1}$, where the degree of the numerator is 2 and the degree of the denominator is 0. The graph of a quadratic equation is a parabola, which has no horizontal asymptote.

793

Simplify Rational Expressions

Before You simplified polynomials.

Now You will simplify rational expressions.

Why So you can model a cost over time, as in Example 5.

Key Vocabulary
• rational expression
• excluded value
• simplest form of a rational expression

A **rational expression** is an expression that can be written as a ratio of two polynomials where the denominator is not 0. A rational expression is undefined when the denominator is 0. A number that makes a rational expression undefined is called an **excluded value**. For example, $\dfrac{2}{x-3}$ is undefined when $x = 3$. So, 3 is an excluded value.

EXAMPLE 1 Find excluded values

Find the excluded values, if any, of the expression.

a. $\dfrac{x+8}{10x}$ **b.** $\dfrac{5}{2y+14}$ **c.** $\dfrac{4v}{v^2-9}$ **d.** $\dfrac{7w+2}{8w^2+w+5}$

Solution

a. The expression $\dfrac{x+8}{10x}$ is undefined when $10x = 0$, or $x = 0$.

▸ The excluded value is 0.

b. The expression $\dfrac{5}{2y+14}$ is undefined when $2y + 14 = 0$, or $x = -7$.

▸ The excluded value is −7.

c. The expression $\dfrac{4v}{v^2-9}$ is undefined when $v^2 - 9 = 0$, or $(v + 3)(v - 3) = 0$. The solutions of the equation are −3 and 3.

▸ The excluded values are −3 and 3.

d. The expression $\dfrac{7w+2}{8w^2+w+5}$ is undefined when $8w^2 + w + 5 = 0$.

The discriminant is $b^2 - 4ac = 1^2 - 4(8)(5) < 0$. So, the quadratic equation has no real roots.

▸ There are no excluded values.

REVIEW DISCRIMINANT
For help with finding the discriminant of a quadratic equation, see p. 678.

✓ **GUIDED PRACTICE** for Example 1

Find the excluded values, if any, of the expression.

1. $\dfrac{x+2}{3x-5}$ $\dfrac{5}{3}$ **2.** $\dfrac{2}{5y^2+2y+3}$ none   **3.** $\dfrac{n-6}{2n^2-5n-12}$ $-\dfrac{3}{2}, 4$ **4.** $\dfrac{2m}{m^2-4}$ −2, 2

SIMPLIFYING A RATIONAL EXPRESSION To simplify a rational expression, you factor the numerator and denominator and then divide out any common factors. A rational expression is in **simplest form** if the numerator and denominator have no factors in common other than 1.

KEY CONCEPT $\qquad\qquad\qquad\qquad\qquad$ *For Your Notebook*

Simplifying Rational Expressions

Let a, b, and c be polynomials where $b \neq 0$ and $c \neq 0$.

Algebra $\dfrac{ac}{bc} = \dfrac{a \cdot \cancel{c}}{b \cdot \cancel{c}} = \dfrac{a}{b}$ $\qquad\qquad$ **Example** $\dfrac{2x + 4}{3x + 6} = \dfrac{2(x + 2)}{3(x + 2)} = \dfrac{2}{3}$

EXAMPLE 2 $\quad$ Simplify expressions by dividing out monomials

Simplify the rational expression, if possible. State the excluded values.

a. $\dfrac{r}{2r}$ $\qquad$ **b.** $\dfrac{5x}{5(x + 2)}$ $\qquad$ **c.** $\dfrac{6m^3 - 12m^2}{18m^2}$ $\qquad$ **d.** $\dfrac{y}{7 - y}$

Solution

a. $\dfrac{r}{2r} = \dfrac{\cancel{r}}{2\cancel{r}}$ $\qquad\qquad$ Divide out common factor.

$\qquad = \dfrac{1}{2}$ $\qquad\qquad\qquad$ Simplify.

▶ The excluded value is 0.

b. $\dfrac{5x}{5(x + 2)} = \dfrac{\cancel{5} \cdot x}{\cancel{5} \cdot (x + 2)}$ $\qquad$ Divide out common factor.

$\qquad = \dfrac{x}{x + 2}$ $\qquad\qquad\qquad$ Simplify.

▶ The excluded value is −2.

c. $\dfrac{6m^3 - 12m^2}{18m^2} = \dfrac{6m^2(m - 2)}{6 \cdot 3 \cdot m^2}$ $\qquad$ Factor numerator and denominator.

$\qquad = \dfrac{\cancel{6m^2}(m - 2)}{\cancel{6} \cdot 3 \cdot \cancel{m^2}}$ $\qquad$ Divide out common factors.

$\qquad = \dfrac{m - 2}{3}$ $\qquad\qquad\qquad$ Simplify.

▶ The excluded value is 0.

d. The expression $\dfrac{y}{7 - y}$ is already in simplest form.

▶ The excluded value is 7.

 GUIDED PRACTICE $\quad$ for Example 2

Simplify the rational expression, if possible. State the excluded values.

5. $\dfrac{4a^3}{22a^6}$ $\quad$ $\dfrac{2}{11a^3}$; 0 $\qquad$ **6.** $\dfrac{2c}{c + 5}$ $\quad$ $\dfrac{2c}{c + 5}$; −5 $\qquad$ **7.** $\dfrac{2s^2 + 8s}{3s + 12}$ $\quad$ $\dfrac{2s}{3}$; −4 $\qquad$ **8.** $\dfrac{8x}{8x^3 + 16x^2}$

$\qquad\qquad\qquad\qquad\qquad\qquad\qquad\qquad\qquad\qquad\qquad\qquad\qquad\qquad\qquad \dfrac{1}{x^2 + 2x}$; 0, −2

Extra Example 3

Simplify $\dfrac{x^2 + x - 12}{x^2 - x - 6}$. State the

excluded values. $\dfrac{x+4}{x+2}$; $-2, 3$

Key Questions to Ask for Example 3

- What step makes it easier to determine excluded values? **If you factor the denominator, you can more easily tell what values would give a zero denominator.**

- Why is -2 an excluded value if the expression simplifies to $\dfrac{x-5}{x-4}$?
You use the original expression to find excluded values. In the original expression, -2 is an excluded value.

Extra Example 4

Simplify $\dfrac{x^2 - 7x + 10}{25 - x^2}$. State the

excluded values. $-\dfrac{x-2}{x+5}$; $-5, 5$

Key Question to Ask for Example 4

- Why can't you rewrite $(4 - x)$ as $(x - 4)$? **$(4 - x)$ is the opposite of $(x - 4)$.**

EXAMPLE 3 **Simplify an expression by dividing out binomials**

Simplify $\dfrac{x^2 - 3x - 10}{x^2 + 6x + 8}$. State the excluded values.

$$\dfrac{x^2 - 3x - 10}{x^2 + 6x + 8} = \dfrac{(x - 5)(x + 2)}{(x + 4)(x + 2)} \qquad \text{Factor numerator and denominator.}$$

$$= \dfrac{(x - 5)\cancel{(x + 2)}}{(x + 4)\cancel{(x + 2)}} \qquad \text{Divide out common factor.}$$

$$= \dfrac{x - 5}{x + 4} \qquad \text{Simplify.}$$

▶ The excluded values are -4 and -2.

INTERPRET THE GRAPH

Although the graphs of y_1 and y_2 appear to pass through $(-2, -3.5)$, the point is not on either graph because -2 is an excluded value of both y_1 and y_2.

CHECK   In the graphing calculator activity on page 560, you saw how to use a graph to check a sum or difference of polynomials.

Check your simplification using a graphing calculator.

Graph $y_1 = \dfrac{x^2 - 3x - 10}{x^2 + 6x + 8}$ and $y_2 = \dfrac{x - 5}{x + 4}$.

The graphs coincide. So, the expressions are equivalent for all values of x other than the excluded values (-4 and -2).

OPPOSITES   When simplifying a rational expression, look for factors that are opposites of each other. For example, $x - 1$ and $1 - x$ are opposites, because $x - 1 = -(1 - x)$.

EXAMPLE 4 **Recognize opposites**

Simplify $\dfrac{x^2 - 7x + 12}{16 - x^2}$. State the excluded values.

$$\dfrac{x^2 - 7x + 12}{16 - x^2} = \dfrac{(x - 3)(x - 4)}{(4 - x)(4 + x)} \qquad \text{Factor numerator and denominator.}$$

$$= \dfrac{(x - 3)(x - 4)}{-(x - 4)(4 + x)} \qquad \text{Rewrite } 4 - x \text{ as } -(x - 4).$$

$$= \dfrac{(x - 3)\cancel{(x - 4)}}{-\cancel{(x - 4)}(4 + x)} \qquad \text{Divide out common factor.}$$

$$= \dfrac{x - 3}{-(4 + x)} = -\dfrac{x - 3}{x + 4} \qquad \text{Simplify.}$$

▶ The excluded values are -4 and 4.

✓ **GUIDED PRACTICE**   for Examples 3 and 4

Simplify the rational expression. State the excluded values.

9. $\dfrac{x^2 + 3x + 2}{x^2 + 7x + 10}$ $\dfrac{x+1}{x+5}$; $-2, -5$ 10. $\dfrac{y^2 - 64}{y^2 - 16y + 64}$ $\dfrac{y+8}{y-8}$; 8 11. $\dfrac{5 + 4z - z^2}{z^2 - 3z - 10}$ $-\dfrac{z+1}{z+2}$; $5, -2$

EXAMPLE 5 Simplify a rational model

CELL PHONE COSTS The average cost C (in dollars per minute) for cell phone service in the United States during the period 1991–2000 can be modeled by

$$C = \frac{46 - 2.2x}{100 - 18x + 2.2x^2}$$

where x is the number of years since 1991. Rewrite the model so that it has only whole number coefficients. Then simplify the model.

1991 cell phone

Solution

$$C = \frac{46 - 2.2x}{100 - 18x + 2.2x^2} \qquad \text{Write model.}$$

$$= \frac{460 - 22x}{1000 - 180x + 22x^2} \qquad \text{Multiply numerator and denominator by 10.}$$

$$= \frac{2(230 - 11x)}{2(500\ \ 90x\ +\ 11x^2)} \qquad \text{Factor numerator and denominator.}$$

$$= \frac{\cancel{2}(230 - 11x)}{\cancel{2}(500 - 90x + 11x^2)} \qquad \text{Divide out common factor.}$$

$$= \frac{230 - 11x}{500 - 90x + 11x^2} \qquad \text{Simplify.}$$

 GUIDED PRACTICE   for Example 5

12. In Example 5, approximate the average cost per minute in 2000.
   about \$.23/min

12.4 EXERCISES

HOMEWORK KEY
○ = **WORKED-OUT SOLUTIONS**
on p. WS1 for Exs. 9, 23, and 43

★ = **STANDARDIZED TEST PRACTICE**
Exs. 2, 33, 34, 35, and 45

SKILL PRACTICE

[A] 1. **VOCABULARY** Copy and complete: A value that makes a rational expression undefined is called a(n) __?__. **excluded value**

2. ★ **WRITING** Is $\frac{(x + 3)(x - 6)}{(x - 3)(6 - x)}$ in simplest form? *Explain.* **See margin.**

EXAMPLE 1
on p. 794
for Exs. 3–10

FINDING EXCLUDED VALUES Find the excluded values, if any, of the expression.

3. $\frac{4x}{20}$ **none**   4. $\frac{13}{2y}$ **0**   5. $\frac{5}{r + 1}$ **−1**   6. $\frac{-s}{3s + 4}$ **−$\frac{4}{3}$**

7. $\frac{-m}{4m^2 - 3m + 9}$ **none** 8. $\frac{n + 2}{n^2 - 64}$ **−8, 8** ⑨ $\frac{-3}{2p^2 - p}$ **0, $\frac{1}{2}$** 10. $\frac{5q}{q^2 - 6q + 9}$ **3**

12.4 Simplify Rational Expressions **797**

Differentiated Instruction

Visual Learners Show students that an excluded value can be represented on a graph by an open circle or dashed vertical line. For **Example 3**, plot the graph of $y = \frac{x - 5}{x + 4}$ and place an open circle at the point $(-2, -3.5)$. The other excluded value can be illustrated by a dashed vertical line at $x = -4$.
See also the *Algebra 1 Toolkit* for more strategies.

Extra Example 5
The average amount of a customer's purchase P applied to a credit card account at a toy store during the period 1998–2004 can be modeled by $P = \frac{24 + 0.8x^2}{0.5 + 0.02x^2}$, where x is the number of years since 1998. Rewrite the model so that it has only whole number coefficients. Then simplify the model. $P = \frac{2400 + 80x^2}{50 + 2x^2}$;

$\frac{1200 + 40x^2}{25 + x^2}$

Key Questions to Ask for Example 5
• How do you approximate the average cost for cell phone service in 2000? **Since 2000 is 9 years since 1991, evaluate the model for $x = 9$.**
• Do you have to use the simplified model to approximate the cost for a particular year? Explain. **Either model will give the same value, but it may be easier to calculate with the simplified model.**

Closing the Lesson
Have students summarize the major points of the lesson and answer the Essential Question: How do you simplify a rational expression?
• **Exclude values that would result in a zero denominator.**
• **Some rational expressions can be simplified by factoring and dividing.**
To simplify a rational expression, factor the numerator and denominator, divide out the common factors, and note excluded values. When factoring, watch for expressions that are opposites.

2. No, after rewriting $6 - x$ in the denominator as $-1(x - 6)$, you can divide out the common factor of $x - 6$ from the numerator and denominator.

797

Assignment Guide

📖 **Answer Transparencies** available for all exercises

Basic:
Day 1: EP p. 946 Exs. 25–30
pp. 797–800
Exs. 1–12, 13–33 odd, 34–36,
40–44, 48, 52, 55, 58

Average:
Day 1: pp. 797–800
Exs. 1, 2, 7–12, 14–32 even, 33–38,
40–45, 49, 53, 56, 59

Advanced:
Day 1: pp. 797–800
Exs. 1, 8–11, 14–32 even, 33–46*,
50, 54, 57, 60

Block:
pp. 797–800
Exs. 1, 2, 7–12, 14–32 even, 33–38,
40–45, 49, 53, 56, 59 (with 12.5)

Differentiated Instruction

See *Algebra 1 Best Practices Toolkit* for suggestions on addressing the needs of a diverse classroom.

Homework Check

For a quick check of student understanding of key concepts, go over the following exercises:

Basic: 4, 14, 19, 28, 40

Average: 6, 16, 24, 30, 41

Advanced: 8, 16, 26, 32, 42

Extra Practice

• Student Edition, p. 946
• Chapter 12 Resource Book:
  Practice levels A, B, C, pp. 45–47

Practice Worksheet

An easily-readable reduced practice page (with answers) for this lesson can be found on p. 762C.

**EXAMPLES
2, 3, and 4**
on pp. 795–796
for Exs. 11–33

23. $\dfrac{1}{h-4}$; $-3, 4$

24. $\dfrac{1}{j-4}$; $2, 4$

25. $\dfrac{-12}{4w-10}$; $0, \dfrac{5}{2}$

26. $\dfrac{2y^3}{2y+3}$; $0, -\dfrac{3}{2}$

27. 3; $0, 4$

28. $\dfrac{7x}{x-1}$; $1, -\dfrac{3}{2}$

29. $\dfrac{s+8}{s-1}$; $1, -8$

30. $\dfrac{t+5}{2t-3}$; $9, \dfrac{3}{2}$

31. $\dfrac{1}{m^2+5m}$; $0, -5$

32. $-\dfrac{1}{3n}$; $-7, 0, 4$

ERROR ANALYSIS *Describe* and correct the error in simplifying the rational expression or in stating the excluded values.

11. $\dfrac{2x^2 - x - 3}{2x^2 - 11x + 12}$

$$\dfrac{2x^2 - x - 3}{2x^2 - 11x + 12} = \dfrac{(x+1)(2x-3)}{(2x-3)(x-4)}$$
$$= \dfrac{(x+1)\cancel{(2x-3)}}{\cancel{(2x-3)}(x-4)}$$
$$= \dfrac{x+1}{x-4}$$

The excluded value is 4. ✗

12. $\dfrac{2(x-5)}{(x-5)(x+2)}$

$$\dfrac{2(x-5)}{(x-5)(x+2)} = \dfrac{2\cancel{(x-5)}}{\cancel{(x-5)}(x+2)}$$
$$= \dfrac{2}{x+2}$$
$$= \dfrac{\cancel{2}}{x+\cancel{2}}$$
$$= \dfrac{1}{x+1}$$

The excluded values are −2 and 5. ✗

SIMPLIFYING EXPRESSIONS Simplify the rational expression, if possible. State the excluded values.

13. $\dfrac{10x}{25}$ $\dfrac{2x}{5}$; none

14. $\dfrac{63}{18y}$ $\dfrac{7}{2y}$; 0

15. $\dfrac{-48a^2}{16a}$ $-3a$; 0

16. $\dfrac{27b^2}{30b^5}$ $\dfrac{9}{10b^3}$; 0

17. $\dfrac{3c + 33}{c + 11}$ 3; -11

18. $\dfrac{d+8}{d-8}$ $\dfrac{d+8}{d-8}$; 8

19. $\dfrac{2u-6}{3-u}$ -2; 3

20. $\dfrac{v+2}{v^2-4}$ $\dfrac{1}{v-2}$; ± 2

21. $\dfrac{2}{f^2-9}$ $\dfrac{2}{f^2-9}$; ± 3

22. $\dfrac{g+4}{g^2-16}$ $\dfrac{1}{g-4}$; ± 4

23. $\dfrac{h+3}{h^2-h-12}$

24. $\dfrac{j-2}{j^2-6j+8}$

25. $\dfrac{-48w}{16w^2 - 40w}$

26. $\dfrac{12y^4}{12y^2 + 18y}$

27. $\dfrac{6z^2 - 24z}{2z^2 - 8z}$

28. $\dfrac{14x^2 + 21x}{2x^2 + x - 3}$

29. $\dfrac{s^2 + 16s + 64}{s^2 + 7s - 8}$

30. $\dfrac{t^2 - 4t - 45}{2t^2 - 21t + 27}$

31. $\dfrac{m+5}{m^3 + 10m^2 + 25m}$

32. $\dfrac{-n^2 - 3n + 28}{3n^3 + 9n^2 - 84n}$

33. ★ **WRITING** Are the rational expressions $\dfrac{x^2 + x}{x^2 - 1}$ and $\dfrac{x^2}{x^2 - x}$ equivalent?

   Explain how you know. What are the excluded values, if any, of the rational expressions? **See margin.**

B 34. ★ **OPEN-ENDED**   Write a rational expression whose excluded values are −3 and −5. **Sample answer:** $\dfrac{1}{x^2 + 8x + 15}$

35. ★ **MULTIPLE CHOICE** The expression $\dfrac{a}{x^2 + 5x - 6}$ simplifies to $\dfrac{2x+5}{x+6}$. What is a? **C**

   Ⓐ $2x^2 + 7x + 5$ Ⓑ $2x^2 + 5x - 1$ Ⓒ $2x^2 + 3x - 5$ Ⓓ $2x^2 + 7x - 5$

▱ **GEOMETRY** Write and simplify a rational expression for the ratio of the perimeter of the given figure to its area.

36. Square $\dfrac{4}{5x}$

37. Rectangle $\dfrac{3(x+2)}{x(x+6)}$

38. Triangle $\dfrac{3}{x}$

C 39. **CHALLENGE** Find two polynomials whose ratio simplifies to $\dfrac{3x-1}{2x+1}$ and whose sum is $5x^2 + 20x$. *Describe* your steps. **See margin.**

○ = **WORKED-OUT SOLUTIONS**
   on p. WS1

★ = **STANDARDIZED TEST PRACTICE**

---

11. When finding the excluded values you must find the values for which the denominator of the original expression, $2x^2 - 11x + 12$, is 0; the excluded values are $\dfrac{3}{2}$ and 4.

12. 2 cannot be divided out of the numerator and denominator of $\dfrac{2}{x+2}$ because 2 is not a factor of the denominator, $x + 2$; $\dfrac{2}{x+2}$.

33. No; the two expressions do not have the same excluded values; the excluded values for $\dfrac{x^2 + x}{x^2 - 1}$ are ± 1, while the excluded values for $\dfrac{x^2}{x^2 - x}$ are 0 and 1. The expressions are not equivalent for $x = 0$ and for $x = -1$.

PROBLEM SOLVING

EXAMPLE 5 [A]
on p. 797
for Exs. 40–43

40. CREDIT CARD FEES The average late payment fee F (in dollars) on a credit card account during the period 1994–2003 can be modeled by

$$F = \frac{12 + 1.6x^2}{1 + 0.04x^2}$$

where x is the number of years since 1994. Rewrite the model so that it has only whole number coefficients. Then simplify the model and approximate the average late payment fee in 2003.

@HomeTutor for problem solving help at classzone.com $F = \frac{300 + 40x^2}{25 + x^2}$; $33.40

41. TELEVISION For the period 1980–2003, the percent p (in decimal form) of non-network television commercials in the United States that lasted 15 seconds can be modeled by

$$p = \frac{0.12x^2 - 0.48}{0.88x^2 + 100}$$

where x is the number of years since 1980. Rewrite the model so that it has only whole number coefficients. Then simplify the model and approximate the percent of non-network television commercials in 2003 that lasted 15 seconds.

@HomeTutor for problem solving help at classzone.com $p = \frac{3x^2 - 12}{22x^2 + 2500}$; about 11%

42. CAR RADIOS A company forecasts that the number R (in thousands) of digital car radios sold annually and the sales S (in millions of dollars) of digital car radios during the period 2004–2007 can be modeled by

$$R = 190x^2 + 55x + 140 \qquad \text{and} \qquad S = 170x + 60$$

where x is the number of years since 2004. Write and simplify a model that gives the average price P (in thousands of dollars) of a digital car radio as a function of x. Then predict the average price in 2007. $P = \frac{34x + 12}{38x^2 + 11x + 28}$; about $280

(43.) HOUSES The total number H of new single-family houses and the number W of new single-family wood houses in the United States during the period 1990–2002 can be modeled by

$$H = 34,500x + 913,000$$
$$\text{and } W = -20,200x + 366,000$$

where x is the number of years since 1990. Write and simplify a model that gives the percent p (in decimal form) of the houses that were wood houses as a function of x. *Describe* how the percent that were wood houses changed during the period 1990–2002. $p = \frac{-202x + 3660}{345x + 9130}$; the percent of wood houses decreased.

[B] **44. AIRPORTS** The total number A of airports and the number P of private airports in the United States during the period 1989–2002 can be modeled by

$$A = 0.18x^3 + 140x + 17,000 \qquad \text{and} \qquad P = 0.16x^3 + 120x + 12,000$$

where x is the number of years since 1989. Using only whole number coefficients, write a model that gives the percent p (in decimal form) of all airports that were private airports. Simplify the model and approximate the percent of airports in 2002 that were private airports.

$p = \frac{8x^3 + 6000x + 600,000}{9x^3 + 7000x + 850,000}$; about 72%

12.4   Simplify Rational Expressions   **799**

Avoiding Common Errors

Exercises 13–32 Some students start to identify excluded values after expressions are simplified. Remind them to use the original expression. If they are in doubt about the excluded values, suggest they check whether the values would give a zero denominator.

🖩 Graphing Calculator

Exercises 13–32 Suggest that students use their graphing calculators to check their simplified expressions. They can use the check in Example 3, page 796, as a guide.

Reading Strategy

Exercises 40–41, 44–45 Encourage students to look carefully at each of the models in these exercises. Suggest that when they rewrite the models using only whole number coefficients, they pay close attention to place value.

---

39. $3x^2 + 11x - 4$, $2x^2 + 9x + 4$; if the ratio of the polynomials simplifies to $\frac{3x - 1}{2x + 1}$, then find a value a such that the ratio of the polynomials can be written in the form $\frac{(x + a)(3x - 1)}{(x + a)(2x + 1)}$. To solve for a, multiply out the factored polynomials, find their sum, and set the sum equal to $5x^2 + 20x$. Then solve for a. Substitute the value of a into the expressions for the polynomials and simplify.

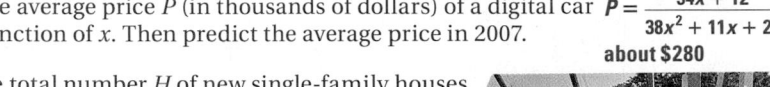

Daily Homework Quiz

📄 Transparency Available

Simplify the rational expression, if possible. Find the excluded values.

1. $\dfrac{12x^3}{18x^5}$ $\dfrac{2}{3}x^2; 0$

2. $\dfrac{2x - 14}{x^2 - 9x + 14}$ $\dfrac{2}{x - 2}; 2, 7$

3. The average cost C (in dollars per hour) for a cleaning service during the period 1994–2003 can be modeled by $C = \dfrac{52 - 1.4x}{10 - 14x + 2.1x^2}$, where x is the number of years since 1994. Rewrite the model so that it has only whole number coefficients. Then simplify the model, if necessary.

$C = \dfrac{520 - 14x}{100 - 140x + 21x^2}$

 Online Quiz

Available at classzone.com

Diagnosis/Remediation

• Practice A, B, C in Chapter 12 Resource Book, pp. 45–47
• Study Guide in Chapter 12 Resource Book, pp. 48–49
• Practice Workbook, pp. 188–189
• @HomeTutor

Challenge

Additional challenge is available in the Chapter 12 Resource Book, p. 53.

Quiz

An easily-readable reduced copy of the quiz (with answers) on Lessons 12.3–12.4 from the Assessment Book can be found on p. 762F.

45b, Quiz 3, 4. See Additional Answers beginning on p. AA1.

45a.

$\dfrac{37{,}500 + 2500x}{125 + x}$; about \$5 million

45c. No; if the price per copy of printed music went up during the period 1988–2002, then the revenue may have increased without the number of copies sold increasing.

45. ★ **EXTENDED RESPONSE** The revenue R (in millions of dollars) from sales of printed music in the United States during the period 1988–2002 can be modeled by

$$R = \frac{300 + 20x}{1 + 0.008x}$$

where x is the number of years since 1988.

a. **Model and Calculate** Rewrite the model so that it has only whole number coefficients. Then simplify the model and approximate the revenue from sales of printed music in 2002.

b. **Graph** Graph the model. *Describe* how revenue changed during the period. **See margin for art; revenue increased.**

c. **Decide** Can you use the model to conclude that the number of copies of printed music sold increased over time? *Explain*.

C 46. **CHALLENGE** The average annual expenses E (in dollars) of a middle income family and the average annual amount T (in dollars) spent on telephone service during the period 1992–2001 can be modeled by

$$E = 1240x + 24{,}800 \qquad \text{and} \qquad T = 31x + 620$$

where x is the number of years since 1992. Write and simplify a model to show that the average annual amount spent on telephone service was 2.5% of the average annual expenses during the period.

$\dfrac{T}{E} = \dfrac{31x + 620}{1240x + 24{,}800}$; $\dfrac{T}{E} = \dfrac{31(x + 20)}{1240(x + 20)}$; $\dfrac{T}{E} = \dfrac{31}{1240}$; $\dfrac{T}{E} = 0.025$. Thus, $T = 0.025E$, so T is 2.5% of E.

MIXED REVIEW

PREVIEW
Prepare for Lesson 12.5 in Exs. 47–54.

Multiply or divide. *(p. 915)*

47. $\dfrac{1}{3} \times \dfrac{1}{3}$ $\dfrac{1}{9}$

48. $\dfrac{2}{7} \times \dfrac{4}{5}$ $\dfrac{8}{35}$

49. $\dfrac{8}{5} \times \dfrac{1}{4}$ $\dfrac{2}{5}$

50. $\dfrac{5}{9} \times \dfrac{9}{10}$ $\dfrac{1}{2}$

51. $\dfrac{1}{4} \div \dfrac{1}{4}$ **1**

52. $\dfrac{2}{5} \div \dfrac{4}{11}$ $\dfrac{11}{10}$

53. $\dfrac{4}{9} \div \dfrac{4}{3}$ $\dfrac{1}{3}$

54. $\dfrac{14}{27} \div \dfrac{7}{4}$ $\dfrac{8}{27}$

Simplify the expression.

55. $9x - 3$

55. $5x - (-4x + 3)$ *(p. 96)*

56. $(-2x^2)^4$ *(p. 489)* $16x^8$

57. $8x^3 \cdot (3x^4)^3$ *(p. 489)* $216x^{15}$

58. $\dfrac{y^6}{8} \cdot \dfrac{2}{y^2}$ *(p. 495)* $\dfrac{y^4}{4}$

59. $\dfrac{12m^4}{n^4} \cdot \left(\dfrac{n}{m^0}\right)^6$ *(p. 495)* $12m^4n^2$

60. $\dfrac{x^2}{y^4} \cdot \left(\dfrac{y^6}{x^{-5}}\right)^{-1}$ *(p. 495)* $\dfrac{1}{x^3y^{10}}$

QUIZ *for Lessons 12.3–12.4*

Divide. *(p. 784)*

1. $(y^2 - 5y + 6) \div (y - 3)$ $y - 2$

2. $(x^2 + 3x - 28) \div (x - 6)$ $x + 9 + \dfrac{26}{x - 6}$

Graph the function. *(p. 784)*   **3–4. See margin.**

3. $y = \dfrac{x + 3}{x - 4}$

4. $y = \dfrac{2x - 1}{x + 3}$

Simplify the rational expression, if possible. State the excluded values. *(p. 794)*

5. $\dfrac{w + 10}{w^2 - 100}$ $\dfrac{1}{w - 10}$; ± 10

6. $\dfrac{250x^3}{14x}$ $\dfrac{125x^2}{7}$; 0

7. $\dfrac{y + 7}{y - 7}$ $\dfrac{y + 7}{y - 7}$; 7

8. $\dfrac{z^2 - 4z - 45}{3z^2 + 25z + 50}$ $\dfrac{z - 9}{3z + 10}$; $-\dfrac{10}{3}$, -5

800

EXTRA PRACTICE for Lesson 12.4, p. 949   **ONLINE QUIZ** at classzone.com

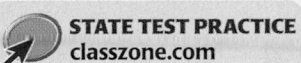

Lessons 12.1–12.4

1. MULTI-STEP PROBLEM A bookseller uses shipping cartons in the shape of rectangular prisms. The cartons have the same size base but vary in height.

BOOKS BOOKS h cm
24 cm
26 cm

a. Write an equation that gives the ratio r of surface area to volume as a function of the height h. Then graph the equation. **See margin.**

b. The lesser the ratio, the more efficient the carton is. *Describe* how the efficiency of the carton changes as the height increases. **The efficiency increases.**

2. GRIDDED ANSWER You and some friends are taking a car trip to an amusement park. Admission costs $50 per person, and everyone will share the combined cost of gas and parking, which is $30. How much more (in dollars) will one person pay if 4 people go on the trip than if 5 people go? **$1.50**

3. OPEN-ENDED A city's population density (in people per square mile) is the ratio of the population of the city to the area (in square miles) of the city. Suppose that a city has a population of 150,000 people and an area of 40 square miles. *Describe* two ways that the population density can decrease to 3125 people per square mile. **See margin.**

4. MULTI-STEP PROBLEM The average amount A (in pounds per person) of fish and shellfish consumed in the United States during the period 1992–2001 can be modeled by

$$A = \frac{52x + 3800}{3.2x + 260}$$

where x is the number of years since 1992.

a. Rewrite the model so that it has only whole number coefficients. Then simplify the model. $A = \dfrac{65x + 4750}{4x + 325}$

b. Approximate the average amount of fish and shellfish consumed per person in 2001. **about 15 pounds per person**

5. EXTENDED RESPONSE A professional baseball team may pay a luxury tax if the team's combined annual salary exceeds a certain amount. In 2003, a team whose combined annual salary exceeded $117 million paid a luxury tax of 17.5% on the amount over $117 million. **a–c. See margin.**

a. Write an equation that gives the percent p (in decimal form) of the salary paid in luxury tax as a function of the salary s (in millions of dollars) for $s > 117$.

b. Graph the function. *Describe* how the percent changed as the salary increased.

c. Was it possible for a team to pay 17.5% of its salary in luxury tax? *Explain.*

6. SHORT RESPONSE You plan to hike a mountain trail that is 15 miles long and stop halfway to camp overnight for 10 hours.

a. Write an equation that gives the combined time t (in hours) for hiking and camping as a function of the average rate r (in miles per hour) at which you hike. Then graph the equation. $t = \dfrac{15}{r} + 10$; **see margin for art.**

b. *Explain* how the graph would change if you camped for 12 hours instead of 10 hours. **See margin.**

7. SHORT RESPONSE The table shows the relationship between the volume V (in liters) and the pressure P (in kilopascals) of a gas in a cylindrical container.

Volume, V (L)	Pressure, P (kPa)
20	1
5	4
2.5	8
1.6	12.5
0.4	50

a, b. See margin.

a. *Explain* why the volume and pressure are inversely related. Then write an equation that relates the volume and the pressure.

b. Suppose that only the height of the container can be changed. *Describe* how the pressure changes as the height increases.

1a. $r = \dfrac{2}{h} + \dfrac{25}{156}$;

$r = \dfrac{2}{h} + \dfrac{25}{156}$

Ratio of surface area to volume
Height (feet)

3. *Sample answer:* The city's population decreases to 125,000 people while its area remains the same; the city's population increases to 156,250 people when 10 square miles of surrounding land are added to its area.

5a. $p = \dfrac{0.175s - 20.475}{s}$

5b.

$p = \dfrac{0.175s - 20.475}{s}$

Percent
Salary (millions of dollars)

The percent increases.

5c. No; the graph in part (b) approaches its horizontal asymptote $p = 0.175$ from below, so the percent of the salary paid in luxury tax is always less than 17.5%.

6a.

$t = \dfrac{15}{r} + 10$

Combined time (hours)
Average rate (mi/h)

6b. The horizontal asymptote would change from $t = 10$ to $t = 12$.

7a. For each pair of values (V, P), the product VP is the same number, 20; $P = \dfrac{20}{V}$.

7b. The pressure decreases.

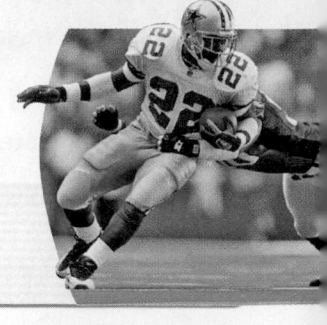

12.5 Multiply and Divide Rational Expressions

Before You multiplied and divided polynomials.

Now You will multiply and divide rational expressions.

Why? So you can describe football data, as in Ex. 35.

Key Vocabulary
- **multiplicative inverse,** *p. 103*
- **polynomial,** *p. 554*
- **rational expression,** *p. 794*

Multiplying and dividing rational expressions is similar to multiplying and dividing numerical fractions.

KEY CONCEPT   *For Your Notebook*

Multiplying and Dividing Rational Expressions

Let a, b, c, and d be polynomials.

Algebra $\dfrac{a}{b} \cdot \dfrac{c}{d} = \dfrac{ac}{bd}$ where $b \neq 0$ and $d \neq 0$

$\dfrac{a}{b} \div \dfrac{c}{d} = \dfrac{a}{b} \cdot \dfrac{d}{c} = \dfrac{ad}{bc}$ where $b \neq 0$, $c \neq 0$, and $d \neq 0$

Examples $\dfrac{x+2}{x} \cdot \dfrac{3}{x^2} = \dfrac{3(x+2)}{x^3}$ $\dfrac{x}{x-1} \div \dfrac{4}{x} = \dfrac{x}{x-1} \cdot \dfrac{x}{4} = \dfrac{x^2}{4(x-1)}$

EXAMPLE 1 Multiply rational expressions involving monomials

Find the product $\dfrac{2x^2}{3x} \cdot \dfrac{6x^2}{12x^3}$.

APPLY EXCLUDED VALUES

When performing operations with rational expressions, remember that the answer may have excluded values. In Example 1, the excluded value is 0.

$\dfrac{2x^2}{3x} \cdot \dfrac{6x^2}{12x^3} = \dfrac{(2x^2)(6x^2)}{(3x)(12x^3)}$ Multiply numerators and denominators.

$= \dfrac{12x^4}{36x^4}$ Product of powers property

$= \dfrac{\cancel{12} \cdot \cancel{x^4}}{3 \cdot \cancel{12} \cdot \cancel{x^4}}$ Factor and divide out common factors.

$= \dfrac{1}{3}$ Simplify.

✓ **GUIDED PRACTICE**   for Example 1

Find the product.

1. $\dfrac{2y^3}{5y} \cdot \dfrac{15y^3}{8y^5}$ **3/4**

2. $\dfrac{7z^2}{4z^3} \cdot \dfrac{z^3}{14z}$ **z/8**

EXAMPLE 2 Multiply rational expressions involving polynomials

Find the product $\dfrac{3x^2 + 3x}{4x^2 - 24x + 36} \cdot \dfrac{x^2 - 4x + 3}{x^2 - x}$.

$$\dfrac{3x^2 + 3x}{4x^2 - 24x + 36} \cdot \dfrac{x^2 - 4x + 3}{x^2 - x}$$

$$= \dfrac{(3x^2 + 3x)(x^2 - 4x + 3)}{(4x^2 - 24x + 36)(x^2 - x)}$$ Multiply numerators and denominators.

$$= \dfrac{3x(x + 1)(x - 3)(x - 1)}{4x(x - 3)(x - 3)(x - 1)}$$ Factor and divide out common factors.

$$= \dfrac{3(x + 1)}{4(x - 3)}$$ Simplify.

CHECK Check your simplification using a graphing calculator.

Graph $y_1 = \dfrac{3x^2 + 3x}{4x^2 - 24x + 36} \cdot \dfrac{x^2 - 4x + 3}{x^2 - x}$

and $y_2 = \dfrac{3(x + 1)}{4(x - 3)}$.

The graphs coincide. So, the expressions are equivalent for all values of x other than the excluded values (0, 1, and 3).

MULTIPLYING BY A POLYNOMIAL When you multiply a rational expression by a polynomial, first write the polynomial as a fraction with a denominator of 1.

EXAMPLE 3 Multiply a rational expression by a polynomial

Find the product $\dfrac{5x}{x^2 + 5x + 6} \cdot (x + 3)$.

$$\dfrac{5x}{x^2 + 5x + 6} \cdot (x + 3)$$

$$= \dfrac{5x}{x^2 + 5x + 6} \cdot \dfrac{x + 3}{1}$$ Rewrite polynomial as a fraction.

$$= \dfrac{5x(x + 3)}{x^2 + 5x + 6}$$ Multiply numerators and denominators.

$$= \dfrac{5x(x + 3)}{(x + 2)(x + 3)}$$ Factor and divide out common factor.

$$= \dfrac{5x}{x + 2}$$ Simplify.

✓ **GUIDED PRACTICE** for Examples 2 and 3

Find the product.

3. $\dfrac{x^2 + x - 2}{x^2 + 2x} \cdot \dfrac{2x^2 + 2x}{5x^2 - 15x + 10}$ $\dfrac{2(x + 1)}{5(x - 2)}$

4. $\dfrac{2w^2}{w^2 - 7w + 12} \cdot (w - 4)$ $\dfrac{2w^2}{w - 3}$

12.5 Multiply and Divide Rational Expressions **803**

Differentiated Instruction

Below Level It may help students to see that the original expressions and the simplified expressions in **Examples 1–3** are equivalent if they substitute values for the variables. Have students substitute 2 for x in the original expression in Example 1 and then compare it to the simplified expression. Have them do the same for Examples 2 and 3. To make sure that they understand the concept, have them substitute 3 for Example 2 and ask them to explain the results.

See also the *Algebra 1 Toolkit* for more strategies.

Motivating the Lesson

A local basketball association wants to report some statistics for a brochure. They have expressions that model the total number of points per game and the total number of free throw points per game for the past 6 years. By learning how to divide rational expressions, you can determine what percent of the total points scored were free throws.

❸ TEACH

Extra Example 1

Find the product $\dfrac{3x^2}{2x} \cdot \dfrac{8x^3}{15x} \cdot \dfrac{4x^3}{5}$

Key Question to Ask for Example 1

• What is the product of powers property? $a^m \cdot a^n = a^{m + n}$

Extra Example 2

Find the product

$\dfrac{3x + 6}{3x^2 + 18x + 27} \cdot \dfrac{x^2 - x - 12}{x^2 - 4}.$

$\dfrac{x - 4}{(x + 3)(x - 2)}$

Extra Example 3

Find the product

$\dfrac{4x^2}{x^2 + 3x - 10} \cdot (x - 2).$ $\dfrac{4x^2}{x + 5}$

Key Question to Ask for Example 3

• Are there any excluded values in the expression? Explain. **The two excluded values are −3 and −2, even though −3 is not an excluded value for the simplified product.**

803

Extra Example 4

Find the quotient

$$\frac{x^2 - 9}{x^2 + 5x + 6} \div \frac{4x^2 - 12x}{x^2 - 2x - 8} \cdot \frac{x - 4}{4x}$$

Key Questions to Ask for Example 4

• How do you find the multiplicative inverse of an expression? **Switch the numerator and denominator.**

• How do you check whether two expressions are multiplicative inverses? **Their product is 1.**

Extra Example 5

Find the quotient

$$\frac{3x^2 + 24x + 36}{6x + 9} \div (x + 2). \ \frac{x + 6}{x + 3}$$

Key Questions to Ask for Example 5

• What are the excluded values? **0, −6**

• What can you tell about the graph

of $y = \dfrac{2x^2 + 16x + 24}{3x^2} \div (x + 6)$

by looking at the expression? **A vertical asymptote is $x = 0$.**

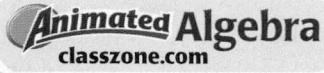
Animated Algebra
classzone.com

An **Animated Algebra** activity is available on-line for **Example 5**. This activity is also available on the **Power Presentations CD-ROM**.

DIVIDING RATIONAL EXPRESSIONS To divide by a rational expression, multiply by its multiplicative inverse.

EXAMPLE 4 **Divide rational expressions involving polynomials**

Find the quotient $\dfrac{7x^2 - 7x}{x^2 + 2x - 3} \div \dfrac{x + 1}{x^2 - 7x - 8}$.

REVIEW INVERSES
For help with finding the multiplicative inverse of a number, see p. 103.

$$\frac{7x^2 - 7x}{x^2 + 2x - 3} \div \frac{x + 1}{x^2 - 7x - 8}$$

$$= \frac{7x^2 - 7x}{x^2 + 2x - 3} \cdot \frac{x^2 - 7x - 8}{x + 1} \qquad \text{Multiply by multiplicative inverse.}$$

$$= \frac{(7x^2 - 7x)(x^2 - 7x - 8)}{(x^2 + 2x - 3)(x + 1)} \qquad \text{Multiply numerators and denominators.}$$

$$= \frac{7x(x - 1)(x - 8)(x + 1)}{(x + 3)(x - 1)(x + 1)} \qquad \text{Factor and divide out common factors.}$$

$$= \frac{7x(x - 8)}{x + 3} \qquad \text{Simplify.}$$

DIVIDING BY A POLYNOMIAL When you divide a rational expression by a polynomial, first write the polynomial as a fraction with a denominator of 1. Then multiply by the multiplicative inverse of the polynomial.

EXAMPLE 5 **Divide a rational expression by a polynomial**

Find the quotient $\dfrac{2x^2 + 16x + 24}{3x^2} \div (x + 6)$.

$$\frac{2x^2 + 16x + 24}{3x^2} \div (x + 6)$$

$$= \frac{2x^2 + 16x + 24}{3x^2} \div \frac{x + 6}{1} \qquad \text{Rewrite polynomial as fraction.}$$

$$= \frac{2x^2 + 16x + 24}{3x^2} \cdot \frac{1}{x + 6} \qquad \text{Multiply by multiplicative inverse.}$$

$$= \frac{2x^2 + 16x + 24}{3x^2(x + 6)} \qquad \text{Multiply numerators and denominators.}$$

$$= \frac{2(x + 2)(x + 6)}{3x^2(x + 6)} \qquad \text{Factor and divide out common factor.}$$

$$= \frac{2(x + 2)}{3x^2} \qquad \text{Simplify.}$$

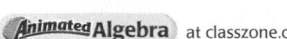 at classzone.com

---

✓ **GUIDED PRACTICE** for Examples 4 and 5

Find the quotient.

5. $\dfrac{m^2 - 4}{2m^2 + 4m} \div \dfrac{6m - 3m^2}{4m + 44} \ \dfrac{-2(m + 11)}{3m^2}$

6. $\dfrac{n^2 - 6n + 9}{12n} \div (n - 3) \ \dfrac{n - 3}{12n}$

Differentiated Instruction

Kinesthetic Learners The excluded values of the quotient are the x-values that make the value of any denominator equal to zero. In **Example 4**, the excluded values include not only $x = -3$, but also $x = -1, 1,$ and 8. Students can find the excluded values by using the TABLE feature of a calculator. Because the quotient is complicated, let $Y_1 = \dfrac{7x^2 - 7x}{x^2 + 2x - 3}$, $Y_2 = \dfrac{x + 1}{x^2 - 7x - 8}$, and $Y_3 = \dfrac{Y_1}{Y_2}$. Make a TABLE of values for Y_3.

See also the *Algebra 1 Toolkit* for more strategies.

EXAMPLE 6 Solve a multi-step problem

ADVERTISING The amount A (in millions of dollars) spent on all advertising and the amount T (in millions of dollars) spent on television advertising in the United States during the period 1970–2003 can be modeled by

$$A = \frac{13{,}000 + 3700x}{1 - 0.015x} \quad \text{and} \quad T = \frac{1800 + 860x}{1 - 0.016x}$$

where x is the number of years since 1970. Write a model that gives the percent p (in decimal form) of the amount spent on all advertising that was spent on television advertising. Then approximate the percent spent on television advertising in 2003.

Solution

STEP 1 **Write** a verbal model. Then write an equation.

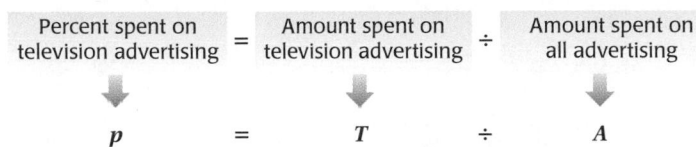

$$p \qquad = \qquad T \qquad \div \qquad A$$

STEP 2 **Find** the quotient.

$p = T \div A$ Write equation.

$= \dfrac{1800 + 860x}{1 - 0.016x} \div \dfrac{13{,}000 + 3700x}{1 - 0.015x}$ **Substitute for T and for A.**

$= \dfrac{1800 + 860x}{1 - 0.016x} \cdot \dfrac{1 - 0.015x}{13{,}000 + 3700x}$ **Multiply by multiplicative inverse.**

$= \dfrac{(1800 + 860x)(1 - 0.015x)}{(1 - 0.016x)(13{,}000 + 3700x)}$ **Multiply numerators and denominators.**

$= \dfrac{\cancel{20}(90 + 43x)(1 - 0.015x)}{(1 - 0.016x)\cancel{(20)}(650 + 185x)}$ **Factor and divide out common factor.**

$= \dfrac{(90 + 43x)(1 - 0.015x)}{(1 - 0.016x)(650 + 185x)}$ **Simplify.**

STEP 3 **Approximate** the percent spent on television advertising in 2003. Because $2003 - 1970 = 33$, $x = 33$. Substitute 33 for x in the model and use a calculator to evaluate.

$$p = \frac{(90 + 43 \cdot 33)(1 - 0.015 \cdot 33)}{(1 - 0.016 \cdot 33)(650 + 185 \cdot 33)} \approx 0.239$$

▶ About 24% of the amount spent on all advertising was spent on television advertising in 2003.

✓ **GUIDED PRACTICE** for Example 6

7. About $63,941 million, about $267,525 million; about 0.239; the answers are the same.

7. In Example 6, find the values of T and of A separately when $x = 33$. Then divide the value of T by the value of A. *Compare* your answer with the answer in Step 3 above.

12.5 **EXERCISES**

HOMEWORK KEY
○ = **WORKED-OUT SOLUTIONS**
on p. WS1 for Exs. 5, 15, and 35
★ = **STANDARDIZED TEST PRACTICE**
Exs. 2, 21, 26, 27, 28, 36, and 37
◆ = **MULTIPLE REPRESENTATIONS**
Ex. 35

④ PRACTICE AND APPLY

Assignment Guide

📖 **Answer Transparencies available for all exercises**

Basic:
Day 1: EP p. 946 Exs. 49–57 odd
pp. 806–809
Exs. 1–10, 12, 22, 23, 47–52
Day 2: pp. 806–809
Exs. 11, 13–21, 24–26, 33–36, 39–46

Average:
Day 1: pp. 806–809
Exs. 1, 2, 4–10, 12, 22, 23, 29, 47–52
Day 2: pp. 806–809
Exs. 11, 13–21, 24–28, 30, 33–37, 39–45 odd

Advanced:
Day 1: pp. 806–809
Exs. 1, 4–10, 22, 23, 29–31*, 47–52
Day 2: pp. 806–809
Exs. 13–21, 24–28, 32–38*, 40–46 even

Block:
pp. 806–809
Exs. 1, 2, 4–10, 12, 22, 23, 29, 47–52
(with 12.4)
pp. 806–809
Exs. 11, 13–21, 24–28, 30, 33–37, 39–45 odd (with 12.6)

Differentiated Instruction

See *Algebra 1 Best Practices Toolkit* for suggestions on addressing the needs of a diverse classroom.

Homework Check

For a quick check of student understanding of key concepts, go over the following exercises:
Basic: 4, 8, 14, 16, 33
Average: 6, 9, 17, 19, 34
Advanced: 7, 10, 18, 20, 35

Extra Practice

• Student Edition, p. 946
• Chapter 12 Resource Book:
Practice levels A, B, C, pp. 58–60

Practice Worksheet

An easily-readable reduced practice page (with answers) for this lesson can be found on p. 762C.

SKILL PRACTICE

A
1. **VOCABULARY** Copy and complete: To divide by a rational expression, multiply by its __?__. **multiplicative inverse**

2. ★ **WRITING** *Describe* how to multiply a rational expression by a polynomial. **See margin.**

EXAMPLES 1, 2, and 3
on pp. 802–803
for Exs. 3–10, 12

MULTIPLYING EXPRESSIONS Find the product.

3. $\dfrac{9p^2}{7} \cdot \dfrac{5}{6p^4}$ **$\dfrac{15}{14p^2}$**

4. $\dfrac{5}{8q^6} \cdot \dfrac{4q^5}{3}$ **$\dfrac{5}{6q}$**

5. $\dfrac{v^2 + v - 12}{5v + 10} \cdot \dfrac{-v - 2}{v^2 + 5v + 4}$ **$\dfrac{-(v-3)}{5(v+1)}$**

6. $\dfrac{y - 2}{-2y^2 - 10y} \cdot \dfrac{4y^2 + 20y}{y^2 - 4}$ **$\dfrac{-2}{y+2}$**

7. $\dfrac{5x}{2x^3 - 17x^2 - 9x} \cdot \dfrac{4x^2 - 20x - 144}{20}$ **$\dfrac{x+4}{2x+1}$**

8. $\dfrac{r^5}{7r^3 + 56r} \cdot (r^2 + 8)$ **$\dfrac{r^4}{7}$**

9. $\dfrac{-3m}{m^2 - 7m + 10} \cdot (m - 5)$ **$\dfrac{-3m}{m-2}$**

10. $\dfrac{2n - 6}{3n^2 - 7n - 6} \cdot (3n^2 + 14n + 8)$ **$2(n+4)$**

EXAMPLES 4 and 5
on p. 804
for Exs. 11, 13–21

ERROR ANALYSIS *Describe* and correct the error in finding the product or quotient. **11–12. See margin.**

11. $\dfrac{x^3}{5} \div \dfrac{15x^3}{2}$

$\dfrac{x^3}{5} \div \dfrac{15x^3}{2} = \dfrac{5}{x^3} \cdot \dfrac{15x^3}{2}$

$= \dfrac{75x^3}{2x^3}$

$= \dfrac{75}{2}$

12. $\dfrac{x - 2}{x + 5} \cdot \dfrac{x}{2 - x}$

$\dfrac{x - 2}{x + 5} \cdot \dfrac{x}{2 - x} = \dfrac{(x - 2)x}{(x + 5)(2 - x)}$

$= \dfrac{(x - 2)x}{(x + 5)(2 - x)}$

$= \dfrac{x}{x + 5}$

DIVIDING EXPRESSIONS Find the quotient.

13. $\dfrac{16r^2}{3} \div \dfrac{12}{5r}$ **$\dfrac{20r^3}{9}$**

14. $\dfrac{25s^{12}}{18} \div \dfrac{5s^6}{2}$ **$\dfrac{5s^6}{9}$**

15. $\dfrac{2w^2 + 5w}{w^2 - 81} \div \dfrac{w^2}{w + 9}$ **$\dfrac{2w + 5}{w(w - 9)}$**

16. $\dfrac{c^2 + c}{c^2 + c - 30} \div \dfrac{c - 6}{c^2 - 11c + 30}$ **$\dfrac{c(c + 1)}{c + 6}$**

17. $\dfrac{a^2 + 3a - 10}{a^2 + 6a - 7} \div \dfrac{9a^3 - 18a^2}{3a^2 + 18a - 21}$ **$\dfrac{a + 5}{3a^2}$**

18. $\dfrac{2x^2 - 9x + 9}{35x + 14} \div \dfrac{-3x^2 + 13x - 12}{15x^2 - 14x - 8}$ **$\dfrac{3 - 2x}{7}$**

19. $\dfrac{4k^2 + 4k - 15}{2k - 3} \div (2k + 5)$ **1**

20. $\dfrac{t^2 - 9t - 22}{5t - 1} \div (5t^2 + 9t - 2)$ **$\dfrac{t - 11}{(5t - 1)^2}$**

21. ★ **MULTIPLE CHOICE** What common factor do you divide out when finding the quotient $\dfrac{x^2 - 3x + 2}{x^2 - 2x - 3} \div \dfrac{x^2 + 4x + 3}{x^2 - 7x + 12}$? **B**

Ⓐ $x - 1$ Ⓑ $x - 3$ Ⓒ $x + 1$ Ⓓ $x + 3$

---

2. First write the polynomial as a fraction with a denominator of 1. Then write the product of the numerators over the product of the denominators, leaving the products in factored form. Factor the numerator and denominator completely and divide out any common factors.

11. To divide by the rational expression $\dfrac{15x^3}{2}$, you must multiply by its multiplicative inverse, $\dfrac{2}{15x^3}$. $\dfrac{x^3}{5} \cdot \dfrac{2}{15x^3} = \dfrac{2x^3}{75x^3} = \dfrac{2}{75}$.

24. $(x^2 + 3x - 18) \div \frac{x+6}{2}$; $2(x-3)$

R TRANSLATING PHRASES Translate the verbal phrase into a product or quotient of rational expressions. Then find the product or quotient.

22. The product of $x + 3$ and the ratio of $x + 5$ to $x^2 - 9$ $(x+3) \cdot \frac{x+5}{x^2-9}$; $\frac{x+5}{x-3}$

23. The product of $8x^2$ and the multiplicative inverse of $2x^3$ $8x^2 \cdot \frac{1}{2x^3}$; $\frac{4}{x}$

24. The quotient of $x^2 + 3x - 18$ and the ratio of $x + 6$ to 2

25. The quotient of the multiplicative inverse of $x^2 - 3x - 4$ and twice the multiplicative inverse of $x^2 - 1$ $\frac{1}{x^2-3x-4} \div \frac{2}{x^2-1}$; $\frac{x-1}{2(x-4)}$

26. ★ MULTIPLE CHOICE What is the quotient $\frac{x^2-1}{-(x+1)} \div (x-1)$? A

     (A) -1 (B) 0 (C) 1 (D) $x^2 - 1$

★ OPEN-ENDED   Let a, b, c, and d be different polynomials. Find two rational expressions $\frac{a}{b}$ and $\frac{c}{d}$ that satisfy the given conditions.

27. The product of the rational expressions is $\frac{x-3}{x+2}$, and the excluded values are $-2, -1, 4$, and 5. Sample answer: $\frac{x^2-2x-3}{x^2-2x-8}, \frac{x^2-9x+20}{x^2-4x-5}$

28. The quotient of the rational expressions is $\frac{x-6}{x+4}$, and the excluded values are $-4, -2, 3$, and 6. Sample answer: $\frac{x^2-4x-12}{x^2-2x-24}, \frac{x^2-x-6}{x^2-9x+18}$

GEOMETRY Write an expression for the area of the figure. Find a value of x less than 5 for which the given dimensions and the area are positive.

29. Rectangle

$\frac{x^2-6x+5}{x+2}$

$\frac{x^2-x-6}{x-5}$

$(x-1)(x-3)$. Sample answer: 0

30. Triangle

$\frac{2x^2+2x-24}{2x+1}$

$\frac{2x^2-x-1}{x-3}$

$(x-1)(x+4)$. Sample answer: 4

C CHALLENGE Let a be a polynomial in the given equation. Find a.

31. $\frac{a}{x+2} \cdot \frac{3x^2+5x-2}{x-4} = 6x^2 + 7x - 3$
$2x^2 - 5x - 12$

32. $\frac{8x^2-2x-3}{x-5} \div \frac{2x+1}{a} = 12x^2 - x - 6$
$3x^2 - 13x - 10$

PROBLEM SOLVING

EXAMPLE 6 A
on p. 805
for Exs. 33–35

33. VEHICLES The total distance M (in billions of miles) traveled by all motor vehicles and the distance T (in billions of miles) traveled by trucks in the United States during the period 1980–2002 can be modeled by

$$M = 1500 + 63x \qquad \text{and} \qquad T = \frac{100 + 2.2x}{1 - 0.014x}$$

where x is the number of years since 1980. Write a model that gives the percent p (in decimal form) of the total motor vehicle distance that was traveled by trucks as a function of x. Then approximate the percent traveled by trucks in 2002. See margin.

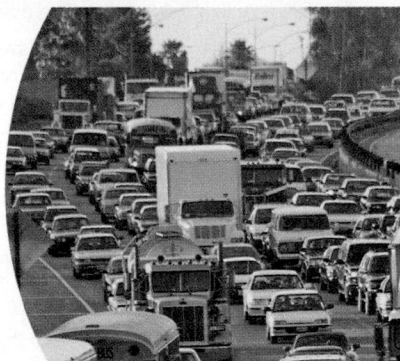

@HomeTutor for problem solving help at classzone.com

Avoiding Common Errors

Exercises 13–21 Watch for students who do not rewrite division as multiplication. Remind students that when they see a division symbol, they should multiply by the reciprocal.

Reading Strategy

Exercises 5, 15, 33 Point out to students that each of these exercises is circled in red, which means that there is a worked-out solution. Encourage them to solve the problem first and then check their solutions against the worked-out solutions.

12. Before dividing out the common factor $(x - 2)$, you must first rewrite the factor $(2 - x)$ in the denominator as $-1(x - 2)$, leaving a factor of -1 in the denominator; $\frac{(x-2)x}{-1(x+5)(x-2)} = \frac{-x}{x+5}$.

33. $p = \frac{100 + 2.2x}{(1 - 0.014x)(1500 + 63x)}$; about 7%

34. CONSUMER SPENDING The average annual amount T (in dollars) spent on reading and entertainment and the average annual amount E (in dollars) spent on entertainment by consumers in the United States during the period 1985–2002 can be modeled by

$$T = \frac{1300 + 84x}{1 + 0.015x} \quad \text{and} \quad E = \frac{1100 + 64x}{1 + 0.0062x}$$

where x is the number of years since 1985. Write a model that gives the percent p (in decimal form) of the amount spent on reading and entertainment that was spent on entertainment as a function of x. Then approximate the percent spent on entertainment in 2000.

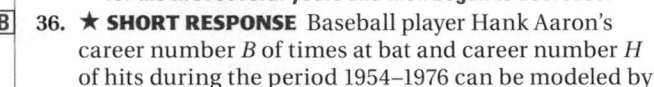 **@HomeTutor** for problem solving help at classzone.com $\quad p = \dfrac{(275 + 16x)(1 + 0.015x)}{(1 + 0.0062x)(325 + 21x)}$; about 90%

35. ◆ **MULTIPLE REPRESENTATIONS** Football player Emmitt Smith's career number Y of rushing yards gained and his career number A of rushing attempts from 1990 (when he started playing professional football) through the 2002 football season can be modeled by

$$Y = \frac{860 + 1800x}{1 + 0.024x} \quad \text{and} \quad A = \frac{230 + 380x}{1 + 0.014x}$$

where x is the number of years since 1990.

a. Writing an Equation A football player's rushing average is the number of rushing yards gained divided by the number of rushing attempts. Write a model that gives Smith's career rushing average R as a function of x for the period 1990–2002. $\quad R = \dfrac{(86 + 180x)(1 + 0.014x)}{(1 + 0.024x)(23 + 38x)}$

b. Making a Table Make a table that shows Smith's approximate career rushing average (rounded to the nearest hundredth) for each year during the period. *Describe* how the career rushing average changed over time. **See margin for table; Smith's career rushing average increased for the first several years and then began to decrease.**

B **36.** ★ **SHORT RESPONSE** Baseball player Hank Aaron's career number B of times at bat and career number H of hits during the period 1954–1976 can be modeled by

$$B = \frac{300 + 700x}{1 + 0.01x} \quad \text{and} \quad H = \frac{62 + 240x}{1 + 0.017x}$$

where x is the number of years since 1954.

a. Model A baseball player's batting average is the number of hits divided by the number of times at bat. Write a model that gives Hank Aaron's career batting average A as a function of x. **See margin.**

b. Decide The table shows Aaron's actual career number of times at bat and actual career number of hits for three different years. For which year does the model give the best approximation of A? *Explain* your choice.

Year	1954	1959	1976
Career times at bat	468	3524	12,364
Career hits	131	1137	3771

1959; using the values in the table to calculate the ratio $\dfrac{H}{B}$ for the three given years gives batting averages A of 0.280 in 1954, 0.323 in 1959, and 0.305 in 1976. Calculating A using the model from part (a) for $x = 0$, 5, and 22 gives batting averages of 0.207 in 1954, 0.321 in 1959, and 0.302 in 1976.

○ = **WORKED-OUT SOLUTIONS**   ★ = **STANDARDIZED**   ◆ = **MULTIPLE**
808   on p. WS1   **TEST PRACTICE**   **REPRESENTATIONS**

35b.

x	1990	1991	1992	1993	1994	1995	1996
R	3.74	4.32	4.42	4.44	4.44	4.42	4.40

x	1997	1998	1999	2000	2001	2002
R	4.38	4.35	4.33	4.30	4.28	4.25

37. ★ EXTENDED RESPONSE The gross revenue R (in millions of dollars) from movie tickets sold and the average movie ticket price P (in dollars) in the United States during the period 1991–2002 can be modeled by

$$R = \frac{4700 - 74x}{1 - 0.053x} \quad \text{and} \quad P = 0.015x^2 + 4.1$$

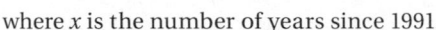

where x is the number of years since 1991.

a–c. See margin.

a. **Model** Write a model that gives the number T of movie tickets sold (in millions) as a function of x.

b. **Describe** Graph the model on a graphing calculator and describe how the number of tickets sold changed over time. Can you use the graph to describe how the gross revenue and ticket prices changed over time? *Explain* your reasoning.

c. **Compare** The table shows the actual number of tickets sold for each year during the period. Make a scatter plot of the data on the same screen as the graph of the model in part (b). *Compare* the scatter plot with the graph of the model.

Year	1991	1992	1993	1994	1995	1996
Tickets (millions)	1141	1173	1244	1292	1263	1339

Year	1997	1998	1999	2000	2001	2002
Tickets (millions)	1388	1481	1465	1421	1487	1639

[C] **38. CHALLENGE** The total amount F (in billions of dollars) spent on food other than groceries and the amount E (in billions of dollars) spent at restaurants in the U.S. during the period 1977–2003 can be modeled by

$$F = \frac{88 + 9.2x}{1 - 0.0097x} \quad \text{and} \quad E = \frac{54 + 6.5x}{1 - 0.012x}$$

where x is the number of years since 1977. Write a model that gives the percent p (in decimal form) of the amount spent on food other than groceries that was spent at restaurants as a function of x. Approximate the percent that was spent at locations other than restaurants in 2002.

$p = \dfrac{(54 + 6.5x)(1 - 0.0097x)}{(1 - 0.012x)(88 + 9.2x)}$; about 26%

MIXED REVIEW

PREVIEW
Prepare for Lesson 12.6 in Exs. 39–52.

Add or subtract. *(p. 914)*

39. $\dfrac{2}{5} + \dfrac{2}{3}$ $1\dfrac{1}{15}$

40. $\dfrac{3}{8} + \dfrac{5}{12}$ $\dfrac{19}{24}$

41. $\dfrac{1}{4} + \dfrac{5}{6}$ $1\dfrac{1}{12}$

42. $\dfrac{7}{9} + \dfrac{8}{21}$ $1\dfrac{10}{63}$

43. $\dfrac{7}{8} - \dfrac{7}{10}$ $\dfrac{7}{40}$

44. $\dfrac{7}{15} - \dfrac{1}{4}$ $\dfrac{13}{60}$

45. $\dfrac{9}{14} - \dfrac{5}{21}$ $\dfrac{17}{42}$

46. $\dfrac{5}{17} - \dfrac{2}{51}$ $\dfrac{13}{51}$

Find the sum, difference, or product. 47–52. See margin.

47. $(25x^2 - 6x) + (4x^2 - 5)$ *(p. 554)*

48. $(7x^2 + 5x + 1) + (-6x^2 + 13x)$ *(p. 554)*

49. $(2x^2 - x + 12) - (3x + 8)$ *(p. 554)*

50. $(7x^2 + 16) - (8x^3 + 3x^2 - 7)$ *(p. 554)*

51. $(5x - 6)(4x - 5)$ *(p. 562)*

52. $(2x + 9)(3x - 7)$ *(p. 562)*

EXTRA PRACTICE for Lesson 12.5, p. 949   ⊘ **ONLINE QUIZ** at classzone.com   809

---

47. $29x^2 - 6x - 5$

48. $x^2 + 18x + 1$

49. $2x^2 - 4x + 4$

50. $-8x^3 + 4x^2 + 23$

51. $20x^2 - 49x + 30$

52. $6x^2 + 13x - 63$

1 PLAN AND PREPARE

Warm-Up Exercises

Find the quotient.

1. $\dfrac{5x}{3} \div 5x^2 \quad \dfrac{1}{3x}$

2. $\dfrac{x^2 - 10x + 16}{2x} \div (x - 2) \quad \dfrac{x - 8}{2x}$

2 FOCUS AND MOTIVATE

Essential Question

Big Idea 2, p. 736

How do you simplify a complex fraction? **Tell students they will learn how to answer this question by treating a complex fraction as division of two rational expressions.**

3 TEACH

Extra Example 1

Simplify the complex fraction.

a. $\dfrac{\frac{8x^2}{5}}{-2x} \quad -\dfrac{4x}{5}$

b. $\dfrac{\frac{x - 4}{x + 4}}{x^2 - 16} \quad \dfrac{1}{(x + 4)^2}$

Key Question to Ask for Example 1

• In part (b), how can you tell which expression represents the complex fraction's numerator? **The longest fraction bar separates the numerator and denominator of the complex fraction.**

NCTM STANDARDS

Standard 1: Understand how operations are related

Standard 2: Analyze situations using algebraic symbols

Extension

Use after Lesson 12.5

Simplify Complex Fractions

GOAL Simplify complex fractions.

Key Vocabulary
• complex fraction

A **complex fraction** is a fraction that contains a fraction in its numerator, denominator, or both. To simplify a complex fraction, divide its numerator by its denominator.

> **READING**
> ⋯⋯⋯⋯⋯⋯⋯⋯⋯
> The widest fraction bar separates the numerator of a complex fraction from the denominator.

KEY CONCEPT   *For Your Notebook*

Simplifying a Complex Fraction

Let a, b, c, and d be polynomials where $b \neq 0$, $c \neq 0$, and $d \neq 0$.

Algebra $\dfrac{\frac{a}{b}}{\frac{c}{d}} = \dfrac{a}{b} \div \dfrac{c}{d} = \dfrac{a}{b} \cdot \dfrac{d}{c}$

Example $\dfrac{\frac{x}{2}}{\frac{x}{3}} = \dfrac{x}{2} \div \dfrac{x}{3} = \dfrac{x}{2} \cdot \dfrac{3}{x} = \dfrac{3x}{2x} = \dfrac{3}{2}$

EXAMPLE 1   **Simplify a complex fraction**

Simplify the complex fraction.

a. $\dfrac{\frac{3x}{2}}{-6x^3} = \dfrac{3x}{2} \div (-6x^3)$ **Write fraction as quotient.**

$= \dfrac{3x}{2} \cdot \dfrac{1}{-6x^3}$ **Multiply by multiplicative inverse.**

$= \dfrac{3x}{-12x^3}$ **Multiply numerators and denominators.**

$= -\dfrac{1}{4x^2}$ **Simplify.**

b. $\dfrac{x^2 - 1}{\frac{x + 1}{x - 1}} = (x^2 - 1) \div \dfrac{x + 1}{x - 1}$ **Write fraction as quotient.**

$= (x^2 - 1) \cdot \dfrac{x - 1}{x + 1}$ **Multiply by multiplicative inverse.**

$= \dfrac{(x^2 - 1)(x - 1)}{x + 1}$ **Multiply numerators and denominators.**

$= \dfrac{\cancel{(x + 1)}(x - 1)(x - 1)}{\cancel{x + 1}}$ **Factor and divide out common factor.**

$= (x - 1)^2$ **Simplify.**

810   Chapter 12   Rational Equations and Functions

EXAMPLE 2   Simplify a complex fraction

Simplify $\dfrac{\dfrac{2x^2 - 8x}{x^2 + 4x + 4}}{\dfrac{x^3 - 16x}{x + 2}}$.

$$\dfrac{\dfrac{2x^2 - 8x}{x^2 + 4x + 4}}{\dfrac{x^3 - 16x}{x + 2}} = \dfrac{2x^2 - 8x}{x^2 + 4x + 4} \div \dfrac{x^3 - 16x}{x + 2}$$ Write fraction as quotient.

$$= \dfrac{2x^2 - 8x}{x^2 + 4x + 4} \cdot \dfrac{x + 2}{x^3 - 16x}$$ Multiply by multiplicative inverse.

$$= \dfrac{(2x^2 - 8x)(x + 2)}{(x^2 + 4x + 4)(x^3 - 16x)}$$ Multiply numerators and denominators.

$$= \dfrac{2x(x - 4)(x + 2)}{(x + 2)(x + 2)x(x + 4)(x - 4)}$$ Factor and divide out common factors.

$$= \dfrac{2}{(x + 2)(x + 4)}$$ Simplify.

PRACTICE

EXAMPLES
1 and 2
on pp. 810–811
for Exs. 1–9

Simplify the complex fraction.

1. $\dfrac{\dfrac{-9x^5}{7}}{-12x^2}$ $\dfrac{3x^3}{28}$

2. $\dfrac{\dfrac{-2}{11x^4}}{18x^4}$ $\dfrac{-1}{99x^8}$

3. $\dfrac{\dfrac{x^2 + 7x}{2x - 6}}{x^2 - 49}$ $\dfrac{x}{2(x - 3)(x - 7)}$

4. $\dfrac{\dfrac{-24x^4}{8x^2}}{-4x^3}$ $12x^5$

5. $\dfrac{\dfrac{x^2 + 4x}{x + 4}}{x^2 - x}$ $x^2(x - 1)$

6. $\dfrac{\dfrac{2x^2 + 5x - 3}{x^2 + 4x + 3}}{15x}$ $\dfrac{15x(2x - 1)}{x + 1}$

7. $\dfrac{\dfrac{x^2 - x - 20}{4}}{\dfrac{x - 5}{10}}$ $\dfrac{5(x + 4)}{2}$

8. $\dfrac{\dfrac{x^2 - 2x - 8}{6x - 3x^2}}{\dfrac{x^3 + 4x^2}{x^2 - 4}}$ $\dfrac{(x - 4)(x + 2)^2}{3x^3(x + 4)}$

9. $\dfrac{\dfrac{2x^2 + 5x - 3}{3x^2 + 4x + 1}}{\dfrac{10x^2 - 5x}{2x^3 - 2x}}$ $\dfrac{2(x + 3)(x - 1)}{5(3x + 1)}$

⬡ **GEOMETRY** Write a rational expression for the ratio of the surface area S of the given solid to its volume V.

10. Sphere $\dfrac{3}{r}$

11. Cone $\dfrac{3(r + \ell)}{rh}$

12. Pyramid with a square base $\dfrac{3(s + 2\ell)}{sh}$

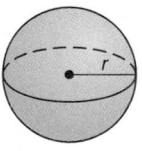

$S = 4\pi r^2$

$V = \dfrac{4\pi r^3}{3}$

$S = \pi r^2 + \pi r \ell$

$V = \dfrac{\pi r^2 h}{3}$

$S = s^2 + 2s\ell$

$V = \dfrac{s^2 h}{3}$

13. Are the complex fractions $\dfrac{\dfrac{a}{b}}{c}$ and $\dfrac{a}{\dfrac{b}{c}}$ equivalent? *Explain* your answer.   **See margin.**

13. No; $\dfrac{\frac{a}{b}}{c} = \dfrac{a}{b} \div c = \dfrac{a}{b} \cdot \dfrac{1}{c} = \dfrac{a}{bc}$ and $\dfrac{a}{\frac{b}{c}} = a \div \dfrac{b}{c} = \dfrac{a}{1} \cdot \dfrac{c}{b} = \dfrac{ac}{b}$. Thus, $\dfrac{\frac{a}{b}}{c} \neq \dfrac{a}{\frac{b}{c}}$.

Extra Example 2

Simplify $\dfrac{\dfrac{3x - 18}{2x^2 + 16x + 30}}{\dfrac{x - 6}{x^2 + 2x - 15}}$ $\dfrac{3(x - 3)}{2(x + 3)}$

Key Questions to Ask for Example 2

- How many fractions make up the complex fraction? **two; one in the numerator and one in the denominator**
- For which fraction do you find the multiplicative inverse? **the one in the denominator**

Closing the Lesson

Have students summarize the major points of the lesson and answer the Essential Question: How do you simplify a complex fraction?

- **A complex fraction contains a fraction in its numerator, denominator, or both.**

To simplify a complex fraction, first write the fraction as a quotient. Then use the reciprocal of the divisor to rewrite the expression as a product. Factor numerators and/or denominators, divide out common factors, and simplify.

❹ PRACTICE AND APPLY

Avoiding Common Errors

Exercises 1–9 Watch for students who separate the complex fraction incorrectly, using part of the numerator as the denominator or vice versa. Remind these students that the longest fraction bar indicates how to rewrite the complex fraction as the division of two rational expressions.

Before	You multiplied and divided rational expressions.
Now	You will add and subtract rational expressions.
Why?	So you can solve work problems, as in Ex. 49.

Key Vocabulary
• **least common denominator (LCD) of rational expressions**

Adding and subtracting rational expressions with the same denominator is similar to adding and subtracting numerical fractions with the same denominator.

KEY CONCEPT *For Your Notebook*

Adding and Subtracting Rational Expressions with the Same Denominator

Let a, b, and c be polynomials where $c \neq 0$.

Algebra $\dfrac{a}{c} + \dfrac{b}{c} = \dfrac{a+b}{c}$ $\qquad$ $\dfrac{a}{c} - \dfrac{b}{c} = \dfrac{a-b}{c}$

Examples $\dfrac{2}{x} + \dfrac{3}{x} = \dfrac{2+3}{x} = \dfrac{5}{x}$ $\qquad$ $\dfrac{5}{4x} - \dfrac{2}{4x} = \dfrac{5-2}{4x} = \dfrac{3}{4x}$

EXAMPLE 1 Add and subtract with the same denominator

a. $\dfrac{5}{3x} + \dfrac{7}{3x} = \dfrac{12}{3x}$ $\qquad$ Add numerators.

$\qquad\qquad = \dfrac{\cancel{3} \cdot 4}{\cancel{3} \cdot x}$ $\qquad$ Factor and divide out common factor.

$\qquad\qquad = \dfrac{4}{x}$ $\qquad$ Simplify.

b. $\dfrac{3x}{x-1} - \dfrac{x+5}{x-1} = \dfrac{3x-(x+5)}{x-1}$ $\qquad$ Subtract numerators.

$\qquad\qquad = \dfrac{2x-5}{x-1}$ $\qquad$ Simplify.

CHECK Check your simplification using a graphing calculator. For part (b), graph $y_1 = \dfrac{3x}{x-1} - \dfrac{x+5}{x-1}$ and $y_2 = \dfrac{2x-5}{x-1}$. The graphs coincide. So, the expressions are equivalent for all values of x other than the excluded value of 1.

GUIDED PRACTICE for Example 1

Find the sum or difference.

1. $\dfrac{2}{y} + \dfrac{y+1}{y}$ $\dfrac{y+3}{y}$

2. $\dfrac{4x+1}{2x-1} - \dfrac{2x-3}{2x-1}$ $\dfrac{2x+4}{2x-1}$

LEAST COMMON DENOMINATOR The **least common denominator (LCD)** of two or more rational expressions is the product of the factors of the denominators of the rational expressions with each common factor used only once.

EXAMPLE 2   Find the LCD of rational expressions

Find the LCD of the rational expressions.

a. $\dfrac{1}{4r}, \dfrac{r+3}{10r^2}$

b. $\dfrac{5}{(x-3)^2}, \dfrac{3x+4}{x^2-x-6}$

c. $\dfrac{3}{c-2}, \dfrac{c+8}{2c+7}$

Solution

a. Find the least common multiple (LCM) of $4r$ and $10r^2$.

$$4r = \boxed{2} \cdot 2 \cdot \boxed{r} \longleftarrow \text{The common factors are circled.}$$
$$10r^2 = \boxed{2} \cdot 5 \cdot \boxed{r} \cdot r$$

AVOID ERRORS
When finding the LCD, be sure to use the common factors only once.

$$\text{LCM} = 2 \cdot r \cdot 2 \cdot 5 \cdot r = 20r^2$$

▶ The LCD of $\dfrac{1}{4r}$ and $\dfrac{r+3}{10r^2}$ is $20r^2$.

b. Find the least common multiple (LCM) of $(x-3)^2$ and x^2-x-6.

$$(x-3)^2 = \boxed{(x-3)} \cdot (x-3)$$
$$x^2-x-6 = \boxed{(x-3)} \cdot (x+2)$$
$$\text{LCM} = (x-3) \cdot (x-3) \cdot (x+2) = (x-3)^2(x+2)$$

▶ The LCD of $\dfrac{5}{(x-3)^2}$ and $\dfrac{3x+4}{x^2-x-6}$ is $(x-3)^2(x+2)$.

c. Find the least common multiple of $c-2$ and $2c+7$.

Because $c-2$ and $2c+7$ cannot be factored, they don't have any factors in common. The least common multiple is their product, $(c-2)(2c+7)$.

▶ The LCD of $\dfrac{3}{c-2}$ and $\dfrac{c+8}{2c+7}$ is $(c-2)(2c+7)$.

 GUIDED PRACTICE for Example 2

Find the LCD of the rational expressions.

3. $\dfrac{1}{28m}, \dfrac{m+1}{7m^3}$

   $28m^3$

4. $\dfrac{2}{x^2+4x-5}, \dfrac{x^2+2}{x^2+7x+10}$

   $(x+5)(x-1)(x+2)$

5. $\dfrac{5a}{a+3}, \dfrac{a+6}{a-4}$

   $(a+3)(a-4)$

DIFFERENT DENOMINATORS To add or subtract rational expressions that have different denominators, use the LCD to write equivalent rational expressions that have the same denominator just as you would for numerical fractions.

Motivating the Lesson

You are planning a 500-mile trip to the Grand Canyon. You estimate that your average speed driving to the Canyon will be greater than your average speed returning home. In this lesson you will learn how to write an equation to model this situation and how to use the model to determine your average speed for the entire trip to and from the Grand Canyon.

❸ TEACH

Extra Example 1
Add or subtract.

a. $\dfrac{2x}{x+2} + \dfrac{x+1}{x+2}$ $\dfrac{3x+1}{x+2}$

b. $\dfrac{4x+1}{5x} - \dfrac{x+3}{5x}$ $\dfrac{3x-2}{5x}$

Extra Example 2
Find the LCD of the rational expressions.

a. $\dfrac{1}{12x}, \dfrac{x+7}{4x^2}$ $12x^2$

b. $\dfrac{4}{x^2-x-6}, \dfrac{3x^2}{(x+2)^2}$

   $(x+2)^2(x-3)$

c. $\dfrac{2x}{x-8}, \dfrac{3x+15}{x+1}$ $(x-8)(x+1)$

Key Question to Ask for Example 2

• If two denominators have repeated factors, such as $2 \cdot 2 \cdot 2 \cdot x$ and $2 \cdot 2 \cdot x \cdot x$, how many times does each factor appear in the LCD? **In the LCD, use the greater number of times it occurs. For these denominators, the LCD is $2 \cdot 2 \cdot 2 \cdot x \cdot x$ or $8x^2$.**

814

Extra Example 3

Find the sum $\dfrac{6}{18x} + \dfrac{4}{6x^2}$. $\dfrac{x+2}{3x^2}$

Key Question to Ask for Example 3

• How did you determine the LCD? The denominators are $2 \cdot 2 \cdot 2 \cdot x \cdot x$ and $2 \cdot 2 \cdot 3 \cdot x \cdot x \cdot x$. Taking each factor the greater number of times, the LCD is $2 \cdot 2 \cdot 2 \cdot 3 \cdot x \cdot x \cdot x$, or $24x^3$.

Extra Example 4

Find the difference $\dfrac{5}{2x} - \dfrac{3x}{x-1}$.

$\dfrac{-6x^2 + 5x - 5}{2x(x-1)}$

Key Question to Ask for Example 4

• In the second step of the example, can you divide out the common factor of $(x+2)$ on the right side of the equation? Explain. **No; $(x+2)$ does not appear in the numerator of one of the terms.**

Extra Example 5

Find the difference
$\dfrac{x+3}{x^2 - 8x + 15} - \dfrac{x+6}{x^2 - x - 20}$.
$\dfrac{4x + 30}{(x-3)(x-5)(x+4)}$

Animated Algebra
classzone.com

An **Animated Algebra** activity is available on-line for **Example 5**. This activity is also available on the **Power Presentations CD-ROM**.

EXAMPLE 3 Add expressions with different denominators

Find the sum $\dfrac{9}{8x^2} + \dfrac{5}{12x^3}$.

$\dfrac{9}{8x^2} + \dfrac{5}{12x^3} = \dfrac{9 \cdot 3x}{8x^2 \cdot 3x} + \dfrac{5 \cdot 2}{12x^3 \cdot 2}$ Rewrite fractions using LCD, $24x^3$.

$= \dfrac{27x}{24x^3} + \dfrac{10}{24x^3}$ Simplify numerators and denominators.

$= \dfrac{27x + 10}{24x^3}$ Add fractions.

EXAMPLE 4 Subtract expressions with different denominators

Find the difference $\dfrac{10}{3x} - \dfrac{7x}{x+2}$.

$\dfrac{10}{3x} - \dfrac{7x}{x+2} = \dfrac{10(x+2)}{3x(x+2)} - \dfrac{7x(3x)}{(x+2)(3x)}$ Rewrite fractions using LCD, $3x(x+2)$.

$= \dfrac{10(x+2) - 7x(3x)}{3x(x+2)}$ Subtract fractions.

$= \dfrac{-21x^2 + 10x + 20}{3x(x+2)}$ Simplify numerator.

EXAMPLE 5 Subtract expressions with different denominators

Find the difference $\dfrac{x+4}{x^2 + 3x - 10} - \dfrac{x-1}{x^2 + 2x - 8}$.

$\dfrac{x+4}{x^2 + 3x - 10} - \dfrac{x-1}{x^2 + 2x - 8}$

$= \dfrac{x+4}{(x-2)(x+5)} - \dfrac{x-1}{(x+4)(x-2)}$ Factor denominators.

$= \dfrac{(x+4)(x+4)}{(x-2)(x+5)(x+4)} - \dfrac{(x-1)(x+5)}{(x+4)(x-2)(x+5)}$ Rewrite fractions using LCD, $(x-2)(x+5)(x+4)$.

$= \dfrac{(x+4)(x+4) - (x-1)(x+5)}{(x-2)(x+5)(x+4)}$ Subtract fractions.

$= \dfrac{x^2 + 8x + 16 - (x^2 + 4x - 5)}{(x-2)(x+5)(x+4)}$ Find products in numerator.

$= \dfrac{4x + 21}{(x-2)(x+5)(x+4)}$ Simplify.

Animated Algebra at classzone.com

AVOID ERRORS
Because you are subtracting $x^2 + 4x - 5$ in the numerator, you need to add the opposite of *every* term in $x^2 + 4x - 5$.

✓ **GUIDED PRACTICE** for Examples 3, 4, and 5

Find the sum or difference.

6. $\dfrac{3}{2x} + \dfrac{7}{5x^4}$ $\dfrac{15x^3 + 14}{10x^4}$ 7. $\dfrac{y}{y+1} + \dfrac{3}{y+2}$ $\dfrac{y^2 + 5y + 3}{(y+1)(y+2)}$ 8. $\dfrac{2z-1}{z^2 + 2z - 8} - \dfrac{z+1}{z^2 - 4}$ $\dfrac{z^2 - 2z - 6}{(z+4)(z-2)(z+2)}$

814   Chapter 12   Rational Equations and Functions

Differentiated Instruction

Auditory Learners Students may find other methods of adding and subtracting fractions easier to recall. In **Example 3**, students can "cross-multiply" to get a numerator of $9 \cdot 12x^3 + 5 \cdot 8x^2$ and then multiply the denominators to get $96x^5$. Students can conclude by simplifying the resulting rational expression, $\dfrac{9 \cdot 12x^3 + 5 \cdot 8x^2}{96x^5}$, as $\dfrac{27x + 10}{24x^3}$.

See also the *Algebra 1 Toolkit* for more strategies.

EXAMPLE 6 **Solve a multi-step problem**

BOAT TRAVEL A boat travels 24 kilometers upstream (against the current) and 24 kilometers downstream (with the current) as shown in the diagram. Write an equation that gives the total travel time t (in hours) as a function of the boat's average speed r (in kilometers per hour) in still water. Find the total travel time if the boat's average speed in still water is 10 kilometers per hour.

Speed of current: 2 kilometers per hour

Direction of current

Solution

STEP 1 **Write** a verbal model. Then write an equation.

$$\begin{array}{c} \text{Total travel} \\ \text{time} \\ \text{(hours)} \end{array} = \begin{array}{c} \text{Distance} \\ \text{upstream} \\ \text{(kilometers)} \\ \hline \text{Speed of boat} \\ \text{going upstream} \\ \text{(kilometers/hour)} \end{array} + \begin{array}{c} \text{Distance} \\ \text{downstream} \\ \text{(kilometers)} \\ \hline \text{Speed of boat} \\ \text{going downstream} \\ \text{(kilometers/hour)} \end{array}$$

> **COMBINE SPEEDS**
> When you go upstream, you subtract the speed of the current from the speed at which you travel in still water. When you go downstream, you add the speeds.

$$t \quad = \quad \frac{24}{r-2} \quad + \quad \frac{24}{r+2}$$

STEP 2 **Find** the sum of the expressions on the right side of the equation.

$t = \dfrac{24}{r-2} + \dfrac{24}{r+2}$ **Write equation.**

$= \dfrac{24(r+2)}{(r-2)(r+2)} + \dfrac{24(r-2)}{(r+2)(r-2)}$ **Rewrite fractions using LCD, $(r-2)(r+2)$.**

$= \dfrac{24(r+2) + 24(r-2)}{(r-2)(r+2)}$ **Add fractions.**

$= \dfrac{48r}{(r-2)(r+2)}$ **Simplify.**

STEP 3 **Calculate** the value of t when $r = 10$.

$$t = \frac{48(10)}{(10-2)(10+2)} = \frac{480}{(8)(12)} = \frac{480}{96} = 5$$

▶ The total travel time is 5 hours.

✓ **GUIDED PRACTICE**   for Example 6

9. **WHAT IF?** In Example 6, suppose the speed of the current is 3 kilometers per hour. Find the total travel time. **about 5.3 h**

Extra Example 6

A rowing crew rows a boat 18 miles upstream (against the current) and 18 miles downstream (with the current). The speed of the current is 3 miles per hour. Write an equation that gives the boat's average speed r (in miles per hour) in still water. Find the total travel time if the boat's average speed in still water is 5 miles per hour. $t = \dfrac{18}{r-3} + \dfrac{18}{r+3}$; **11.25 h**

Closing the Lesson

Have students summarize the major points of the lesson and answer the Essential Question: How do you add or subtract rational expressions?

• **Rational expressions can be added or subtracted by using the rules for adding and subtracting rational numbers.**

• **To find the least common denominator (LCD) of two rational expressions, find the product of the factors of each denominator. If the denominators have a common factor, use it just once. If either denominator has repeated factors, the LCD also will have repeated factors.**

When adding or subtracting rational expressions with the same denominator, write the sum or difference of the numerators over the common denominator and simplify. When adding or subtracting rational expressions with different denominators, start by using the LCD to write equivalent rational expressions.

12.6 **EXERCISES**

HOMEWORK
KEY
○ = **WORKED-OUT SOLUTIONS**
on p. WS1 for Exs. 7, 29, and 45
★ = **STANDARDIZED TEST PRACTICE**
Exs. 2, 32, 44, and 48

④ PRACTICE AND APPLY

Assignment Guide

📝 **Answer Transparencies**
available for all exercises

Basic:
Day 1: pp. 816–819
Exs. 1–17, 19–21, 25, 26, 58–62
Day 2: pp. 816–819
Exs. 18, 22–24, 27–35, 42–47, 50–57

Average:
Day 1: pp. 816–819
Exs. 1, 2, 7–17, 19–21, 25, 26, 29, 30, 35, 36, 58–62
Day 2: pp. 816–819
Exs. 18, 22–24, 27–34, 37–40, 42–48, 50–56 even

Advanced:
Day 1: pp. 816–819
Exs. 1, 2, 7–17, 19–21, 25, 26, 35, 36, 58–62
Day 2: pp. 816–819
Exs. 22–24, 27, 28, 31–34, 37, 41–49*, 51–57 odd

Block:
pp. 816–819
Exs. 1, 2, 7–17, 19–21, 25, 26, 29, 30, 35, 36, 58–62 (with 12.5)
pp. 816–819
Exs. 18, 22–24, 27–34, 37–40, 42–48, 50–56 even (with 12.7)

Differentiated Instruction

See *Algebra 1 Best Practices Toolkit*
for suggestions on addressing the
needs of a diverse classroom.

Homework Check

For a quick check of student under-
standing of key concepts, go over
the following exercises:
Basic: 8, 20, 23, 25, 42
Average: 10, 21, 24, 26, 44
Advanced: 11, 22, 30, 31, 46

Extra Practice

- Student Edition, p. 946
- Chapter 12 Resource Book:
  Practice levels A, B, C, pp. 69–71

Practice Worksheet

An easily-readable reduced
practice page (with answers)
for this lesson can be found
on p. 762C.

SKILL PRACTICE

[A] 1. **VOCABULARY** Copy and complete: The __?__ of two rational expressions is the product of the factors of their denominators with each common factor used only once.   **least common denominator**

2. ★ **WRITING** *Describe* your steps in rewriting the expressions $\dfrac{1}{x+2}$ and $\dfrac{2x}{x^2-4}$ so that they have the same denominator. **See margin.**

EXAMPLE 1
on p. 812
for Exs. 3–11

ADDING AND SUBTRACTING EXPRESSIONS Find the sum or difference.

3. $\dfrac{2}{5x} + \dfrac{3}{5x}$ $\dfrac{1}{x}$

4. $\dfrac{y+1}{2y} + \dfrac{5}{2y}$ $\dfrac{y+6}{2y}$

5. $\dfrac{6z}{z^2} - \dfrac{2z}{z^2}$ $\dfrac{4}{z}$

6. $\dfrac{7}{a+2} - \dfrac{3a}{a+2}$ $\dfrac{7-3a}{a+2}$

⑦. $\dfrac{h}{b-3} + \dfrac{b+1}{b-3}$ $\dfrac{2b+1}{b-3}$

8. $\dfrac{c+2}{c-9} + \dfrac{c+5}{c-9}$ $\dfrac{2c+7}{c-9}$

9. $\dfrac{7}{m^2+1} - \dfrac{8}{m^2+1}$ $\dfrac{-1}{m^2+1}$

10. $\dfrac{2n+1}{n^2-16} - \dfrac{n}{n^2-16}$ $\dfrac{n+1}{n^2-16}$

11. $\dfrac{3r}{r^2+r-7} + \dfrac{1}{r^2+r-7}$ $\dfrac{3r+1}{r^2+r-7}$

EXAMPLE 2
on p. 813
for Exs. 12–17, 32

FINDING THE LCD Find the LCD of the rational expressions.

12. $\dfrac{1}{24x}, \dfrac{x+2}{6x^3}$ $24x^3$

13. $\dfrac{3}{15v^2}, \dfrac{v^2-4}{20v^3}$ $60v^3$

14. $\dfrac{4w}{w+5}, \dfrac{w+3}{w-2}$ $(w+5)(w-2)$

15. $\dfrac{s-1}{s+2}, \dfrac{s+2}{s-1}$ $(s+2)(s-1)$

16. $\dfrac{1}{t^2-4t}, \dfrac{6}{t^2-2t-8}$ $t(t+2)(t-4)$

17. $\dfrac{u+9}{u^2+8u+7}, \dfrac{-3}{u^2-2u-3}$ $(u+7)(u+1)(u-3)$

EXAMPLES 3, 4, and 5
on p. 814
for Exs. 18–31

ERROR ANALYSIS *Describe* and correct the error in finding the sum or difference. **18, 19. See margin.**

18. $\dfrac{8}{2x+3} - \dfrac{4x}{x+2}$

19. $\dfrac{5x}{x-4} + \dfrac{2}{x+3}$

$$\dfrac{8}{2x+3} - \dfrac{4x}{x+2} = \dfrac{8-4x}{2x+3-(x+2)}$$
$$= \dfrac{8-4x}{2x+3-x-2}$$ ✗
$$= \dfrac{8-4x}{x+1}$$

$$\dfrac{5x}{x-4} + \dfrac{2}{x+3} = \dfrac{5x(x-4)+2(x+3)}{(x-4)(x+3)}$$
$$= \dfrac{5x^2-20x+2x+6}{(x-4)(x+3)}$$ ✗
$$= \dfrac{5x^2-18x+6}{(x-4)(x+3)}$$

ADDING AND SUBTRACTING EXPRESSIONS Find the sum or difference. **20–31. See margin.**

20. $\dfrac{5x}{4} + \dfrac{2}{5x}$

21. $\dfrac{13}{3y} + \dfrac{2}{11y}$

22. $\dfrac{7}{2z} - \dfrac{2}{3z^2}$

23. $\dfrac{7r}{r-2} - \dfrac{2r}{r-3}$

24. $\dfrac{s}{5s-2} - \dfrac{1}{4s+1}$

25. $\dfrac{c+3}{c-6} + \dfrac{c}{3c+10}$

26. $\dfrac{d-5}{d+7} + \dfrac{d-5}{4d}$

27. $\dfrac{f+3}{7f} - \dfrac{3f}{f+4}$

28. $\dfrac{1}{g^2+5g+6} - \dfrac{1}{g^2-4}$

㉙. $\dfrac{2j}{j^2-1} + \dfrac{j-1}{j^2-7j+6}$

30. $\dfrac{k+7}{k^2+6k+9} + \dfrac{k-5}{k^2-5k-24}$

31. $\dfrac{v+2}{2v^2-v-15} - \dfrac{v-2}{v^2+2v-15}$

2. Write each denominator in factored form: $(x+2)$ and $(x+2)(x-2)$.
The least common denominator (LCD) will have all the factors of both
denominators, using any common factor only once: the denominator of
the second fraction, $(x+2)(x-2)$, is the LCD. Write the first fraction
with the LCD by multiplying its numerator and its denominator by $(x-2)$:
$\dfrac{x-2}{(x+2)(x-2)}$.

32. ★ **MULTIPLE CHOICE** Which is a factor of the LCD of $\dfrac{3}{x^2 - 4x}$ and $\dfrac{4x}{x + 2}$? **B**

   (A) 3   **(B)** $x - 4$ **(C)** $4x$ **(D)** $x - 2$

[B] **33.** 🔺 **GEOMETRY** The height h of a rectangular prism is given by

$$h = \frac{S}{2(\ell + w)} - \frac{\ell w}{\ell + w}$$

where S is the surface area, ℓ is the length, and w is the width. Find the difference of the expressions on the right side of the equation. $\dfrac{s - 2\ell w}{2(\ell + w)}$

USING ORDER OF OPERATIONS Use the order of operations to write the expression as a single rational expression.

34. $2\left(\dfrac{x}{x + 1}\right) - 3\left(\dfrac{x - 4}{x + 2}\right)$ $\dfrac{-x^2 + 13x + 12}{(x + 1)(x + 2)}$ **35.** $5\left(\dfrac{3x}{x - 2} + \dfrac{4}{x^2 + 6x - 16}\right)$ $\dfrac{15x^2 + 120x + 20}{(x - 2)(x + 8)}$

36. $\dfrac{x - 3}{x^2 + 9x + 20} + \dfrac{5x}{x + 2} \cdot \dfrac{12}{x + 4}$ $\dfrac{61x^2 + 299x - 6}{(x + 5)(x + 4)(x + 2)}$ **37.** $\dfrac{x + 5}{x - 9} - \dfrac{3x^2 + 2x - 1}{x + 4} \div \dfrac{x^2 - 3x - 4}{x^2 - 16}$ $\dfrac{-3x^2 + 29x - 4}{x - 9}$

WRITING EQUATIONS For the given hyperbola, write an equation of the form $y = \dfrac{a}{b}$ where a and b are first-degree polynomials.

38. $y = \dfrac{2x + 4}{x - 1}$

39. $y = \dfrac{-4x - 16}{x + 2}$

40. $y = \dfrac{-3x - 8}{x + 6}$

38.   **39.**   **40.**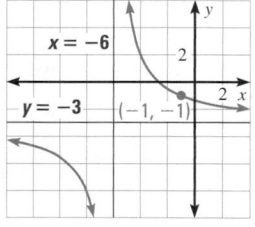

41. **CHALLENGE** Let a, b, c, and d be first-degree polynomials. Find two rational expressions $\dfrac{a}{b}$ and $\dfrac{c}{d}$ such that $\dfrac{a}{b} - \dfrac{c}{d} = \dfrac{5x + 7}{(x + 2)(x + 3)}$.

    Sample answer: $\dfrac{-3}{x + 2}, \dfrac{-8}{x + 3}$

PROBLEM SOLVING

EXAMPLE 6 **[A]**
on p. 815
for Exs. 42–46

42. **CANOEING** A canoeist travels 16 miles upstream (against the current) and 16 miles downstream (with the current). The speed of the current is 1 mile per hour. Write an equation that gives the total travel time t (in hours) as a function of the canoeist's average speed r (in miles per hour) in still water. Then find the total travel time if the canoeist's average speed in still water is 6 miles per hour. $t = \dfrac{32r}{(r - 1)(r + 1)}$; about 5.5 h

   @HomeTutor   for problem solving help at classzone.com

43. **DRIVING** Matt drives 200 miles to another city. On the drive back home, his average speed decreases by 5 miles per hour. Write an equation that gives the total driving time t (in hours) as a function of his average speed r (in miles per hour) when driving to the city. Then find the total driving time if he drives to the city at an average speed of 50 miles per hour.

   @HomeTutor   for problem solving help at classzone.com $t = \dfrac{400r - 1000}{r(r - 5)}$; about 8.4 h

---

Avoiding Common Errors

Exercises 3–11, 20–31 Watch for students who divide out common factors before adding or subtracting. Remind students that they must combine the expressions before they look for common factors in the numerator and denominator.

Exercises 20–31 Students sometimes find the correct LCD but calculate an incorrect numerator for the equivalent rational expression. Suggest that students check their calculations for this type of error.

Teaching Strategy

Exercises 34–37 Before students begin these exercises, you may want to ask them to describe the steps they will take to rewrite each of the exercises. Make sure students know that they must distribute the factor outside the parentheses to each term inside the parentheses.

20. $\dfrac{25x^2 + 8}{20x}$

21. $\dfrac{149}{33y}$

22. $\dfrac{21z - 4}{6z^2}$

23. $\dfrac{5r^2 - 17r}{(r - 2)(r - 3)}$

24. $\dfrac{4s^2 - 4s + 2}{(5s - 2)(4s + 1)}$

25. $\dfrac{4c^2 + 13c + 30}{(c - 6)(3c + 10)}$

26. $\dfrac{5d^2 - 18d - 35}{4d(d + 7)}$

27. $\dfrac{-20f^2 + 7f + 12}{7f(f + 4)}$

28. $\dfrac{-5}{(g + 2)(g + 3)(g - 2)}$

29. $\dfrac{3j^2 - 12j - 1}{(j - 1)(j + 1)(j - 6)}$

30. $\dfrac{2k^2 - 3k - 71}{(k - 8)(k + 3)^2}$

31. $\dfrac{-v^2 + 6v + 20}{(2v + 5)(v - 3)(v + 5)}$

---

18. Rational expressions are not subtracted by subtracting their numerators and subtracting their denominators. Instead, you must write the expressions with a common denominator and then subtract the numerators over the common denominator; $\dfrac{8}{2x + 3} - \dfrac{4x}{x + 2} =$

$\dfrac{8(x + 2)}{(2x + 3)(x + 2)} - \dfrac{4x(2x + 3)}{(2x + 3)(x + 2)} = \dfrac{8x + 16 - 8x^2 - 12x}{(2x + 3)(x + 2)} = \dfrac{-8x^2 - 4x + 16}{(2x + 3)(x + 2)}$.

19. See Additional Answers beginning on p. AA1.

44. ★ **SHORT RESPONSE** An airplane makes a round trip between two destinations as shown in the diagram. The airplane flies against the wind when traveling west and flies with the wind when traveling east. Assume that the speed of the wind remains constant during each flight.

Chicago, IL ——— 670 miles ——— Philadelphia, PA

Speed of airplane in still air: 300 miles per hour

  a. **Model** Write an equation that gives the total flying time t (in hours) as a function of the speed w (in miles per hour) of the wind. Then find the total flying time if the speed of the wind is 15 miles per hour. **a, b. See margin.**

  b. **Decide** For what value of w does the flying time one way take half as long as the total flying time? *Explain* your reasoning.

45. **ELEVATORS** According to the law in one state, the minimum weight W (in pounds) that a passenger elevator must hold is given by

$$W = \frac{2A^2}{3} + \frac{200A}{3} \text{ if } A \le 50 \qquad \text{and} \qquad W = \frac{7A^2}{150} + (125A - 1367) \text{ if } A > 50$$

where A represents the area (in square feet) of the elevator platform.

  a. Write the right side of each equation as a single rational expression. **See margin.**

  b. What is the minimum weight that an elevator must hold if the area of the platform is 30 square feet? 60 square feet? **2600 lb; 6301 lb**

46. **MULTI-STEP PROBLEM** A parallel electric circuit consists of a power source and several parallel resistors through which electricity can flow. For a parallel circuit with two resistors, let r_1 represent the resistance (in ohms) of one resistor, and let r_2 represent the resistance (in ohms) of the other resistor.

Parallel Circuit

  a. **Model** The total resistance r_T is equal to the multiplicative inverse of $\dfrac{1}{r_1} + \dfrac{1}{r_2}$. Write $\dfrac{1}{r_1} + \dfrac{1}{r_2}$ as a single rational expression. Then write an equation that gives r_T in terms of r_1 and r_2. $r_T = \dfrac{r_1 r_2}{r_2 + r_1}$

  b. **Calculate** Find the total resistance when one resistor has a resistance of 2 ohms and the other resistor has a resistance of 6 ohms. **1.5 ohms**

47. **RADIO STATIONS** Radio stations use either amplitude modulation (AM) broadcasting or frequency modulation (FM) broadcasting. The percent a (in decimal form) of commercial radio stations that used AM broadcasting during the period 1990–2003 can be modeled by

$$a = \frac{2.8 + 0.085x}{5.3 + 0.30x}$$

where x is the number of years since 1990. Write a model that gives the percent f (in decimal form) of commercial radio stations that used FM broadcasting as a function of x. Then approximate the value of f in 2003. $f = \dfrac{2.5 + 0.215x}{5.3 + 0.30x}$; about 58%

○ = **WORKED-OUT SOLUTIONS** on p. WS1   ★ = **STANDARDIZED TEST PRACTICE**

48. ★ **EXTENDED RESPONSE** The axle load for a tow vehicle is the weight (in pounds) that an axle on the vehicle supports. The rear axle load R and the front axle load F are given by the formulas

$$R = \frac{t(w + h)}{w} \quad \text{and} \quad F = \frac{th}{w}$$

where t represents the weight (in pounds) that presses down on the hitch by a trailer and w and h represent the distances (in feet) shown.

Tow vehicle   Hitch   Trailer

Front axle   Rear axle
├──── w ────┼─ h ─┤

a. Calculate For a certain tow vehicle, $t = 300$, $w = 9$, and $h = 3.5$. Find the rear axle load and the front axle load. $416\frac{2}{3}$ **lb, $116\frac{2}{3}$ lb**

b. Compare Find the difference of the rear axle load and the front axle load found in part (a). *Compare* your answer with the given value of t.
300 lb; the answers are the same.

c. Model Write an equation that gives t in terms of R and F. *Justify* your answer algebraically. $t = R - F; R - F = \dfrac{t(w + h)}{w} - \dfrac{th}{w} = \dfrac{tw + th - th}{w} = \dfrac{tw}{w} = t$

C **49. CHALLENGE** You and your friend plan to spend 10 minutes mowing your family's lawn together. You can mow the entire lawn alone in 30 minutes.

a. Write an equation that gives the fraction y of the lawn that you and your friend can mow in 10 minutes as a function of the time t (in minutes) that your friend can mow the entire lawn alone. $y = \dfrac{t + 30}{3t}$

b. Suppose your friend can mow the entire lawn alone in 20 minutes. Can the entire lawn be mowed if you and your friend work together for 10 minutes? *Explain.* **No; to find the fraction of the lawn that you and your friend can mow in 10 minutes, find the value of y when $t = 20$ in the equation in part (a): $y = \dfrac{20 + 30}{3(20)} = \dfrac{50}{60} = \dfrac{5}{6}$. You and your friend can mow only of the lawn in 10 minutes.**

MIXED REVIEW

PREVIEW
Prepare for
Lesson 12.7
in Exs. 50–57.

Solve the equation or proportion.

50. $-4(f - 5) = -16$ *(p. 148)* **9**

51. $2x + 11 + 3x = 21$ *(p. 148)* **2**

52. $5g - 18 = 4g - 3$ *(p. 154)* **15**

53. $7.5k = 5(2k + 1)$ *(p. 154)* **−2**

54. $\dfrac{7}{3} = \dfrac{m}{6}$ *(p. 168)* **14**

55. $\dfrac{14}{10} = \dfrac{v}{15}$ *(p. 168)* **21**

56. $x^2 - 9x + 14 = 0$ *(p. 583)* **7, 2**

57. $-7m^2 + 56 = 0$ *(p. 653)* **$\pm 2\sqrt{2}$**

58. SPORTS An athlete kicks a football upward from the ground with an initial vertical velocity of 64 feet per second. After how many seconds does the football land on the ground? *(p. 575)* **4 sec**

Factor the expression.

59. $12x^2 - 24x$ *(p. 575)* **$12x(x - 2)$**

60. $x^2 - 9x - 22$ *(p. 583)* **$(x - 11)(x + 2)$**

61. $x^2 + 15x + 56$ *(p. 583)* **$(x + 8)(x + 7)$**

62. $100 - 9x^2$ *(p. 600)* **$(10 - 3x)(10 + 3x)$**

⑤ ASSESS AND RETEACH

Daily Homework Quiz

▨ **Transparency Available**

Find the sum or difference.

1. $\dfrac{4}{2x} + \dfrac{x + 1}{3}$ $\dfrac{x^2 + x + 6}{3x}$

2. $\dfrac{x - 6}{x - 1} - \dfrac{x - 1}{3x}$ $\dfrac{2x^2 - 16x - 1}{(x - 1)(3x)}$

3. $\dfrac{2x}{x^2 + 6x - 16} + \dfrac{x + 3}{x^2 - 3x + 2}$

  $\dfrac{3x^2 + 9x + 24}{(x + 8)(x - 2)(x - 1)}$

4. You hike 4 miles up a hill and then 4 miles back down the hill. Your speed hiking up the hill is 1.5 miles per hour less than your speed hiking back down. Find the total time of your hike if you hiked 2.5 miles per hour up the hill. **5.6 h**

◉ **Online Quiz**

Available at **classzone.com**

Diagnosis/Remediation

- Practice A, B, C in Chapter 12 Resource Book, pp. 69–71
- Study Guide in Chapter 12 Resource Book, pp. 72–73
- Practice Workbook, pp. 192–193
- @HomeTutor

Challenge

Additional challenge is available in the Chapter 12 Resource Book, p. 76.

Before You simplified rational expressions.

Now You will solve rational equations.

Why? So you can calculate a hockey statistic, as in Ex. 31.

Key Vocabulary
• **rational equation**
• **cross product,** *p. 168*
• **extraneous solution,** *p. 730*
• **least common denominator (LCD) of rational expressions,** *p. 813*

A **rational equation** is an equation that contains one or more rational expressions. One method for solving a rational equation is to use the cross products property. You can use this method when both sides of the equation are single rational expressions.

EXAMPLE 1 Use the cross products property

Solve $\frac{6}{x + 4} = \frac{x}{2}$. Check your solution.

REVIEW CROSS PRODUCTS
For help with using the cross products property, see p. 168.

$$\frac{6}{x + 4} = \frac{x}{2} \qquad \text{Write original equation.}$$

$$12 = x^2 + 4x \qquad \text{Cross products property}$$

$$0 = x^2 + 4x - 12 \qquad \text{Subtract 12 from each side.}$$

$$0 = (x + 6)(x - 2) \qquad \text{Factor polynomial.}$$

$$x + 6 = 0 \quad or \quad x - 2 = 0 \qquad \text{Zero-product property}$$

$$x = -6 \quad or \quad x = 2 \qquad \text{Solve for } x.$$

▸ The solutions are -6 and 2.

CHECK If $x = -6$:   If $x = 2$:

$$\frac{6}{-6 + 4} \overset{?}{=} \frac{-6}{2} \qquad \frac{6}{2 + 4} \overset{?}{=} \frac{2}{2}$$

$$-3 = -3 ✓ \qquad 1 = 1 ✓$$

✓ **GUIDED PRACTICE** for Example 1

Solve the equation. Check your solution.

1. $\frac{5}{y - 2} = \frac{y}{3}$ **-3, 5**

2. $\frac{2}{z + 5} = \frac{z}{7}$ **-7, 2**

USING THE LCD Given an equation with fractional coefficients such as $\frac{2}{3}x + \frac{1}{6} = \frac{3}{4}$, you can multiply each side by the least common denominator (LCD), 12. The equation becomes $8x + 2 = 9$, which you may find easier to solve than the original equation. You can use this method to solve a rational equation.

EXAMPLE 2 **Multiply by the LCD**

Solve $\dfrac{x}{x-2} + \dfrac{1}{5} = \dfrac{2}{x-2}$. Check your solution.

$$\dfrac{x}{x-2} + \dfrac{1}{5} = \dfrac{2}{x-2}$$ Write original equation.

$$\dfrac{x}{x-2} \cdot 5(x-2) + \dfrac{1}{5} \cdot 5(x-2) = \dfrac{2}{x-2} \cdot 5(x-2)$$ Multiply by LCD, $5(x-2)$.

$$\dfrac{x \cdot 5(x-2)}{x-2} + \dfrac{5(x-2)}{5} = \dfrac{2 \cdot 5(x-2)}{x-2}$$ Multiply and divide out common factors.

$$5x + x - 2 = 10$$ Simplify.

$$6x - 2 = 10$$ Combine like terms.

$$6x = 12$$ Add 2 to each side.

$$x = 2$$ Divide each side by 6.

AVOID ERRORS
Be sure to identify the excluded values for the rational expressions in the original equation.

The solution appears to be 2, but the expressions $\dfrac{x}{x-2}$ and $\dfrac{2}{x-2}$ are undefined when $x = 2$. So, 2 is an extraneous solution.

▶ There is no solution.

EXAMPLE 3 **Factor to find the LCD**

Solve $\dfrac{3}{x-7} + 1 = \dfrac{8}{x^2 - 9x + 14}$. Check your solution.

Solution

Write each denominator in factored form. The LCD is $(x-2)(x-7)$.

$$\dfrac{3}{x-7} + 1 = \dfrac{8}{(x-2)(x-7)}$$

$$\dfrac{3}{x-7} \cdot (x-2)(x-7) + 1 \cdot (x-2)(x-7) = \dfrac{8}{(x-2)(x-7)} \cdot (x-2)(x-7)$$

$$\dfrac{3(x-2)(x-7)}{x-7} + (x-2)(x-7) = \dfrac{8(x-2)(x-7)}{(x-2)(x-7)}$$

$$3(x-2) + (x^2 - 9x + 14) = 8$$

$$x^2 - 6x + 8 = 8$$

$$x^2 - 6x = 0$$

$$x(x-6) = 0$$

$$x = 0 \text{ or } x - 6 = 0$$

$$x = 0 \text{ or } \quad x = 6$$

▶ The solutions are 0 and 6.

CHECK If $x = 0$:

$$\dfrac{3}{0-7} + 1 \overset{?}{=} \dfrac{8}{0^2 - 9 \cdot 0 + 14}$$

$$\dfrac{4}{7} = \dfrac{4}{7} \checkmark$$

If $x = 6$:

$$\dfrac{3}{6-7} + 1 \overset{?}{=} \dfrac{8}{6^2 - 9 \cdot 6 + 14}$$

$$-2 = -2 \checkmark$$

12.7 Solve Rational Equations **821**

Motivating the Lesson
You and a friend work together during the summer to mow and trim lawns. You know that you can finish the work alone twice as fast as when your friend works alone. If you know the time it takes the two of you to complete a job together, you can write an equation to find the amount of time it would take you to do the job alone.

❸ TEACH

Extra Example 1
Solve $\dfrac{8}{x+6} = \dfrac{x}{2}$. Check your solution. **−8 and 2; both solutions check.**

Key Question to Ask for Example 1
• When is it appropriate to use cross products to solve a rational equation? **Use cross products if both sides of the equation are single rational expressions.**

Extra Example 2
Solve $\dfrac{2x}{x+3} + \dfrac{1}{3} = \dfrac{-6}{x+3}$. Check your solution. **There is no solution. The solution appears to be −3, but the expressions $\dfrac{2x}{x+3}$ and $\dfrac{-6}{x+3}$ are undefined when $x = -3$.**

Extra Example 3
Solve $\dfrac{4}{x-1} + 1 = \dfrac{-10}{x^2 - 9x + 8}$. Check your solution. **−2 and 7; both solutions check.**

Differentiated Instruction

Visual Learners Teach students to use the factored form as a way to visualize the solution. In **Example 3**, first visualize $x^2 - 9x + 14$ in the factored form $(x-2)(x-7)$. Next visualize $\dfrac{3}{x-7}$ as $\dfrac{3}{x-7} \cdot 1$, or $\dfrac{3}{x-7} \cdot \dfrac{x-2}{x-2}$. Finally, the constant 1 is the fraction $\dfrac{(x-2)(x-7)}{(x-2)(x-7)}$. Now that all of the fractions have the same denominator, the numerators can be used to write the equation $3(x-2) + (x-2)(x-7) = 8$ which can be solved for x.

See also the *Algebra 1 Toolkit* for more strategies.

EXAMPLE 4 Solve a multi-step problem

PAINT MIXING You have an 8 pint mixture of paint that is made up of equal amounts of yellow paint and blue paint. To create a certain shade of green, you need a paint mixture that is 80% yellow. How many pints of yellow paint do you need to add to the mixture?

ANOTHER WAY
For an alternative method for solving the problem in Example 4, turn to page 827 for the **Problem Solving Workshop.**

Solution

Because the amount of yellow paint equals the amount of blue paint, the mixture has 4 pints of yellow paint. Let p represent the number of pints of yellow paint that you need to add.

STEP 1 **Write** a verbal model. Then write an equation.

$$\frac{4 + p}{8 + p} = 0.8$$

STEP 2 **Solve** the equation.

$$\frac{4 + p}{8 + p} = 0.8 \qquad \text{Write equation.}$$

$$4 + p = 0.8(8 + p) \qquad \text{Cross products property}$$

$$4 + p = 6.4 + 0.8p \qquad \text{Distributive property}$$

$$0.2p = 2.4 \qquad \text{Rewrite equation.}$$

$$p = 12 \qquad \text{Solve for } p.$$

▶ You need to add 12 pints of yellow paint.

CHECK $\quad\dfrac{4 + p}{8 + p} = 0.8 \qquad$ **Write original equation.**

$$\frac{4 + 12}{8 + 12} \stackrel{?}{=} 0.8 \qquad \text{Substitute 12 for } p.$$

$$\frac{16}{20} \stackrel{?}{=} 0.8 \qquad \text{Simplify numerator and denominator.}$$

$$0.8 = 0.8 \ \checkmark \qquad \text{Write fraction as decimal. Solution checks.}$$

 GUIDED PRACTICE for Examples 2, 3, and 4

Solve the equation. Check your solution.

3. $\dfrac{a}{a + 4} + \dfrac{1}{3} = \dfrac{-12}{a + 4}$ **−10**

4. $\dfrac{n}{n - 11} - 1 = \dfrac{22}{n^2 - 5n - 66}$ **−4**

5. **WHAT IF?** In Example 4, suppose you need a paint mixture that is 75% yellow. How many pints of yellow paint do you need to add to the mixture? **8 pints**

12.7 EXERCISES

HOMEWORK KEY
○ = WORKED-OUT SOLUTIONS
on p. WS1 for Exs. 7, 15, and 33
★ = STANDARDIZED TEST PRACTICE
Exs. 2, 24, 28, and 35

SKILL PRACTICE

[A] 1. **VOCABULARY** The equation $\frac{3}{x-1} = \frac{7}{x} + 4$ is an example of a(n) __?__ . **rational equation**

2. ★ **WRITING** *Describe* two methods for solving a rational equation. Which method can you use to solve any kind of rational equation? *Explain.* **See margin.**

EXAMPLE 1
on p. 820
for Exs. 3–13, 24

SOLVING EQUATIONS Solve the equation. Check your solution.

3. $\frac{5}{r} = \frac{r}{20}$ **±10**

4. $\frac{3}{s-13} = \frac{s}{10}$ **−2, 15**

5. $\frac{2}{t} = \frac{10}{t-6}$ **−1½**

6. $\frac{2}{c+3} = \frac{-5}{c-1}$ **−1⁶⁄₇**

7. $\frac{2m}{m+4} = \frac{3}{m-1}$ **−1½, 4**

8. $\frac{n-3}{n-6} = \frac{n+1}{n+5}$ **1²⁄₇**

9. $\frac{w}{2} = \frac{15}{w+1}$ **−6, 5**

10. $\frac{2x}{4-x} = \frac{x}{x-4}$ **0**

11. $\frac{2y}{y-3} = \frac{24}{y}$ **6**

ERROR ANALYSIS *Describe* and correct the error in solving the equation. **12, 13. See margin.**

12. $\frac{x+1}{2x+2} = \frac{3}{2x}$

$$\frac{x+1}{2x+2} = \frac{3}{2x}$$
$$(x+1)2x = 3(2x+2)$$
$$2x^2 + 2x = 6x + 6$$
$$2x^2 - 4x - 6 = 0$$
$$2(x-3)(x+1) = 0$$
$$x - 3 = 0 \quad \text{or} \quad x + 1 = 0$$
$$x = 3 \quad \text{or} \quad x = -1$$

The solutions are 3 and −1.

13. $\frac{4x+1}{8x-1} = \frac{3}{5}$

$$\frac{4x+1}{8x-1} = \frac{3}{5}$$
$$5(4x+1) = 3(8x-1)$$
$$20x + 1 = 24x - 3$$
$$1 = 4x - 3$$
$$4 = 4x$$
$$1 = x$$

The solution is 1.

EXAMPLES 2 and 3
on p. 821
for Exs. 14–23

SOLVING EQUATIONS Solve the equation. Check your solution.

14. $\frac{6x}{x-11} + 1 = \frac{3}{x-11}$ **2**

15. $\frac{z}{z+7} - 3 = \frac{-1}{z+7}$ **−10**

16. $\frac{a+7}{a+4} - 1 = \frac{a+10}{2a+8}$ **no solution**

17. $\frac{1}{b+3} + 2 = \frac{b^2-3}{b^2+12b+27}$ **−22**

18. $\frac{m}{m-2} - \frac{3m}{m-4} = \frac{-2m+2}{m^2-6m+8}$ **1**

19. $\frac{3n}{n+1} - \frac{12}{n^2-1} + \frac{n+4}{n-1}$ **2 ± 2√3**

20. $\frac{3}{p-1} - \frac{2}{p-1} = \frac{-6}{p^2-3p+2}$ **−4**

21. $\frac{5}{q+4} = \frac{q}{q-3} + \frac{2q-27}{q^2+q-12}$ **no solution**

22. $\frac{r+2}{r^2+6r-7} = \frac{8}{r^2+3r-4}$ **−6, 8**

23. $\frac{9}{s^2-4} = \frac{4-5s}{s-2}$ **−⅕, −1**

24. ★ **OPEN-ENDED** Write a rational equation that can be solved using the cross products property. Then solve the equation. *Sample answer:* $\frac{x}{x+1} = \frac{2}{x+3}$; **−2, 1**

---

2. Method 1: Use the cross products property, Method 2: Multiply each side of the equation by the LCD of all the rational expressions in the equation. Method 2 can be used for any rational equation, but Method 1 can be used only for rational equations for which both sides are single rational expressions.

12. The solutions must be checked in the original equation. The solution $x = -1$ is extraneous because it is an excluded value for the original equation. The correct solution is 3.

13. The distributive property must be used to find the product of 5 and $(4x + 1)$; $5(4x + 1) = 3(8x - 1)$, $20x + 5 = 24x - 3$, $8 = 4x$, $2 = x$. The solution is 2.

4 PRACTICE AND APPLY

Assignment Guide

Answer Transparencies available for all exercises

Basic:
Day 1: EP p. 946 Exs. 43–48
pp. 823–826
Exs. 1–8, 12–19, 24–26, 31–35, 39–53 odd

Average:
Day 1: pp. 823–826
Exs. 1, 2, 7–13, 19–29, 31–37, 40–52 even

Advanced:
Day 1: pp. 823–826
Exs. 1, 2, 8–11, 20–38*, 40–52 even

Block:
pp. 823–826
Exs. 1, 2, 7–13, 19–29, 31–37, 40–52 even (with 12.6)

Differentiated Instruction

See *Algebra 1 Best Practices Toolkit* for suggestions on addressing the needs of a diverse classroom.

Homework Check

For a quick check of student understanding of key concepts, go over the following exercises:

Basic: 6, 14, 18, 31, 32
Average: 8, 20, 22, 32, 33
Advanced: 10, 21, 23, 33, 34

Extra Practice

• Student Edition, p. 946
• Chapter 12 Resource Book: Practice levels A, B, C, pp. 79–81

Practice Worksheet

An easily-readable reduced practice page (with answers) for this lesson can be found on p. 762C.

B 25. **REASONING** Consider the equation $\frac{2}{x - a} = \frac{x}{x - a}$ where a is a real number. For what value(s) of a does the equation have exactly one solution? no solution? *Explain* your answers. **See margin.**

26. **USING ANOTHER METHOD** Another way to solve a rational equation is to write each side of the equation as a single rational expression and then use the cross products property. Use this method to solve the equation $\frac{x}{x + 1} + \frac{x - 2}{2} = \frac{2x - 1}{4}$. **3**

27. **SOLVING SYSTEMS OF EQUATIONS** Consider the following system:

$$y = 3x + 1$$

$$y = \frac{-5}{x - 3} - 6$$

a. Solve the system algebraically. $\left(\frac{8}{3}, 9\right), (-2, -5)$

b. Check your solution by graphing the equations. **See margin.**

28. ★ **MULTIPLE CHOICE** Let a be a real number. How many solutions does the equation $\frac{2}{x - a} = \frac{1}{x + a} + \frac{2a}{x^2 - a^2}$ have? **A**

(A) Zero   (B) One   (C) Two   (D) Infinitely many

29. **REASONING** Is the expression $\frac{x + a}{x + 1 + a}$ ever equivalent to $\frac{x}{x + 1}$ for some nonzero value of a? *Justify* your answer algebraically. **See margin.**

C 30. **CHALLENGE** Let a and b be real numbers. The solutions of the equation $ax + b = \frac{30}{x + 2} - 1$ are -8 and 8. What are the values of a and b? *Explain* your answer.
$a = \frac{1}{2}, b = -2.$ **Sample answer:** Replacing x in the equation with -8 and then again with 8 gives two equations in two variables, a and b. Solving this system of two equations yields $a = \frac{1}{2}$ and $b = -2$.

PROBLEM SOLVING

EXAMPLE 4 **A**
on p. 822
for Exs. 31–34

31. **ICE HOCKEY** In ice hockey, a goalie's save percentage (in decimal form) is the number of shots blocked by a goalie divided by the number of shots made by an opposing team. Suppose a goalie has blocked 160 out of 200 shots. How many consecutive shots does the goalie need to block in order to raise the save percentage to 0.840? **50 consecutive shots**

@HomeTutor for problem solving help at classzone.com

32. **RUNNING TIMES** You are running a 6000 meter charity race. Your average speed in the first half of the race is 50 meters per minute faster than your average speed in the second half. You finish the race in 27 minutes. What is your average speed in the second half of the race? **250 m/min**

@HomeTutor for problem solving help at classzone.com

824

○ = **WORKED-OUT SOLUTIONS** on p. WS1   ★ = **STANDARDIZED TEST PRACTICE**

33. **CLEANING SOLUTIONS** You have a cleaning solution that consists of 2 cups of vinegar and 7 cups of water. You need a cleaning solution that consists of 5 parts water and 1 part vinegar in order to clean windows. How many cups of water do you need to add to your cleaning solution so that you can use it to clean windows? **3 c**

34. **MULTI-STEP PROBLEM** Working together, a painter and an assistant can paint a certain room in 2 hours. The painter can paint the room alone in half the time it takes the assistant to paint the room alone. Let t represent the time (in hours) that the painter can paint the room alone.

a. Copy and complete the table.

Person	Fraction of room painted each hour	Time (hours)	Fraction of room painted
Painter	$\frac{1}{t}$	2	? $\frac{2}{3}$
Assistant	? $\frac{1}{2t}$	2	? $\frac{1}{3}$

b. *Explain* why the sum of the expressions in the fourth column of the table must be 1. **See margin.**

c. Write a rational equation that you can use to find the time that the painter takes to paint the room alone. Then solve the equation. $\frac{2}{t} + \frac{1}{t} = 1$; **3 h**

d. How long does the assistant take to paint the room alone? **6 h**

B **35.** ★ **EXTENDED RESPONSE** You and your sister can rake a neighbor's front lawn together in 30 minutes. Your sister takes 1.5 times as long as you to rake the lawn by herself.

a. **Solve** Write an equation that you can use to find the time t (in minutes) you take to rake the lawn by yourself. Then solve the equation. $\frac{30}{t} + \frac{30}{1.5t} = 1$; **50 min**

b. **Compare** With more experience, both of you can now rake the lawn together in 20 minutes, and your sister can rake the lawn alone in the same amount of time as you. Tell how you would change the equation in part (a) in order to describe this situation. Then solve the equation. **Change each 30 to 20, and change 1.5 to 1; 40 min.**

c. **Explain** *Explain* why your solution of the equation in part (b) makes sense. Then justify your explanation algebraically for any given amount of time that both of you rake the lawn together. **See margin.**

36. **TELEVISION** The average time t (in minutes) that a person in the United States watched television per day during the period 1950–2000 can be modeled by

$$t = \frac{265 + 8.85x}{1 + 0.0114x}$$

where x is the number of years since 1950.

a. Approximate the year in which a person watched television for an average of 6 hours per day. **1970**

b. About how many years had passed when the average time a person spent watching television per day increased from 5 hours to 7 hours? **about 32 yr**

Exercise 33 Some students may prefer one of the alternative methods, shown on pages 827–828, for solving this problem. Suggest that students make themselves familiar with the three methods (Example 4 on page 822 and the two alternative methods), and identify which method they prefer.

34b. The expressions in the fourth column represent the fractions of the room painted by each person in 2 hours. Because the painter and assistant can paint the whole room in 2 hours, the sum of the fractions must be 1 (one whole room).

35c. Because you now both rake at the same rate, whenever you work together, the time it takes to rake a portion of the lawn will be half the time it takes either of you to rake that portion alone. Suppose you rake together for m minutes. Then you each rake $\frac{m}{40}$ of the lawn, and together you rake $\frac{m}{40} + \frac{m}{40} = \frac{2m}{40} = \frac{m}{20}$ of the lawn. To rake $\frac{m}{20}$ of the lawn alone would take you $2m$ minutes.

Daily Homework Quiz

Transparency Available

Solve the equation.

1. $\frac{7}{x-4} = \frac{x}{3}$ **−3 and 7**

2. $\frac{x+9}{x+6} - 2 = \frac{x+12}{2x+12}$ **no solution**

3. $\frac{3}{x-2} + 1 = \frac{1}{x^2+x-6}$ **−5 and 1**

4. You have a 6-ounce spice blend that is made up of equal parts of basil and oregano. A recipe calls for a blend that is 60% basil. How many ounces of basil do you need to add to the blend? **1.5 oz**

Online Quiz

Available at **classzone.com**

Diagnosis/Remediation

- Practice A, B, C in Chapter 12 Resource Book, pp. 79–81
- Study Guide in Chapter 12 Resource Book, pp. 82–83
- Practice Workbook, pp. 194–195
- @HomeTutor

Challenge

Additional challenge is available in the Chapter 12 Resource Book, p. 86.

Quiz

An easily-readable reduced copy of the quiz (with answers) on Lessons 12.5–12.7 from the Assessment Book can be found on p. 762F.

37. From 8 psi to 7 psi; substitute the given psi values for p in the given equation and then solve for a: for $p = 10$, $a \approx 10{,}722$; for $p = 9$, $a \approx 13{,}536$; for $p = 8$, $a \approx 16{,}600$; for $p = 7$, $a \approx 19{,}948$. The change in altitude when the atmospheric pressure changes from 10 psi to 9 psi is about $13{,}536 - 10{,}722 = 2814$, and the change in altitude when the atmospheric pressure changes from 8 psi to 7 psi is about $19{,}948 - 16{,}600 = 3348$.

---

37. SCIENCE Atmospheric pressure, measured in pounds per square inch (psi), is the pressure exerted on an object by the weight of the atmosphere above the object. The atmospheric pressure p (in psi) can be modeled by

$$p = \frac{14.55(56{,}267 - a)}{55{,}545 + a}$$

where a is the altitude (in feet). Is the change in altitude greater when the atmospheric pressure changes from 10 psi to 9 psi or from 8 psi to 7 psi? *Explain* your answer. **See margin.**

C **38. CHALLENGE** Butterfat makes up about 1% of the volume of milk in 1% milk. Butterfat can make up no more than 0.2% of the volume of milk in skim milk. A container holds 15 fluid ounces of 1% milk. How many fluid ounces of butterfat must be removed in order for the milk to be considered skim milk? Round your answer to the nearest hundredth. **0.12 fl oz**

MIXED REVIEW

PREVIEW
Prepare for Lesson 13.1 in Exs. 39–44.

Write the fraction as a decimal and as a percent. Round decimals to the nearest thousandth. Round percents to the nearest tenth of a percent. *(p. 916)*

39. $\frac{1}{4}$ **0.25, 25%**   40. $\frac{1}{8}$ **0.125, 12.5%**   41. $\frac{7}{10}$ **0.7, 70%**

42. $\frac{24}{25}$ **0.96, 96%**   43. $\frac{25}{30}$ **0.833, 83.3%**   44. $\frac{7}{2}$ **3.5, 350%**

Evaluate the expression.

45. $(9^2 - 7) \div 2$ *(p. 8)* **37**   46. $6[4 - (16 - 14)^2]$ *(p. 8)* **0**   47. $\sqrt{289}$ *(p. 110)* **17**

48. $\pm\sqrt{1600}$ *(p. 110)* **±40**   49. $\frac{3^2}{3^{-7}}$ *(p. 495)* **19,683**   50. $\frac{4^2}{4^5}$ *(p. 495)* $\frac{1}{64}$

51. $\left(-\frac{1}{8}\right)^3$ *(p. 495)* $-\frac{1}{512}$ 52. $\frac{1.61 \times 10^{-7}}{2.3 \times 10^{-3}}$ *(p. 512)* **7 × 10⁻⁵**   53. $(1.2 \times 10^6)^2$ *(p. 512)* **1.44 × 10¹²**

QUIZ for Lessons 12.5–12.7

Find the product or quotient. *(p. 802)*

1. $\frac{5}{8x^2} \cdot \frac{4x^3}{15}$ $\frac{x}{6}$

2. $\frac{3y^2 + 6y}{y^2 - 16} \div \frac{y^2}{y - 4}$ $\frac{3(y+2)}{y(y+4)}$

Find the sum or difference. *(p. 812)*

3. $\frac{8a}{a+11} - \frac{5a-1}{a+11}$ $\frac{3a+1}{a+11}$

4. $\frac{6n}{n+3} + \frac{n-1}{n^2+5n+6}$ $\frac{6n^2+13n-1}{(n+3)(n+2)}$

Solve the equation. Check your solution. *(p. 820)*

5. $\frac{2z}{z+5} = \frac{z}{z-3}$ **0, 11**

6. $\frac{2x}{x} + \frac{3-x}{x+1} = \frac{-4}{x^2+x}$ **−4**

7. **BATTING AVERAGES** A softball player's batting average is the number of hits divided by the number of times at bat. A softball player has a batting average of .200 after 90 times at bat. How many consecutive hits does the player need in order to raise the batting average to .250? *(p. 820)* **6 hits**

Using ALTERNATIVE METHODS

Another Way to Solve Example 4, page 822

MULTIPLE REPRESENTATIONS In Example 4 on page 822, you saw how to solve a problem about mixing paint by using a rational equation. You can also solve the problem by using a table or by reinterpreting the problem.

PROBLEM

PAINT MIXING You have an 8 pint mixture of paint that is made up of equal amounts of yellow paint and blue paint. To create a certain shade of green, you need a paint mixture that is 80% yellow. How many pints of yellow paint do you need to add to the mixture?

METHOD 1

Use a Table One alternative approach is to use a table.

The mixture has 8 pints of paint. Because the mixture has an equal amount of yellow paint and blue paint, the mixture has $8 \div 2 = 4$ pints of yellow paint.

STEP 1 **Make** a table that shows the percent of the mixture that is yellow paint after you add various amounts of yellow paint.

Yellow paint (pints)	Paint in mixture (pints)	Percent of mixture that is yellow paint
4	8	$\frac{4}{8} = 50\%$
6	10	$\frac{6}{10} = 60\%$
8	12	$\frac{8}{12} \approx 67\%$
10	14	$\frac{10}{14} \approx 71\%$
12	16	$\frac{12}{16} = 75\%$
14	18	$\frac{14}{18} \approx 78\%$
15	19	$\frac{15}{19} \approx 79\%$
16	20	$\frac{16}{20} = 80\%$

A mixture with 6 pints of yellow paint is the result of adding 2 pints of yellow paint to the mixture.

This amount of yellow paint gives you the percent yellow you want.

STEP 2 **Find** the number of pints of yellow paint needed. Subtract the number of pints of yellow paint already in the mixture from the total number of pints of yellow paint you have: $16 - 4 = 12$.

▶ You need to add 12 pints of yellow paint.

Alternative Strategy

Example 4 on page 822 can be solved by using a table or by reinterpreting the problem. When using a table, students should be careful to organize the table to include all existing data and to show all of the data they need to solve the problem. Reinterpreting the problem as a ratio allows students to write an equation whose solution has fewer steps than solving a rational equation.

Avoiding Common Errors

In Method 1, some students may forget to perform Step 2 after they have found the percent of the mixture that is yellow paint. Remind students that the original mixture already contains some yellow paint, and that they need to subtract this amount from the total amount needed.

In Step 1, some students may think that $\frac{4}{5}$ to $\frac{1}{5}$ means the ratio is $4:5$. It may help these students to ask how many pints of yellow paint would be in a mixture that contains 5 pints of yellow and blue paint, given the ratio of 4 pints of yellow paint to 1 pint of blue paint.

1. See Additional Answers beginning on p. AA1.

2. Because Jill already has $1000 in the mutual fund she only needs to add $2250 − $1000 = $1250 to the account.

3, 5. See Additional Answers beginning on p. AA1.

METHOD 2   **Reinterpret Problem** Another alternative approach is to reinterpret the problem.

STEP 1 **Reinterpret** the problem. A mixture with 80% yellow paint means that $\frac{4}{5}$ of the mixture is yellow and $\frac{1}{5}$ of the mixture is blue. So, the ratio of yellow paint to blue paint needs to be $4:1$. You need 4 times as many pints of yellow paint as pints of blue paint.

STEP 2 **Write** a verbal model. Then write an equation. Let p represent the number of pints of yellow paint that you need to add.

Pints of yellow paint already in mixture	+	Pints of yellow paint you need to add	= 4 ·	Pints of blue paint in mixture
4	+	p	= 4 ·	4

STEP 3 **Solve** the equation.

$4 + p = 4 \cdot 4$ **Write equation.**

$4 + p = 16$ **Multiply.**

$p = 12$ **Subtract 4 from each side.**

▶ You need to add 12 pints of yellow paint to the mixture.

PRACTICE

1. **INVESTING** Jill has $10,000 in various investments, including $1000 in a mutual fund. Jill wants the amount in the mutual fund to make up 20% of the amount in all of her investments. How much money should she add to the mutual fund? Solve this problem using two different methods. **See margin.**

2. **ERROR ANALYSIS** *Describe* and correct the error in solving Exercise 1. **See margin.**

Amount in mutual fund	Amount in all investments	Percent in mutual fund
1000	10,000	10%
1400	10,400	About 13%
1800	10,800	About 17%
2250	11,250	20%

Jill needs to add $2250 to her mutual fund. ✗

3. **BASKETBALL** A basketball player has made 40% of 30 free throw attempts so far. How many consecutive free throws must the player make in order to increase the percent of free throw attempts made to 50%? Solve this problem using two different methods. **See margin.**

4. **WHAT IF?** In Exercise 3, suppose the basketball player instead wants to increase the percent of free throw attempts made to 60%. How many consecutive free throws must the player make? **15 free throws**

5. **SNOW SHOVELING** You and your friend are shoveling snow out of a driveway. You can shovel the snow alone in 50 minutes. Both of you can shovel the snow in 30 minutes when working together. How many minutes will your friend take to shovel the snow alone? Solve this problem using two different methods. **See margin.**

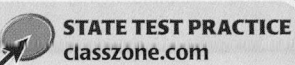
Lessons 12.5–12.7

1. **MULTI-STEP PROBLEM** For the period 1991–2002, the average total revenue T (in dollars per admission) that a movie theater earned and the average revenue C (in dollars per admission) from concessions in the United States can be modeled by

$$T = \frac{0.018x^2 + 5.4}{1 - 0.0011x^2} \quad \text{and} \quad C = \frac{0.013x^2 + 1.1}{0.0011x^2 + 1}$$

where x is the number of years since 1991.

a. Write a model that gives the percent p (in decimal form) of the average total revenue per admission that came from concessions as a function of x. **See margin.**

b. About what percent of the average total revenue came from concessions in 2001? **about 27%**

2. **SHORT RESPONSE** The diagram of the truck shows the distance between the first axle and the last axle for each of two groups of consecutive axles.

Axle 1   Axle 2 Axle 3   Axle 4 Axle 5
├── 20 ft ──┤
├──────── 35 ft ────────┤

The maximum weight W (to the nearest 500 pounds) that a truck on a highway can carry on a group of consecutive axles is given by the formula

$$W = 500\left(\frac{d}{n-1} + 12n + 36\right)$$

where d is the distance (in feet) between the first axle and the last axle of the group and n is the number of axles in the group.

a. Rewrite the expression on the right side of the equation as a single rational expression. Then find the maximum weight that the truck shown can carry on axles 1–3. $\frac{500(12n^2 + 24n + d - 36)}{n-1}$; **41,000 lb**

b. Can the truck carry 65,500 pounds on axles 2–5? *Explain* your answer. **See margin.**

3. **MULTI-STEP PROBLEM** A rower travels 5 miles upstream (against the current) and 5 miles downstream (with the current). The speed of the current is 1 mile per hour.

a. Write an equation that gives the total travel time t (in hours) as a function of the rower's average speed r (in miles per hour) in still water. $\frac{10r}{(r-1)(r+1)}$

b. Find the total travel time if the rower's average speed in still water is 7 miles per hour. **about 1.5 h**

4. **GRIDDED ANSWER** You take 7 minutes to fill your washing machine tub using only the cold water valve. You take 4 minutes to fill the tub using both the cold water valve and the hot water valve. How many minutes will you take to fill the tub using only the hot water valve? $9\frac{1}{3}$ **min**

5. **OPEN-ENDED** *Describe* a real-world situation that can be modeled by the equation $\frac{115 + x}{170 + x} = 0.75$. *Explain* what the solution of the equation means in this situation. **See margin.**

6. **EXTENDED RESPONSE** The number D (in thousands) of all college degrees earned and the number M (in thousands) of master's degrees earned in the United States during the period 1984–2001 can be modeled by

$$D = \frac{1800 + 17x^2}{1 + 0.0062x^2} \quad \text{and} \quad M = \frac{280 + 2.5x^2}{1 + 0.0040x^2}$$

where x is the number of years since 1984.

a. Write a model that gives the percent p (in decimal form) of all college degrees earned that were master's degrees. **See margin.**

b. Approximate the percent of all college degrees earned that were master's degrees in 2000. **about 19.1%**

c. Graph the equation in part (a) on a graphing calculator. *Describe* how the percent of college degrees that were master's degrees changed during the period. Can you use the graph to describe how the *number* of master's degrees changed during the period? *Explain.* **See margin.**

1a. $p = \frac{(0.013x^2 + 1.1)(1 - 0.0011x^2)}{(0.0011x^2 + 1)(0.018x^2 + 5.4)}$

2b. No; for the group of axles from axle 2 to axle 5, $d = 35$ feet and $n = 4$. Substitute these values into the expression for W to find the maximum weight this group of axles can carry: $\frac{500[12(4)^2 + 24(4) + 35 - 36]}{4 - 1} \approx$ 48,000 pounds. 65,500 pounds is greater than 48,000 pounds, so the truck cannot carry a weight of 65,500 pounds between axle 2 and axle 5.

5. *Sample answer:* A basketball player who has made 115 free throws out of 170 attempts wants to raise his free throw shooting percentage to 75%; the solution $x = 50$ means that the basketball player would have to make 50 consecutive free throws in order to raise his free throw shooting percentage to 75%.

6a. $p = \frac{(280 + 2.5x^2)(1 + 0.0062x^2)}{(1 + 0.0040x^2)(1800 + 17x^2)}$

6c. The percent of college degrees that were master's degrees increased from 1984–2001; no. *Sample answer:* The graph only shows what percent of college degrees are master's degrees, it does not show the number of college degrees that are master's degrees so you cannot describe how the number of master's degrees changed during the period.

Additional Resources

The following resources are available to help review the materials in this chapter.

Chapter 12 Resource Book

- Chapter Review Games and Activities, p. 87
- Cumulative Practice, Chs. 1–12, pp. 89–90

Student Resources in Spanish

eWorkbook

@HomeTutor

Vocabulary Practice

Vocabulary practice is available at **classzone.com**.

BIG IDEAS

For Your Notebook

Big Idea 1

Graphing Rational Functions

The graphs of $y = \dfrac{a}{x}$ $(a \neq 0)$ and $y = \dfrac{a}{x-h} + k$ $(a \neq 0)$ are hyperbolas that have two symmetrical branches. The characteristics of the functions and their graphs are given below. To graph a rational function whose numerator and denominator are first-degree polynomials, you can first use long division to rewrite the function so that it has the form $y = \dfrac{a}{x-h} + k$.

Function	Vertical asymptote	Horizontal asymptote	Domain	Range
$y = \dfrac{a}{x}$	$x = 0$	$y = 0$	All real numbers except $x = 0$	All real numbers except $y = 0$
$y = \dfrac{a}{x-h} + k$	$x = h$	$y = k$	All real numbers except $x = h$	All real numbers except $y = k$

Big Idea 2

Performing Operations on Rational Expressions

Performing operations on rational expressions is similar to performing operations on numerical fractions. Any common factors in the numerator and denominator should be divided out, and the original expression should be used when finding excluded values.

Operation	Rule
Multiplication	$\dfrac{a}{b} \cdot \dfrac{c}{d} = \dfrac{ac}{bd}$ where $b \neq 0$ and $d \neq 0$
Division	$\dfrac{a}{b} \div \dfrac{c}{d} = \dfrac{a}{b} \cdot \dfrac{d}{c}$ where $b \neq 0$, $c \neq 0$, and $d \neq 0$
Addition	Same denominator: $\dfrac{a}{c} + \dfrac{b}{c} = \dfrac{a+b}{c}$ where $c \neq 0$ Different denominators: Use LCD of rational expressions.
Subtraction	Same denominator: $\dfrac{a}{c} - \dfrac{b}{c} = \dfrac{a-b}{c}$ where $c \neq 0$ Different denominators: Use LCD of rational expressions.

Big Idea 3

Solving Rational Equations

You can use the following steps to solve a rational equation.

1. Rewrite the rational equation by using the cross products property or by multiplying each side by the least common denominator (LCD) of the rational expressions in the equation.

2. Solve the rewritten equation.

3. Check for extraneous solutions.

REVIEW KEY VOCABULARY

- inverse variation, *p. 765*
- constant of variation, *p. 765*
- hyperbola, branches of a hyperbola, asymptotes of a hyperbola, *p. 767*
- rational function, *p. 775*
- rational expression, *p. 794*
- excluded value, *p. 794*
- simplest form of a rational expression, *p. 795*
- least common denominator (LCD) of rational expressions, *p. 813*
- rational equation, *p. 820*

VOCABULARY EXERCISES

1. Copy and complete: A(n) _?_ of a hyperbola is a line that the hyperbola approaches but doesn't intersect. **asymptote**

2. **WRITING** *Explain* how you can use an LCD to solve a rational equation. **See margin.**

3. Identify the vertical asymptote and horizontal asymptote of the graph of $y = \dfrac{-5}{x+2} - 4$. **$x = -2$, $y = -4$**

REVIEW EXAMPLES AND EXERCISES

Use the review examples and exercises below to check your understanding of the concepts you have learned in each lesson of Chapter 12.

12.1 Model Inverse Variation
pp. 765–772

EXAMPLE

The variables x and y vary inversely, and $y = 14$ when $x = 4$. Write the inverse variation equation that relates x and y. Then find the value of y when $x = 7$.

$y = \dfrac{a}{x}$ Write inverse variation equation.

$14 = \dfrac{a}{4}$ Substitute 4 for *x* and 14 for *y*.

$56 = a$ Simplify.

▶ The inverse variation equation is $y = \dfrac{56}{x}$. When $x = 7$, $y = \dfrac{56}{7} = 8$.

EXERCISES

EXAMPLES 4 and 5 on pp. 767–768 for Exs. 4–7

Given that y varies inversely with x, use the specified values to write an inverse variation equation that relates x and y. Then find y when $x = 5$. **$y = \dfrac{-36}{x}$, −7.2**

4. $x = 9$, $y = 2$ **$y = \dfrac{18}{x}$, 3.6**

5. $x = 3$, $y = 21$ **$y = \dfrac{63}{x}$, 12.6**

6. $x = -6$, $y = 6$

7. Tell whether the ordered pairs $(-10, 0.8)$, $(-4, 2)$, $(5, -1.6)$, and $(16, -0.5)$ represent inverse variation. If so, write the inverse variation equation. **See margin.**

Chapter Review **831**

Extra Example 12.1

The variables x and y vary inversely, and $y = 8$ when $x = 3$. Write the inverse variation equation that relates x and y. Then find the value of y when $x = 12$. **$y = \dfrac{24}{x}$; 2**

2. Multiply each side of the equation by the least common denominator of all the rational expressions in the equation. This will make all the denominators in the equation equal to 1 and allow you to identify the equation as linear or quadratic in form.

7. inverse variation; $y = \dfrac{-8}{x}$

Extra Example 12.2

Graph $y = \dfrac{1}{x+3} + 2$.

Extra Example 12.3

Divide $x^2 + 4x + 8$ by $x + 2$.

$x + 2 + \dfrac{4}{x+2}$

8.

$y = \dfrac{4}{x} + 1$

9.

$y = \dfrac{1}{x-6}$

10.

$y = \dfrac{2}{x+1} + 1$

15.

$a = \dfrac{500 + 2d}{d}$

12.2 Graph Rational Functions

pp. 775–782

EXAMPLE

Graph $y = \dfrac{-1}{x-2} - 3$.

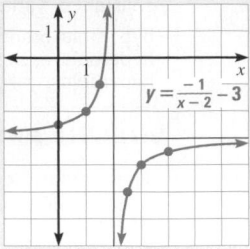

$y = \dfrac{-1}{x-2} - 3$

STEP 1 **Identify** the asymptotes of the graph. The vertical asymptote is $x = 2$, and the horizontal asymptote is $y = -3$.

STEP 2 **Plot** several points on each side of the vertical asymptote.

STEP 3 **Graph** two branches that pass through the plotted points and approach the asymptotes.

EXERCISES

EXAMPLES
2, 3, and 4
on pp. 776–777
for Exs. 8–10

Graph the function. 8–10. See margin.

8. $y = \dfrac{4}{x} + 1$

9. $y = \dfrac{1}{x-6}$

10. $y = \dfrac{2}{x+1} + 1$

12.3 Divide Polynomials

pp. 784–791

EXAMPLE

Divide $x^2 + 7x - 2$ by $x - 2$.

$$
\begin{array}{r}
x + 9 \\
x - 2 \overline{\smash{)}\, x^2 + 7x - 2} \\
\underline{x^2 - 2x} \\
9x - 2 \\
\underline{9x - 18} \\
16
\end{array}
$$

Multiply x and $x - 2$.

Subtract $x^2 - 2x$. Bring down -2.

Multiply 9 and $x - 2$.

Subtract $9x - 18$.

▶ $(x^2 + 7x - 2) \div (x - 2) = x + 9 + \dfrac{16}{x-2}$

EXERCISES

EXAMPLES
2, 3, 4, 5, and 7
on pp. 785–787
for Exs. 11–15

Divide.

11. $(x^2 + 12x + 35) \div (x + 7)$ $x + 5$

12. $(y^2 - 5y - 8) \div (y - 3)$ $y - 2 + \dfrac{-14}{y-3}$

13. $(4z + z^2 - 1) \div (5 + z)$ $z - 1 + \dfrac{4}{z+5}$

14. $(3a^2 - 2) \div (3 + 3a)$ $a - 1 + \dfrac{1}{3+3a}$

15. CHARITY DONATIONS Sean intends to collect $500 in individual donations for a charity. His company will contribute $2 for every donation collected. Write and graph an equation that gives the average amount a (including the company contribution) that the charity will receive per individual donation as a function of the number d of donations. $a = \dfrac{500 + 2d}{d}$

832 Chapter 12 Rational Equations and Functions

12.4 Simplify Rational Expressions

pp. 794–800

EXAMPLE

Simplify $\dfrac{x^2 - 3x - 18}{x^2 + 11x + 24}$. State the excluded values.

$$\dfrac{x^2 - 3x - 18}{x^2 + 11x + 24} = \dfrac{(x + 3)(x - 6)}{(x + 3)(x + 8)} \qquad \text{Factor numerator and denominator.}$$

$$= \dfrac{\cancel{(x + 3)}(x - 6)}{\cancel{(x + 3)}(x + 8)} \qquad \text{Divide out common factor.}$$

$$= \dfrac{x - 6}{x + 8} \qquad \text{Simplify.}$$

▶ The excluded values are −8 and −3.

EXERCISES

EXAMPLES
1, 2, 3, and 4
on pp. 794–796
for Exs. 16–21

Find the excluded values, if any, of the expression.

16. $\dfrac{x + 3}{2x - 4}$ **2**

17. $\dfrac{3}{y^2 - 4y - 12}$ **−2, 6**

18. $\dfrac{8z}{9z^2 - 1}$ **$\pm\dfrac{1}{3}$**

Simplify the expression, if possible. State the excluded values.

19. $\dfrac{5m^3 - 15m^2}{20m^2}$ **$\dfrac{m - 3}{4}$; 0**

20. $\dfrac{3n^2 - n - 2}{2n^2 - 3n + 1}$ **$\dfrac{3n + 2}{2n - 1}$; $\dfrac{1}{2}$, 1**

21. $\dfrac{4 - r^2}{r^2 - r - 2}$ **$\dfrac{-(r + 2)}{r + 1}$; −1, 2**

12.5 Multiply and Divide Rational Expressions

pp. 802–809

EXAMPLE

Find the quotient $\dfrac{5x^2 + 3x - 2}{4x} \div (5x - 2)$.

$$\dfrac{5x^2 + 3x - 2}{4x} \div (5x - 2) = \dfrac{5x^2 + 3x - 2}{4x} \div \dfrac{5x - 2}{1} \qquad \text{Rewrite polynomial as fraction.}$$

$$= \dfrac{5x^2 + 3x - 2}{4x} \cdot \dfrac{1}{5x - 2} \qquad \text{Multiply by multiplicative inverse.}$$

$$= \dfrac{5x^2 + 3x - 2}{4x(5x - 2)} \qquad \text{Multiply numerators and denominators.}$$

$$= \dfrac{(5x - 2)(x + 1)}{4x(5x - 2)} \qquad \text{Factor and divide out common factor.}$$

$$= \dfrac{x + 1}{4x} \qquad \text{Simplify.}$$

EXERCISES

EXAMPLES
3 and 4
on pp. 803–804
for Exs. 22–24

Find the product or quotient.

22. $\dfrac{-x^3}{x^2 + 5x - 14} \cdot (2 - x)$ **$\dfrac{x^3}{x + 7}$**

23. $\dfrac{6v^8}{2v^5} \div \dfrac{8v}{14v^5}$ **$\dfrac{21v^7}{4}$**

24. $\dfrac{w^2 - 9}{2w + 1} \div \dfrac{w + 3}{4w^2 - 1}$ **$(w - 3)(2w - 1)$**

Chapter Review **833**

Extra Example 12.4

Simplify $\dfrac{x^2 - 6x - 16}{x^2 + 8x + 12}$. State the excluded values. $\dfrac{x - 8}{x + 6}$; −6, −2

Extra Example 12.5

Find the product $\dfrac{2x}{x^2 + 3x - 4} \cdot (x + 4)$. $\dfrac{2x}{x - 1}$

12.6 Add and Subtract Rational Expressions
pp. 812–819

EXAMPLE

Find the difference $\dfrac{x}{x-4} - \dfrac{5}{x+3}$.

$$\dfrac{x}{x-4} - \dfrac{5}{x+3} = \dfrac{x(x+3)}{(x-4)(x+3)} - \dfrac{5(x-4)}{(x+3)(x-4)}$$
Rewrite fractions using LCD, $(x-4)(x+3)$.

$$= \dfrac{x(x+3) - 5(x-4)}{(x-4)(x+3)}$$
Subtract fractions.

$$= \dfrac{x^2 - 2x + 20}{(x-4)(x+3)}$$
Simplify numerator.

EXERCISES

Find the sum or difference.

**EXAMPLES
1, 3, 5, and 6**
on pp. 812–815
for Exs. 25–28

25. $\dfrac{x+13}{5x-3} - \dfrac{9x-20}{5x-3}$ $\dfrac{-8x+33}{5x-3}$

26. $\dfrac{5}{6a} + \dfrac{1}{9a^3}$ $\dfrac{15a^2+2}{18a^3}$

$\dfrac{5c^2 - 13c - 48}{(c+1)(c-4)(c+2)}$

27. $\dfrac{6}{c+1} - \dfrac{c}{c^2 - 2c - 8}$

28. **BICYCLING** You ride your bike to a beach that is 15 miles away. Your average speed on the way home is 5 miles per hour less than your average speed on the way to the beach. Write an equation that gives the total travel time t (in hours) as a function of your average speed r (in miles per hour) on the way to the beach. Then find the total travel time if you biked to the beach at an average speed of 15 miles per hour. $\dfrac{30r - 75}{r(r-5)}$; **2.5 h**

12.7 Solve Rational Equations
pp. 820–826

EXAMPLE

Solve $\dfrac{2x}{x-1} + \dfrac{2}{3} = \dfrac{10}{x-1}$.

$$\dfrac{2x}{x-1} + \dfrac{2}{3} = \dfrac{10}{x-1}$$
Write original equation.

$$\dfrac{2x}{x-1} \cdot 3(x-1) + \dfrac{2}{3} \cdot 3(x-1) = \dfrac{10}{x-1} \cdot 3(x-1)$$
Multiply each expression by LCD, $3(x-1)$.

$$\dfrac{2x \cdot 3(x-1)}{(x-1)} + \dfrac{2 \cdot 3(x-1)}{3} = \dfrac{10 \cdot 3(x-1)}{(x-1)}$$
Divide out common factors.

$$6x + 2x - 2 = 30$$
Simplify.

$$8x - 2 = 30$$
Combine like terms.

$$x = 4$$
Solve for x.

EXERCISES

Solve the equation. Check your solution.

**EXAMPLES
1, 2, and 3**
on pp. 820–821
for Exs. 29–31

29. $\dfrac{18}{x-3} = \dfrac{x}{3}$ **−6, 9**

30. $\dfrac{4}{y+6} - 2 = \dfrac{20}{y^2 + 3y - 18}$ **−2, 1**

31. $\dfrac{1}{z+3} - \dfrac{5}{6} = \dfrac{2}{z+3}$ $\dfrac{-21}{5}$

Given that y varies inversely with x, use the specified values to write an inverse variation equation that relates x and y. Then find y when $x = 3$.

1. $x = 2, y = 5$ $\quad y = \dfrac{10}{x}; \dfrac{10}{3}$

2. $x = 9, y = 9$ $\quad y = \dfrac{81}{x}; 27$

3. $x = \dfrac{9}{2}, y = 4$ $\quad y = \dfrac{18}{x}; 6$

4. Tell whether the table represents inverse variation. If so, write the inverse variation equation.
inverse variation; $y = \dfrac{-5}{x}$

x	−10	−2	4	5	20
y	0.5	2.5	−1.25	−1	−0.25

Graph the function.
5–7. See margin.

5. $y = \dfrac{-6}{x}$

6. $y = \dfrac{2}{x-5} + 2$

7. $y = \dfrac{3x-1}{x+4}$

Divide.

8. $(v^2 - 16v + 49) \div (v - 8)$ $\quad v - 8 + \dfrac{-15}{v-8}$

9. $(8w - 2w^2 - 6) \div (w - 1)$ $\quad -2w + 6$

10. $(6x^2 + x) \div (2x + 1)$ $\quad 3x - 1 + \dfrac{1}{2x+1}$

Simplify the expression, if possible. State the excluded values.

11. $\dfrac{42x^4}{3x^2}$ $\quad 14x^2; 0$

12. $\dfrac{2y-8}{4-y}$ $\quad -2; 4$

13. $\dfrac{z^2 - 4z - 77}{z^2 - 13z + 22}$ $\quad \dfrac{z+7}{z-2}; 2, 11$

Find the sum, difference, product, or quotient. **14–19. See margin.**

14. $\dfrac{r^2 - 9r + 18}{r^2 + 11r + 30} \cdot \dfrac{r+5}{r^2 - 36}$

15. $\dfrac{s^2 + 3s - 10}{s^2 - 9} \div \dfrac{s-2}{s+3}$

16. $\dfrac{x^2 - 9x}{x+3} \div (x^2 - 6x - 27)$

17. $\dfrac{4}{m+2} - \dfrac{3m}{m-3}$

18. $\dfrac{2n+7}{n-1} - \dfrac{8n}{n+5}$

19. $\dfrac{p+1}{p^2-49} + \dfrac{p-1}{p^2 + 10p + 21}$

Solve the equation. Check your solution.

20. $\dfrac{7}{u+1} = \dfrac{4}{u+4}$ $\quad -8$

21. $\dfrac{t+11}{t-11} = \dfrac{11t+121}{t^2 - 6t - 55}$ $\quad 6, -11$

22. $\dfrac{8}{x+4} = \dfrac{5x}{x^2 - 2x - 24} - 1$ $\quad -9, 8$

23. **GOLF** Your local golf club offers two payment options to anyone who wants to use its course. For the first option, you pay a one-time fee of $750 to join for the season plus $25 each time you use the golf course. For the second option, you instead pay $45 each time you use the golf course.

 a. Using the first option, write an equation that gives your average cost C (in dollars) per use of the golf course as a function of the number g of times you use the golf course. Then graph the equation. **See margin.**

 b. Use the graph to approximate the number of times you need to use the golf course before the average cost is less than $45. **38 times**

24. **CLEANING** You and your brother start a house cleaning business for the summer. Your brother needs twice the time you need to clean a certain room. Working together, the two of you need 60 minutes to clean the room.

 a. Write an equation that you can use to find the time t (in minutes) you need to clean the room by yourself. Then solve the equation. $\dfrac{60}{t} + \dfrac{60}{2t} = 1$

 b. How long will each of you need to clean the room individually?
 You need 90 minutes and your brother needs 180 minutes.

Additional Resources

Assessment Book
- Chapter Test, Levels A, B, C, pp. 171–176
- Standardized Chapter Test, pp. 177–178
- SAT/ACT Chapter Test, pp. 179–180
- Alternative Assessment, pp. 181–182

Test Generator CD-ROM

Chapter Test

Easily-readable reduced copies (with answers) of Chapter Test B, the Standardized Chapter Test, and the Alternative Assessment from the Assessment Book can be found on pp. 762G–762H.

14. $\dfrac{r-3}{(r+6)^2}$

15. $\dfrac{s+5}{s-3}$

16. $\dfrac{x}{(x+3)^2}$

17. $\dfrac{-3m^2 - 2m - 12}{(m+2)(m-3)}$

18. $\dfrac{-6n^2 + 25n + 35}{(n-1)(n+5)}$

19. $\dfrac{2p^2 - 4p + 10}{(p-7)(p+7)(p+3)}$

23a. $C = \dfrac{750 + 25g}{g}$;

5.

6. $y = \dfrac{2}{x-5} + 2$

7. $y = \dfrac{3x-1}{x+4}$

Encourage students to check their answers against the context of the question, including any diagrams, tables, or graphs, to make sure that they have answered the right question and that their answer makes sense in the context of the question. This strategy is also useful when calculations are complex and the likelihood of error is high.

Avoiding Common Errors

It is easy to misread diagrams or other graphics if students are in a hurry to finish a question. Urge students to take enough time to check that their answers match diagrams and graphs.

CONTEXT-BASED MULTIPLE CHOICE QUESTIONS

Some of the information you need to solve a context-based multiple choice question may appear in a table, a diagram, or a graph.

PROBLEM 1

Gary competes in the triathlon described in the flyer. His average biking speed is 8 times his average swimming speed. His average running speed is 4 times his average swimming speed. He takes 0.75 minute to transition from swimming to biking and 0.25 minute to transition from biking to running. He finishes the triathlon in 2 hours 25 minutes. What is his average swimming speed?

OAK CITY TRIATHLON

July 29, 8 A.M.

Swim: 1.5 kilometers
Bike: 40 kilometers
Run: 10 kilometers

(A) 0.0625 kilometer per minute   (B) 0.125 kilometer per minute

(C) 0.25 kilometer per minute   (D) 0.5 kilometer per minute

Plan

INTERPRET THE INFORMATION Use the distance for each stage of the triathlon and Gary's average speed for each stage to write a rational equation that describes the situation. Then solve the equation to find his average swimming speed.

Solution

STEP 1
....
Use the information in the problem to write an equation that describes the situation.

The time that Gary takes to complete each stage of the triathlon is the distance of the stage divided by the average speed for that stage. The sum of the times of each stage and the transition times equals 2 hours 25 minutes, or 145 minutes. Let x represent Gary's average swimming speed (in kilometers per minute).

$$\frac{1.5}{x} + \frac{40}{8x} + \frac{10}{4x} + 0.75 + 0.25 = 145$$

STEP 2
....
Solve the equation to find Gary's average swimming speed.

$$\frac{1.5}{x} \cdot 8x + \frac{40}{8x} \cdot 8x + \frac{10}{4x} \cdot 8x + 0.75 \cdot 8x + 0.25 \cdot 8x = 145 \cdot 8x$$

$$\frac{1.5 \cdot 8x}{x} + \frac{40 \cdot 8x}{8x} + \frac{10 \cdot 8x}{4x} + 0.75 \cdot 8x + 0.25 \cdot 8x = 145 \cdot 8x$$

$$12 + 40 + 20 + 6x + 2x = 1160x$$

$$72 + 8x = 1160x$$

$$0.0625 = x$$

Gary's average swimming speed is 0.0625 kilometer per minute.

The correct answer is A. (A) (B) (C) (D)

PROBLEM 2

The graph of which function is shown?

A $y = \dfrac{2}{x-3} + 4$ **B** $y = \dfrac{2}{x+3} + 4$

C $y = \dfrac{1}{x+3} + 4$ **D** $y = \dfrac{1}{x+4} - 3$

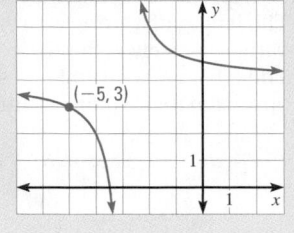

$(-5, 3)$

Plan

INTERPRET THE GRAPH The graph is a hyperbola that represents a rational function of the form $y = \dfrac{a}{x-h} + k$. Use the asymptotes and the fact that $(-5, 3)$ lies on the graph to find the function.

Solution

STEP 1
Find the values of h and k.

The hyperbola has a vertical asymptote of $x = -3$ and a horizontal asymptote of $y = 4$. So, the function has the form $y = \dfrac{a}{x-(-3)} + 4$, or $y = \dfrac{a}{x+3} + 4$.

STEP 2
Find the value of a.

To find the value of a, substitute the coordinates of $(-5, 3)$ into the function.

$3 = \dfrac{a}{-5+3} + 4$ **Substitute −5 for x and 3 for y.**

$2 = a$ **Solve for a.**

The function is $y = \dfrac{2}{x+3} + 4$. The correct answer is B. **A** **B** **C** **D**

PRACTICE

1. A community service club is recruiting volunteers to work at a charity event. The table shows the number of hours that each volunteer needs to work for various numbers of volunteers that the club recruits. If the club recruits 50 volunteers, how many hours does each volunteer need to work? **B**

Volunteers	Work time (hours/person)
20	4
25	3.2
32	2.5

   A 1 hour   **B** 1.6 hours   **C** 2 hours   **D** 2.8 hours

2. What is the area of the right triangle shown? **A**

   A $\dfrac{x^2 - 12x + 35}{2}$ **B** $\dfrac{x^2 + 12x - 35}{2}$

   C $\dfrac{x^2 + 12x - 35}{4}$ **D** $x^2 - 12x + 35$

$\dfrac{x^2 - 2x - 35}{x + 9}$

$\dfrac{x^2 + 4x - 45}{x + 5}$

Standardized Test Preparation   **837**

MULTIPLE CHOICE

In Exercises 1–3, use the following information.
The length of a string on a stringed instrument varies inversely with the frequency of vibration. The table gives several notes and their approximate frequencies (in hertz).

Note	Frequency (Hz)
C	65.4
D	73.4
E	82.4
F	87.3
G	98.0

1. The string corresponding to which note has the shortest length? **D**

  (A) C note   **(B)** D note

  (C) E note   **(D)** G note

2. If the string that produces the C note has a length of 42 centimeters, what is the approximate length of the string that produces the F note? **B**

  (A) 28 cm   **(B)** 31 cm

  (C) 35 cm   **(D)** 46 cm

3. If the string that produces the D note has a length of 56 centimeters, what is the approximate length of the string that produces the G note? **C**

  (A) 31 cm   **(B)** 35 cm

  (C) 42 cm   **(D)** 65 cm

4. Which equation gives the ratio r of the surface area of the rectangular prism to its volume as a function of the height h? **A**

  (A) $r = \dfrac{2}{h} + 0.7$ **(B)** $r = \dfrac{1}{20h} + 0.7$

  (C) $r = \dfrac{1}{20h} + 28$ **(D)** $r = \dfrac{2}{h} + 0.05$

5. Which point lies on the hyperbola shown? **D**

  (A) $(-7, 2.5)$ **(B)** $(-9, 2.6)$

  (C) $(9, 3.4)$ **(D)** $(11, 3.2)$

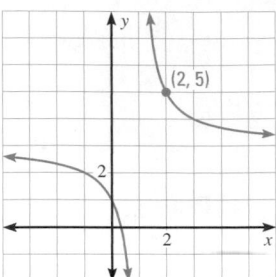

In Exercises 6–8, use the following information.

Jan is hiking a trail and plans to rest for 2 hours along the way. The hyperbola shown is the graph of her combined time t (in hours) for hiking and resting as a function of her average hiking speed r (in miles per hour).

6. If $r = 5$, what is the value of t? **B**

  (A) 5   **(B)** 6

  (C) 7   **(D)** 10

7. What is the length of the trail? **B**

  (A) 10 miles   **(B)** 20 miles

  (C) 30 miles   **(D)** 40 miles

8. Suppose Jan's combined time for hiking and resting is 8 hours 15 minutes. What is her average hiking speed? **B**

  (A) 3 mi/h   **(B)** 3.2 mi/h

  (C) 3.4 mi/h   **(D)** 3.6 mi/h

GRIDDED ANSWER

9. The variables x and y vary inversely, and $y = 15$ when $x = 2$. What is the value of y when $x = 5$? **6**

10. You and your friend wash cars to raise money for your school club. Both of you can wash a certain car in 10 minutes when working together. Your friend can wash the car alone in twice the time that you can wash the car alone. How many minutes do you take to wash the car alone? **15 min**

11. What is the remainder when you divide $2x^2 - 5x + 10$ by $2x + 1$? **13**

12. What is the excluded value of the rational expression $\dfrac{6x^2 + 19x - 7}{x^2 - 8x + 16}$? **4**

13. You and several friends are planning a ski trip. Your plane ticket costs $180. A ski lodge costs $2000 to rent. Everyone will share the cost of renting the ski lodge equally. How much more money (in dollars) would you spend if 8 people go on the trip than if 10 people go? **$50**

SHORT RESPONSE

14. A town's two street sweepers can clean the streets together in 20 hours. The older sweeper takes 4 times as long as the newer sweeper to clean the streets by itself.

  a. Write an equation that you can use to find the time t (in hours) that the newer sweeper takes to clean the streets by itself. Then solve the equation. $\dfrac{20}{t} + \dfrac{20}{4t} = 1$; **25 h**

  b. Suppose that the older sweeper takes only twice as long as the newer sweeper to clean the streets by itself. Will the two sweepers take 10 hours to clean the streets together? *Explain.* **See margin.**

15. Your cousin is driving 500 miles to your house. On her way, she takes a 45 minute lunch break. Write and graph an equation that gives the total time t (in hours) of your cousin's trip as a function of her average driving speed r (in miles per hour). How would the graph change if she took a 60 minute lunch break? *Explain* your answer. **See margin.**

EXTENDED RESPONSE

16. The table shows the taxes paid for various incomes.

  a. Write a linear equation that gives the taxes paid t (in dollars) as a function of the income i (in dollars). $t = 0.06i - 180$

  b. Write a rational equation that gives the percent p (in decimal form) of income that is paid in taxes as a function of the income i (in dollars). Use the equation to find the income of a person who pays 4.5% of income in taxes. $p = \dfrac{0.06i - 180}{i}$; **$12,000**

  c. Does the function in part (b) make sense for incomes less than $3000? *Justify* your answer algebraically. **See margin.**

Income (dollars)	Taxes paid (dollars)
10,000	420
15,000	720
20,000	1020
25,000	1320

17. A greeting card company offers you the opportunity to sell its cards, but you must first pay the company a one-time fee of $300 plus $2 for each card that you sell.

  a. Write and graph an equation that gives the average cost C per card (including the fee) as a function of the number of cards s that you sell. $c = \dfrac{300 + 2s}{s}$; **see margin for art.**

  b. You want to sell enough cards so that the average cost per card (including the fee) drops to $3. Write and solve an equation to find the number of cards that you need to sell. $\dfrac{300 + 2s}{s} = 3$; **300 cards**

  c. Is it possible for you to sell enough cards so that the average cost per card drops to $1.75? *Explain* your answer. **See margin.**

Margin

15.

The horizontal asymptote will move from $t = 0.75$ to $t = 1$. *Sample answer:* The equation would change from $t = \dfrac{500}{r} + 0.75$ to $t = \dfrac{500}{r} + 1$, which changes the horizontal asymptote to 1 instead of 0.75.

16c. No; a person cannot pay a negative amount of tax, so the equation in part (b) only makes sense for incomes i for which $t \geq 0$. Solve the inequality $0.06i - 180 \geq 0$ to get $i \geq 3000$.

17a. $C = \dfrac{300 + 2s}{s}$;

17c. No; as the graph in part (a) shows, the average cost decreases as the number of cards sold increases, but the average cost C never gets as low as $2.00 (or $1.75) because $C = 2$ is the horizontal asymptote of the graph.

14b. No; from part (a) we know that the new sweeper takes 25 hours to clean the streets by itself, so the old sweeper takes $2(25) = 50$ hours to clean the streets by itself. In 1 hour the new sweeper cleans $\dfrac{1}{25}$ of the streets and the old sweeper cleans $\dfrac{1}{50}$ of the streets. To find the number of hours t it takes them to clean the streets together, solve the equation $\dfrac{t}{25} + \dfrac{t}{50} = 1$. The solution is $t = 16\dfrac{2}{3}$ hours.

REGULAR SCHEDULE
Pre-AP For pacing and assignments for a Pre-AP course, see the *Algebra 1 Toolkit*.

Lesson	Les. Day	BASIC	AVERAGE	ADVANCED
13.1	Day 1	SRH p. 932 Exs. 4–8; pp. 846–848 Exs. 1–15, 19–21, 24–26	pp. 846–848 Exs. 1, 2–12 even, 13–17, 19–22, 24–26	pp. 846–848 Exs. 1, 2–6 even, 10, 12, 13–26*
13.2	Day 1	pp. 853–855 Exs. 1–19	pp. 853–855 Exs. 1–19	pp. 853–855 Exs. 1–19
	Day 2	pp. 853–855 Exs. 20–29, 32–36, 40–43	pp. 853–855 Exs. 22–30, 32–38, 40–43	pp. 853–855 Exs. 24–43*
13.3	Day 1	pp. 858–859 Exs. 1–17, 23–25, 28–33	pp. 858–859 Exs. 1–5, 6–14 even, 15–20, 23–26, 28–33	pp. 858–859 Exs. 1–3, 10–33*
13.4	Day 1	SRH p. 915 Exs. 1, 2, 6, 7; pp. 864–867 Exs. 1–8, 30–34	pp. 864–867 Exs. 1, 2, 5–8, 18, 19, 30–34	pp. 864–867 Exs. 1, 2, 6–8, 18, 19, 21*, 30–34
	Day 2	pp. 864–867 Exs. 9–17, 22–25, 28, 29	pp. 864–867 Exs. 11–17, 20, 22–26, 28, 29	pp. 864–867 Exs. 11–17, 20, 22–29*
13.5	Day 1	pp. 873–874 Exs. 1–10, 13–16, 19–27	pp. 873–874 Exs. 1, 2, 4–11, 13–17, 19–27	pp. 873–874 Exs. 1, 2, 5–27*
13.6	Day 1	pp. 877–878 Exs. 1–14, 19–21, 24	pp. 877–878 Exs. 1, 2, 4–10, 13–17, 19–22, 24	pp. 877–878 Exs. 1, 5–9, 13–24*
13.7	Day 1	pp. 883–885 Exs. 1–9, 17, 20	pp. 883–885 Exs. 1, 2, 4–9, 17, 20, 21	pp. 883–885 Exs. 1, 4–9, 17, 20, 21
	Day 2	pp. 883–885 Exs. 10–13, 18, 19, 23–27	pp. 883–885 Exs. 10–15, 18, 19, 23–27	pp. 883–885 Exs. 11–16*, 18, 19, 22–27*
13.8	Day 1	pp. 889–892 Exs. 1–7, 15, 16	pp. 889–892 Exs. 1, 2, 4–7, 15, 16, 21, 22	pp. 889–892 Exs. 1, 2, 4–6, 15, 16, 21, 22
	Day 2	pp. 889–892 Exs. 8–12, 17–19, 21–24	pp. 889–892 Exs. 8–13, 17–19, 23, 24	pp. 889–892 Exs. 8–14*, 17–20*, 23, 24
Review	Day 1	pp. 896–900 Exs. 1–25	pp. 896–900 Exs. 1–25	pp. 896–900 Exs. 1–25
Assess	Day 1	Chapter 13 Test	Chapter 13 Test	Chapter 13 Test
Yearly Pacing		Chapter 13 Total – 14 days	Chapters 1–13 Total – 160 days	Remaining – 0 days

*Challenge Exercises EP = Extra Practice SRH = Skills Review Handbook

BLOCK SCHEDULE

DAY 1	DAY 2	DAY 3	DAY 4	DAY 5	DAY 6	DAY 7
13.1	**13.2 (CONT.)**	**13.4**	**13.5**	**13.7**	**13.8**	**REVIEW**
pp. 846–848 Exs. 1, 2–12 even, 13–17, 19–22, 24–26	pp. 853–855 Exs. 22–30, 32–38, 40–43	pp. 864–867 Exs. 1, 2, 5–8, 11–20, 22–26, 28–34	pp. 873–874 Exs. 1, 2, 4–11, 13–17, 19–27	pp. 883–885 Exs. 1, 2, 4–15, 17–21, 23–27	pp. 889–892 Exs. 1, 2, 4–13, 15–19, 21–24	pp. 896–900 Exs. 1–25
13.2	**13.3**		**13.6**			**ASSESS**
pp. 853–855 Exs. 1–19	pp. 858–859 Exs. 1–5, 6–14 even, 15–20, 23–26, 28–33		pp. 877–878 Exs. 1, 2, 4–10, 13–17, 19–22, 24			Chapter 13 Test
Yearly Pacing	Chapter 13 Total – 7 days		Chapters 1–13 Total – 80 days		Remaining – 0 days	

RESOURCE MANAGER

Chapter Resource Book

CHAPTER SUPPORT

| Parents as Partners (Chapter Overview with home involvement exercises and activity) | | | | | | | p. 1 | |

LESSON SUPPORT	13.1	13.2	13.3	13.4	13.5	13.6	13.7	13.8
Teaching Guide/Lesson Plan	p. 3	p. 14	p. 24	p. 36	p. 48	p. 58	p. 71	p. 85
Activity Masters			p. 26	p. 38				
Technology Activities & Keystrokes	p. 5		p. 27			p. 60	p. 73	p. 87
Activity Support Masters								
Practice (3 levels)	p. 6	p. 16	p. 28	p. 39	p. 50	p. 63	p. 74	p. 88
Study Guide	p. 9	p. 19	p. 31	p. 42	p. 53	p. 66	p. 80	p. 94
Catch-Up for Absent Students	p. 11	p. 21	p. 33	p. 44	p. 55	p. 68	p. 82	p. 96
Problem Solving/Application	p. 12	p. 22	p. 34	p. 45	p. 56	p. 69	p. 83	p. 97
Challenge Practice	p. 13	p. 23	p. 35	p. 47	p. 57	p. 70	p. 84	p. 98

REVIEW

Chapter Review Games and Activities	p. 99	Cumulative Practice	p. 101
Project with Rubric	p. 100	Resource Book Answers	A1

Transparencies	13.1	13.2	13.3	13.4	13.5	13.6	13.7	13.8
Warm-Up/Daily Homework Quiz	✔	✔	✔	✔	✔	✔	✔	✔
Notetaking Guide	✔	✔	✔	✔	✔	✔	✔	✔
Teacher Support	✔			✔				✔
Answer Transparencies	✔	✔	✔	✔	✔	✔	✔	✔

ASSESSMENT BOOK

Quizzes	p. 183	SAT/ACT Chapter Test	p. 193
Chapter Tests (3 levels)	p. 185	Alternative Assessment with Rubric	p. 195
Standardized Chapter Test	p. 191	Cumulative Test	p. 197

TECHNOLOGY

- Easy Planner
- Test and Practice Generator
- Power Presentations
- @HomeTutor
- Activity Generator
- Animated Algebra
- Classzone.com
- eEdition Plus Online
- eWorkbook Plus Online
- Easy Grader Online

ADDITIONAL RESOURCES

- Worked-Out Solution Key
- Notetaking Guide
- Practice Wookbook
- Algebra 1 Toolkit
- Benchmark Tests
- Reteaching and Remediation
- Spanish Study Guide
- Spanish Assessment Book
- Student Resources in Spanish
- Multi-Language Visual Glossary

13 Lesson Practice Level B

LESSON 13.1 Practice B
For use with pages 843–848

3. 36; 1, 1; 1, 2; 1, 3; 1, 4; 1, 5; 1, 6; 2, 1; 2, 2; 2, 3; 2, 4; 2, 5; 2, 6; 3, 1; 3, 2; 3, 3; 3, 4; 3, 5; 3, 6; 4, 1; 4, 2; 4, 3; 4, 4; 4, 5; 4, 6; 5, 1; 5, 2; 5, 3; 5, 4; 5, 5; 5, 6; 6, 1; 6, 2; 6, 3; 6, 4; 6, 5; 6, 6

Find the number of possible outcomes in the sample space. Then list the possible outcomes.

1. A bag contains 6 blue cards numbered 1–6 and 8 red cards numbered 1–8. You choose a card at random.
14; blue 1; blue 2; blue 3; blue 4; blue 5; blue 6; red 1; red 2; red 3; red 4; red 5; red 6; red 7; red 8

2. You roll one 3-sided number cube and toss two coins.
2. 12; 1, H, H; 1, H, T; 1, T, H; 1, T, T; 2, H, H; 2, H, T; 2, T, H; 2, T, T; 3, H, H; 3, H, T; 3, T, H; 3, T, T

3. You roll two number cubes. See above.

In Exercises 4–9, refer to the spinner shown. The spinner is divided into sections with the same area.

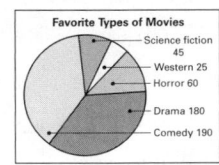

4. What is the probability that the spinner stops on an even number? $\frac{4}{9}$

5. What is the probability that the spinner stops on an odd number? $\frac{5}{9}$

6. You spin the spinner 24 times. It stops on 27 twice. What is the experimental probability of stopping on 27? $\frac{1}{12}$

7. You spin the spinner 30 times. It stops on a multiple of 3 five times. What is the experimental probability of stopping on a multiple of 3? $\frac{1}{6}$

8. What are the odds in favor of stopping on a multiple of 4? $\frac{1}{3}$

9. What are the odds against stopping on a multiple of 6? $\frac{7}{2}$

10. **Favorite Spectator Sport** A survey asked a total of 180 students in your school about their favorite spectator sports. The table shows the results of the survey.

Sport	Basketball	Soccer	Football	Baseball	Volleyball	Wrestling	Hockey
Number of students	40	20	45	20	16	18	21

a. What is the probability that a randomly selected student who participated in this survey chose football as his or her favorite spectator sport? $\frac{1}{4}$

b. What is the probability that a randomly selected student who participated in this survey chose wrestling or hockey as his or her favorite spectator sport? $\frac{13}{60}$

c. What are the odds in favor of a randomly selected student who participated in this survey choosing basketball as his or her favorite spectator sport? $\frac{2}{7}$

11. **Movies** A local movie theater did a survey of students to determine their favorite types of movies. The circle graph shows the results of the survey.

Favorite Types of Movies
- Science fiction 45
- Western 25
- Horror 60
- Drama 180
- Comedy 190

a. What is the probability that a randomly selected student chose science fiction as his or her favorite type of movie?

b. What is the probability that a randomly selected student chose drama or comedy as his or her favorite type of movie? **11. a.** $\frac{9}{100}$ **b.** $\frac{37}{50}$

LESSON 13.2 Practice B
For use with pages 851–855

4. the number of permutations of 14 objects taken 3 at a time
5. the number of permutations of 24 objects taken 10 at a time
6. the number of permutations of 30 objects taken 20 at a time

Find the number of ways you can arrange (a) all of the letters in the given word and (b) 2 of the letters in the word.

1. TACK **a.** 24 **b.** 12
2. MAR **a.** 6 **b.** 6
3. GAMER **a.** 120 **b.** 20

Write the meaning of the notation in words. See above.

4. $_{14}P_3$
5. $_{24}P_{10}$
6. $_{30}P_{20}$

Evaluate the expression.

7. 6! 720
8. 9! 362,880
9. 11! 39,916,800

10. $\frac{8!}{3!}$ 6720
11. $\frac{12!}{9!}$ 1320
12. $\frac{15!}{14!}$ 15

13. $_6P_3$ 120
14. $_4P_4$ 24
15. $_{15}P_3$ 2730

16. $_8P_7$ 40,320
17. $_{10}P_6$ 151,200
18. $_5P_0$ 1

Complete the statement using >, <, or =.

19. $_6P_4 \underline{\ ?\ } _4P_1$ >
20. $_8P_6 \underline{\ ?\ } _{10}P_8$ <
21. $_3P_0 \underline{\ ?\ } _6P_5$ <

22. $_6P_3 \underline{\ ?\ } _4P_1$ >
23. $_{24}P_1 \underline{\ ?\ } _4P_4$ =
24. $_7P_5 \underline{\ ?\ } _{12}P_3$ >

25. **Summer Reading List** At the beginning of the summer, you have 6 books to read. In how many orders can you read the books? 720

26. **Air Conditioning Repair** An air conditioner repair person has repairs to make at 7 different homes. The destinations are all so close, it doesn't matter the order in which the repairs are made. In how many orders can the repairs be made? 5040

27. **Boat Racing** You are in a boat racing competition. In each heat, 4 boats race and the positions of the boats are randomly assigned.

a. In how many ways can a position be assigned? 24

b. What is the probability that you are chosen to be in the last position? *Explain* how you found your answer.

c. What is the probability that you are chosen to be in the first or second position of the heat that you are racing in? *Explain* how you found your answer.

d. What is the probability that you are chosen to be in the second or third position of the heat that you are racing in? *Compare* your answer with that in part (c).

28. **Math Exam** On an exam, you are asked to list the 6 steps to solving a particular kind of problem in order. You guess the order of the steps at random. What is the probability that you choose the correct order? $\frac{1}{720}$

27. b. $\frac{1}{4}$; The number of ways to be chosen to be in last position is given by 3!. The total number of ways a position is chosen is 4! = 24. So, the probability is $\frac{3!}{4!} = \frac{1}{4}$. **c.** $\frac{1}{2}$; You can be chosen to be in the first position 6 out of 24 ways and you can be chosen to be in the second position 6 out of 24 ways, so you can be chosen to be in the first or second position 12 out of 24 ways. **d.** $\frac{1}{2}$; You can be chosen to be in the second position 6 out of 24 ways and you can be chosen to be in the third position 6 out of 24 ways, so you can be chosen to be in the second or third position 12 out of 24 ways. The answers are the same.

LESSON 13.3 Practice B
For use with pages 856–859

Evaluate the expression.

1. $_8C_4$ 70
2. $_5C_5$ 1
3. $_{12}C_0$ 1

4. $_7C_1$ 7
5. $_{15}C_{11}$ 1365
6. $_{10}C_3$ 120

7. $_6C_5$ 6
8. $_4C_2$ 6
9. $_{16}C_8$ 12,870

Complete the statement using >, <, or =.

10. $_{10}C_6 \underline{\ ?\ } _8C_5$ >
11. $_{22}C_3 \underline{\ ?\ } _{18}C_4$ <
12. $_9C_6 \underline{\ ?\ } _9C_3$ =

13. $_8C_2 \underline{\ ?\ } _{15}C_{14}$ >
14. $_7C_7 \underline{\ ?\ } _{14}C_{14}$ =
15. $_5C_3 \underline{\ ?\ } _8C_3$ <

In Exercises 16–18, tell whether the question can be answered using combinations or permutations. Explain your choice, then answer the question.

16. Five students from the 90 students in your class not running for class president will be selected to count the ballots for the vote for class president. In how many ways can the 5 students be selected? combinations; Answers will vary. 43,949,268

17. Twenty students are running for 3 different positions on student council. In how many ways can the 3 positions be filled? permutations; Answers will vary. 6840

18. To complete a quiz, you must answer 3 questions from a list of 6 questions. In how many ways can you complete the quiz? combinations; Answers will vary. 20

19. **Sweaters** The buyer for a retail store must decide which sweaters to stock for the upcoming fall season. A sweater from one manufacturer comes in 5 different colors and 3 different textures. The buyer decides that the store will stock the sweater in 3 different colors and 2 different textures. How many different sweaters are possible? 30

20. **Greeting Cards** A greeting card company packages 4 different cards together that are randomly selected from 10 different cards with a different animal on each card. What is the probability that one of the cards in a package is the card that has a dog on it? $\frac{2}{5}$

21. **Open-Mike Night** A coffee shop offers an open-mike night for poetry. Tonight, 15 people would like to read, but there is only enough time to have 7 people read.

a. Seven of the 15 people that would like to read are randomly chosen. How many combinations of 7 readers from the group of people that would like to read are possible? 6435

b. You and your friend are part of the group that would like to read. What is the probability that you and your friend are chosen? What is the probability that you are chosen first and your friend is chosen second? Which event is more likely to occur? $\frac{1}{5}$; $\frac{1}{5}$; They are equally likely to occur.

Practice B
For use with pages 861–867

1. overlapping; $\frac{4}{9}$

In Exercises 1–4, you draw a card from a bag that contains 4 yellow cards numbered 1–4 and 5 blue cards numbered 1–5. Tell whether the events A *and* B are *mutually exclusive* or *overlapping*. Then find P(A *or* B).

1. Event A: You choose a card with an even number.
Event B: You choose a number 4 card.

2. Event A: You choose a yellow card.
Event B: You choose a number 5 card.
mutually exclusive; $\frac{5}{9}$

3. Event A: You choose a blue number 3 card.
Event B: You choose a blue card.
overlapping; $\frac{5}{9}$

4. Event A: You choose a card with an odd number.
Event B: You choose a blue card.
overlapping; $\frac{7}{9}$

In Exercises 5 and 6, tell whether the events A *and* B are *dependent* or *independent*. Then find P(A *and* B).

5. A bag contains 6 red balls and 5 green balls. You randomly draw one ball, replace it, and randomly draw a second ball.
Event A: The first ball is green.
Event B: The second ball is green. independent; $\frac{25}{121}$

6. You write each of the letters of the word BRILLIANT on pieces of paper and place them in a bag. You randomly draw one letter, do not replace it, then randomly draw a second letter.
Event A: The first letter is an L.
Event B: The second letter is a T. dependent; $\frac{1}{36}$

7. Eating Habits A survey of 500 students in a school found that about 100 households consist of only vegetarians, 240 consist of vegetarians and non-vegetarians, and 160 consist of non-vegetarians.
   a. What is the probability that one of the households surveyed, chosen at random, consists of vegetarians or non-vegetarians? $\frac{13}{25}$
   b. What is the probability that one of the households surveyed, chosen at random, consists of vegetarians and non-vegetarians? $\frac{12}{25}$
   c. *Explain* how your answers to parts (a) and (b) are related. The sum of the probabilities is 1.

8. Coordinating Time You study with a group for an upcoming math competition on Mondays, Tuesdays, and Thursdays. You volunteer at a hospital on Mondays, Wednesdays, and Thursdays.
   a. Make a Venn diagram that shows the days of the week that you participate in each activity.
   b. Your class is taking a field trip that could be scheduled for any day of the week (Monday through Friday). Find the probability that it is scheduled for a day when you are studying with your group or are volunteering. $\frac{4}{5}$

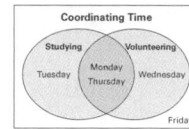

Coordinating Time

Studying — Volunteering
Tuesday — Monday Thursday — Wednesday
Friday

Practice B
For use with pages 871–874

1. music store customers; self-selected sample
3. likely to result in a biased sample
4. not likely to result in a biased sample

In Exercises 1 and 2, identify the population and classify the sampling method.

1. The manager of a music store wants to evaluate how customers rate the selection of music the store has in stock. Customers are given comment cards with their receipts.

2. Your school's administrators want to know if students are satisfied with the choices of activities for activity period. In each grade, every seventh student in alphabetical order is surveyed. all students in school; systematic sample

Tell whether the survey method used is likely to result in a biased sample.

3. A bicycling club wants to gather information about biking conditions throughout a city. A survey for bicycle riders is posted on the club's website.

4. A management company that owns several apartment buildings wants to gather information about tenant satisfaction with the condition of the apartments. They send a survey to 30 random tenants in each of the buildings.

In Exercises 5 and 6, tell whether the question is potentially biased. *Explain* your answer.

5. Don't you think that the lunch menu should include grilled chicken rather than pizza because grilled chicken is healthier for you? See below.

6. Do you think that the city's excess revenue should be spent on road repairs or building a new sports stadium? See below.

In Exercises 7–9, explain why the question is biased. Then rewrite it so that it is not.

7. Don't you agree that it is better to offer an accounting class as an elective rather than a computer programming class? See below.

8. Don't you agree that a science center would be more fun to go to than a planetarium? See below.

9. Would you pay even higher taxes to fund a new highway? biased because it suggests that taxes are already high; Would you use your taxes to fund a new highway?

10. Bus Stop Conditions A newspaper does a report on the condition of the bus stops in a large city. Part of the report includes a survey of people living in the area. The survey is done by asking people at a mall what they think of local bus stops. Is the sample likely to be biased? *Explain.* Answers will vary.

11. After-School Activities You plan a report on the participation of students at your school in after-school activities on your school's website. *Describe* how you could choose a representative sample. *Justify* your sampling method. Answers will vary.

5. biased because it suggests that grilled chicken is healthier than pizza
6. not biased because a particular response is not encouraged
7. biased because it suggests that accounting class is better than a computer programming class; Which class should your school offer as an elective, an accounting class or a computer programming class?
8. biased because it suggests that going to a science center is more fun than going to a planetarium; Where would you like to go, to a science center or to a planetarium?

Practice B
For use with pages 875–878

1. mean: 5; median: 5; modes: 1, 5
2. mean: 68; median: 67.5; mode: 81
3. mean: 19; median: 22; mode: 25
4. mean: 16; median: 13.5; modes: 8, 28

Find the mean, median, and mode(s) of the data.

1. 6, 1, 3, 8, 5, 11, 1, 5
2. 60, 81, 52, 75, 59, 81
3. 15, 27, 10, 25, 9, 22, 25
4. 23, 6, 8, 14, 28, 8, 13, 28
5. 16, 11, 14, 30, 22, 9, 19, 15
mean: 17; median: 15.5; mode: none
6. 4.2, 2.2, 3.7, 2.8, 1.1
mean: 2.8; median: 2.8; mode: none

For the set of data, determine which measure of central tendency best represents the data.

7. 89, 86, 96, 87, 100, 86 median
8. 38, 35, 40, 36, 36, 33, 42, 37, 39, 34 median
9. 50, 47, 48, 49, 72, 47, 54, 50 median
10. 115, 112, 127, 116, 123, 113 median
11. 87, 77, 151, 105, 65, 141, 104, 166 mean
12. 100, 106, 180, 41, 161, 292, 116, 213 mean

14. range: 10; mean absolute deviation: 2.88

Find the range and mean absolute deviation of the data. Round to the nearest hundredth, if necessary. 13. range: 6; mean absolute deviation: 1.68

13. 10, 7, 13, 10, 8
14. 110, 114, 104, 108, 106
16. range: 8; mean absolute deviation: 2.25
15. range: 13; mean
15. 87, 75, 85, 77, 74, 82 absolute deviation: 4.67
16. 15, 17, 15, 17, 21, 17, 15, 23
17. 40, 46, 41, 46, 49, 49, 46, 44, 44
range: 9; mean absolute deviation: 2.44
18. 50.8, 51.6, 51.9, 52, 52.5, 52.8, 53.1
range: 2.3; mean absolute deviation: 0.6

19. Bean Plants The heights (in inches) of eight bean plants are 28, 36, 41, 50, 35, 42, 46, and 52.
b. mean: 41.25; median: 41.5; mode: none
   a. What is the range of the bean plant heights? 24
c. either the mean or the median because they are both close to all of the data
   b. Find the mean, median, and mode(s) of the bean plant heights.
   c. Which measure of central tendency best represents the data? *Explain.*

20. Hotel Stay You are planning a trip to Washington, D.C. and are looking up hotel room rates. On the Internet, you find the following rates for a one-night stay in a hotel in Washington, D.C.
20. b. mean; because it is closer to all of the data
$109, $126.50, $175.95, $139, $77.50, $145, $162.35, $173, $181.50, $105
   a. Find the mean, median, and mode(s) of the rates. mean: 139.48; median: 142; mode: none
   b. Which measure of central tendency best represents the data? *Explain.*

21. Temperature The high and low temperatures for the last seven days are given.
High temperatures: 81°F, 78°F, 83°F, 89°F, 90°F, 87°F, 89°F 21. c. The range of the lows is greater than the range of the highs, so the lows cover a wider interval than the highs.
Low temperatures: 64°F, 53°F, 62°F, 66°F, 68°F, 69°F, 67°F
   a. Find the mean, median, and mode of each data set. Round your answers to the nearest tenth. highs: mean: 85.3; median: 87; mode: 89; lows: mean: 64.1; median: 66; mode: none
   b. For each data set, determine which measure of central tendency best represents the data. *Explain.* both the medians because they are closer to all of the data
   c. *Compare* the spreads of data by using the range.
   d. *Compare* the spreads of data by using the mean absolute deviation. Round your answers to the nearest hundredth. The mean absolute deviation of the highs is greater, so the average variation from the mean is greater for the highs than the lows.

13 Lesson Practice Level B

Give two possible keys for the stem-and-leaf plot.

1.
```
4 | 1 1 5        4|1 = 41; 4|1 = 4.1
5 | 0 2 7 8
6 | 3 9
7 | 4 5 6 9
8 | 0 1 3
```

2.
```
0 | 0 2 3 8 9       1|0 = 10; 1|0 = 1.0
1 | 0 2 5 5 8
2 | 4 6 8
3 | 3 3 4 5
4 | 6 7
```

Make a stem-and-leaf plot of the data.

3. 21, 10, 14, 26, 8, 30, 17, 15, 34, 27, 36, 20, 7, 19, 25, 33, 19, 32, 12, 25

```
0 | 7 8                 Key: 1|0 = 10
1 | 0 2 4 5 7 9 9
2 | 0 1 5 5 6 7
3 | 0 2 3 4 6
```

4. 52, 66, 61, 82, 51, 60, 62, 54, 73, 70, 89, 85, 74, 53, 61, 75, 89, 85, 77, 55

```
5 | 1 2 3 4 5          Key: 5|1 = 51
6 | 0 1 1 2 6
7 | 0 3 4 5 7
8 | 2 5 5 9 9
```

5. 3, 5, 11, 34, 28, 19, 4, 6, 14, 17, 22, 30, 1, 1, 9, 10, 24, 27, 33, 20, 9, 1

```
0 | 1 1 3 4 4 5 6 9 9   Key: 1|0 = 10
1 | 0 1 4 7 9
2 | 0 2 4 7 8
3 | 0 3 4
```

6. 0.1, 3.6, 2.2, 1.0, 2.1, 1.1, 0.2, 3.5, 3.1, 2.4, 0.3, 1.5, 2.3, 0.5, 1.2

```
0 | 1 2 3 5            Key: 0|1 = 0.1
1 | 0 1 2 5
2 | 1 2 3 4
3 | 1 5 6
```

Make a histogram of the data.

7. 78, 96, 72, 108, 82, 108, 99, 118, 94, 100, 86, 74

8. 58, 55, 65, 69, 66, 53, 60, 68, 61, 52, 66, 51

9. 4, 2.7, 3.2, 3, 3.7, 2.9, 3.1, 2.6, 3.4, 3, 3.6, 2.9

10. 18, 17.1, 15.5, 16.3, 15.2, 17.4, 16.6, 17.2, 15.1

11. **Mountains** The table shows the heights of the world's 14 tallest mountains (in thousands of meters). Make a stem-and-leaf plot of the data.

Mountain	Height	Mountain	Height
Aconagua	7.0	Mt. Damavand	5.8
Annapurna	8.1	Mt. Everest	8.8
Cotopoxi	5.9	Mt. Godwin Austen (K-2)	8.8
Illampu	6.6	Mt. Logan	6.1
Kanchenjuga	8.6	Mt. Makalu	8.5
Kilimanjaro	5.9	Mt. McKinley	6.2
Lenin	7.1	Orizaba	5.7

```
5 | 7 8 9 9           Key: 5|7 = 5.7
6 | 1 2 6
7 | 0 1
8 | 1 5 6 6 8
```

12. **Books** A survey asked people how many books they have read in the last month. The results are shown in the table.

Books	0–5	6–11	12–17	18–23
Frequency	12	4	3	1

a. Make a histogram of the data.

b. What is the probability that a person surveyed, chosen at random, has read 0–5 books in the last month? $\frac{3}{5}$

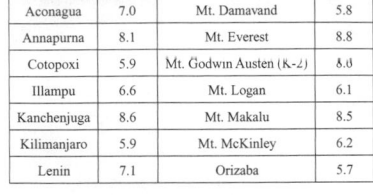

Identify the median, quartiles, and interquartile range of the data from the box-and-whisker plot. See below.

1.

2.

3.

4.
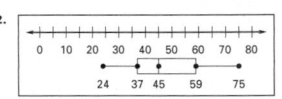

Make a box-and-whisker plot of the data.

5. 11, 33, 39, 27, 25, 31, 28, 33, 31, 49

6. 10, 16, 18, 10, 13, 7, 10, 13, 2, 48

7. 108, 124, 92, 110, 117, 102, 100, 98, 120

8. 350, 225, 300, 314, 210, 321, 275, 290, 310

In Exercises 9 and 10, use the box-and-whisker plot.

9. About what percent of the data are greater than 25? 75%

10. About what percent of the data are less than 34? 50%

1. median: 46; lower quartile: 39; upper quartile: 52; interquartile range: 13
2. median: 45; lower quartile: 37; upper quartile: 59; interquartile range: 22
3. median: 170; lower quartile: 159; upper quartile: 184; interquartile range: 25
4. median: 4.4; lower quartile: 2.9; upper quartile: 5.3; interquartile range: 2.4

Make a box-and-whisker plot of the data. Identify any outliers.

11. 17, 38, 22, 15, 13, 24, 18, 10, 20, 13, 17, 12

38 is an outlier

12. 134, 115, 105, 100, 115, 134, 200, 310, 124

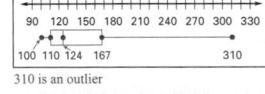

310 is an outlier

13. 45, 30, 30, 17, 15, 27, 23, 25, 26, 30, 33, 30

45 is an outlier

14. 730, 640, 500, 719, 620, 645, 740, 703, 690

no outliers

15. **Gas Prices** The prices of a gallon of gasoline (in dollars) for selected countries in 2003 are listed below.

Australia: $2.20   Canada: $2.02
Germany: $4.58   Japan: $3.47
Mexico: $2.09   Taiwan: $2.16
United States: $1.59

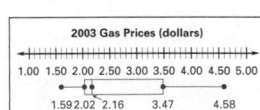

a. Make a box-and-whisker plot of the gasoline prices.

b. Which countries, if any, had gasoline prices that can be considered outliers? no outliers

16. **Supreme Court Justices** The stem-and-leaf plot shows the lengths of the terms (in years) of Supreme Court justices appointed from 1902 until 1986.

Stems | Leaves
```
0 | 1 3 3 4 4 5 5 5 5 5 6 6 7 7 7 8 9
1 | 0 0 1 2 3 5 5 5 6 6 6 6 6 7 8 9 9
2 | 2 3 3 4 4 6 6 9
3 | 1 3 4 6
```

Key: 1|5 = 15

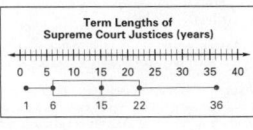

a. Make a box-and-whisker plot of the lengths of the terms.

b. William Douglas has served the longest so far with a term of 36 years. Can his term be considered an outlier? *Explain* why or why not. no, because 36 < 22 + 1.5(6)

840E

CHAPTER 13 Quiz 1
For use after Lessons 13.1–13.4

In Exercises 1 and 2, use the following information.

A box contains 10 green balls and 6 red balls. You choose a ball at random.

1. What is the probability that you select a green ball?

2. What is the probability that you select a red ball?

In Exercises 3 and 4, use the following information.

A bucket contains 10 balls numbered as follows: 1, 2, 2, 3, 3, 3, 3, 4, 4, 5.
A single ball is randomly chosen from the bucket.

3. What is the probability of drawing a ball numbered 3?

4. What is the probability of drawing a ball with a number greater than 3?

5. Consider the number of permutations of the letters in the word BOATS. In how many ways can you arrange all of the letters?

Evaluate the expression.

6. $_4P_2$ 7. $_5P_3$

8. $_5C_2$ 9. $_6C_3$

Answers

1. $\frac{5}{8}$

2. $\frac{3}{8}$

3. $\frac{2}{5}$

4. $\frac{3}{10}$

5. 120

6. 12

7. 60

8. 10

9. 20

CHAPTER 13 Quiz 2
For use after Lessons 13.5–13.8

In Exercises 1 and 2, use the following information.

A community hospital conducts a survey to determine patient satisfaction. One hundred patients are randomly selected to complete the survey.

1. Identify the population.

2. Classify the sampling method.

In Exercises 3 and 4, find the range and mean absolute deviation of the data. Round to the nearest hundredth, if necessary.

3. 13, 21, 17, 8, 19, 18   4. 83, 90, 49, 57, 74, 63, 32

5. Make a histogram of the data: 1.4, 2.5, 1.7, 2.0, 1.6, 2.2, 2.7, 1.5, 2.3.

6. Make a stem-and-leaf plot of the data: 24, 12, 6, 31, 8, 17, 35, 15.

```
0 | 6 8       Key: 1 | 2 = 12
1 | 2 5 7
2 | 4
3 | 1 5
```

In Exercises 7 and 8, use the following information.

The ages of senior citizens who play on a chess team are given in years: 77, 65, 78, 70, 71, 86, 73, 65, 75, 69, 68.

7. Make a box-and-whisker plot of the data.

8. Identify any outliers.

Answers

1. all selected patients

2. random sample

3. 13; 3.67

4. 58; 15.71

5. See left.

6. See left.

7. See left.

8. 86

CHAPTER 13 Chapter Test B
For use after Chapter 13

In Exercises 1–3, use the following information.

Cystic fibrosis is an inherited disease that effects the functioning of the glands. F is the normal gene and f is the mutant gene. Any gene combination with an F results in healthy offspring. Suppose each parent has the same gene combination Ff.

1. Use a Punnett square to list the possible outcomes for their offspring.

2. What is the probability that a child will have cystic fibrosis?

3. What are the odds against a child being a carrier of cystic fibrosis?

4. The table shows the data collected from a citizen's group concerned about the safety of three intersections in their community. Find the probability that a randomly chosen vehicle will be involved in an accident at each intersection. Which intersection is the most dangerous? Explain.

Intersection	1	2	3
Number of vehicles (per day)	8330	25,250	3640
Number of accidents (per year)	110	175	45

Evaluate the expression.

5. 0!   6. $_{10}P_4$ 7. $_7C_3$

Tell whether the question can be answered using combinations or permutations. Explain your choice, then answer the question.

8. On a sailboat there are 6 signal flags. The order the flags are strung on the mast determines the signal being sent. How many 3-flag signals can the captain send?

9. You are taking an online algebra quiz in which 6 questions are randomly selected from a test bank containing 50 questions. How many versions of the quiz are possible?

In Exercises 10 and 11, refer to a bag containing 13 red balls numbered 1–13 and 5 green balls numbered 14–18.

10. You choose a ball at random. What is the probability that you choose a red or an even numbered ball?

11. You randomly choose 2 balls from the bag at the same time. What is the probability that you choose a red ball and a green ball?

Answers

1. FF, Ff, Ff, ff

2. $\frac{1}{4}$

3. 1 : 1

4. $\frac{11}{833}, \frac{7}{1010}, \frac{9}{728}$

Intersection #1

because the probability

is the highest.

5. 1

6. 5040

7. 35

8. permutations; the

order of the flags is

important; 120

9. combinations; the

order of the

questions is not

important; 15,890,700

10. $\frac{8}{9}$

11. $\frac{65}{306}$

CHAPTER 13 Chapter Test B continued
For use after Chapter 13

In Exercises 12-14, use the following information.

A manager of a buffet-style restaurant wants to gather information about his customers' perceptions of the cleanliness of the restaurant. The first 25 people leaving the restaurant are briefly interviewed.

12. Identify the population.   13. Classify the sampling method.

14. Tell whether the survey method used is likely to result in a biased sample.

Find the mean, median, and mode(s) of the data.

15. 1, 2, 5, 7, 8, 18, 22   16. 14, 12, 17, 15, 11, 12, 11, 13

Find the range and mean absolute deviation of the data. Round to the nearest hundredth, if necessary.

17. 48, 93, 87, 93, 59, 70   18. 1, 3, 6, 7, 5

In Exercises 19–21, use the following information.

A survey asked people how many minutes they talked during a long-distance phone call. The results are: 15, 7, 25, 10, 18, 10, 10, 23, 4, 12, 8, 6.

19. Make a stem-and-leaf plot of the data.

```
0 | 4 6 7 8
1 | 0 0 0 2 5 8
2 | 3 5        Key: 2 | 3 = 23
```

20. Make a histogram of the data.

21. What is the probability that a randomly chosen long-distance phone call was more than 15 minutes?

In Exercises 22–24, use the box-and-whisker plot.

22. About what percent of the data are less than 45?

23. About what percent of the data are greater than 37?

24. Which value, if any, is an outlier?

Answers

12. all patrons of

the restaurant

13. convenience sample

14. The restaurant may

lack cleanliness later

in the day or during

other shifts, so the

method may result in

a biased sample.

15. 9; 7; none

16. 13; 12.5; 12 and 11

17. 45; 16

18. 6; 1.92

19. See left.

20. See left.

21. $\frac{1}{4}$

22. 75%

23. 50%

24. 64

13 Assessment

Multiple Choice

1. How many possible outcomes are there when you roll two number cubes and toss one coin?   C

(A) 13   (B) 36   (C) 72   (D) 144

2. The probability of an event occurring is $7:10$. What are the odds against the event?   A

(A) $3:10$ (B) $10:3$
(C) $3:17$ (D) $10:7$

3. According to a meteorologist, there is a 60% chance of thunderstorms today. What are the odds that it will *not* storm?   C

(A) $3:5$ (B) $2:3$
(C) $2:5$ (D) $1:25$

4. How many ways can you arrange all the letters in the word MATH?   D

(A) 4   (B) 6   (C) 12   (D) 24

5. The judges of the science fair will be awarding ribbons for first, second, and third place, plus a ribbon for honorable mention out of 15 entries. Which expression gives the number of ways the judges can award first place, second place, third place, and honorable mention?   B

(A) $\frac{4!}{11!}$ (B) $\frac{15!}{11!}$ (C) $\frac{11!}{15!}$ (D) $\frac{11!}{4!}$

6. You need to go to the library, grocery store, and pharmacy. In how many orders can you visit these places?   B

(A) 3   (B) 6   (C) 9   (D) 12

7. What is the value of $_8P_5$?   C

(A) 56   (B) 120
(C) 6720   (D) 40,320

8. What is the value of $_6C_3$?   A

(A) 20   (B) 120   (C) 240   (D) 1200

9. How many combinations of 3 letters can you make from the list A, B, C, D, and E?   A

(A) 10   (B) 20   (C) 30   (D) 60

10. You are ordering a 3-topping pizza from a pizzeria. You have 10 topping choices. How many different pizzas are possible?   B

(A) 60   (B) 120   (C) 720   (D) 5040

11. You roll a number cube. What is the probability that you will roll an even number *or* a number greater than 4?   C

(A) $0.1\overline{6}$ (B) 0.5 (C) $0.\overline{6}$ (D) $0.8\overline{3}$

12. You flip a coin and roll a number cube. What is the probability that the coin shows tails and the number cube shows a 3?   D

(A) $\frac{2}{3}$ (B) $\frac{1}{2}$ (C) $\frac{1}{6}$ (D) $\frac{1}{12}$

13. A jar contains 6 red marbles, 5 blue marbles, and 9 green marbles. What is the probability of randomly choosing a blue marble and then another blue marble if the first marble is not replaced?   B

(A) $\frac{1}{20}$ (B) $\frac{1}{19}$ (C) $\frac{1}{18}$ (D) $\frac{1}{16}$

14. Which of the following statements is *not* potentially biased?   C

(A) Do you prefer creamy macaroni and cheese or bland rice?

(B) Don't you feel the city is wasting money by building that new stadium?

(C) Do you prefer shopping online or in the stores?

(D) Don't you agree that the driving age should be raised to 18 so as to decrease the number of accidents?

---

15. What is the mean absolute deviation of the data? Round your answer to the nearest hundredth if necessary.   D

36.2, 3.4, 76.4, 5.5, 2.8, 84.8

(A) 22.54   (B) 28.72
(C) 32.6   (D) 30.95

In Exercises 16 and 17, use the stem-and-leaf plot.

Set A   Set B
```
        2 0 | 1 | 2 5 7 8 8
  8 7 4 1 | 2 | 1 3 4 6
9 5 3 1 0 | 3 |
8 7 4 1 1 | 4 | 2 5 8 9 9
```

16. What is the range of data set A?   C

(A) 36   (B) 37   (C) 38   (D) 48

17. What is the mean of data set B? Round your answer to the nearest hundredth if necessary.   D

(A) 24.89   (B) 25.48
(C) 27.32   (D) 29.07

18. In a box-and-whisker plot, each whisker represents about what percent of the data?   A

(A) 25%   (B) 50%   (C) 75%   (D) 100%

Gridded Answer

19. What is the median of the following data set?

0.2, 0.5, 0.2, 1.2, 0.8, 1.4, 0.6, 1.8

21. a. $\frac{6}{11}$ **b.** $\frac{2}{3}, \frac{3}{7}, \frac{1}{3}$

c. The star player is most likely to make attempted 3-point shots during games with a point difference of 0–7 points at the end of the game because the probability of the player making them is $\frac{2}{3}$, rather than $\frac{3}{7}$ and $\frac{1}{3}$.

Short Response

20. The stem-and-leaf plot shows the number of years spent teaching by teachers in your school.

```
0 | 0 3 5 5 8 8 9
1 | 0 1 2 2 4 5 7
2 | 0 1 7 9
3 | 6
```

a. Make a box-and-whisker plot of the data.   See above.

b. Mrs. Smith has been teaching for 36 years. Can the number of years she has spent teaching be considered an outlier? *Explain* your reasoning.

20. a.

20. b. Yes, 36 would be considered an outlier because it is more than 1.5 times the upperquartile.

Extended Response

21. The table shows last season's 3-point shot statistics for your school's star basketball player.

	Point Difference at end of game		
	0–7 points	8–14 points	≥ 15 points
3-point shots attempted	12	7	3
3-point shots made	8	3	1

a. During last season, what was the probability that your school's star basketball player would make an attempted 3-point shot, regardless of the point difference? Write your answer in fraction form.   See left.

b. Find the probabilities that the star player made an attempted 3-point shot when the point difference at the end of the game was 0–7 points, 8–14 points, and at least 15 points. Write your answers in fraction form.   See left.

c. During what kind of games is the star player most likely to make attempted 3-point shots. *Justify* your conclusion. See left.

840G

Alternative Assessment and Math Journal

For use after Chapter 13

Journal

1. Write a survey question that is biased in some way and explain the reason. Rewrite the question so that it is no longer biased.

Multi-Step Problem

2. The data given represent the heights (in inches) of a class of ninth grade students. The first row are the heights of the girls in the class and the second row are the heights of the boys.

Girls: 60, 58, 63, 54, 65, 66, 65, 67, 64, 59

Boys: 62, 65, 60, 69, 70, 68, 61, 65, 71, 67

a. A student is randomly selected from the class, what is the probability that the student is over 60 inches tall?

b. A student is randomly selected from the class, what is the probability that the student is a girl and over 60 inches tall?

c. A student is randomly selected from the class, what is the probability that the student is a boy or over 60 inches tall?

d. Determine the mean, median, and mode(s) of the students' heights.

e. Compare the spread of the data for the girls and boys heights using the range and the mean absolute deviation.

f. Make a stem-and-leaf plot of the entire set of data.

g. Make a box-and-whisker plot of the data for each group.

1. Complete answers should include: a survey question that is biased, an explanation of the reason for the bias; an edited survey question that is no longer biased.

2. a. $\frac{3}{4} = 0.75$ b. $\frac{3}{10} = 0.3$ c. $\frac{4}{5} = 0.8$ d. 63.95; 65; 65

e. Girls: range = 13, mean absolute deviation = 3.48; Boys: range = 11, mean absolute deviation = 3.2

f. Students' Heights

g.

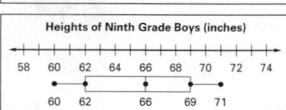

Alternative Assessment Rubric *continued*

For use after Chapter 13

Journal Solution

1. Complete answers should include:

- a survey question that is biased.
- an explanation of the reason for the bias.
- an edited survey question that is no longer biased.

Multi-Step Problem Solution

2. a. $\frac{3}{4} = 0.75$ b. $\frac{3}{10} = 0.3$ c. $\frac{4}{5} = 0.8$ d. 63.95; 65; 65

e. Girls: range = 13, mean absolute deviation = 3.48; Boys: range = 11, mean absolute deviation = 3.2

f. Students' Heights

```
        Girls           Boys
       9 8 4 | 5 |
7 6 5 5 4 3 0 | 6 | 0 1 2 5 5 7 8 9
             | 7 | 0 1
```

g.

Heights of Ninth Grade Girls (inches)

```
  52   54   56   58   60   62   64   66   68
        54         59      63.5 65   67
```

Heights of Ninth Grade Boys (inches)

```
  58   60   62   64   66   68   70   72   74
        60   62         66      69   71
```

Multi-Step Problem Rubric

4 The student answers all parts of the problem correctly and completely. The student shows all work. The student's work is neat.

3 The student answers all parts of the problem. The student's work may contain one or two errors in the calculations or plots. The student shows most work. The student's work is neat.

2 The student answers all parts of the problem, but there are more than two errors in the calculations or plots. The student shows some work. The student's work is sloppy.

1 The student does not complete all parts of the problem. The student's work has several errors in the calculations and plots. The student's work is sloppy, or no work is shown.

In Chapter 13, students use sample spaces to calculate probabilities and odds. They identify and use the number of permutations or the number of combinations in a set of objects to calculate the probability of an event. They find the probability of compound events by identifying whether the events are mutually exclusive or overlapping, or whether the events are dependent or independent. Students analyze data by identifying sampling methods and potentially biased samples and questions. They compare measures of central tendency: the mean, median, and mode; and they compare measures of dispersion: the range and mean absolute deviation. They analyze and display data in stem-and-leaf plots, histograms, and box-and-whisker plots.

Prerequisite Skills

- Finding the mean, median, and mode(s) of data
- Using a display to analyze data

Additional resources for reviewing prerequisite skills are:

- Skills Review Handbook, pp. 909–937
- @HomeTutor

13 Probability and Data Analysis

13.1 **Find Probabilities and Odds**

13.2 **Find Probabilities Using Permutations**

13.3 **Find Probabilities Using Combinations**

13.4 **Find Probabilities of Compound Events**

13.5 **Analyze Surveys and Samples**

13.6 **Use Measures of Central Tendency and Dispersion**

13.7 **Interpret Stem-and-Leaf Plots and Histograms**

13.8 **Interpret Box-and-Whisker Plots**

Before

In previous courses, you learned the following skills, which you'll use in Chapter 13: finding the mean, median, and mode(s) of data and using a display to analyze data.

Prerequisite Skills

VOCABULARY CHECK

1. Copy and complete: The ? of a numerical data set is the middle number when the values are written in numerical order. **median**

SKILLS CHECK

Find the mean, median, and mode(s) of the data. *(Review p. 918 for 13.6.)*

2. 0.2, 1.3, 0.9, 1.5, 2.1, 1.8, 0.6
1.2, 1.3, no mode

3. 103, 121, 111, 194, 99, 160, 134, 160
135.25, 127.5, 160

In Exercises 4 and 5, use the bar graph, which shows the numbers of adults who participate in leisure activities, according to the results of a survey.
(Review p. 933 for 13.7.)

Leisure Activities

Activity	Number of participants
Bake	37
Play cards	53
Read books	82

Number of participants: 0 20 40 60 80 100

4. Which activities have fewer than 60 participants? **baking, playing cards**

5. Of those surveyed, how many more read books than play cards? **29 people**

@HomeTutor Prerequisite skills practice at classzone.com

840

Chapter 13 Resource Book

- Teaching Guide/Lesson Plan (pp. 3, 14, 24, 36, 48, 58, 71, 85)
- Project with Rubric (p. 100)

Assessment and Intervention

- Assessment Book (pp. 183–196)
- Benchmark Tests
- Reteaching and Remediation Book

Interactive Technology

- Easy Planner
- Power Presentations CD-ROM
- Activity Generator CD-ROM
- Animated Algebra
- Test Generator CD-ROM
- Online Quizzes
- eWorkbook
- eEdition
- @HomeTutor

Resources for English Learners

- Quick Reference for English Learners
- Spanish Study Guide
- Multi-Language Visual Glossary
- Student Resources in Spanish

In Chapter 13, you will apply the big ideas listed below and reviewed in the Chapter Summary on page 895. You will also use the key vocabulary listed below.

Big Ideas

1 Finding probabilities of simple and compound events
2 Analyzing sets of data
3 Making and interpreting data displays

KEY VOCABULARY
- outcome, *p. 843*
- event, *p. 843*
- probability, *p. 843*
- odds, *p. 845*
- permutation, *p. 851*
- combination, *p. 856*

- compound event, *p. 861*
- survey, *p. 871*
- sample, *p. 871*
- measure of dispersion, *p. 876*
- range, *p. 876*
- stem-and-leaf plot, *p. 881*

- frequency, *p. 882*
- histogram, *p. 882*
- box-and-whisker plot, *p. 887*
- interquartile range, *p. 888*
- outlier, *p. 889*

You can use probability and data analysis to make predictions. For example, you can use data about a kicker's past successes in football games to find the chance of his success in the future.

Animated Algebra

The animation illustrated below for Exercise 22 on page 848 helps you to answer this question: What is the probability that the kicker makes an attempted field goal?

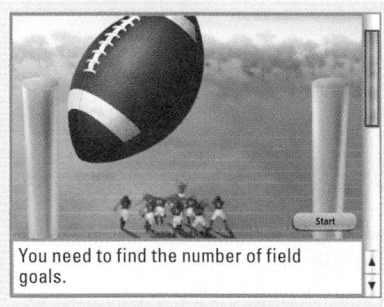

You need to find the number of field goals.

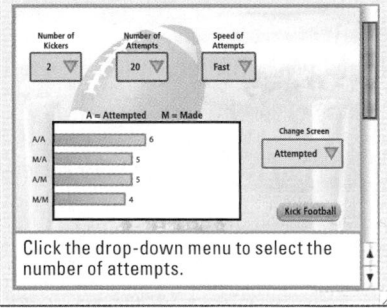

Click the drop-down menu to select the number of attempts.

Animated **Algebra** at classzone.com

Other animations for Chapter 13: pages 845, 856, 875, and 887

Algebra 1 Toolkit
- Reading Strategies for Chapter 13, pp. 33–34
- Differentiated Instruction Notes, pp. 89–92
- English Learners Notes, pp. 121–122
- Inclusion Notes, pp. 153–154
- Teaching Strategies with Sample Worksheets, pp. 155–178
- Using Technology in the Classroom, pp. 179–184
- Tips for New Teachers, pp. 209–210
- Math Background Notes, pp. 235–236
- Pre-AP Strategies and Copymasters, pp. 302–303, 512–533
- Teacher Survival Activities, pp. 579–580, 605–606
- Bulletin Board Idea, p. 619
- Teacher Tool Transparencies, following p. 620

13.1 Find a Probability

MATERIALS • paper bag

QUESTION What is the chance that you would select the initials of a student in your class from a bag of letters?

You can perform an experiment and record the results to approximate the likelihood of selecting the initials of a student in your class.

EXPLORE Perform an experiment

STEP 1 *Select letters*

Write each of the 26 letters of the alphabet on separate pieces of paper. Put all of the letters into a bag. Select a letter at random (without looking into the bag). Replace the letter and select a second letter at random.

STEP 2 *Record the results*

Record the results of the selections in a table like the one shown.

- If the first letter is the first initial of any student in your class, put a tally mark in the "first initial" column.
- If the second letter is the last initial of any student in your class, put a tally mark in the "last initial" column.
- If the two letters are the first and last initials of any student in your class, put a tally mark in the "both initials" column, but do not put a tally mark in the other columns.

Perform this experiment 30 times.

	First initial	Last initial	Both initials
Tally	JHT	JHT II	I
Frequency	?	?	?

STEP 3 *Record the frequencies*

Record the *frequency*, the total number of tally marks, of each possible result.

DRAW CONCLUSIONS Use your observations to complete these exercises
1–3. Answers may vary.

1. For what fraction of the times that you performed the experiment did you select the first initial of a student in your class? the last initial? both?

2. Which of these results do you think is least likely to happen if you repeat the experiment 30 more times? *Explain* your choice.

3. **REASONING** You perform the experiment 90 times. How many times do you expect to select both the first and last initials of a student in your class? *Explain* how you made your prediction.

13.1 Find Probabilities and Odds

Before	You made organized lists and tree diagrams.
Now	You will find sample spaces and probabilities.
Why?	So you can find the likelihood of an event, as in Example 2.

Key Vocabulary
• outcome
• event
• sample space
• probability
• odds

A possible result of an experiment is an **outcome**. For instance, when you roll a number cube there are 6 possible outcomes: a 1, 2, 3, 4, 5, or 6. An **event** is an outcome or a collection of outcomes, such as rolling an odd number. The set of all possible outcomes is called a **sample space**.

EXAMPLE 1 Find a sample space

You flip a coin and roll a number cube. How many possible outcomes are in the sample space? List the possible outcomes.

Solution

> **REVIEW TREE DIAGRAMS**
> For help with tree diagrams, see p. 931.

Use a tree diagram to find the outcomes in the sample space.

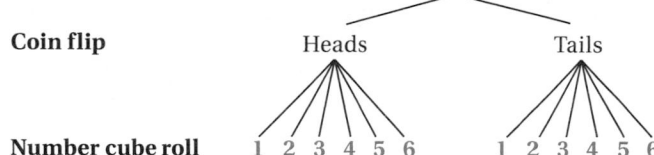

Coin flip   Heads   Tails

Number cube roll   1 2 3 4 5 6   1 2 3 4 5 6

The sample space has 12 possible outcomes. They are listed below.

Heads, 1   Heads, 2   Heads, 3   Heads, 4   Heads, 5   Heads, 6
Tails, 1   Tails, 2   Tails, 3   Tails, 4   Tails, 5   Tails, 6

✓ **GUIDED PRACTICE**   for Example 1

1. You flip 2 coins and roll a number cube. How many possible outcomes are in the sample space? List the possible outcomes.
   24 outcomes; HH1, HH2, HH3, HH4, HH5, HH6, HT1, HT2, HT3, HT4, HT5, HT6, TH1, TH2, TH3, TH4, TH5, TH6, TT1, TT2, TT3, TT4, TT5, TT6

PROBABILITY The **probability of an event** is a measure of the likelihood, or chance, that the event will occur. Probability is a number from 0 to 1 and can be expressed as a decimal, fraction, or percent.

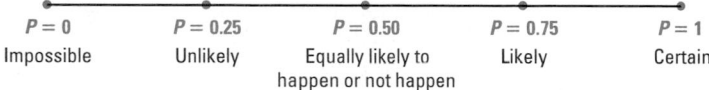

| $P = 0$ | $P = 0.25$ | $P = 0.50$ | $P = 0.75$ | $P = 1$ |
| Impossible | Unlikely | Equally likely to happen or not happen | Likely | Certain |

① PLAN AND PREPARE

Warm-Up Exercises
📑 **Transparency Available**

1. Use a tree diagram to find the number of possible outfits you can make using one shirt and one pair of shorts if you have 3 shirts and 4 pairs of shorts. **12 outfits**

2. Use an organized list to find the number of possible ways to travel to and from Chicago if you can travel by car, bus, train, or airplane. **16 ways**

Notetaking Guide
📑 **Transparency Available**
Promotes interactive learning and notetaking skills, pp. 296–298.

Pacing
Basic: 1 day
Average: 1 day
Advanced: 1 day
Block: 0.5 block with 13.2
• See *Teaching Guide/Lesson Plan*.

② FOCUS AND MOTIVATE

Essential Question
Big Idea 1, p. 841

How do you find the probability an event? **Tell students they will learn how to answer this question by comparing favorable and possible outcomes in a theoretical situation and successes and trials in an experimental situation.**

NCTM STANDARDS
Standard 5: Understand basic concepts of probability; Apply basic concepts of probability

---

Resource Planning Guide

Chapter Resource Book
• Teaching Guide/Lesson Plan (pp. 3–4)
• Practice levels A, B, C (pp. 6–8)
• Study Guide (pp. 9–10)
• Catch-up for Absent Students (p. 11)
• Application (p. 12)
• Challenge (p. 13)

Workbooks
• Notetaking Guide (pp. 296–298)
• Practice Workbook (pp. 196–197)

Teaching Options
• **Power Presentations CD-ROM** provides dynamic electronic teaching resources for the classroom.
• **Activity Generator CD-ROM** provides editable activities for all ability levels.

Interactive Technology
• Easy Planner
• Power Presentations CD-ROM
• Activity Generator CD-ROM
• Animated Algebra
• Test Generator CD-ROM
• Online Quiz
• eWorkbook
• eEdition
• @HomeTutor

Resources for English Learners
• Quick Reference for English Learners
• Spanish Study Guide
• Multi-Language Visual Glossary
• Student Resources in Spanish

See also the *Algebra 1 Toolkit* for more strategies for meeting individual needs.

THEORETICAL PROBABILITY The outcomes for a specified event are called *favorable outcomes*. When all outcomes are equally likely, the **theoretical probability** of the event can be found using the following:

$$\text{Theoretical probability} = \frac{\text{Number of favorable outcomes}}{\text{Total number of outcomes}}$$

The probability of event A is written as $P(A)$.

EXAMPLE 2 Find a theoretical probability

T-SHIRTS You and your friends designed T-shirts with silk screened emblems, and you are selling the T-shirts to raise money. The table below shows the number of T-shirts you have in each design. A student chooses a T-shirt at random. What is the probability that the student chooses a red T-shirt?

	Gold emblem	Silver emblem
Green T-shirt	10	8
Red T-shirt	6	6

Solution

You and your friends have a total of $10 + 6 + 8 + 6 = 30$ T-shirts. So, there are 30 possible outcomes. Of all the T-shirts, 12 T-shirts are red. There are 12 favorable outcomes.

$$P(\text{red T-shirt}) = \frac{\text{Number of favorable outcomes}}{\text{Total number of outcomes}}$$

$$= \frac{\text{Number of red T-shirts}}{\text{Total number of T-shirts}}$$

$$= \frac{12}{30}$$

$$= \frac{2}{5}$$

✓ **GUIDED PRACTICE** for Example 2

2. **T-SHIRTS** In Example 2, what is the probability that the student chooses a T-shirt with a gold emblem? $\frac{8}{15}$

3. You toss a coin and roll a number cube. What is the probability that the coin shows tails and the number cube shows 4? $\frac{1}{12}$

EXPERIMENTAL PROBABILITY An **experimental probability** is based on repeated *trials* of an experiment. The number of trials is the number of times the experiment is performed. Each trial in which a favorable outcome occurs is called a *success*.

$$\text{Experimental probability} = \frac{\text{Number of successes}}{\text{Number of trials}}$$

EXAMPLE 3 **Standardized Test Practice**

Each section of the spinner shown has the same area. The spinner was spun 20 times. The table shows the results. For which color is the experimental probability of stopping on the color the same as the theoretical probability?

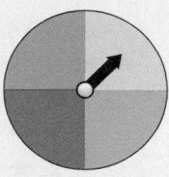

Spinner Results			
Red	Green	Blue	Yellow
5	9	3	3

(A) Red   (B) Green   (C) Blue   (D) Yellow

Solution

The theoretical probability of stopping on each of the four colors is $\frac{1}{4}$. Use the outcomes in the table to find the experimental probabilities.

$P(\text{red}) = \frac{5}{20} = \frac{1}{4}$ $P(\text{green}) = \frac{9}{20}$ $P(\text{blue}) = \frac{3}{20}$ $P(\text{yellow}) = \frac{3}{20}$

▸ The correct answer is A. (A) (B) (C) (D)

Animated Algebra at classzone.com

ODDS The odds of an event compare the number of favorable and unfavorable outcomes when all outcomes are equally likely.

$$\text{Odds in favor} = \frac{\text{Number of favorable outcomes}}{\text{Number of unfavorable outcomes}}$$

$$\text{Odds against} = \frac{\text{Number of unfavorable outcomes}}{\text{Number of favorable outcomes}}$$

EXAMPLE 4 **Find the odds**

READING
Odds are read as the ratio of one number to another. For instance, the odds $\frac{3}{1}$ are read as "three to one." Odds are usually written as $a : b$.

SPINNER In Example 3, find the odds against stopping on green.

Solution

The 4 possible outcomes are all equally likely. Green is the 1 favorable outcome. The other 3 colors are unfavorable outcomes.

$$\text{Odds against green} = \frac{\text{Number of unfavorable outcomes}}{\text{Number of favorable outcomes}} = \frac{3}{1} \text{ or } 3 : 1.$$

 GUIDED PRACTICE   for Examples 3 and 4

4. In Example 3, for which color is the experimental probability of stopping on the color greater than the theoretical probability? **green**

5. In Example 3, what are the odds in favor of stopping on blue? $\frac{1}{3}$ **or 1 : 3**

13.1 Find Probabilities and Odds   **845**

Extra Example 3
A bag contains one blue, one green, one yellow, and one red ball. A ball is drawn at random from the bag and then replaced. The table shows the results for 24 drawings. For which color of ball is the experimental probability of drawing the color the same as the theoretical probability?

Random Drawing Results			
Blue	Green	Yellow	Red
4	6	9	5

(A) Blue   (B) Green
(C) Red   (D) Yellow
The correct answer is B.

An **Animated Algebra** activity is available on-line for **Example 3**. This activity is also available on the **Power Presentations CD-ROM**.

Extra Example 4
In Extra Example 3, find the odds in favor of drawing a yellow ball. **3 : 5**

Closing the Lesson
Have students summarize the major points of the lesson and answer the Essential Question: How do you find the probability of an event?

• **Theoretical probability is based on all possible outcomes being equally likely.**

• **Experimental probability is based on repeated trials, which is the number of times the experiment is performed.**

The theoretical probability of an event is the ratio of the number of favorable outcomes to the total number of outcomes. The experimental probability of an event is the ratio of the number of successes of the experiment to the number of trials.

845

13.1 **EXERCISES**

HOMEWORK KEY
○ = WORKED-OUT SOLUTIONS
on p. WS1 for Exs. 3 and 21

★ = STANDARDIZED TEST PRACTICE
Exs. 2, 14–16, 21, and 22

④ PRACTICE AND APPLY

Assignment Guide

📑 Answer Transparencies available for all exercises

Basic:
Day 1: SRH p. 932 Exs. 4–8
pp. 846–848
Exs. 1–15, 19–21, 24–26

Average:
Day 1: pp. 846–848
Exs. 1, 2–12 even, 13–17, 19–22, 24–26

Advanced:
Day 1: pp. 846–848
Exs. 1, 2–6 even, 10, 12, 13–26*

Block:
pp. 846–848
Exs. 1, 2–12 even, 13–17, 19–22, 24–26 (with 13.2)

Differentiated Instruction

See *Algebra 1 Best Practices Toolkit* for suggestions on addressing the needs of a diverse classroom.

Homework Check

For a quick check of student understanding of key concepts, go over the following exercises:

Basic: 4, 7, 9, 11, 21
Average: 5, 9, 12, 19, 21
Advanced: 6, 10, 14, 20, 21

Extra Practice

• Student Edition, p. 950
• Chapter 13 Resource Book: Practice levels A, B, C, pp. 6–8

Practice Worksheet

An easily-readable reduced practice page (with answers) for this lesson can be found on p. 840C.

2. *Sample answer:* The probability of an event is the number of favorable outcomes divided by the number of possible outcomes, while the odds in favor of an event is the number of favorable outcomes divided by the number of unfavorable outcomes.

SKILL PRACTICE

[A] 1. **VOCABULARY** Copy and complete: A number that describes the likelihood of an event is the __?__ of the event. **probability**

2. ★ **WRITING** *Explain* how the probability of an event differs from the odds in favor of the event when all outcomes are equally likely. **See margin.**

EXAMPLE 1
on p. 843
for Exs. 3–6

SAMPLE SPACE In Exercises 3–6, find the number of possible outcomes in the sample space. Then list the possible outcomes.

3. A bag contains 4 red cards numbered 1–4, 4 white cards numbered 1–4, and 4 black cards numbered 1–4. You choose a card at random.
12 outcomes; R1, R2, R3, R4, W1, W2, W3, W4, B1, B2, B3, B4

4. You toss two coins.
4 outcomes; HH, TT, HT, TH

5. You roll a number cube and toss three coins. **See margin.**

6. You roll two number cubes. **See margin.**

EXAMPLE 2
on p. 844
for Exs. 7–8

PROBABILITY AND ODDS In Exercises 7–13, refer to the spinner shown. The spinner is divided into sections with the same area.

7. What is the probability that the spinner stops on a multiple of 3? $\frac{9}{10}$

8. **ERROR ANALYSIS** *Describe* and correct the error in finding the probability of stopping on a multiple of 9.

$$\frac{\text{Number of favorable outcomes}}{\text{Total number of outcomes}} = \frac{2}{10} = \frac{1}{5}$$ ✗

There are 3 favorable outcomes (landing on 9, 18, and 27); $\frac{3}{10}$.

EXAMPLE 3
on p. 845
for Exs. 9–10

9. You spin the spinner 30 times. It stops on 12 three times. What is the experimental probability of stopping on 12? $\frac{1}{10}$

10. You spin the spinner 10 times. It stops on an even number 6 times. What is the experimental probability of stopping on an even number? $\frac{3}{5}$

EXAMPLE 4
on p. 845
for Exs. 11–14

11. What are the odds in favor of stopping on a multiple of 4? $\frac{3}{7}$ or 3 : 7

12. What are the odds against stopping on a number less than 12? $\frac{7}{3}$ or 7 : 3

13. **ERROR ANALYSIS** *Describe* and correct the error in finding the odds in favor of stopping on a multiple of 3. **See margin.**

$$\text{Odds in favor of a multiple of 3} = \frac{\text{Number of favorable outcomes}}{\text{Total number of outcomes}} = \frac{9}{10} \text{ or } 9 : 10$$ ✗

[B] 14. ★ **MULTIPLE CHOICE** The odds in favor of an event are 5 : 8. What are the odds against the event? **D**

   (A) 3 : 8   (B) 8 : 3   (C) 5 : 8   (D) 8 : 5

15. ★ **OPEN-ENDED** *Describe* a real-world event whose probability is 0. *Describe* another real-world event whose probability is 1.
Sample answer: **Rolling a standard number cube and getting a 0, flipping a coin and getting heads or tails.**

---

5. 48; HHH1, HHH2, HHH3, HHH4, HHH5, HHH6, HHT1, HHT2, HHT3, HHT4, HHT5, HHT6, HTH1, HTH2, HTH3, HTH4, HTH5, HTH6, HTT1, HTT2, HTT3, HTT4, HTT5, HTT6, THH1, THH2, THH3, THH4, THH5, THH6, THT1, THT2, THT3, THT4, THT5, THT6, TTH1, TTH2, TTH3, TTH4, TTH5, TTH6, TTT1, TTT2, TTT3, TTT4, TTT5, TTT6

6. 36 outcomes; 1-1, 1-2, 1-3, 1-4, 1-5, 1-6, 2-1, 2-2, 2-3, 2-4, 2-5, 2-6, 3-1, 3-2, 3-3, 3-4, 3-5, 3-6, 4-1, 4-2, 4-3, 4-4, 4-5, 4-6, 5-1, 5-2, 5-3, 5-4, 5-5, 5-6, 6-1, 6-2, 6-3, 6-4, 6-5, 6-6

13. See Additional Answers beginning on p. AA1.

16. ★ MULTIPLE CHOICE According to a meteorologist, there is a 40% chance that it will rain today. What are the odds in favor of rain? **B**

(A) 2 : 5   (B) 2 : 3   (C) 3 : 2   (D) 4 : 1

17. NUMBER CUBES Make a table showing all of the possible sums that result from rolling two number cubes. (Columns represent the possible outcomes of the first number cube. Rows represent the possible outcomes of the second number cube. The cells of the table represent the sums of the two outcomes.) Then find the probability of rolling each sum. **See margin.**

C **18. CHALLENGE** A bag holds red, white, and blue marbles. You randomly draw a marble from the bag. The odds against drawing a white marble are 47 : 3.

     a. There are fewer than 100 marbles in the bag. How many marbles are in the bag? *Justify* your answer. **See margin.**

     b. The probability of drawing a red marble is 0.5. What is the probability of drawing a blue marble? *Explain* how you found your answer. **See margin.**

PROBLEM SOLVING

EXAMPLE 2 A
on p. 844
for Exs. 19–20

19. MUSIC PROGRAM You have created a playlist of 7 songs on your MP3 player. You play these songs in a random shuffle, where each song has an equally likely chance of being played. What is the probability that the second song on the list will be played first? $\frac{1}{7}$

@HomeTutor for problem solving help at classzone.com

20. SURVEY A survey asked a total of 600 students (100 male students and 100 female students who were 11, 13, and 15 years old) about their exercise habits. The table shows the numbers of students who said they exercise 2 hours or more each week.

	11 years	13 years	15 years
Female	53	57	51
Male	65	68	67

     a. What is the probability that a randomly selected female student who participated in this survey exercises 2 hours or more each week? $\frac{161}{300}$

     b. What is the probability that a randomly selected 15-year-old student who participated in this survey exercises 2 hours or more each week? $\frac{59}{100}$

     c. What is the probability that a randomly selected student who participated in this survey exercises 2 hours or more each week? $\frac{361}{600}$

     @HomeTutor for problem solving help at classzone.com

EXAMPLES
2 and 4
on pp. 844–845
for Ex. 21

21. **★ SHORT RESPONSE** Suppose there are 15 girls and 12 boys in your homeroom. The teacher chooses one student representative at random. What is the probability that a boy is chosen? What are the odds in favor of choosing a boy? *Explain* how the probablity and odds are related. **See margin.**

13.1 Find Probabilities and Odds   **847**

Avoiding Common Errors

Exercises 7, 9–14 Students often confuse probabilities and odds and experimental and theoretical probability. Remind students that experimental probabilities are based on the number of trials or experiments, and that theoretical probability and odds are based on equally likely outcomes. Suggest that students check each of their answers against the respective formulas for probabilities and odds.

Study Strategy

Exercise 16 Suggest that students ask themselves what the chances are that it will not rain and then compare favorable chances to unfavorable chances to find the odds.

An **Animated Algebra** activity is available on-line for **Exercise 22**. This activity is also available on the **Power Presentations CD-ROM**.

18a. 50 marbles. *Sample answer:* The odds against picking a white marble says that the number of non-white marbles to white marbles must be 47 : 3. The only pair of numbers that simplifies to this ratio and whose sum is less than 100 total marbles is 47 and 3. There are 47 non-white marbles and 3 white marbles, for a total of 50 marbles.

18b. 0.44. *Sample answer:* There are 50 marbles in the bag, and half of them are blue. So there are 25 blue marbles and 3 white marbles. The rest are red, so there are 22 red marbles. The probability that a red marble is drawn is $\frac{22}{50} = 0.44$.

21. See Additional Answers beginning on p. AA1.

17.

	1	2	3	4	5	6
1	2	3	4	5	6	7
2	3	4	5	6	7	8
3	4	5	6	7	8	9
4	5	6	7	8	9	10
5	6	7	8	9	10	11
6	7	8	9	10	11	12

$P(2) = \frac{1}{36}$; $P(3) = \frac{1}{18}$; $P(4) = \frac{1}{12}$; $P(5) = \frac{1}{9}$; $P(6) = \frac{5}{36}$; $P(7) = \frac{1}{6}$; $P(8) = \frac{5}{36}$; $P(9) = \frac{1}{9}$; $P(10) = \frac{1}{12}$; $P(11) = \frac{1}{18}$; $P(12) = \frac{1}{36}$

1. The table shows the number of students in your history class. Your teacher chooses one student at random to give an oral report. What is the probability the student is female? $\frac{7}{15}$

	9th Grade	10th Grade
Male	12	4
Female	8	6

2. A bag contains 8 white marbles, 6 red marbles, and 12 blue marbles. Find the odds against choosing a white marble. **9:4**

🔎 Online Quiz

Available at **classzone.com**

Diagnosis/Remediation

- Practice A, B, C in Chapter 13 Resource Book, pp. 6–8
- Study Guide in Chapter13 Resource Book, pp. 9–10
- Practice Workbook, pp. 196–197
- @HomeTutor

Challenge

Additional challenge is available in the Chapter 13 Resource Book, p. 13.

848

22b. 0–7: $\frac{4}{5}$, 8–14: $\frac{7}{11}$, ≥15: $\frac{2}{3}$

22c. Games where the point difference is 0–7. *Sample answer:* In these games he makes 80% of his field goals, while during his other games he made about 64%.

23a. A representative. *Sample answer:* The data in the table show that about 94% of representatives that ran for re-election were re-elected, while only about 84% of senators running for re-election were re-elected.

B **22.** ★ **EXTENDED RESPONSE** The table shows the 2003 regular season field goal statistics for kicker Adam Vinatieri.

	Point difference at end of game		
	0–7 points	8–14 points	≥ 15 points
Field goals attempted	20	11	3
Field goals made	16	7	2

a. During the 2003 regular season, what was the probability that Adam Vinatieri would make an attempted field goal, regardless of the point difference? $\frac{25}{34}$

b. Find the probabilities that Vinatieri made an attempted field goal when the point difference at the end of the game was 0–7 points, 8–14 points, and at least 15 points.

c. During what kinds of games was Adam Vinatieri most likely to make attempted field goals? *Justify* your answer.

Animated Algebra classzone.com

C **23.** **CHALLENGE** The table shows the results of Congressional elections that involved incumbent candidates (representatives or senators who ran for re-election) during the period 1980–2000.

	Incumbent representatives		Incumbent senators	
	Ran	Re-elected	Ran	Re-elected
Presidential election year	2373	2235	163	130
Midterm election year	1984	1873	145	130

a. Did a representative or a senator have a better chance of being re-elected? *Justify* your answer using the data in the table.

b. Did a member of Congress have a better chance of being re-elected during a presidential election year than during a midterm election year? *Justify* your answer.
23b. No. *Sample answer:* Members of Congress have about a 94% chance of being re-elected during midterm election years, and about a 0.93 chance in presidential election years.

MIXED REVIEW

PREVIEW
Prepare for Lesson 13.2 in Exs. 24–26.

Use the indicated counting method to answer the question. *(p. 931)*

24. You have 3 posters to hang beside each other on a wall. In how many different ways can you hang the posters? (Make a list.) **6 ways**

25. Members of a credit union choose a personal identification number (PIN) for their debit card. The PIN consists of 4 digits from 0 to 9. Digits cannot be repeated. How many PINs are possible? (Use the counting principle.)
5040 PINs

26. Weekly pottery classes are offered on Monday, Wednesday, and Thursday. On each of those days there is a class at 5:00 and a class at 7:00. How many classes are offered? (Make a tree diagram.) **6 classes**

Perform Simulations

GOAL Perform simulations to make predictions.

Key Vocabulary
• simulation

A **simulation** is an experiment that you can perform to make predictions about real-world situations.

EXAMPLE 1 Perform a simulation

CONCESSION PRIZES Each time you buy an item from the concession stand at a baseball stadium, you receive a prize coupon, chosen at random. There is an equal chance of winning each prize from the following list: hot dog, popcorn, peanuts, pretzel, ice cream, and small drink. About how many times must you buy an item from the concession stand before you win each prize at least once?

Solution

You can perform a simulation to answer the question.

STEP 1 **Write** each prize on a separate piece of paper. Put the pieces of paper in a container.

STEP 2 **Draw** a piece of paper from the container at random. Record the result in a table like the one shown. Put the piece of paper back in the container. Repeat until you put a tally mark in the last empty cell of the table.

Prize	Hot dog	Popcorn	Peanuts	Pretzel	Ice cream	Small drink
Tally	I	IIII	II	JHT	JHT I	II

The sum of all of the tally marks is the number of times you must buy an item from the concession stand before you win each prize at least once.

▶ In this simulation, you must buy an item from the concession stand 20 times.

USING A GRAPHING CALCULATOR You can also use the random integer generator on a graphing calculator to perform simulations.

The random integer generator is found by pressing the `MATH` key and selecting the PRB menu. It is the fifth item on the list and is displayed as randInt(.

```
MATH NUM CPX  PRB
1:rand
2:nPr
3:nCr
4:!
5:randInt(
6:randNorm
```

---

① PLAN AND PREPARE

Warm-Up Exercises

1. You bought 4 raffle tickets for a weekend trip for two in New York City. If 120 tickets were sold, what is the probability you will win the raffle? $\frac{1}{30}$

2. A sports store is giving away 4 basketballs, 6 footballs, and 8 soccer balls in a random drawing. If you are the first to draw a winning ticket, what is the probability you will win a football? $\frac{1}{3}$

② FOCUS AND MOTIVATE

Essential Question
Big Idea 1, p.841

How do you perform simulations to make predictions? **Tell students they will learn how to answer this question by using the results of experiments to make predictions.**

③ TEACH

Extra Example 1
Each time you buy an item at a movie store, you receive one of eight prize coupons chosen at random. There is an equal chance of winning each prize. Perform a simulation to predict the number of items you must buy before you win each prize at least once? **Answers will vary.**

NCTM STANDARDS

Standard 5: Understand basic concepts of probability

Standard 10: Use representations to solve problems

EXAMPLE 2 Perform a simulation using technology

GAME CARDS You receive a game card with every purchase at a sandwich shop. Each card has two circles to scratch. One circle reveals a prize, and the other says "Not a Winner." You cannot claim a prize if you scratch both circles. There is a $\frac{1}{6}$ chance that a card is for a CD, a $\frac{1}{2}$ chance that it is for a drink, and a $\frac{1}{3}$ chance that it is for a sandwich. About how many game cards must you scratch before you win a CD?

Solution

STEP 1 Use List 1 to show whether you scratch the circle with the prize. Generate a list of 50 random 1s and 0s. Each 1 means that you scratch the circle with the prize, and each 0 means that you scratch "Not a Winner."

Press **STAT** and select Edit. Highlight L_1. Enter randInt(0,1,50).

STEP 2 Use List 2 to show whether your game card contains the CD as the prize. Generate a list of 50 random integers from 1 to 6. Each 1 represents a prize card with a CD.

Highlight L_2. Enter randInt(1,6,50).

STEP 3 **Compare** the results of your two lists using List 3. Multiply the numbers from List 1 and List 2. Each 0 in List 3 means that you chose the wrong circle, so the prize does not matter. Because $1 \cdot 1 = 1$, you chose the correct circle *and* your card contains the CD prize when you see a 1 in L_3.

Highlight L_3. Enter L_1*L_2.

STEP 4 **Find** the first occurrence of a 1 in List 3. In this simulation, you can see that the first occurrence of a 1 in List 3 happens after 4 trials.

▶ For this simulation, you must scratch 4 game cards before you win a CD.

PRACTICE

EXAMPLE 1
on p. 849
for Exs. 1–3

1. In Example 1, suppose you can receive a prize coupon for nachos in addition to the items listed in the example. About how many times must you buy an item from the concession stand before you win each prize at least once? *Explain* how you found your answer. **Answers will vary.**

EXAMPLE 2
on p. 850
for Exs. 2–3

2. In Example 2, about how many game cards must you scratch before you win one of each prize? *Explain* how you found your answer. **Answers will vary.**

3. In Example 2, there are 3 prizes. *Explain* why the results of the simulation would be inaccurate if you generated random integers from 1 to 3. **See margin.**

850   Chapter 13   Probability and Data Analysis

3. *Sample answer:* There are 3 prizes to win, but since the prizes do not have an equal likelihood of being won, generating a list of random integers from 1 to 3 wouldn't represent the situation. The probability of winning a CD is $\frac{1}{6}$, so if there were only 3 possible outcomes in the simulation you couldn't represent winning a CD properly.

13.2 Find Probabilities Using Permutations

Before You used the counting principle.

Now You will use the formula for the number of permutations.

Why? So you can find the number of possible arrangements, as in Ex. 38.

Key Vocabulary
• permutation
• *n* factorial

A **permutation** is an arrangement of objects in which order is important. For instance, the 6 possible permutations of the letters A, B, and C are shown.

ABC   ACB   BAC   BCA   CAB   CBA

EXAMPLE 1   Count permutations

Consider the number of permutations of the letters in the word JULY.

a. In how many ways can you arrange all of the letters?

b. In how many ways can you arrange 2 of the letters?

Solution

a. Use the counting principle to find the number of permutations of the letters in the word JULY.

REVIEW COUNTING PRINCIPLE
For help with using the counting principle, see p. 931.

$$\begin{array}{c}\text{Number of} \\ \text{permutations}\end{array} = \begin{array}{c}\text{Choices for} \\ \text{1st letter}\end{array} \cdot \begin{array}{c}\text{Choices for} \\ \text{2nd letter}\end{array} \cdot \begin{array}{c}\text{Choices for} \\ \text{3rd letter}\end{array} \cdot \begin{array}{c}\text{Choices for} \\ \text{4th letter}\end{array}$$

$$= 4 \quad \cdot \quad 3 \quad \cdot \quad 2 \quad \cdot \quad 1$$

$$= 24$$

▶ There are 24 ways you can arrange all of the letters in the word JULY.

b. When arranging 2 letters of the word JULY, you have 4 choices for the first letter and 3 choices for the second letter.

$$\begin{array}{c}\text{Number of} \\ \text{permutations}\end{array} = \begin{array}{c}\text{Choices for} \\ \text{1st letter}\end{array} \cdot \begin{array}{c}\text{Choices for} \\ \text{2nd letter}\end{array}$$

$$= 4 \cdot 3$$

$$= 12$$

▶ There are 12 ways you can arrange 2 of the letters in the word JULY.

✓ GUIDED PRACTICE   for Example 1

1. In how many ways can you arrange the letters in the word MOUSE? **120 ways**

2. In how many ways can you arrange 3 of the letters in the word ORANGE? **120 ways**

---

① PLAN AND PREPARE

Warm-Up Exercises

▣ Transparency Available

1. There are 8 football teams in your district and 7 teams in a neighboring district. How many teams can you match up for games? **56**

2. A padlock has 9 numbers and uses 3 of them in sequence to open the lock. If you randomly choose 3 numbers, what is the probability that you choose the correct sequence? $\frac{1}{729}$

Notetaking Guide

▣ Transparency Available

Promotes interactive learning and notetaking skills, pp. 299–301.

Pacing

Basic: 2 days

Average: 2 days

Advanced: 2 days

Block: 0.5 block with 13.1
0.5 block with 13.3

• See *Teaching Guide/Lesson Plan*.

② FOCUS AND MOTIVATE

Essential Question

Big Idea 1, p. 841

How do you use the formula for permutations? **Tell students they will learn how to answer this question by finding the number of arrangements of *n* objects.**

NCTM STANDARDS

Standard 5: Apply basic concepts of probability

Standard 6: Build knowledge through problem solving

Resource Planning Guide

Chapter Resource Book
• Teaching Guide/Lesson Plan (pp. 14–15)
• Practice levels A, B, C (pp. 16–18)
• Study Guide (pp. 19–20)
• Catch-up for Absent Students (p. 21)
• Problem Solving Workshop (p. 22)
• Challenge (p. 23)

Workbooks
• Notetaking Guide (pp. 299–301)
• Practice Workbook (pp. 198–199)

Teaching Options
• **Power Presentations CD-ROM** provides dynamic electronic teaching resources for the classroom.
• **Activity Generator CD-ROM** provides editable activities for all ability levels.

Interactive Technology
• Easy Planner
• Power Presentations CD-ROM
• Activity Generator CD-ROM
• Animated Algebra
• Test Generator CD-ROM
• Online Quiz
• eWorkbook
• eEdition
• @HomeTutor

Resources for English Learners
• Quick Reference for English Learners
• Spanish Study Guide
• Multi-Language Visual Glossary
• Student Resources in Spanish

See also the *Algebra 1 Toolkit* for more strategies for meeting individual needs.

852

Motivating the Lesson

You want to photograph five of your friends. If you know how to calculate permutations, you can find the number of ways you can arrange them in a row for a photograph.

❸ TEACH

Extra Example 1

Consider the number of permutations of the letters in the word BRIGHTEN.

a. In how many ways can you arrange all of the letters?
40,320 ways

b. In how many ways can you arrange 2 of the letters? **56 ways**

Key Questions to Ask for Example 1

• How can you tell that order is important for this exercise? **The word "arrange" means to put in order, so order is important.**

• Why are there 3 choices for the second letter? **There are 4 letters in the word *July*. Once one has been chosen for the first letter, there are 3 letters left from which to choose the second letter.**

Extra Example 2

You have 14 CDs. You can arrange 12 of the 14 in a CD wallet. In how many ways can you arrange the CDs in the CD wallet?
43,589,145,600 ways

Key Questions to Ask for Example 2

• What permutations formula would you use to find the number of ways the band might arrange 10 of the 12 songs? $_{12}P_{10} = \dfrac{12!}{2!}$

FACTORIAL In Example 1, you evaluated the expression $4 \cdot 3 \cdot 2 \cdot 1$. This expression can be written as 4! and is read "4 *factorial*." For any positive integer n, the product of the integers from 1 to n is called n **factorial** and is written as $n!$. The value of 0! is defined to be 1.

$$n! = n \cdot (n-1) \cdot (n-2) \cdot \ldots \cdot 3 \cdot 2 \cdot 1 \text{ and } 0! = 1$$

In Example 1, you also found the permutations of four objects taken two at a time. You can find the number of permutations using the formulas below.

KEY CONCEPT   *For Your Notebook*

Permutations

Formulas	Examples
The number of permutations of n objects is given by: $$_nP_n = n!$$	The number of permutations of 4 objects is: $$_4P_4 = 4! = 4 \cdot 3 \cdot 2 \cdot 1 = 24$$
The number of permutations of n objects taken r at a time, where $r \le n$, is given by: $$_nP_r = \frac{n!}{(n-r)!}$$	The number of permutations of 4 objects taken 2 at a time is: $$_4P_2 = \frac{4!}{(4-2)!} = \frac{4 \cdot 3 \cdot 2!}{2!} = 12$$

EXAMPLE 2 Use a permutations formula

CD RECORDING Your band has written 12 songs and plans to record 9 of them for a CD. In how many ways can you arrange the songs on the CD?

Solution

To find the number of permutations of 9 songs chosen from 12, find $_{12}P_9$.

DIVIDE COMMON FACTORS
When you divide out common factors, remember that 3! is a factor of 12!.

$_{12}P_9 = \dfrac{12!}{(12-9)!}$ Permutations formula

$= \dfrac{12!}{3!}$ Subtract.

$= \dfrac{12 \cdot 11 \cdot 10 \cdot 9 \cdot 8 \cdot 7 \cdot 6 \cdot 5 \cdot 4 \cdot \cancel{3!}}{\cancel{3!}}$ Expand factorials. Divide out common factor, 3!.

$= 79,833,600$ Multiply.

▶ There are 79,833,600 ways to arrange 9 songs out of 12.

 GUIDED PRACTICE   for Example 2

3. **WHAT IF?** In Example 2, suppose your band has written 15 songs. You will record 9 of them for a CD. In how many ways can you arrange the songs on the CD? **1,816,214,400 ways**

Differentiated Instruction

Below Level Have students work in pairs to confirm that the permutations formula works. Suggest that they make a list of the number of ways the letters in the word SAID can be arranged and then find the arrangements using the permutations formula. Ask them to make a similar list for two of the letters in the word. Then lead students to see the usefulness of the permutations formula by having them examine what happens to the number of permutations as the number of letters in a word increases. See also the *Algebra 1 Toolkit* for more strategies.

EXAMPLE 3 Find a probability using permutations

PARADE For a town parade, you will ride on a float with your soccer team. There are 12 floats in the parade, and their order is chosen at random. Find the probability that your float is first and the float with the school chorus is second.

Solution

STEP 1 **Write** the number of possible outcomes as the number of permutations of the 12 floats in the parade. This is $_{12}P_{12} = 12!$.

STEP 2 **Write** the number of favorable outcomes as the number of permutations of the other floats, given that the soccer team is first and the chorus is second. This is $_{10}P_{10} = 10!$.

STEP 3 **Calculate** the probability.

$$P\left(\begin{array}{c}\text{soccer team is first}\\ \text{chorus is second}\end{array}\right) = \frac{10!}{12!} \qquad \text{Form a ratio of favorable to possible outcomes.}$$

$$= \frac{\cancel{10!}}{12 \cdot 11 \cdot \cancel{10!}} \qquad \text{Expand factorials. Divide out common factor, 10!.}$$

$$= \frac{1}{132} \qquad \text{Simplify.}$$

✔ **GUIDED PRACTICE** for Example 3

4. WHAT IF? In Example 3, suppose there are 14 floats in the parade. Find the probability that the soccer team is first and the chorus is second. $\frac{1}{182}$

13.2 EXERCISES

HOMEWORK KEY

○ = **WORKED-OUT SOLUTIONS**
on p. WS1 for Exs. 21 and 35

★ = **STANDARDIZED TEST PRACTICE**
Exs. 2, 11, 30, 33, and 35

◆ = **MULTIPLE REPRESENTATIONS**
Ex. 34

SKILL PRACTICE

 1. VOCABULARY Copy and complete: An arrangement of objects in which order is important is called a(n) __?__ . **permutation**

2. ★ WRITING *Explain* what the notation $_9P_2$ means. What is the value of this expression? **The number of permutations containing 2 items chosen from a group of 9 possible items; 72**

EXAMPLES 1 and 2 on pp. 851–852 for Exs. 3–11

COUNTING PERMUTATIONS Find the number of ways you can arrange (a) all of the letters in the given word and (b) 2 of the letters in the word.

3. AT
a. 2 ways; b. 2 ways

4. TRY
a. 6 ways; b. 6 ways

5. GAME
a. 24 ways; b. 12 ways

6. CAT
a. 6 ways; b. 6 ways

7. WATER
a. 120 ways; b. 20 ways

8. ROCK
a. 24 ways; b. 12 ways

9. APRIL
a. 120 ways; b. 20 ways

10. FAMILY
a. 720 ways; b. 30 ways

11. ★ OPEN-ENDED *Describe* a real-world situation where the number of possibilities is given by $_5P_2$. *Sample answer:* **5 people are running in a race. How many different results can there be for first and second place?**

Differentiated Instruction

Visual Learners For Step 2 in **Example 3**, draw a simple diagram to show why the number of outcomes is 10!.

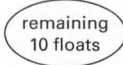
1st   2nd
| soccer team | chorus | remaining 10 floats |

The number of permutations of the remaining 10 floats is given by $_{10}P_{10} = 10!$.

See also the *Algebra 1 Toolkit* for more strategies.

Ten students in your science class are giving reports on endangered animals. The order of the reports is chosen at random. Find the probability that your report on the humpback whale is first and your friend's report on the American crocodile is second. $\frac{1}{90}$

Closing the Lesson

Have students summarize the major points of the lesson and answer the Essential Question: How do you use the formula for permutations?

• **A permutation is an arrangement of objects in which order is important.**

• **The product of positive integers from 1 to *n* is called *n* factorial ($n!$). 4! is $4 \cdot 3 \cdot 2 \cdot 1$ or 24.**

Use the formula $_nP_n = n!$ to find the arrangement of *n* objects. You can arrange 5 objects in $_5P_5 = 5!$ ways, or $5 \cdot 4 \cdot 3 \cdot 2 \cdot 1 = 120$ ways. Use the permutations formula $_nP_r = \frac{n!}{(n-r)!}$ to find the number of permutations of *n* objects taken *r* at a time. You can arrange 2 of 5 objects in $\frac{5!}{(5-2)!} = \frac{5!}{3!}$, or 20 ways.

To find a probability using permutations, use formulas to write a ratio of favorable to possible outcomes.

Assignment Guide

Answer Transparencies available for all exercises

Basic:
Day 1: pp. 853–855
Exs. 1–19
Day 2: pp. 853–855
Exs. 20–29, 32–36, 40–43

Average:
Day 1: pp. 853–855
Exs. 1–19
Day 2: pp. 853–855
Exs. 22–30, 32–38, 40–43

Advanced:
Day 1: pp. 853–855
Exs. 1–19
Day 2: pp. 853–855
Exs. 24–43*

Block:
pp. 853–855
Exs. 1–19 (with 13.1)
pp. 853–855
Exs. 22–30, 32–38, 40–43
(with 13.3)

Differentiated Instruction

See *Algebra 1 Best Practices Toolkit* for suggestions on addressing the needs of a diverse classroom.

Homework Check

For a quick check of student under-standing of key concepts, go over the following exercises:
Basic: 6, 13, 22, 32, 34
Average: 8, 15, 24, 33, 35
Advanced: 10, 17, 26, 36, 37

Extra Practice

- Student Edition, p. 950
- Chapter 13 Resource Book: Practice levels A, B, C, pp. 16–18

Practice Worksheet

An easily-readable reduced practice page (with answers) for this lesson can be found on p. 840C.

EXAMPLE 2
on p. 852
for Exs. 12–30

FACTORIALS AND PERMUTATIONS Evaluate the expression.

12. $1!$ **1**   **13.** $3!$ **6**   **14.** $0!$ **1**   **15.** $5!$ **120**

16. $8!$ **40,320**   **17.** $10!$ **3,628,800**   **18.** $12!$ **479,001,600**   **19.** $13!$ **6,227,020,800**

20. $_5P_2$ **20**   **21.** $_7P_3$ **210**   **22.** $_9P_1$ **9**   **23.** $_6P_5$ **720**

24. $_8P_8$ **40,320**   **25.** $_{12}P_0$ **1**   **26.** $_{30}P_2$ **870**   **27.** $_{25}P_5$ **6,375,600**

28. The denominator of the fraction should be $(11 - 7)!$, not $(11 - 7)$;
$$\frac{11!}{(11 - 7)!} = \frac{11!}{4!} = 1,663,200.$$

29. The denominator of the fraction should be $(5 - 3)!$, not $3!$;
$$\frac{5!}{(5 - 3)!} = \frac{5!}{2!} = 60.$$

B **ERROR ANALYSIS** *Describe* and correct the error in evaluating the expression.

28.
$$_{11}P_7 = \frac{11!}{(11 - 7)} = \frac{11!}{4} = 9,979,200 \quad \times$$

29.
$$_5P_3 = \frac{5!}{3!} = \frac{5 \cdot 4 \cdot 3!}{3!} = 20 \quad \times$$

30. ★ **MULTIPLE CHOICE** The judges in an art contest award prizes for first, second, and third place out of 11 entries. Which expression gives the number of ways the judges can award first, second, and third place? **C**

(A) $\frac{3!}{11!}$ (B) $\frac{8!}{11!}$ (C) $\frac{11!}{8!}$ (D) $\frac{11!}{3!}$

31. **CHALLENGE** Consider a set of 4 objects and a set of n objects.

a. Are there more permutations of all 4 of the objects or of 3 of the 4 objects? *Justify* your answer using an organized list. **a–b. See margin.**

b. In general, are there more permutations of n objects taken n at a time or of n objects taken $n - 1$ at a time? *Justify* your answer using the formula for the number of permutations.

PROBLEM SOLVING

EXAMPLE 2 **A**
on p. 852
for Exs. 32–33

32. **MOVIES** Six friends go to a movie theater. In how many different ways can they sit together in a row of 6 empty seats? **720 ways**

@HomeTutor for problem solving help at classzone.com

33. ★ **MULTIPLE CHOICE** You plan to visit 4 stores during a shopping trip. In how many orders can you visit these stores? **C**

(A) 4   (B) 16   (C) 24   (D) 256

@HomeTutor for problem solving help at classzone.com

EXAMPLE 3
on p. 853
for Exs. 34–38

34. ◆ **MULTIPLE REPRESENTATIONS** You and your friend are two of 4 servers working a shift in a restaurant. The host assigns tables of new diners to the servers in a particular order. This order remains the same, so that all servers are likely to wait on the same number of tables by the end of the shift.

a. **Making a List** List all the possible orders in which the host can assign tables to the servers. **See margin.**

b. **Using a Formula** Use the formula for permutations to find the number of ways in which the host can assign tables to the servers. **24 ways**

c. **Describe in Words** What is the likelihood that you and your friend are assigned the first 2 tables? *Explain* your answer using probability. **See margin.**

854

○ = **WORKED-OUT SOLUTIONS** on p. WS1

★ = **STANDARDIZED TEST PRACTICE**

◆ = **MULTIPLE REPRESENTATIONS**

31a. They are the same; 4 of 4 items: ABCD, ABDC, ACBD, ACDB, ADBC, ADCB, BACD, BADC, BCDA, BCAD, BDAC, BDCA, CABD, CADB, CBAD, CBDA, CDAB, CDBA, DABC, DACB, DBAC, DBCA, DCAB, DCBA; 3 of 4 items: ABC, ABD, ACB, ACD, ADB, ADC, BAC, BAD, BCD, BCA, BDA, BDC, CAB, CAD, CBA, CBD, CDA, CDB, DAB, DAC, DBA, DBC, DCA, DCB.

31b. See Additional Answers beginning on p. AA1.

35. ★ **SHORT RESPONSE** Every student in your history class is required to present a project in front of the class. Each day, 4 students make their presentations in an order chosen at random by the teacher. You make your presentation on the first day.

    a. What is the probability that you are chosen to be the first or second presenter on the first day? *Explain* how you found your answer.

    b. What is the probability that you are chosen to be the second or third presenter on the first day? *Compare* your answer with that in part (a).
    $\frac{1}{2}$; the answers are the same.

[B]

36. **HISTORY EXAM** On an exam, you are asked to list 5 historical events in the order in which they occurred. You guess the order of the events at random. What is the probability that you choose the correct order? $\frac{1}{120}$

37. **SPIRIT** You make 6 posters to hold up at a basketball game. Each poster has a letter of the word TIGERS. You and 5 friends sit next to each other in a row. The posters are distributed at random. What is the probability that TIGERS is spelled correctly when you hold up the posters? $\frac{1}{720}$

38. **BAND COMPETITION** Seven marching bands will perform at a competition. The order of the performances is determined at random. What is the probability that your school band will perform first, followed by the band from the one other high school in your town? $\frac{1}{42}$

[C]

39. **CHALLENGE** You are one of 10 students performing in a school talent show. The order of the performances is determined at random. The first five performers go on stage before the intermission, while the remaining five performers go on stage after the intermission.

    a. What is the probability that you are the last performer before the intermission and your rival performs immediately before you? $\frac{1}{90}$

    b. What is the probability that you are *not* the first performer? $\frac{9}{10}$

MIXED REVIEW

PREVIEW
Prepare for
Lesson 13.3 in
Exs. 40–43.

40. You are randomly assigned a day of the week to work an extra shift at your part-time job. Find the probability that you are assigned to work on Saturday. *(p. 843)* $\frac{1}{7}$

41. You choose a letter at random out of a bag that contains one of each letter of the alphabet. Find the probability that you choose the letter K. *(p. 843)* $\frac{1}{26}$

42. You roll a number cube. Find the probability that you roll an even number. *(p. 843)* $\frac{1}{2}$

43. You toss a coin twice. Find the probability that the coin shows tails twice. *(p. 843)* $\frac{1}{4}$

EXTRA PRACTICE for Lesson 13.2, p. 950   ⬯ **ONLINE QUIZ** at classzone.com   855

Before You used permutations to count possibilities.
Now You will use combinations to count possibilities.
Why? So you can find the probability of an event, as in Example 3.

Key Vocabulary
• combination

A **combination** is a selection of objects in which order is *not* important. For instance, in a drawing for 3 identical prizes, you would use combinations, because the order of the winners would not matter. If the prizes were different, you would use permutations, because the order would matter.

EXAMPLE 1 Count combinations

Count the combinations of two letters from the list A, B, C, D.

Solution

List all of the permutations of two letters in the list A, B, C, D. Because order is not important in a combination, cross out any duplicate pairs.

| AB | AC | AD | ~~BA~~ | BC | ~~BD~~ | ← BD and DB are the same pair. |
| ~~CA~~ | ~~CB~~ | CD | ~~DA~~ | ~~DB~~ | ~~DC~~ | |

▶ There are 6 possible combinations of 2 letters from the list A, B, C, D.

Animated Algebra at classzone.com

✓ GUIDED PRACTICE for Example 1

1. Count the combinations of 3 letters from the list A, B, C, D, E.
   10 combinations

COMBINATIONS In Example 1, you found the number of combinations of objects by making an organized list. You can also find the number of combinations using the following formula.

KEY CONCEPT *For Your Notebook*

Combinations

Formula
The number of combinations of n objects taken r at a time, where $r \le n$, is given by:

$$_nC_r = \frac{n!}{(n-r)! \cdot r!}$$

Example
The number of combinations of 4 objects taken 2 at a time is:

$$_4C_2 = \frac{4!}{(4-2)! \cdot 2!} = \frac{4 \cdot 3 \cdot 2!}{2! \cdot (2 \cdot 1)} = 6$$

EXAMPLE 2 Use the combinations formula

LUNCH MENU You order a sandwich at a restaurant. You can choose 2 side dishes from a list of 8. How many combinations of side dishes are possible?

Solution

The order in which you choose the side dishes is not important. So, to find the number of combinations of 8 side dishes taken 2 at a time, find $_8C_2$.

$$_8C_2 = \frac{8!}{(8-2)! \cdot 2!} \qquad \text{Combinations formula}$$

$$= \frac{8!}{6! \cdot 2!} \qquad \text{Subtract.}$$

$$= \frac{8 \cdot 7 \cdot 6!}{6! \cdot (2 \cdot 1)} \qquad \begin{array}{l}\text{Expand factorials.}\\ \text{Divide out common factor, 6!.}\end{array}$$

$$= 28 \qquad \text{Simplify.}$$

▶ There are 28 different combinations of side dishes you can order.

EXAMPLE 3 Find a probablity using combinations

PHOTOGRAPHY A yearbook editor has selected 14 photos, including one of you and one of your friend, to use in a collage for the yearbook. The photos are placed at random. There is room for 2 photos at the top of the page. What is the probability that your photo and your friend's photo are the two placed at the top of the page?

Solution

STEP 1 **Write** the number of possible outcomes as the number of combinations of 14 photos taken 2 at a time, or $_{14}C_2$, because the order in which the photos are chosen is not important.

$$_{14}C_2 = \frac{14!}{(14-2)! \cdot 2!} = \frac{14!}{12! \cdot 2!} = \frac{14 \cdot 13 \cdot 12!}{12! \cdot (2 \cdot 1)} = 91$$

STEP 2 **Find** the number of favorable outcomes. Only one of the possible combinations includes your photo and your friend's photo.

STEP 3 **Calculate** the probability.

$$P(\text{your photo and your friend's photos are chosen}) = \frac{1}{91}$$

 GUIDED PRACTICE for Examples 2 and 3

2. WHAT IF? In Example 2, suppose you can choose 3 side dishes out of the list of 8 side dishes. How many combinations are possible? **56 combinations**

3. WHAT IF? In Example 3, suppose there are 20 photos in the collage. Find the probability that your photo and your friend's photo are the two placed at the top of the page. $\frac{1}{190}$

13.3 Find Probabilities Using Combinations **857**

Differentiated Instruction

Advanced Have students create two situations in which 2 out of 16 objects are selected, with order important in one of the situations and not important in the other. Ask students to use the situations to compare and contrast permutations and combinations, explaining why the number of selections is greater in one than the other, and describing the relationship between the two. Tell students it may be necessary to create several situations in which order is and is not important to be able to describe the relationship between permutations and combinations.

See also the *Algebra 1 Toolkit* for more strategies.

Motivating the Lesson

You sing in a chorus after school. The director will choose at random 2 songs out of 5 for the chorus to learn to sing. You can use combinations to help find the probability that the director will choose your two favorite songs.

❸ TEACH

Extra Example 1

Count the combinations of 2 letters from the list A, B, C, D, E. **10**

Animated Algebra
classzone.com

An **Animated Algebra** activity is available on-line for **Example 1**. This activity is also available on the **Power Presentations CD-ROM**.

Extra Example 2

You can choose 2 courses out of a list of 6. How many combinations of electives are possible? **15**

Extra Example 3

Your teacher randomly chooses 2 out of 18 students to give an impromptu debate on freedom of the press in high school newspapers. What is the probability that your teacher chooses you and your best friend? $\frac{1}{153}$

Closing the Lesson

Have students summarize the major points of the lesson and answer the Essential Question: How do you use combinations to count possibilities?

- A combination is a selection of objects in which order is not important.

Use the formula $_nC_r = \frac{n!}{n-r} \cdot r!$ to find the number of combinations of *n* objects taken *r* at a time.

13.3 EXERCISES

HOMEWORK KEY
○ = **WORKED-OUT SOLUTIONS**
  on p. WS1 for Exs. 7 and 25

★ = **STANDARDIZED TEST PRACTICE**
  Exs. 2, 14–20, and 25

④ PRACTICE AND APPLY

Assignment Guide

📑 Answer Transparencies
available for all exercises

Basic:
Day 1: pp. 858–859
Exs. 1–17, 23–25, 28–33

Average:
Day 1: pp. 858–859
Exs. 1–5, 6–14 even, 15–20, 23–26, 28–33

Advanced:
Day 1: pp. 858–859
Exs. 1–3, 10–33*

Block:
pp. 858–859
Exs. 1–5, 6–14 even, 15–20, 23–26, 28–33 (with 13.2)

Differentiated Instruction

See *Algebra 1 Best Practices Toolkit* for suggestions on addressing the needs of a diverse classroom.

Homework Check

For a quick check of student understanding of key concepts, go over the following exercises:
Basic: 3, 8, 16, 23, 24
Average: 4, 10, 17, 24, 25
Advanced: 3, 12, 18, 25, 26

Extra Practice

• Student Edition, p. 950
• Chapter 13 Resource Book: Practice levels A, B, C, pp. 28–30

Practice Worksheet

An easily-readable reduced practice page (with answers) for this lesson can be found on p. 840C.

16. Combinations; the order in which the students are picked for the group does not matter, 8,214,570 groups.

17. Permutations; since the roles are different, the order in which students are selected for the roles matters, 720 ways.

18. Combinations; the order in which you answer the questions does not matter, 45 ways.

858

SKILL PRACTICE

EXAMPLE 1
on p. 856
for Exs. 3, 4

EXAMPLE 2
on p. 857
for Exs. 5–15

2. In a combination, the order in which the objects are arranged is not important. In a permutation, the order is important.

4. Each combination is duplicated, since the order of the letters does not matter. AB and BA are the same, as are CA and AC and BC and CB; list: AB, AC, BC.

5. *Sample answer:* The answer given was $_9P_4$ not $_9C_4$;
$$\frac{9!}{(9-4)! \cdot 4!} =$$
$$\frac{9!}{5! \cdot 4!} = 126.$$

⎡A⎤ 1. **VOCABULARY** Copy and complete: A(n) __?__ is a selection of objects in which order is not important. **combination**

2. ★ **WRITING** *Explain* how a combination differs from a permutation. **See margin.**

3. **COMBINATIONS** How many combinations of 3 letters from the list A, B, C, D, E, F are possible? **20 combinations**

4. **ERROR ANALYSIS** *Describe* and correct the error in listing all of the possible combinations of 2 letters from the list A, B, C. **See margin.**

AB	BA	CA
AC	BC	CB
✕

5. **ERROR ANALYSIS** *Describe* and correct the error in evaluating $_9C_4$. **See margin.**

$$_9C_4 = \frac{9!}{(9-4)!} = \frac{9!}{5!} = 3024 \quad ✕$$

COMBINATIONS Evaluate the expression.

6. $_5C_1$ **5**   ⑦ $_8C_5$ **56**   8. $_9C_9$ **1**   9. $_8C_6$ **28**

10. $_{12}C_3$ **220**   11. $_{11}C_4$ **330**   12. $_{15}C_8$ **6435**   13. $_{20}C_5$ **15,504**

14. ★ **MULTIPLE CHOICE** What is the value of $_{10}C_6$? **C**

Ⓐ 7   Ⓑ 60   Ⓒ 210   Ⓓ 151,200

⎡B⎤ 15. ★ **MULTIPLE CHOICE** You have the first season of your favorite television show on a set of DVDs. The set contains 13 episodes. You have time to watch 3 episodes. How many combinations of 3 episodes can you watch? **A**

Ⓐ 286   Ⓑ 572   Ⓒ 1716   Ⓓ 589,680

★ **SHORT RESPONSE** In Exercises 16–19, tell whether the question can be answered using *combinations* or *permutations*. *Explain* your choice, then answer the question. **16–19. See margin.**

16. Four students from your class of 120 students will be selected to organize a fundraiser. How many groups of 4 students are possible?

17. Ten students are auditioning for 3 different roles in a play. In how many ways can the 3 roles be filled?

18. To complete an exam, you must answer 8 questions from a list of 10 questions. In how many ways can you complete the exam?

19. In how many ways can 5 people sit in a car that holds 5 passengers?

20. ★ **WRITING** Which is greater, $_6P_r$ or $_6C_r$? *Justify* your answer. **See margin.**

⎡C⎤ 21. **REASONING** Write an equation that relates $_nP_r$ and $_nC_r$. *Explain* your reasoning. **See margin.**

22. **CHALLENGE** Prove that $_nC_r = {}_nC_{n-r}$. *Explain* why this makes sense. **See margin.**

---

19. Permutations; the arrangement of people in the car matters, 120 ways.

20–22. See Additional Answers beginning on p. AA1.

Differentiated Instruction

Kinesthetic Learners Some students may have trouble distinguishing between combinations and permutations. For **Exercises 3 and 4**, have students write single letters on index cards and use the cards to compute combinations and permutations by sorting them. Provide additional exercises to be solved using the cards, such as distinguishing $_3C_2 = 3$ from $_3P_2 = 6$, and distinguishing $_5C_2 = 10$ from $_5P_2 = 20$.

See also the *Algebra 1 Toolkit* for more strategies.

EXAMPLE 2 [A]
on p. 857
for Ex. 23

23. RESTAURANT You are ordering a burrito with 2 main ingredients and 3 toppings. The menu below shows the possible choices. How many different burritos are possible? **840 burritos**

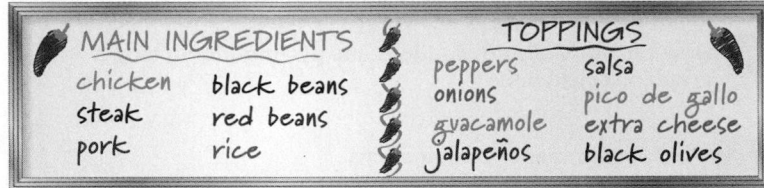

@HomeTutor for problem solving help at classzone.com

EXAMPLE 3
on p. 857
for Exs. 24–26

24. WORK SCHEDULE You work 3 evenings each week at a bookstore. Your supervisor assigns you 3 evenings at random from the 7 possibilities. What is the probability that your schedule this week includes working on Friday? $\frac{3}{7}$

@HomeTutor for problem solving help at classzone.com

25. ★ **SHORT RESPONSE** On a television game show, 9 members of the studio audience are randomly selected to be eligible contestants.

   a. Six of the 9 eligible contestants are randomly chosen to play a game on the stage. How many combinations of 6 players from the group of eligible contestants are possible? **84 combinations**

   b. You and your two friends are part of the group of 9 eligible contestants. What is the probability that all three of you are chosen to play the game on stage? *Explain* how you found your answer. **See margin.**

26. $\frac{1}{435}$; $\frac{1}{870}$; **my best friend and I are chosen, regardless of order.** [B]

26. REPRESENTATIVES Your teacher chooses 2 students at random to represent your homeroom. The homeroom has a total of 30 students, including your best friend. What is the probability that you and your best friend are chosen? What is the probability that you are chosen first and your best friend is chosen second? Which event is more likely to occur?

[C] **27. CHALLENGE** There are 30 students in your class. Your science teacher will choose 5 students at random to complete a group project. Find the probability that you and your 2 best friends in the science class are chosen to work in the group. *Explain* how you found your answer. **See margin.**

PREVIEW
Prepare for
Lesson 13.4 in
Exs. 28–32.

Find the product. *(p. 915)*

28. $\frac{1}{6} \cdot \frac{4}{5}$ $\frac{2}{15}$

29. $\frac{4}{25} \cdot \frac{7}{24}$ $\frac{7}{150}$

30. $\frac{13}{30} \cdot \frac{5}{26}$ $\frac{1}{12}$

31. $\frac{7}{24} \cdot \frac{4}{51}$ $\frac{7}{306}$

32. You roll a number cube. What is the probability that you roll a multiple of 3? *(p. 843)* $\frac{1}{3}$

33. In how many ways can you arrange 3 letters from the list P, Q, R, S, T, L? *Explain* how you found your answer. *(p. 851)* **120 ways.** *Sample answer:* Calculate $_6P_3$.

EXTRA PRACTICE for Lesson 13.3, p. 950   ⟳ **ONLINE QUIZ** at classzone.com   859

13.3 Find Permutations and Combinations

QUESTION How can you find combinations and permutations using a graphing calculator?

EXAMPLE 1 Find the number of combinations

STARTERS There are 15 players on your softball team, but only 9 of them can be the starting players in one game. How many combinations of starting players are possible?

Solution

You are finding $_nC_r$ where $n = 15$ and $r = 9$. Enter 15 for n. Press MATH . Go to the PRB menu and select $_nC_r$. Then enter 9 for r.

▶ There are 5005 possible combinations of starting players.

EXAMPLE 2 Find the number of permutations

BATTING ORDER Before each softball game, your coach announces the batting order of the 9 starting players. This is the order in which the starting players will bat. How many batting orders can be formed using 9 players on your team of 15 players?

Solution

You are finding $_nP_r$ where $n = 15$ and $r = 9$. Enter 15 for n. Press MATH . Go to the PRB menu and select $_nP_r$. Then enter 9 for r.

▶ There are 1,816,214,400 possible batting orders.

PRACTICE

Evaluate the expression.

1. $_7C_4$ **35**
2. $_6C_6$ **1**
3. $_{10}C_3$ **120**
4. $_{16}C_8$ **12,870**
5. $_9P_5$ **15,120**
6. $_7P_6$ **5040**
7. $_{11}P_8$ **6,652,800**
8. $_{12}P_5$ **95,040**

9. **GROUP PROJECT** Your teacher selects 3 students from a class of 28 students to work on a project in a group. Within the group, one member must be the writer, one must be the researcher, and one must be the presenter.

   a. How many different groups of 3 can your teacher select? **3276 groups**

   b. After the group is formed, in how many ways can the roles in the group be assigned? **6 ways**

13.4 Find Probabilities of Compound Events

Before You found the probability of a simple event.

Now You will find the probability of a compound event.

Why? So you can analyze scientific data, as in Ex. 23.

Key Vocabulary
• compound event
• mutually exclusive events
• overlapping events
• independent events
• dependent events

> **REVIEW VENN DIAGRAMS**
> For help with using Venn diagrams, see p. 930.

A **compound event** combines two or more events, using the word *and* or the word *or*. To find the probability that either event *A* or event *B* occurs, determine how the events are related. **Mutually exclusive events** have no common outcomes. **Overlapping events** have at least one common outcome.

For instance, suppose you roll a number cube.

Mutually Exclusive Events

Event A: Roll a 3.

Event B: Roll an even number.

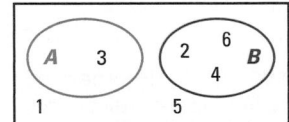

Set *A* has **1** number, and set *B* has **3** numbers.

$$P(3 \text{ or even}) = \frac{1}{6} + \frac{3}{6}$$

$$P(A \text{ or } B) = P(A) + P(B)$$

Overlapping Events

Event A: Roll an odd number.

Event B: Roll a prime number.

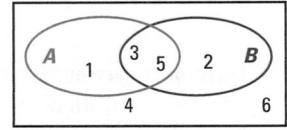

Set *A* has **3** numbers, and set *B* has **3** numbers. There are **2** numbers in both sets.

$$P(\text{odd or prime}) = \frac{3}{6} + \frac{3}{6} - \frac{2}{6}$$

$$P(A \text{ or } B) = P(A) + P(B) - P(A \text{ and } B)$$

EXAMPLE 1 Find the probability of *A* or *B*

You roll a number cube. Find the probability that you roll a 2 or an odd number.

Solution

Because 2 is an even number, rolling a 2 and rolling an odd number are mutually exclusive events.

$$P(2 \text{ or odd}) = P(2) + P(\text{odd})$$

$$= \frac{1}{6} + \frac{3}{6}$$

$$= \frac{4}{6}$$

$$= \frac{2}{3}$$

① PLAN AND PREPARE

Warm-Up Exercises

📄 **Transparency Available**

Find the product.

1. $\frac{2}{5} \cdot \frac{3}{4}$ $\frac{3}{10}$ **2.** $\frac{7}{8} \cdot \frac{2}{7}$ $\frac{1}{4}$

3. $\frac{12}{15} \cdot \frac{8}{14}$ $\frac{16}{35}$ **4.** $\frac{18}{52} \cdot \frac{17}{51}$ $\frac{3}{26}$

5. A bag contains 3 green, 5 blue, and 6 yellow marbles. What is the probability of selecting a yellow marble at random? $\frac{3}{7}$

Notetaking Guide

📄 **Transparency Available**

Promotes interactive learning and notetaking skills, pp. 305–307.

Pacing

Basic: 2 days

Average: 2 days

Advanced: 2 days

Block: 1 block

• See *Teaching Guide/Lesson Plan.*

② FOCUS AND MOTIVATE

Essential Question

Big Idea 1, p. 841

How do you find the probability of compound events? **Tell students they will learn how to answer this question by finding probabilities of mutually exclusive events or overlapping events and independent or dependent events.**

NCTM STANDARDS

Standard 9: Grasp connections among mathematical ideas

Standard 10: Create representations to communicate mathematical ideas

Resource Planning Guide

Chapter Resource Book
• Teaching Guide/Lesson Plan (pp. 36–37)
• Activity Master (p. 38)
• Practice levels A, B, C (pp. 39–41)
• Study Guide (pp. 42–43)
• Catch-up for Absent Students (p. 44)
• Problem Solving Workshop (p. 45)
• Challenge (p. 47)

Workbooks
• Notetaking Guide (pp. 305–307)
• Practice Workbook (pp. 202–204)

Teaching Options
• **Power Presentations CD-ROM** provides dynamic electronic teaching resources for the classroom.
• **Activity Generator CD-ROM** provides editable activities for all ability levels.

Interactive Technology
• Easy Planner
• Power Presentations CD-ROM
• Activity Generator CD-ROM
• Animated Algebra
• Test Generator CD-ROM
• Online Quiz
• eWorkbook
• eEdition
• @HomeTutor

Resources for English Learners
• Quick Reference for English Learners
• Spanish Study Guide
• Multi-Language Visual Glossary
• Student Resources in Spanish

See also the *Algebra 1 Toolkit* for more strategies for meeting individual needs.

Motivating the Lesson

You are one out of 50 students who will be selected at random to recite one of their poems or play one of their songs. If you know how to find the probability of compound events, you can determine your chances of being selected for one or the other of these performances.

❸ TEACH

Extra Example 1

You roll a number cube. Find the probability of rolling a 1 or a number greater than 4. $\frac{1}{2}$

Key Question to Ask for Example 1

• How is a mutually exclusive compound probability similar to a simple probability? **Each of the probabilities in a mutually exclusive compound event is represented as the ratio of the number of favorable outcomes to the number of possible outcomes, just as in a simple probability.**

Extra Example 2

You roll a number cube. Find the probability of rolling an odd number or a number less than 5. $\frac{5}{6}$

Key Question to Ask for Example 2

• Why do you subtract the probability of the overlapping event in a compound probability? **The overlapping event is a subset of both events. You need to subtract its probability so that it is not included twice.**

EXAMPLE 2 **Find the probability of *A* or *B***

You roll a number cube. Find the probability that you roll an even number or a prime number.

Solution

Because 2 is both an even number and a prime number, rolling an even number and rolling a prime number are overlapping events. There are 3 even numbers, 3 prime numbers, and 1 number that is both.

$$P(\text{even or prime}) = P(\text{even}) + P(\text{prime}) - P(\text{even and prime})$$

$$= \frac{3}{6} + \frac{3}{6} - \frac{1}{6}$$

$$= \frac{5}{6}$$

✓ **GUIDED PRACTICE** for Examples 1 and 2

1. You roll a number cube. Find the probability that you roll a 2 or a 5. $\frac{1}{3}$

2. You roll a number cube. Find the probability that you roll a number less than 4 or an odd number. $\frac{2}{3}$

INDEPENDENT AND DEPENDENT EVENTS To find the probability that event *A* and event *B* both occur, determine how the events are related. Two events are **independent events** if the occurrence of one event has no effect on the occurrence of the other. Two events are **dependent events** if the occurrence of one event affects the occurrence of the other.

For instance, consider the probability of choosing a green marble and then a blue marble from the bag shown. If you choose one marble and replace it before choosing the second, then the events are independent. If you do not replace the first marble, then the sample space has changed, and the events are dependent.

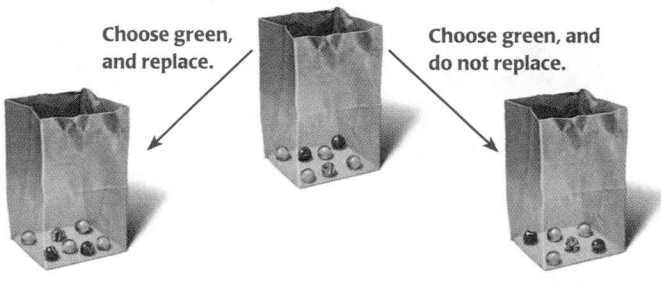

Choose green, and replace.   Choose green, and do not replace.

Independent Events	**Dependent Events**
With replacement:	Without replacement:
$P(\text{green and blue}) = \frac{4}{7} \cdot \frac{1}{7} = \frac{4}{49}$	$P(\text{green and blue}) = \frac{4}{7} \cdot \frac{1}{6} = \frac{2}{21}$
$P(A \text{ and } B) = P(A) \cdot P(B)$	$P(A \text{ and } B) = P(A) \cdot P(B \text{ given } A)$

Differentiated Instruction

Inclusion To help students associate *or* with addition, and *and* with multiplication, students can use a simple example. The sample space {H, T} for one toss of a coin gives $P(\text{heads or tails}) = 1$. Using addition, $P(\text{heads or tails}) = \frac{1}{2} + \frac{1}{2} = 1$. So, *or* means addition. Similarly, the sample space {HH, HT, TH, TT} for two tosses of a coin gives $P(\text{heads and then tails}) = \frac{1}{4}$. By multiplication, $P(\text{heads and then tails}) = \frac{1}{2} \cdot \frac{1}{2} = \frac{1}{4}$. So, *and* means multiplication. See also the *Algebra 1 Toolkit* for more strategies.

EXAMPLE 3 Find the probability of *A* and *B*

BUS SCHEDULE You take a city bus from your neighborhood to a location within walking distance of your school. The express bus arrives at your neighborhood between 7:30 and 7:36. The local bus arrives at your neighborhood between 7:30 and 7:40. You arrive at the bus stop at 7:33. Find the probability that you have missed both the express bus and the local bus.

ANOTHER WAY
For alternative methods for solving the problem in Example 3, turn to page 868 for the **Problem Solving Workshop**.

Solution

The events are independent. The arrival of one bus does not affect the arrival of the other bus.

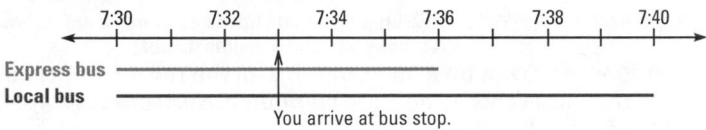

There are 6 minutes when the express bus can arrive. You are not at the bus stop for 3 of those minutes.

$P(\text{you miss express bus}) = \frac{3}{6} = \frac{1}{2}$

There are 10 minutes when the local bus can arrive. You are not at the bus stop for 3 of those minutes.

$P(\text{you miss local bus}) = \frac{3}{10}$

Multiply the probabilities of the two events:

$P(\text{you miss both buses}) = \frac{1}{2} \cdot \frac{3}{10} = \frac{3}{20}$

▶ The probability that you miss the express bus and the local bus is $\frac{3}{20}$.

EXAMPLE 4 Find the probability of *A* and *B*

PEN COLORS A box contains 3 blue pens and 5 black pens. You choose one pen at random, do not replace it, then choose a second pen at random. What is the probability that both pens are blue?

Solution

Because you do not replace the first pen, the events are dependent. Before you choose a pen, there are 8 pens, and 3 of them are blue. After you choose a blue pen, there are 7 pens left and 2 of them are blue.

$P(\text{blue and then blue}) = P(\text{blue}) \cdot P(\text{blue given blue})$

$= \frac{3}{8} \cdot \frac{2}{7} = \frac{6}{56} = \frac{3}{28}$

 GUIDED PRACTICE for Examples 3 and 4

3. **MARBLES** A bag contains 4 red, 5 green, and 2 blue marbles. You randomly draw 2 marbles, one at a time. Find the probabililty that both are red if:
   a. you replace the first marble. $\frac{16}{121}$ **b.** you do not replace the first marble. $\frac{6}{55}$

13.4 Find Probabilities of Compound Events **863**

Extra Example 3
An acceptable two-digit code, made from the digits 1 through 9, consists of an even number followed by an odd number. You choose two numbers at random. Find the probability that you have chosen an acceptable code. $\frac{20}{81}$

Extra Example 4
A bag contains 4 blue marbles and 8 yellow marbles. You choose one marble at random, do not replace it, and then choose a second marble at random. What is the probability that both marbles are blue? $\frac{1}{11}$

Closing the Lesson
Have students summarize the major points of the lesson and answer the Essential Question: How do you find the probability of compound events?

- A compound event combines two or more events using the word *and* or the word *or*.
- Mutually exclusive events have no common outcomes, while overlapping events have at least one common outcome.
- Independent events are ones in which the occurrence of one event has no effect on the occurrence of the other. Two events are dependent if the occurrence of one event affects the occurrence of the other.

To find the probability that event A *or* event B occurs, determine if the events are mutually exclusive or overlapping. If mutually exclusive, add the probabilities. If overlapping, add the probabilities and subtract the probability of the overlapping event. To find the probability of events A *and* B occurring, multiply the probabilities of the events.

HOMEWORK
KEY

○ = **WORKED-OUT SOLUTIONS**
on p. WS1 for Exs. 5 and 23

★ = **STANDARDIZED TEST PRACTICE**
Exs. 2, 8, 13, 20, and 24

◆ = **MULTIPLE REPRESENTATIONS**
Ex. 25

4 PRACTICE AND APPLY

Assignment Guide

📖 Answer Transparencies
available for all exercises

Basic:
Day 1: SRH p. 915 Exs. 1, 2, 6, 7
pp. 864–867
Exs. 1–8, 30–34
Day 2: pp. 864–867
Exs. 9–17, 22–25, 28, 29

Average:
Day 1: pp. 864–867
Exs. 1, 2, 5–8, 18, 19, 30–34
Day 2: pp. 864–867
Exs. 11–17, 20, 22–26, 28, 29

Advanced:
Day 1: pp. 864–867
Exs. 1, 2, 6–8, 18, 19, 21*, 30–34
Day 2: pp. 864–867
Exs. 11–17, 20, 22–29*

Block:
pp. 864–867
Exs. 1, 2, 5–8, 11–20, 22–26, 28–34

Differentiated Instruction

See *Algebra 1 Best Practices Toolkit*
for suggestions on addressing the
needs of a diverse classroom.

Homework Check

For a quick check of student under-
standing of key concepts, go over
the following exercises:
Basic: 4, 8, 10, 22, 24
Average: 5, 11, 23, 24, 25
Advanced: 6, 12, 23, 24, 25

Extra Practice

• Student Edition, p. 950
• Chapter 13 Resource Book:
Practice levels A, B, C, pp. 39–41

Practice Worksheet

An easily-readable reduced
practice page (with answers)
for this lesson can be found
on p. 840C.

SKILL PRACTICE

A 1. **VOCABULARY** Copy and complete: The probability of __?__ events is found
using the formula $P(A \text{ and } B) = P(A) \cdot P(B \text{ given } A)$. **dependent**

2. ★ **WRITING** *Explain* how overlapping events differ from mutually
exclusive events. **Overlapping events have one or more outcomes in common,
mutually exclusive events do not.**

EXAMPLES 1 and 2
on pp. 861–862
for Exs. 3–8

PROBABILITY OF A OR B In Exercises 3–6, you roll a number cube. Tell
whether the events *A* and *B* are *mutually exclusive* or *overlapping*.
Then find $P(A \text{ or } B)$.

3. **Event A:** Roll a 6. **mutually exclusive,** $\frac{2}{3}$
   Event B: Roll a prime number.

4. **Event A:** Roll an even number.
   Event B: Roll a 5. **mutually exclusive;** $\frac{2}{3}$

5. **Event A:** Roll an odd number.
   Event B: Roll a number less than 5. $\frac{5}{6}$
   overlapping;

6. **Event A:** Roll a multiple of 3.
   Event B: Roll an even number. **overlapping;** $\frac{2}{3}$

7. To find the
probability
that you draw
a yellow *or* a
blue marble,
the individual
probabilities
should be added,
not multiplied;
$\frac{7}{16} + \frac{5}{16} = \frac{12}{16} = \frac{3}{4}$.

7. **ERROR ANALYSIS** A bag contains
7 yellow marbles, 4 red marbles, and
5 blue marbles. *Describe* and correct the
error in finding the probability that you
randomly draw a yellow or blue marble.
See margin.

$$P(\text{yellow or blue}) = P(\text{yellow}) \cdot P(\text{blue})$$
$$= \frac{7}{16} \cdot \frac{5}{16} = \frac{35}{256}$$

8. ★ **MULTIPLE CHOICE** A bag contains tiles with the numbers 1–10 on them.
You randomly choose a tile from the bag. What is the probability that you
choose an even number or a number less than 5? **A**

Ⓐ 0.7 Ⓑ 0.8 Ⓒ 0.9 Ⓓ 1

EXAMPLES 3 and 4
on p. 863
for Exs. 9–12

PROBABILITY OF A AND B In Exercises 9–12, tell whether the events
A and *B* are *dependent* or *independent*. Then find $P(A \text{ and } B)$.

9. You roll two number cubes.
   Event A: You roll a 2 first.
   Event B: You roll a 5 second. **independent;** $\frac{1}{36}$

10. You write each of the letters of the word BIOLOGY on pieces of paper and
place them in a bag. You randomly draw one letter, do not replace it, then
randomly draw a second letter.
Event A: The first letter is O.
Event B: The second letter is B. **dependent;** $\frac{1}{21}$

11. You flip a coin and roll a number cube.
Event A: The coin shows heads.
Event B: The number cube shows 2. **independent;** $\frac{1}{12}$

12. A box contains 3 milk chocolates, 3 white chocolates, and 4 dark
chocolates. You choose a chocolate at random, eat it, then choose a
second chocolate at random.
Event A: You choose a dark chocolate.
Event B: You choose a dark chocolate. **dependent;** $\frac{2}{15}$

864 Chapter 13 Probability and Data Analysis

13. ★ **MULTIPLE CHOICE** A vase holds 7 red roses and 5 pink roses. You randomly choose a rose, place it in a different vase, then randomly choose another rose. What is the approximate probability that both the first and second roses are red? **B**

    (A) 0.29   **(B)** 0.32   **(C)** 0.34   **(D)** 0.37

B **CHESS PIECES** In Exercises 14–17, consider a bag that contains all of the chess pieces in a set, as shown in the diagram.

	King	Queen	Bishop	Rook	Knight	Pawn
Black	1	1	2	2	2	8
White	1	1	2	2	2	8

14. You choose one piece at random. Find the probability that you choose a black piece or a queen. $\frac{17}{32}$

15. You choose one piece at random, replace it, then choose a second piece at random. Find the probability that you choose a rook, then a bishop. $\frac{1}{64}$

16. You choose one piece at random, do not replace it, then choose a second piece at random. Find the probability that you choose a king, then a pawn. $\frac{1}{31}$

17. **ERROR ANALYSIS** *Describe* and correct the error in finding the probability that you randomly choose a pawn and a second pawn, without replacement.

$$P(\text{pawn and pawn}) = P(\text{pawn}) \cdot P(\text{pawn})$$
$$= \frac{16}{32} \cdot \frac{16}{32} = \frac{1}{4}$$

In Exercises 18 and 19, use the following information. Two mutually exclusive events for which one or the other must occur are called *complementary* events. If events A and B are complementary events, then $P(A) + P(B) = 1$.

18. **WEATHER** A local meteorologist reports that there is a 70% chance of rain tomorrow. What is the probability that it will *not* rain tomorrow? **30%**

19. **BASKETBALL** You make 31% of your attempted 3-point shots. What is the probability that you miss your next attempted 3-point shot? **69%**

20. ★ **WRITING** You write the letters of the word WISDOM on pieces of paper and place them in a bag. You randomly choose 2 letters from the bag at the same time. *Explain* whether these events are independent or dependent. What is the probability that you choose the letters S and D?

C **21.** **CHALLENGE** The sections of the spinner shown all have the same area. You spin the spinner.

    a. Find the probability that the spinner stops on red *or* a prime number *or* a multiple of 3. You may want to draw a Venn diagram to find the answer. $\frac{7}{8}$

    b. Write a general formula for $P(A$ or B or $C)$ where A, B, and C are overlapping events. *Explain* your reasoning. **See margin.**

### Sidebar notes (left margin)

17. If you first draw a pawn and then do not replace it, the probability of drawing a second pawn is not $\frac{16}{32}$, but $\frac{15}{31}$, $\frac{16}{32} \cdot \frac{15}{31} = \frac{15}{62}$.

20. Dependent. *Sample answer*: Even though two pieces of paper are selected at the same time, the selection of one piece of paper affects the selection of the other, so the events are dependent; $\frac{1}{15}$.

### Sidebar notes (right margin)

Avoiding Common Errors

Exercises 3–12 Some students may add probabilities when finding $P(A$ *and* $B)$ and multiply probabilities when finding $P(A$ *or* $B)$. Remind these students that they add when the conjunction is *or* and multiply when the conjunction is *and*.

Study Strategy

Exercises 3–8, 9–16 Suggest that students ask themselves key questions when trying to determine whether events are mutually exclusive or overlapping or whether the events are dependent or independent. For example, when finding $P(A$ *or* $B)$, students could ask: *If I choose A, could I also be choosing B?* When finding $P(A$ *and* $B)$, students can ask: *After I find the probability of A, do I then want to find the probability of B or the probability of B given A?*

21b. $P(A) + P(B) + P(C) - P(A$ *and* $B) - P(A$ *and* $C) - P(B$ *and* $C) + P(A$ *and* B *and* $C)$; when $P(A) + P(B) + P(C)$ is added, the overlap of each set is counted twice so it must be subtracted. When you subtract the overlap of each set the overlap of all three sets gets subtracted 3 times, so it must be added one time.

PROBLEM SOLVING

EXAMPLES
3 and 4
on p. 863
for Exs. 22–23

22. CONTEST You can win concert tickets from a radio station if you are the first person to call when the song of the day is played, or if you are the first person to correctly answer the trivia question. The song of the day is played between 5:00 and 5:30 P.M. The trivia question is asked between 5:15 and 5:45 P.M. You begin listening to the radio station at 5:20. Find the probability that you miss the song of the day and the trivia question. $\frac{1}{9}$

@HomeTutor for problem solving help at classzone.com

23. WALRUS When a walrus forages for food, it waves its flipper to move sediment 70% of the time. When using the flipper wave technique, a walrus uses its right flipper 89% of the time. Find the probability that a walrus foraging for food uses a flipper and it is the right flipper. **62.3%**

@HomeTutor for problem solving help at classzone.com

EXAMPLES
1, 2, 3, and 4
on pp. 861–863
for Ex. 24

24. ★ SHORT RESPONSE A survey of 887,403 households found that 270,658 households have a dog, 326,591 have a cat, and 81,641 have both.

a. What is the probability that one of the households surveyed, chosen at random, has a dog and a cat? **about 0.092**

b. What is the probability that one of the households surveyed, chosen at random, has a dog or a cat? **0.58**

c. *Explain* how your answers to parts (a) and (b) are related. **See margin.**

EXAMPLES B
1 and 2
on pp. 861–862
for Ex. 25

25. ◆ MULTIPLE REPRESENTATIONS You have student government meetings on Monday and Wednesday. You tutor in the morning on Monday, Thursday, Friday, and Saturday.

a. **Making a Table** Make a table that shows your schedule for the week. **See margin.**

b. **Drawing a Diagram** Make a Venn diagram that shows the days of the week that you participate in each activity. **See margin.**

c. **Using a Formula** Your class is taking a field trip that could be scheduled for any day of the week. Find the probability that it is scheduled for a day when you tutor or have a student government meeting. $\frac{5}{7}$

26. EARTH SCIENCE The table shows the ranges of annual mean temperature and precipitation for 57 cities in the U.S. Find the probability that a city in this study has an annual mean temperature in the range 39°F–52°F or an annual precipitation in the range 0–24 inches. $\frac{35}{57}$

Precipitation (inches)	Temperature (degrees Fahrenheit)	
	39–52	53–66
0–24	7	7
25–49	21	22

○ = **WORKED-OUT SOLUTIONS** on p. WS1   ★ = **STANDARDIZED TEST PRACTICE**   ◆ = **MULTIPLE REPRESENTATIONS**

25a.

	Mon	Tues	Wed	Thurs	Fri	Sat	Sun
	st. gov.		st. gov.				
	tutor			tutor	tutor	tutor	

C 27. **CHALLENGE** You have 5 tickets to a play. You invite 4 friends to see the play. You hand out the tickets at random. One ticket is for an aisle seat, and the other tickets are for the next 4 seats in the row.

   a. What is the probability that you will get the aisle seat? $\frac{1}{5}$

   b. What is the probability that you will get the aisle seat and your best friend will get the ticket for the seat next to you? $\frac{1}{20}$

   c. *Explain* how you could solve the problem in part (b) using permutations. **See margin.**

MIXED REVIEW

PREVIEW
Prepare for Lesson 13.5 in Exs. 28–29.

In Exercises 28 and 29, the spinner shown has sections with equal area. *(p. 843)*

28. You flip a coin and spin the spinner. How many possible outcomes are in the sample space? List the possible outcomes.
16 outcomes; H1, H2, H3, H4, H5, H6, H7, H8, T1, T2, T3, T4, T5, T6, T7, T8

29. You roll a number cube and spin the spinner. How many possible outcomes are in the sample space? List the possible outcomes.
See margin.

Evaluate the expression.

30. $_5P_3$ *(p. 851)* **60**   31. $_{15}P_0$ *(p. 851)* **1**   32. $_{15}C_0$ *(p. 856)* **1**   33. $_5C_3$ *(p. 856)* **10**

34. **ELECTIVES** Your school offers 10 elective courses each semester. You have time in your schedule for 2 of these courses. How many combinations of 2 elective courses can you choose? *(p. 856)* **45 combinations**

QUIZ *for Lessons 13.1–13.4*

1. **MARBLES** A bag contains 16 red marbles and 8 white marbles. You select a marble at random. *(p. 843)*

   a. What is the probability that you select a red marble? $\frac{2}{3}$

   b. What are the odds in favor of selecting a red marble? **2 : 1**

2. **PASSWORD** The password for an e-mail account is the word FISH followed by a 3-digit number. The 3-digit number contains the digits 1, 2, and 3. How many different passwords are possible? *(p. 851)* **6**

3. **SHUFFLE** A CD plays on random shuffle. The CD has 12 songs on it. Your CD player selects a song at random, plays it, then selects a second song at random. No song is repeated until every song has been played. What is the probability that song 3 is played first and song 1 is played second? *(p. 851)* $\frac{1}{132}$

8. $\frac{8}{15}$,
overlapping.
Sample answer:
The events are overlapping because numbers like 3 and 11 are both odd and prime.

Evaluate the expression.

4. $_5P_4$ *(p. 851)* **120**   5. $_8P_5$ *(p. 851)* **6720**   6. $_5C_2$ *(p. 856)* **10**   7. $_8C_5$ *(p. 856)* **56**

8. **NUMBER TILES** Tiles numbered 1–30 are placed in a bag. You select a tile at random. Find the probability that you select an odd number or a prime number. Are the events mutually exclusive or overlapping? *Explain.* *(p. 861)*

---

29. 48 outcomes; 1-1, 1-2, 1-3, 1-4, 1-5, 1-6, 1-7, 1-8, 2-1, 2-2, 2-3, 2-4, 2-5, 2-6, 2-7, 2-8, 3-1, 3-2, 3-3, 3-4, 3-5, 3-6, 3-7, 3-8, 4-1, 4-2, 4-3, 4-4, 4-5, 4-6, 4-7, 4-8, 5-1, 5-2, 5-3, 5-4, 5-5, 5-6, 5-7, 5-8, 6-1, 6-2, 6-3, 6-4, 6-5, 6-6, 6-7, 6-8

---

⑤ ASSESS AND RETEACH

Daily Homework Quiz
Transparency Available

1. A bag contains 4 yellow marbles, 3 blue marbles, and 5 red marbles. You randomly draw a marble, replace it, and draw another marble. What is the probability that you draw a red marble and a yellow marble? $\frac{5}{36}$

2. A survey of 100 students at your school found that 58 students ride the bus, 22 drive to school, 14 walk, and 6 get a ride from a relative. If one of the students surveyed is chosen at random, what is the probability the student either drives to school or walks? $\frac{9}{25}$

Online Quiz

Available at **classzone.com**

Diagnosis/Remediation
- Practice A, B, C in Chapter 13 Resource Book, pp. 39–41
- Study Guide in Chapter13 Resource Book, pp. 42–43
- Practice Workbook, pp. 202–204
- @HomeTutor

Challenge
Additional challenge is available in the Chapter 13 Resource Book, p. 47.

Quiz
An easily-readable reduced copy of the quiz (with answers) on Lessons 13.1–13.4 from the Assessment Book can be found on p. 840F.

Using ALTERNATIVE METHODS

Alternative Strategy

Example 3 on page 863 can be solved by performing a simulation or by using geometry. Point out to students that the simulation in Method 1 gives a probability close to Example 3 on page 863, but not the same as the example. Be sure students realize that different simulations will give different probabilities. Method 2 can help students visualize the relationship between possible and favorable outcomes.

Graphing Calculator

If students need help generating random numbers to perform a simulation, refer them to the directions for the simulations they performed in the extension on page 849.

Teaching Strategy

You may want students to compare their simulations to see how closely they approximate the probability calculated by using the formula in Example 3 in Lesson 13.4 and by using geometry in alternative method 2.

Another Way to Solve Example 3, page 863

MULTIPLE REPRESENTATIONS In Example 3 on page 863, you saw how to solve the problem about a bus schedule by using a number line and a formula. You can also solve the problem by performing a simulation or using geometry.

PROBLEM

> **BUS SCHEDULE** You take a city bus from your neighborhood to a location within walking distance of your school. The express bus arrives at your neighborhood between 7:30 and 7:36. The local bus arrives at your neighborhood between 7:30 and 7:40. You arrive at the bus stop at 7:33. Find the probability that you have missed both the express bus and the local bus.

METHOD 1 **Performing a Simulation** One alternative approach is to perform a simulation.

STEP 1 **Read** the problem. Notice that there is a 6 minute interval when the express bus could arrive and a 10 minute interval when the local bus could arrive. Let 1 represent the first minute, from 7:30 to 7:31, that a bus could arrive. Let 2 represent the second minute, from 7:31 to 7:32, that a bus could arrive. Continue to number the minutes when a bus could arrive.

STEP 2 **Generate** random integers. Use a graphing calculator to generate a random integer from 1 to 6. This number represents the minute that the express bus arrives. Then generate a random integer from 1 to 10. This number represents the minute that the local bus arrives. Perform this simulation 10 times.

You are not at the bus stop until the fourth minute, so if both numbers that you generate are less than 4, then you miss both buses.

First number	5	4	2	5	2	1	2	3	3	1
Second number	9	1	1	8	4	7	9	10	6	2
Miss both buses?	No	No	Yes	No	No	No	No	No	No	Yes

STEP 3 **Find** the experimental probability that you miss both buses.

$$P(\text{miss both buses}) = \frac{2}{10} = \frac{1}{5}$$

METHOD 2 **Using Geometry** Another approach is to use geometry. Use the formula for the area of a rectangle to find the number of possible outcomes and the number of favorable outcomes.

STEP 1 **Draw** a rectangle whose side lengths represent the number of minutes that each bus could arrive.

STEP 2 **Draw** a square within the rectangle to represent the number of minutes that you are *not* at the bus stop.

STEP 3 **Calculate** the area of the rectangle that represents the time a bus could arrive. Also calculate the area of the square that represents the time that you are *not* at the bus stop.

Time a bus could arrive: Time you are *not* at bus stop:
$A = 6 \cdot 10 = 60$ $A = 3 \cdot 3 = 9$

STEP 4 **Find** the probability that you miss both buses by forming the ratio of the areas from step 2.

$$P(\text{miss both buses}) = \frac{9}{60} = \frac{3}{20}$$

PRACTICE

1. **WHAT IF?** In the problem on page 868, suppose you arrive at 7:34. What is the probability that you miss both buses? $\frac{4}{15}$

2. **VISITING FRIENDS** Two friends are planning to visit you this evening. You expect one friend to arrive at your house between 7:00 and 7:30 P.M. You expect the other friend to arrive between 7:10 and 7:20 P.M. You have to run an errand from 7:00 until 7:15 P.M. What is the probability that you are home when both friends arrive? Solve this problem using two different methods. $\frac{1}{4}$

3. **WHAT IF?** In Exercise 2, suppose a third friend plans to visit you this evening. This friend plans to arrive at your house between 7:00 and 7:20 P.M. What is the probability that you are home when all three of your friends arrive? *Explain* how you found your answer.
See margin.

4. **RAFFLE** You enter two different raffles during your neighborhood's street fair. The winner of the first raffle will be announced between 6:00 and 6:30 P.M. The winner of the second raffle will be announced between 6:15 and 6:45 P.M. You leave the fair at 5:00 P.M. and return at 6:20 P.M. What is the probability that you hear the winner of each raffle announced? Solve this problem using two different methods. $\frac{5}{18}$

5. **ERROR ANALYSIS** A student solved the problem in Exercise 4 as shown. *Describe* and correct the error. **See margin.**

$$P(\text{hear both winners}) = \frac{\text{Favorable time}}{\text{Total time}}$$

$$= \frac{10 \text{ minutes}}{30 \text{ minutes}} = \frac{1}{3}$$

Using Alternative Methods   **869**

3. $\frac{1}{16}$. *Sample answer:* The third friend can arrive any time in a 20 minute span, and I will be away from the house for 15 of those minutes. The probability is $\frac{1}{4}$ that I will be home when the third friend arrives. Since the three friends arrive independently of each other, you can multiply the probability that you are home when the other two friends arrive by $\frac{1}{4}$ to calculate the probability that you are home when all three friends arrive; $\frac{1}{4} \cdot \frac{1}{4} = \frac{1}{16}$.

5. *Sample answer:* The times at which each raffle is announced is independent, so the two probabilities should be calculated separately and then multiplied; $\frac{10}{30} \cdot \frac{25}{30} = \frac{1}{3} \cdot \frac{5}{6} = \frac{5}{18}$.

Lessons 13.1–13.4

1. MULTI-STEP PROBLEM There are 5743 known amphibian species in the world. Of these, 1856 species are judged to be at risk of extinction, and another 113 species may already be extinct.

The Puerto Rican crested toad is at risk of extinction.

a. Find the probability that an amphibian species chosen at random is at risk of extinction or may already be extinct. **about 0.343**

b. Find the probability that two different amphibian species, each chosen at random, are at risk of extinction. **about 0.104**

2. MULTI-STEP PROBLEM You are ordering an omelet with two ingredients. You can choose from the following list: cheese, mushrooms, onions, tomatoes, peppers, sausage, ham, and steak.

a. Make an organized list of all the possible omelets that you can order. **See margin.**

b. Use a permutation or combination formula to find the number of possible omelets. **28 omelets**

3. MULTI-STEP PROBLEM In NCAA women's basketball tournaments from 1982 to 2003, teams seeded, or ranked, number one have won 283 games and lost 71 games in the tournament. Suppose a team is chosen at random from all those that have been seeded number one.

a. What is the probability that the team won a game in the tournament? $\frac{283}{354}$

b. What are the odds in favor of the team's having won a game in the tournament? **283 : 71**

4. SHORT RESPONSE A meteorologist reports that there is a 15% chance of snow tomorrow. What are the odds in favor of snow tomorrow? *Explain* how you found your answer. **See margin.**

5. OPEN-ENDED *Describe* a real-world situation in which the number of possible arrangements is given by $_{10}P_2$. **See margin.**

6. SHORT RESPONSE In the United States there are 21 states (not including Washington, D.C.) with teams in the National Football League and 17 states with Major League Baseball teams. There are 15 states that have both types of teams. Suppose a state is chosen at random.

a. Find the probability that the state has either a National Football League team or a Major League Baseball team. $\frac{23}{50}$

b. There are 21 states that have a team in the National Basketball Association. What additional information would you need in order to find the probability that the state chosen at random has either a team in the National Basketball Association or a Major League Baseball team? *Explain* your reasoning. **See margin.**

7. EXTENDED RESPONSE A survey asked a total of 400 students, 100 male students and 100 female students who were 13 and 15 years old, about their eating habits. The table shows the numbers of students who said that they eat fruit every day.

	13 years old	15 years old
Male	60	53
Female	61	58

a. Find the probability that a female student, chosen at random from the students surveyed, eats fruit every day. **0.595**

b. Find the probability that a 15-year-old student, chosen at random from the students surveyed, eats fruit every day. **0.555**

c. You select a student at random from the students surveyed. Find the odds against the student's eating fruit every day. *Explain* your reasoning. **See margin.**

8. GRIDDED ANSWER A music club gives you 6 free CDs for joining. You would like to own 11 of the free CDs that are offered. How many combinations of 6 CDs from the 11 CDs can you choose? **462 combinations**

2a. cheese, mushrooms; cheese, onions; cheese, tomatoes; cheese, peppers; cheese, sausage; cheese, ham; cheese, steak; mushrooms, onions; mushrooms, tomatoes; mushrooms, peppers; mushrooms, sausage; mushrooms, ham; mushrooms, steak; onions, tomatoes; onions, peppers; onions, sausage; onions, ham; onions, steak; tomatoes, peppers; tomatoes, sausage; tomatoes, ham; tomatoes, steak; peppers, sausage; peppers, ham; peppers, steak; sausage, ham; sausage, steak; ham, steak

4. 3:17. *Sample answer:* 15% is equivalent to $\frac{3}{20}$. There is a $\frac{17}{20}$ chance that it will not snow. So, the odds in favor of snow are $\frac{3}{20} : \frac{17}{20} = 3:17$.

5. *Sample answer:* A club of 10 students is choosing a president and vice-president. How many choices could the club make?

6b. How many states have a team in both the National Basketball Association and in Major League Baseball. *Sample answer:* The probability that the state has a team in the National Basketball Association or a Major League Baseball team is the sum of the probability that the state has a team in the National Basketball Association and the probability that the state has a Major League Baseball team minus the probability that the state has a team in both the National Basketball Association and in Major League Baseball.

7c. 21:29. *Sample answer:* The total number of students from the survey who eat fruit every day is 232. The total number of students surveyed is 400, so 168 students surveyed do not eat fruit every day. Therefore, the odds against a random student from the survey eating fruit is 168:232, or 21:29.

13.5 Analyze Surveys and Samples

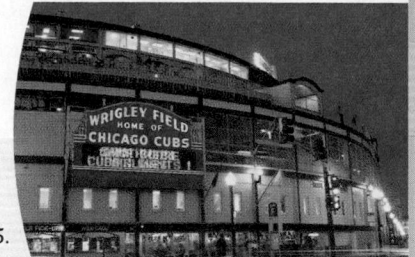

Before	You found experimental probabilities.
Now	You will identify populations and sampling methods.
Why?	So you can analyze surveys of sports fans, as in Ex. 15.

Key Vocabulary
• survey
• population
• sample
• biased sample
• biased question

A **survey** is a study of one or more characteristics of a group. The entire group you want information about is called a **population**. You may find it difficult to survey an entire population. Instead, you can survey a **sample**, which is a part of the population. Five types of samples are listed below.

KEY CONCEPT   *For Your Notebook*

Sampling Methods

In a **random sample**, every member of the population has an equal chance of being selected.

In a **stratified random sample**, the population is divided into distinct groups. Members are selected at random from each group.

In a **systematic sample**, a rule is used to select members of the population.

In a **convenience sample**, only members of the population who are easily accessible are selected.

In a **self-selected sample**, members of the population select themselves by volunteering.

EXAMPLE 1 **Classify a sampling method**

EMPLOYEE SAFETY The owners of a company with several factories conduct a survey to determine whether employees are informed about safety regulations. At each factory, 50 employees are chosen at random to complete the survey. Identify the population and classify the sampling method.

Solution

The population is all company employees. Because the population is divided into distinct groups (individual factories), with employees chosen at random from each group, the sample is a stratified random sample.

 GUIDED PRACTICE for Example 1

1. **WHAT IF?** In Example 1, suppose the owners survey each employee whose last name begins with M. Classify the sampling method. **systematic**

Resource Planning Guide

Chapter Resource Book
• Teaching Guide/Lesson Plan (pp. 48–49)
• Practice levels A, B, C (pp. 50–52)
• Study Guide (pp. 53–54)
• Catch-up for Absent Students (p. 55)
• Application (p. 56)
• Challenge (p. 57)

Workbooks
• Notetaking Guide (pp. 308–310)
• Practice Workbook (pp. 204–205)

Teaching Options
• **Power Presentations CD-ROM** provides dynamic electronic teaching resources for the classroom.
• **Activity Generator CD-ROM** provides editable activities for all ability levels.

Interactive Technology
• Easy Planner
• Power Presentations CD-ROM
• Activity Generator CD-ROM
• Animated Algebra
• Test Generator CD-ROM
• Online Quiz
• eWorkbook
• eEdition
• @HomeTutor

Resources for English Learners
• Quick Reference for English Learners
• Spanish Study Guide
• Multi-Language Visual Glossary
• Student Resources in Spanish

See also the *Algebra 1 Toolkit* for more strategies for meeting individual needs.

① PLAN AND PREPARE

Warm-Up Exercises
⎙ **Transparency Available**
A spinner has 5 sections of equal area, with sections numbered 1–5.
1. You toss a coin and spin the spinner. How many outcomes are in the sample space? **10**
2. You spin the spinner twice. How many outcomes are in the sample space? **25**

Notetaking Guide
⎙ **Transparency Available**
Promotes interactive learning and notetaking skills, pp. 308–310.

Pacing
Basic: 1 day
Average: 1 day
Advanced: 1 day
Block: 0.5 block with 13.6
• See *Teaching Guide/Lesson Plan.*

② FOCUS AND MOTIVATE

Essential Question
Big Idea 2, p. 841
How do you identify populations and sampling methods? **Tell students they will learn how to answer this question by analyzing surveys and samples.**

NCTM STANDARDS
Standard 5: Devise questions that can be addressed with data
Standard 8: Communicate thinking clearly to others

Motivating the Lesson

You want to know how many students participate in Internet chat rooms. By learning how to identify populations and sampling methods, you can design an unbiased survey.

③ TEACH

Extra Example 1

Owners of a computer store survey customers to see whether they should expand their game selection. They survey customers in the game aisle. Identify the population and classify the sampling method. **Population: store customers; Method: convenience sampling**

Extra Example 2

In Extra Example 1, suppose owners randomly survey all customers at the store on a Saturday. Is the method likely to result in a biased sample? **Saturday customers may reflect different buying attitudes than weekday customers, so the method may result in a biased sample.**

Extra Example 3

Tell whether the question is potentially biased. Explain your answer. *Do you think the city should renovate the library?* **It does not encourage a particular response, so the question is not biased.**

Closing the Lesson

Have students summarize the major points of the lesson and answer the Essential Question: How do you identify populations and sampling methods?

• **A population is the entire group you want information about.**

Identify populations by looking for all members of a group affected by a survey. Identify sampling methods by deciding if they represent the selected population.

BIASED SAMPLES A sample chosen for a survey should be representative of the population. A **biased sample** is a sample that is not representative. In a biased sample, parts of the population may be over-represented or under-represented.

Random samples and stratified random samples (as in Example 1) are the most likely types of samples to be representative. A systematic sample may be representative if the rule used to choose individuals is not biased.

EXAMPLE 2 Identify a potentially biased sample

In Example 1, suppose the owners question 50 workers chosen at random from one factory. Is the method likely to result in a biased sample?

Solution

Workers at other factories may hold significantly different opinions, so the method may result in a biased sample.

BIASED QUESTIONS A question that encourages a particular response is a **biased question**. Survey questions should be worded to avoid bias.

EXAMPLE 3 Identify potentially biased questions

Tell whether the question is potentially biased. Explain your answer. If the question is potentially biased, rewrite it so that it is not.

a. Don't you agree that the voting age should be lowered to 16 because many 16-year-olds are responsible and informed?

b. Do you think the city should risk an increase in pollution by allowing expansion of the Northern Industrial Park?

Solution

a. This question is biased because it suggests that lowering the voting age is a good thing to do. An unbiased question is "Do you think the voting age should be lowered to 16?"

b. This question is biased because it suggests that the proposed expansion will be bad for the environment. An unbiased question is "Do you think the city should allow expansion of the Northern Industrial Park?"

✓ **GUIDED PRACTICE** for Examples 2 and 3

2. **SOCCER** In a survey about Americans' interest in soccer, the first 25 people admitted to a high school soccer game were asked, "How interested are you in the world's most popular sport, soccer?"
   a, b. See margin.
   a. Is the sampling method likely to result in a biased sample? *Explain*.

   b. Is the question potentially biased? *Explain* your answer. If the question is potentially biased, rewrite it so that it is not.

872 Chapter 13 Probability and Data Analysis

Differentiated Instruction

English Learners Students should be aware that there can be more than one way to rewrite a biased question as an unbiased one. In **Example 3b**, the basic question is biased because it asks if you agree to increasing pollution. An equally valid, unbiased question, would be "Do you think the city will have an increase in pollution by allowing the expansion of the Northern Industrial Park?"
See also the *Algebra 1 Toolkit* for more strategies.

13.5 EXERCISES

HOMEWORK KEY
○ = WORKED-OUT SOLUTIONS
on p. WS1 for Exs. 3 and 15
★ = STANDARDIZED TEST PRACTICE
Exs. 2, 6, and 17

SKILL PRACTICE

[A]

1. **VOCABULARY** Copy and complete: In a(n) __?__ sample, participants are chosen using a rule. **systematic**

2. ★ **WRITING** *Explain* how a sample is related to a population.
A sample is a portion of a population.

POPULATIONS AND SAMPLES In Exercises 3–5, identify the population and classify the sampling method.

EXAMPLE 1
on p. 871
for Exs. 3–6

3. **RESTAURANT SERVICE** A restaurant manager wants to evaluate the restaurant's quality of service. Diners are given mail-in comment cards.
people who have eaten at the restaurant, self-selected

4. **EXTRACURRICULAR ACTIVITIES** Your school wants to know if students are satisfied with the school's extracurricular activities. In each grade, every tenth student on an alphabetized list is surveyed.
students at your school, systematic

5. **CUSTOMER SATISFACTION** An airline wants to gather information on passenger satisfaction during a flight. A computer randomly selects 30 passengers to complete a survey. **passengers of the airline, random**

6. ★ **MULTIPLE CHOICE** Scientists wanted to gather information about the birds in a particular region. They chose observation sites and asked bird watchers at those sites to record the number and types of birds they saw in 3 minutes. What population was being studied? **A**

   (A) Birds   (B) Sites   (C) Scientists   (D) Bird watchers

EXAMPLE 2
on p. 872
for Exs. 7–8

BIASED SAMPLES Tell whether the sampling method used is likely to result in a biased sample. *Explain*.

7. **NEIGHBORHOOD WATCH** A family wants to gather information from other residents on their street about forming a neighborhood watch. They survey every third house on both sides of the street. **Not likely. *Sample answer:* The sample should represent the neighborhood.**

8. **NURSE SURVEY** The American Nurses Association wanted to gather information about the working environment for nurses in hospitals. A survey for nurses was posted on the association's website. **See margin.**

EXAMPLE 3 [B]
on p. 872
for Exs. 9–11

BIASED QUESTIONS In Exercises 9 and 10, tell whether the question is potentially biased. *Explain* your answer. **9, 10. See margin.**

9. Do you support the incumbent's tax plan or the challenger's tax plan?

10. Do you prefer the ease of shopping online or the fun of going to a mall?

12. Sample answer: Both manufacturers can make this claim if they used biased survey questions, techniques, or samples.

11. **ERROR ANALYSIS** *Describe* and correct the error in revising the survey question "Don't you think the minimum driving age should be lower?" so that it is not biased. **See margin.**

> Not biased:
> Is the minimum driving age too high or too low? ✗

[C]

12. **CHALLENGE** Two toothpaste manufacturers each claim that 4 out of every 5 dentists use their brand exclusively. Both manufacturers can support their claims with survey results. *Explain* how this is possible.

13.5 Analyze Surveys and Samples   **873**

---

p. 872
2a–b. See Additional Answers beginning on p. AA1.

p. 873
8. **Likely.** *Sample answer:* Since it is a self-selected sample, only the nurses with extreme views are likely to take the time to respond, and the results of the survey will be swayed toward either extreme negative or positive views.

9. **Not potentially biased.** *Sample answer:* This question simply presents the two choices.

---

4 PRACTICE AND APPLY

Assignment Guide

📄 Answer Transparencies available for all exercises

Basic:
Day 1: pp. 873–874
Exs. 1–10, 13–16, 19–27

Average:
Day 1: pp. 873–874
Exs. 1, 2, 4–11, 13–17, 19–27

Advanced:
Day 1: pp. 873–874
Exs. 1, 2, 5–27*

Block:
pp. 873–874
Exs. 1, 2, 4–11, 13–17, 19–27
(with 13.6)

Differentiated Instruction

See *Algebra 1 Best Practices Toolkit* for suggestions on addressing the needs of a diverse classroom.

Homework Check

For a quick check of student understanding of key concepts, go over the following exercises:

Basic: 4, 7, 9, 13, 14
Average: 5, 8, 10, 14, 15
Advanced: 6, 8, 11, 15, 16

Extra Practice

• Student Edition, p. 950
• Chapter 13 Resource Book:
  Practice levels A, B, C, pp. 50–52

Practice Worksheet

An easily-readable reduced practice page (with answers) for this lesson can be found on p. 840C.

10. **Potentially biased.** *Sample answer:* Even though it presents both choices in a favorable light, the question is not neutral and is likely to affect the survey's results.

11. *Sample answer:* The new question presumes that the driving age should be changed, and does not present the option that it should remain the same; "What do you think about the current driving age?"

ASSESS AND RETEACH
5

Daily Homework Quiz

 Transparency Available

Identify the population and classify the sampling method.

1. You want to know if students would like year-round schools. You survey every fifth student entering first period classes. **Population: all students at a school; systematic sample**

2. A theater owner asks people in line to see a horror movie if they think the theater should show more comedies. Explain whether the survey method is likely to result in a biased survey. **People who go to horror movies may prefer horror to comedy, so the survey may be biased.**

Online Quiz

Available at **classzone.com**

Diagnosis/Remediation

- Practice A, B, C in Chapter 13 Resource Book, pp. 50–52
- Study Guide in Chapter13 Resource Book, pp. 53–54
- Practice Workbook, pp. 204–205
- @HomeTutor

Challenge

Additional challenge is available in the Chapter 13 Resource Book, p. 57.

13. *Sample answer:* This question is phrased to prompt people into agreeing that the athletic field is more important than the science lab; "Which do you think the school needs more: a new athletic field or a new science lab?"

14. *Sample answer:* This question suggests that prices are already too high, and is likely to make respondents more likely to say no; "Would you pay higher concert ticket prices to finance a new arena?"

16, 17b, 18. See Additional Answers beginning on p. AA1.

EXAMPLES [A]
2 and 3
on p. 872
for Exs. 13–16

In Exercises 13 and 14, explain why the question is biased. Then rewrite it so that it is not. 13, 14. See margin.

13. Don't you agree that the school needs a new athletic field more than a new science lab?

@HomeTutor for problem solving help at classzone.com

14. Would you pay even higher concert ticket prices to finance a new arena?

@HomeTutor for problem solving help at classzone.com

15. No. *Sample answer:* Only some of the fans are able to attend games, and those who attend games may have different player preferences than thos who do not attend games.

(15.) **BASEBALL** Every Major League Baseball (MLB) season, players are chosen to represent the two leagues in an All-Star game. At each MLB park, fans are given ballots to vote for their favorite players. Are the ballots collected at the Chicago Cubs' park, Wrigley Field, necessarily representative of the opinions of all Chicago Cubs fans? *Explain.*

16. **WATER SAMPLING** Scientists designed a project in which students performed tests on local water sources each day. Students from 18 countries participated in the project. The results of the survey were used to assess the quality of the world's fresh water. Is the sample likely to be biased? *Explain.* **See margin.**

17a. *Sample answer:* Obtain a list of everyone at the school and select names randomly using a random number generator.

[B]
17. ★ **SHORT RESPONSE** You plan to report on the academic performance of students in your school for your school newspaper.

a. *Describe* how you could choose a representative sample.

b. Write an unbiased question you could use to collect information on how many hours per night a student studies. *Explain* why your question is unbiased. **See margin.**

[C]
18. **CHALLENGE** A systematic sample of a population is used for a survey containing unbiased questions. *Explain* how it is possible for the survey to be biased. *Describe* a situation in which this might occur. **See margin.**

MIXED REVIEW

PREVIEW
Prepare for Lesson 13.6 in Exs. 19–23.

Order the numbers from least to greatest. *(p. 909)*

19. 0.02, 0.015, 0.021, 0.012
0.012, 0.015, 0.02, 0.021

20. 6.51, 6.15, 6.02, 6.23
6.02, 6.15, 6.23, 6.51

21. 12.3, 11.9, 11.09, 12.08
11.09, 11.9, 12.08, 12.3

Find the mean, median, and mode(s) of the data. *(p. 918)*

22. Cost (in dollars) of computer monitors: 296, 215, 426, 390, 351, 215, 289
about $311.71, $296, $215

23. Size (in megabytes) of files to be downloaded: 10.9, 12.1, 6.4, 2.8, 5.1, 7.6
about 7.483 MB, 7 MB, no mode

Evaluate the expression.

24. $_5P_3$ *(p. 851)* **60**

25. $_{10}P_4$ *(p. 851)* **5040**

26. $_8C_4$ *(p. 856)* **70**

27. $_7C_2$ *(p. 856)* **21**

EXTRA PRACTICE for Lesson 13.5, p. 950   **ONLINE QUIZ** at classzone.com

13.6 Use Measures of Central Tendency and Dispersion

Before You analyzed surveys and samples.

Now You will compare measures of central tendency and dispersion.

Why? So you can analyze and compare data, as in Example 1.

Key Vocabulary
• measure of dispersion
• range
• mean absolute deviation

KEY CONCEPT
For Your Notebook

Measures of Central Tendency

The **mean**, or *average*, of a numerical data set is denoted by $\bar{x}$, which is read as "*x*-bar." For the data set $x_1, x_2, \ldots, x_n$, the mean is $\bar{x} = \dfrac{x_1 + x_2 + \ldots + x_n}{n}$.

The **median** of a numerical data set is the middle number when the values are written in numerical order. If the data set has an even number of values, the median is the mean of the two middle values.

The **mode** of a data set is the value that occurs most frequently. There may be one mode, no mode, or more than one mode.

EXAMPLE 1 Compare measures of central tendency

The heights (in feet) of 8 waterfalls in the state of Washington are listed below. Which measure of central tendency best represents the data?

1000, 1000, 1181, 1191, 1200, 1268, 1328, 2584

Solution

$\bar{x} = \dfrac{1000 + 1000 + 1181 + 1191 + 1200 + 1268 + 1328 + 2584}{8} = \dfrac{10{,}752}{8} = 1344$

The median is the mean of the two middle values, 1191 and 1200, or 1195.5.

The mode is 1000.

▶ The median best represents the data. The mode is significantly less than most of the data, and the mean is significantly greater than most of the data.

Animated Algebra at classzone.com

✓ **GUIDED PRACTICE** for Example 1

1. **WHAT IF?** In Example 1, suppose you eliminate the greatest data value, 2584. Which measure of central tendency best represents the remaining data? *Explain* your reasoning. *Sample answer:* **Median; the median, 1191, is close to the data points.**

---

① PLAN AND PREPARE

Warm-Up Exercises

📑 **Transparency Available**

1. Order from least to greatest:
   10.14, 11.2, 10.1, 10.08, 11.21
   10.08, 10.1, 10.14, 11.2, 11.21

2. Jenna scored the following points in her last five basketball games: 28, 18, 24, 22, and 18. What is Jenna's average score for the 5 games? **22 points**

Notetaking Guide

📑 **Transparency Available**

Promotes interactive learning and notetaking skills, pp. 311–313.

Pacing

Basic: 1 day

Average: 1 day

Advanced: 1 day

Block: 0.5 block with 13.5

• See *Teaching Guide/Lesson Plan*.

② FOCUS AND MOTIVATE

Essential Question

Big Idea 2, p. 841

How do you compare measures of central tendency and dispersion? **Tell students they will learn how to answer this question by using the mean, median, mode, range, and mean absolute deviation to analyze data.**

NCTM STANDARDS

Standard 2: Analyze situations using algebraic symbols

Standard 5: Use proper statistical methods to analyze data

Resource Planning Guide

Chapter Resource Book
• Teaching Guide/Lesson Plan (pp. 58–59)
• Activity Master (p. 60)
• Practice levels A, B, C (pp. 63–65)
• Study Guide (pp. 66–67)
• Catch-up for Absent Students (p. 68)
• Problem Solving Workshop (p. 69)
• Challenge (p. 70)

Workbooks
• Notetaking Guide (pp. 311–313)
• Practice Workbook (pp. 206–207)

Teaching Options
• **Power Presentations CD-ROM** provides dynamic electronic teaching resources for the classroom.
• **Activity Generator CD-ROM** provides editable activities for all ability levels.

Interactive Technology
• Easy Planner
• Power Presentations CD-ROM
• Activity Generator CD-ROM
• Animated Algebra
• Test Generator CD-ROM
• Online Quiz
• eWorkbook
• eEdition
• @HomeTutor

Resources for English Learners
• Quick Reference for English Learners
• Spanish Study Guide
• Multi-Language Visual Glossary
• Student Resources in Spanish

See also the *Algebra 1 Toolkit* for more strategies for meeting individual needs.

Motivating the Lesson

You follow the career of a baseball player. You can use measures of central tendency and dispersion to analyze and compare statistical data gathered on the player.

❸ TEACH

Extra Example 1

The lengths (in miles) of the 10 longest rivers in the U.S. are listed below. Which measure of central tendency best represents the data?

1290, 1310, 1420, 1450, 1460, 1900, 1900, 1980, 2340, 2540

the mean or the median, since both are close to the middle of the data

Animated Algebra
classzone.com

An **Animated Algebra** activity is available on-line for **Example 1**. This activity is also available on the **Power Presentations CD-ROM**.

Extra Example 2

The top 5 finishing times (in seconds) for swimmers in two women's races are given. Times for the 50-yard free are in set A and for the 100-yard free in set B. Compare the spread of the data for the two sets using (a) the range and (b) the mean absolute deviation.
A: 24.32, 24.34, 24.48, 24.82, 25.02
B: 52.90, 52.96, 52.98, 53.02, 53.24
Data in set A cover a wider interval than data in set B. The average variation from the mean is greater for set A than for set B.

Closing the Lesson

Have students summarize the major points of the lesson and answer the Essential Question: How do you compare measures of central tendency and dispersion?

• **Measures of central tendency are the mean, median, and mode.**

• **Measures of dispersion are range and mean absolute deviation.**

Compare mean, median, and mode to find which measure best represent most of the data. Compare measures of dispersion to find which data set covers a wider interval.

876

MEASURES OF DISPERSION A **measure of dispersion** describes the dispersion, or spread, of data. Two such measures are the *range*, which gives the length of the interval containing the data, and the *mean absolute deviation*, which gives the average variation of the data from the mean.

REVIEW ABSOLUTE VALUE
For help with absolute value, see p. 66.

KEY CONCEPT
For Your Notebook

Measures of Dispersion

The **range** of a numerical data set is the difference of the greatest value and the least value.

The **mean absolute deviation** of the data set $x_1, x_2, \ldots, x_n$ is given by:

$$\text{Mean absolute deviation} = \frac{|x_1 - \overline{x}| + |x_2 - \overline{x}| + \ldots + |x_n - \overline{x}|}{n}$$

EXAMPLE 2 Compare measures of dispersion

RUNNING The top 10 finishing times (in seconds) for runners in two men's races are given. The times in a 100 meter dash are in set A, and the times in a 200 meter dash are in set B. Compare the spread of the data for the two sets using (**a**) the range and (**b**) the mean absolute deviation.

A: 10.62, 10.94, 10.94, 10.98, 11.05, 11.13, 11.15, 11.28, 11.29, 11.32

B: 21.37, 21.40, 22.23, 22.23, 22.34, 22.34, 22.36, 22.60, 22.66, 22.73

Solution

a. A: $11.32 - 10.62 = 0.7$ B: $22.73 - 21.37 = 1.36$

▶ The range of set B is greater than the range of set A. So, the data in B cover a wider interval than the data in A.

b. The mean of set A is 11.07, so the mean absolute deviation is:

$$\frac{|10.62 - 11.07| + |10.94 - 11.07| + \ldots + |11.32 - 11.07|}{10} = 0.164$$

The mean of set B is 22.226, so the mean absolute deviation is:

$$\frac{|21.37 - 22.226| + |21.40 - 22.226| + \ldots + |22.73 - 22.226|}{10} = 0.3364$$

▶ The mean absolute deviation of set B is greater, so the average variation from the mean is greater for the data in B than for the data in A.

REVIEW NEGATIVE NUMBERS
When using the formula for mean absolute deviation, you will encounter negative numbers. For help with negative numbers, see p. 64.

2a. The range of finishing times for the men's 400 m dash (6.79) is greater than the range for set A (0.7).
2b. The mean absolute deviation is greater for the men's 400 m dash (1.7246) than it is for set A (0.164).

✓ **GUIDED PRACTICE**   for Example 2

2. **RUNNING** The top 10 finishing times (in seconds) for runners in a men's 400 meter dash are 46.89, 47.65, 48.15, 49.05, 49.19, 49.50, 49.68, 51.09, 53.31, and 53.68. *Compare* the spread of the data with that of set A in Example 2 using (**a**) the range and (**b**) the mean absolute deviation.

876   Chapter 13 Probability and Data Analysis

Differentiated Instruction

Auditory Learners Students may have difficulty with relating the mathematical notation in a formula to its meaning. The mean absolute deviation can be verbalized as *the average of all of the distances of the data points from the mean*.

See also the *Algebra 1 Toolkit* for more strategies.

13.6 EXERCISES

HOMEWORK KEY
○ = WORKED-OUT SOLUTIONS
on p. WS1 for Exs. 7 and 19
★ = STANDARDIZED TEST PRACTICE
Exs. 2, 9, 17, 19, and 22

SKILL PRACTICE

A 1. **VOCABULARY** Copy and complete: The value that occurs most frequently in a data set is called the __?__ of the data. **mode**

2. ★ **WRITING** How are measures of central tendency and measures of dispersion used to compare data? **See margin.**

EXAMPLE 1
on p. 875
for Exs. 3–10

MEASURES OF CENTRAL TENDENCY Find the mean, median, and mode(s) of the data.

3. 1, 1, 1, 2, 3, 3, 5, 5, 6 **3, 3, 1**

4. 9, 10, 12, 15, 16 **12.4, 12, no mode**

5. 13, 16, 19, 20, 22, 25, 30, 31 **22, 21, no mode**

6. 14, 15, 15, 14, 14, 16, 18, 15
   15.125, 15, 14 and 15

7. 5.52, 5.44, 3.60, 5.76, 3.80, 7.22
   5.223, 5.48, no mode

8. 300, 320, 341, 348, 360, 333
   333.6, 337, no mode

9. ★ **MULTIPLE CHOICE** What is the median of the data set? **B**

   0.7, 0.3, 0.7, 0.8, 0.9, 0.4, 1.0, 1.6, 1.2

   (A) 0.7   **(B)** 0.8   **(C)** 0.9   **(D)** 1.0

10. **ERROR ANALYSIS** *Describe* and correct the error in finding the median of the data set.
    The list needs to be ordered before you can find the median; 2, 3, 4, 4, 6, 6, 7, 8, 8, the median is 6.

    7 4 6 2 4 6 8 8 3

    The median is 4. ✗

EXAMPLE 2 B
on p. 876
for Exs. 11–16

MEASURES OF DISPERSION Find the range and mean absolute deviation of the data. Round to the nearest hundredth, if necessary.

11. 30, 35, 20, 85, 60 **65, 21.2**

12. 111, 135, 115, 120, 145, 130 **34, 10.67**

13. 30, 45, 52, 48, 100, 45, 42, 45 **70, 12.56**

14. 505, 510, 480, 550, 495, 500 **70, 15.56**

15. 1.25, 1.50, 1.70, 0.85, 1.00, 1.25 **0.85, 0.23**

16. 38.2, 80.1, 2.6, 84.2, 2.5, 5.5 **81.7, 31.98**

17. Sample answer: The range only considers the two extreme values, while the mean absolute deviation is affected by all of the values.

17. ★ **WRITING** *Explain* why the mean absolute deviation of a data set is generally a better measure of dispersion than the range.

C 18. **CHALLENGE** Write a data set that has a mean of 10, a median of 10, and modes of 5 and 8. *Sample answer:* **5, 5, 8 , 8, 10, 11, 13, 14, 16**

PROBLEM SOLVING

EXAMPLE 1 A
on p. 875
for Exs. 19–20

19. ★ **SHORT RESPONSE** The weights (in pounds) of ten pumpkins are 22, 21, 24, 24, 5, 24, 5, 23, 24, and 24.

   a. What is the range of the pumpkin weights? **19 lb**

   b. Find the mean, median, and mode(s) of the pumpkin weights. **19.6 lb, 23.5 lb, 24 lb**

   c. Which measure of central tendency best represents the data? *Explain.*
   See margin.

   @HomeTutor for problem solving help at classzone.com

2. *Sample answer:* **Measures of central tendency and measures of dispersion are useful in comparing data by providing numbers that represent how spread apart the data are and where the center of the data is. These numbers can be compared for different data sets, providing a picture of the relative position and spread of the data sets.**

19c. **Median.** *Sample answer:* **The mode is the greatest data value and the mean is less than 8 of the 10 data values.**

---

4 PRACTICE AND APPLY

Assignment Guide
📄 Answer Transparencies available for all exercises

Basic:
Day 1: pp. 877–878
Exs. 1–14, 19–21, 24

Average:
Day 1: pp. 877–878
Exs. 1, 2, 4–10, 13–17, 19–22, 24

Advanced:
Day 1: pp. 877–878
Exs. 1, 5–9, 13–24*

Block:
pp. 877–878
Exs. 1, 2, 4–10, 13–17, 19–22, 24
(with 13.5)

Differentiated Instruction
See *Algebra 1 Best Practices Toolkit* for suggestions on addressing the needs of a diverse classroom.

Homework Check
For a quick check of student understanding of key concepts, go over the following exercises:
Basic: 4, 10, 12, 19, 21
Average: 6, 14, 16, 20, 21
Advanced: 8, 16, 17, 20, 21

Extra Practice
• Student Edition, p. 950
• Chapter 13 Resource Book:
  Practice levels A, B, C, pp. 63–65

Practice Worksheet
An easily-readable reduced practice page (with answers) for this lesson can be found on p. 840C.

1. The list shows the number of e-mails Brennan sent in 8 days. Find the mean, median, and mode(s) of the data. Which measure of central tendency best represents the data?

45, 25, 38, 42, 51, 52, 24, 51
Mean: 41, Median: 43.5, Mode: 51; the median best represents the data since the mean is toward the lower end of the data and the mode is toward the upper end.

2. Find the range and mean absolute deviation of the data. Round to the nearest hundredth, if necessary.

38, 43, 56, 84, 98, 99, 102, 103
Range: 65; mean absolute deviation: 24.16

Online Quiz

Available at **classzone.com**

Diagnosis/Remediation

- Practice A, B, C in Chapter 13 Resource Book, pp. 63–65
- Study Guide in Chapter13 Resource Book, pp. 66–67
- Practice Workbook, pp. 206–207
- @HomeTutor

Challenge

Additional challenge is available in the Chapter 13 Resource Book, p. 70.

22a. Mean: about 67, median: 40. *Sample answer:* **The median better represents the data because the mean is highly affected by the Mississippi River, which is substantially higher than the other rivers.**

22b. 39.33; yes. *Sample answer:* **It is a better representation because the extremely high relative value of the Mississippi river greatly inflated the mean in part (a).**

22c, 23b. See Additional Answers beginning on p. AA1.

---

20. POPULATION The population densities (in people per square mile) for each of the 10 most densely populated states in 2003 were 719.0, 418.5, 315.6, 563.6, 820.6, 1164.6, 406.5, 279.3, 275.9, and 1029.9.

  a. Find the mean, median, and mode(s) of the data set. **599.35, 491.05, no mode**

  b. Which measure of central tendency best represents the data? *Explain.* **See margin.**

@HomeTutor for problem solving help at classzone.com

EXAMPLE 2 B
on p. 876
for Ex. 21

21. BOWLING The average scores of the bowlers on two different bowling teams are given. *Compare* the spreads of the data sets using (**a**) the range and (**b**) the mean absolute deviation.

  Team 1: 162, 150, 173, 202   **Team 2:** 140, 153, 187, 196

20b. Mean and median. *Sample answer:* **The mean and median are both close to the center of the data. Since there is no mode, it does not represent the data values.**

21a. The range for Team 2 is 56 and the range for Team 1 is 52, so the scores for Team 2 cover a slightly greater range.

22. ★ EXTENDED RESPONSE The Mississippi River discharges an average of 230 million tons of sediment per year. The average sediment discharges (in millions of tons per year) of the seven U.S. rivers with the greatest discharges are 230, 80, 65, 40, 25, 15, and 11. For parts (a)–(c) below, round your answers to the nearest whole number, if necessary. **a–c. See margin.**

  a. Find the mean and median of the data. Which measure represents the data better? *Explain.*

  b. Find the mean of the data for the other six rivers, excluding the Mississippi River. Does this mean represent the data better than the mean you found in part (a)? *Explain.*

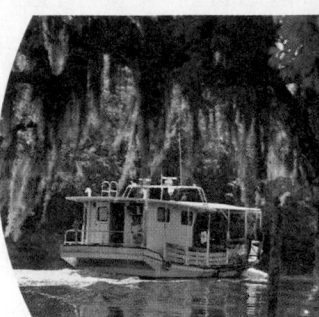
Fishing boat on the Mississippi River

  c. Find the range and mean absolute deviation of the data for all seven rivers. *Describe* what the measures tell you about the dispersion of the data.

21b. The mean absolute deviation for Team 1 is 15.75 and the mean deviation for Team 2 is 22.5, so the scores for Team 2 are more dispersed.

C

23. CHALLENGE So far, you have scored 84, 92, 76, 88, and 76 on five of the six tests you will take in a particular class. Your goal is to finish the year with a test average of 85 or greater.

  a. Let x represent your last test score. Write an expression for the mean of your test scores. Then write and solve an inequality to find the possible scores you can achieve in order to meet your goal. $\dfrac{416 + x}{6}$; $\dfrac{416 + x}{6} \geq 85$, $x \geq 94$

  b. After the last test, your teacher tells you that the median of your six test scores is 86. Can you tell whether you met your goal? *Explain.* **See margin.**

MIXED REVIEW

PREVIEW
Prepare for Lesson 13.7 in Ex. 24.

24. POPULATION The bar graph shows the populations of Alabama, Kentucky, Mississippi, and Tennessee (the East South Central states) according to the U.S. Census of 2000. *(p. 933)*

  a. What was the total population of the four states? **16.9 million**

  b. How much greater was the population of Tennessee than the population of Kentucky? **1.7 million**

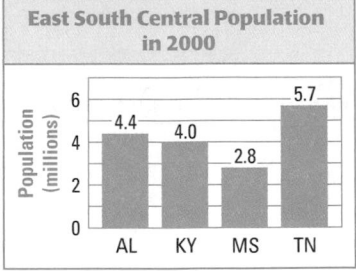
East South Central Population in 2000

---

878   **EXTRA PRACTICE** for Lesson 13.6, p. 950   🧭 **ONLINE QUIZ** at classzone.com

Calculate Variance and Standard Deviation

GOAL Find the variance and standard deviation of a data set.

Key Vocabulary
• variance
• standard deviation

In addition to range and mean absolute deviation, *variance* and *standard deviation* are also measures of dispersion that can be used to describe the spread of a set of data.

KEY CONCEPT   *For Your Notebook*

Variance and Standard Deviation

The **variance** of a numerical data set is denoted by σ^2, which is read as "sigma squared." For the data set $x_1, x_2, \ldots, x_n$, the variance is given by:

$$\sigma^2 = \frac{(x_1 - \overline{x})^2 + (x_2 - \overline{x})^2 + \ldots + (x_n - \overline{x})^2}{n}$$

The **standard deviation** of a numerical data set is denoted by σ, which is read as "sigma." For the data set $x_1, x_2, \ldots, x_n$, the standard deviation is the square root of the variance and is given by:

$$\sigma = \sqrt{\frac{(x_1 - \overline{x})^2 + (x_2 - \overline{x})^2 + \ldots + (x_n - \overline{x})^2}{n}}$$

EXAMPLE 1   **Find variance and standard deviation**

E-MAIL SIZES The sizes of e-mails (in kilobytes) in your inbox are 1, 2, 2, 7, 4, 1, 10, 3, and 6. Find the variance and standard deviation of the data.

Solution

STEP 1 Find the mean.

$$\overline{x} = \frac{1 + 2 + 2 + 7 + 4 + 1 + 10 + 3 + 6}{9} = \frac{36}{9} = 4$$

STEP 2 Find the variance.

$$\sigma^2 = \frac{(1 - 4)^2 + (2 - 4)^2 + \ldots + (6 - 4)^2}{9} = \frac{76}{9} = 8.444\ldots$$

STEP 3 Find the standard deviation.

$$\sigma = \sqrt{\sigma^2} = \sqrt{8.444\ldots} \approx 2.9$$

▶ The variance is about 8.4, and the standard deviation is about 2.9.

IMPROVE ACCURACY
The more accurate the value of σ^2 you use to calculate σ, the more accurate the value of σ you obtain. In the final answer, both results are rounded.

Extension: Calculate Variance and Standard Deviation   **879**

USING A CALCULATOR You can use a graphing calculator to find the standard deviation of a data set.

EXAMPLE 2 Find standard deviation

HOUSEHOLDS In 2000 the numbers (in thousands) of households in the 13 states with Atlantic Ocean coastline are given. Find the standard deviation of the data.

299 6338 3006 518 1981 2444 475 3065
7057 3132 408 1534 2699

Solution

STEP 1 **Enter** the data into a graphing calculator. Press [STAT] and select Edit. Enter the data into List 1 (L_1).

STEP 2 **Calculate** the standard deviation. Press [STAT]. From the CALC menu select 1-Var Stats.

On this screen, σ_x stands for standard deviation.

▸ The standard deviation of the data is about 2056.

PRACTICE

EXAMPLE 1
on p. 879
for Exs. 1–3

Use the formulas for variance and standard deviation to find the variance and standard deviation of the data. Round to the nearest tenth, if necessary.

1. 4, 5, 3, 2, 4, 7, 8, 9, 4, 6, 7, 8, 9, 1 **6.3, 12.5**

2. 14, 16, 19, 20, 28, 7, 24, 15, 16, 30, 33, 24 **52.1, 17.2**

3. 110, 205, 322, 608, 1100, 240, 185, 552, 418, 300 **76,656.6, 276.9**

EXAMPLE 2
on p. 880
for Exs. 4–7

In Exercises 4–6, use a graphing calculator to find the standard deviation of the data. Round to the nearest tenth, if necessary.

4. 3.5, 3.8, 4.1, 3.0, 3.8, 3.6, 3.3, 4.0, 3.8, 3.9, 3.2, 3.0, 3.3, 4.2, 3.0 **0.4**

5. 66, 43, 9, 28, 7, 5, 90, 9, 78, 6, 69, 55, 28, 43, 10, 54, 13, 88, 21, 4 **29.1**

6. 1002, 1540, 480, 290, 2663, 3800, 690, 1301, 1750, 2222, 4040, 800 **1192.5**

7. **REASONING** The heights (in feet) of 9 pecan trees are 72, 84, 81, 78, 80, 86, 70, 80, and 88. For parts (a)–(c) below, round your answers to the nearest tenth.

   a. Find the standard deviation of the data. **5.6**

   b. Suppose you include a pecan tree with a height of 136 feet. *Predict* the effect of the additional data on the standard deviation of the data set.

   c. Find the standard deviation of the new data set in part (b). *Compare* the results to your prediction in part (b).

13.7 Interpret Stem-and-Leaf Plots and Histograms

Before	You found measures of central tendency and dispersion.
Now	You will make stem-and-leaf plots and histograms.
Why?	So you can analyze historical data, as in Ex. 20.

Key Vocabulary
• stem-and-leaf plot
• frequency
• frequency table
• histogram

A **stem-and-leaf plot** is a data display that organizes data based on their digits. Each value is separated into a *stem* (the leading digit(s)) and a *leaf* (the last digit). A stem-and-leaf plot has a key that tells you how to read the data. A stem-and-leaf plot shows how the data are distributed.

EXAMPLE 1 Make a stem-and-leaf plot

BASEBALL The number of home runs hit by the 20 baseball players with the best single-season batting averages in Major League Baseball since 1900 are listed below. Make a stem-and-leaf plot of the data.

14, 25, 8, 8, 7, 7, 19, 37, 39, 18, 42, 23, 4, 32, 14, 21, 3, 12, 19, 41

Solution

STEP 1 Separate the data into stems and leaves.

Home Runs

Stem	Leaves
0	8 8 7 7 4 3
1	4 9 8 4 2 9
2	5 3 1
3	7 9 2
4	2 1

Key: 1 | 4 = 14 home runs

STEP 2 Write the leaves in increasing order.

Home Runs

Stem	Leaves
0	3 4 7 7 8 8
1	2 4 4 8 9 9
2	1 3 5
3	2 7 9
4	1 2

Key: 1 | 4 = 14 home runs

INTERPRET INTERVALS
Each stem in a stem-and-leaf plot defines an interval. For instance, the stem 2 represents the interval 20–29. The data values in this interval are 21, 23, and 25.

✓ GUIDED PRACTICE for Example 1

1. **U.S. HISTORY** The years in which each of the first 20 states were admitted to the Union are listed below. Make a stem-and-leaf plot of the years.
   See margin.
   1788, 1787, 1788, 1816, 1792, 1812, 1788, 1788, 1817, 1788, 1787, 1788, 1789, 1803, 1787, 1790, 1788, 1796, 1791, 1788

2. **REASONING** In Example 1, describe the distribution of the data on the intervals represented by the stems. Are the data clustered together in a noticeable way? *Explain.*

2. *Sample answer:* The data are clustered from 3–19. Over half of the values are from 3–19.

13.7 Interpret Stem-and-Leaf Plots and Histograms **881**

1 PLAN AND PREPARE

Warm-Up Exercises
📄 Transparency Available

1. The data give the ages of people in an art class. Find the mean, median, and mode of the data.
   38, 15, 13, 32, 13, 17, 29, 43
   mean: 25, median: 23, mode: 13

2. Find the range and the mean absolute deviation of the data.
   8, 3, 3, 8, 9, 2, 3 **6, about 2.41**

Notetaking Guide
📄 Transparency Available
Promotes interactive learning and notetaking skills, pp. 314–316.

Pacing
Basic: 2 days
Average: 2 days
Advanced: 2 days
Block: 1 block
• See *Teaching Guide/Lesson Plan.*

2 FOCUS AND MOTIVATE

Essential Question
Big Idea 3, p. 841

How do you make stem-and-leaf plots and histograms? **Tell students they will learn how to answer this question by organizing the data and then displaying the results in a graph.**

NCTM STANDARDS
Standard 5: Collect, organize, and display data; Develop inferences that are based on data

Resource Planning Guide

Chapter Resource Book
• Teaching Guide/Lesson Plan (pp. 71–72)
• Activity Master (p. 73)
• Practice levels A, B, C (pp. 74–79)
• Study Guide (pp. 80–81)
• Catch-up for Absent Students (p. 82)
• Application (p. 83)
• Challenge (p. 84)

Workbooks
• Notetaking Guide (pp. 314–316)
• Practice Workbook (pp. 208–210)

Teaching Options
• **Power Presentations CD-ROM** provides dynamic electronic teaching resources for the classroom.
• **Activity Generator CD-ROM** provides editable activities for all ability levels.

Interactive Technology
• Easy Planner
• Power Presentations CD-ROM
• Activity Generator CD-ROM
• Animated Algebra
• Test Generator CD-ROM
• Online Quiz
• eWorkbook
• eEdition
• @HomeTutor

Resources for English Learners
• Quick Reference for English Learners
• Spanish Study Guide
• Multi-Language Visual Glossary
• Student Resources in Spanish

See also the *Algebra 1 Toolkit* for more strategies for meeting individual needs.

Motivating the Lesson

You volunteer at an animal shelter on the weekends. The director of the shelter wants you to analyze the number of hours volunteers work. By knowing how to organize data in stem-and-leaf plots and histograms, you can display the data in an appropriate graph.

③ TEACH

Extra Example 1

A software developer advertised a position at its home office. The list below shows the number of applications the office received per day. Make a stem-and-leaf plot of the data.

9, 8, 24, 18, 27, 25, 24, 38, 32, 29, 41, 56, 42, 38, 40, 47, 32, 52, 39, 41

Software Applications

Stem	Leaves
0	8 9
1	8
2	4 4 5 7 9
3	2 2 8 8 9
4	0 1 1 2 7
5	2 6

Key: 3|2 = 32 applications

Extra Example 2

The back-to-back stem-and-leaf plot shows the ages of participants in two yoga classes. Compare the ages of the participants in the two yoga classes.

Yoga Class Ages

Class 1		Class 2
9	1	8 8 9 9
6 5 4 4	2	0 0 1 3
7 4 2 2	3	0 0

Key: 2|2|0 = 22, 20

Participants in Class 2 are generally younger than participants in Class 1.

EXAMPLE 2 Interpret a stem-and-leaf plot

GYMNASTICS The back-to-back stem-and-leaf plot shows the ages of members of the U.S men's and women's 2004 Olympic gymnastics teams. Compare the ages of the gymnasts on the two teams.

2004 Olympic Gymnast Ages

Men		Women
	1	6 6 8 8
7 4 3 1 1	2	5 6
0	3	

Key: 1|2|5 = 21, 25

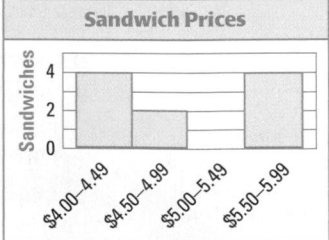

Solution

Consider the distribution of the data. The interval for 10–19 years old contains more than half of the female gymnasts. The interval for 20–29 years old contains more than half of the male gymnasts. The clustering of the data shows that the men's team was generally older than the women's team.

FREQUENCY The **frequency** of an interval is the number of data values in that interval. A stem-and-leaf plot shows the frequencies of intervals determined by the stems. A **frequency table** is also used to group data values into equal intervals, with no gaps between intervals and no intervals overlapping.

A **histogram** is a bar graph that displays data from a frequency table. Each bar represents an interval. Because intervals have equal size, the bars have equal width. A bar's length indicates the frequency. There is no space between bars.

❖ EXAMPLE 3 Make a histogram

SANDWICH PRICES The prices (in dollars) of sandwiches at a restaurant are listed below. Make a histogram of the data.

4.00, 4.00, 4.25, 4.50, 4.75, 4.25, 5.95, 5.50, 5.50, 5.75

Solution

CHOOSE AN INTERVAL SIZE
To choose the interval size for a frequency table, divide the range of the data by the number of intervals you want the table to have. Use the quotient as an approximate interval size.

STEP 1 Choose intervals of equal size that cover all of the data values. Organize the data using a frequency table.

Prices	Sandwiches
$4.00–4.49	IIII
$4.50–4.99	II
$5.00–5.49	
$5.50–5.99	IIII

STEP 2 Draw the bars of the histogram using the intervals from the frequency table.

Sandwich Prices

Differentiated Instruction

Kinesthetic Learners Stem-and-leaf plots and histograms place statistical data in equally spaced groups, or "bins." It may be helpful to write numerical data on slips of paper for students to sort and place in small boxes. Then they can construct the appropriate histogram or stem-and-leaf plot, and see how it corresponds to the sorted data.

See also the *Algebra 1 Toolkit* for more strategies.

3. *Sample answer:* Most of the data for the females is between 10% and 30%, while most of the data for males is between 20% and 40%. There is considerable overlap, but in general the male students watch more television than do the female students.

3. TELEVISION The back-to-back stem-and-leaf plot shows the percents of students in 24 countries who report watching television for 4 or more hours each day. *Compare* the data for female and male students.

Female		Male
9 9 9 8 8 8 6 6 5 4	1	7 8 9
6 6 5 4 3 3 0 0	2	0 1 2 2 4 5 5 6 6 7 7 8
8 3 2 2 1	3	4 6 6 8 8 9
1	4	0 6 6

Key: 4 | 1 | 7 = 14%, 17%

4. PRECIPITATION The average number of days each month with precipitation of 0.01 inch or more in Buffalo, New York, are 20, 17, 16, 14, 13, 11, 10, 10, 11, 12, 16, and 19. Make a histogram of the data. **See margin.**

13.7 **EXERCISES**

HOMEWORK KEY

○ = **WORKED-OUT SOLUTIONS** on p. WS1 for Exs. 3 and 19

★ = **STANDARDIZED TEST PRACTICE** Exs. 2, 8, 9, 15, and 20

SKILL PRACTICE

A

1. VOCABULARY Copy and complete: The number of data values in an interval is the __?__ of that interval. **frequency**

2. ★ WRITING *Explain* how a histogram differs from a bar graph. *Sample answer:* A histogram displays the frequency of numerical data. A bar graph displays categorical data.

EXAMPLE 1
on p. 881
for Exs. 3–7

STEM-AND-LEAF PLOTS Make a stem-and-leaf plot of the data.

3–6. See margin.

3. 17, 31, 42, 33, 38, 20, 24, 30, 39, 38, 35, 20, 55

4. 2, 8, 17, 7, 14, 20, 32, 5, 33, 6, 6, 8, 11, 9

5. 121, 124, 133, 111, 109, 182, 105, 127, 156, 179, 142

6. 1.23, 1.05, 1.11, 1.29, 1.31, 1.19, 1.45, 1.22, 1.19, 1.35

7. ERROR ANALYSIS *Describe* and correct the error in making a stem-and-leaf plot of the following data: 18, 19, 18, 19, 20, 20, 21, 22, 18, 19, 20, 21, 23, 21. **There is no key given for the stem-and-leaf plot; Key: 1|8 = 18.**

1	8 8 8 9 9 9
2	0 0 0 1 1 1 2 3

STEM-AND-LEAF PLOT In Exercises 8 and 9, consider the back-to-back stem-and-leaf plot that shows data sets *A* and *B*.

8. ★ MULTIPLE CHOICE What is the median of data set *A*? **C**

(A) 21   (B) 32
(C) 33   (D) 34

9. ★ MULTIPLE CHOICE What is the range of data set *B*? **C**

(A) 18   (B) 19
(C) 20   (D) 21

Set A		Set B
1 1 1	2	
4 3 3 2	3	1 2 2
2 0	4	1 1 3 4
	5	0 1

Key: 2 | 3 | 1 = 32, 31

13.7 Interpret Stem-and-Leaf Plots and Histograms **883**

---

p. 881

1.
Stem	Leaves
178	7 7 7 8 8 8 8 8 8 8 9 9
179	0 1 2 6
180	3
181	2 6 7

Key: 178|7 = 1787

p. 883

3.
Stem	Leaves
1	7
2	0 0 4
3	0 1 3 5 8 8 9
4	2
5	5

Key: 1|7 = 17

4.
Stem	Leaves
0	2 5 6 6 7 8 8 9
1	1 4 7
2	0
3	2 3

Key: 0|2 = 2

p. 883

Guided Practice Ex. 4. See Additional Answers beginning on p. AA1.

Extra Example 3
The number of song requests per day for a two week period at a radio station are shown below. Make a histogram of the data.

12, 22, 18, 26, 31, 34, 17, 26, 28, 10, 20, 14, 15, 32

Song Requests

Closing the Lesson

Have students summarize the major points of the lesson and answer the Essential Question: How do you make stem-and-leaf plots and histograms?

• A stem-and-leaf plot organizes data based on their digits, with the leading digit(s) in stems and the last digit in leaves.

• A histogram is a bar graph that displays data from a frequency table, with no space between bars and bars of equal width.

To make a stem-and-leaf plot, separate the data into stems and leaves. Each stem represents an interval, such as 0 represents 0–9. Write the leaves in increasing order and make a key that tells how to read the data. To make a histogram, choose equal intervals that cover all of the data, organize the data using a frequency table, and then use the intervals from the frequency table to draw the bars of the histogram.

5.
Stem	Leaves
10	5 9
11	1
12	1 4 7
13	3
14	2
15	6
16	
17	9
18	2

Key: 10|5 = 105

6.
Stem	Leaves
1.0	5
1.1	1 9 9
1.2	2 3 9
1.3	1 5
1.4	5

Key: 1.0|5 = 1.05

Assignment Guide

📖 **Answer Transparencies** available for all exercises

Basic:
Day 1: pp. 883–885
Exs. 1–9, 17, 20
Day 2: pp. 883–885
Exs. 10–13, 18, 19, 23–27

Average:
Day 1: pp. 883–885
Exs. 1, 2, 4–9, 17, 20, 21
Day 2: pp. 883–885
Exs. 10–15, 18, 19, 23–27

Advanced:
Day 1: pp. 883–885
Exs. 1, 4–9, 17, 20, 21
Day 2: pp. 883–885
Exs. 11–16*, 18, 19, 22–27*

Block:
pp. 883–885
Exs. 1, 2, 4–15, 17–21, 23–27

Differentiated Instruction

See *Algebra 1 Best Practices Toolkit* for suggestions on addressing the needs of a diverse classroom.

Homework Check

For a quick check of student understanding of key concepts, go over the following exercises:
Basic: 4, 10, 17, 18, 20
Average: 5, 12, 17, 18, 20
Advanced: 6, 14, 17, 19, 20

Extra Practice

- Student Edition, p. 950
- Chapter 13 Resource Book: Practice levels A, B, C, pp. 74–79

Practice Worksheet

An easily-readable reduced practice page (with answers) for this lesson can be found on p. 840C.

10–14. See Additional Answers beginning on p. AA1.

EXAMPLE 3
on p. 882
for Exs. 10–14

10. ERROR ANALYSIS *Describe* and correct the error in creating a histogram using the frequency table below. **See margin.**

Ages	0–9	10–19	20–29	30–39
Frequency	III	₩TI		IIII

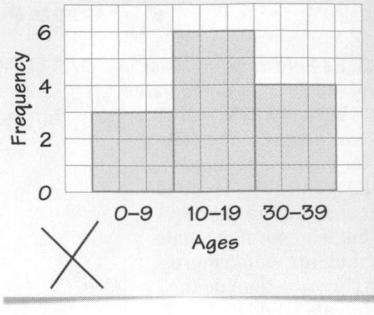

B HISTOGRAMS Make a histogram of the data.
11–14. See margin.

11. 55, 82, 94, 75, 61, 69, 77, 98, 81, 83, 75, 90, 51

12. 12, 0, 22, 31, 14, 7, 7, 45, 31, 28, 21, 25, 25, 18

13. 0.01, 0.13, 0.09, 1.10, 1.33, 0.99, 0.50, 0.95, 1.05, 1.50, 0.75, 1.01

14. 111, 109, 224, 657, 284, 120, 119, 415, 180, 105, 208, 108

15. ★ **WRITING** *Explain* why a histogram can show the distribution of the data below better than a stem-and-leaf plot. **See margin.**

15, 21, 18, 10, 12, 11, 17, 18, 16, 12, 20, 12, 17, 16

C 16. CHALLENGE Create a stem-and-leaf plot that has the same distribution of data as the histogram shown. *Explain* the steps you took to create the stem-and-leaf plot.
See margin for art. *Sample answer:* **I created values for each interval of the histogram that would have generated the frequencies shown in the histogram, then plotted the values on a stem-and-leaf plot.**

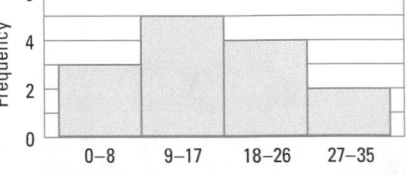

PROBLEM SOLVING

EXAMPLE 1 A
on p. 881
for Ex. 17

17. HEIGHTS The heights (in inches) of players on a boys' basketball team are as follows: 80, 76, 81, 69, 81, 78, 74, 68, 78, 74, 81, 72, 69, 81, 70. Make a stem-and-leaf plot of the heights. **See margin.**

@HomeTutor for problem solving help at classzone.com

EXAMPLE 3
on p. 882
for Exs. 18–19

18. SURVEY A survey asked people how many 8 ounce glasses of water they drink in one day. The results are below. Make a histogram of the data.

3, 0, 9, 1, 4, 2, 11, 5, 3, 6, 0, 5, 7, 8, 5, 2, 9, 6, 10, 2, 4 **See margin.**

@HomeTutor for problem solving help at classzone.com

19. MEMORY A survey asked people how many phone numbers they have memorized. The results are shown in the table.

Phone numbers	1–5	6–10	11–15	16–20	21–25
Frequency	88	85	50	28	14

a. Make a histogram of the data. **See margin.**

b. What is the probability that a person surveyed, chosen at random, has 11–25 phone numbers memorized? $\frac{92}{265}$

○ = WORKED-OUT SOLUTIONS on p. WS1   ★ = STANDARDIZED TEST PRACTICE

---

15. *Sample answer:* **A histogram can show a variety of intervals, but a stem-and-leaf plot can only show intervals that are powers of 10. The given data range from 10 to 20, so a stem-and-leaf plot would place all the data into only two intervals, making it difficult to see trends within the data. The histogram could use an interval of 3 or 4.**

16. *Sample:*

Stem	Leaves
0	5 6 7
1	0 1 2 3 4
2	0 1 2 3
3	0 1

Key: 0 | 5 = 5

17, 18, 19a. See Additional Answers beginning on p. AA1.

EXAMPLE 2
on p. 882
for Ex. 20

20. ★ **EXTENDED RESPONSE** The back-to-back stem-and-leaf plot shows the numbers of days the House of Representatives and the Senate spent in session each year from 1996 to 2004.

a. What was the median number of days the House of Representatives spent in session? the Senate?
132 days; 149 days

b. What is the range of the number of days the House of Representatives spent in session? the Senate?
32 days; 41 days

c. *Compare* the data for the House of Representatives and the Senate. What does the distribution of the data tell you?

Days in Session

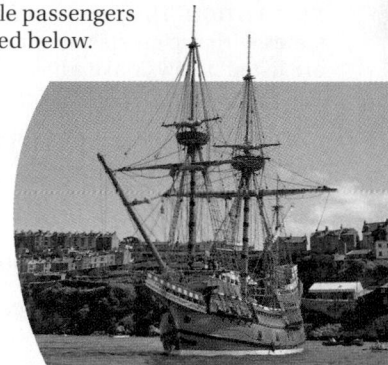

House		Senate
9 0	11	
3 2	12	
7 5 3 2	13	2 3
2	14	1 3 9
	15	3
	16	2 7
	17	3

Key: 2 | 14 | 1 = 142, 141

20c. *Sample answer:* The Senate generally spends more time in session than the House of Representatives and has more variation in the number of days they spend in session.

B

21c. $\frac{1}{3}$. *Sample answer:* Since 13 of the 39 passengers, or $\frac{1}{3}$ of them, were ages 18–29, we can predict that another passenger about whom we have no information has a $\frac{1}{3}$ probability of being in that age group.

C

21. **MAYFLOWER** The known ages (in years) of adult male passengers on the *Mayflower* at the time of its departure are listed below.

21, 34, 29, 38, 30, 54, 39, 20, 35, 64, 37, 45, 21, 25, 55, 45, 40, 38, 38, 21, 21, 20, 34, 38, 50, 41, 48, 18, 32, 21, 32, 49, 30, 42, 30, 25, 38, 25, 20

a. Make a stem-and-leaf plot of the ages. **See margin.**

b. Find the median age and range of the ages.
median: 34 yr, range: 46 yr

c. According to one source, the age of passenger Thomas English was unknown at the time of the *Mayflower's* departure. What is the probability that he was 18–29 years old? *Explain* your reasoning.

Replica of the *Mayflower*

22. **CHALLENGE** Refer to the histogram shown.

a. Find the midpoint of each interval. Multiply each midpoint by the frequency of its interval. Add these products. Divide the sum by the sum of all the frequencies. **a, b. See margin.**

b. Does the your final result in part (a) best approximate the mean, the median, or the mode of the data? *Explain* your answer.

MIXED REVIEW

PREVIEW
Prepare for Lesson 13.8 in Exs. 23–25.

Find the mean, median, and mode(s) of the data. *(p. 918)*

23. Ages of family members (in years): 62, 35, 51, 28, 22, 25, 16, 58, 30, 14
34.1 yr, 29 yr, no mode

24. Minutes of exercise each day: 35, 20, 25, 20, 0, 30, 45, 40, 20, 30, 35, 0
25 min, 27.5 min, 20 min

25. Hours worked per week: 10, 9, 11, 12, 8, 15, 20, 9, 16, 14, 15, 12
about 12.6 h; 12 h; 9 h; 12 h, and 15 h

Tell whether the question is potentially biased. *Explain* your answer. If the question is biased, rewrite it so that it is not. *(p. 871)* **26, 27. See margin.**

26. Don't you agree that science fiction movies are boring?

27. Is your ideal vacation a trip to Florida or a trip to Alaska?

---

26. *Sample answer:* This question is potentially biased because it encourages the respondent to agree. A better question would be "What do you think of science fiction movies?"

27. *Sample answer:* This question is potentially biased because it assumes that the respondent's ideal vacation is one of the two choices. A less biased question would be "Would you rather take a trip to Florida or Alaska?" or "Tell me about your ideal vacation."

---

⑤ ASSESS AND RETEACH

Daily Homework Quiz

📖 **Transparency Available**

The data show the hours Henry worked at a photo shop over a 10-week period.

21, 2, 10, 4, 12, 4, 10, 9, 8, 9

1. Make a stem-and-leaf plot of the data.

Hours at the Photo Shop

Stem	Leaves
0	2 4 4 8 9 9
1	0 0 2
2	1

Key: 1 | 0 = 10 hours

2. Describe the data in the stem-and-leaf plot in Exercise 1. **Henry generally works fewer than 10 hours per week.**

3. Make a histogram of the data.

⊘ **Online Quiz**

Available at **classzone.com**

Diagnosis/Remediation

- Practice A, B, C in Chapter 13 Resource Book, pp. 74–79
- Study Guide in Chapter 13 Resource Book, pp. 80–81
- Practice Workbook, pp. 208–210
- @HomeTutor

Challenge

Additional challenge is available in the Chapter 13 Resource Book, p. 84.

21a, 22a–b. See Additional Answers beginning on p. AA1.

QUESTION How can you use a graphing calculator to make a histogram?

EXAMPLE Make a histogram

POPULATION The populations (in thousands) of metropolitan areas in the states with the greatest metropolitan populations in the United States in 2000 are listed below. Make a histogram of the data.

4527 32,750 14,837 5667 10,542 4390 4911 6101 8169 3795 8414
17,473 5437 9214 10,392 3862 17,692 5528 4899 3640

STEP 1 *Enter the data*
Go to the STAT menu and choose Edit. Enter the data into List 1.

STEP 2 *Select histogram*
Go to the STAT PLOT screen. Select Plot 1. Use the settings shown below.

STEP 3 *Set the viewing window*
Go to the WINDOW screen. Use the settings shown below.

STEP 4 *Graph*
Press **GRAPH**. Use the *trace* feature to move from bar to bar.

DRAW CONCLUSIONS

1. *Describe* the distribution of the population data in the example above. **See margin.**

2. **BOWLING** Use a graphing calculator to make a histogram of the following bowling scores: 200, 210, 105, 300, 180, 175, 162, 110, 140, 300, 152, 165, 175, 115, 250, 270, 145, 182, 164, 122, 141, 135, 189, 170, 151, 158. **See margin.**

2.

Bowling Scores

13.8 Interpret Box-and-Whisker Plots

Before	You made stem-and-leaf plots and histograms.
Now	You will make and interpret box-and-whisker plots.
Why?	So you can compare sets of scientific data, as in Ex. 19.

Key Vocabulary
- box-and-whisker plot
- quartile
- interquartile range
- outlier

A **box-and-whisker plot** organizes data values into four groups. Ordered data are divided into lower and upper halves by the median. The median of the lower half is the **lower quartile**. The median of the upper half is the **upper quartile**.

EXAMPLE 1 Make a box-and-whisker plot

SONG LENGTHS The lengths of songs (in seconds) on a CD are listed below. Make a box-and-whisker plot of the song lengths.

$$173, 206, 179, 257, 198, 251, 239, 246, 295, 181, 261$$

Solution

STEP 1 **Order** the data. Then find the median and the quartiles.

Lower half   Median   Upper half

173, 179, **181**, 198, 206, **239**, 246, 251, **257**, 261, 295

Lower quartile   Upper quartile

STEP 2 **Plot** the median, the quartiles, the maximum value, and the minimum value below a number line.

STEP 3 **Draw** a box from the lower quartile to the upper quartile. Draw a vertical line through the median. Draw a line segment (a "whisker") from the box to the maximum and another from the box to the minimum.

Animated Algebra at classzone.com

✓ **GUIDED PRACTICE** for Example 1

1. Make a box-and-whisker plot of the ages of eight family members: 60, 15, 25, 20, 55, 70, 40, 30. **See margin.**

1 PLAN AND PREPARE

Warm-Up Exercises

📋 **Transparency Available**

Find the mean, median, and mode(s) of the data.

1. 8, 12, 15, 17, 18, 26 **16, 16, no mode**

2. 186, 144, 201, 164, 182, 164 **173.50, 173, 164**

3. The monthly charge for seven dial-up internet service providers are listed. What is the mean price? $10, $22, $17, $11, $16, $23, $25 **about $17.71**

Notetaking Guide

📋 **Transparency Available**

Promotes interactive learning and notetaking skills, pp. 317–319.

Pacing

Basic: 2 days

Average: 2 days

Advanced: 2 days

Block: 1 block

- See *Teaching Guide/Lesson Plan.*

2 FOCUS AND MOTIVATE

Essential Question

Big Idea 3, p. 841

How do you make and interpret box-and-whisker plots? **Tell students they will learn how to answer this question by organizing data values into four groups, each containing 25% of the data.**

NCTM STANDARDS

Standard 5: Collect, organize, and display data; Develop inferences that are based on data

Resource Planning Guide

Chapter Resource Book
- Teaching Guide/Lesson Plan (pp. 85–86)
- Activity Master (p. 87)
- Practice levels A, B, C (pp. 88–93)
- Study Guide (pp. 94–95)
- Catch-up for Absent Students (p. 96)
- Problem Solving Workshop (p. 97)
- Challenge (p. 98)

Workbooks
- Notetaking Guide (pp. 317–319)
- Practice Workbook (pp. 211–213)

Teaching Options
- **Power Presentations CD-ROM** provides dynamic electronic teaching resources for the classroom.
- **Activity Generator CD-ROM** provides editable activities for all ability levels.

Interactive Technology
- Easy Planner
- Power Presentations CD-ROM
- Activity Generator CD-ROM
- Animated Algebra
- Test Generator CD-ROM
- Online Quiz
- eWorkbook
- eEdition
- @HomeTutor

Resources for English Learners
- Quick Reference for English Learners
- Spanish Study Guide
- Multi-Language Visual Glossary
- Student Resources in Spanish

See also the *Algebra 1 Toolkit* for more strategies for meeting individual needs.

Motivating the Lesson

You want to compare the weather in two cities before your family takes a vacation in one of them. You can easily compare the two places by making box-and-whisker plots to display the weather data from past years.

❸ TEACH

Extra Example 1

The prices (in dollars) of 27-inch television sets at an electronics store are given below. Make a box-and-whisker plot of the television prices.

188, 225, 192, 239, 271, 286, 224, 334, 316, 275

Animated **Algebra**
classzone.com

An **Animated Algebra** activity is available on-line for **Example 1**. This activity is also available on the **Power Presentations CD-ROM**.

Extra Example 2

The box-and-whisker plots below show the normal monthly wind speeds (in miles per hour) in Athens and Savannah, Georgia.

a. For how many months is Athens' wind speed more than 8.3 miles per hour? **3 months**

b. Compare the wind speeds in the two cities. **Wind speed is more variable in Athens, but in general is stronger in Savannah.**

INTERPRET A BOX-AND-WHISKER PLOT A box-and-whisker plot separates data into four groups: the two parts of the box and the two whiskers. Each part contains approximately the same number of data values.

INTERPRET VARIATION
....
The interquartile range measures the variation in the middle half of the data and ignores the extreme values, whose variation may not be representative of the data.

Each whisker represents about 25% of the data.

The box on each side of the median represents about 25% of the data.

You know that the range of a data set is the difference of the maximum value and the minimum value. The **interquartile range** of a data set is the difference of the upper quartile and the lower quartile.

EXAMPLE 2 Interpret a box-and-whisker plot

PRECIPITATION The box-and-whisker plots below show the normal precipitation (in inches) each month in Dallas and in Houston, Texas.

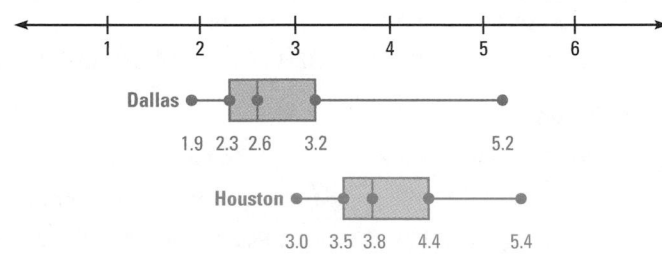

a. For how many months is Houston's precipitation less than 3.5 inches?

b. Compare the precipitation in Dallas with the precipitation in Houston.

Solution

INTERPRET QUARTILES
....
When the number of data values is a multiple of 4, the median and quartiles will divide the data into four groups of *exactly* the same size.

a. For Houston, the lower quartile is 3.5. A whisker represents 25% of the data, so for 25% of 12 months, or 3 months, Houston has less than 3.5 inches of precipitation.

b. The median precipitation for a month in Dallas is 2.6 inches. The median for Houston is 3.8 inches. In general, Houston has more precipitation.

For Dallas, the interquartile range is $3.2 - 2.3$, or 0.9 inch. For Houston, the interquartile range is $4.4 - 3.5 = 0.9$ inch. So, the cities have the same variation in the middle 50% of the data. The range for Dallas is greater than the range for Houson. When all the data are considered, Dallas has more variation in precipitation.

✓ **GUIDED PRACTICE** for Example 2

2. **PRECIPITATION** In Example 2, for how many months was the precipitation in Dallas more than 2.6 inches? **6 mo**

888 Chapter 13 Probability and Data Analysis

Differentiated Instruction

Below Level Have students work with values that are easier to manipulate so that they can concentrate on dividing the data into groups and learning the vocabulary. For example, they could make a box-and-whiskers plot that displays the number of e-mail messages a friend receives. The number of messages could be 6, 9, 12, 8, 6, 4, 5, 10, 8, 9, and 11, with median 8, lower quartile 6, upper quartile 10, minimum value 4, and maximum value 12.
See also the *Algebra 1 Toolkit* for more strategies.

OUTLIERS A value that is widely separated from the rest of the data in a data set is called an **outlier**. Typically, a data value is considered to be an outlier if it is greater than the upper quartile by more than 1.5 times the interquartile range or if it is less than the lower quartile by more than 1.5 times the interquartile range.

 EXAMPLE 3 **Standardized Test Practice**

> The normal monthly amounts of precipitation (in inches) in Dallas are: 1.9, 2.4, 3.1, 3.2, 5.2, 3.2, 2.1, 2.0, 2.4, 4.1, 2.6, 2.6. These data were used to create the box-and-whisker plot in Example 2. Which value, if any, is an outlier?
>
> **(A)** 1.9   **(B)** 5.2   **(C)** 1.9 and 5.2   **(D)** No outlier

Solution

From Example 2, you know the interquartile range of the data is 0.9 inch. Find 1.5 times the interquartile range: 1.5(0.9) = 1.35.

From Example 2, you also know that the lower quartile is 2.3 and the upper quartile is 3.2. A value less than 2.3 − 1.35 = 0.95 is an outlier. A value greater than 3.2 + 1.35 = 4.55, is an outlier. Notice that 5.2 > 4.55.

▶ The correct answer is B. **(A) (B) (C) (D)**

✓ **GUIDED PRACTICE** for Example 3

3. Which value, if any, is an outlier in the data set? **D**

    3.7, 3.0, 3.4, 3.6, 5.2, 5.4, 3.2, 3.8, 4.3, 4.5, 4.2, 3.7

    (A) 3.0   **(B)** 5.4   **(C)** 3.0 and 5.4   **(D)** No outlier

13.8 **EXERCISES**

HOMEWORK KEY
◯ = **WORKED-OUT SOLUTIONS**
on p. WS1 for Exs. 3 and 17

★ = **STANDARDIZED TEST PRACTICE**
Exs. 2, 8, 9, 18, and 19

SKILL PRACTICE

Ⓐ 1. **VOCABULARY** What is the interquartile range of a data set?
       the difference of the upper quartile and the lower quartile

    2. ★ **WRITING** *Explain* how you can identify an outlier in a data set. **See margin.**

EXAMPLE 1
on p. 887
for Exs. 3–7

BOX-AND-WHISKER PLOTS Make a box-and-whisker plot of the data. 3–6. See margin.

③ 1, 7, 0, 7, 2, 6, 3, 6, 0, 7, 8   4. 10, 1, 7, 5, 1, 8, 5, 4, 6, 5, 9, 12

5. 52, 20, 24, 45, 35, 32, 39, 42, 23, 64   6. 0.8, 0.4, 0.3, 0.6, 0.7, 0.2, 0.7, 0.9

13.8 Interpret Box-and-Whisker Plots   **889**

Differentiated Instruction

Kinesthetic Learners Ordering data can be difficult to do on paper. For problems similar to **Example 3**, have students write each data value on a small self-stick note so they can sort the data by moving the self-stick notes on their desk or on a sheet of paper.

See also the *Algebra 1 Toolkit* for more strategies.

p. 887
Guided Practice Ex. 1

Assignment Guide

📖 Answer Transparencies available for all exercises

Basic:
Day 1: pp. 889–892
Exs. 1–7, 15, 16
Day 2: pp. 889–892
Exs. 8–12, 17–19, 21–24

Average:
Day 1: pp. 889–892
Exs. 1, 2, 4–7, 15, 16, 21, 22
Day 2: pp. 889–892
Exs. 8–13, 17–19, 23, 24

Advanced:
Day 1: pp. 889–892
Exs. 1, 2, 4–6, 15, 16, 21, 22
Day 2: pp. 889–892
Exs. 8–14*, 17–20*, 23, 24

Block:
pp. 889–892
Exs. 1, 2, 4–13, 15–19, 21–24

Differentiated Instruction

See *Algebra 1 Best Practices Toolkit* for suggestions on addressing the needs of a diverse classroom.

Homework Check

For a quick check of student understanding of key concepts, go over the following exercises:
Basic: 4, 8, 11, 15, 17
Average: 5, 9, 12, 16, 18
Advanced: 6, 10, 13, 17, 19

Extra Practice

• Student Edition, p. 950
• Chapter 13 Resource Book:
  Practice levels A, B, C, pp. 88–93

Practice Worksheet

An easily-readable reduced practice page (with answers) for this lesson can be found on p. 840C.

7. ERROR ANALYSIS *Describe* and correct the error in creating a box-and-whisker plot of the data 0, 2, 4, 0, 6, 10, 8, 12, 5.
Sample answer: The upper quartile is incorrect. The upper quartile should be the median of 8 and 10, or 9; see margin for art.

BOX-AND-WHISKER PLOT In Exercises 8–10, use the box-and-whisker plot.

EXAMPLE 2
on p. 888
for Exs. 8–10

8. ★ **MULTIPLE CHOICE** About what percent of the data are greater than 20? **A**

(A) 25%   (B) 50%   (C) 75%   (D) 100%

9. ★ **MULTIPLE CHOICE** About what percent of the data are less than 15? **B**

(A) 25%   (B) 50%   (C) 75%   (D) 100%

10. ERROR ANALYSIS *Describe* and correct the error in interpreting the box-and-whisker plot. *Sample answer:* The box represents 50% of the data values; about 50% of the data values lie between 11 and 20.

> About 25% of the data values lie between 11 and 20.

EXAMPLES B
1 and 3
on pp. 887, 889
for Exs. 11–13

OUTLIERS Make a box-and-whisker plot of the data. Identify any outliers. 11–13. See margin.

11. Hours worked per week: 15, 15, 10, 12, 22, 10, 8, 14, 18, 22, 18, 15, 12, 11, 10

12. Prices of MP3 players: $124, $95, $105, $110, $95, $124, $300, $190, $114

13. Annual salaries: $30,000, $35,000, $48,000, $68,500, $32,000, $38,000

C **14. CHALLENGE** Two data sets have the same mean, the same interquartile range, and the same range. Is it possible for the box-and-whisker plots of such data sets to be different? *Justify* your answer by creating data sets that fit the situation. **Yes.** *Sample answer:* A: 0, 2, 4, 6, 8; B: –1, 3, 4, 7, 7

PROBLEM SOLVING

EXAMPLE 1 A
on p. 887
for Exs. 15–16

15. SEAWAY The average sailing times to the Atlantic Ocean from several ports on the St. Lawrence Seaway are shown on the map. Make a box-and-whisker plot of the sailing times. **See margin.**

@HomeTutor   for problem solving help at classzone.com

890

○ = **WORKED-OUT SOLUTIONS** on p. WS1
★ = **STANDARDIZED TEST PRACTICE**

7.

11.

There are no outliers.

12.

$300 is an outlier.

13.

There are no outliers.

16. BASEBALL STATISTICS In 2004, Ichiro Suzuki scored 101 runs. The numbers of runs he scored against different opposing teams are listed below. Make a box-and-whisker plot of the numbers of runs scored. **See margin.**

Runs scored: 18, 8, 4, 8, 2, 8, 0, 9, 0, 4, 2, 5, 9, 1, 2, 1, 2, 11, 7

@HomeTutor for problem solving help at classzone.com

**EXAMPLES
1 and 3**
on pp. 887, 889
for Exs. 17–18

17.) RETAIL SALES The retail sales (in billions of dollars) of the nine U.S. states with the highest retail sales in 2002 are listed below.

California: $153.1   Florida: $118.2   Georgia: $38.4

Illinois: $52.4   New Jersey: $35.8   New York: $54.7

Ohio: $50.7   Pennsylvania: $49.9   Texas: $107.0

a. Make a box-and-whisker plot of the retail sales. **See margin.**

b. Which states, if any, had retail sales in 2002 that can be considered outliers? **none**

18b. Sample answer: Ronald Reagan's age is more than 1.5 times the interquartile range of 7 away from the upper quartile.

18. ★ SHORT RESPONSE The stem-and-leaf plot shows the ages of the first 43 presidents of the United States when they first took the oath of office.

```
4 | 2 3 6 6 7 8 9 9

5 | 0 0 1 1 1 1 2 2 4 4 4 4 5 5 5 5 6 6 6 7 7 7 7 8

6 | 0 1 1 1 2 4 4 5 8 9
```
                                        Key: 4 | 2 = 42 years

a. Make a box-and-whisker plot of the ages. **See margin.**

b. Ronald Reagan was the oldest United States president, and Theodore Roosevelt was the youngest. Can either of these presidents' ages be considered outliers? *Explain* why or why not.

EXAMPLE 2 [B]
on p. 888
for Ex. 19

19. ★ EXTENDED RESPONSE The box-and-whisker plots show the diameters (in kilometers) of craters on Jupiter's moons Callisto and Ganymede.

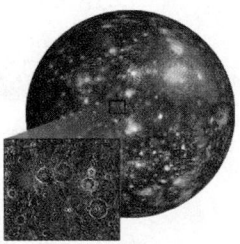

Callisto

19b. Sample answer: Chesapeake Bay is larger than between 50% and 75% of the craters on both Callisto and Ganymede.

19c. Sample answer: Vredefort is larger than at least 75% of the craters on both Callisto and Ganymede.

a. *Compare* the diameters of craters on Callisto with the diameters of craters on Ganymede. **See margin.**

b. The largest crater in the United States is the Chesapeake Bay in Virginia, with a diameter of 90 kilometers. *Compare* the diameter of the Chesapeake Bay with diameters of craters on Callisto and Ganymede.

c. The largest crater on Earth is Vredefort in South Africa, with a diameter of 300 kilometers. *Compare* the diameter of Vredefort with the diameter of craters on Callisto and Ganymede.

13.8 Interpret Box-and-Whisker Plots   **891**

15.

Avoiding Common Errors

Exercises 3–6, 11–13 Caution students to pay attention to the values they use to determine the median and quartiles. A common error is using the median to determine the quartiles when there is an odd number of values in the data set.

Mathematical Reasoning

Exercise 14 To get students started on this exercise, you may want to ask if two data sets can have the same range and the same mean, but different medians. Ask the students, as a class, to come up with an example.

⊘ Internet Reference

Exercise 18 For additional information about the presidents of the United States, visit www.whitehouse.gov/history/presidents/index2.html

Teaching Strategy

Exercise 19 You may want to use this exercise to discuss outliers and interquartile range. First have students calculate outliers for Callisto and Ganymede and then point out how the outliers affect the range but not the interquartile range. Ask students to explain whether the range or the interquartile range best describes the spread of the data.

16.

17a.

18a.

19a. Sample answer: The craters on Ganymede are generally smaller than the craters on Callisto. The lower extreme, lower quartile, median, upper quartile, and upper extreme values are all lower for Ganymede than for Callisto.

Daily Homework Quiz

📖 Transparency Available

1. Hiking trails (in miles) of moderate difficulty in Arizona's Mazatzal Wilderness Area are listed below. Make a box-and-whisker plot of the data.

4.2, 5.7, 7, 3.3, 3.1, 3, 3.5, 3, 7.5, 4.2, 7.5, 6.6

2. About what percent of the trails are greater than 4.2 miles in length? **50%**

🌐 **Online Quiz**

Available at **classzone.com**

Diagnosis/Remediation

• Practice A, B, C in Chapter 13 Resource Book, pp. 88–93
• Study Guide in Chapter13 Resource Book, pp. 94–95
• Practice Workbook, pp. 211–213
• @HomeTutor

Challenge

Additional challenge is available in the Chapter 13 Resource Book, p. 98.

Quiz

An easily-readable reduced copy of the quiz (with answers) on Lessons 13.5–13.8 from the Assessment Book can be found on p. 840F.

20, Quiz 4–6. See Additional Answers beginning on p. AA1.

20. CHALLENGE The box-and-whisker plots show the heights (in inches) of singers in a chorus, according to their voice parts. A soprano part has the highest pitch, followed by alto, tenor, and bass, respectively. Draw a conclusion about voice parts and heights. *Justify* your conclusion. **See margin.**

MIXED REVIEW

Make a stem-and-leaf plot of the data. *(p. 881)* **21, 22. See margin.**

21. 56, 55, 54, 57, 28, 28, 53, 52, 56, 28, 25, 23, 17, 51, 54, 23, 20, 10

22. 71, 60, 39, 43, 81, 32, 33, 41, 37, 34, 51, 41, 32, 34, 48, 35, 36, 58

Make a histogram of the data. *(p. 881)* **23, 24. See margin.**

23. 1.24, 2.45, 1.11, 2.09, 2.19, 1.99, 1.75, 1.65, 2.10, 2.30

24. 1.5, 5.12, 7.5, 7.1, 7.14, 9.7, 10.24, 1.3, 1.6, 1.6, 3.3, 3.12

QUIZ *for Lessons 13.5–13.8*

1. HOTEL SURVEY A hotel manager leaves guest comment cards in each room. Identify the population and classify the sampling method. *(p. 871)*
all the hotel's guests, self-selected

In Exercises 2 and 3, find the range and mean absolute deviation of the data. Round to the nearest hundredth, if necessary. *(p. 875)*

2. 62, 63, 70, 40, 50, 60 **30, 8.33**

3. 14, 18, 22, 14, 14, 6, 17 **16, 3.43**

4. Make a histogram of the data: 44, 52, 60, 47, 65, 40, 49, 45, 32, 68, 39. *(p. 881)*
See margin.

5. Make a stem-and-leaf plot of the data: 1.8, 2.2, 1.2, 2.8, 3.6, 3.3, 1.8, 2.2. *(p. 881)* **See margin.**

6. TEST SCORES The scores on a math exam are given below. Make a box-and-whisker plot of the data. Identify any outliers. *(p. 887)* **See margin.**

76, 55, 88, 92, 79, 85, 90, 88, 85, 92, 100, 91, 90, 86, 88

21.

Stem	Leaves
1	0 7
2	0 3 3 5 8 8 8
3	
4	
5	1 2 3 4 4 5 6 6 7

Key: 1 | 0 = 10

22.

Stem	Leaves
3	2 2 3 4 4 5 6 7 9
4	1 1 3 8
5	1 8
6	0
7	1
8	1

Key: 3 | 2 = 32

23, 24. See Additional Answers beginning on p. AA1.

13.8 Draw Box-and-Whisker Plots

QUESTION   How can you use a graphing calculator to make a box-and-whisker plot?

EXAMPLE   Make a box-and-whisker plot

REPTILE SPECIES The number of known reptile species per 10,000 square kilometers in the countries of Asia (excluding the Middle East) and of Central America, South America, and the Caribbean are listed below. Make box-and-whisker plots of the numbers of species.

Asia: 36, 26, 49, 11, 32, 35, 27, 58, 91, 26, 8, 8, 12, 12, 23, 110, 4, 51, 41, 41, 62, 350, 77, 18, 81, 23, 18, 59

Central America, South America, and the Caribbean: 81, 125, 47, 69, 57, 107, 77, 73, 35, 123, 69, 116, 87, 37, 45, 53, 20, 124, 126, 35, 73, 60, 64

STEP 1 *Enter the data*
Enter the data for Asia into List 1. Enter the data for Central America, South America, and the Caribbean into List 2.

STEP 2 *Select box-and-whisker plot*
Go to the STAT PLOT screen and select the box-and-whisker plot for both Plot 1 and Plot 2. The Xlist for Plot 1 should be L_1, so that it displays the data from List 1. The Xlist for Plot 2 should be L_2, so that it displays the data from List 2. Make sure both plots are on.

STEP 3 *Set the viewing window*
Press **ZOOM** 9 to set the window so that it shows all of the data.

STEP 4 *Graph*
Press **GRAPH**. Use the trace feature to examine the box-and-whisker plots more closely. Notice that the graphing calculator refers to the lower quartile as Q_1 and the upper quartile as Q_3.

DRAW CONCLUSIONS

1. **REPTILE SPECIES** *Compare* the number of reptile species per 10,000 square kilometers in the countries of Central America, South America, and the Caribbean with the number in Asia. **See margin.**

2. **BIRD SPECIES** The number of threatened bird species per 10,000 square kilometers in the countries of two regions are listed below. Make box-and-whisker plots of the data and compare the data for the two regions.
   See margin.
   Middle East and Northern Africa: 13, 8, 11, 14, 12, 8, 4, 3, 5, 2, 11, 5, 11, 7, 6, 14, 4, 13

   North and South America: 5, 50, 41, 27, 103, 18, 64, 53, 3, 26, 64, 2, 11, 22

13.8 Interpret Box-and-Whisker Plots   **893**

---

1. *Sample answer:* **Although Asia has an outlier that is greater than any value in Central America, South America, and the Caribbean's data set, in general Asia's data is lower. The lower extreme, lower quartile, median, and upper quartile are all lower for Asia than for Central America, South America, and the Caribbean.**

2.

Sample answer: **Generally, there are more threatened bird species in North and South America than in the Middle East and Northern Africa. There is also a much greater range of values in North and South America.**

---

① PLAN AND PREPARE

Learn the Method
• Students will use a graphing calculator to make a box-and-whisker plot.
• After the activity, students can use a graphing calculator to check their solutions in Exercises 3–6 and 11–13 in Lesson 13.8.

Keystroke Help
Keystrokes for several models of calculators are available in blackline format in the *Chapter 13 Resource Book*.

② TEACH

Tips for Success
If necessary, tell students to adjust Xmin and Xmax in the viewing window so they can clearly see both plots.

Extra Example
The number of recorded green turtle nests and leatherback turtle nests during the years 1996–2004 on a Florida island are listed below. Make box-and-whiskers plots of the number of nests.
Green turtle: 31, 10, 93, 22, 166, 21, 106, 81, 70
Leatherback turtle: 13, 21, 7, 20, 21, 35, 16, 18, 6

③ ASSESS AND RETEACH

What do the interquartile ranges of the two plots tell you? **The interquartile ranges tell you that the number of green turtle nests varied greatly during the 9-year period, while the number of leatherback turtle nests remained fairly consistent.**

Left margin answers:

1a.

Age	People
20–29	III
30–39	IIIII
40–49	IIII I
50–59	IIII II
60–69	III

1b.

2a. population: all the doctor's patients, sampling method: systematic sample

2b. *Sample answer:* The sample is likely to be biased because those patients who cannot visit on Tuesdays cannot be represented, and they are likely to have different opinions about scheduling than those who can visit on Tuesdays.

4a. store A: mean: $257, median: $245, mode: $200, $260; store B: mean: $237.50, median: $210, mode: $200. *Sample answer:* The mean; the mean is not influenced by a very high or a very low price, so it is a good representation.

4b. store A: range: $350, mean absolute deviation: $63; store B: range: $250, mean absolute deviation: $57.50. *Sample answer:* Store A; it has a greater range and a greater mean absolute deviation.

4c. Yes. *Sample answer:* At store A, the interquartile range is 80, with an upper quartile of 280. All values at Store A greater than $400 are outliers, so the $500 DVD player is an outlier. At store B, the interquartile range is 60 with an upper quartile of 250. All values at store B above $340 are outliers, so the $350 and $400 DVD player are outliers.

Lessons 13.5–13.8

1. **MULTI-STEP PROBLEM** The ages of people who attended an opening reception for a theater production are listed below.

   54, 25, 28, 64, 30, 42, 33, 50, 27, 35, 40, 39, 41, 52, 49, 48, 56, 60, 58, 37, 56, 45, 57, 62
   a, b. See margin.

   a. Make a frequency table of the data.

   b. Make a histogram of the data.

2. **MULTI-STEP PROBLEM** A doctor would like to extend her office hours to better accommodate her patients. She asks each patient who visits her office on Tuesday which day the patient thinks the hours should be extended. **a, b. See margin.**

   a. Identify the population and classify the sampling method.

   b. Tell whether the survey method used is likely to result in a biased sample.

3. **GRIDDED ANSWER** The average lengths (in hours) of several morning commutes are listed below. How many minutes is the mean commute? **37.5 min**

   0.25, 0.20, 0.50, 0.50, 0.50, 0.05, 0.65, 1.00, 1.50, 0.75, 0.50, 1.10, 0.60, 0.80, 1.00, 0.10

4. **EXTENDED RESPONSE** The prices (in dollars) of portable DVD players at two different stores are listed below.

   Store A: 280, 200, 260, 230, 200, 150, 300, 260, 500, 190

   Store B: 350, 190, 230, 250, 400, 200, 200, 220, 185, 150 **a–c. See margin.**

   a. Find the mean, median, and mode(s) of each data set. Which measure of central tendency best represents each data set? *Explain* your reasoning.

   b. Find the range and mean absolute deviation of each data set. Which store's prices are more spread out? *Explain.*

   c. Can any of the prices of the portable DVD players be considered outliers? *Explain* your reasoning.

5. **OPEN-ENDED** A clothing store sells several different styles of jeans. The mean price of the jeans is $27. The median price of the jeans is $27.50. The mode of the prices is $20. Make a list of prices of jeans that has these measures of central tendency.
   See margin.

6. **SHORT RESPONSE** The back-to-back stem-and-leaf plot below shows the lengths (in meters) of the eight best men's and women's final long jump results from the 2004 Olympics. *Compare* the lengths of the jumps by men with those by women. **See margin.**

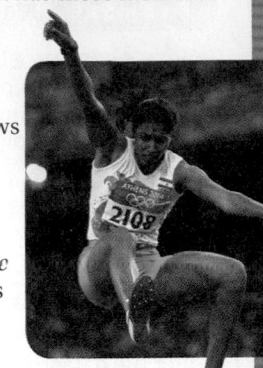

Lengths (in meters) of Long Jump

Men		Women
	6	7 8 8 9
	7	0 0 0 1
6 5 3 3 2 2 2 0	8	

Key: 0|7|1 = 7.0 m, 7.1 m

7. **SHORT RESPONSE** The stem-and-leaf plot shows the number of games lost by 15 NCAA football coaches with the greatest career winning percentages after at least 10 years of coaching.

1	1 2 3 6 7 7 8
2	1 3 3 4 5 9
3	6
4	9

   Key: 2|1 = 21 games

   a. Make a box-and-whisker plot of the data. **See margin.**

   b. Tom Osborne had a winning percentage of 83.6% over his career and lost 49 games. Can the number of games lost by Tom Osborne be considered an outlier? *Explain* your reasoning.
   Yes. *Sample answer:* The interquartile range is 9, and 49 is more than 9 · 1.5 = 13.5 years greater than the upper quartile of 25.

894   Chapter 13   Probability and Data Analysis

---

5. *Sample answer:* 20, 20, 27, 28, 30, 37

6. *Sample answer:* The men jumped farther than the women.

7a.

BIG IDEAS

For Your Notebook

Big Idea 1

Finding Probabilities of Simple and Compound Events

To find $P(A)$ when...	
all outcomes are equally likely, use $P(A) = \dfrac{\text{Number of favorable outcomes}}{\text{Number of possible outcomes}}$	you perform an experiment, use $P(A) = \dfrac{\text{Number of successes}}{\text{Number of trials}}$

To find $P(A$ or $B)$ when...	...use this formula
events A and B have no common outcomes	$P(A$ or $B) = P(A) + P(B)$
events A and B have at least one common outcome	$P(A$ or $B) = P(A) + P(B) - P(A$ and $B)$

To find $P(A$ and $B)$ when...	...use this formula
events A and B are independent	$P(A$ and $B) = P(A) \cdot P(B)$
events A and B are dependent	$P(A$ and $B) = P(A) \cdot P(B$ given $A)$

Big Idea 2

Analyzing Sets of Data

You can find values that represent a typical data value using the following measures of central tendency:

> mean, median, and mode

You can find values that describe the spread of data using the following measures of dispersion:

> range, mean absolute deviation, and interquartile range

Big Idea 3

Making and Interpreting Data Displays

Use an appropriate display to show the distribution of a set of numerical data.

A **stem-and-leaf plot** organizes data based on their digits.

Stem	Leaves				
1	0	1	1	2	3
2	0	0	0	2	

Key: 1 | 0 = 10

A **histogram** shows the frequency of data on intervals of equal size, with no gaps or overlaps.

A **box-and-whisker plot** organizes data into four groups of approximately equal size.

Additional Resources

The following resources are available to help review the materials in this chapter.

Chapter 13 Resource Book

- Chapter Review Games and Activities, p. 99
- Cumulative Practice, Chs. 1–13, pp. 101–102

Student Resources in Spanish

eWorkbook

@HomeTutor

Vocabulary Practice

Vocabulary practice is available at **classzone.com**

Extra Example 13.1

A bag contains 12 green markers, 6 blue markers, and 8 yellow markers. You choose a marker at random. Find the probability you choose a blue marker. $\frac{3}{13}$

REVIEW KEY VOCABULARY

- outcome, event, *p. 843*
- sample space, *p. 843*
- probability of an event, *p. 843*
- theoretical, experimental probability, *p. 844*
- odds in favor, odds against, *p. 845*
- permutation, *p. 851*
- *n* factorial, *p. 852*
- combination, *p. 856*
- compound event, *p. 861*
- mutually exclusive events, *p. 861*

- overlapping events, *p. 861*
- independent events, *p. 862*
- dependent events, *p. 862*
- survey, *p. 871*
- population, *p. 871*
- sample: random, stratified random, systematic, convenience, self-selected, *p. 871*
- biased sample, *p. 872*
- biased question, *p. 872*
- mean, median, mode, *p. 875*

- measure of dispersion, *p. 876*
- range, *p. 876*
- mean absolute deviation, *p. 876*
- stem-and-leaf plot, *p. 881*
- frequency, frequency table, *p. 882*
- histogram, *p. 882*
- box-and-whisker plot, *p. 887*
- lower quartile, upper quartile, *p. 887*
- interquartile range, *p. 888*
- outlier, *p. 889*

VOCABULARY EXERCISES

Copy and complete the statement.

1. An event that combines two or more events is a(n) _?_ . **compound event**

2. A possible result of an experiment is a(n) _?_ . **outcome**

3. **WRITING** *Compare* theoretical probability and experimental probability.
   Sample answer: **Theoretical probability is based on knowing the likelihood of all possible outcomes of an event. Experimental probability is based on the results of an experiment.**

REVIEW EXAMPLES AND EXERCISES

Use the review examples and exercises below to check your understanding of the concepts you have learned in each lesson of Chapter 13.

13.1 Find Probabilities and Odds
pp. 843–848

> **EXAMPLE**
>
> A bag contains 15 red checkers and 15 black checkers. You choose a checker at random. Find the probability that you choose a black checker.
>
> $$P(\text{black checker}) = \frac{\text{Number of black checkers}}{\text{Total number of checkers}} = \frac{15}{30} = \frac{1}{2}$$

EXERCISES

EXAMPLE 2
on p. 844
for Exs. 4–5

4. **CHECKERS** In the example above, suppose an extra red checker is added to the bag. Find the probability of randomly choosing a black checker. $\frac{15}{31}$

5. **BAG OF LETTERS** A bag contains tiles. Each tile has one letter from the word HAPPINESS on it. You choose a tile at random. What is the probability that you choose a tile with the letter S? $\frac{2}{9}$

13.2 Find Probabilities Using Permutations

pp. 851–855

EXAMPLE

You need to enter a 4 digit code in order to enter the building where you work. The digits are 4 different numbers from 1 to 5. You forgot the code and try to guess it. Find the probability that you guess correctly.

STEP 1 Write the number of possible outcomes as the number of permutations of 4 out of the 5 possible digits. This is $_5P_4$.

$$_5P_4 = \frac{5!}{(5-4)!} = \frac{5!}{1!} = 5! = 5 \cdot 4 \cdot 3 \cdot 2 \cdot 1 = 120$$

STEP 2 Find the probability. Because only one of the permutations is the correct code, the probability that you guess the correct code is $\frac{1}{120}$.

EXERCISES

EXAMPLE 2
on p. 852
for Exs. 6–10

Evaluate the expression.

6. $_7P_6$ **5040**   7. $_6P_2$ **30**   8. $_8P_5$ **6720**   9. $_{13}P_{10}$
1,037,836,800

10. **MUSIC** You downloaded 6 songs. You randomly choose 4 of these songs to play. Find the probability that you play the first 4 songs you downloaded in the order in which you downloaded them. $\frac{1}{360}$

13.3 Find Probabilities Using Combinations

pp. 856–859

EXAMPLE

For your government class, you must choose 3 states in the United States to research. You may choose your states from the 6 New England states. How many combinations of states are possible?

The order in which you choose the states is not important. So, to find the number of combinations of 6 states taken 3 at a time, find $_6C_3$.

$$_6C_3 = \frac{6!}{(6-3)! \cdot 3!} \quad \text{Combinations formula}$$

$$= \frac{6 \cdot 5 \cdot 4 \cdot 3!}{3! \cdot (3 \cdot 2 \cdot 1)} \quad \text{Expand factorials.}$$
Divide out common factor, 3!.

$$= 20 \quad \text{Simplify.}$$

EXERCISES

EXAMPLE 2
on p. 857
for Exs. 11–15

Evaluate the expression.

11. $_7C_6$ **7**   12. $_6C_2$ **15**   13. $_8C_5$ **56**   14. $_{13}C_{10}$ **286**

15. **TICKETS** You win 5 tickets to a concert. In how many ways can you choose 4 friends out of a group of 9 to take with you to the concert? **126 ways**

Chapter Review **897**

Extra Example 13.2
The coach for the swimming team randomly chooses 2 of the 12 members of the team to talk to local reporters about an upcoming meet. What is the probability that the coach chooses you and your twin brother? $\frac{1}{132}$

Extra Example 13.3
Your dog has 6 puppies. You can choose 2 of the 6 to keep. How many choices of two puppies are possible? **15 choices**

Extra Examples 13.4

1. You roll a number cube. Find the probability that the number is 2 or an odd number. $\frac{2}{3}$

2. A bag contains 3 red chips, 2 white chips, 4 blue chips, and 6 yellow chips. You choose a chip at random and then return it to the bag. You choose another chip at random. What is the probability that both chips are red? $\frac{1}{25}$

13.4 Find Probabilities of Compound Events

pp. 861–867

EXAMPLE

The sections of the spinner shown all have the same area. You spin the spinner. Find the probability that the spinner stops on red or on an even number.

Because 24 is an even number on a red section, stopping on red and stopping on an even number are overlapping events.

$P(\text{red or even}) = P(\text{red}) + P(\text{even}) - P(\text{red and even})$

$= \frac{3}{8} + \frac{3}{8} - \frac{1}{8}$

$= \frac{5}{8}$

EXERCISES

EXAMPLES
1 and 2
on pp. 861–862
for Exs. 16–19

You spin the spinner shown above. Find the specified probability.

16. $P(\text{green or odd})$ $\frac{7}{8}$ **17.** $P(\text{blue or prime number})$ $\frac{3}{8}$

18. $P(\text{blue or even})$ $\frac{3}{4}$ **19.** $P(\text{red or multiple of 3})$ $\frac{5}{8}$

EXAMPLE

A bag contains 5 red marbles, 3 blue marbles, 6 white marbles, and 2 green marbles. You choose one marble at random, put the marble aside, then choose a second marble at random. What is the probability that both marbles are blue?

Because you do not replace the first marble, the events are dependent. Before you choose a marble, there are 16 marbles, and 3 of them are blue. After you choose a blue marble, there are 2 blue marbles among 15 marbles left.

$P(\text{blue and then blue}) = P(\text{blue}) \cdot P(\text{blue given blue})$

$= \frac{3}{16} \cdot \frac{2}{15}$

$= \frac{6}{240}$

$= \frac{1}{40}$

EXERCISES

EXAMPLES
3 and 4
on p. 863
for Exs. 20–21

You randomly choose 2 marbles from the bag described in the example above. Find the probability that both are green if:

20. you replace the first marble. $\frac{1}{64}$ **21.** you don't replace the first marble. $\frac{1}{120}$

898 Chapter 13 Probability and Data Analysis

13.5 Analyze Surveys and Samples

pp. 871–874

EXAMPLE

You want to determine what type of music is the favorite of students in your grade. You survey every third student from an alphabetical list of students in your grade. You ask each surveyed student, "What is your favorite type of music, classical or country?"

Identify the population and classify the sampling method. Tell whether the question is potentially biased. Explain your answer. If the question is potentially biased, rewrite it so that it is not.

The population is all students in your grade. Because you use the rule "survey every third student," the sample is a systematic sample.

The question is biased, because it does not allow students to choose a type of music other than classical or country. An unbiased question is "What is your favorite type of music?"

EXERCISES

EXAMPLE 1
on p. 871
for Ex. 22

22. **SURVEY** In the example above, suppose you create a questionaire and distribute one to every student in your grade. There is a box in the cafeteria where students can drop off completed questionaires during lunch. Identify the sampling method. **self-selected**

13.6 Use Measures of Central Tendency and Dispersion

pp. 875–878

EXAMPLE

The amounts of snowfall (in inches) in one town for 8 months of the year are listed below. Find the mean, median, and mode(s) of the data. Which measure of central tendency best represents the data?

0.5, 0.5, 1.5, 2.0, 3.5, 4.5, 16.5, 30.5

$$\bar{x} = \frac{0.5 + 0.5 + 1.5 + 2.0 + 3.5 + 4.5 + 16.5 + 30.5}{8} = \frac{59.5}{8} = 7.4375 \text{ inches}$$

The median is the mean of the two middle values, 2.0 and 3.5, or 2.75 inches.

The mode is 0.5 inch.

The median best represents the data. The mean is greater then most of the data values. The mode is less than most of the data values.

EXERCISES

EXAMPLES
1 and 2
on pp. 875–876
for Ex. 23

23. **BASEBALL STATISTICS** The numbers of home runs hit by baseball player Manny Ramirez against several different opposing teams over 3 seasons are 5, 1, 10, 5, 5, 4, 1, 0, 7, 2, 1, 1, 1, 9, 6, 1, 2, 6, 2, 19, 6, and 17.

   a. Find the mean, median, and mode(s) of the data. **about 5.045, 4.5**

   b. Which measure of central tendency best represents the data? *Explain.*
   See margin.

Extra Example 13.5

You want to determine whether the students at your school think the cafeteria serves nutritious food. You randomly choose students standing in the cafeteria line during first period lunch. You ask each student, "Do you think the cafeteria should serve better food?"

Identify the population and classify the sampling method. Tell whether the question is potentially biased. Explain your answer. If the question is potentially biased, rewrite it so that it is not.

The population is all students at your school. The sampling method is convenience.

The question is biased because the word "better" is ambiguous. An unbiased question is "Do you think the cafeteria serves nutritious food?"

Extra Example 13.6

Your test scores for English and science are shown below. Compare the scores using the range and the mean absolute deviation.

English: 82, 76, 84, 82
Science: 91, 84, 88, 90
English: range is 8 and mean absolute deviation is 2.5
Science: range is 7 and mean absolute deviation is 2.25
The range of English test scores is greater. The mean absolute deviation for the English scores is also greater.

23b. Median. *Sample answer:*
The mode is much lower than many of the values, and the mean is affected by the two extreme values (17 and 19) that are much greater than the rest of the data. So, the median best represents the data.

Extra Example 13.7

The back-to-back stem-and-leaf plot shows the prices (in dollars) of oak trees and maple trees at a nursery. Compare the prices of the two trees at the nursery.

Tree Prices

Oak		Maple
3 1 0	4	0 0 2 3 3
7 5 5	5	1 1 2 3 5 5
8 7 6 5 4	6	0 2 2
8 8 5 5	7	2

Key: 5|5|1 = $55, $51

The median price of oak trees is $65, while the median price of maple trees is $52. In general, oak trees cost more than maple trees at the nursery.

Extra Example 13.8

Make a box-and-whisker plot of the prices of oak trees in the extra example above.

24.

Stem	Leaves
0	0 0 0 0 0 5
1	0 0 5
2	0 0 0 0 5 5
3	0 0 5
4	0 5

Key: 1|0 = 10 minutes

25.

13.7 Interpret Stem-and-Leaf Plots and Histograms
pp. 881–885

EXAMPLE

The prices (in dollars) of several books are listed below. Make a stem-and-leaf plot of the prices.

14, 15, 9, 19, 21, 29, 12, 25, 10, 8, 15, 13, 15, 20

STEP 1 Separate the data into stems and leaves

Book Prices

Stem	Leaves
0	9 8
1	4 5 9 2 0 5 3 5
2	1 9 0 5

Key: 1 | 4 = $14

STEP 2 Write the leaves in increasing order.

Book Prices

Stem	Leaves
0	8 9
1	0 2 3 4 5 5 5 9
2	0 1 5 9

Key: 1 | 4 = $14

EXERCISES

EXAMPLE 1
on p. 881
for Ex. 24

24. EXERCISING The minutes per day that the students in a class spend exercising are listed below. Make a stem-and-leaf plot of the data. **See margin.**

20, 25, 0, 10, 0, 30, 35, 20, 45, 25, 40, 0, 0, 0, 5, 10, 20, 15, 20, 30

13.8 Interpret Box-and-Whisker Plots
pp. 887–892

EXAMPLE

Make a box-and-whisker plot of the book prices in the example above.

Order the data. Then find the median and quartiles.

Upper quartile   Median = 15   Lower quartile

8 9 10 **12** 13 14 15 15 15 19 **20** 21 25 29

Plot the median, the quartiles, the maximum value, and the minimum value below a number line. Draw the box and the whiskers.

EXERCISES

EXAMPLE 1
on p. 887
for Ex. 25

25. EXERCISING Use the data in Exercise 24 to make a box-and-whisker plot of the minutes per day that the students in the class spend exercising. **See margin.**

900 Chapter 13 Probability and Data Analysis

You roll a number cube. Find (a) the probability that the number rolled is as described and (b) the odds in favor of rolling such a number.

1. a 4 **a.** $\frac{1}{6}$ **b. 1 : 5**

2. an even number **a.** $\frac{1}{2}$ **b. 1 : 1**

3. a number less than 5 **a.** $\frac{2}{3}$ **b. 2 : 1**

4. a multiple of 3 **a.** $\frac{1}{3}$ **b. 1 : 2**

Evaluate the expression.

5. $_7P_2$ **42**

6. $_8P_3$ **336**

7. $_6C_3$ **20**

8. $_{12}C_7$ **792**

Tell whether the question can be answered using *combinations* or *permutations*. *Explain* your choice, then answer the question.

9. Eight swimmers participate in a race. In how many ways can the swimmers finish in first, second, and third place?

10. A restaurant offers 7 different side dishes. In how many different ways can you choose 2 side dishes? **Combinations; order does not matter since the side dishes can be selected in either order; 21 ways.**

In Exercises 11 and 12, refer to a bag containing 12 tiles numbered 1–12.

11. You choose a tile at random. What is the probability that you choose a number less than 10 or an odd number. $\frac{5}{6}$

12. You choose a tile at random, replace it, and choose a second tile at random. What is the probability that you choose a number greater than 3, then an odd number. $\frac{3}{8}$

13. **GOVERNMENT PROJECT** City officials want to know whether residents will support construction of a new library. This question appears on the ballot in the citywide election: "Do you support a tax increase to replace the old, deteriorating library with a brand new one?"Is the question potentially biased? *Explain* your answer. If the question is potentially biased, rewrite it so that it is not. **See margin.**

14. **BASKETBALL** The back-to-back stem-and-leaf plot shows the heights (in inches) of the players on a high school's basketball teams. **a–d. See margin.**

Basketball Players' Heights

	Girls		Boys	
9 7 7 6 6 5 3 3	6	9 9 9
3 2 1 1 0	7	0 0 0 2 4 4 6 6 7 7 7 8

Key: 3 | 6 | 9 = 63 in., 69 in.

a. Find the mean, median, and mode(s) of each data set. Which measure of central tendency best represents each data set? *Explain*.

b. Find the range and mean absolute deviation of each data set. Which team's heights are more spread out? *Explain*.

c. Make a box-and-whisker plot of each data set.

d. *Compare* the boys' heights with the girls' heights.

9. Permutations; order matters since there are first, second, and third places; 336 ways.

Chapter Test   **901**

Additional Resources

Assessment Book

- Chapter Test, Levels A, B, C, pp. 185–190
- Standardized Chapter Test, pp. 191–192
- SAT/ACT Chapter Test, pp. 193–194
- Alternative Assessment, pp. 195–196

Test Generator CD-ROM

Chapter Test

Easily-readable reduced copies (with answers) of Chapter Test B, the Standardized Chapter Test, and the Alternative Assessment from the Assessment Book can be found on pp. 840F–840H.

14a. Girls: mean: about 67.92, median: 67, mode: 66, 67, and 71; Boys: mean: 73.2, median: 74, mode: 69, 70, and 77

14b. Girls: range: 10, mean absolute deviation: 2.84; Boys: range: 9, mean absolute deviation: 3.12. *Sample answer:* Boys; their range is less, but their mean absolute deviation is greater which indicates that, on the average, the points are farther away from the mean.

14c.

14d. *Sample answer:* Generally, the boys are taller than the girls. 50% of the boys are taller than all of the girls. Each group's data is almost equally dispersed, with the boy's having a slightly greater interquartile range.

13. Yes. *Sample answer:* The question suggests that the current library is old and deteriorating and that a new library would be an improvement; "Are you for or against a tax increase to build a new library to replace the old one?"

Using Rubrics

The rubric given on the pupil page is a sample of a three-level rubric. Other rubrics may contain four, five, or six levels. For more information on rubrics, see the *Algebra 1 Toolkit*.

Test-Taking Strategy

Encourage students to write down what they need to include when they are asked to display data in a graph. They should take a couple of minutes to think about the values or labels they need to show in their displays. After they have created the display, they can check it against their list to make sure that they have included all of the elements of the particular display. Tell students that using a checklist will increase their chances of getting full credit for the graph because it is easy to overlook a single element among many.

Avoiding Common Errors

Students often answer the questions in a short response test question, but fail to explain their answers. Remind students to check that they have answered all parts of the question.

Scoring Rubric

Full Credit
- solution is complete and correct

Partial Credit
- solution is complete but has errors, *or*
- solution is without error but incomplete

No Credit
- no solution is given, *or*
- solution makes no sense

SHORT RESPONSE QUESTIONS

> **PROBLEM**

The lengths (in inches) of several goldfish are listed below. Make a box-and-whisker plot of the lengths. Can any of the goldfish lengths be considered outliers? *Explain* why or why not.

$$8, 5, 4, 5, 4, 5, 4, 3, 4, 8$$

Below are sample solutions to the problem. Read each solution and the comments in blue to see why the sample represents full credit, partial credit, or no credit.

SAMPLE 1: Full credit solution

First, order the lengths from least to greatest.

$$3, 4, 4, 4, 4, 5, 5, 5, 8, 8$$

Then, plot the median, the quartiles, the maximum value, and the minimum value below a number line. Draw the box and whiskers.

▸ The box-and-whisker plot is correct, and the student explained how it was drawn.

The interquartile range of the goldfish lengths is $5 - 4 = 1$, and 1.5 times the interquartile range is $1.5 \cdot 1 = 1.5$.

▸ The question is answered correctly and includes an explanation.

A length that is less than $4 - 1.5 = 2.5$ would be an outlier. A length that is greater than $5 + 1.5 = 6.5$ would also an outlier. So, the two fish lengths of 8 inches are outliers.

SAMPLE 2: Partial credit solution

▸ The box-and-whisker plot is incorrect. The student has not identified the median.

The interquartile range of the lengths is $5 - 4 = 1$, and $1 \cdot 1.5 = 1.5$.

▸ The answer and reasoning are correct.

A length that is less than $4 - 1.5 = 2.5$ is an outlier. A length that is greater than $5 + 1.5 = 6.5$ is an outlier. So, the two fish lengths of 8 inches are outliers.

SAMPLE 3: Partial credit solution

The box-and-whisker plot is correct.

The answer is correct, but the reasoning is incorrect.

The interquartile range of the goldfish lengths is $5 - 4 = 1$.

A length that is less than $4 - 1 = 3$ is an outlier. A length that is greater than $5 + 1 = 6$ is an outlier. So, the two fish lengths of 8 inches are outliers.

SAMPLE 4: No credit solution

There is no box-and-whisker plot. The answer is incorrect.

The value 3 is an outlier because it is a very small goldfish.

PRACTICE   Apply the Scoring Rubric

Score the solution to the problem below as *full credit, partial credit,* or *no credit. Explain* your reasoning.

> **PROBLEM** The number of runs scored by 13 players on a baseball team are listed below. Make a box-and-whisker plot of the data. Can any of the values be considered outliers? *Explain* why or why not.
>
> 24, 20, 20, 11, 17, 6, 16, 16, 6, 5, 1, 5, 4

1. Partial credit. *Sample answer:* the box-and-whisker plot is correct, but there is no reasoning given for determining that there are no outliers.

1.

There are no outliers in the data set.

2. Full credit. *Sample answer:* The box-and-whisker plot is correct, and the reasoning is correct.

2.

The interquartile range is 13.5, and $1.5 \cdot 13.5 = 20.25$. No values are less than $5 - 20.25 = -15.25$ or greater than $18.5 + 20.25 = 38.75$. So, there are no outliers.

Mathematical Reasoning

Tell students that it is a good idea to show their work so that a test reviewer can see how they arrived at their answers. They should show their work even if they use a calculator or mental math.

1b. $\frac{2}{5}$. *Sample answer:* Since the books are selected randomly, each book has an equal $\frac{1}{5}$ chance of being in the first, second, third, fourth, or fifth position. Since being selected first and being selected second are mutually exclusive, to find the probability that the longest book is first or second you can add the probability that it is selected first to the probability that it is selected second, $\frac{1}{5} + \frac{1}{5} = \frac{2}{5}$.

2a.

2b. No. *Sample answer:* The extreme values are less than 1.5 times the interquartile range from the nearest quartile.

3b. Median. *Sample answer:* The mean is affected by the outlier 46, and there are 2 modes.

4b. Combinations. *Sample answer:* It doesn't matter in which order you select the 3 toppings.

5a.

6a. *Sample answer:* You could select individuals sitting in randomly selected seats at a basketball game.

6b. *Sample answer:* What kind of food would you be most likely to buy at a basketball game?

7b. $\frac{27}{40}$. *Sample answer:* $\frac{27}{40}$ is the sum of the answer from part (a) and the probability of selecting a medium short-sleeve T-shirt or a large long-sleeve T-shirt.

SHORT RESPONSE

1. Your English teacher gives you a list of 5 books that you are required to read over summer vacation. You read the books in a random order.

 a. In how many different ways can you read the 5 books? **120 ways**

 b. What is the probability that you read the longest book first or second? *Explain* how you found this probability. **See margin.**

2. The median ages (in years) of residents of 13 towns in a county are listed below.

> 39, 35, 34, 40, 33, 30, 37,
> 27, 33, 29, 33, 31, 35
> **a, b. See margin.**

 a. Make a box-and-whisker plot of the ages.

 b. Can any of the ages be considered outliers? *Explain* why or why not.

3. The lengths (in seconds) of songs on one CD are listed below.

> 136, 249, 434, 136, 299,
> 227, 270, 270, 46, 254

 a. Find the mean, median, and mode(s) of the song lengths. **232.1 sec, 251.5 sec, 136 sec and 270 sec**

 b. Which measure of central tendency best represents the data? *Explain*. **See margin.**

4. You are ordering a pizza with 3 toppings. There are 8 toppings available.

 a. How many possible pizzas with 3 toppings can you order? **56 pizzas**

 b. Did you answer the question in part (a) using combinations or permutations? *Explain* your choice. **See margin.**

5. The prices (in dollars) of several mobile phones sold by one retailer are listed below.

> 350, 395, 429, 300, 569, 200, 500, 10,
> 234, 245, 440, 50, 800, 390, 440, 338

 a. Make a box-and-whisker plot of the mobile phone prices. **See margin.**

 b. Which prices, if any, can be considered outliers? *Explain*. **$800. Sample answer: 800 is more than 1.5 times the interquartile range of 100.5 from the upper quartile, 440.**

6. You want to find out what kinds of food items would be most popular to sell to people who attend basketball games at your high school. You decide to conduct a survey. **a, b. See margin.**

 a. *Describe* how you could choose a representative sample.

 b. Write an unbiased question that you could use to collect information on what kinds of food items people would be most likely to purchase during a basketball game. *Explain* why your question is unbiased.

7. The student council has ordered T-shirts for everyone who participated in a recent fundraiser. The table below shows the number of each type of T-shirt ordered. You reach into the box of T-shirts and choose one at random.

	Medium	Large
Long sleeve	9	10
Short sleeve	8	13

 a. What is the probability that you choose a medium long-sleeve T-shirt? $\frac{9}{40}$

 b. What is the probability that you choose a medium T-shirt or a long-sleeve T-shirt? *Explain* how this probability is related to the probability you found in part (a). **See margin.**

8. The back-to-back stem-and-leaf plot shows the prices (in dollars) of 15 dinners at two competing restaurants. *Compare* the prices at the two restaurants.

Dinner Prices

Restaurant A		Restaurant B
9 9 9 8	0	
7 7 5 5 2 2 1 0	1	0 2 2 3 5 6 6 8
1 0 0	2	1 2 4 4 5 5 5

Key: 0 | 2 | 1 = $20, $21

Sample answer: Generally, Restaurant B is more expensive. Restaurant A has cheaper options than does Restaurant B, and Restaurant B has several dinners that are more expensive than anything at Restaurant A.

904   Chapter 13   Probability and Data Analysis

MULTIPLE CHOICE

9. The odds in favor of an event are 3 : 4. What is the probability of the event? **B**

- **(A)** $\frac{1}{4}$
- **(B)** $\frac{3}{7}$
- **(C)** 75%
- **(D)** $\frac{3}{4}$

10. A bag contains 4 red marbles, 3 green marbles, and 5 blue marbles. You randomly choose a marble from the bag. What is the probability that you choose a blue marble? **B**

- **(A)** $\frac{1}{5}$
- **(B)** $\frac{5}{12}$
- **(C)** $\frac{5}{11}$
- **(D)** $\frac{5}{7}$

11. You roll a number cube. What is the probability that you roll a multiple of 2 or a multiple of 3? **C**

- **(A)** $\frac{1}{6}$
- **(B)** $\frac{1}{3}$
- **(C)** $\frac{2}{3}$
- **(D)** $\frac{5}{6}$

GRIDDED ANSWER

12. What is the value of $_4P_3$? **24**

13. In how many ways can you arrange the letters in the word BEACH? **120 ways**

14. What is the range of the given data set? **55**

32, 41, 29, 28, 40, 78, 56, 23, 61, 30

15. The stem-and-leaf plot shows the ages (in years) of members of one family. What is the median age? **39 yr**

```
0 | 8  9
1 | 0  4  6  7
2 | 0
3 | 9
4 | 2  3  3  4  5
5 |
6 | 8  9
```

Key: 0 | 8 = 8 years

EXTENDED RESPONSE

16. A survey asked 500 teenagers where they would like to live. Of those surveyed, 150 teenagers would like to live in a large city. A participant in this survey is chosen at random.

a. What is the probability that the participant would like to live in a large city? $\frac{3}{10}$

b. What are the odds in favor of the participant's wanting to live in a large city? **3 : 7**

c. *Explain* how the probability in part (a) and odds in part (b) are related. **See margin.**

17. The histogram shows the diameters (in kilometers) of Jupiter's ten largest moons. **a–c. See margin.**

a. *Describe* the distribution of the data in the histogram. In your description, mention whether the data appear to be spread out or clumped in a certain way.

b. The diameters (in kilometers) of Saturn's ten largest moons are listed below.

97, 209, 256, 536, 560, 764, 2575, 180, 718, 110

Make a histogram of the diameters.

c. *Compare* the distribution of diameters of Jupiter's moons with the distribution of diameters of Saturn's moons.

Jupiter's Largest Moons

Frequency vs Diameter (km): 1–1375, 1376–2750, 2751–4125, 4126–5500

16c. *Sample answer:* The odds in favor is the ratio of the numerator from part (a) to the denominator minus the numerator from part (a).

17a. *Sample answer:* Most of the data is clumped in the first interval. The remainder of the data is in the third and fourth intervals. So, most of the data is relatively small and the remainder is relatively large.

17b.

Saturn's Largest Moons

Frequency vs Diameter (km): 0–650, 651–1300, 1301–1950, 1951–2600

17c. *Sample answer:* Like Jupiter, most of the data for Saturn is clumped in the first interval. Relative to Jupiter, however, Saturn's moons are small. The largest of Saturn's moons would fall in the second interval in the Jupiter graph, and the majority of Saturn's moons are much smaller than this.

Additional Resources

The following resources are available to help review the materials in Chapters 1–13.

Chapter Resource Books

- Chapter 11 CRB, Cumulative Review, pp. 64–65
- Chapter 12 CRB, Cumulative Review, pp. 89–90
- Chapter 13 CRB, Cumulative Review, pp. 101–102

Assessment Book

- Cumulative Test, Chapters 8–13, pp. 197–200
- Cumulative Test, Chapters 1–13, pp. 201–204

7.

8.

9.

12.

13.

14.

Evaluate the expression.

1. $2^4 \cdot 3 - 16 \div 4$ *(p. 8)* **44**
2. $|-125| - 34$ *(p. 80)* **91**
3. $\pm\sqrt{2025}$ *(p. 110)* **±45**

Solve the equation.

4. $7 - 2x = 13$ *(p. 141)* **−3**
5. $-8x + 15 + 5x = 9$ *(p. 148)* **2**
6. $5(2x + 3) = 4x$ *(p. 154)* **−2.5**

Graph the equation. 7–9. See margin.

7. $x = 7$ *(p. 215)*
8. $y = 2x + 3$ *(p. 244)*
9. $4y - 2x = 1$ *(p. 244)*

Write an equation in slope-intercept form of the line with the given characteristics.

10. passes through $(-2, -8)$ and $(3, -5.5)$ *(p. 292)* $y = \frac{1}{2}x - 7$
11. slope: -8; passes through $(1, -5)$ *(p. 292)* $y = -8x + 3$

Solve the inequality. Graph your solution. 12–14. See margin for art.

12. $4x - 6 \le 8x - 2$ *(p. 369)* $x \ge -1$
13. $-2 \le x - 6 < 18$ *(p. 380)* $4 \le x < 24$
14. $2x < 6$ or $4x \ge 8$ *(p. 380)* **all real numbers**

Solve the linear system.

15. $x = 4y + 3$ *(p. 435)* $(4, \frac{1}{4})$
    $2x - 4y = 7$
16. $3x - 7y = 20$ *(p. 451)* **(−5, −5)**
    $-11x + 10y = 5$
17. $-9x + 6y = 0$ *(p. 451)* **no solution**
    $-12x + 8y = 5$

Simplify the expression. Write your answer using only positive exponents.

18. $(2x^3)^4 \cdot x^9$ *(p. 489)* $16x^{21}$
19. $(-9x^3)^2\left(-\frac{1}{4}x^6\right)$ *(p. 489)* $\dfrac{-81x^{12}}{4}$
20. $\dfrac{(3x)^{-3}y^3}{x^2y^{-1}}$ *(p. 503)* $\dfrac{y^4}{27x^5}$

Factor the polynomial.

21. $a^2 - 15a - 54$ *(p. 583)* $(a - 18)(a + 3)$
22. $-3b^2 - 22b - 7$ *(p. 593)* $-(3b + 1)(b + 7)$
23. $4f^2 + 4fg + g^2$ *(p. 600)* $(2f + g)^2$
24. $p^2(p - 5) + 9(5 - p)$ *(p. 606)* $(p - 5)(p - 3)(p + 3)$

Solve the equation.

25. $(x + 7)(x - 3) = 0$ *(p. 575)* **−7, 3**
26. $9x^2 - 28x + 3 = 0$ *(p. 652)* $\frac{1}{9}$, 3
27. $8x^2 + 7 = 36x - 9$ *(p. 661)* $\frac{1}{2}$, 4
28. $\sqrt{x + 8} + 10 = 2$ *(p. 729)* **no solution**

Find the distance between the two points. *(p. 744)*

29. $(5, 2)$, $(7, 14)$ $2\sqrt{37}$
30. $(-8, 6)$, $(5, 0)$ $\sqrt{205}$
31. $(2.5, 7)$, $(2.5, -8)$ **15**

Find the sum, difference, product, or quotient.

32. $\dfrac{x - 2}{x + 5} \cdot \dfrac{x + 5}{x - 8}$ *(p. 802)* $\dfrac{x - 2}{x - 8}$
33. $\dfrac{x^3 - 16x}{x^2 + 3x} \div (x - 4)$ *(p. 802)* $\dfrac{x + 4}{x + 3}$
34. $\dfrac{16}{2x^4} \cdot \dfrac{7x^3}{2x}$ *(p. 802)* $\dfrac{28}{x^2}$
35. $\dfrac{2x}{3 - x} + \dfrac{x - 9}{3 - x}$ *(p. 812)* **−3**
36. $\dfrac{1}{x + 6} + \dfrac{4x}{x + 6}$ *(p. 812)* $\dfrac{4x + 1}{x + 6}$
37. $\dfrac{9}{x^2 - 3x} - \dfrac{3}{x - 3}$ *(p. 812)* $\dfrac{9 - 3x}{x^2 - 3x}$

Evaluate the expression.

38. $_6P_1$ *(p. 851)* **6**
39. $_8P_3$ *(p. 851)* **336**
40. $_7C_3$ *(p. 856)* **35**
41. $_{10}C_6$ *(p. 856)* **210**

42. You roll a number cube. What is the probability that you roll a 5? *(p. 843)* $\frac{1}{6}$

43. You roll a number cube. What is the probability that you roll a 2 or an even number? *(p. 861)* $\frac{1}{2}$

44. You choose a number from 1 to 20 at random. What is the probability that you choose a prime number? *(p. 843)* $\frac{2}{5}$

45. You choose a number from 1 to 20 at random. What is the probability that you choose a multiple of 6? *(p. 843)* $\frac{3}{20}$

46. A bag contains 2 red marbles, 4 green marbles, and 4 blue marbles. You choose one marble at random, put the marble back into the bag, then choose a second marble at random. What is the probability that you choose 2 red marbles? *(p. 861)* $\frac{1}{25}$

47. **MARATHON** Two runners are training for a marathon. When running a practice distance of 26.2 miles, one runner begins running 6 minutes after the other. The speed of the first runner is 11.4 miles per hour. The speed of the second runner is 12 miles per hour. After how many minutes does the second runner pass the first runner? *(p. 435)* **Sample answer: 120 min after the first runner starts**

48. **STONE ARCH** The shape of a stone arch can be modeled by the graph of the equation $y = -0.5x^2 + 4x + 4$ where x is the horizontal distance (in feet) from one end of the arch and y is its height (in feet) above the ground. What is the maximum height of the arch? *Explain* how you found your answer. *(p. 628)* **See margin.**

49. **GUY WIRE** A guy wire supports an antenna tower, as shown at the right. The bottom of the wire is secured in the ground 30 feet from the base of the tower. The top of the wire is secured to the tower at a height of 30 feet above the ground. How long is the wire? Round your answer to the nearest tenth of a foot. *(p. 737)* **42.4 ft**

50. **HEATING RATES** An electric heater takes 8 minutes to heat an entire apartment to the desired temperature. A wood stove and an electric heater together take 6 minutes to heat the apartment. How many minutes does it take the wood stove alone to heat the apartment to the desired temperature? *(p. 820)* **24 min**

51. **FLIGHTS** You are traveling from Boston, Massachusetts, to Richmond, Virginia. The prices (in dollars) of airline tickets for different flights between the cities are listed below.

    176, 191, 195, 197, 197, 204, 204, 204, 204,
    204, 206, 206, 206, 206, 206, 217, 217, 221

    a. What is the range of the prices? *(p. 875)* **$45**

    b. Make a stem-and-leaf plot of the prices. *(p. 881)* **b–d. See margin.**

    c. Make a box-and-whisker plot of the prices. *(p. 887)*

    d. Can any of these prices be considered outliers? *Explain* why or why not. *(p. 887)*

Contents of Student Resources

Skills Review Handbook

Comparing and Ordering Decimals

A **number line** is a line whose points are associated with numbers. You can use a number line to compare and order decimals. From left to right, the numbers on a number line appear in order from least to greatest.

EXAMPLE Copy and complete the statement using <, >, or =.

a. 9.67 __?__ 9.59

9.67 is to the right of 9.59,
so 9.67 is greater than 9.59.

▸ 9.67 > 9.59

b. 0.08 __?__ 0.12

0.08 is to the left of 0.12,
so 0.08 is less than 0.012.

▸ 0.08 < 0.012

EXAMPLE Order the numbers 0.4, 0.56, 0.48, and 0.515 from least to greatest.

Graph all the numbers on a number line.

Write the numbers as they appear on the number line from left to right.

▸ The numbers in order from least to greatest are 0.4, 0.48, 0.515, and 0.56.

PRACTICE

Copy and complete the statement using <, >, or =.

1. 1.48 __?__ 1.413 >
2. 0.809 __?__ 0.81 <
3. 5.47 __?__ 5.43 >
4. 0.01 __?__ 0.005 >
5. 35.2 __?__ 35 >
6. 6.24 __?__ 6.2 >
7. 1.674 __?__ 1.678 <
8. 20.05 __?__ 20.3 <
9. 9.018 __?__ 9.017 >

Order the numbers from least to greatest.

10. 2.5, 2.3, 2.45, 2.38
    2.3, 2.38, 2.45, 2.5
11. 7.01, 7.13, 7.3, 7.03
    7.01, 7.03, 7.13, 7.3
12. 10.19, 10.2, 10, 10.4
    10, 10.19, 10.2, 10.4
13. 0.3, 0.47, 0.9, 0.15
    0.15, 0.3, 0.47, 0.9
14. 1.3, 1.05, 1.11, 1.0
    1.0, 1.05, 1.11, 1.3
15. 12.6, 10.9, 11, 11.9
    10.9, 11, 11.9, 12.6
16. 6.1, 6.89, 7.25, 7
    6.1, 6.89, 7, 7.25
17. 3.1, 3.3, 0.3, 1.33
    0.3, 1.33, 3.1, 3.3
18. 5.46, 5.4, 5.64, 5.6
    5.4, 5.46, 5.6, 5.64

Factors and Multiples

A **prime number** is a whole number that is greater than 1 and has exactly two whole number factors, 1 and itself. A **composite number** is a whole number that is greater than 1 and has more than two whole number factors. The table below shows that the first five prime numbers are 2, 3, 5, 7, and 11.

Number	Product(s)	Factor(s)	Prime or composite?
1	1 · 1	1	Neither
2	1 · 2	1, 2	Prime
3	1 · 3	1, 3	Prime
4	1 · 4, 2 · 2	1, 2, 4	Composite
5	1 · 5	1, 5	Prime
6	1 · 6, 2 · 3	1, 2, 3, 6	Composite
7	1 · 7	1, 7	Prime
8	1 · 8, 2 · 4	1, 2, 4, 8	Composite
9	1 · 9, 3 · 3	1, 3, 9	Composite
10	1 · 10, 2 · 5	1, 2, 5, 10	Composite
11	1 · 11	1, 11	Prime
12	1 · 12, 2 · 6, 3 · 4	1, 2, 3, 4, 6, 12	Composite

When you write a composite number as a product of prime numbers, you are writing its **prime factorization**. You can use a **factor tree** to write the prime factorization of a number.

EXAMPLE   **Write the prime factorization of 120.**

Write 120 at the top of your factor tree. Draw two branches and write 120 as the product of two factors. Continue to draw branches until all the factors are prime numbers (shown in red). Here are two possible factor trees for 120.

Start with 120 = 2 · 60.

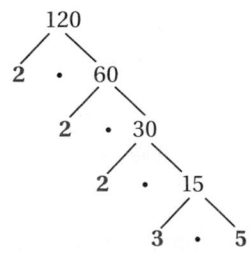

Start with 120 = 10 · 12.

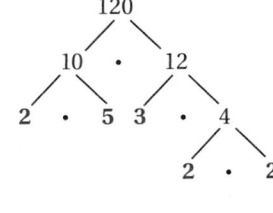

Both factor trees show that $120 = 2 \cdot 2 \cdot 2 \cdot 3 \cdot 5$, or $120 = 2^3 \cdot 3 \cdot 5$.

▸ The prime factorization of 120 is $2^3 \cdot 3 \cdot 5$.

For two or more nonzero whole numbers, a **common factor** is a whole number that is a factor of each number. The **greatest common factor (GCF)** of two or more nonzero whole numbers is the greatest of their common factors.

EXAMPLE Find the greatest common factor of 30 and 42.

Write the prime factorization of each number. The greatest common factor is the product of the common prime factors.

$$30 = 2 \cdot 3 \cdot 5 \qquad \text{and} \qquad 42 = 2 \cdot 3 \cdot 7$$

The common prime factors are 2 and 3. The GCF is the product $2 \cdot 3 = 6$.

▶ The greatest common factor of 30 and 42 is 6.

A **multiple** of a whole number is the product of the number and any nonzero whole number. A **common multiple** of two or more whole numbers is a multiple of each number. The **least common multiple (LCM)** of two or more whole numbers is the least of their common multiples.

EXAMPLE Find the least common multiple of 10 and 15.

Write the prime factorization of each number. The least common multiple is the product of the factors, using each common prime factor only once.

$$10 = 2 \cdot 5 \qquad \text{and} \qquad 15 = 3 \cdot 5$$

The common prime factor is 5. The LCM is the product $2 \cdot 3 \cdot 5 = 30$.

▶ The least common multiple of 10 and 15 is 30.

PRACTICE

Write the prime factorization of the number if it is not a prime number. If the number is prime, write *prime*.

1. 28 $2^2 \cdot 7$
2. 16 2^4
3. 11 **prime**
4. 100 $2^2 \cdot 5^2$
5. 81 3^4
6. 49 7^2
7. 60 $2^2 \cdot 3 \cdot 5$
8. 53 **prime**
9. 180 $2^2 \cdot 3^2 \cdot 5$
10. 19 **prime**
11. 51 $3 \cdot 17$
12. 72 $2^3 \cdot 3^2$

Find the greatest common factor of the pair of numbers.

13. 4, 8 **4**
14. 5, 6 **1**
15. 60, 18 **6**
16. 2, 10 **2**
17. 36, 27 **9**
18. 15, 21 **3**
19. 12, 16 **4**
20. 24, 108 **12**
21. 48, 88 **8**
22. 8, 12 **4**
23. 20, 28 **4**
24. 3, 5 **1**

Find the least common multiple of the pair of numbers.

25. 6, 9 **18**
26. 3, 8 **24**
27. 5, 45 **45**
28. 16, 20 **80**
29. 10, 65 **130**
30. 12, 15 **60**
31. 9, 30 **90**
32. 8, 9 **72**
33. 2, 14 **14**
34. 28, 32 **224**
35. 7, 49 **49**
36. 4, 6 **12**

Finding Equivalent Fractions and Simplifying Fractions

A **fraction** is a number of the form $\frac{a}{b}$ where a is the **numerator** and b is the **denominator**. The value of b cannot be 0.

The number lines show the graphs of two fractions, $\frac{1}{2}$ and $\frac{2}{4}$.

These fractions represent the same number. Two fractions that represent the same number are called **equivalent fractions**.

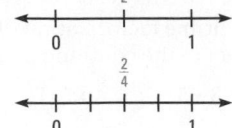

To write equivalent fractions, you can multiply or divide the numerator and the denominator by the same nonzero number.

EXAMPLE Write two fractions that are equivalent to $\frac{6}{8}$.

Multiply the numerator and denominator by 3.

$$\frac{6}{8} = \frac{6 \times 3}{8 \times 3} = \frac{18}{24} \quad \textbf{Equivalent fraction}$$

Divide the numerator and denominator by 2.

$$\frac{6}{8} = \frac{6 \div 2}{8 \div 2} = \frac{3}{4} \quad \textbf{Equivalent fraction}$$

A fraction is in **simplest form** when its numerator and its denominator have no common factors besides 1.

EXAMPLE Write the fraction $\frac{10}{15}$ in simplest form.

Divide the numerator and denominator by 5, the greatest common factor of 10 and 15.

$$\frac{10}{15} = \frac{10 \div 5}{15 \div 5} = \frac{2}{3} \quad \textbf{Simplest form}$$

PRACTICE

Write two fractions that are equivalent to the given fraction. **1–5. Sample answers are given.**

1. $\frac{9}{12}$ $\frac{3}{4}$ and $\frac{18}{24}$
2. $\frac{4}{6}$ $\frac{2}{3}$ and $\frac{8}{12}$
3. $\frac{1}{2}$ $\frac{2}{4}$ and $\frac{3}{6}$
4. $\frac{2}{5}$ $\frac{4}{10}$ and $\frac{6}{15}$
5. $\frac{10}{14}$ $\frac{5}{7}$ and $\frac{20}{28}$

Write the fraction in simplest form.

6. $\frac{16}{24}$ $\frac{2}{3}$
7. $\frac{3}{12}$ $\frac{1}{4}$
8. $\frac{30}{48}$ $\frac{5}{8}$
9. $\frac{5}{40}$ $\frac{1}{8}$
10. $\frac{8}{20}$ $\frac{2}{5}$

11. $\frac{4}{16}$ $\frac{1}{4}$
12. $\frac{64}{72}$ $\frac{8}{9}$
13. $\frac{35}{100}$ $\frac{7}{20}$
14. $\frac{21}{81}$ $\frac{7}{27}$
15. $\frac{44}{55}$ $\frac{4}{5}$

16. $\frac{15}{20}$ $\frac{3}{4}$
17. $\frac{12}{28}$ $\frac{3}{7}$
18. $\frac{15}{39}$ $\frac{5}{13}$
19. $\frac{24}{78}$ $\frac{4}{13}$
20. $\frac{60}{96}$ $\frac{5}{8}$

Mixed Numbers and Improper Fractions

A **mixed number** is the sum of a whole number and a fraction. An **improper fraction** is a fraction with a numerator that is greater than or equal to the denominator.

The shaded part of the model at the right represents the mixed number $2\frac{1}{4}$ and the improper fraction $\frac{9}{4}$.

EXAMPLE Write $5\frac{7}{8}$ as an improper fraction.

$5\frac{7}{8} = 5 + \frac{7}{8}$ Definition of mixed number

$= \frac{40}{8} + \frac{7}{8}$ 1 whole $= \frac{8}{8}$, so 5 wholes $= \frac{40}{8}$.

$= \frac{47}{8}$ Add.

EXAMPLE Write $\frac{17}{5}$ as a mixed number.

$$5\overline{)17}\ \ ^{3}$$
$$\underline{15}$$
$$2$$

Divide the numerator by the denominator: $17 \div 5$.
The quotient is 3 and the remainder is 2.

▶ $\frac{17}{5} = 3\frac{2}{5}$ Write the remainder as a fraction, $\frac{\text{remainder}}{\text{divisor}}$.

PRACTICE

Write the mixed number as an improper fraction.

1. $1\frac{2}{3}$ $\frac{5}{3}$
2. $3\frac{1}{4}$ $\frac{13}{4}$
3. $10\frac{3}{10}$ $\frac{103}{10}$
4. $2\frac{3}{5}$ $\frac{13}{5}$
5. $4\frac{1}{2}$ $\frac{9}{2}$

6. $9\frac{1}{3}$ $\frac{28}{3}$
7. $1\frac{11}{12}$ $\frac{23}{12}$
8. $2\frac{3}{4}$ $\frac{11}{4}$
9. $6\frac{5}{8}$ $\frac{53}{8}$
10. $5\frac{9}{16}$ $\frac{89}{16}$

11. $8\frac{1}{8}$ $\frac{65}{8}$
12. $6\frac{3}{5}$ $\frac{33}{5}$
13. $7\frac{2}{9}$ $\frac{65}{9}$
14. $2\frac{3}{13}$ $\frac{29}{13}$
15. $12\frac{2}{3}$ $\frac{38}{3}$

Write the improper fraction as a mixed number.

16. $\frac{5}{2}$ $2\frac{1}{2}$
17. $\frac{12}{5}$ $2\frac{2}{5}$
18. $\frac{15}{8}$ $1\frac{7}{8}$
19. $\frac{25}{4}$ $6\frac{1}{4}$
20. $\frac{37}{3}$ $12\frac{1}{3}$

21. $\frac{7}{4}$ $1\frac{3}{4}$
22. $\frac{27}{8}$ $3\frac{3}{8}$
23. $\frac{29}{10}$ $2\frac{9}{10}$
24. $\frac{69}{16}$ $4\frac{5}{16}$
25. $\frac{54}{5}$ $10\frac{4}{5}$

26. $\frac{31}{4}$ $7\frac{3}{4}$
27. $\frac{22}{5}$ $4\frac{2}{5}$
28. $\frac{13}{3}$ $4\frac{1}{3}$
29. $\frac{43}{9}$ $4\frac{7}{9}$
30. $\frac{35}{11}$ $3\frac{2}{11}$

Adding and Subtracting Fractions

To add or subtract two fractions with the same denominator, write the sum or difference of the numerators over the denominator.

Sum and Difference Rules ($c \neq 0$)

$$\frac{a}{c} + \frac{b}{c} = \frac{a+b}{c} \qquad \frac{a}{c} - \frac{b}{c} = \frac{a-b}{c}$$

EXAMPLE Add or subtract: **a.** $\frac{1}{10} + \frac{3}{10}$ **b.** $\frac{7}{8} - \frac{3}{8}$

a. $\frac{1}{10} + \frac{3}{10} = \frac{4}{10}$ Add numerators.   **b.** $\frac{7}{8} - \frac{3}{8} = \frac{4}{8}$ Subtract numerators.

         $= \frac{2}{5}$ Simplify. $= \frac{1}{2}$ Simplify.

The **least common denominator (LCD)** of two fractions is the least common multiple of the denominators. To add or subtract two fractions with different denominators, use the LCD of the fractions to write equivalent fractions that have the same denominator.

EXAMPLE Add: $\frac{1}{4} + \frac{5}{6}$

The LCD of the fractions is 12, so write $\frac{1}{4}$ as $\frac{1 \times 3}{4 \times 3} = \frac{3}{12}$ and $\frac{5}{6}$ as $\frac{5 \times 2}{6 \times 2} = \frac{10}{12}$.

$\frac{1}{4} + \frac{5}{6} = \frac{3}{12} + \frac{10}{12}$ Write equivalent fractions.

       $= \frac{13}{12}$ Add.

       $= 1\frac{1}{12}$ Write as a mixed number.

PRACTICE

Add or subtract.

1. $\frac{1}{16} + \frac{3}{16}$ $\frac{1}{4}$ **2.** $\frac{1}{5} + \frac{2}{5}$ $\frac{3}{5}$ **3.** $\frac{7}{12} - \frac{5}{12}$ $\frac{1}{6}$ **4.** $\frac{2}{3} - \frac{1}{3}$ $\frac{1}{3}$ **5.** $\frac{5}{8} + \frac{3}{8}$ **1**

6. $\frac{3}{4} + \frac{3}{4}$ $1\frac{1}{2}$ **7.** $\frac{7}{8} - \frac{3}{8}$ $\frac{1}{2}$ **8.** $\frac{17}{20} + \frac{9}{20}$ $1\frac{3}{10}$ **9.** $\frac{7}{10} + \frac{1}{2}$ $1\frac{1}{5}$ **10.** $\frac{3}{10} + \frac{3}{5}$ $\frac{9}{10}$

11. $\frac{3}{8} - \frac{3}{16}$ $\frac{3}{16}$ **12.** $\frac{1}{3} + \frac{1}{10}$ $\frac{13}{30}$ **13.** $\frac{7}{12} - \frac{1}{16}$ $\frac{25}{48}$ **14.** $\frac{2}{3} - \frac{1}{4}$ $\frac{5}{12}$ **15.** $\frac{5}{6} + \frac{7}{8}$ $1\frac{17}{24}$

16. $\frac{3}{4} - \frac{5}{8}$ $\frac{1}{8}$ **17.** $\frac{3}{4} - \frac{1}{5}$ $\frac{11}{20}$ **18.** $\frac{5}{12} + \frac{2}{3}$ $1\frac{1}{12}$ **19.** $1 - \frac{1}{5}$ $\frac{4}{5}$ **20.** $4 - \frac{3}{16}$ $3\frac{13}{16}$

21. $2\frac{5}{8} + 4\frac{1}{8}$ $6\frac{3}{4}$ **22.** $2\frac{9}{10} - 1\frac{7}{10}$ $1\frac{1}{5}$ **23.** $1\frac{5}{6} + 3\frac{1}{6}$ **5**   **24.** $2\frac{1}{2} + 2\frac{3}{8}$ $4\frac{7}{8}$ **25.** $1\frac{3}{4} - \frac{11}{16}$ $1\frac{1}{16}$

Multiplying and Dividing Fractions

To multiply two fractions, write the product of the numerators over the product of the denominators.

Product Rule ($b, d \neq 0$)

$$\frac{a}{b} \times \frac{c}{d} = \frac{ac}{bd}$$

EXAMPLE Multiply: $\frac{3}{5} \times \frac{7}{8}$

$\frac{3}{5} \times \frac{7}{8} = \frac{3 \times 7}{5 \times 8}$ **Use product rule.**

$= \frac{21}{40}$ **Simplify.**

Two nonzero numbers whose product is 1 are **reciprocals**. For example, 6 and $\frac{1}{6}$ are reciprocals because $6 \times \frac{1}{6} = 1$. Every number except 0 has a reciprocal.

To divide by a fraction, multiply by its reciprocal.

Quotient Rule ($b, c, d \neq 0$)

$$\frac{a}{b} \div \frac{c}{d} = \frac{a}{b} \times \frac{d}{c}$$

EXAMPLE Divide: $\frac{5}{7} \div \frac{3}{4}$

The reciprocal of $\frac{3}{4}$ is $\frac{4}{3}$ because $\frac{3}{4} \times \frac{4}{3} = 1$, so multiply $\frac{5}{7}$ by $\frac{4}{3}$.

$\frac{5}{7} \div \frac{3}{4} = \frac{5}{7} \times \frac{4}{3}$ **Use quotient rule.**

$= \frac{20}{21}$ **Use product rule.**

PRACTICE

Multiply or divide.

1. $\frac{3}{4} \times \frac{2}{3}$ **$\frac{1}{2}$**
2. $\frac{1}{5} \times \frac{5}{8}$ **$\frac{1}{8}$**
3. $\frac{1}{6} \div \frac{1}{3}$ **$\frac{1}{2}$**
4. $\frac{2}{3} \div \frac{2}{3}$ **1**
5. $\frac{9}{10} \div \frac{4}{5}$ **$1\frac{1}{8}$**

6. $\frac{1}{12} \times \frac{3}{4}$ **$\frac{1}{16}$**
7. $\frac{3}{8} \times \frac{1}{8}$ **$\frac{3}{64}$**
8. $\frac{5}{6} \div \frac{1}{4}$ **$3\frac{1}{3}$**
9. $\frac{1}{2} \times \frac{1}{4}$ **$\frac{1}{8}$**
10. $\frac{7}{10} \div \frac{5}{8}$ **$1\frac{3}{25}$**

11. $\frac{3}{4} \div \frac{1}{2}$ **$1\frac{1}{2}$**
12. $\frac{5}{6} \times \frac{3}{10}$ **$\frac{1}{4}$**
13. $\frac{2}{5} \div \frac{4}{5}$ **$\frac{1}{2}$**
14. $\frac{9}{10} \times \frac{1}{3}$ **$\frac{3}{10}$**
15. $\frac{1}{4} \div \frac{7}{8}$ **$\frac{2}{7}$**

16. $\frac{3}{16} \times \frac{2}{5}$ **$\frac{3}{40}$**
17. $\frac{2}{5} \div 20$ **$\frac{1}{50}$**
18. $18 \times \frac{1}{3}$ **6**
19. $\frac{1}{10} \times 6$ **$\frac{3}{5}$**
20. $24 \div \frac{3}{8}$ **64**

21. $5\frac{1}{2} \times \frac{9}{16}$ **$3\frac{3}{32}$**
22. $8\frac{1}{4} \div \frac{3}{10}$ **$27\frac{1}{2}$**
23. $1\frac{7}{8} \times 2\frac{1}{3}$ **$4\frac{3}{8}$**
24. $3\frac{3}{4} \div 6\frac{1}{2}$ **$\frac{15}{26}$**
25. $2\frac{1}{2} \div 1\frac{7}{8}$ **$1\frac{1}{3}$**

Fractions, Decimals, and Percents

A **percent** is a fraction whose denominator is 100. The symbol for percent is %. In the model at the right, there are 100 squares in all, and 49 of the 100 squares are shaded. You can write the shaded part of the model as a fraction, a decimal, or a percent.

Fraction: forty-nine out of one hundred, or $\frac{49}{100}$

Decimal: forty-nine hundredths, or 0.49

Percent: forty-nine percent, or 49%

EXAMPLE   Write the fraction as a decimal: **a.** $\frac{1}{8}$ **b.** $\frac{5}{12}$

a. $\begin{array}{r} 0.125 \\ \hline 1\overline{)8.000} \end{array}$ **Divide.**

▶ $\frac{1}{8} = 0.125$

b. $\begin{array}{r} 0.41666\ldots \\ 12\overline{)5.00000\ldots} \end{array}$ **Divide.**

▶ $\frac{5}{12} = 0.41666\ldots = 0.41\overline{6}$

EXAMPLE   Write the decimal as a fraction: **a.** **0.7**   **b.** **0.32**

a.   0.7 = seven tenths

$= \frac{7}{10}$

b.   0.32 = thirty-two hundredths

$= \frac{32}{100}$

$= \frac{8}{25}$

To write a percent as a decimal, move the decimal point two places to the left and remove the percent sign.

EXAMPLE   Write the percent as a decimal: **a.** **16%**   **b.** **5%**

a.   16% = 16%

$= 0.16$

b.   5% = 05%

$= 0.05$

To write a decimal as a percent, move the decimal point two places to the right and write a percent sign.

EXAMPLE   Write the decimal as a percent: **a.** **0.83**   **b.** **0.195**

a.   0.83 = 0.83

$= 83\%$

b.   0.195 = 0.195

$= 19.5\%$

EXAMPLE   **Write the percent as a fraction:**   **a. 98%**   **b. 5%**

a. $98\% = \dfrac{98}{100}$ **Definition of percent**   **b.** $5\% = \dfrac{5}{100}$ **Definition of percent**

       $= \dfrac{49}{50}$ **Simplify.** $= \dfrac{1}{20}$ **Simplify.**

To write a fraction as a percent, you may be able to rewrite the fraction using a denominator of 100. If the denominator of the fraction is not a factor of 100, you can first write the fraction as a decimal and then as a percent.

EXAMPLE   **Write the fraction as a percent:**   **a.** $\dfrac{2}{5}$ **b.** $\dfrac{5}{8}$

a. $\dfrac{2}{5} = \dfrac{2(20)}{5(20)}$ **Write as a fraction with denominator 100.**   **b.** $\dfrac{5}{8} = 0.625$ **Write as a decimal.**

       $= \dfrac{40}{100} = 40\%$ **Write as a percent.** $= 62.5\%$ **Write as a percent.**

The table below gives commonly used fractions, decimals, and percents written in increasing order.

$\dfrac{1}{100} = 0.01 = 1\%$	$\dfrac{1}{16} = 0.0625 = 6.25\%$	$\dfrac{1}{10} = 0.1 = 10\%$	$\dfrac{1}{8} = 0.125 = 12.5\%$
$\dfrac{1}{5} = 0.2 = 20\%$	$\dfrac{1}{4} = 0.25 = 25\%$	$\dfrac{1}{3} = 0.\overline{3} \approx 33.3\%$	$\dfrac{3}{8} = 0.375 = 37.5\%$
$\dfrac{2}{5} = 0.4 = 40\%$	$\dfrac{1}{2} = 0.5 = 50\%$	$\dfrac{3}{5} = 0.6 = 60\%$	$\dfrac{5}{8} = 0.625 = 62.5\%$
$\dfrac{2}{3} = 0.\overline{6} \approx 66.7\%$	$\dfrac{3}{4} = 0.75 = 75\%$	$\dfrac{4}{5} = 0.8 = 80\%$	$\dfrac{7}{8} = 0.875 = 87.5\%$

PRACTICE

Write the percent as a decimal and as a fraction.

1. 70%   **0.7,** $\dfrac{7}{10}$ 2. 12%   **0.12,** $\dfrac{3}{25}$ 3. 3%   **0.03,** $\dfrac{3}{100}$ 4. 55%   **0.55,** $\dfrac{11}{20}$ 5. 35%   **0.35,** $\dfrac{7}{20}$

6. 9%   **0.09,** $\dfrac{9}{100}$ 7. 110%   **1.1, 1**$\dfrac{1}{10}$ 8. 225%   **2.25, 2**$\dfrac{1}{4}$ 9. 0.3%   **0.003,** $\dfrac{3}{1000}$ 10. 0.5%   **0.005,** $\dfrac{1}{200}$

Write the decimal as a fraction and as a percent.

11. 0.28 $\dfrac{7}{25}$**, 28%**   12. 0.13 $\dfrac{13}{100}$**, 13%**   13. 0.05 $\dfrac{1}{20}$**, 5%**   14. 0.36 $\dfrac{9}{25}$**, 36%**   15. 0.52 $\dfrac{13}{25}$**, 52%**

16. 0.004 $\dfrac{1}{250}$**, 0.4%**   17. 0.025 $\dfrac{1}{40}$**, 2.5%**   18. 4 $\dfrac{4}{1}$**, 400%**   19. 1.5 $\dfrac{3}{2}$**, 150%**   20. 2.3 $\dfrac{23}{10}$**, 230%**

Write the fraction as a decimal and as a percent. Round decimals to the nearest thousandth. Round percents to the nearest tenth of a percent.

21. $\dfrac{3}{16}$ **0.188, 18.8%**   22. $\dfrac{1}{9}$ **0.111, 11.1%**   23. $\dfrac{61}{100}$ **0.61, 61%**   24. $\dfrac{3}{20}$ **0.15, 15%**   25. $\dfrac{19}{100}$ **0.19, 19%**

26. $\dfrac{17}{25}$ **0.68, 68%**   27. $\dfrac{9}{25}$ **0.36, 36%**   28. $\dfrac{5}{6}$ **0.833, 83.3%**   29. $\dfrac{4}{7}$ **0.571, 57.1%**   30. $\dfrac{5}{12}$ **0.417, 41.7%**

Mean, Median, and Mode

Three measures of central tendency are mean, median, and mode.

The **mean** of a data set is the sum of the values divided by the number of values.	The **median** of a data set is the middle value when the values are written in numerical order. If a data set has an even number of values, the median is the mean of the two middle values.	The **mode** of a data set is the value that occurs most often. A data set can have no mode, one mode, or more than one mode.

EXAMPLE Find the mean, median, and mode(s) of the data in the table.

Mean

Add the values. Then divide by 8, the number of values.

Sum = 251 + 222 + 222 + 220 + 215 + 207 + 188 + 178
  = 1703

▶ Mean = $\frac{1703}{8}$ = 212.875

Median

Write the values in order from least to greatest. Then find the middle value(s).

178, 188, 207, **215**, **220**, 222, 222, 251

Find the mean of the two middle values.

▶ Median = $\frac{215 + 220}{2}$ = $\frac{435}{2}$ = 217.5

Mode

Find the value that occurs most often.

▶ Mode = 222

Lengths of School Years	
Country	School year (days)
China	251
Korea	222
Taiwan	222
Japan	220
Israel	215
Switzerland	207
Canada	188
United States	178

PRACTICE

Find the mean, median, and mode(s) of the data.

1. Test scores: 90, 88, 95, 94, 87, 85, 92, 99, 100, 94 **92.4; 93; 94**

2. Daily high temperatures (°F) for a week: 68, 70, 67, 68, 75, 75, 74 **71°F; 70°F; 68°F and 75°F**

3. Ages of employees: 24, 52, 21, 55, 39, 49, 28, 33, 52, 41, 30, 64, 45 **41 yr; 41 yr; 52 yr**

4. Numbers of students in classes: 21, 24, 27, 28, 25, 18, 22, 25, 26, 22, 27, 20 **23.75; 24.5; 22, 25, and 27**

5. Movie ticket prices: $6.75, $7.50, $7.25, $6.75, $6.25, $7.50, $7.25, $6.75, $7 **$7; $7; $6.75**

6. Hourly rates of pay: $14.50, $8.75, $7, $11, $16.50, $18, $12, $10.25 **$12.25; $11.50; no mode**

7. Numbers of children in families: 0, 0, 1, 1, 1, 2, 2, 2, 2, 2, 3, 3, 4, 4, 4, 5 **2.25; 2; 2**

8. Ages of students in a high school class: 3 sixteen-year-olds, 10 seventeen-year-olds, and 7 eighteen-year-olds **17.2 yr; 17 yr; 17 yr**

Classifying Triangles and Quadrilaterals

A **polygon** is a closed plane figure whose sides are segments that intersect only at their endpoints. Each endpoint is called a **vertex** of the polygon. Polygons are classified by the number of sides they have.

Triangle	Quadrilateral	Pentagon	Hexagon	Octagon
3 sides	4 sides	5 sides	6 sides	8 sides

Triangles are classified by their angle measures. If two angles have the same measure, they are **congruent angles**. In a diagram, matching arcs are used to show congruent angles.

A **right angle** measures 90° and is marked by a square corner. An **acute angle** measures less than 90°, and an **obtuse angle** measures more than 90°. The sum of the measures of the angles of a triangle is 180°.

Equiangular triangle	Right triangle	Acute triangle	Obtuse triangle
3 congruent angles	1 right angle	3 acute angles	1 obtuse angle

Triangles are also classified by their side lengths. If two sides have the same length, they are **congruent sides**. In a diagram, matching tick marks are used to show congruent sides.

Scalene triangle	Isosceles triangle	Equilateral triangle
No congruent sides	At least 2 congruent sides	3 congruent sides

---

EXAMPLE **Classify the figure using all names that apply.**

List the characteristics of the figure.

  The figure is a polygon with 3 sides, so it is a triangle.

  The triangle has no congruent sides, so it is a scalene triangle.

  The triangle includes one right angle, so it is a right triangle.

▶ The figure is a scalene right triangle.

Skills Review Handbook **919**

Two sides of a figure are parallel if the lines that contain the sides do not intersect. In a diagram, triangles (▶) are used to show parallel sides. Quadrilaterals are classified by whether they have parallel sides, congruent sides, or right angles.

Trapezoid Quadrilateral with exactly one pair of opposite sides parallel	**Parallelogram** Quadrilateral with both pairs of opposite sides parallel	**Rhombus** Parallelogram with 4 congruent sides	**Rectangle** Parallelogram with 4 right angles	**Square** Parallelogram with 4 right angles and 4 congruent sides

EXAMPLE Classify the figure using all names that apply.

List the characteristics of the figure.

The figure is a polygon with four sides, so it is a quadrilateral.

Both pairs of opposite sides of the quadrilateral are parallel, so the figure is a parallelogram.

The parallelogram has four right angles, so it is a rectangle.

▶ The figure is a quadrilateral, a parallelogram, and a rectangle.

PRACTICE

Classify the figure using all names that apply.

1. isosceles right triangle

2. quadrilateral, parallelogram, rectangle, rhombus, square

3. pentagon

4. quadrilateral, trapezoid

5. hexagon

6. obtuse isosceles triangle

7. parallelogram, rhombus

8. equilateral, equiangular acute triangle

9. quadrilateral, parallelogram

The Coordinate Plane

Just as you use a number line to graph numbers, you use a *coordinate plane* to graph *ordered pairs* of numbers.

A **coordinate plane** has a horizontal **x-axis** and a vertical **y-axis** that intersect at a point called the **origin**. The origin is labeled O.

In an **ordered pair**, the first number is the **x-coordinate** and the second number is the **y-coordinate**. The coordinates of the origin are (0, 0). The ordered pair (4, 5) is graphed at the right.

13–24.

EXAMPLE Give the coordinates of points *A* and *B*.

Point *A* is 5 units to the right of the origin and 2 units up, so the *x*-coordinate is 5 and the *y*-coordinate is 2.

▸ The coordinates of point *A* are (5, 2).

Point *B* is 0 units to the right or left of the origin and 4 units up, so the *x*-coordinate is 0 and the *y*-coordinate is 4.

▸ The coordinates of point *B* are (0, 4).

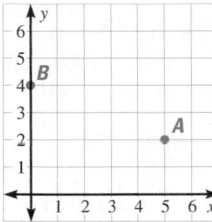

EXAMPLE Plot the points *C*(1, 3) and *D*(3, 0) in a coordinate plane.

To plot the point *C*(1, 3), begin at the origin and move 1 unit to the right, then 3 units up.

To plot the point *D*(3, 0), begin at the origin and move 3 units right, then 0 units up.

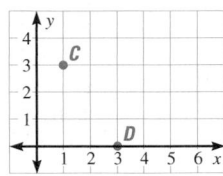

PRACTICE

Give the coordinates of the point.

1. *A* **(5, 4)**
2. *B* **(0, 1)**
3. *C* **(10, 8)**
4. *D* **(1, 9)**
5. *E* **(9, 2)**
6. *F* **(7, 0)**
7. *G* **(2, 6)**
8. *H* **(7, 7)**
9. *J* **(10, 0)**
10. *K* **(4, 8)**
11. *L* **(0, 5)**
12. *M* **(3, 1)**

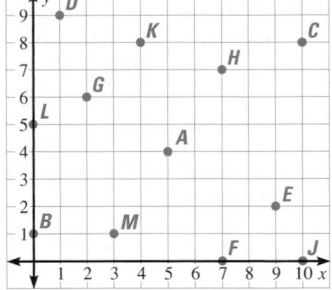

Plot the point in a coordinate plane.
13–24. See margin.
13. *M*(1, 7)
14. *N*(2, 1)
15. *P*(4, 4)
16. *Q*(0, 3)
17. *R*(4, 0)
18. *S*(6, 8)
19. *T*(3, 6)
20. *U*(8, 4)
21. *V*(7, 0)
22. *W*(0, 8)
23. *X*(3, 5)
24. *Z*(5, 6)

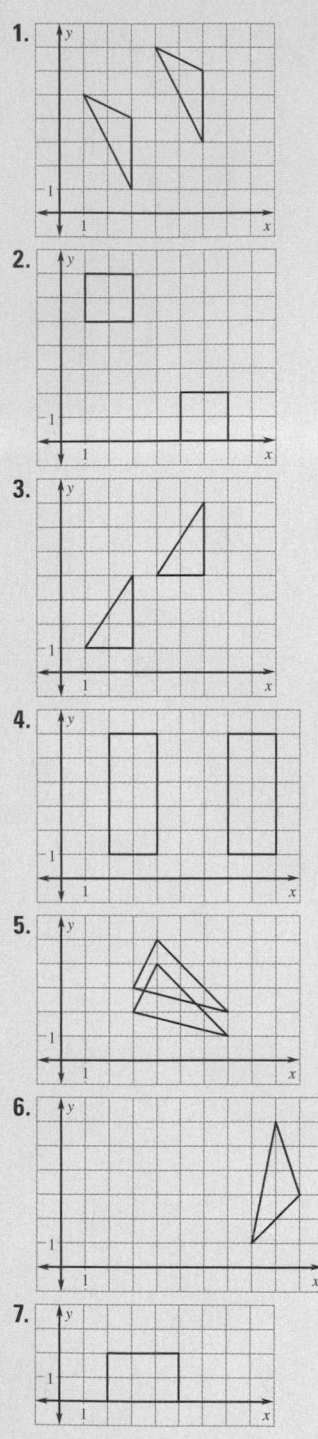

1.

2.

3.

4.

5.

6.

7.

Transformations

A **transformation** is a change made to the location, size, or shape of a figure. The new figure formed by a transformation is called an **image**. In this book, original figures are shown in blue and images in red.

A **translation** is a transformation in which each point of a figure moves the same distance in the same direction. A figure and its translated image are identical in size and shape.

EXAMPLE **Translate the triangle 4 units to the right and 1 unit up.**

From each vertex of the triangle, move 4 units to the right and 1 unit up to plot the image of the vertex. Draw segments connecting the images of the vertices.

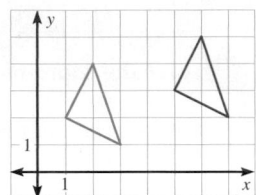

A **reflection** is a transformation in which a figure is reflected, or flipped, in a line, called the *line of reflection*. A figure and its reflected image are identical in size and shape.

EXAMPLE **Reflect the line segment in the given line.**

For each endpoint, find the distance from the endpoint to the line of reflection. Move the same distance on the opposite side of the line of reflection and plot the image point. Draw a segment connecting the image points.

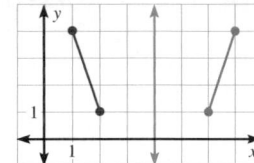

A **dilation** is a transformation in which a figure stretches or shrinks with respect to a fixed point called the *center of dilation*. (The examples and exercises below all have the origin as the center of dilation.) A figure and its dilated image have the same shape.

The **scale factor** of a dilation is the ratio of a side length of the image to the corresponding side length of the original figure. A figure *stretches* if its scale factor is greater than 1. A figure *shrinks* if its scale factor is between 0 and 1.

EXAMPLE **Dilate the rectangle using a scale factor of 3.**

Multiply each coordinate of each vertex by 3 to find the coordinates of the image. Plot the image of each vertex. Connect the image points to form a rectangle.

$(1, 1) \rightarrow (3, 3)$　　　$(1, 2) \rightarrow (3, 6)$

$(3, 2) \rightarrow (9, 6)$　　　$(3, 1) \rightarrow (9, 3)$

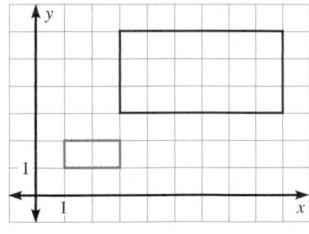

EXAMPLE Dilate the triangle using a scale factor of $\frac{1}{2}$.

Multiply each coordinate of each vertex by $\frac{1}{2}$ to find the coordinates of the image. Plot the image of each vertex. Connect the image points to form a triangle.

$(2, 6) \rightarrow$ **(1, 3)**

$(2, 2) \rightarrow$ **(1, 1)**

$(6, 4) \rightarrow$ **(3, 2)**

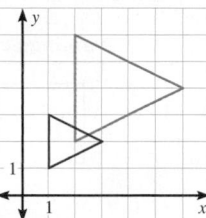

PRACTICE

The coordinates of the vertices of a polygon are given. Draw the polygon. Then find the coordinates of the vertices of the image after the specified translation, and draw the image. 1–5. See margin for art.

1. (1, 5), (3, 4), (3, 1); translate 3 units to the right and 2 units up **(4, 7), (6, 6), (6, 3)**

2. (5, 0), (7, 0), (7, 2), (5, 2); translate 4 units to the left and 5 units up **(1, 5), (3, 5), (3, 7), (1, 7)**

3. (4, 4), (6, 4), (6, 7); translate 3 units to the left and 3 units down **(1, 1), (3, 1), (3, 4)**

4. (2, 1), (4, 1), (4, 6), (2, 6); translate 5 units to the right **(7, 1), (9, 1), (9, 6), (7, 6)**

5. (4, 5), (7, 2), (3, 3); translate 1 unit down **(4, 4), (7, 1), (3, 2)**

For the figure shown, find the coordinates of the vertices of the image after a reflection in the given line. Then draw the image. 6–8. See margin for art.

6.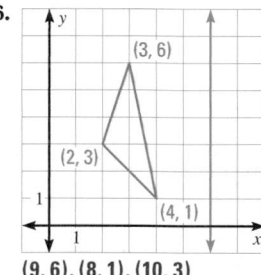

(9, 6), (8, 1), (10, 3)

7.

(2, 0), (5, 0), (5, 2), (2, 2)

8.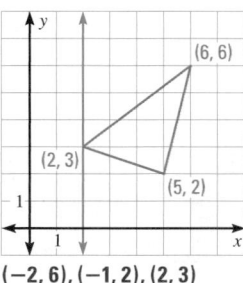

(−2, 6), (−1, 2), (2, 3)

The coordinates of the vertices of a polygon are given. Draw the polygon. Then find the coordinates of the vertices of the image after the specified dilation, and draw the image. 9–13. See margin for art.

9. (1, 2), (2, 4), (5, 3); dilate using a scale factor of 2 **(2, 4), (4, 8), (10, 6)**

10. (2, 6), (6, 6), (6, 2), (2, 2); dilate using a scale factor of $\frac{1}{2}$ **(1, 3), (3, 3), (3, 1), (1, 1)**

11. (1, 3), (3, 3), (3, 1), (1, 1); dilate using a scale factor of 4 **(4, 12), (12, 12), (12, 4), (4, 4)**

12. (3, 9), (6, 9), (6, 3); dilate using a scale factor of $\frac{1}{3}$ **(1, 3), (2, 3), (2, 1)**

13. (0, 2), (4, 4), (6, 0); dilate using a scale factor of $1\frac{1}{2}$ **(0, 3), (6, 6), (9, 0)**

Skills Review Handbook **923**

8.

9.

10.

11.

12.

13.

Perimeter and Area

The **perimeter** P of a figure is the distance around it.

Perimeter of a Square	Perimeter of a Rectangle	Perimeter of a Triangle
		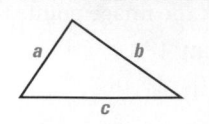
$P = s + s + s + s$ $= 4s$	$P = \ell + w + \ell + w$ $= 2\ell + 2w$	$P = a + b + c$

EXAMPLE   Find the perimeter of the figure.

a. Square

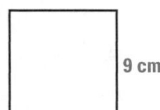

9 cm

$P = 4s$

$= 4(9)$

$= 36$ cm

b. Rectangle

7 m

11 m

$P = 2\ell + 2w$

$= 2(11) + 2(7)$

$= 22 + 14 = 36$ m

c. Triangle

8 ft

6 ft   10 ft

$P = a + b + c$

$= 6 + 8 + 10$

$= 24$ ft

The **area** A of a figure is the number of square units enclosed by the figure.

Area of a Square	Area of a Rectangle	Area of a Parallelogram
		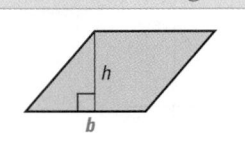
$A = s^2$	$A = \ell w$	$A = bh$

Area of a Triangle	Area of a Trapezoid
$A = \frac{1}{2}bh$	$P = \frac{1}{2}(b_1 + b_2)h$

EXAMPLE Find the area of the figure.

a. Rectangle

15 cm

9 cm

$A = \ell w$

$= 9(15)$

$= 135 \text{ cm}^2$

b. Triangle

6 in.

12 in.

$A = \frac{1}{2}bh$

$= \frac{1}{2}(12)(6)$

$= 36 \text{ in.}^2$

c. Parallelogram

32 yd

25 yd

$A = bh$

$= 25(32)$

$= 800 \text{ yd}^2$

PRACTICE

Find the perimeter of the figure.

1. Square **36 ft**

9 ft

2. Rectangle **28 mm**

8 mm

6 mm

3. Triangle **20 ft**

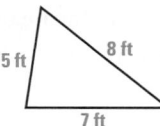

5 ft   8 ft

7 ft

Find the area of the figure.

4. Square **400 in.²**

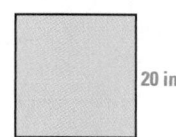

20 in.

5. Rectangle **66 yd²**

6 yd

11 yd

6. Triangle **52 m²**

8 m

13 m

7. Parallelogram **110 in.²**

11 in.

10 in.

8. Trapezoid **130 m²**

17 m

10 m

9 m

9. Parallelogram **21 ft²**

3 ft

7 ft

10. Trapezoid **234 m²**

13 m

24 m   12 m

11. Triangle **70 yd²**

14 yd

10 yd

12. Rectangle **144 in.²**

8 in.

18 in.

Circumference and Area of a Circle

A circle consists of all points in a plane that are the same distance from a fixed point called the **center**.

The distance between the center and any point on the circle is the **radius**. The distance across the circle through the center is the **diameter**. The diameter of a circle is twice its radius.

The **circumference** of a circle is the distance around the circle. For any circle, the ratio of its circumference to its diameter is π (pi), a number that is approximately equal to 3.14 or $\frac{22}{7}$.

Circumference and Area of a Circle

To find the circumference C of a circle with radius r or diameter d, use the formula $C = 2\pi r$ or $C = \pi d$.

To find the area A of a circle with radius r, use the formula $A = \pi r^2$.

EXAMPLE Find the circumference and area of the circle. Give your answers in terms of π and as decimals rounded to the nearest tenth.

5 cm

Circumference

$C = 2\pi r$

$\quad = 2\pi(5)$

$\quad = 10\pi$ cm   **Exact answer**

$\quad \approx 10(3.14)$

$\quad = 31.4$ cm   **Decimal approximation**

Area

$A = \pi r^2$

$\quad = \pi(5^2)$

$\quad = 25\pi$ cm^2 **Exact answer**

$\quad \approx 25(3.14)$

$\quad = 78.5$ cm^2 **Decimal approximation**

PRACTICE

Find the circumference and area of the circle. Give your answers in terms of π and as decimals rounded to the nearest tenth.

1.

6 in.

12π in. or 37.7 in.,
36π in.^{2} or 113.0 in.^{2}

2.

3 cm

6π cm or 18.8 cm,
9π cm^2 or 28.3 cm^2

3.

8 in.

16π in. or 50.2 in.,
64π in.^{2} or 201.0 in.^{2}

4.
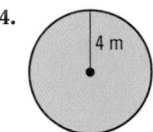
4 m

8π m or 25.1 m,
16π m^2 or 50.2 m^2

5.

4 ft

4π ft or 12.6 ft,
4π ft^2 or 12.6 ft^2

6.

14 cm

14π cm or 44.0 cm,
49π cm^2 or 153.9 m^2

7.

18 m

18π m or 56.5 m,
81π m^2 or 254.3 m^2

8.
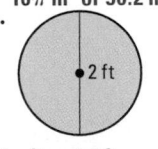
2 ft

2π ft or 6.3 ft,
π ft^2 or 3.1 ft^2

Surface Area and Volume

A **solid** is a three-dimensional figure that encloses part of space. The **surface area** S of a solid is the sum of the areas of all of its surfaces. The **volume** V of a solid is the amount of space that the solid occupies. In the formulas for surface area and volume, the number π (pi) is approximately equal to 3.14 or $\frac{22}{7}$.

Right Rectangular Prism	Right Circular Cylinder

$S = 2B + Ph \qquad V = Bh$
$\quad = 2\ell w + 2hw + 2\ell h \qquad = \ell wh$

$S = 2B + Ch \qquad V = Bh$
$\quad = 2\pi r^2 + 2\pi rh \qquad = \pi r^2 h$

Regular Pyramid	Right Circular Cone	Sphere

$S = B + \frac{1}{2}P\ell \qquad V = \frac{1}{3}Bh$

$S = B + C\ell \qquad V = \frac{1}{3}Bh$
$\quad = \pi r^2 + \pi r\ell \qquad = \frac{1}{3}\pi r^2 h$

$S = 4\pi r^2 \qquad V = \frac{4}{3}\pi r^3$

In this book, the adjectives *right* and *circular* will be assumed and therefore will not be used in naming solids.

EXAMPLE Find the surface area of the solid.

a. Sphere

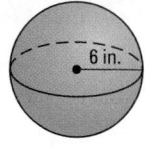

$S = 4\pi r^2$

$\quad = 4\pi(6^2)$

$\quad = 144\pi \text{ in.}^2$

$\quad \approx 144(3.14)$

$\quad \approx 452.2 \text{ in.}^2$

b. Cylinder

1 m

5 m

$S = 2\pi r^2 + 2\pi rh$

$\quad = 2\pi(1^2) + 2\pi(1)(5)$

$\quad = 2\pi + 10\pi$

$\quad = 12\pi \text{ m}^2$

$\quad \approx 12(3.14) \approx 37.7 \text{ m}^2$

c. Cone

5 in.

3 in.

$S = \pi r^2 + \pi r\ell$

$\quad = \pi(3^2) + \pi(3)(5)$

$\quad = 9\pi + 15\pi$

$\quad = 24\pi \text{ in.}^2$

$\quad \approx 24(3.14) \approx 75.4 \text{ in.}^2$

EXAMPLE Find the volume of the solid.

a. Rectangular prism

$$V = Bh$$
$$= 25(8)$$
$$= 200 \text{ ft}^3$$

b. Regular pyramid

$$V = \frac{1}{3}Bh$$
$$= \frac{1}{3}(36)6$$
$$= 72 \text{ yd}^3$$

c. Cone

$$V = \frac{1}{3}Bh$$
$$= \frac{1}{3}\pi(3^2)(6)$$
$$= 18\pi \text{ in.}^3$$
$$\approx 18(3.14) \approx 56.5 \text{ in.}^3$$

PRACTICE

Find the surface area and volume of the solid. For spheres, cylinders, and cones, give your answers in terms of π and as decimals rounded to the nearest tenth.

1. Rectangular prism

320 cm², 336 cm³

2. Cylinder 72π in.² or 226.1 in.², 80π in.³ or 251.2 in.³

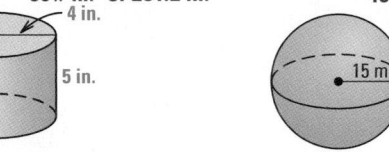

3. Sphere 900π m² or 2826 m², 4500π m³ or 14,130 m³

4. Cylinder 136π ft² or 427.0 ft², 208π ft³ or 653.1 ft³

5. Cone 200π in.² or 628 in.², 320π in.³ or 1004.8 in.³

6. Rectangular prism

94 mm², 60 mm³

7. Regular pyramid 96 in.², 48 in.³

8. Sphere 100π in.² or 314 in.², 166⅔π in.³ or 523.3 in.³

9. Cylinder 1888π in.² or 5928.3 in.², 11,008π in.³ or 34,565.1 in.³

10. Rectangular prism 150 cm², 125 cm³

11. Cone 96π m² or 301.4 m², 96π m³ or 301.4 m³

12. Regular pyramid 360 cm², 400 cm³

Converting Units of Measurement

The Table of Measures on page 956 gives many statements of equivalent measures. You can write two different conversion factors for each statement, as shown below. Each conversion factor is equal to 1.

Statement of Equivalent Measures	Conversion Factors	
100 cm = 1 m	$\dfrac{100 \text{ cm}}{1 \text{ m}} = 1$	$\dfrac{1 \text{ m}}{100 \text{ cm}} = 1$

To convert from one unit of measurement to another, multiply by a conversion factor that will eliminate the starting unit and result in the desired unit.

Convert meters to centimeters:

Use $\dfrac{100 \text{ cm}}{1 \text{ m}}$.

$3 \cancel{\text{m}} \times \dfrac{100 \text{ cm}}{1 \cancel{\text{m}}} = 300 \text{ cm}$

Convert centimeters to meters:

Use $\dfrac{1 \text{ m}}{100 \text{ cm}}$.

$400 \cancel{\text{cm}} \times \dfrac{1 \text{ m}}{100 \cancel{\text{cm}}} = 4 \text{ m}$

Sometimes you need to use more than one conversion factor.

EXAMPLE   Copy and complete: 2 d = __?__ sec

STEP 1   **Find** the appropriate statements of equivalent measures.

24 h = 1 d, 60 min = 1 h, and 60 sec = 1 min

STEP 2   **Write** conversion factors.

$\dfrac{24 \text{ h}}{1 \text{ d}}, \dfrac{60 \text{ min}}{1 \text{ h}},$ and $\dfrac{60 \text{ sec}}{1 \text{ min}}$

STEP 3   **Multiply** by conversion factors to convert days to seconds.

$2 \cancel{\text{d}} \times \dfrac{24 \cancel{\text{h}}}{1 \cancel{\text{d}}} \times \dfrac{60 \cancel{\text{min}}}{1 \cancel{\text{h}}} \times \dfrac{60 \text{ sec}}{1 \cancel{\text{min}}} = 172{,}800 \text{ sec}$

▶ 2 d = 172,800 sec

PRACTICE

Copy and complete.

1. 300 sec = __?__ min **5**
2. 2.6 g = __?__ kg **0.0026**
3. 64 oz = __?__ lb **4**
4. 4 gal = __?__ qt **16**
5. 72 in. = __?__ ft **6**
6. 94 mm = __?__ cm **9.4**
7. 42 ft = __?__ yd **14**
8. 5 d = __?__ h **120**
9. 3 m = __?__ cm **300**
10. 2 yd = __?__ in. **72**
11. 70 L = __?__ mL **70,000**
12. 10 mi = __?__ ft **52,800**
13. 1.5 ton = __?__ lb **3000**
14. 4500 mL = __?__ L **4.5**
15. 15,000 mg = __?__ g **15**
16. 1 mi = __?__ in. **63,360**
17. 80 fl oz = __?__ qt **2.5**
18. 5 gal = __?__ c **80**
19. 1 km = __?__ mm **1,000,000**
20. 20 c = __?__ qt **5**
21. 8 h = __?__ sec **28,800**

930

1.

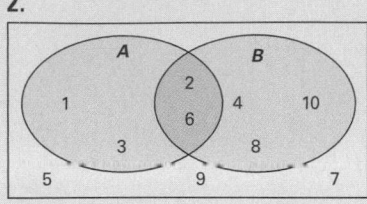

2.

4a. Sometimes; there are whole numbers that are even and less than 10 that are factors of 6 such as 2 and 6, but there are also whole numbers that are even and less than 10 that are not factors of 6 such as 4, 8, and 10.

4b. Sometimes; there are factors of 6 that are less than 10 that are even such as 2 and 6, but there are also factors of 6 that are less than 10 that are odd such as 1 and 3.

Venn Diagrams and Logical Reasoning

A **Venn diagram** uses shapes to show how sets are related.

EXAMPLE Draw a Venn diagram of the whole numbers less than 10 where set A consists of prime numbers and set B consists of even numbers.

Whole numbers less than 10:
0, 1, 2, 3, 4, 5, 6, 7, 8, 9

Set A: 2, 3, 5, 7

Set B: 0, 2, 4, 6, 8

Both set A and set B: 2

Neither set A nor set B: 1, 9

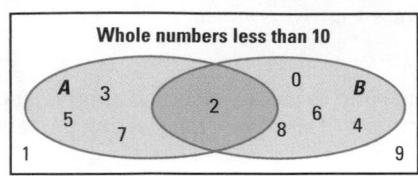

You can use a Venn diagram to answer questions about sets.

EXAMPLE Use the Venn diagram above to answer the question.

  a. Is the statement below *true* or *false*? Explain.

  No whole number less than 10 is prime.

  ▸ False. The whole number 2 is less than 10 and is prime.

  b. Is the statement below *always*, *sometimes*, or *never* true? Explain.

  A whole number less than 10 is either even or prime.

  ▸ Sometimes. Each of the numbers 0, 2, 3, 4, 5, 6, 7, and 8 are either even or prime, but the numbers 1 and 9 are not even and not prime.

PRACTICE

Draw a Venn diagram of the sets described. 1, 2. See margin.

  1. Of the whole numbers less than 10, set A consists of factors of 10 and set B consists of odd numbers.

  2. Of the whole numbers less than 10, set A consists of factors of 6 and set B consists of even numbers.

Use the Venn diagrams you drew in Exercises 1 and 2 to answer the question.

  3. Are the following statements *true* or *false*? Explain.

    a. *If a whole number less than 10 is odd, then it must be a factor of 10.*

    b. *A whole number less than 10 that is a factor of 10 must be odd.*

  4. Are the following statements *always*, *sometimes*, or *never* true? Explain.
     a, b. See margin.
    a. *A whole number that is even and less than 10 is a factor of 6.*

    b. *A factor of 6 that is less than 10 is even.*

3a. False; there are whole numbers less than 10 that are odd but are not factors of 10, such as 3, 7, and 9. 3b. False; there is a whole number less than 10 that is a factor of 10 but is not odd, 2.

930 Student Resources

Counting Methods

There are several methods for counting the number of possibilities in a situation.

EXAMPLE   **Make a list to find the number of possible lunch specials.**

Pair each soup with each sandwich.

    Chicken soup with turkey sandwich

    Chicken soup with tuna sandwich

    Chicken soup with cheese sandwich

    Tomato soup with turkey sandwich

    Tomato soup with tuna sandwich

    Tomato soup with cheese sandwich

Count the number of lunch specials in the list.

▶ There are 6 possible lunch specials.

Lunch Special $6.95	
Choose 1 soup and 1 sandwich.	
Soups	**Sandwiches**
Chicken	Turkey
Tomato	Tuna
	Cheese

EXAMPLE   **Draw a tree diagram to find the number of possible lunch specials given the choices in the example above.**

Arrange the soups and sandwiches in a tree diagram.

Soup	Sandwich	Lunch
	Turkey	Chicken soup, turkey sandwich
Chicken	Tuna	Chicken soup, tuna sandwich
	Cheese	Chicken soup, cheese sandwich
	Turkey	Tomato soup, turkey sandwich
Tomato	Tuna	Tomato soup, tuna sandwich
	Cheese	Tomato soup, cheese sandwich

▶ There are 6 possible lunch specials.

Another way to count the number of possible lunch specials described in the examples above is to multiply. Since there are 2 choices of soup and 3 choices of sandwich, there are $2 \times 3 = 6$ possible lunch specials. This method uses the counting principle.

The Counting Principle
If one event can occur in m ways, and for each of these ways a second event can occur in n ways, then the number of ways that the two events can occur together is $m \cdot n$.

The counting principle can be extended to three or more events.

EXAMPLE Greta must choose a 4-digit password for her cell phone mailbox. Use the counting principle to find the number of possible 4-digit passwords.

For each of the 4 digits in the password, there are 10 choices: 0, 1, 2, 3, 4, 5, 6, 7, 8, and 9.

10 choices for first digit	×	10 choices for second digit	×	10 choices for third digit	×	10 choices for fourth digit

$10 \times 10 \times 10 \times 10 = 10{,}000$

▶ There are 10,000 possible 4-digit passwords.

PRACTICE

In Exercises 1–3, use the indicated counting method to answer the question.

1. Andrew, Bettina, and Carl are triplets. In how many different ways can the triplets stand in a row for a photo? (Make a list.) **6 ways**

2. The sign at the right shows the color and size choices for school T-shirts. How many different types of school T-shirts are available? (Draw a tree diagram.) **12 types of T-shirts**

School T-Shirts $9.99	
Choose 1 color and 1 size.	
Colors:	**Sizes:**
Black, Gold, or White	S, M, L, or XL

3. A 3-letter monogram consists of the first letter of a person's first name, middle name, and last name. For example, Matthew David Weaver's monogram is MDW. How many different 3-letter monograms are possible? (Use the counting principle.) **17,576 3-letter monograms**

In Exercises 4–8, answer the question using any counting method you choose.

4. How many different pizzas with 2 different toppings are available for the large pizza special advertised at the right? **28 pizzas**

Large Pizza Special	
Any 2 toppings for $12.49	
Pepperoni	Black olive
Sausage	Green pepper
Ground beef	Red onion
Extra cheese	Mushroom

5. Lance must choose 4 characters for his computer password. Each character can be any letter A–Z or any digit 0–9. How many different computer passwords are possible? **1,679,616 computer passwords**

6. Mia must choose 3 whole numbers less than 50 for her locker combination. The numbers may be repeated. How many different locker combinations are possible? **125,000 locker combinations**

7. A restaurant offers a dinner special. You can choose a main course, a vegetable, and a salad from a choice of 6 main courses, 4 vegetables, and 3 salads. How many different dinners are available? **72 dinners**

8. Each day Scott walks, rides the bus, or gets a ride to school. He has each of the same possibilities for getting home each day. How many combinations of travel to and from school does Scott have? **9 combinations of travel**

Bar Graphs

You can use a **bar graph** to display and compare data that are in categories.

EXAMPLE

Use the bar graph, which shows the medals won by the United States in the 2004 Summer Olympics. **(a) Did the United States win more gold medals, silver medals, or bronze medals? (b) How many more silver medals than bronze medals did the United States win?**

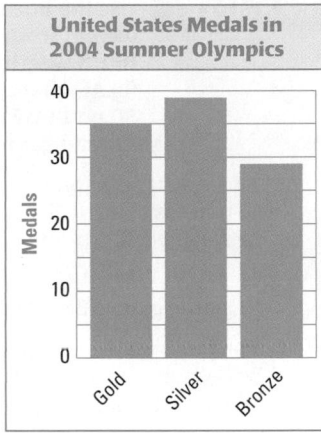

a. The longest bar on the graph is for silver medals won.

▸ The United States won more silver medals than any other type.

b. The bar for silver medals shows 39 silver medals won. The bar for bronze medals shows 29 gold medals won.

$39 - 29 - 10$

▸ The United States won 10 more silver medals than bronze medals.

PRACTICE

In Exercises 1–3, use the bar graph above.

1. The United States won fewer of which type of medal than any other type? **bronze**

2. How many more silver medals than gold medals did the United States win? **4 more silver medals**

3. How many medals did the United States win altogether? **103 medals**

In Exercises 4–11, use the bar graph below, which shows the top medal-winning countries in the 2002 Winter Olympics.

4. Which country won the most medals? How many medals did it win? **Germany; 37 medals**

5. How many medals did Norway win? **25 medals**

6. Which two countries won 17 medals each? **Canada and Austria**

7. Which country won the same number of medals as France? **Switzerland**

8. How many countries won more than 15 medals? **5 countries**

9. Which country won twice as many medals as Austria? **United States**

10. How many medals did Russia and Italy win altogether? **26 medals**

11. How many medals did the top 3 medal-winning countries win? **96 medals**

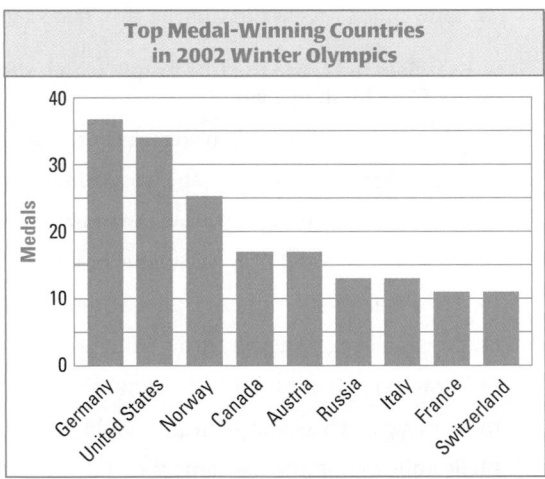

Line Graphs

You can use a **line graph** to show how numerical data change over time.

EXAMPLE Use the line graph, which shows Charlie's weight from birth to 5 years old. (a) How much weight did Charlie gain in 5 years? (b) At what age did Charlie weigh 30 pounds? (c) In which year did Charlie gain the most weight?

Charlie's Weight

a. The lowest point on the graph shows that Charlie weighed 10 pounds at birth. The highest point on the graph shows he weighed 42.5 pounds at age 5.

$42.5 - 10 = 32.5$

▶ Charlie gained 32.5 pounds in 5 years.

b. The point on the graph to the right of 30 on the weight axis corresponds to an age of 2.

▶ Charlie weighed 30 pounds at age 2.

c. The graph is steepest from birth to age 1.

▶ Charlie gained the most weight in his first year.

PRACTICE

In Exercises 1–5, use the line graph above.

1. How much did Charlie weigh on his first birthday? **about 24 lb**

2. How old was Charlie when he weighed 40 pounds? **about 4.2 years old**

3. In which year did Charlie gain the least weight? **between ages 4 and 5**

4. How much weight did Charlie gain his first year? **about 14 lb**

5. How much weight did Charlie gain from age 1 to age 4? **about 15 lb**

In Exercises 6–14, use the line graph, which shows Abby's height from birth to 4 years old.

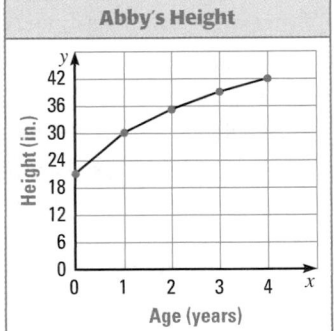

Abby's Height

6. How tall was Abby when she was born? **about 21 in.**

7. How old was Abby when she was 35 inches tall? **about 2 years old**

8. In which year did Abby grow the most? **her first year**

9. In which year did Abby grow the least? **between ages 3 and 4**

10. How many inches did Abby grow from age 3 to age 4? **about 3 in.**

11. In which year did Abby grow 5 inches? **between ages 1 and 2**

12. How many inches did Abby grow in 4 years? **about 21 in.**

13. At what age was Abby's height double her height at birth? **about 4 yr**

14. If Abby maintains the same growth rate from age 4 to age 5 that she had from age 3 to age 4, how tall will she be when she is 5? **about 45 in.**

Circle Graphs

You can use a **circle graph** to display data as sections of a circle. The entire circle represents all of the data. The sections of the circle may be labeled using the actual data or the data expressed as fractions, decimals, or percents. When the data are expressed as fractions, decimals, or percents, the sum of the data is 1.

EXAMPLE Use the circle graph, which shows the string musicians in a college orchestra. (a) What percent of the string musicians in the orchestra play the cello? (b) Which instrument do almost half the string musicians in the orchestra play?

String Musicians

Violin 49%
Bass 9%
Viola 21%
Cello 21%

a. The cello section of the circle is labeled 21%.

   ▸ Of the string musicians in the orchestra, 21% play cello.

b. The violin section of the circle is labeled 49%, which is almost 50%. Also, the violin section of the circle is almost half the total area of the circle.

   ▸ Almost half of the string musicians in the orchestra play the violin.

PRACTICE

In Exercises 1–4, use the circle graph above.

1. What percent of the string musicians in the orchestra play the bass? **9%**

2. How does the number of string musicians who play the viola compare with the number of string musicians who play the cello? **They are equal.**

3. The violinists are divided evenly into two groups, first violin and second violin. What percent of the string musicians are in each of these groups? **24.5%**

4. If there are 57 string musicians in the orchestra, how many musicians play each type of instrument? **28 play violin, 12 play cello, 12 play viola, and 5 play bass**

In Exercises 5–10, use the circle graph, which shows the types of instruments played by musicians in a college band.

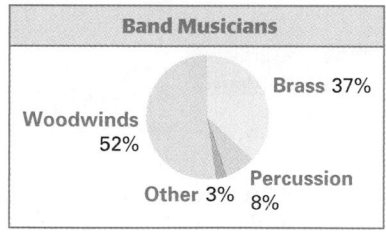

Band Musicians

Brass 37%
Woodwinds 52%
Other 3%
Percussion 8%

5. What percent of the musicians in the band play a brass instrument? **37%**

6. Which type of instrument do 8% of the musicians in the band play? **percussion**

7. Which type of instrument do more than half of the musicians in the band play? **woodwinds**

8. The instruments in the "Other" category are harp, string bass, and keyboard. What percent of the band musicians play one of these instruments? **3%**

9. In this band, which type of instrument is played by about 5 times as many musicians as play percussion instruments? **brass**

10. There are 91 musicians in the band. How many more musicians play a woodwind than play a percussion instrument? **40 more musicians**

Problem Solving Strategies

The following are strategies that you can use to solve problems.

Strategy	When to use	How to use
Draw a diagram	Draw a diagram when a problem involves any relationships that you can represent visually.	Draw a diagram that shows the given information. Label any unknowns in your diagram and look for relationships between givens and unknowns.
Look for a pattern	Look for a pattern when a problem includes a series of numbers or diagrams that you need to analyze.	Look for a pattern in any given information. Apply, extend, or generalize the pattern to help you solve the problem.
Guess, check, and revise	Guess, check, and revise when you need a place to start or you want to see what happens for a particular number.	Make a reasonable guess. Check to see if your guess solves the problem. If it does not, revise your guess and check again.
Act it out	Act out a problem that involves any relationships that you can represent with physical objects and movement.	Act out the problem, using objects described in the problem or other items that represent those objects.
Make a list or table	Make a list or table when you need to record, generate, or organize information.	Generate a list systematically, accounting for all possibilities. Look for relationships across rows or down columns within a table.
Solve a simpler or related problem	Solve a simpler or related problem when a problem seems difficult and can be made easier by using simpler numbers or conditions.	Think of a way to make the problem easier. Solve the simpler or related problem. Use what you learned to help you solve the original problem.
Work backward	Work backward when a problem gives you an end result and you need to find beginning conditions.	Work backward from the given information until you solve the problem. Work forward through the problem to check your answer.
Break into parts	Break into parts when a problem cannot be solved all at once, but can be solved in parts or stages.	Break the problem into parts and solve each part. Put the answers together to help you solve the original problem.

EXAMPLE Fletcher baked brownies in a rectangular pan that measures 9 inches by 13 inches. He wants to cut rectangular brownies that are at least 2 inches on each side, with all brownies the same size. What is the greatest number of brownies Fletcher can cut?

Draw a diagram of the rectangular pan. Label the sides with their lengths. Think about each side of the rectangle.

13 in.

9 in.

$9 \div 2 = 4.5$, so cut 4 brownies along the 9 inch side.
Check: $9 \div 4 = 2.25$, and $2.25 > 2$.

$13 \div 2 = 6.5$, so cut 6 brownies along the 13 inch side.
Check: $13 \div 6 \approx 2.17$, and $2.17 > 2$.

Use your diagram to count the brownies: $4 \times 6 = 24$.

▶ The greatest number of brownies Fletcher can cut is 24.

1. Four friends hosted a party. The table shows the amount of money each friend spent. The friends want to share the party expenses equally, and Pam will pay the entire amount she owes to one person. Who owes money to whom? **See margin.**

Person	Party expenses
Barb	$11 for drinks
Bonnie	$15 for food
Pam	$6 for invitations
Holly	$8 for decorations

2. Six people can be seated at a rectangular table, with one person at each end. How many people can be seated at five of these tables if they are placed end to end? **22 people**

3. Bob is 55 years old. In 5 years, Bob will be twice as old as his son. How old is Bob's son? **25 years old**

4. Maddie and Rob are sharing a pack of 25 pens. Maddie offers to let Rob have 3 pens for every 2 pens she gets. If they use the entire package of pens, how many pens will each person get? **Rob: 15 pens, Maddie: 10 pens**

5. In how many different ways can you make $.50 in change using quarters, dimes, and nickels? **10 ways**

6. The diagram shows two cuts through the center of a pizza. How many cuts through the center are needed to divide a pizza into 12 equal pieces? **6 cuts**

7. Deb is flying to Seattle. Her flight leaves at 4:15 P.M. She wants to arrive at the airport 2 hours early to check in and get through security. The taxi ride from her office to the airport takes about 30 minutes. What time should Deb ask the taxi driver to pick her up at the office? **1:45 P.M.**

8. Dan wants to enclose a rectangular area with a fence. He has 12 fence posts to use, and the fence posts will be placed 10 feet apart. The diagram shows a possible shape for the area. Find another shape that would use all the fence posts, placed 10 feet apart, and would increase the area by 100 square feet. **a square with 4 posts on each side**

9. A soccer league has a 7 week season, and there are 7 teams in the league. Each team plays a game with every other team once during the season. How many soccer games must be played each week of the season? **3 soccer games per week**

10. Julia is setting up a display of cracker boxes at a grocery store. She wants one box in the top row, two boxes in the second row down, three boxes in the third row down, and so on, as shown. Each box is 8 inches tall, and her display will be 6 feet tall. How many cracker boxes will be in the display? **45 cracker boxes**

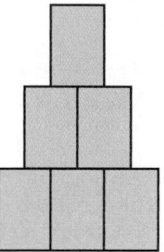

11. Five friends line up for tetherball. William is first in line, Mac is between Quinn and Benjamin, and Nate is next to William and Benjamin. Which friend is last in line? **Quinn**

12. The 4 members of the Buckner family usually drink 3 gallons of milk altogether each week. For 12 weeks in the summer, they will have a fifth family member staying with them. How many gallons of milk would you expect the 5 family members to drink over the 12 weeks? **45 gal**

1. Pam owes $4 that she can pay to Bonnie who is owed a total of $5. Holly should pay both Barb and Bonnie $1.

29. Sample answer: You know the temperature in Quito in degrees Celsius and the temperature in Miami in degrees Fahrenheit. You need to find out which one is greater.

30. Sample answer: You know the rate and time Katherine walked each day. You need to find out the distance she walked during the 2 days.

32.

Input	2	4	6	8
Output	7.5	10	12.5	15

33.

34.

35.

36.

Chapter 1

Evaluate the expression.

1.1 **1.** $k + 9$ when $k = 7$ **16** **2.** $21 - x$ when $x = 3$ **18** **3.** $3.5 + t$ when $t = 0.9$ **4.4** **4.** $y - \frac{3}{8}$ when $y = \frac{7}{12}$ $\frac{5}{24}$

5. $\frac{m}{4}$ when $m = 9.6$ **2.4** **6.** $1.5t$ when $t = 2.3$ **3.45** **7.** z^3 when $z = \frac{2}{3}$ $\frac{8}{27}$ **8.** p^4 when $p = 0.2$ **0.0016**

1.2 **9.** $25 - 7 + 8$ **26** **10.** $67 - 3 \cdot 4$ **55** **11.** $8^2 \div 4 + 12$ **28** **12.** $9 + 6 \div 3$ **11**

13. $\frac{3^3 - 7}{2}$ **10** **14.** $\frac{1}{3}(7 - 5.5)^2$ **0.75** **15.** $3 + 4(3 + 24)$ **111** **16.** $\frac{3}{5}[27 - (2 + 5)]^2$ **240**

1.3 **Translate the verbal phrase into an expression.**

17. $\frac{3}{4}$ of a number m $\frac{3}{4}m$

18. the quotient of a number x and 7 $\frac{x}{7}$

19. the difference of a number y and 3 $y - 3$

20. 6 more than 3 times a number n $3n + 6$

1.3 **Write an expression for the situation.**

21. Number of minutes left in a 45 minute class after m minutes have gone by $45 - m$

22. Number of meters in c centimeters $\frac{c}{100}$

1.4 **Write an equation or an inequality.**

23. The product of 12 and the difference of a number r and 4 is 72. $12 \cdot (r - 4) = 72$

24. The difference of a number q and 18 is greater than 10 and less than 15. $10 < q - 18 < 15$

1.4 **Solve the equation using mental math.**

25. $d - 13 = 25$ **38** **26.** $12z = 96$ **8** **27.** $23 - m = 7$ **16** **28.** $\frac{k}{6} = 12$ **72**

1.5 **In Exercises 29 and 30, identify what you know and what you need to find out. You do *not* need to solve the problem.** **29, 30. See margin.**

29. One day the temperature in Quito, Ecuador, was 20°C. The temperature in Miami, Florida was 75°F. Which temperature was higher?

30. On Monday, Katherine walked at a rate of 0.08 mile per minute for 40 minutes. On Tuesday, she walked at a rate of 0.07 mile per minute for 50 minutes. How far did Katherine walk altogether?

1.6 **31.** Identify the domain and range of the function.
domain: 3, 4, 5, 6; range: 9, 11, 13, 15

Input	3	4	5	6
Output	9	11	13	15

1.6 **32.** The domain of the function $y = 1.25x + 5$ is 2, 4, 6, and 8. Make a table for the function. Identify the range of the function.
See margin for table; range: 7.5, 10, 12.5, 15.

1.7 **Graph the function.**
33–36. See margin.

33. $y = x + 2$; domain: 0, 1, 2, and 3

34. $y = 3x - 3$; domain: 1, 2, 3, and 4

35. $y = 1.5x$; domain: 0, 20, 40, and 60

36. $y = \frac{1}{4}x + 2$; domain: 0, 4, 8, and 12

Chapter 2

2.1 Graph the numbers on a number line. Then tell which number is greater. **1–4. See margin for art.**

1. 0 and −4 **0**
2. 2 and −2 **2**
3. −5 and −3 **−3**
4. −6 and 4 **4**

2.1 Tell whether each number in the list is a whole number, an integer, or a rational number. Then order the numbers from least to greatest. **5–7. See margin.**

5. $0.25, -\frac{1}{8}, -\frac{1}{10}, -\frac{1}{5}$

6. $-2.5, -3, \frac{5}{2}, -\frac{9}{4}$

7. $-4, 3, -5, 0$

2.2 Find the sum.

8. −6 + 10 **4**
9. −25 + (−36) **−61**
10. −75 + 58 **−17**
11. 8 + (−15) + 7 **0**

12. −2.8 + 4.3 **1.5**
13. −8.2 + (−11.5) **−19.7**
14. $3\frac{2}{3} + (-5\frac{3}{8})$ **$-1\frac{17}{24}$**
15. $-12\frac{3}{5} + 8\frac{1}{6}$ **$-4\frac{13}{30}$**

2.3 Find the difference.

16. −17 − 20 **−37**
17. 16 − (−50) **66**
18. −9 − (−12) **3**
19. $\frac{4}{5} - \frac{1}{2}$ **$\frac{3}{10}$**

20. $-\frac{1}{2} - \frac{2}{3}$ **$-1\frac{1}{6}$**
21. $-\frac{1}{3} - \left(-\frac{3}{4}\right)$ **$\frac{5}{12}$**
22. −6.4 − 15 **−21.4**
23. −12.8 − (−5.6) **−7.2**

2.3 Evaluate the expression when $x = 1.5$ and $y = -4$.

24. $y - x$ **−5.5**
25. $-y - (-x)$ **5.5**
26. $x - (10 - y)$ **−12.5**
27. $-7 - (x - y)$ **−12.5**

2.4 Find the product.

28. $-\frac{2}{3}(-36)$ **24**
29. $64\left(-\frac{5}{8}\right)$ **−40**
30. −4.1(−3.5) **14.35**
31. (1.1)(−0.5)(−4) **2.2**

2.4 Identify the property illustrated. **32–37. See margin.**

32. $(-5)(8)(2) = (-5)(2)(8)$
33. $6 \cdot (7 \cdot 2) = (6 \cdot 7) \cdot 2$
34. $1(mn) = mn$
35. $0 \cdot (134) = 0$
36. $y \cdot (-1) = (-1) \cdot y$
37. $(-1)(-9) = 9$

2.5 Use the distributive property to write an equivalent expression.

38. $8(x + 4)$ **$8x + 32$**
39. $5(6 - y)$ **$30 - 5y$**
40. $(m + 7)(-8)$ **$-8m - 56$**
41. $-3(k - 14)$ **$-3k + 42$**

42. $\frac{3}{5}(-15r - 5)$ **$-9r - 3$**
43. $\frac{7}{12}(24s + 12)$ **$14s + 7$**
44. $(9v - 18)\frac{1}{3}$ **$3v - 6$**
45. $-\frac{5}{6}(-6w - 30)$ **$5w + 25$**

2.6 Find the quotient.

46. −35 ÷ 7 **−5**
47. −92 ÷ (−4) **23**
48. $36 \div \left(-\frac{3}{4}\right)$ **−48**
49. $-56 \div \left(-\frac{7}{8}\right)$ **64**

50. $\frac{5}{9} \div (-5)$ **$-\frac{1}{9}$**
51. $-\frac{5}{12} \div \frac{1}{2}$ **$-\frac{5}{6}$**
52. $-\frac{4}{3} \div \frac{4}{3}$ **−1**
53. $-\frac{5}{6} \div \left(-\frac{6}{5}\right)$ **$\frac{25}{36}$**

2.7 Evaluate the expression.

54. $-\sqrt{36}$ **−6**
55. $\pm\sqrt{400}$ **±20**
56. $\sqrt{6400}$ **80**
57. $\pm\sqrt{144}$ **±12**

2.7 Approximate the square root to the nearest integer.

58. $\sqrt{135}$ **12**
59. $-\sqrt{75}$ **−9**
60. $-\sqrt{160}$ **−13**
61. $\sqrt{250}$ **16**

5. Each number is a rational number; $-\frac{1}{5}, -\frac{1}{8}, -\frac{1}{10}, 0.25.$

6. −3 is an integer, the rest are rational numbers; $-3, -2.5, -\frac{9}{4}, \frac{5}{2}.$

7. 3 and 0 are whole numbers, −4 and −5 are integers; −5, −4, 0, 3.

32. Commutative property of multiplication

33. Associative property of multiplication

34. Identity property of multiplication

35. Property of zero

36. Commutative property of multiplication

37. Property of −1

EXTRA PRACTICE

Chapter 4, p. 941

1.

2.

3.

4.

5.

6.

7.

8.

9.

Chapter 3

Solve the equation. Check your solution.

3.1

1. $x + 4 = 20$ **16**

2. $8 = m - 13$ **21**

3. $t + 2 = -10$ **−12**

4. $z - 8 = -7$ **1**

5. $7h = 63$ **9**

6. $-4t = -44$ **11**

7. $\frac{b}{4} = 13$ **52**

8. $\frac{y}{-3} = 8$ **−24**

3.2

9. $4x + 3 = 27$ **6**

10. $6m - 4 = 14$ **3**

11. $50 = 7y - 6$ **8**

12. $\frac{t}{4} - 3 = 9$ **48**

13. $\frac{x}{7} + 3 = -2$ **−35**

14. $6p - 2p = 28$ **7**

3.3

15. $6x + 3x + 8 = 35$ **3**

16. $12w - 5 - 3w = 40$ **5**

17. $4d - 3 - 2d = -15$ **−6**

18. $7m + 3(m + 2) = -24$ **−3**

19. $5x - 3(x - 5) = 13$ **−1**

20. $\frac{3}{4}(2y - 8) = 6$ **8**

3.4

21. $8x - 4 = 3x + 6$ **2**

22. $10 - 2x = 3x - 20$ **6**

23. $5 - 5x = 14 - 8x$ **3**

24. $3(2y - 5) = 4y - 7$ **4**

25. $9 + 4y = 2(3 - y)$ **−$\frac{1}{2}$**

26. $3x - 3 = \frac{3}{4}(2x + 12)$ **8**

3.5 Solve the proportion. Check your solution.

27. $\frac{7}{2} = \frac{x}{16}$ **56**

28. $\frac{m}{9} = \frac{6}{27}$ **2**

29. $\frac{z}{4} = \frac{48}{12}$ **16**

30. $\frac{30}{50} = \frac{t}{10}$ **6**

3.5 Write the sentence as a proportion. Then solve the proportion.

31. 5 is to 7 as 15 is to x. $\frac{5}{7} = \frac{15}{x}$; **21**

32. 9 is to 3 as x is to 12. $\frac{9}{3} = \frac{x}{12}$; **36**

33. g is to 9 as 16 is to 12. $\frac{g}{9} = \frac{16}{12}$; **12**

34. 6 is to 18 as y is to 3. $\frac{6}{18} = \frac{y}{3}$; **1**

3.6 Solve the proportion. Check your solution.

35. $\frac{12}{x} = \frac{6}{7}$ **14**

36. $\frac{6x}{4} = \frac{18}{12}$ **1**

37. $\frac{7}{x + 13} = \frac{4}{12}$ **8**

38. $\frac{y + 5}{y} = \frac{10}{8}$ **20**

39. $\frac{2x + 6}{x} = \frac{7}{2}$ **4**

40. $\frac{3b}{5b - 7} = \frac{8}{11}$ **8**

41. $\frac{8}{2x + 12} = \frac{6}{x + 8}$ **−2**

42. $\frac{4.8 - 2x}{8} = \frac{0.4 + x}{10}$ **1.6**

3.7 Use a proportion to answer the question.

43. What percent of 96 is 12? **12.5%**

44. What number is 35% of 18? **6.3**

45. 14 is 40% of what number? **35**

46. What percent of 125 is 30? **24%**

3.7 Use the percent equation to answer the question.

47. What number is 250% of 18? **45**

48. What percent of 58 is 8.7? **15%**

49. 30.1 is 35% of what number? **86**

50. What number is 70% of 250? **175**

3.8 Solve the literal equation for x. Then use the solution to solve the specific equation.

51. $ax - b = c$; $6x - 5 = 25$ $x = \frac{c + b}{a}$; **5**

52. $a(b - x) = c$; $2(8 - x) = -6$ $x = b - \frac{c}{a}$; **11**

3.8 Write the equation so that y is a function of x.

53. $5x + y = 10$
$y = -5x + 10$

54. $8x - 2y = 16$
$y = 4x - 8$

55. $7x + 3y = 6 - 5x$
$y = -4x + 2$

56. $21 = 6x + 7y$
$y = -\frac{6}{7}x + 3$

10.

11.

12.

Chapter 4

4.1 Plot the point in a coordinate plane. *Describe* the location of the point. **1–8. See margin for art.**

1. $K(-4, -2)$
Quadrant III
2. $L(5, 0)$
on the x–axis
3. $M(3, -1)$
Quadrant IV
4. $N(-2, 2)$
Quadrant II

5. $P(0, 4)$
on the y-axis
6. $Q(-3.5, 5)$
Quadrant II
7. $R(2.5, 6)$
Quadrant I
8. $S(-1, -1.5)$
Quadrant III

4.1 Graph the function with the given domain. Then identify the range of the function. **9, 10. See margin for art.**

9. $y = -2x + 2$; domain: $-2, -1, 0, 1, 2$
range: $-2, 0, 2, 4, 6$

10. $y = \frac{1}{2}x - 3$; domain: $-4, -2, 0, 2, 4$
range: $-5, -4, -3, -2, -1$

4.2 Graph the equation. **11–18. See margin.**

11. $y - x = 3$ **12.** $y + 3x = 5$ **13.** $y - 4x = 10$ **14.** $y = 4$

15. $2x - y = 0$ **16.** $3x + y = 0$ **17.** $3x + 2y = -6$ **18.** $x = 0.5$

4.3 Find the x-intercept and the y-intercept of the graph of the equation. **19–22. See margin.**

19. $2x - y = 12$ **20.** $-5x - 2y = 20$ **21.** $-4x + 1.5y = 4$ **22.** $y = \frac{3}{4}x - 15$

4.3 Graph the equation. Label the points where the line crosses the axes. **23–26. See margin.**

23. $y = 3x - 6$ **24.** $4x + 5y = -20$ **25.** $\frac{2}{3}x + \frac{1}{2}y = 10$ **26.** $0.3x - y = 6$

4.4 Find the slope of the line that passes through the points.

27. $(4, 2)$ and $(6, 8)$ **3**   **28.** $(-3, 0)$ and $(2, -5)$ **−1**   **29.** $(-5, 3)$ and $(-8, 10)$ $-\frac{7}{3}$

30. $(9, 4)$ and $(0, 1)$ $\frac{1}{3}$ **31.** $(-2, 5)$ and $(-2, 10)$ **no slope**   **32.** $(6, -4)$ and $(4, -4)$ **0**

4.5 Identify the slope and y-intercept of the line with the given equation. **33–36. See margin.**

33. $y = 7x + 8$ **34.** $y = 10x - 6$ **35.** $y = 3 - 4x$ **36.** $y = x$

4.5 Rewrite the equation in slope-intercept form. Then identify the slope and the y-intercept of the line. **37–40. See margin.**

37. $2x + y = 8$ **38.** $10x - y = 20$ **39.** $5x + 2y = 10$ **40.** $-2x - y = 3$

4.5 Graph the equation. **41–44. See margin.**

41. $y = 2x - 4$ **42.** $y = -\frac{3}{4}x + 1$ **43.** $2x + y = 1$ **44.** $-2x + 3y = -9$

4.6 Graph the direct variation equation. **45–52. See margin.**

45. $y = 2x$ **46.** $y = -x$ **47.** $y = 4x$ **48.** $5x + y = 0$

49. $x - 2y = 0$ **50.** $3x + y = 0$ **51.** $2y = 9x$ **52.** $y - \frac{5}{4}x = 0$

4.7 Find the value of x so that the function has the given value.

53. $f(x) = -7x - 3$; -17 **2**   **54.** $g(x) = 5x - 4$; 12 $\frac{16}{5}$ **55.** $t(x) = 3x + 1$; -11 **−4**

4.7 Graph the function. Compare the graph with the graph of $f(x) = x$. **56–59. See margin.**

56. $m(x) = x - 2$ **57.** $t(x) = x + 4$ **58.** $z(x) = 6x$ **59.** $h(x) = -2x$

EXTRA PRACTICE

16.

17.

18.

19. x-int: 6, y-int: -12

20. x-int: -4, y-int: -10

21. x-int: -1, y-int: $\frac{8}{3}$

22. x-int: 20, y-int: -15

23–26. See Additional Answers beginning on p. AA1.

33. slope: 7, y-intercept: 8

34. slope: 10, y-intercept: -6

35. slope: -4, y-intercept: 3

36. slope: 1, y-intercept: 0

37. $y = -2x + 8$; slope: -2, y-intercept: 8

38. $y = 10x - 20$; slope: 10, y-intercept: -20

39. $y = -\frac{5}{2}x + 5$; slope: $-\frac{5}{2}$, y-intercept: 5

40. $y = -2x - 3$; slope: -2, y-intercept: -3

41–52, 56–59. See Additional Answers beginning on p. AA1.

13.

14.

15.

941

Chapter 5

13.

14.

15.

16–18. Sample answers are given.

16. $y - 2 = 7(x + 4)$

17. $y - 9 = \frac{1}{2}(x - 3)$

18. $y + 2 = -2(x - 10)$

28.

29.

30.

31.

EXTRA PRACTICE

5.1 Write an equation of the line with the given slope and y-intercept.

1. slope: 3
y-intercept: 6
$y = 3x + 6$

2. slope: -2
y-intercept: 4
$y = -2x + 4$

3. slope: 5
y-intercept: -1
$y = 5x - 1$

4. slope: -1
y-intercept: -3
$y = -x - 3$

5. slope: $\frac{1}{2}$
y-intercept: -5
$y = \frac{1}{2}x - 5$

6. slope: $-\frac{7}{10}$
y-intercept: 8
$y = \frac{7}{10}x + 8$

5.2 Write an equation of the line that passes through the given point and has the given slope *m*.

7. $(3, 8)$; $m = 2$
$y = 2x + 2$

8. $(-1, 5)$; $m = -4$
$y = -4x + 1$

9. $(-6, 3)$; $m = \frac{2}{3}$
$y = \frac{2}{3}x + 7$

5.2 Write an equation of the line that passes through the given points.

10. $(2, 4)$, $(5, 13)$
$y = 3x - 2$

11. $(1, -2)$, $(-2, 13)$
$y = -5x + 3$

12. $\left(2, \frac{1}{3}\right)$, $(6, 3)$
$y = \frac{2}{3}x - 1$

5.3 Graph the equation. **13–15. See margin.**

13. $y - 3 = -3(x + 4)$

14. $y + 5 = -2(x - 1)$

15. $y - 6 = \frac{2}{3}(x - 3)$

5.3 Write an equation in point-slope form of the line that passes through the given points. **16–18. See margin.**

16. $(-4, 2)$, $(-2, 16)$

17. $(3, 9)$, $(-7, 4)$

18. $(10, -2)$, $(12, -6)$

5.4 Write an equation in standard form of the line that passes through the given point and has the given slope *m* or that passes through the two given points.

19. $(2, 7)$, $m = -4$
$4x + y = 15$

20. $(5, 11)$, $m = 3$
$3x - y = 4$

21. $(1, -2)$, $(-2, 4)$
$2x + y = 0$

5.5 Write an equation of the line that passes through the given point and is parallel to the given line.

22. $(5, 4)$, $y = 3x + 5$
$y = 3x - 11$

23. $(-3, -7)$, $y = -5x - 2$
$y = -5x - 22$

24. $(8, -3)$, $y = \frac{3}{4}x + 5$
$y = \frac{3}{4}x - 9$

5.5 Write an equation of the line that passes through the given point and is perpendicular to the given line.

25. $(-12, -2)$, $y = 3x + 2$
$y = -\frac{1}{3}x - 6$

26. $(15, -11)$, $y = \frac{3}{5}x - 8$
$y = -\frac{5}{3}x + 14$

27. $(7, -6)$, $4x + 6y = 7$
$y = \frac{3}{2}x - \frac{33}{2}$

5.6 Make a scatter plot of the data in the table. Draw a line of fit. Write an equation of the line. **28, 29. See margin for art.**

28.

x	1	2	3	3.5	4	4.5	5
y	20	35	40	55	60	45	60

Sample answer: $y = 9.2x + 14.7$

29.

x	10	20	30	40	50	60
y	55	45	45	40	35	20

Sample answer: $y = -0.6x + 61$

5.7 Make a scatter plot of the data. Find the equation of the best-fitting line. Approximate the value of *y* for $x = 7$. **30–31. See margin for art.**

30.

x	0	2	4	6	8
y	0.5	3	4	5.5	7

$y = 0.78x + 0.9$; 6.36

31.

x	0	1	3	6	8
y	5	8	12	15	14

$y = 1.1x + 6.7$; 14.4

Chapter 6, p. 943

1.

2.

3.

4.

5.

6.

7.

8.

9.

Chapter 6

Solve the inequality. Graph your solution. 1–24. See margin for art.

6.1
1. $y - 2 > 3$
$y > 5$

2. $5 + x \le 2$
$x \le -3$

3. $4 \ge x - 3$
$x \le 7$

4. $m + 3 < 2$
$m < -1$

5. $2 + n \le 4\frac{1}{2}$ $n \le 2\frac{1}{2}$

6. $2\frac{3}{4} + n < -3\frac{5}{8}$
$n < -6\frac{3}{8}$

7. $1\frac{7}{8} > 6\frac{3}{4} + z$ $z < -4\frac{7}{8}$

8. $3\frac{2}{5} \ge 1\frac{1}{3} + k$ $k \le 2\frac{1}{15}$

9. $-8.5 \le t - 10$
$t \ge 1.5$

10. $r + 4 < -0.7$
$r < -4.7$

11. $-6.9 > -1.4 + y$
$y < -5.5$

12. $1.48 - m \ge -3.13$
$m \le 4.61$

6.2
13. $3p \le 27$
$p \le 9$

14. $-13t > 26$
$t < -2$

15. $\frac{x}{3} \ge 2$
$x \ge 6$

16. $\frac{y}{-2} < 5$
$y > -10$

17. $-6m \ge -9$
$m \le \frac{3}{2}$

18. $-3 \ge \frac{n}{2}$
$n \le -6$

19. $0.3z \le 2.4$
$z \le 8$

20. $25 > -2.5s$
$s > -10$

21. $4.8z \le 3.2$
$z \ge \frac{2}{3}$

22. $0.09d < -1.8$
$d < -20$

23. $\frac{y}{0.3} > -15$
$y > -4.5$

24. $-1.8t < 9$
$t > -5$

6.3 Solve the inequality, if possible. Graph your solution. 25–33. See margin for art.

25. $3x + 5 \ge 20$
$x \ge 5$

26. $6z - 5 < 13$
$z < 3$

27. $8(t + 4) > -8$
$t > -5$

28. $7 - 8n \le 4n - 17$
$n \ge 2$

29. $8(m + 2) < 4(5 + 2m)$
all real numbers

30. $6d - 4 - 3d \ge 14$
$d \ge 6$

31. $\frac{2}{3}y + 28 > 20 + 2y$
$y < 6$

32. $6(-5 + 3p) \ge 3(6p - 10)$
all real numbers

33. $\frac{5}{6}(12z - 24) > \frac{2}{5}(25z - 25)$
no solution

6.4 Solve the inequality. Graph your solution. 34–42. See margin for art.

34. $2 \le y - 4 < 7$
$6 \le y < 11$

35. $-27 < 9x < 27$
$-3 < x < 3$

36. $2 < 6z - 10 < 20$
$2 < z < 5$

37. $15 < \frac{5}{9}(18a - 9) \le 30$
$2 < a \le 3\frac{1}{2}$

38. $2v > 12$ or $v + 2 < 6$
$v > 6$ or $v < 4$

39. $3r + 7 < -5$ or $32 \le 7r + 46$
$r < -4$ or $r \ge -2$

40. $-4m < 8$ or $2m - 2 < -12$
$m > -2$ or $m < -5$

41. $9t - 20 \ge 4t$ or $4 < \frac{1}{-2}t$
$t \ge 4$ or $t < -8$

42. $-n - 1 > 1$ or $2n + 8 > n + 8$
$n < -2$ or $n > 0$

6.5 Solve the equation, if possible.

43. $|x| = 8$
± 8

44. $|y| = -10$
no solution

45. $|m + 6| = 5$
$-11, -1$

46. $|4z - 2| = 14$
$-3, 4$

47. $|t - 7| = 21$
$-14, 28$

48. $6|z - 4| = 36$
$-2, 10$

49. $4|6s + 11| = -52$
no solution

50. $|r + 3| - 16 = -4$
$-15, 9$

51. $|5r| + 10 = 15$
$-1, 1$

52. $2|3s + 4| = 14$
$-3\frac{2}{3}, 1$

53. $-4|7v + 2| = 32$
no solution

54. $12\left|\frac{5}{6}w - 4\right| - 4 = 8$
$3\frac{3}{5}, 6$

6.6 Solve the inequality. Graph your solution. 55–66. See margin for art.

55. $|x| \le 3$
$-3 \le x \le 3$

56. $|y| \ge 5$
$y \le -5$ or $y \ge 5$

57. $|s| > 1.2$
$s < -1.2$ or $s > 1.2$

58. $|q| < \frac{2}{5}$
$-\frac{2}{5} < q < \frac{2}{5}$

59. $|x + 2| > 6$
$x < -8$ or $x > 4$

60. $|y + 3| \le 5$
$-8 \le y \le 2$

61. $|8 - m| < 3$
$5 < m < 11$

62. $|4n - 1| \ge 7$
$n \le -\frac{3}{2}$ or $n \ge 2$

63. $3|p - 3| \le 12$
$-1 \le p \le 7$

64. $|3q + 2| - 3 \ge 8$
$q \le -\frac{13}{3}$ or $q \ge 3$

65. $2|5a - 1| + 3 \le 11$
$-\frac{3}{5} \le a \le 1$

66. $4\left|\frac{2}{3}c + 2\right| < 64$
$-27 < c < 21$

6.7 Graph the inequality.
67–78. See margin.

67. $y \ge x + 5$

68. $y < x - 1$

69. $4x + y > 3$

70. $x \le -5$

71. $3(x - 8) \le 6y$

72. $2x - y \ge -2$

73. $y > 8$

74. $2(x - 1) \ge 1 - y$

75. $x - 8 \le y + 2$

76. $2x \ge -2y$

77. $3(y - 8) > x - 9$

78. $2(-x - 1) \ge 4 + y$

EXTRA PRACTICE

19.

20.

21.

22.

23.

24.

25.

26.

27.

28.

29.

30.

31.

32.

33.

34–42, 55–78. See Additional
Answers beginning on p. AA1.

10.

11.

12.

13.

14.

15.

16.

17.

18.

25.

26.

27.

34.

35.

36.

37.

Chapter 7

7.1 Solve the linear system by graphing. Check your solution.

1. $y = x - 1$
$y = -x + 5$ **(3, 2)**

2. $y = 3x + 12$
$y = -4x - 2$ **(−2, 6)**

3. $x - y = 4$
$x + y = -2$ **(1, −3)**

4. $4x - y = 10$
$x = 4$ **(4, 6)**

5. $3x - 2y = -5$
$4x + 3y = -18$ **(−3, −2)**

6. $\frac{2}{3}x + \frac{1}{3}y = \frac{16}{3}$
$-\frac{2}{5}x + y = \frac{8}{5}$ **(6, 4)**

7.2 Solve the linear system using substitution.

7. $y = 2x + 6$
$x = y - 3$ **(−3, 0)**

8. $y = 3x + 5$
$x + y = -1$ $\left(-\frac{3}{2}, \frac{1}{2}\right)$

9. $x = 2y - 5$
$2x - y = 11$ **(9, 7)**

10. $2x - y = 0$
$r + 3y = -56$ **(−8, −16)**

11. $1.5x - 2.5y = 22$
$x - y = 10$ **(3, −7)**

12. $\frac{1}{2}x + \frac{3}{4}y = 5$
$x - \frac{1}{2}y = 6$ **(7, 2)**

Solve the linear system using elimination.

7.3 **13.** $x + 2y = 2$
$-x + 3y = 13$ **(−4, 3)**

14. $3x - 4y = -16$
$x - 4y = -40$ **(12, 13)**

15. $3x + 2y = -31$
$5x + 2y = -49$ **(−9, −2)**

16. $5x + 4y = 6$
$7x + 4y = 14$ $\left(4, -\frac{7}{2}\right)$

17. $10y - 3x = -41$
$3x - 5y = 16$ **(−3, −5)**

18. $4x - 3y = 39$
$7y = 4x - 79$ $\left(\frac{9}{4}, -10\right)$

7.4 **19.** $x + y = -3$
$5x + 7y = -9$ **(−6, 3)**

20. $5x + 2y = -19$
$10x - 7y = -16$ **(−3, −2)**

21. $8x - 3y = 61$
$2x - 5y = -23$ **(11, 9)**

22. $4x - 3y = -2$
$6x + 4y = 31$ $\left(\frac{5}{2}, 4\right)$

23. $5x - 2y = 53$
$2x + 6y = 11$ $\left(10, -\frac{3}{2}\right)$

24. $15x - 8y = 6$
$25x - 12y = 16$ $\left(\frac{14}{5}, \frac{9}{2}\right)$

7.5 Graph the linear system. Then use the graph to tell whether the linear
system has *one solution*, *no solution*, or *infinitely many solutions*. **25–27. See margin for art.**

25. $2x + y = -3$
$y = -2x + 5$
no solution

26. $2y - 4x = 10$
$-2y - 2x = 8$
one solution

27. $10x + 5y = -15$
$y = -2x - 3$
infinitely many solutions

7.5 Solve the linear system using substitution or elimination.

28. $y - 3x = 5$
$x = y - 5$ **(0, 5)**

29. $2y - 3x = 36$
$y = 3x - 12$ **(20, 48)**

30. $5x + 5y = -32$
$3x + 3y = 14$ **no solution**

31. $4x + 6y = 11$
$y = -\frac{2}{3}x + 7$ **no solution**

32. $3y - 3x = 12$
$y = x - 4$ **no solution**

33. $x + 2y = -30$
$y = \frac{1}{2}x + 15$ **(−30, 0)**

7.6 Graph the system of inequalities. **34–39. See margin.**

34. $y \geq -5$
$y \leq -2$

35. $x \geq -3$
$y < 1$

36. $y < -2x - 3$
$x - y > -4$

37. $x + 4y \geq -8$
$y - 4x < 8$
$x > -1$

38. $x > 3$
$x < 5$
$y > -2$
$y \leq 0$

39. $x + y > 3$
$x - y > 5$
$x + 2y \leq 8$
$x - 5y > 10$

38.

39.

Chapter 8

Simplify the expression. In exercises involving numerical bases only, write your answer using exponents.

8.1 **1.** $5^3 \cdot 5^4$ $\mathbf{5^7}$ 　　**2.** $6 \cdot 6^7$ $\mathbf{6^8}$ 　　**3.** $(-2)^3 \cdot (-2)^6$ $\mathbf{(-2)^9}$ 　**4.** $(2^8)^2$ $\mathbf{2^{16}}$

5. $[(-4)^3]^2$ $\mathbf{(-4)^6}$ 　　**6.** $(8 \cdot 4)^5$ $\mathbf{32^5}$ 　　**7.** $m^5 \cdot m^2$ $\mathbf{m^7}$ 　　**8.** $n^2 \cdot n^4 \cdot n^5$ $\mathbf{n^{11}}$

9. $(y^3)^5$ $\mathbf{y^{15}}$ 　　**10.** $(-2x)^3$ $\mathbf{-8x^3}$ 　　**11.** $(3d^2)^3 \cdot 2d^2$ $\mathbf{54d^8}$ 　**12.** $(-4s^2)^3(2s^3)^6$ $\mathbf{-4096s^{24}}$

8.2 **13.** $\dfrac{8^7}{8^2}$ $\mathbf{8^5}$ 　　**14.** $\dfrac{4^6 \cdot 4^2}{4^3}$ $\mathbf{4^5}$ 　　**15.** $\left(-\dfrac{2}{3}\right)^5$ $\mathbf{-\dfrac{2^5}{3^5}}$ 　**16.** $10^{12} \cdot \dfrac{1}{10^7}$ $\mathbf{10^5}$

17. $7^9 \cdot \left(\dfrac{1}{7}\right)^4$ $\mathbf{7^5}$ 　**18.** $\dfrac{1}{t^9} \cdot t^{13}$ $\mathbf{t^4}$ 　　**19.** $\left(\dfrac{p}{q}\right)^7$ $\mathbf{\dfrac{p^7}{q^7}}$ 　　**20.** $\left(\dfrac{6x^9}{3y^4}\right)^2$ $\mathbf{\dfrac{4x^{18}}{y^8}}$

21. $\left(\dfrac{4y^5}{3}\right)^3 \cdot \dfrac{1}{y^6}$ $\mathbf{\dfrac{64y^9}{27}}$ 　**22.** $\left(\dfrac{2}{u^2}\right)^3 \cdot \left(\dfrac{3u^4}{z^2}\right)^4$ $\mathbf{\dfrac{648u^{10}}{z^8}}$ 　**23.** $\left(\dfrac{5x^3y^4}{2x^2y}\right)^2$ $\mathbf{\dfrac{25x^2y^6}{4}}$ 　**24.** $\dfrac{6a^4b^5}{ab} \cdot \left(\dfrac{2ab}{a^2b^2}\right)^3$ $\mathbf{48b}$

8.3 Evaluate the expression.

25. 3^{-4} $\mathbf{\dfrac{1}{81}}$ 　　　**26.** $(-5)^{-3}$ $\mathbf{-\dfrac{1}{125}}$ 　**27.** 7^0 $\mathbf{1}$ 　　　**28.** $4^{-5} \cdot 4^3$ $\mathbf{\dfrac{1}{16}}$

29. $\left(\dfrac{1}{2}\right)^{-3}$ $\mathbf{8}$ 　　　**30.** $(3^{-2})^3$ $\mathbf{\dfrac{1}{729}}$ 　**31.** $\dfrac{1}{2^{-5}}$ $\mathbf{32}$ 　　　**32.** $\dfrac{8^{-4}}{8^{-6}}$ $\mathbf{64}$

8.3 Simplify the expression. Write your answer using only positive exponents.

33. y^{-10} $\mathbf{\dfrac{1}{y^{10}}}$ 　　**34.** $(3c)^{-4}$ $\mathbf{\dfrac{1}{81c^4}}$ 　**35.** $10b^{-3}c^5$ $\mathbf{\dfrac{10c^5}{b^3}}$ 　**36.** $(2d^5e^{-2})^{-3}$ $\mathbf{\dfrac{e^6}{8d^{15}}}$

37. $\dfrac{x^{-4}}{y^{-5}}$ $\mathbf{\dfrac{y^5}{x^4}}$ 　　**38.** $\dfrac{1}{6t^{-5}u^3}$ $\mathbf{\dfrac{t^5}{6u^3}}$ 　**39.** $\dfrac{3}{(-2z)^{-5}}$ $\mathbf{-96z^5}$ 　**40.** $\dfrac{(2e)^{-4}g^5}{e^5g^{-3}}$ $\mathbf{\dfrac{g^8}{16e^9}}$

8.4 If the number is written in scientific notation, write it in standard form. If the number is written in standard form, write it in scientific notation.

41. 0.87 $\mathbf{8.7 \times 10^{-1}}$ 　**42.** 378.4 $\mathbf{3.784 \times 10^2}$ 　**43.** 0.000359 $\mathbf{3.59 \times 10^{-4}}$ 　**44.** $465{,}000{,}000$ $\mathbf{4.65 \times 10^8}$

45. 5.3×10^5 $\mathbf{530{,}000}$ 　**46.** 1.67×10^{-4} $\mathbf{0.000167}$ 　**47.** 8×10^{-6} $\mathbf{0.000008}$ 　**48.** 9.0001×10^2 $\mathbf{900.01}$

8.4 Evaluate the expression. Write your answer in scientific notation.

49. $\dfrac{3 \times 10^2}{8 \times 10^6}$ $\mathbf{3.75 \times 10^{-5}}$ 　　**50.** $(8.5 \times 10^{10})(3.7 \times 10^{-5})$ $\mathbf{3.145 \times 10^6}$ 　**51.** $\dfrac{2.4 \times 10^{-5}}{6 \times 10^{-8}}$ $\mathbf{4 \times 10^2}$

Graph the function. 52–67. See margin.

8.5 **52.** $y = 3^x$ 　　**53.** $y = 1.25^x$ 　　**54.** $y = \left(\dfrac{9}{4}\right)^x$ 　　**55.** $y = 5 \cdot 2^x$

56. $y = \dfrac{1}{3} \cdot 2^x$ 　　**57.** $y = -\dfrac{1}{2} \cdot 5^x$ 　　**58.** $y = -5 \cdot 2^x$ 　　**59.** $y = -\dfrac{1}{3} \cdot 4^x$

8.6 **60.** $y = \left(\dfrac{1}{3}\right)^x$ 　**61.** $y = (0.2)^x$ 　**62.** $y = 3 \cdot (0.2)^x$ 　**63.** $y = 2 \cdot \left(\dfrac{1}{3}\right)^x$

64. $y = 4 \cdot \left(\dfrac{1}{3}\right)^x$ 　**65.** $y = \dfrac{1}{2} \cdot \left(\dfrac{1}{3}\right)^x$ 　**66.** $y = -2 \cdot \left(\dfrac{1}{3}\right)^x$ 　**67.** $y = -\dfrac{3}{4} \cdot \left(\dfrac{1}{3}\right)^x$

8.6 **68.** Tell whether the table represents an exponential function. If so, write a rule for the function.
exponential; $y = 5 \cdot 2^x$

x	-1	0	1	2	3
y	$\dfrac{5}{2}$	5	10	20	40

Extra Practice   **945**

55.

56.

57.

58.

59.

60.

61.

62.

63–67. See Additional Answers beginning on p. AA1.

52.

53.

54.

Chapter 10, p. 947

1.

The graph is a vertical stretch by a factor of 4 of the graph of $y = x^2$.

2.

The graph is a vertical stretch by a factor of 5 and a reflection in the x-axis of the graph of $y = x^2$.

3.

The graph is a vertical shrink by a factor of $\frac{1}{2}$ of the graph of $y = x^2$.

4.

The graph is a vertical shrink by a factor of $\frac{2}{5}$ and a reflection in the x-axis of the graph of $y = x^2$.

5.

The graph is a vertical translation 3 units up of the graph of $y = x^2$.

946

The graph is a vertical translation 2 units down of the graph of $y = x^2$.

The graph is a vertical stretch by a factor of 3 and a vertical translation 4 units up of the graph of $y = x^2$.

EXTRA PRACTICE

Chapter 9

Find the sum or difference.

9.1

1. $(6x^2 + 7) + (x^2 - 9)$
$7x^2 - 2$

2. $(8y^2 - 3y - 10) + (-11y^2 + 2y - 7)$
$-3y^2 - y - 17$

3. $(10m^2 - 7m + 2) - (3m^2 - 2m + 5)$
$7m^2 - 5m - 3$

4. $(2t^3 - 3t^2 + 5t) - (6t^3 + 3t^2 - 5t)$
$-4t^3 - 6t^2 + 10t$

5. $(6b^3 + 12b^2 - b) - (15b^2 + 7b - 8)$
$6b^3 - 3b^2 - 8b + 8$

6. $(r^2 - 8 + 4r^3 + 5r) - (7r^3 - 3r^2 + 5)$
$-3r^3 + 4r^2 + 5r - 13$

Find the product.

9.2

7. $5x^4(2x^3 - 3x^2 + 5x - 1)$
$10x^7 - 15x^6 + 25x^5 - 5x^4$

8. $(x^2 + 4x + 2)(x + 7)$
$x^3 + 11x^2 + 30x + 14$

9. $(2x + 3)(4x + 2)$
$8x^2 + 16x + 6$

10. $(2x - 5x + 6)(3x - 2)$
$6x^3 - 19x^2 + 28x - 12$

11. $(3x - 7)(x + 5)$
$3x^2 + 8x - 35$

12. $(9t - 2)(2t - 3)$
$18t^2 - 31t + 6$

9.3

13. $(x + 10)^2$
$x^2 + 20x + 100$

14. $(m + 8)(m - 8)$
$m^2 - 64$

15. $(4x - 2)(4x + 2)$
$16x^2 - 4$

16. $(3x - 4y)(3x + 4y)$
$9x^2 - 16y^2$

17. $(6 - 3t)(6 + 3t)$
$36 - 9t^2$

18. $(-11x - 4y)^2$
$121x^2 + 88xy + 16y^2$

9.4 Solve the equation.

19. $(m + 8)(m - 2) = 0$ $-8, 2$

20. $(2y - 6)(y + 3) = 0$ ± 3

21. $(5y - 3)(2y - 4) = 0$ $\frac{3}{5}, 2$

22. $3b^2 + 9b = 0$ $-3, 0$

23. $-12m^2 - 3m = 0$ $-\frac{1}{4}, 0$

24. $14k^2 = 28k$ $0, 2$

9.5 Factor the trinomial.

25. $y^2 + 7y + 12$ $(y + 3)(y + 4)$

26. $x^2 - 12x + 35$ $(x - 7)(x - 5)$

27. $x^2 + 5x - 36$ $(x - 4)(x + 9)$

28. $q^2 + 3q - 40$
$(q - 5)(q + 8)$

29. $m^2 - 29m + 100$
$(m - 25)(m - 4)$

30. $y^2 + 14y - 72$
$(y - 4)(y + 18)$

9.5 Solve the equation.

31. $m^2 - 7m + 10 = 0$ $2, 5$

32. $p^2 - 7p = 18$ $-2, 9$

33. $z^2 - 13z + 24 = -12$ $4, 9$

34. $n^2 + 8 = 6n$ $2, 4$

35. $r^2 - 15r = -8r - 10$ $2, 5$

36. $c^2 - 8 = -13c + 6$ $-14, 1$

9.6 Factor the trinomial.

37. $-x^2 + 5x - 6$
$-(x - 3)(x - 2)$

38. $3k^2 - 10k + 8$
$(3k - 4)(k - 2)$

39. $4k^2 - 12k + 5$ $(2k - 1)(2k - 5)$

40. $6t^2 - 5t - 6$ $(2t - 3)(3t + 2)$

41. $-3s^2 - 7s - 2$
$-(3s + 1)(s + 2)$

42. $2v^2 - 5v + 3$ $(2v - 3)(v - 1)$

9.6 Solve the equation.

43. $-3x^2 + 14x - 8 = 0$ $\frac{2}{3}, 4$

44. $8t^2 + 6t = 9$ $-\frac{3}{2}, \frac{3}{4}$

45. $2x^2 + 3x - 2 = 0$ $-2, \frac{1}{2}$

46. $3p^2 - 28 = 17p$ $-\frac{4}{3}, 7$

47. $16m^2 - 1 = -15m$ $-1, \frac{1}{16}$

48. $t(6t - 7) = 3$ $-\frac{1}{3}, \frac{3}{2}$

9.7 Factor the polynomial.

49. $y^2 - 36$ $(y + 6)(y - 6)$

50. $9y^2 - 49$ $(3y - 7)(3y + 7)$

51. $12y^2 - 27$ $3(2y - 3)(2y + 3)$

52. $x^2 - 8x + 16$ $(x - 4)^2$

53. $4x^2 - 12x + 9$ $(2x - 3)^2$

54. $27x^2 - 36x + 12$ $3(3x - 2)^2$

55. $g^2 + 10g + 25$ $(g + 5)^2$

56. $9b^2 + 24b + 16$ $(3b + 4)^2$

57. $4w^2 + 28w + 49$ $(2w + 7)^2$

9.8 Factor the polynomial completely.

58. $2x^2 + 8x + 6$ $(2x + 2)(x + 3)$

59. $3z^2 - 16z + 5$
$(3z - 1)(z - 5)$

60. $5m^2 - 23m + 12$
$(5m - 3)(m - 4)$

61. $3y^3 + 15y^2 + 2y + 10$
$(3y^2 + 2)(y + 5)$

62. $30z^3 - 14z^2 - 8z$
$z(10z - 8)(3z + 1)$

63. $98m^3 - 18m$
$2m(7m - 3)(7m + 3)$

64. $8h^2k - 32k$
$8k(h - 2)(h + 2)$

65. $2h^3 - 3h^2 - 18h + 27$
$(h + 3)(h - 3)(2h - 3)$

66. $-12z^3 + 12z^2 - 3z$
$-3z(2z - 1)^2$

946 Student Resources

Chapter 10

10.1 Graph the function. Compare the graph with the graph of $y = x^2$. **1–8. See margin.**

1. $y = 4x^2$ 2. $y = -5x^2$ 3. $y = \frac{1}{2}x^2$ 4. $y = -\frac{2}{5}x^2$

5. $y = x^2 + 3$ 6. $y = x^2 - 2$ 7. $y = 3x^2 + 4$ 8. $y = -4x^2 - 3$

10.2 Graph the function. Label the vertex and axis of symmetry. **9–14. See margin.**

9. $y = x^2 + 4x + 4$ 10. $y = -x^2 - 2x + 3$ 11. $y = 2x^2 - 6x + 5$

12. $y = 3x^2 + 12x + 8$ 13. $y = -2x^2 + 6$ 14. $y = \frac{3}{4}x^2 - 3x$

10.3 Solve the equation by graphing.

15. $x^2 + 3x - 10 = 0$ **−5, 2**   16. $x^2 + 14 = 9x$ **2, 7**   17. $-x^2 + 3x = -18$ **−3, 6**

18. $2x^2 + 3x - 20 = 0$ **−4, $\frac{5}{2}$**   19. $2x^2 + x = 6$ **−2, $\frac{3}{2}$**   20. $\frac{1}{2}x^2 - x = 12$ **−4, 6**

10.4 Solve the equation. Round the solutions to the nearest hundredth, if necessary.

21. $2x^2 - 20 = 78$ **±7**   22. $3y^2 + 16 = 4$ **no solution**   23. $16y^2 - 6 = 3$ **± 0.75**

24. $48 - x^2 = -52$ **±10**   25. $5m^2 - 5 = 10$ **±1.73**   26. $2 - 5t^2 = 4$ **no solution**

10.5 Solve the equation by completing the square. Round the solutions to the nearest hundredth, if necessary.

27. $x^2 + 4x - 21 = 0$ **−7, 3**   28. $g^2 - 10g = 24$ **−2, 12**   29. $w^2 - 7w + 6 = 0$ **1, 6**

30. $y^2 - \frac{3}{4}y = \frac{1}{4}$ **−0.25, 1**   31. $x^2 - 6x + 3 = 0$ **0.55, 5.45**   32. $4m^2 + 8m - 7 = 0$ **−2.66, 0.66**

10.6 Use the quadratic formula to solve the equation. Round the solutions to the nearest hundredth, if necessary.

33. $h^2 + 6h - 72 = 0$ **−12, 6**   34. $3x^2 - 7x + 2 = 0$ **0.33, 2**   35. $2k^2 - 5k + 2 = 0$ **0.5, 2**

36. $n^2 + 1 = 5n$ **0.21, 4.79**   37. $2z + 4 = 3z^2$ **−0.87, 1.54**   38. $5x^2 - 4x = 2$ **−0.35, 1.15**

10.7 Tell whether the equation has *two solutions*, *one solution*, or *no solution*.

39. $m^2 - 2m + 1 = 0$
one solution
40. $3x^2 + 6x + 2 = 0$
two solutions
41. $2q^2 + 3q + 5 = 0$
no solution
42. $\frac{3}{4}x^2 - x + 2 = 0$
no solution
43. $2w^2 - 5w + 6 = 8$
two solutions
44. $2y^2 + 10y - 5 = 3y^2 - 30$
two solutions

10.8 Tell whether the table of values represents a *linear function*, an *exponential function*, or a *quadratic function*. Then write an equation for the function. **45–48. See margin.**

45.

x	−1	0	1	2	3
y	3	0	3	12	27

46.

x	0	1	2	3	4
y	−5	−2	1	4	7

47.

x	1	2	3	4	5
y	1	2	4	8	16

48.

x	−2	−1	0	1	2
y	18	14	10	6	2

9.

10.

11.

12.

13.

14.

45. quadratic function; $y = 3x^2$

46. linear function; $y = 3x - 5$

47. exponential function;
$y = 0.5 \cdot 2^x$

48. linear function; $y = -4x + 10$

8.

The graph is a vertical stretch by a factor of 4, a vertical translation 3 units down, and a reflection in the *x*-axis of $y = x^2$.

1.

Domain: $x \geq 0$, range: $y \geq 0$; the graph is a vertical stretch by a factor of 6 of the graph of $y = \sqrt{x}$.

2.

Domain: $x \geq 0$, range: $y \geq 0$; the graph is a vertical shrink by a factor of $\frac{1}{5}$ of the graph of $y = \sqrt{x}$.

3.

Domain: $x \geq 0$, range: $y \leq 0$; the graph is a vertical stretch by a factor of 8 and a reflection in the x-axis of the graph of $y = \sqrt{x}$.

4.

Domain: $x \geq 0$, range: $y \leq 0$; the graph is a vertical shrink by a factor of $\frac{2}{5}$ and a reflection in the x-axis of the graph of $y = \sqrt{x}$.

5.

Domain: $x \geq 0$, range: $y \geq 3$; the graph is a vertical translation 3 units up of the graph of $y = \sqrt{x}$.

Chapter 11

11.1 Graph the function and identify its domain and range. Compare the graph with the graph of $y = \sqrt{x}$. **1–9. See margin.**

1. $y = 6\sqrt{x}$ **2.** $y = \frac{1}{5}\sqrt{x}$ **3.** $y = -8\sqrt{x}$

4. $y = -\frac{2}{5}\sqrt{x}$ **5.** $y = \sqrt{x} + 3$ **6.** $y = \sqrt{x} - 5$

7. $y = \sqrt{x - 2}$ **8.** $y = \sqrt{x + 5}$ **9.** $y = \sqrt{x - 4} + 2$

11.2 Simplify the expression.

10. $\sqrt{98}$ $7\sqrt{2}$ **11.** $\sqrt{300}$ $10\sqrt{3}$ **12.** $\sqrt{128x^3}$ $8x\sqrt{2x}$ **13.** $\sqrt{17} \cdot \sqrt{17}$ 17

14. $\sqrt{112} \cdot \sqrt{63}$ 84 **15.** $\sqrt{11g} \cdot 5\sqrt{g}$ $5g\sqrt{11}$ **16.** $4m\sqrt{m} \cdot \sqrt{5m}$ **17.** $\sqrt{27x^5} \cdot \sqrt{48x}$ $36x^3$

                                                                    $4m^2\sqrt{5}$

18. $\sqrt{\frac{19}{49}}$ $\frac{\sqrt{19}}{7}$ **19.** $\sqrt{\frac{1}{6x^2}}$ $\frac{\sqrt{6}}{6x}$ **20.** $\frac{3}{\sqrt{5}}$ $\frac{3\sqrt{5}}{5}$ **21.** $\frac{\sqrt{7}}{\sqrt{8k}}$ $\frac{\sqrt{14k}}{4k}$

22. $\sqrt{\frac{5}{27}}$ $\frac{\sqrt{15}}{9}$ **23.** $2\sqrt{3} + \sqrt{7} + \sqrt{3}$ **24.** $2\sqrt{11} + \sqrt{99}$ $5\sqrt{11}$ **25.** $\sqrt{45} + 3\sqrt{20}$ $9\sqrt{5}$

                                     $3\sqrt{3} + \sqrt{7}$

26. $\sqrt{3}(12 - \sqrt{15})$ **27.** $3\sqrt{6}(4\sqrt{6} - \sqrt{600})$ **28.** $(6 - \sqrt{7})(6 - \sqrt{7})$ **29.** $(4 - \sqrt{13})(10 + \sqrt{13})$

     $12\sqrt{3} - 3\sqrt{5}$ -108 $43 - 12\sqrt{7}$ $27 - 6\sqrt{13}$

11.3 Solve the equation. Check for extraneous solutions.

30. $6\sqrt{x} - 30 = 0$ **25**   **31.** $\sqrt{8x} + 5 = 13$ **8**   **32.** $\sqrt{x + 3} + 5 = 16$ **118**

33. $3\sqrt{4x + 1} - 2 = 25$ **20**   **34.** $\sqrt{3x - 12} = \sqrt{5x - 26}$ **7**   **35.** $\sqrt{2x + 10} - \sqrt{x + 7} = 0$ **−3**

36. $\sqrt{\frac{1}{2}x + 10} - \sqrt{2x - 8} = 0$ **12**   **37.** $x = \sqrt{11x - 10}$ **1, 10**   **38.** $x = \sqrt{20 - x}$ **4**

39. $5x = \sqrt{20x - 3}$ $\frac{1}{5}, \frac{3}{5}$ **40.** $\sqrt{-4x + 5} = 3x$ $\frac{5}{9}$ **41.** $x + 1 = \sqrt{6 - 2x}$ **1**

11.4 Let a and b represent the lengths of the legs of a right triangle, and let c represent the length of the hypotenuse. Find the unknown length.

42. $a = 6, b = 8$ $c = 10$ **43.** $a = 10, c = 26$ $b = 24$ **44.** $b = 40, c = 41$ $a = 9$

45. $a = 2, c = 5$ $b = \sqrt{21}$ **46.** $a = 4, b = 7$ $c = \sqrt{65}$ **47.** $b = 8, c = 11$ $a = \sqrt{57}$

11.4 Tell whether the triangle with the given side lengths is a right triangle.

48. $a = 10, b = 24, c = 26$ **49.** $a = 2, b = 4, c = 6$ **50.** $a = 14, b = 15, c = 21$
     right triangle   **not a right triangle**   **not a right triangle**
51. $a = 16, b = 30, c = 34$ **52.** $a = 1.4, b = 4.8, c = 5$ **53.** $a = 13, b = 84, c = 95$
     right triangle   **right triangle**   **not a right triangle**

11.5 Find the distance between the two points.

54. $(5, 10), (2, 6)$ **5**   **55.** $(2, 8), (7, -4)$ **13**   **56.** $(3, -3), (4, 1)$ $\sqrt{17}$

57. $(6, 1.5), (2.5, -4)$ $\sqrt{42.5}$ **58.** $\left(1, \frac{2}{5}\right), \left(\frac{1}{2}, -\frac{4}{5}\right)$ **1.3**   **59.** $\left(-\frac{3}{8}, 1\right), \left(\frac{5}{8}, \frac{1}{2}\right)$ $\frac{\sqrt{5}}{2}$

11.5 Find the midpoint of the line segment with the given endpoints.

60. $(6, -2), (8, -6)$ $(7, -4)$ **61.** $(0, -5), (-4, 8)$ $(-2, 1.5)$ **62.** $(0, -6), (0, 2)$ $(0, -2)$

63. $(10, 0), (-8, 0)$ $(1, 0)$ **64.** $(-5, -3), (-8, -7)$ $(-6.5, -5)$ **65.** $\left(5, -\frac{1}{2}\right), \left(8, -\frac{5}{2}\right)$ $6 1/2, -1\frac{1}{2}$

6–9. See Additional Answers beginning on p. AA1.

Chapter 12

12.1 Graph the inverse variation equation. **1–4. See margin.**

1. $y = \dfrac{-1}{x}$
2. $y = \dfrac{8}{x}$
3. $y = \dfrac{12}{x}$
4. $y = \dfrac{-14}{x}$

12.1 Given that y varies inversely with x, use the specified values to write an inverse variation equation that relates x and y. Then find the value of y when $x = 2$.

5. $x = 3, y = 4$ $y = \dfrac{12}{x}; 6$
6. $x = -2, y = 5$ $y = -\dfrac{10}{x}; -5$
7. $x = -4, y = -15$ $y = \dfrac{60}{x}; 30$

8. $x = 8, y = -6$ $y = \dfrac{-48}{x}; -24$
9. $x = -7, y = -7$ $y = \dfrac{49}{x}; 24.5$
10. $x = -11, y = 11$ $y = \dfrac{-121}{x}; -60.5$

12.2 Graph the function. **11–18. See margin.**

11. $y = \dfrac{6}{x}$
12. $y = \dfrac{-6}{x}$
13. $y = \dfrac{1}{5x}$
14. $y = \dfrac{1}{x} + 6$

15. $y = \dfrac{1}{x - 4}$
16. $y = \dfrac{1}{x - 5} + 3$
17. $y = \dfrac{4}{x + 2} - 3$
18. $y = \dfrac{-2}{x + 1} - 3$

12.3 Divide.

19. $(30x^4 - 12x^3 + 6x^2) \div (-6x)$ $-5x^3 + 2x^2 - x$
20. $(9y^2 + 3y - 6) \div (3y - 2)$ $3y + 3$

21. $(3v^2 + 2v + 12) \div (v + 2)$ $3v - 4 + \dfrac{20}{v + 2}$
22. $(-24w - 11 + 8w^2) \div (2 + 4w)$ $2w - 7 + \dfrac{3}{4w + 2}$

23. $(9m^2 - 6) \div (3m - 4)$ $3m + 4 + \dfrac{10}{3m - 4}$
24. $(-2 + 25n^2) \div (2 + 5n)$ $5n - 2 + \dfrac{2}{5n + 2}$

12.4 Simplify the rational expression, if possible. State the excluded values. **25–32. See margin.**

25. $\dfrac{44x^3}{24x}$
26. $\dfrac{3y + 6}{y + 2}$
27. $\dfrac{3a - 15}{4a - 20}$
28. $\dfrac{2b - 8}{4 - b}$

29. $\dfrac{r^2 - 2r - 15}{r^2 + r - 6}$
30. $\dfrac{s + 3}{2s^2 + 3s - 9}$
31. $\dfrac{2m^2 + 8m - 24}{3m^3 + 24m^2 + 36m}$
32. $\dfrac{6n^3 - 18n^2}{3n^3 - 27n}$

Find the sum, difference, product, or quotient.

12.5 33. $\dfrac{x^2 + 3x - 10}{2x - 4} \cdot \dfrac{5x}{x^2 + 2x - 15}$ $\dfrac{5x}{2x - 6}$
34. $\dfrac{2y^6}{6y^3 + 8y^2} \cdot (3y + 4)$ y^4

35. $\dfrac{3r^2 - 12}{r - 2} \div \dfrac{2r^2 + 7r + 6}{2r^2 - r - 6}$ $3r - 6$
36. $\dfrac{3s^2 + 11s + 10}{s + 2} \div (-3s^2 + s + 10)$ $-\dfrac{1}{s - 2}$

12.6 37. $\dfrac{8}{5t} + \dfrac{3}{2t^2}$ $\dfrac{16t + 15}{10t^2}$
38. $\dfrac{3}{u + 2} + \dfrac{4}{2u + 1}$ $\dfrac{10u + 11}{(u + 2)(2u + 1)}$

39. $\dfrac{3}{c^2 - 9} - \dfrac{2}{2c^2 - 3c - 9}$ $\dfrac{4c + 3}{(c + 3)(c - 3)(2c + 3)}$
40. $\dfrac{k + 4}{k^2 + 4k + 4} - \dfrac{k - 4}{k^2 - k - 6}$ $\dfrac{3k - 4}{(k + 2)^2(k - 3)}$

12.7 Solve the equation. Check your solution.

41. $\dfrac{2}{x + 2} = \dfrac{x - 5}{9}$ $-4, 7$
42. $\dfrac{y}{y - 1} + \dfrac{1}{4} = \dfrac{6}{y - 1}$ 5

43. $\dfrac{z}{z + 3} + 2 = \dfrac{5}{z - 1}$ $-\dfrac{7}{3}, 3$
44. $\dfrac{1}{w + 5} - \dfrac{2}{w + 3} = \dfrac{6}{w^2 + 5w + 6}$ $-11, -4$

45. $\dfrac{3}{h + 4} - 4 = \dfrac{6}{h^2 + h - 12}$ $-3, \dfrac{11}{4}$
46. $\dfrac{2}{a + 2} - \dfrac{5}{a + 2} = \dfrac{4}{a^2 + 4a + 4}$ $-\dfrac{10}{3}$

13.

14–18. See Additional Answers beginning on p. AA1.

25. $\dfrac{11x^2}{6}$, excluded value is 0.

26. 3, excluded value is −2.

27. $\dfrac{3}{4}$, excluded value is 5.

28. −2, excluded value is 4.

29. $\dfrac{r - 5}{r - 2}$, excluded values are 2 and −3.

30. $\dfrac{1}{2s - 3}$, excluded values are −3 and $\dfrac{3}{2}$.

31. $\dfrac{2m - 4}{3m^2 + 6m}$, excluded values are −6, −2, and 0.

32. $\dfrac{2n}{n + 3}$, excluded values are −3, 0, and 3.

Extra Practice **949**

EXTRA PRACTICE

18. population: parents or guardians of high school students, sampling method: systematic sample

19. Yes. *Sample answer:* The sampling method might be biased because only the parents or guardians of students are called and not other spectators.

20. Potentially biased. *Sample answer:* The question does not present any alternatives to the system being updated.

22.

Key: 6 | 9 = 69

23.

Chapter 13

13.1 In Exercises 1 and 2, use the following information. A bag contains 3 red, 3 blue, and 3 yellow marbles. You toss a coin and then draw a marble out of the bag at random.

1. Find the number of possible outcomes in the sample space. Then list the possible outcomes. **6 possible outcomes; heads, yellow; heads, red; heads, blue; tails, yellow; tails, red; tails, blue**

2. What is the probability that the coin shows tails and the marble is blue? $\frac{1}{6}$

13.1 3. You toss a coin 3 times. What are the odds against the coin's showing heads twice and tails once? **5 : 3**

13.2 4. In how many ways can you arrange the letters in the word SPRING? **720 ways**

5. In how many ways can you arrange 3 of the letters in the word TULIP? **60 ways**

13.2 Evaluate the expression.

6. $7!$ **5040**   7. $_8P_3$ **336**   8. $_{10}P_3$ **720**   9. $_5P_5$ **120**

13.3 10. You can choose 3 books from a list of 5 books to read for English class. How many combinations of 3 books are possible? **10 combinations**

13.3 Evaluate the expression.

11. $_6C_2$ **15**   12. $_7C_3$ **35**   13. $_{10}C_4$ **210**   14. $_{20}C_{15}$ **15,504**

13.4 In Exercises 15 and 16, you roll a number cube. Tell whether the events A and B are *mutually exclusive* or *overlapping*. Then find $P(A \text{ or } B)$.

15. **Event A:** Roll a 5.   **overlapping;** $\frac{1}{2}$
    Event B: Roll a prime number.

16. **Event A:** Roll a 4.   **mutually exclusive;** $\frac{1}{2}$
    Event B: Roll a multiple of 3.

13.4 17. A bag contains 3 red, 4 blue, and 5 yellow marbles. You randomly draw two marbles, one at a time. Find the probability that both are blue if (a) you replace the first marble and (b) you do not replace the first marble. **a.** $\frac{1}{9}$ **b.** $\frac{1}{11}$

13.5 In Exercises 18–20, use the following information. **18–20. See margin.**

Some parents want to gather information about updating the sound system in the high school auditorium. They obtain a list of high school students and call the parents or guardians of every 20th student on the list. The question they ask is "Don't you think the sound system in the high school auditorium needs updating?"

18. Identify the population and classify the sampling method.

19. Is the sampling method used likely to result in a biased sample? *Explain.*

20. Tell whether the question is potentially biased. *Explain* your answer.

In Exercises 21–23, use the following numbers of stories in the world's ten tallest buildings: 101, 88, 88, 108, 88, 88, 80, 69, 102, 78.

13.6 21. Find the mean, median, mode(s), range, and mean absolute deviation of the data. Round to the nearest hundredth, if necessary.
mean: 89, median: 88, mode: 88, range: 39, mean absolute deviation: 8.8

13.7 22. Make a histogram and a stem-and-leaf plot of the data. **See margin.**

13.8 23. Make a box-and-whisker plot of the data. Identify any outliers. **See margin for art; no outliers.**

Tables

Symbols

Symbol	Meaning	Page
$3 \cdot x$ $3x$ $3(x)$	3 times x	2
$\dfrac{a}{b}$	a divided by b, $b \neq 0$	2
a^4	the fourth power of a, or $a \cdot a \cdot a \cdot a$	3
( )	parentheses—a grouping symbol	9
[ ]	brackets—a grouping symbol	9
$=$	is equal to	21
$<$	is less than	21
$>$	is greater than	21
$\leq$	is less than or equal to	21
$\geq$	is greater than or equal to	21
$\stackrel{?}{=}$	is equal to?	22
(x, y)	ordered pair	43
$\ldots$	continues on	64
$-a$	the opposite of a	66
$\lvert a \rvert$	the absolute value of a	66
$\begin{bmatrix} 1 & 0 \\ 0 & 1 \end{bmatrix}$	matrix	94
$\dfrac{1}{a}$	the reciprocal of a, $a \neq 0$	103
$\sqrt{a}$	the nonnegative square root of a, $a \geq 0$	110
$\pm$	plus or minus	110
$\approx$	is approximately equal to	112
$a : b$	the ratio of a to b	162

Symbol	Meaning	Page
$\cong$	is congruent to	174
$\sim$	is similar to	174
A'	the image of point A	213
m	slope	235
b	y-intercept	244
a	constant of variation	253
$f(x)$	the value of the function f at x	262
a^{-n}	$\dfrac{1}{a^n}$, $a \neq 0$	503
$\sqrt[3]{a}$	the cube root of a	510
$c \times 10^n$	scientific notation, $1 \leq c < 10$ and n is an integer	512
$P(A)$	the probability of an event A	844
$n!$	n factorial, or $n \cdot (n-1) \cdot \ldots \cdot 2 \cdot 1$, n is a nonnegative integer	852
$_nP_r$	the number of permutations of n objects taken r at a time, $r \leq n$	852
$_nC_r$	the number of combinations of n objects taken r at a time, $r \leq n$	856
$\overline{x}$	x bar, the mean of numerical data	875
σ^2	variance, the square of standard deviation	879
σ	standard deviation, the nonnegative square root of variance	879

Geometric Formulas

Pythagorean Theorem (p. 737)	**Square (p. 924)**	**Rectangle (p. 924)**
  In a right triangle, $a^2 + b^2 = c^2$ where a and b are the lengths of the legs and c is the length of the hypotenuse.	 **Area** $\quad\quad$ **Perimeter** $A = s^2$ $\quad\quad$ $P = 4s$	 **Area** $\quad\quad$ **Perimeter** $A = \ell w$ $\quad\quad$ $P = 2\ell + 2w$
Parallelogram (p. 924)	**Triangle (p. 924)**	**Trapezoid (p. 924)**
  Area $A = bh$	 **Area** $A = \frac{1}{2}bh$	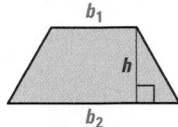 **Area** $A = \frac{1}{2}(b_1 + b_2)h$
Circle (p. 926)	**Prism (p. 927)**	**Cylinder (p. 927)**
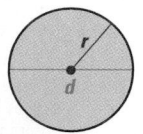 **Circumference** $\quad$ **Area** $C = \pi d$ or $\quad\quad\quad$ $A = \pi r^2$ $C = 2\pi r$	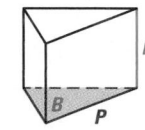 **Surface Area** $\quad$ **Volume** $S = 2B + Ph$ $\quad$ $V = Bh$	 **Surface Area** $\quad$ **Volume** $S = 2B + Ch$ $\quad$ $V = Bh$ $\quad = 2\pi r^2 + 2\pi rh$ $\quad = \pi r^2 h$
Pyramid (p. 927)	**Cone (p. 927)**	**Sphere (p. 927)**
  Surface Area $\quad$ **Volume** $S = B + \frac{1}{2}P\ell$ $\quad$ $V = \frac{1}{3}Bh$	 **Surface Area** $\quad$ **Volume** $S = B + \pi r\ell$ $\quad$ $V = \frac{1}{3}Bh$ $\quad = \pi r^2 + \pi r\ell$ $\quad\quad = \frac{1}{3}\pi r^2 h$	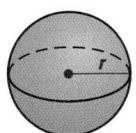 **Surface Area** $\quad$ **Volume** $S = 4\pi r^2$ $\quad$ $V = \frac{4}{3}\pi r^3$

Other Formulas

Slope (p. 235)	The slope m of a nonvertical line passing through the two points (x_1, y_1) and (x_2, y_2) is $m = \dfrac{y_2 - y_1}{x_2 - x_1}$.
Compound interest (p. 523)	$y = a(1 + r)^t$ where y is the account balance, a is the initial investment, r is the annual interest rate (in decimal form), and t is the time in years.
Quadratic formula (p. 671)	The real-number solutions of the quadratic equation $ax^2 + bx + c = 0$ are $x = \dfrac{-b \pm \sqrt{b^2 - 4ac}}{2a}$ where $a \neq 0$ and $b^2 - 4ac \geq 0$.
Distance formula (p. 744)	The distance d between any two points (x_1, y_1) and (x_2, y_2) is $d = \sqrt{(x_2 - x_1)^2 + (y_2 - y_1)^2}$.
Midpoint formula (p. 745)	The midpoint M of the line segment with endpoints $A(x_1, y_1)$ and $B(x_2, y_2)$ is $M\left(\dfrac{x_1 + x_2}{2}, \dfrac{y_1 + y_2}{2}\right)$.
Theoretical probability (p. 844)	The probability of an event when all the outcomes are equally likely is $P(\text{event}) = \dfrac{\text{Number of favorable outcomes}}{\text{Total number of outcomes}}$.
Experimental probability (p. 844)	For repeated trials of an experiment, the probability of an event is $P(\text{event}) = \dfrac{\text{Number of successes}}{\text{Number of trials}}$.
Permutations (p. 852)	The number of permutations of n objects taken r at a time, where $r \leq n$, is given by $_nP_r = \dfrac{n!}{(n - r)!}$.
Combinations (p. 856)	The number of combinations of n objects taken r at a time, where $r \leq n$, is given by $_nC_r = \dfrac{n!}{(n - r)! \cdot r!}$.
Probability of mutually exclusive or overlapping events (p. 861)	If A and B are mutually exclusive events, then $P(A \text{ or } B) = P(A) + P(B)$. If A and B are overlapping events, then $P(A \text{ or } B) = P(A) + P(B) - P(A \text{ and } B)$.
Probability of independent or dependent events (p. 862)	If A and B are independent events, then $P(A \text{ and } B) = P(A) \cdot P(B)$. If A and B are dependent events, then $P(A \text{ and } B) = P(A) \cdot P(B \text{ given } A)$.

TABLES

Properties

Properties of Addition and Multiplication

Commutative Properties (pp. 75, 89) The order in which you add two numbers does not change the sum. The order in which you multiply two numbers does not change the product.	$a + b = b + a$ $a \cdot b = b \cdot a$
Associative Properties (pp. 75, 89) The way you group three numbers in a sum does not change the sum. The way you group three numbers in a product does not change the product.	$(a + b) + c = a + (b + c)$ $(a \cdot b) \cdot c = a \cdot (b \cdot c)$
Identity Properties (pp. 75, 89) The sum of a number and the additive identity, 0, is the number. The product of a number and the multiplicative identity, 1, is the number.	$a + 0 = 0 + a = a$ $a \cdot 1 = 1 \cdot a = a$
Inverse Properties (pp. 75, 103) The sum of a number and its additive inverse, or opposite, is 0. The product of a nonzero number and its multiplicative inverse, or reciprocal, is 1.	$a + (-a) = -a + a = 0$ $a \cdot \frac{1}{a} = \frac{1}{a} \cdot a = 1 \ (a \neq 0)$
Distributive Property (p. 96) You can multiply a number and a sum by multiplying each term of the sum by the number and then adding these products. The same property applies to the product of a number and a difference.	$a(b + c) = ab + ac$ $(b + c)a = ba + ca$ $a(b - c) = ab - ac$ $(b - c)a = ba - ca$

Properties of Equality

Addition Property of Equality (p. 134) Adding the same number to each side of an equation produces an equivalent equation.	If $x - a = b$, then $x - a + a = b + a$, or $x = b + a$.
Subtraction Property of Equality (p. 134) Subtracting the same number from each side of an equation produces an equivalent equation.	If $x + a = b$, then $x + a - a = b - a$, or $x = b - a$.
Multiplication Property of Equality (p. 135) Multiplying each side of an equation by the same nonzero number produces an equivalent equation.	If $\frac{x}{a} = b$ and $a \neq 0$, then $a \cdot \frac{x}{a} = a \cdot b$, or $x = ab$.
Division Property of Equality (p. 135) Dividing each side of an equation by the same nonzero number produces an equivalent equation.	If $ax = b$ and $a \neq 0$, then $\frac{ax}{a} = \frac{b}{a}$, or $x = \frac{b}{a}$.

Properties of Inequality

Addition and Subtraction Properties of Inequality (pp. 357, 358) Adding or subtracting the same number on each side of an inequality produces an equivalent inequality.	If $a < b$, then $a + c < b + c$ and $a - c < b - c$. If $a > b$, then $a + c > b + c$ and $a - c > b - c$.
Multiplication and Division Properties of Inequality (pp. 363, 364) Multiplying or dividing each side of an inequality by a *positive* number produces an equivalent inequality. Multiplying or dividing each side of an inequality by a *negative* number and *reversing the direction of the inequality symbol* produces an equivalent inequality.	If $a < b$ and $c > 0$, then $ac < bc$ and $\dfrac{a}{c} < \dfrac{b}{c}$. If $a < b$ and $c < 0$, then $ac > bc$ and $\dfrac{a}{c} > \dfrac{b}{c}$.

Properties of Exponents

Product of Powers Property (p. 489) To multiply powers having the same base, add the exponents.	$a^m \cdot a^n = a^{m+n}$
Power of a Power Property (p. 490) To find a power of a power, multiply exponents.	$(a^m)^n = a^{mn}$
Power of a Product Property (p. 490) To find a power of a product, find the power of each factor and multiply.	$(ab)^m = a^m b^m$
Quotient of Powers Property (p. 495) To divide powers having the same nonzero base, subtract exponents.	$\dfrac{a^m}{a^n} = a^{m-n},\ a \neq 0$
Power of a Quotient Property (p. 496) To find a power of a quotient, find the power of the numerator and the power of the denominator and divide.	$\left(\dfrac{a}{b}\right)^m = \dfrac{a^m}{b^m},\ b \neq 0$

Other Properties

Cross Products Property (p. 168) The cross products of a proportion are equal.	If $\dfrac{a}{b} = \dfrac{c}{d}$ $(b, d \neq 0)$, then $ad = bc$.
Product Property of Radicals (p. 719) The square root of a product equals the product of the square roots of the factors.	$\sqrt{ab} = \sqrt{a} \cdot \sqrt{b},\ a \geq 0$ and $b \geq 0$
Quotient Properties of Radicals (p. 720) The square root of a quotient equals the quotient of the square roots of the numerator and denominator.	$\sqrt{\dfrac{a}{b}} = \dfrac{\sqrt{a}}{\sqrt{b}},\ a \geq 0$ and $b > 0$

TABLES

Measures

Time

60 seconds (sec) = 1 minute (min)	365 days ⎤
60 minutes = 1 hour (h)	52 weeks (approx.) ⎬ = 1 year
24 hours = 1 day	12 months ⎦
7 days = 1 week	10 years = 1 decade
4 weeks (approx.) = 1 month	100 years = 1 century

Metric	United States Customary
Length	**Length**
10 millimeters (mm) = 1 centimeter (cm)	12 inches (in.) = 1 foot (ft)
100 cm ⎤ = 1 meter (m)	36 in. ⎤ = 1 yard (yd)
1000 mm ⎦	3 ft ⎦
1000 m = 1 kilometer (km)	5280 ft ⎤ = 1 mile (mi)
	1760 yd ⎦
Area	**Area**
100 square millimeters = 1 square centimeter	144 square inches (in.^{2}) = 1 square foot (ft^2)
(mm^2) (cm^2)	9 ft^2 = 1 square yard (yd^2)
10,000 cm^2 = 1 square meter (m^2)	43,560 ft^2 ⎤ = 1 acre (A)
10,000 m^2 = 1 hectare (ha)	4840 yd^2 ⎦
Volume	**Volume**
1000 cubic millimeters = 1 cubic centimeter	1728 cubic inches (in.^{3}) = 1 cubic foot (ft^3)
(mm^3) (cm^3)	27 ft^3 = 1 cubic yard (yd^3)
1,000,000 cm^3 = 1 cubic meter (m^3)	
Liquid Capacity	**Liquid Capacity**
1000 milliliters (mL) ⎤ = 1 liter (L)	8 fluid ounces (fl oz) = 1 cup (c)
1000 cubic centimeters (cm^3) ⎦	2 c = 1 pint (pt)
1000 L = 1 kiloliter (kL)	2 pt = 1 quart (qt)
	4 qt = 1 gallon (gal)
Mass	**Weight**
1000 milligrams (mg) = 1 gram (g)	16 ounces (oz) = 1 pound (lb)
1000 g = 1 kilogram (kg)	2000 lb = 1 ton
1000 kg = 1 metric ton (t)	
Temperature Degrees Celsius (°C)	**Temperature Degrees Fahrenheit (°F)**
0°C = freezing point of water	32°F = freezing point of water
37°C = normal body temperature	98.6°F = normal body temperature
100°C = boiling point of water	212°F = boiling point of water

TABLES

Squares and Square Roots

No.	Square	Sq. Root	No.	Square	Sq. Root	No.	Square	Sq. Root
1	1	1.000	51	2601	7.141	101	10,201	10.050
2	4	1.414	52	2704	7.211	102	10,404	10.100
3	9	1.732	53	2809	7.280	103	10,609	10.149
4	16	2.000	54	2916	7.348	104	10,816	10.198
5	25	2.236	55	3025	7.416	105	11,025	10.247
6	36	2.449	56	3136	7.483	106	11,236	10.296
7	49	2.646	57	3249	7.550	107	11,449	10.344
8	64	2.828	58	3364	7.616	108	11,664	10.392
9	81	3.000	59	3481	7.681	109	11,881	10.440
10	100	3.162	60	3600	7.746	110	12,100	10.488
11	121	3.317	61	3721	7.810	111	12,321	10.536
12	144	3.464	62	3844	7.874	112	12,544	10.583
13	169	3.606	63	3969	7.937	113	12,769	10.630
14	196	3.742	64	4096	8.000	114	12,996	10.677
15	225	3.873	65	4225	8.062	115	13,225	10.724
16	256	4.000	66	4356	8.124	116	13,456	10.770
17	289	4.123	67	4489	8.185	117	13,689	10.817
18	324	4.243	68	4624	8.246	118	13,924	10.863
19	361	4.359	69	4761	8.307	119	14,161	10.909
20	400	4.472	70	4900	8.367	120	14,400	10.954
21	441	4.583	71	5041	8.426	121	14,641	11.000
22	484	4.690	72	5184	8.485	122	14,884	11.045
23	529	4.796	73	5329	8.544	123	15,129	11.091
24	576	4.899	74	5476	8.602	124	15,376	11.136
25	625	5.000	75	5625	8.660	125	15,625	11.180
26	676	5.099	76	5776	8.718	126	15,876	11.225
27	729	5.196	77	5929	8.775	127	16,129	11.269
28	784	5.292	78	6084	8.832	128	16,384	11.314
29	841	5.385	79	6241	8.888	129	16,641	11.358
30	900	5.477	80	6400	8.944	130	16,900	11.402
31	961	5.568	81	6561	9.000	131	17,161	11.446
32	1024	5.657	82	6724	9.055	132	17,424	11.489
33	1089	5.745	83	6889	9.110	133	17,689	11.533
34	1156	5.831	84	7056	9.165	134	17,956	11.576
35	1225	5.916	85	7225	9.220	135	18,225	11.619
36	1296	6.000	86	7396	9.274	136	18,496	11.662
37	1369	6.083	87	7569	9.327	137	18,769	11.705
38	1444	6.164	88	7744	9.381	138	19,044	11.747
39	1521	6.245	89	7921	9.434	139	19,321	11.790
40	1600	6.325	90	8100	9.487	140	19,600	11.832
41	1681	6.403	91	8281	9.539	141	19,881	11.874
42	1764	6.481	92	8464	9.592	142	20,164	11.916
43	1849	6.557	93	8649	9.644	143	20,449	11.958
44	1936	6.633	94	8836	9.695	144	20,736	12.000
45	2025	6.708	95	9025	9.747	145	21,025	12.042
46	2116	6.782	96	9216	9.798	146	21,316	12.083
47	2209	6.856	97	9409	9.849	147	21,609	12.124
48	2304	6.928	98	9604	9.899	148	21,904	12.166
49	2401	7.000	99	9801	9.950	149	22,201	12.207
50	2500	7.071	100	10,000	10.000	150	22,500	12.247

TABLES

A

absolute deviation (p. 392) The absolute deviation of a number x from a given value is the absolute value of the difference of x and the given value:

$$\text{absolute deviation} = |x - \text{given value}|$$

desviación absoluta (pág. 392) La desviación absoluta de un número x con respecto a un valor dado es el valor absoluto de la diferencia entre x y el valor dado:

$$\text{desviación absoluta} = |x - \text{valor dado}|$$

If the absolute deviation of x from 2 is 3, then $|x - 2| = 3$.

Si la desviación absoluta de x con respecto a 2 es 3, entonces $|x - 2| = 3$.

---

absolute value (p. 66) The absolute value of a number a is the distance between a and 0 on a number line. The symbol $|a|$ represents the absolute value of a.

valor absoluto (pág. 66) El valor absoluto de un número a es la distancia entre a y 0 en una recta numérica. El símbolo $|a|$ representa el valor absoluto de a.

$|2| = 2$, $|-5| = 5$, and $|0| = 0$

$|2| = 2$, $|-5| = 5$, y $|0| = 0$

---

absolute value equation (p. 390) An equation that contains an absolute value expression.

ecuación de valor absoluto (pág. 390) Ecuación que contiene una expresión de valor absoluto.

$|x + 2| = 3$ is an absolute value equation.

$|x + 2| = 3$ es una ecuación de valor absoluto.

---

additive identity (p. 76) The number 0 is the additive identity, because the sum of any number and 0 is the number: $a + 0 = 0 + a = a$.

identidad aditiva (pág. 76) El número 0 es la identidad aditiva ya que la suma de cualquier número y 0 es ese número: $a + 0 = 0 + a = a$.

$$-2 + 0 = -2, \, 0 + \tfrac{3}{4} = \tfrac{3}{4}$$

---

additive inverse (p. 76) The additive inverse of a number a is its opposite, $-a$. The sum of a number and its additive inverse is 0: $a + (-a) = -a + a = 0$.

inverso aditivo (pág. 76) El inverso aditivo de un número a es su opuesto, $-a$. La suma de un número y su inverso aditivo es 0: $a + (-a) = -a + a = 0$.

The additive inverse of -5 is 5, and $-5 + 5 = 0$.

El inverso aditivo de -5 es 5, y $-5 + 5 = 0$.

---

algebraic expression (p. 2) An expression that consists of numbers, variables, and operations. Also called *variable expression*.

expresión algebraica (pág. 2) Expresión formada por números, variables y operaciones.

$5n$, $\tfrac{14}{y}$, $6 + c$, and $8 - x$ are algebraic expressions.

$5n$, $\tfrac{14}{y}$, $6 + c$ y $8 - x$ son expresiones algebraicas.

arithmetic sequence (p. 309) A sequence in which the difference between consecutive terms is constant.	2, 8, 14, 20, 26, . . . is an arithmetic sequence in which the difference between consecutive terms is 6.
progresión aritmética (pág. 309) Progresión en la que la diferencia entre los términos consecutivos es constante.	2, 8, 14, 20, 26, . . . es una progresión aritmética en la que la diferencia entre los términos consecutivos es 6.
asymptotes of a hyperbola (p. 767) Lines that a hyperbola approaches but does not intersect.	*See* hyperbola.
asíntotas de una hipérbola (pág. 767) Rectas a las que la hipérbola se acerca pero sin cortarlas.	*Ver* hipérbola.
axis of symmetry (p. 628) The line that passes through the vertex and divides the parabola into two symmetric parts. **eje de simetría** (pág. 628) La recta que pasa por el vértice y divide a la parábola en dos partes simétricas.	 The axis of symmetry of the graph of $y = -x^2 + 2x + 1$ is the line $x = 1$. El eje de simetría de la gráfica de $y = -x^2 + 2x + 1$ es la recta $x = 1$.

B

base of a power (p. 3) The number or expression that is used as a factor in a repeated multiplication.	In the power 3^4, the base is 3.
base de una potencia (pág. 3) El número o la expresión que se usa como factor en la multiplicación repetida.	En la potencia 3^4, la base es 3.
best-fitting line (p. 335) The line that most closely follows a trend in data, found using technology. **mejor recta de regresión** (pág. 335) La recta que se ajusta más a la tendencia de los datos y que sólo se encuentra mediante tecnología.	 The graph shows the best-fitting line for the data in the scatter plot. La gráfica muestra la mejor recta de regresión para los datos del diagrama de dispersión.

biased question (p. 872) A question that encourages a particular response.	"Don't you agree that the voting age should be lowered to 16 because many 16-year-olds are responsible and informed?" is a biased question.
pregunta capciosa (pág. 872) Pregunta que impulsa a dar una respuesta determinada.	"¿No estás de acuerdo en que se debe bajar la edad para votar a los 16 años ya que muchos jóvenes de 16 años son responsables y están bien informados?" es una pregunta capciosa.
biased sample (p. 872) A sample that is not representative of the population.	The members of a school's basketball team would form a biased sample for a survey about whether to build a new gym.
muestra sesgada (pág. 872) Muestra que no es representativa de la población.	Los miembros del equipo de baloncesto de una escuela formarían una muestra sesgada si participaran en una encuesta sobre si quieren que se construya un nuevo gimnasio.
binomial (p. 555) A polynomial with two terms.	$t^3 - 4t$ and $2x + 5$ are binomials.
binomio (pág. 555) Polinomio con dos términos.	$t^3 - 4t$ y $2x + 5$ son binomios.
box-and-whisker plot (p. 887) A data display that organizes data values into four groups using the minimum value, lower quartile, median, upper quartile, and maximum value. **gráfica de frecuencias acumuladas** (pág. 887) Presentación de datos que organiza los valores de los datos en cuatro grupos usando el valor mínimo, el cuartil inferior, la mediana, el cuartil superior y el valor máximo.	
branches of a hyperbola (p. 767) The two symmetrical parts of a hyperbola.	*See* hyperbola.
ramas de una hipérbola (pág. 767) Las dos partes simétricas de la hipérbola.	*Ver* hipérbola.

C

coefficient (p. 97) The number part of a term with a variable part.	The coefficient of $-6x$ is -6.
coeficiente (pág. 97) La parte numérica de un término que tiene una variable.	El coeficiente de $-6x$ es -6.
combination (p. 856) A selection of objects in which order is *not* important.	There are 6 combinations of two of the letters from the list A, B, C, D: AB, AC, AD, BC, BD, and CD.
combinación (pág. 856) Selección de objetos en la que el orden *no* es importante.	Hay 6 combinaciones de dos de las letras de la lista A, B, C, D: AB, AC, AD, BC, BD y CD.

common difference (p. 309) The constant difference between consecutive terms of an arithmetic sequence.	2, 8, 14, 20, 26, . . . is an arithmetic sequence with a common difference of 6.
diferencia común (pág. 309) La diferencia constante entre los términos consecutivos de una progresión aritmética.	2, 8, 14, 20, 26, . . . es una progresión aritmética con una diferencia común de 6.
common ratio (p. 539) The ratio of any term of a geometric sequence to the previous term of the sequence.	The sequence 5, 10, 20, 40, . . . is a geometric sequence with common ratio 2.
razón común (pág. 539) La razón entre cualquier término de una progresión geométrica y el término anterior de la progresión.	La progresión 5, 10, 20, 40, . . . es una progresión geométrica con una razón común de 2.
completing the square (p. 663) The process of rewriting a quadratic expression so that it is a perfect square trinomial.	To write $x^2 - 16x$ as a perfect square trinomial, add $\left(\frac{-16}{2}\right)^2$, or $(-8)^2$. This gives $x^2 - 16x + (-8)^2 = (x - 8)^2$.
completar el cuadrado (pág. 663) El proceso de escribir una expresión cuadrática de manera que sea un trinomio cuadrado perfecto.	Para escribir $x^2 - 16x$ como trinomio cuadrado perfecto, suma $\left(\frac{-16}{2}\right)^2$, o $(-8)^2$. Así resulta $x^2 - 16x + (-8)^2 = (x - 8)^2$.
complex fraction (p. 810) A fraction that contains a fraction in its numerator, denominator, or both.	$\frac{\frac{3x}{2}}{-6x^3}$ and $\frac{\frac{x^2-1}{x+1}}{x-1}$ are complex fractions.
fracción compleja (pág. 810) Fracción que contiene una fracción en su numerador, en su denominador o en ambos.	$\frac{\frac{3x}{2}}{-6x^3}$ y $\frac{\frac{x^2-1}{x+1}}{x-1}$ son fracciones complejas.
compound event (p. 861) An event that combines two or more events, using the word *and* or the word *or*.	When you roll a number cube, the event "roll a 2 or an odd number" is a compound event.
suceso compuesto (pág. 861) Suceso que combina dos o más sucesos usando la palabra *y* o la palabra *o*.	Cuando lanzas un cubo numerado, el suceso "salir el 2 ó número impar" es un suceso compuesto.
compound inequality (p. 380) Two inequalities joined by *and* or *or*.	$-2 < x$ *and* $x < 1$, which can be written as $-2 < x < 1$, is a compound inequality, as is $x < -1$ *or* $x > 0$.
desigualdad compuesta (pág. 380) Dos desigualdades unidas por *y* u *o*.	$-2 < x$ *y* $x < 1$, que puede escribirse $-2 < x < 1$, es una desigualdad compuesta, al igual que $x < -1$ ó $x > 0$.
compound interest (p. 523) Interest that is earned on both an initial investment and on previously earned interest.	You deposit $250 in an account that earns 4% interest compounded yearly. After 5 years, your account balance is $y = 250(1 + 0.04)^5 \approx$ $304.16.
interés compuesto (pág. 523) Interés obtenido tanto sobre la inversión inicial como sobre el interés conseguido anteriormente.	Depositas $250 en una cuenta al 4% anual de interés compuesto. Después de 5 años, el balance de la cuenta es $y = 250(1 + 0.04)^5 \approx$ $304.16.

conditional statement (p. 66) A statement with a hypothesis and a conclusion. **enunciado condicional** (pág. 66) Enunciado que tiene una hipótesis y una conclusión.	**conditional statement** **enunciado condicional** If a is > 0, then $\lvert a \rvert = a$. hypothesis conclusion hipótesis conclusión
congruent figures (p. 174) Figures that have the same size and shape. The symbol $\cong$ indicates congruence. **figuras congruentes** (pág. 174) Figuras que tienen igual tamaño y forma. El símbolo $\cong$ indica la congruencia.	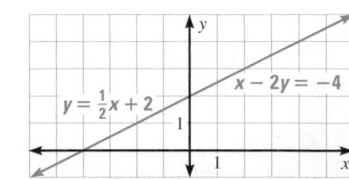 $\triangle ABC \cong \triangle DEF$
conjecture (p. 117) A statement that is believed to be true but not yet shown to be true. **conjetura** (pág. 117) Enunciado que se considera verdadero sin que haya sido demostrado todavía.	**A conclusion reached using inductive reasoning is a conjecture.** **Una conclusión que se saca mediante el razonamiento inductivo es una conjetura.**
consistent dependent system (p. 459) A linear system with infinitely many solutions. The graphs of the equations of a dependent system coincide. **sistema dependiente compatible** (pág. 459) Sistema lineal con infinitas soluciones. Las gráficas de las ecuaciones de un sistema dependiente coinciden.	 **The linear system $x - 2y = -4$ and $y = \frac{1}{2}x + 2$ is a consistent dependent system because the graphs of the equations coincide.** **El sistema lineal $x - 2y = -4$ e $y = \frac{1}{2}x + 2$ es un sistema dependiente compatible ya que las gráficas de las ecuaciones coinciden.**
consistent independent system (p. 427) A linear system with exactly one solution. The graphs of the equations of a consistent independent system intersect. **sistema independiente compatible** (pág. 427) Sistema lineal con una sola solución. Las gráficas de las ecuaciones de un sistema independiente compatible se cortan.	**The linear system $3x - 2y = 2$ and $x + y = 4$ is a consistent independent system because the graphs of the equations intersect.** **El sistema lineal $3x - 2y = 2$ y $x + y = 4$ es un sistema independiente compatible ya que las gráficas de las ecuaciones se cortan.**

constant of variation (pp. 253, 765) The nonzero constant a in a direct variation equation $y = ax$ or in an inverse variation equation $y = \frac{a}{x}$.	The constant of variation in the direct variation equation $y = \frac{2}{3}x$ is $\frac{2}{3}$, and the constant of variation in the inverse variation equation $y = \frac{-1}{x}$ is -1.
constante de variación (págs. 253, 765) La constante a distinta de cero de una ecuación de variación directa $y = ax$ o de una ecuación de variación inversa $y = \frac{a}{x}$.	La constante de variación de la ecuación de variación directa $y = \frac{2}{3}x$ es $\frac{2}{3}$, y la constante de variación de la ecuación de variación inversa $y = \frac{-1}{x}$ es -1.
constant term (p. 97) A term with a number part but no variable part.	In the expression $3x + (-4) + (-6x) + 2$, the constant terms are -4 and 2.
término constante (pág. 97) Término que tiene una parte numérica sin variable.	En la expresión $3x + (-4) + (-6x) + 2$, los términos constantes son -4 y 2.
continuous function (p. 223) A function with a graph that is unbroken. **función continua** (pág. 223) Función con una gráfica no interrumpida.	
convenience sample (p. 871) A sample in which only members of a population who are easily accessible are selected.	You can select a convenience sample of a school's student population by choosing only students who are in your classes.
muestra de conveniencia (pág. 871) Muestra en la que se selecciona sólo a los miembros de una población fácilmente accesibles.	Para seleccionar una muestra de conveniencia de la población de estudiantes de una escuela, puedes escoger sólo a los estudiantes que están en tus clases.
converse of a conditional (p. 319) A statement formed by interchanging the hypothesis and the conclusion. The converse of a true statement is not necessarily true.	The converse of the statement "If $x = 5$, then $|x| = 5$" is "If $|x| = 5$, then $x = 5$." The original statement is true, but the converse is false.
recíproco de un condicional (pág. 319) Enunciado formado al intercambiar la hipótesis y la conclusión. El recíproco de un enunciado verdadero no es necesariamente verdadero.	El recíproco del enunciado "Si $x = 5$, entonces $|x| = 5$" es "Si $|x| = 5$, entonces $x = 5$". El enunciado original es verdadero, pero el recíproco es falso.

correlation (p. 325) The relationship between paired data. The paired data have *positive correlation* if *y* tends to increase as *x* increases, *negative correlation* if *y* tends to decrease as *x* increases, and *relatively no correlation* if *x* and *y* have no apparent relationship.

correlación (pág. 325) La relación entre los pares de datos. Los pares de datos presentan una *correlación positiva* si *y* tiende a aumentar al aumentar *x*, una *correlación negativa* si *y* tiende a disminuir al aumentar *x* y una *correlación nula* si *x* e *y* no tienen ninguna relación aparente.

Positive correlation
Correlación positiva

Negative correlation
Correlación negativa

Relatively no correlation
Correlación nula

---

corresponding parts (p. 174) A pair of sides or angles that have the same relative position in two figures.

partes correspondientes (pág. 174) Par de lados o ángulos que tienen la misma posición relativa en dos figuras.

$\angle A$ and $\angle J$ are corresponding angles.
$\overline{AB}$ and $\overline{JK}$ are corresponding sides.

$\angle A$ y $\angle J$ son ángulos correspondientes.
$\overline{AB}$ y $\overline{JK}$ son lados correspondientes.

---

counterexample (p. 66) An example used to show that an if-then statement is false.

contraejemplo (pág. 66) Ejemplo utilizado para demostrar que un enunciado de "si…, entonces…" es falso.

The statement "If a number is a whole number, then the number is positive" is false because 0 is a whole number that is not a positive number.

El enunciado "Si un número es un número natural, entonces es positivo" es falso ya que 0 es un número natural que no es positivo.

---

cross product (p. 168) In a proportion, a cross product is the product of the numerator of one ratio and the denominator of the other ratio. The cross products of a proportion are equal.

producto cruzado (pág. 168) En una proporción, un producto cruzado es el producto del numerador de una de las razones y el denominador de la otra razón. Los productos cruzados de una proporción son iguales.

The cross products of the proportion
$\frac{3}{4} = \frac{6}{8}$ are $3 \cdot 8 = 24$ and $4 \cdot 6 = 24$.

Los productos cruzados de la proporción
$\frac{3}{4} = \frac{6}{8}$ son $3 \cdot 8 = 24$ y $4 \cdot 6 = 24$.

---

cube root (p. 510) If $b^3 = a$, then *b* is the cube root of *a*.

raíz cúbica (pág. 510) Si $b^3 = a$, entonces *b* es la raíz cúbica de *a*.

2 is the cube root of 8 because $2^3 = 8$.

2 es la raíz cúbica de 8 ya que $2^3 = 8$.

decay factor (p. 534) The expression $1 - r$ in the exponential decay model $y = a(1 - r)^t$.	In the exponential decay model $P = 41(0.995)^t$, the decay factor is 0.995.
factor de decrecimiento (pág. 534) La expresión $1 - r$ del modelo de decrecimiento exponencial $y = a(1 - r)^t$.	En el modelo de decrecimiento exponencial $P = 41(0.995)^t$, el factor de decrecimiento es 0.995.
decay rate (p. 534) The variable r in the exponential decay model $y = a(1 - r)^t$.	In the exponential decay model $P = 41(0.995)^t$, the decay rate is 0.005, because $0.995 = 1 - 0.005$.
tasa de decrecimiento (pág. 534) La variable r del modelo de decrecimiento exponencial $y = a(1 - r)^t$.	En el modelo de decrecimiento exponencial $P = 41(0.995)^t$, la tasa de decrecimiento es 0.005 ya que $0.995 = 1 - 0.005$.
deductive reasoning (p. 118) A form of reasoning in which a conclusion is based on statements that are assumed or shown to be true.	$(x + 2) + (-2)$ $= x + [2 + (-2)]$ Associative property of addition $= x + 0$ Inverse property of addition $= x$ Identity property of addition
razonamiento deductivo (pág. 118) Tipo de razonamiento en el que una conclusión se basa en enunciados que se suponen o se demuestran verdaderos.	$(x + 2) + (-2)$ $= x + [2 + (-2)]$ Propiedad asociativa de la suma $= x + 0$ Propiedad del elemento inverso de la suma $= x$ Propiedad de identidad de la suma
degree of a monomial (p. 554) The sum of the exponents of the variables in the monomial. The degree of a nonzero constant term is 0.	The degree of $\frac{1}{2}ab^2$ is $1 + 2$, or 3.
grado de un monomio (pág. 554) La suma de los exponentes de las variables del monomio. El grado de un término constante distinto de cero es 0.	El grado de $\frac{1}{2}ab^2$ es $1 + 2$, ó 3.
degree of a polynomial (p. 554) The greatest degree of the terms of the polynomial.	The polynomial $2x^2 + x - 5$ has degree of 2.
grado de un polinomio (pág. 554) El mayor grado de los términos del polinomio.	El polinomio $2x^2 + x - 5$ tiene un grado de 2.
dependent events (p. 862) Two events such that the occurrence of one event affects the occurrence of the other event.	A bag contains 3 red marbles and 5 white marbles. You randomly draw one marble, do not replace it, then randomly draw another marble. The events "draw a red marble first" and "draw a white marble second" are dependent events.
sucesos dependientes (pág. 862) Dos sucesos tales que la ocurrencia de uno de ellos afecta a la ocurrencia del otro.	Una bolsa contiene 3 canicas rojas y 5 blancas. Sacas al azar una canica sin reemplazarla y luego sacas al azar otra canica. Los sucesos "sacar primero una canica roja" y "sacar después una canica blanca" son sucesos dependientes.

ENGLISH-SPANISH GLOSSARY

dependent variable (p. 36) The output variable of a function.	In the function equation $y = x + 3$, y is the dependent variable.
variable dependiente (pág. 36) La variable de salida de una función.	En la ecuación de función $y = x + 3$, y es la variable dependiente.
dimensions of a matrix (p. 94) If a matrix has m rows and n columns, the dimensions of the matrix are written as $m \times n$.	The dimensions of a matrix with 2 rows and 3 columns are 2×3 ("2 by 3").
dimensiones de una matriz (pág. 94) Si una matriz tiene m filas y n columnas, las dimensiones de la matriz se escriben $m \times n$.	Las dimensiones de una matriz con 2 filas y 3 columnas son 2×3 ("2 por 3").
direct variation (p. 253) The relationship of two variables x and y if there is a nonzero number a such that $y = ax$. If $y = ax$, then y is said to vary directly with x.	The equation $2x - 3y = 0$ represents direct variation because it is equivalent to the equation $y = \frac{2}{3}x$. The equation $y = x + 5$ does *no*t represent direct variation.
variación directa (pág. 253) La relación entre dos variables x e y si hay un número a distinto de cero tal que $y = ax$. Si $y = ax$, entonces se dice que y varía directamente con x.	La ecuación $2x - 3y = 0$ representa una variación directa ya que es equivalente a la ecuación $y = \frac{2}{3}x$. La ecuación $y = x + 5$ *no* representa una variación directa.
discrete function (p. 223) A function with a graph that consists of isolated points. **función discreta** (pág. 223) Función cuya gráfica consta de puntos aislados.	
discriminant (p. 678) The expression $b^2 - 4ac$ of the assciated equation $ax^2 + bx + c = 0$; also the expression under the radical sign in the quadratic formula.	The value of the discriminant of the equation $3x^2 - 2x - 7 = 0$ is: $$b^2 - 4ac = (-2)^2 - 4(3)(-7) = 88$$
discriminante (pág. 678) La expresión $b^2 - 4ac$ de la ecuación asociada $ax^2 + bx + c = 0$; también es la expresión colocada bajo el signo radical de la fórmula cuadrática.	El valor del discriminante de la ecuación $3x^2 - 2x - 7 = 0$ es: $$b^2 - 4ac = (-2)^2 - 4(3)(-7) = 88$$
distance formula (p. 744) The distance d between any two points (x_1, y_1) and (x_2, y_2) is $d = \sqrt{(x_2 - x_1)^2 + (y_2 - y_1)^2}$.	The distance d between $(-1, 3)$ and $(5, 2)$ is: $$d = \sqrt{(5 - (-1))^2 + (2 - 3)^2} = \sqrt{37}$$
fórmula de la distancia (pág. 744) La distancia d entre dos puntos cualesquiera (x_1, y_1) y (x_2, y_2) es $d = \sqrt{(x_2 - x_1)^2 + (y_2 - y_1)^2}$.	La distancia d entre $(-1, 3)$ y $(5, 2)$ es: $$d = \sqrt{(5 - (-1))^2 + (2 - 3)^2} = \sqrt{37}$$

distributive property (p. 96) A property that can be used to find the product of a number and a sum or difference:

$$a(b + c) = ab + ac$$

$$(b + c)a = ba + ca$$

$$a(b - c) = ab - ac$$

$$(b - c)a = ba - ca$$

propiedad distributiva (pág. 96) Propiedad que sirve para hallar el producto de un número y una suma o una diferencia:

$$a(b + c) = ab + ac$$

$$(b + c)a = ba + ca$$

$$a(b - c) = ab - ac$$

$$(b - c)a = ba - ca$$

$$3(4 + 2) = 3(4) + 3(2),$$
$$(8 - 6)4 = (8)4 - (6)4$$

---

domain of a function (p. 35) The set of all inputs of a function.

dominio de una función (pág. 35) El conjunto de todas las entradas de una función.

See function.

Ver función.

E

element of a matrix (p. 94) Each number in a matrix.

elemento de una matriz (pág. 94) Cada número de la matriz.

See matrix.

Ver matriz.

---

element of a set (p. 71) Each object in a set. Also called a *member* of a set.

elemento de un conjunto (pág. 71) Cada objeto de un conjunto; llamado también *miembro* de un conjunto.

5 is an element of the set of whole numbers, $W = \{0, 1, 2, 3, \ldots\}$.

5 es un elemento del conjunto de los números naturales, $W = \{0, 1, 2, 3, \ldots\}$.

---

empty set (p. 71) The set with no elements, written as Ø.

conjunto vacío (pág. 71) El conjunto que no tiene ningún elemento, escrito Ø.

The set of negative whole numbers = Ø.

El conjunto de los números naturales negativos = Ø.

---

equation (p. 21) An open sentence that contains the symbol =.

ecuación (pág. 21) Expresión con variables que contiene el símbolo =.

$2k - 8 = 12$ is an equation.

$2k - 8 = 12$ es una ecuación.

---

equivalent equations (p. 134) Equations that have the same solution(s).

ecuaciones equivalentes (pág. 134) Ecuaciones que tienen la misma solución o soluciones.

$x + 7 = 4$ and $x = -3$ are equivalent equations.

$x + 7 = 4$ y $x = -3$ son ecuaciones equivalentes.

ENGLISH-SPANISH GLOSSARY

equivalent expressions (p. 96) Two expressions that have the same value for all values of the variable.	$3(x + 2) + x$ and $4x + 6$ are equivalent expressions.
expresiones equivalentes (pág. 96) Dos expresiones que tienen el mismo valor para todos los valores de la variable.	$3(x + 2) + x$ y $4x + 6$ son expresiones equivalentes.
equivalent inequalities (p. 357) Inequalities that have the same solutions.	$2t < 4$ and $t < 2$ are equivalent inequalities, because the solutions of both inequalities are all real numbers less than 2.
desigualdades equivalentes (pág. 357) Desigualdades con las mismas soluciones.	$2t < 4$ y $t < 2$ son desigualdades equivalentes ya que las soluciones de ambas son todos los números reales menores que 2.
evaluate an algebraic expression (p. 2) To find the value of an algebraic expression by substituting a number for each variable.	The value of $n - 1$ when $n = 3$ is $3 - 1 = 2$.
evaluar una expresión algebraica (pág. 2) Hallar el valor de una expresión algebraica mediante la sustitución de cada variable por un número.	El valor de $n - 1$ cuando $n = 3$ es $3 - 1 = 2$.
event (p. 843) An outcome or a collection of outcomes.	When you roll a number cube, "roll an odd number" is an event.
suceso (pág. 843) Caso o colección de casos.	Cuando lanzas un cubo numerado, "salir número impar" es un suceso.
excluded value (p. 794) A number that makes a rational expression undefined.	3 is an excluded value of the expression $\frac{2}{x - 3}$ because 3 makes the value of the denominator 0.
valor excluido (pág. 794) Número que hace que una expresión racional sea indefinida.	3 es un valor excluido de la expresión $\frac{2}{x - 3}$ ya que 3 hace que el valor del denominador sea 0.
experimental probability (p. 844) A probability based on repeated trials of an experiment. The experimental probability of an event is the ratio of the number of successes (trials in which a favorable outcome occurs) to the number of trials.	You spin a spinner 20 times and it stops on yellow 3 times. The experimental probability that the spinner stops on yellow is $\frac{3}{20}$, 15%, or 0.15.
probabilidad experimental (pág. 844) Probabilidad basada en la realización repetida de las pruebas de un experimento. La probabilidad experimental de un suceso es la razón entre el número de resultados deseados (pruebas en las que se produce un caso favorable) y el número de pruebas.	Giras una ruleta 20 veces y ésta se detiene en el amarillo 3 veces. La probabilidad experimental de que la ruleta se detenga en el amarillo es $\frac{3}{20}$, 15% ó 0.15.
exponent (p. 3) The number or variable that represents the number of times the base of a power is used as a factor.	In the power 3^4, the exponent is 4.
exponente (pág. 3) El número o la variable que representa la cantidad de veces que se usa la base de una potencia como factor.	En la potencia 3^4, el exponente es 4.

exponential decay (p. 533) When $a > 0$ and $0 < b < 1$, the function $y = ab^x$ represents exponential decay. When a quantity decays exponentially, it decreases by the same percent over equal time periods. The exponential decay model is $y = a(1 - r)^t$.

decrecimiento exponencial (pág. 533) Cuando $a > 0$ y $0 < b < 1$, la función $y = ab^x$ representa el decrecimiento exponencial. Cuando una cantidad decrece de forma exponencial, disminuye en el mismo porcentaje durante períodos de tiempo iguales. El modelo de decrecimiento exponencial es $y = a(1 - r)^t$.

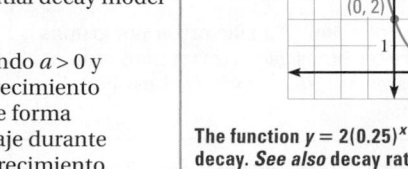

The function $y = 2(0.25)^x$ represents exponential decay. *See also* decay rate *and* decay factor.

La función $y = 2(0.25)^x$ representa el decrecimiento exponencial. *Ver también* tasa de decrecimiento *y* factor de decrecimiento.

---

exponential function (p. 520) A function of the form $y = ab^x$ where $a \neq 0$, $b > 0$, and $b \neq 1$.

función exponencial (pág. 520) Función de la forma $y = ab^x$, donde $a \neq 0$, $b > 0$ y $b \neq 1$.

The functions $y = 2 \cdot 3^x$ and $y = -2 \cdot \left(\frac{1}{2}\right)^x$ are exponential functions.

See also exponential growth *and* exponential decay.

Las funciones $y = 2 \cdot 3^x$ e $y = -2 \cdot \left(\frac{1}{2}\right)^x$ son funciones exponenciales.

Ver también crecimiento exponencial *y* decrecimiento exponencial.

---

exponential growth (p. 522) When $a > 0$ and $b > 1$, the function $y = ab^x$ represents exponential growth. When a quantity grows exponentially, it increases by the same percent over equal time periods. The exponential growth model is $y = a(1 + r)^t$.

crecimiento exponencial (pág. 522) Cuando $a > 0$ y $b > 1$, la función $y = ab^x$ representa el crecimiento exponencial. Cuando una cantidad crece de forma exponencial, aumenta en el mismo porcentaje durante períodos de tiempo iguales. El modelo de crecimiento exponencial es $y = a(1 + r)^t$.

The functions $y = 3 \cdot 2^x$ and $y = 2^x$ represent exponential growth. *See also* growth rate *and* growth factor.

Las funciones $y = 3 \cdot 2^x$ e $y = 2^x$ representan el crecimiento exponencial. *Ver también* tasa de crecimiento *y* factor de crecimiento.

---

extraneous solution (p. 730) A solution of a transformed equation that is not a solution of the original equation.

solución extraña (pág. 730) Solución de una ecuación transformada que no es solución de la ecuación original.

When you square both sides of the radical equation $\sqrt{6 - x} = x$, the resulting equation has two solutions, 2 and -3, but -3 is an extraneous solution because it does not satisfy the original equation $\sqrt{6 - x} = x$.

Al elevar al cuadrado ambos miembros de la ecuación radical $\sqrt{6 - x} = x$, la ecuación resultante tiene dos soluciones, 2 y -3, pero -3 es una solución extraña ya que no satisface la ecuación original $\sqrt{6 - x} = x$.

factor by grouping (p. 606) To factor a polynomial with four terms by grouping, factor a common monomial from pairs of terms, and then look for a common binomial factor.

factorizar por grupos (pág. 606) Para factorizar por grupos un polinomio con cuatro términos, factoriza un monomio común a partir de los pares de términos y luego busca un factor binómico común.

$$x^3 + 3x^2 + 5x + 15 = (x^3 + 3x^2) + (5x + 15)$$
$$= x^2(x + 3) + 5(x + 3)$$
$$= (x + 3)(x^2 + 5)$$

factor completely (p. 607) A factorable polynomial with integer coefficients is factored completely if it is written as a product of unfactorable polynomials with integer coefficients.

factorizar completamente (pág. 607) Un polinomio que puede descomponerse en factores y que tiene coeficientes enteros está completamente factorizado si está escrito como producto de polinomios que no pueden descomponerse en factores y que tienen coeficientes enteros.

The polynomial $x^3 - x$ is *not* factored completely when written as $x(x^2 - 1)$ but is factored completely when written as $x(x + 1)(x - 1)$.

El polinomio $x^3 - x$ no está completamente factorizado cuando se escribe $x(x^2 - 1)$, pero sí está completamente factorizado cuando se escribe $x(x + 1)(x - 1)$.

family of functions (p. 263) A group of functions with similar characteristics.

familia de funciones (pág. 263) Grupo de funciones con características similares.

Functions that have the form $f(x) = mx + b$ constitute the family of linear functions.

Las funciones que tienen la forma $f(x) = mx + b$ constituyen la familia de las funciones lineales.

formula (p. 30) An equation that relates two or more quantities.

fórmula (pág. 30) Ecuación que relaciona dos o más cantidades.

The formula $d = rt$ relates the distance traveled to the rate of speed and travel time.

La fórmula $d = rt$ relaciona la distancia recorrida con la velocidad y el tiempo transcurrido.

frequency (p. 882) The frequency of an interval is the number of data values in that interval.

frecuencia (pág. 882) La frecuencia de un intervalo es el número de datos de valores que hay en ese intervalo.

See frequency table *and* histogram.

Ver tabla de frecuencias *e* histograma.

frequency table (p. 882) A data display that groups data into equal intervals with no gaps between intervals and no intervals overlapping.

tabla de frecuencias (pág. 882) Presentación de datos en la que se agrupan los datos en intervalos iguales sin que haya interrupciones entre los intervalos y sin intervalos superpuestos.

Prices Precios	Sandwiches Sándwiches
$4.00–4.49	IIII
$4.50–4.99	II
$5.00–5.49	
$5.50–5.99	IIII

function (p. 35) A function consists of:
- A set called the domain containing numbers called inputs, and a set called the range containing numbers called outputs.
- A pairing of inputs with outputs such that each input is paired with exactly one output.

función (pág. 35) Una función consta de:
- Un conjunto llamado dominio que contiene los números conocidos como entradas, y otro conjunto llamado rango que contiene los números conocidos como salidas.
- Una correspondencia entre las entradas y las salidas tal que a cada entrada le corresponde una sola salida.

The pairing in the table below is a function, because each input is paired with exactly one output.

La correspondencia que aparece en la tabla de abajo es una función ya que a cada entrada le corresponde una sola salida.

Input, x Entrada, x	0	1	2	3	4
Output, y Salida, y	3	4	5	6	7

The domain is the set of inputs: 0, 1, 2, 3, and 4.
The range is the set of outputs: 3, 4, 5, 6, and 7.

El dominio es el conjunto de entradas: 0, 1, 2, 3 y 4.
El rango es el conjunto de salidas: 3, 4, 5, 6 y 7.

---

function notation (p. 262) A way to name a function using the symbol $f(x)$ instead of y. The symbol $f(x)$ is read as "the value of f at x" or as "f of x."

notación de función (pág. 262) Forma de nombrar una función usando el símbolo $f(x)$ en lugar de y. El símbolo $f(x)$ se lee "el valor de f en x" o "f de x".

The function $y = 2x - 9$ can be written in function notation as $f(x) = 2x - 9$.

La función $y = 2x - 9$ escrita en notación de función es $f(x) = 2x - 9$.

---

geometric sequence (p. 539) A sequence in which the ratio of any term to the previous term is constant. The constant ratio is called the common ratio.

progresión geométrica (pág. 539) Progresión en la que la razón entre cualquier término y el término anterior es constante. La razón constante se llama razón común.

The sequence 5, 10, 20, 40, . . . is a geometric sequence with common ratio 2.

La progresión 5, 10, 20, 40, . . . es una progresión geométrica cuya razón común es 2.

---

graph of an equation in two variables (p. 215) The set of points in a coordinate plane that represent all solutions of the equation.

gráfica de una ecuación con dos variables (pág. 215) El conjunto de puntos de un plano de coordenadas que representa todas las soluciones de la ecuación.

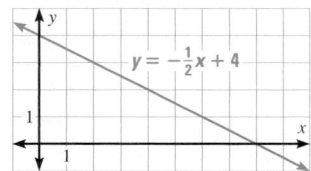

The line is the graph of the equation $y = -\frac{1}{2}x + 4$.

La recta es la gráfica de la ecuación $y = -\frac{1}{2}x + 4$.

graph of an inequality in one variable (p. 356) On a number line, the set of points that represent all solutions of the inequality.	 **Graph of** $x < 3$ **Gráfica de** $x < 3$
gráfica de una desigualdad con una variable (pág. 356) En una recta numérica, el conjunto de puntos que representa todas las soluciones de la desigualdad.	
graph of an inequality in two variables (p. 405) In a coordinate plane, the set of points that represent all solutions of the inequality. **gráfica de una desigualdad con dos variables** (pág. 405) En un plano de coordenadas, el conjunto de puntos que representa todas las soluciones de la desigualdad.	 The graph of $y > 4x - 3$ is the shaded half-plane. La gráfica de $y > 4x - 3$ es el semiplano sombreado.
graph of a system of linear inequalities (p. 466) The graph of all solutions of the system. **gráfica de un sistema de desigualdades lineales** (pág. 466) La gráfica de todas las soluciones del sistema.	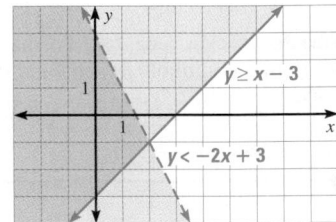 The graph of the system $y < -2x + 3$ and $y \geq x - 3$ is the intersection of the half-planes. La gráfica del sistema $y < -2x + 3$ e $y \geq x - 3$ es la intersección de los semiplanos.
growth factor (p. 522) The expression $1 + r$ in the exponential growth model $y = a(1 + r)^t$. **factor de crecimiento** (pág. 522) La expresión $1 + r$ del modelo de crecimiento exponencial $y = a(1 + r)^t$.	In the exponential growth model $C = 11{,}000(1.069)^t$, the growth factor is 1.069. En el modelo de crecimiento exponencial $C = 11{,}000(1.069)^t$, el factor de crecimiento es 1.069.
growth rate (p. 522) The variable r in the exponential growth model $y = a(1 + r)^t$. **tasa de crecimiento** (pág. 522) La variable r del modelo de crecimiento exponencial $y = a(1 + r)^t$.	In the exponential growth model $C = 11{,}000(1.069)^t$, the growth rate is 0.069. En el modelo de crecimiento exponencial $C = 11{,}000(1.069)^t$, la tasa de crecimiento es 0.069.

half-plane (p. 405) In a coordinate plane, the region on either side of a boundary line.

semiplano (pág. 405) En un plano de coordenadas, la región situada a cada lado de una recta límite.

See graph of an inequality in two variables.

Ver gráfica de una desigualdad con dos variables.

---

histogram (p. 882) A bar graph that displays data from a frequency table. Each bar represents an interval, and the length of each bar indicates the frequency.

histograma (pág. 882) Gráfica de barras que presenta los datos de una tabla de frecuencias. Cada barra representa un intervalo, y la longitud de cada barra indica la frecuencia.

Sandwich Prices
Precios de los Sándwiches

---

hyperbola (p. 767) The graph of the inverse variation equation $y = \frac{a}{x}$ ($a \neq 0$) or the graph of a rational function of the form $y = \frac{a}{x - h} + k$ ($a \neq 0$). A hyperbola has two symmetrical parts called branches. A hyperbola approaches but doesn't intersect lines called asymptotes.

hipérbola (pág. 767) La gráfica de la ecuación de variación inversa $y = \frac{a}{x}$ ($a \neq 0$) o la gráfica de una función racional de la forma $y = \frac{a}{x - h} + k$ ($a \neq 0$). La hipérbola tiene dos partes simétricas llamadas ramas. La hipérbola se acerca a las rectas llamadas asíntotas pero sin cortarlas.

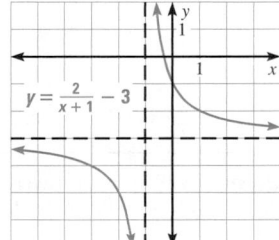

$$y = \frac{2}{x + 1} - 3$$

The graph of $y = \frac{2}{x + 1} - 3$ is a hyperbola. The asymptotes of the hyperbola are the lines $x = -1$ and $y = -3$.

La gráfica de $y = \frac{2}{x + 1} - 3$ es una hipérbola. Las asíntotas de la hipérbola son las rectas $x = -1$ e $y = -3$.

---

hypotenuse (p. 737) The hypotenuse of a right triangle is the side opposite the right angle.

hipotenusa (pág. 737) La hipotenusa de un triángulo rectángulo es el lado opuesto al ángulo recto.

hypotenuse
hipotenusa

identity (p. 156) An equation that is true for all values of the variable.

identidad (pág. 156) Ecuación que es verdadera para todos los valores de la variable.

The equation $2x + 10 = 2(x + 5)$ is an identity.

La ecuación $2x + 10 = 2(x + 5)$ es una identidad.

if-then statement (p. 66) A conditional statement with an *if* part and a *then* part. The *if* part contains the hypothesis, and the *then* part contains the conclusion.

enunciado de "si…, entonces…" (pág. 66) Enunciado condicional con una parte de *si* y otra de *entonces*. La parte de *si* contiene la hipótesis, y la parte de *entonces* contiene la conclusión.

If $a = -1$, then $|a| = 1$.
The hypothesis is $a = -1$.
The conclusion is $|a| = 1$.

Si $a = -1$, entonces $|a| = 1$.
La hipótesis es $a = -1$.
La conclusión es $|a| = 1$.

---

inconsistent system (p. 459) A linear system with no solution. The graphs of the equations of an inconsistent system are parallel lines.

sistema incompatible (pág. 459) Sistema lineal sin solución. Las gráficas de las ecuaciones de un sistema incompatible son rectas paralelas.

The linear system $y = 2x + 1$ and $y = 2x - 3$ is inconsistent because the graphs of the equations are parallel lines.

El sistema lineal $y = 2x + 1$ e $y = 2x - 3$ es incompatible ya que las gráficas de las ecuaciones son rectas paralelas.

---

independent events (p. 862) Two events such that the occurrence of one event has no effect on the occurrence of the other event.

sucesos independientes (pág. 862) Dos sucesos tales que la ocurrencia de uno de ellos no afecta a la ocurrencia del otro.

You roll a number cube twice. The events "roll a 3 first" and "roll a 6 second" are independent events.

Lanzas un cubo numerado dos veces. Los sucesos "salir primero el 3" y "salir después el 6" son sucesos independientes.

---

independent variable (p. 36) The input variable of a function.

variable independiente (pág. 36) La variable de entrada de una función.

In the function equation $y = x + 3$, x is the independent variable.

En la ecuación de función $y = x + 3$, x es la variable independiente.

---

inductive reasoning (p. 117) A form of reasoning in which a conclusion is based on several examples.

razonamiento inductivo (pág. 117) Tipo de razonamiento en el que la conclusión se basa en varios ejemplos.

You add several pairs of odd numbers and notice that the sum is even. You conclude that the sum of any two odd numbers is even.

Sumas varias parejas de números impares y observas que la suma es par. Sacas la conclusión de que la suma de dos números impares cualesquiera es par.

---

inequality (p. 21) An open sentence that contains one of the symbols $<$, $\leq$, $>$, or $\geq$.

desigualdad (pág. 21) Expresión con variables que contiene uno de los siguientes signos: $<$, $\leq$, $>$ o $\geq$.

$6n \geq 24$ and $x - 2 < 7$ are inequalities.

$6n \geq 24$ y $x - 2 < 7$ son desigualdades.

input (p. 35) A number in the domain of a function.	*See* function.
entrada (pág. 35) Número del dominio de una función.	*Ver* función.
integers (p. 64) The numbers . . . , $-3, -2, -1, 0, 1, 2, 3, . . . ,$ consisting of the negative integers, zero, and the positive integers.	-8 and 46 are integers. $-8\frac{1}{2}$ and 46.2 are *not* integers.
números enteros (pág. 64) Los números . . . , $-3, -2, -1,$ $0, 1, 2, 3, . . . ,$ que constan de los números enteros negativos, cero y los números enteros positivos.	-8 y 46 son números enteros. $-8\frac{1}{2}$ y 46.2 *no* son números enteros.
intercept form of a quadratic function (p. 641) A quadratic function in the form $y = a(x - p)(x - q)$ where $a \neq 0$. The x-intercepts of the graph of the function are p and q.	The quadratic function $y = -(x + 1)(x - 5)$ is in intercept form. The intercepts of the graph of the function are -1 and 5.
forma de intercepto de una función cuadrática (pág. 641) Función cuadrática de la forma $y = a(x - p)(x - q)$, donde $a \neq 0$. Los interceptos en x de la gráfica de la función son p y q.	La función cuadrática $y = -(x + 1)(x - 5)$ está en la forma de intercepto. Los interceptos de la gráfica de la función son -1 y 5.
interquartile range (p. 888) The difference of the upper and the lower quartiles of a data set.	The interquartile range of the data set below is $23 - 10 = 13$. lower upper quartile quartile $\downarrow$ $\downarrow$ 8 **10** 14 17 20 **23** 50
rango intercuartílico (pág. 888) La diferencia entre el cuartil superior y el cuartil inferior de un conjunto de datos.	El rango intercuartílico del siguiente conjunto de datos es $23 - 10 = 13$. cuartil cuartil inferior superior $\downarrow$ $\downarrow$ 8 **10** 14 17 20 **23** 50
intersection (p. 71) The intersection of two sets A and B is the set of all elements in *both* A and B. The intersection of A and B is written as $A \cap B$.	
intersección (pág. 71) La intersección de dos conjuntos A y B es el conjunto de todos los elementos *tanto de A como de B*. La intersección de A y B se escribe $A \cap B$.	
	$A \cap B = \{2\}$
inverse operations (p. 134) Two operations that undo each other.	Addition and subtraction are inverse operations. Multiplication and division are also inverse operations.
operaciones inversas (pág. 134) Dos operaciones que se anulan entre sí.	La suma y la resta son operaciones inversas. La multiplicación y la división también son operaciones inversas.

inverse variation (p. 765) The relationship of two variables x and y if there is a nonzero number a such that $y = \frac{a}{x}$. If $y = \frac{a}{x}$, then y is said to vary inversely with x.	The equations $xy = 4$ and $y = \frac{-1}{x}$ represent inverse variation.
variación inversa (pág. 765) La relación entre dos variables x e y si hay un número a distinto de cero tal que $y = \frac{a}{x}$. Si $y = \frac{a}{x}$, entonces se dice que y varía inversamente con x.	Las ecuaciones $xy = 4$ e $y = \frac{-1}{x}$ representan una variación inversa.
irrational number (p. 111) A number that cannot be written as the quotient of two integers. The decimal form of an irrational number neither terminates nor repeats.	$\sqrt{945} = 30.74085\ldots$ is an irrational number. $1.666\ldots$ is *not* an irrational number.
número irracional (pág. 111) Número que no puede escribirse como cociente de dos números enteros. La forma decimal de un número irracional no termina ni se repite.	$\sqrt{945} = 30.74085\ldots$ es un número irracional. $1.666\ldots$ *no* es un número irracional.

L

leading coefficient (p. 554) When a polynomial is written so that the exponents of a variable decrease from left to right, the coefficient of the first term is the leading coefficient.	The leading coefficient of the polynomial $2x^3 + x^2 - 5x + 12$ is 2.
coeficiente inicial (pág. 554) Cuando un polinomio se escribe de tal manera que los exponentes de una variable disminuyen de izquierda a derecha, el coeficiente del primer término es el coeficiente inicial.	El coeficiente inicial del polinomio $2x^3 + x^2 - 5x + 12$ es 2.
least common denominator (LCD) of rational expressions (p. 813) The product of the factors of the denominators of the rational expressions with each common factor used only once.	The LCD of $\frac{5}{(x-3)^2}$ and $\frac{3x+4}{(x-3)(x+2)}$ is $(x-3)^2(x+2)$.
mínimo común denominador (m.c.d.) de las expresiones racionales (pág. 813) El producto de los factores de los denominadores de las expresiones racionales usando cada factor común una sola vez.	El m.c.d. de $\frac{5}{(x-3)^2}$ y $\frac{3x+4}{(x-3)(x+2)}$ es $(x-3)^2(x+2)$.
legs of a right triangle (p. 737) The two sides that form the right angle. **catetos de un triángulo rectángulo** (pág. 737) Los dos lados que forman el ángulo recto.	leg cateto leg cateto
like terms (p. 97) Terms that have the same variable parts. Constant terms are also like terms.	In the expression $3x + (-4) + (-6x) + 2$, $3x$ and $-6x$ are like terms, and -4 and 2 are like terms.
términos semejantes (pág. 97) Términos que tienen las mismas variables. Los términos constantes también son términos semejantes.	En la expresión $3x + (-4) + (-6x) + 2$, $3x$ y $-6x$ son términos semejantes, y -4 y 2 también son términos semejantes.

line of fit (p. 326) A line used to model the trend in data having a positive or negative correlation.

recta de regresión (pág. 326) Recta utilizada para representar la tendencia de los datos que presentan una correlación positiva o negativa.

The graph shows a line of fit for the data in the scatter plot.

La gráfica muestra una recta de regresión para los datos del diagrama de dispersión.

---

linear equation (p. 216) An equation whose graph is a line.

ecuación lineal (pág. 216) Ecuación cuya gráfica es una recta.

See standard form of a linear equation.

Ver forma general de una ecuación lineal.

---

linear extrapolation (p. 336) Using a line or its equation to approximate a value outside the range of known values.

extrapolación lineal (pág. 336) El uso de una recta o su ecuación para hallar por aproximación un valor situado fuera del rango de los valores conocidos.

X=11.75   Y=1200

The best-fitting line can be used to estimate that when $y = 1200$, $x \approx 11.75$.

La mejor recta de regresión puede utilizarse para estimar que cuando $y = 1200$, $x \approx 11.75$.

---

linear function (p. 217) The equation $Ax + By = C$ represents a linear function provided $B \neq 0$.

función lineal (pág. 217) La ecuación $Ax + By = C$ representa una función lineal siempre que $B \neq 0$.

The equation $2x - y = 3$ represents a linear function. The equation $x = 3$ does *not* represent a function.

La ecuación $2x - y = 3$ representa una función lineal. La ecuación $x = 3$ *no* representa una función.

---

linear inequality in two variables (p. 405) An inequality that is the result of replacing the $=$ sign in a linear equation with $<, \leq, >,$ or $\geq$.

desigualdad lineal con dos variables (pág. 405) Desigualdad que se obtiene al reemplazar el símbolo $=$ de la ecuación lineal por $<, \leq, >$ o $\geq$.

$x - 3y < 6$ is a linear inequality in two variables, x and y.

$x - 3y < 6$ es una desigualdad lineal con dos variables, x e y.

linear interpolation (p. 335) Using a line or its equation to approximate a value between two known values.

interpolación lineal (pág. 335) El uso de una recta o su ecuación para hallar por aproximación un valor situado entre dos valores conocidos.

The best-fitting line can be used to estimate that when $x = 1$, $y \approx 16.4$.

La mejor recta de regresión puede utilizarse para estimar que cuando $x = 1$, $y \approx 16.4$.

---

linear regression (p. 335) The process of finding the best-fitting line to model a set of data.

regresión lineal (pág. 335) El proceso de hallar la mejor recta de regresión para representar un conjunto de datos.

You can use a graphing calculator to perform linear regression on a data set.

Puedes usar una calculadora de gráficas para realizar una regresión lineal a un conjunto de datos.

---

literal equation (p. 184) An equation in which letters are used to replace the coefficients and constants of another equation.

ecuación literal (pág. 184) Ecuación en la que se usan letras para reemplazar los coeficientes y las constantes de otra ecuación.

The equation $5(x + 3) = 20$ can be written as the literal equation $a(x + b) = c$.

La ecuación $5(x + 3) = 20$ puede escribirse como la ecuación literal $a(x + b) = c$.

---

lower quartile (p. 887) The median of the lower half of an ordered data set.

The lower quartile of the data set below is 10.

$$
\begin{array}{cc}
\text{lower} & \\
\text{quartile} & \text{median} \\
\downarrow & \downarrow \\
8 \ \mathbf{10} \ 14 \ 17 & 20 \ 23 \ 50
\end{array}
$$

cuartil inferior (pág. 887) La mediana de la mitad inferior de un conjunto de datos ordenados.

El cuartil inferior del siguiente conjunto de datos es 10.

$$
\begin{array}{cc}
\text{cuartil} & \\
\text{inferior} & \text{mediana} \\
\downarrow & \downarrow \\
8 \ \mathbf{10} \ 14 \ 17 & 20 \ 23 \ 50
\end{array}
$$

matrix, matrices (p. 94) A rectangular arrangement of numbers in rows and columns. Each number in a matrix is an element, or *entry*.

matriz, matrices (pág. 94) Disposición rectangular de números colocados en filas y columnas. Cada número de la matriz es un elemento, o *entrada*.

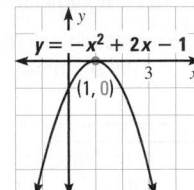

$$A = \begin{bmatrix} 0 & 4 & -1 \\ -3 & 2 & 5 \end{bmatrix} \quad \begin{array}{l} \text{2 rows} \\ \text{2 filas} \end{array}$$

3 columns
3 columnas

Matrix *A* has 2 rows and 3 columns. The element in the first row and second column is 4.

La matriz *A* tiene 2 filas y 3 columnas. El elemento de la primera fila y la segunda columna es 4.

---

maximum value (p. 636) For $y = ax^2 + bx + c$ where $a < 0$, the y-coordinate of the vertex is the maximum value of the function.

valor máximo (pág. 636) Para $y = ax^2 + bx + c$ donde $a < 0$, la coordenada y del vértice es el valor máximo de la función.

$y = -x^2 + 2x - 1$

$(1, 0)$

The maximum value of the function $y = -x^2 + 2x - 1$ is 0.

El valor máximo de la función $y = -x^2 + 2x - 1$ es 0.

---

mean (p. 875) For the numerical data set $x_1, x_2, \ldots, x_n$, the mean, or average, is:
$$\overline{x} = \frac{x_1 + x_2 + \ldots + x_n}{n}$$

media (pág. 875) Para el conjunto de datos numéricos $x_1, x_2, \ldots, x_n$, la media, o el promedio, es:
$$\overline{x} = \frac{x_1 + x_2 + \ldots + x_n}{n}$$

The mean of 5, 9, 14, 23 is $\dfrac{5 + 9 + 14 + 23}{4} = \dfrac{51}{4} = 12.75$.

La media de 5, 9, 14, 23 es $\dfrac{5 + 9 + 14 + 23}{4} = \dfrac{51}{4} = 12.75$.

---

mean absolute deviation (p. 876) The mean absolute deviation of the data set $x_1, x_2, \ldots, x_n$ is a measure of dispersion given by:
$$\frac{|x_1 - x| + |x_2 - x| + \ldots + |x_n - x|}{n}$$

desviación absoluta media (pág. 876) La desviación absoluta media del conjunto de datos $x_1, x_2, \ldots, x_n$ es una medida de dispersión dada por:
$$\frac{|x_1 - x| + |x_2 - x| + \ldots + |x_n - x|}{n}$$

The mean absolute deviation of the data set 3, 9, 13, 23 is:
$$\frac{|3 - 12| + |9 - 12| + |13 - 12| + |23 - 12|}{4} = 6$$

La desviación absoluta media del conjunto de datos 3, 9, 13, 23 es:
$$\frac{|3 - 12| + |9 - 12| + |13 - 12| + |23 - 12|}{4} = 6$$

---

measure of dispersion (p. 876) A measure that describes the dispersion, or spread, of data.

medida de dispersión (pág. 876) Medida que describe la dispersión, o extensión, de los datos.

See range *and* mean absolute deviation.

Ver rango y desviación absoluta media.

median (p. 875) The median of a numerical data set is the middle number when the values are written in numerical order. If the data set has an even number of values, the median is the mean of the two middle values.

mediana (pág. 875) La mediana de un conjunto de datos numéricos es el número central cuando los valores se escriben en orden numérico. Si el conjunto de datos tiene un número par de valores, la mediana es la media de los dos valores centrales.

The median of 5, 9, 14, 23 is the mean of 9 and 14, or $\frac{9 + 14}{2} = 11.5$.

La mediana de 5, 9, 14, 23 es la media de 9 y 14, ó $\frac{9 + 14}{2} = 11.5$.

---

midpoint (p. 745) The midpoint of a line segment is the point on the segment that is equidistant from the endpoints.

punto medio (pág. 745) El punto medio de un segmento de recta es el punto del segmento que es equidistante de los extremos.

M is the midpoint of $\overline{AB}$.

M en el punto medio de $\overline{AB}$.

---

midpoint formula (p. 745) The midpoint M of the line segment with endpoints $A(x_1, y_1)$ and $B(x_2, y_2)$ is $M\left(\frac{x_1 + x_2}{2}, \frac{y_1 + y_2}{2}\right)$.

fórmula del punto medio (pág. 745) El punto medio M del segmento de recta cuyos extremos son $A(x_1, y_1)$ y $B(x_2, y_2)$ es $M\left(\frac{x_1 + x_2}{2}, \frac{y_1 + y_2}{2}\right)$.

The midpoint M of the line segment with endpoints $(-1, -2)$ and $(3, -4)$ is:

$$\left(\frac{-1 + 3}{2}, \frac{-2 + (-4)}{2}\right) = (1, -3)$$

El punto medio M del segmento de recta cuyos extremos son $(-1, -2)$ y $(3, -4)$ es:

$$\left(\frac{-1 + 3}{2}, \frac{-2 + (-4)}{2}\right) = (1, -3)$$

---

minimum value (p. 636) For $y = ax^2 + bx + c$ where $a > 0$, the y-coordinate of the vertex is the minimum value of the function.

valor mínimo (pág. 636) Para $y = ax^2 + bx + c$ donde $a > 0$, la coordenada y del vértice es el valor mínimo de la función.

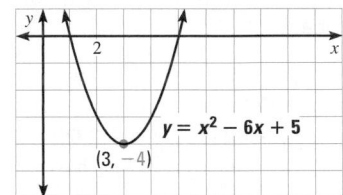

The minimum value of the function $y = x^2 - 6x + 5$ is -4.

El valor mínimo de la función $y = x^2 - 6x + 5$ es -4.

---

mode (p. 875) The mode of a data set is the value that occurs most frequently. There may be one mode, no mode, or more than one mode.

moda (pág. 875) La moda de un conjunto de datos es el valor que ocurre más veces. Puede haber una moda, más de una moda o ninguna moda.

The mode of the data set 4, 7, 9, 11, 11, 12, 18 is 11.

La moda del conjunto de datos 4, 7, 9, 11, 11, 12, 18 es 11.

monomial (p. 554) A number, variable, or the product of a number and one or more variables with whole number exponents.	$10, 3x, \frac{1}{2}ab^2$, and $-1.8m^5$ are monomials.
monomio (pág. 554) Un número, una variable o el producto de un número y una o más variables que tienen exponentes expresados por números naturales.	$10, 3x, \frac{1}{2}ab^2$ y $-1.8m^5$ son monomios.
multiplicative identity (p. 89) The number 1 is the multiplicative identity, because the product of any number and 1 is the number: $a \cdot 1 = 1 \cdot a = a$.	
identidad multiplicativa (pág. 89) El número 1 es la identidad multiplicativa ya que el producto de cualquier número y 1 es ese número: $a \cdot 1 = 1 \cdot a = a$.	$3.6(1) = 3.6, 1(-7) = -7$
multiplicative inverse (p. 103) The multiplicative inverse of a nonzero number a is its reciprocal, $\frac{1}{a}$. The product of a nonzero number and its multiplicative inverse is 1: $a \cdot \frac{1}{a} = \frac{1}{a} \cdot a = 1, a \neq 0$.	The multiplicative inverse of $-\frac{1}{5}$ is -5 because $-\frac{1}{5} \cdot (-5) = 1$.
inverso multiplicativo (pág. 103) El inverso multiplicativo de un número a distinto de cero es su recíproco, $\frac{1}{a}$. El producto de un número distinto de cero y su inverso multiplicativo es 1: $a \cdot \frac{1}{a} = \frac{1}{a} \cdot a = 1, a \neq 0$.	El inverso multiplicativo de $-\frac{1}{5}$ es -5 ya que $-\frac{1}{5} \cdot (-5) = 1$.
mutually exclusive events (p. 861) Events that have no common outcome.	When you roll a number cube, "roll a 3" and "roll an even number" are mutually exclusive events.
sucesos mutuamente excluyentes (pág. 861) Sucesos que no tienen ningún caso en común.	Cuando lanzas un cubo numerado, "salir el 3" y "salir número par" son sucesos mutuamente excluyentes.

N

n factorial (p. 852) For any positive integer n, n factorial, written $n!$, is the product of the integers from 1 to n; $0! = 1$.	
factorial de n (pág. 852) Para cualquier número entero positivo n, el factorial de n, escrito $n!$, es el producto de los números enteros de 1 a n; $0! = 1$.	$5! = 5 \cdot 4 \cdot 3 \cdot 2 \cdot 1 = 120$
negative exponent (p. 503) If $a \neq 0$, then a^{-n} is the reciprocal of a^n; $a^{-n} = \frac{1}{a^n}$.	
exponente negativo (pág. 503) Si $a \neq 0$, entonces a^{-n} es el recíproco de a^n; $a^{-n} = \frac{1}{a^n}$.	$3^{-2} = \frac{1}{3^2} = \frac{1}{9}$

negative integers (p. 64) The integers that are less than 0. **números enteros negativos** (pág. 64) Los números enteros menores que 0.	$-1, -2, -3, -4, \ldots$

O

odds against (p. 845) When all outcomes are equally likely, the odds against an event is the ratio of the number of unfavorable outcomes to the number of favorable outcomes. **probabilidad en contra** (pág. 845) Cuando todos los casos son igualmente posibles, la probabilidad en contra de que ocurra un suceso es la razón entre el número de casos desfavorables y el número de casos favorables.	When you roll a number cube, the odds against rolling a number less than 5 is $\frac{2}{4} = \frac{1}{2}$, or 1 : 2. Cuando lanzas un cubo numerado, la probabilidad en contra de que salga un número menor que 5 es $\frac{2}{4} = \frac{1}{2}$, ó 1 : 2.
odds in favor (p. 845) When all outcomes are equally likely, the odds in favor of an event is the ratio of the number of favorable outcomes to the number of unfavorable outcomes. **probabilidad a favor** (pág. 845) Cuando todos los casos son igualmente posibles, la probabilidad a favor de que ocurra un suceso es la razón entre el número de casos favorables y el número de casos desfavorables.	When you roll a number cube, the odds in favor of rolling a number less than 5 is $\frac{4}{2} = \frac{2}{1}$, or 2 : 1. Cuando lanzas un cubo numerado, la probabilidad a favor de que salga un número menor que 5 es $\frac{4}{2} = \frac{2}{1}$, ó 2 : 1.
open sentence (p. 21) A mathematical statement that contains two algebraic expressions and a symbol that compares them. **expresión con variables** (pág. 21) Enunciado matemático que contiene dos expresiones algebraicas y un símbolo que las compara.	$2k - 8 = 12$ and $6n \geq 24$ are open sentences. $2k - 8 = 12$ y $6n \geq 24$ son expresiones con variables.
opposites (p. 66) Two numbers that are the same distance from 0 on a number line but are on opposite sides of 0. **opuestos** (pág. 66) En una recta numérica, dos números que están a la misma distancia de 0 pero en lados opuestos de 0.	 4 and −4 are opposites. 4 y −4 son opuestos.
order of magnitude of a quantity (p. 491) The power of 10 nearest the quantity. **orden de magnitud de una cantidad** (pág. 491) La potencia de 10 más próxima a la cantidad.	The order of magnitude of 91,000 is 10^5, or 100,000. El orden de magnitud de 91,000 es 10^5, ó 100,000.

order of operations (p. 8) Rules for evaluating an expression involving more than one operation.

To evaluate $24 - (3^2 + 1)$, evaluate the power, then add within the parentheses, and then subtract:
$$24 - (3^2 + 1) = 24 - (9 + 1) = 24 - 10 = 14$$

orden de operaciones (pág. 8) Reglas para evaluar una expresión relacionada con más de una operación.

Para evaluar $24 - (3^2 + 1)$, evalúa la potencia, suma las cantidades entre paréntesis y después resta:
$$24 - (3^2 + 1) = 24 - (9 + 1) = 24 - 10 = 14$$

---

outcome (p. 843) A possible result of an experiment.

When you roll a number cube, there are 6 possible outcomes: a 1, 2, 3, 4, 5, or 6.

caso (pág. 843) Resultado posible de un experimento.

Cuando lanzas un cubo numerado, hay 6 casos posibles: 1, 2, 3, 4, 5 ó 6.

---

outlier (p. 889) A value that is widely separated from the rest of the data in a data set. Typically, a value that is greater than the upper quartile by more than 1.5 times the interquartile range or is less than the lower quartile by more than 1.5 times the interquartile range.

The interquartile range of the data set below is $23 - 10 = 13$.

lower quartile	upper quartile
↓	↓

8 **10** 14 17 20 **23** 50

The data value 50 is greater than $23 + 1.5(13) = 42.5$, so it is an outlier.

valor extremo (pág. 889) En un conjunto de datos, valor muy alejado del resto de los datos. Generalmente, un valor mayor que el cuartil superior en más de 1.5 veces el rango intercuartílico o menor que el cuartil inferior en más de 1.5 veces el rango intercuartílico.

El rango intercuartílico del siguiente conjunto de datos es $23 - 10 = 13$.

cuartil inferior	cuartil superior
↓	↓

8 **10** 14 17 20 **23** 50

El valor 50 es mayor que $23 + 1.5(13) = 42.5$, por lo que es un valor extremo.

---

output (p. 35) A number in the range of a function.

See function.

salida (pág. 35) Número que pertenece al rango de una función.

Ver función.

---

overlapping events (p. 861) Events that have at least one common outcome.

When you roll a number cube, "roll a 3" and "roll an odd number" are overlapping events.

sucesos de intersección (pág. 861) Sucesos que tienen al menos un caso en común.

Cuando lanzas un cubo numerado, "salir el 3" y "salir número impar" son sucesos de intersección.

parabola (p. 628) The U-shaped graph of a quadratic function.

parábola (pág. 628) La gráfica en forma de U de una función cuadrática.

The graph of $y = x^2 - 6x + 5$ is a parabola.

La gráfica de $y = x^2 - 6x + 5$ es una parábola.

---

parallel lines (p. 246) Two lines in the same plane that do not intersect.

rectas paralelas (pág. 246) Dos rectas del mismo plano que no se cortan.

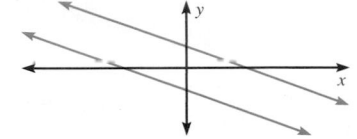

---

parent linear function (p. 263) The function $f(x) = x$, which is the most basic function in the family of linear functions.

función lineal básica (pág. 263) La función $f(x) = x$, que es la más básica de la familia de las funciones lineales.

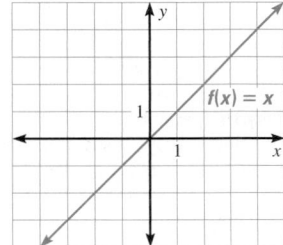

---

parent quadratic function (p. 628) The function $y = x^2$, which is the most basic function in the family of quadratic functions.

función cuadrática básica (pág. 628) La función $y = x^2$, que es la más básica de la familia de las funciones cuadráticas.

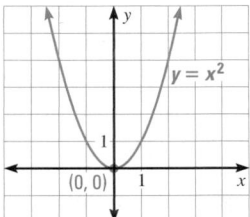

---

parent square root function (p. 710) The function $y = \sqrt{x}$, which is the most basic function in the family of square root functions.

función con raíz cuadrada básica (pág. 710) La función $y = \sqrt{x}$, que es la más básica de la familia de las funciones con raíz cuadrada.

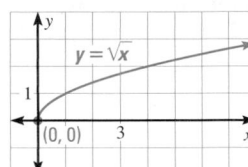

percent of change (p. 182) A percent that indicates how much a quantity increases or decreases with respect to the original amount. Percent of change, $p\% = \dfrac{\text{Amount of increase or decrease}}{\text{Original amount}}$	The percent of change, $p\%$, from 140 to 189 is: $p\% = \dfrac{189 - 140}{140} = \dfrac{49}{140} = 0.35 = 35\%$
porcentaje de cambio (pág. 182) Porcentaje que indica cuánto aumenta o disminuye una cantidad con respecto a la cantidad original. Porcentaje de cambio, $p\% = \dfrac{\text{Cantidad de aumento o disminución}}{\text{Cantidad original}}$	El porcentaje de cambio, $p\%$, de 140 a 189 es: $p\% = \dfrac{189 - 140}{140} = \dfrac{49}{140} = 0.35 = 35\%$
percent of decrease (p. 182) The percent of change in a quantity when the new amount of the quantity is less than the original amount.	*See* percent of change.
porcentaje de disminución (pág. 182) El porcentaje de cambio de una cantidad cuando la nueva cantidad es menor que la cantidad original.	*Ver* porcentaje de cambio.
percent of increase (p. 182) The percent of change in a quantity when the new amount of the quantity is greater than the original amount.	*See* percent of change.
porcentaje de aumento (pág. 182) El porcentaje de cambio de una cantidad cuando la nueva cantidad es mayor que la cantidad original.	*Ver* porcentaje de cambio.
perfect square (p. 111) A number that is the square of an integer.	49 is a perfect square, because $49 = 7^2$.
cuadrado perfecto (pág. 111) Número que es el cuadrado de un número entero.	49 es un cuadrado perfecto ya que $49 = 7^2$.
perfect square trinomials (p. 601) Trinomials of the form $a^2 + 2ab + b^2$ and $a^2 - 2ab + b^2$.	$x^2 + 6x + 9$ and $x^2 - 10x + 25$ are perfect square trinomials.
trinomios cuadrados perfectos (pág. 601) Trinomios de la forma $a^2 + 2ab + b^2$ y $a^2 - 2ab + b^2$.	$x^2 + 6x + 9$ y $x^2 - 10x + 25$ son trinomios cuadrados perfectos.
permutation (p. 851) An arrangement of objects in which order is important.	There are 6 permutations of the numbers 1, 2, and 3: 123, 132, 213, 231, 312, and 321.
permutación (pág. 851) Disposición de objetos en la que el orden es importante.	Existen 6 permutaciones de los números 1, 2 y 3: 123, 132, 213, 231, 312 y 321.
perpendicular lines (p. 320) Two lines in the same plane that intersect to form a right angle.	Horizontal and vertical lines are perpendicular to each other.
rectas perpendiculares (pág. 320) Dos rectas del mismo plano que al cortarse forman un ángulo recto.	Las rectas horizontales y verticales son perpendiculares entre sí.

point-slope form (p. 302) An equation of a nonvertical line written in the form $y - y_1 = m(x - x_1)$ where the line passes through a given point (x_1, y_1) and has a slope of m.	The equation $y + 3 = 2(x - 4)$ is in point-slope form. The graph of the equation is a line that passes through the point $(4, -3)$ and has a slope of 2.
forma punto-pendiente (pág. 302) Ecuación de una recta no vertical escrita en la forma $y - y_1 = m(x - x_1)$, donde la recta pasa por un punto dado (x_1, y_1) y tiene pendiente m.	La ecuación $y + 3 = 2(x - 4)$ está en la forma punto-pendiente. La gráfica de la ecuación es una recta que pasa por el punto $(4, -3)$ y tiene pendiente 2.
polynomial (p. 554) A monomial or a sum of monomials, each called a term of the polynomial.	$9, 2x^2 + x - 5$, and $7bc^3 + 4b^4c$ are polynomials.
polinomio (pág. 554) Monomio o suma de monomios; cada uno se llama término del polinomio.	$9, 2x^2 + x - 5$ y $7bc^3 + 4b^4c$ son polinomios.
population (p. 871) The entire group that you want information about.	A magazine invites its readers to mail in answers to a questionnaire rating the magazine. The population consists of all the magazines' readers.
población (pág. 871) El grupo entero sobre el que se desea información.	Una revista invita a sus lectores a enviar por correo las respuestas a un cuestionario sobre la calidad de la revista. La población está formada por todos los lectores de la revista.
positive integers (p. 64) The integers that are greater than 0. **números enteros positivos** (pág. 64) Los números enteros mayores que 0.	$1, 2, 3, 4, \ldots$
power (p. 3) An expression that represents repeated multiplication of the same factor. **potencia** (pág. 3) Expresión que representa la multiplicación repetida del mismo factor.	81 is a power of 3, because $81 = 3 \cdot 3 \cdot 3 \cdot 3 = 3^4$. 81 es una potencia de 3 ya que $81 = 3 \cdot 3 \cdot 3 \cdot 3 = 3^4$.
probability of an event (p. 843) A number from 0 to 1 that measures the likelihood, or chance, that the event will occur. **probabilidad de un suceso** (pág. 843) Número de 0 a 1 que mide la posibilidad de que ocurra un suceso.	*See* experimental probability *and* theoretical probability. *Ver* probabilidad experimental *y* probabilidad teórica.
proportion (p. 163) An equation that states that two ratios are equivalent: $\frac{a}{b} = \frac{c}{d}$ where $b \neq 0$ and $d \neq 0$. **proporción** (pág. 163) Ecuación que establece que dos razones son equivalentes: $\frac{a}{b} = \frac{c}{d}$ donde $b \neq 0$ y $d \neq 0$.	$\frac{3}{4} = \frac{6}{8}$ and $\frac{11}{6} = \frac{x}{30}$ are proportions. $\frac{3}{4} = \frac{6}{8}$ y $\frac{11}{6} = \frac{x}{30}$ son proporciones.

Pythagorean theorem (p. 737) If a triangle is a right triangle, then the sum of the squares of the lengths a and b of the legs equals the square of the length c of the hypotenuse: $a^2 + b^2 = c^2$.

teorema de Pitágoras (pág. 737) Si un triángulo es rectángulo, entonces la suma de los cuadrados de las longitudes a y b de los catetos es igual al cuadrado de la longitud c de la hipotenusa: $a^2 + b^2 = c^2$.

$$5^2 + 12^2 = 13^2$$

Q

quadrants (p. 206) The four regions into which the coordinate plane is divided by the x-axis and the y-axis.

cuadrantes (pág. 206) Las cuatro regiones en las que el eje de x y el eje de y dividen al plano de coordenadas.

quadratic equation (p. 643) An equation that can be written in the standard form $ax^2 + bx + c = 0$ where $a \neq 0$.

ecuación cuadrática (pág. 643) Ecuación que puede escribirse en la forma general $ax^2 + bx + c = 0$, donde $a \neq 0$.

The equations $x^2 - 2x = 3$ and $0.1x^2 = 40$ are quadratic equations.

$x^2 - 2x = 3$ y $0.1x^2 = 40$ son ecuaciones cuadráticas.

quadratic formula (p. 671) The formula below that can be used to find the solutions of the quadratic equation $ax^2 + bx + c = 0$ when $a \neq 0$ and $b^2 - 4ac \geq 0$:
$$x = \frac{-b \pm \sqrt{b^2 - 4ac}}{2a}$$

fórmula cuadrática (pág. 671) La fórmula de abajo puede utilizarse para hallar las soluciones de la ecuación cuadrática $ax^2 + bx + c = 0$ cuando $a \neq 0$ y $b^2 - 4ac \geq 0$:
$$x = \frac{-b \pm \sqrt{b^2 - 4ac}}{2a}$$

To solve $3x^2 + 5x - 8 = 0$, substitute 3 for a, 5 for b, and -8 for c in the quadratic formula:
$$x = \frac{-5 \pm \sqrt{5^2 - 4(3)(-8)}}{2(3)}$$
$x = 1$ or $x = -\frac{8}{3}$

Para resolver $3x^2 + 5x - 8 = 0$, sustituye a por 3, b por 5 y c por -8 en la fórmula cuadrática:
$$x = \frac{-5 \pm \sqrt{5^2 - 4(3)(-8)}}{2(3)}$$
$x = 1$ ó $x = -\frac{8}{3}$

quadratic function (p. 628) A nonlinear function that can be written in the standard form $y = ax^2 + bx + c$ where $a \neq 0$.

función cuadrática (pág. 628) Función no lineal que puede escribirse en la forma general $y = ax^2 + bx + c$, donde $a \neq 0$.

$y = 2x^2 + 5x - 3$ is a quadratic function.

$y = 2x^2 + 5x - 3$ es una función cuadrática.

radical equation (p. 729) An equation that contains a radical expression with a variable in the radicand.	$2\sqrt{x} - 8 = 0$ and $\sqrt{3x - 17} = \sqrt{x + 21}$ are radical equations.
ecuación radical (pág. 729) Ecuación que contiene una expresión radical en cuyo radicando aparece una variable.	$2\sqrt{x} - 8 = 0$ y $\sqrt{3x - 17} = \sqrt{x + 21}$ son ecuaciones radicales.
radical expression (p. 710) An expression that contains a radical, such as a square root, cube root, or other root.	$3\sqrt{2x}$ and $\sqrt[3]{x - 1}$ are radical expressions.
expresión radical (pág. 710) Expresión que contiene un radical, como una raíz cuadrada, una raíz cúbica u otra raíz.	$3\sqrt{2x}$ y $\sqrt[3]{x - 1}$ son expresiones radicales.
radical function (p. 710) A function that contains a radical expression with the independent variable in the radicand.	$y = \sqrt[3]{2x}$ and $y = \sqrt{x + 2}$ are radical functions.
función radical (pág. 710) Función que contiene una expresión radical y en cuyo radicando aparece la variable independiente.	$y = \sqrt[3]{2x}$ e $y = \sqrt{x + 2}$ son funciones radicales.
radicand (p. 110) The number or expression inside a radical symbol.	The radicand of $\sqrt{9}$ and $-\sqrt{9}$ is 9.
radicando (pág. 110) El número o la expresión que aparece bajo el signo radical.	El radicando de $\sqrt{9}$ y $-\sqrt{9}$ es 9.
random sample (p. 871) A sample in which every member of the population has an equal chance of being selected.	You can select a random sample of a school's student population by having a computer randomly choose 100 student identification numbers.
muestra aleatoria (pág. 871) Muestra en la que cada miembro de la población tiene igual probabilidad de ser seleccionado.	Para seleccionar una muestra aleatoria de la población de estudiantes de una escuela, puedes usar la computadora para elegir al azar 100 números de identificación estudiantil.
range of a data set (p. 876) The range of a numerical data set is a measure of dispersion. It is the difference of the greatest value and the least value.	The range of the data set 4, 7, 9, 11, 11, 12, 18 is $18 - 4 = 14$.
rango de un conjunto de datos (pág. 876) El rango de un conjunto de datos numéricos es una medida de dispersión. Es la diferencia entre los valores mayor y menor.	El rango del conjunto de datos 4, 7, 9, 11, 11, 12, 18 es $18 - 4 = 14$.
range of a function (p. 35) The set of all outputs of a function.	*See* function.
rango de una función (pág. 35) El conjunto de todas las salidas de una función.	*Ver* función.

rate (p. 17) A fraction that compares two quantities measured in different units.	$\dfrac{110 \text{ miles}}{2 \text{ hours}}$ and $\dfrac{55 \text{ miles}}{1 \text{ hour}}$ are rates.
relación (pág. 17) Fracción que compara dos cantidades medidas en unidades diferentes.	$\dfrac{110 \text{ millas}}{2 \text{ horas}}$ y $\dfrac{55 \text{ millas}}{1 \text{ hora}}$ son relaciones.
rate of change (p. 237) A comparison of a change in one quantity with a change in another quantity. In real-world situations, you can interpret the slope of a line as a rate of change.	You pay \$7 for 2 hours of computer use and \$14 for 4 hours of computer use. The rate of change is $\dfrac{\text{change in cost}}{\text{change in time}} = \dfrac{14 - 7}{4 - 2} = 3.5$, or \$3.50 per hour.
relación de cambio (pág. 237) Comparación entre el cambio producido en una cantidad y el cambio producido en otra cantidad. En situaciones de la vida real, se puede interpretar la pendiente de una recta como una relación de cambio.	Pagas \$7 por usar la computadora 2 horas y \$14 por usarla 4 horas. La relación de cambio es $\dfrac{\text{cambio en el costo}}{\text{cambio en el tiempo}} = \dfrac{14 - 7}{4 - 2} = 3.5$, o \$3.50 por hora.
ratio (p. 162) A comparison of two numbers using division. The ratio of a and b, where $b \neq 0$, can be written as a to b, as $a : b$, or as $\dfrac{a}{b}$.	The ratio of 5 wins to 2 losses can be written as 5 to 2, as $5 : 2$, or as $\dfrac{5}{2}$.
razón (pág. 162) Comparacion de dos números mediante la división. La razón entre a y b, donde $b \neq 0$, puede escribirse a a b, $a : b$ o $\dfrac{a}{b}$.	La razón de 5 victorias a 2 derrotas puede escribirse 5 a 2, $5 : 2$ ó $\dfrac{5}{2}$.
rational equation (p. 820) An equation that contains one or more rational expressions.	The equations $\dfrac{6}{x + 4} = \dfrac{x}{2}$ and $\dfrac{x}{x - 2} + \dfrac{1}{5} = \dfrac{2}{x - 2}$ are rational equations.
ecuación racional (pág. 820) Ecuación que contiene una o más expresiones racionales.	$\dfrac{6}{x + 4} = \dfrac{x}{2}$ y $\dfrac{x}{x - 2} + \dfrac{1}{5} = \dfrac{2}{x - 2}$ son ecuaciones racionales.
rational expression (p. 794) An expression that can be written as a ratio of two polynomials where the denominator is not 0.	$\dfrac{x + 8}{10x}$ and $\dfrac{5}{x^2 - 1}$ are rational expressions.
expresión racional (pág. 794) Expresión que puede escribirse como razón de dos polinomios, donde el denominador no es 0.	$\dfrac{x + 8}{10x}$ y $\dfrac{5}{x^2 - 1}$ son expresiones racionales.
rational function (p. 775) A function whose rule is given by a fraction whose numerator and denominator are polynomials and whose denominator is not 0.	The equations $y = \dfrac{-1}{x}$ and $y = \dfrac{2x - 1}{x - 2}$ are rational functions.
función racional (pág. 775) Función cuya regla viene dada por una fracción cuyo numerador y denominador son polinomios y cuyo denominador no es 0.	Las ecuaciones $y = \dfrac{-1}{x}$ e $y = \dfrac{2x - 1}{x - 2}$ son funciones racionales.

ENGLISH-SPANISH GLOSSARY

rational number (p. 64) A number that can be written as $\frac{a}{b}$ where a and b are integers and $b \neq 0$.

$4 = \frac{4}{1}, 0 = \frac{0}{1}, 2\frac{1}{3} = \frac{7}{3}, -\frac{3}{4} = \frac{-3}{4}$, and $0.6 = \frac{3}{5}$ are all rational numbers.

número racional (pág. 64) Número que puede escribirse $\frac{a}{b}$, donde a y b son números enteros y $b \neq 0$.

$4 = \frac{4}{1}, 0 = \frac{0}{1}, 2\frac{1}{3} = \frac{7}{3}, -\frac{3}{4} = \frac{-3}{4}$ y $0.6 = \frac{3}{5}$ son todos números racionales.

---

rationalizing the denominator (p. 721) The process of eliminating a radical from an expression's denominator by multiplying the expression by an appropriate form of 1.

To rationalize the denominator of $\frac{5}{\sqrt{7}}$, multiply the expression by $\frac{\sqrt{7}}{\sqrt{7}}$:

$$\frac{5}{\sqrt{7}} = \frac{5}{\sqrt{7}} \cdot \frac{\sqrt{7}}{\sqrt{7}} = \frac{5\sqrt{7}}{\sqrt{49}} = \frac{5\sqrt{7}}{7}$$

racionalizar el denominador (pág. 721) El proceso de eliminar el radical del denominador de una expresión multiplicando la expresión por la forma apropiada de 1.

Para racionalizar el denominador de $\frac{5}{\sqrt{7}}$, multiplica la expresión por $\frac{\sqrt{7}}{\sqrt{7}}$:

$$\frac{5}{\sqrt{7}} = \frac{5}{\sqrt{7}} \cdot \frac{\sqrt{7}}{\sqrt{7}} = \frac{5\sqrt{7}}{\sqrt{49}} = \frac{5\sqrt{7}}{7}$$

---

real numbers (p. 112) The set of all rational and irrational numbers.

$8, -6.2, \frac{6}{7}, \pi$, and $\sqrt{2}$ are real numbers.

números reales (pág. 112) El conjunto de todos los números racionales e irracionales.

$8, -6.2, \frac{6}{7}, \pi$ y $\sqrt{2}$ son números reales.

---

reflection (p. 213) A reflection flips a figure in a line.

reflexión (pág. 213) Una reflexión vuelca una figura en una recta.

line of reflection
recta de reflexión

---

relation (p. 49) Any pairing of a set of inputs with a set of outputs.

relación (pág. 49) Cualquier correspondencia establecida entre un conjunto de entradas y un conjunto de salidas.

The pairing in the table below is a relation, but it is *not* a function.

La correspondencia en la tabla de abajo es una relación, pero *no* es una función.

Input Entrada	4	4	5	6	7
Output Salida	0	1	2	3	4

---

roots (p. 575) The solutions of an equation in which one side is zero and other side is a product of polynomial factors.

The roots of the equation $(x - 4)(x + 2) = 0$ are 4 and -2.

raíces (pág. 575) Las soluciones de una ecuación en la que un miembro es cero y el otro miembro es el producto de factores polinómicos.

Las raíces de la ecuación $(x - 4)(x + 2) = 0$ son 4 y -2.

sample (p. 871) A part of a population.	**To predict the results of an election, a survey is given to a sample of voters.**
muestra (pág. 871) Parte de una población.	**Para predecir los resultados de una elección, se realiza una encuesta entre una muestra de votantes.**
sample space (p. 843) The set of all possible outcomes.	**When you toss two coins, the sample space is heads, heads; heads, tails; tails, heads; and tails, tails.**
espacio muestral (pág. 843) El conjunto de todos los casos posibles.	**Cuando lanzas al aire dos monedas, el espacio muestral es cara, cara; cara, cruz; cruz, cara; y cruz, cruz.**
scalar (p. 95) A real number that is multiplied by each element in a matrix.	*See* **matrix.**
escalar (pág. 95) Número real que se multiplica por cada elemento de una matriz.	*Ver* **matriz.**
scalar multiplication (p. 95) Multiplication of each element in a matrix by a real number, called a scalar.	**The matrix is multiplied by the scalar 3.** $$3\begin{bmatrix} 1 & 2 \\ 0 & -1 \end{bmatrix} = \begin{bmatrix} 3 & 6 \\ 0 & -3 \end{bmatrix}$$
multiplicación escalar (pág. 95) Multiplicación de cada elemento de una matriz por un número real llamado escalar.	**La matriz se multiplica por el escalar 3.** $$3\begin{bmatrix} 1 & 2 \\ 0 & -1 \end{bmatrix} = \begin{bmatrix} 3 & 6 \\ 0 & -3 \end{bmatrix}$$
scale (p. 170) A ratio that relates the dimensions of a scale drawing or scale model and the actual dimensions.	**The scale 1 in. : 12 ft on a floor plan means that 1 inch in the floor plan represents an actual distance of 12 feet.**
escala (pág. 170) Razón que relaciona las dimensiones de un dibujo a escala o un modelo a escala con las dimensiones reales.	**La escala 1 pulg : 12 pies en un diagrama de planta significa que 1 pulgada en el diagrama de planta representa una distancia real de 12 pies.**
scale drawing (p. 170) A two-dimensional drawing of an object in which the dimensions of the drawing are in proportion to the dimensions of the object.	**A floor plan of a house is a scale drawing.**
dibujo a escala (pág. 170) Dibujo bidimensional de un objeto en el que las dimensiones del dibujo guardan proporción con las dimensiones del objeto.	**El diagrama de planta de una casa es un dibujo a escala.**
scale model (p. 170) A three-dimensional model of an object in which the dimensions of the model are in proportion to the dimensions of the object.	**A globe is a scale model of Earth.**
modelo a escala (pág. 170) Modelo tridimensional de un objeto en el que las dimensiones del modelo guardan proporción con las dimensiones del objeto.	**El globo terráqueo es un modelo a escala de la Tierra.**

scatter plot (p. 325) A graph used to determine whether there is a relationship or trend between paired data.

diagrama de dispersión (pág. 325) Gráfica utilizada para determinar si hay una relación o tendencia entre los pares de datos.

scientific notation (p. 512) A number is written in scientific notation when it is of the form $c \times 10^n$ where $1 \le c < 10$ and n is an integer.

notación científica (pág. 512) Un número está escrito en notación científica cuando es de la forma $c \times 10^n$, donde $1 \le c < 10$ y n es un número entero.

Two million is written in scientific notation as 2×10^6, and 0.547 is written in scientific notation as 5.47×10^{-1}.

El número dos millones escrito en notación científica es 2×10^6, y 0.547 escrito en notación científica es 5.47×10^{-1}.

self-selected sample (p. 871) A sample in which members of the population select themselves by volunteering.

muestra autoseleccionada (pág. 871) Muestra en la que los miembros de la población se seleccionan a sí mismos ofreciéndose a participar.

You can obtain a self-selected sample of a school's student population by asking students to return surveys to a collection box.

Para obtener una muestra autoseleccionada de la población de estudiantes de una escuela, puedes pedir a los estudiantes que hagan la encuesta que la depositen en un recipiente de recogida.

sequence (p. 309) An ordered list of numbers.

progresión (pág. 309) Lista ordenada de números.

$-4, 1, 6, 11, 16, \ldots$ is a sequence.

$-4, 1, 6, 11, 16, \ldots$ es una progresión.

set (p. 71) A collection of distinct objects.

conjunto (pág. 71) Colección de objetos diferenciados.

The set of whole numbers is $W = \{0, 1, 2, 3, \ldots\}$.

El conjunto de los números naturales es $W = \{0, 1, 2, 3, \ldots\}$.

similar figures (p. 174) Figures that have the same shape but not necessarily the same size. Corresponding angles of similar figures are congruent, and the ratios of the lengths of corresponding sides are equal. The symbol $\sim$ indicates that two figures are similar.

figuras semejantes (pág. 174) Figuras que tienen la misma forma pero no necesariamente el mismo tamaño. Los ángulos correspondientes de las figuras semejantes son congruentes, y las razones de las longitudes de los lados correspondientes son iguales. El símbolo $\sim$ indica que dos figuras son semejantes.

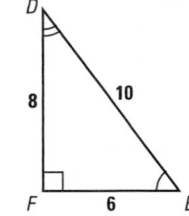

$\triangle ABC \sim \triangle DEF$

simplest form of a radical expression (p. 719) A radical expression that has no perfect square factors other than 1 in the radicand, no fractions in the radicand, and no radicals appearing in the denominator of a fraction.

In simplest form, $\sqrt{32}$ is written as $4\sqrt{2}$, and $\dfrac{5}{\sqrt{7}}$ is written as $\dfrac{5\sqrt{7}}{7}$.

forma más simple de una expresión radical (pág. 719) Expresión radical que no tiene en el radicando fracciones ni factores cuadrados perfectos distintos de 1 y que no tiene radicales en el denominador de las fracciones.

En la forma más simple, $\sqrt{32}$ se escribe $4\sqrt{2}$, y $\dfrac{5}{\sqrt{7}}$ se escribe $\dfrac{5\sqrt{7}}{7}$.

---

simplest form of a rational expression (p. 795) A rational expression whose numerator and denominator have no factors in common other than 1.

The simplest form of $\dfrac{2x}{x(x-3)}$ is $\dfrac{2}{x-3}$.

forma más simple de una expresión racional (pág. 795) Expresión racional cuyo numerador y denominador no tienen más factores en común que el 1.

La forma más simple de $\dfrac{2x}{x(x-3)}$ es $\dfrac{2}{x-3}$.

---

simulation (p. 849) An experiment that you can perform to make predictions about real-world situations.

Each box of Oaties contains 1 of 6 prizes.

The probability of getting each prize is $\dfrac{1}{6}$.

To predict the number of boxes of cereal you must buy to win all 6 prizes, you can roll a number cube 1 time for each box of cereal you buy. Keep rolling until you have rolled all 6 numbers.

simulación (pág. 849) Experimento que se puede realizar para hacer predicciones sobre situaciones de la vida real.

Cada paquete de Oaties contiene 1 de un total de 6 premios. La probabilidad de obtener cada premio es $\dfrac{1}{6}$. Para predecir el número de paquetes de cereales que debes comprar para poder conseguir los 6 premios, puedes lanzar un cubo numerado 1 vez por cada paquete de cereales que compres. Sigue lanzando el cubo hasta obtener los 6 números.

---

slope (p. 235) The slope m of a nonvertical line is the ratio of the vertical change (the *rise*) to the horizontal change (the *run*) between any two points on the line: $m = \dfrac{y_2 - y_1}{x_2 - x_1}$.

pendiente (pág. 235) La pendiente m de una recta no vertical es la razón del cambio vertical (*distancia vertical*) al cambio horizontal (*distancia horizontal*) entre dos puntos cualesquiera de la recta: $m = \dfrac{y_2 - y_1}{x_2 - x_1}$.

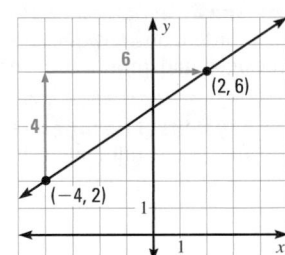

The slope of the line shown is $\dfrac{4}{6}$, or $\dfrac{2}{3}$.

La pendiente de la recta indicada es $\dfrac{4}{6}$, ó $\dfrac{2}{3}$.

slope-intercept form (p. 244) A linear equation written in the form $y = mx + b$ where m is the slope and b is the y-intercept of the equation's graph.	$y = 3x + 4$ is in slope-intercept form. The slope of the line is 3, and the y-intercept is 4.
forma pendiente-intercepto (pág. 244) Ecuación lineal escrita en la forma $y = mx + b$, donde m es la pendiente y b es el intercepto en y de la gráfica de la ecuación.	$y = 3x + 4$ está en la forma pendiente-intercepto. La pendiente de la recta es 3, y el intercepto en y es 4.
solution of an equation in one variable (p. 22) A number that produces a true statement when substituted for the variable in an equation.	The number 3 is a solution of the equation $8 - 2x = 2$, because $8 - 2(3) = 2$.
solución de una ecuación con una variable (pág. 22) Número que, al sustituirse por la variable de la ecuación, produce una expresión verdadera.	El número 3 es una solución de la ecuación $8 - 2x = 2$ ya que $8 - 2(3) = 2$.
solution of an equation in two variables (p. 215) An ordered pair that produces a true statement when the coordinates of the ordered pair are substituted for the variables in the equation.	$(1, -4)$ is a solution of $3x - y = 7$, because $3(1) - (-4) = 7$.
solución de una ecuación con dos variables (pág. 215) Par ordenado que, al ser sustituidas sus coordenadas por las variables de la ecuación, produce una expresión verdadera.	$(1, -4)$ es una solución de $3x - y = 7$ ya que $3(1) - (-4) = 7$.
solution of an inequality in one variable (p. 22) A number that produces a true statement when substituted for the variable in an inequality.	The number 3 is a solution of the inequality $5 + 3n \le 20$, because $5 + 3(3) = 14$ and $14 \le 20$.
solución de una desigualdad con una variable (pág. 22) Número que, al sustituirse por la variable de la desigualdad, produce una expresión verdadera.	El número 3 es una solución de la desigualdad $5 + 3n \le 20$ ya que $5 + 3(3) = 14$ y $14 \le 20$.
solution of an inequality in two variables x and y (p. 405) An ordered pair (x, y) that produces a true statement when the values of x and y are substituted into the inequality.	$(-1, 2)$ is a solution of the inequality $x - 3y < 6$ because $-1 - 3(2) = -7$ and $-7 < 6$.
solución de una desigualdad con las dos variables x e y (pág. 405) Par ordenado (x, y) que, al sustitutirse los valores de x e y en la desigualdad, produce una expresión verdadera.	$(-1, 2)$ es una solución de la desigualdad $x - 3y < 6$ ya que $-1 - 3(2) = -7$ y $-7 < 6$.
solution of a system of linear equations (p. 427) An ordered pair that is a solution of each equation in the system.	$(3, 2)$ is a solution of the system of linear equations $$x + 2y = 7$$ $$3x - 2y = 5$$ because each equation is a true statement when 3 is substituted for x and 2 is substituted for y.
solución de un sistema de ecuaciones lineales (pág. 427) Par ordenado que es una solución de cada ecuación del sistema.	$(3, 2)$ es una solución del sistema de ecuaciones lineales $$x + 2y = 7$$ $$3x - 2y = 5$$ ya que cada ecuación es una expresión verdadera cuando x se sustituye por 3 e y se sustituye por 2.

solution of a system of linear inequalities (p. 466) An ordered pair that is a solution of each inequality in the system.	(6, −5) is a solution of the system of inequalities $$x - y > 7$$ $$2x + y < 8$$ because each inequality is a true statement when 6 is substituted for x and −5 is substituted for y.
solución de un sistema de desigualdades lineales (pág. 466) Par ordenado que es una solución de cada desigualdad del sistema.	(6, −5) es una solución del sistema de desigualdades $$x - y > 7$$ $$2x + y < 8$$ ya que cada desigualdad es una expresión verdadera cuando x se sustituye por 6 e y se sustituye por −5.
square root (p. 110) If $b^2 = a$, then b is a square root of a. The radical symbol $\sqrt{\ }$ represents a nonnegative square root.	The square roots of 9 are 3 and −3, because $3^2 = 9$ and $(-3)^2 = 9$. So, $\sqrt{9} = 3$ and $-\sqrt{9} = -3$.
raíz cuadrada (pág. 110) Si $b^2 = a$, entonces b es una raíz cuadrada de a. El signo radical $\sqrt{\ }$ representa una raíz cuadrada no negativa.	Las raíces cuadradas de 9 son 3 y −3 ya que $3^2 = 9$ y $(-3)^2 = 9$. Así pues, $\sqrt{9} = 3$ y $-\sqrt{9} = -3$.
square root function (p. 710) A radical function whose equation contains a square root with the independent variable in the radicand.	$y = 2\sqrt{x + 2}$ and $y = \sqrt{x} + 3$ are square root functions.
función con raíz cuadrada (pág. 710) Función radical representada por una ecuación con una raíz cuadrada en cuyo radicando aparece la variable independiente.	$y = 2\sqrt{x + 2}$ e $y = \sqrt{x} + 3$ son funciones con raíz cuadrada.
standard deviation (p. 879) The standard deviation of a numerical data set $x_1, x_2, \ldots, x_n$ is a measure of dispersion denoted by σ and computed as the square root of the variance. $$\sigma = \sqrt{\frac{(x_1 - \overline{x})^2 + (x_2 - \overline{x})^2 + \ldots + (x_n - \overline{x})^2}{n}}$$	The standard deviation of the data set 3, 9, 13, 23 is: $$\sigma = \sqrt{\frac{(3 - 12)^2 + (9 - 12)^2 + (13 - 12)^2 + (23 - 12)^2}{4}}$$ $$= \sqrt{53} \approx 7.3$$
desviación típica (pág. 879) La desviación típica de un conjunto de datos numéricos $x_1, x_2, \ldots, x_n$ es una medida de dispersión designada por σ y calculada como raíz cuadrada de la varianza. $$\sigma = \sqrt{\frac{(x_1 - \overline{x})^2 + (x_2 - \overline{x})^2 + \ldots + (x_n - \overline{x})^2}{n}}$$	La desviación típica del conjunto de datos 3, 9, 13, 23 es: $$\sigma = \sqrt{\frac{(3 - 12)^2 + (9 - 12)^2 + (13 - 12)^2 + (23 - 12)^2}{4}}$$ $$= \sqrt{53} \approx 7.3$$
standard form of a linear equation (p. 216) $Ax + By = C$, where A, B, and C are real numbers and A and B are not both zero.	The linear equation $y = 2x - 3$ can be written in standard form as $2x - y = 3$.
forma general de una ecuación lineal (pág. 216) $Ax + By = C$, donde A, B y C son números reales, y A y B no son ambos cero.	La ecuación lineal $y = 2x - 3$ puede escribirse en la forma general como $2x - y = 3$.

standard form of a quadratic equation (p. 643) A quadratic equation in the form $ax^2 + bx + c = 0$ where $a \neq 0$.	The quadratic equation $x^2 - 2x - 3 = 0$ is in standard form.
forma general de una ecuación cuadrática (pág. 643) Ecuación cuadrática de la forma $ax^2 + bx + c = 0$, donde $a \neq 0$.	La ecuación cuadrática $x^2 - 2x - 3 = 0$ está en la forma general.
standard form of a quadratic function (p. 628) A quadratic function in the form $y = ax^2 + bx + c$ where $a \neq 0$.	The quadratic function $y = 2x^2 + 5x - 3$ is in standard form.
forma general de una función cuadrática (pág. 628) Función cuadrática de la forma $y = ax^2 + bx + c$, donde $a \neq 0$.	La función cuadrática $y = 2x^2 + 5x - 3$ está en la forma general.
stem-and-leaf plot (p. 881) A data display that organizes data based on their digits. **tabla arborescente** (pág. 881) Presentación de datos que organiza los datos basándose en sus dígitos.	Stem / Raíces Leaves / Hojas 0 | 8 9 1 | 0 2 3 4 5 5 5 9 2 | 1 1 5 9 Key: / Clave: 1 | 9 = \$19
stratified random sample (p. 871) A sample in which a population is divided into distinct groups, and members are selected at random from each group. **muestra aleatoria estratificada** (pág. 871) Muestra en la que la población está dividida en grupos diferenciados, y los miembros de cada grupo se seleccionan al azar.	You can select a stratified random sample of a school's student population by having a computer randomly choose 25 students from each grade level. Para seleccionar una muestra aleatoria estratificada de la población de estudiantes de una escuela, puedes usar la computadora para elegir al azar a 25 estudiantes de cada grado.
survey (p. 871) A study of one or more characteristics of a group. **encuesta** (pág. 871) Estudio de una o más características de un grupo.	A magazine invites its readers to mail in answers to a questionnaire rating the magazine. Una revista invita a sus lectores a enviar por correo las respuestas a un cuestionario sobre la calidad de la revista.
system of linear equations (p. 427) Two or more linear equations in the same variables; also called a *linear system*. **sistema de ecuaciones lineales** (pág. 427) Dos o más ecuaciones lineales con las mismas variables; llamado también *sistema lineal*.	The equations below form a system of linear equations: $x + 2y = 7$ $3x - 2y = 5$ Las siguientes ecuaciones forman un sistema de ecuaciones lineales: $x + 2y = 7$ $3x - 2y = 5$

system of linear inequalities in two variables (p. 466) Two or more linear inequalities in the same variables; also called a *system of inequalities*.	The inequalities below form a system of linear inequalities in two variables: $$x - y > 7$$ $$2x + y < 8$$
sistema de desigualdades lineales con dos variables (pág. 466) Dos o más desigualdades lineales con las mismas variables; llamado también *sistema de desigualdades*.	Las siguientes desigualdades forman un sistema de desigualdades lineales con dos variables: $$x - y > 7$$ $$2x + y < 8$$
systematic sample (p. 871) A sample in which a rule is used to select members of the population.	You can select a systematic sample of a school's student population by choosing every tenth student on an alphabetical list of all students at the school.
muestra sistemática (pág. 871) Muestra en la que se usa una regla para seleccionar a los miembros de la población.	Para seleccionar una muestra sistemática de la población de estudiantes de una escuela, puedes elegir a cada décimo estudiante de una lista ordenada alfabéticamente de todos los estudiantes de la escuela.

terms of an expression (p. 97) The parts of an expression that are added together.	The terms of the expression $3x + (-4) + (-6x) + 2$ are $3x$, -4, $-6x$, and 2.
términos de una expresión (pág. 97) Las partes de una expresión que se suman.	Los términos de la expresión $3x + (-4) + (-6x) + 2$ son $3x$, -4, $-6x$ y 2.
theoretical probability (p. 844) When all outcomes are equally likely, the theoretical probability of an event is the ratio of the number of favorable outcomes to the total number of possible outcomes. The probability of event A is written as $P(A)$.	A bag of 20 marbles contains 8 red marbles. The theoretical probability of randomly choosing a red marble from the bag is $\frac{8}{20} = \frac{2}{5}$, 40%, or 0.4.
probabilidad teórica (pág. 844) Cuando todos los casos son igualmente posibles, la probabilidad teórica de un suceso es la razón entre el número de casos favorables y el número total de casos posibles. La probabilidad del suceso A se escribe $P(A)$.	Una bolsa de 20 canicas contiene 8 canicas rojas. La probabilidad teórica de sacar al azar una canica roja de la bolsa es $\frac{8}{20} = \frac{2}{5}$, 40% ó 0.4.
transformation (p. 213) For a given set of points, a transformation produces an image by applying a rule to the coordinates of the points.	Translations, vertical stretches, vertical shrinks, and reflections are transformations.
transformación (pág. 213) Para un conjunto dado de puntos, una transformación produce una imagen al aplicar una regla a las coordenadas de los puntos.	Las traslaciones, las expansiones verticales, las contracciones verticales y las reflexiones son transformaciones.

ENGLISH-SPANISH GLOSSARY

translation (p. 213) A translation moves every point in a figure the same distance in the same direction.

traslación (pág. 213) Una traslación desplaza cada punto de una figura la misma distancia en la misma dirección.

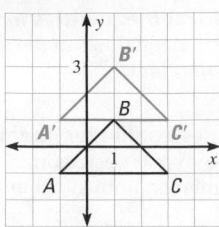

$\triangle$*ABC* is translated up 2 units.

$\triangle$*ABC* es trasladada 2 unidades hacia arriba.

---

trinomial (p. 555) A polynomial with three terms.

trinomio (pág. 555) Polinomio con tres términos.

$2x^2 + x - 5$ is a trinomial.

$2x^2 + x - 5$ es un trinomio.

U

union (p. 71) The union of two sets *A* and *B* is the set of all elements in *either A* or *B*. The union of *A* and *B* is written as $A \cup B$.

unión (pág. 71) La unión de dos conjuntos *A* y *B* es el conjunto de todos los elementos en *A o B*. La unión de *A* y *B* se escribe $A \cup B$.

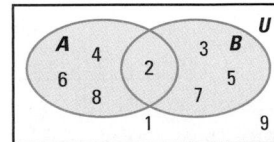

$A \cup B = \{2, 3, 4, 5, 6, 7, 8\}$

---

unit rate (p. 17) A rate in which the denominator of the fraction is 1 unit.

relación unitaria (pág. 17) Relación en la que el denominador de la fracción es 1 unidad.

$\frac{55 \text{ miles}}{1 \text{ hour}}$, or 55 mi/h, is a unit rate.

$\frac{55 \text{ millas}}{1 \text{ hora}}$, ó 55 mi/h, es una relación unitaria.

---

universal set (p. 71) The set of all elements under consideration, written as *U*.

conjunto universal (pág. 71) El conjunto de todos los elementos en cuestión, escrito *U*.

If the universal set is the set of positive integers, then $U = \{1, 2, 3, \ldots\}$.

Si el conjunto universal es el conjunto de los números enteros positivos, entonces $U = \{1, 2, 3, \ldots\}$.

---

upper quartile (p. 887) The median of the upper half of an ordered data set.

The upper quartile of the data set below is 23.

$$\begin{array}{ccc} & & \text{upper} \\ \text{median} & & \text{quartile} \\ \downarrow & & \downarrow \\ \end{array}$$
8 10 14 17 20 **23** 50

cuartil superior (pág. 887) La mediana de la mitad superior de un conjunto de datos ordenados.

El cuartil superior del siguiente conjunto de datos es 23.

$$\begin{array}{ccc} & & \text{cuartil} \\ \text{mediana} & & \text{superior} \\ \downarrow & & \downarrow \\ \end{array}$$
8 10 14 17 20 **23** 50

ENGLISH-SPANISH GLOSSARY

variable (p. 2) A letter that is used to represent one or more numbers.

variable (pág. 2) Letra que sirve para representar uno o más números.

In the expressions $5n$, $n + 1$, and $8 - n$, the letter n is the variable.

En las expresiones $5n$, $n + 1$ y $8 - n$, la letra n es la variable.

---

variance (p. 879) The variance of a numerical data set $x_1, x_2, \ldots, x_n$ is a measure of dispersion denoted by σ^2 and given by:
$$\sigma^2 = \frac{(x_1 - \overline{x})^2 + (x_2 - \overline{x})^2 + \ldots + (x_n - \overline{x})^2}{n}$$

varianza (pág. 879) La varianza de un conjunto de datos numéricos $x_1, x_2, \ldots, x_n$ es una medida de dispersión designada por σ^2 y dada por:
$$\sigma^2 = \frac{(x_1 - \overline{x})^2 + (x_2 - \overline{x})^2 + \ldots + (x_n - \overline{x})^2}{n}$$

The variance of the data set 3, 9, 13, 23 is:
$$\sigma^2 = \frac{(3 - 12)^2 + (9 - 12)^2 + (13 - 12)^2 + (23 - 12)^2}{4}$$
$$= 53$$

La varianza del conjunto de datos 3, 9, 13, 23 es:
$$\sigma^2 = \frac{(3 - 12)^2 + (9 - 12)^2 + (13 - 12)^2 + (23 - 12)^2}{4}$$
$$= 53$$

---

verbal model (p. 16) A verbal model describes a real-world situation using words as labels and using math symbols to relate the words.

modelo verbal (pág. 16) Un modelo verbal describe una situación de la vida real mediante palabras que la exponen y símbolos matemáticos que relacionan esas palabras.

A verbal model and algebraic expression for dividing a dollars in a tip jar among 6 people:

Un modelo verbal y una expresión algebraica utilizados para dividir entre 6 personas a dólares del recipiente de las propinas:

Amount in jar Cantidad del recipiente	÷	Number of people Número de personas
a	÷	6

---

vertex form of a quadratic function (p. 669) A quadratic function in the form $y = a(x - h)^2 + k$ where $a \neq 0$. The vertex of the graph of the function is (h, k).

forma de vértice de una función cuadrática (pág. 669) Función cuadrática de la forma $y = a(x - h)^2 + k$, donde $a \neq 0$. El vértice de la gráfica de la función es (h, k).

The quadratic function $y = -2(x + 1)^2 - 5$ is in vertex form. The vertex of the graph of the function is $(-1, -5)$.

La función cuadrática $y = -2(x + 1)^2 - 5$ está en la forma de vértice. El vértice de la gráfica de la función es $(-1, -5)$.

ENGLISH-SPANISH GLOSSARY

vertex of a parabola (p. 628) The lowest or highest point on a parabola.

vértice de una parábola (pág. 628) El punto más bajo o más alto de la parábola.

The vertex of the graph of $y = -x^2 + 2x + 1$ is the point (1, 2).

El vértice de la gráfica de $y = -x^2 + 2x + 1$ es el punto (1, 2).

---

vertical motion model (p. 577) A model for the height of an object that is propelled into the air but has no power to keep itself in the air.

The vertical motion model for an object thrown upward with an initial vertical velocity of 20 feet per second from an initial height of 8 feet is $h = -16t^2 + 20t + 8$ where h is the height (in feet) of the object t seconds after it is thrown.

modelo de movimiento vertical (pág. 577) Modelo para representar la altura de un objeto que es lanzado hacia arriba pero que no tiene potencia para mantenerse en el aire.

El modelo de movimiento vertical de un objeto lanzado hacia arriba con una velocidad vertical inicial de 20 pies por segundo desde una altura inicial de 8 pies es $h = -16t^2 + 20t + 8$, donde h es la altura (en pies) del objeto t segundos después del lanzamiento.

---

vertical shrink (p. 213) A vertical shrink moves every point in a figure toward the x-axis, while points on the x-axis remain fixed.

contracción vertical (pág. 213) La contracción vertical desplaza cada punto de una figura en dirección del eje de x, mientras los puntos del eje de x permanecen fijos.

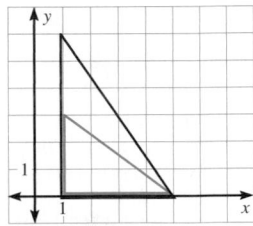

The black triangle is shrunk vertically to the green triangle.

El triángulo negro se contrae verticalmente hacia el triángulo verde.

vertical stretch (p. 213) A vertical stretch moves every point in a figure away from the *x*-axis, while points on the *x*-axis remain fixed.

expansión vertical (pág. 213) La expansión vertical desplaza cada punto de una figura alejándose del eje de *x*, mientras los puntos del eje de *x* permanecen fijos.

The black triangle is stretched vertically to the green triangle.

El triángulo negro se expande verticalmente hacia el triángulo verde.

whole numbers (p. 64) The numbers 0, 1, 2, 3, ...

0, 8, and 106 are whole numbers.
−1 and 0.6 are *not* whole numbers.

números naturales (pág. 64) Los números 0, 1, 2, 3, ...

0, 8 y 106 son números naturales.
−1 y 0.6 *no* son números naturales.

x-intercept (p. 225) The *x*-coordinate of a point where a graph crosses the *x*-axis.

intercepto en x (pág. 225) La coordenada *x* de un punto donde la gráfica corta al eje de *x*.

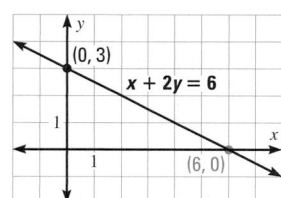

The *x*-intercept is 6.

El intercepto en *x* es 6.

y-intercept (p. 225) The *y*-coordinate of a point where a graph crosses the *y*-axis.

intercepto en y (pág. 225) La coordenada *y* de un punto donde la gráfica corta al eje de *y*.

The *y*-intercept is 3.

El intercepto en *y* es 3.

ENGLISH-SPANISH GLOSSARY

zero exponent (p. 503) If $a \neq 0$, then $a^0 = 1$. **exponente cero** (pág. 503) Si $a \neq 0$, entonces $a^0 = 1$.	$(-7)^0 = 1$
zero of a function (p. 337) An x-value for which $f(x) = 0$ (or $y = 0$). **cero de una función** (pág. 337) Un valor x para el que $f(x) = 0$ (o $y = 0$).	**The zero of $f(x) = 2x - 4$ is 2 because $f(2) = 0$.** El cero de $f(x) = 2x - 4$ es 2 ya que $f(2) = 0$.

Credits

Images; **569** © Alan Carey/Photo Researchers, Inc.; **571** *top left* © Ulrike Schanz/Animals Animals; **571** *top* © Fritz Prenzel/Animals Animals; **573** *top* © Royalty-Free/Corbis; **573** *football* © PhotoDisc/Getty Images; **573** *grass* © PowerPhotos/PhotoSpin; **574** © Royalty-Free/Corbis; **575** © Aase Bjerner; **577** © George Holton/Photo Researchers, Inc.; **579** © James H. Robinson/Photo Researchers, Inc.; **583** © Richard Berenholtz/Corbis; **588** © Richard Berenholtz/Corbis; **593** © Picture Finders LTD/eStock Photo; **595** © Mike Powell/Getty Images; **598** *bottom right* © Martin Harvey/Natural History Photographic Agency; **598** *top left* © Richard Hutchings/Photo Researchers, Inc.; **598** *top center* © Kevin Peterson/Getty Images; **598** *top right* © Rubberball Productions/Getty Images; **600** © Scott Camazine/Alamy; **602** © HIRB/Index Stock Imagery; **606** © Lawrence M. Sawyer/Getty Images; **614** © Brian Drake/SportsChrome; **626–627** © Bill Stevenson/Alamy; **628** © Digital Vision/Getty Images; **631** © Roger Ressmeyer/Corbis; **635** *top right* © Ric Ergenbright; **637** © Dwight Condrowoki; **639** Courtesy of Dallas Convention Center; **643** *top right* © Jeff Greenberg/PhotoEdit; **648** © Rhoda Peacher/R Photographs; **652** *top right* © Rhoda Peacher/R Photographs; **658** © Kim Karpeles; **661** © Amwell/Getty Images; **663** *center* © Jonathan Nourok/PhotoEdit; **671** © Adam Woolfitt/Corbis; **678** © Jeff Gross/Getty Images; **682** © Davis Barber/PhotoEdit; **684** © David A. Northcott/Corbis ; **687** © John Kelly/Getty Images; **689** © David A. Northcott/Corbis; **690** © Davies & Starr/Getty Images; **708–709** © Robert Holland/Getty Images; **710** © Michael Newman/PhotoEdit; **715** © Vince Streano/Corbis; **716** *top right* © Tim Zurowski/Corbis; **716** *top left* © Darrell Gulin/Corbis; **719** © John Elk/Elk Photography; **726** © Tony Freeman/PhotoEdit; **729** © Robert Winslow/Animals Animals; **731** © Iconica/Photonica/Getty Images; **733** Jacques Descloitres/MODIS Rapid Response Team, NASA/GSFC; **735** *right* © Galen Rowell/Corbis; **735** *left* © Philip Gould/Corbis; **737** © Joseph Pobereskin/Getty Images; **744** © Scott Goodwin/Boston MedFlight; **762–763** © Roland Birke/Phototake; **765** *top right* © Dwight Cendrowski; **768** © Tony Freeman/PhotoEdit; **770** © Rhoda Peacher/R Photographs; **771** *both* © GK Hart/Vikki Hart/Getty Images; **772** *top right* © Lee Snider/Corbis; **775** © Matt York, Staff/AP/Wide World Photos; **778** © Richard Cummins/Corbis; **781** © Phillip Colla/www.OceanLight.com; **784** © Ace Stock Limited/Alamy; **787** © Michael Newman/PhotoEdit; **790** © Rubberball Productions/Getty Images; **791** © Carolina Biological Supply Company/Phototake; **794** © Allana Wesley White/Corbis; **797** © 2005, Motorola, Inc./ Reproduced with Permission from Motorola, Inc. ; **799** © Zigy Kaluzny/Getty Images; **800** © Tom Stewart/Corbis; **802** © Adrees A. Latif/Reuters/Corbis; **807** © David Butow/Corbis; **808** © Ron Kuntz/Bettmann/Corbis; **809** © Bob Daemmrich/PhotoEdit; **812** © Michael Mahovlich/Masterfile; **820** © David Stoecklein/Corbis; **824** © Paul J. Sutton/Duomo/Corbis; **825** © Jim West/Jim West Photography; **840–841** © Comstock Production Department/Alamy; **840** *ball* © PhotoDisc/Getty Images; **843** © Michelle D. Bridwell/PhotoEdit; **847** © Royalty-Free/Corbis; **848** © Matt Brown/NewSport/Corbis; **851** © Mary Kate Denny/PhotoEdit; **856** © Don Smetzer/Getty Images; **857** *both* © Stockbyte/Royalty-Free; **861** © Tim Davis/Corbis; **870** © Dante Fenolio/Photo Researchers, Inc.; **871** © New Moon/Panoramic Images; **872** © Tom Carter/PhotoEdit; **874** © David Young-Wolff/PhotoEdit; **875** © PictureChasers.com 2005; **876** © Alan Thornton/Getty Images; **878** © Leslie Parr/Getty Images; **881** © Paul Conklin/PhotoEdit; **882** © 2003 Robyn Beck/Staff/AFP/Getty; **885** © Bettmann/Corbis; **887** DLR/NASA; **894** © Mark Dadswell/Staff/Getty Images.

Illustration and Map

Argosy **1**, **63**, **131**, **205**, **281**, **355**, **425**, **487**, **553**, **627**, **631**, **633**, **709**, **763**, **841**; Steve Cowden **32**, **40** *center*, **240**, **258**, **308**, **323** *center right*, **440** *bottom center*, **446**, **465**, **615**, **646**, **654**, **668**, **675**, **715**, **733**, **750**, **752** *bottom left*, **781**, **855**; Stephen Durke **634**, **648** *center*, **658**, **741** *both*, **741**; John Francis **815**; Patrick Gnan/Deborah Wolfe, Ltd. **228**, **249**, **323** *bottom right*, **468**, **526**, **567**, **588** *both*, **588**, **591**, **742**, **865**; Sharon and Joel Harris **514**; Mark Heine/Deborah Wolfe **28**; Steve McEntee **640**, **683**, **702**; Karen Minot **890**; Laurie O'Keefe **866**; Tony Randazzo **508**, **604**, **819**; Mark Schroeder **690**; Dan Stuckenschneider **20**, **116**, **145**, **146**, **152** *center*, **221**, **231** *center*, **315**, **361**, **373**, **381**, **385**, **411**, **471**, **494**, **525**, **564**, **609**, **612** *top right*, **612** *bottom right*, **612**, **648** *bottom*, **667**, **680**, **725**, **772** *both*, **772**, **829**, **862**; Matt Zang/American Artists **511**, **657**, **722**, **749**, **771**, **891**.

Worked-Out Solutions

This section of the book provides step-by-step solutions to exercises with circled exercise numbers. These solutions provide models that can help guide your work with the homework exercises.

The separate **Selected Answers** section follows this section. It provides numerous answers that you can use to check your own answers.

Chapter 1

Lesson 1.1 (pp. 5–7)

19. three tenths to the fourth power; $(0.3)^4 =$
$0.3 \cdot 0.3 \cdot 0.3 \cdot 0.3$

35. $\left(\frac{3}{5}\right)^3 = \frac{3}{5} \cdot \frac{3}{5} \cdot \frac{3}{5} = \frac{27}{125}$

51. a. Total length $= 3.5 + 5.5 + 3 = 12$

The total length is 12 inches.

b. Evaluate $12f$ for $f = 12$: $12(12) = 144$

The area of water surface needed is 144 square inches.

Lesson 1.2 (pp. 10–12)

16. $\frac{1}{6}(6 + 18) - 2^2 = \frac{1}{6}(6 + 18) - 4$

$= \frac{1}{6}(24) - 4$

$= 4 - 4 = 0$

35. a. Total cost $= 3 \cdot 0.99 + 2 \cdot 9.95$

$= 2.97 + 19.90 = 22.87$

The total cost is $22.87.

b. Amount of money left $= 25 - 22.87 = 2.13$

The amount you have left is $2.13.

Lesson 1.3 (pp. 18–20)

11. 7 less than twice a number k

Less than is subtraction after the next term, and twice a number is two times a number. The expression is $2k - 7$.

35.

$$\boxed{\begin{array}{c}\text{Number of}\\\text{months in}\\y\text{ years}\end{array}} = \boxed{\begin{array}{c}\text{Number of}\\\text{months in}\\\text{one year}\end{array}} + \boxed{\begin{array}{c}\text{Number of}\\\text{years}\end{array}}$$

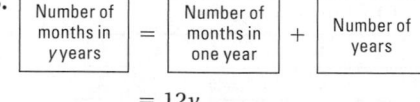

$= 12y$

The number of months is $12y$.

33. a. 48 ounce container:

$$\frac{\$2.64}{48 \text{ ounces}} = \frac{\$2.64 \div 48}{48 \text{ ounces} \div 48} = \frac{\$.055}{1 \text{ ounce}}$$

The unit rate is $.055 per ounce.

64 ounce container:

$$\frac{\$3.84}{64 \text{ ounces}} = \frac{\$3.84 \div 64}{64 \text{ ounces} \div 64} = \frac{\$.06}{1 \text{ ounce}}$$

The unit rate is $.06 per ounce.

b. Since $.055 is less than $.06, the 48 ounce container costs less per ounce.

c. Write a verbal model and an expression. Let n be the number of ounces.

$$\boxed{\text{Savings}} = \boxed{\begin{array}{c}\text{Unit rate for}\\64 \text{ ounce}\\\text{container}\end{array}} \cdot \boxed{\begin{array}{c}\text{Number}\\\text{of}\\\text{ounces}\end{array}} -$$

$$\boxed{\begin{array}{c}\text{Unit rate for}\\48 \text{ ounce}\\\text{container}\end{array}} \cdot \boxed{\begin{array}{c}\text{Number}\\\text{of}\\\text{ounces}\end{array}}$$

$= 0.06n - 0.055n$

Evaluate the expression when $n = 192$.

$0.06(192) - 0.055(192) = 0.96$

The amount of money you save is $.96.

Lesson 1.4 (pp. 24–26)

7. 5 more than a number is written as $t + 5$.

The product of 9 and the quantity 5 more than a number t is written as $9(t + 5)$.

The product of 9 and the quantity 5 more than a number t is less than 6 is written as $9(t + 5) < 6$.

41. Write a verbal model. Then write an equation. Let w be the winning team's time.

U.S. team's time	−	Winning team's time	=	Difference in time

$$173 - w = 6$$

Use mental math to solve the equation. Think: 173 less what number is 6?

Because $173 - 167 = 6$, the solution is 167 hours.

Lesson 1.5 (pp. 31–33)

5. You know that the temperature in Rome, Italy, is 30°C, and the temperature in Dallas, Texas, is 83°F

You want to find out which temperature is higher.

17. Step 1: You know the total weight of your backpack and its contents is $13\frac{3}{8}$ pounds. The total weight you want to carry is no more than 15 pounds. The weight of each bottle of water is $\frac{3}{4}$ pound. You want to find out how many extra bottles of water you can add to your backpack.

Step 2: Write a verbal model that represents what you want to find out. Then write an equation and solve it.

Step 3: Let n be the number of extra bottles of water.

Weight of backpack	+	Weight of each bottle of water	·	Number of extra bottles of water	=	Total weight

$$13\frac{3}{8} + \frac{3}{4}n = 15$$
$$13\frac{3}{8} - 13\frac{3}{8} + \frac{3}{4}n = 15 - 13\frac{3}{8}$$
$$\frac{3}{4}n = 1\frac{5}{8}$$
$$\frac{4}{3} \cdot \frac{3}{4}n = \frac{4}{3} \cdot \frac{13}{8}$$
$$n = \frac{13}{6}, \text{ or } n = 2\frac{1}{6}$$

Since you cannot carry a fraction of a bottle, round down to 2 bottles.

Step 4: You know that 2 is a solution; check to see if 3 could be a solution. The additional bottle of water weighs $\frac{3}{4}$ pound. Since $14\frac{7}{8}$ pounds is only $\frac{1}{8}$ pound less than the maximum of 15 pounds, and $\frac{3}{4} > \frac{1}{8}$, adding another bottle weighing $\frac{3}{4}$ pound would make the total weight more than 15 pounds. Therefore, the number of extra bottles of water you can add to your backpack is 2 bottles.

Lesson 1.6 (pp. 38–40)

7. The pairing is not a function because the input $\frac{3}{4}$ is paired with two outputs, 3 and 5.

23. You have 10 quarters that you can use for a parking meter.

a. Each time you put 1 quarter in the meter, you have 1 less quarter, so the <u>number of quarters left</u> is a function of <u>the number of quarters used</u>.

b. Let y represent the number of quarters you have left.

Number of quarters you have left	=	Total number of quarters	−	Number of quarters you have used so far

$$y = 10 - x$$

The domain of the function is: 0, 1, 2, 3, 4, 5, 6, 7, 8, 9, and 10.

c. Make a table of inputs, x, and use $y = 10 - x$ to find the corresponding outputs.

Input, x	0	1	2	3	4	5
Output, y	10	9	8	7	6	5

Input, x	6	7	8	9	10
Output, y	4	3	2	1	0

The range of the function is: 0, 1, 2, 3, 4, 5, 6, 7, 8, 9, and 10.

Lesson 1.7 (pp. 46–48)

3. Make an input-output table using the given domain values.

x	0	1	2	3	4	5
y	3	4	5	6	7	8

Plot a point for each ordered pair (x, y).

17. Number of voters v as a function of time t in years since 1984.

Years since 1984	Voters	Voters (millions)
0	92,652,680	93
4	91,594,693	92
8	104,405,155	104
12	96,456,345	96
16	105,586,274	106

The t-values range from 0 to 16, so label the t-axis from 0 to 20 in increments of 2 units. The v-values (in millions) range from 93 to 106, so label the v-axis from 90 to 110 in increments of 2 units.

Chapter 2

Lesson 2.1 (pp. 67–70)

7. Graph -5 and -6 on a number line.

On the number line, -5 is to the right of -6, so $-5 > -6$. The number -5 is greater.

29. If $a = -6.1$, then $-a = -(-6.1) = 6.1$.

If $a = -6.1$, then $|a| = |-6.1| = 6.1$.

53. Graph the numbers on a number line.

Read the numbers from left to right: $-206, -170, -135, 2, 5$.

From lowest elevation to highest elevation, the locations are Fondo, Frink, Alamorio, Calexico, and Date City.

13. $-8.7 + 4.2 = -(|8.7| - |4.2|)$

$\qquad = -(8.7 - 4.2) = -4.5$

35. $-2.6 + (-3.4) + 7.6 = [-2.6 + (-3.4)] + 7.6$

$\qquad = -6 + 7.6 = 1.6$

55. a. You know the first lens has a strength of -4.75 diopters and the second lens has a strength of 6.25 diopters.

You want to know the strength of the new lens.

Calculate the sum of -4.75 and 6.25:

$-4.75 + 6.25 = 1.5$

The strength of the new lens is 1.5 diopters.

b. You know the first lens has a strength of -2.5 diopters and the second lens has a strength of -1.25 diopters.

You want to know the strength of the new lens.

Calculate the sum of -2.5 and -1.25:

$-2.5 + (-1.25) = -3.75$

The strength of the new lens is -3.75 diopters.

c. You know the first lens has a strength of 1.5 diopters and the second lens has a strength of -3.75 diopters. The greater the absolute value of the strength of a lens, the stronger the lens.

You want to know which new lens is stronger.

Find the absolute value of each lens in part (a) and part (b) and choose the greater.

$|1.5| = 1.5 \qquad |-3.75| = 3.75$

The new lens in part (b) has a greater absolute value, and is therefore stronger.

Lesson 2.3 (pp. 82–84)

3. $13 - (-5) = 13 + 5 = 18$

21. When $x = 7.1$ and $y = -2.5$,

$$-y - (1.9 - x) = -(-2.5) - (1.9 - 7.1)$$
$$= 2.5 - [1.9 - (-7.1)]$$
$$= 2.5 - (-5.2)$$
$$= 2.5 + 5.2 = 7.7$$

43. Write a verbal model. Then write an equation.

Change in temperature	=	Temperature inside	−	Temperature outside

$C = i - t$

Substitute 12.2 for i and -2.4 for t.

$C = 12.2 - (-2.4)$

$C = 12.2 + 2.4 = 14.6$

The change in temperature was 14.6°C.

Lesson 2.4 (pp. 91–93)

11. $-1.9(3.3)(7) = (-6.27)(7) = -43.89$

31. $-2(-6)(-7z) = [-2(-6)](-7z)$

$$= 12(-7z)$$
$$= [12 \cdot (-7)]z$$
$$= -84z$$

51. Write a verbal model.

Total value	=	Original price per share	·	Number of shares	+

		Change in price per share	·	Number of shares

Calculate the original price.

Original price = ($3.50)(50) = $175

Calculate the change in price.

Change in price = (−$.25)(50) = −$12.50

Calculate the total value.

Total value = (3.50)(50) + (−0.25)(50)

$$= 175 + (-12.50) = 162.50$$

The total value is $162.50.

Lesson 2.5 (pp. 99–101)

9. $(p - 3)(-8) = p(-8) - 3(-8) = -8p + 24$

23. Write the expression as a sum:
$7x^2 + (-10) + (-2x^2) + 5$

Terms: $7x^2$, -10, $-2x^2$, 5

Like terms: $7x^2$ and $-2x^2$; -10 and 5

Coefficients: 7, -2

Constant terms: -10, 5

51. Write a verbal model. Then write an equation.

Total cost	=	Number of movies rented	·

$$\left(\begin{array}{ccc} \text{Regular cost of a rental} & = & \text{Discount per movie} \end{array} \right)$$

$C = 3(r - 2)$ or $C = 3r - 6$

Find the value of C when $r = 3.99$.

$C = 3(3.99 - 2)$

$$= 3(3.99) - 3(2)$$
$$= 11.97 - 6 = 5.97$$

The total cost is $5.97.

Lesson 2.6 (pp. 106–108)

13. $-1 \div \left(-\dfrac{7}{2}\right) = -1 \cdot \left(-\dfrac{7}{2}\right) = \dfrac{2}{7}$

35. $\dfrac{9z - 6}{-3} = (9z - 6) \div (-3)$

$$= (9z - 6) \cdot \left(-\frac{1}{3}\right)$$
$$= 9z \cdot \left(-\frac{1}{3}\right) - 6 \cdot \left(-\frac{1}{3}\right)$$
$$= -3z + 2$$

53. To find the daily mean temperature for a day, find the sum of the high and low temperatures for that day and then divide the sum by 2.

$$\text{Mean} = \frac{-10.6 + (-18.9)}{2} = \frac{-29.5}{2} = -14.75$$

The daily mean temperature was −14.75°C.

Lesson 2.7 (pp. 113–116)

9. Since $50^2 = 2500$, $\pm\sqrt{2500} = \pm50$.

19. Write a compound inequality that compares $-\sqrt{86}$ with both $-\sqrt{100}$ and $-\sqrt{81}$.

$-\sqrt{100} < -\sqrt{86} < -\sqrt{81}$

Take the square root of each number.

$-10 < -\sqrt{86} < -9$

Because 86 is closer to 81 than to 100, $-\sqrt{86}$ is closer to -9 than to -10. So $-\sqrt{86}$ is about -9.

49. You need to find the side length s of the mazes such that s^2 is the given area in square feet, so s is the positive square root of the area. Then identify the side length as rational or irrational.

Dallas: $s^2 = 1225$, $s = 35$; rational

San Francisco: $s^2 = 576$, $s = 24$; rational

Corona: $s^2 = 2304$, $s = 48$; rational

Waterville: $s^2 = 900$, $s = 30$; rational

The side lengths are 35 feet, 24 feet, 48 feet, and 30 feet. All the lengths are rational numbers.

Chapter 3

Lesson 3.1 (pp. 137–140)

13.
$$-2 = n - 6$$
$$-2 + 6 = n - 6 + 6$$
$$4 = n$$

55. Let w represent the width of the trampoline.

$$A = \ell \cdot w$$
$$187 = 17 \cdot w$$
$$\frac{187}{17} = \frac{17w}{17}$$
$$11 = w$$

The width of the trampoline is 11 feet.

Lesson 3.2 (pp. 144–146)

13.
$$7 = \frac{5}{6}c - 8$$
$$7 + 8 = \frac{5}{6}c - 8 + 8$$
$$15 = \frac{5}{6}c$$
$$\frac{6}{5} \cdot 15 = \frac{6}{5} \cdot \frac{5}{6}c$$
$$18 = c$$

19.
$$-32 = -5k + 13k$$
$$-32 = 8k$$
$$\frac{-32}{8} = \frac{8k}{8}$$
$$-4 = k$$

39. Write a verbal model. Then write an equation. Let h be the number of half-side advertisements.

$$\boxed{\text{Total budget}} = \boxed{\text{Cost per month}} \cdot \boxed{\text{Number of full bus wrap advertisements}} +$$
$$\boxed{\text{Cost per month}} \cdot \boxed{\text{Number of half-side advertisements}}$$

$6000 = 2000(1) + 800h$

$6000 = 2000 + 800h$

Solve the equation.

$$6000 = 2000 + 800h$$
$$6000 - 2000 = 2000 - 2000 + 800h$$
$$4000 = 800h$$
$$\frac{4000}{800} = \frac{800h}{800}$$
$$5 = h$$

The museum can have 5 half-side advertisements.

Lesson 3.3 (pp. 150–153)

17.
$$-3 = 12y - 5(2y - 7)$$
$$-3 = 12y - 10y + 35$$
$$-3 = 2y + 35$$
$$-3 - 35 = 2y + 35 - 35$$
$$-38 = 2y$$
$$\frac{-32}{8} = \frac{2y}{2}$$
$$-19 = y$$

39. Let x be the amount of space you should leave between posters (in feet).

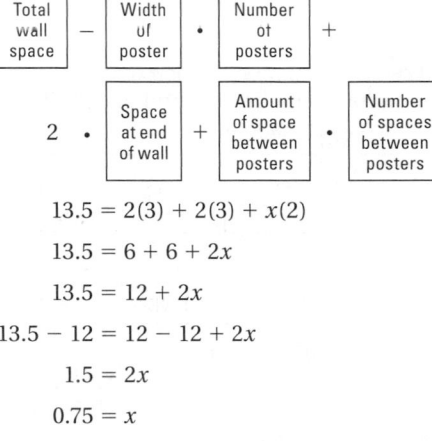

$$13.5 = 2(3) + 2(3) + x(2)$$
$$13.5 = 6 + 6 + 2x$$
$$13.5 = 12 + 2x$$
$$13.5 - 12 = 12 - 12 + 2x$$
$$1.5 = 2x$$
$$0.75 = x$$

You should leave 0.75 foot between each poster.

Lesson 3.4 (pp. 157–159)

13.
$$40 + 14j = 2(-4j - 13)$$
$$40 + 14j = -8j - 26$$
$$40 + 14j + 8j = -8j + 8j - 26$$
$$40 + 22j = -26$$
$$40 - 40 + 22j = -26 - 40$$
$$22j = -66$$
$$j = -3$$

51. Let x represent the number of years. So $33x$ represents the increase in the number of students taking Spanish, and $2x$ represents the decreased number of students who are taking French.

$$555 + 33x = 3(230 - 2x)$$
$$555 + 33x = 690 - 6x$$
$$555 + 33x + 6x = 690 - 6x + 6x$$
$$555 + 39x = 690$$
$$555 - 555 + 39x = 690 - 555$$
$$39x = 135$$
$$x \approx 3.5$$

So it will be after 3 more school years, or in about 4 years, when the number of students taking Spanish will be 3 times the number of students taking French.

Lesson 3.5 (pp. 165–167)

17.
$$\frac{16}{48} = \frac{n}{36}$$
$$36 \cdot \frac{16}{48} = 36 \cdot \frac{n}{36}$$
$$\frac{576}{48} = n$$
$$12 = n$$

49. Find the total number of pizzas:
$$96 + 144 + 240 = 480.$$

The ratio of large pizzas to all pizzas is
$$\frac{\text{number of large pizzas}}{\text{total number of pizzas}} = \frac{240}{480} = \frac{1}{2}.$$

Lesson 3.6 (pp. 171–173)

13.
$$\frac{11}{w} = \frac{33}{w + 24}$$
$$11(w + 24) = 33w$$
$$11w + 264 = 33w$$
$$11w - 11w + 264 = 33w - 11w$$
$$264 = 22w$$
$$12 = w$$

39. The ratio of model to height is $\dfrac{\text{height of model}}{\text{actual height}}$. Write and solve a proportion.

$$\frac{1}{25} = \frac{x}{443.2}$$
$$443.2 = 25x$$
$$17.728 = x$$

The height of the model is 17.728 meters.

Lesson 3.7 (pp. 179–181)

13. $a = p\% \cdot b$
$$= 115\% \cdot 60$$
$$= 1.15 \cdot 60$$
$$= 69 \qquad 69 \text{ is } 115\% \text{ of } 60.$$

35. a. The survey shows that 36% of the 250 listeners who participated in the survey are "tired of" the song.

$$a = p\% \cdot b$$
$$= 36\% \cdot 250$$
$$= 0.36 \cdot 250$$
$$= 90$$

90 listeners are "tired of" the song.

b. The survey shows that 14% of the 250 listeners who participated in the survey "love" the song.

$$a = p\% \cdot b$$
$$= 14\% \cdot 250$$
$$= 0.14 \cdot 250$$
$$= 35$$

35 listeners "love" the song.

Lesson 3.8 (pp. 187–189)

17.
$$30 = 9x - 5y$$
$$30 + 5y = 9x - 5y + 5y$$
$$30 + 5y = 9x$$
$$30 - 30 + 5y = 9x - 30$$
$$5y = 9x - 30$$
$$y = \frac{9}{5}x - 6$$

33. a. $C = 12x + 25$
$$C - 25 = 12x + 25 - 25$$
$$C - 25 = 12x$$
$$\frac{C - 25}{12} = x$$

b. \$145: $\dfrac{C - 25}{12} = x$
$$\frac{145 - 25}{12} = x$$
$$10 = x$$

For \$145, you bowled 10 league nights.

\$181: $\dfrac{C - 25}{12} = x$
$$\frac{181 - 25}{12} = x$$
$$13 = x$$

For \$181, you bowled 13 league nights.

\$205: $\dfrac{C - 25}{12} = x$
$$\frac{205 - 25}{12} = x$$
$$15 = x$$

For \$205, you bowled 15 league nights.

Chapter 4

Lesson 4.1 (pp. 209–212)

15. To plot $Q(-1, 5)$, begin at the origin. First move 1 unit to the left, then 5 units up. Point Q is in Quadrant II.

25. First create a table of values by substituting the domain values into the function.

x	y = 2x − 5
−2	y = 2(−2) − 5 = −9
−1	y = 2(−1) − 5 = −7
0	y = 2(0) − 5 = −5
1	y = 2(1) − 5 = −3
2	y = 2(2) − 5 = −1

The table gives the ordered pairs (−2, −9), (−1, −7), (0, −5), (1, −3), and (2, −1).

Graph the function by plotting these points. The range of the function is the y-values from the table: −9, −7, −5, −3, −1.

37. The table represents a function because there is exactly one low temperature for each day in the first week of February.

To graph the data, plot the ordered pairs (day, record low).

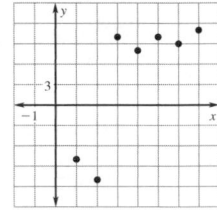

Lesson 4.2 (pp. 219–221)

3. Test (−2, 3):

$$2y + x = 4$$

$$2(3) + (−2) = 4 \quad \text{Substitute −2 for } x \text{ and 3 for } y.$$

$$6 + (−2) = 4$$

$$4 = 4 ✓$$

So, (−2, 3) is a solution of 2y + x = 4.

11. First, solve the equation for y.

$$y + x = 2$$

$$y + x − x = 2 − x$$

$$y = 2 − x$$

Use this equation to create a table of values.

x	−2	−1	0	1	2
y	4	3	2	1	0

Plot at least three of the points whose ordered pairs (x, y) are indicated by the table. Draw a line through the plotted points.

37. a.

Since the scientist is studying the organisms in the first 4 kilometers of Earth's crust, the domain of the function is 0 ≤ d ≤ 4. The range of the function is 20 ≤ T ≤ 120. The temperature 4 kilometers from the surface is 120°C.

b. Notice in the table for part (a) that the temperatures between 20°C and 95°C occur when the distance from the surface is between 0 kilometers and 3 kilometers.

The domain of the function is now 0 ≤ d ≤ 3 and the range is 20 ≤ T ≤ 95. So this section of crust is 3 kilometers deep.

Lesson 4.3 (pp. 229–232)

21. Substitute 0 for y in y = −4x + 3 and solve for x.

$$0 = −4x + 3$$

$$−3 = −4x$$

$$\frac{3}{4} = x$$

The x-intercept is $\frac{3}{4}$.

Substitute 0 for x in y = −4x + 3 and solve for y.

$$y = −4(0) + 3 = 0 + 3 = 3$$

The y-intercept is 3.

Plot the two points that correspond to the intercepts and draw a line through them.

47. a. If $v = 0$ in the function $f = 180 - 1.5v$, then $f = 180 - 1.5(0)$, and $f = 180$. This is the intercept on the vertical axis, and it represents the area (in square feet) available for flowers when no vegetables are planted.

Letting $f = 0$ gives $0 = 180 - 1.5v$, $1.5v = 180$, and $v = 120$. This is the intercept on the horizontal axis, and it represents the area (in square feet) available for vegetables when no flowers are planted.

b.

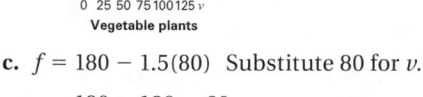

The domain is $0 \le v \le 120$. The range is $0 \le f \le 180$.

c. $f = 180 - 1.5(80)$ Substitute 80 for v.

$= 180 - 120 = 60$

There are 60 square feet left to plant flowers.

Lesson 4.4 (pp. 239–242)

11. Let $(x_1, y_1) = (1, 3)$ and $(x_2, y_2) = (3, -2)$.

$$m = \frac{y_2 - y_1}{x_2 - x_1} = \frac{-2 - 3}{3 - 1} = \frac{-5}{2} \text{ or } -\frac{5}{2}$$

37. a. rate of change $= \dfrac{\text{change in temperature}}{\text{change in time}}$

0–1.5 hours:
$$\frac{1000 - 250}{1.5 - 0} = \frac{750}{1.5} = 500 \text{ degrees per hour}$$

1.5–2.5 hours:
$$\frac{1300 - 1000}{2.5 - 1.5} = \frac{300}{1} = 300 \text{ degrees per hour}$$

2.5–4.65 hours:
$$\frac{1680 - 1300}{4.65 - 2.5} = \frac{380}{2.15} \approx 177 \text{ degrees per hour}$$

4.65–8.95 hours:
$$\frac{1920 - 1680}{8.95 - 4.65} = \frac{240}{4.3} \approx 56 \text{ degrees per hour}$$

The time interval with the greatest rate of change was from 0 hours to 1.5 hours.

b. The time interval that showed the least rate of change was from 4.65 hours to 8.95 hours.

Lesson 4.5 (pp. 247–250)

11.
$$4x + y = 1$$
$$4x - 4x + y = 1 - 4x$$
$$y = -4x + 1$$

The slope is -4 and the y-intercept is 1.

21. The equation $y = -6x + 1$ is in slope-intercept form. The slope is -6 and the y-intercept is 1. Locate the point $(0, 1)$, which corresponds to the intercept. Use the slope to find a second point, $(1, -5)$. Draw a line through the points.

41. a.

b. On the graph, the vertical distance between the lines is about 30 when $t = 3$. To verify this estimate, substitute 3 in $d = 55t$: $d = 55(3) = 165$. Now substitute 3 in $d = 65t$: $d = 65(3) = 195$. Subtract: $195 - 165 = 30$. Driving at the maximum speed limit, a driver could travel 30 miles farther after 1995 than before 1995.

Lesson 4.6 (pp. 256–259)

7. Solve the equation for y: $8x + 2y = 0$
$$2y = -8x$$
$$y = -4x$$

Because $8x + 2y = 0$ can be written in the form $y = ax$, it does represent direct variation. The constant of variation is -4.

21. When solved for y, the equation is $y = -4x$. The slope of the line is the constant of variation, -4. The graph of a direct variation equation always passes through $(0, 0)$. The slope can be used to locate a second point from the origin, like $(1, -4)$. Draw a line through the points.

43. a. Compare the ratio $\frac{f}{w}$ or all three data pairs:

$$\frac{2.50}{10} = 0.25, \frac{3.75}{15} = 0.25, \frac{7.50}{30} = 0.25$$

Because the ratios are all equal, f varies directly with w.

b. Since $\frac{f}{w} = 0.25$, multiply both sides by w to obtain the direct variation equation $f = 0.25w$.

The computer weighs 18 pounds, so substitute 18 for w.

$$f = 0.25(18) = 4.50$$

The printer weighs 10 pounds, so substitute 10 for w.

$$f = 0.25(10) = 2.50$$

The total recycling fee for the computer and printer is $\$4.50 + \$2.50 = \$7.00$.

Lesson 4.7 (pp. 265–268)

3. Substitute -2, 0, and 3 for x.

$$f(-2) = 12(-2) + 1 = -24 + 1 = -23$$
$$f(0) = 12(0) + 1 = 0 + 1 = 1$$
$$f(3) = 12(3) + 1 = 36 + 1 = 37$$

17. Substitute -13 for $j(x)$.

$$-13 = 4x + 11$$
$$-13 - 11 = 4x + 11 - 11$$
$$-24 = 4x$$
$$\frac{-24}{4} = \frac{4x}{4}$$
$$-6 = x$$

39. a. Create a table of values for the function.

x	f(x)
0	$0.10(0) + 2.75 = 2.75$
5	$0.10(5) + 2.75 = 3.25$
10	$0.10(10) + 2.75 = 3.75$
15	$0.10(15) + 2.75 = 4.25$
20	$0.10(20) + 2.75 = 4.75$

Use the ordered pairs given by the table to graph the function.

The domain of the function is $0 \leq x \leq 20$ and the range is $2.75 \leq f(x) \leq 4.75$.

b. Substitute 4.55 for $f(x)$.

$$4.55 = 0.10x + 2.75$$
$$4.55 - 2.75 = 0.10x + 2.75 - 2.75$$
$$1.8 = 0.10x$$
$$\frac{1.8}{0.10} = \frac{0.10x}{0.10}$$
$$18 = x$$

When $x = 18$, $f(x) = 4.55$. In 1998, 18 years after 1980, the average price of a movie ticket was $\$4.55$.

Chapter 5

Lesson 5.1 (pp. 286–289)

11. Determine the slope: $m = \frac{\text{rise}}{\text{run}} = \frac{-1}{2} = $ or $-\frac{1}{2}$.

The line crosses the y-axis at $(0, 0)$, so the y-intercept is 0.

Substitute $-\frac{1}{2}$ for m and 0 for b in the slope-intercept form $y = mx + b$: $y = -\frac{1}{2}x$.

19. Calculate the slope:
$$m = \frac{y_2 - y_1}{x_2 - x_1} = \frac{4 - 0}{0 - (-1)} = \frac{4}{1} = 4.$$

The line crosses the y-axis at $(0, 4)$, so the y-intercept is 4.

Substitute 4 for m and 4 for b in the slope-intercept form $y = mx + b$: $y = 4x + 4$.

47. Let C be the cost of a visit to the aquarium and t be the time parked there. The total cost C is given by the function $C = 3h + 30$, where h is the number of hours parked at the aquarium.

Evaluate the function for $h = 4$:
$C = 3(4) + 30 = 12 + 30 = 42$

The total cost is $42.

Lesson 5.2 (pp. 296–299)

5. The slope is given. To find the y-intercept, substitute the slope, -5, and the coordinates of the given point $(-4, 7)$ into the equation $y = mx + b$, and solve for b.

$y = mx + b$

$7 = -5(-4) + b$

$7 = 20 + b$

$-13 = b$

The equation of the line is $y = -5x - 13$.

11. Calculate the slope:
$m = \dfrac{y_2 - y_1}{x_2 - x_1} = \dfrac{7 - 4}{2 - 1} = \dfrac{3}{1} = 3$.

To find the y-intercept, substitute the slope, 3, and the coordinates of either given point into the equation $y = mx + b$, and solve for b. Using $(1, 4)$,

$y = mx + b$

$4 = 3(1) + b$

$4 = 3 + b$

$1 = b$

The equation of the line is $y = 3x + 1$.

49. Let T be the total time (in minutes) for cooking a roast that weighs p pounds and t be the extra time needed (in minutes). The equation $T = 30p + t$ models the situation.

For a 2 pound roast, the total time was 1 hour 25 minutes, or 85 minutes. Find the extra time t needed by substituting 85 for T and 2 for p, and solving for t.

$85 = 30(2) + t$

$85 = 60 + t$

$25 = t$

Find the value of T for a 3 pound roast by substituting 3 for p.

$T = 30(3) + 25 = 90 + 25 = 115$

You need 115 minutes, or 1 hour 55 minutes, to cook a 3 pound roast.

Lesson 5.3 (pp. 305–308)

3. Substitute 2 for x_1, 1 for y_1, and 2 for m in the point-slope form $y - y_1 = m(x - x_1)$:
$y - 1 = 2(x - 2)$.

39. The rate of change is given as $10,000 per year. Let y be the annual sales (in dollars) and x be the number of years since 1994. From the given information about 1997, one data pair is $(3, 97000)$. Use the point-slope form of an equation.

$y - y_1 = m(x - x_1)$

$y - 97000 = 10000(x - 3)$

$y - 97000 = 10000x - 30000$

$y = 10000x + 67000$

To find the sales in 2000, use the equation above with $x = 2000 - 1994$, or 6.

$y = 10000(6) + 67000$

$= 60000 + 67000 = 127000$

The annual sales in 2000 were $127,000.

Lesson 5.4 (pp. 314–316)

17. Calculate the slope:
$m = \dfrac{y_2 - y_1}{x_2 - x_1} = \dfrac{-4 - 4}{4 - (-8)} = \dfrac{-8}{12}$ or $-\dfrac{2}{3}$.

Use either point to write an equation in point-slope form. Using $(-8, 4)$:

$y - y_1 = m(x - x_1)$

$y - 4 = -\dfrac{2}{3}[x - (-8)]$

$y - 4 = -\dfrac{2}{3}(x + 8)$

Rewrite the equation in standard form.

$y - 4 = -\dfrac{2}{3}x - \dfrac{16}{3}$

$\dfrac{2}{3}x + y - 4 = -\dfrac{16}{3}$

$\dfrac{2}{3}x + y = -\dfrac{4}{3}$ (or $2x + 3y = -4$)

39. a. Let n be the number of ounces in a box of wheat cereal.

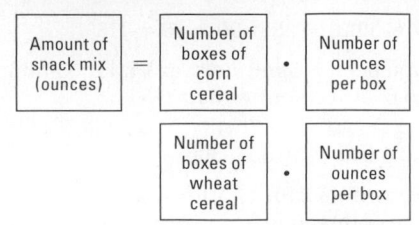

$$120 = 5 \cdot 12 + 4 \cdot n$$
$$120 = 60 + 4n$$
$$60 = 4n$$
$$15 = n$$

There are 15 ounces in a box of wheat cereal.

b. Let c be the number of boxes of corn cereal and let w be the number of boxes of wheat cereal you use. Use the verbal model from part (a).

$$120 = c \cdot 12 + w \cdot 15$$
$$120 = 12c + 15w \text{ or } 12c + 15w = 120$$

c. Substitute different values for c and w in the equation for part (b).

If $c = 0$, then $12(0) + 15w = 120$, and $w = 8$; you can use 0 boxes of corn cereal and 8 boxes of wheat cereal.

If $c = 5$, then $12(5) + 15w = 120$, and $w = 4$; you can use 5 boxes of corn cereal and 4 boxes of wheat cereal.

If $c = 10$, then $12(10) + 15w = 120$, and $w = 0$; you can use 10 boxes of corn cereal and 0 boxes of wheat cereal.

Lesson 5.5 (pp. 322–324)

19. The slope of the line $y = 3x - 12$ is 3, so the slope of the perpendicular line is $-\frac{1}{3}$.

Use the slope $-\frac{1}{3}$ and the point $(-9, 2)$ to find the y-intercept of the line.

$$y = mx + b$$
$$2 = -\frac{1}{3}(-9) + b$$
$$2 = 3 + b$$
$$-1 = b$$

The equation of the line through $(-9, 2)$ that is perpendicular to the line $y = 3x - 12$ is $y = -\frac{1}{3}x - 1$.

33. a. Let w represent the weight of the blue whale calves and let d represent the number of days since birth.

The rate of change is 200 pounds per day. Use this value and the birth weights to write an equation for each calf.

First calf: $w_1 = 200d + 6000$
Second calf: $w_2 = 200d + 6250$

b. Substitute 30 for d in each equation from part (a).

$$w_1 = 200(30) + 6000 = 12{,}000$$

After 30 days, the first calf weighs 12,000 pounds.

$$w_2 = 200(30) + 6250 = 12{,}250$$

After 30 days, the second calf weighs 12,250 pounds.

c. The graphs of the equations in part (a) are parallel, since the two equations have the same slope, 200. The w-intercept of the second line is 250 greater than the w-intercept of the first line.

Lesson 5.6 (pp. 328–331)

7. The ordered pairs from the table are (1.2, 10), (1.8, 7), (2.3, 5), (3.0, −1), (4.4, −4), and (5.2, −8).

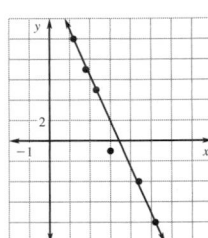

Use the points (1.2, 10) and (5.2, −8) to find the slope of the line of fit.

$$m = \frac{y_2 - y_1}{x_2 - x_1} = \frac{-8 - 10}{5.2 - 1.2} = \frac{-18}{4} = -4.4.$$

Use the slope −4.4 and the point (5.2, −8) to find the y-intercept of the line.

$$y = mx + b$$
$$-8 = -4.4(5.2) + b$$
$$-8 = -22.88 + b$$
$$14.88 = b$$

A line of fit is $y = -4.4x + 14.88$.

17. a. The ordered pairs from the diagram are (86, −86), (80, −65), (75, −54), (70, −40), (65, −26), (60, −21), and (52, −4).

b. Draw a line that appears to fit the points.

Sample:

Use the points (60, −21) and (80, −65) to find the slope of the line of fit.

$$m = \frac{y_2 - y_1}{x_2 - x_1} = \frac{-21 - (-65)}{60 - 80} = \frac{44}{-20} = -2.2$$

Use the slope −2.2 and the point (80, −65) to find the *y*-intercept of the line.

$$y = mx + b$$

$$-65 = -2.2(80) + b$$

$$-65 = -176 + b$$

$$111 = b$$

A line of fit is $y = -2.2x + 111$.

c. The slope of the line of fit models the rate of change. So the temperature changes at an approximate rate of −2.2°C per kilometer of increasing altitude.

Lesson 5.7 (pp. 338–341)

3. Enter the data list on a graphing calculator. Create a scatter plot.

Perform a linear regression using the paired data. An equation of the best-fitting line is approximately $y = 2.6x + 2.5$.

Graph the best-fitting line. Use the trace feature and arrow keys to find the value of y when $x = 5$. For $x = 5$, $y = 15.5$.

19. a. Enter the data list on a graphing calculator. Make a scatter plot.

b. Perform a linear regression using the paired data. An equation of the best-fitting line is approximately $y = 0.03x + 1.23$ where y is the recommended space (in square feet) and x is a pig's weight (in pounds).

c. Evaluate $y = 0.03x + 1.23$ for $x = 250$.

$$y = 0.03(250) + 1.23 = 7.5 + 1.23 = 8.73$$

The model predicts that about 8.73 square feet of space is needed for a pig weighing 250 pounds.

Chapter 6

Lesson 6.1 (pp. 359–361)

7. The open circle means that 10 is not a solution of the inequality. Because the arrow points to the left, all numbers less than 10 are solutions. An inequality represented by the graph is $x < 10$.

15.
$$w + 14.9 > -2.7$$
$$w + 14.9 - 14.9 > -2.7 - 14.9$$
$$w > -17.6$$

33. a. Let s represent score you can earn.

| Your score | + | Score you can earn | > | Competitor's total score |

$$129.49 + s > (127.04 + 129.98)$$
$$129.49 + s > 257.02$$
$$129.49 + s - 129.49 > 257.02 - 129.49$$
$$s > 127.53$$

The score you can earn must be greater than 127.53.

b. Yes; since 128.13 > 127.53, you will beat your competitor.

No; since 126.78 < 127.53, you will not beat your competitor.

No; when your score is 127.53, you and your competitor will tie.

Lesson 6.2 (pp. 366–368)

5. $-6y < -36$

$$\frac{-6y}{-6} > \frac{-36}{-6}$$ Reverse the inequality symbol when dividing by -6.

$y > 6$

9. $\dfrac{g}{6} > 20$

$6 \cdot \dfrac{g}{6} > 6 \cdot (-20)$

$g > -120$

39. $48 \leq 15 \cdot w$

$$\frac{48}{15} \leq \frac{15w}{15}$$

$3.2 \leq w$

The minimum width of the molding must be greater than or equal to 3.2 inches, or the width must be at least 3.2 inches.

Lesson 6.3 (pp. 372–374)

5. $8v - 3 \geq -11$

$8v \geq -8$

$v \geq -1$

19. $3(s - 4) \geq 2(s - 6)$

$3s - 12 \geq 2s - 12$

$3s \geq 2s$

$3s - 2s \geq 2s - 2s$

$s \geq 0$

39. a. The area of the habitat is (20 feet)(50 feet) = 1000 square feet. Since 500 square feet are needed for the first two swans, $1000 - 500 = 500$ square feet are left for the other swans. 500 square feet can hold up to $500 \div 125 = 4$ more swans; so, the maximum number of swans is $2 + 4 = 6$ swans.

b. The area of the new habitat is $[(20 + 20)\text{ feet}][(50 + 20)\text{ feet}] = (40\text{ feet})(70\text{ feet}) = 2800$ square feet. Since $2800 - 1000 = 1800$, the additional area is 1800 square feet. 1800 square feet can hold up to $1800 \div 125 = 14.4$ more swans; so the possible number of additional swans is at most 14 swans. The habitat can hold at most 14 more swans.

Lesson 6.4 (pp. 384–387)

7. Let s be the speed of a vehicle that is traveling within the posted speed limits.

$40 \leq s \leq 60$

11. Separate the compound inequality $-1 \leq -4m \leq 16$ into two inequalities.

$-1 \leq -4m$ *and* $-4m \leq 16$

$\dfrac{-1}{-4} \geq \dfrac{-4m}{-4}$ *and* $\dfrac{-4m}{-4} \geq \dfrac{16}{-4}$

$\dfrac{1}{4} \geq m$ *and* $m \geq -4$

The inequality can be written as $-4 \leq m \leq \dfrac{1}{4}$.

41. An inequality representing values for p is $0.02 \leq p \leq 0.04$.

$0.02 \leq \dfrac{f}{d} \leq 0.04$ Substitute $\dfrac{f}{d}$ for p.

$0.02 \leq \dfrac{f}{160} \leq 0.04$ Substitute 160 for w.

$3.2 \leq f \leq 6.4$

The possible amounts of food f eaten per day by a deer is greater or equal to 3.2 pounds and less than or equal to 6.4 pounds.

Lesson 6.5 (pp. 393–395)

11. Rewrite the absolute value equation $|3p + 7| = 4$ as two equations.

$3p + 7 = 4$ *or* $3p + 7 = -4$

$3p = -3$ *or* $3p = -11$

$p = -1$ *or* $p = -3\dfrac{2}{3}$

The solutions are -1 and $-3\dfrac{2}{3}$.

23. $|x - 1| + 5 = 2$

$|x - 1| = -3$

The absolute value of a number is never negative. So, there are no solutions.

45. a. Let s represent your friend's scores last year.

$$\boxed{\text{Absolute deviation}} = \left| \boxed{\text{Score}} - \boxed{\text{Mean score}} \right|$$

$2.213 = |s - 54.675|$

$2.213 = s - 54.675$

$56.888 = s$

$or \ -2.213 = s - 54.675$

$52.462 = s$

His least score earned was 52.462, and his greatest score was 56.888 points.

b. Let t represent your friend's scores this year. Find his greatest score for this year. Then find the difference between this year's greatest score and last year's greatest score.

$0.45 = |t - 56.738|$

$0.45 = t - 56.738$

$57.188 = t$

$or \ -0.45 = t - 56.738$

$56.288 = t$

His greatest score was 57.188 points. This score is $57.188 - 56.888$, or 0.3 point more than his greatest score last year.

Lesson 6.6 (pp. 401–403)

9. Rewrite $|d + 4| \geq 3$ as a compound inequality.

$d + 4 \leq -3 \quad or \quad d + 4 \geq 3$

$d \leq -7 \quad or \quad d \geq -1$

![number line from -12 to 4 with closed points at -7 and -1, shading outward]

15. $5\left|\frac{1}{2}r + 3\right| > 5$

$\left|\frac{1}{2}r + 3\right| > 1$

$\frac{1}{2}r + 3 < -1 \quad or \quad \frac{1}{2}r + 3 > 1$

$\frac{1}{2}r < -4 \quad or \quad \frac{1}{2}r > -2$

$r < -8 \quad or \quad r > -4$

![number line from -14 to 2 with open points at -8 and -4]

37. Let t represent the oven temperature.

$$\left| \boxed{\substack{\text{Oven} \\ \text{temperature}}} - \boxed{\substack{\text{Measured} \\ \text{temperature}}} \right| \leq \boxed{\substack{\text{Absolute} \\ \text{deviation}}}$$

$|t - 346| \leq 2$

$-2 \leq t - 346 \leq 2$

$344 \leq t \leq 348$

The temperature is at least 344°F and at most 348°F. You should continue to preheat; the temperature is still below 350°F.

Lesson 6.7 (pp. 409–412)

5. Substitute -1 for x and -4 for y in the inequality $y - x > -2$.

$-4 - (-1) > 2$

$-3 > 2$ ✗

Since -3 is not greater than 2, the ordered pair $(-1, -4)$ is not a solution.

19. Graph the equation $y = 3x + 5$. The symbol of the given inequality is $<$, so use a dashed line. Since the line does not pass through the origin, test the ordered pair $(0, 0)$ in $y < 3x + 5$.

$0 < 3(0) + 5$

$0 < 5$ ✓

Shade the half-plane that contains $(0, 0)$ because $(0, 0)$ is a solution of the inequality.

57. a. Let m be the number of muffins and let ℓ be the number of loaves of bread. An inequality modeling this situation is $\frac{1}{6}m + \frac{1}{2}\ell \leq 12$.

To graph $\frac{1}{6}m + \frac{1}{2}\ell \leq 12$, first graph the equation $\frac{1}{6}m + \frac{1}{2}\ell = 12$ in Quadrant I; the inequality symbol is $\leq$, so use a solid line.

Next, test $(12, 12)$ in $\frac{1}{6}m + \frac{1}{2}\ell \leq 12$.

$\frac{1}{6}(12) + \frac{1}{2}(12) \leq 12$

$2 + 6 \leq 12$ ✓

Finally, shade the part of Quadrant I that contains (12, 12), because (12, 12) is a solution of the inequality.

b. $\frac{1}{6}m + \frac{1}{2}(4) \le 12$ Substitute 4 for ℓ.

$$\frac{1}{6}m + 2 \le 12$$

$$\frac{1}{6}m \le 10$$

$$m \le 60$$

You can make up to 60 muffins.

Chapter 7

Lesson 7.1 (pp. 430–433)

15. Graph both equations.

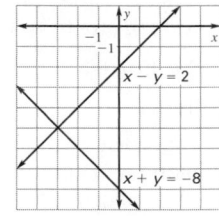

The lines appear to intersect at $(-3, -5)$.

Check: Substitute -3 for x and -5 for y in each equation.

$x - y = 2$	$x + y = -8$
$-3 - (-5) = 2$	$-3 + (-5) = -8$
$2 = 2 ✓$	$-8 = -8 ✓$

So, $(-3, -5)$ is the solution of the system.

31. The two lines appear to intersect at (50, 50). If the value of t is 50, then the year is $1990 + 50$, or 2040. So, the percent of eighth graders who watch 1 hour or less of television will equal the percent of eighth graders who watch 1 hour or more of television in the year 2040.

Lesson 7.2 (pp. 439–441)

13. Solve $x + y = -3$ for x: $x = -y - 3$.

Substitute $-y - 3$ for x in the other equation and solve for y.

$$5(-y - 3) + 2y = 9$$

$$-5y - 15 + 2y = 9$$

$$-3y - 15 = 9$$

$$-3y = 24$$

$$y = -8$$

Substitute -8 for y in the equation $x = -y - 3$.

$$x = -(-8) - 3 = 5$$

The solution of the linear system is $(5, -8)$.

33. a. Write a system of two linear equations.

Use the given verbal model to write the first equation: $x \cdot 1.5 = y \cdot 1.2$, or $1.5x = 1.2y$.

Since the length of the dowel is 9 inches, the second equation is $x + y = 9$.

Solve $x + y = 9$ for x: $x = -y + 9$.

Substitute $-y + 9$ for x in the equation $1.5x = 1.2y$ and solve for y.

$$1.5x = 1.2y$$

$$1.5(-y + 9) = 1.2y$$

$$-1.5y + 13.5 = 1.2y$$

$$13.5 = 2.7y$$

$$5 = y$$

Substitute 5 for y in the equation $x = -y + 9$.

$$x = -5 + 9 = 4$$

The solution is (4, 5). So the string should be placed 4 inches from point A.

Lesson 7.3 (pp. 447–450)

17. Rewrite the first equation so that the x-term is first. Subtract the equations to eliminate the variable x, then solve for y.

$$\begin{array}{r} 6x - 8y = 36 \\ \underline{6x - 8y = 15} \\ -7y = 21 \\ y = -3 \end{array}$$

Substitute -3 for y in either equation.

$$6x - (-3) = 15$$
$$6x + 3 = 15$$
$$6x = 12$$
$$x = 2$$

The solution of the linear system is $(2, -3)$.

41. Write a system of equations. Let x be the cost of a monophonic ring tone and let y be the cost of a polyphonic ring tone.

$3 \cdot x + 2 \cdot y = 12.85$ ← Julie's total cost

$1 \cdot x + 2 \cdot y = 8.95$ ← Tate's total cost

Subtract the equations to eliminate y.

$$3x + 2y - 12.05$$
$$\underline{3x + 2y = 8.95}$$
$$2x = 3.90$$
$$x = 1.95$$

Substitute 1.95 for x in either equation.

$$1.95 + 2y = 8.95$$
$$2y = 7.00$$
$$y = 3.50$$

The solution of the linear system is $(1.95, 3.50)$. The cost of a monophonic ring tone is \$1.95 and the cost of a polyphonic ring tone is \$3.50.

Lesson 7.4 (pp. 4542457)

15. Begin by multiplying $9x + 2y = 39$ by 2 and $6x + 13y = -9$ by 3 so that the coefficient of x is the same in both equations. Then subtract the equations to eliminate x. Solve for y.

$9x + 2y = 39$ $\boxed{\times 2}$ $18x + 34y = 78$

$6x + 13y = -9$ $\boxed{\times 3}$ $\underline{18x + 39y = -27}$

$$-35y = 105$$
$$y = -3$$

Substitute -3 for y in either original equations.

$9x + 2(-3) = 39$ Use the equation
$\qquad\qquad\quad 9x + 2y = 39$.

$$9x - 6 = 39$$
$$9x = 45$$
$$x = 5 \qquad \text{The solution is } (5, -3).$$

39. Let x be the number of pies and y be the number of batches of applesauce.

$5x + 4y = 169$ ← Granny Smith apples

$3x + 2y = 95$ ← Golden Delicious apples

Now begin to solve the system by multiplying $5x + 4y = 169$ by 3 and $3x + 2y = 95$ by 5 so that the coefficient of x is the same in both equations. Then subtract the equations to eliminate x. Solve for y.

$5x + 4y = 169$ $\boxed{\times 3}$ $15x + 12y = 507$

$3x + 2y = 95$ $\boxed{\times 5}$ $\underline{15x + 10y = 475}$

$$2y = 32$$
$$y = 16$$

Substitute 16 for y in either original equations.

$$3x + 2(16) = 95$$
$$3x + 32 = 95$$
$$3x = 63$$
$$x = 21$$

The solution is $(21, 16)$. The apples can be used to make 21 pies and 16 batches of applesauce.

Lesson 7.5 (pp. 462–465)

11.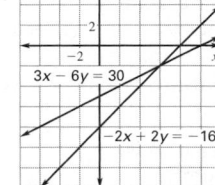

The lines intersect, so the linear system has one solution.

37. Write a system of equations. Let x be the cost of a coach ticket and let y be the cost of a business class ticket.

$150x + 80y = 22,860$ ← Washington, D.C.

$170x + 100y = 27,280$ ← York City

Solve the linear system using elimination. Multiply the Washington, D.C. equation by 5 and the New York City equation by 4.

$$750x + 400y = 114,300$$
$$680x + 400y = 109,120$$
$$70x = 5180$$
$$x = 74$$

Worked-Out Solutions **WS17**

Substitute 74 for x in either original equations.

$$170(74) + 100y = 27,280$$
$$12,580 + 100y = 27,280$$
$$100y = 14,700$$
$$y = 147$$

The solution is (74, 147). Since there is one solution to the system, there is enough information to determine the cost of one coach ticket.

Lesson 7.6 (pp. 469–472)

13. The graph of the system is the intersection of the two half-planes when both inequalities are graphed in the same coordinate plane.

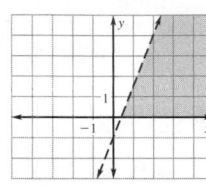

39. a. Let x be the person's age in years and let y be the target heart rate (in beats per minute). A person's maximum heart rate is given by $220 - x$, so 70% of this value is $0.7(220 - x)$ and 85% of this value is $0.85(220 - x)$. So the range for the target heart rate is given by the compound inequality $0.7(220 - x) \le y \le 0.85(220 - x)$, or $154 - 0.70x \le y \le 187 - 0.85x$. This compound inequality can be rewritten as the two inequalities $y \ge 154 - 0.70x$ and $y \le 187 - 0.85x$. The age range for which the heart rate calculations is valid is given as $20 \le x \le 65$.

The system of inequalities is:

$$y \ge 154 - 0.70x$$
$$y \le 187 - 0.85x$$
$$20 \le x \le 65$$

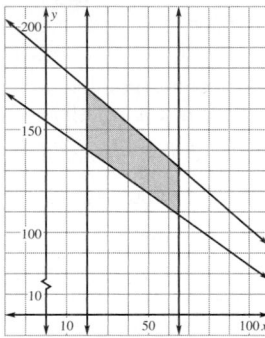

b. No; substituting 40 for x in the inequality $0.70(220 - x) \le y \le 0.85(220 - x)$ gives a range of $126 \le y \le 153$. Since 104 and 120 are both less than 126, his heart rate stays below 70% of the maximum heart rate and is not in the target range for his age.

Chapter 8

Lesson 8.1 (pp. 492–494)

31.
$$(-10x^6)^2 \cdot x^2 = (-10 \cdot x^6)^2 \cdot x^2$$
$$= (-10)^2 \cdot (x^6)^2 \cdot x^2$$
$$= 100 \cdot x^{6 \cdot 2} \cdot x^2$$
$$= 100 \cdot x^{12} \cdot x^2$$
$$= 100 \cdot x^{12 + 2}$$
$$= 100x^{14}$$

55. a. For 10 ounces of gold, there are $10^1 \cdot 10^{23} = 10^{1 + 23}$, or 10^{24} atoms of gold; for 100 ounces of gold, there are $10^2 \cdot 10^{23} = 10^{25}$ atoms of gold; for 1000 ounces of gold, there are $10^3 \cdot 10^{23} = 10^{26}$ atoms of gold; for 10,000 ounces of gold, there are $10^4 \cdot 10^{23} = 10^{27}$ atoms of gold; and for 100,000 ounces of gold, there are $10^5 \cdot 10^{23} = 10^{28}$ atoms of gold.

b. The power of 10 closest to 96,000 is 10^5, or 100,000. So there were about $10^5 \cdot 10^{23} = 10^{5 + 23}$, or 10^{28} atoms of gold extracted from the mine.

Lesson 8.2 (pp. 498–501)

33.
$$\left(\frac{3x^3}{2y^2}\right) \cdot \frac{1}{x^2} = \frac{(3y^3)^2}{(2y)^2} \cdot \frac{1}{x^2}$$
$$= \frac{3^2 \cdot (x^3)^2}{2^2 \cdot y^2} \cdot \frac{1}{x^2}$$
$$= \frac{9x^6}{4y^2} \cdot \frac{1}{x^2}$$
$$= \frac{9x^6}{4x^2y^2}$$
$$= \frac{9x^4}{4y^2}$$

51. Convert the speed of the spacecraft to kilometers per second.

$$\frac{10^4 \text{ m}}{1 \text{ sec}} \cdot \frac{1 \text{ km}}{10^3 \text{ m}} = \frac{10^{4-3} \text{ km}}{1 \text{ sec}} = \frac{10^1 \text{ km}}{1 \text{ sec}}$$

So the speed of the spacecraft is 10 kilometers per second.

Use the quotient of powers property to calculate the number of seconds it would take to make the trip.

$$\frac{10^{13}\text{ km}}{10^{1}\text{ km/sec}} = 10^{13-1}\text{ sec} = 10^{12}\text{ sec}$$

Calculate the number of seconds in a year (using 365 days = 1 year).

$$\frac{60\text{ sec}}{1\text{ min}} \cdot \frac{60\text{ min}}{1\text{ h}} \cdot \frac{24\text{ h}}{1\text{ day}} \cdot \frac{365\text{ day}}{1\text{ yr}} = \frac{31,356,000\text{ sec}}{1\text{ yr}}$$

Now convert the trip time, 10^{12} seconds, to years.

$$10^{12}\text{ sec} \div \frac{31,536,000\text{ sec}}{1\text{ yr}} \approx 31,710\text{ yr}$$

It would take about 31,710 years for the spacecraft to reach Alpha Centauri.

Lesson 8.3 (pp. 506–508)

11. $\left(\frac{2}{7}\right)^{-2} = \frac{1}{\left(\frac{2}{7}\right)^{2}} = \frac{1}{\frac{4}{49}} = \frac{49}{4}$

53. To find the number of red blood cells in the entire sample, multiply the sample size, 10^{-2} liters, by the ratio 10^{7} red blood cells per 10^{-6} liters.

$$10^{-2}\text{ L} \cdot \frac{10^{7}\text{ red blood cells}}{10^{-6}\text{ L}}$$

$$= \frac{10^{-2} \cdot 10^{7}}{10^{-6}}\text{ red blood cells}$$

$$= 10^{-2+7-(-6)}\text{ red blood cells}$$

$$= 10^{11}\text{ red blood cells}$$

The entire sample would contain about 10^{11} red blood cells.

Lesson 8.4 (pp. 515–518)

3. Since 8.5 is already between 1 and 10, you move the decimal point 0 places and the exponent is 0: $8.5 = 8.5 \times 10^{0}$.

17. Since the exponent is 7, move the decimal point 7 places to the right: $7.5 \times 10^{7} = 75,000,000$.

53. Divide the number of pounds of cotton by the number of acres.

$$\frac{9.7 \times 10^{8}}{6.9 \times 10^{5}} = \frac{9.7}{6.9} \times \frac{10^{8}}{10^{5}}$$

$$\approx 1.4058 \times 10^{3} \approx 1405.8$$

The average number of pounds produced per acre was about 1406 pounds per acre.

Lesson 8.5 (pp. 523–527)

13. Make a table of values by choosing values for x and finding the corresponding values for y. The domain of the function is all real numbers.

x	−2	−1	0	1	2	3
y	$0.\overline{4}$	$0.\overline{6}$	1	1.5	2.25	3.375

Plot the points from the table and draw a smooth curve through them.

The table and the graph show that the range of the function is all positive real numbers.

41. a. Use the exponential growth model, $y = a(1 + r)^{t}$.

For tree 1 (with 6% = 0.06), substitute A for y, 154 for a, and 0.06 for r.

$$A = 154(1 + 0.06)^{t} = 154(1.06)^{t}$$

For tree 2 (with 10% = 0.1), substitute A for y, 113 for a, and 0.1 for r.

$$A = 113(1 + 0.1)^{t} = 113(1.1)^{t}$$

The functions are $A = 154(1.06)^{t}$ for tree 1 and $A = 113(1.1)^{t}$ for tree 2.

b. Using the *intersect* feature of the graphing calculator, the graphs intersect at about the point (8.4, 250.6). So, the trees will be the same height in about 8.4 years.

Lesson 8.6 (pp. 535–538)

7. Make a table of values by choosing values for x and finding the corresponding values for y. The domain of the function is all real numbers.

x	−2	−1	0	1	2
y	25	5	1	$\frac{1}{5}$	$\frac{1}{25}$

Plot the points from the table and draw a smooth curve through them.

The table and the graph show that the range of the function is all positive real numbers.

49. Let V be the value of the boat (in dollars) and let t be the time (in years since 2003).

Use the exponential decay model, $y = a(1 - r)^t$, to write a function for the value of the boat over time. Substitute V for y, 4000 for a, and 0.07 for r.

$V = 4000(1 - 0.07)^t$

$\quad = 4000(0.93)^t$

In 2006, the value of t is $2006 - 2003$, or 3.

$V = 4000(0.93)^3 \approx \$3217.43$

The value of the boat in 2006 is about \$3217. The family should not sell the boat, since the \$3000 offer is less than the value of the boat.

Chapter 9

Lesson 9.1 (pp. 557–559)

21. $(6c^2 + 3c + 9) - (3c - 5)$

$\qquad = 6c^2 + 3c + 9 - 3c + 5$

$\qquad = 6c^2 + (3c - 3c) + (9 + 5)$

$\qquad = 6c^2 + 14$

39. a. Add the models for the number of books of each type sold to find a model T for the total number (in millions) of books sold.

$T = A + J$

$= (9.5t^3 - 58t^2 + 66t + 500) +$
$(-15t^2 + 64t + 360)$

$= 9.5t^3 + (-58t^2 - 15t^2) + (66t + 64t) +$
$(500 + 360)$

$= 9.5t^3 - 73t^2 + 130t + 860$

b. To find the total number (in millions) of books sold in the years 1998 and 2002, substitute the number of years since 1998 for t in the model. Then compare the results.

For 1998, $t = 1998 - 1998 = 0$:

$M = 9.5(0)^3 - 73(0)^2 + 130(0) + 860 = 860$

There were 860 million books sold in 1998.

For 2002, $t = 2002 - 1998 = 4$:

$M = 9.5(4)^3 - 73(4)^2 + 130(4) + 860$

$\quad = 9.5(64) - 73(16) + 130(4) + 860$

$\quad = 608 - 1168 + 520 + 860$

$\quad = 820$

There were 820 million books sold in 2002.

More books were sold in 1998 than in 2002.

Lesson 9.2 (pp. 565–568)

23. $(5x + 2)(-3x^2 + 4x - 1)$

$= 5x(-3x^2 + 4x - 1) + 2(-3x^2 + 4x - 1)$

$= 15x^3 + 20x^2 - 5x - 6x^2 + 8x - 2$

$= -15x^3 + (20x^2 - 6x^2) + (-5x + 8x) - 2$

$= -15x^3 + 14x^2 + 3x - 2$

51. a. Substitute 0 for t in each function:

$R = -336(0)^2 + 1730(0) + 12{,}300 = 12{,}300$

$P = 0.00351(0)^2 - 0.0249(0) + 0.171 = 0.171$

Since t is the number of years since 1997, the product $R \cdot P$ when $t = 0$ represents the amount (in million of dollars) spent in 1997 on sound recordings in the U.S. by people between 15 and 19 years old.

b. $R \cdot P = (-336t^2 + 1730t + 12{,}300) \cdot$
$(0.00351t^2 - 0.0249t + 0.171)$

$= -336t^2(0.00351t^2 - 0.0249t + 0.171) +$
$1730t(0.00351t^2 - 0.0249t + 0.171) +$
$12{,}300(0.00351t^2 - 0.0249t + 0.171)$

$= -1.17936t^4 + 8.3664t^3 - 57.456t^2 +$
$6.0723t^3 - 43.077t^2 + 295.83t +$
$43.173t^2 - 306.27t + 2103.3$

$= -1.17936t^4 + (8.3664t^3 + 6.0723t^3) +$
$(-57.456t^2 - 43.077t^2 + 43.173t^2) +$
$(295.83t - 306.27t) + 2103.3$

$= -1.17936t^4 + 14.4387t^3 - 57.36t^2 -$
$10.44t + 2103.3$

So, $R \cdot P \approx -1.18t^4 + 14.4t^3 - 57.4t^2 - 10.4t + 2100$.

c. For 2002, $t = 2002 - 1997 = 5$. Substitute 5 for t in the equation for part (b).

$$R \cdot P \approx -1.18(5)^4 + 14.4(5)^3 - 57.4(5)^2 - 10.4(5) + 2100$$

$$\approx -1.18(625) + 14.4(125) - 57.4(25) - 10.4(5) + 2100$$

$$\approx -737.50 + 1800 - 1435 - 52 + 2100$$

$$\approx 1675.5$$

In 2002, people between the ages of 15 and 19 years old spent about 1680 million dollars (or $1,680,000,000) on sound recordings.

Lesson 9.3 (pp. 572–574)

11. $(t + 4)(t - 4) = t^2 - 4^2 = t^2 - 16$

41. a.

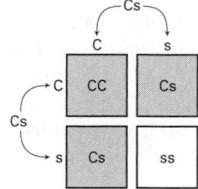

b. Model the gene from each parent with $0.5C + 0.5s$. There is an equal chance that the child inherits a straight thumb gene or a curved thumb gene from each parent. The possible gene combinations of the child can be modeled by $(0.5C + 0.5s)^2$, or

$$(0.5C)^2 + 2(0.5C)(0.5s) + (0.5s)^2$$

$$= 0.25C^2 + 0.5Cs + 0.25s^2$$

c. Consider the coefficients in the polynomial found in part (b). The coefficients show that $25\% + 50\% = 75\%$ of the possible gene combinations will contain a C, and thus result in a child with a curved thumb.

Lesson 9.4 (pp. 578–580)

3. $(x - 5)(x + 3) = 0$

$x - 5 = 0 \quad or \quad x + 3 = 0$

$x = 5 \quad or \quad x = -3$

The solutions of the equation are 5 and -3.

55. a. The initial vertical velocity is given as 4.9 meters per second and the rabbit starts from the ground, so $v = 4.9$ and $s = 0$ in the vertical motion model.

$$h = -4.9t^2 + vt + s$$

$$= -4.9t^2 + 4.9t + 0$$

$$= -4.9t^2 + 4.9t$$

b. When the rabbit lands, its height above the ground is 0 meters. A reasonable domain for t can be found by substituting 0 for h and solving for t.

$$0 = -4.9t^2 + 4.9t$$

$$0 = 4.9t(-t + 1)$$

$4.9t = 0 \quad or \quad -t + 1 = 0$

$t = 0 \quad or \quad t = 1$

Since a height of 0 represents when the rabbit is on the ground, $t = 1$ second represents how long it takes for the rabbit to land back on the ground after jumping at $t = 0$ seconds. So, a reasonable domain is all real numbers greater than or equal to 0 and less than or equal to 1, or $0 \le t \le 1$.

Lesson 9.5 (pp. 586–589)

7. In $z^2 + 8z - 48$, $c = -48$. Since c is negative, p and q must have different signs.

Factors of −48	Sum of factors	
−48, 1	$-48 + 1 = -47$	✗
48, −1	$48 + (-1) = 47$	✗
−24, 2	$-24 + 2 = -22$	✗
24, −2	$24 + (-2) = 22$	✗
−16, 3	$-16 + 3 = -13$	✗
16, −3	$16 + (-3) = 13$	✗
−12, 4	$-12 + 4 = -8$	✗
12, −4	$12 + (-4) = 8$	← Correct

So, $z^2 + 8z - 48 = (z + 12)(z - 4)$.

61. Let x be the original length of the sides of the square photo. Then the length of the trimmed photo is $(x - 6)$ inches and its width is $(x - 5)$ inches. The formula $A = \ell \cdot w$ models the area of the trimmed photo which is 20 square inches.

$$A = \ell \cdot w$$
$$20 = (x - 6)(x - 5)$$
$$20 = x^2 - 11x + 30$$
$$0 = x^2 - 11x + 10$$
$$0 = (x - 10)(x - 1)$$
$$x - 10 = 0 \quad or \quad x - 1 = 0$$
$$x = 10 \quad or \quad x = 1$$

So, the original square photo had a side length of 10 inches or 1 inch. But an original length of 1 inch does not make sense in this situation, so the side length of the original square photo was 10 inches. Therefore, the perimeter of the original square photo was 4(10), or 40 inches.

Lesson 9.6 (pp. 596–599)

5. Factor -1 from each term of the trinomial:
$-y^2 + 2y + 8 = -\left(y^2 - 2y - 8\right)$.

In $y^2 - 2y - 8$, $c = -8$. Since c is negative, the factors of c must have different signs.

Factors of −8	Possible factorization	Middle term when multiplied	
−8, 1	$(y - 8)(y + 1)$	$y - 8y = -7y$	✗
8, −1	$(y + 8)(y - 1)$	$-y + 8y = 7y$	✗
−4, 2	$(y - 4)(y + 2)$	$2y - 4y = -2y$	← Correct
4, −2	$(y + 4)(y - 2)$	$-2y + 4y = 2y$	✗

So, $y^2 - 2y - 8 = (y - 4)(y + 2)$. Therefore,

$$-y^2 + 2y + 8 = -\left(y^2 - 2y - 8\right)$$
$$= -(y - 4)(y + 2)$$

25. $\quad 4s^2 + 11s - 3 = 0$
$$(4s - 1)(s + 3) = 0$$
$$4s - 1 = 0 \quad or \quad s + 3 = 0$$
$$s = \frac{1}{4} \quad or \quad s = -3$$

61. Let w be the width of the Parthenon's base. Then $2w + 8$ is the length of the base. The formula $A = \ell \cdot w$ models the area of the rectangular base which is 2170 square meters.

$$A = \ell \cdot w$$
$$2170 = (2w + 8) \cdot w$$
$$2170 = 2w^2 + 8w$$
$$0 = 2w^2 + 8w - 2170$$
$$0 = 2\left(w^2 + 4w - 1085\right)$$
$$0 = 2(w + 35)(w - 31)$$
$$w + 35 = 0 \quad or \quad w - 31 = 0$$
$$w = -35 \quad or \quad w = 31$$

The solutions are -35 and 31.

Since the width cannot be negative, reject -35 as a solution. So, the width is 31 meters and the length is $2(31) + 8$, or 70 meters. Therefore, the base of the Parthenon has length 70 meters and width 31 meters.

Lesson 9.7 (pp. 603–605)

11. $49a^2 + 14a + 1 = (7a)^2 + 2(7a \cdot 1) + 1^2$
$$= (7a + 1)^2$$

49. Use the vertical motion model with $h = 54$, $v = 56$, and $s = 5$.

$$h = -16t^2 + vt + s$$
$$54 = -16t^2 + 56t + 5$$
$$0 = -16t^2 + 56t - 49$$
$$0 = -\left(16t^2 - 56t + 49\right)$$
$$0 = -\left[(4t)^2 - 2(4t \cdot 7) + 7^2\right]$$
$$0 = -(4t - 7)^2$$
$$0 = (4t - 7)^2$$
$$4t - 7 = 0$$
$$t = 1.75$$

The ball reaches a height of 54 feet in 1.75 seconds. Since there is one solution for t, the ball reaches a height of 54 feet just once.

Lesson 9.8 (pp. 610–613)

13. $x^3 + x^2 + 2x + 2 = (x^3 + x^2) + (2x + 2)$

$$= x^2(x + 1) + 2(x + 1)$$

$$= (x + 1)(x^2 + 2)$$

23. $x^4 - x^2 = x^2(x^2 - 1) = x^2(x - 1)(x + 1)$

71. a. Substitute 0 for h in $h = -4.9t^2 + 3.9t + 1$.

$$0 = -4.9t^2 + 3.9t + 1$$

$$0 = -(4.9t^2 - 3.9t - 1)$$

$$0 = -(4.9t + 1)(t - 1)$$

$$4.9t + 1 = 0 \qquad or \qquad t - 1 = 0$$

$$t \approx -0.20 \quad or \qquad t = 1$$

The zeros are 1 and about -0.2.

b. The zero $t \approx -0.2$ has no meaning in this situation because t represents time which cannot be negative. The zero $t = 1$ means that the pallino hits the ground (where $h = 0$) 1 second after it is thrown.

Chapter 10

Lesson 10.1 (pp. 632–634)

7. Make a table of values for $y = -2x^2$.

x	−2	−1	0	1	2
y	−8	−2	0	−2	−8

Plot the points from the table. Draw a smooth curve through the points.

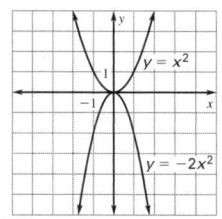

The graphs of $y = -2x^2$ and $y = x^2$ have the same vertex, $(0, 0)$, and the same axis of symmetry, $x = 0$. However, the graph of $-2x^2$ is narrower than the graph of $y = x^2$, and it opens down. This is because the graph of $y = -2x^2$ is a vertical stretch (by a factor of 2) with a reflection in the x-axis of the graph of $y = x^2$.

41. a.

b. From the graph, the wind speed that will produce a force of 1 pound per square foot on a sail is about 16 knots. Using the function to check: $F = 0.004(16)^2 = 1.024$.

c. From the graph, the wind speed that will produce a force of 5 pounds per square foot on a sail is about 35 knots. Using the function to check: $F = 0.004(35)^2 = 4.9$.

Lesson 10.2 (pp. 638–640)

9. For $y = -\frac{2}{3}x^2 - 1$, $a = -\frac{2}{3}$ and $b = 0$.

$$x = -\frac{b}{2a} = \frac{0}{2\left(-\frac{2}{3}\right)} = 0$$

The axis of symmetry is $x = 0$.

The x-coordinate of the vertex, $-\frac{b}{2a}$, is 0. To find the y-coordinate, substitute 0 for x in the function and find y: $y = -\frac{2}{3}(0)^2 - 1 = -1$. The vertex is $(0, -1)$.

41. The highest point of each parabolic arch is at the vertex of the parabola. The height h is the y-coordinate of the vertex.

To find the x-coordinate of the vertex, use

$x = -\frac{b}{2a}$ with $a = -0.0019$ and $b = 0.71$.

$$x = -\frac{b}{2a} = -\frac{0.71}{2(-0.0019)} \approx 187$$

Substitute 187 for x in the given equation to find the y-coordinate of the vertex.

$$y = -0.0019(187)^2 + 0.71(187) \approx 66.3$$

The height h at the highest point of the arch is about 66 feet.

Lesson 10.3 (pp. 647–649)

5. Write the equation $x^2 + 6x = -8$ in standard form: $x^2 + 6x + 8 = 0$.

Graph the function $y = x^2 + 6x + 8$.

 The x-intercepts are -4 and -2.

So, the solutions of $x^2 + 6x = -8$ are -4 and -2.

51. The width of the road can be found by finding the distance between the x-intercepts of the graph $y = -0.0017x^2 + 0.041x$.

Graph the function $y = -0.0017x^2 + 0.041x$ on a graphing calculator.

Use the *trace* feature of the graphing calculator to find the x-intercepts. There are two x-intercepts, one at 0 and one at approximately 24.12.

To the nearest tenth of a foot, the width of the road is 24.1 feet.

Lesson 10.4 (pp. 655–658)

25. $7c^2 = 100$

$$c^2 = \frac{100}{7}$$

$$c = \pm\sqrt{\frac{100}{7}}$$

$$c \approx \pm 3.78 \quad \text{Use a calculator.}$$

59. First, solve the formula for D: $D = \pm\sqrt{\dfrac{w}{0.0018ds}}$.

Since D cannot be negative in this situation, use the positive square root only.

a. For amethyst, substitute 1 for w, 4.5 for d, and 2.65 for s.

$$D = \sqrt{\frac{1}{0.0018(4.5)(2.65)}} \approx 6.83$$

The diameter is about 6.8 millimeters.

b. For diamond, substitute 1 for w, 4.5 for d, and 3.52 for s.

$$D = \sqrt{\frac{1}{0.0018(4.5)(3.52)}} \approx 5.92$$

The diameter is about 5.9 millimeters.

c. For ruby, substitute 1 for w, 4.5 for d, and 4.00 for s.

$$D = \sqrt{\frac{1}{0.0018(4.5)(4.00)}} \approx 5.55$$

The diameter is about 5.6 millimeters.

Lesson 10.5 (pp. 666–668)

19.

$$z^2 + 11z = -\frac{21}{4}$$

$$z^2 + 11z + \left(\frac{11}{2}\right)^2 = -\frac{21}{4} + \left(\frac{11}{2}\right)^2$$

$$\left(z + \frac{11}{2}\right)^2 = -\frac{21}{4} + \frac{121}{4}$$

$$\left(z + \frac{11}{2}\right)^2 = 25$$

$$z + \frac{11}{2} = \pm 5$$

$$z = -\frac{11}{2} \pm 5$$

The solutions of the equation are

$-\dfrac{11}{2} + 5 = -0.5$ and $-\dfrac{11}{2} - 5 = -10.5$.

47. a. Convert \$1,904,000 to thousands of dollars: $1,904,000 \div 1000 = 1904$.

Substitute 1904 for y in $y = 7x^2 - 4x + 392$: $1904 = 7x^2 - 4x + 392$.

$$7x^2 - 4x + 392 = 1904$$

$$7x^2 - 4x = 1512$$

$$x^2 - \frac{4}{7}x = 216$$

$$x^2 - \frac{4}{7}x + \left(\frac{2}{7}\right)^2 = 216 + \left(\frac{2}{7}\right)^2$$

$$\left(x - \frac{2}{7}\right)^2 = 216\frac{4}{49}$$

$$x - \frac{2}{7} = \pm\sqrt{216\frac{4}{49}}$$

$$x = \frac{2}{7} \pm \sqrt{216\frac{4}{49}}$$

Using a calculator, the solutions are about 14.99 and about -14.41.

The negative value does not make sense in this situation because the function does not model the years prior to 1985. So, the year when the average salary was \$1,904,000 was $1985 + 15$, or 2000.

b. First, graph the function $y = 7x^2 - 4x - 392$ for $x \geq 0$. Then draw a dashed line at about $y = 1904$ until it intersects the curve. Draw a dashed line from this point down to the x-axis. The x-value here is about 15. So, the year when the average salary was $1,904,000 is about 1985 + 15, or 2000.

Lesson 10.6 (pp. 674–676)

19. Write $6z^2 = 2z^2 + 7z + 5$ in standard form: $4z^2 - 7z - 5 = 0$.

Use the quadratic formula, with $a = 4$, $b = -7$, and $c = -5$.

$$z = \frac{-(-7) \pm \sqrt{(-7)^2 - 4(4)(-5)}}{2(4)} = \frac{7 \pm \sqrt{129}}{8}$$

Using a calculator, the solutions are about 2.29 and about −0.54.

47. For 16,000,000 subscribers, $y = 16$ in the function.

$$16 = 0.7x^2 - 4.3x + 5.5$$
$$0 = 0.7x^2 - 4.3x - 10.5$$

Use the quadratic formula, with $a = 0.7$, $b = -4.3$, and $c = -10.5$.

$$x = \frac{-(-4.3) \pm \sqrt{(-4.3)^2 - 4(0.7)(-10.5)}}{2(0.7)}$$
$$= \frac{4.3 \pm \sqrt{47.89}}{1.4} \quad \text{Use a calculator.}$$

The solutions are about 8.01 and about −1.87.

The negative value does not make sense in this situation because the function does not model the years prior to 1985. So, the year when the number of subscribers was 16,000,000 was 1985 + 8, or 1993.

Lesson 10.7 (pp. 681–683)

9. Find the value of the discriminant. Substitute 25 for a, −16 for b, and 0 for c.

$$b^2 - 4ac = (-16)^2 - 4(25)(0) = 256$$

Since 256 > 0, the equation has two solutions.

47. In order for the child not to have to bend over, the height y of the arch must be at least 4 feet. Use the given quadratic equation with 4 substituted for y.

$$4 = -0.18x^2 + 1.6x$$
$$0 = -0.18x^2 + 1.6x - 4$$

Find the value of the discriminant. Substitute −0.18 for a, 1.6 for b, and −4 for c.

$$b^2 - 4ac = (1.6)^2 - 4(-0.18)(-4) = -0.32$$

Because the discriminant is negative, there are no solutions of the equation $0 = -0.18x^2 + 1.6x - 4$, meaning that the height of an arch is less than 4 feet. So, a child who is 4 feet tall would not be able to walk under one of the arches without having to bend over.

Lesson 10.8 (pp. 688–691)

7. linear function

13.

x	−2	−1	0	1	2
y	−4	−1	0	−1	−4

First differences: +3 +1 −1 −3

Second differences: −2 −2 −2

The second differences are equal, so the table of values represents a quadratic function.

The equation has the form $y = ax^2$. Find the value of a by using the coordinates of a point (other than the origin) that lies on the graph, such as $(-1, -1)$.

$$y = ax^2$$
$$-1 = a(-1)^2$$
$$-1 = a$$

An equation for the function is $y = -x^2$.

25. a.

Folds	1	2	3	4	5
Sections	2	4	8	16	32

b.

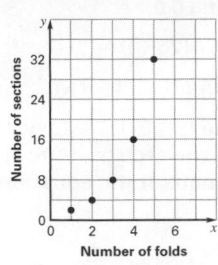

Both the graph and the table show that the data can be modeled by an exponential function.

c. Write an exponential equation of the form $y = ab^x$. From the table, the number of sections increases by a factor of 2, so $b = 2$. Find the value of a using one of the data pairs, such as $(3, 8)$.

$$y = ab^x$$

$$8 = a(2)^3$$

$$1 = a$$

The exponential equation is $y = 2^x$.

To find the number of sections created by 7 folds, substitute 7 for x in $y = 2^x$:
$y = 2^7 = 128$.

Chapter 11

Lesson 11.1 (pp. 713–716)

7. Make a table. Because the square root of a negative number is undefined, x must be nonnegative. So the domain of the function is $x \geq 0$.

x	0	1	2	3	4
y	0	1.5	2.1	2.6	3

Plot the ordered pairs from the table and then draw a smooth curve through the points. From the graph, it can seen that the range of the function is $y \geq 0$.

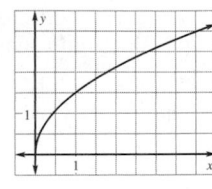

The graph of $y = -\frac{3}{2}\sqrt{x}$ is a vertical stretch $\left(\text{by a factor of } \frac{3}{2}\right)$ of the graph of $y = \sqrt{x}$.

23. Make a table. Because the square root of a negative number is undefined, the value of $x - 1$ must be nonnegative: $x - 1 \geq 0$. So the domain of the function is $x \geq 1$.

x	1	2	3	4	5
y	0	1	2.1	1.7	2

Plot the ordered pairs from the table and then draw a smooth curve through the points.

From the graph, it can seen that the range of the function is $y \geq 0$.

The graph of $y = \sqrt{x - 1}$ is a horizontal translation (of 1 unit to the right) of the graph of $y = \sqrt{x}$.

45. Because the square root of a negative number is undefined, h must be nonnegative. So the domain of the function is $h \geq 0$.

h	0	0.25	0.5	0.75	1
s	0	5.45	7.7	9.4	10.9

Plot the ordered pairs from the table and then draw a smooth curve through the points. From the graph, it can seen that the range of the function is $y \geq 0$.

The maximum height reached is about 0.9 meter when the long jumper's speed before jumping is 10.25 meters per second.

Lesson 11.2 (pp. 723–726)

9.
$$\sqrt{81m^3} = \sqrt{81 \cdot m^2 \cdot m}$$
$$= \sqrt{81} \cdot \sqrt{m^2} \cdot \sqrt{m}$$
$$= 9m\sqrt{m}$$

37.
$$9\sqrt{32} + \sqrt{2} = 9\sqrt{16 \cdot 2} + \sqrt{2}$$
$$= 9\sqrt{16} \cdot \sqrt{2} + \sqrt{2}$$
$$= 9 \cdot 4 \cdot \sqrt{2} + \sqrt{2}$$
$$= 36\sqrt{2} + \sqrt{2}$$
$$= (36 + 1)\sqrt{2}$$
$$= 37\sqrt{2}$$

69. a. $30 \div \$6$ per square yard $= 5$ square yards

b. s yd $= \sqrt{\dfrac{S \text{ yd}^2}{6}} = \sqrt{\dfrac{S}{6} \cdot \dfrac{\text{yd}^2}{1}}$

$= \sqrt{\dfrac{S}{6}} \cdot \sqrt{\dfrac{\text{yd}^2}{1}} = \sqrt{\dfrac{S}{6}}$ yd

Therefore s yd $= \sqrt{\dfrac{S}{6}}$ yd, and the units check.

c. Substitute 5 for s in the formula $s = \sqrt{\dfrac{S}{6}}$:

$\sqrt{\dfrac{5}{6}} \approx 0.9$.

To the nearest tenth of a yard, the edge length of the largest footrest you can cover with 5 square yards of fabric is 0.9 yard.

Lesson 11.3 (pp. 732–734)

11. $\sqrt{6 - 2x} + 12 = 21$

$\sqrt{6 - 2x} = 9$

$6 - 2x = 81$

$-2x = 75$

$x = -\dfrac{75}{2}$, or $-37\dfrac{1}{2}$

37. Substitute 20 for y in the given function.

$\sqrt{18x + 272} = 20$

$18x + 272 = 400$

$18x = 128$

$x = \dfrac{128}{18}$, or about 7.1

So, the annual banana consumption in the United States reached 20 pounds per person in the year $1970 + 7$, or 1977.

Lesson 11.4 (pp. 740–742)

9. $a^2 + b^2 = c^2$

$8^2 + 12^2 = c^2$ Substitute 8 for a and 12 for b.

$208 = c^2$

$\sqrt{208} = c$ Positive square root only.

$4\sqrt{13} = c$

23. Check to see if $a^2 + b^2 = c^2$ when $a = 2$, $b = 3$, and $c = 4$.

$2^2 + 3^2 \stackrel{?}{=} 4^2$

$4 + 9 \stackrel{?}{=} 16$

$13 \neq 16$ Not a right triangle

35. Check to see if $87^2 + 173^2 = 190^2$ when $a = 87$, $b = 173$, and $c = 190$.

$87^2 + 173^2 \stackrel{?}{=} 190^2$

$7569 + 29{,}929 \stackrel{?}{=} 36{,}100$

$37498 \neq 36100$

So, the triangle is not a right triangle. The sum of the squares of the lengths of the two shorter sides is not equal to the square of the length of the longer side.

Lesson 11.5 (pp. 747–750)

7. Let $(x_1, y_1) = (-4, 1)$ and $(x_2, y_2) = (3, -1)$.

$d = \sqrt{(x_2 - x_1)^2 + (y_2 - y_1)^2}$

$= \sqrt{(3 - (-4))^2 + (-1 - 1)^2}$

$= \sqrt{7^2 + (-2)^2} = \sqrt{53}$

23. Let $(x_1, y_1) = (6, -3)$ and $(x_2, y_2) = (4, -7)$.

$\left(\dfrac{x_1 + x_2}{2}, \dfrac{y_1 + y_2}{2} \right) = \left(\dfrac{6 + 4}{2}, \dfrac{-3 + (-7)}{2} \right) = (5, -5)$

49. a. The coordinates of the anchor are $(2, 3)$, the coordinates of the sword are $(9, 2)$, and the coordinates of the cup are $(8, 5)$.

Distance between the anchor and sword: Let $(x_1, y_1) = (2, 3)$ and $(x_2, y_2) = (9, 2)$.

$d = \sqrt{(9 - 2)^2 + (2 - 3)^2}$

$= \sqrt{7^2 + (-1)^2} = \sqrt{50}$

Distance between the anchor and cup: Let $(x_1, y_1) = (2, 3)$ and $(x_2, y_2) = (8, 5)$.

$d = \sqrt{(8 - 2)^2 + (5 - 3)^2}$

$= \sqrt{6^2 + (2)^2} = \sqrt{40}$

Since $\sqrt{40} < \sqrt{50}$, the anchor and the cup are closer together.

b. By examining the survey grid, the belt buckle and the sword are closest together; they are 3 units, or 150 feet, apart.

Again, by examining the survey grid, the two objects farthest apart are either the anchor and cup or the anchor and sword. The result in part (a) shows that the anchor and the sword are farthest apart; they are $\sqrt{50}$ units, or $50\sqrt{50} \approx 354$ feet, apart.

Chapter 12

Lesson 12.1 (pp. 769–772)

17. Make a table by choosing several integer values of x and finding the values of y. Notice that x cannot be 0, and that y will never be 0.

x	−7	−5	−2	−1	0	1	2	5	7
y	1	1.2	3.5	7	—	−7	−3.5	−1.2	−1

Plot the points (x, y) from the table.

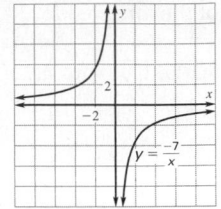

Connect the points in Quadrant II by drawing a smooth curve through them. Draw a separate curve though the points in Quadrant IV.

33. Because y varies inversely with x, the equation has the form $y = \dfrac{a}{x}$. Use the fact that $x = -22$ when $y = -6$ to find the value of a.

$-6 = \dfrac{a}{-22}$, so $a = -6(-22)$, or 132

An equation that relates x and y is $y = \dfrac{132}{x}$. When $x = 2$, $y = \dfrac{132}{2}$, or 66.

57. a. An inverse variation equation can be used to model the data if each pair of points (ℓ, f) fits the same equation. Use $f = \dfrac{a}{\ell}$ to test the data.

For (42.1, 523): $523 = \dfrac{a}{42.1}$, so $a \approx 22{,}000$

For (37.5, 587): $587 = \dfrac{a}{37.5}$, so $a \approx 22{,}000$

For (33.4, 659): $659 = \dfrac{a}{33.4}$, so $a \approx 22{,}000$

For (31.5, 698): $698 = \dfrac{a}{31.5}$, so $a \approx 22{,}000$

Since the value of a is about the same for each pairing, the inverse equation $f = \dfrac{22{,}000}{\ell}$ can be used to model the data.

To graph $f = \dfrac{22{,}000}{\ell}$, make a table of values, plot the points (ℓ, f), and then draw a smooth curve through them. Use only positive values for ℓ since the length of a string cannot be negative.

ℓ	880	440	293.3	220
f	25	50	75	100

b. Use the equation found in part (a) with $a = 29.4$.

$f = \dfrac{22{,}000}{29.4} \approx 748.3$

The frequency is about 748 hertz.

c. The frequency increases as the length of the string decreases. Yes, the length in part (b), 29.4 centimeters, is shorter than those in the table, but it has the greatest frequency.

Lesson 12.2 (pp. 779–782)

7. Make a table of values for x and y.

x	$-\frac{1}{4}$	$-\frac{1}{2}$	0	$\frac{1}{4}$	$\frac{1}{2}$
y	1	$\frac{1}{2}$	—	−1	$-\frac{1}{2}$

Plot the points (x, y) from the table. Connect the points in Quadrant II by drawing a smooth curve through them. Draw a separate curve though the points in Quadrant IV.

The graph of $y = \dfrac{-1}{4x}$ is a vertical shrink with a reflection in the x-axis of the graph of $y = \dfrac{1}{x}$.

21. The vertical asymptote of the graph is $x = -7$ and the horizontal asymptote is $y = 5$. Plot several points on each side of the vertical asymptote, such as $(-9, 3)$, $(-8, 1)$, $(-5, 7)$, and $(-3, 6)$. Draw the two branches of the graph that pass through the plotted points and approach the asymptotes.

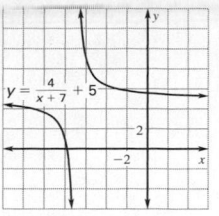

41. a. Use a verbal model to write an equation.

$C = 22 \div (r + 2)$, or $C = \dfrac{22}{r + 2}$

b. The graph shows that as the number of rentals increases, the average cost per rental decreases.

From the graph, the number of additional rentals needed per month so that the average cost is $1.50 per rental is 13 additional rentals.

Lesson 12.3 (pp. 788–791)

7.
$$
\begin{array}{r}
3v + 5 \\
v - 2\overline{)3v^2 - v - 10} \\
\underline{3v^2 - 6v} \\
5v - 10 \\
\underline{5v - 10} \\
0
\end{array}
$$

25. Rewrite the function in the form $y = \dfrac{a}{x - h} + k$.

$$
\begin{array}{r}
2 \\
x - 1\overline{)2x - 4} \\
\underline{2x - 2} \\
-2
\end{array}
\qquad \text{So, } y = \dfrac{-2}{x - 1} + 2.
$$

The asymptotes of the graph can be identified from the equation. The vertical asymptote is $x = 1$ and the horizontal asymptote is $y = 2$. Plot several points on each side of the vertical asymptote, such as $(-1, 3)$, $(0, 4)$, $(2, 0)$, and $(3, 1)$. Draw the two branches of the graph.

45. a. Since t is defined as the time for 1000 minutes or more, the domain of the function is $t \geq 1000$. The average cost C is found by adding the monthly fee to the product of the number of minutes over 1000 and the per-minute charge for those minutes, and then dividing that sum by the total number of minutes of use. The equation is $C = \dfrac{40 + 0.40(t - 1000)}{t}$, or $C = \dfrac{0.4t - 360}{t}$, where $t \geq 1000$.

b. Choose values of $t \geq 1000$.

t	1000	1100	1200	1300	1400	1500
C	0.04	0.073	0.10	0.123	0.143	0.16

The average cost per minute increases as the number of minutes over 1000 increases.

c. From the graph you can see that the number of minutes used is about 1030 minutes if the average cost is $.05 per minute.

Lesson 12.4 (pp. 797–800)

9. The expression $\dfrac{-3}{2p^2 - p}$ is undefined when $2p^2 - p = 0$.

$$2p^2 - p = 0$$
$$p(2p - 1) = 0$$
$$p = 0 \quad or \quad 2p - 1 = 0$$
$$p = \dfrac{1}{2}$$

The excluded values are 0 and $\dfrac{1}{2}$.

23. $\dfrac{h+3}{h^2-h-12} = \dfrac{h+3}{(h-4)(h+3)}$

$\qquad = \dfrac{\cancel{h+3}}{(h-4)\cancel{(h+3)}}$

$\qquad = \dfrac{1}{h-4}$

The excluded values are 4 and -3.

43. The percent of wood houses can be found by using the formula $p = \dfrac{W}{H}$.

$p = \dfrac{-20{,}200x + 366{,}000}{34{,}500x + 913{,}000} = \dfrac{-202x + 3660}{345x + 9130}$

To determine how the percent changed during the period 1990–2002, evaluate the function for several values of x.

For 1990, $x = 0$: $\dfrac{-202(0) + 3660}{345(0) + 9130} = \dfrac{3660}{9160} \approx 0.40$

In 1990, about 40% of new single-family houses were wood houses.

For 1994, $x = 4$: $\dfrac{-202(4) + 3660}{345(4) + 9130} = \dfrac{2852}{10{,}546} \approx 0.27$

In 1994, about 27% of new single-family houses were wood houses.

For 1998, $x = 8$: $\dfrac{-202(8) + 3660}{345(8) + 9130} = \dfrac{2044}{11{,}890} \approx 0.17$

In 1998, about 17% of new single-family houses were wood houses.

For 2002, $x = 12$:

$\dfrac{-202(12) + 3660}{345(12) + 9130} = \dfrac{1236}{13{,}270} \approx 0.09$

In 2002, about 9% of new single-family houses were wood houses.

The percent of wood houses decreased steadily from 1990 to 2002.

Lesson 12.5 (pp. 806–809)

5. $\dfrac{v^2 + v - 12}{5v + 10} \cdot \dfrac{-v - 2}{v^2 + 5v + 4}$

$= \dfrac{(v^2 + v - 12)(-v - 2)}{(5v + 10)(v^2 + 5v + 4)}$

$= \dfrac{\cancel{(v+4)}(v-3)(-1)\cancel{(v+2)}}{5\cancel{(v+2)}\cancel{(v+4)}(v+1)}$

$= \dfrac{-(v - 3)}{5(v + 1)}$

15. $\dfrac{2w^2 + 5w}{w^2 - 81} \div \dfrac{w^2}{w + 9} = \dfrac{2w^2 + 5w}{w^2 - 81} \cdot \dfrac{w + 9}{w^2}$

$= \dfrac{(2w^2 + 5w)(w + 9)}{(w^2 - 81)(w^2)}$

$= \dfrac{\cancel{(w)}(2w + 5)\cancel{(w + 9)}}{\cancel{(w + 9)}(w - 9)\cancel{(w)}(w)}$

$= \dfrac{2w + 5}{w(w - 9)}$

35. a. Use the formula $R = Y \div A$.

$R = \dfrac{860 + 1800x}{1 + 0.024x} \div \dfrac{230 + 380x}{1 + 0.014x}$

$= \dfrac{860 + 1800x}{1 + 0.024x} \cdot \dfrac{1 + 0.014x}{230 + 380x}$

$= \dfrac{(860 + 1800x)(1 + 0.014x)}{(1 + 0.024x)(230 + 380x)}$

$= \dfrac{\cancel{(10)}(86 + 180x)(1 + 0.014x)}{(1 + 0.024x)\cancel{(10)}(23 + 38x)}$

$= \dfrac{(86 + 180x)(1 + 0.014x)}{(1 + 0.024x)(23 + 38x)}$

b.

x	0	1	2	3	4	5	6
R	3.74	4.32	4.42	4.44	4.44	4.42	4.40

x	7	8	9	10	11	12
R	4.38	4.35	4.33	4.30	4.28	4.25

Smith's career rushing average increased for the first several years, and then began to decrease.

Lesson 12.6 (pp. 816–819)

7. $\dfrac{b}{b-3} + \dfrac{b+1}{b-3} = \dfrac{b+b+1}{b-3} = \dfrac{2b+1}{b-3}$

29. $\dfrac{2j}{j^2 - 1} + \dfrac{j - 1}{j^2 - 7j + 6}$

$= \dfrac{2j}{(j-1)(j+1)} + \dfrac{j-1}{(j-1)(j-6)}$

$= \dfrac{2j(j-6)}{(j-1)(j+1)(j-6)} + \dfrac{(j-1)(j+1)}{(j-1)(j-6)(j+1)}$

$= \dfrac{2j(j-6) + (j-1)(j+1)}{(j-1)(j+1)(j-6)}$

$= \dfrac{2j^2 - 12j + j^2 - 1}{(j-1)(j+1)(j-6)}$

$= \dfrac{3j^2 + 12j - 1}{(j-1)(j+1)(j-6)}$

45. a. For $A \le 50$: $\dfrac{2A^2}{3} + \dfrac{200A}{3} = \dfrac{2A^2 + 200A}{3}$

For $A > 50$, $\dfrac{7A^2}{150} + (125A - 1367)$

$= \dfrac{7A^2}{150} + \dfrac{150(125A - 1367)}{150}$

$= \dfrac{7A^2 + 150(125A - 1367)}{150}$

$= \dfrac{7A^2 + 18{,}750A - 205{,}050}{150}$

b. For $A = 30$ ft^2, use the formula for $A \le 50$:

$W = \dfrac{2(30)^2 + 200(30)}{3} = \dfrac{7800}{3} = 2600$

The minimum weight this elevator must hold is 2600 pounds.

For $A = 60$ ft^2, use the formula for $A > 50$:

$W = \dfrac{7(60)^2 + 18{,}750(60) - 205{,}050}{150}$

$= \dfrac{945{,}150}{150} = 6301$

The minimum weight this elevator must hold is 6301 pounds.

Lesson 12.7 (pp. 823–826)

7.
$$\dfrac{2m}{m+4} = \dfrac{3}{m-1}$$

$$2m^2 - 2m = 3m + 12$$

$$2m^2 - 5m - 12 = 0$$

$$(2m + 3)(m - 4) = 0$$

$$2m + 3 = 0 \quad or \quad m - 4 = 0$$

$$m = -1\tfrac{1}{2} \quad or \quad m = 4$$

15.
$$\dfrac{z}{z+7} - 3 = \dfrac{-1}{z+7}$$

$$\dfrac{z}{z+7} \cdot (z+7) - 3(z+7) = \dfrac{-1}{z+7} \cdot (z+7)$$

$$\dfrac{z(z+7)}{z+7} - 3(z+7) = \dfrac{-1(z+7)}{z+7}$$

$$z - 3z - 21 = -1$$

$$-2z = 20$$

$$z = -10$$

---

33. Let w be the number of cups of water needed.

$$\dfrac{\text{Cups of water in cleaning solution} + \text{Cups of water needed}}{\text{Cups of cleaning solution} + \text{Cups of water needed}} = \text{Desired fraction of water in mixture}$$

$$\dfrac{7 + w}{9 + w} = \dfrac{5}{6}$$

$$(7 + w)6 = (9 + w)5$$

$$42 + 6w = 45 + 5w$$

$$w = 3$$

You need to add 3 cups of water to the cleaning solution.

Chapter 13

Lesson 13.1 (pp. 846–848)

3. Use a tree diagram to find the possible outcomes in the sample space.

The sample space has 12 possible outcomes. The outcomes are: Red 1, Red 2, Red 3, Red 4, White 1, White 2, White 3, White 4, Black 1, Black 2, Black 3, Black 4.

21. Since there are 15 girls and 12 boys, there are a total of 27 students. So there are 27 possible outcomes.

$P(\text{boy}) = \dfrac{\text{Number of boys}}{\text{Total number of students}} = \dfrac{12}{27} = \dfrac{4}{9}$

Odds in favor of choosing a boy

$= \dfrac{\text{Number of boys}}{\text{Number of girls}} = \dfrac{12}{15} = \dfrac{4}{5}$

Sample answer: The probability and odds of choosing a boy are related because they each compare the number of favorable outcomes to another number. The probability of choosing a boy compares the number of boys to the total number of outcomes possible, while the odds of choosing a boy compare the number of boys to the total number of outcomes less the number of boys.

Lesson 13.2 (pp. 853–855)

21. $_7P_3 = \dfrac{7!}{(7-3)!} = \dfrac{7!}{4!} = \dfrac{7 \cdot 5 \cdot \cancel{4!}}{\cancel{4!}} = 210$

35. a. The total number of possible outcomes for the order on the first day is the number of permutations of the 4 student presenters on that day: $_4P_4 = 4!$.

The number of favorable outcomes (being chosen to be the first or second presenter) is the number of permutations of the 3 other presenters, given that you are chosen to be the first or second presenter. This is $_3P_3 = 3!$ if you are the first presenter and also $_3P_3 = 3!$ if you are the second presenter.

P(1st or 2nd presenter)
$= P$(1st presenter) $+ P$(2nd presenter)

$= \dfrac{3!}{4!} + \dfrac{3!}{4!} = \dfrac{1}{4} + \dfrac{1}{4}$, or $\dfrac{1}{2}$

The probability that you are the first or the second presenter is $\dfrac{1}{2}$.

b. The number of possible outcomes is still $4!$. The number of favorable outcomes is again $_3P_3 = 3!$ for you being the second presenter and $_3P_3 = 3!$ for you being the third presenter.

P(2nd or 3rd presenter)
$= P$(2nd presenter) $+ P$(3rd presenter)

$= \dfrac{3!}{4!} + \dfrac{3!}{4!} = \dfrac{1}{4} + \dfrac{1}{4}$, or $\dfrac{1}{2}$

The probability that you are the second or the third presenter is $\dfrac{1}{2}$.

This answer is the same as the answer in part (a).

Lesson 13.3 (pp. 858–859)

7. $_8C_5 = \dfrac{8!}{(8-5)!5!} = \dfrac{8!}{3!5!} = \dfrac{8 \cdot 7 \cdot 6 \cdot \cancel{5!}}{3! \cdot \cancel{5!}} = 56$

25. a. The number of possible outcomes is the number of combinations of the 9 contestants taken 6 at a time, or 9C6, because the order in which the contestants are chosen is not important.

$_9C_6 = \dfrac{9!}{(9-5)!5!} = \dfrac{9!}{3!6!} = \dfrac{9 \cdot 8 \cdot 7 \cdot \cancel{6!}}{3! \cdot \cancel{6!}} = 84$

There are 84 possible combinations of 6 players from the group of eligible contestants.

b. Find the number of favorable outcomes, those where you and your two friends are 3 of the 6 contestants selected to play. The order of the selections is not important. The favorable outcomes are those where only 3 of the other 6 eligible contestants are chosen. So the number of favorable combinations is $_6C_3 = 20$. Therefore, the probability that you and your friends are chosen is $\dfrac{20}{84}$, or $\dfrac{5}{21}$.

Lesson 13.4 (pp. 864–867)

5. Rolling an odd number on a number cube and rolling a number less than 5 are overlapping events as shown in the diagram. There are two numbers less than 5 that are odd, 1 and 3.

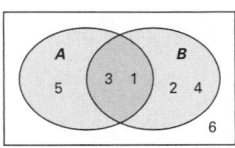

The probability of rolling an odd number is $\dfrac{3}{6} = \dfrac{1}{2}$, the probability of rolling a number less than 5 is $\dfrac{4}{6} = \dfrac{2}{3}$, and the probability of rolling a number that is both odd and less than 5 is $\dfrac{2}{6} = \dfrac{1}{3}$.

Using the formula for finding the probability of overlapping events,

$P(A \text{ or } B) = P(A) + P(B) - P(A \text{ and } B)$

$= \dfrac{3}{6} + \dfrac{4}{6} - \dfrac{2}{6} = \dfrac{5}{6}$

23. Let Event A be using a flipper to forage for food and let Event B be using the right flipper if the flipper wave technique is used. These two events are dependent.

$P(A) = 70\% = 0.7$ and
$P(B \text{ given } A) = 89\% = 0.89$

Using the formula for finding the probability of dependent events,

$P(A \text{ and } B) = P(A) \cdot P(B \text{ given } A)$
$= 0.7 \cdot 0.89 = 0.623$, or 62.3%

The probability that a walrus foraging for food uses a flipper and that it is the right flipper is 62.3%.

Lesson 13.5 (pp. 873–874)

3. The population is all persons who dine at the restaurant. Because the diners ultimately decide whether or not to take part in the survey by mailing their comment cards, this is a self-selected sample.

15. Ballots collected at Wrigley Field are not necessarily representative of the opinions of all Chicago Cubs fans. *Sample answer:* Only some of the Chicago Cubs' fans are able to attend games, and those who attend games may have different player preferences than those who do not attend games.

Lesson 13.6 (pp. 877–878)

7. Mean:

$$x = \frac{5.52 + 5.44 + 3.60 + 5.76 + 3.80 + 7.22}{6}$$

$$= \frac{31.34}{6} = 5.2233...$$

So, the mean of the data is $5.22\overline{3}$.

Median: The ordered list of numbers is: 3.60, 3.80, 5.44, 5.52, 5.76, 7.22. There are two middle values, 5.44 and 5.52. Therefore, the median is $\frac{5.44 + 5.52}{2} = 5.48$.

Each data value appears just once, so there is no mode.

19. a. The range of the pumpkin weights is the difference of the greatest value and the least value; $24 - 5 = 19$ pounds.

b. Mean: $\overline{x} =$

$$\frac{22 + 21 + 24 + 24 + 5 + 24 + 5 + 23 + 24 + 24}{10}$$

$$= \frac{196}{10} = 19.6$$

The mean of the pumpkin weights is 19.6 pounds.

Median: The ordered list of weights is: 5, 5, 21, 22, 23, 24, 24, 24, 24, 24. There are two middle values, 23 and 24. So, the median is 23.5 pounds.

Mode: The weight that occurs most frequently is 24 pounds.

c. The median best represents the data. *Sample answer:* The mode is the greatest data value and the mean is less than 8 of the 10 data values.

Lesson 13.7 (pp. 883–885)

3. First, separate the data into stems and leaves.

Key: 1|7 = 17

Now rewrite the leaves in increasing order.

Key: 1|7 = 17

19. a. Draw the bars of the histogram using the intervals from the frequency table.

b. Use the table to determine the total number of people surveyed: $88 + 85 + 50 + 28 + 14 = 265$.

Determine the number of favorable outcomes. This number is the sum of the number of people in the 11–15 range, the 16–20 range, and the 21–25 range.

$$P(11\text{–}25) = \frac{\text{Number of favorable outcomes}}{\text{Total number of outcomes}}$$

$$= \frac{50 + 28 + 14}{265} = \frac{92}{265}$$

Lesson 13.8 (pp. 889–892)

3. Write the data in order from least to greatest. Find the median and the quartiles.

Plot the median, the quartiles, the maximum value, and the minimum value below a number line. Draw a box from the lower quartile to the upper quartile. Draw a vertical line through the median. Draw a line segment from the side of the box to the maximum value and another from the other side of the box to the minimum value.

17. a. Order the data, and then find the median and the quartiles.

lower quartile: $\dfrac{\$38.4 + \$49.9}{2} = \$44.15$

median: $\$52.4$

upper quartile: $\dfrac{\$107.0 + \$118.2}{2} = \$112.06$

Use the median, the quartiles, the maximum value, and the minimum value to draw the box-and-whisker plot.

b. To check if any of the data are outliers, find the inner quartile range: $112.6 - 44.15 = 68.45$. An outlier would be any value greater than $1.5(68.45) + 112.6 = 215.275$ or less than $44.15 - 1.5(68.45) = -58.525$. Since all the data values are within these two values, there are no outliers. So, none of the states had retail sales that can be considered outliers.

Selected Answers

Chapter 1

1.1 Skill Practice (pp. 5–6) **1.** exponent: 12, base: 6
3. 60 **5.** 12 **7.** 12 **9.** 3 **11.** 10 **13.** $\frac{1}{3}$ **17.** seven to the third power, $7 \cdot 7 \cdot 7$ **19.** three tenths to the fourth power, $0.3 \cdot 0.3 \cdot 0.3 \cdot 0.3$ **21.** n to the seventh power, $n \cdot n \cdot n \cdot n \cdot n \cdot n \cdot n$ **23.** t to the fourth power, $t \cdot t \cdot t \cdot t$ **25.** The base was used as the exponent and the exponent was used as the base; $5^4 = 5 \cdot 5 \cdot 5 \cdot 5 = 625$. **27.** 100 **29.** 1331 **31.** 243 **33.** 1296 **35.** $\frac{27}{125}$
37. $\frac{1}{216}$ **39.** 1.21 **41.** 40.5 **43.** 9.6

1.1 Problem Solving (pp. 6–7) **49.** 162.5 cm **51. a.** 12 in.
b. 144 in.^{2} **53.** New England Patriots

1.2 Skill Practice (pp. 10–11) **1.** Square 4. **3.** 8 **5.** 14
7. $3\frac{3}{5}$ **9.** $63\frac{3}{4}$ **11.** 21 **13.** 73.5 **15.** $12\frac{1}{2}$ **17.** 48 **21.** $\frac{1}{2}$ was multiplied by 6 before squaring 6; $20 - \frac{1}{2} \cdot 6^2 =$
$20 - \frac{1}{2} \cdot 36 = 20 - 18 = 2$. **23.** 29 **25.** 126 **27.** 0.75
29. 3 **33.** $(2 \times 2 + 3)^2 - (4 + 3) \times 5$

1.2 Problem Solving (pp. 11–12) **35. a.** $22.87 **b.** $2.13
37. *Sample answer:* $(3 \times 4) + 5$ **39. a.** $380, $237.99;
$142.01 **b.** *Sample answer:* You could write an expression showing the difference of your income and expenses as $P = 10s - (4.50m + 12.99)$.

1.2 Graphing Calculator Activity (p. 13) **1.** 5 **3.** 0.429
5. 0.188 **7.** 40.9 BMI units

1.3 Skill Practice (pp. 18–19) **1.** rate **3.** $x + 8$ **5.** $\frac{1}{2}m$
7. $7 - n$ **9.** $\frac{2t}{12}$ **11.** $2k - 7$ **15.** $4v$ **17.** $\frac{16}{p}$ **19.** $7 - d$
21. $12y$ **23.** 1.5 pints per serving **25.** $6.80 per share
27. Feet should cancel out; $54. **29.** $19.50 for 1 h

1.3 Problem Solving (pp. 19–20) **31.** $19.95t + 3$; $102.75
33. a. $.055, $.06 **b.** 48 oz container **c.** $.96 **35.** $500
37. a. $12g + h + \frac{1}{4}c$ **b.** 247; 376.75; 242

1.4 Skill Practice (pp. 24–25) **1.** *Sample answer:*
$3x + 5 = 20$ **3.** $42 + n = 51$ **5.** $9 - \frac{t}{6} = 5$ **7.** $9(t + 5) < 6$
9. $8 < b + 3 < 12$ **11.** $10 < t - 7 < 20$ **13.** $p \geq 12.99
15. The wrong inequality symbol is used; $\frac{t}{4.2} \leq 15$.

17. solution **19.** not a solution **21.** not a solution
23. solution **25.** solution **27.** not a solution **29.** 5
31. 12 **33.** 9 **35.** $3x - 2 = x + 5$; solution

1.4 Problem Solving (pp. 25–26) **39.** 7.5 mi **41.** 167 h
43. $100 **45. a.** $6r + 5(10 - r) \geq 55$ **b.** Yes; you will earn $30 running errands and $25 walking dogs;
$30 + 25 = 55$. **c.** Yes; if you work 10 hours running errands, you will earn $60. You will not meet your goal if you work all 10 hours walking dogs.

1.5 Skill Practice (p. 31) **1.** *Sample answer:* $d = rt$
3. You know how many collars you've made, how much you have spent to make them, and how much money you want to make. You need to find what to charge for each collar so you make $90. **5.** You know the temperature in Rome and the temperature in Dallas. You know the formula to convert Fahrenheit temperatures to Celsius temperatures. You need to find the higher temperature. **7.** The formula for perimeter should be used, not area; $P = 2\ell + 2w$;
$P = 2(200) + 2(150) = 700$; $10(700) = 7000.
9. $P = I - E$

1.5 Problem Solving (pp. 32–33) **15.** 110.25 in.^{2}
17. 2 water bottles **19. a.** 960 ft **b.** 480 ft

21. a.

Room size (feet)	1 by 1	2 by 2	3 by 3	4 by 4	5 by 5
Remaining area (square feet)	431	428	423	416	407

b. $1 \leq s \leq 5$; 5 ft

1.5 Problem Solving Workshop (p. 34)

1. 9 pieces of cake; Draw a diagram of a 9 inch by 11 inch pan and divide it into 3 inch by 3 inch pieces. From the diagram you see that the cake can be divided into 9 pieces of cake.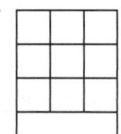
3. The equation should be $3x + 6 = 12$ because there are only 3 spaces between the 4 floats; $3(2) + 6 = 12$.

1.6 Skill Practice (pp. 38–39) **1.** input; output
3. domain: 0, 1, 2, and 3, range: 5, 7, 15, and 44
5. domain: 6, 12, 21, and 42, range: 5, 7, 10, and 17
7. not a function **9.** The pairing is a function. Each input is paired with only one output.

11. *Sample:*

Input	Output
0	5
1	6
2	7
3	7
4	9
5	10

15.

Input	4	5	7	8	12
Output	7.5	8.5	10.5	11.5	15.5

range: 7.5, 8.5, 10.5, 11.5, and 15.5

17.

Input	4	6	9	11
Output	5	6	7.5	8.5

range: 5, 6, 7.5, and 8.5

19.

Input	0	2	4	6
Output	$\frac{1}{2}$	1	$1\frac{1}{2}$	2

range: $\frac{1}{2}$, 1, $1\frac{1}{2}$, and 2

21. $y = x - 8$

1.6 Problem Solving (pp. 39–40) **23. a.** the number of quarters left; the number of quarters used **b.** $y = 10 - x$; domain: 0, 1, 2, 3, 4, 5, 6, 7, 8, 9, and 10
c.

Input	0	1	2	3	4	5	6	7	8	9	10
Output	10	9	8	7	6	5	4	3	2	1	0

range: 0, 1, 2, 3, 4, 5, 6, 7, 8, 9, and 10
25. $y = 100 + 20m$; independent variable: m, the number of months; dependent variable: y, the amount of money saved; domain: $m > 0$, range: $y \geq 100$; $340
27. a.

2	3	4	5
A, B, C	D, E, F	G, H, I	J, K, L

6	7	8	9
M, N, O	P, Q, R, S	T, U, V	W, X, Y, Z

No; because there is more than one output for each input.

b.

A	B	C	D	E	F	G	H	I	J	K	L
2	2	2	3	3	3	4	4	4	5	5	5

M	N	O	P	Q	R	S	T	U	V	W	X	Y	Z
6	6	6	7	7	7	7	8	8	8	9	9	9	9

Yes; because there is only one output for each input.

1.6 Graphing Calculator Activity (p. 41) **1.** 50°F; scroll down until you see the output 10, look to see that the input is 50.

3.

Input	0	1	2	3
Output	5	5.75	6.5	7.25

5.

Input	1	2	3	4
Output	7	14.5	22	29.5

1.7 Skill Practice (pp. 46–47) **1.** domain; range

3. **5.** **7.**

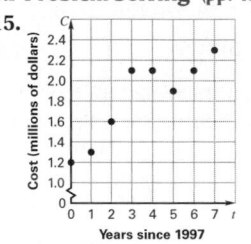

9. The domain and range are graphed backwards.

11. $y = 2x - 2$; domain: 1, 2, 3, and 4, range: 0, 2, 4, and 6

1.7 Problem Solving (pp. 47–48)

15.

17.

Years since 1984	Voters	Voters (millions)
0	92,652,680	93
4	91,594,693	92
8	104,405,155	104
12	96,456,345	96
16	105,586,274	106

19. a. increases **b.** Yes; 27.5 grams is between the mass of an egg that is just under 38 millimeters long and an egg that is just over 38 millimeters long.

Extension (p. 50) **1.** function **3.** not a function
5. function **7.** Not a function. *Sample answer:* There
could be many students whose first names have
4 letters, for instance, but their last names could all
have a different number of letters. **9.** Function; for
each of your birthdays, you have only one height.

Chapter Review (pp. 53–56) **1.** 7, 12 **3.** algebraic
expression **5.** 16 **7.** 10 **9.** 400 **11.** 25 in.^{2} **13.** 9 **15.** 8
17. $\frac{1}{3}$ **19.** 52 **21.** 18 **23.** $z - 5$ **25.** $3x^2$ **27.** $2.95n + 2.19$
29. $13 + t \geq 24$ **31.** solution **33.** 240 ft^2
35.

Input	10	12	15	20	21
Output	5	7	10	15	16

   range: 5, 7, 10, 15, and 16
37. $y = x + 4$ **39.**

Chapter 2

2.1 Skill Practice (pp. 67–68) **1.** rational number
3. Zero is in the set of whole numbers, but not in
the set of positive integers. **5–13.** Check students'
graphs. **5.** 7 **7.** -5 **9.** 5 **11.** -1 **13.** -2 **15.** 1.6:
rational number, 1: whole number, integer, rational
number, -4: integer, rational number, 0: whole
number, integer, rational number; $-4, 0, 1, 1.6$
17. $-\frac{2}{3}$: rational number, -0.6: rational number, -1:
integer, rational number, $\frac{1}{3}$: rational number; -1,
$-\frac{2}{3}, -0.6, \frac{1}{3}$ **19.** 16: whole number, integer, rational
number, -1.66: rational number, $\frac{5}{3}$: rational number,
-1.6: rational number; $-1.66, -1.6, \frac{5}{3}, 16$ **21.** -4.99:
rational number, 5: whole number, integer, rational
number, $\frac{16}{3}$: rational number, -5.1: rational number;
$-5.1, -4.99, 5, \frac{16}{3}$ **23.** $-6, 6$ **25.** 18, 18 **27.** $-13.4, 13.4$
29. 6.1, 6.1 **31.** $1\frac{1}{9}, 1\frac{1}{9}$ **33.** $-\frac{3}{4}, \frac{3}{4}$ **35.** Hypothesis: a
number is a positive integer, conclusion: the number
is a whole number; true. **37.** Hypothesis: a number
is positive, conclusion: its opposite is positive; false.
Sample answer: The opposite of 2 is -2, a negative
number. **41.** $-|-0.2|$ is a negative number. *Sample
answer:* In the number $-|-0.2|$, remove both
negative signs. **43.** 1 **45.** 1.75 **47.** 2.25 **49.** 1.5

2.1 Problem Solving (pp. 69–70) **53.** Fondo, Frink,
Alamorio, Calexico, Date City **55.** -3.4; the absolute
value of -3.4 is less than the absolute value of -3.8,
so it is closer to 0, the exact pitch. **57. a.** 500 Hz
b. The intensity decreases until 1000 Hz and then
increases. **59. a.** Sun, Sirius, Canopus, Arcturus,
Capella, Achernar; Canopus, Achernar, Arcturus,
Capella, Sirius, Sun **b.** Rigel's apparent magnitude
is greater than the Sun's apparent magnitude, so it
is dimmer than the Sun; Rigel's absolute magnitude
is less than the Sun's absolute magnitude, so it is
brighter than the Sun. **c.** No. *Sample answer:* The
apparent magnitude of Arcturus is less than the
apparent magnitude of Achernar, but the absolute
magnitude of Arcturus is greater than the absolute
magnitude of Achernar.

Extension (p. 72) **1.** $\{1, 3, 5, 6, 7, 9\}, \{3, 9\}$ **3.** $\{0, 1, 2, 3,$
$4, 5, 6, 7, 8, 9, 10\}, \varnothing$ **5.** $R = \{2, 4, 6, 8, 10\}, f = \{(1, 2),$
$(2, 4), (3, 6), (4, 8), (5, 10)\}$ **7.** $R = \{4, 8, 12, 16, 20\},$
$f = \{(1, 4), (5, 8), (9, 12), (13, 16), (17, 20)\}$ **9.** the set
of integers, $\varnothing$

2.2 Skill Practice (pp. 77–78) **1.** 0 **3.** -8 **5.** 6 **7.** -13
9. -6 **11.** -20 **13.** -4.5 **15.** 6.6 **17.** -15.2 **19.** $7\frac{1}{15}$
21. $1\frac{16}{45}$ **23.** $-20\frac{23}{24}$ **25.** The numbers have different
signs, so their absolute values should have been
subtracted, $17 + (-31) = -14$. **27.** Associate
property of addition **29.** Identity property of
addition **31.** Commutative property of addition
33. -49 **35.** 1.6 **37.** $5\frac{19}{60}$ **39.** -3 **41.** -9.5 **43.** $7\frac{23}{60}$
45. 0 **47.** 7.4 **49.** $-(-18) + (-18); 0$

2.2 Problem Solving (pp. 78–79) **53.** 7°F
55. a. 1.5 diopters **b.** -3.75 diopters **c.** part (b)
57. a. your friend **b.** No, if you score 2 double eagles,
you will have the same score.

2.3 Skill Practice (pp. 82–83) **1.** $-3 + (-6)$ **3.** 18 **5.** -8
7. 14.1 **9.** -25.8 **11.** $-\frac{1}{3}$ **13.** $\frac{3}{4}$ **15.** 8 was substituted
for y instead of -8; $3 - (-8) + 2 = 3 + 8 + 2 = 13$.
17. 4.6 **19.** 10.6 **21.** 7.7 **23.** 7.6 **25.** 1.8 **27.** 107°F
29. -1280 m **31.** 127.1 mi **33.** 8 **35.** -4.2 **37.** 16.4
39. *Sample answer:* You are overdrawn on your
checking account by \$23. You write two more checks
for \$14 and \$8. What is your balance?; $-\$45$

2.3 Problem Solving (pp. 83–84)
43. 14.6°C **45. a.** $d = t - 342$

b.

t	d
341.7	−0.3
343.8	1.8
340.9	−1.1
342.7	0.7

341.7 and 340.9; you can tell if $t - 342$ is negative.
47. a. 6°; 19° **b.** −4°

2.3 Spreadsheet Activity (p. 85) **1.** 6 hand grips
3. 4.902; the difference in the lengths has the smallest absolute value.

2.4 Skill Practice (pp. 91–92) **1.** 1 **3.** −28 **5.** 90
7. −36 **9.** 7 **11.** −43.89 **13.** −40 **15.** −80 **17.** $2\frac{2}{5}$
19. Multiplicative property of zero **21.** Identity property of multiplication **23.** Associative property of multiplication **25.** Identity property of multiplication **27.** Multiplicative property of −1
29. 18x; 18x, same signs, product is positive.
31. −84z; 12(−7z), product of −2 and −6 is 12; [12 • (−7)]z, associative property of multiplication; −84(z), product of 12 and −7 is −84; −84z, multiply.
33. −40c; 2(4)(−5c), product of $-\frac{1}{5}$ and −10 is 2;
8(−5c), product of 2 and 4 is 8; [8 • (−5)]c, associative property of multiplication; −40(c), product of 8 and −5 is −40; −40c, multiply.
35. 16.8r^2; [−6r • (−2.8)]r, associative property of multiplication; [−6 • (−2.8) • r]r, commutative property of multiplication; (16.8r)r, product of −6 and −2.8 is 16.8; 16.8(r • r), associative property of multiplication; 16.8r^2, multiply **37.** −0.4 **39.** −12.6
41. −6.6 **43.** −1(7) = −7, not 7; −1(7)(−3)(−2x) = −7(−3)(−2x) = 21(−2x) = −42x **45.** true **47.** true

2.4 Problem Solving (pp. 92–93) **51.** $162.50
55. a. $f = 11{,}250 + (−30t)$, $f = 135{,}000 + (−240t)$
b. 11,160 gal, 134,280 gal **c.** Rhododendron; 45,000 gal; the Rhododendron takes 375 hours to burn all of its fuel; the Spokane takes 562.5 hours to burn all of its fuel; to find the number of hours the Rhododendron will take to burn all its fuel, use the equations in part (a) and find the additive inverse of 11,250, then divide it by −30; to find the number of hours the Spokane will take to burn all its fuel, use the equations in part (a) and find the additive inverse of 135,000, then divide it by −240.

Extension (p. 95) **1.** $\begin{bmatrix} 16 & 4 \\ 8 & 12 \end{bmatrix}$ **3.** $\begin{bmatrix} -15 & -4 & -9 \\ -2 & 2 & -5 \end{bmatrix}$

5. Cannot be performed. **7.** $\begin{bmatrix} -28 & -49 \\ 3\frac{1}{2} & 3\frac{1}{9} \end{bmatrix}$ **9.** $\begin{bmatrix} -72 \\ 20.4 \\ 4.2 \end{bmatrix}$

11.

Calcium (mg)	Potassium (mg)
263.52	290.36
270.84	341.6
246.44	324.52

13. $\begin{bmatrix} -41 & -99 \\ 78 & 91 \end{bmatrix}$

2.5 Skill Practice (pp. 99–100) **1.** 4, −9 **3.** The negative was not distributed to the −8; $5y - (2y - 8) = 5y - 2y + 8 = 3y + 8$. **5.** $4x + 12$ **7.** $5m + 25$ **9.** $-8p + 24$
11. $4r - 6$ **13.** $6v^2 + 6v$ **15.** $2x^2 - 6x$ **17.** $\frac{1}{4}m - 2$
19. $4n - 6$ **21.** terms: −7, 13x, 2x, 8; like terms: −7 and 8, 13x and 2x; coefficients: 13, 2; constant terms: −7, 8 **23.** terms: $7x^2$, −10, $-2x^2$, 5; like terms: $7x^2$ and $-2x^2$, −10 and 5; coefficients: 7, −2; constant terms: −10, 5 **25.** terms: 2, 3xy, −4xy, 6; like terms: 2 and 6, 3xy and −4xy; coefficients: 3, −4; constant terms: 2, 6 **29.** 5y **31.** $9a - 2$ **33.** $8r + 8$ **35.** $3m + 5$
37. $10w - 35$ **39.** $15s + 6$ **41.** $34 - 24w$; $72 - 108w$
43. $38.97 **45.** $11.88 **47.** $2(6 + x) + (x - 5)$; $3x + 7$

2.5 Problem Solving (pp. 100–101)
51. $C = 3r - 6$; $5.97 **53.** $s = d(x + y + z)$

2.5 Problem Solving Workshop (p. 102)
1. $330 **3.** $287.50

2.6 Skill Practice (pp. 106–107) **1.** multiplicative inverse **3.** $-\frac{1}{18}$ **5.** −1 **7.** $-1\frac{1}{3}$ **9.** $-\frac{3}{13}$ **11.** −7 **13.** $\frac{2}{7}$
15. −3 **17.** $-2\frac{1}{2}$ **19.** $\frac{2}{7}$ **21.** −22 **25.** $-1\frac{2}{3}$ **27.** $2\frac{1}{4}$
29. $-2\frac{1}{5}$ **31.** 0.1 **33.** $3x - 7$ **35.** $-3z + 2$ **37.** $\frac{1}{2} - 2\frac{1}{2}q$
39. $3a + 1\frac{1}{4}$ **41.** $4 - 3c$ **43.** −2 was added instead of subtracted; $\frac{-15x - 10}{-5} = (-15x - 10) \cdot \left(-\frac{1}{5}\right) = -15x\left(-\frac{1}{5}\right) - 10\left(-\frac{1}{5}\right) = 3x + 2$ **45.** $-1\frac{1}{3}$ **47.** $\frac{1}{3}$

2.6 Problem Solving (pp. 107–108) **53.** −14.75°C
57. a. −0.034 **b.** Yes; it will improve to −0.012.
c. If the player had the same number of aces as service errors, then $a = e$, so $f = \frac{a - a}{s} = 0$; if all the serves were aces, a would be equal to s and e would be 0, so $f = \frac{s - 0}{s} = \frac{s}{s} = 1$; if all the serves were errors, then $e = s$ and $a = 0$, so $f = \frac{0 - s}{s} = \frac{-s}{s} = -1$.

2.7 Skill Practice (pp. 113–114) **1.** real numbers **3.** 2
5. −3 **7.** 14 **9.** ±50 **11.** −15 **13.** ±13 **15.** 3 **17.** −2
19. −9 **21.** 14 **25.** $-\sqrt{12}$: real number, irrational number, −3.7: real number, rational number, $\sqrt{9}$: real number, rational number, integer, whole number, 2.9: real number, rational number; −3.7, $-\sqrt{12}$, 2.9, $\sqrt{9}$

27. $\sqrt{8}$: real number, irrational number, $-\frac{2}{5}$: real number, rational number, -1: real number, rational number, integer, 0.6: real number, rational number, $\sqrt{6}$: real number, irrational number; -1, $-\frac{2}{5}$, 0.6, $\sqrt{6}$, $\sqrt{8}$ **29.** -8.3: real number, rational number, $-\sqrt{80}$: real number, irrational number, $-\frac{17}{2}$: real number, rational number, -8.25: real number, rational number, $-\sqrt{100}$: real number, rational number, integer; $-\sqrt{100}$, $-\sqrt{80}$, $-\frac{17}{2}$, -8.3, -8.25

31. If a number is a real number, then it is an irrational number; false. *Sample answer:* 3 is a real number and a rational number. **33.** If a number is an irrational number, then it is not a whole number; true. **35.** 2 **37.** -42 **39.** 63 **41.** -16

2.7 Problem Solving (pp. 115–116) **47.** 60 in. **49.** 35 ft; 24 ft; 48 ft; 30 ft; they are all rational numbers. **51.** 3; square each fraction, $\left(\frac{265}{153}\right)^2 < 3$, $\left(\frac{1351}{780}\right)^2 > 3$ so the value of x is 3. **53. a.** 144 tiles **b.** 16 ft. *Sample answer:* If the homeowner can buy 144 tiles that are each 256 square inches, then the total area is (144 tiles)(256 square inches per tile) = 36,864 square inches. Divide 36,864 square inches by 144 square inches to find the number of square feet, 256 square feet. If the area of the square is 256 square feet, take the square root of 256 to find the side length, 16 feet.

Extension (p. 118) **1.** *Sample answer:* $3 - 5 = -2$, $-2(6) = -12$, $-12 \div 3 = -4$, $-4 + 10 = 6$; $-2 - 5 = -7$, $-7(6) = -42$, $-42 \div 3 = -14$, $-14 + 10 = -4$; $10 - 5 = 5$, $5(6) = 30$, $30 \div 3 = 10$, $10 + 10 = 20$; double the number; $\frac{(x-5)6}{3} + 10 = (x-5)2 + 10 = 2x - 10 + 10 = 2x$ **3.** Distributive property; Subtraction rule; Associative property of addition; Inverse property of addition; Identity property of addition; Divide

Chapter Review (pp. 121–124) **1.** terms: $-3x$, -5, $-7x$, -9; coefficients: -3, -7; constant terms: -5, -9; like terms: $-3x$ and $-7x$, -5 and -9 **3.** real number, rational number **5.** real number, rational number, integer **7.** -6, -5.2, $-\frac{3}{8}$, $-\frac{1}{4}$, 0.3 **9.** 0.2, 0.2 **11.** $-\frac{7}{8}$, $\frac{7}{8}$ **13.** 3 **15.** -3.5 **17.** $-1\frac{3}{14}$ **19.** $-\$.23$ million **21.** -10 **23.** -6.1 **25.** $-\frac{31}{36}$ **27.** $2\frac{1}{2}$ **29.** -60 **31.** -18 **33.** $6x$; $x \cdot (-18) = -\frac{1}{3}(-18)(x)$, commutative property of multiplication; $6(x)$, product of $-\frac{1}{3}$ and -18; $6x$, multiply **35.** 2.74 ft **37.** $-3y - 27$ **39.** $3x + 8$

41. $9n - 3\frac{1}{2}$ **43.** -14 **45.** $\frac{2}{3}$ **47.** $3x - 5$ **49.** $2n + 1$ **51.** -6 **53.** ± 15 **55.** -7 **57.** 17 **59.** $-\sqrt{4}$, -0.3, 0, 1.25, $\sqrt{11}$

Chapter 3

3.1 Skill Practice (pp. 137–138) **1.** inverse operations **3.** 3 **5.** 5 **7.** -3 **9.** 7 **11.** 17 **13.** 4 **17.** 4 **19.** 6 **21.** -15 **23.** 15 **25.** 48 **27.** 22 **29.** 3.8 should have been subtracted from *both* sides; $x + 3.8 - 3.8 = 2.3 - 3.8$, $x = -1.5$. **31.** 3.5 **33.** -1.1 **35.** -2.05 **37.** $\frac{5}{8}$ **39.** 0.06 **41.** 96 **43.** 12 **45.** -56 **47.** $\frac{3}{5}$ **49.** $54 = 12x$; 4.5 in.

3.1 Problem Solving (pp. 139–140) **53.** 1046.6 ft **55.** 11 ft **57. a.** $\frac{4}{7}x = 200$ **b.** Plants; if you solve the equation in part (a) you find that there are 350 species of birds.

59. a.

t	d
1	6.5
2	13
3	19.5
4	26
5	32.5

b.   4 sec

c. $26 = 6.5t$; 4 sec **61. a.** 171 hits **b.** 215 hits **c.** No; if Mueller had less hits than Wells but had a higher batting average, he must have had less at bats than Wells.

3.2 Skill Practice (pp. 144–145) **1.** like terms **3.** 4 **5.** 2 **7.** -3 **9.** 6 **11.** 40 **13.** 18 **15.** 4 **17.** 9 **19.** -4 **23.** The division of $-2x + x$ by -2 is done incorrectly. *Sample answer:* If like terms are combined as the first step, the second line would be $-x = 10$ and the final result would be $x = -10$. **25.** $y = 2x + 4$; -7 **27.** 4 **29.** 5 **31.** 0.5 **33.** 15.9 **35.** 6.9

3.2 Problem Solving (pp. 145–146) **37.** 28 classes **39.** 5 half-side advertisements **41.** Yes; the equation $\$542 = \$50 + 6x$ gives the monthly cost of a guitar that costs $\$542$. Solving the equation gives $x = \$82$ per month, so you can afford the guitar. **43. a.** $y = 12x$

b.

x (hours)	Marissa	Ryan	Total
1	5	7	12
2	10	14	24
3	15	21	36
4	20	28	48
5	25	35	60

c.

about 4.5 h

3.2 Problem Solving Workshop (p. 147)
1. 7 players **3.** 4 chairs

3.3 Skill Practice (pp. 150–151) **1.** $\frac{5}{3}$ **3.** 3 **5.** 6 **7.** −2
9. −8 **11.** −8 **13.** 4 **15.** −9 **17.** −19 **19.** 12 **21.** −2
23. −9 **25.** −3 times −6 is 18, not −18; $5x − 3x + 18 = 2$, $2x + 18 = 2$, $2x = −16$, $x = −8$. **27.** 2 **29.** 3 **31.** −5
33. 2 **35.** 9.5 in., 6 in.; if you use the perimeter formula $P = 2\ell + 2w$ and substitute $3.5 + w$ for ℓ, the solution is $w − 6$.

3.3 Problem Solving (pp. 152–153) **39.** 0.75 ft
41. a. 34 mo **b.** 307 ft per mo **c.** After the work crews merged; before the work crews merged they were working at a rate of $117 + 137 = 254$ feet per month, and after merging at a rate of 307 feet per month.

3.4 Skill Practice (pp. 157–158) **1.** identity **3.** −2
5. −4 **7.** −7 **9.** 8 **11.** −4 **13.** −3 **17.** *Sample answer:*
Distribute the 3 to get $6z − 15 = 2z + 13$, then subtract $2z$ from each side to get $4z − 15 = 13$, next add 15 to each side to get $4z = 28$, finally divide each side by 4 to get $z = 7$. **19.** 2 **21.** −7 **23.** no solution **25.** no solution **27.** The 3 was not distributed to both terms; $3x + 15 = 3x + 15$, $15 = 15$, so the equation is an identity. **29.** *Sample answer:* $5x + 4 = 5x$; the number $5x$ cannot be equal to 4 more than itself.
31. 2 **33.** −4 **35.** 6 **37.** identity **39.** 2 **41.** 10
43. identity **45.** $16x + 12$

3.4 Problem Solving (pp. 158–159) **49.** 9 nights
51. about 4 yr **53. a.** $23.4t = 24(t − 0.3)$; 12 sec
b. about 4.4 sec **c.** No; it would take 12 seconds for the sheepdog to catch up to the collie and it only takes 4.4 seconds for the collie to complete the last leg.

3.4 Spreadsheet Activity (p. 160) **1.** 2 **3.** 4

3.5 Skill Practice (pp. 165–166) **1.** ratios **3.** no; 7 to 9
5. yes **7.** $\frac{6}{5}$ **9.** 22 **11.** 48 **13.** 15 **15.** 40 **17.** 12
21. Multiply each side by 6, not $\frac{1}{6}$; $6 \cdot \frac{3}{4} = 6 \cdot \frac{x}{6}$, $4\frac{1}{2} = x$. **23.** $\frac{3}{8} = \frac{x}{32}$; 12 **25.** $\frac{x}{4} = \frac{8}{16}$; 2 **27.** $\frac{b}{10} = \frac{7}{2}$; 35
29. $\frac{12}{18} = \frac{d}{27}$; 18 **31.** 1.8 **33.** 2.4 **35.** 4 **37.** 4 **39.** 2
41. 3.5 **43.** Yes. *Sample answer:* $\frac{3}{6} = \frac{4}{8}$

3.5 Problem Solving (pp. 166–167) **45.** $\frac{2}{145}$ **47.** $\frac{2}{5}$
49. $\frac{1}{2}$ **51.** 45 goals **53. a.** $\frac{10}{23}$ **b.** 110 lift tickets
c. 40 snowboarders

3.6 Skill Practice (pp. 171–172) **1.** cross product **3.** 6
5. 24 **7.** 1 **9.** −49 **11.** 2 **13.** 12 **17.** Use the cross products property to multiply 4 by x and 16 by 3; $4 \cdot x = 3 \cdot 16$, $4x = 48$, $x = 12$. **19.** 15 **21.** 10 **23.** 5.5
25. −3.4 **27.** 4.2 **29.** −5.9 **31. a.** Multiplication property of equality **b.** Multiply **c.** Simplify

3.6 Problem Solving (pp. 172–173) **33.** 5 c **35.** 90 km
37. 7.5 km **39.** 17.728 m **41.** 80 yd; find the actual length of the field by using the ratio 1 in. : 20 yd, then use that number to find the width of the soccer field by using the ratio 3 : 2.

Extension (p. 175) **1.** 24 in. **3.** 16 m **5.** 37.5 ft

3.7 Skill Practice (pp. 179–180) **1.** percent: 15, base: 360, part: 54 **3.** 36% **5.** 28 **7.** 150 **9.** 70% **11.** 6% **13.** 69
15. 25 **17.** 95 **21.** 76.5% needs to be changed to 0.765; $153 = 0.765 \cdot b$, $b = 200$. **23.** 96% **25.** 150 **27.** 6%
29. 30% **31.** No. *Sample answer:* The area of the smaller square would be 16% of the area of the larger square because the percent needs to be squared.

3.7 Problem Solving (pp. 180–181) **33.** 8%
35. a. 90 listeners **b.** 35 listeners **37.** 59.3%; 16.5%; 13.2%; 11% **39. a.** $48 **b.** $66.25 **c.** The bicycle in part (a); it will cost $192, the bicycle in part (b) will cost $198.75.

Extension (p. 183) **1.** increase; 25% **3.** decrease; 45%
5. decrease; 33% **7.** 20.3 **9.** 35.2 **11.** 20% increase
13. 48.0 people per square mile

3.8 Skill Practice (pp. 187–188) **1.** literal equation
3. $x = \frac{c}{b − a}$; −2 **5.** $x = bc − a$; 9 **7.** $x = a(c − b)$; 28
9. b should have been subtracted from both sides, not added; $ax = −b$, $x = −\frac{b}{a}$. **11.** $y = 7 − 2x$ **13.** $4 − 3x = y$
15. $2 + \frac{6}{7}x = y$ **17.** $\frac{9}{5}x − 6 = y$ **19.** $y = \frac{1}{2}x + \frac{1}{3}$
21. $h = \frac{S − 2B}{P}$ **25.** $y = 18 − 5x$
27. $\ell = \frac{S}{\pi r} − r$; 13.03 cm **29.** *Sample answer:* You want to find how long it will take to drive 150 miles if you drive at an average rate of 55 miles per hour.

3.8 Problem Solving (pp. 188–189) **33. a.** $x = \frac{C − 25}{12}$
b. 10 nights; 13 nights; 15 nights **35.** Divide each side by the total bill, b, to get $\frac{a}{b} = p\%$.

Chapter Review (pp. 192–196) **1.** scale drawing
3. If you collect like terms you get $10x = 10x$, so any value of x will make it true. **5.** Subtract $6x$ from each side, then divide each side by -2. **7.** 13 **9.** -15
11. -36 **13.** 2 **15.** 18 **17.** 5 **19.** 2 **21.** -6 **23.** 14
25. 1 **27.** -4 **29.** no solution **31.** 7 **33.** identity
35. 3 **37. a.** 4 **b.** 116 **39.** 15 **41.** 10.5 **43.** 70 **45.** 28
47. 1 **49.** 10 **51.** 650 words **53.** 16.5 **55.** 37.5%

57. 1500 general admission tickets **59.** $y = \frac{3}{2}x + 9$

61. a. $h = \dfrac{V}{\ell w}$ **b.** 15 in.

Cumulative Review (pp. 202–203) **1.** 27 **3.** 11 **5.** 42
7. solution **9.** not a solution **11.** not a solution

13. $-6\frac{5}{6}$ **15.** -19.1 **17.** -21 **19.** 6 **21.** 3 **23.** 13.9

25. 58.8 **27.** -11 **29.** 6 **31.** $4\frac{2}{3}$ **33.** 3 **35.** 8.5 **37.** 15

39. 23 **41.** 1.2 **43.** 18 pieces **45.** $-\$.34$; $-\$.45$;
$-\$.25$; $\$1.02$; $\$.08$ **47.** 140 people **49. a.** 2 players
b. 7 players **c.** 11 players

Chapter 4

4.1 Skill Practice (pp. 209–210) **1.** 5; -3 **3.** $(3, -2)$
5. $(4, 4)$ **7.** $(4, -1)$ **9.** $(-5, 4)$ **11.** $(-4, -1)$

15–21.

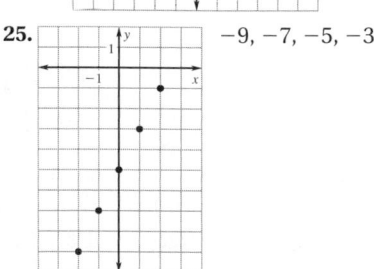

15. Quadrant II
17. origin
19. y-axis
21. Quadrant IV

25.

$-9, -7, -5, -3, -1$

27.

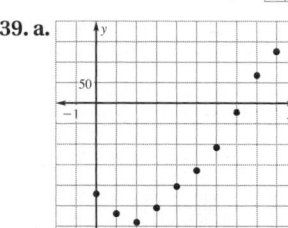

$-2, -1, 0, 1, 2$

29. Quadrant IV; the x-coordinate is positive and the y-coordinate is negative so the point is in Quadrant IV.

31. Quadrant II; the x-coordinate is negative and the y-coordinate is positive so the point is in Quadrant II.
33. If the x-coordinate is 0, then the point is on the y-axis. If the y-coordinate is 0, then the point is on the x-axis.

4.1 Problem Solving (pp. 210–212)
37. There is exactly one low temperature for each day in February.

39. a.

b. *Sample answer:* From 1992 to 1999 the federal deficit was decreasing.

41. a.

Height (in.)		
Reported	**Measured**	**Difference**
70	68	2
70	67.5	2.5
78.5	77.5	1
68	69	-1
71	72	-1
70	70	0

Weight (lb)		
Reported	**Measured**	**Difference**
154	146	8
141	143	-2
165	168	-3
146	143	3
220	223	-3
176	176	0

b. $(2, 8)$, $(2.5, -2)$, $(1, -3)$, $(-1, 3)$, $(-1, -3)$, $(0, 0)$

Extension (p. 214) **1.** Translation; a translation moves every point the same distance in the same direction so it will have the same shape and size as the original figure. **3.** Subtract 4 from each y-coordinate. **5.** Add 2 to each y-coordinate. **7.** $(0, 1), (0, 3), (2, 3), (2, 1)$ **9.** $(0, 0), (0, -2), (2, -2), (2, 0)$ **11.** $(0, 0), (0, -1), (2, -1), (2, 0)$ **13.** $(-1, 4), (-1, 6), (1, 6), (1, 4)$ **15.** Use the transformation $(x, y) \rightarrow (x, -y)$.

4.2 Skill Practice (pp. 219–220) **1.** linear function **3.** solution **5.** solution **7.** not a solution **9.** The 8 should be substituted for x and 11 for y, $11 - 8 \neq -3$, so $(8, 11)$ is not a solution.

11.

13.

15.

17.

19.

21.

23. C **25.** B

27.

$y \geq 3$

29.

$y = -6$

31.
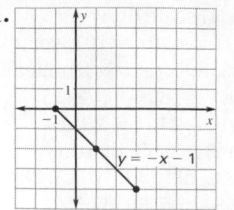
$-4 \leq y \leq 0$

4.2 Problem Solving (pp. 220–221)

35.

domain: $0 \leq f \leq 4$, range: $0 \leq w \leq 2$; 2 lb

37. a.

domain: $0 \leq d \leq 4$, range: $20 \leq T \leq 120$; $120°C$

b.
domain: $0 \leq d \leq 3$, range: $20 \leq T \leq 95$; 3 km

39. a.
domain: $t \geq 0$, range: $r \geq 0$

b. Domain: $0 \leq t \leq 4$, range: $0 \leq r \leq 480$; the graph was a ray, but is now a segment.

41. a.

4.2 Graphing Calculator Activity (p. 222) **1.** 5.6 **3.** −5.3

Extension (p. 224)

1.
discrete

3. discrete

5. continuous
7. Discrete; you can only rent a whole number of DVDs.

9. Continuous; it makes sense to talk about the weight of water for any volume of water. 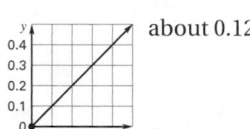 about 0.12

4.3 Skill Practice (pp. 229–230) **1.** x-intercept **3.** The intercepts are switched around; the x-intercept is -2, and the y-intercept is 1. **5.** 3, -3 **7.** 1, 4 **9.** 12, -3 **11.** 64, 4 **13.** $\frac{1}{2}$, 7 **15.** 20, -12

17. **19.**

21. **23.**

25. **27.**

29. 3, -2

31. **33.**

35. **39.** B **41.** Yes; yes; a horizontal line does not have an x-intercept if $y \neq 0$, a vertical line does not have a y-intercept if $x \neq 0$.

4.3 Problem Solving (pp. 230–232)
45. a. $x = 14$, $y = 7$

b. *Sample answer:* 2 and 6, 4 and 5, 6 and 4
47. a. v-intercept: 120, f-intercept: 180; the v-intercept means there are no flowers planted, the f-intercept means there are no vegetables planted.

b. domain: $0 \leq v \leq 120$, range: $0 \leq f \leq 180$

c. 60 ft^2 **49.** 12.5 h. *Sample answer:* Since the tank will be empty when it needs to be refilled, replace w in the function with 0 and then solve the resulting equation for t.

4.4 Skill Practice (pp. 239–241) **1.** slope **3.** The denominator should be $2 - 5$, not $5 - 2$; $m = \frac{6 - 3}{2 - 5} = \frac{3}{-3} = -1$. **5.** undefined **7.** The slope was calculated using $\frac{\text{run}}{\text{rise}}$, not $\frac{\text{rise}}{\text{run}}$; $m = \frac{0 - 3}{12 - 6} = \frac{-3}{6} = -\frac{1}{2}$. **9.** undefined **11.** $-\frac{5}{2}$ **13.** 1 **15.** 0 **19.** $2.25 per day; it costs $2.25 per day to rent a movie. **21.** 0.3 **23.** 0.1 **25.** -15 **27.** -2 **29.** -3 **31.** -15 **33.** Yes; the slope of the line containing both points is -3.

4.4 Problem Solving (pp. 241–242) **37. a.** 0 h to 1.5 h
b. 4.65 h to 8.95 h **39.** *Sample answer:* The elevation
of the hiker increases for about 60 minutes, then
stays the same for about 30 minutes, then decreases
for the last 60 minutes.

4.5 Skill Practice (pp. 247–248) **1.** parallel **3.** 2, 1 **5.** −3, 6
7. $\frac{2}{3}$, −1 **11.** $y = -4x + 1$; −4, 1 **13.** $y = 2x + 3$; 2, 3
15. $y = -\frac{2}{5}x - 2$; $-\frac{2}{5}$, −2 **17.** B **19.** C

21. **23.**

25. **27.**

29. **31.** red, blue, and green
33. Parallel; the slopes are
both 3. **35.** Not parallel;
the slopes are −4 and $-\frac{1}{4}$.
37. −2

4.5 Problem Solving (pp. 248–250)
41. a. **b.** 30 mi

43. a. The slopes are the
amount of money
earned per hour, the
a-intercepts show the
amount of money
made at 0 hours.
b. $80

Extension (p. 252) **1.** −2 **3.** −4 **5.** $\frac{1}{2}$ **7.** 2000 **9.** 2000

4.6 Skill Practice (pp. 256–257) **1.** direct variation
3. direct variation; 1 **5.** not direct variation **7.** direct
variation; −4

11. **13.**

15. **17.**

19. 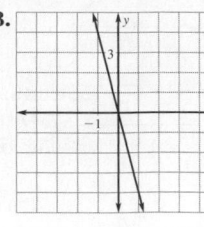 **21.**

23. $y = -x$; −8 **25.** $y = -\frac{3}{4}x$; −6 **27.** not direct
variation **29.** $y = 3x$ **31.** $y = \frac{1}{2}x$ **33.** $y = x$ **35.** $y = 4x$
37. $y = -\frac{7}{26}x$

4.6 Problem Solving (pp. 258–259) **41. a.** $v = \frac{3}{2}t$ **b.** 12 h
43. a. Compare the ratios, $\frac{f}{w}$, for all data pairs (w, f).
Since the ratios all equal 0.25, *f* varies directly with *w*.
b. $f = 0.25w$; $7
45. a. *Sample answer:*

d	C (dollars)
1	1.5
2	3
3	4.5

b. **c.** $C = 1.5d$; yes; it is in the form
$y = ax$; $33.

SA10 Selected Answers

4.6 Problem Solving Workshop (p. 261) **1.** 110 tbsp.
Sample answer: Use the proportion $\frac{20}{100} = \frac{22}{x}$.
3. Because 7 is half of 14, you can take half of 5.88
to find 7 words cost $2.94. Because 21 is 3 times 7,
multiply $2.94 by 3 to get $8.82. **5.** The proportion
should be $\frac{6}{96} = \frac{10}{x}$; $\frac{6}{96} = \frac{10}{x}$, $960 = 6x$, $x = 160$.

4.7 Skill Practice (pp. 265–266) **1.** function notation
3. $-23, 1, 37$ **5.** $14, -2, -26$ **7.** $13, 0, -19.5$
9. $2\frac{1}{5}, 3, 4\frac{1}{5}$ **11.** $-7\frac{1}{2}, -6, -3\frac{3}{4}$ **15.** 3 **17.** -6
19. -7.5 **21.** 3.5

23.
Because the graphs of
g and f have the same
slope, $m = 1$, the lines are
parallel. The y-intercept
of the graph of g is 5 more
than the y-intercept of the
graph of f.

25.
Because the graphs of
q and f have the same
slope, $m = 1$, the lines are
parallel. The y-intercept
of the graph of q is 1 less
than the y-intercept of the
graph of f.

27.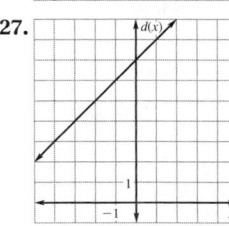
Because the graphs of
d and f have the same
slope, $m = 1$, the lines are
parallel. The y-intercept
of the graph of d is 7 more
than the y-intercept of the
graph of f.

29.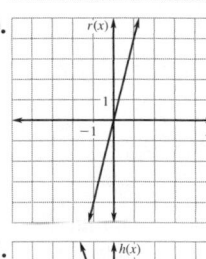
Because the slope of the
graph of r is greater than
the slope of the graph of f,
the graph of r rises faster
from left to right. The
y-intercept for both graphs
is 0, so both lines pass
through the origin.

31.
Because the slope of the
graph of h is negative, the
graph of h falls from left to
right. The y-intercept for
both graphs is 0, so both
lines pass through the
origin.

33.
Because the slope of the
graph of g is less than the
slope of the graph of f,
the graph of g rises slower
from left to right. The
y-intercept for both graphs
is 0, so both lines pass
through the origin.

37. Since the graphs of g and h have the same slope,
$m = 0$, the lines are parallel. The y-intercept of the
graph of h is 2 less than the y-intercept of the graph
of g.

4.7 Problem Solving (pp. 267–268)

39. a.
domain: $0 \le x \le 20$,
range: $2.75 \le f(x) \le 4.75$
b. 18; in 1998, 18 years
after 1980, the price of a
movie ticket was $4.55.

41.
Domain: $x \ge 0$,
range: $d(x) \ge 0$;
1.5 h; substitute 15 for $d(x)$
to get the equation
$15 = 10x$, solve for x.

43.
Because the slope of the
graph of r is greater than
the slope of the graph of s,
the graph of r rises faster
from left to right. The
y-intercept for both graphs
is 0, so both lines pass
through the origin.

45. a. See graph in part (b); domain: $1 \le x \le 31$, range:
$11.53 \le \ell(x) \le 12.43$.

b.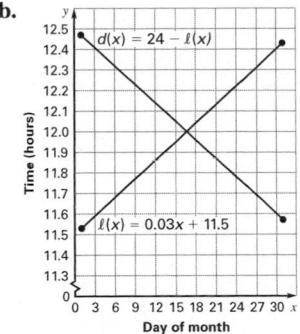
domain:
$11.53 \le \ell(x) \le 12.43$,
range:
$11.57 \le d(x) \le 12.47$

1. slope **3.** *Sample answer:* Make a table, use intercepts, and use the slope and *y*-intercept.

5–7.

5. Quadrant I
7. Quadrant III

9. **11.**

13.

15. $-\dfrac{1}{3}$ **17.** -2

19.

21. about 1.4 sec

23. direct variation; $-\dfrac{1}{2}$

25. **27.**

29. 11

31. Because the graphs of *j* and *f* have the same slope, $m = 1$, the lines are parallel. The *y*-intercept of the graph of *j* is 6 less than the *y*-intercept of the graph of *f*.

33. Because the slope of the graph of *t* is greater than the slope of the graph of *f*, the graph of *t* rises faster from left to right. The *y*-intercept of the graph of *t* is 1 more than the *y*-intercept of the graph of *f*.

Chapter 5

5.1 Skill Practice (pp. 286–287) **1.** slope **3.** $y = 2x + 9$
5. $y = -3x$ **7.** $y = \dfrac{2}{3}x - 9$ **11.** $y = -\dfrac{1}{2}x$ **13.** $y = \dfrac{2}{3}x - 8$
15. $y = -2x - 2$ **17.** The slope should be $\dfrac{0-4}{5-0}$, $y = -\dfrac{4}{5}x + 4$. **19.** $y = 4x + 4$ **21.** $y = -\dfrac{4}{3}x$
23. $y = 2x - 2$ **25.** $y = -x - 5$ **27.** $y = -0.0625x + 4$
29. $y = -4x - 24$ **31.** $y = -2x + 7$ **33.** $y = -\dfrac{4}{5}x - 1$
35. $y = \dfrac{2}{3}x + 3$ **37.** $y = -3x + 9$ **39.** $y = x - 3$
41. $y = -2x + 1$ **43.** No; the slope of the line is undefined, the equation is $x = 3$, which is not in slope-intercept form.

5.1 Problem Solving (pp. 288–289) **45. a.** $C = 44m + 48$
b. \$312 **47.** $C = 3h + 30$; \$42

49. a.

x (years since 1970)	y (km²)
0	5.2
10	4.1
20	3.0
30	1.9

b. The area of the glaciers changed -1.1 square kilometers between every 10 year interval. **c.** $y = -0.11x + 5.2$; -0.11 km²

51. a. $t = 0.7d + 2$ **b.** 16 min

5.1 Graphing Calculator Activity (pp. 290–291)
1. $y = -2x + 5$ **3.** $y = 2x + 1.5$ **5.** $y = 1.5x + 2$
7. $y = 4x - 3$ **9.** $y = 0.5x + 1$; substitute 2 for x, 2 for y, and solve for b.

5.2 Skill Practice (pp. 296–297) **1.** y-intercept
3. $y = 3x - 2$ **5.** $y = -5x - 13$ **7.** $y = -\frac{3}{4}x + 2$
9. -3 was substituted for x instead of y and 6 was substituted for y instead of x, $-3 = -2(6) + b$, $-3 = -12 + b$, $9 = b$. **11.** $y = 3x + 1$ **13.** $y = -\frac{2}{5}x - 1$
15. $y = -\frac{3}{4}x + \frac{35}{8}$ **17.** $y = 4x - 15$ **19.** $y = -\frac{1}{2}x + \frac{1}{2}$
21. $y = \frac{1}{3}x - \frac{4}{3}$ **23.** $y = -2x + 11$ **25.** $y = -\frac{1}{2}x + 8$
27. $y = x - 2$ **31.** $y = -\frac{2}{3}x + 6$ **33.** $y = 6x - 4$
35. Yes; you can substitute m and the coordinates of the point in $y = mx + b$, solve for b, and write the equation. **37.** Yes; you can find the slope of the line, then substitute the y-intercept for b, and write the equation. **39.** $y = \frac{9}{2}x - \frac{1}{2}$ **41.** The lines $y = \frac{3}{2}x - \frac{1}{2}$ and $y = \frac{9}{2}x - \frac{1}{2}$ and the lines $y = \frac{9}{2}x - \frac{1}{2}$ and $y = \frac{3}{2}x + \frac{11}{2}$ intersect because they have different slopes; the lines $y = \frac{3}{2}x - \frac{1}{2}$ and $y = \frac{3}{2}x + \frac{11}{2}$ will not intersect because they have the same slope, so they are parallel.
43. The three points do not lie on the same line. If you find the equation of the line between two of the points and then check to see that the third point is a solution, you can see they do not lie on the same line.
45. The three points do not lie on the same line. If you find the equation of the line between two of the points and then check to see that the third point is a solution, you can see they do not lie on the same line.

5.2 Problem Solving (pp. 298–299) **47.** $\frac{3}{4}$ ft/yr; 6 ft
49. 115 min or 1 h 55 min; substitute 30 for m, 2 for x, and 85 for y into the equation $y = mx + b$ to find $b = 25$. Then substitute 3 for x into the equation $y = 30x + 25$ to solve for y. **51. a.** about 584 newspapers **b.** $y = 11.8x + 584$ **c.** about 938 newspapers
53. a. $d = -18t + 234$

b.

The slope is the rate that the hurricane is traveling, the y-intercept represents the distance from the town at 12 P.M.

c. 1 A.M.; find the t-intercept to find the value of t when the distance to the town is 0; substitute 0 for d and solve for t; $t = 13$, so you need to add 13 hours to 12 P.M. to get 1 A.M.

5.2 Problem Solving Workshop (p. 301) **1.** $5; $19
3. No; if the cost of the 60 inch bookshelf changes, the cost no longer increases at a constant rate. **5.** The student assumes that there is no fixed fee by using a proportion; $93 - 57 = 36$, $36 \div 2 = 18$, $57 + 18 = 75$.

5.3 Skill Practice (pp. 305–306) **1.** -2; $(-5, 5)$ **3.** $y - 1 = 2(x - 2)$ **5.** $y + 1 = -6(x - 7)$ **7.** $y - 2 = 5(x + 8)$
9. $y + 3 = -9(x + 11)$ **11.** $y + 12 = -\frac{2}{5}(x - 5)$
13. The form is $y - y_1$, so the left side should be $y - (-5)$ or $y + 5$; $y + 5 = -2(x - 1)$.

15.
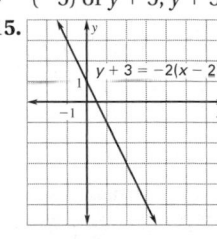
$y + 3 = -2(x - 2)$

17.
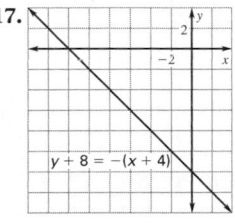
$y + 8 = -(x + 4)$

19.
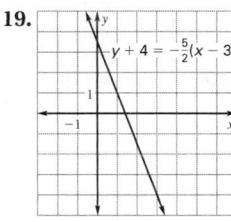
$y + 4 = -\frac{5}{2}(x - 3)$

21. $y - 4 = (x - 1)$ or $y - 1 = (x + 2)$
23. $y - 2 = -2(x - 7)$ or $y - 12 = -2(x - 2)$
25. $y + 1 = -\frac{3}{5}(x + 4)$ or $y + 7 = -\frac{3}{5}(x - 6)$

27. $y + 20 = 8(x + 3)$ or $y - 36 = 8(x - 4)$
29. A point was not substituted into the equation, the y-coordinates of the two points were substituted; $y - 2 = \frac{2}{3}(x - 1)$. **31.** No; because the increase is not at a constant rate, the situation cannot be modeled by a linear equation. **33.** No; because the increase is not at a constant rate, the situation cannot be modeled by a linear equation.

5.3 Problem Solving (pp. 307–308) **37. a.** $y = 130x + 530$
b. $1570 **39.** $y = 10000x + 67000$; $127,000 **41. a.** Since the cost increases at a constant rate of $.49 per print, the situation can be modeled by a linear equation.
b. *Sample answer:* $y - 1.98 = 0.49(x - 1)$ **c.** $1.49
d. $1.79 **43. a.** $y - 17.6 = -0.06(x - 60)$ **b.** 16.4 ft/sec

Extension (p. 310) **1.** yes; 2, -1 **3.** yes; -43, -50

5. **7.**

9.

11. $a_n = 51 + (n-1)21$; 2130 **13.** $a_n = \frac{1}{4} + (n-1)\frac{1}{8}$; $12\frac{5}{8}$ **15.** $a_n = 1 + (n-1)\frac{1}{3}$; 34

5.4 Skill Practice (p. 314) **1.** standard form **3.** point-slope form **5–9.** Sample answers are given.
5. $2x + 2y = -20$, $3x + 3y = -30$ **7.** $x - 2y = -9$, $-2x + 4y = 18$ **9.** $3x - y = -4$, $6x - 2y = -8$
11. $-x + y = 5$ **13.** $2x + y = 5$ **15.** $\frac{3}{2}x + y = -10$
17. $\frac{2}{3}x + y = -\frac{4}{3}$ **19.** $-\frac{4}{3}x + y = -1$ **21.** $-\frac{1}{2}x + y = 1$
23. $y = 2$, $x = 3$ **25.** $y = 3$, $x = -1$ **27.** $y = 4$, $x = -1$
29. $(1, -4)$ was substituted incorrectly, 1 should be substituted for x and -4 substituted for y, $A(1) - 3(-4) = 5$, $A + 12 = 5$, $A = -7$. **31.** 4; $4x + 3y = 5$
33. -4; $-x - 4y = 10$ **35.** -5; $-5x - 3y = -5$

5.4 Problem Solving (pp. 315–316) **39. a.** 15 oz
b. $12c + 15w = 120$ **c.** 10 corn, 0 wheat; 5 corn, 4 wheat; 0 corn, 8 wheat **41. a.** $100\ell + 40s = 1600$

b.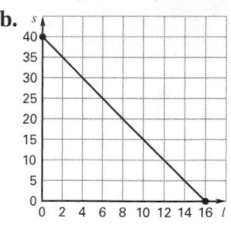

c.

Large rafts	Small rafts
16	0
14	5
12	10
10	15
8	20
6	25
4	30
2	35
0	40

43. $2\ell + 2w = 60$. *Sample answer:*

Length (ft)	Width (ft)
5	25
10	20
15	15
20	10
25	5

5.5 Skill Practice (pp. 322–323) **1.** perpendicular
3. $y = 2x + 5$ **5.** $y = -\frac{3}{5}x + 2$ **7.** $y = 6x + 1$
9. $y = 2x + 9$ **11.** $y = 3x + 30$ **13.** parallel: a and b; perpendicular: none **15.** parallel: none; perpendicular: a and b **17.** The line through points $(6, 4)$ and $(4, 1)$ is perpendicular to the line through points $(1, 3)$ and $(4, 1)$; the slope of the line through the points $(6, 4)$ and $(4, 1)$ is $\frac{3}{2}$, the slope of the line through the points $(1, 3)$ and $(4, 1)$ is $-\frac{2}{3}$. The slopes are negative reciprocals, so the lines are perpendicular.
19. $y = -\frac{1}{3}x - 1$ **21.** $y = -2x + 24$ **23.** $y = -\frac{3}{4}x - 4$
25. $y = -\frac{1}{2}x - \frac{1}{2}$ **27.** $(2, 1)$ was substituted incorrectly, 2 should be substituted for x, and 1 should be substituted for y; $1 = 2(2) + b$, $1 = 4 + b$, $-3 = b$.
29. Yes; the slope of the line through $(4, 3)$ and $(3, -1)$ is 4 and the slope of the line through $(-3, 3)$ and $(1, 2)$ is $-\frac{1}{4}$. The slopes are negative reciprocals, so the lines are perpendicular.

5.5 Problem Solving (pp. 323–324) **33. a.** $w = 200d + 6000$; $w = 200d + 6250$ **b.** 12,000 lb; 12,250 lb
c. The graphs of the lines are parallel because they have the same slope, 200. The w-intercept of the second line is 250 more than the w-intercept of the first line. **35.** Different registration fees; because the lines are parallel, the rate of change, the monthly fee, for each must be equal. Therefore, the students paid different registration fees.

5.6 Skill Practice (pp. 328–329) **1.** increase **3.** positive correlation **5.** negative correlation
7. 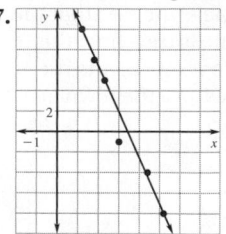 *Sample answer:* $y = -4.4x + 14.88$

9. The line does not have approximately half the data above it and half below it.

11. *Sample answer:* The amount of time driving a car and the amount of gas left in the gas tank

13.

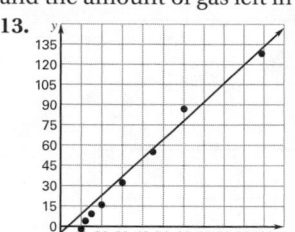

Positive correlation. *Sample answer:* $y = 1.49x - 13$

5.6 Problem Solving (pp. 330–331)

17. a.

b. *Sample answer:* $y = -2.2x + 111$
c. *Sample answer:* -2.2 degrees per kilometer

19. *Sample answer:* $y = 12.6x + 32$

5.6 Graphing Calculator Activity (p. 333)
1. See art in Exercise 3; negative correlation.

3.

5. *Sample answer:* You cannot use the best-fitting line to predict future sales because the data do not show a strong correlation.

5.7 Skill Practice (pp. 338–339)
1. linear interpolation

3.

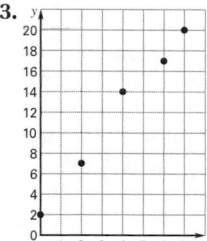

$y = 2.6x + 2.5$; 15.5

5.

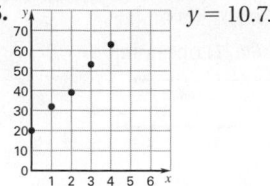

$y = 10.7x + 20$; 127

7. $2\frac{2}{3}$ **9.** -16 **11.** 1.5 **13.** To find the zero of a function, substitute 0 for y, not x; $0 = 2.3x - 2$, $2 = 2.3x$, $x = \frac{20}{23}$. **15.** a and b were not substituted correctly; $y = 4.47x + 23.1$.

5.7 Problem Solving (pp. 339–341)
19. a.

b. $y = 0.03x + 1.23$ **c.** about 8.73 ft^2
21. a. $y = -197.6x + 3542$ **b.** about 17.9; 17.9 years from 1985, or 2002, the number of people living in high noise areas will be 0; no.

5.7 Internet Activity (p. 342)
1. Answers may vary. **3.** Answers may vary.

Chapter Review (pp. 345–348) **1.** negative **3.** The zero of a function is the x-value of the function when $y = 0$; it is the x-intercept of the graph. **5.** $y = \frac{4}{9}x + 5$
7. $y = -1.25x + 25$; \$22.50 **9.** $y = x + 3$ **11.** $y - 7 = -6(x - 4)$ or $y - 1 = -6(x - 5)$ **13.** $y + 2 = -\frac{6}{11}(x + 3)$ or $y + 8 = -\frac{6}{11}(x - 8)$ **15.** $4x + y = -1$
17. $0.07r + 0.04s = 5$. *Sample answer:* 4 organza, 118 satin; 8 organza, 111 satin; 12 organza, 104 satin
19. a. $y = -2x + 1$ **b.** $y = \frac{1}{2}x - 4$

21.

positive correlation

6.1 Skill Practice (pp. 359–360) **1.** open, left of -8

3. $s \leq 60$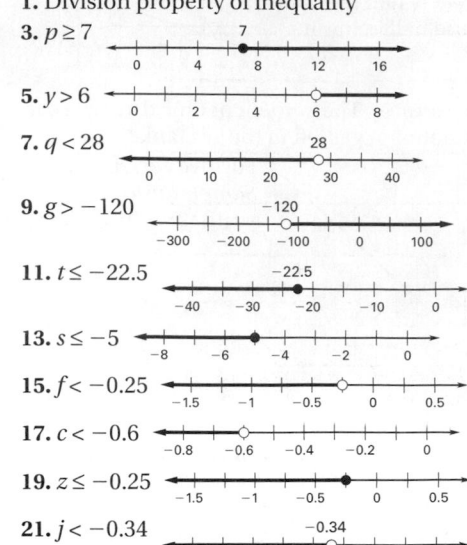

5. $h > 48$

7. $x < 10$ **9.** $x \geq -2$

11. $y \geq -16$

13. $n \leq -\frac{1}{5}$

15. $w > -17.6$

17. $s \geq 9$

19. $q > -1\frac{1}{6}$

21. $d > -6.84$

23. The number line should be shaded to the right of -3, not the left.

25. $n - 15 \leq 37$; $n \leq 52$

27. $x < 21.6$ **29.** No; no; there are infinitely many solutions of an inequality, so it is not possible to check them all. One solution might check in the inequality while another does not. For example, if you incorrectly solve $x + 7 > 10$ as $x > 2$, the solution $x = 4$ checks in the original inequality.

6.1 Problem Solving (pp. 360–361) **31.** at least 8350 points **33. a.** $s > 127.53$ **b.** Yes; no; no; $128.13 > 127.53$; $126.78 < 127.53$; when your score is 127.53, you and your competitor will tie. **35.** *Sample answer:* You want to improve on your personal best of 16 points scored in a basketball game. In the first three quarters of the game, you scored 14 points. Write and solve an inequality to find the possible numbers of points that you can score in the fourth quarter to give yourself a new personal best; $x \geq 3$, if you score at least 3 points in the fourth quarter, you will have a new personal best.

37. a.

Original price, x ($)	19,459	19,989	20,549	22,679	23,999
Final price, y ($)	16,459	16,989	17,549	19,679	20,999

b. $w - 3000 \leq 17000$, $w \leq \$20{,}000$

6.2 Skill Practice (pp. 366–367) **1.** Division property of inequality

3. $p \geq 7$

5. $y > 6$

7. $q < 28$

9. $g > -120$

11. $t \leq -22.5$

13. $s \leq -5$

15. $f < -0.25$

17. $c < -0.6$

19. $z \leq -0.25$

21. $j < -0.34$

23. $r > -54$

25. $m > -24$

27. In both cases, you divide both sides of the inequality by a; when $a > 0$, you do not reverse the inequality symbol, but when $a < 0$, you do. **29.** Both sides of the inequality were multiplied by a positive number, so the inequality symbol should not have been reversed; $x \leq -63$.

31. $-15y \leq 90$; $y \geq -6$

33. $\dfrac{w}{24} \geq -\dfrac{1}{6}$; $w \geq -4$

6.2 Problem Solving (pp. 367–368) **37.** at least 200 words **39.** at least 3.2 in. **41. a.** $h \leq 16$ horses **b.** No; the area added by increasing both the length and the width by 20 feet can be divided into 2 rectangles (80 feet by 20 feet and 82 feet by 20 feet) and 1 square (20 feet by 20 feet). The 400 square feet of the square is large enough to hold one horse, and the rectangular areas will be able to hold additional horses. **c.** $h \leq 23$ horses; the area of the new corral is $(80 + 15)(82 + 15) = 9215$ square feet. Find the possible numbers of horses h the corral can hold by solving the inequality $9215 \geq 400h$; $h \leq 23.04$.

6.3 Skill Practice (pp. 372–373)

1. equivalent inequalities

3. $x > 5$

5. $v \geq -1$

7. $r \geq 1\frac{1}{7}$

9. $m > 3$

11. $p < \frac{1}{2}$

13. $d > -10$

15. The inequality symbol was not reversed when dividing both sides by -3; $x \leq -13$. **17.** all real numbers **19.** $s \geq 0$ **21.** all real numbers **23.** no solution **25.** no solution **27.** no solution

29. $3x + 4 < 40$; $x < 12$

31. $5x + 2 > 9x - 4$; $x < 2$

35. $\frac{1}{2} \cdot 8(x + 1) \leq 44$; $x \leq 10$

6.3 Problem Solving (pp. 373–374) **37.** at most 11 songs **39. a.** Up to 6 swans; the area of the habitat is (20 feet)(50 feet) = 1000 square feet. 500 square feet are needed for the first two swans and the remaining $1000 - 500 = 500$ square feet can hold up to $500 \div 125 = 4$ more swans; so, the maximum number of swans is $2 + 4 = 6$ swans. **b.** at most 14 more swans

41. a.

Pitches per inning, p	15	16	17	18	19
Total number of pitches, t	98	101	104	107	110

b. $53 + 3p \leq 105$, $p \leq 17\frac{1}{3}$, $p \leq 17$ pitches

6.3 Problem Solving Workshop (p. 376) **1.** at least 9 batches **3.** at most 6 games **5.** less than 7.9 min/mi

Extension (p. 378) **1.** $x > 3$ **3.** $x < 213.75$

6.4 Skill Practice (pp. 384–385)

1. compound inequality

3. $2 < x < 6$

5. $-1.5 \leq x < 9.2$

7. $40 \leq s \leq 60$

9. $1 < x \leq 6$

11. $-4 \leq m \leq \frac{1}{4}$

13. $-\frac{1}{3} \leq p < 2$

15. $r < 2$ or $r \geq 7$

17. $v < -5$ or $v > 5$

19. $g < -2\frac{1}{3}$ or $g > 10$

21. 3 was subtracted from only two of the three expressions of the inequality; $1 < -2x < 6$, $-\frac{1}{2} > x > -3$.

23. $x + 5 < 8$ or $x - 3 > 5$; $x < 3$ or $x > 8$

25. $-8 \leq 3(x - 1) \leq 10$; $1\frac{1}{3} \leq x \leq 7\frac{1}{3}$

29. true **31.** False. *Sample answer:* $a = -3$ is a solution of $x > 5$ or $x \leq -4$, but it is not a solution of $x > 5$.

6.4 Problem Solving (pp. 385–387)

37. $-2600 \leq e \leq -100$

41. 3.2 lb $\leq f \leq 6.4$ lb **43. a.** $\frac{5}{9}(F - 32) < 0$ or $\frac{5}{9}(F - 32) > 100$, $F < 32°F$ or $F > 212°F$

b.

°F	23	86	140	194	239
°C	−5	30	60	90	115

23°F, 239°F

45. a. $8 \leq \frac{w}{300} \leq 10$, $2400 \leq w \leq 3000$; 2400 watts to 3000 watts **b.** Yes; no; the amplification per person for 350 people is $\frac{2900}{350} \approx 8.3$ watts, which is between 8 watts and 10 watts, the amplification per person for 400 people is $\frac{2900}{400} = 7.25$ watts, which is not between 8 watts and 10 watts. **c.** 4800 watts; because each person requires at least 8 watts of amplification, and you want to be sure to provide enough amplification for 600 people, you need at least $8(600) = 4800$ watts of amplification.

6.4 Graphing Calculator Activity (p. 388) **1.** $4 < x < 7$; the graphs are the same. **3–7.** Displays should show the graphs of the following inequalities. **3.** $3 \leq x \leq 7$ **5.** $8 \leq x \leq 48$ **7.** $x \leq 4\frac{1}{2}$ or $x \geq 5$

6.5 Skill Practice (pp. 393–394) **1.** absolute value equation **3.** 5, −5 **5.** 0.7, −0.7 **7.** $\frac{1}{2}$, −$\frac{1}{2}$ **9.** 4, −10 **11.** −1, −3$\frac{2}{3}$ **13.** 2, −9 **15.** 4, 9 **17.** 8$\frac{1}{2}$, −3$\frac{1}{2}$ **19.** −$\frac{1}{2}$, −2$\frac{1}{2}$ **21.** The absolute value symbol was removed without writing the second equation, $x + 4 = -13$; $x = 9$ or $x = -17$. **23.** no solution **25.** −4.5, −5.5 **27.** −3, 6 **29.** 13$\frac{1}{2}$, 14$\frac{1}{2}$ **31.** $\frac{1}{4}$, −1$\frac{1}{4}$ **33.** 13, −3 **35.** −7.5, −10.7 **37.** The distance between x and 3 is 7, 10, −4; $x − 3 = 7$ or $x − 3 = −7$, 10, −4; the solutions are the same. **39.** $5\left|2x + 9\right| = 15$; −3, −6

6.5 Problem Solving (pp. 394–395) **43.** 235 sec, 245 sec
45. a. 52.462 points, 56.888 points **b.** 0.3 point
47. a. $p - \left|s - 450\right|$ **b.** 300 points, 600 points
49. a. June 2005; November 2005 **b.** Yes; make a table of values for (m, p) using integer values of m from 0 to 8. Look for the lowest value of p in the table.

Extension (p. 397)

1. 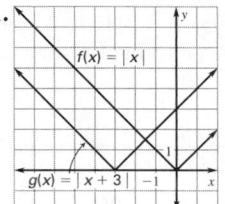 The graph of g is 3 units to the left of the graph of f.

3. 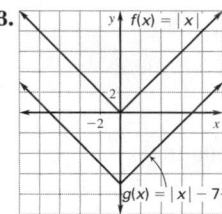 The graph of g is 7 units below the graph of f.

5. 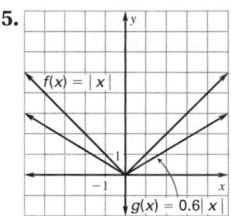 The graph of g opens up and is wider than the graph of f.

7.

x	1	2	3	4	5
$g(x)$	8	6	4	6	8

The graph of g is the graph of f moved 3 units right and 4 units up, and made narrower.

6.6 Skill Practice (pp. 401–402)
1. equivalent inequalities
3. $-4 < x < 4$
5. $h < -4.5$ or $h > 4.5$
7. $-\frac{3}{5} \le t \le \frac{3}{5}$
9. $d \le -7$ or $d \ge -1$
11. $m < -20$ or $m > 8$
13. $c \le -3$ or $c \ge \frac{1}{2}$
15. $r < -8$ or $r > -4$
17. $u \le -3\frac{1}{5}$ or $u \ge 6\frac{2}{5}$
19. $v < 6$ or $v > 34$
23. The compound inequality should use *or*: $x + 4 > 13$ or $x + 4 < -13$; $x > 9$ or $x < -17$.
25. $\left|x - 6\right| \le 4$; $2 \le x \le 10$
27. $\left|-4x - 7\right| + 3 > 10$; $x < -3.5$ or $x > 0$
29. true **31.** False. *Sample answer:* 20

6.6 Problem Solving (pp. 402–403) **35.** at least 470 words and at most 530 words **37.** $\left|t - 346\right| \le 2$, at least 344°F and at most 348°F; continue to preheat; the temperature is still below 350°F. **39. a.** 10.02 m/sec² **b.** 0.88 m/sec²

6.7 Skill Practice (pp. 409–410) **1.** solution **3.** not a solution **5.** not a solution **7.** not a solution **9.** solution **11.** not a solution **13.** solution

17.
$y > x + 3$

19.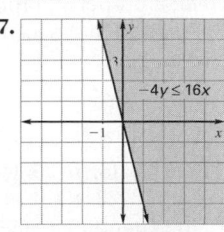
$y < 3x + 5$

21.
$x + y < -8$

23.
$x + 8y > 16$

25.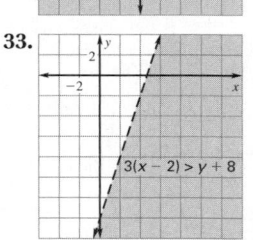
$2(x + 2) > 7y$

27.
$-4y \le 16x$

29.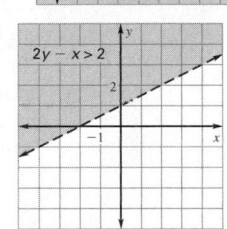
$y < -3$

31.
$x > -2$

33.
$3(x - 2) > y + 8$

35.
$\frac{1}{2}(x + 2) + 3y < 8$

37. The wrong half-plane is shaded.

$2y - x > 2$

39. No; $(0, 0)$ is a point on the boundary line $2x = -5y$.

41. $-2y \le x + 6$
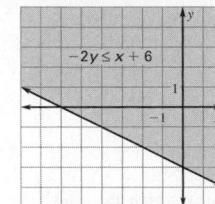

43. $x + 4y < -3$

$x + 4y < -3$

45. $y \le \frac{5}{7}x - \frac{9}{7}$ **47.** $y > 0$ **49.** $y < 0$

6.7 Problem Solving (pp. 410–412)

53.
$x + y \le 860$

Sample answer: The solution $(450, 400)$ means that the bobsled can weigh 450 pounds when the combined weight of the athletes is 400 pounds.

55. a. $15x + 10y \ge 100$

b.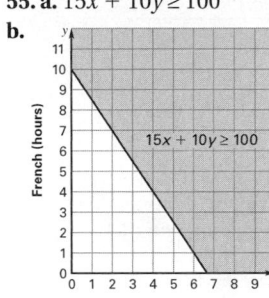
$15x + 10y \ge 100$

Sample answer: $(4, 8)$, $(5, 3)$, $(6, 1)$

c. *Sample answer:*

Spanish time (hours)	4	5	6
French time (hours)	8	3	1
Total earnings (dollars)	140	105	100

57. a. $\frac{1}{6}m + \frac{1}{2}\ell \le 12$
b. $m \le 60$

$\frac{1}{6}m + \frac{1}{2}\ell \le 12$

59. a. $x + y \le 30$

Sample answer: (20, 4), (25, 5), (26, 2)

b. Yes; no; (0, 30) means that you do not take a duffel and have a 30 pound bedroll, while (30, 0) means you take a 30 pound duffel and do not take a bedroll. You need to bring both a duffel and a bedroll.

Chapter Review (pp. 415–418) **1.** $|x - 19| = 8$ **3.** The boundary line is solid if the inequality symbol is $\le$ or $\ge$, the boundary line is dashed if the inequality symbol is $<$ or $>$, choose a test point that is not on the boundary line. If the ordered pair is a solution to the inequality, shade the half-plane that contains the test point; if it not a solution, shade the other half-plane.

5. $x > -18$

7. $s < -2.7$

9. $n > 36$

11. $y \ge 9$

13. $g < 7$

15. $x \ge 3$

17. no solution

19. at most 5 tickets

21. $-1 < x < 3\frac{2}{3}$

23. $w \le \frac{1}{2}$ or $w > 2$

25. $-4, -8$ **27.** $5, 1$ **29.** $1\frac{1}{6}, \frac{1}{6}$

31. $m \le -8$ or $m \ge 8$

33. $-1 < g < 2\frac{1}{3}$

35. $j < -1\frac{1}{2}$ or $j > 10\frac{1}{2}$

37. solution **39.** solution

41.

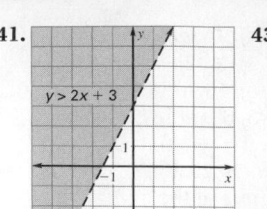

$y > 2x + 3$

43.

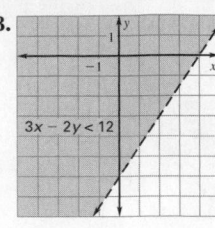

$3x - 2y < 12$

Chapter 7

7.1 Skill Practice (pp. 430–432) **1.** solution **3.** solution **5.** not a solution **9.** (4, 2)

11. The solution $(3, -1)$ does not satisfy Equation 2. The graph of Equation 2 is incorrect; if properly graphed, the lines would intersect at $(-3, -3)$.

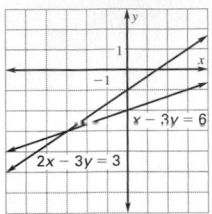

$x - 3y = 6$
$2x - 3y = 3$

13. (4, 0) **15.** $(-3, -5)$ **17.** $(10, -15)$ **19.** $(7, -5)$ **21.** $(-5, 2)$ **23.** (3, 6) **25.** (4, 6) **27.** *Sample answer:* $m = 0$ and $b = 2$ **29. a.** 4 **b.** 4 **c.** *Sample answer:* Each side of the equation is set equal to y. **d.** *Sample answer:* Set each side of the equation equal to y to create a system of two equations. Then solve the system using the graph-and-check method.

7.1 Problem Solving (pp. 432–433) **31.** 2040 **33.** 15 small cards and 10 large cards **35. a.** $y = 5x + 15$, $y = 8x$

b.

Tickets	Cost for members	Cost for non-members
1	$20	$8
2	$25	$16
3	$30	$24
4	$35	$32
5	$40	$40
6	$45	$48

c.

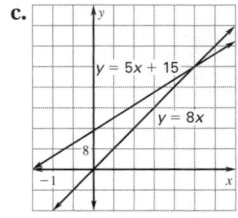

$y = 5x + 15$
$y = 8x$

When you rent 6 or more movies. *Sample answer:* The graph for a non-member is below the graph for a member up through 4 movies. For 5 movies, the cost is the same. The graph for members is lower than the graph for non-members for 6 or more movies.

7.1 Graphing Calculator Activity (p. 434)
1. $(-1.5, 2.5)$ **3.** $(0.2, -1.44)$

7.2 Skill Practice (pp. 439–440) **1.** *Sample answer:*
$y = x + 1$, $y = 2x + 1$ **3.** (5, 3) **5.** (2, −1) **7.** (−4, 5)
9. (6, 7) **11.** (2, −2) **13.** (5, −8) **15.** (0, 2) **17.** (1.4, −4.4)
19. *Sample answer:* In Step 3, 6 is substituted for
y instead of x; $y = 9 − 3(6)$, $y = −9$, the solution is
(6, −9). **21.** (4, −120) **23.** (3, 7) **25.** (6, −3) **27.** (0, −6)
29. *Sample answer:* The graphs of the equations
should intersect at the solution you found using the
substitution method.

7.2 Problem Solving (pp. 440–441) **31.** 96 bags of
popcorn; 48 pretzels **33.** 4 in. *Sample answer:* (4, 5)
is the solution to the appropriate linear system, so x
should equal 4. **35.** 50 milliliters of 1% hydrochloric
acid solution and 50 milliliters of 5% hydrochloric
acid solution **37.** Yes. *Sample answer:* The cheetah
would have to run at 88 feet per second for
23.3 seconds to catch the gazelle.

7.2 Problem Solving Workshop (p. 442) **1.** 5 mi

7.3 Skill Practice (pp. 447–448) **1.** *Sample answer:*
$x + y = 10$, $x − y = 5$ **3.** (1, 6) **5.** (−1, −5) **7.** (5, 7)
9. (−1, 2) **11.** (5, 3) **13.** (4, 5) **17.** (2, −3) **19.** (−18, 4)
21. (4, −3) **23.** *Sample answer:* The two equations
should be subtracted rather than added; $6x = 8$, $x = \frac{4}{3}$.
25. (26, 14) **27.** (−4, 12) **29.** (−2, 5) **31.** (5, 25)
33. (−2, 8) **35.** $\ell = 4.5$ ft, $w = 2.5$ ft

7.3 Problem Solving (pp. 449–450) **39.** speed in still
water: 4.6 m/sec, speed of current: 0.3 m/sec
41. monophonic ring tone: $1.95, polyphonic ring
tone: $3.50 **43. a.** flight to Phoenix: 400 mi/h, flight
to Charlotte: 450 mi/h **b.** $s + w = 450$, $s − w = 400$;
plane: 425 mi/h, wind: 25 mi/h

7.4 Skill Practice (pp. 454–455) **1.** 36 **3.** (1, 1) **5.** (5, −4)
7. (2, 1) **9.** (−7, −12) **11.** (5, 6) **13.** (4, 4) **15.** (5, −3)
17. $\left(4\frac{2}{7}, 5\right)$ **19.** *Sample answer:* The two equations
should be subtracted rather than added; $−x = −9$,
$x = 9$. **21.** (2, −1) **23.** $\left(−4\frac{5}{22}, −2\frac{1}{11}\right)$ **25.** (5, 4)
27. (10, 2) **29.** (2, −1) **31.** $\left(\frac{1}{3}, −\frac{2}{3}\right)$ **33. a.** $2\ell + 2w = 18$,
$6\ell + 4w = 46$ **b.** length: 15 in., width: 8 in.

7.4 Problem Solving (pp. 456–457) **37.** 5 hardcover
books **39.** 21 pies, 16 batches of applesauce
41. $16.50; a small costs $2.90, and a large costs $3.90;
$3(2.90) + 2(3.90) = 16.50$. **43.** $800; $1200

7.5 Skill Practice (pp. 462–464) **1.** inconsistent system
3. *Sample answer:* The lines have the same slope
but different intercepts. **5.** B; one solution **7.** A;
infinitely many solutions

9. **11.**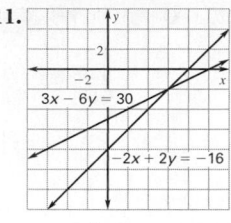

infinitely many solutions   one solution

13.   no solution

15. (−3, 4) **17.** (3, 7) **19.** (2, 2) **21.** no solution
23. (0, 3) **27.** infinitely many solutions **29.** infinitely
many solutions **31.** infinitely many solutions
33. *Sample answer:* $7x − 8y = −9$, $7x − 8y = 4$

7.5 Problem Solving (pp. 464–465) **37.** Yes. *Sample
answer:* There is one solution to the resulting linear
system. **39. a.** $d = \frac{t}{3}$, $d = \frac{t}{3} − 5$

b. 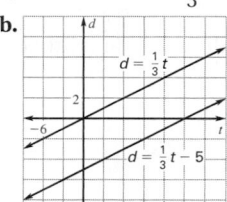   *Sample answer:* No, since
the lines are parallel, the
two climbers will never be
at the same distance at the
same time.

7.6 Skill Practice (pp. 469–470) **1.** solution **3.** not a
solution **5.** not a solution **7.** A

9. **11.**

13. **15.**

17.

19.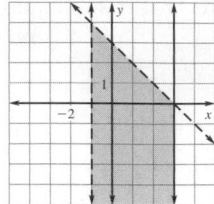

23. The graph is shaded to include $x + y > 3$, not $x + y < 3$.

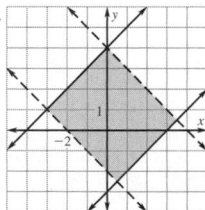

25. $y > -1, y < 4$ **27.** $y \le 5x + 1, y > x - 2$ **29.** $y \le x - 3,$ $y > -2x - 1, y > -6$

31.

33. No; there are no possible values for x and y that satisfy both equations.

7.6 Problem Solving (pp. 471–472)

37. $14x + 7y < 70,$ $x + y < 8, x \ge 0, y \ge 0$

39. a. $20 \le x \le 65, 154 - 0.7x \le y \le 187 - 0.85x$

b. No. *Sample answer:* The heart rate is below 70% of the maximum heart rate.

Chapter Review (pp. 475–478) **1.** system of linear inequalities **3.** *Sample answer:* Graph each inequality then shade the region that is the intersection of the solutions to each inequality. Then check the solution with a test point. **5.** $(2, -5)$ **7.** $(4, -1)$ **9.** $(5, 1)$ **11.** 4 tubes of paint, 8 brushes **13.** $(1, -2)$ **15.** $(6, 10)$ **17.** $(-7, 8)$ **19.** $(-2, 5)$ **21.** $(4, 5)$ **23.** $(1, 6)$ **25.** No solution. *Sample answer:* When the variables are eliminated, a false statement remains, which means there is no solution. **27.** One solution. *Sample answer:* The lines have different slopes, so there is only one solution.

29.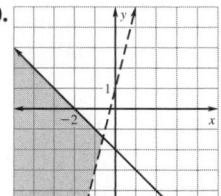

31. Let m represent the number of matinee movies and n represent the number of evening movies; $5m + 8n \le 40, m \ge 0, n \ge 0$.

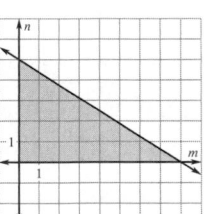

Cumulative Review (pp. 484–485) **1.** 62 **3.** 55 **5.** -50 **7.** solution **9.** not a solution **11.** solution **13.** $5y - 1$ **15.** $-g + 4$ **17.** $-3 + \frac{4}{7}x$ **19.** 29 **21.** -7 **23.** -3 **25.** -3 **27.** $4\frac{4}{9}$

29.

31.

33.

35. $y = -x + 3$ **37.** $y + 10 = -2(x - 1)$ or $y - 2 = -2(x + 5)$ **39.** $y + 2 = \frac{10}{3}(x + 9)$ or $y - 8 = \frac{10}{3}(x + 6)$

41. $y - 4 = -\frac{1}{3}(x - 2)$ or $y - 2 = -\frac{1}{3}(x - 8)$

43. $x < -4$

45. $x \geq 7$

47. $x > -5$

49. $x \geq -6$

51. $-1 < x < 2$

53. $-5 < x < 5$

55. $(1, 4)$ **57.** $(2, -3)$ **59.** \$.02 **61. a.** The ratio $\frac{p}{\ell}$ is always the same, so p varies directly with ℓ.
b. $p = 2.5\ell$ **63.** $-4 < F < 113$

Chapter 8

8.1 Skill Practice (pp. 492–493) **1.** order of magnitude
3. 4^8 **5.** 3^4 **7.** $(-7)^9$ **9.** 2^{14} **11.** 3^{10} **13.** $(-5)^{12}$
15. $15^3 \cdot 29^3$ **17.** $132^6 \cdot 9^6$ **19.** x^6 **21.** z^6 **23.** x^{10}
25. $(b - 2)^{12}$ **27.** $25x^2$ **29.** $49x^2y^2$ **31.** $100x^{14}$
33. $96d^{22}$ **35.** $12p^{19}$ **37.** $108x^{29}$ **39.** *Sample answer:*
The exponents should be added, not multiplied;
$c^1 \cdot c^4 \cdot c^5 = c^{1 + 4 + 5} = c^{10}$. **43.** 2 **45.** 2
47. $-3267x^{12}y^{13}$ **49.** $1000r^{17}s^6t^{17}$

8.1 Problem Solving (pp. 493–494) **53.** 10^{26} m
55. a.

Ounces of gold	10	100	1000	10,000	100,000
Number of atoms	10^{24}	10^{25}	10^{26}	10^{27}	10^{28}

b. $10^5 \cdot 10^{23}$; 10^{28} atoms **57.** 10^{27}

8.2 Skill Practice (pp. 498–500) **1.** base, exponent **3.** 5^4
5. 3^4 **7.** $(-4)^3$ **9.** 10^6 **11.** $\frac{1}{3^5}$ **13.** $\frac{5^4}{4^4}$ **15.** 7^7 **17.** 3^8

21. y^7 **23.** $\frac{a^9}{y^9}$ **25.** $\frac{p^4}{q^4}$ **27.** $-\frac{64}{x^3}$ **29.** $\frac{64c^3}{d^6}$ **31.** $\frac{x^4}{9y^6}$
33. $\frac{9x^4}{4y^2}$ **35.** $\frac{3m^7}{8n^6}$ **39.** 8 **41.** 4 **43.** $54s^3t^3$ **45.** $\frac{27x^{11}y^5}{25}$
47. Identity property of multiplication; Multiply fractions; Quotient of powers property

8.2 Problem Solving (pp. 500–501)

49. a.

Step	Number of new squares	Side length of new square
1	$4 = 4^1$	$\frac{1}{2} = \left(\frac{1}{2}\right)^1$
2	$16 = 4^2$	$\frac{1}{4} = \left(\frac{1}{2}\right)^2$
3	$64 = 4^3$	$\frac{1}{8} = \left(\frac{1}{2}\right)^3$
4	$256 = 4^4$	$\frac{1}{16} = \left(\frac{1}{2}\right)^4$

b. $\frac{4^4}{4^2}$; 16 times

51. about 31,710 yr **53.** 31^3 times greater

8.3 Skill Practice (pp. 506–507) **1.** Product of powers property and definition of zero exponent; the expression simplifies using the product of powers property to 3^0, which by definition equals 1. **3.** $\frac{1}{64}$
5. $-\frac{1}{3}$ **7.** 1 **9.** 1 **11.** $\frac{49}{4}$ **13.** undefined **15.** $\frac{1}{32}$ **17.** $\frac{1}{32}$
19. 27 **21.** $\frac{1}{243}$ **23.** $\frac{8}{3}$ **25.** 16 **27.** 3^0 is not equivalent to 0, but to 1; $-6 \cdot 3^0 = -6 \cdot 1 = -6$. **29.** $\frac{2}{y^3}$ **31.** $\frac{1}{121h^2}$
33. $\frac{5}{m^3n^4}$ **35.** 1 **37.** $\frac{1}{x^5y^2}$ **39.** $\frac{y^8}{15x^{10}}$ **41.** $243d^3$
43. $\frac{3x^{12}y^5}{4}$ **49.** *Sample answer:* It approaches 0.

8.3 Problem Solving (pp. 507–508) **51.** about 10^5 grains of rice **53.** about 10^{11} red blood cells
55. a.

Number of folds	0	1	2	3
Fraction of original area	1	$\frac{1}{2}$	$\frac{1}{4}$	$\frac{1}{8}$

b. $\left(\frac{1}{2}\right)^x$ **57. a.** 112.5 watts **b.** $I = 9d^{-2}$ **c.** The intensity is divided by 4.

Extension (p. 510) **1.** 1000 **3.** $\frac{1}{729}$ **5.** $\frac{1}{3}$ **7.** 81 **9.** $\frac{1}{216}$
11. $-\frac{1}{4}$ **13.** *Sample answer:* $b^3 = a$, substitute a^k for b to create $(a^k)^3 = a$; $a^{3k} = a^1$ by the power of a power property. Solving for k, $3k = 1$ so $k = \frac{1}{3}$.

8.4 Skill Practice (pp. 515–516) **1.** No; 0.5 is not a number greater than or equal to 1.0 and less than 10. **3.** 8.5×10^1 **5.** 8.24×10^1 **7.** 7.2×10^7

9. 1.06525×10^6 **11.** 1.06×10^9 **13.** 9×10^{14}
17. 75,000,000 **19.** 30,300 **21.** 15,440,000,000
23. 0.00000000044 **25.** 0.0000000852
27. 0.0000012034 **29.** 6.7×10^3; 12,439; 2×10^4;
45,000 **31.** 9.8×10^{-6}; 0.00008; 0.0005; 5×10^{-3};
8.2×10^{-3}; 0.04065 **33.** < **37.** > **39.** 6.6×10^{-4}
41. 7.29×10^{-9} **43.** 3×10^{-3} **45.** 1.25×10^{-22}
47. 1.96×10^6 **49.** *Sample answer:* 2.8×10^1 and
1×10^3; 11.2×10^5 and 4.0×10^1

8.4 Problem Solving (pp. 516–518) **51. a.** 1.4×10^{-4};
2.5×10^{-1}; 1.67×10^2; 555 **b.** the elephant beetle
and the walking stick **53.** 1406 pounds per acre
55. a. About 3.67; the radius of the Earth is about
3.67 times greater than the radius of the moon.
b. About 49.30; the volume of the Earth is about
49.30 times greater than the volume of the moon.
c. The ratio of the volumes is the cube of the ratio
of the radii. **57.** 4 in. by 6 in. **59. a.** 4.9 L **b.** about
2.58×10^6 L, about 2.58×10^7 L, about 2.06×10^8 L
c. Underestimates. *Sample answer:* They are
calculated when a person is at rest. When a person
is not resting, the rate will go up.

8.4 Graphing Calculator Activity (p. 519) **1.** 2.7×10^{13}
3. 2.5×10^{19} **5. a.** about 6.10×10^{18} g **b.** about
3.05×10^{41} atoms

8.5 Skill Practice (pp. 523–524) **1.** growth factor **3.** The
graph would be a vertical stretch. *Sample answer:*
Since the y-values of $y = 2 \cdot 5^x$ are double those of
$y = 5^x$. **5.** $y = 125 \cdot 5^x$ **7.** $y = \frac{1}{9} \cdot 3^x$

9. domain: all real numbers,
range: all positive real
numbers

11. domain: all real numbers,
range: all positive real numbers

13. domain: all real numbers,
range: all positive real numbers

15. domain: all real numbers,
range: all positive real numbers

17. domain: all real numbers,
range: all positive real
numbers

19. domain: all real numbers,
range: all positive real numbers

21. The percent increase was not written as a
decimal; $0.27(1 + 0.02)^3 = 0.27(1.02)^3 = \$.29$.

23. 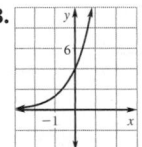 The graph is a vertical stretch.

25. The graph is a vertical shrink.

27. The graph is a vertical stretch.

29. The graph is a vertical stretch
with a reflection in the x-axis.

31. The graph is a vertical shrink with
a reflection in the x-axis.

33. The graph is a vertical stretch with a reflection in the x-axis.

35. 200%. *Sample answer:* A growth rate of 200% would create a growth factor of $1 + 2 = 3$, which would represent the tripling of the population every year.

8.5 Problem Solving (pp. 525–527) **39. a.** Let x represent the number of years since 2001 and $f(x)$ represent the number of computers (in hundreds of millions); $f(x) = 6 \cdot (1.1)^x$. **b.** about 1,286,153,286 computers **41. a.** tree 1: $A = 154 \cdot (1.06)^t$, tree 2: $A = 113 \cdot (1.1)^t$

b. about 8.4 yr

45. $y = 25.96(1.059)^x$; about 145 Hz **47.** $1266.77
49. $1271.24

8.5 Problem Solving Workshop (pp. 528–529)
1. a. Let t represent the number of years since 1997 and F represent the bus fare; $F = 20(1.12)^t$. **b.** $22.40
c. 2000. *Sample answer:* Make a table of values.
3. a. $T = 7.5(1.039)^t$ **b.** about 37.4 million

8.6 Skill Practice (pp. 535–536) **1.** $1 - r$ **3.** exponential function; $y = 8 \cdot 4^x$ **5.** exponential function; $y = 2\left(\frac{1}{3}\right)^x$

7. 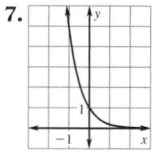 domain: all real numbers, range: all positive real numbers

9. domain: all real numbers, range: all positive real numbers

11. domain: all real numbers, range: all positive real numbers

13. domain: all real numbers, range: all positive real numbers

15. 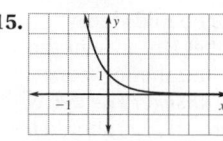 domain: all real numbers, range: all positive real numbers

17. domain: all real numbers, range: all positive real numbers

21. 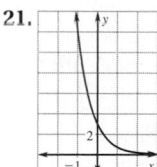 The graph is a vertical stretch.

23. The graph is a vertical shrink.

25. The graph is a vertical stretch.

27. The graph is a vertical stretch with a reflection in the x-axis.

29. The graph is a vertical shrink with a reflection in the x-axis.

31. The graph is a vertical stretch with a reflection in the x-axis.

33. C **35.** initial amount: 90,000 people, decay factor: 0.975, decay rate: 2.5%; Let P represent the population and t represent the number of years; $P = 90,000(0.975)^t$. **37.** *Sample answer:* The decay rate, r, is 0.14. So the decay factor $(1 - r)$ should be 0.86, not 0.14; $y = 25,000(0.86)^t$. **39.** exponential decay; $y = 8 \cdot 0.6^x$ **41. a.** The graph is a vertical shrink. **b.** The graph is a vertical stretch with a reflection in the x-axis. **c.** The graph is a vertical shift up 1 unit. **45.** *Sample answer:* Since the quantity loses the same percent each time period, the amount y remaining after x time periods can be modeled using the exponential function $y = a(1 - r)^x$. After 1 time period, when x is 1, $y = a(1 - r)^1$, or $a(1 - r)$.

8.6 Problem Solving (pp. 537–538) **47.** Let V represent the value of the cell phone and t represent the number of years since purchase, $V = 125(0.8)^t$; $64. **49.** No. *Sample answer:* The boat's value is about $3217. **51. a.** decay factor: 0.9439, decay rate: 5.61% **b.** about 1.431 in. **c.** about 0.716 in. **53. a.** $y = 4(0.995)^x$, $y = 3.5(0.995)^x$

b. 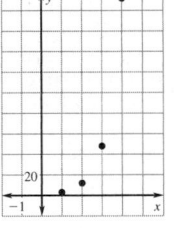 **c.** about 52 yr

Extension (p. 540)

1. geometric **3.** arithmetic

5. geometric

7. $a_n = (-5)^{n-1}$; 15,625 **9.** $a_n = 432\left(\frac{1}{6}\right)^{n-1}$; $\frac{1}{108}$

Chapter Review (pp. 543–546) **1.** decay, decay factor **3.** Exponential decay; $b = 0.85$ which is between 0 and 1, therefore it's exponential decay. **5.** Exponential growth; $b = 2.1$ which is greater than 1, therefore it's exponential growth. **7.** $(-3)^8$ **9.** y^{20} **11.** $(b + 2)^{24}$ **13.** $-64x^2y^2$ **15.** 10^{21} **17.** 5^3 **19.** 17^4 **21.** $\frac{49x^{10}}{y^4}$ **23.** $\frac{6r^{15}}{7s^5}$ **25.** 1 **27.** $\frac{27}{8}$ **29.** 10^6 **31.** 0.000075 **33.** 4.0625×10^{13}

35. domain: all real numbers, range: all positive real numbers

37. domain: all real numbers, range: all positive real numbers

39. The graph is a vertical stretch with a reflection in the x-axis.

41. exponential decay; $y = 3 \cdot \left(\frac{1}{3}\right)^x$

Chapter 9

9.1 Skill Practice (pp. 557–558) **1.** monomial **3.** $9m^5$; 5, 9 **5.** $2x^2y^2 - 8xy$; 4, 2 **7.** $3z^4 + 2z^3 - z^2 + 5z$; 4, 3 **11.** not a polynomial; variable exponent **13.** polynomial; 1, binomial **15.** polynomial; 3, trinomial **17.** $13a^2 - 4$ **19.** $m^2 + 9m + 9$ **21.** $6c^2 + 14$ **23.** $-2n^3 + n - 12$ **25.** $-15d^3 + 3d^2 - 3d + 2$ **27.** Two unlike terms, $-4x^2$ and $8x$, were combined; $-2x^3 - 4x^2 + 8x + 1$. **29.** $2x^2 + 6x - 9$, $4x^2 - 4x - 5$ **31.** $12x - 3$ **33.** $-x^2 + 10xy + y^2$ **35.** $6a^2b - 6a + 4b - 19$

9.1 Problem Solving (pp. 558–559) **37.** about 39,800,000 people **39. a.** $T = 9.5t^3 - 73t^2 + 130t + 860$ **b.** 1998; substitute $t = 0$ into the equation for T to find the number of books shipped in 1998 to get 860 million books. Substitute 4 into the equation for T to find the number of books shipped in 2002 to get 820 million books. More books were shipped in 1998. **41. a.** $D = -0.44t^2 + 49t + 19.7$ **b.** about 855 decisions **c.** about 61%; Cy Young's career lasted $1911 - 1890 = 21$ years. To find the number of wins in his career, find the value of W when $t = 21$; about 525 wins. From part (b), we know that the total number of decisions in his career is about 855, so to find the percent of the decisions that were wins, find $525 \div 855 \approx 0.614$, or about 61%.

9.1 Graphing Calculator Activity (p. 560)
1. $7x^2 + 2x + 1$ **3.** correct

9.2 Skill Practice (pp. 565–566) **1.** binomials
3. $2x^3 - 3x^2 + 9x$ **5.** $4z^6 + z^5 - 11z^4 - 6z^2$ **7.** $9a^7 - 5a^6 - 13a^5$ **9.** $x^2 - x - 6$ **11.** $4b^2 - 31b + 21$
13. $12k^2 + 23k - 9$ **15.** The second term of the first binomial is -5, not 5, so the entries in the second row of the diagram should be $-15x$ and -5; $3x^2 - 14x - 5$. **17.** $y^2 + y - 30$ **19.** $77w^2 + 34w - 15$
21. $s^3 + 10s^2 + 19s - 20$ **23.** $-15x^3 + 14x^2 + 3x - 2$
25. $54z^3 - 21z^2 - 14z + 5$ **27.** $10r^2 + r - 3$
29. $8m^2 + 46m + 63$ **31.** $48x^2 - 88x + 35$
33. $3p^2 - 3p - 9$ **35.** $-3c^3 - 45c^2 + 23c - 10$
37. $2x^2 + x - 45$ **39.** $x^2 + 8x + 15$ **41.** $80 - 6x^2$
43. $2x^2 - 10x - 132$ **45.** $2x^4 - 11x^3 - 20x^2 - 7x$; graph $Y_1 = (x^2 - 7x)(2x^2 + 3x + 1)$ and $Y_2 = 2x^4 - 11x^3 - 20x^2 - 7x$ in the same viewing window. Because the graphs coincide, the expressions for Y_1 and Y_2 must be equivalent.

9.2 Problem Solving (pp. 567–568) **49. a.** $4x^2 + 84x + 440$ **b.** 840 in.^{2} **51. a.** $12,300 million, 0.171; for $t = 0$, the amount of money (in millions of dollars) people between 15 and 19 years old spent on sound recordings in the U.S. in 1997 **b.** $R \cdot P \approx -1.18t^4 + 14.4t^3 - 57.4t^2 - 10.4t + 2100$ **c.** about $1680 million **53. a.** *Sample answer:* $T = t + 90$; use the data points from 1995−1999: (5, 95), (6, 96), (7, 97), (8, 98), (9, 99). All these points lie on a line with slope $m = 1$; use any one of the points to find the y-intercept $b = 90$. The other data points, (0, 92), (10, 101), and (11, 102), lie close to the line $T = t + 90$. **b.** $V = -0.0015t^3 - 0.103t^2 + 2.949t + 6.21$ **c.** about 24.2 million households, about 22.2 million households

9.3 Skill Practice (p. 572) **1.** *Sample answer:* $x - 5$, $x + 5$ **3.** $x^2 + 16x + 64$ **5.** $4y^2 + 20y + 25$

7. $n^2 - 22n + 121$ **9.** The middle term of the product, $2(s)(-3) = -6s$, was left out; $s^2 - 6s + 9$.
11. $t^2 - 16$ **13.** $4x^2 - 1$ **15.** $49 - w^2$ **19.** Use the sum and difference pattern to find the product $(20 - 4)(20 + 4)$. **21.** Use the square of a binomial pattern to find the product $(20 - 3)^2$. **23.** $r^2 + 18rs + 81s^2$ **25.** $9m^2 - 121n^2$ **27.** $9m^2 - 42mn + 49n^2$
29. $9f^2 - 81$ **31.** $9x^2 + 48xy + 64y^2$ **33.** $4a^2 - 25b^2$
35. $9x^2 - 0.25$ **37.** $9x^2 - 3x + 0.25$

9.3 Problem Solving (pp. 573–574)
41. a.

b. $0.25C^2 + 0.5Cs + 0.25s^2$
c. 75%

43. a. 88.1%; the areas of the four regions are: 2 complete passes: $0.655^2 \approx 0.429$ square units; 1 complete pass, 1 incomplete pass: $0.655(0.345) \approx 0.226$ square units; 1 incomplete pass, 1 complete pass: $0.345(0.655) \approx 0.226$ square units; and 2 incomplete passes: $0.345^2 \approx 0.119$ square units. The regions that involve at least one complete pass cover $0.429 + 0.226 + 0.226 = 0.881$ square units, or 88.1% of the whole square region. **b.** The outcome of each attempted pass is modeled by $0.655C + 0.345I$, so the possible outcomes of two attempted passes is modeled by $(0.655C + 0.345I)^2 = 0.429C^2 + 0.452CI + 0.119I^2$. Because any combination of outcomes with a C results in at least one completed pass, the coefficients of the first two terms show that 42.9% + 45.2% = 88.1% of the outcomes will have at least one completed pass, and the coefficient of the last term shows that 11.9% of the outcomes will have two incomplete passes.

9.4 Skill Practice (pp. 578–579) **1.** The vertical motion model is the equation $h = -16t^2 + vt + s$, where h is the height (in feet) of a projectile after t seconds in the air, given an initial velocity of v feet per second and an initial height of s feet. **3.** 5, -3 **5.** 13, 14
7. 7, $-\frac{4}{3}$ **9.** ± 3 **11.** $-\frac{11}{3}$, -1 **13.** $-\frac{5}{2}$, $\frac{5}{7}$ **17.** $2(x + y)$
19. $s(3s^3 + 16)$ **21.** $7w^2(w^3 - 5)$ **23.** $5n(3n^2 + 5)$
25. $\frac{1}{2}x^4(5x^2 - 1)$ **27.** 0, -6 **29.** 0, $\frac{7}{2}$ **31.** 0, $-\frac{1}{3}$
33. 0, 2 **35.** 0, $-\frac{5}{2}$ **37.** 0, $-\frac{2}{7}$ **41.** $2ab(4a - 3b)$
43. $v(v^2 - 5v + 9)$ **45.** $3q^2(2q^3 - 7q^2 - 5)$ **47.** 0, $\frac{1}{2}$

9.4 Problem Solving (pp. 579–580) **51.** about 0.69 sec
53. 0, about 0.28; the zero $t = 0$ seconds means that
the penguin begins at a height of 0 feet in the air as
it leaves the water; the zero $t \approx 0.28$ second means
that the penguin lands back in the water (at a
height of 0 feet in the air) after about 0.28 second.
55. a. $h = -4.9t^2 + 4.9t$ **b.** $0 \le h \le 1$; a reasonable
domain for the function will cover the time from
when the rabbit leaves the ground until the rabbit
lands back on the ground; these times t are the
zeros of the function, 0 seconds and 1 second.
57. a. $w(w + 2) = w(10 - w)$ **b.** 4 ft **c.** 48 ft^2

9.5 Skill Practice (pp. 586–587) **1.** factors
3. $(x + 3)(x + 1)$ **5.** $(b - 9)(b - 8)$ **7.** $(z + 12)(z - 4)$
9. $(y - 9)(y + 2)$ **11.** $(x + 10)(x - 7)$
13. $(m - 15)(m + 8)$ **15.** $(p + 16)(p + 4)$
17. $(c + 11)(c + 4)$ **19.** In order to have a product
of $+24$, p and q must have the same sign;
$(m - 6)(m - 4)$. **21.** $10, -3$ **23.** $-10, 5$ **25.** $-5, -4$
27. $-22, -1$ **31.** $-3, -2$ **33.** $9, 5$ **35.** $17, -3$ **37.** $14, 2$
39. $-9, 8$ **41.** $-17, -2$ **43.** 20 in., 5 in. **45.** 26 yd, 6 yd
47. $(x - 2y)^2$ **49.** $(c + 9d)(c + 4d)$ **51.** $(a + 5b)(a - 3b)$
53. $(m - 7n)(m + 6n)$ **55.** $(g + 10h)(g - 6h)$

9.5 Problem Solving (pp. 588–589) **59.** 10 cm^2
61. 40 in.; the side lengths of the rectangular picture
can be represented by $x - 5$ and $x - 6$; the area of
the picture is 20 square inches, so to find the side
length x of the original square picture, solve the
equation $(x - 5)(x - 6) = 20$. The equation has two
solutions, 10 and 1, but when $x = 1$ inch, both $x - 5$
and $x - 6$ are negative, which does not make sense in
this situation. So, $x = 10$ inches, and the perimeter of
the original picture was $4(10) = 40$ inches.

9.5 Problem Solving Workshop (p. 591) **1.** 2 ft **3.** 9 ft

9.6 Skill Practice (pp. 596–597) **1.** roots **3.** To factor
the polynomial that has a leading coefficient of
1, $x^2 - x - 2$, you only need to find factors of the
constant term, -2, that add to the coefficient of the
middle term, -1. To factor the polynomial that has
a leading coefficient that is not 1, $6x^2 - x - 2$, you
must also take into account how the factors of the
leading coefficient, 6, affect the coefficient of the
middle term. **5.** $-(y - 4)(y + 2)$ **7.** $(5w - 1)(w - 1)$
9. $(6s + 5)(s - 1)$ **11.** $(2c - 1)(c - 3)$
13. $-(2h + 1)(h - 3)$ **15.** $(2x + 3)(5x - 9)$
17. $(3z + 7)(z - 2)$ **19.** $(2n + 3)(2n + 5)$

21. $(3y - 4)(2y + 1)$ **23.** $-\frac{7}{2}, 5$ **25.** $\frac{1}{4}, -3$ **27.** $\frac{3}{4}, -\frac{1}{2}$
29. $-\frac{1}{4}, \frac{2}{5}$ **31.** $\frac{1}{3}, -5$ **33.** $\frac{2}{5}, 1$ **35.** $\frac{11}{2}, -3$ **37.** $-\frac{4}{3}, \frac{1}{2}$
39. The factorization of the polynomial should be
$(3x + 2)(4x - 1)$ instead of $(3x - 1)(4x + 2)$; $-\frac{2}{3}, \frac{1}{4}$.
41. $9\frac{1}{2}$ in.; to find the width, solve the equation
$w(4w + 1) = 3$ to get $w = \frac{3}{4}$ or $w = -1$. The width
cannot be negative, so the width is $\frac{3}{4}$ inch. Then the
length is $4\left(\frac{3}{4}\right) + 1 = 4$ inches, and the perimeter is
$2\left(\frac{3}{4}\right) + 2(4) = 9\frac{1}{2}$ inches. **43.** 5, 7 **45.** $-\frac{7}{3}, 2$ **47.** $\frac{7}{2}, -\frac{3}{2}$
49. $-\frac{1}{4}, \frac{5}{2}$ **53.** $2x^2 - 9x - 5 = 0$; any root $x = \frac{r}{s}$ of
$ax^2 + bx + c = 0$ comes from setting the factor $sx - r$
equal to 0 after $ax^2 + bx + c$ is written in factored
form; so, the roots $-\frac{1}{2}$ and 5 come from the factors
$2x - (-1)$, or $2x + 1$, and $x - 5$. The product of these
factors is $(2x + 1)(x - 5) = 2x^2 - 10x + x - 5 =$
$2x^2 - 9x - 5$.

9.6 Problem Solving (pp. 598–599) **59. a.** $24x^2 + 48x + 24$
b. 4 in., 2 in. **61.** 70 m, 31 m

9.7 Skill Practice (pp. 603–604) **1.** perfect square
3. $(x + 5)(x - 5)$ **5.** $(9c + 2)(9c - 2)$
7. $-3(m + 4n)(m - 4n)$ **9.** $(x - 2)^2$ **11.** $(7a + 1)^2$
13. $\left(m + \frac{1}{2}\right)^2$ **15.** $4(c + 10)(c - 10)$
17. $(2s + 3r)(2s - 3r)$ **19.** $8(3 + 2y)(3 - 2y)$
21. $(2x)^2 - 3^2$ is in the form $a^2 - b^2$, so it must
be factored using the difference of two squares
pattern, not the perfect square trinomial pattern;
$9(2x + 3)(2x - 3)$. **25.** -4 **27.** ± 3 **29.** -2 **31.** ± 12
33. $\pm \frac{7}{2}$ **35.** $\frac{5}{6}$ **37.** $\pm \frac{4}{3}$ **39.** 0, 1

9.7 Problem Solving (pp. 604–605) **47.** 2.5 sec **49.** Once;
the ball's height (in feet) is modeled by the equation
$h = -16t^2 + 56t + 5$, where t is the time (in seconds)
since it was thrown. To find when the height is
54 feet, substitute 54 for h and solve the equation
$54 = -16t^2 + 56t + 5$, or $16t^2 - 56t + 49 = 0$.
Because the left side of the equation factors as a
perfect square trinomial, $(4t - 7)^2$, the equation has
only one solution, $\frac{7}{4}$; so, the ball reaches a height
of 54 feet only once, after $\frac{7}{4}$ seconds. **51. a.** $4d^2 - 9$
b. 10 in.

9.8 Skill Practice (pp. 610–611) **1.** The polynomial is written as a monomial or as a product of a monomial and one or more prime polynomials. **3.** $(x - 8)(x + 1)$ **5.** $(z - 4)(6z - 7)$ **7.** $(b + 5)(b^2 - 3)$ **9.** $(x + 13)(x - 1)$ **11.** $(z - 1)(12 + 5z^2)$ **13.** $(x + 1)(x^2 + 2)$ **15.** $(z - 4)(z^2 + 3)$ **17.** $(a + 13)(a^2 - 5)$ **19.** $(5n - 4)(n^2 + 5)$ **21.** $(y + 1)(y + 5x)$ **23.** $x^2(x - 1)(x + 1)$ **25.** $3n^3(n - 4)(n + 4)$ **27.** $3c^7(5c - 1)(5c + 1)$ **29.** $8s^2(2s - 1)(2s + 1)$ **31.** cannot be factored **33.** $3w^2(w + 4)^2$ **35.** $(b - 5)(b - 2)(b + 2)$ **37.** $(9t - 1)(t^2 + 2)$ **39.** $7ab^3(a - 3)(a + 3)$ **43.** $-1, \pm 2$ **45.** $\frac{7}{4}, \pm 2$ **47.** $0, -5, -3$ **49.** $0, \pm 9$ **51.** $0, \pm 2$ **53.** $-\frac{1}{3}, \pm 1$

55. No; when the polynomial is factored completely, the equation becomes $(x + 2)(x^2 + 3) = 0$. When the factor $x^2 + 3$ is set equal to 0, the resulting equation, $x^2 + 3 = 0$, or $x^2 = -3$, has no real number solutions because x^2 cannot be negative. **57.** 12 ft, 4 ft, 2 ft **59.** $(2b - a)(2b - 3)(2b + 3)$ **61.** $(3x + 4)(2x - 1)$ **63.** $(4n - 3)(3n - 1)$ **65.** $(3w + 2)(7w - 2)$

9.8 Problem Solving (pp. 612–613) **69. a.** $4w^2 + 16w$ **b.** 4 in. long by 4 in. wide by 8 in. high **71. a.** 1, about -0.2 **b.** The zero $t \approx -0.2$ has no meaning because t, which represents time in seconds, cannot be negative in this situation. The zero $t = 1$ means that the ball lands on the ground 1 second after you throw it. **73. a.** $-h^3 + 5h^2 + 36h$ **b.** 4 in. long by 9 in. wide by 5 in. high, 3 in. long by 10 in. wide by 6 in. high **c.** 4 in. long by 9 in. wide by 5 in. high; the 4-inch long box has a surface area of 202 square inches and the 3-inch long box has a surface area of 216 square inches.

Chapter Review (pp. 616–620) **1.** degree of the polynomial **3.** A factorable polynomial with integer coefficients is factored completely if it is written as a product of unfactorable polynomials with integer coefficients. *Sample answer:* $3x(x - 4)(2x + 1)$ **5.** A **7.** $x^3 - 8x^2 + 15x$ **9.** $11y^5 + 4y^2 - y - 3$ **11.** $5s^3 - 7s + 13$ **13.** $x^3 - 5x^2 + 7x - 3$ **15.** $x^2 - 2x - 8$ **17.** $z^2 - 3z - 88$ **19.** $18n^2 + 27n + 7$ **21.** $3x^2 + 10x - 8$ **23.** $36y^2 + 12y + 1$ **25.** $16a^2 - 24a + 9$ **27.** $9s^2 - 25$

29. $0, 11$ **31.** $0, 9$ **33.** $0, \frac{1}{3}$ **35.** $(s + 11)(s - 1)$ **37.** $(a + 12)(a - 7)$ **39.** $(x + 8)(x - 4)$ **41.** $(c + 5)(c + 3)$ **43.** $\frac{1}{7}, 1$ **45.** $\frac{2}{3}, -2$ **47.** $-\frac{3}{2}, -3$ **49.** 3 sec **51.** $(z - 15)(z + 15)$ **53.** $12(1 - 2n)(1 + 2n)$ **55.** $(4p - 1)^2$ **57.** 1 sec **59.** $(y + 3)(y + x)$ **61.** $5s^2(s - 5)(s + 5)$ **63.** $2z(z + 6)(z - 5)$ **65.** $(2b + 3)(b - 2)(b + 2)$

Chapter 10

10.1 Skill Practice (pp. 632–633) **1.** parabola **3.** C **5.** B

7. The graph is a vertical stretch (by a factor of 2) with a reflection in the x-axis of the graph of $y = x^2$.

9. 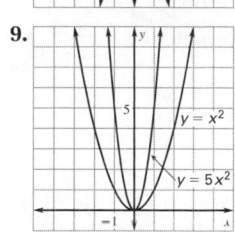 The graph is a vertical stretch (by a factor of 5) of the graph of $y = x^2$.

11. 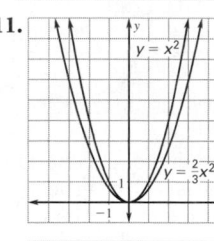 The graph is a vertical shrink $\left(\text{by a factor of } \frac{2}{3}\right)$ of the graph of $y = x^2$.

13. 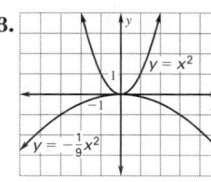 The graph is a vertical shrink $\left(\text{by a factor of } \frac{1}{9}\right)$ with a reflection in the x-axis of the graph of $y = x^2$.

15. 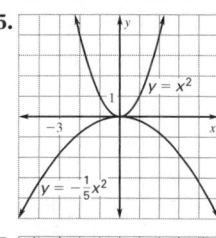 The graph is a vertical shrink $\left(\text{by a factor of } \frac{1}{5}\right)$ with a reflection in the x-axis of the graph of $y = x^2$.

17. 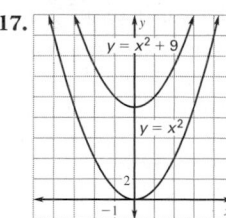 The graph is a vertical translation (of 9 units up) of the graph of $y = x^2$.

19. The graph is a vertical translation (of 4 units down) of the graph of $y = x^2$.

21. 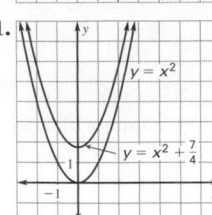 The graph is a vertical translation $\left(\text{of } \frac{7}{4} \text{ units up}\right)$ of the graph of $y = x^2$.

23. The graph of $y = x^2 - 2$ should be shifted 2 units down, not 2 units up. The vertex should be at $(0, -2)$.

25. 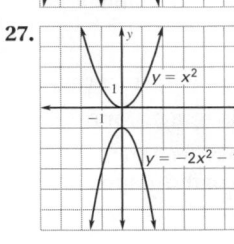 The graph is a reflection in the x-axis with a vertical translation (of 5 units up) of the graph of $y = x^2$.

27. 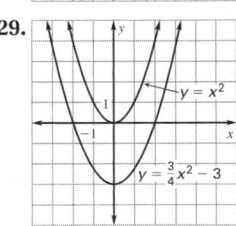 The graph is a vertical stretch (by a factor of 2) with a vertical translation (of 1 unit down) and a reflection in the x-axis of the graph of $y = x^2$.

29. The graph is a vertical shrink $\left(\text{by a factor of } \frac{3}{4}\right)$ with a vertical translation (of 3 units down) of the graph of $y = x^2$.

31. The graph is a vertical shrink $\left(\text{by a factor of } \frac{1}{2}\right)$ with a vertical translation (of 5 units down) of the graph of $y = x^2$.

35. Translate the graph of f 5 units down.

10.1 Problem Solving (pp. 633–634)

41. a.   **b.** about 16 knots
c. about 35 knots

43. a.

b. No. *Sample answer:* Let D be the diameter of a rope with 4 times the breaking weight of a rope with breaking weight d. Then $8900D^2 = 4(8900d^2)$; $D^2 = 4d^2$; $D = \sqrt{4d^2}$; $D = 2d$. Thus, the diameter of the rope with 4 times the breaking weight is only two times the diameter of the other rope.

10.2 Skill Practice (pp. 638–639) **1.** When the function is in standard form, $y = ax^2 + bx + c$, it will have a minimum value if $a > 0$ and a maximum value if $a < 0$. **3.** $x = 2$, $(2, -2)$ **5.** $x = 4$, $(4, 26)$

7. $x = -\frac{1}{2}$, $\left(-\frac{1}{2}, -\frac{3}{2}\right)$ **9.** $x = 0$, $(0, -1)$ **11.** $x = 6$, $(6, 7)$

13. The equation of the axis of symmetry is $x = \frac{-b}{2a}$, not $x = \frac{b}{2a}$; $x = \frac{-b}{2a} = \frac{-16}{2(2)}$, $x = -4$.

15.   **17.**

19. **21.**

23. **25.**

9. **11.**

13. **15.**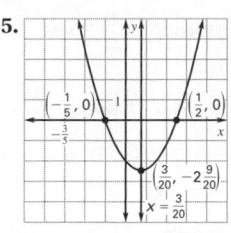

29. maximum value; 7 **31.** maximum value; -8

33. maximum value; $\frac{81}{8}$ **35.** maximum value; 54

37. The graph of $y = x^2 + 4x + 1$ is a horizontal translation (of 4 units left) of the graph of $y = x^2 - 4x + 1$.

10.2 Problem Solving (pp. 639–640) **41.** about 66 ft

43. about 243 ft

Extension (p. 642)

1. 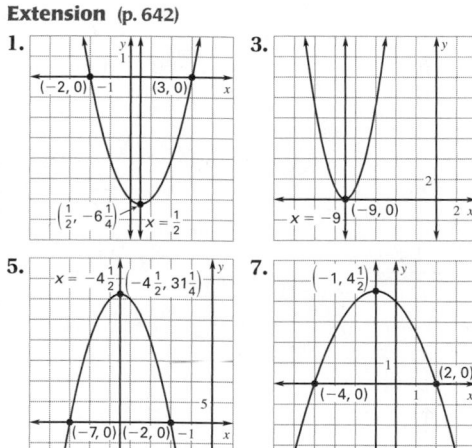 **3.**

5. **7.**

10.3 Skill Practice (pp. 647–648) **1.** $2x^2 - 9x + 11 = 0$
3. 4, 1 **5.** $-4, -2$ **7.** 8, -2 **9.** 3 **11.** -5 **13.** -7
15. no solution **17.** no solution **19.** $-6, 2$ **21.** Any solution of a quadratic equation is an x-intercept of the graph of the related quadratic function. The x-intercept of the function shown in the graph is 2, not 4; the only solution of the equation is 2. **23.** $-3, 4$

25. $-5, 2$ **27.** $-5, 4$ **29.** 1, 11 **31.** $-1\frac{1}{2}, 1$ **33.** $\frac{1}{2}$

35. no solution **37.** $-3.4, -0.6$ **39.** $-1.4, 3.4$
41. 0.8, 6.2 **43.** $-1.3, 0.8$ **45.** $-4.7, -1.3$

10.3 Problem Solving (pp. 648–649) **51.** 24.1 ft **53.** 16 ft; the distance from the nozzle to the circle is the distance between the x-intercepts of $y = -0.75x^2 + 6x$. Substitute 0 for y and solve for x: $0 = -0.75x^2 + 6x$ has solutions 0 and 8. The radius of the display circle is 8 feet, so the diameter is 16 feet.

10.3 Graphing Calculator Activity (pp. 650–651)

1. $1\frac{2}{3}$ **3.** -3.75 **5.** about -3.5 **7.** $-1.11, 3.61$

9. $-1.61, 5.61$ **11.** 0.90, 2.18 **13.** $-7.03, 2.15$ **15.** 0; the maximum or minimum value of a quadratic function occurs at the vertex of the parabola that is the graph of the function. When a quadratic function has only one zero, its graph has only one x-intercept, which must also be the x-coordinate of the vertex of the parabola. Then the y-coordinate of the vertex is 0, so the maximum or minimum value of the function is 0.

10.4 Skill Practice (pp. 656–657) **1.** square root **3.** ± 1

5. ± 10 **7.** 0 **9.** $\pm\frac{1}{2}$ **11.** $\pm\frac{7}{3}$ **13.** 0 **17.** ± 2.65 **19.** no solution **21.** 0 **23.** ± 2.24 **25.** ± 3.78 **27.** ± 1.32

31. Negative numbers do not have real number square roots, so $\pm\sqrt{-\frac{11}{7}}$ are not real numbers; there is no solution. **33.** 0.76, 5.24 **35.** -8.16, -1.84 **37.** -16.65, -11.35 **39.** -5.69, 3.69 **41.** ± 4 **43.** ± 1.41 **45.** 0.37, 13.63 **47.** 12 in. **49.** 11.66 ft **51.** $\pm\frac{6}{5}$, or ± 1.2. *Sample answer:* Rewrite the decimal as a fraction and then take square roots of each side of the equation: $x^2 = \frac{144}{100}$, so $x = \pm\sqrt{\frac{144}{100}} = \pm\frac{12}{10} = \pm\frac{6}{5}$ or ± 1.2.

10.4 Problem Solving (pp. 657–658) **59. a.** 6.8 mm **b.** 5.9 mm **c.** 5.6 mm **61. a.** $D = 4 \pm \sqrt{\frac{16V}{L}}$ **b.** 11.1 ft, 10.7 ft, 10.3 ft, 10.0 ft

10.4 Problem Solving Workshop (p. 660) **1.** about 1.5 sec **3. a.** $V = 25x^2$ **b.** length: about 9 in., width: 5 in., height: about 1.8 in.

c.

Height, x (inches)	1.7	1.8	1.9
Width (inches)	5	5	5
Length, $5x$ (inches)	8.5	9	9.5
Volume, V (cubic inches)	72.25	81	90.25

The volume in the table closest to 83 cubic inches is 81 cubic inches. To the nearest tenth of an inch, the height of the box is about 1.8 inches. The length of the box is $5x \approx 9$ inches, and the width is 5 inches. **5.** To rewrite the equation $6 = -16t^2 + 54$ so that one side is 0, you must subtract 6 from each side; $0 = -16t^2 + 48$, replace 48 with the closest perfect square, 49. $0 = -16t^2 + 49 = -(16t^2 - 49) = -(4t + 7)(4t - 7)$, so the approximate solutions of this equation are $\pm\frac{7}{4}$. Disregard the negative solution because time cannot be negative; so, it takes about $\frac{7}{4}$, or 1.75, seconds for the shoe to hit the net.

10.5 Skill Practice (pp. 666–667) **1.** completing the square **3.** 9; $(x + 3)^2$ **5.** 4; $(x - 2)^2$ **7.** $\frac{9}{4}$; $\left(x - \frac{3}{2}\right)^2$ **9.** 1.44; $(x + 1.2)^2$ **11.** $\frac{4}{9}$; $\left(x - \frac{2}{3}\right)^2$ **13.** $-12, 2$ **15.** $-6, 12$ **17.** $-7, 3$ **19.** $-10.5, -0.5$ **21.** $-0.80, 8.80$ **23.** $-2.5, -0.5$ **27.** The perfect square trinomial $x^2 - 2x + 1$ factors as $(x - 1)^2$ not $(x + 1)^2$, $(x - 1)^2 = 5$, $x - 1 = \pm\sqrt{5}$, $x = 1 \pm \sqrt{5}$. **29.** $-11.57, -0.43$ **31.** $-1.91, 0.91$ **33.** $-0.96, 6.96$ **35.** $-0.79, 2.21$ **37.** $-3.68, -0.32$ **39.** $-0.25, 0.75$ **41.** 4.87

10.5 Problem Solving (pp. 667–668) **45.** 3 ft **47. a.** $1904 = 7x^2 - 4x + 392$, 2000

b.

When $y \approx 1904$; the value of x is about 15. So the year 2000 (1985 + 15) found in part (a) is correct.

49. Yes; to find the number of days x after which the stock price was \$23.50 per share, substitute 23.5 for y and solve for x by completing the square to find that the solutions are 10 and 30. You could have sold the stock for \$23.50 per share 10 days after you purchased it.

Extension (p. 670)

1.

3.

5.

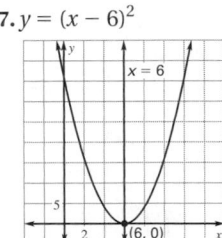

7. $y = (x - 6)^2$

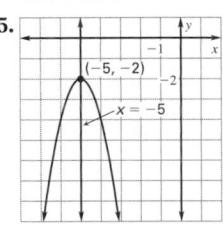

9. $y = -(x - 5)^2 + 4$

11. $y = -3(x + 1)^2 + 2$

13. $y = \frac{1}{4}(x + 6)^2 + 1$

10.6 Skill Practice (pp. 674–675) **1.** quadratic formula
3. −13, 8 **5.** −2, 2.33 **7.** −3.27, 4.27 **9.** −2.5
11. −0.63, 2.13 **13.** −2, 7 **15.** −1, 1.29 **17.** 3.27, 6.73
19. −0.54, 2.29 **21.** −0.66, 1.09 **23.** −1.77, −0.57
27. Before identifying the values of a, b, and c,
the equation must be written in standard form
$ax^2 + bx + c = 0$; $-2x^2 + 3x - 1 = 0$, so $c = -1$,
not 1; $x = \dfrac{-3 \pm \sqrt{3^2 - 4(-2)(-1)}}{2(-2)}$, $x = \dfrac{-3 \pm \sqrt{1}}{-4}$, $x = \dfrac{1}{2}$
and $x = 1$. **29–33.** Sample answers are given.
29. Using square roots, the equation can be written
in the form $x^2 = d$. **31.** Factoring, the expression
$m^2 + 5m + 6$ factors easily. **33.** Quadratic formula,
the equation does not factor easily. **35.** 4 **37.** 6
39. −1.94, 2.19 **41.** −0.41, 2.41 **43.** 5; 13 m by 7 m

10.6 Problem Solving (pp. 675–676)
47. 1993 **49. a.** 2001 **b.**

10.7 Skill Practice (pp. 681–682) **1.** $x = \dfrac{-b \pm \sqrt{b^2 - 4ac}}{2a}$,
$b^2 - 4ac$ should be circled. **3.** no solution **5.** two
solutions **7.** one solution **9.** two solutions **11.** two
solutions **13.** one solution **15.** two solutions **17.** no
solution **21.** Before calculating the discriminant,
the equation must be written in standard form:
$3x^2 - 7x + 5$. Thus, c is 5, not 9, so $b^2 - 4ac =$
$(-7)^2 - 4(3)(5) = 49 - 60 = -11$, the equation has
no solution. **23.** 2 **25.** 0 **27.** 0 **29.** 1 **31–33.** Sample
answers are given for parts (a) and (c). **31. a.** 0 **b.** 1
c. 2 **33. a.** 8 **b.** 9 **c.** 10 **35.** On; the value of the
discriminant is $(-6)^2 - 4(3)(3) = 0$, so the graph has
exactly one x-intercept. A parabola that has exactly
one x-intercept must have its vertex on the x-axis.
37. Below; $a < 0$, so the graph opens down. The
value of the discriminant is $(10)^2 - 4(-15)(-25) =$
$-1400 < 0$, so the graph has no x-intercepts; a
parabola that opens down and has no x-intercepts
must have its vertex below the x-axis. **39.** On; the
value of the discriminant is $(-24)^2 - 4(9)(16) = 0$,
so the graph has exactly one x-intercept; a parabola
that has exactly one x-intercept must have its vertex
on the x-axis. **41. a.** $314 = 2w^2 + 40w + 64$ **b.** 2
c. −25, 5; the width w cannot be negative, so the
solution −25 meters does not make sense in the
context of the problem. The solution 5 meters does
makes sense in the context of the problem.

10.7 Problem Solving (pp. 682–683) **45. a.** Substitute
25 for y in the equation and then write the resulting
quadratic equation in standard form: $25 = 0.06x^2 -$
$4x + 87$, or $0 = 0.06x^2 - 4x + 62$. Evaluate the
discriminant: $b^2 - 4ac = (-4)^2 - 4(0.06)(62) = 1.12$.
Since the discriminant is positive, we know that
the equation $25 = 0.06x^2 - 4x + 87$ does have
solutions, so it is possible for a parakeet to consume
25 milliliters of oxygen per gram of body mass
per hour. **b.** 24.5 km/h and 42.2 km/h **47.** No;
to determine if there is any point of the arch at a
height of 4 feet, substitute 4 for y in the equation
and then determine if the equation has any positive
solutions. The equation is $4 = -0.18x^2 + 1.6x$, or
$0 = -0.18x^2 + 1.6x - 4$. Evaluate the discriminant:
$b^2 - 4ac = (1.6)^2 - 4(-0.18)(-4) = -0.32$. Since the
discriminant is negative, we know the equation has
no solution; thus, a child who is 4 feet tall cannot
walk under one of the arches without having to
bend over. **49. a.** $h = -16t^2 + 32t + 6$ **b.** no **c.** yes;
about 0.8 sec and about 1.4 sec

10.8 Skill Practice (pp. 688–689) **1.** exponential
function **3.** B **5.** A **7.** linear function **9.** exponential
function **11.** quadratic function **13.** quadratic
function; $y = -x^2$ **15.** linear function; $y = 3x + 1$
17. exponential function; $y = 4\left(\dfrac{1}{4}\right)^x$ **19.** The x- and
y-values were reversed when substituting the
coordinates of the ordered pair (2, 10) into the
equation $y = ax^2$. Substituting 2 for x and 10 for
y gives $10 = a(2)^2$, $a = 2.5$; so, the equation is
$y = 2.5x^2$. **21.** $A = \left(\dfrac{\sqrt{3}}{4}\right)s^2$; $25\sqrt{3}$ cm^2

10.8 Problem Solving (pp. 689–691)
23. linear function; $y = 0.34x + 24.6$
25. a.

Folds	1	2	3	4	5
Sections	2	4	8	16	32

b.

exponential function
c. $y = 2^x$; 128 sections

27. a. quadratic function; $d = 0.82t^2$ **b.** 0.205 ft
c. The period decreases by about 71%. For example, consider $t = 4$ for $d = 13.12$. To find t for 50% of d, solve $0.5(13.12) = 0.82t^2$; $t \approx 2.83$, and $\frac{2.83}{4} = 0.708$, so the period decreased by about 71%. Consider $t = 2$ for $d = 3.28$. To find t for 50% of d, solve $0.5(3.28) = 0.82t^2$; $t \approx 1.41$, and $\frac{1.41}{2} = 0.705$, so the period decreased by about 71%. Consider $t = 1$ for $d = 0.82$. To find t for 50% of d, solve $0.5(0.82) = 0.82t^2$; $t \approx 0.707$, and $\frac{0.707}{1} = 0.707$, so the period decreased by about 71%.

10.8 Graphing Calculator Activity (pp. 692–693)
1. $y = 15{,}600(0.866)^x$
3. $y = 179(0.987)^x$, $y = 0.040x^2 - 4.13x + 197$

The exponential model; although the quadratic model appears to fit the given data points more closely than the exponential model does, the graph shows that after the last data point, (60, 90), the quadratic model implies increasing temperatures as time goes on, while the exponential model shows gradually decreasing temperatures as time goes on; the exponential model is a more accurate model of what will happen as the hot chocolate continues to cool.

Chapter Review (pp. 696–700)
1. axis of symmetry **3.** maximum

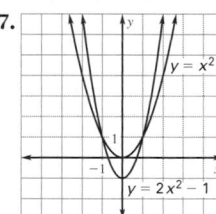

The graph is a vertical stretch (by a factor of 4) with a reflection in the x-axis of the graph of $y = x^2$.

7.

The graph is a vertical stretch (by a factor of 2) with a vertical translation (of 1 unit down) of the graph of $y = x^2$.

9.

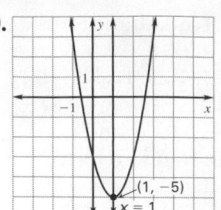

11. no solution **13.** $-8, 1$ **15.** no solution **17.** ± 0.76
19. 2.71, 5.29 **21.** 0.32, -6.32 **23.** $-0.62, 1.62$
25. $-3.89, 0.39$ **27.** 0.16, 1.24 **29.** $-1.22, 1$
31. no solution **33.** two solutions **35.** two solutions
37. exponential function

Cumulative Review (pp. 706–707) **1.** 3 **3.** 0.2 **5.** -1
7.

9.

11.

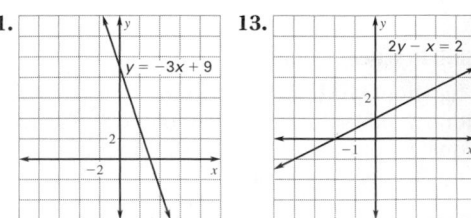

13.

15. $y = \frac{1}{5}x + 3$ **17.** $y = -2x + 19$
19. $x < -36$
21. $b \geq -1$
23. $-\frac{3}{2} \leq c \leq 7$
25. all real numbers **27.** $-729r^3$ **29.** $\frac{81x^3}{y^2}$
31.

33. $-x^2 + 12x + 12$ **35.** $2z^2 + 11z - 63$
37. $-3q^3 + 11q - 2$ **39.** $4k^2 - 44k + 121$
41. $(x + 12)(x - 6)$ **43.** $(5d + 6)^2$
45. $(z - 6)(z + 2)(z - 2)$

47. 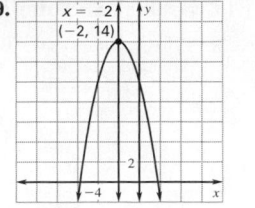 **49.**

51. ±3.32 **53.** 0.5, 3 **55.** −0.57, 1 **57.** $475
59. length 19 in., width: 8 in.

61. a. 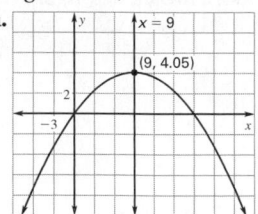 **b.** 18 ft

Chapter 11

11.1 Skill Practice (pp. 713–714) **1.** radical function

3. 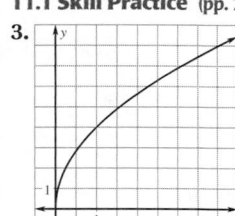 domain: $x \geq 0$, range: $y \geq 0$; vertical stretch by a factor of 4

5. 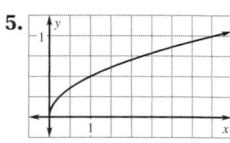 domain: $x \geq 0$, range: $y \geq 0$; vertical shrink by a factor of 0.5

7. 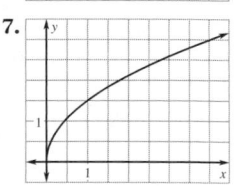 domain: $x \geq 0$, range: $y \geq 0$; vertical stretch by a factor of $\frac{3}{2}$

9. domain: $x \geq 0$, range: $y \leq 0$; vertical stretch by a factor of 3 with a reflection in the x-axis

11. 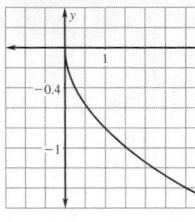 domain: $x \geq 0$, range: $y \leq 0$; vertical shrink by a factor of 0.8 with a reflection in the x-axis

13. domain: $x \geq 0$, range: $y \leq 0$; vertical shrink by a factor of $\frac{1}{4}$ with a reflection in the x-axis

17. domain: $x \geq 0$, range: $y \geq 1$; vertical translation 1 unit up

19. domain: $x \geq 0$, range: $y \geq -3$; vertical translation 3 units down

21. domain: $x \geq 0$, range: $y \geq \frac{3}{4}$; vertical translation $\frac{3}{4}$ unit up

23. domain: $x \geq 1$, range: $y \geq 0$; horizontal translation 1 unit right

25. domain: $x \geq -2$, range: $y \geq 0$; horizontal translation 2 units left

27. domain: $x \geq -1.5$, range: $y \geq 0$; horizontal translation 1.5 units left

31.

33.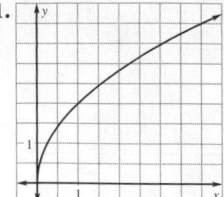

11.1 Graphing Calculator Activity (p. 717)

1. domain: $x \geq 0$, range: $y \geq 0$

35.

37.

3. 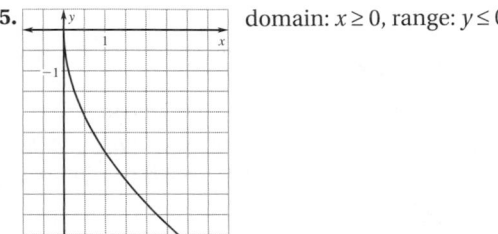 domain: $x \geq 0$, range: $y \geq 0$

11.1 Problem Solving (pp. 715–716)

43. a. domain: $x \geq 0$, range: $y \geq 0$

b. about 1024 ft

5. domain: $x \geq 0$, range: $y \leq 0$

45. domain: $x \geq 0$, range: $y \geq 0$; about 0.9 m

7. domain: $x \geq 0$, range: $y \geq 0$

47. a. 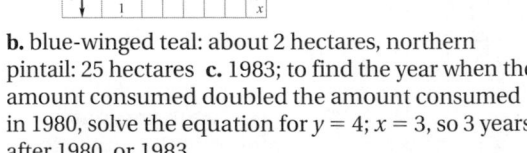 blue-winged teal's domain: $x \geq 0$, range: $y \geq 0$, northern pintail's domain: $x \geq 0$, range: $y \geq 0$

$y = 0.7\sqrt{x}$

$y = 0.2\sqrt{x}$

b. blue-winged teal: about 2 hectares, northern pintail: 25 hectares **c.** 1983; to find the year when the amount consumed doubled the amount consumed in 1980, solve the equation for $y = 4$; $x = 3$, so 3 years after 1980, or 1983.

9. 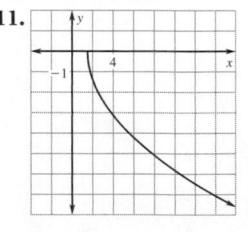 domain: $x \geq -\frac{4}{3}$, range: $y \geq 0$

11. domain: $x \geq \frac{3}{2}$, range: $y \leq 0$

13. a.

domain: $x \geq 0$, range: $y \geq 0$

b. about 154.3 m

11.2 Skill Practice (pp. 723–724) **1.** rationalizing the denominator **3.** $2\sqrt{5}$ **5.** $4\sqrt{6}$ **7.** $5\sqrt{5b}$ **9.** $9m\sqrt{m}$
11. $5\sqrt{6}$ **13.** $2x\sqrt{7}$ **15.** $2a^2b^2\sqrt{b}$ **17.** mn **19.** $\frac{2}{7}$ **21.** $\frac{a\sqrt{a}}{11}$
25. *Sample answer:* Simplify $\sqrt{45}$ to $\sqrt{9} \cdot \sqrt{5} = 3\sqrt{5}$.
Then multiply $3\sqrt{5} \cdot \sqrt{5} = 3 \cdot 5 = 15$. Or, combine
the expressions to create $\sqrt{45 \cdot 5} = \sqrt{225} = 15$.
27. $\frac{4\sqrt{3}}{3}$ **29.** $\frac{\sqrt{13}}{13}$ **31.** $\frac{\sqrt{2x}}{2x}$ **33.** $\frac{2\sqrt{6n}}{3n^2}$ **35.** $-5\sqrt{5}$
37. $37\sqrt{2}$ **39.** $7\sqrt{7} - 5\sqrt{14}$ **41.** $21\sqrt{2} + 6\sqrt{6}$
43. $18 - \sqrt{2}$ **45.** $6\sqrt{7} + 6\sqrt{3} + 2\sqrt{14} + 2\sqrt{6}$
47. $16s^3t\sqrt{2rt}$ **49.** $\frac{h\sqrt{10gf}}{5f^2}$ **51.** $\frac{\sqrt{5}}{10}$ **53.** $\frac{3\sqrt{x} + 4x\sqrt{x}}{x^2}$
55. $\frac{\sqrt{7} - 1}{6}$ **57.** $\frac{7\sqrt{10} + 2\sqrt{5}}{47}$ **59.** $3\sqrt{7} - 3\sqrt{6}$
61. $-2\sqrt{3} - 3\sqrt{2}$ **63.** $(a\sqrt{b} + c\sqrt{d})(a\sqrt{b} - c\sqrt{d}) =$
$a^2b - ac\sqrt{bd} + ac\sqrt{bd} - c^2d = a^2b - c^2d$ **65.** $-x$

11.2 Problem Solving (pp. 725–726) **67.** about 9.54%
69. a. 5 yd^2 **b.** The side length s is in yd, and $\sqrt{\frac{S}{6}}$ is
$\sqrt{\text{yd}^2} = \text{yd}$. **c.** 0.9 yd **71. a.** $S = \frac{\sqrt{hw}}{60}$ **b.** Yes. *Sample
answer:* If the mass stays the same, then the greater
the height the greater the body surface area will be.

Extension (pp. 727–728) **1.** $-2 - \sqrt{2}, -2 + \sqrt{2}$
3. $-4 - 2\sqrt{2}, -4 + 2\sqrt{2}$ **5.** $-1 - \frac{2\sqrt{3}}{3}, -1 + \frac{2\sqrt{3}}{3}$
7. $\frac{1}{5} - \frac{\sqrt{11}}{5}, \frac{1}{5} + \frac{\sqrt{11}}{5}$ **9.** $\frac{1}{2} - \frac{\sqrt{13}}{2}, \frac{1}{2} + \frac{\sqrt{13}}{2}$
11. $\frac{7}{2} - \frac{\sqrt{61}}{2}, \frac{7}{2} + \frac{\sqrt{61}}{2}$ **13.** $2 - \sqrt{2}, 2 + \sqrt{2}$
15. $-\frac{\sqrt{6}}{3}, \frac{\sqrt{6}}{3}$ **17.** $-\frac{1}{6} - \frac{\sqrt{73}}{6}, -\frac{1}{6} + \frac{\sqrt{73}}{6}$ **21.** Sum: $-\frac{b}{a}$,
product: $\frac{c}{a}$. *Sample answer:* $y = 2x^2 - 4x + 1$

11.3 Skill Practice (pp. 732–733) **1.** extraneous
solution **3.** 4 **5.** 48 **7.** 29 **9.** 8 **11.** $-\frac{75}{2}$ **13.** 47 **15.** -2
17. 7 **19.** no real solutions **23.** 1 **25.** $\frac{3}{8}, \frac{1}{2}$ **27.** -2

29. *Sample answer:* The solution $x = -9$ does not
check in the original equation, so it is an extraneous
solution. The only real solution is $x = 2$. **31.** no real
solutions **33.** $\frac{16}{5}$

11.3 Problem Solving (pp. 733–734) **37.** 1977 **39.** 2.1 m

11.4 Skill Practice (pp. 740–741) **1.** hypotenuse
3. $b = 4$ **5.** $c = \sqrt{61}$ **7.** $c = 8\sqrt{2}$ **9.** $c = 4\sqrt{13}$ **11.** $a = 8$
13. $a = 1.6$ **17.** 2, 4 **19.** 3, 4, 5, or 7, 24, 25 **21.** 2 in.,
6 in. **23.** not a right triangle **25.** not a right triangle
27. right triangle **31.** *Sample answer:* Let $m = 3$
and $n = 6$. Then $a = 6^2 - 3^2 = 27$, $b = 2(3)(6) = 36$,
$c = 6^2 + 3^2 = 45$; substitute the values from the
equation for a, b, and c in the Pythagorean theorem:
$(n^2 - m^2)^2 + (2mn)^2 = (n^2 + m^2)^2$. Simplify to
$n^4 - 2m^2n^2 + m^4 + 4m^2n^2 = n^4 + 2m^2n^2 + m^4$;
$-2m^2n^2 + 4m^2n^2 = 2m^2n^2$; $2 = 2$. The equations
are equal, so by the converse of the Pythagorean
theorem, the lengths a, b, and c are a Pythagorean
triple.

11.4 Problem Solving (pp. 741–742) **33.** 16 ft **35.** No;
the sum of the squares of the two shorter sides
is not equal to the square of the longer side.
37. a. $\sqrt{6}$ **b.** $\sqrt{8}$ **c.** $\sqrt{n + 1}$. *Sample answer:* A list of
the hypotenuse lengths for the first few triangles is
$\sqrt{2}, \sqrt{3}, \sqrt{4}, \sqrt{5}, \ldots$. A general formula for this series
is $c_n = \sqrt{n + 1}$.

11.5 Skill Practice (pp. 747–748) **1.** midpoint **3.** 1
5. 5 **7.** $\sqrt{53}$ **9.** $2\sqrt{17}$ **11.** $\sqrt{397}$ **13.** $\sqrt{73}$ **17.** 1, 25
19. -11, 1 **21.** -7, 15 **23.** $(5, -5)$ **25.** $(1, -4)$
27. $(-11, -6)$ **29.** $(-2, 0)$ **31.** $(-8, -4.5)$
33. $(-21, -33)$ **35.** *Sample answer:* The square of
the difference in the x values and the square of the
difference in the y values should be added, not
subtracted; $d = \sqrt{(3 - (-17))^2 + (8 - (-2))^2} =$
$\sqrt{400 + 100} = \sqrt{500} = 10\sqrt{5}$. **39.** $(8, -2)$ **41.** right
triangle **43.** not a right triangle **45.** *Sample answer:*
Use the distance formula to find the distance
between the midpoint and each of the endpoints.
If they are equal, the midpoint is equidistant from
each endpoint.

11.5 Problem Solving (pp. 748–750) **47. a.** 10 mi
b. $\sqrt{2}$ times greater **49. a.** the anchor and the cup
b. the belt buckle and the sword; the anchor and the
sword **51.** Yes; yes; all of them; the quadrilateral is
a square.

11.5 Problem Solving Workshop (p. 751) **1. a.** Natural
History Museum **b.** 0.24 mi

Chapter Review (pp. 754–756) **1.** It is a vertical stretch by a factor of 3 of the graph of $y = \sqrt{x}$. **3.** converse of the Pythagorean theorem

5.
domain: $x \geq 0$, range: $y \leq 0$; vertical stretch by a factor of 2 with a reflection in the x-axis

7.
domain: $x \geq -7$, range: $y \geq 0$; horizontal translation of 7 units to the left

9. $11x\sqrt{x}$ **11.** $7x\sqrt{7}$ **13.** $\frac{2\sqrt{5}}{5}$ **15.** $2\sqrt{2} - 2\sqrt{3}$ **17.** 784 **19.** 5 **21.** no real solutions **23.** $c = \sqrt{218}$ **25.** $b = \sqrt{57}$ **27.** $a = \sqrt{209}$ **29.** 2036 ft **31.** 10 **33.** $(3.5, -4)$ **35.** $(5, -2)$

Chapter 12

12.1 Skill Practice (pp. 769–770) **1.** -3 **3.** direct variation **5.** neither **7.** inverse variation **9.** direct variation **11.** inverse variation **13.** direct variation

15. **17.**

19. **21.**

23. **25.**

27. An inverse variation equation is in the form $y = \frac{a}{x}$, not $y = ax$; $8 = \frac{a}{2}$, $16 = a$. The correct inverse variation equation is $y = \frac{16}{x}$. **29.** $y = \frac{21}{x}$; 10.5 **31.** $y = \frac{-13}{x}$; -6.5 **33.** $y = \frac{132}{x}$; 66 **35.** $y = \frac{-18}{x}$; -9 **37.** $y = \frac{20}{x}$; 10 **39.** $y = \frac{70}{x}$; 35 **41.** $y = \frac{66}{x}$; 33 **45.** not inverse variation **47.** inverse variation; $y = \frac{24}{x}$ **49.** $2\pi r = C$; direct variation **51.** $Bh = 400$; inverse variation

12.1 Problem Solving (pp. 770–772) **55.** $d = \frac{175,000}{p}$; 350 units **57. a.** yes; $f = \frac{22,000}{\ell}$

b. about 748 Hz **c.** The frequency increases; yes. **59. a.** $s = \frac{35}{a}$ inverse variation

b. 4; when $s = 4$, the diameter of the aperture is $a = \frac{35}{4} = 8.75$ millimeters, and when $s = 8$, the diameter of the aperture is $a = \frac{35}{8} = 4.375$ millimeters.

1. $x = 3$, $y = -6$

3. Domain: all real numbers except 0, range: all real numbers except 0; the graph is a vertical stretch of the graph of $y = \frac{1}{x}$.

5. Domain: all real numbers except 0, range: all real numbers except 0; the graph is a vertical stretch of the graph of $y = \frac{1}{x}$ that is then reflected in the x-axis.

7. Domain: all real numbers except 0, range: all real numbers except 0; the graph is a vertical shrink of the graph of $y = \frac{1}{x}$ that is then reflected in the x-axis.

9. Domain: all real numbers except 0, range: all real numbers except -5; the graph is a vertical translation (of 5 units down) of the graph of $y = \frac{1}{x}$.

11. Domain: all real numbers except 0, range: all real numbers except 8; the graph is a vertical translation (of 8 units up) of the graph of $y = \frac{1}{x}$.

13. Domain: all real numbers except -3, range: all real numbers except 0; the graph is a horizontal translation (of 3 units left) of the graph of $y = \frac{1}{x}$.

15. Domain: all real numbers except -8, range: all real numbers except 0; the graph is a horizontal translation (of 8 units left) of the graph of $y = \frac{1}{x}$.

17. 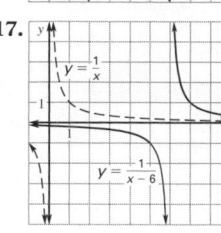 Domain: all real numbers except 6, range: all real numbers except 0; the graph is a horizontal translation (of 6 units right) of the graph of $y = \frac{1}{x}$.

19.

21.

23.

25.

27.

29. *Sample answer:* $y = \frac{1}{x + 1} + 2$ **31.** To identify the asymptotes of the hyperbola, write its equation in the form $y = \frac{a}{x - h} + k$: $y = \frac{-2}{x - 6} + 7$; thus the horizontal asymptote is $y = 7$, not $y = -7$. **33.** $y = \frac{-28}{x + 2} + 5$

35. $y = \frac{-28}{x + 4} - 4$

37. a. $h = \dfrac{100}{b_2 + 4}$

domain: $b_2 > 0$, range: $0 < h < 25$ **b.** about 13

12.2 Problem Solving (pp. 780–782)

39. $C = \dfrac{900}{p} + 400p$

41. a. $C = \dfrac{22}{r + 2}$

b.

13 additional rentals

43.

Domain: $d \geq 32.8$, range: $0 \leq p < 0.859$; the percent of time gliding increases.

12.3 Skill Practice (pp. 788–789) **1.** monomial
3. $2x^2 - 3x + 4$ **5.** $-2r^3 + 5r + 12$ **7.** $3v + 5$
9. $m - 4$ **11.** $a - 4 + \dfrac{-1}{a - 1}$ **13.** $3p - 13 + \dfrac{18}{3 + p}$
15. $x + 3 + \dfrac{-12}{6 + x}$ **17.** $-t - 3 + \dfrac{-4}{t - 3}$ **21.** When subtracting $8x - 24$ from $8x - 9$, the result is $-9 - (-24) = -9 + 24 = 15$; $(8x - 9) \div (x - 3) = 8 + \dfrac{15}{x - 3}$.

23.

25.

27.

29.

31. $\dfrac{7}{6} + \dfrac{2}{\ell}$ **35.** 10 **37.** -5

12.3 Problem Solving (pp. 789–791)

43. $C = \dfrac{80 + 3d}{d}$

45. a. $C = \dfrac{0.4t - 360}{t}$

b.

The average cost increases.
c. about 1030 min

47. a.

The number of households with VCRs increased.

b. No; as x increases, the graph of the function approaches its horizontal asymptote $y = 120$ from below, so the value of y will never exceed 120 million if this model applies to years beyond 2000.

49. a. $y = \dfrac{2r + 2\ell}{r\ell}$

b. More efficient; the graph in part (a) shows that as the length increases, the ratio decreases, implying that the microorganism becomes more efficient at performing metabolic tasks. **c.** The microorganism's efficiency would increase. *Sample answer:* Suppose the length is fixed at 50 micrometers. Then $y = \frac{2r + 100}{50r}$, or $y = \frac{2}{r} + 0.04$. This equation has the same graph as the graph shown in part (a); from the graph we see that as the radius increases, the ratio decreases, implying that the microorganism's efficiency increases.

12.3 Graphing Calculator Activity (pp. 792–793)

1. vertical: $x = 2$, horizontal: $y = 0$

3. vertical: none, horizontal: $y = 0$

5. vertical: $x = -3$, $x = 3$, horizontal: $y = 0$

9. vertical: $x = 1$, horizontal: $y = 5$

11. vertical: none, horizontal: $y = 3$

13. vertical: $x = -1$, $x = 1$, horizontal: $y = 3$

15. Vertical lines $x = a$, where a is an x-value that makes the denominator of the rational function equal to 0. **17.** $y = a$, where a is the quotient of the leading coefficient of the numerator and the leading coefficient of the denominator.

12.4 Skill Practice (pp. 797–798) **1.** excluded value

3. none **5.** -1 **7.** none **9.** $0, \frac{1}{2}$ **11.** When finding the excluded values you must find the values for which the denominator of the original expression, $2x^2 - 11x + 12$, is 0; the excluded values are $\frac{3}{2}$ and 4.

13. $\frac{2x}{5}$; none **15.** $-3a$; 0 **17.** 3; -11 **19.** -2; 3

21. $\frac{2}{f^2 - 9}$; ± 3 **23.** $\frac{1}{h - 4}$; $-3, 4$ **25.** $\frac{-6}{2w - 5}$; $0, \frac{5}{2}$

27. 3; 0, 4 **29.** $\frac{s + 8}{s - 1}$; $-8, 1$ **31.** $\frac{1}{m^2 + 5m}$; 0, -5 **33.** No; the two expressions do not have the same excluded values; the excluded values for $\frac{x^2 + x}{x^2 - 1}$ are ± 1, while the excluded values for $\frac{x^2}{x^2 - x}$ are 0 and 1. The expressions are not equivalent for $x = 0$ and for $x = -1$. **37.** $\frac{3(x + 2)}{x(x + 6)}$

12.4 Problem Solving (pp. 799–800)

41. $p = \frac{3x^2 - 12}{22x^2 + 2500}$; about 11% **43.** $p = \frac{-202x + 3660}{345x + 9130}$; the percent of wood houses decreased.

45. a. $\frac{37,500 + 2500x}{125 + x}$; about \$5 million

b. revenue increased

c. No; if the price per copy of printed music went up during the period 1988–2002, then the revenue may have increased without the number of copies sold increasing.

12.5 Skill Practice (pp. 806–807) **1.** multiplicative inverse **3.** $\dfrac{15}{14p^2}$ **5.** $\dfrac{-(v-3)}{5(v+1)}$ **7.** $\dfrac{x+4}{2x+1}$ **9.** $\dfrac{-3m}{m-2}$

11. To divide by the rational expression $\dfrac{15x^3}{2}$, you

must multiply by its multiplicative inverse, $\dfrac{2}{15x^3}$;

$\dfrac{x^3}{5} \cdot \dfrac{2}{15x^3} = \dfrac{2x^3}{75x^3} = \dfrac{2}{75}$. **13.** $\dfrac{20r^3}{9}$ **15.** $\dfrac{2w+5}{w(w-9)}$ **17.** $\dfrac{a+5}{3a^2}$

19. 1 **23.** $8x^2 \cdot \dfrac{1}{2x^3}; \dfrac{4}{x}$ **25.** $\dfrac{1}{x^2-3x-4} \div \dfrac{2}{x^2-1}; \dfrac{x-1}{2(x-4)}$

27. *Sample answer:* $\dfrac{x^2-2x-3}{x^2-2x-8}, \dfrac{x^2-9x+20}{x^2-4x-5}$

29. $(x-1)(x-3)$. *Sample answer:* 0

12.5 Problem Solving (pp. 807–809)

33. $p = \dfrac{100+2.2x}{(1-0.014x)(1500+63x)}$; about 7%

35. a. $R = \dfrac{(86+180x)(1+0.014x)}{(1+0.024x)(23+38x)}$

b.

Year	1990	1991	1992	1993	1994	1995	1996
Rushing average, *R* (yards per attempt)	3.74	4.32	4.42	4.44	4.44	4.42	4.40

Year	1997	1998	1999	2000	2001	2002
Rushing average, *R* (yards per attempt)	4.38	4.35	4.33	4.30	4.28	4.25

Smith's career rushing average increased for the first several years and then began to decrease.

37. a. $T = \dfrac{4700-74x}{(1-0.053x)(0.015x^2+4.1)}$

b.

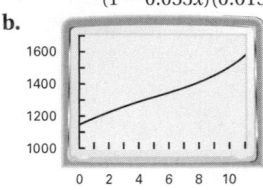

The number of tickets increased. No; the graph only shows how the *ratio* of the gross revenue and the ticket prices changed. *R* and *P* could go up and/or down while their ratio increases.

c.

The points of the scatter plot are very close to the graph of the model for all years except 1998, 1999, and 2002.

Extension (p. 811) **1.** $\dfrac{3x^3}{28}$ **3.** $\dfrac{x}{2(x-3)(x-7)}$ **5.** $x^2(x-1)$

7. $\dfrac{5(x+4)}{2}$ **9.** $\dfrac{2(x+3)(x-1)}{5(3x+1)}$ **11.** $\dfrac{3(r+\ell)}{rh}$

13. No; $\dfrac{\frac{a}{b}}{c} = \dfrac{a}{b} \div c = \dfrac{a}{b} \cdot \dfrac{1}{c} = \dfrac{a}{bc}$ and $\dfrac{a}{\frac{b}{c}} = a \div \dfrac{b}{c} = $

$\dfrac{a}{1} \cdot \dfrac{c}{b} = \dfrac{ac}{b}$. Thus, $\dfrac{\frac{a}{b}}{c} \neq \dfrac{a}{\frac{b}{c}}$.

12.6 Skill Practice (pp. 816–817) **1.** least common denominator **3.** $\dfrac{1}{x}$ **5.** $\dfrac{4}{z}$ **7.** $\dfrac{2b+1}{b-3}$ **9.** $\dfrac{-1}{m^2+1}$

11. $\dfrac{3r+1}{r^2+r-7}$ **13.** $60v^3$ **15.** $(s+2)(s-1)$

17. $(u+7)(u+1)(u-3)$ **19.** To rewrite each rational expression using the least common denominator, you must multiply its numerator by the factor of the LCD that is missing from the denominator; the numerator $5x$ should be multiplied by $(x+3)$ and the numerator 2 should be multiplied by $(x-4)$;

$\dfrac{5x}{x-4} + \dfrac{2}{x+3} = \dfrac{5x(x+3)}{(x-4)(x+3)} + \dfrac{2(x-4)}{(x-4)(x+3)} =$

$\dfrac{5x^2+15x+2x-8}{(x-4)(x+3)} = \dfrac{5x^2+17x--8}{(x-4)(x+3)}$.

21. $\dfrac{149}{33y}$ **23.** $\dfrac{5r^2-17r}{(r-2)(r-3)}$ **25.** $\dfrac{4c^2+13c+30}{(c-6)(3c+10)}$

27. $\dfrac{-20f^2+7f+12}{7f(f+4)}$ **29.** $\dfrac{3j^2-12j-1}{(j+1)(j-1)(j-6)}$

31. $\dfrac{-v^2+6v+20}{(2v+5)(v-3)(v+5)}$ **33.** $\dfrac{s-2\ell w}{2(\ell+w)}$

35. $\dfrac{15x^2+120x+20}{(x-2)(x+8)}$ **37.** $\dfrac{-3x^2+29x-4}{x-9}$

39. $y = \dfrac{-4x-16}{x+2}$

12.6 Problem Solving (pp. 817–819) **43.** $t = \dfrac{400r-1000}{r(r-5)}$;

about 8.4 h **45. a.** $\dfrac{2A^2-200A}{3}; \dfrac{7A^2+18,750A-250,050}{150}$

b. 2600 lb; 6301 lb **47.** $f = \dfrac{2.5+0.215x}{5.3+0.30x}$; about 58%

12.7 Skill Practice (pp. 823–824) **1.** rational equation

3. ± 10 **5.** $-1\dfrac{1}{2}$ **7.** $-1\dfrac{1}{2}, 4$ **9.** $-6, 5$ **11.** 6 **13.** The distributive property must be used to find the product of 5 and $(4x+1)$; $5(4x+1) = 3(8x-1)$, $20x+5 = 24x-3$, $8 = 4x$, $2 = x$. The solution is 2.

15. -10 **17.** -22 **19.** $2 \pm 2\sqrt{3}$ **21.** no solution

23. $-\dfrac{1}{5}, -1$ **25.** All real numbers except 2; 2; two fractions with equal denominators must also have equal numerators, so $x = 2$, and the denominator of both fractions is $2 - a$. The equation has this one solution as long as the denominator $2 - a$ is not 0; so, the equation has no solution when $a = 2$.

27. a. $\left(\frac{8}{3}, 9\right)$, $(-2, -5)$ **b.**

29. No; suppose that $\dfrac{x + a}{x + 1 + a} = \dfrac{x}{x + 1}$. Then, using the cross products property, $(x + 1)(x + a) = x(x + 1 + a)$; $x^2 + xa + x + a = x^2 + x + xa$; $x^2 + x(a + 1) + a = x^2 + x(1 + a)$. Then, subtracting $x^2 + x(1 + a)$ from both sides gives the result $a = 0$; so, the only value of a for which the equation is true is 0.

12.7 Problem Solving (pp. 824–826) **31.** 50 consecutive shots **33.** 3 c **35. a.** $\dfrac{30}{t} + \dfrac{30}{1.5t} = 1$; 50 min **b.** Change each 30 to 20, and change 1.5 to 1; 40 min. **c.** Because you now both rake at the same rate, whenever you work together, the time it takes to rake a portion of the lawn will be half the time it takes either of you to rake that portion alone. Suppose you rake together for m minutes. Then you each rake $\dfrac{m}{40}$ of the lawn, and together you rake $\dfrac{m}{40} + \dfrac{m}{40} = \dfrac{2m}{40} = \dfrac{m}{20}$ of the lawn. To rake $\dfrac{m}{20}$ of the lawn alone would take you $2m$ minutes. **37.** From 8 psi to 7 psi; substitute the given psi values for p in the given equation and then solve for a: for $p = 10$, $a \approx 10{,}722$; for $p = 9$, $a \approx 13{,}536$; for $p = 8$, $a \approx 16{,}600$; for $p = 7$, $a \approx 19{,}948$. The change in altitude when the atmospheric pressure changes from 10 psi to 9 psi is about $13{,}536 - 10{,}722 = 2814$, and the change in altitude when the atmospheric pressure changes from 8 psi to 7 psi is about $19{,}948 - 16{,}600 = 3348$.

12.7 Problem Solving Workshop (p. 828)
1. $1250 **3.** 6 free throws **5.** 75 min

Chapter Review (pp. 831–834) **1.** asymptote **3.** $x = -2$, $y = -4$ **5.** $y = \dfrac{63}{x}$, 12.6 **7.** inverse variation; $y = \dfrac{-8}{x}$

9.

11. $x + 5$ **13.** $z - 1 + \dfrac{4}{z + 5}$

15. $a = \dfrac{500 + 2d}{d}$

17. $-2, 6$ **19.** $\dfrac{m - 3}{4}$; 0 **21.** $\dfrac{-(r + 2)}{r + 1}$; $-1, 2$ **23.** $\dfrac{21v^7}{4}$ **25.** $\dfrac{-8x + 33}{5x - 3}$ **27.** $\dfrac{5c^2 - 13c - 48}{(c + 1)(c - 4)(c + 2)}$ **29.** $-6, 9$ **31.** $\dfrac{-21}{5}$

Chapter 13

13.1 Skill Practice (pp. 846–847) **1.** probability
3. 12 outcomes; R1, R2, R3, R4, W1, W2, W3, W4, B1, B2, B3, B4 **5.** 48; HHH1, HHH2, HHH3, HHH4, HHH5, HHH6, HHT1, HHT2, HHT3, HHT4, HHT5, HHT6, HTH1, HTH2, HTH3, HTH4, HTH5, HTH6, HTT1, HTT2, HTT3, HTT4, HTT5, HTT6, THH1, THH2, THH3, THH4, THH5, THH6, THT1, THT2, THT3, THT4, THT5, THT6, TTH1, TTH2, TTH3, TTH4, TTH5, TTH6, TTT1, TTT2, TTT3, TTT4, TTT5, TTT6

7. $\dfrac{9}{10}$ **9.** $\dfrac{1}{10}$ **11.** $\dfrac{3}{7}$ or $3 : 7$ **13.** *Sample answer:* Odds in favor is the number of favorable outcomes divided by the number of unfavorable outcomes; odds in favor of a multiple of $3 = \dfrac{\text{Number of favorable outcomes}}{\text{Number of unfavorable outcomes}} = \dfrac{9}{1}$ or $9 : 1$. **15.** *Sample answer:* Rolling a standard number cube and getting a 0, flipping a coin and getting heads or tails.

17.

	1	2	3	4	5	6
1	2	3	4	5	6	7
2	3	4	5	6	7	8
3	4	5	6	7	8	9
4	5	6	7	8	9	10
5	6	7	8	9	10	11
6	7	8	9	10	11	12

$P(2) = \dfrac{1}{36}$; $P(3) = \dfrac{1}{18}$; $P(4) = \dfrac{1}{12}$; $P(5) = \dfrac{1}{9}$; $P(6) = \dfrac{5}{36}$; $P(7) = \dfrac{1}{6}$; $P(8) = \dfrac{5}{36}$; $P(9) = \dfrac{1}{9}$; $P(10) = \dfrac{1}{12}$; $P(11) = \dfrac{1}{18}$; $P(12) = \dfrac{1}{36}$

13.1 Problem Solving (pp. 847–848) **19.** $\dfrac{1}{7}$ **21.** $\dfrac{4}{9}$; $\dfrac{4}{5}$. *Sample answer:* The probability and odds of choosing a boy are related because both compare the number of boys to another number. The probability of choosing a boy compares the number of boys to the total number of outcomes, while the odds of choosing a boy compare the number of boys to the total number of outcomes minus the number of boys.

Extension (p. 850) **1.** Answers will vary. **3.** *Sample answer:* There are 3 prizes to win, but since the prizes do not have an equal likelihood of being won, generating a list of random integers from 1 to 3 would not represent the situation. The probability of winning a CD is $\frac{1}{6}$, so if there were only 3 possible outcomes in the simulation you could not represent winning a CD properly.

13.2 Skill Practice (pp. 853–854) **1.** permutation
3. a. 2 ways **b.** 2 ways **5. a.** 24 ways **b.** 12 ways
7. a. 120 ways **b.** 20 ways **9. a.** 120 ways **b.** 20 ways
11. *Sample answer:* 5 people are running in a race. How many different results can there be for first and second place? **13.** 6 **15.** 120 **17.** 3,628,800
19. 6,227,020,800 **21.** 210 **23.** 720 **25.** 1 **27.** 6,375,600
29. The denominator should be $(5 - 3)! = 2!$, not 3!;
$$_5P_3 = \frac{5!}{(5 - 3)!} = \frac{5!}{2!} = 60.$$

13.2 Problem Solving (pp. 854–855) **35. a.** $\frac{1}{2}$. *Sample answer:* Make a list of possible permutations, count the number in which you are first or second, and divide it by the total number of outcomes. **b.** $\frac{1}{2}$; the answers are the same. **37.** $\frac{1}{720}$

13.3 Skill Practice (p. 858) **1.** combination
3. 20 combinations **5.** *Sample answer:* The answer given is for $_9P_4$, not $_9C_4$; $_9C_4 = \frac{9!}{(9 - 4)! \cdot 4!} = \frac{9!}{5! \cdot 4!} = 126$. **7.** 56 **9.** 28 **11.** 330 **13.** 15,504 **17.** Permutations; since the roles are different, the order in which students are selected for the roles matters; 720 ways.
19. Permutations; the arrangement of people in the car matters; 120 ways. **21.** $_nC_r = {_nP_r} \cdot \frac{1}{r!}$. *Sample answer:* To find the number of combinations, you find the number of permutations and then divide by the number of ways the items being chosen can be arranged, or $r!$.

13.3 Problem Solving (p. 859) **23.** 840 burritos
25. a. 84 combinations **b.** $\frac{5}{21}$. *Sample answer:* There are 84 possible outcomes of the choice. Find the number of combinations that include you and your 2 friends. After you and your friends are chosen, 3 other contestants from a pool of 6 can be chosen in any combination, so the number of favorable combinations is $_6C_3 = 20$. The probability that you and your friends are chosen is $\frac{20}{84} = \frac{5}{21}$.

13.3 Graphing Calculator Activity (p. 860) **1.** 35 **3.** 120
5. 15,120 **7.** 6,652,800 **9. a.** 3276 groups **b.** 6 ways

13.4 Skill Practice (pp. 864–865) **1.** dependent
3. mutually exclusive; $\frac{2}{3}$ **5.** overlapping; $\frac{5}{6}$ **7.** To find the probability that you draw a yellow *or* a blue marble, the individual probabilities should be added, not multiplied; $\frac{7}{16} + \frac{5}{16} = \frac{12}{16} = \frac{3}{4}$.
9. independent; $\frac{1}{36}$ **11.** independent; $\frac{1}{12}$ **15.** $\frac{1}{64}$
17. If you first draw a pawn and then do not replace it, the probability of drawing a second pawn is not $\frac{16}{32}$, but $\frac{15}{31}$; $\frac{16}{32} \cdot \frac{15}{31} = \frac{15}{62}$. **19.** 69%

13.4 Problem Solving (pp. 866–867) **23.** 62.3%
25. a.

Mon	Tues	Wed	Thurs	Fri	Sat	Sun
st. gov.		st. gov.				
tutor			tutor	tutor	tutor	

b. 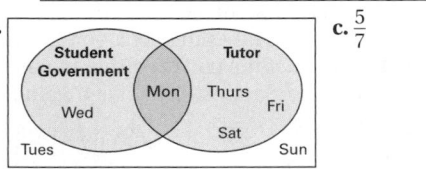 **c.** $\frac{5}{7}$

13.4 Problem Solving Workshop (pp. 868–869)
1. $\frac{4}{15}$ **3.** $\frac{1}{16}$. *Sample answer:* The third friend can arrive any time in a 20 minute span, and I will be away from the house for 15 of those minutes. The probability is $\frac{1}{4}$ that I will be home when the third friend arrives. Since the three friends arrive independently of each other, you can multiply the probability that you are home when the other two friends arrive by $\frac{1}{4}$ to calculate the probability that you are home when all three friends arrive; $\frac{1}{4} \cdot \frac{1}{4} = \frac{1}{16}$.
5. *Sample answer:* The times at which each raffle is announced is independent, so the two probabilities should be calculated separately and then multiplied; $\frac{10}{30} \cdot \frac{25}{30} = \frac{1}{3} \cdot \frac{5}{6} = \frac{5}{18}$.

13.5 Skill Practice (p. 873) **1.** systematic **3.** people who have eaten at the restaurant, self-selected
5. passengers of the airline, random **7.** Not likely. *Sample answer:* The sample should represent the neighborhood. **9.** Not potentially biased. *Sample answer:* This question simply presents the two choices.

11. *Sample answer:* The new question presumes that the driving age should be changed, and does not present the option that it should remain the same; "What do you think about the current driving age?"

13.5 Problem Solving (p. 874) **13.** *Sample answer:* This question is phrased to prompt people into agreeing that the athletic field is more important than the science lab; "Which do you think the school needs more: a new athletic field or a new science lab?" **15.** No. *Sample answer:* Only some of the fans are able to attend games, and those who attend games may have different player preferences than those who do not attend games. **17. a.** *Sample answer:* Obtain a list of everyone at the school and select names randomly using a random number generator. **b.** *Sample answer:* "How many hours per night do you study?"; This question is unbiased because it does not prompt respondents to give any particular answer.

13.6 Skill Practice (p. 877) **1.** mode **3.** 3, 3, 1 **5.** 22, 21, no mode **7.** 5.223, 5.48, no mode **11.** 65, 21.2 **13.** 70, 12.56 **15.** 0.85, 0.23 **17.** *Sample answer:* The range only considers the two extreme values, while the mean absolute deviation is affected by all of the values.

13.6 Problem Solving (pp. 877–878) **19. a.** 19 **b.** 19.6 lb, 23.5 lb, 24 lb **c.** Median. *Sample answer:* The mode is the greatest data value and the mean is less than 8 of the 10 data values. **21. a.** The range for Team 2 is 56 and the range for Team 1 is 52, so the scores for Team 2 cover a slightly wider range. **b.** The mean absolute deviation for Team 1 is 15.75 and the mean absolute deviation for Team 2 is 22.5, so the scores for Team 2 are more dispersed.

Extension (pp. 879–880) **1.** 6.3, 2.5 **3.** 76,656.6; 276.9 **5.** 29.1 **7. a.** 5.6 **b.** *Sample answer:* Since 136 is much greater than the mean, the standard deviation will increase. **c.** 17.7. *Sample answer:* The standard deviation more than tripled, so the prediction was correct.

13.7 Skill Practice (pp. 883–884) **1.** frequency

3.

Stem	Leaves
1	7
2	0 0 4
3	0 1 3 5 8 8 9
4	2
5	5

Key: 1 | 7 = 17

5.
Stem	Leaves
10	5 9
11	1
12	1 4 7
13	3
14	2
15	6
16	
17	9
18	2

Key: 10 | 5 = 105

7. There is no key given for the stem-and-leaf plot; Key: 1 | 8 = 18.

11. **13.**

15. *Sample answer:* A histogram can show a variety of intervals, but a stem-and-leaf plot can only show intervals that are powers of 10. The given data range from 10 to 20, so a stem-and-leaf plot would place all the data into only two intervals, making it difficult to see trends within the data. The histogram could use an interval of 3 or 4.

13.7 Problem Solving (pp. 884–885)

17.
Heights

Stem	Leaves
6	8 9 9
7	0 2 4 4 6 8 8
8	0 1 1 1 1

Key: 6 | 8 = 68 in.

19. a. **b.** $\dfrac{92}{265}$

Phone Number Memorization

21. a.

Ages of *Mayflower* Passengers

Stem	Leaves
1	8
2	0 0 0 1 1 1 1 1 5 5 5 9
3	0 0 0 2 2 4 4 5 7 8 8 8 8 8
4	0 1 2 5 5 8 9
5	0 4 5
6	4

Key: 1 | 8 = 18 years

b. median: 34 yr, range: 46 yr **c.** $\frac{1}{3}$. *Sample answer:*

Since 13 of the 39 passengers or $\frac{1}{3}$ of them were ages 18–29, we can predict that another passenger about whom we have no information has a $\frac{1}{3}$ probability of being in that age group.

13.7 Graphing Calculator Activity (p. 886) **1.** *Sample answer:* The majority of the data are at the lower end of the scale, between 3000 and 12,000, with the highest frequency between 3000 and 6000.

13.8 Skill Practice (pp. 889–890) **1.** the difference of the upper quartile and the lower quartile

3.

5.

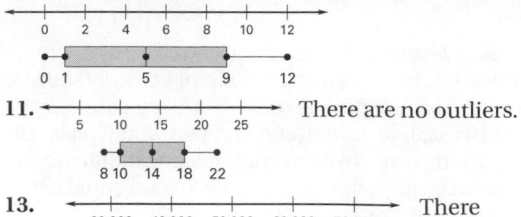

7. Sample answer: The upper quartile is incorrect. The upper quartile should be the median of 8 and 10, or 9.

11. There are no outliers.

13. There are no outliers.

13.8 Problem Solving (pp. 890–892)

15.

17. a. **b.** none

19. a. Sample answer: The craters on Ganymede are generally smaller than the craters on Callisto. The lower extreme, lower quartile, median, upper quartile, and upper extreme values are all lower for Ganymede than for Callisto. **b. Sample answer:** Chesapeake Bay is larger than between 50% and 75% of the craters on both Callisto and Ganymede. **c. Sample answer:** Vredefort is larger than at least 75% of the craters on both Callisto and Ganymede.

Chapter Review (pp. 896–900) **1.** compound event **3. Sample answer:** Theoretical probability is based on knowing the likelihood of all possible outcomes of an event. Experimental probability is based on the results of an experiment. **5.** $\frac{2}{9}$ **7.** 30 **9.** 1,037,836,800 **11.** 7

13. 56 **15.** 126 ways **17.** $\frac{3}{8}$ **19.** $\frac{5}{8}$ **21.** $\frac{1}{120}$ **23. a.** about 5.045, 4.5, 1 **b.** Median. **Sample answer:** The mode is much lower than many of the values, and the mean is affected by the two extreme values (17 and 19) that are much greater than the rest of the data. So, the median best represents the data.

25.

Cumulative Review (pp. 906–907) **1.** 44 **3.** ±45 **5.** 2

7. **9.**

11. $y = -8x + 3$

13. $4 \le x < 24$

15. $\left(4, \frac{1}{4}\right)$ **17.** no solution **19.** $\frac{-81x^{12}}{4}$

21. $(a - 18)(a + 3)$ **23.** $(2f + g)^2$ **25.** $-7, 3$ **27.** $\frac{1}{2}, 4$

29. $2\sqrt{37}$ **31.** 15 **33.** $\frac{x + 4}{x + 3}$ **35.** -3 **37.** $\frac{9 - 3x}{x^2 - 3x}$

39. 336 **41.** 210 **43.** $\frac{1}{2}$ **45.** $\frac{3}{20}$ **47. Sample answer:** 120 min after the first runner starts **49.** 42.4 ft

51. a. \$45

b.

Stem	Leaves
17	6
18	
19	1 5 7 7
20	4 4 4 4 4 6 6 6 6
21	7 7
22	1

Key: 17|6 = \$176

c.

d. Yes. **Sample answer:** The interquartile range is 9, so any data value more than 13.5 less than the lower quartile of 197 or greater than the upper quartile of 206 can be considered outliers. 176 and 221 are both outliers.

Skills Review Handbook

Comparing and Ordering Decimals (p. 909) **1.** > **3.** > **5.** > **7.** < **9.** > **11.** 7.01, 7.03, 7.13, 7.3 **13.** 0.15, 0.3, 0.47, 0.9 **15.** 10.9, 11, 11.9, 12.6 **17.** 0.3, 1.33, 3.1, 3.3

Factors and Multiples (pp. 910–911) **1.** $2^2 \cdot 7$ **3.** prime **5.** 3^4 **7.** $2^2 \cdot 3 \cdot 5$ **9.** $2^2 \cdot 3^2 \cdot 5$ **11.** $3 \cdot 17$ **13.** 4 **15.** 6 **17.** 9 **19.** 4 **21.** 8 **23.** 4 **25.** 18 **27.** 45 **29.** 130 **31.** 90 **33.** 14 **35.** 49

Finding Equivalent Fractions and Simplifying Fractions (p. 912) **1–5.** Sample answers are given. **1.** $\frac{3}{4}$ and $\frac{18}{24}$ **3.** $\frac{2}{4}$ and $\frac{3}{6}$ **5.** $\frac{5}{7}$ and $\frac{20}{28}$ **7.** $\frac{1}{4}$ **9.** $\frac{1}{8}$ **11.** $\frac{1}{4}$ **13.** $\frac{7}{20}$ **15.** $\frac{4}{5}$ **17.** $\frac{3}{7}$ **19.** $\frac{4}{13}$

Mixed Numbers and Improper Fractions (p. 913) **1.** $\frac{5}{3}$ **3.** $\frac{103}{10}$ **5.** $\frac{9}{2}$ **7.** $\frac{23}{12}$ **9.** $\frac{53}{8}$ **11.** $\frac{65}{8}$ **13.** $\frac{65}{9}$ **15.** $\frac{38}{3}$ **17.** $2\frac{2}{5}$ **19.** $6\frac{1}{4}$ **21.** $1\frac{3}{4}$ **23.** $2\frac{9}{10}$ **25.** $10\frac{4}{5}$ **27.** $4\frac{2}{5}$ **29.** $4\frac{7}{9}$

Adding and Subtracting Fractions (p. 914) **1.** $\frac{1}{4}$ **3.** $\frac{1}{6}$
5. 1 **7.** $\frac{1}{2}$ **9.** $1\frac{1}{5}$ **11.** $\frac{3}{16}$ **13.** $\frac{25}{48}$ **15.** $1\frac{17}{24}$ **17.** $\frac{11}{20}$ **19.** $\frac{4}{5}$
21. $6\frac{3}{4}$ **23.** 5 **25.** $1\frac{1}{16}$

Multiplying and Dividing Fractions (p. 915) **1.** $\frac{1}{2}$ **3.** $\frac{1}{2}$
5. $1\frac{1}{8}$ **7.** $\frac{3}{64}$ **9.** $\frac{1}{8}$ **11.** $1\frac{1}{2}$ **13.** $\frac{1}{2}$ **15.** $\frac{2}{7}$ **17.** $\frac{1}{50}$ **19.** $\frac{3}{5}$
21. $3\frac{3}{32}$ **23.** $4\frac{3}{8}$ **25.** $1\frac{1}{3}$

Fractions, Decimals, and Percents (pp. 916–917)
1. 0.7, $\frac{7}{10}$ **3.** 0.03, $\frac{3}{100}$ **5.** 0.35, $\frac{7}{20}$ **7.** 1.1, $1\frac{1}{10}$
9. 0.003, $\frac{3}{1000}$ **11.** $\frac{7}{25}$, 28% **13.** $\frac{1}{20}$, 5% **15.** $\frac{13}{25}$, 52%
17. $\frac{1}{40}$, 2.5% **19.** $\frac{3}{2}$, 150% **21.** 0.188, 18.8% **23.** 0.61,
61% **25.** 0.19, 19% **27.** 0.36, 36% **29.** 0.571, 57.1%

Mean, Median, and Mode (p. 918) **1.** 92.4; 93; 94
3. 41 yr; 41 yr; 52 yr **5.** $7; $7; $6.75 **7.** 2.25; 2; 2

Classifying Triangles and Quadrilaterals (pp. 919–920)
1. isosceles right triangle **3.** pentagon
5. hexagon **7.** parallelogram, rhombus
9. quadrilateral, parallelogram

The Coordinate Plane (p. 921) **1.** (5, 4) **3.** (10, 8)
5. (9, 2) **7.** (2, 6) **9.** (10, 0) **11.** (0, 5)
13–23.

Transformations (pp. 922–923)
1.
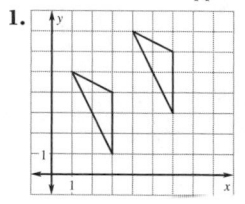
(4, 7), (6, 6), (6, 3)
3.
(1, 1), (3, 1), (3, 4)
5.

(4, 4), (7, 1), (3, 2)

7. (2, 0), (5, 0), (5, 2), (2, 2)

9.
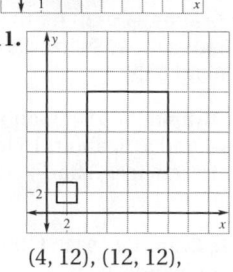
(2, 4), (4, 8), (10, 6)

11.
(4, 12), (12, 12),
(12, 4), (4, 4)

13.

(0, 3), (6, 6), (9, 0)

Perimeter and Area (pp. 924–925) **1.** 36 ft **3.** 20 ft
5. 66 yd^2 **7.** 110 in.^{2} **9.** 21 ft^2 **11.** 70 yd^2

Circumference and Area of a Circle (p. 926) **1.** 12π in.
or 37.7 in., 36π in.^{2} or 113.0 in.^{2} **3.** 16π in. or 50.2 in.,
64π in.^{2} or 201.0 in.^{2} **5.** 4π ft or 12.6 ft, 4π ft^2 or
12.6 ft^2 **7.** 18π m or 56.5 m, 81π m^2 or 254.3 m^2

Surface Area and Volume (pp. 927–928) **1.** 320 cm^2,
336 cm^3 **3.** 900π m^2 or 2826 m^2, 4500π m^3 or
14,130 m^3 **5.** 200π in.^{2} or 628 in.^{2}, 320π in.^{3} or
1004.8 in.^{3} **7.** 96 in.^{2}, 48 in.^{3} **9.** 1888π in.^{2} or
5928.3 in.^{2}, $11,008\pi$ in.^{3} or 34,565.1 in.^{3} **11.** 96π m^2
or 301.4 m^2, 96π m^3 or 301.4 m^3

Converting Units of Measurement (p. 929) **1.** 5 **3.** 4
5. 6 **7.** 14 **9.** 300 **11.** 70,000 **13.** 3000 **15.** 15 **17.** 2.5
19. 1,000,000 **21.** 28,800

Venn Diagrams and Logical Reasoning (p. 930)
1.
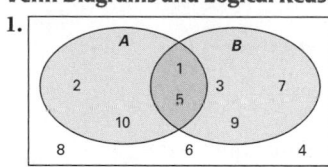

3. a. False; there are whole numbers less than 10 that
are odd but are not factors of 10, such as 3, 7, and 9.
b. False; there is a whole number less than 10 that is
a factor of 10 but is not odd, 2.

Counting Methods (pp. 931–932) **1.** 6 ways
3. 17,576 3-letter monograms **5.** 1,679,616 computer passwords **7.** 72 dinners

Bar Graphs (p. 933) **1.** bronze **3.** 103 medals
5. 25 medals **7.** Switzerland **9.** United States
11. 96 medals

Line Graphs (p. 934) **1.** about 24 lb **3.** between ages 4 and 5 **5.** about 15 lb **7.** about 2 years old
9. between ages 3 and 4 **11.** between ages 1 and 2
13. about 4 yr

Circle Graphs (p. 935) **1.** 9% **3.** 24.5% **5.** 37%
7. woodwinds **9.** brass

Problem Solving Strategies (pp. 936–937) **1.** Pam owes $4 that she can pay to Bonnie who is owed a total of $5. Holly should pay both Barb and Bonnie $1.
3. 25 years old **5.** 10 ways **7.** 1:45 P.M. **9.** 3 soccer games per week **11.** Quinn

Extra Practice

Chapter 1 (p. 938) **1.** 16 **3.** 4.4 **5.** 2.4 **7.** $\frac{8}{27}$ **9.** 26
11. 28 **13.** 10 **15.** 111 **17.** $\frac{3}{4}m$ **19.** $y - 3$ **21.** $45 - m$
23. $12 \cdot (r - 4) = 72$ **25.** 38 **27.** 16 **29.** *Sample answer:* You know the temperature in Quito in degrees Celsius and the temperature in Miami in degrees Fahrenheit. You need to find out which one is greater.
31. domain: 3, 4, 5, 6; range: 9, 11, 13, 15

33.   **35.**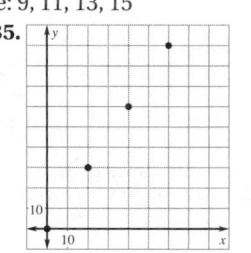

Chapter 2 (p. 939)
1.   0

3.   −3

5. Each number is a rational number; $-\frac{1}{5}, -\frac{1}{8}, -\frac{1}{10},$ 0.25. **7.** 3 and 0 are whole numbers, −4 and −5 are integers; −5, −4, 0, 3. **9.** −61 **11.** 0 **13.** −19.7
15. $-4\frac{13}{30}$ **17.** 66 **19.** $\frac{3}{10}$ **21.** $\frac{5}{12}$ **23.** −7.2 **25.** 5.5
27. −12.5 **29.** −40 **31.** 2.2 **33.** Associative property of multiplication **35.** Property of zero **37.** Property of −1

39. $30 - 5y$ **41.** $-3k + 42$ **43.** $14s + 7$ **45.** $5w + 25$
47. 23 **49.** 64 **51.** $-\frac{5}{6}$ **53.** $\frac{25}{36}$ **55.** ±20 **57.** ±12
59. −9 **61.** 16

Chapter 3 (p. 940) **1.** 16 **3.** −12 **5.** 9 **7.** 52 **9.** 6 **11.** 8
13. −35 **15.** 3 **17.** −6 **19.** −1 **21.** 2 **23.** 3 **25.** $-\frac{1}{2}$
27. 56 **29.** 16 **31.** $\frac{5}{7} = \frac{15}{x}$; 21 **33.** $\frac{g}{9} = \frac{16}{12}$, 12 **35.** 14
37. 8 **39.** 4 **41.** −2 **43.** 12.5% **45.** 35 **47.** 45 **49.** 86
51. $x = \frac{c + b}{a}$; 5 **53.** $y = -5x + 10$ **55.** $y = -4x + 2$

Chapter 4 (p. 941)

1.   **3.**
Quadrant III   Quadrant IV

5.   **7.**
on the y-axis   Quadrant I

9.   **11.**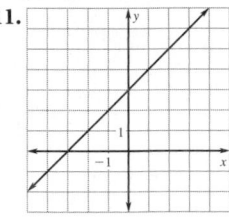
range: −2, 0, 2, 4, 6

13.   **15.**

17.   **19.** x-intercept: 6, y-intercept: −12
21. x-intercept: −1, y-intercept: $\frac{8}{3}$

23.

25.

27. 3 **29.** $-\frac{7}{3}$ **31.** no slope **33.** slope: 7, y-intercept: 8

35. slope: -4, y-intercept: 3 **37.** $y = -2x + 8$; slope: -2,
y-intercept: 8 **39.** $y = -\frac{5}{2}x + 5$; slope: $-\frac{5}{2}$,
y-intercept: 5

41.

43.

45.

47.

49.

51.

53. 2 **55.** -4

57.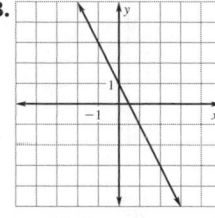

The graph is a vertical translation 4 units up of $f(x) = x$.

59.

The graph is a vertical stretch by a factor of 2 with a reflection in the x-axis of $f(x) = x$.

Chapter 5 (p. 942) **1.** $y = 3x + 6$ **3.** $y = 5x - 1$
5. $y = \frac{1}{2}x - 5$ **7.** $y = 2x + 2$ **9.** $y = \frac{2}{3}x + 7$
11. $y = -5x + 3$

13.

15.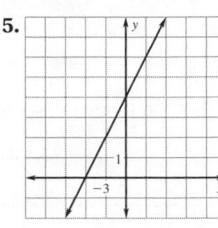

17. *Sample answer:* $y - 9 = \frac{1}{2}(x - 3)$ **19.** $4x + y = 15$

21. $2x + y = 0$ **23.** $y = -5x - 22$ **25.** $y = -\frac{1}{3}x - 6$

27. $y = \frac{3}{2}x - \frac{33}{2}$

29.

Sample answer:
$y = -0.6x + 61$

31.

$y = 1.1x + 6.7$; 14.4

Chapter 6 (p. 943)

1. $y > 5$

3. $x \le 7$

5. $n \le 2\frac{1}{2}$

7. $z < -4\frac{7}{8}$

9. $t \ge 1.5$

11. $y < -5.5$

13. $p \le 9$

15. $x \ge 6$

17. $m \le \frac{3}{2}$

19. $z \le 8$

21. $z \leq \frac{2}{3}$

23. $y > -4.5$

25. $x \geq 5$

27. $t > -5$

29. all real numbers

31. $y < 6$

33. no solution

35. $-3 < x < 3$

37. $2 < a \leq 3.5$

39. $r < -4$ or $r \geq -2$

41. $t \geq 4$ or $t < -8$

43. ± 8 **45.** $-11, -1$ **47.** $-14, 28$ **49.** no solution

51. $-1, 1$ **53.** no solution

55. $-3 \leq x \leq 3$

57. $s < -1.2$ or $s > 1.2$

59. $x < -8$ or $x > 4$

61. $5 < m < 11$

63. $-1 \leq p \leq 7$

65. $-\frac{3}{5} \leq a \leq 1$

67.

69.

71.

73.

75.

77.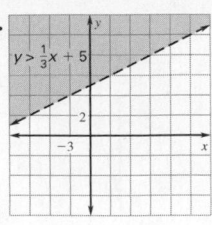

Chapter 7 (p. 944) **1.** $(3, 2)$ **3.** $(1, -3)$ **5.** $(-3, -2)$
7. $(-3, 0)$ **9.** $(9, 7)$ **11.** $(3, -7)$ **13.** $(-4, 3)$ **15.** $(-9, -2)$
17. $(-3, -5)$ **19.** $(-6, 3)$ **21.** $(11, 9)$ **23.** $\left(10, -\frac{3}{2}\right)$

25.   **27.**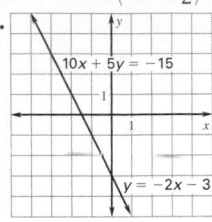

no solution   infinitely many solutions
29. $(20, 48)$ **31.** no solution **33.** $(-30, 0)$

35.   **37.**

39.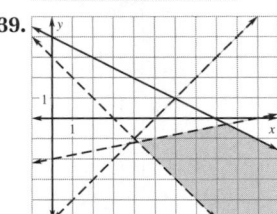

Chapter 8 (p. 945) **1.** 5^7 **3.** $(-2)^9$ **5.** $(-4)^6$ **7.** m^7 **9.** y^{15}
11. $54d^8$ **13.** 8^5 **15.** $-\frac{2^5}{3^5}$ **17.** 7^5 **19.** $\frac{p^7}{q^7}$ **21.** $\frac{64y^9}{27}$
23. $\frac{25x^2y^6}{4}$ **25.** $\frac{1}{81}$ **27.** 1 **29.** 8 **31.** 32 **33.** $\frac{1}{y^{10}}$ **35.** $\frac{10c^5}{b^3}$
37. $\frac{y^5}{x^4}$ **39.** $-96z^5$ **41.** 8.7×10^{-1} **43.** 3.59×10^{-4}
45. $530{,}000$ **47.** 0.000008 **49.** 3.75×10^{-5} **51.** 4×10^2

53.

55.

57.

59.

61.

63.

65.

67.

3. The graph is a vertical shrink by a factor of $\frac{1}{2}$ of $y = x^2$.

5. The graph is a vertical translation 3 units up of $y = x^2$.

7. The graph is a vertical stretch by a factor of 3 with a vertical translation 4 units up of $y = x^2$.

9.

11.

13.

Chapter 9 (p. 946) **1.** $7x^2 - 2$ **3.** $7m^2 - 5m - 3$
5. $6b^3 - 3b^2 - 8b + 8$ **7.** $10x^7 - 15x^6 + 25x^5 - 5x^4$
9. $8x^2 + 16x + 6$ **11.** $3x^2 + 8x - 35$ **13.** $x^2 + 20x + 100$
15. $16x^2 - 4$ **17.** $36 - 9t^2$ **19.** $-8, 2$ **21.** $\frac{3}{5}, 2$
23. $-\frac{1}{4}, 0$ **25.** $(y + 3)(y + 4)$ **27.** $(x - 4)(x + 9)$
29. $(m - 25)(m - 4)$ **31.** $2, 5$ **33.** $4, 9$ **35.** $2, 5$
37. $-(x - 3)(x - 2)$ **39.** $(2k - 1)(2k - 5)$
41. $-(3s + 1)(s + 2)$ **43.** $\frac{2}{3}, 4$ **45.** $-2, \frac{1}{2}$ **47.** $-1, \frac{1}{16}$
49. $(y + 6)(y - 6)$ **51.** $3(2y - 3)(2y + 3)$ **53.** $(2x - 3)^2$
55. $(g + 5)^2$ **57.** $(2w + 7)^2$ **59.** $(3z - 1)(z - 5)$
61. $(3y^2 + 2)(y + 5)$ **63.** $2m(7m - 3)(7m + 3)$
65. $(h + 3)(h - 3)(2h - 3)$

15. $-5, 2$ **17.** $-3, 6$
19. $-2, \frac{3}{2}$ **21.** ± 7
23. ± 0.75 **25.** ± 1.73
27. $-7, 3$ **29.** $1, 6$
31. $0.55, 5.45$
33. $-12, 6$ **35.** $0.5, 2$
37. $-0.87, 1.54$

39. one solution **41.** no solution **43.** two solutions
45. quadratic function; $y = 3x^2$ **47.** exponential
function; $y = 0.5 \cdot 2^x$

Chapter 10 (p. 947)
1. The graph is a vertical stretch by a factor of 4 of $y = x^2$.

Chapter 11 (p. 948)
1. Domain: $x \geq 0$, range: $y \geq 0$; the graph is a vertical stretch by a factor of 6 of the graph of $y = \sqrt{x}$.

Selected Answers **SA51**

3. Domain: $x \geq 0$, range: $y \leq 0$; the graph is a vertical stretch by a factor of 8 with a reflection in the x-axis of the graph of $y = \sqrt{x}$.

5. Domain: $x \geq 0$, range: $y \geq 3$; the graph is a vertical translation 3 units up of the graph of $y = \sqrt{x}$.

7. Domain: $x \geq 2$, range: $y \geq 0$; the graph is a horizontal translation 2 units right of the graph of $y = \sqrt{x}$.

9. 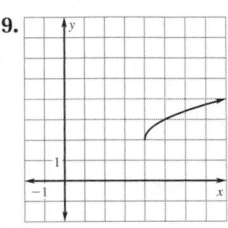 Domain: $x \geq 4$, range: $y \geq 2$; the graph is a vertical translation 2 units up and a horizontal translation 4 units right of the graph of $y = \sqrt{x}$.

11. $10\sqrt{3}$ **13.** 17 **15.** $5g\sqrt{11}$ **17.** $36x^3$ **19.** $\dfrac{\sqrt{6}}{6x}$ **21.** $\dfrac{\sqrt{14k}}{4k}$ **23.** $3\sqrt{3} + \sqrt{7}$ **25.** $9\sqrt{5}$ **27.** -108 **29.** $27 - 6\sqrt{13}$ **31.** 8 **33.** 20 **35.** -3 **37.** $1, 10$ **39.** $\dfrac{1}{5}, \dfrac{3}{5}$ **41.** 1 **43.** $b = 24$ **45.** $b = \sqrt{21}$ **47.** $a = \sqrt{57}$ **49.** not a right triangle **51.** right triangle **53.** not a right triangle **55.** 13 **57.** $\sqrt{42.5}$ **59.** $\dfrac{\sqrt{5}}{2}$ **61.** $(-2, 1.5)$ **63.** $(1, 0)$ **65.** $\left(6\dfrac{1}{2}, -1\dfrac{1}{2}\right)$

Chapter 12 (p. 949)

1. 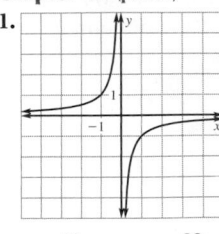 **3.**

5. $y = \dfrac{12}{x}; 6$ **7.** $y = \dfrac{60}{x}; 30$ **9.** $y = \dfrac{49}{x}; 24.5$

11. 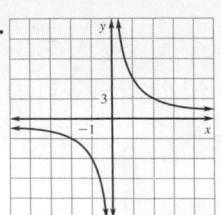 **13.**

15. **17.**

19. $-5x^3 + 2x^2 - x$ **21.** $3v - 4 + \dfrac{20}{v + 2}$ **23.** $3m + 4 + \dfrac{10}{3m - 4}$ **25.** $\dfrac{11x^2}{6}$, excluded value is 0. **27.** $\dfrac{3}{4}$, excluded value is 5. **29.** $\dfrac{r - 5}{r - 2}$, excluded values are 2 and -3.

31. $\dfrac{2m - 4}{3m^2 + 6m}$, excluded values are -6, -2, and 0.

33. $\dfrac{5x}{2x - 6}$ **35.** $3r - 6$ **37.** $\dfrac{16t + 15}{10t^2}$

39. $\dfrac{4c + 3}{(c + 3)(c - 3)(2c + 3)}$ **41.** $-4, 7$ **43.** $-\dfrac{7}{3}, 3$ **45.** $-3, \dfrac{11}{4}$

Chapter 13 (p. 950) **1.** 6 possible outcomes; heads, yellow; heads, red; heads, blue; tails, yellow; tails, red; tails, blue **3.** $5:3$ **5.** 60 ways **7.** 336 **9.** 120 **11.** 15 **13.** 210 **15.** overlapping; $\dfrac{1}{2}$ **17. a.** $\dfrac{1}{9}$ **b.** $\dfrac{1}{11}$

19. Yes. *Sample answer:* The sampling method might be biased because only the parents or guardians of students are called and not other spectators. **21.** mean: 89, median: 88, mode: 88, range: 39, mean absolute deviation: 8.8

23. There are no outliers.

Teacher's Edition Index

A

Absolute deviation, 392–395
  relative, 403
Absolute error, 392
Absolute value, 66–69, 390
  equations, 390–395, 417
  functions, 396–397
  inequalities, 398–403, 418
ACT, *See* Standardized Test Preparation
Act it out, problem solving strategy, 936–937
Activities, *See also* Graphing calculator
  adding integers, 73
  collecting and organizing data, 334
  completing the square, 662
  determining the discriminant, 677
  distance formula, 743
  dividing polynomials, 783
  exponential models, 530
  factoring a trinomial, 582, 592
  finding probability, 842
  graphing rational functions, 773–774
  inequalities with negative coefficients, 362
  linear inequalities in two variables, 404
  linear systems and elimination, 443
  logical reasoning, 318
  modeling data from the internet, 342
  modeling linear relationships, 282
  modeling one-step equations, 132–133
  multiplication by –1, 87
  multiplying binomials, 561
  patterns and expressions, 14
  products and powers, 488
  properties of radicals, 718
  the Pythagorean theorem, 736
  relationships between dimensions of a rectangle, 764
  scatter plots and functions, 42
  slope and y-intercept, 243
  slopes of lines, 234
  solving linear systems using tables, 426
  spreadsheet
    equations with variables on both sides, 160
    subtract real numbers, 85
  statements with *and* and *or*, 379
  writing if-then statements, 109
  zero and negative exponents, 502
Activity Notes
  Investigating Algebra, 14, 42, 73, 109, 132–133, 234, 243, 282, 318, 334, 362, 379, 404, 426, 443, 488, 502, 530, 561, 582, 592, 662, 677, 718, 736, 743, 764, 773–774, 783, 842

Technology, 13, 41, 85, 160, 222, 290, 332–333, 388, 434, 519, 560, 650–651, 692–693, 717, 792–793, 860, 886, 893
Acute angle, 919
Addition
  of fractions, 914
  of inequalities, 356–361, 415
  integer, 73
  in linear equations, 134–140, 191
  matrix, 94–95
  of polynomials, 555–559, 615, 616
  properties, 75–79, 120, 134, 357
  of radicals, 721–726
  of rational expressions, 812–819, 830, 834
  real number, 74–79, 120, 122
  for solving linear systems, 444–450, 476–477
Addition property of equality, 134, 191
Addition property of inequality, 357
Additive identity, 76
Additive inverse, 76
Algebra tiles
  for adding integers, 73
  for completing the square, 662
  for dividing polynomials, 783
  for factoring trinomials, 582, 592
  for modeling equations, 132–133
  for modeling linear systems, 443
  for multiplying binomials, 561
Alternative method, *See* Another Way; Problem Solving Workshop
Analyze, exercises, 69, 70, 109, 207, 218, 237, 488, 690
***And* statements,** 379, 414
  for compound inequalities, 380–385
Angle(s)
  classifying, 919
  congruent, 919
Animated Algebra, *Throughout. See for example* 1, 63, 131, 205, 281, 354, 425, 487, 553, 627, 709, 763, 841
Another Way, 76, 98, 105, 135, 150, 154, 169, 175, 183, 260–261, 293, 312, 370, 382, 383, 437, 442, 451, 452, 514, 522, 528–529, 585, 590–591, 645, 652, 659–660, 671, 824, 868–869
Applications
  advertising, 47, 145, 246, 261, 675, 799, 805
  apparel, 233, 258, 347, 394, 450, 481, 668, 844
  archery, 100
  architecture, 741
  art, 6, 32, 115, 181, 197, 249, 461, 476, 485

astronomy, 65, 70, 164, 269, 383, 493, 494, 498, 500, 516, 517, 518, 551, 633, 722, 891, 905
baseball, 27, 31, 119, 140, 289, 324, 337, 374, 402, 468, 483, 556, 559, 599, 613, 614, 657, 667, 694, 742, 801, 808, 826, 860, 870, 874, 881, 891, 899, 903
basketball, 23, 147, 152, 190, 203, 231, 259, 392, 423, 537, 828, 865, 870, 884, 901
biking, 23, 250, 259, 295, 300–301, 352, 419, 687, 770, 834
biology, 190, 298, 323, 548, 551, 573, 581, 682, 716, 733, 791, 874, 893
botany, 507, 880
business, 78, 85, 128, 146, 155, 166, 246, 252, 265, 267, 275, 279, 285, 301, 305, 307, 315, 324, 332, 340, 367, 373, 419, 430, 437, 442, 482, 501, 526, 558, 581, 661, 683, 692, 693, 713, 770, 829, 835, 839, 873, 891
camping, 20, 102, 324, 558
chemistry, 79, 173, 255, 316, 352, 402, 441, 458, 493, 550
collections, 27, 162, 426, 522
construction, 61, 115, 129, 153, 188, 195, 473, 567, 580, 588, 591, 612, 621, 648, 667, 694, 739, 752, 759, 768, 791
consumer economics, 11, 12, 17, 27, 30, 31, 32, 35, 51, 54, 57, 60, 123, 153, 158, 161, 180, 181, 183, 200, 218, 231, 237, 249, 256, 269, 277, 278, 294, 298, 305, 307, 317, 343, 345, 350, 352, 360, 368, 371, 374, 375, 378, 389, 400, 423, 449, 458, 473, 479, 483, 558, 789, 790, 797
contests, 108, 394, 395, 402, 423, 471, 634, 640, 648, 683, 735, 866
crafts, 139, 203, 241, 272, 432, 449, 453, 472, 581, 585, 598, 614, 665
dancing, 145
design, 27, 336, 564, 565, 567, 588, 591, 598, 844
domestic animals, 159, 161, 196, 343, 419, 668
education, 44, 129, 158, 166, 180, 195, 197, 252, 365, 389, 411, 413, 450, 559, 590, 604, 707, 829, 848, 855, 858, 859, 867, 897
employment, 25, 26, 60, 102, 125, 143, 146, 188, 190, 249, 258, 268, 367, 408, 411, 413, 422, 465, 473, 547, 602, 707, 825, 828, 854, 855, 859
energy, 631, 634

INDEX

Compound event, 861–867, 895, 898
Compound inequalities, 21, 380–388, 417
 and absolute value, 398–403
Compound interest, 523, 525, 527
Concept Summary, 45, 105, 156, 179, 214,
 264, 294, 400, 454, 462, 533, 607, 646,
 673
Concepts, *See* Big Ideas; Concept Summary;
 Key Concept
Conclusion, 66–68
 conjecture and, 117–118
Conditional statement, 66–68, 109, 113,
 114
 converse of, 318, 319
Cone
 surface area of, 927–928
 volume of, 927–928
Congruent angles, 919
Congruent figures, 174
Congruent sides, 919
Conjecture, 117–118
 exercises, 774, 793
Conjugates, 724
Connections, *See* Applications
Constant term, 97, 309, 554
Constant of variation, 253, 254, 765
Continuous function, 223–224
Convenience sample, 871
Converse
 of the Pythagorean theorem, 739–742,
 753
 of a statement, 318, 319, 575
Conversion factor, 929
Coordinates
 of ordered pairs, 206, 921
 of transformations, 213–214, 922–923
Coordinate graph, 206–214
Coordinate plane, 206, 921
 distance in, 743–750, 753, 756
 graphing linear equations in, 215–222
 graphing systems of inequalities in,
 466–472
 midpoints in, 745–750, 753, 756
 plotting points in, 206–214, 271
 transformations in, 213–214, 922–923
Correlation
 describing, 325–342
 paired data, 325
Correlation coefficient, 333
Corresponding parts, of similar figures,
 174–175
Counterexample, 66–67, 318, 464
Counting methods, 931–932
Counting principle, 851, 931
Critical thinking, *See* Reasoning
Cross products property, 168
 to solve proportions, 168–173, 195
 to solve rational equations, 820–828
Cube root, 510
 fractional exponents and, 509–510

Cumulative Review, 202–203, 484–485,
 706–707, 906–907
Cylinder
 surface area of, 927–928
 volume of, 927–928

D

Daily Homework Quiz, *Occurs at the end of
 each exercise set*
Data, *See also* Equation(s); Graphs;
 Inequalities; Modeling; Statistics
 analyzing
 correlation, 325–342
 using exponential regression, 692–693
 using extrapolation, 336–342
 fitting a line to data, 325–342, 348
 using interpolation, 335–342
 interquartile range, 888
 using linear regression, 332–333,
 335–342
 using mean absolute deviation,
 876–878
 using measures of central tendency,
 875–878, 918
 using measures of dispersion, 876–880
 outliers, 889
 predicting from, 333–342, 348
 using quadratic regression, 692–693
 using standard deviation, 879–880
 variance, 879–880
 gathering, 334, 342
 bias in, 872, 899
 from the Internet, 342
 populations, 871
 sampling, 871–874, 899
 organizing, 334
 in a back-to-back stem-and-leaf plot,
 882, 883, 885
 in a bar graph, 933
 in a box-and-whisker plot, 887–893,
 895, 900, 902–903
 in a circle graph, 935
 in a frequency table, 882, 884
 in a histogram, 882–886, 895
 in a line graph, 934
 in a matrix, 94–95
 in a scatter plot, 42, 325–342
 in a stem-and-leaf plot, 881–885, 895,
 900
 in a table, 147, 442, 502, 677
Decay factor, 534
Decay rate, 534
Decimal(s)
 commonly used, 917
 comparing, 909
 fractions, percents, and, 916–917
 ordering, 909
 repeating, 65
 scientific notation and, 512–519, 542, 545

Deductive reasoning, *See also* Reasoning,
 118
Degree
 of a monomial, 554
 of a polynomial, 554
Denominator, 912
Dependent events, 862–867, 895, 898
Dependent variable, 36
Diagnosing readiness, *See* Readiness
Diagrams
 drawing to solve problems, 34, 438
 interpreting data from, 549–550, 836
 mapping, 35–36, 38
 tree, 843, 910, 931
 Venn, 64, 71–72, 112, 379, 861, 930
Diameter, of a circle, 926
Difference, common, 309
Difference of two squares pattern, 600–605
Differentiated Instruction, 3, 5, 9, 11, 16,
 24, 29, 30, 31, 36, 44, 47, 65, 66, 77,
 81, 89, 90, 97, 104, 111, 135, 136,
 143, 151, 156, 158, 163, 169, 177,
 187, 207, 208, 216, 217, 226, 236,
 237, 245, 256, 263, 285, 294, 295,
 303, 312, 313, 320, 326, 336, 359,
 364, 370, 382, 383, 385, 392, 393,
 402, 406, 428, 429, 432, 436, 438,
 446, 452, 460, 467, 490, 496, 498,
 504, 514, 515, 521, 523, 533, 555,
 556, 557, 563, 570, 584, 585, 594,
 601, 607, 629, 636, 645, 646, 653,
 654, 664, 665, 672, 679, 680, 685,
 711, 712, 720, 721, 730, 738, 745,
 767, 776, 786, 787, 797, 803, 804,
 814, 821, 844, 852, 853, 857, 858,
 862, 872, 876, 882, 888, 889
Dilation, 922–923
Dimension(s), of a matrix, 94
Direct variation, 253–261, 274, 276, 765, 767
Discrete function, 207, 223–224
Discrete mathematics,
 counting methods, 931–932
 counting principle, 851
 inductive reasoning, 117–118
 matrices, 94–95
 mutually exclusive events, 861, 864
 sequences, 309–310, 539–540
 set theory, 71–72
 tree diagram, 497, 843, 910, 931
Discriminant, 677–683, 700
Dispersion, measures of, 876–878, 895, 899
Distance formula, in the coordinate plane,
 743–750, 753, 756
Distance traveled formula, 30, 446
Distributive property, 96–101, 123
 for multiplying polynomials, 562–568
 for simplifying radical expressions,
 721–726
 for solving equations, 148–153

INDEX

INDEX

T

INDEX

Chapter 1

1.5 Skill Practice (p. 31) **5.** You know the temperature in Rome and the temperature in Dallas. You know the formula to convert Fahrenheit temperatures to Celsius temperatures. You need to find the higher temperature. **6.** The formula for perimeter is wrong; $P = 2\ell + 2w$; $P = 2(200) + 2(150) = 700$; $\$10(700) = \$7000$. **7.** The formula for perimeter should be used, not area; $P = 2\ell + 2w$; $P = 2(200) + 2(150) = 700$; $\$10(700) = \$7000$.

1.6 Problem Solving (pp. 39–40)

27. a.

2	3	4	5
A, B, C	D, E, F	G, H, I	J, K, L

6	7	8	9
M, N, O	P, Q, R, S	T, U, V	W, X, Y, Z

No; because there is more than one output for each input.

b.

A	B	C	D	E	F	G	H	I	J	K	L
2	2	2	3	3	3	4	4	4	5	5	5

M	N	O	P	Q	R	S	T	U	V	W	X	Y	Z
6	6	6	7	7	7	7	8	8	8	9	9	9	9

Yes; because there is only one output for each input.

1.7 Skill Practice (pp. 46–47)

3. **4.** **5.**

6. **7.** **8.**

1.7 Problem Solving (pp. 47–48) **20. a.** *Sample answer:* Count the number of blocks between the men's and women's times. Each block represents 10 minutes.

Quiz for Lessons 1.6–1.7 (p. 48)

1.

Input	0	2	3	4	5
Output	12	8	6	4	2

4. **5.**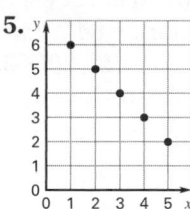

Chapter 2

2.1 Skill Practice (pp. 67–68) **52.** $a < 0$; $a > 0$; $a = 0$. *Sample answer:* When a number a is negative, its opposite will be positive, which is greater than a. When a number a is positive, its opposite will be negative, which is less than a. When a is 0, its opposite is 0, which is equal to a.

2.3 Spreadsheet Activity (p. 85)

Step 2.

	A	B	C
1	Grip	Length (in.)	Difference
2	1	4.878	−0.122
3	2	4.902	−0.098
4	3	5.115	0.115
5	4	5.13	0.13
6	5	4.877	−0.123
7	6	4.874	−0.126
8	7	4.799	0.201
9	8	4.819	−0.181
10	9	4.879	−0.121
11	10	5.124	0.124

4.

	A	B	C
1	Grip	Length (in.)	Difference
2	1	4.871	−0.129
3	2	5.019	0.019
4	3	5.112	0.112
5	4	4.987	−0.013
6	5	5.067	0.067
7	6	4.899	−0.101
8	7	4.859	−0.141
9	8	5.132	0.132
10	9	5.126	0.126
11	10	5.093	0.093

2.4 Skill Practice (pp. 91–92) **28.** $16y$; $y(16)$, product of -2 and -8; $16y$, commutative property of multiplication **29.** $18x$; $18x$, same signs, product is positive. **30.** $-3q$; $\left[\frac{3}{5}(-5)\right]q$, associative property of multiplication; $-3(q)$, product of $\frac{3}{5}$ and -5 is -3; $-3q$, multiply. **31.** $-84z$; $12(-7z)$, product of -2 and -6 is 12; $[12 \cdot (-7)]z$, associative property of multiplication; $-84(z)$, product of 12 and -7 is -84; $-84z$, multiply. **32.** $42z$; $20(-2.1)(-z)$, product of -5 and -4 is 20; $-42(-z)$, product of 20 and -2.1 is -42; $42z$, multiply. **33.** $-40c$; $2(4)(-5c)$, product of $-\frac{1}{5}$ and -10 is 2; $8(-5c)$, product of 2 and 4 is 8; $[8 \cdot (-5)]c$, associative property of multiplication; $-40(c)$, product of 8 and -5 is -40; $-40c$, multiply. **34.** $5t^2$; $(t)(-t)(-5)$, commutative property of multiplication; $-t^2(-5)$, product of t and $-t$ is $-t^2$; $(-5)(-t^2)$, commutative property of multiplication; $5t^2$, multiply. **35.** $16.8r^2$; $[-6r \cdot (-2.8)]r$, associative property of multiplication; $[-6 \cdot (-2.8) \cdot r]r$, commutative property of multiplication; $(16.8r)r$, product of -6 and -2.8 is 16.8; $16.8(r \cdot r)$, associative property of multiplication; $16.8r^2$, multiply. **36.** $-\frac{3}{10}m^2$; $-\frac{3}{10}(-m)(-m)$, product of $\frac{1}{3}$ and $-\frac{9}{10}$ is $-\frac{3}{10}$; $-\frac{3}{10}m^2$, multiply.

2.5 Problem Solving Workshop (p. 102) **3.** 287.50; Method 1: Write an equation for a, the total amount earned as a function of d, the number of hours spent making deliveries; $a = 9.50d + 8(35 - d)$ or $a = 1.5d + 280$. Substitute 5 for d, giving you $a = \$287.50$; Method 2: Break the problem into parts. Find the amount earned working 5 hours making deliveries: \$9.50 per hour • 5 hours = \$47.50. Find the number of hours spent working at the register: 35 hours − 5 hours = 30 hours. Find the amount earned working at the register for 30 hours: \$8 per hour • 30 hours = \$240. Add the amount earned making deliveries to the amount earned working at the register: \$47.50 + \$240 = \$287.50.

2.7 Skill Practice (pp. 113–114) **24.** $\sqrt{49}$: real number, rational number, integer, whole number, 8: real number, rational number, integer, whole number, $-\sqrt{4}$: real number, rational number, integer, -3: real number, rational number, integer; -3, $-\sqrt{4}$, $\sqrt{49}$, 8 **25.** $-\sqrt{12}$: real number, irrational number, -3.7: real number, rational number, $\sqrt{9}$: real number, rational number, integer, whole number, 2.9: real number, rational number; -3.7, $-\sqrt{12}$, 2.9, $\sqrt{9}$ **26.** -11.5: real number, rational number, $-\sqrt{121}$: real number, rational number, integer, -10: real number, rational number, integer, $\frac{25}{2}$: real number, rational number, $\sqrt{144}$: real number, rational number, integer, whole number; -11.5, $-\sqrt{121}$, -10, $\sqrt{144}$, $\frac{25}{2}$

27. $\sqrt{8}$: real number, irrational number, $-\frac{2}{5}$: real number, rational number, -1: real number, rational number, integer, 0.6: real number, rational number, $\sqrt{6}$: real number, irrational number; -1, $-\frac{2}{5}$, 0.6, $\sqrt{6}$, $\sqrt{8}$

28. $-\frac{8}{3}$: real number, rational number, $-\sqrt{5}$: real number, irrational number, 2.6: real number, rational number, -1.5: real number, rational number, $\sqrt{5}$: real number, irrational number; $-\frac{8}{3}$, $-\sqrt{5}$, -1.5, $\sqrt{5}$, 2.6 **29.** -8.3: real number, rational number, $\sqrt{80}$: real number, irrational number, $-\frac{17}{2}$: real number, rational number, -8.25: real number, rational number, $-\sqrt{100}$: real number, rational number, integer; $-\sqrt{100}$, $-\sqrt{80}$, $-\frac{17}{2}$, -8.3, -8.25

2.7 Problem Solving (pp. 115–116)

54. a.

Quotient of pyramids	Quotient of area of bases	Quotient of side length of bases
Khafre / Menafaure	3.9	2.0
Khufu / Menafaure	4.6	2.1
Khufu / Khafre	1.2	1.1

The quotient of the areas is the square of the quotient of the side lengths.

Chapter 3

3.2 Problem Solving (pp. 145–146)

43. b.

x (h)	Marissa	Ryan	Total
1	5	7	12
2	10	14	24
3	15	21	36
4	20	28	48
5	25	35	60

3.2 Problem Solving Workshop (p. 147)

1. 7 players; Method 1: Use the equation $600 + 25x = 775$ to get $x = 7$; Method 2: Make a table that lists the number of non-members and the amount the team would pay. The team has 7 members who are not club members.

Non-members	Total fee (dollars)
0	600
1	625
2	650
3	675
4	700
5	725
6	750
7	775

3. 4 chairs; Method 1: Use the equation $220 + 35x = 370$ to get $x \approx 4.3$; Method 2: Make a table that lists the number of chairs and the total cost of the table and chairs; because you cannot afford $395 for 5 chairs, you can afford to buy 4 chairs.

Chairs	Total cost (dollars)
1	255
2	290
3	325
4	360
5	395

3.4 Problem Solving (pp. 158–159)

52. b.

Visits	Members' cost (dollars)	Non-members' cost (dollars)
5	380	80
10	400	160
15	420	240
20	440	320
25	460	400
30	480	480
35	500	560

3.4 Spreadsheet Activity (p. 160)

4. a–b.

	A	B	C	D
1	Possible solutions	Left side	Right side	Difference
2	0	38.5	0	38.5
3	1	33.7	6.2	27.5
4	2	28.9	12.4	16.5
5	3	24.1	18.6	5.5
6	4	19.3	24.8	−5.5
7	5	14.5	31	−16.5
8	6	9.7	37.2	−27.5
9	7	4.9	43.4	−38.5
10	8	0.1	49.6	−49.5
11	9	−4.7	55.8	−60.5
12	10	−9.5	62	−71.5

Chapter 4

4.1 Guided Practice (pp. 206–208)

3–6. 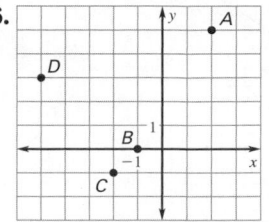   **7.**

4.1 Skill Practice (pp. 209–210)

29. Quadrant IV; the x-coordinate is positive and the y-coordinate is negative so the point is in Quadrant IV. **30.** Quadrant IV; the x-coordinate is positive and the y-coordinate is negative so the point is in Quadrant IV. **31.** Quadrant II; the x-coordinate is negative and the y-coordinate is positive so the point is in Quadrant II. **32.** Quadrant III; the x-coordinate is negative and the y-coordinate is negative so the point is in Quadrant III.

4.2 Guided Practice (pp. 215–218)

2.   **3.**

4.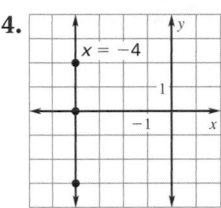

4.2 Skill Practice (pp. 219–220)

11.   **12.**

13.   **14.**

15.   **16.**

17.

18.

$3x + 2y = 8$

$x - 2y = 3$

19.

$x = 0$

20.

$y = 0$

21.

$y = -4$

22.

$x = 2$

26.

$y = 3x - 2$

27.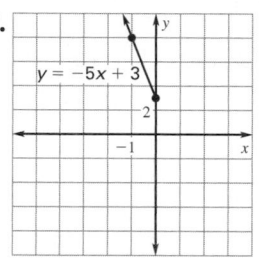

$y = -5x + 3$

28.

$y = 4$

29.

$y = -6$

30.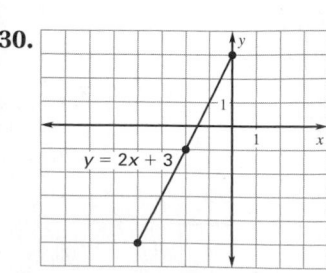

$y = 2x + 3$

31.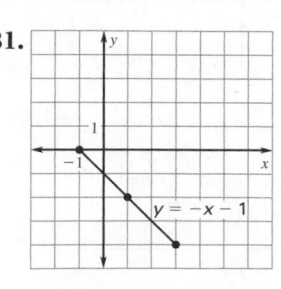

$y = -x - 1$

4.2 Problem Solving (pp. 220–221)

40. a.

t (seconds)	h (feet)
0	5
1	19
2	33
3	47
4	61
5	75
6	89
7	103
8	117
9	131
10	145

b.

$h = 5 + 14t$

41. a.

$y = 30$

$y = 2.5x$

Extension (p. 224)

1.

2.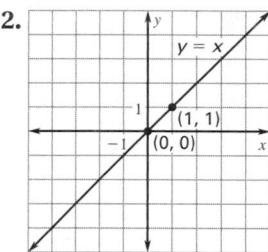

$y = x$

$(1, 1)$

$(0, 0)$

3.

4.

5.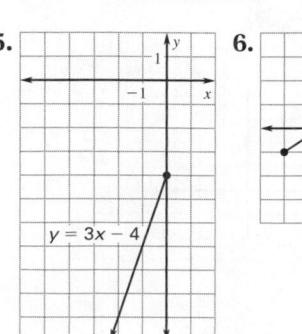

$y = 3x - 4$

6.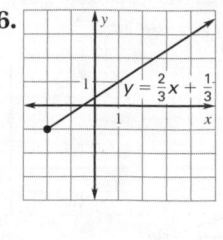

$y = \frac{2}{3}x + \frac{1}{3}$

4.3 Skill Practice (pp. 229–230)

16.

17.

18.

19.

20.

21.

22.

23.

24.

25.

26.

27.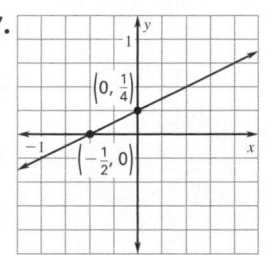

4.3 Problem Solving (pp. 230–232)

50. b.

Quiz for Lessons 4.1–4.3 (p. 232)

1–3.

4.

5.

6.

13.

4.4 Problem Solving (pp. 241–242)

41. a.   **b.**   **c.**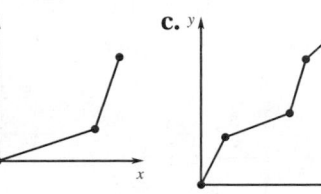

4.5 Guided Practice (pp. 244–246)

4.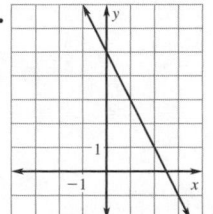

4.5 Problem Solving (pp. 248–250)

45. a.

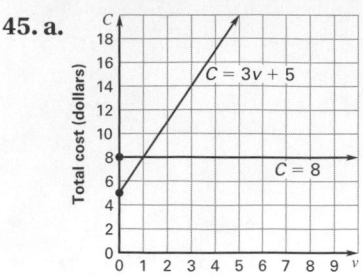

Quiz for Lessons 4.4–4.5 (p. 250)

7.

8.

9.

10. a.

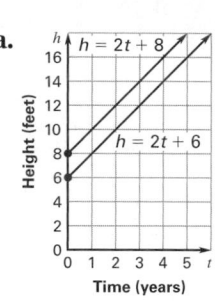

4.6 Skill Practice (pp. 256–257)

11.

12.

13.

14.

15.

16.

17.

18.

19.

20.

21.

22.

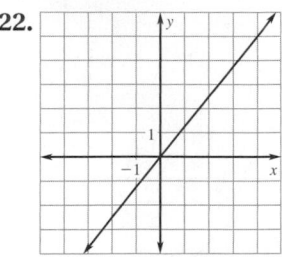

4.6 Mixed Review (p. 259)

48.

49.

50.

51.

52.

53.

54.

55.

56.

4.7 Skill Practice (pp. 265–266)

23.

Because the graphs of *g* and *f* have the same slope, *m* = 1, the lines are parallel. The *y*-intercept of the graph of *g* is 5 more than the *y*-intercept of the graph of *f*.

24.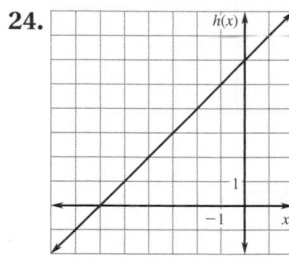

Because the graphs of *h* and *f* have the same slope, *m* = 1, the lines are parallel. The *y*-intercept of the graph of *h* is 6 more than the *y*-intercept of the graph of *f*.

25.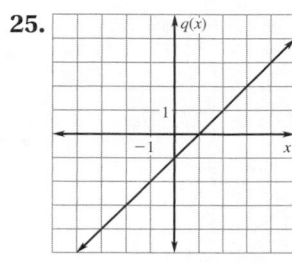

Because the graphs of *q* and *f* have the same slope, *m* = 1, the lines are parallel. The *y*-intercept of the graph of *q* is 1 less than the *y*-intercept of the graph of *f*.

26.

Because the graphs of *m* and *f* have the same slope, *m* = 1, the lines are parallel. The *y*-intercept of the graph of *m* is 6 less than the *y*-intercept of the graph of *f*.

27.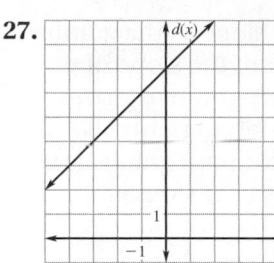

Because the graphs of *d* and *f* have the same slope, *m* = 1, the lines are parallel. The *y*-intercept of the graph of *d* is 7 more than the *y*-intercept of the graph of *f*.

28.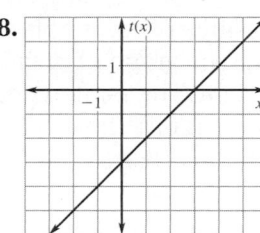

Because the graphs of *t* and *f* have the same slope, *m* = 1, the lines are parallel. The *y*-intercept of the graph of *t* is 3 less than the *y*-intercept of the graph of *f*.

29.

Because the slope of the graph of *r* is greater than the slope of the graph of *f*, the graph of *r* rises faster from left to right. The *y*-intercept for both graphs is 0, so both lines pass through the origin.

30.

Because the slope of the graph of *w* is greater than the slope of the graph of *f*, the graph of *w* rises faster from left to right. The *y*-intercept for both graphs is 0, so both lines pass through the origin.

31.

Because the slope of the graph of *h* is negative, the graph of *h* falls from left to right. The *y*-intercept for both graphs is 0, so both lines pass through the origin.

32.

Because the slope of the graph of k is negative, the graph of k falls from left to right. The y-intercept for both graphs is 0, so both lines pass through the origin.

33.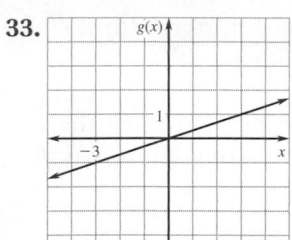

Because the slope of the graph of g is less than the slope of the graph of f, the graph of g rises slower from left to right. The y-intercept for both graphs is 0, so both lines pass through the origin.

34.

Because the slope of the graph of m is negative, the graph of m falls from left to right. The y-intercept for both graphs is 0, so both lines pass through the origin.

36. a.

b.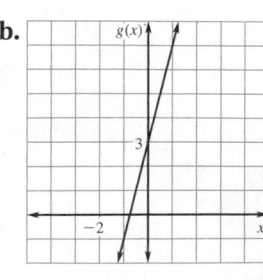

Because the slope of the graph of g is greater than the slope of the graph of f, the graph of g rises faster from left to right. The y-intercept for both graphs is the same, so both lines pass through the point $(0, 3)$.

c.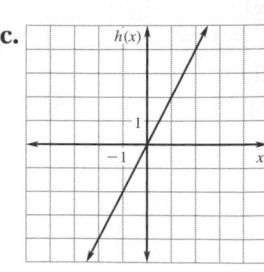

Because the graphs of h and f have the same slope, $m = 2$, the lines are parallel. The y-intercept of the graph of h is 3 less than the y-intercept of the graph of f.

4.7 Problem Solving (pp. 267–268)

42.

Because the graphs of g and f have the same slope, $m = 40$, the lines are parallel. The y-intercept of the graph of g is 80 less than the y-intercept of the graph of f.

43.

Because the slope of the graph of r is greater than the slope of the graph of s, the graph of r rises faster from left to right. The y-intercept for both graphs is 0, so both lines pass through the origin.

45. b.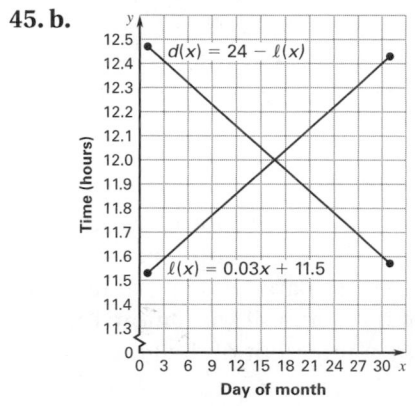

4.7 Mixed Review (p. 268)

55.

56.

57.

58.

59.   **60.**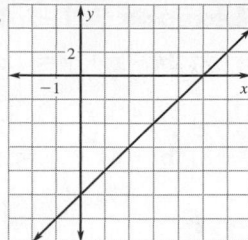

Quiz for Lessons 4.6–4.7 (p. 268)

8.   Because the slope of the graph of g is negative, the graph of g falls from left to right. The y-intercept for both graphs is 0, so both lines pass through the origin.

9. 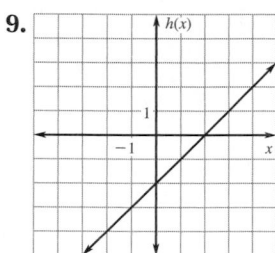 Because the graphs of h and f have the same slope, $m = 1$, the lines are parallel. The y-intercept of the graph of h is 2 less than the y-intercept of the graph of f.

Chapter Review (pp. 271–274)

31.   Because the graphs of j and f have the same slope, $m = 1$, the lines are parallel. The y-intercept of the graph of j is 6 less than the y-intercept of the graph of f.

32.   Because the slope of the graph of k is negative, the graph of k falls from left to right. The y-intercept for both graphs is 0, so both lines pass through the origin.

33.   Because the slope of the graph of t is greater than the slope of the graph of f, the graph of t rises faster from left to right. The y-intercept of the graph of t is 1 more than the y-intercept of the graph of f.

Chapter Test (p. 275)

16.   **17.**

18.

Chapter 5

5.3 Guided Practice (pp. 302–305)

2.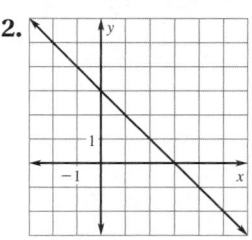

5.3 Skill Practice (pp. 305–306) **31.** No; because the increase is not at a constant rate, the situation cannot be modeled by a linear equation. **32.** Yes; because the rate is increasing at a constant rate, the situation can be modeled by a linear equation. *Sample answer:* $y - 1.2 = \frac{1}{5}(x - 1)$.

33. No; because the increase is not at a constant rate, the situation cannot be modeled by a linear equation. **34.** Yes; because the rate is decreasing at a constant rate, the situation can be modeled by a linear equation. *Sample answer:* $y - 16 = -3(x + 3)$.

5.3 Mixed Review (p. 308)

48.   **49.**

50.

51.

52.

53.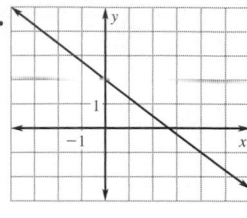

Extension (p. 310)

4.

5.

6.

7.

8.

9.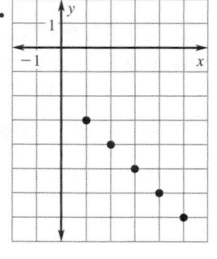

5.4 Skill Practice (p. 314) **5–10.** Sample answers are given. **5.** $2x + 2y = -20, 3x + 3y = -30$ **6.** $x + 2y = 3,$ $10x + 20y = 30$ **7.** $x - 2y = -9, -2x + 4y = 18$ **8.** $-3x - 4y = 2, -6x - 8y = 4$ **9.** $3x - y = -4, 6x - 2y = -8$ **10.** $2x - 4y = 5, -4x + 8y = -10$

5.4 Problem Solving (pp. 315–316)

43. *Sample answer:*

Length (ft)	Width (ft)
5	25
10	20
15	15
20	10
25	5

Quiz for Lessons 5.1–5.4 (p. 316) **7. a.** $y - 2 = x + 5$ or $y - 3 = x + 4$ **b.** $-x + y = 7$ **8. a.** $y + 9 = \frac{4}{3}(x + 6)$ or $y + 1 = \frac{4}{3}x$ **b.** $-\frac{4}{3}x + y = -1$ **9. a.** $y - 1 = 4(x - 1)$ or $y - 9 = 4(x - 3)$ **b.** $-4x + y = -3$

Chapter 6

6.1 Guided Practice (pp. 357–358)

1.

4.

5.

6.

6.1 Skill Practice (pp. 359–360)

10.

11.

12.

13.

14.

15.

16.

17.

18.

19.

20.

21.

22.

23.

6.1 Problem Solving (pp. 360–361)

36. 2 axles:
$w \le 19{,}800$ lb, 3 axles: $w \le 39{,}800$ lb, 4 axles: $w \le 54{,}800$ lb,
5 axles: $w \le 65{,}800$ lb; no; the total weight, 34,200 pounds,
would exceed the maximum weight allowed, 34,000 pounds.

37. a.

Original price, x ($)	19,459	19,989	20,549	22,679	23,999
Final price, y ($)	16,459	16,989	17,549	19,679	20,999

6.2 Skill Practice (pp. 366–367)

3.

4.

5.

6.

7.

8.

9.

10.

11.

12.

13.

14.

15.

16.

17.

18.

19.

20.

21.

22.

23.

24.

25.

26.

6.2 Problem Solving (pp. 367–368)

41. b. No; the area added by increasing both the length and the width by 20 feet can be divided into 2 rectangles (80 feet by 20 feet and 82 feet by 20 feet) and 1 square (20 feet by 20 feet). The 400 square feet of the square is large enough to hold one horse, and the rectangular areas will be able to hold additional horses.

Quiz for Lessons 6.1–6.2 (p. 368)

1. **2.**

3. **4.**

5. **6.**

7. **8.**

9.

6.3 Problem Solving (pp. 373–374)

41. a.

Pitches per inning, p	15	16	17	18	19
Total number of pitches, t	98	101	104	107	110

42. c. More than $875; for price $p > 400$, the tax paid in the 4% sales tax state is $0.04p$, and the tax paid in the other state is $0.05(p - 175)$, or $0.05p - 8.75$. To find the values of p for which the first expression is less than the second, solve the inequality $0.04p < 0.05p - 8.75$ to get $p > \dfrac{8.75}{0.01}$, or $p > 875$. Check $p = \$900$: The tax paid in the 4% sales tax state is $0.04(\$900) = \$36$ and the tax paid in the other state is $0.05(\$900 - \$175) = \$36.25$.

6.3 Problem Solving Workshop (p. 376) **2.** At most 4 games; Method 1: Work backward. Begin with $400 and subtract the cost of the console to find out how much money you have to spend on games: $400 − $259 = $141. Make a table of values showing the amount of money you have left after buying various numbers of games.

Number of games bought	Amount of money left
0	$141
1	$112
2	$83
3	$54
4	$25

After buying 4 games, you will not have enough money left to buy a fifth. You can buy at most 4 games. Method 2: Use a graph. Write and graph an equation that gives the total amount of money y you spend as a function of the number of games x that you buy: $y = 29x + 259$. Graph $y = 400$ on the same coordinate plane.

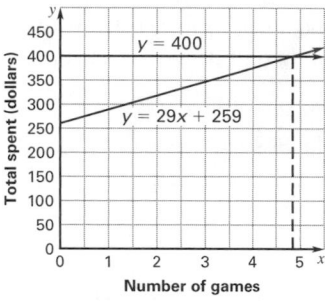

The graphs intersect between $x = 4$ and $x = 5$. Because you can spend at most $400, the solutions are the x-coordinates of the points on the graph of $y = 29x + 259$ that lie on or below the graph of $y = 400$. Only integer values of x make sense in this situation, so you can buy at most 4 games. **4.** At most 7 weeks; Method 1: Work backward. Begin with $247 and make a table of values showing the amount of money you have left in your account after various numbers of $20 withdrawals.

Number of $20 withdrawals	Amount of money left in account
0	$247
1	$227
2	$207
3	$187
4	$167
5	$147
6	$127
7	$107
8	$87

If you make $20 withdrawals for 8 weeks your account balance will fall below the required $100, so you can make $20 withdrawals for at most 7 weeks. Method 2: Use a graph. Write and graph an equation that gives the total amount of money y in your account as a function of the number x of $20 withdrawals that you make: $y = -20x + 247$. Graph $y = 100$ on the same coordinate plane.

The graphs intersect between $x = 7$ and $x = 8$. Because your account must have at least $100, the solutions are the x-coordinates of the points on the graph of $y = 29x + 259$ that lie on or below the graph of $y = 100$. Only integer values of x make sense in this situation, so you can make $20 withdrawals for at most 7 weeks.

6.4 Guided Practice (pp. 380–383)

6.4 Skill Practice (pp. 384–385)

9.

10.

11.

12.

13.

14.

15.

16.

AA12

17.

18.

19.

20.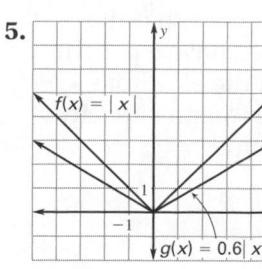

Extension (pp. 396–397)

1. 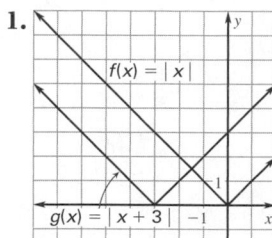 The graph of g is 3 units to the left of the graph of f.

2. 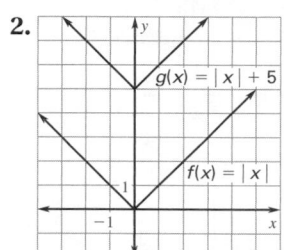 The graph of g is 5 units above the graph of f.

3. 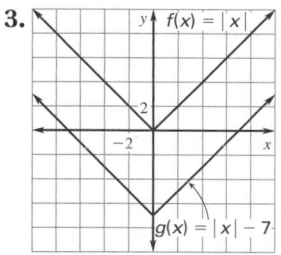 The graph of g is 7 units below the graph of f.

4. 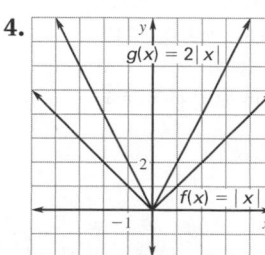 The graph of g opens up and is narrower than the graph of f.

5. 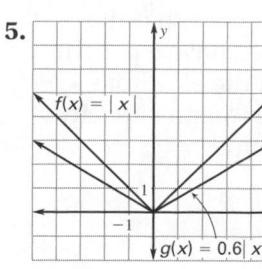 The graph of g opens up and is wider than the graph of f.

6. 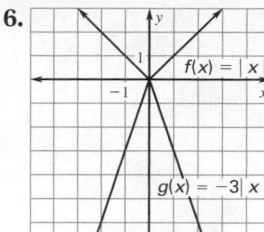 The graph of g opens down and is narrower than the graph of f.

6.6 Problem Solving (pp. 402–403)

38. a.

Measured compression, p (lb)	275	325	375	425	475
Absolute deviation from 350 (lb)	75	25	25	75	125

6.6 Mixed Review (p. 403)

42.

43.

44.

45.

46.

47.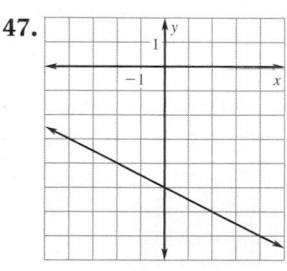

6.7 Skill Practice (pp. 409–410)

17.

18.

19.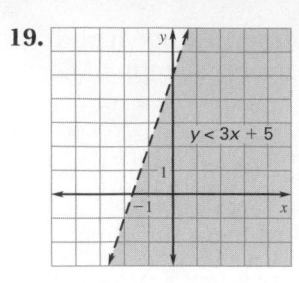

$y < 3x + 5$

20.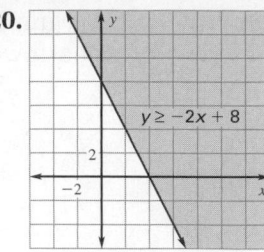

$y \geq -2x + 8$

21.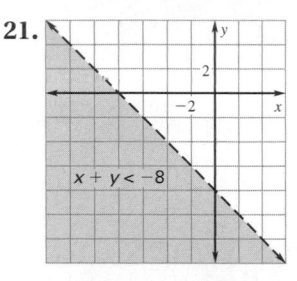

$x + y < -8$

22.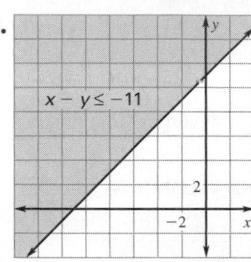

$x - y \leq -11$

23.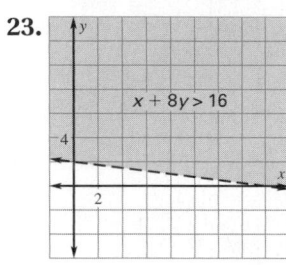

$x + 8y > 16$

24.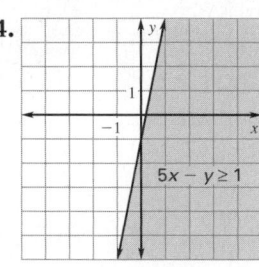

$5x - y \geq 1$

25.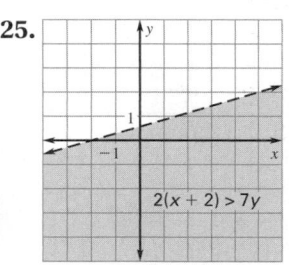

$2(x + 2) > 7y$

26.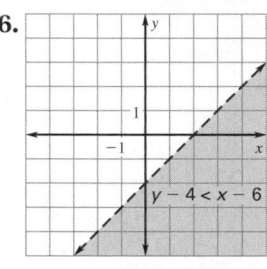

$y - 4 < x - 6$

27.

$-4y \leq 16x$

28.

$6(2x) \geq -24y$

29.

$y < -3$

30.

$x \geq 5$

31.

$x > -2$

32.

$y \leq 4$

33.

$3(x - 2) > y + 8$

34.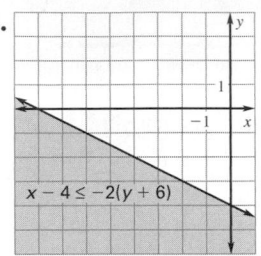

$x - 4 \leq -2(y + 6)$

35.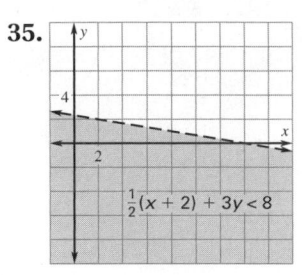

$\frac{1}{2}(x + 2) + 3y < 8$

36.

$2(x + 1) \geq \frac{1}{4}y - 1$

37.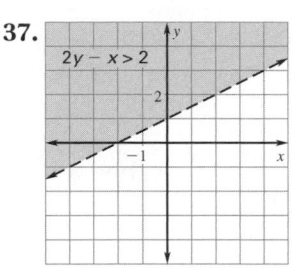

$2y - x > 2$

38.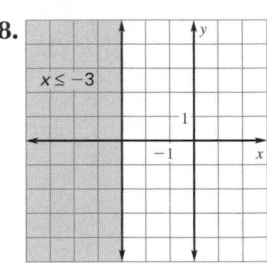

$x \leq -3$

6.7 Problem Solving (pp. 410–412)

53.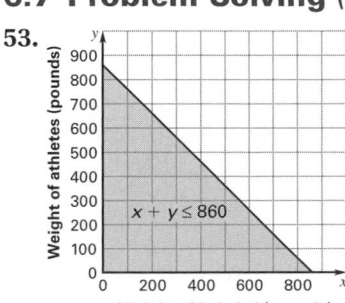

Sample answer: The solution (450, 400) means that the bobsled can weigh 450 pounds when the combined weight of the athletes is 400 pounds.

Weight of athletes (pounds) — Weight of bobsled (pounds)

$x + y \leq 860$

54.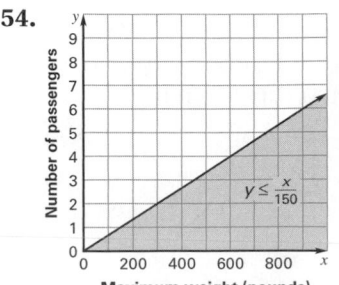

Sample answer: The solution (1200, 8) means that the elevator can have 8 passengers when the elevator's maximum weight capacity is 1200 pounds.

Number of passengers — Maximum weight (pounds)

$y \leq \frac{x}{150}$

60. a.

b. Greater than 80% and up to 100%; substitute $x = 30$ into the inequality to get $y > 110 - 30$, so the investor should invest more than 80% of his money in stocks. The investor cannot invest more than 100% of his money in stocks.

61. a. sinks:

floats:

6.7 Mixed Review (p. 412)

71.

72.

73.

74.

75.

76.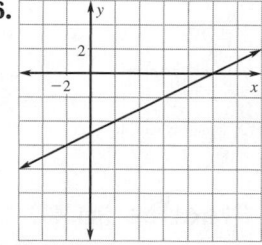

Quiz for Lessons 6.5–6.7 (p. 412)

4. **5.**

6. **7.**

8. **9.**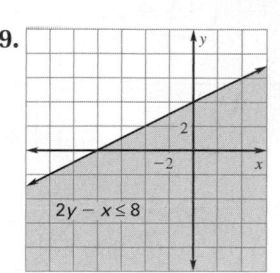

Chapter Test (p. 419)

29.

30.

31.

Chapter 7

7.3 Mixed Review (p. 450)

46.

47.

48.   **49.**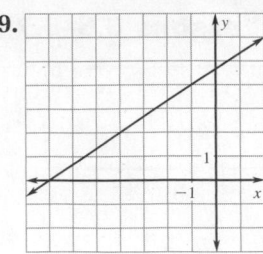

7.4 Mixed Review (p. 457)

45.   **46.**

47.   **48.**

49.   **50.**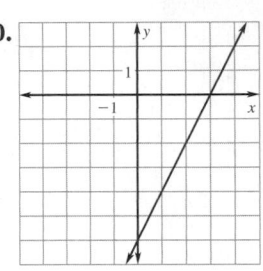

7.5 Mixed Review (p. 465)

46.   **47.**

48.   **49.**

50.   **51.**

52.   **53.**

54.   **55.**

56.   **57.**

58.   **59.**

60.   **61.**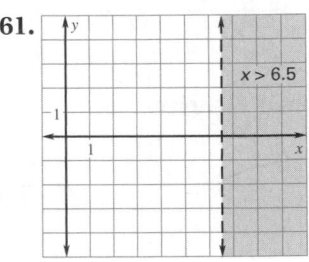

7.6 Guided Practice (pp. 467–468)

1.   **2.**

3.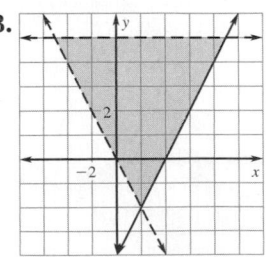

7.6 Skill Practice (pp. 469–470)

9.   **10.**

11.

12.

13.

14.

15.

16.

17.

18.

19.

20.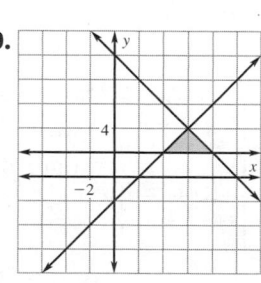

7.6 Problem Solving (pp. 471–472)

41. a.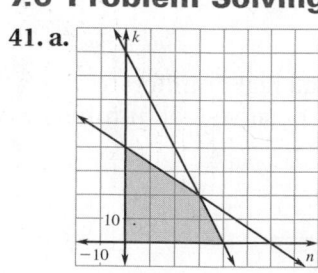

Quiz for Lessons 7.5–7.6 (p. 472)

1.

2.

3.

4.

5.

6.

7.

8.

9.

Chapter 8

8.1 Mixed Review (p. 494)

66.

67.

68.

69.

70.

71.

$x \geq -3$

72.

$y < 1.5$

73.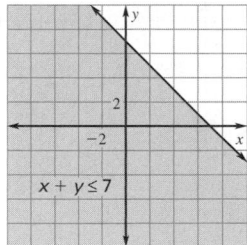

$x + y \leq 7$

74.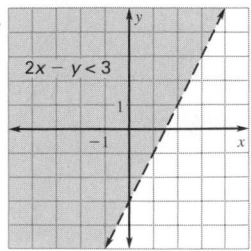

$2x - y < 3$

8.4 Mixed Review (p. 518)

69.

70.

71.

72.

73.

74.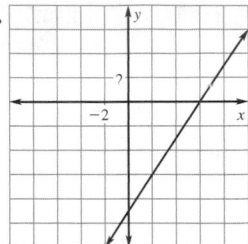

8.5 Guided Practice (pp. 520–523)

2.

3.

4.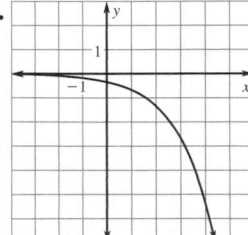

8.5 Skill Practice (pp. 523–524)

9.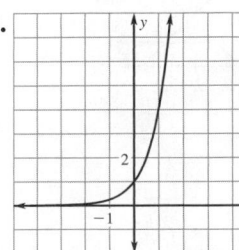

domain: all real numbers, range: all positive real numbers

10.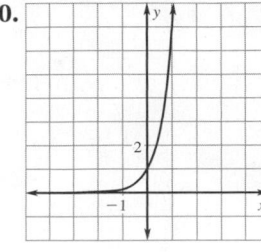

domain: all real numbers, range: all positive real numbers

11. domain: all real numbers, range: all positive real numbers

12. domain: all real numbers, range: all positive real numbers

13. domain: all real numbers, range: all positive real numbers

14. domain: all real numbers, range: all positive real numbers

15. 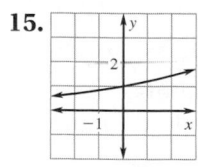 domain: all real numbers, range: all positive real numbers

16. domain: all real numbers, range: all positive real numbers

17. domain: all real numbers, range: all positive real numbers

18. 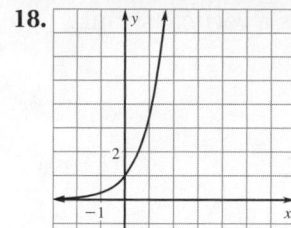 domain: all real numbers, range: all positive real numbers

19. domain: all real numbers, range: all positive real numbers

20. 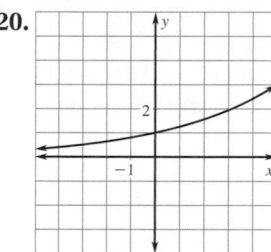 domain: all real numbers, range: all positive real numbers

22. The graph is a vertical stretch.

23. The graph is a vertical stretch.

24. 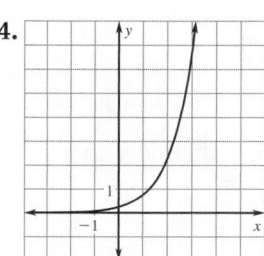 The graph is a vertical shrink.

25. 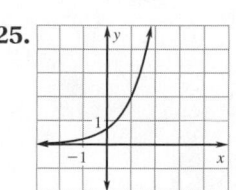 The graph is a vertical shrink.

26. The graph is a vertical shrink.

27. The graph is a vertical stretch.

28. 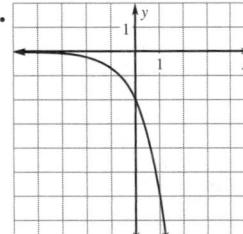 The graph is a vertical stretch with a reflection in the *x*-axis.

29. 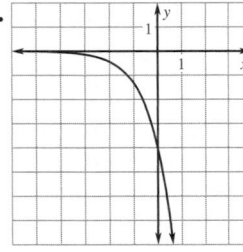 The graph is a vertical stretch with a reflection in the *x*-axis.

30. 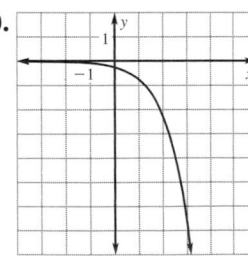 The graph is a vertical shrink with a reflection in the *x*-axis.

31. 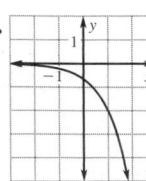 The graph is a vertical shrink with a reflection in the *x*-axis.

32. The graph is a vertical shrink with a reflection in the *x*-axis.

33. The graph is a vertical stretch with a reflection in the *x*-axis.

8.6 Guided Practice (pp. 531–534)

2.   **3.**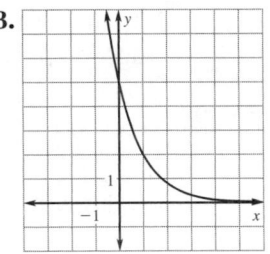

8.6 Skill Practice (pp. 535–536)

7. 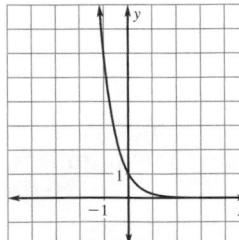 domain: all real numbers, range: all positive real numbers

8. domain: all real numbers, range: all positive real numbers

9. domain: all real numbers, range: all positive real numbers

10. domain: all real numbers, range: all positive real numbers

11. domain: all real numbers, range: all positive real numbers

12. 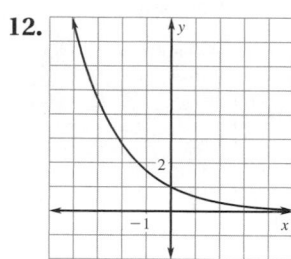 domain: all real numbers, range: all positive real numbers

13. domain: all real numbers, range: all positive real numbers

14. 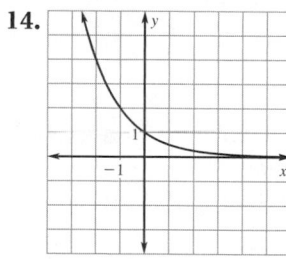 domain: all real numbers, range: all positive real numbers

15. domain: all real numbers, range: all positive real numbers

16. 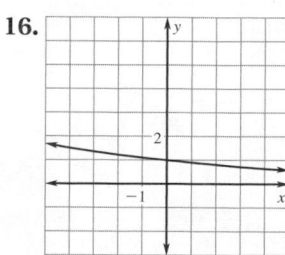 domain: all real numbers, range: all positive real numbers

17. domain: all real numbers, range: all positive real numbers

18. 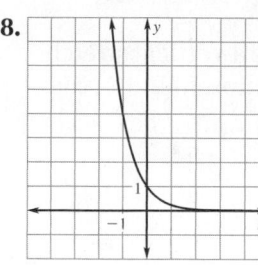 domain: all real numbers, range: all positive real numbers

20. 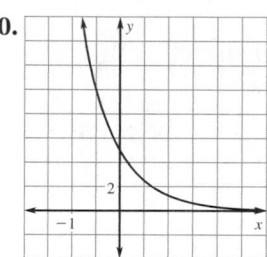 The graph is a vertical stretch.

21. 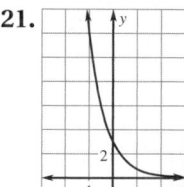 The graph is a vertical stretch.

22. 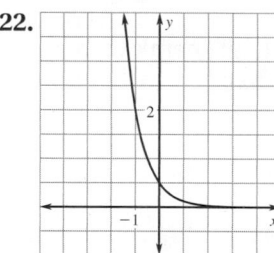 The graph is a vertical shrink.

23. The graph is a vertical shrink.

24. 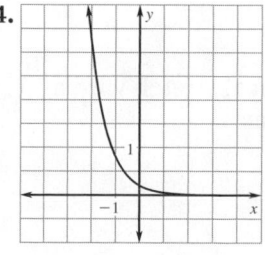 The graph is a vertical shrink.

25. The graph is a vertical stretch.

26. 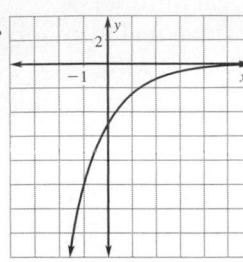 The graph is a vertical stretch with a reflection in the x-axis.

27. The graph is a vertical stretch with a reflection in the x-axis.

28. 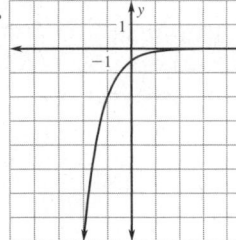 The graph is a vertical shrink with a reflection in the x-axis.

29. 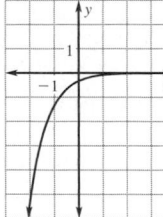 The graph is a vertical shrink with a reflection in the x-axis.

30. 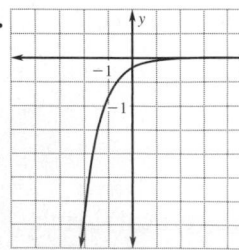 The graph is a vertical shrink with a reflection in the x-axis.

31. The graph is a vertical stretch with a reflection in the x-axis.

Quiz for Lessons 8.5–8.6 (p. 538)

1.

2.

3.

4.

5.

6.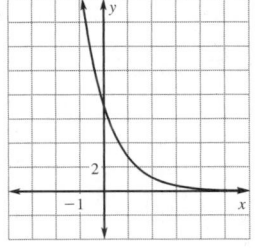

Extension (p. 540)

1.

2.

3.

4.

5.   **6.**

3.

Chapter 9

9.1 Mixed Review (p. 559)

49.   **50.**

5. **6.**

51.   **52.**

53.   **54.**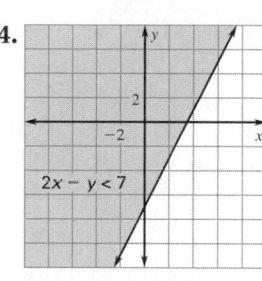

9.2 Investigating Algebra Activity (p. 561)

1.   **2.**

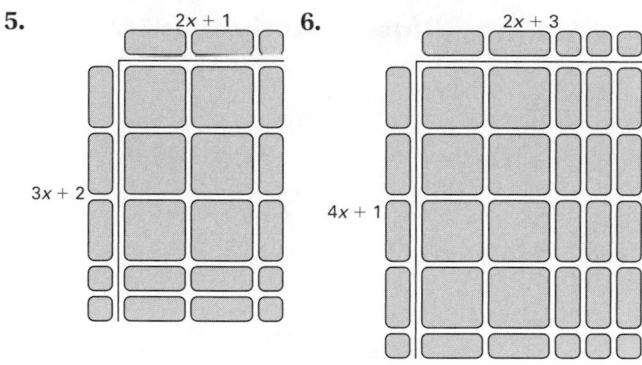

9.3 Skill Practice (p. 572) **2.** The square of a binomial is a trinomial. To find the first term of the trinomial, square the first term of the binomial. To find the second term of the trinomial, find twice the product of the terms of the binomial, using the sign of the second term. To find the third term of the trinomial, square the second term of the binomial.

9.3 Problem Solving (pp. 573–574) **43. a.** 88.1%; the areas of the four regions are: 2 complete passes: $0.655^2 \approx 0.429$ square units; 1 complete pass, 1 incomplete pass: $0.655(0.345) \approx 0.226$ square units; 1 incomplete pass, 1 complete pass: $0.345(0.655) \approx 0.226$ square units; and 2 incomplete passes: $0.345^2 \approx 0.119$ square units. The regions that involve at least one complete pass cover $0.429 + 0.226 + 0.226 = 0.881$ square units, or 88.1% of the whole square region. **b.** The outcome of each attempted pass is modeled by $0.655C + 0.345I$, so the possible outcomes of two attempted passes is modeled by $(0.655C + 0.345I)^2 = 0.429C^2 + 0.452CI + 0.119I^2$. Because any combination of outcomes with a C results in at least one completed pass, the coefficients of the first two terms show that 42.9% + 45.2% = 88.1% of the outcomes will have at least one completed pass, and the coefficient of the last term shows that 11.9% of the outcomes will have two incomplete passes.

9.4 Problem Solving (pp. 579–580) **59. a.** 8 ft; the zeros of the function, 0 and 8, are the x-intercepts of the graph, which represent the edges of the base of the doorway. The distance between 0 and 8 on the x-axis is 8 units, so the width of the doorway at its base is 8 feet. **b.** 8 ft; the center of the base is the midpoint of the segment joining the x-intercepts 0 and 8, so at the center of the base $x = 4$. The doorway's highest point will be the point $(4, y)$ on the graph of $y = -0.5x(x - 8)$. Substitute $x = 4$ into the equation for y to find the height: $y = -0.5(4)(4 - 8) = 8$ feet.

9.5 Investigating Algebra Activity (p. 582)

2. **3.**

4. **5.**

6. **7.**

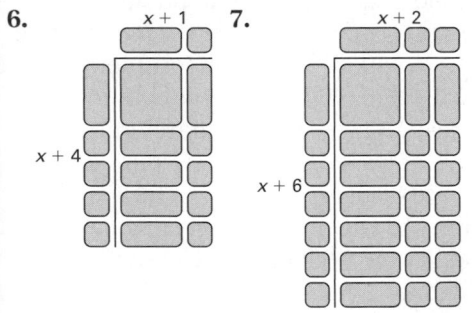

9.6 Investigating Algebra Activity (p. 592)

2. **3.**

4.

5.

6.

7.

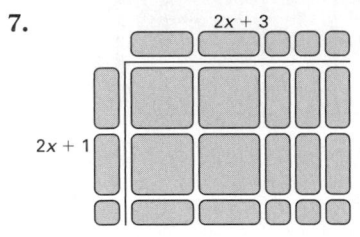

9.6 Skill Practice (pp. 596–597) **52.** $x^2 + x - 6 = 0$; any root $x = r$ of $x^2 + bx + c = 0$ comes from setting the factor $x - r$ equal to zero after $x^2 + bx + c$ is written in factored form; so, the roots -3 and 2 come from the factors $x - (-3)$, or $x + 3$, and $x - 2$. The product of these factors is $(x + 3)(x - 2) = x^2 - 2x + 3x - 6 = x^2 + x - 6$.

53. $2x^2 - 9x - 5 = 0$; any root $x = \frac{r}{s}$ of $ax^2 + bx + c = 0$ comes from setting the factor $sx - r$ equal to zero after $ax^2 + bx + c$ is written in factored form; so, the roots $-\frac{1}{2}$ and 5 come from the factors $2x - (-1)$, or $2x + 1$, and $x - 5$. The product of these factors is $(2x + 1)(x - 5) = 2x^2 - 10x + x - 5 = 2x^2 - 9x - 5$. **54.** $12x^2 + 13x + 3 = 0$; any root $x = \frac{r}{s}$ of $ax^2 + bx + c = 0$ comes from setting the factor $sx - r$ equal to zero after $ax^2 + bx + c$ is written in factored form; so, the roots $-\frac{3}{4}$ and $-\frac{1}{3}$ come from the factors $4x - (-3)$, or $4x + 3$, and $3x - (-1)$, or $3x + 1$. The product of these factors is $(4x + 3)(3x + 1) = 12x^2 + 4x + 9x + 3 = 12x^2 + 13x + 3$.

9.7 Problem Solving (pp. 604–605)

52. d. 6 rows; let x = the number of chairs in the last row, so that the sum of the odd integers from 15 to x is 120. x can be written in the form $2n - 1$. 15 is the eighth odd integer and x is the nth odd integer, so the sum of the odd integers from 15 to x can be found as described in part (c): the sum of the first n odd integers minus the sum of the first 7 odd integers, $n^2 - 7^2$, or $n^2 - 49$. The total number of chairs is to be 120, so this leads to the equation $n^2 - 49 = 120$, or $n^2 - 169 = 0$. This equation has two solutions, 13 and -13. Disregard the solution -13 because n cannot be negative in this situation. So, x is the thirteenth odd integer. The numbers of chairs in the rows go from the eighth odd integer (15) to the thirteenth odd integer (25). There are $13 - 8 + 1 = 6$ rows of chairs.

9.7 Mixed Review (p. 605)

62.

63.

64.

65.

66.

67.

68.

69.

70.
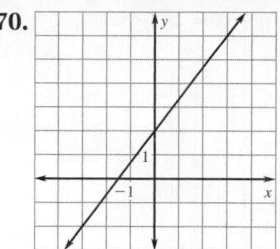

9.8 Mixed Review (p. 613)

75.

76.

77.

78.

79.

80.

81.

82.

83.

84.

85.

86.

Chapter 10

10.1 Guided Practice (pp. 629–631)

1. 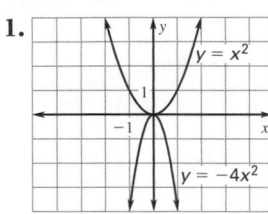 The graph is a vertical stretch (by a factor of 4) with a reflection in the x-axis of the graph of $y = x^2$.

2. 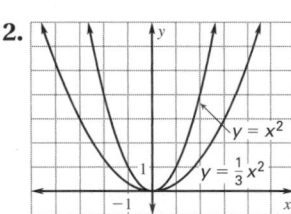 The graph is a vertical shrink $\left(\text{by a factor of } \frac{1}{3}\right)$ of the graph of $y = x^2$.

3. 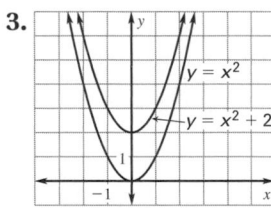 The graph is a vertical translation (of 2 units up) of the graph of $y = x^2$.

10.1 Skill Practice (pp. 632–633)

6. 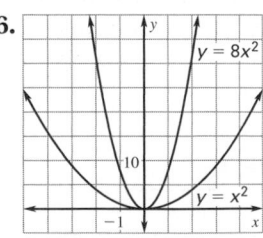 The graph is a vertical stretch (by a factor of 8) of the graph of $y = x^2$.

7. 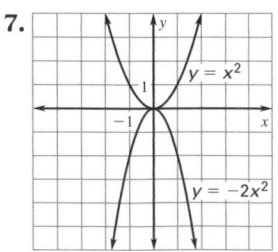 The graph is a vertical stretch (by a factor of 2) with a reflection in the x-axis of the graph of $y = x^2$.

8. 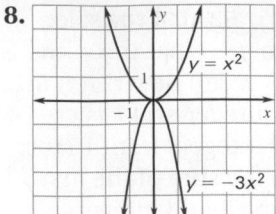 The graph is a vertical stretch (by a factor of 3) with a reflection in the x-axis of the graph of $y = x^2$.

9. The graph is a vertical stretch (by a factor of 5) of the graph of $y = x^2$.

10. 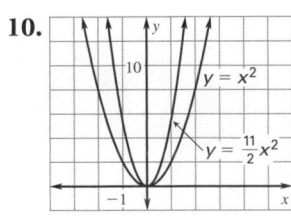 The graph is a vertical stretch $\left(\text{by a factor of } \frac{11}{2}\right)$ of the graph of $y = x^2$.

11. 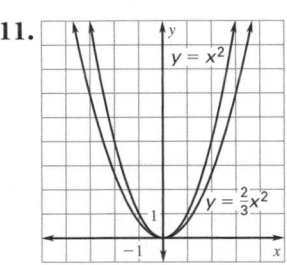 The graph is a vertical shrink $\left(\text{by a factor of } \frac{2}{3}\right)$ of the graph of $y = x^2$.

12. 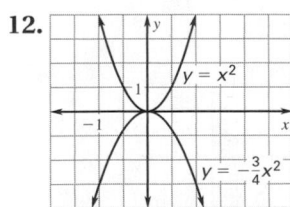 The graph is a vertical shrink $\left(\text{by a factor of } \frac{3}{4}\right)$ with a reflection in the x-axis of the graph of $y = x^2$.

13. 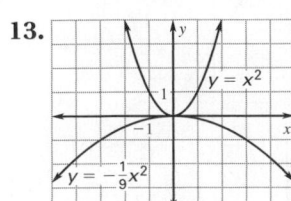 The graph is a vertical shrink $\left(\text{by a factor of } \frac{1}{9}\right)$ with a reflection in the x-axis of the graph of $y = x^2$.

14. 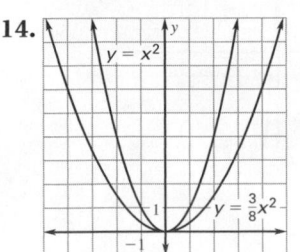 The graph is a vertical shrink $\left(\text{by a factor of } \frac{3}{8}\right)$ of the graph of $y = x^2$.

15. The graph is a vertical shrink $\left(\text{by a factor of } \frac{1}{5}\right)$ with a reflection in the x-axis of the graph of $y = x^2$.

16. The graph is a vertical translation (of 7 units down) of the graph of $y = x^2$.

17. 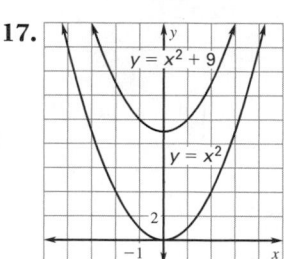 The graph is a vertical translation (of 9 units up) of the graph of $y = x^2$.

18. 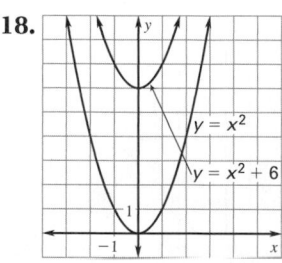 The graph is a vertical translation (of 6 units up) of the graph of $y = x^2$.

19. The graph is a vertical translation (of 4 units down) of the graph of $y = x^2$.

20. 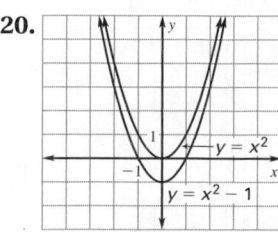 The graph is a vertical translation (of 1 unit down) of the graph of $y = x^2$.

21. The graph is a vertical translation $\left(\text{of } \frac{7}{4} \text{ units up}\right)$ of the graph of $y = x^2$.

24. 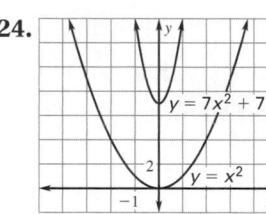 The graph is a vertical stretch (by a factor of 7) with a vertical translation (of 7 units up) of the graph of $y = x^2$.

25. 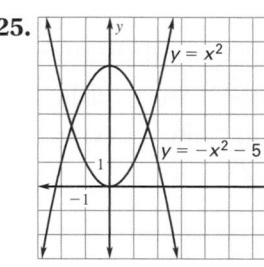 The graph is a reflection in the x-axis with a vertical translation (of 5 units up) of the graph of $y = x^2$.

26. The graph is a vertical stretch (by a factor of 2) with a vertical translation (of 12 units down) of the graph of $y = x^2$.

27. The graph is a vertical stretch (by a factor of 2) with a vertical translation (of 1 unit down) and a reflection in the x-axis of the graph of $y = x^2$.

28. 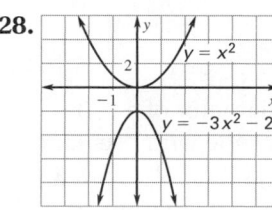 The graph is a vertical stretch (by a factor of 3) with a vertical translation (of 2 units down) and a reflection in the x-axis of the graph of $y = x^2$.

29.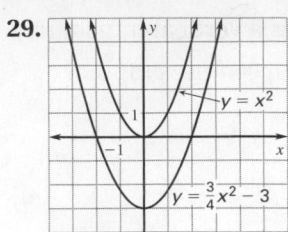

The graph is a vertical shrink $\left(\text{by a factor of } \frac{3}{4}\right)$ with a vertical translation (of 3 units down) of the graph of $y = x^2$.

30.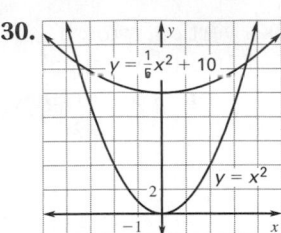

The graph is a vertical shrink $\left(\text{by a factor of } \frac{1}{5}\right)$ with a vertical translation (of 10 units up) of the graph of $y = x^2$.

31.

The graph is a vertical shrink $\left(\text{by a factor of } \frac{1}{2}\right)$ with a vertical translation (of 5 units down) of the graph of $y = x^2$.

32.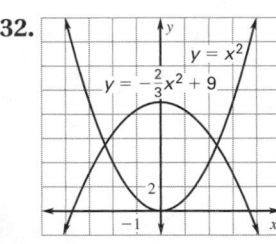

The graph is a vertical shrink $\left(\text{by a factor of } \frac{2}{3}\right)$ with a vertical translation (of 9 units up) and a reflection in the x-axis of the graph of $y = x^2$.

10.1 Problem Solving (pp. 633–634)

43. a.

b. No. *Sample answer:* Let D be the diameter of a rope with 4 times the breaking weight of a rope with breaking weight d. Then $8900D^2 = 4(8900d^2)$; $D^2 = 4d^2$; $D = \sqrt{4d^2}$; $D = 2d$. Thus, the diameter of the rope with 4 times the breaking weight is only two times the diameter of the other rope.

44. a.   **b.**

c. The graph of $y = -16t^2 + 30$ is a reflection in the x-axis and a vertical translation (of 30 units up) of the graph of $y = 16t^2$. To use the graph of $y = -16t^2 + 30$, estimate the t-value of the point that has a y-value of 20 feet, which is the height of the egg after it falls 10 feet. To use the graph of $y = 16t^2$, estimate the t-value of the point that has a y-value of 10 feet.

10.2 Skill Practice (pp. 638–639)

15.   **16.**

17.   **18.**

19.   **20.**

21.   **22.**

23.

24.

25.

26.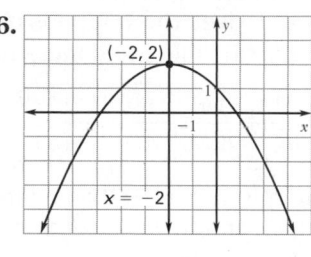

10.2 Problem Solving (pp. 639–640)

43.

Extension (p. 642)

1.

2.

3.

4.

5.

6.

7.

8.

9.

10.

11.

12.

13.

14.

15.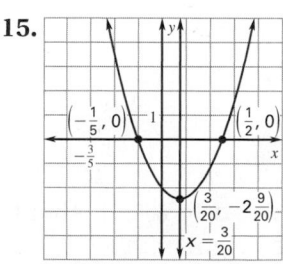

Quiz for Lessons 10.1–10.3 (p. 649)

1.

The graph is a vertical shrink $\left(\text{by a factor of } \frac{1}{2}\right)$ with a reflection in the x-axis of the graph of $y = x^2$.

2.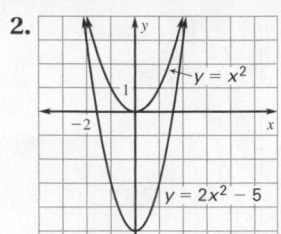

The graph is a vertical stretch (by a factor of 2) with a vertical translation (of 5 units down) of the graph of $y = x^2$.

3.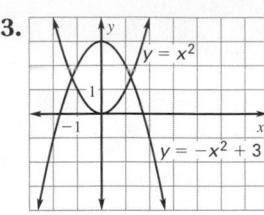

The graph is a vertical translation (of 3 units up) with a reflection in the x-axis of the graph of $y = x^2$.

4.

5.

6.

7.

8.

9.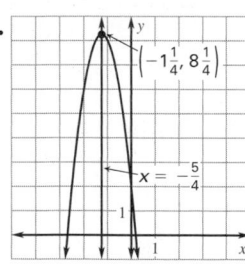

10.4 Problem Solving Workshop (p. 660) **1.** About 1.5 sec; Method 1: Use factoring. The height h (in feet) of the ball t seconds after it is dropped is modeled by $h = -16t^2 + 45$. To find the time it takes the ball to reach a height of 10 feet, substitute 10 for h and solve for t: $10 = -16t^2 + 45$, or $0 = -16t^2 + 35$. Replace 35 with the closest perfect square and factor: $0 = -16t^2 + 36$; $0 = -4(4t^2 - 9)$; $0 = -4(2t + 3)(2t - 3)$; $2t + 3 = 0$ *or* $2t - 3 = 0$; $t = -\frac{3}{2}$ or $t = \frac{3}{2}$. The time cannot be negative, so disregard the negative solution; the ball is in the air about 1.5 seconds.

Method 2: Use a table. The height h (in feet) of the ball t seconds after it is dropped is modeled by $h = -16t^2 + 45$. Make a table that shows the height h of the ball for values of t in increments of 1 second:

Time, t (sec)	0	1	2
Height, h (ft)	45	29	−19

Look in the table for the time interval in which the ball reaches a height of 10 feet; this happens between 1 and 2 seconds. Make a second table using increments of 0.1 second:

Time, t (sec)	1.0	1.1	1.2	1.3	1.4	1.5
Height, h (ft)	29.00	25.64	21.96	17.96	13.64	9

The height in the table that is closest to 10 feet is 9 feet. To the nearest tenth of a second, the ball is in the air for about 1.5 seconds.

3. b. length: about 9 in., width: 5 in., height: about 1.8 in.

c.

Height, x (in.)	1.7	1.8	1.9
Width (in.)	5	5	5
Length, $5x$ (in.)	8.5	9	9.5
Volume, V (in.³)	72.25	81	90.25

The volume in the table closest to 83 cubic inches is 81 cubic inches. To the nearest tenth of an inch, the height of the box is about 1.8 inches. The length of the box is $5x \approx 9$ inches, and the width is 5 inches.

Extension (p. 670)

1.

2.

3.

4.

5.

6.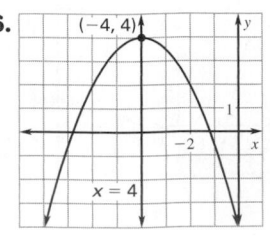

7. $y = (x - 6)^2$

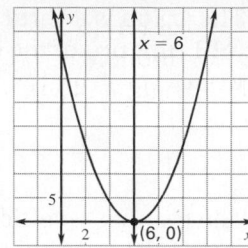

8. $y = (x + 4)^2 - 1$

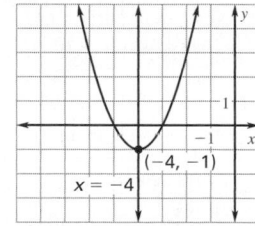

9. $y = -(x - 5)^2 + 4$

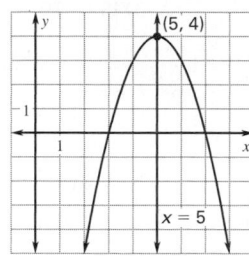

10. $y = 2(x - 3)^2 + 1$

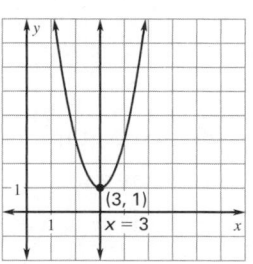

11. $y = -3(x + 1)^2 + 2$

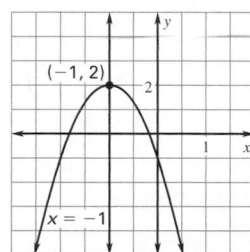

12. $y = -\frac{1}{2}(x + 6)^2 - 3$

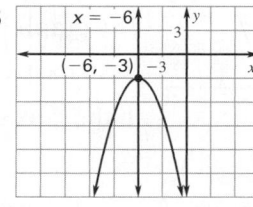

10.6 Mixed Review (p. 676)

56.

57.

58.

59.

60.

61.

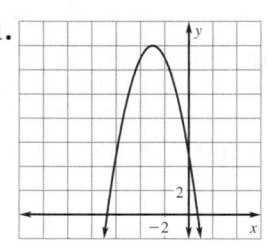

10.7 Investigating Algebra Activity (p. 677)

2. When $b^2 - 4ac$ is positive, $b^2 - 4ac$ has two square roots, one positive and one negative, so there are two different solutions to the quadratic equation $ax^2 + bx + c = 0$: $\dfrac{-b + \sqrt{b^2 - 4ac}}{2a}$ and $\dfrac{-b - \sqrt{b^2 - 4ac}}{2a}$. When $b^2 - 4ac$ is zero, $\sqrt{b^2 - 4ac} = 0$, so there is only one solution to the quadratic equation $ax^2 + bx + c = 0$: $\dfrac{-b \pm 0}{2a} = -\dfrac{b}{2a}$. When $b^2 - 4ac$ is negative, there is a negative number under the radical in the quadratic formula. Because negative numbers do not have real-number square roots, the quadratic formula cannot be evaluated and the quadratic equation $ax^2 + bx + c = 0$ has no real solution.

10.7 Skill Practice (pp. 681–682)
41.c. -25, 5; the width w cannot be negative, so the solution -25 meters does not make sense in the context of the problem. The solution 5 meters does makes sense in the context of the problem.

42. a. $k < \dfrac{1}{24}$ **b.** $\dfrac{1}{24}$ **c.** $k > \dfrac{1}{24}$ **43. a.** $k < -3 \text{ or } k > 3$ **b.** ± 3

c. $-3 < k < 3$ **44. a.** $k > -\dfrac{25}{64}$ **b.** $-\dfrac{25}{64}$ **c.** $k < -\dfrac{25}{64}$

10.7 Problem Solving (pp. 682–683)
45. a. Substitute 25 for y in the equation and then write the resulting quadratic equation in standard form: $25 = 0.06x^2 - 4x + 87$, or $0 = 0.06x^2 - 4x + 62$. Evaluate the discriminant: $b^2 - 4ac = (-4)^2 - 4(0.06)(62) = 1.12$. Since the discriminant is positive, we know that the equation $25 = 0.06x^2 - 4x + 87$ does have solutions, so it is possible for a parakeet to consume 25 milliliters of oxygen per gram of body mass per hour.

47. No; to determine if there is any point of the arch at a height of 4 feet, substitute 4 for y in the equation and then determine if the equation has any positive solutions. The equation is $4 = -0.18x^2 + 1.6x$, or $0 = -0.18x^2 + 1.6x - 4$. Evaluate the discriminant: $b^2 - 4ac = (1.6)^2 - 4(-0.18)(-4) = -0.32$. Since the discriminant is negative, we know the equation has no solution; thus, a child who is 4 feet tall cannot walk under one of the arches without having to bend over. **50. b.** Yes; no; $28,900; to decide if a weekly revenue of $28,000 is possible, check the discriminant of the equation $28,000 = -100x^2 + 1400x + 24,000$, or $0 = -100x^2 + 1400x - 4000$. The discriminant is 36. Since the discriminant is positive, it may be possible to receive a weekly revenue of $28,000. To decide if a weekly revenue of $30,000 is possible, check the discriminant of the equation $30,000 = -100x^2 + 1400x + 24,000$, or $0 = -100x^2 + 1400x - 6000$. The discriminant is -44. Since the discriminant is negative, it is not possible to receive a weekly revenue of $30,000. Since $r = -100x^2 + 1400x + 24,000$ is equivalent to the quadratic equation $0 = -100x^2 + 1400x + (24,000 - r)$, the maximum revenue r will occur when this equation has exactly one solution, or when its discriminant is 0. Solve $1400^2 - 4(-100)(24,000 - r) = 0$ for r; $r = \$28,900$.

10.7 Mixed Review (p. 683)

51.

52.

53.

54.

55.

56.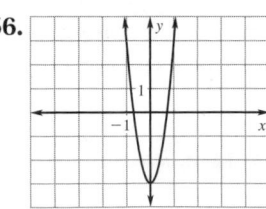

10.8 Mixed Review (p. 691)

35.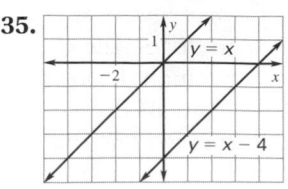
The graph is a vertical translation (of 4 units down) of the graph of $y = x$.

36.
The graph is a vertical translation (of 1 unit up) of the graph of $y = x$.

37.
The graph is a vertical stretch (by a factor of 8) of the graph of $y = x$.

38.
The graph is a reflection in the x-axis of the graph of $y = x$.

39.
The graph is a vertical shrink $\left(\text{by a factor of } \frac{1}{4}\right)$ of the graph of $y = x$.

40.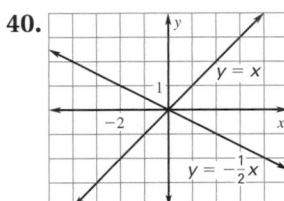
The graph is a vertical shrink $\left(\text{by a factor of } \frac{1}{2}\right)$ with a reflection in the x-axis of the graph of $y = x$.

41.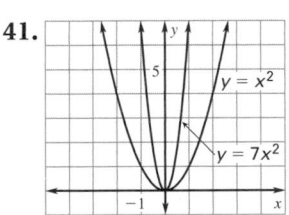
The graph is a vertical stretch (by a factor of 7) of the graph of $y = x^2$.

42.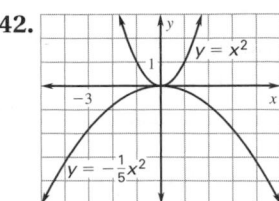
The graph is a vertical shrink $\left(\text{by a factor of } \frac{1}{5}\right)$ with a reflection in the x-axis of the graph of $y = x^2$.

43. The graph is a vertical stretch (by a factor of 2) with a vertical translation (of 3 units up) of the graph of $y = x^2$.

Cumulative Review (pp. 706–707)

18.

19.

20.

21.

22.

23.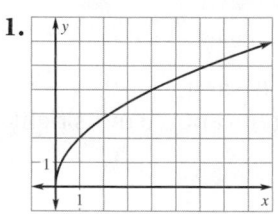

Chapter 11

11.1 Guided Practice (pp. 711–713)

1. 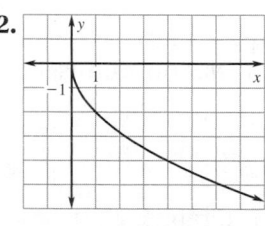 domain: $x \geq 0$, range: $y \geq 0$; vertical stretch by a factor of 2

2. 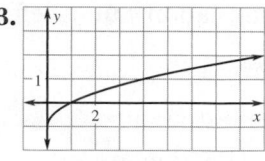 domain: $x \geq 0$, range: $y \leq 0$; vertical stretch by a factor of 2 and a reflection in the x-axis

3. 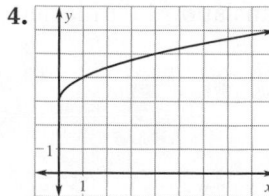 domain: $x \geq 0$, range: $y \geq -1$; vertical translation of 1 unit down

4. domain: $x \geq 0$, range: $y \geq 3$; vertical translation of 3 units up

11.1 Skill Practice (pp. 713–714)

3. 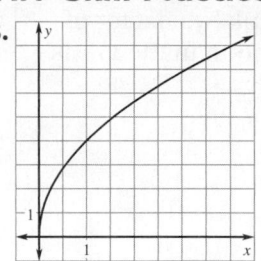 domain: $x \geq 0$, range: $y \geq 0$; vertical stretch by a factor of 4

4. 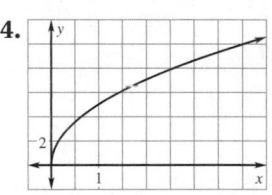 domain: $x \geq 0$, range: $y \geq 0$; vertical stretch by a factor of 5

5. 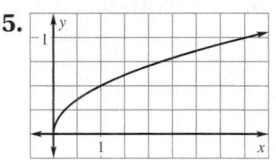 domain: $x \geq 0$, range: $y \geq 0$; vertical shrink by a factor of 0.5

6. 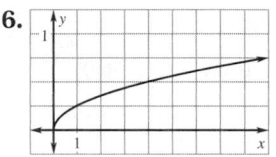 domain: $x \geq 0$, range: $y \geq 0$; vertical shrink by a factor of 0.25

7. 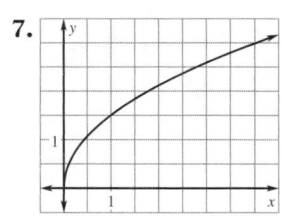 domain: $x \geq 0$, range: $y \geq 0$; vertical stretch by a factor of $\frac{3}{2}$

8. 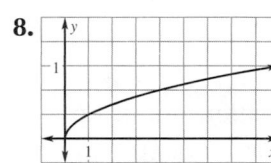 domain: $x \geq 0$, range: $y \geq 0$; vertical shrink by a factor of $\frac{1}{3}$

9. 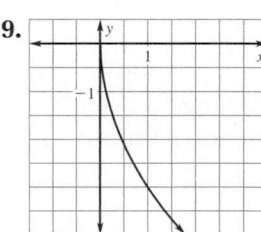 domain: $x \geq 0$, range: $y \leq 0$; vertical stretch by a factor of 3 with a reflection in the x-axis

10. 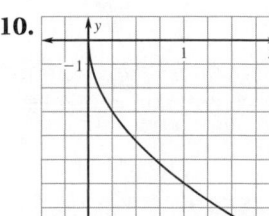 domain: $x \geq 0$, range: $y \leq 0$; vertical stretch by a factor of 6 with a reflection in the x-axis

11. domain: $x \geq 0$, range: $y \leq 0$; vertical shrink by a factor of 0.8 with a reflection in the x-axis

12. 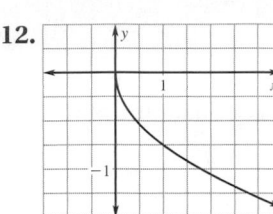 domain: $x \geq 0$, range: $y \leq 0$; vertical shrink by a factor of 0.75 with a reflection in the x-axis

13. 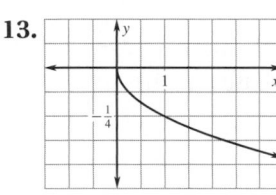 domain: $x \geq 0$, range: $y \leq 0$; vertical shrink by a factor of $\frac{1}{4}$ with a reflection in the x-axis

14. 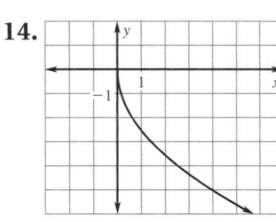 domain: $x \geq 0$, range: $y \leq 0$; vertical stretch by a factor of $\frac{5}{2}$ with a reflection in the x-axis

17. 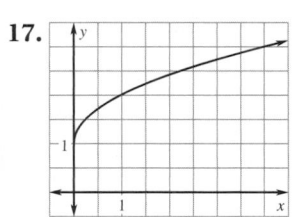 domain: $x \geq 0$, range: $y \geq 1$; vertical translation 1 unit up

18. 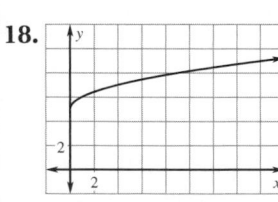 domain: $x \geq 0$, range: $y \geq 5$; vertical translation 5 units up

19. 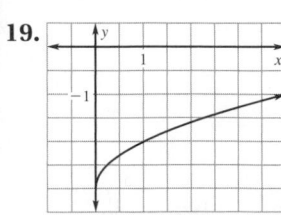 domain: $x \geq 0$, range: $y \geq -3$; vertical translation 3 units down

20. domain: $x \geq 0$, range: $y \geq -4$; vertical translation 4 units down

21. domain: $x \geq 0$, range: $y \geq \frac{3}{4}$; vertical translation $\frac{3}{4}$ unit up

22. 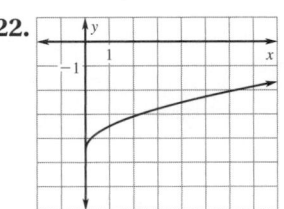 domain: $x \geq 0$, range: $y \geq -4.5$; vertical translation 4.5 units down

23. 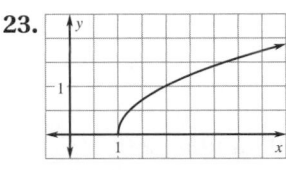 domain: $x \geq 1$, range: $y \geq 0$; horizontal translation 1 unit right

24. 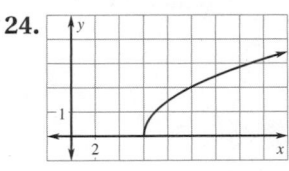 domain: $x \geq 6$, range: $y \geq 0$; horizontal translation 6 units right

25. 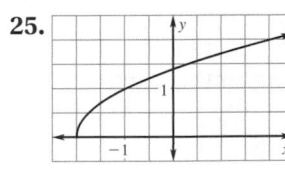 domain: $x \geq -2$, range: $y \geq 0$; horizontal translation 2 units left

26. 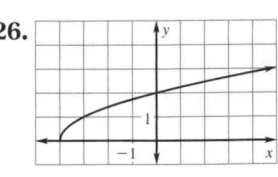 domain: $x \geq -4$, range: $y \geq 0$; horizontal translation 4 units left

27. 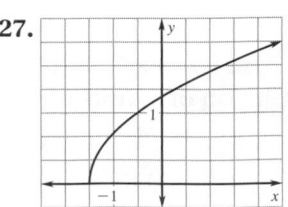 domain: $x \geq -1.5$, range: $y \geq 0$; horizontal translation 1.5 units left

28. domain: $x \geq \frac{1}{2}$, range: $y \geq 0$;

horizontal translation $\frac{1}{2}$ unit right

30. **31.**

32. **33.**

34. **35.**

36. **37.**

38.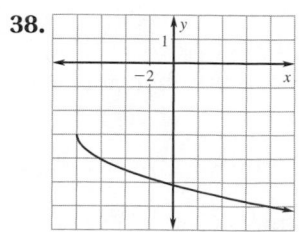

11.1 Problem Solving (pp. 715–716)

47. a. 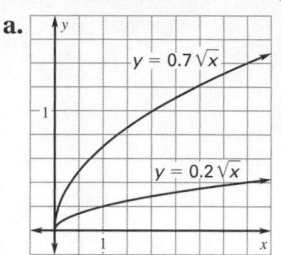 blue-winged teal's domain: $x \geq 0$, range: $y \geq 0$, northern pintail's domain: $x \geq 0$, range: $y \geq 0$

48. a. 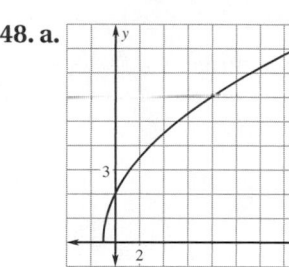 **c.** 1983; to find the year when the amount consumed doubled the amount consumed in 1980, solve the equation for $y = 4$; find $x = 3$, so 3 years after 1980, or 1983.

11.1 Graphing Calculator Activity (p. 717)

1. 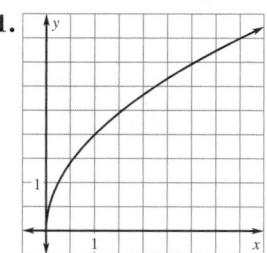 domain: $x \geq 0$, range: $y \geq 0$

2. 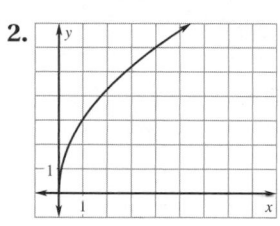 domain: $x \geq 0$, range: $y \geq 0$

3. 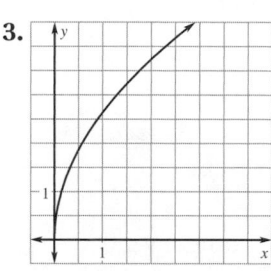 domain: $x \geq 0$, range: $y \geq 0$

4. 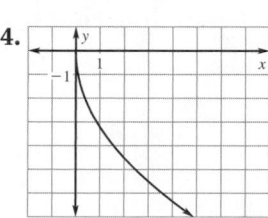 domain: $x \geq 0$, range: $y \leq 0$

5. domain: $x \geq 0$, range: $y \leq 0$

6. 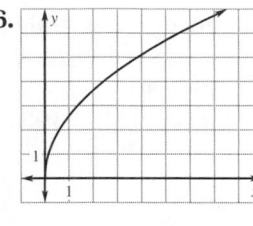 domain: $x \geq 0$, range: $y \geq 0$

7. 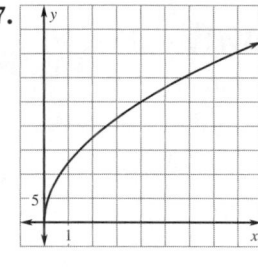 domain: $x \geq 0$, range: $y \geq 0$

8. 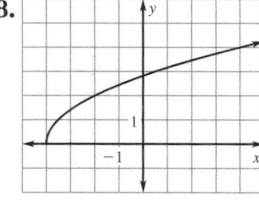 domain: $x \geq -4$, range: $y \geq 0$

9. 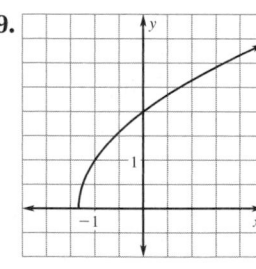 domain: $x \geq -\frac{4}{3}$, range: $y \geq 0$

10. 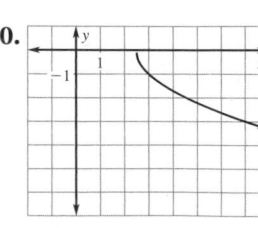 domain: $x \geq \frac{5}{2}$, range: $y \leq 0$

11. 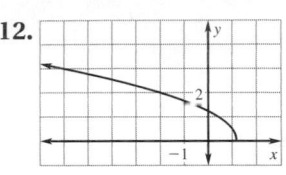 domain: $x \geq \frac{3}{2}$, range: $y \leq 0$

12. 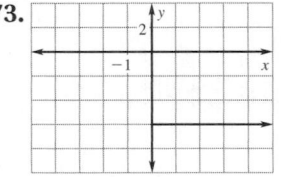 domain: $x \leq \frac{6}{5}$, range: $y \geq 0$

11.2 Mixed Review (p. 726)

73. 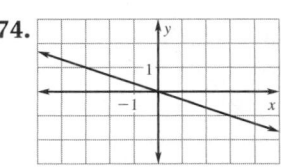 domain: $x \geq 0$, range: $y = -6$

74. 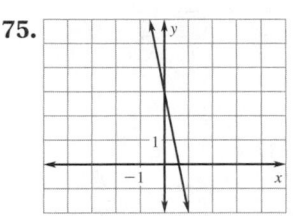 domain: all real numbers, range: all real numbers

75. domain: all real numbers, range: all real numbers

76. domain: all real numbers, range: all real numbers

77. 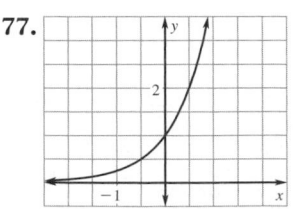 domain: all real numbers, range: $y \geq 0$

78. domain: all real numbers, range: $y \geq 0$

79. 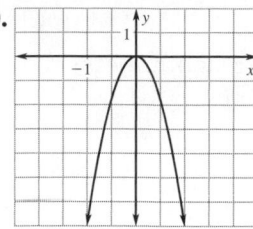 domain: all real numbers, range: $y \leq 0$

80. domain: all real numbers, range: $y \geq 2$

81. domain: all real numbers, range: $y \geq -\dfrac{49}{3}$

Extension (pp. 727–728)

19. Substitute $\dfrac{-b + \sqrt{b^2 - 4ac}}{2a}$ for x:

$$a\left(\frac{-b + \sqrt{b^2 - 4ac}}{2a}\right) + b\left(\frac{-b + \sqrt{b^2 - 4ac}}{2a}\right) + c = 0$$

$$a\left(\frac{b^2 - 2b\sqrt{b^2 - 4ac} + b^2 - 4ac}{4a^2}\right) + \frac{-b^2 + b\sqrt{b^2 - 4ac}}{2a} + c = 0$$

$$\frac{b^2}{4a} - \frac{b\sqrt{b^2 - 4ac}}{2a} + \frac{b^2}{4a} - c - \frac{b^2}{2a} + \frac{b\sqrt{b^2 - 4ac}}{2a} + c = 0$$

$$0 = 0$$

Substitute $\dfrac{-b - \sqrt{b^2 - 4ac}}{2a}$ for x:

$$a\left(\frac{-b - \sqrt{b^2 - 4ac}}{2a}\right) + b\left(\frac{-b - \sqrt{b^2 - 4ac}}{2a}\right) + c = 0$$

$$a\left(\frac{b^2 + 2b\sqrt{b^2 - 4ac} + b^2 - 4ac}{4a^2}\right) + \frac{-b^2 - b\sqrt{b^2 - 4ac}}{2a} + c = 0$$

$$\frac{b^2}{4a} + \frac{b\sqrt{b^2 - 4ac}}{2a} + \frac{b^2}{4a} - c - \frac{b^2}{2a} - \frac{b\sqrt{b^2 - 4ac}}{2a} + c = 0$$

$$0 = 0$$

22. $a \leq 12$. *Sample answer:* For a quadratic equation to have one or two real solutions, the value of $b^2 - 4ac$ must be greater than or equal to 0. Substituting values and solving: $12^2 - 4 \cdot a \cdot 3 \geq 0$, $a \leq 12$.

11.4 Mixed Review (p. 742)

39.

40.

41.

42.

43.

44.

45.

46.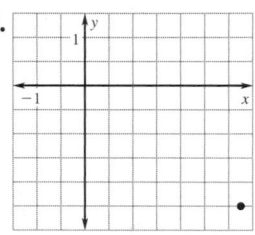

11.5 Mixed Review (p. 750)

59.

60.

61.

62.

63.

64.

Chapter 12

12.1 Skill Practice (pp. 769–770)

15.
$y = \frac{2}{x}$

16.
$y = \frac{-1}{x}$

17.
$y = \frac{-7}{x}$

18.
$y = \frac{10}{x}$

19.
$y = \frac{-5}{x}$

20.
$y = \frac{18}{x}$

21.
$y = \frac{9}{x}$

22.
$y = \frac{-2}{x}$

23.
$y = \frac{15}{x}$

24.
$y = \frac{6}{x}$

25.
$y = \frac{-12}{x}$

26.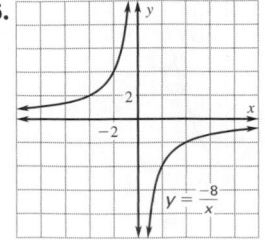
$y = \frac{-8}{x}$

12.1 Mixed Review (p. 772)

63.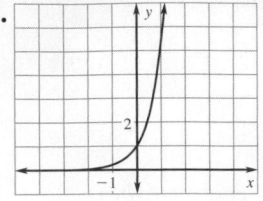
domain: all real numbers, range: $y > 0$

64.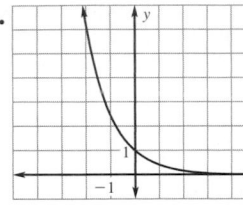
domain: all real numbers, range: $y > 0$

65.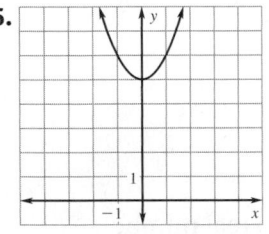
domain: all real numbers, range: $y \geq 5$

66.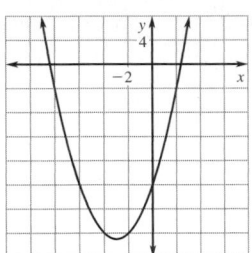
domain: all real numbers, range: $y \geq -29$

67.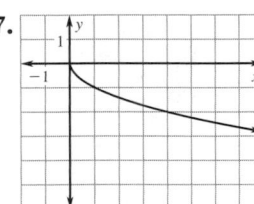
domain: $x \geq 0$, range: $y \leq 0$

68.
domain: $x \geq 1$, range: $y \geq 1$

12.2 Guided Practice (pp. 776–778)

1.
Domain: all real numbers except 0, range: all real numbers except 0; the graph is a vertical stretch of the graph of $y = \frac{1}{x}$ that is then reflected in the x-axis.

$y = \frac{1}{x}$

$y = \frac{-4}{x}$

2. Domain: all real numbers except 0, range: all real numbers except -4; the graph is a vertical translation (of 4 units down) of the graph of $y = \frac{1}{x}$.

3. Domain: all real numbers except -5, range: all real numbers except 0; the graph is a horizontal translation (of 5 units left) of the graph of $y = \frac{1}{x}$.

4. The graph of $y = \frac{1}{x + 3}$ is a horizontal translation (of 3 units left) of the graph of $y = \frac{1}{x}$.

12.2 Skill Practice (pp. 779–780)

3. 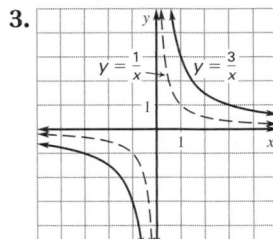 Domain: all real numbers except 0, range: all real numbers except 0; the graph is a vertical stretch of the graph of $y = \frac{1}{x}$.

4. 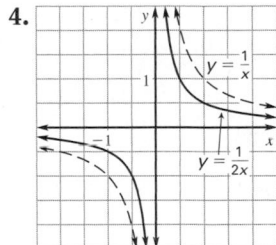 Domain: all real numbers except 0, range: all real numbers except 0; the graph is a vertical shrink of the graph of $y = \frac{1}{x}$.

5. 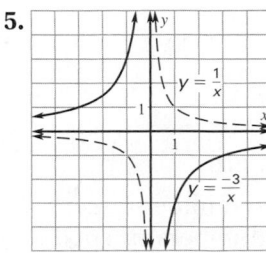 Domain: all real numbers except 0, range: all real numbers except 0; the graph is a vertical stretch of the graph of $y = \frac{1}{x}$ that is then reflected in the x-axis.

6. 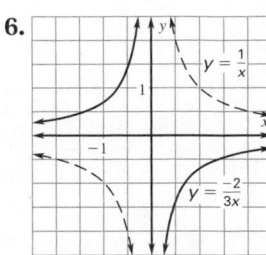 Domain: all real numbers except 0, range: all real numbers except 0; the graph is a vertical shrink of the graph of $y = \frac{1}{x}$ that is then reflected in the x-axis.

7. Domain: all real numbers except 0, range: all real numbers except 0; the graph is a vertical shrink of the graph of $y = \frac{1}{x}$ that is then reflected in the x-axis.

8. Domain: all real numbers except 0, range: all real numbers except 7; the graph is a vertical translation (of 7 units up) of the graph of $y = \frac{1}{x}$.

9. Domain: all real numbers except 0, range: all real numbers except -5; the graph is a vertical translation (of 5 units down) of the graph of $y = \frac{1}{x}$.

10. 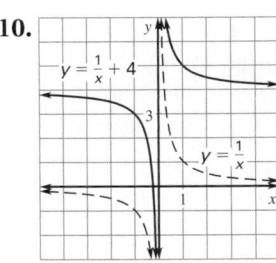 Domain: all real numbers except 0, range: all real numbers except 4; the graph is a vertical translation (of 4 units up) of the graph of $y = \frac{1}{x}$.

11. 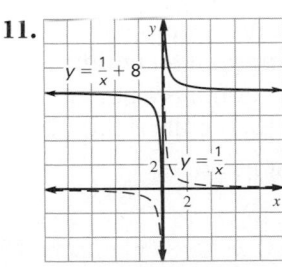 Domain: all real numbers except 0, range: all real numbers except 8; the graph is a vertical translation (of 8 units up) of the graph of $y = \frac{1}{x}$.

12. Domain: all real numbers except 0, range: all real numbers except -6; the graph is a vertical translation (of 6 units down) of the graph of $y = \frac{1}{x}$.

13.

Domain: all real numbers except −3, range: all real numbers except 0; the graph is a horizontal translation (of 3 units left) of the graph of $y = \frac{1}{x}$.

14.

Domain: all real numbers except 7, range: all real numbers except 0; the graph is a horizontal translation (of 7 units right) of the graph of $y = \frac{1}{x}$.

15.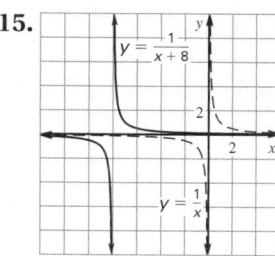

Domain: all real numbers except −8, range: all real numbers except 0; the graph is a horizontal translation (of 8 units left) of the graph of $y = \frac{1}{x}$.

16.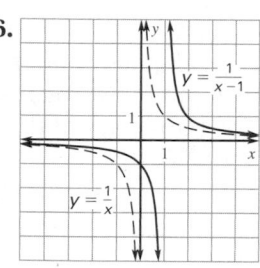

Domain: all real numbers except 1, range: all real numbers except 0; the graph is a horizontal translation (of 1 unit right) of the graph of $y = \frac{1}{x}$.

17.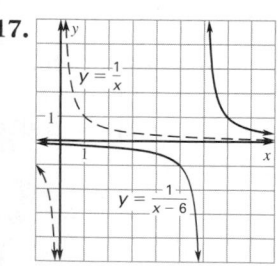

Domain: all real numbers except 6, range: all real numbers except 0; the graph is a horizontal translation (of 6 units right) of the graph of $y = \frac{1}{x}$.

19.

20.

21.

22.

23.

24.

25.

26.

27.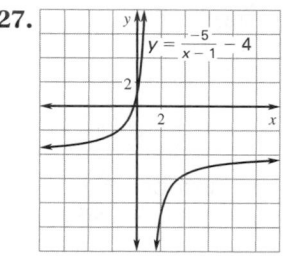

12.2 Problem Solving (pp. 780–782)

45. a.

Quiz for Lessons 12.1–12.2 (p. 782)

7.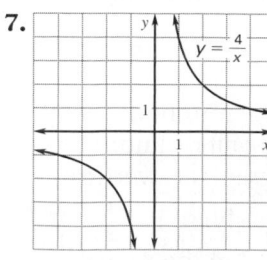

domain: all real numbers except 0, range: all real numbers except 0

8. 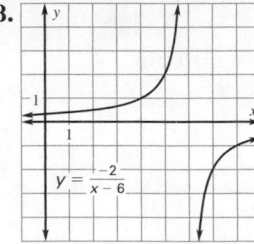 domain: all real numbers except 6, range: all real numbers except 0

$$y = \frac{-2}{x - 6}$$

9. 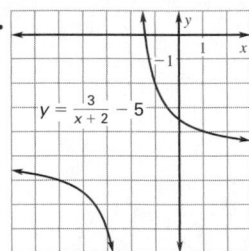 domain: all real numbers except −2, range: all real numbers except −5

$$y = \frac{3}{x + 2} - 5$$

12.3 Investigating Algebra Activity (p. 783)

2. $2x + 3$

3. $2x + 3 + \dfrac{1}{x + 3}$

4. $2x + 1 + \dfrac{4}{2x + 1}$

5. $x + 1 + \dfrac{4}{2x + 3}$

6. $3x + 1 + \dfrac{1}{x + 2}$

7. $4x + 2 + \dfrac{3}{x + 1}$

12.3 Skill Practice (pp. 788–789)

22.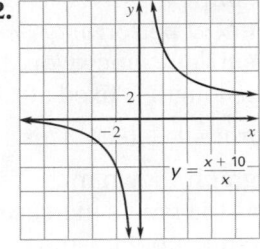

$$y = \frac{x + 10}{x}$$

23.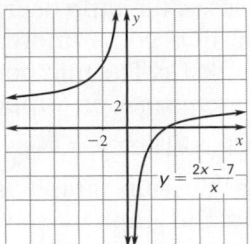

$$y = \frac{2x - 7}{x}$$

24.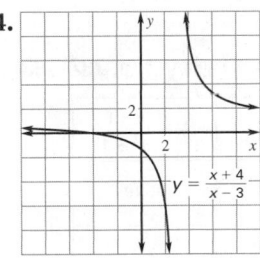

$$y = \frac{x + 4}{x - 3}$$

25.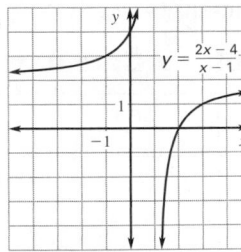

$$y = \frac{2x - 4}{x - 1}$$

26.

$$y = \frac{5x + 2}{x + 3}$$

27.

$$y = \frac{6x - 4}{x + 5}$$

28.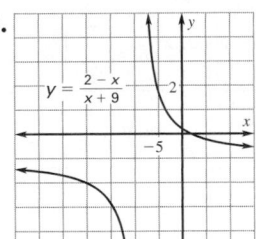

$$y = \frac{2 - x}{x + 9}$$

29.

$$y = \frac{2 + 4x}{x - 3}$$

30.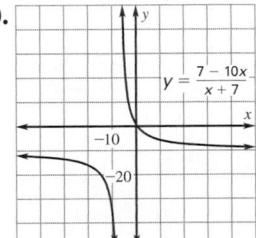

$$y = \frac{7 - 10x}{x + 7}$$

12.3 Problem Solving (pp. 789–791)

49. a. $y = \dfrac{2r + 2\ell}{r\ell}$;

$$y = \frac{2}{\ell} + 0.04$$

Length (micrometers)

AA41

b. More efficient; the graph in part (a) shows that as the length increases, the ratio decreases, implying that the microorganism becomes more efficient at performing metabolic tasks. **c.** The microorganism's efficiency would increase. *Sample answer:* Suppose the length is fixed at 50 micrometers. Then $y = \dfrac{2r + 100}{50r}$, or $y = \dfrac{2}{r} + 0.04$. This equation has the same graph as the graph shown in part (a); from the graph we see that as the radius increases, the ratio decreases, implying that the microorganism's efficiency increases.

12.3 Graphing Calculator Activity (pp. 792–793)

7.

	$y = \dfrac{8}{x - 2}$	$y = \dfrac{4}{6x - 7}$	$y = \dfrac{x - 9}{x^2 + 1}$
Vertical asymptotes	$x = 2$	$x = \dfrac{7}{6}$	none
x-values for which y is undefined	2	$\dfrac{7}{6}$	none
Horizontal asymptotes	$y = 0$	$y = 0$	$y = 0$
Degree of numerator	0	0	1
Degree of denominator	1	1	2

	$y = \dfrac{x + 5}{x^2 + 4x + 4}$	$y = \dfrac{x + 1}{4x^2 - 36}$	$y = \dfrac{5}{10x^2 + 9}$
Vertical asymptotes	$x = -2$	$x = -3,$ $x = 3$	none
x-values for which y is undefined	-2	$-3, 3$	none
Horizontal asymptotes	$y = 0$	$y = 0$	$y = 0$
Degree of numerator	1	1	0
Degree of denominator	2	2	2

8. vertical: $x = -9$, horizontal: $y = -6$

9. vertical: $x = 1$, horizontal: $y = 5$

10. vertical: $x = \dfrac{9}{2}$, horizontal: $y = 5$

11. vertical: none, horizontal: $y = 3$

12. vertical: $x = \dfrac{-4}{3}, x = \dfrac{4}{3}$, horizontal: $y = 3$

13. vertical: $x = -1, x = 1$, horizontal: $y = 3$

14.

	$y = \dfrac{-6x}{x + 9}$	$y = \dfrac{5x - 12}{x - 1}$	$y = \dfrac{10x}{2x - 9}$
Vertical asymptotes	$x = -9$	$x = 1$	$x = \dfrac{9}{2}$
x-values for which y is undefined	-9	1	$\dfrac{9}{2}$
Horizontal asymptotes	$y = -6$	$y = 5$	$y = 5$
Degree of numerator	1	1	1
Degree of denominator	1	1	1
Quotient of leading coefficients	-6	5	5

	$y = \dfrac{12x^2 - 7}{4x^2 + 2}$	$y = \dfrac{27x^2 - x}{9x^2 - 16}$	$y = \dfrac{18x^2 - 1}{6x^2 - 6}$
Vertical asymptotes	none	$x = \dfrac{-4}{3}, x = \dfrac{4}{3}$	$x = -1, x = 1$
x-values for which y is undefined	none	$\dfrac{-4}{3}, \dfrac{4}{3}$	$-1, 1$
Horizontal asymptotes	$y = 3$	$y = 3$	$y = 3$
Degree of numerator	2	2	2
Degree of denominator	2	2	2
Quotient of leading coefficients	3	3	3

12.4 Problem Solving (pp. 799–800)

45. b.

$$R = \frac{37500 + 2500x}{125 + x}$$

x-axis: Years since 1988; *y*-axis: Revenue (millions of dollars)

Quiz for Lessons 12.3–12.4 (p. 800)

3.

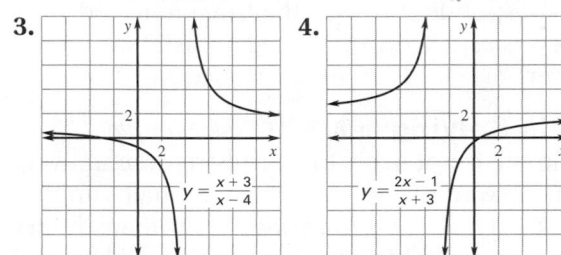

$$y = \frac{x + 3}{x - 4}$$

4.

$$y = \frac{2x - 1}{x + 3}$$

12.6 Skill Practice (pp. 816–817)

19. To rewrite each rational expression using the least common denominator, you must multiply its numerator by the factor of the LCD that is missing from the denominator: the numerator $5x$ should be multiplied by $(x + 3)$ and the numerator 2 should be multiplied by $(x - 4)$; $\dfrac{5x}{x - 4} + \dfrac{2}{x + 3} =$

$\dfrac{5x(x + 3)}{(x - 4)(x + 3)} + \dfrac{2(x - 4)}{(x - 4)(x + 3)} = \dfrac{5x^2 + 15x + 2x - 8}{(x - 4)(x + 3)} = \dfrac{5x^2 + 17x - 8}{(x - 4)(x + 3)}.$

12.7 Problem Solving Workshop (p. 828)

1. $1250; Method 1: Use a table. Make a table that shows the percent of Jill's investment money that is in the mutual fund after various amounts are added to the mutual fund.

Amount in mutual fund ($)	Amount in all investments ($)	Percent in mutual fund (%)
1000	10,000	10
1200	10,200	about 11.8
1400	10,400	about 13.5
1600	10,600	about 15
1800	10,800	about 16.7
2000	11,000	about 18.1
2050	11,050	about 18.6
2100	11,100	about 18.9
2150	11,150	about 19.3
2200	11,200	about 19.6
2250	11,250	20

Method 2: Reinterpret the problem. When 20% of Jill's investment money is in the mutual fund, $\frac{1}{5}$ of her money will be in the mutual fund and $\frac{4}{5}$ of her money will be in other accounts. The ratio of money in the mutual fund to money in other accounts (which is $10,000 − $1000 = $9000) needs to be 1 : 4. Let a = amount of money (in dollars) added to the mutual fund and write a proportion: $\dfrac{1000 + a}{9000} = \dfrac{1}{4}$. Solving for a gives $a = 1250$, so Jill needs to add $1250 to the mutual fund. **3.** 6 free throws; Method 1: Use a table. Make a table that shows the percent of free throw attempts made after various numbers of consecutive successful free throw attempts.

Number of consecutive successful free throw attempts	Total number of free throw attempts	Percent of free throw attempts made
12	30	40%
13	31	about 42%
14	32	about 44%
15	33	about 45%
16	34	about 47%
17	35	about 49%
18	36	50%

Method 2: Reinterpret the problem. When 50% of the free throw attempts have been successful, the number of attempts made will equal the number of attempts not made. After the first 30 attempts, the number of attempts made is 0.40(30) = 12, and the number of attempts not made is 0.60(30) = 18. Let n = number of consecutive successful free throw attempts and write an equation that shows that the number of attempts made and the number of attempts not made are equal: $12 + n = 18$. Solving for n gives $n = 6$, so the basketball player needs to make 6 consecutive free throws. **5.** 75 minutes; Method 1: Use a table. Make a table that shows the total time it takes you and your friend to shovel the driveway together for various amounts of time that it takes your friend to shovel the driveway alone.

Time m for your friend to shovel the driveway alone (min)	Time for you to shovel the driveway alone (min)	Time it takes to shovel the driveway together (min)
50	50	25
55	50	about 26
60	50	about 27
65	50	about 28
70	50	about 29
75	50	30

Method 2: Reinterpret the problem. Because you can shovel the driveway alone in 50 minutes, during each of the 30 minutes that you and your friend work together you shovel $\frac{1}{50}$ of the driveway. So, in 30 minutes you have shoveled $\frac{30}{50}$, or $\frac{3}{5}$ of the driveway. Your friend shovels $\frac{2}{5}$ of the driveway in 30 minutes, so 30 minutes is $\frac{2}{5}$ of the time that it will take your friend to shovel the whole driveway. Let m be the number of minutes it takes your friend to shovel the whole driveway and write an equation: $30 = \frac{2}{5}m$. Solving for m gives $m = 75$ minutes, so it takes your friend 75 minutes to shovel the driveway alone.

Chapter 13

13.1 Skill Practice (pp. 846–847) 13. *Sample answer:* Odds in favor is the number of favorable outcomes divided by the number of unfavorable outcomes; odds in favor of a multiple of $3 = \frac{\text{Number of favorable outcomes}}{\text{Number of unfavorable outcomes}} = \frac{9}{1}$ or $9:1$. **21.** $\frac{4}{9}; \frac{4}{5}$. *Sample answer:* The probability and odds of choosing a boy are related because both compare the number of boys to another number. The probability of choosing a boy compares the number of boys to the total number of outcomes, while the odds of choosing a boy compare the number of boys to the total number of outcomes minus the number of boys.

13.2 Skill Practice (pp. 853–854) 31. b. There are the same number of permutations. *Sample answer:* The formula for n objects taken n at a time is $\frac{n!}{(n-n)!} = n!$, while the formula for n objects taken $n-1$ at a time is $\frac{n!}{(n-(n-1))!} = \frac{n!}{1!} = n!$. Thus, both formulas are equal.

13.3 Skill Practice (p. 858) 20. $_6P_r \geq {_6C_r}$. *Sample answer:* The formula for $_6C_r$ is the same as $_6P_r$ multiplied by $\frac{1}{r!}$. For any value of $r > 1$, this will result in $_6C_r$ being less than $_6P_r$. If $r = 1$ or $r = 0$ then the values will be the same. **21.** $_nC_r = {_nP_r} \cdot \frac{1}{r!}$. *Sample answer:* To find the number of combinations, you find the number of permutations and then divide by the number of ways the items being chosen can be arranged, or $r!$. **22.** $_nC_{n-r} = \frac{n!}{[n-(n-r)]! \cdot (n-r)!} = \frac{n!}{r! \cdot (n-r)!} = \frac{n!}{(n-r)! \cdot r!} = {_nC_r}$. *Sample answer:* When you select a combination of r items from a group of n, you divide the group into 2 sections: a group of r selected items and a group of $n - r$ items that were not selected. Since each combination you select results in a unique combination of items not selected, the number of combinations of r items you can select from a group of n is the same as the number of combinations of $(n - r)$ items you cannot select in the group of n.

13.3 Problem Solving (p. 859) 27. $\frac{351}{142,506} \approx 0.25\%$. *Sample answer:* The number of possible groups chosen is $_{30}C_5 = 142{,}506$. To find the number of groups that include me and my 2 best friends, find the number of combinations of students to fill the remaining group once me and my 2 best friends have been chosen, or $_{27}C_2 = 351$. There are 351 favorable groups out of 142,506 possible groups.

13.5 Guided Practice (pp. 871–872) 2. a. Yes. *Sample answer:* All the people sampled were visiting a soccer game, so they may be more likely than the American population to be interested in soccer. **b.** Yes. *Sample answer:* The question suggests that soccer is popular and may encourage respondents to say they are interested in soccer. *Sample answer:* "How interested or disinterested are you in soccer?"

13.5 Problem Solving (p. 874) 16. Yes. *Sample answer:* The sample is not likely to be truly representative of the world's fresh water since it was such a small sample of the population. **17. b.** *Sample answer:* "How many hours per night do you study?" This question is unbiased because it does not prompt respondents to give any particular answer. **18.** *Sample answer:* If the rule used to select the systematic survey is not representative then the results will be biased; if a survey designed to determine the favorite clothes shops of students at a school selected all the students who were over 6 feet tall, this might bias the results towards shops that sold clothes for tall people.

13.6 Problem Solving (pp. 877–878) 22. c. Range: 219, mean absolute deviation: 50.7. *Sample answer:* The range is much higher than the mean which indicates that the data covers a wide spread of values. The mean absolute deviation tells you that the data points are not very close to the mean. **23. b.** No. *Sample answer:* If your median is 86, it means the final test score was greater than or equal to 88. You may or may not have scored greater than 94.

13.7 Guided Practice (pp. 881–883)

4. *Sample:*

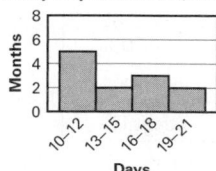

13.7 Skill Practice (pp. 883–884)

10. *Sample answer:* The range 20–29 even though it has a frequency of 0 needs to be included on the axis. Without it the histogram gives a distorted view of the spread of data.

11.

12.

13.

14.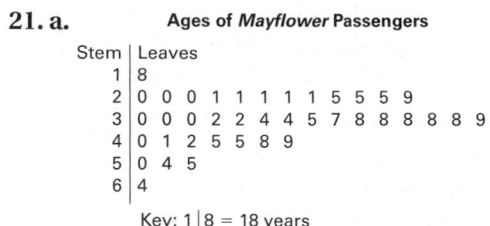

13.7 Problem Solving (pp. 884–885)

17.
Heights

Stem	Leaves
6	8 9 9
7	0 2 4 4 6 8 8
8	0 1 1 1 1

Key: 6│8 = 68 in.

18.
Water Intake

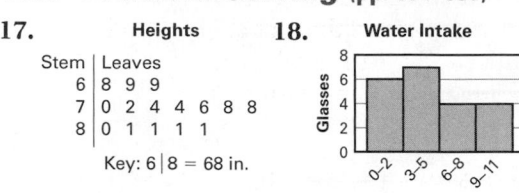

19. a. Phone Number Memorization

21. a.
Ages of *Mayflower* Passengers

Stem	Leaves
1	8
2	0 0 0 1 1 1 1 1 5 5 5 9
3	0 0 0 2 2 4 4 5 7 8 8 8 8 8 9
4	0 1 2 5 5 8 9
5	0 4 5
6	4

Key: 1│8 = 18 years

22. a. 29.5, 39.5, 49.5, 59.5, 69.5; 4100.5, 6833.5, 7573.5, 5950, 4865; 29,322.5; 46.177 **b.** The mean. *Sample answer:* By estimating likely average values for each interval, a sum was found for all the data values that created the histogram. This sum was divided by the total number of data values, to create an estimate of the mean.

13.8 Skill Practice (pp. 889–890) 2. *Sample answer:* Find the interquartile range and multiply it by 1.5. Add the result to the upper quartile, and subtract it from the lower quartile. Any data values outside these values are outliers.

13.8 Problem Solving (pp. 890–892) 20. *Sample answer:* Generally, the lower the voice part the taller the singer in the chorus. 50% of the bass parts are between 68 and 72 inches, while 50% of the tenors are between 66.5 and 71.5 inches, 50% of the altos are between 63 and 67 inches, and sopranos are the shortest with 50% between 62.5 and 66 inches. Around 75% of all bass singers are taller than all sopranos and around 50% of tenors are taller than all sopranos.

13.8 Mixed Review (p. 892)

23.

24.

Quiz for Lessons 13.5–13.8 (p. 892)

4.

5.
Stem	Leaves
1	2 8 8
2	2 2 8
3	3 6

Key: 1│2 = 1.2

6. 55 is an outlier.

Extra Practice

Chapter 4 (p. 941)

23. **24.**

25. **26.**

41. **42.**

43. **44.**

45.

46.

47.

48.

49.

50.

51.

52.

56. 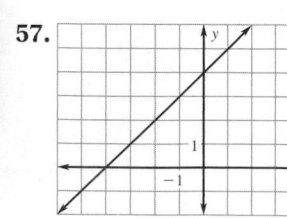 The graph is a vertical translation 2 units down of $f(x) = x$.

57. 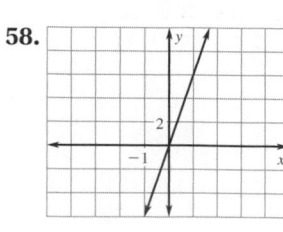 The graph is a vertical translation 4 units up of $f(x) = x$.

58. The graph is a vertical stretch by a factor of 6 of $f(x) = x$.

59. The graph is a vertical stretch by a factor of 2 and a reflection in the x-axis of $f(x) = x$.

Chapter 6 (p. 943)

34.

35.

36.

37. 3.5

38.

39.

40.

41.

42.

55.

56.

57. −1.2 ... 1.2

58. $-\frac{2}{5}$ ... $\frac{2}{5}$

59.

60.

61.

62. $-\frac{3}{2}$

63. −1 ... 7

64. $-4\frac{1}{3}$

65.

66.

67.

68.

69.

70.

71.

72.

73.

74.

75.

76.

77.

78.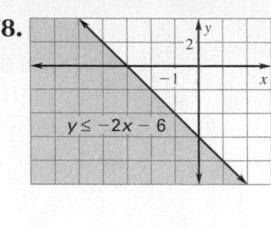

Chapter 8 (p. 945)

63.

64.

65.

66.

67.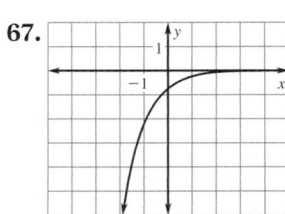

Chapter 11 (p. 948)

6.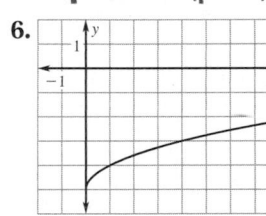
Domain: $x \geq 0$, range: $y \geq -5$; the graph is a vertical translation 5 units down of the graph of $y = \sqrt{x}$.

7.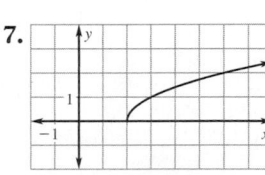
Domain: $x \geq 2$, range: $y \geq 0$; the graph is a horizontal translation 2 units right of the graph of $y = \sqrt{x}$.

8.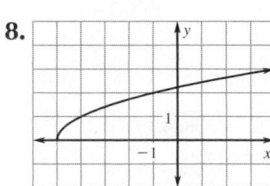
Domain: $x \geq -5$, range: $y \geq 0$; the graph is a horizontal translation 5 units left of the graph of $y = \sqrt{x}$.

9. Domain: $x \geq 4$, range: $y \geq 2$; the graph is a vertical translation 2 units up and a horizontal translation 4 units right of the graph of $y = \sqrt{x}$.

Chapter 12 (p. 949)

14.

15.

16.

17.

18.